Lesko's Free Money For Entrepreneurs:

How To Start Or Expand A Business With Government Grants, Low Interest Loans, Contacts and Free Services

by **Matthew Lesko**

with **Mary Ann Martello**

Researchers
Cindy Owens, Jean Neuner,
Bev Matson, Chelsea Noble, Dixie St. John

Production
Beth Meserve

Marketing
Kim McCoy

Support
Mercedes Sundeen

Cover
Tom Ford

LESKO'S FREE MONEY FOR ENTREPRENEURS, Copyright 2004 by Matthew Lesko and Mary Ann Martello. All rights reserved. Printed in the United States of America. Published by Information USA, Inc., P.O. Box E, Kensington, MD 20895; {www.lesko.com}.

Clip art used in this publication © Dynamic Graphics, Inc.; Totem Graphics; One Mile Up; Tech Pool; Image Club Graphics, Inc.; and Corel Corp.

FIRST EDITION

Library of Congress Cataloging-in-Publication date
    Lesko, Matthew
    Martello, Mary Ann

Lesko's Free Money For Entrepreneurs

ISBN # 1-878346-69-5

Most books by Matthew Lesko are available at special quantity discounts for bulk purchases for sales promotions, premiums, fund-raising or educational use. Special books or book excerpts also can be created to fit specific needs.

For details, write Information USA, Special Markets, Attention: Kim McCoy, P.O. Box E, Kensington, MD 20895; or 1-800-797-7811, Marketing; {www.lesko.com}.

Other books available from Matthew Lesko:

Free Money To Change Your Life

Free Money To Change Your Life
    6-hour instructional audio cassette/CD

Lesko's Info-Power III

Government Giveaways for Entrepreneurs IV

Free Legal Help

Free Health Care

Gobs and Gobs of Free Stuff

Free Stuff For Busy Moms

Free Stuff For Women's Health, Fitness and Nutrition

Free College Money And Training For Women

Free Money And Help For Women Entrepreneurs

Free Money to Change Your Life CD-ROM

Free Money For Your Retirement

How to Write and Get a Grant

Free Money To Pay Your Bills

For ordering information on any of Matthew Lesko's publications, call 1-800-UNCLE-SAM, or contact his web site at www.lesko.com.

Table of Contents

Introduction

Every year over 1 million entrepreneurs receive money from the government. And for one of the major government business programs, you have a 66% of getting the money. So why play your state lottery where you only have a one in a million chance of winning and there is only one or a handful of winners? Instead, you can

apply to one of the thousands of other government programs where over 1 million entrepreneurs are winners every year and in some of these programs 2 out of every 3 people who apply get the money. And remember, state lotteries are just another government method of getting tax money. So playing the lottery is like paying more in taxes.

Most people don't apply to these programs and play the lottery because the lottery is the only government program that advertises. The government does not spend a dime advertising the thousands of government programs that are available for entrepreneurs. You have to find out about them yourself. That's where we come in.

Types Of Money

Businesses and entrepreneurs now have a single source that identifies all the money programs for businesses with copies of official applications that can be completed and submitted for funding. We identify every money source the government has available including:

♦ **Grants**: money that you do not have to pay back

♦ **Loans**: at interest rates below market or at market value, and from organizations seeking to help both established businesses and the first time entrepreneur

♦ **Loan Guarantees**: to ensure that a bank will provide you with the funds you need, a government agency or nonprofit organization will guarantee that if you are unable to repay your loan they will pay it for you

♦ **Government Contracts**: better than a loan or even a grant, this is the government's largest source of business money for any kind of business

♦ **Tax Credits**: real dollars back on your taxes from federal, state and local governments for performing certain entrepreneurial endeavors

♦ **Venture Capital**: public or private investors who are looking for new ideas in need of financial assistance

♦ **Free Services To Help You Get The Money**: these government or nonprofit organizations specialize in assisting new or growing businesses get the financing and help they need

Sources Of Money

To get government money for your business venture you just can't go to the government in Washington, DC to get it all. That used to be the case years ago, but times have changed. The federal government in Washington is just one of the many places where entrepreneurs can turn for free money and help to insure their success. Here are the sources we include in the book.

Federal Government: Programs that are national in scope. You can apply to these programs from anywhere in the United States. They are grants, venture capital, loans, and loan guarantees.

State Government: Grants, venture capital, loans, loan guarantees that are offered at the state level. These programs are only for those businesses and entrepreneurs doing business or plan to do business within the boundaries of the state.

Local Government: Grants, venture capital, and loans that are offered at the county, city or other local jurisdiction. It is normally a requirement that your business or venture be located within a given jurisdiction to receive these funds.

NonProfit Organizations: Organizations that raise monies from government or private sources and, in turn, make loans or grants to entrepreneurs.

Small-Business-Friendly Banks: The banks listed here are determined as "small-business-friendly banks" according to a study conducted the U.S. SBA Office of Advocacy. The data was taken from reports submitted by 9,000 commercial banks to the U.S. Federal Reserve Board describing their loan activity.

Grants for Entrepreneur Training: Federal and state training programs allow grants to be used for individuals to take courses and other training in entrepreneurship.

Entrepreneur Employment Money: More and more states are allowing individuals to use their unemployment money as income while they start their own business.

Free Help In Selling To The Government: These nonprofit and government supported organizations offer free or very low cost services to businesses and entrepreneurs who are looking to sell their products or services to federal, state or local governments.

Free and Low Cost Services To Businesses: These government and nonprofit organizations offer free and low cost services to businesses and entrepreneurs. In addition to help with financing and business plan preparation they can help with taxes, management, marketing, public relations, legal matters, and more.

Venture Capital: Private investors and sometimes government organizations will provide money to new, young and growing companies in exchange for a partial ownership or a royalty arrangement.

Who Can Benefit From This Book?

You can be a first time entrepreneur who doesn't even know how to spell the word "entrepreneur" or you can be a Vice President of a Fortune 500 Conglomerate. Either way, you will immediately see the tremendous value in having a single source for all the available applications for little known free and low cost government money programs.

- Why be turned <u>down by your local bank</u> for money to start a new business when there are government agencies that have set up special money programs just for entrepreneurs who can't get money elsewhere?

- Why ask your friends and relatives for money to <u>work on your invention</u> when there are government agencies that provide free grant money to work on your idea?

- Why give up on your dream of being an entrepreneur <u>just because you have no money</u>, when there are public and private programs that will pay to train you as an entrepreneur and offer you money to start your dream?

- <u>Why use your company's money</u> to train your employees in the new computer software or the latest in customer service skills when you can pay for it with a free government grant?.

- Why pay for <u>new office space or a factory</u> with your own money when government agencies will pay for it for you with grants and low interest loans?

- Why borrow money at high interest rates from commercial banks when government offices provide money at <u>below market interest rates</u>?

- Why not have the government finance <u>your next overseas sale</u> at a favorable interest rate?

- Why not have the government give your company grants and low interest loans the next time you want to <u>expand your business</u>?

- Why not have the government do the marketing for you to make <u>billions in government contracts</u>?

- Why not take advantage of all the money and services that this country has to offer to entrepreneurs when <u>your tax dollars are paying for them</u>?

Who Gets This Money?

Because over 1,000,000 entrepreneurs and businesses every year use these government money programs to start or grow their businesses, the people who use these programs come in all kinds of shapes and sizes. It can be big business and big time entrepreneurs like:
- Donald Trump
- H. Ross Perot
- Nike Shoes
- Federal Express

Before they entered the White House, George W. Bush and Richard Cheney took advantage of these government money programs for their businesses. They're not dumb. They know where the money is.

While running Halliburton Company, Vice President Candidate Dick Cheney received over $1.5 billion from the U.S. Export-Import Bank and the Overseas Private Investment Bank to finance his overseas sales. He also received over $2.3 billion in federal contracts during the 5-year period he was in charge.

Presidential Candidate Bush received $200 million worth of government money to build a new stadium while he was in charge of the Texas Rangers baseball team. In five years this project raised the value of his original $606,302 investment to $14.9 million.

But this money is not just for fat cats. It's also for people like:

- Blanca Basson received $30,000 to start a music jingle business in her home,
- Keith Ross and Gil Rodrigues got $100,00 to start a coffee shop,

- Michelle and Mark Levendoski received $35,000 to start their own exclusive hair salon, and
- Michael Williams received over $1,000,000 for his consulting business.

You Don't have 2,500 Hours

That's a conservative estimate of how long it took us to find and collect all the information for this book. And I feel that we are probably the country's leading expert in government money programs. Imagine how long it would take a non-expert to collect this information? Sure, you can do it. There is no magic to what we do. It is mostly just a lot of hard work. But the average person does not have the time, the patience, nor the expertise to take on such a task. And instead of doing it yourself, if you hired someone, even at $10 an hour to do it, it would cost $25,000 to gather this information.

Lesko's Free Money For Business gives you the easiest way to take ONE BIG GIANT STEP towards getting free and cheap money for your business. You won't have to spend the thousands of hours it takes in chasing down these little-known programs. And more importantly, you won't have to deal with the bureaucratic dance of wrong numbers, unanswered phones and voice mail in order to get the necessary applications.

This Is Earth, Not Heaven

If life were perfect, you could just fill out the applications, mail them in, and sit back and wait for the money. But there are a lot of things in life that don't go perfectly. Actually most things in life don't run perfectly at all. No matter what you are doing, life will continue to put up hurdles and little glitches all along the way. If these hurdles and glitches weren't there, then it wouldn't be life. It would be heaven. And we're not there yet.

Here are some things you can do that will cut down on the glitches, lower the hurdles and ultimately increase your chances of getting the money:

1) **Call First**: This can't hurt. Try to get as much additional information about the program as you can. Talk with someone at the office so that you can get a name of someone to keep as contact. Those who are most successful in using the system are those that are not afraid to do three things: Call. Call. Call.

2) **Make It Personal**: Remember, it's the bureaucrats at these offices who have power over the money. The more you can personalize your application the easier it will be to get the money. These bureaucrats are actually human beings. It may

be hard to understand that, but they are. Think of it as being back in school when you would go and brown nose the teacher. The good brown nosers would meet with the teacher after class and not only talk about school, but would talk about their life. Show the teacher pictures of their dog. Talk about how much they like baseball. Anything to get the teacher to relate to them, not as a student but as a person. Once the teacher sees a student as a person, it's hard to flunk them no matter how bad they are. These bureaucrats have the power to pass or fail you on your money exam. So the more they get to know you as a person, the more likely they are to help you pass the test. So when you are talking to them don't be afraid to talk about personal stuff along with the professional. The more they get to know you as a person, the more likely they are to help you pass the test. And they certainly have the power to help, because they are the ones who give out the money.

3) **How To Treat A Bureaucrat**: When you are calling around the government getting a lot of voice mail or being put on hold, it's hard to remember how important that person is who finally answers the telephone. That's the person who can give you the money. So how well you treat them can determine your success or failure in getting what you need. When the person answers the phone, if you start yelling because you've been sitting on hold for the past 10 minutes, you will not sound like you are going  to be the highlight of any bureaucrat's day. That bureaucrat gets paid the same amount of money whether they help you for free for 2 weeks or if they hang up on you right after you say hello. What you have to do is try to get that person to want to spend time with you. You want them to enjoy talking with you. The more comfortable they are in talking with you, the more likely they are to share inside information that will increase your chances and make it easier for you to get the money. It's basic common sense things can be easily forgotten, like: a) Don't be nasty when they answer the phone because the first words out of your mouth can set the stage for the entire conversation. b) Don't act like you hate them except for the fact that they are sitting on the money (even though it may be true) because this will come through in your conversation and they will not want to help you. c) Send "thank you" notes when people are exceptionally nice because it is the best way to ensure that you are remembered the next time you call. I can go on and on but simply put …. TREAT PEOPLE LIKE YOU WANT TO BE TREATED.

4) **Belly To Belly Cash Flow:** If speaking well on the phone increases your odds of getting the cash, then face to face will do even that much more. This may not be practical or even possible all the time, but it is certainly another way for a bureaucrat to put a face with an application and this will make it that much harder for her to just say "no".

5) **Don't Wait**: I really mean don't wait until the last minute to apply. Especially with those offices that only give out money at certain times of the year. As deadline time approaches, the bureaucrats can become too busy to provide you with any individualized help. So the best strategy is to call early and to call often.

6) **There's Always Next Year:** Sure the government runs out of money. It happens every year. But the good news is that the office will get their coffers filled again for the following year. That's why it is important to remember that if you talk to an office and they say they have run out of money, ask them when their fiscal year ends. Because the day after that you can call again. That's the day they get another year's worth of money.

7) **Get A Copy Of The Test Ahead Of Time**: Wouldn't it have been great if when you were in school you had a way to get a copy of the test days before you took the exam? Well, it's legal when you're getting government money. Under the Freedom of Information Act laws at the federal level and in most states, successful applications for government money are available for view to the public. Remember this is taxpayer's money they're giving out, and as a taxpayer you have a right to see how they are spending it. It may not be the easiest thing to do, but under the law you can get them. The caveat you may run into is that the agency has the right to block out those portions of the applications when it may reveal confidential information about the applicant, like detailed financial information. You may want to weigh the benefits of having such a document against the hassle of the procedure for getting one. One way to help you decide is by carefully looking at the questions on a blank application and try to understand how seeing a completed one might help. Many applications require only that information which is so personal to you that seeing others may be of no value at all.

8) **Consider A Little Move:** Who cares if your business is 10 miles from your home if someone will give your $100,000 to put it there. Some programs even offer special incentives to establish your business in certain zip codes. Different counties and cities offer different financial incentives, and even state governments offer different incentives for establishing businesses in different areas. So make sure you look through all the local programs before you decide on which ones to apply. It may pay  you to move a little. You may want to even consider looking at another state. Having the business you love may out weigh the hassle of locating it in another county or even another state. You can also have your business in one state and live in another. The people giving out the money don't care where you live. They only care where you put your business.

9) **Bad Credit Can Make You Eligible:** Remember this is the government and a lot of things just don't make sense. We are not here to explain why some programs exist, but we are here simply to show you that they <u>do</u> exist. And it's true, there are programs that are set up for entrepreneurs to get money to start a business if they have less than stellar credit. Actually many government programs have been established primarily to serve people who can't get money elsewhere. Yours is not the reason why, yours is just to apply.

10) **No Doesn't Mean No**: The older I get the more I believe that the only time "no" means "no" is in sexual harassment cases. There are times when bureaucrats will say, "no, you don't qualify," or "no, we don't give money for what you want to  do," just because it's the easiest thing to say or they don't really know what they are talking about. A few years back, Steven Stern, a young man from Boston, saw me on the David Letterman show telling the audience about a government program that gives money to teenage entrepreneurs. He contacted the appropriate office and they said that he could not apply for the money because it was only for teenagers who lived in small towns and Boston was not considered a small town. Steven tracked me down and asked what he could do. I wasn't sure, but said that before you give up get a copy of the program's literature. When he got the literature he read it closely. It certainly said that the money was indeed for teens in small towns, but a separate line also stated that it was for teens who wanted to start lawnmower service businesses. That was exactly what Steven wanted to do. He contacted the office and after he told them what their own literature said, they gave him the money. And that $2,000 he got to start a start a lawn mower service business earned him over $10,000 a year to put himself through college.

A "no" may also be changed to a "yes" because an office may be trying to get rid of more of their money towards the end of their fiscal year because not enough people have applied for it. Or a "no" may become a "yes" because the official misunderstood the real importance of your project or is simply not creative enough to understand how to bend the objective of your project to meet the objectives of the money program.

11) **Apply Everywhere**: If you're not sure exactly which program to apply to, then apply everywhere. The worst thing that can happen is that you get too much money. That's a nice problem to have. You can always give it back. You can also take the approach of thinking nationally, but acting locally. Keep in mind that there are federal programs you can eventually turn to, but start applying at the local level first and see how you do. The local level is where officials are going to be more sensitive to your needs and have a better understanding of you and your project. Then you can turn to the state and then go up to the federal government.

12) **The Columbo Effect:** There was a detective series on television back in the 70's and 80's called Columbo and it starred Peter Falk. (I'm showing my age here.) He was a sloppy person who always wore a raincoat that looked like he slept in it. When he was interviewing suspects he always took the approach of being very humble even to the point of acting dumb and unassuming. But at the end of the interview, even while he was walking out the door, and the suspect thought that she was in the clear, Columbo would turn around and ask one more question that would cut right to the heart of the matter and expose the suspect as the real criminal. Now, your mission is not to expose any bureaucratic wrong doing, but you do want to ask one last question before you leave your conversation. Especially if the encounter proved to be unproductive in getting the money you need. The question you have to ask while walking out the door is, "Do you know of anywhere else to get money?" Remember that you contacted these people believing that they can help get you money, so if they don't have any themselves it is certainly possible that if they have been in their business for awhile they may know of other colleagues or offices that run other programs. Even try to get them to stretch their imagination a little or even ask other people in their office. You have nothing to lose and everything to gain.

13) **Maybe You Don't Need All The Money You Think You Do:** Many people who are thinking of starting or expanding a business believe that money will solve all their problems. But it's not always so. Think about doing your business with just a little or maybe, no money at all. Anyone can do things with a lot of money, but a true entrepreneur does it with little or no money. It's easy to spend lots of money buying the latest hi-tech equipment and spending big money on advertising and then hoping for the best. But can you get customers without spending money on advertising and then borrowing someone's equipment when you need it to do the work? Many businesses today only take a phone and a business card to be in business. This is certainly true of service businesses and even many information businesses. You can be a web designer or a pet sitter and all you need is a business card to show you are in business. The key to being in any business is getting customers.

A Caution About Web Site Address

Our web site address listed in the descriptions of the programs may be lengthy because, when possible, we try to give you the address that goes directly to the page that describes the program. If you have trouble using a web site address or it appears to not be active, there are a number of things you can do before you start searching on your own. You may be able to get there by not using the complete address. For example if you put in {www.choosemaryland.com/finance/medaaf.htm} and you receive a notice that "Page cannot be found," try putting in {www.choosemaryland.com} and work your way thru the site where you would like to go. Sometimes simply retyping the address in your web browser instead of clicking though an address in a document will find success. These techniques should definitely be tried before you try to attack unruly search engines.

There's Always More

We have dozens of the country's best researchers working on this project and no matter how hard we try we will never have every single program available. Just like your local telephone book, as soon as it is in print it is out of date. We are constantly updating to keep this material as current as we possibly can. But things change daily and even hourly in our society. As a result you may find a program that has been cancelled since we updated your edition or there may 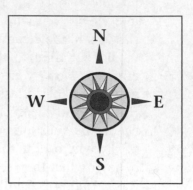 even be additional programs that our researchers failed to uncover. So keep an open mind. Be aware that there may be programs that are not in our database yet. And enjoy the excitement of discovering that pearl that even the experts are not aware of.

Happy Hunting
Matthew Lesko

Who's Lesko?

Matthew Lesko is the founder of three successful information companies including one of the country's first information brokerage businesses. Lesko served as an information and government money consultant to thousands of private clients including many of the country's Fortune 500 companies. He has written over 100 books on the money and information available from government and other non-traditional sources. Two of his books were New York Times Best Sellers and two received awards for the Best Reference Book of the Year from the American Library Association. He also has written columns for Good Housekeeping Magazine, The Chicago Sun Times, and the New York Times Syndicate. You may have seen him with his fancy glasses, bow tie, question mark suit, and acting goofy on shows like Oprah, Larry King, Letterman, Jay Leno, Home Shopping, C-Span, and The Today Show.

Lesko is undoubtly the most qualified person the United States to present all these little-known sources of business money. So don't settle for less. When you want to know about grants get the best. The Washington Post calls Lesko, "the Guru Of Government Giveaways."

State Money and Help For Your Business

Who Can Use State Money?

All states require that funds be used solely by state residents. But that shouldn't limit you to exploring possibilities only in the state in which you currently reside. If you reside in Maine, but Massachusetts agrees to give you $100,000 to start your own business, it would be worth your while to consider moving to Massachusetts. Shop around for the best deal.

Types Of State Money And Help Available

Each state has different kinds and amounts of money and assistance programs available, but these sources of financial and counseling help are constantly being changed. What may not be available this year may very well be available next. Therefore, in the course of your exploration, you might want to check in with the people who operate the business "hotlines" to discover if anything new has been added to the states' offerings.

Many states have trade assistance, agricultural and rural development offices, marketing and technological development assistance, and women and minority offices. In addition loans or loan guarantees may be available through different organizations. Grants to start a business are few and far between, but that shouldn't stop you. There is frequently free job training assistance to get your new employees up to speed. You may find tax incentives and credits that can save you thousands each year. Site location and marketing research is often free and can be the difference between success and failure. Try to take advantage of all these wonderful opportunities.

Described below are the major kinds of programs offered by most of the states.

Information

Hotlines or One-Stop Shops are available in many states through a toll-free number that hooks you up with someone who will either tell you what you need to know or refer you to someone who can. These hotlines are invaluable — offering information on everything from business permit regulations to obscure financing programs. Most states also offer some kind of booklet that tells you to how to start-up a business in that state. Ask for it. It will probably be free.

Small Business Advocates operate in all fifty states and are part of a national organization (the National Association of State Small Business Advocates) devoted to helping small business people function efficiently with their state governments. They are a good source for help in cutting through bureaucratic red tape.

Funding Programs

Free Money can come in the form of grants, and works the same as free money from the federal government. You do not have to pay it back.

Loans from state governments work in the same way as those from the federal government -- they are given directly to entrepreneurs. Loans are usually at interest rates below the rates charged at commercial institutions and are also set aside for those companies which have trouble getting a loan elsewhere. This makes them an ideal source for riskier kinds of ventures.

Loan Guarantees are similar to those offered by the federal government. For this program, the state government will go to the bank with you and co-sign your loan. This, too, is ideal for high risk ventures which normally would not get a loan.

Interest Subsidies On Loans is a unique concept not used by the federal government. In this case, the state will subsidize the interest rate you are charged by a bank. For example, if the bank gives you a loan for $50,000 at 10 percent per year interest, your interest payments will be $5,000 per year. With an interest subsidy you might have to pay only $2,500 since the state will pay the other half. This is like getting the loan at 5 percent instead of 10 percent.

Industrial Revenue Bonds Or General Obligation Bonds are a type of financing that can be used to purchase only fixed assets, such as a factory or equipment. In the case of Industrial Revenue Bonds the state will raise money from the general public to buy your equipment. Because the state acts as the middleman, the people who lend you the money do not have to pay federal taxes on the interest they charge you. As a result, you get the money cheaper because they get a tax break. If the state issues General Obligation Bonds to buy your equipment, the arrangement will be similar to that for an Industrial Revenue Bond except that the state promises to repay the loan if you cannot.

Matching Grants supplement and abet federal grant programs. These kinds of grants could make an under-capitalized project go forward. Awards usually hinge on the usefulness of the project to its surrounding locality.

Loans To Agricultural Businesses are offered in states with large rural, farming populations. They are available solely to farmers and/or agribusiness entrepreneurs.

Loans To Exporters are available in some states as a kind of gap financing to cover the expenses involved in fulfilling a contract.

Energy Conservation Loans are made to small businesses to finance the installation of energy-saving equipment or devices.

Special Regional Loans are ear-marked for specific areas in a state that may have been hard hit economically or suffer from under-development. If you live in one of these regions, you may be eligible for special funds.

High Tech Loans help fledgling companies develop or introduce new products into the marketplace.

Loans To Inventors help the entrepreneur develop or market new products.

Local Government Loans are used for start-up and expansion of businesses within the designated locality.

Childcare Facilities Loans help businesses establish on-site daycare facilities.

Loans To Women And/Or Minorities are available in almost every state from funds specifically reserved for economically disadvantaged groups.

Many federally funded programs are administered by state governments. Among them are the following programs:

The SBA 7(A) Guaranteed and ***Direct Loan*** program can guarantee up to 90 percent of a loan made through a private lender (up to $750,000), or make direct loans of up to $150,000.

The SBA 504 establishes Certified Development Companies whose debentures are guaranteed by the SBA. Equity participation of the borrower must be at least 10 percent, private financing 60 percent and CDC participation at a maximum of 40 percent, up to $750,000.

Small Business Innovative Research Grants (SBIR) award between $20,000 to $50,000 to entrepreneurs to support six months of research on a technical innovation. They are then eligible for up to $500,000 to develop the innovation.

Small Business Investment Companies (SBIC) license, regulate and provide financial assistance in the form of equity financing, long-term loans, and management services.

Community Development Block Grants are available to cities and counties for the commercial rehabilitation of existing buildings or structures used for business, commercial, or industrial purposes. Grants of up to $500,000 can be made. Every $15,000 of grant funds invested must create at least one full-time job, and at least 51 percent of the jobs created must be for low and moderate income families.

Farm Service Agency (FSA) Emergency Disaster Loans are available in counties where natural disaster has substantially affected farming, ranching or aquaculture production.

Farm Service Agency (FSA) Farm Loan Guarantees are made to family farmers and ranchers to enable them to obtain funds from private lenders. Funds must be used for farm ownership, improvements, and operating purposes.

Farm Service Agency (FSA) Farm Operating Loans to meet operating expenses, finance recreational and nonagricultural enterprises, to add to family income, and to pay for mandated safety and pollution control changes are available at variable interest rates. Limits are $200,000 for an insured farm operating loan and $400,000 for a guaranteed loan.

Farm Service Agency (FSA) Farm Ownership Loans can be used for a wide range of farm improvement projects. Limits are $200,000 for an insured loan and $300,000 for a guaranteed loan.

Farm Service Agency (FSA) Soil And Water Loans must be used by individual farmers and ranchers to develop, conserve, and properly use their land and water resources and to help abate pollution. Interest rates are variable; each loan must be secured by real estate.

Farm Service Agency (FSA) Youth Project Loans enable young people to borrow for income-producing projects sponsored by a school or 4H club.

Assistance Programs

Management Training is offered by many states in subjects ranging from bookkeeping to energy conservation.

Business Consulting is offered on almost any subject. Small Business Development Centers are the best source for this kind of assistance.

Market Studies to help you sell your goods or services within or outside the state are offered by many states. They all also have State Data Centers which not only collect demographic and other information about markets within the state, but also have access to federal data which can pinpoint national markets. Many states also provide the services of graduate business students at local universities to do the legwork and analysis for you.

Business Site Selection is done by specialists in every state who will identify the best place to locate a business.

Licensing, Regulation, and Permits information is available from most states through "one-stop shop" centers by calling a toll-free number. There you'll get help in finding your way through the confusion of registering a new business.

Employee Training Programs offer on-site training and continuing education opportunities.

Research And Development assistance for entrepreneurs is a form of assistance that is rapidly increasing as more and more states try to attract high technology-related companies. Many states are even setting up clearing houses so that small businesses can have one place to turn to find expertise throughout a statewide university system.

Procurement Programs have been established in some states to help you sell products to state, federal, and local governments.

Export Assistance is offered to identify overseas markets. Some states even have overseas offices to drum up business prospects for you.

Assistance In Finding Funding is offered in every state, particularly through regional Small Business Development Centers. They will not only identify funding sources in the state and federal governments but will also lead you through the complicated application process.

Special Help For Minorities And Women is available in almost every state to help boost the participation of women and minorities in small business ventures. They offer special funding programs and, often, one-on-one counseling to assure a start-up success.

Venture Capital Networking is achieved through computer databases that hook up entrepreneurs and venture capitalists. This service is usually free of charge. In fact, the demand for small business investment opportunities is so great that some states require the investor to pay to be listed.

Inventors Associations have been established to encourage and assist inventors in developing and patenting their products.

Annual Governors' Conferences give small business people the chance to air their problems with representatives from state agencies and the legislature.

Small Business Development Centers (SBDCs), funded jointly by the federal and state governments, are usually associated with the state university system. SBDCs are a god-send to small business people. They will not only help you figure out if your business project is feasible, but also help you draw up a sensible business plan, apply for funding, and check in with you frequency once your business is up and running to make sure it stays that way.

Tourism programs are prominent in states whose revenues are heavily dependent on the tourist trade. They are specifically aimed at businesses in the tourist industries.

Small Business Institutes at local colleges use senior level business students as consultants to help develop business plans or plan expansions.

Technology Assistance Centers help high tech companies and entrepreneurs establish new businesses and plan business expansions.

On-Site Energy Audits are offered free of charge by many states to help control energy costs and improve energy efficiency for small businesses. Some states also conduct workshops to encourage energy conservation measures.

Minority Business Development Centers offer a wide range of services from initial counseling on how to start a business to more complex issues of planning and growth.

Business Information Centers (BICs) provide the latest in high-tech hardware, software, and telecommunications to help small businesses get started. BIC is a place where business owners and aspiring business owners can go to use hardware/software, hard copy books, and publications to plan their business, expand an existing business, or venture into new business areas. Also, on-site counseling is available.

U.S. Small Business Administration (SBA) Programs

The SBA offices listed under each state can provide you with detailed information on the following programs:

Small Business Innovative Research Grants (SBIR): Phase I awards between $20,000 to $50,000 to entrepreneurs to support six months of research on a technical innovation. Phase II grants are an additional $500,000 for development. Private sector investment funds must follow.

International Trade Loans: Guaranteed long-term loans through private lenders to develop or expand export markets, or to recover from the effects of import competition. Maximum guaranteed loan is $1,000,000 for fixed assets and an additional $250,000 for working capital and/or export revolving line of credit.

Contract Loan: Short-term loans are available to small businesses to finance the costs of labor and materials on contracts for which the proceeds are assignable. Program guarantees up to 90 percent of loans not in excess of $750,000. Qualifying small businesses must be in business for at least 12 calendar months prior to the date of the loan application.

General Contractor Loans: Small general construction contractors may obtain short-term loans or loan guarantees for residential or commercial construction or rehabilitation of property to be sold. The SBA will guarantee up to 90 percent of qualifying loans made by private lenders up to a maximum of $750,000. Direct loans can be up to $150,000.

7(a) Loan Guaranty Program: This program is used to fund the varied long-term needs of small businesses. It is designed to promote small business formation and growth by guaranteeing long-term loans to qualified firms. Can guarantee up to $750,000, generally between 70%-90% of the loan value, at an interest rate not to exceed 2.75 over the prime lending rate. Maturities are up to 10 years for working capital; up to 25 years for fixed assets.

7(a) Loan Guaranty Program
Low Documentation Loan Program (LowDoc): Purpose is to reduce the paperwork involved in loan requests of $100,000 or less. A one-page application is used and it relies on the strength of the individual applicant's character and credit history.

7(a) Loan Guaranty Program
GreenLine Program: Intended to finance short-term, working-capital needs of small businesses. Loan advances are usually made against a borrower's certified level of inventory and accounts payable.

7(a) Loan Guaranty Program
Vietnam-Era and Disabled Veteran Loan Program: Assists disabled veterans of any era who can't secure business financing from private sector or other guaranty loan sources. Veterans can apply for loans to establish a small business or expand an existing small business. The maximum is $150,000.

7(a) Loan Guaranty Program
Handicapped Assistance Loans: Assists individuals with disabilities and public/private nonprofit organizations for the employment of the handicapped. Financing is available for starting/acquiring or operating a small business. There are 2 programs of assistance: HAL-1 and HAL-2.

> *HAL-1:* Financial assistance is available to state and federal-chartered organizations that operate in the interest of disabled individuals. Applicants must provide evidence that the business is operated in the interest of handicapped individuals.

> *HAL-2:* Financial assistance is provided to handicapped persons who provide evidence that their business is a for-profit operation, qualifies as a small business, is 100% owned by 1 or more handicapped individuals, and the handicapped owner(s) must actively participate in managing the business.

7(a) Loan Guaranty Program
Women's Prequalification Loan Program: Provides women business owners a pre-

authorized loan guaranty commitment. It provides a quick response to loan requests of $250,000 or less.

7(a) Loan Guaranty Program
Secondary Market: Lenders who hold business loans guaranteed by the SBA may improve profitability and liquidity by selling the guaranteed portions of those loans in the secondary market. Banks, savings and loan companies/ credit unions and pension funds, and insurance companies are frequent buyers.

8(a) Participant Loan Programs: Makes financial assistance available to 8(a) certified firms. Applicants must be participants in the 8(a) Program and eligible for contractual assistance. Loans can be made directly or through lending institutions under the agency's immediate participation or guaranty programs. Loans may be used for facilities/equipment or working capital.

7(m) MicroLoan Demonstration Program: Aimed at small businesses needing small-scale financing/technical assistance for start-up or expansion. Short-term loans of up to $25,000 are made to small businesses for the purchase of machinery and equipment, furniture and fixtures, inventory, supplies and working capital.

502 Local Development Company Program: Provides long-term, fixed asset financing through certified development companies. Proceeds are provided as follows: 50% by an unguaranteed bank loan, 40% by an SBA guaranteed debenture, 10% by the small business customer. The maximum SBA debenture is $1 million.

504 Certified Development Company Program: Provides long-term, fixed asset financing through certified development companies. Proceeds are provided as follows: 50% by an unguaranteed bank loan, 40% by an SBA guaranteed debenture, 10% by the small business customer. The maximum SBA debenture is $1 million.

Surety Bond Program
Prior Approval Program: Aimed at small construction/ service contractors; surety/insurance companies; minority/ women's groups; federal/state agencies; state insurance departments; federal/state and other procurement officials.

Surety Bond Program
Preferred Surety Bond (PSB) Program: Aimed at small construction and service contractors; surety/insurance companies; minority and women's groups; federal/state agencies; state insurance departments; federal and state and other procurement officials. The decision to issue a surety bond guarantee is made by participating sureties. There are participating sureties authorized by SBA to issue/monitor and service bonds without prior SBA approval. SBA guarantees surety bonds for construction, service/supply contracts up to $1.25 million.

Export Working Capital Program (EWCP): Replaces the Export Revolving Line of Credit Program. EWCP will allow up to a 90% guarantee on private-sector loans of up to $750,000 for working capital. Loans can be for single or multiple export sales and can be extended for pre-shipment working capital and post-shipment exposure coverage.

Disaster Assistance Loan Program: A disaster-assistance loan program for nonagricultural victims. Eligibility is based on financial criteria. Interest rates fluctuate according to statutory formulas. There is a lower rate available to applicants without credit available elsewhere, not to exceed 4%, and a higher interest rate for those with credit available elsewhere, not to exceed 8%.

Disaster Assistance to Businesses
Loans for Physical Damage: Available to qualified businesses for uninsured losses up to $1.5 million for businesses of any size to repair/replace business property to pre-disaster conditions. Loans may be used to replace/repair equipment, fixtures, inventory, and leasehold improvements.

Disaster Assistance to Businesses
Economic Injury Disaster Loan (EIDL): For businesses that sustain economic injury as a result of a disaster. Working capital loans are made to help businesses pay ordinary/necessary expenses which would have been payable barring disaster. Maximum loan amounts is $1.5 million EIDL and physical damage loans combined unless the business meets the criteria for major source of employment.

Disaster Assistance to Businesses
Loan for Major Source of Employment (MSE): For business, large and small, and nonprofit organizations. The $1.5 million limit may be waived for businesses that employ 250 or more in an affected area.

Disaster Assistance to Individual Homeowners and Renters:
Real Property: Loans available to qualified homeowner/ renter applicants for uninsured losses up to $200,000 to repair/ restore a primary residence to pre-disaster condition. Homeowners may apply for an additional 20% for disaster mitigation. This is a long-term program for individual disaster losses.

Disaster Assistance to Individuals Homeowners and Renters:
Personal Property: Loans available to qualified homeowner/ renter applicants for uninsured losses up to $40,000 to repair/ replace personal property such as clothing, furniture, cars, etc.

Government Contracting
Certificate of Competency: Helps small businesses to receive government contracts by providing an appeal process to low-bidder businesses denied government contracts by contracting officers for perceived lack of ability to satisfactorily perform.

Government Contracting
Prime Contract: Program increases small business opportunities in the federal acquisition process through initiation of small business set-asides, identification of new small business sources, counseling small businesses on how to do business with the federal government, and assessment of compliance with the Small Business Act through surveillance reviews.

Government Contracting
Breakout Program: Promotes/influences and enhances the break-out of historically sole-source items for full and open competition in order to effect significant savings to the federal government.

Government Contracting
Natural Resources Sales Assistance Program:
Timber Sales: Set-aside program maintains small businesses in the forest products industry by providing them with preferential bidding opportunities for purchasing timber offered by the federal government. Joint operation of the SBA and federal timber-selling agencies throughout the U.S.

National Small Business Tree Planting Program: Allocates grants to the states/trust territories for the purpose of contracting with small businesses to plant trees on land owned and controlled by state/local governments. Federal dollars are matched by community funds.

Government Contracting
Procurement Automated Source System (PASS): A computerized database of small businesses nationwide which are interested in federal procurement opportunities. Information on each company includes a summary of capabilities, ownership and qualifications.

Small Business Technology Transfer Program (STTR) Pilot Program: This is similar in philosophy and objectives to the SBIR program. It has a requirement that the small firm competing for the Small Business Technology Transfer Program (STTR) Research and Development (R&D) project must collaborate with a nonprofit research institution. This is a joint venture project from the initial bid submission to project completion. Available to small high-tech R&D firms.

Alabama

* Alabama Development Office
401 Adams Avenue, Suite 670   800-248-0033
Montgomery, AL 36130-4106   334-242-0400
www.ado.state.al.us/finance1.htm   Fax: 334-242-2414
Alabama offers a variety of financial options aimed at starting and growing your business. They offer one-stop support and incentives that will tailor programs to meet individual companies needs. The Alabama Development Office administers the following programs: *Industrial Revenue Bonds, Industrial Development Grants, Linked Deposits, Revolving Loan Funds, Infrastructure Grant Program, Appalachian Regional Grant Program, Commercial Lending Sources, Tennessee Valley Authority Economic Development Loan Fund, Alabama Industrial Access Road and Bridge Program.*

* Rural Development
USDA Rural Development
4121 Carmichael Road, Suite 601   334-279-3400
Montgomery, AL 36106-3683   Fax: 334-279-3403
www.rurdev.usda.gov/al
There are many forms of grants and loans provided by the

Alabama Rural Development Office. Funds are available in the form of guaranteed loans through a local lender, and direct loans and grants directly from the U.S. Treasury, they include *Rural Business Enterprise Grants, Rural Business Opportunity Grants, Business and Industry Direct Loan Program, Business and Industry Guaranteed Loan Program, Intermediary Relending Program, Rural Economic Development Zero Interest Loans, Rural Economic Development Grants and Rural Cooperative Development Grants*. Contact your state office for additional information.

* Alabama Department of Revenue

P.O. Box 327001   334-242-1170
Montgomery, AL 36132-7001   Fax: 334-242-0550
www.ador.state.al.us

The Alabama Department of Revenue administers several tax incentives for existing, expanding and new industries. They are a one-stop office for tax forms, filing information, laws and tax publications.

* Alabama Technology Network

500 Beacon Parkway West   205-943-4808
Birmingham, AL 35209   Fax: 205-943-4813
www.atn.org

The Alabama Technology Network helps manufacturers in Alabama improve their global competitiveness through technical assistance, workforce training and technology transfer. They provide ten network centers that will provide assistance to Alabama's existing industries.

* Department of Agriculture and Industry

P.O. Box 3336
Montgomery, AL 36109   334-240-7100
agri-ind.state.al.us

Supplies both information and technical support to farmers, businesses and consumers.

* Alabama Industrial Development and Training

One Technology Court
Montgomery, AL 36116   334-242-4158
www.aidt.edu

Offers recruiting, assessing and training potential employees; developing and producing training materials, and locating facilities; and, delivering customized services.

* Alabama International Trade Center

University of Alabama
Box 870396
Tuscaloosa, AL 35498-0396   205-348-7621
www.aitc.ua.edu

Services offered include foreign market research, strategic planning and consulting, implementation recommendations, training seminars and general information.

* Office of Minority Business Enterprise

401 Adams Ave.   334-242-2224
Montgomery, AL 36130   800-447-4191
www.adeca.alabama.gov/content/dir/dir_ombe.aspx

Assists minorities in achieving effective and equitable participation in the American free enterprise system and in overcoming social and economic disadvantages that have

limited their participation in the past. Management and technical assistance is provided to minority firms on request.

* State Treasurer's Office

Linked Deposits
Room S-106
The State Capitol Building
Montgomery, AL 36130   334-242-7500
www.treasury.state.al.us

The Alabama State Treasury administers the *Linked Deposit Program*, which provides low interest loans to small business owners and farmers starting new businesses or maintaining existing ones.

* Loans For Farmers

Farm Service Agency
U.S. Department of Agriculture
4121 Carmichael Road, Suite 600   334 279-3501
Montgomery, AL 36106-2872   Fax: 334-279-3550
http://www.fsa.usda.gov/al/

The Farm Service Agency provides Direct and Guaranteed Loans to farmers through a variety of programs, including:

Farm Ownership Loans: purchase farmland, construct or repair buildings and other fixtures, and promote soil and water conservation. Up to $200,000.

Operating Loans: purchase items needed for a successful farm operation, such as livestock, farm equipment, feed, seed, fuel, farm chemicals, insurance, and other operating expenses. Can also be used to pay for minor improvements. Up to $200,000.

Beginning Farmer and Rancher Loans: provides funds to beginning and farmers and ranchers who are unable to obtain financing elsewhere.

Downpayment Farm Ownership Loans for Beginning Farmers: helps beginning farmers and ranchers purchase a farm or ranch. Also provides a way for retiring farmers to transfer their land to a future generation of farmers and ranchers. Applicant must have a downpayment of 10% and FSA with finance 40%, with the remaining balance from a commercial lender. Purchase price cannot exceed $250,000.

Loans to Socially Disadvantaged Farmers/Ranchers: helps socially disadvantaged applicants buy and operate family-size farms and ranches.

Youth Loans: Made to youths to establish and operate income-producing projects with the participation in 4-H clubs, Future Farmers of America, and similar organizations. Up to $5,000.

Emergency Loan Assistance: provides loans to help producers recover from production and physical losses due to drought, flooding, and other natural disasters, or quarantine. Up to $500,000.

Beginning Farmer and Rancher Land Contract Guarantee Pilot Program: "prompt payment guarantee" from FSA. FSA will provide payment to seller two times if the beginning farmer does not pay. Program is tested in IN, IA, ND, OR, PA and WI.

Farm Ownership and Operating Loan Guarantees: FSA will guarantee loans up to $782,000.

* Small Business Administration

801 Tom Martin Drive   205-290-7101
Birmingham, AL 35211   Fax: 205-290-7404
http://www.sba.gov/al/

The Alabama SBA provides counseling and training along with a start-up kit to help you as you begin your own business. Their services include a Women's Business Ownership Representative to assist women business owners, an International Trade Specialist is to assist businesses interested in exporting and a Veterans Affairs Program.

Alaska

* Department of Community and Economic Development

P.O. Box 11080   907-465-2017
Juneau, AK 99811   Fax: 907-465-3767
www.dced.state.ak.us

The Department of Community and Economic Development should be your first stop in starting your own business in Alaska. They oversee many agencies critical to your businesses success including: Community and Business Development, International Trade and Market Development, Industrial Development and Export Authority and many more.

* Rural Development

800 W. Evergreen, Suite 201   907-761-7705
Palmer, AK 99645   Fax: 907-761-7783
www.rurdev.usda.gov/ak

The Rural Development Team of Alaska is dedicated to providing rural Alaskans with a wide variety of programs designed to assist community and businesses. Loans and grants are available to entrepreneurs to develop and maintain local business and industry.

* Alaska Department of Revenue

Tax Division
P.O. Box 110420   907-465-2320
Juneau, AK 99811-0420   Fax: 907-465-2375
www.revenue.state.ak.us

Although Alaska has no state income tax or sales tax, the Department of Revenue can provide the entrepreneur with information on regulations and other tax issues concerning their business.

* International Trade and Market Development

P.O. Box 110804   907-465-2017
Juneau, AK 99811-0804   Fax: 907-465-3767
www.dced.state.ak.us/trade

The International Trade and Market Development, a division of the Community and Economic Development Office provides representatives to help promote Alaska's products and services by providing information and access to markets overseas, including government-to-government relations.

* Small Business Administration

510 L Street, Suite 310   907-271-4022
Anchorage, AK 99501-1952   800-755-7034
www.sba.gov/ak   Fax: 907-271-4545

The Alaska SBA's goal is to assist entrepreneurs in many aspects of business. They provide counseling and training along with a start-up kit to help you as you begin your own business.

* Buy Alaska

University of Alaska
Small Business Development Center
430 W. 7th Avenue, Suite 110   907-274-7232
Anchorage, AK 99501   800-478-7232
www.buyalaska.com

The Buy Alaska Program's mission is to assist businesses, consumers, and government entities in finding competitive Alaskan sources for goods and services with the goal of keeping more dollars in Alaska. The Buy Alaska Program offers the free service of researching buying needs and "matching" buyers with sellers. Businesses and consumers seeking to buy competitively-priced goods and services can get help from Buy Alaska in identifying local Alaskan vendors and providers from which to make their purchases.

* Alaska Science and Technology Foundation

4500 Diplomacy Drive, Suite 515   907-272-4333
Anchorage, AK 99508   Fax: 907-274-6228
www.dced.state.ak.us/astf/index.cfm

The mission of the Alaska Science and Technology Foundation is to enhance the development and application of science and technology for the benefit of Alaskans. The Foundation provides grants in five areas: *Major Individual Grants, Small Grants, Group Project Grants, Direct Grants to Teachers,* and *Small Business Innovation Research Bridging Grants.*

* Alaska Growth Capital

3900 C Street, Suite 302   907-339-6760
Anchorage, AK 99507   888-315-4904
www.akgrowth.com   Fax: 907-339-6771

This is a commercial financial institution, licensed and regulated by the State of Alaska. It is not regulated as a bank, but rather as a Business and Industrial Development Corporation (BIDCO). BIDCOs do not accept deposits and do not provide consumer lending. BIDCOs focus exclusively on financing businesses.

* Power Project Fund

Alaska Energy Authority
813 W. Northern Lights Blvd.   907-269-3000
Anchorage, AK 99503   Fax: 907-269-3004
www.aidea.org/powerloan.htm

Provides loans to local utilities, local governments or independent power producers for the development or upgrade of electric power facilities, including conservation, bulk fuel storage and waste energy conservation, or potable water supply projects. Loan term is related to the life of the project.

* The Polaris Fund

Jim Yarmon
c/o Yarmon Investments
840 K Street, #201
Anchorage, AK 99501   907-276-4466
www.alaska.net/~jimyarm/polhome.htm

The purpose of the Polaris Fund is to finance young companies with potential to achieve profitable sales by providing equity capital. Ideal companies should have an experienced management team, an innovative, distinctive product with a $100-$500 million growing market and a well-defined channel for sales. Polaris investments are usually in the $100,000 to $500,000 range, and favor companies that align Polaris closely with management.

* Business Incentive Program

Bill Paulick
Division of Trade & Development
P.O. Box 110804
Juneau, AK 99811-0804   907-465-3961
Email: Bill_Paulick@commerce.state.ak.us

Under this program companies will be reimbursed (rather than be paid up front) for designated portions of relocation costs, site development costs, special employee training not covered by other programs, and special analysis of sites in Alaska. The program was passed into law in April 1998 and is limited to $3 million annually.

* Small Business Economic Development Revolving Loan Fund

Alaska Department of Commerce and Economic
  Development
Division of Investments
P.O. Box 34159   800-478-LOAN
Juneau, AK 99803   907-465-2510
www.dced.state.ak.us/investments

This program was established in 1987 in conjunction with the U.S. Department of Commerce, Economic Development Administration (EDA). The purpose of the program is to provide private sector employment in the areas designated by EDA. The maximum loan amount is $300,000. Applicants are required to obtain additional private, non-public financing of approximately twice the amount requested. The interest rate of prime minus 4 points is set by the Loan Administration Board consisting of three members from the existing divisional loan committee and two members from the private sector. The board is responsible for setting loan policy and for making all major loan decisions.

* Commercial Fishing Revolving Loan Fund

Alaska Department of Community and Economic
  Development
Division of Investments
P.O. Box 34159
Juneau, AK 99803   907-465-2510
www.dced.state.ak.us/investments

Commercial fishing loans are available for various purposes at prime plus two percent (up to a maximum of 10.5%) for a 15-year term. All loans must be secured by adequate collateral.

* Alaska Employment Service

Work Opportunity Tax Credit Coordinator
P.O. Box 25509   907-465-5953
Juneau, AK 99802   Fax: 907-465-8753

Work Opportunity Tax Credit (WOTC): Offers employers tax credits as an incentive to hire people from seven target groups including Alaska Temporary Assistance Program (ATAP) and Aid for Families with Dependent Children (AFDC) recipients, food stamp recipients, veterans, vocational rehabilitation recipients, ex-felons, and high risk youth. The credit amount is 40% of up to $6,000 in qualified first year wages with a maximum credit of $2,400.

Welfare-to-Work Tax Credit (W2W): The W2W tax credit is available for hiring long-term ATAP and AFDC clients. The W2W tax credit is 35% of the first $10,000 in wages paid the first year, and 50% of the first $10,000 paid for the second year. The maximum tax credit is $3,500 the first year and $5,000 the second year for a total of $8,500.

* Exploration Incentive

Department of Natural Resources
Division of Oil and Gas
550 West 7th Ave., Suite 800
Anchorage, AK 99501   907-269-8900
www.dog.dnr.state.ak.us/oil/programs/incentives/incenti
ves.htm

Up to $30 million in qualifying costs can be credited against future state corporate income tax, mining license tax and production royalties. Geophysical and geochemical surveys, trenching, bulk sampling, drilling, metallurgical testing and underground exploration are included as qualifying costs. Unused credit can be retained for 15 years and may be assigned to successors in interest.

* Alaska Industrial Development and Export Authority (AIDEA)

813 West Northern Lights   907-269-3000
Anchorage, AK 99503-6690   800-300-8534
http://www.aidea.org/   Fax: 907-269-3044

The Alaska Industrial Development and Export Authority's (AIDEA) mission is to encourage economic growth and diversification in Alaska. AIDEA finances businesses, helping to diversify the economy of Alaska and creating jobs for Alaskans. AIDEA also oversees the Alaska Energy Authority. The AIDEA has many programs; contact them directly to see if they have one to fit your business needs.

Loan Participation Program: provides long-term financing to Alaska businesses for new or existing projects, or for the refinancing of existing loans. This program has helped diversify the Alaskan economy by providing financing for a large variety of commercial facilities ranging from office buildings, warehouses and retail establishments to hotels, fishing vessels and manufacturing facilities. Financing is available for up to 15 years for personal property and up to 25 years for real property.

Business and Export Assistance Loan Guarantee: the program is designed to assist small to medium sized Alaskan businesses. The guarantee is applied to loans made to eligible Alaska business enterprises for real property, tangible personal property, working capital and export transactions. Through the program AIDEA is authorized to guarantee up to 80% of a loan, not to exceed $1 million, originated by eligible financial institutions. A part of this program, aimed at small businesses in rural areas, provides a streamlined application process for secured and unsecured loan guarantees up to $100,000.

Conduit Revenue Bond Program: Manufactures can apply for tax-exempt financing through small-issue manufacturing bonds. The bonds can be used to finance a manufacturing facility.

* Alaska Department of Natural Resources

Division of Agriculture
1800 Glenn Hwy, Suite 12   907-745-7200
Palmer, AK 99645-6736   Fax: 907-745-7242
www.dnr.state.ak.us/ag/ag_arlf.htm

Agricultural Revolving Loan Fund: Available to individual farmers, ranchers, homesteaders, partnerships or corporations who are Alaska residents and can demonstrate experience in the farming business. Provides direct short term loans (1-year) up to $200,000. Product processing and land clearing loans up to $250,000, farm development loans up to $1 million. Interest rates at 5 percent with varying pay back periods.

* Division of Energy

Alaska Energy Authority/AIDEA
813 West Northern Lights Blvd.   907-269-3036
Anchorage, AK 99503   Fax: 907-269-3044
www.aidea.org/loanfund.htm

Bulk Fuel Revolving Loan Fund: Assists communities in purchasing bulk fuel oil. A private individual who has a written endorsement from the government body of the community is eligible. Loan amount may not exceed 90 percent of the wholesale price of the fuel being purchased. Maximum loan amount is $200,000. Loan must be repaid within one year.

* Fisheries Research and Development Grants

National Oceanic and Atmospheric Administration
National Marine Fisheries Services
P.O. Box 21668   907-586-7221
Juneau, AK 99802-1668   Fax: 907-586-7249
www.fakr.noaa.gov/omi/grants

The Grants Program Office of the National Marine Fisheries Service, Alaska Region administers a broad range of financial assistance and programs. The programs provide financial assistance for research and development projects to benefit the U.S. fishing industry.

* Alaska Commercial Fishing and Agriculture Bank (CFAB)

P.O. Box 92070
Anchorage, AK 99509   907-276-2007
www.cfabalaska.com

Established by Alaska Statute, CFAB is a private lending cooperative in which borrowers become members. Loans may be made for harvesting, marketing, or processing of fish or agriculture products. Interest rates are determined by the periodic sale of Farm Credit bonds in the national market.

* State Conservationist

USDA - Natural Resources Conservation Service
800 W. Evergreen Avenue, Suite 100   907-761-7760
Palmer, AK 99645   Fax: 907-761-7790
http://www.ak.nrcs.usda.gov/programs/index.html

The Natural Resources Conservation Service assists owners of America's private land conserve their soil, water and other natural resources. They offer many programs to achieve harmony between people and the land. The voluntary program *Environmental Quality Incentives Program (EQIP)* is for Alaskan farmers and ranchers that are concerned about environmental quality. EQIP offers financial and technical help to assist eligible participants install and implement conservation programs.

* Conservation Grants

Alaska Conservation Foundation
441 West 5th Avenue, Suite 502   907-276-1917
Anchorage, AK 99501   Fax: 907-274-4145
www.akcf.org

The Alaska Conservation Foundation is a foundation committed to the environment that receives and awards grants to protect the Alaska ecosystems and sustainable communities for the Alaskan people. The Foundation provides a number of grants for a variety of needs including: *General Grantmaking, Rapid Response Grants, Sustainable Community Development Grants, Watchable Wildlife Conservation Trust Grants* and more.

* Alaska Economic Development Resource Guide

Division of Community and Business Development
Department of Community and
    Economic Development
550 W 7th, Suite 770   907-269-4580
Anchorage, AK 99501   Fax: 907-269-4539
http://www.dced.state.ak.us/cbd/edrg/EDRG.htm

This publication describes more than 120 assistance programs for Alaskan individuals and businesses. It is available for $7 for a hard copy or you can obtain a free copy at the above web site.

* Alaska Product Preference and Forest Product Preference Programs

Department of Community and
    Economic Development
Division of Community and Business Development
550 W 7th, Suite 1770   907-269-8110
Anchorage, AK 99507   Fax: 907-269-8125
http://www.dced.state.ak.us/cbd/prodpref/prodpref.htm

These programs provide incentives for Alaska businesses responding to bids or proposals for state contracts by giving them preferential consideration. The Alaska Product Preference Program and the Alaska Forest Product Preference Program can provide a cost preference of up to 7%.

* Loans For Farmers

Farm Service Agency
U.S. Department of Agriculture
800 West Evergreen St., Suite 216   907-761-7738
Palmer, AK 99645-6539   Fax: 907-761-7789
http://www.fsa.usda.gov/ak/

The Farm Service Agency provides Direct and Guaranteed Loans to farmers through a variety of programs, including:

Farm Ownership Loans: purchase farmland, construct or repair buildings and other fixtures, and promote soil and water conservation. Up to $200,000.

Operating Loans: purchase items needed for a successful farm operation, such as livestock, farm equipment, feed, seed, fuel, farm chemicals, insurance, and other operating expenses. Can also be used to pay for minor improvements. Up to $200,000.

Beginning Farmer and Rancher Loans: provides funds to beginning and farmers and ranchers who are unable to obtain financing elsewhere.

Downpayment Farm Ownership Loans for Beginning Farmers: helps beginning farmers and ranchers purchase a farm or ranch. Also provides a way for retiring farmers to transfer their land to a future generation of farmers and ranchers. Applicant must have a downpayment of 10% and FSA with finance 40%, with the remaining balance from a commercial lender. Purchase price cannot exceed $250,000.

Loans to Socially Disadvantaged Farmers/Ranchers: helps socially disadvantaged applicants buy and operate family-size farms and ranches.

Youth Loans: Made to youths to establish and operate income-producing projects with the participation in 4-H clubs, Future Farmers of America, and similar organizations. Up to $5,000.

Emergency Loan Assistance: provides loans to help producers recover from production and physical losses due to drought, flooding, and other natural disasters, or quarantine. Up to $500,000.

Beginning Farmer and Rancher Land Contract Guarantee Pilot Program: "prompt payment guarantee" from FSA. FSA will provide payment to seller two times if the beginning farmer does not pay. Program is tested in IN, IA, ND, OR, PA and WI.

Farm Ownership and Operating Loan Guarantees: FSA will guarantee loans up to $782,000.

Arizona

* Arizona Department of Commerce
Executive Tower, Suite 600
1700 W. Washington   800-528-8421
Phoenix, AZ 85007   602-771-1100
www.azcommerce.com

If you are thinking about starting a business or already have a business in Arizona, you should get to know the Department of Commerce. They provide a wealth of information about all aspects of business including financial options.

Arizona Business Connection: A resource center for information, referrals and advice for every stage of small business development. Representatives are available to answer questions and provide a free custom packet.

Small Business Advocate: Works with chambers of commerce and other groups to develop policies and programs that will address fundamental statewide issues of concern to all small businesses.
- Develops customized packets of information and licenses required for small business start-up, expansion, and relocation.
- Provides the booklet *Guide To Establishing and Operating a Business In Arizona* which includes an extensive directory and resources for referrals and networking opportunities.
- Provides coordination and publicity for programs and services that assist minority and women business owners, and assists state agencies in certification of minority and women owned businesses.
- Conducts seminars to help local companies procure goods and services from qualified firms.
- Assists entrepreneurs in resolving matters involving state government offices.
- The High Technology Division aids and assists the growth of high technology companies in Arizona.

The Community Planning Staff: Provides technical assistance on development-related issues, such as community-strategic planning, land-use planning, design review, zoning and infrastructure development, and financing. Provides direct assistance to rural communities in organizing an economic development program or effort, and evaluating community resources. Provides assistance with downtown revitalization projects. Provides support for rural community tourism development efforts. This program helps organizations responsible for retention and expansion develop a program to retain and encourage expansion of existing businesses.

Arizona's Work Force Recruitment and Job Training Program: Provides job training assistance to businesses creating net new jobs in Arizona. The program is designed to provide companies with a well equipped work force while ensuring maximum leverage of state and federal training funds.

Strategic Finance Division: Offers a wide range of loan and grant programs which provide economic development resources for companies relocating to or expanding in Arizona including the following:
- *Commerce & Economic Development Commission (CEDC):* A low-interest rate loan program funded by proceeds from the Arizona Lottery. The CEDC's activities include:
  - *Direct Assistance To Arizona Business*: to provide expansion capital to existing companies.
  - *Technology Sector Capital*: financing that supports the development and growth of high-tech industries.
  - *Intermediary Participation Program*: partnerships with other groups that provide economic development loans.
  - A CEDC loan can be used to purchase fixed assets. A grant component tied to specific wage levels may also be available. In general, projects are weighted based on job creation, the presence of other investors and projected tax revenues. Final loan approval is determined by a six-member commission appointed by the Governor of Arizona. Attractive terms and a fixed interest rate are available.

Revolving Energy Loans for Arizona (RELA): A loan fund to promote and assist energy-related projects and companies. Arizona nonprofit entities, political subdivisions or companies that purchase energy-conserving products for use in their own facilities are eligible. In addition, manufacturers of energy-conserving products may apply. Loan requests may range from $10,000 to $500,000 up to a maximum of 60% of total project costs. The RELA program offers a 5% interest rate and variable terms depending on energy payback.

Economic Strength Projects (ESP) offers grants for road construction. This is a very competitive program based on the economic impact of applicant projects in the community in which it will be located. Applications are submitted by a town, city or county.

The Enterprise Zones Program: Offers income tax credits and property tax reclassification for eligible companies meeting employment and industry requirements. Benefits are based on net new job creation, employment of economically disadvantaged or dislocated workers and location in an enterprise zone.

Minority/Women-Owned Business Enterprises Office: Acts as a resource and advocate for women and minority small businesses. Services include: a statewide directory of women/minority-owned businesses, Professional Women's conference sponsorship, newsletter containing calendar of events and relevant articles, marketing to state agencies and businesses, and certification seminars.

* Arizona Rural Business Program
Arizona Rural Development Office
3003 North Central, Suite 900   602-280-8701
Phoenix, AZ 85012-2906   Fax: 602-280-8708
http://www.rurdev.usda.gov/az/RBuss.htm

The Arizona Rural Business Program is committed to the creation of viable new and improved business and cooperatives in rural Arizona. The program delivers a variety of assistance to businesses including: *Business and Industry Guaranteed Loans, Intermediary Relending Program, Rural Business Enterprise Grants* and *Rural Cooperative Development Grants.*

* Arizona Department of Revenue

3191 N. Washington
Chandler, AZ 85225   602-225-2060
http://www.revenue.state.az.us

The Arizona Department of Revenue doesn't just collect taxes; it also offers a variety of information for the small business owner. They offer the guides *A-Z Taxes for Small Business Program* and *Business Basics: A Guide to Taxes for Arizona.* In addition they will provide Business Seminars, Education Classes and Tax Credit information.

* Loans For Farmers

Farm Service Agency
U.S. Department of Agriculture
77 East Thomas Road, Suite 240
Phoenix, AZ 85012   602-640-5200
http://www.fsa.usda.gov/az/AZ.htm

The Farm Service Agency provides Direct and Guaranteed Loans to farmers through a variety of programs, including:

Farm Ownership Loans: purchase farmland, construct or repair buildings and other fixtures, and promote soil and water conservation. Up to $200,000.

Operating Loans: purchase items needed for a successful farm operation, such as livestock, farm equipment, feed, seed, fuel, farm chemicals, insurance, and other operating expenses. Can also be used to pay for minor improvements. Up to $200,000.

Beginning Farmer and Rancher Loans: provides funds to beginning and farmers and ranchers who are unable to obtain financing elsewhere.

Downpayment Farm Ownership Loans for Beginning Farmers: helps beginning farmers and ranchers purchase a farm or ranch. Also provides a way for retiring farmers to transfer their land to a future generation of farmers and ranchers. Applicant must have a downpayment of 10% and FSA with finance 40%, with the remaining balance from a commercial lender. Purchase price cannot exceed $250,000.

Loans to Socially Disadvantaged Farmers/Ranchers: helps socially disadvantaged applicants buy and operate family-size farms and ranches.

Youth Loans: Made to youths to establish and operate income-producing projects with the participation in 4-H clubs, Future Farmers of America, and similar organizations. Up to $5,000.

Emergency Loan Assistance: provides loans to help producers recover from production and physical losses due to drought, flooding, and other natural disasters, or quarantine. Up to $500,000.

Beginning Farmer and Rancher Land Contract Guarantee Pilot Program: "prompt payment guarantee" from FSA. FSA will provide payment to seller two times if the beginning farmer does not pay. Program is tested in IN, IA, ND, OR, PA and WI.

Farm Ownership and Operating Loan Guarantees: FSA will guarantee loans up to $782,000.

* Small Business Administration (SBA)

2828 N. Central Ave., #800   602-745-7200
Phoenix, AZ 85004-1093   Fax: 602-745-7210
www.sba.gov/az

The Arizona District Small Business Administration Office delivers a variety of programs and services, such as startup and operational assistance through small business training and counseling, financial assistance for startup's, operational and disaster help, business opportunities, such as government contracting, subcontracting, procurement, and much more.

Arkansas

* Arkansas Department of Economic Development

1 State Capitol Mall   501-682-1121
Little Rock, AR 72201   800-ARKANSAS
www.aedc.state.ar.us   Fax: 501-682-7394

Existing Workforce Training Program (EWTP): Provides financial assistance to Arkansas manufacturing industries for upgrading the skills of their existing workforce. Secondary objectives are to build the capacity within their state-supported institutions to supply the ongoing training needs of Arkansas industries and to increase industry participation in the state's School-to-Work initiative.

ScrapMatch: A program designed to help Arkansas manufacturers find markets for their industrial scrap materials, thereby lowering the cost of doing business. ScrapMatch uses an electronic data management system to match industrial waste generators with secondary material markets.

Industrial Waste Minimization Program and Resource Recovery: Reduction, reuse, and recycling of industrial waste is the Industrial Waste Minimization Program's focus. By-product and surplus asset marketing assistance are also provided. The program provides on-site waste reduction audits and technical assistance to industry.

Customized Training Incentive Program: Provides intensive pre-employment training for Arkansas workers to meet the increasing technical employment needs of the state's new and expanding businesses. Additionally, financial assistance to manufacturing industries for upgrading the skills of their existing workforce is also available.

Bond Guaranty Programs: For companies that have a financial history but are unable to sell industrial revenue bonds to the public, the Arkansas Economic Development Commission (AEDC) can assure bond holders of repayment by guaranteeing up to $4 million of a bond issue. The state's guaranty allows the bonds to be sold at a higher credit rating, therefore lowering the effective interest rate for the company. The AEDC charges a 5% fee for guaranteeing issues of this type.

Economic Development District Revolving Funds: Several planning and development districts in Arkansas have revolving loan funds for economic development purposes. The loans are limited to $100,000 per business, must involve specific levels of job creation, and must be matched by a bank loan.

Create Rebate Program: Companies hiring specified net new full-time permanent employees within 24 months after completion of an approved expansion and/or new location project can be eligible to receive a financial incentive to be used for a specific purpose. This incentive ranges from 3.9% to 5% in areas with an unemployment rate in excess of 10%, or more than 3% above the state's average unemployment rate for the preceding calendar year.

Industrial Revenue Bonds: Provide manufacturers with below-market financing. Interest on tax exempt issues is normally 80% of prime, but this may vary depending on terms of the issue. For real estate loans, 15 years is the most common term. The primary goal of this financing program is to enable manufacturers to purchase land, buildings, and equipment to expand their operations.

Arkansas Economic Development Act (AEDA): To utilize the AEDA program, companies must sign a financial agreement prior to construction outlining the terms of the incentives and stipulations. There are two basic incentives provided: A state corporate income tax credit up to 100% of the total amount of annual debt service paid to the lender financing a project; Refund of sales and use taxes on construction materials, machinery, and equipment associated with a project during the period specified by the financial agreement.

Advantage Arkansas Program: A job tax credit program for qualifying new and expanding companies which provides corporate income tax credits and sales and use tax refunds to companies locating or expanding in Arkansas.

Free Port Law: No tax on goods in transit or raw materials and finished goods destined for out-of-state sales; no sales tax on manufacturing equipment, pollution control facilities, or raw materials; no property tax on textile mills.

Day Care Facility Incentive Program: Companies can receive a sales and use tax refund on the initial cost of construction materials and furnishings purchased to build and equip an approved child care facility. Additionally, a corporate income tax credit of 3.9% of the total annual payroll of the workers employed exclusively to provide childcare service, or a $5,000 income tax credit for the first year the business provides its employees with a day care facility is also available.

Tourism Development: Provides state sales tax credits up to 10% of approved project costs for the creation or expansion of eligible tourist attractions exceeding $500,000, and 25% of project costs exceeding $1,000,000.

Recycling Equipment Tax Credit: Allows taxpayers to receive a tax credit for the purchase of equipment used exclusively for reduction, reuse, or recycling of solid waste material for commercial purposes, whether or not for profit, and the cost of installation of such equipment by outside contractors. The amount of the credit shall equal 30% of the cost of eligible equipment and installation costs.

Motion Picture Incentive Act: Qualifying motion picture production companies spending in excess of $500,000 within six months, or $1 million within 12 months may receive a refund of state sales and use taxes paid on qualified expenditures incurred in conjunction with a film, telefilm, music video, documentary, episodic television show, or commercial advertisement.

Biotechnology Development and Training Act: Offers three different income tax credits to taxpayers furthering biotechnical business development. The first credit is a 5% income tax credit applied to costs to build and equip eligible biotechnical facilities. The second credit allows a 30% income tax credit both for eligible employee training costs

and for contract with state-supported institutions for higher education to conduct qualified cooperative research projects. The third credit allows an income tax credit for qualified research in biotechnology, including but not limited to the cost of purchasing, licensing, developing, or protecting intellectual property. This credit is equal to 20% of the amount the cost of qualified research exceeds the cost of such resource in the base year.

The *Arkansas Economic Development Commission's (AEDC)* international offices assist Arkansas companies in exporting their products and services by arranging personalized meetings with potential distributors, sales representatives or end users in the countries targeted for AEDC's export promotion efforts. In addition to this service, they also offer the following:
- Market research
- Assisting companies exhibiting in international trade fairs
- Planning and coordinating trade missions
- Obtaining trade leads
- Representing and/or advising companies on export transactions
- Accompanying company representatives on export sales trips
- Promoting companies in meetings with prospective buyers

* USDA Rural Development
Shirley Tucker
Director for Rural Business Cooperative Programs
700 West Capitol, Room 3416   501-301-3280
Little Rock, AR 72201-3225   Fax: 501-301-3294
www.rurdev.usda.gov/ar

The Rural Business-Cooperative Service provides loans to help develop emerging businesses that will bring employment opportunities to rural areas. Grants are available for public bodies and private nonprofit corporations to facilitate development of small emerging private business enterprises in rural areas. They offer the following assistance: *Business and Industry Guaranteed Loans, Intermediary Relending Program, Rural Business Enterprise and Opportunity Grants* and *Rural and Economic Development Loans and Grants.*

* Environmental Permitting Services
Arkansas Department of Environmental Quality
8001 National Dr.
Little Rock, AR 72219   501-682-0821
www.adez.state.ar.us/custsvs/businessasst.htm

The Arkansas Department of Environmental Quality works in a pro-business manner with companies looking to locate or expand operations in Arkansas. The agency recognizes the need for business growth in Arkansas while maintaining their state's positive environmental quality.

* Arkansas Capital Corporation
2005 S. Commerce St.   501-374-9247
Little Rock, AR 72201   800-216-7237
http://acc.arccapital.com

A privately-owned, nonprofit organization established in 1957 to serve as an alternative source of financing for companies in Arkansas. Its main goal is to improve the economic climate in the state by providing long-term, fixed-rate loans to Arkansas companies. As a preferred lender for the Small Business Administration, ACC makes loans to existing operations and business start-ups for everything from new construction and equipment to working capital. ACC loans may be used in combination with bank loans, municipal bond issues, or other sources of financing.

* ASTA Investment Fund

Arkansas Science and Technology Authority
100 Main St., Suite 450
Little Rock, AR 72201   501-324-8755
www.accessarkansasscience.org/seed.html

The Arkansas Science and Technology Authority (ASTA) administers a special Investment Fund of $2.9 million which can provide seed capital for new and developing technology-based companies through loans, royalty agreements, and limited stock purchases.

* Arkansas Development Finance Authority (ADFA)

P.O. Box 8023
423 Main Street, Suite 500   501-682-5905
Little Rock, AR 72203   Fax: 501-682-5859
www.accessarkansas.org/adfa

Industrial Development Bond Guaranty Program: Offers taxable and tax exempt bond financing to both small and large businesses. Umbrella bonds, available to small businesses, spread the costs of the bond issue among all of the borrowers. ADFA also can provide interim financing for approved projects awaiting bond issuance. Available to manufacturing facilities.

Export Finance: Short-term loans to businesses based on export transactions. Financing is provided through the exporter's local bank which funds 10 percent of the loan value.

Beginning Farmer Loan Program: assists beginning farmers acquire agricultural property at lower interest rates.

Speculative Building Loan Program: provides a source of financing to Industrial Development Corps. interested in building spec. industrial facilities.

Capital Access Program: creates a method for making slightly higher risk loans more attractive to participating lending institutions.

Waste Water Revolving Loan Fund: provides low interest rate financing to municipalities wishing to improve their waste water treatment facilities.

Cooperative Revolving Loan Fund: provides low interest rate loans to agricultural cooperatives who are producing/marketing fruit & vegetable products.

Disadvantaged Business Enterprise Program: provides banks with working capital guarantees for disadvantaged business enterprise contractors.

Intermediary Relending Loan Program: $3 million Federal loan to ADFA which can be relended to businesses and communities in rural Arkansas.

Port Facilities Revolving Loan Program: supports investment in port facilities for Arkansas' navigable waterways.

Aquaculture Program: coordinates the aquaculture industry in Arkansas.

Farm Mediation Program: provides a forum for farmers and lenders to resolve loan debt service payment problems.

Farm Link Program: a listing service that links up retiring farmers with aspiring farmers.

Crop and Livestock Loan Program: provides a 50% guarantee to a commercial lender making a loan to a 4-H or FFA member.

* Arkansas Science and Technology Authority

423 Main St., Suite 200   501-683-4400
Little Rock, AR 72201   Fax: 501-683-4420
www.accessarkansasscience.org

Promotes science and technology in both the public and private sectors and works to support scientific research and job creating technology development. The following is a listing of some of the programs offered.

Applied Research Grant Programs: For companies in need of research and development and would welcome working with an Arkansas college or university to have this work completed on a cost-sharing basis.

The Technology Development Program: provides assistance in development and commercialization of new technology-based products and processes through innovative technology development projects.

Seed Capital Investment Program: Program seeks to invest in innovative Arkansas companies that utilize new products or processes in their businesses. Does not fund entire projects, just the initial working capital portion of the financing package.

* Loans For Farmers

Farm Service Agency
U.S. Department of Agriculture
700 West Capitol Avenue, Room 3416   501-301-3050
Little Rock, AR 72201-3225   Fax: 501-301-3088
http://www.fsa.usda.gov/ar/ar.htm

The Farm Service Agency provides Direct and Guaranteed Loans to farmers through a variety of programs, including:

Farm Ownership Loans: purchase farmland, construct or repair buildings and other fixtures, and promote soil and water conservation. Up to $200,000.

Operating Loans: purchase items needed for a successful farm operation, such as livestock, farm equipment, feed, seed, fuel, farm chemicals, insurance, and other operating expenses. Can also be used to pay for minor improvements. Up to $200,000.

Beginning Farmer and Rancher Loans: provides funds to beginning and farmers and ranchers who are unable to obtain financing elsewhere.

Downpayment Farm Ownership Loans for Beginning Farmers: helps beginning farmers and ranchers purchase a farm or ranch. Also provides a way for retiring farmers to transfer their land to a future generation of farmers and ranchers. Applicant must have a downpayment of 10% and FSA with finance 40%, with the remaining balance from a commercial lender. Purchase price cannot exceed $250,000.

Loans to Socially Disadvantaged Farmers/Ranchers: helps socially disadvantaged applicants buy and operate family-size farms and ranches.

Youth Loans: Made to youths to establish and operate income-producing projects with the participation in 4-H clubs, Future Farmers of America, and similar organizations. Up to $5,000.

Emergency Loan Assistance: provides loans to help producers recover from production and physical losses due to drought, flooding, and other natural disasters, or quarantine. Up to $500,000.

Beginning Farmer and Rancher Land Contract Guarantee Pilot Program: "prompt payment guarantee" from FSA. FSA will provide payment to seller two times if the beginning farmer does not pay. Program is tested in IN, IA, ND, OR, PA and WI.

Farm Ownership and Operating Loan Guarantees: FSA will guarantee loans up to $782,000.

* Small Business Administration (SBA)

2120 Riverfront Dr., #100	501-324-5871
Little Rock, AR 72202-1794	Fax: 501-324-5199
www.sba.gov/ar	

The Arkansas District Small Business Administration Office delivers a variety of programs and services, such as startup and operational assistance through small business training and counseling, financial assistance for startup's, operational and disaster help, business opportunities, such as government contracting, subcontracting, procurement, and much more.

* Arkansas Capital Corporation

Arkansas Capital Corporation	800-216-7237
200 S. Commerce	501-374-9247
Little Rock, AR 72201	Fax: 501-374-9425

Arkansas Capital Corporation	800-705-9295
700 Research Center Blvd., Suite 1608	479-444-8881
Fayetteville, AR 72701	Fax: 479-444-8882

Arkansas Capital Corporation	
P.O. Box 1403	
2905 King Street	870-923-8002
Jonesboro, AR 72403	888-726-9229
Contact: Mike Taylor	Fax: (870) 932-0135

Arkansas Capital Corporation	
The Chamber Building	870-352-2853
119 W. 3rd Street	888-870-8685
Fordyce, AR 71742	Fax: 870-352-5126
Contact: Ms. Bryn Bagwell	
www.arcapital.com	

A private, nonprofit corporation that provides fixed-rate financing for projects which do not meet the requirements for conventional bank loans. Projects must increase or maintain employment, and major portion of loan must be used for fixed assets.

California

* California Trade and Commerce Agency

1102 Q Street, Suite 6000	800-303-6000
Sacramento, CA 95814	916-322-1394
http://commerce.ca.gov/state/ttca/ttca_homepage.jsp	

California's business resources are many and varied with many local and regional programs. The following is not all-inclusive:

Office of Small Business: Offers workshops, seminars, individual counseling, and publications for those interested in small businesses. They have information and expertise in dealing with state, federal, and local agencies.

The Loan Guarantee Program: Assists small businesses that cannot qualify for bank loans. Normally, 80% of the loan amount, with the guaranteed portion of the loan not exceeding $350,000 is offered. Microloans, up to $25,000, are fully guaranteed.

Fishing Vessel: Direct loans to finance commercial fishing vessel equipment and modifications that result in fuel savings. Loans are from $10,000 to $25,000.

Hazardous Waste: Direct loans to finance equipment or a production practice that reduces waste or lessens hazardous properties. The minimum loan is $20,000. The maximum loan is $150,000.

Small Corporate Offering Registration Network: Raise up to $1 million by issuing shares directly to investors through a state-registered public offering.

Sudden and Severe Economic Dislocation (SSED): The California Trade and Commerce Agency provides gap financing to businesses in areas of the state affected by plant and military base closures, defense downsizing, industry layoffs, presidentially declared disasters and other economic problems which have contributed to job loss in California.

Old Growth Diversification Revolving Loan Fund: The California Trade and Commerce Agency provides low cost capital to businesses that create jobs in targeted timber-dependent areas. Businesses may borrow from $5,000 to $150,000 at a reduced interest rate to purchase machinery and equipment or for working capital.

Net Operating Loss Carryover: Allows businesses that experience a loss for the year to carry this loss forward to the next year in order to offset income in the following year.

Enterprise Zone Program: Encourages business development in 39 designated areas through numerous special zone incentives.

Local Agency Military Base Recovery Area: Designations which are similar to enterprise zones allowing communities to extend the aforementioned California tax credits to companies locating in a LAMBRA zone.

International Trade and Investment: Acts as a catalyst to create jobs in California through vigorous and sustained promotion of exports to global markets and foreign investment into the Golden State. They have offices in California and ten foreign locations. They offer promotion of California products and companies abroad through the Office of Export Development, current information on foreign market opportunities, the Special American Business Internship Training Program, and assistance with attracting foreign investment through the California Office of Foreign Investment. They also provide exporting financial assistance for going global through several economic development programs provided by the California Export Finance Office, a division of California's Trade and Commerce Agency. The maximum guarantee amount is $750,000. That is 90% of an $833,000 loan.

* Rural Development Authority

Charles Clendenin, Program Director
Rural Business-Cooperative Service
430 G Street, Agcy. 4169   530-792-5800
Davis, CA 95616   Fax: 530-792-5837
www.rurdev.usda.gov/ca

This service is responsible for business development programs including guaranteed loans to rural business and industries, grants to facilitate development of small and emerging private business enterprises in rural areas, and revolving loan programs that finance rural businesses. The RBS administers programs directed toward increasing rural job opportunities, facilitating development of small and emerging private business enterprises, and improving the economic and environmental climate of rural communities.

* California State Treasurer's Office

915 Capitol Mall
Sacramento, CA 95814
Mailing address:
Post Office Box 942809
915 Capitol Mall C-15
Sacramento, CA 94209-0001   916-653-2995
http://www.treasurer.ca.gov/

The California Treasurer's Office has information on a variety of bonds for businesses and offers publications on many business topics.

* Energy Technology Export Program

California Energy Commission
1516 Ninth St., MS-45
Sacramento, CA 95814   916-654-4528
www.energy.ca.gov

The California Energy Commission assists California companies through several energy export programs.

* California Capital Access Program

California Pollution Control Financing Authority
Attention: SBAF Program Manager
915 Capitol Mall, Room 466
Sacramento, CA 95814   916-654-5610
www.treasurer.ca.gov/cpcfa/cpcfa.htm

The California Pollution Control Financing Authority (CPCFA) provides a form of loan portfolio insurance which provides up to 100% coverage on certain loan defaults, encouraging banks and other financial institutions to make loans to small businesses that fall just outside of most banks' conventional underwriting standards. The maximum loan amount is $2.5 million. The maximum premium CPCFA will pay is $100,000 (per loan).

* California Industrial Development Financing Advisory Commission (CEDFAC)

California Industrial Development Financing Advisory
  Commission
915 Capitol Mall
Sacramento, CA 95814   916-653-3843
www.treasurer.ca.gov/CIDFAC/cidfac.htm

The Treasurer's office assists California manufacturing businesses in funding capital expenditures for acquisitions or expansions. Allows a business to borrow funds at competitive rates through the issuance of tax-exempt bonds enhanced by a letter of credit. The maximum face amount of an IDB bond issue is $10 million per applicant per public jurisdiction.

* Loans For Farmers

Farm Service Agency
U.S. Department of Agriculture
430 G Street, Suite 4161
Davis, CA 95616-4161   530-792-5520
http://www.fsa.usda.gov/ca/

The Farm Service Agency provides Direct and Guaranteed Loans to farmers through a variety of programs, including:

Farm Ownership Loans: purchase farmland, construct or repair buildings and other fixtures, and promote soil and water conservation. Up to $200,000.

Operating Loans: purchase items needed for a successful farm operation, such as livestock, farm equipment, feed, seed, fuel, farm chemicals, insurance, and other operating expenses. Can also be used to pay for minor improvements. Up to $200,000.

Beginning Farmer and Rancher Loans: provides funds to beginning and farmers and ranchers who are unable to obtain financing elsewhere.

Downpayment Farm Ownership Loans for Beginning Farmers: helps beginning farmers and ranchers purchase a farm or ranch. Also provides a way for retiring farmers to transfer their land to a future generation of farmers and ranchers. Applicant must have a downpayment of 10% and FSA with finance 40%, with the remaining balance from a commercial lender. Purchase price cannot exceed $250,000.

Loans to Socially Disadvantaged Farmers/Ranchers: helps socially disadvantaged applicants buy and operate family-size farms and ranches.

Youth Loans: Made to youths to establish and operate income-producing projects with the participation in 4-H clubs, Future Farmers of America, and similar organizations. Up to $5,000.

Emergency Loan Assistance: provides loans to help producers recover from production and physical losses due to drought, flooding, and other natural disasters, or quarantine. Up to $500,000.

Beginning Farmer and Rancher Land Contract Guarantee Pilot Program: "prompt payment guarantee" from FSA. FSA will provide payment to seller two times if the beginning farmer does not pay. Program is tested in IN, IA, ND, OR, PA and WI.

Farm Ownership and Operating Loan Guarantees: FSA will guarantee loans up to $782,000.

* Small Business Administration (SBA)

Los Angeles District Office
330 N. Brand, Suite 1200   818-552-3210
Glendale, CA 91203   Fax: 818-552-3260

Mark Quinn
Small Business Administration (SBA)
455 Market, 6th Floor   415-744-6820
San Francisco, CA 94105-2420   Fax: 415-744-6812
www.sba.gov/ca
Local Offices
Fresno   559-487-5791
          Fax: 559-487-5636
Sacramento   916-930-3700
          Fax: 916-930-3737

San Diego   619-557-7250
                                         619-557-5894

Santa Ana   714-550-7420
                                         714-550-0191

The California Small Business Administration Office delivers a variety of programs and services, such as startup and operational assistance through small business training and counseling, financial assistance for startup's, operational and disaster help, business opportunities, such as government contracting, subcontracting, procurement, and much more.

Colorado

* Office of Economic Development and International Trade

1625 Broadway, Suite 1710   303-892-3840
Denver, CO 80202   800-592-5920
www.state.co.us /oed/index.cfm   Fax: 303-892-3848
                                   TDD: 800-659-2656
The Office of Economic Development (OED) works with companies starting, expanding or relocating in Colorado. OED offers a wide range of services to assist new and existing businesses of every size.

Colorado Business Assistance Center: Acting as the first point of contact for the Colorado Small Business Development Center Network, the Colorado Business Assistance Center (BAC) is a one-stop shop for new and existing business owners for information regarding all of their federal, state and local licensing requirements. The BAC provides referrals to other state assistance programs around the state. The BAC distributes the *Colorado Business Resource Guide*, a comprehensive guide to starting and operating a business in Colorado.

Revolving Loan Fund Programs (RLFs): Administered locally in 14 geographic regions covering the rural areas of the state. RLFs have considerable flexibility to make small loans of two or three thousand dollars up to $250,000. Applicants can be existing or startup businesses.

Larger Business Loans: Between $100,000 and $250,000 are provided by OBD through thc Community Development Block Grant Business Loans Program when the local government is willing to assume the risk on the loan in order to create or retain jobs. Larger loans may be considered on a case by case basis.

Economic Development Commission: Will provide interest rate write-downs, low interest rate loans or subsidies to companies interested in relocating to or expanding in Colorado.

Private Activity Bonds (PABs): Provide a tax-exempt financing vehicle for facilities and equipment used in the manufacture or production of tangible personal property.

Sales Tax Exemptions: For purchases over $500 on machinery and machine tools purchased for use in manufacturing; Purchases of electricity, coal, gas, or fuel oil for use in processing, manufacturing, and all industrial uses; Sale of tangible personal property for testing, modification, inspection, or similar types of activities in Colorado; Interstate long distance telephone charges.

Local Governments: May provide incentive payments or property tax credits based on the amount of increased property taxes for qualifying new business activity in their jurisdictions.

Colorado International Trade Office (ITO): Responsible for assisting Colorado companies with all aspects of exporting, including counseling, protocol, leading trade missions, and conducting trade shows abroad. By promoting Colorado exports and attracting foreign investment, the ITO helps to build Colorado's identity as an international business center, encouraging foreign buyers to look to Colorado for products and services. The ITO is open to the public and most services are rendered at no cost.

Women's Business Office: Strives to keep the women entrepreneurs of Colorado informed about pertinent issues through all modes of communication.

Office of Economic Development Minority Business Office: Acts as a clearinghouse to disseminate information to the minority business community. Promotes economic development for minority businesses in cooperation with the state economic development activities. Establishes networks between majority and minority business sectors. Promotes minority participation in state procurement. Assists Colorado in achieving its Minority Procurement Goals of 17%. Works with the Minority Business Advisory Council and the minority community in promoting minority business development.

* USDA Rural Development

Community & Business Programs Assistant
April Dahlager
655 Parfet Street, Room E-100   720-544-2909
Lakewood, CO 80215   Fax: 720-544-2972
www.rurdev.usda.gov/co
Areas of operation: Chaffe, Clear Creek, Eagle, Garfield, Gilpin, Grand, Jackson, Lake, Moffat, Park, Rio Blanco, Routt and Summit Counties

Community & Business Programs Specialist/
   Cooperative Services
Dolores Sanchez-Maes
655 Parfet Street, Room E-100   720-544-2927
Lakewood, CO 80215   Fax: 720-544-2972
www.rurdev.usda.gov/co
Areas of operation :Cheyenne, Crowley, Elbert, El Paso, Fremont, Kiowa, Kit Carson, Lincoln, Pueblo and Teller Counties.

Community & Business Programs Specialist
Linda Sundine
655 Parfet Street, Room E-100   720-544-2929
Lakewood, CO 80215   Fax: 720-544-2972
www.rurdev.usda.gov/co
Areas of operations: Adams, Araphaoe, Broomfield, Boulder, Denver, Douglas, Jefferson, Larimer, Logan, Morgan, Phillips, Sedgwick, Washington, Weld and Yuma counties.

Community and Business Program Loan Specialist
Fred Eanes
422 1st Street   719-846-3681
Trinidad, CO 81082   Fax: 719-846-0525
www.rurdev.usda.gov/co
Area of operation: Alamosa, Baca, Bent, Conejos, Costilla, Custer, Huerfano, Las Animas, Mineral, Otero, Prowers, Rio Grande and Saguache counties.

Community and Business Program Loan Specialist
Sue McWilliams

628 West 5th Street   970-565-8416, ext. 4
Cortez, CO 81321   Fax: 970-565-8797
www.rurdev.usda.gov/co
Areas of operation: Archuleta, Delta, Dolores, Gunnison, Hinsdale, La Plata, Mesa, Montezuma, Montrose, Ouray, Pitkin, San Juan and San Miguel counties.

The Colorado Rural Business Programs are designed to aide in the improvement, development, and financing of rural communities by enhancing the economic climate or rural businesses. Rural Business assistance is delivered through several programs: *Business and Industry Loans, Rural Business Opportunity and Enterprise Grants, Intermediary Relending Program, Rural Economic Development Loan and Grant Programs* and *Biobased Products and Bioenergy.*

* Colorado Housing and Finance Authority (CHFA)

1981 Blake St.   303-297-2432
Denver, CO 80202   1-800-877-2432 in Colorado
www.colohfa.org
The Colorado Housing and Finance Authority (CHFA) is a public enterprise working to finance affordable housing, business and economic growth opportunities for Colorado. CHFA's Business Finance Division provides a wide variety of programs, including loan programs specific to businesses located in rural communities, women- and minority-owned businesses, manufacturers in the state, and nonprofit organizations committed to better serving the needs of Colorado citizens.

ACCESS Program (SBA 504 Program): A first mortgage program for established small businesses acquiring land, buildings, and equipment, which generally requires 10% equity on the part of the borrower. CHFA may participate with a local lender or may directly originate the first mortgage while SBA provides a second mortgage generally resulting in a 90% loan to value. {www.colohfa.org/bf_access.shtml}

Business & Industry Loan Program: Targeted for businesses located in communities with populations under 50,000, the loan may be used to finance real estate, equipment and machinery. The loan offers a fixed rate on fully amortized terms of 3 to 25 years and is partially guaranteed by Rural Business Cooperative Service, a division of the U.S. Department of Agriculture. {www.colohfa.org/bf_B&I_1.shtml}

QAL Program: This program provides land, equipment and machinery financing to farm and ranch operations. The financing is made available through local banks and participation with Rural Business Cooperative Services. Loans are made at below market interest rates for terms up to 30 years. {www.colohfa.org/bf_qal.shtml}

CHFA Direct Real Estate Program: real estate financing program where CHFA originates a direct loan for up to 85% of the project cost, and provides a fixed rate for the entire term of the transaction. Allows for financing of machinery and equipment, as long as it is part of the real estate transaction.

Nonprofit Real Estate Program: CHFA provides affordable financing of real estate for nonprofits.

The Rural Development Loan Program: provides financing for businesses located in rural areas. CHFA makes direct loans up to $150,000.

Quality Investment Capital (QIC) Program: CHFA purchases the guaranteed portion of the SBA 7(a) loans, and the borrower is able to take advantage of a long-term fixed rate loan.

Manufacturing Revenue Bond Program: Tax-exempt Private Activity Bond financing targeted to small manufacturers. Provides financing of real estate, machinery, and equipment associated with expansion.

Brownsfields Revolving Loan Fund: Fund used to finance cleanup of environmentally contaminated commercial properties for future reuse or redevelopment.

* Colorado Agricultural Development Authority (CADA)

700 Kipling, #4000   303-239-4114
Lakewood, CO 80215   Fax: 303-239-4125
www.ag.state.co.us/mkt/cada.html
Colorado Value-Added Feasibility Grant Program: May be used only for the development of a report or study that analyzes the feasibility of processing an agricultural commodity produced in Colorado. Maximum award s $15,000. Grants must be equally matched with a cash or in-kind contribution by applicant. Businesses need the approval of the local government where the proposed project is to be located.

Specialty Crops Program: Provides $10,000-$25,000 for developing solutions to agricultural production problems for specialty crops.

Beginning Farmer Loan Program: May borrow up to $250,000 for agricultural property; $250,000 for farm equipment; $62,500 for breeding cattle and used equipment. Must be beginning farmer. Can be used in conjunction with the Farm Service Agency Beginning Farmer Program.

* Loans For Farmers

Farm Service Agency
U.S. Department of Agriculture
655 Parfet Street   720-544-2876
Lakewood, CO 80215   Fax: 720-544-2966
http://www.fsa.usda.gov/co/co.htm
The Farm Service Agency provides Direct and Guaranteed Loans to farmers through a variety of programs, including:

Farm Ownership Loans: purchase farmland, construct or repair buildings and other fixtures, and promote soil and water conservation. Up to $200,000.

Operating Loans: purchase items needed for a successful farm operation, such as livestock, farm equipment, feed, seed, fuel, farm chemicals, insurance, and other operating expenses. Can also be used to pay for minor improvements. Up to $200,000.

Beginning Farmer and Rancher Loans: provides funds to beginning and farmers and ranchers who are unable to obtain financing elsewhere.

Downpayment Farm Ownership Loans for Beginning Farmers: helps beginning farmers and ranchers purchase a farm or ranch. Also provides a way for retiring farmers to transfer their land to a future generation of farmers and ranchers. Applicant must have a downpayment of 10% and FSA with finance 40%, with the remaining balance from a commercial lender. Purchase price cannot exceed $250,000.

Loans to Socially Disadvantaged Farmers/Ranchers: helps socially disadvantaged applicants buy and operate family-size farms and ranches.

Youth Loans: Made to youths to establish and operate income-producing projects with the participation in 4-H clubs, Future Farmers of America, and similar organizations. Up to $5,000.

Emergency Loan Assistance: provides loans to help producers recover from production and physical losses due to drought, flooding, and other natural disasters, or quarantine. Up to $500,000.

Beginning Farmer and Rancher Land Contract Guarantee Pilot Program: "prompt payment guarantee" from FSA. FSA will provide payment to seller two times if the beginning farmer does not pay. Program is tested in IN, IA, ND, OR, PA and WI.

Farm Ownership and Operating Loan Guarantees: FSA will guarantee loans up to $782,000.

* Small Business Administration (SBA)

721 19th St., Suite 426   303-844-2607
Denver, CO 80202-2517   Fax: 303-844-6468
www.sba.gov/co

The Colorado Small Business Administration Office delivers a variety of programs and services, such as startup and operational assistance through small business training and counseling, financial assistance for startup's, business opportunities and much more.

* Colorado Department of Local Affairs

Division of Grants and Financial Assistance
1313 Sherman St., Room 500   303-866-2771
Denver, CO 80203   Fax: 303-866-4819
www.dola.state.co.us

The Colorado Department of Local Affairs mission is to help local governments deal with the financial assistance and technical assistance needs of businesses on a community level. The Department of Grants and Financial Assistance provide a variety of help to the residents of Colorado including the *Community Development and Service Block Grants* and *The Conservation Trust Fund*.

* Colorado Venture Management

2575 Park Lane, Suite 200   303-440-4055
Lafayette, CO 80026   Fax: 303-440-4636
www.coloradovca.org
Email: ewetherbee@cvmequity.com

CVM Equity Fund: Provides equity financing for start-up businesses in the state through private venture capital partnerships. CVM will run the seed capital fund. Focus is on start-up and early stage investments in service and technology-based businesses. Investments will be considered in the range of $25,000 to $300,000.

Connecticut

* Economic Resource Center

Connecticut Department of Economic and Community
   Development   860-571-7136
805 Brooks St., Bldg. 4   800-392-2122
Rocky Hill, CT 06067-3405   Fax: 860-571-7150

www.cerc.com

One Stop Centers: Authorized to enable businesses to obtain many necessary permits and licenses in one location.

Connecticut Economic Resource Center (CERC): A nonprofit private-sector organization formed and managed through a unique partnership of utility/telecommunication companies and state government. The CERC coordinates Connecticut's business-to-business marketing and recruitment efforts on behalf of the state. As a one-stop gateway to the state's programs and services for business, the CERC helps businesses obtain quick and accurate information in the areas of financing, export assistance, licensing, manufacturing programs, job training, utility, telecommunications and real estate help, all at no cost.

Business Resource Index: The Connecticut Economic Resource Center's website {www.cerc.com} offers a large and comprehensive database of programs and services for businesses. The database contains information from the public and private sectors on federal, state and local levels including license and permit information. The *Business Resource Index* is divided into three major sections, each of which can be searched individually or collectively. The sections include *Resources By Agency*, *Licensing*, and *Helpful Fact Sheets*. Available business resources are often divided by city or region. Listings are extensive. To illustrate, a search with the keyword "Small Business" yielded 119 documents including loans, technical assistance, consulting services, grants, and economic development assistance among others. As an example, the Entrepreneurial Loan Program offers loans up to $100,000 insured by the Connecticut Development Authority, for the benefit of start-up and early stage business anywhere in Connecticut. The website also features a real estate search engine enabling the user to input parameters such as size of building and desired location to aid with business site selection.

Technology Extension Program: Provides direct technical assistance to small and mid-sized manufacturing firms.

Institute for Industrial and Engineering Technology: Offers assistance with process improvement, technical training, procurement, human resources, business incubators, and others.

Program Finder: A comprehensive computer database of available commercial and industrial properties.

Demographic and Economic Analysis: Services include industry profiles, competitive intelligence, regional analysis, survey research, bench marking and evaluation.

* Connecticut Development Authority

999 West St.
Rocky Hill, CT 06067   860-258-7800
www.cda.state.ct.us/

The Connecticut Development Authority works to ensure that Connecticut businesses have access to capital to accelerate business formation and expansion and to create and retain jobs. The CDA works with private lending and business professionals to provide loan guarantees and direct loans for working capital, equipment and real estate. The CDA offers the following financing programs:

URBANK: Loans up to $500,000 for any small business enterprise in targeted communities that are unable to obtain conventional financing.

Business Loans: Up to $10 million for medium size enterprises.

Industrial Revenue Bonds: Low rate, tax exempt financing for manufacturers, utilities, certain nonprofits and others.

Job Training Finance Program: Pays up to 25% of the cost of improving skills of manufacturing workers.

Custom Job Training Program: Department of Labor will pay up to 50% for eligible training expenses.

Guaranteed and Participating Loans: For Connecticut companies to accelerate business formation and expansion and retain and create jobs.

Brownsfields Grants and Financing: Grants up to $10,000 for redevelopment and productive use of Brownfield sites.

Information Technology Grants and Loans: Loans and grants as incentives to developers of new projects in high technology, information technology, research, biosciences, and pharmaceuticals.

Equity-Equivalent Investment: Equity and subordinated capital to accelerate business formation and expansion.

Direct Loans: CDA has a direct loan program that strives to stimulate economic development. Eligible businesses can apply for funds up to $5 million.

SBA 504: This program provides long-term, low cost financing for fixed assets. There is a 10% equity investment requirement for businesses applying for the up to $2,500,000 loan.

* Department of Economic and Community Development

State of Connecticut
Department of Economic and Community Development
505 Hudson Street
Hartford, CT 06106-7107   860-270-8000
www.ct.gov/ecd

Economic and Manufacturing Assistance Fund: Program includes loans, defense diversification project funding, tax credits and funding for new machinery and equipment.

Naugatuck Valley Loan Fund: Fund can be used to purchase land or buildings, construction, renovation, rehabilitation, and/or the purchase and installation of machinery and equipment. Maximum loan is $200,000.

* Rural Development Offices

Norwich Service Center
238 West Town Street   860-859-5218 ext. 3004
Norwich, CT 06360   Fax: 860-859-5223
Serving Windham and New London Counties

Windsor Service Center
100 Northfield Drive, 4th Floor   860-688-7725 ext. 4
Windsor, CT 06095-4729   Fax: 860-688-7979
www.rurdev.usda.gov/ma
Serving Tolland, Middlesex, Hartford, Litchfield, New Haven and Fairfield Counties.

The Southern New England Office administers the USDA Rural Development Program in Connecticut with service

centers in Windsor and Norwich. They offer Business Development Programs that are available in rural areas, which are outside the boundary of a city or town of 50,000 or more inhabitants and are immediately adjacent urbanized area. They offer the following programs to assist businesses: *Business & Industry Loans, Rural Business Enterprise Grants* and *Intermediary Relending Program Loans.*

* State of Connecticut Department of Revenue Services

25 Sigourney Street   860-297-5962
Hartford, CT 06106   800-382-9463 (In-state)
www.drs.state.ct.us   Fax: 860-297-5698

When you start your new business the Department of Revenue Services has some help for you. They publish a pamphlet called *Getting Started in Business* to guide you through many of your tax questions. They also offer other assistance for entrepreneurs, call to see how they can help your business.

* Community Economic Development Fund

50-G Weston St.   800-656-4613
Hartford, CT 06120   860-249-3800
www.cedf.com

CEDF provides loans to start-up and existing businesses who have difficulty obtaining traditional financing or need flexible terms. Programs include:

Standard Loan Program: Loans from $5,000-$250,000 for start-up or existing businesses.

Grow Your Business Loan: Businesses three years old or more can qualify for loans up to $250,000.

SBA Microloan Program: For loans up to $35,000.

Microloan Guarantee Program for Women and Minority Owned Businesses: Helps women and minority owned businesses obtain flexible financing with loans from $5,000-$50,000.

CT Inner City Business Loan Guarantee Program: Guarantees for small business loans in designated industry clusters in Waterbury, Hartford, new Britain, Bridgeport, and New Haven. Loans are for $50,000-$250,000.

* Connecticut Venture Group

1895-B Post Rd.
Fairfield, CT 06430   203-256-5955
www.ct-venture.org

Connecticut Venture Group: A nonprofit membership organization that brings entrepreneurs and investors together.

Innovations Technology Financing: Offers a wide range of support from research assistance to financing for product development and marketing.

* Minority and Small Business Contractors Set-Aside Program

Department of Economic and Community Development
Attn: Set Aside Unit
505 Hudson St.
Hartford, CT 06106   860-270-8025
www.ct.gov/ecd

Procurement Program: Set-Aside Program requires state

agencies and political subdivisions to set aside 25% of their budget for construction, housing rehabilitation and the purchasing of supplies. These services are awarded to certified small business contractors, minority businesses, enterprises, nonprofit corporations and individuals with a disability. 25% of this amount is to be awarded to certified minority owned firms.

Minority Supplier Development Council: A nonprofit organization whose mission is to foster business relationships between corporations and certified minority businesses. Services include training seminars, matchmaking activities, bid notifications, networking functions and a large trade expo.

* Connecticut Innovation, Inc. (CII)

999 West St.	860-563-5851
Rocky Hill, CT 06067	Fax: 860-563-4877
www.ctinnovations.com	

Connecticut Innovations is the state's corporation dedicated to technology development, making risk capital investments in high technology companies throughout the state. They offer a wide range of support from research assistance to financing for product development and marketing. Connecticut Innovations offers the following programs:

Yankee Ingenuity Technology Competition: The Yankee Ingenuity Technology Competition provides royalty-based, market driven funding for applied high technology research and development projects that lead to marketable products of processes. The purpose of this initiative is to encourage collaborations between Connecticut colleges and universities and Connecticut business and industry for the development and commercialization of products or processes with high potential to contribute to long-term, sustainable economic growth in Connecticut.

Connecticut Innovations Resource Center: The Connecticut Innovations Resource Center is a high-tech information clearinghouse and a gateway to resources available from Connecticut Innovations. The Center maintains a complete listing of educational programs and services and state and federal resources to assist in converting ideas into products. The Center offers: Access to business planning materials; Guidelines for Connecticut Innovations' programs; Directories and databases of high-tech companies in Connecticut, to assist in the identification of growth industries, companies and localities, and the identification of export companies; Information on federal R & D grant programs and state assistance programs; and Sources of private and public financing.

Eli Whitney Fund: Focuses on information technology, bioscience, photonics, and energy and environmental systems. Investments range from $500,000 to $2 million.

Connecticut BioSeed Fund: Helps accelerate the growth of early stage biotech enterprises. Up to $500,000 for young Connecticut companies.

Technology Test Bed Program: State agency or facility can serve as a demonstration site for one of Connecticut Innovations companies and can receive support to defray costs.

Next Generation Ventures: Venture capital to support entrepreneurial high tech companies.

Bioscience Facilities Fund: A $55 million fund to support the expansion of biotechnology laboratory space in Connecticut.

Funding may be offered in the form of lease or loan guarantee and/or direct investments.

Connecticut Clean Energy Fund: Promotes investment in renewable energy resources, e.g. fuel cells, landfill gas, and tidal, wind and solar power.

* Loans For Farmers

Farm Service Agency	
U.S. Department of Agriculture	
344 Merrow Road, Suite B	860-871-2944
Tolland, CT 06084	Fax: 860-279-4184
http://www.fsa.usda.gov/ct/	

The Farm Service Agency provides Direct and Guaranteed Loans to farmers through a variety of programs, including:

Farm Ownership Loans: purchase farmland, construct or repair buildings and other fixtures, and promote soil and water conservation. Up to $200,000.

Operating Loans: purchase items needed for a successful farm operation, such as livestock, farm equipment, feed, seed, fuel, farm chemicals, insurance, and other operating expenses. Can also be used to pay for minor improvements. Up to $200,000.

Beginning Farmer and Rancher Loans: provides funds to beginning and farmers and ranchers who are unable to obtain financing elsewhere.

Downpayment Farm Ownership Loans for Beginning Farmers: helps beginning farmers and ranchers purchase a farm or ranch. Also provides a way for retiring farmers to transfer their land to a future generation of farmers and ranchers. Applicant must have a downpayment of 10% and FSA with finance 40%, with the remaining balance from a commercial lender. Purchase price cannot exceed $250,000.

Loans to Socially Disadvantaged Farmers/Ranchers: helps socially disadvantaged applicants buy and operate family-size farms and ranches.

Youth Loans: Made to youths to establish and operate income-producing projects with the participation in 4-H clubs, Future Farmers of America, and similar organizations. Up to $5,000.

Emergency Loan Assistance: provides loans to help producers recover from production and physical losses due to drought, flooding, and other natural disasters, or quarantine. Up to $500,000.

Beginning Farmer and Rancher Land Contract Guarantee Pilot Program: "prompt payment guarantee" from FSA. FSA will provide payment to seller two times if the beginning farmer does not pay. Program is tested in IN, IA, ND, OR, PA and WI.

Farm Ownership and Operating Loan Guarantees: FSA will guarantee loans up to $782,000.

* Small Business Administration (SBA)

330 Main St.	860-240-4700
Hartford, CT 06106	Fax: 860-240-4659
www.sba.gov/ct	

The Connecticut Small Business Administration Office delivers a variety of programs and services, such as startup and operational assistance through small business training and counseling, financial assistance for startup's, business opportunities and much more.

Delaware

* Delaware Economic Development Office
John S. Riley
99 Kings Highway
P.O. Box 1401   302-739-4271
Dover, DE 19903   Fax: 302-739-5749
www.state.de.us/dedo/index.htm
Offers referrals to appropriate state agencies and other organizations. Free tabloid, *Small Business Start-Up Guide* is available. Provides support for new businesses and coordinates the efforts of organizations statewide that assist small businesses.

Workforce Development Section: Works to ensure the availability of a skilled, multilevel workforce for new and existing Delaware businesses. Helps employers obtain, upgrade and retain suitable workers, by helping Delawareans gain the education and training to get and keep quality jobs and steady employment. {www.delawareworkforce.com}

Business Research Section: Collects, analyzes and distributes statistical data on the state's economy and business climate and develops research regarding the economic vitality of the State of Delaware

Delaware Tourism Office: Assists the tourism industry.

The State Data Center: Provides economic and demographic data for Delaware.

Business Magazine: Maintained by the Delaware State Chamber of Commerce (DSCC), it is the state's central location for listing business-related events.

Green Industries Initiative: Targets specific businesses for receipt of financial and technical assistance to further the goals of Governor Castle's Executive Order #82 and Delaware's Pollution Prevention Program. The State of Delaware provides corporate income tax credits and/or gross receipts tax reductions for existing Delaware firms and those choosing Delaware as a location for new operations. The type of financial assistance is dependent upon the category under which assistance is requested.

Industrial Revenue Bonds: Statewide financial assistance to new or expanding businesses through the issuance of bonds (IRBs). The maximum for IRBs issued annually in Delaware is $150 million.

Economic Development Loan Program: Assists Delaware businesses to finance projects when 100% financing cannot be obtained through a bank. The program does require 70% bank financing. The remaining 30% is financed through the program up to a maximum of $450,000. In most cases the interest rate for monies loaned through the Economic Development Loan Program is 60% of the prime lending interest rate.

The Delaware Access Program: Designed to give banks a flexible and extremely non-bureaucratic tool to make business loans that are somewhat riskier than a conventional bank loan, in a manner consistent with safety and soundness. It is designed to use a small amount of public resources to generate a large amount of private bank financing, thus

providing access to bank financing for many Delaware businesses that might otherwise not be able to obtain such access. The program sets minimum and maximum limits for the borrower's payment. At a minimum, it must be at least 1-1/2% of the loan amount. The maximum is 3-1/2%. (The premium payment, and other up-front expenses, may be financed as part of the loan.)

Small Business Innovation Research (SBIR): Bridge grant assistance to encourage Delaware businesses to participate in the federal Small Business Innovation Research (SBIR) grant program. The SBIR program requires that 1.25% of all federal research dollars be made available to small businesses. Phase I awardees are granted up to $100,000 by the federal government.

The Delaware Innovation Fund: Assists in the initial capitalization of pre-seed and seed stage enterprises within the State of Delaware. The Fund provides financial and technical assistance to Delaware based businesses which have the potential to launch innovative products and processes into national markets, to create new jobs, and to make a significant contribution to the economic diversity and the technology base of Delaware's communities.

Demonstration Funding: Limited one-time availability, provides $10,000 to $25,000 to aid in establishing patents, business plans and proof of concept issues.

Commercialization Funding: Ranging from $25,000 to $250,000, this funding is used to begin the commercialization process of early-stage businesses and may be available in multiple years.

Venture Capital Funds: Three funds — Anthem Capital, L.P., Triad Investors Corporation, and Blue Rock Capital — have the ability to fund a variety of seed stage, early stage, and later stage companies in both technology-related and non-technology fields. The investment focus of each fund varies. Investments can range from $150,000 for seed stage companies up to $2,000,000 or more for later stage companies.

Export Trading Company Exemption: Delaware exporters who qualify as an Export Trading Company can receive exemption from Delaware income and mercantile taxes.

* USDA/Rural Development
4607 South DuPont Highway   302-697-4300
Post Office Box 400   TTY: 302-697-4303
Camden, DE 19934   Fax: 302-697-4390
www.rurdev.usda.gov/de
The Community & Business Programs Division consists of the Rural Utilities Service (RUS) and the Rural Business & Cooperative Service (RBS). RUS programs assist rural America in building infrastructure by providing loans and grants for water and wastewater disposal systems, solid waste disposal systems, storm drainage systems and advanced telecommunications. RBS programs help provide financial as well as technical assistance to businesses, nonprofit organizations, educational institutions and cooperatives. The financial assistance is provided in the form of loans, guaranteed loans and grants.

* State of Delaware Department of Finance
Division of Business Revenue
820 N. French Street   302-577-8205
Wilmington, DE 19801   Fax: 302-577-8202
http://www.state.de.us/revenue/

800-292-7826 (Delaware only)
The Office of Business Taxes provide businesses information on registering a business, obtaining a license and doing business in Delaware.

* Advanced Technology Centers (ATCs)
Delaware Economic Development Office
820 French St.
Wilmington, DE 19801   302-577-8496
www.state.de.us

Public/private partnerships designed to bolster Delaware's technology base and to create and retain quality high-tech jobs. The State of Delaware has committed $11 million to date in grants to establish five Centers. Funding for the program comes from the state's 21st Century Fund. Amounts are not available without a specific inquiry.

* Wilmington Economic Development Corporation
100 W. 10th St., Suite 706
Wilmington, DE 19801   302-571-9088
www.wedco.org

Projects located within the city limits of Wilmington may also apply for financing through the Wilmington Economic Development Corporation (WEDCO). Financing programs offered include SBA Section 504 Loans, Revolving Loan Funds, and other special purpose financing.

* Sussex County Office of Economic Development
P.O. Box 589
9 S. Dupont Hwy.
Georgetown, DE 19947   302-855-7770
www.sussexcounty.net/depts/econdev/index.html

Operates an Industrial Revenue Bond program with a cap of $15 million each year for industrial projects in the County. Project review requires a letter of commitment for placement of the bond before a project recommendation is made by the Industrial Revenue Bond Review Committee to Sussex County Council (political jurisdiction). The Industrial Revenue Bond process may require as little as five weeks from inception to bond closing.

* Minority Business Programs
Office of Minority and Women Business Enterprise (M/WBE)
Mary Schreiber, Director
Department of Administrative Service
410 Federal Street
Margaret O'Neill Bldg.
Dover, DE 19901   302-739-7830
www.state.de.us/omwbe/

The office sponsors activities ranging from training workshops for agencies, regional workshops for minority and women-owned businesses to orientation sessions for newly certified minority-owned business enterprises. They assist government agencies to use certified minority and women-owned businesses when purchasing and contracting for the state.

* International Trade Section
Delaware Economic Development Office
820 French St.
Carvel State Office Bldg., 10th Floor

Wilmington, DE 19801   302-577-8464
www.state.de.us

A one-stop resource for exporter assistance and international trade information in Delaware.

* Loans For Farmers
Farm Service Agency
U.S. Department of Agriculture
1201 College Park Drive, Suite 101   302-678-4250
Dover, DE 19904-8713   Fax: 320-678-9100
http://www.fsa.usda.gov/de/

The Farm Service Agency provides Direct and Guaranteed Loans to farmers through a variety of programs, including:

Farm Ownership Loans: purchase farmland, construct or repair buildings and other fixtures, and promote soil and water conservation. Up to $200,000.

Operating Loans: purchase items needed for a successful farm operation, such as livestock, farm equipment, feed, seed, fuel, farm chemicals, insurance, and other operating expenses. Can also be used to pay for minor improvements. Up to $200,000.

Beginning Farmer and Rancher Loans: provides funds to beginning and farmers and ranchers who are unable to obtain financing elsewhere.

Downpayment Farm Ownership Loans for Beginning Farmers: helps beginning farmers and ranchers purchase a farm or ranch. Also provides a way for retiring farmers to transfer their land to a future generation of farmers and ranchers. Applicant must have a downpayment of 10% and FSA with finance 40%, with the remaining balance from a commercial lender. Purchase price cannot exceed $250,000.

Loans to Socially Disadvantaged Farmers/Ranchers: helps socially disadvantaged applicants buy and operate family-size farms and ranches.

Youth Loans: Made to youths to establish and operate income-producing projects with the participation in 4-H clubs, Future Farmers of America, and similar organizations. Up to $5,000.

Emergency Loan Assistance: provides loans to help producers recover from production and physical losses due to drought, flooding, and other natural disasters, or quarantine. Up to $500,000.

Beginning Farmer and Rancher Land Contract Guarantee Pilot Program: "prompt payment guarantee" from FSA. FSA will provide payment to seller two times if the beginning farmer does not pay. Program is tested in IN, IA, ND, OR, PA and WI.

Farm Ownership and Operating Loan Guarantees: FSA will guarantee loans up to $782,000.

* Small Business Administration (SBA)
824 N. Market St.   302-573-6294
Wilmington, DE 19801-3011   Fax: 302-573-6060
www.sba.gov/de

The Delaware Small Business Administration Office delivers a variety of programs and services, such as startup and operational assistance through small business training and counseling, financial assistance for startup's, business opportunities and much more.

District of Columbia

* Office of Economic Development

John A. Wilson Building
1350 Pennsylvania Ave., NW, Suite 317
Washington, DC 20004   202-727-6365
www.dcbiz.dc.gov/main.shtm

Welcome To Washington D.C. Online: A useful website with links to business & finance opportunities in the district.

The DC Office of International Business: OIB was created to support the District of Columbia's development and expansion of local business through international trade and joint-venture partnerships, and to attract outside investment to the District of Columbia. Programs offered include:
- *International Trade Counseling and Technical Program*: OIB offers counseling and assistance on all aspects of international business to firms, organizations and residents of the District of Columbia.
- *Resource Center for International Trade Information*: Offers country market profiles, current export licensing regulations, information on trade and financing, a comprehensive database of trade resources and a directory of Washington-based international firms.
- *Trade and Investment Program*: Offers a database of local, small and medium sized businesses, using criteria and categories useful for the analysis of the local market; match making potential for local small business, and investment needs; facilitates trade and investment leads; identifies overseas markets for local goods and services; supports trade and investment missions; hosts foreign buying delegations; works in tandem with its sister agencies in devising strategies and marketing activities to attract foreign investment and business entities to the District of Columbia; establishes regular and close relationships with the diplomatic community, chambers of commerce and other regional and state agencies to identify export and investment opportunities for local and area businesses.
- *OIB Seminar Series*: Provides hands-on training through an eight week course designed to provide concise, nuts-and-bolts instructions on how to conduct import, export, and joint venture transactions. Topics cover every aspect of international trade with emphasis on small business involvement. Upon successful completion of the course, participants receive a "Certificate of Achievement."
- *OIB Internship Program*: OIB offers a high school and college internship program that provides local youth with on-the-job training, skill development and an orientation to international trade.
- *reSTORE DC Main Streets*: designated local Main Street programs receive technical assistance, training and more. Nonprofits may apply for $80,000 grant.
- *reSTORE DC Commercial Development Technical Assistance Program*: awards technical assistance and grants to assist commercial revitalization activities that enhance neighborhood business districts. Nonprofits are eligible for grants from $500-$25,000.
- *reSTORE DC Commercial Property Acquisition and Development Program*: awards grants to assist in acquiring or developing commercial real estate projects that enhance neighborhood business districts. Nonprofits may apply for $10,000 to $250,000.

* Small Business Assistance

Office of Local Business Development
Government of District of Columbia

One Judiciary Square
441 4th St., NW, Suite 970N
Washington, DC 20001   202-727-3900
www.olbd.washingtondc.gov

Certified small, local, and/or disadvantaged business enterprises are given priority consideration for contracts offered by District agencies and on publicly-assisted projects. Company must be certified by OLBD.

* Transferable Development Rights

Local Business Development
441 4th St., NW, Suite 970N
Washington, DC 20001   202-727-3900
http://olbd.washingtondc.gov

Permits businesses to purchase the right to develop at higher densities in designated TDR "receiving zones."

* Business Location Assistance

D.C. Chamber of Commerce
1213 K Street, NW
Washington, DC 20005   202-347-7201
www.dcchamber.org

D.C. Building Industry Association
5100 Wisconsin Ave., NW, Suite 301
Washington, DC 20016   202-966-8665
www.dcbia.org

* Bond Financing and General Information

D.C. Enterprise and Revenue Bond Program
1350 Pennsylvania Avenue, NW, Suite 317
Washington, DC 20004   202-727-6365
www.dcbiz.dc.gov/info/rb.shtm

Qualified businesses located in the Enterprise Zone, nonprofit and manufacturing businesses throughout the city can apply for below market rate loans. The funds can be used for a variety of capital projects.

* Local and Minority Business Development

DC Department of Local Business Development
DC Department of Human Rights and
Minority Business Development
441 4th Street, NW, Suite 970   202-727-3900
Washington, DC 20001   Fax: 202-724-3786
www.oibd.dc.gov

Minority Business Opportunity Commission: Promotes equal opportunity in all aspects of District life and fosters minority business development through:
- *Business Marketing Directory*: listing of Local, Small, Disadvantaged and Minority Business Enterprises.
- *Minority Business Certification Program*
- *Technical Assistance Program*: Aids minority business enterprises through workshops, contracting conferences, referrals and the MBOC Directory to bid and compete on District Government contracts.
- *Bonding Assistance Program*: Establishes a financial assurance pool to serve as limited collateral for surety bonds on public construction projects awarded by the DC government.

* Department of Housing and Community Development

801 N. Capitol St., NE, 8th Floor   202-442-7200
Washington, DC 20002   Fax: 202-442-8391

www.dhcd.dcgov.org

Apartment Improvement Program: provides technical assistance to owners of rental housing for property improvements.

Construction Assistance Program: helps nonprofit land trusts acquire land and buildings for development of low-income housing.

Community Land Acquisition Program: helps nonprofit land trusts acquire land and buildings for development.

Distressed Properties Improvement Program: provides tax relief and other financial incentives to property owners if they are willing to make repairs.

Housing Finance for Elderly, Dependent, and Disabled: provides financing to commercial and nonprofit applicants to develop community-based residential facilities that house individuals with special needs.

Housing Production Trust Fund: provides financial assistance to nonprofit and commercial developers to plan and build low to moderate-income housing and related facilities.

Low Income Housing Tax Credit Program: available to developers that provide new or rehabilitated rental housing.

Community Based Services: supports nonprofit organizations that provide comprehensive housing counseling services.

Emergency Shelter Grant Program: improves the quality of existing emergency shelters for the homeless.

Enterprise Community Program: provides residents in enterprise communities with the resources and training needed to achieve upward mobility.

Multi-Family Housing Rehabilitation Loan Program: low-cost interim construction financing and permanent financing for the rehabilitation of residential properties that contain five or more units.

Neighborhood Development Assistance Program: provides administrative support to Community Development Corporations for neighborhood development projects and neighborhood revitalization activities.

Tenant Purchase Technical Assistance Program: provides technical service assistance to nonprofit organizations that provide legal counseling, loan packaging, and other services to low and moderate-income tenant groups that try to purchase their existing housing units.

* Employment Training Tax Credits
DC Department of Employment Services
609 H St., NE
Washington, DC 20002   202-724-7000
http://does.dc.gov
The Department of Employment Services helps develop Washington's workforce through training and education.

Customized Training Program: employers are reimbursed for funds spent to train District residents as skilled employees.

Enterprise Zone Employment Tax Credit: annual employment tax credit for 20% of wages paid to DC resident employees (up to $3,000 per employee).

Work Opportunity Credit: annual employment tax credit of up to $2,400 per employee in tax credits for employees that meet eligibility criteria.

Welfare to Work Program: Up to $8,500 per employee in tax credits for employees that meet eligibility criteria ($5,000 for year one).

Metro Tech Program: cost of training/certification of information technology professionals is borne by Metro Tech.

* Office of Banking & Financial Institutions
1400 L Street, NW, Suite 400
Washington, DC 20005   202-727-1563
http://dbfi.dc.gov/main.shtm
The general mission of the office is to promote a climate in which financial institutions will organize to do business in the District of Columbia and contribute to the economic development of the District through the increased availability of capital and credit and to expand advantageous financial services to the public in a nondiscriminatory manner.

* Loans For Farmers
Farm Service Agency
U.S. Department of Agriculture
1400 Independence Ave. S.W.
Mail Stop 0506
Washington, DC 20250-0506   202-720-7809
http://www.fsa.usda.go/pas/default.asp
The Farm Service Agency provides Direct and Guaranteed Loans to farmers through a variety of programs, including:

Farm Ownership Loans: purchase farmland, construct or repair buildings and other fixtures, and promote soil and water conservation. Up to $200,000.

Operating Loans: purchase items needed for a successful farm operation, such as livestock, farm equipment, feed, seed, fuel, farm chemicals, insurance, and other operating expenses. Can also be used to pay for minor improvements. Up to $200,000.

Beginning Farmer and Rancher Loans: provides funds to beginning and farmers and ranchers who are unable to obtain financing elsewhere.

Downpayment Farm Ownership Loans for Beginning Farmers: helps beginning farmers and ranchers purchase a farm or ranch. Also provides a way for retiring farmers to transfer their land to a future generation of farmers and ranchers. Applicant must have a downpayment of 10% and FSA with finance 40%, with the remaining balance from a commercial lender. Purchase price cannot exceed $250,000.

Loans to Socially Disadvantaged Farmers/Ranchers: helps socially disadvantaged applicants buy and operate family-size farms and ranches.

Youth Loans: Made to youths to establish and operate income-producing projects with the participation in 4-H clubs, Future Farmers of America, and similar organizations. Up to $5,000.

Emergency Loan Assistance: provides loans to help producers recover from production and physical losses due to drought, flooding, and other natural disasters, or quarantine. Up to $500,000.

Beginning Farmer and Rancher Land Contract Pilot Program: "prompt payment guarantee" from FSA. FSA will provide payment to seller two times if the beginning farmer does not pay. Program is tested in IN, IA, ND, OR, PA and WI.

Farm Ownership and Operating Loan Guarantees: FSA will guarantee loans up to $782,000.

* Washington District Small Business Administration

1110 Vermont Ave. NW, 9th Floor	202-606-4000
Washington, DC 20005	Fax: 202-606-4225
www.sba.gov/dc	

The District of Columbia Small Business Administration Office delivers a variety of programs and services, such as startup and operational assistance through small business training and counseling, financial assistance for startup's, business opportunities and much more.

* DC Marketing Center/DC Business Connections

1213 K St., NW	
Washington, DC 20005	202-638-7333
www.dcmarketingcenter.com/business	

A public/private partnership between the District of Columbia 's Office of the Deputy Mayor for Planning and Economic Development and private sector sponsors. Through DC Business Connections, participating Washington-based companies have the opportunity to establish a unique communication forum with the Government of the District of Columbia to address important issues associated with conducting business in the District.

Florida

* Florida Economic Development Council

P.O. Box 3186	850-201-FEDC
Tallahassee, FL 32315	Fax: 850-201-3330
www.fedc.net	

or

Enterprise Florida	
390 North Orange Avenue, Suite 1300	407-316-4600
Orlando, FL 32801	Fax: 407-316-4599
www.eflorida.com	

Enterprise Florida: Offers information and referral services for current and potential small business owners. Also serves as ombudsman to small businesses to help resolve problems being experienced with state agencies. They sponsor workshops and business forums and an annual Small Business Development Workshop that brings together local, state, and federal agency representatives. Distributes and publishes the *Florida New Business Guide Checklist* for small businesses.

Innovation and Commercialization Centers: Sponsored by Enterprise Florida, Technology Development Corporation provides services and assistance designed to help entrepreneurs and emerging technology-based companies grow, launch new products and succeed in the marketplace. Services include business planning, market development, technology access, commercialization assistance, financial expertise and additional services.
- *Vendor Bid System*: An online computer service allowing searches for state bids that fit a particular business.

- *Quick Response Training*: Up to 18 months of employee training for businesses that produce exportable goods or services, create new jobs and employ Florida workers who require customized entry-level skills training.
- *Info-bid*: Helps businesses locate bid opportunities to sell to federal, state and local government agencies, as well as some commercial firms.

The Economic Development Transportation Fund: Commonly referred to as the "Road Fund," provides funding to units of local government for the elimination of transportation problems that adversely impact a specific company's location or expansion decision. Up to $2,000,000 may be provided to a local government to implement the improvements.

The Florida Recycling Loan Program: Provides funding for machinery and equipment for manufacturing, processing, or conversion systems utilizing materials which have been or will be recycled; collection systems are not eligible. Direct Loans — Maximum to $200,000; minimum of $20,000. Maximum amount for leveraged loans will be $200,000, or 40% of total eligible costs, whichever is less. {www.ffcfc.com}

Florida Export Finance Corporation: Makes available pre- and post-shipment working capital to small and medium size Florida exporters. Programs include state-supported direct loans and guarantees as well as packaging services that provide access to EXIM Bank and SBA export finance and working capital guaranty programs. Direct loans for the lesser of 90% of the product cost or $50,000. Loan guarantees for the lesser of 90% of a loan provided by a lender or $500,000. No minimum size. {www.dos.state.fk.us/fefc}

Rural Revolving Loan Program: Designed to provide gap funding for economic development projects in rural counties. Loan size to $200,000 or 10% of the project being assisted, whichever is less.

Florida Venture Finance Directory: Acts as a "wholesaler" in providing information to assist in the guidance of financing searches, Capital Development developed and published *The Florida Venture Finance Directory*. The *Directory* serves as an effective tool for economic development organizations (primary distributors) to assist local businesses in their fund raising efforts. 407-316-4646

Venture Capital Network Development: Financial support, within budget limitations, is provided to a limited number of venture capital conferences at which Florida entrepreneurs have opportunity to present their ventures to members of the venture capital community. Enterprise Florida also is specifically interested in supporting initiatives leading to increased participation of private individual investors in Florida business ventures.

The Technology Investment Fund: Makes co-investments with Florida companies in promising technology-related projects with near-term commercial potential. Investments fall within a range of $25,000 to $250,000, depending upon the project's scope, commercial potential, matching funds, leveraged funds, the number and quality of other proposals received and the amount of funding requested in the highest ranked proposals.

Minority Business Development Centers: Offers existing and potential minority entrepreneurs a wide range of free services, from initial counseling on how to start a business to the more complex issues of planning and growth.

Office of Supplier Diversity: Responsible for certifying minority business enterprises to do business with state agencies.

Black Business Venture Corporation: A vehicle for initiating business acquisitions and engaging in real estate development. Serves a twofold purpose: to provide real and/or commercial office space for Black businesses; and to address the larger community needs such as local employment and retail centers.

Manufacturing Facility Bond Pool: This allows manufacturing land acquisition, new facility construction, and new equipment purchases with low-cost financing

Florida First Business Bond Pool: Funding for job creation projects that address air or water quality or solid waste management issues.

Front Porch Microcredit Loan Program: This program involves both technical training and a loan for qualified businesses in the Front Porch Community. The loan portion provides capital to small business entrepreneurs that may not have otherwise qualified for conventional financing. Up to $15,000 of funding can be used for startups of cottage industries and micro-enterprises.

Urban Incentives: Businesses located in many urban areas may be eligible for incentive awards and lower wage qualification thresholds.

* Florida Rural Development Office

4440 NW, 25th Place	352-338-3402
Gainesville, FL 32606	Fax: 352-338-3405
www.rurdev.usda.gov/fl	

The Rural Development Office in Florida offers a variety of opportunities to businesses in rural areas. The Rural Business-Cooperative Service offers the following programs: Business & Industry Guaranteed Loans, Business and Industry Direct Loans, Intermediary Relending Loans, Rural Business Enterprise Grants, Rural Economic Development Loans and Grants, Cooperative Development Services, and Rural Business Opportunity Grants.

* State of Florida Department of Revenue

5050 W. Tennessee Street	850-488-6800
Tallahassee, FL 32399-0100	800-352-3671 (FL only)
www.myflorida.com/dor/businesses/	

The Department of Revenue provides information to new business owner and publishes a New Business Owner's Guide.

* Division of International Trade

Enterprise Florida, Inc.
2801 Ponce de Leon Blvd
Suite 700
Miami, Florida 33134   305-569-2650
Fax: 305-569-2686
www.eflorida.com

Enterprise Florida, Inc. is a partnership between Florida's government and business leaders and is the principal economic development organization for the State of Florida. Enterprise Florida's mission is to increase economic opportunities for all Floridians, by supporting the creation of quality jobs and globally competitive businesses. It pursues this mission in cooperation with its statewide network of economic development partners.

Export Counseling: Enterprise Florida's Division of International Trade provides an export counseling service for Florida manufacturers and service companies whose interest in and commitment to exporting is genuine. Export counseling sessions normally take the form of one-on-one meetings at the business location or an EFI office. Contact: Manny Mencia Enterprise Florida International Trade Division, Coral Gables, 305-569-2650

Enterprise Florida's Division of International Trade offers small and medium-sized Florida businesses interested in doing business internationally the opportunity to participate in overseas trade events and marketing missions. Open to all businesses registered in the state of Florida interested in doing business internationally, Enterprise Florida market-site trade events are professionally planned missions that feature one-on-one, prearranged appointments with business executives interested in the specific product lines or services of participants. Contact: Enterprise Florida International Trade Division, Coral Gables, 305-569-2650

* The Economic Development Commission

Mr. Darrell Kelley, President & CEO
Mr. Michael Bobroff, Executive Vice President
Economic Development Commission of Mid-Florida, Inc.
301 East Pine Street, Suite 900   407-422-7159
Orlando, FL 32801-1992   Fax: 407-843-9514
Email: bobroff@business-orlando.org
http://www.business-orlando.org
Serving the counties of Lake, Orange, Osceola, and Seminole

Mr. W.D. Higginbotham, Jr.
Director of Economic Development
2009 NW 67 Place, Suite A   352-955-2200
Gainesville, FL 32653-1603   Fax: 352-955-2209
Email: higginbotham@ncfrpc.org
http://www.originalflorida.org
Serving the counties of Alachua, Bradford, Columbia, Dixie, Gilchrist, Hamilton, Lafayette, Madison, Suwannee, Taylor, and Union

Ms. Betty Neale, Executive Director
P.O. Box 1196
5813 Olive Road   863-385-4900
Sebring, FL 33872-6041   Fax: 863-385-4808
Email: bnc@strato.net
www.fhredi.com
Serving the counties of DeSoto, Glades, Hardee, Hendry, Highlands, and Okeechobee

Mr. Stuart Rogel, Executive Director
Mr. Mike Evans, Business Development
4300 West Cypress Street   813-878-2208, ext. 23
Tampa, FL 33607   Fax: 813-872-9356
Email: srogel@tampabay.org
Email: mevans@tampabay.org
www.tampabay.org
Serving the counties of Hernando, Hillsborough, Manatee, Pasco, Pinellas, Sarasota, and Polk

The Economic Development Commission (EDC) is an organization that helps business. They are dedicated to meeting the needs of today's industries and creating a competitive economic climate where businesses can thrive. To meet this goal, the EDC provides key services and support, which range from relocation and expansion expertise to export counsel to long-term planning with our community partners.

* Florida Black Business Investment Board
1711 S. Gadsen St.
Tallahassee, FL 32301   850-487-4850
www.fbbib.com

Oversees the state's investment in black business investment corporations, which provide technical assistance and loans to black-owned businesses.

Black Business Investment Corporations: Provides loans, loan guarantees, joint ventures, limited partnerships or any combination thereof.

* Office of Supplier Diversity
Florida Department of Management Services
4050 Esplanade Way, Suite 360
Tallahassee, FL 32399-0950   850-487-0915
http://mbaao.fdles.state.fl.us

The Office of Supplier Diversity (OSD) is responsible for certifying minority business enterprises to do business with state agencies. Develops statewide initiative to help minority and women-owned business prosper in Florida and the global marketplace.

* Florida Export Finance Corporation
10400 NW 33 Street, Suite 200   786-845-0400
Miami, FL 33172-5092   Fax: 786-845-0404
www.dos.state.fl.us/fefc

The Florida Export Finance Corporation Loans and Guarantees are available for exporters in Florida that have been turned down by at least one potential lender. They will guarantee a revolving line of credit up to $50,000. Businesses can also benefit from information, technical and counseling assistance.

* Florida Manufacturing Extension Partnership
1180 Celebration Blvd.
Celebration, Fl 34747   321-939-4000
www.floridamep.org

Services are available to small, and medium sized manufactures in the Florida. Businesses can obtain help in the following areas: plant layout, health and safety issues, marketing and business development, technology transfer/processing improvements and access to workforce training and capital services.

* Economic Development and Commercial Revitalization
Bureau of Community Assistance
2555 Shumard Oak Blvd.   850-487-3644
Tallahassee, FL 32399-2100   Fax: 850-922-5609
www.dca.state.fk.us/fhcd.programs/cdbgp/index.htm

Small City Community Development Block Grant (CDBG): Available to cities populations of 50,000 or less or counties with populations of less than 200,000. Designed to address and resolve specific community and economic development needs for low and moderate income families. The state sets aside CDBG funds to assist private entities for the purpose of creating or retaining jobs for low and moderate income persons. Funds can be used for the acquisition, construction, rehabilitation, or installation of commercial or industrial buildings, structures and other real property and for public and private improvements.

* Loans For Farmers
Farm Service Agency
U.S. Department of Agriculture
4440 N.W. 25th Pl., Suite 1   352-379-4500
Gainesville, FL 32614-1030   Fax: 352-379-4580
http://www.fsa.usda.gov/fl/

The Farm Service Agency provides Direct and Guaranteed Loans to farmers through a variety of programs, including:

Farm Ownership Loans: purchase farmland, construct or repair buildings and other fixtures, and promote soil and water conservation. Up to $200,000.

Operating Loans: purchase items needed for a successful farm operation, such as livestock, farm equipment, feed, seed, fuel, farm chemicals, insurance, and other operating expenses. Can also be used to pay for minor improvements. Up to $200,000.

Beginning Farmer and Rancher Loans: provides funds to beginning and farmers and ranchers who are unable to obtain financing elsewhere.

Downpayment Farm Ownership Loans for Beginning Farmers: helps beginning farmers and ranchers purchase a farm or ranch. Also provides a way for retiring farmers to transfer their land to a future generation of farmers and ranchers. Applicant must have a downpayment of 10% and FSA with finance 40%, with the remaining balance from a commercial lender. Purchase price cannot exceed $250,000.

Loans to Socially Disadvantaged Farmers/Ranchers: helps socially disadvantaged applicants buy and operate family-size farms and ranches.

Youth Loans: Made to youths to establish and operate income-producing projects with the participation in 4-H clubs, Future Farmers of America, and similar organizations. Up to $5,000.

Emergency Loan Assistance: provides loans to help producers recover from production and physical losses due to drought, flooding, and other natural disasters, or quarantine. Up to $500,000.

Beginning Farmer and Rancher Land Contract Guarantee Pilot Program: "prompt payment guarantee" from FSA. FSA will provide payment to seller two times if the beginning farmer does not pay. Program is tested in IN, IA, ND, OR, PA and WI.

Farm Ownership and Operating Loan Guarantees: FSA will guarantee loans up to $782,000.

* Small Business Administration (SBA)
Small Business Administration (SBA)
7825 Baymeadows Way, Suite 100B   904-443-1900
Jacksonville, FL 32256   Fax: 904-443-1980
www.sba.gov/fl/north

Small Business Administration (SBA)
100 S. Biscayne Blvd., 7th Floor   305-536-5521
Miami, FL 33131   Fax: 305-536-5058
www.sba.gov/

The Florida Small Business Administration Office delivers a variety of programs and services, such as startup and operational assistance through small business training and counseling, financial assistance for startups, business opportunities and much more.

Georgia

* Office of Economic Development

Georgia Department of Community Affairs
60 Executive Park South, NE
Suite 250   404-679-4940
Atlanta, GA 30329-2231   Fax: 800-736-1155
www.dca.state.ga.us

Georgia Department of Community Affairs (DCA): Responsible for state administration of many incentive programs as well as providing technical assistance in the area of economic development to local governments, development authorities, and private for-profit entities. Provides information on financing programs and other services offered by the state government.

DCA maintains a highly skilled and extremely dedicated graphics and editorial staff to ensure that the information it gathers is effectively digested and promptly disseminated. Some of the department's many publications include:
- *Small Business Resource Guide*: Manual for small business owners with useful instruction, organization addresses and telephone numbers and resources.
- *Georgia's Communities-Planning, Growing, Achieving*: Publication contains information about various federal, state, and local financing programs that benefit businesses located in Georgia.
- *Economic Development Financing Packet*
- *Regional Development Center Listing*: List of Georgia's 16 RDCs with addresses and telephone numbers.

One-Stop Environmental Permitting: Georgia offers one-stop environmental permitting through its Department of Natural Resources, Environmental Protection Division. The state has the full authority of the U.S. Environmental Protection Agency (EPA) to issue permits that meet Federal standards, thus allowing a single permit to meet all requirements.

Industrial Revenue Bonds: Taxable and tax-exempt industrial revenue bond financing is available through the state or local development authorities at competitive, below-prime rates.

Supplier Choice Power: Georgia companies with electricity demands of 900 kilowatts or higher may choose among competing suppliers, taking advantage of a competitive market. This cost-saving option has been available to Georgia consumers long before deregulation of the industry was even contemplated.

The Employment Incentive Program: A financing program that may be used in conjunction with traditional private financing to carry out economic development projects which will result in employment of moderate and low income persons. Amounts not available.

Community Home Investment Program (CHIP): Created by the National Affordable Housing Act of 1990, the Home Investment Partnerships (HOME) Program is the first federally funded block grant designed to address state and local affordable housing concerns with a maximum amount awarded per local government applicant of $200,000.

Immediate Threat and Danger Program: Funds community development, having a particular urgency because existing conditions pose a serious and immediate threat to the health or welfare of the community. The maximum amount an applicant may receive is $50,000, which shall not exceed half of total project cost.

Local Development Fund: A state funded grant program that provides local governments with matching funds for community improvement projects. The maximum grant amount is $10,000 for single community projects and $20,000 for multi-community projects.

Appalachian Regional Commission (ARC): An economic development program providing matching grant funds to eligible applicants for projects that will benefit the entire 35-county area of Appalachian Georgia.

Appalachian Region Business Development Revolving Loan Fund: A $2.2 million pool that can be used in the Appalachian Region for loans to projects that create or save jobs. The maximum loan amount is $200,000 per qualifying business, or 50% of total project cost, whichever is less. There is no maximum project cost and no minimum loan amount.

Regional Assistance Program (RAP): Grants are available on a competitive basis to local governments, development authorities, and regional development centers for regional industrial parks and similar facilities, regional water and sewer treatment facilities, regional transportation and communication facilities, regional marketing and recruitment programs, and other projects important to regional economic development. Grants will be available up to $250,000 per multi-county or regional economic development implementation project with no minimum match required.

Business Retention and Expansion Process: Provides a process for local governments, chambers and/or development authorities to survey existing industries and identify the perceptions and potential problems of private sector firms concerning issues like future plans, international trade, labor and manpower, local government services, energy requirements, and community linkages.

Surety Bond Guarantee Program: Enables small contractors to obtain the surety bonds necessary to compete for government and non-government contracts.

Industrial Enterprise Zones: The City of Atlanta, as authorized under a special provision of Georgia law, has designated two industrial parks as industrial enterprise zones. Companies in both the Atlanta and Southside industrial parks receive 100% freeport on all three classes of inventory and may receive real property tax reduction for up to 25 years. All buildings constructed in these enterprise zones are exempted from local property taxes at levels that begin at 100%. These exemptions decrease in increments of 20% every five years. New businesses in both parks are eligible for a $2,500-per job tax credit for a payroll of ten or more persons.

Bond Allocation Program: Businesses that are looking to construct or improve manufacturing facilities, single and multi-family housing projects can benefit from this program. Economic development projects must keep or create one job for every $125,000 of funding.

Industrial Development Bond Financing: Long-term, low-rate financing for businesses looking to improve or construct manufacturing facilities. Up to $10 million is available per project.

The Redevelopment Fund Program: The Redevelopment Fund provides flexible financial assistance to local governments to assist them in implementing challenging economic and community development projects that cannot be undertaken with existing public sector grant and loan programs.

Downtown Development Revolving loan Fund (DDRLF): The Downtown Development Revolving Loan Fund is designed to assist non-entitlement cities and counties in implementing quality downtown development projects. Loans may be used for a variety of public or private projects that involve infrastructure improvements, real estate development or redevelopment, and, in some cases, purchase or lease of equipment.

Georgia Academy for Economic Development: The Academy is a consortium of public and private economic development organizations providing economic development training throughout Georgia. These professionals serve as the Academy's program leaders and resource experts.

* Rural Development Administration
Community and Business Programs Division
Georgia State Office
335 East Hancock Ave.   706-546-2162
Athens, GA 30610   Fax: 706-546-2152
www.rurdev.usda.gov/ga
Special Grant Programs
Recycling and Waste Reduction Grants: Objectives are to reduce or eliminate pollution of water resources and improve planning and management of solid waste sites. Grants may be used to evaluate current landfill conditions to determine threats to water resources; provide technical assistance and/or training to enhance operator skills in the maintenance and operations of active landfills; provide technical assistance and/or training to help communities reduce the solid waste stream; and provide technical assistance and/or training for operators of landfills which are closed or will be closed in the near future.

Value-Added Agricultural Producer Grants: The Value-Added Agricultural Producer Grants program is designed to encourage independent producers of agricultural commodities to process their raw products into marketable goods, thereby increasing farm income. There are four entities that may apply for funds. They are: Independent Producer, Farm or Ranch Cooperative, Agricultural Producer Groups and Majority-Controlled Producer Based Business Ventures. Funds for eligible products may be used for planning and working capital. Contact Craig Scroggs at 333 Phillips Dr., McDonough, GA 30253 or by email at craig.scroggs@ga.usda.gov

Rural Business Enterprise Grants: This grant program supports the development of small emerging private business enterprises in rural areas. Small or emerging businesses generally employ 50 or fewer employees and have less than $1,000,000 in projected gross revenues. The grants may be used to acquire and develop land, construct or make repairs to buildings/equipment, technical assistance, providing financial assistance and other business purposes. Contact the office or web site for a complete listing.

State Historic Preservation Tax Incentives: Designed to encourage rehabilitation of both residential and commercial historic buildings that might otherwise be neglected. The law provides an owner of historic property which has undergone substantial rehabilitation an eight-year freeze on property tax assessments. For the ninth year, the assessment increases by 50% of the difference between the recorded first year value and the current fair market value. In the tenth and following years the tax assessment will then be based on the current fair market value. The rehabilitation project must meet a rehabilitation test. If the property is: *Residential* (owner occupied C rehabilitation must increase the fair market value of the building by at least 50%. *Mixed-use* (primarily residential and partially income-producing property) C rehabilitation must increase the fair market value of the building by at least 75%. *Commercial and Professional Use* (income producing property) C rehabilitation must increase the fair market value of the building by at least 100%.

Business and Industry Loans: This Direct Loan Program provides loans to private parties, who can't obtain credit elsewhere and to public bodies. This assistance is available in areas outside of the city with a population of 50,000 or less. Loans can be used for improving, developing or financing business and industry, employment and to improve the economic and environmental rural community, including pollution control. The maximum loan available is $10 million.

Renewable Energy System and Energy Efficiency Improvement Program: This grant, loan and loan guarantee program is available to farmers, ranchers and rural small businesses to purchase renewable energy systems and for making energy efficiency improvements. Grants for Renewable Energy Systems are limited to $500,000. Grants for Energy Efficiency Improvements are limited to $250,000.

* The Phoenix Fund
Atlanta Development Authority
86 Pryor St., Suite 300   404-880-4100
Atlanta, GA 30303   Fax: 404-880-9333
www.atlantada.com
A program created to assist small and medium-sized businesses providing loan amounts from $10,000-$100,000 for construction or renovation of privately-owned commercial buildings, equipment purchases needed to operate a business, and, in some cases, working capital.

* The Georgia Procurement Assistance Center
Georgia Tech Economic Development Institute
760 Spring Street, Suite 330   404-953-3155
Atlanta, GA 30332-0640   Fax: 404-953-3169
www.edi.gatech.edu/gtpac
Assists firms in their efforts to do business with the federal government. The Center helps firms solicit bids and locate procurement opportunities with the Department of Defense and area military facilities seeking certain goods and services. Although assistance is given upon request to any firm, the majority of clients are small and disadvantaged businesses.

* Atlanta Regional Export Assistance Center
285 Peachtree Center Avenue   404-657-1961
Atlanta, GA 30303   Fax: 404-657-1970
www.dtae.org/econdev/gitdn.html
The Atlanta Export Assistance Center offers the following resources: Marketing Assistance, Resource Center, Financial Assistance, The Atlanta Export Assistance Center combines

the export promotion and finance resources of the following eight agencies: U.S. Department of Commerce, U.S. Small Business Administration, The Georgia Department of Agriculture, The Georgia Department of Industry, Trade & Tourism, The Georgia Housing and Finance Authority, Georgia's Institute of Technology's Center for International Standards and Quality, and the Service Corps of Retired Executives.

The *Atlanta Region* houses consulates, trade offices, and Chambers of Commerce for 44 countries. These organizations provide assistance with foreign exporting, importing and investing.

International Trade Data Network (ITDN): A not-for-profit data multiplier, GDITT provides the business community with the timely, detailed market intelligence needed to be competitive in the global arena.

* Minority Small Business Resource Organizations
Atlanta Business League
PO Box 92363
931 Martin Luther King Dr.   404-584-8126
Atlanta, GA 30314   Fax: 404-584-0445
www.theabl.org

Atlanta Public Schools
Contract Compliance Office
130 Trinity Avenue, SW, 4th Floor
Atlanta, GA 30303   404-827-2436
www.atlanta.k12.ga.us/inside_aps/finance/contractsw/de
  fault.htm

Business Development Center – NAACP
2034 Metropolitan Parkway, SW
Atlanta, GA 30315   404-761-1266
www.atlantanaacp.org

Department of Commerce
Minority Business Development Agency (MBDA)
Summit Building, Room 1715
401 West Peachtree Street, NW   404-730-3300
Atlanta, GA 30308   Fax: 404-730-3313

Small Business Administration
Minority Small Business Division
233 Peachtree Road, NW, Suite 1900
Atlanta, GA 30303   404-331-0100
www.sba.gov/ga

These organizations provide a variety of technical counseling and financial assistance to minority small businesses:

* Department of Administrative Services
Governor's Small Business Center
200 Piedmont Ave., SE
West Tower, Suite 1804   800-495-0053
Atlanta, GA 30334-9010   404-656-6315
www.doas.state.ga.us

The mission of the Governor's Small Business Center is to contribute to Georgia's economic growth by increasing opportunities for new, emerging and established Georgia-based small and minority businesses to improve their operations, build business alliances, develop joint ventures and promote their businesses.

New Vendor Orientation: these monthly sessions provide general information on how to become a registered vendor

with the state, marketing strategies and more. These sessions are also offered online at {http://www2.state.ga.us/depart ments/doas/gsbc/newvendor.html}.

Small and Minority Business Coordinators: this program is designed to inform you of procurement opportunities with their specific agencies. In addition, they provide state purchasing agencies with a vendor list to increase bid opportunities to small and minority businesses.

Governor's Mentor-Protégé Program: The Governor's Mentor-Protégé Program pairs leading Georgia companies with emerging businesses for mentoring relationships that can increase their odds of success.

* First Stop Business Information Center
Suite 315, West Tower   404-656-7061
2 Martin Luther King, Jr. Drive   800 656-4558
Atlanta, GA 30334   Fax: 404-657-6380
Email: firststop@sos.state.ga.us
www.sos.state.ga.us/firststop

The First Stop Business Information Center provides the small business owner and the prospective entrepreneur with a central point of information and contacts for state regulatory requirements for operating a small business. The primary objective of this center is to facilitate sustainable small business development in Georgia by offering a central location for determination of what licenses and permits must be obtained and maintained by individuals and businesses conducting their enterprises in our great state.

* Small Business Assistance Program
Georgia Department of Natural Resources
Georgia Environmental Protection Division
4244 International Parkway   404-362-4842
Suite 120   888-373-5947
Atlanta, GA 30354   877-427-6255
www.gasmallbiz.org   Fax: 404-651-5778

Georgia Department of Natural Resources created a Small Business Assistance Program (SBAP) in 1993. The goal of the SBAP is to help small businesses comply with clean air requirements in Georgia. Air quality regulations require many small businesses to obtain permits, install pollution control equipment, and maintain extensive records on emissions.

* Office of Adult Literacy Programs
GEA Office
1800 Century Place, NE   404-679-1644
Atlanta, GA 30345   Fax: 404-679-4911
State Office of Adult Literacy   404-679-1625
www.dtae.org/adultlit.html   Fax: 404-679-1630

Georgia Department of Technical and Adult Education
Georgia Department of Revenue
Georgia Tax Credit for Adult Basic Skills Education: Designed to encourage businesses to provide or sponsor basic skills education programs for their employees. The program provides tax credits under Article 2 of Chapter 7 of Title 48 of the Official Code of Georgia Annotated, 48-7-41. The amount of tax credit shall be equal to one-third of the costs of education per full-time equivalent student, or $150 per full-time equivalent student, whichever is less, for each employee who has successfully completed an approved adult basic skills education program. The tax credit granted to any employer pursuant to the Code shall not exceed the amount of the taxpayer's income liability for the taxable year as computed without regard to this Code section.

* Georgia Department of Technical and Adult Education

Michael Jones, Manager
1800 Century Pl., Suite 300   404-679-1700
Atlanta, GA 30345-4304   Fax: 404-679-1710
www.dtae.org

Quick Start: The State of Georgia's internationally known training program for new and expanding business and industries. Quick Start directly provides a full range of high quality customized training services at no cost to client companies. These services cover not only job specific skills but also automation, productivity enhancement and human resource development training. Examples: Statistical Process Control, Programmable Logic Controller, and Team Skills training. Also provides comprehensive training for office operations such as corporate headquarters, billing and remittance centers, and telecommunications operations such as customer service centers.

* Georgia Department of Labor

Assistant Commissioner
Job Training Division
148 International Blvd., NE, Suite 650   404-232-3775
Atlanta, GA 30303   Fax: 404-651-9377
www.dol.state.ga.us

The Department of Labor is responsible for implementing the federal Workforce Investment Act (WIA). There are over 45 One-Stop service locations throughout the state to assist in job training for both the employee and employer.

* The Community Investment Services Department

Federal Home Loan Bank
1475 Peachtree St., NE   404-888-8000
Atlanta, GA 30309-3037   800-536-9650
www.fhlbatl.com

Federal Home Loan Bank

Community Investment Services: The fund provides long-term funds to its member institutions for lending in their communities. Funds may be used to assist first-time home buyers, for loans to small businesses, for the rehabilitation of historic districts, for community redevelopment programs, and for home mortgages for low- and moderate-income families. The maturities offered are up to 20 years at fixed rates.

* Georgia Environmental Facilities Authority

Paul Burks, Executive Director
2090 Equitable Bldg.
100 Peachtree St.   404-656-0938
Atlanta, GA 30303   Fax: 404-656-6416
www.gefa.org

The Georgia Environmental Facilities Authority will responsively and responsibly provide environmental and energy efficiency financing, coordination and education to governmental units and nonprofit organizations so that they can use available resources in an environmentally sensitive manner for all Georgians.

Recycling And Waste Reduction Grants: The purpose of this grant program is to assist local governments in planning, expanding, improving and implementing waste reduction programs in Georgia. The grants are designed to provide much needed technical and financial assistance to Georgia local governments for recycling and waste reduction infrastructure. The goal of the grants is to help local governments foster an integrated approach to waste reduction through waste minimization, recycling, composting and other innovative programs.

Clean Water State Revolving Loan Fund (CWSRF): This federally funded program is administered by the Environmental Facilities Authority for waste water projects. Low interest loans are available for a variety of water quality and wastewater treatment projects that include: construction of new wastewater treatment plants, installing sewer lines, purchasing street and storm sewer cleaning equipment and others.

Drinking Water State Revolving Loan Fund (DWSRF): This federally funded program is administered by the Environmental Facilities Authority for drinking water projects. Low interest loans are available for a variety of public health related water supply projects that include: replacing aging infrastructure, installing or upgrading treatment facilities to improve drinking water quality, maintain compliance and many others.

Georgia Fund Loans through this state bond funded program finance all types of water and sewer projects including water and sewer lines, treatment plants, pumping stations, and water storage tanks. Loans from this program range from $20,000 to $3 million. Over 70% of communities receiving Georgia Fund are in rural areas. Contact Dan Clarke for additional information at (404) 656-0940 .

Environmental Emergency Loans: Environmental emergency loans are available at any time for projects needed to protect community health or safety. The interest rate is only 2.0%. The maximum loan amount is $200,000, but this can be combined with other GEFA loan programs to fully finance projects that cost more than $100,000. Contact James Thompson for more information at (404) 656-4046 .

Construction Loans: GEFA offers up to $1,000,000 in interim financing for applicants with a known source of permanent financing, such as Special Purpose Local Option Sales Taxes (SPLOST), a United States Department of Agriculture loan, etc.

Solid Waste Facility Financing: GEFA offers low interest loans of up to $1 million for solid waste capital projects that serve local governments. Also, to help minimize their waste streams, cities and counties can purchase facilities and equipment for new recycling or waste reduction programs through GEFA recycling and waste reduction grant funds.

GEFA / ENERGY: As the State Energy Office, the GEFA Division of Energy Resources is the primary agency for energy programs, grants, and educational materials. Through a broad array of programs ranging from Home Energy Clinics for the residential sector and the installation of weatherization materials in low income homes to assisting fleets to use clean alternative fuels, GEFA annually assists thousands of citizens throughout the state.

* Loans For Farmers

Farm Service Agency
U.S. Department of Agriculture
355 East Hancock Avenue
Room 102 Mail Stop 100   706-546-2266
Athens, GA 30601-2775   Fax: 706-546-2151
http://www.fsa.usda.gov/ga/

The Farm Service Agency provides Direct and Guaranteed Loans to farmers through a variety of programs, including:

Farm Ownership Loans: purchase farmland, construct or repair buildings and other fixtures, and promote soil and water conservation. Up to $200,000.

Operating Loans: purchase items needed for a successful farm operation, such as livestock, farm equipment, feed, seed, fuel, farm chemicals, insurance, and other operating expenses. Can also be used to pay for minor improvements. Up to $200,000.

Beginning Farmer and Rancher Loans: provides funds to beginning and farmers and ranchers who are unable to obtain financing elsewhere.

Downpayment Farm Ownership Loans for Beginning Farmers: helps beginning farmers and ranchers purchase a farm or ranch. Also provides a way for retiring farmers to transfer their land to a future generation of farmers and ranchers. Applicant must have a downpayment of 10% and FSA with finance 40%, with the remaining balance from a commercial lender. Purchase price cannot exceed $250,000.

Loans to Socially Disadvantaged Farmers/Ranchers: helps socially disadvantaged applicants buy and operate family-size farms and ranches.

Youth Loans: Made to youths to establish and operate income-producing projects with the participation in 4-H clubs, Future Farmers of America, and similar organizations. Up to $5,000.

Emergency Loan Assistance: provides loans to help producers recover from production and physical losses due to drought, flooding, and other natural disasters, or quarantine. Up to $500,000.

Beginning Farmer and Rancher Land Contract Guarantee Pilot Program: "prompt payment guarantee" from FSA. FSA will provide payment to seller two times if the beginning farmer does not pay. Program is tested in IN, IA, ND, OR, PA and WI.

Farm Ownership and Operating Loan Guarantees: FSA will guarantee loans up to $782,000.

* Small Business Administration (SBA)

Small Business Administration
233 Peachtree St., NE, Suite 1900   404-331-0100
Atlanta, GA 30303   Fax: 404-331-0101
www.sba.gov/ga

The Georgia Small Business Administration Office delivers a variety of programs and services, such as startup and operational assistance through small business training and counseling, financial assistance for startup's, business opportunities and much more

* Georgia Development Authority

Agricultural Loan Division
2082 E. Exchange Pl., Suite 102   770-414-3400
Tucker, GA 30084   Fax: 770-414-3407
www.gda.georgia.gov

Georgia business owners have a fast, convenient way to register their business with the State of Georgia. By visiting www.georgia.gov and clicking the Online Business Registration Section, business owners will be able to register for a state sales tax identification number and a provisional Federal Employee Identification Number (FEIN). Obtaining a state sales tax identification number and a provisional

Federal Employee Identification Number (FEIN) used to take several days.

* Intellectual Capital Partnership Program

Office of Economic Development
University System of Georgia
270 Washington Street, SW   404-656-2275
Atlanta, GA 30334   Fax: 404-657-1489
www.icapp.org

The Intellectual Capital Partnership Program provides one-stop entry to the intellectual capital of the University of Georgia, which includes educational programs, facility expertise, and research and development facilities.

* Coastal Venture Investment Forum

210 Technology Circle
Savannah, GA 31407   912-681-0213
www.coastalvif.org/

The Coastal Venture Forum is designed to promote the development of promising businesses located within the coastal region of Georgia. VIF assists by reviewing business plans to determine if private investment is warranted.

* The Business Improvement Loan Fund Program

Atlanta Development Authority
86 Pryor Street, Suite 300   404-880-4100
Atlanta, GA 30303   Fax: 404-880-9333
www.atlantada.com

The Business Improvement Loan Fund Program is designed to encourage the revitalization of targeted business districts in Atlanta, and to support commercial /industrial development in other eligible areas. District loans and loan participation up to $50,000 are available to businesses that are not able to obtain a market rate loan.

* GRASP Enterprises

241 Peachtree Street, NE, Suite 200   404-659-5955
Atlanta, GA 30303   Fax: 404-880-9561
www.graspnet.org

GRASP Enterprises, Inc. is a nonprofit business development agency providing business programs and support services to metro Atlanta's small business community. Their mission is to enable aspiring entrepreneurs and existing small businesses achieve a stronger competitive position, larger market share, and greater chance of long term survival by providing a comprehensive and complete business solution. The organization's services include: Atlanta Women's Business Center, Business Training, Business Consulting, Business Financing, and Incubator Services.

Hawaii

* Department of Business, Economic Development and Tourism

P.O. Box 2359
Honolulu, HI 96804
No. 1 Capitol District Bldg.
250 S. Hotel Street   808-586-2423
Honolulu, HI 96813   Fax: 808-587-2790
www.hawaii.gov/dbedt/index.html

Small Business Information Service: Responsible for providing referrals and information on government licenses, permits and procurement, funding source, and entrepreneurship training.

Business Services Division: Helps new and existing businesses with direct business loans, community development projects, information programs, licensing and permit information and referral, and business advocacy.

Hawaii Small Business Innovation Research Grant Program: Its purpose is to expand science and technology-based economic development in Hawaii, increase revenues and quality job opportunities in the State. {www.htdc.org/sbir}
- Federal SBIR Program: Phase I awards determine the feasibility of a new technology and are valued up to $100,000. Phase II awards are a continuation of successful Phase I efforts. Phase II awards typically involve developing a prototype and are valued up to $750,000
- Hawaii SBIR Matching Grant Program: To encourage Hawaii companies to participate in the program, the High Technology Development Corporation provides a matching grant of up to $25,000 to Hawaii companies that receive Phase I awards

State of Hawaii Government: May finance exports through its Department of Business, Economic Development & Tourism's Hawaii Capital Loan Program (HCLP). The loan program's objective is to provide standard commercial loans to small businesses unable to get financing from private lenders. With an average loan award amount of $250,000 (maximum $1 million) for terms of up to 20 years, HCLP is available to all SBA- defined small businesses with two bank turndowns. The interest rate is set at a very attractive prime rate minus 1%, which is not to exceed 7.5%.

U.S. Department of Commerce-Commercial Service (Honolulu District office): The trade specialist at the Honolulu District office assists U.S. companies seeking to expand into export markets. The Honolulu District office provides companies with trade leads, foreign market research, and information on trade events, seminars, and conferences.

Local Chambers of Commerce: Provide exporters with copies of and instructions for completing a general Certificate of Origin. This certificate is a notarized statement authenticating the country of origin of an export good.

Thai Trade Representative Office: Focuses primarily on the promotion of Thailand products in Hawaii.

Research and Economic Analysis Division: This division provides accurate timely statistical and economic information for Hawaii businesses, including access to information and services available from other government sources in the State of Hawaii, nationally and internationally. There are 15,000 titles relating to business, government and economic development in the State of Hawaii with an emphasis on statistical information.

* Rural Development
U.S. Department of Agriculture
Rural Development
Room 311, Federal Building
154 Waianuenue Avenue   808-933-8380
Hilo, HI 96720   Fax: 808-933-8327
www.rurdev.usda.gov/hi
Business And Industry Guarantee And Direct Loans: The guaranteed B&I program provides financial assistance to

rural businesses by offering guarantees to lenders as an incentive to extend credit in rural areas. If credit is not available elsewhere, Rural Development may provide direct loans to rural borrowers. Loan funds may be used to support the establishment or expansion of businesses, for working capital, machinery and equipment, buildings and real estate, and certain types of debt refinancing. Businesses involved in forestry, aquaculture, growing of hydroponics and mushrooms and commercial nurseries are eligible for assistance in addition to businesses involved in producing value-added products. The primary purpose is to create and maintain employment and improve the economic climate in rural communities.

Intermediary Relending Program: The Intermediary Relending Program allows an eligible intermediary organization to borrow funds directly from Rural Development at a one percent interest rate for the purpose of establishing a revolving fund. The revolving fund is used to provide a source of funds to businesses located in rural areas for business and community development purposes that would not otherwise qualify for commercial loans.

Rural Business Enterprise Grant (RBEG): Rural Business Enterprise Grants are used to finance and facilitate development of private business enterprises. The purpose of the grant is to assist public bodies and nonprofit corporations finance and facilitate development of small and emerging private business enterprises located in areas outside the boundary of a city of 50,000 or more and its immediate adjacent urbanized area. RBEGs are awarded on a competing basis.

Rural Business Opportunity Grant (RBOG): Rural Business Opportunity Grant funds provide for technical assistance, training, and planning activities that improve economic conditions in rural areas. Applicants must be located in rural areas (this includes all areas other than cities of more than 10,000 people). Nonprofit corporations and public bodies are eligible. Funding is available to be distributed on a national competition basis. The RBOG program can be used to promote sustainable economic development in rural communities with exceptional needs. Making grants to organizations to provide for economic development planning, technical assistance, or training accomplishes this.

Hawaii Capital Loan Program: This loan provides loans to small businesses for financing construction, land acquisition, machinery, supplies or working capital for business owners unable to secure financing from conventional sources.

Native Hawaiian Revolving Loan Fund: This lending program is for Native Hawaiians to increase sustainable Native Hawaiian-owned businesses by providing economic independence, commitment and fiscal responsibility through entrepreneurial/job development.

* Employment and Training Fund Program
Oahu Branch
Honolulu Office
830 Punchbowl Street, Room 112   808-586-8715
Honolulu, HI 96813   Fax: 808-586-8724

Hawaii Branch
Hilo Office
180 Kinoole Street, Room 205   808-974-4126
Hilo, HI 96720   Fax: 808-974-4125

Kona Office
74-5565 Luhia Street   808- 327-4770
Kailua-Kona, HI 96740   Fax: 808-327-4774

Kauai Branch
Kauai Office
3100 Kuhio Hwy., C-9   808- 274-3056
Lihue, HI 96766   Fax: 808-274-3059

Maui Branch
Maui Office
2064 Wells Street, Room 108   808-984-2091
Wailuku, HI 96793   Fax: 808-984-2090

Molokai Office
75 Makaena Street   808-553-1755
Kaunakakai, HI 96748   Fax: 808-553-1754

This program provides business specific training, upgrade training, new occupational skills training, management skills training, and other similar activities are available to both employers and individuals. {http://dlir.state.hi.us}.

* The Honolulu Minority Business Development Center

1088 Bishop Street, Suite 2506   808-521-6221
Honolulu, HI 96813   Fax: 808-524-3313
www.mbdc-honolulu.com

The objectives of the Honolulu Minority Business Development Center are to 1) promote the creation and/or expansion of viable and competitive minority-owned businesses, 2) increase contracting opportunities from public and private sources for minority-owned businesses, and 3) provide management and technical assistance to qualified minority individuals and firms in the areas of planning, finance, construction assistance and general management to improve the overall performance, profit and net worth of minority firms.

* Business Action Center

State Department of Business
Economic Development and Tourism
1130 N. Nimitz Hwy., Suite A-220
Honolulu, HI 96817   808-586-2545
www.hawaii.gov/dbedt/br26.html

Provides Hawaii's entrepreneurs with the information, business forms, licenses and permits they need to make their small business dreams a reality.

* Pacific Business Center Program

College of Business Administration
University of Hawaii at Manoa
2404 Maile Way, A413   808-956-6286
Honolulu, HI 96822   Fax: 808-956-6278
www.hawaii.edu/pbcp

The Pacific Business Center matches faculty, students, and facilities at the University of Hawaii at Manoa with requests for assistance from businesses and community development organizations in Hawaii and the U.S. territories in the Pacific Islands. Consultation with program staff is free of charge, and after that clients may be assessed a modest consulting fee to pay faculty and students working on individual projects.

* Alu Like, Inc.

Career Education
458 Keawe St.

Honolulu, HI 96813   808-535-6700
www.alulike.org

Alu-Like, Inc. offers a wide range of office support services and technical assistance to all individuals regardless of race. The organization charges a nominal fee, and has several sites.

* Hawaii Island Economic Development Board

PMB-281
200 Kanoelehua Ave.   808-966-5416
Hilo, HI 96720   Fax: 808-966-6792
www.hiedb.org

HIEDB's mission is to facilitate federal resource programs and implement appropriate economic development projects. HIEDB provides valuable information and contacts for area businesses and industries, as well as key liaison to federal, state, county and private sector resources in financing, business planning, permitting, legal advice and other business services.

* High Technology Development Corporation

2800 Woodlawn Dr., Suite 100   888-677-4292
Honolulu, HI 96822   808-539-3806
www.htdc.org

Promotes the growth of commercial high-technology industry and assists in promoting hi-tech products and software.

* Hawaii Department Of Agriculture

Agricultural Loan Division
1428 S. King St.
Honolulu, HI 96814   808-973-9460
www.hawaiiag.org/hdoa/

The Agricultural Loan Program is intended to provide financing to "Qualified Farmers" and "New Farmers" engaged in agricultural production of food, feed and fiber. Loans can be made to qualifying sole proprietorships, corporations, partnerships and cooperatives. In addition, qualifying corporations and cooperatives can obtain funding for enterprises engaged in marketing, purchasing, processing and for those who provide certain farm business services.

Aquaculture Loan Program: Aquaculture means the production of aquatic plant and animal life in a controlled salt, brackish, or freshwater environment situated on real property. Loans can be made to "Qualified Aquaculturists" organized as sole proprietorships, corporations, cooperatives and partnerships.

* Hawaii Strategic Development Corporation

No. 1 Capitol District Building
250 South Hotel Street, Suite 503
P.O. Box 2359   808-587-3829
Honolulu, HI 96804   Fax: 808-587-3832
www.htdc.org/hsdc

The Hawaii Strategic Development Corporation (HSDC) is a state agency designed to provide capital, mainly to technology-oriented businesses, from public and private sources. The HSDC provides both seed and venture capital through limited partnerships.

* Maui Research & Technology Center

590 Lipoa Parkway
Kihei, HI 96753   808-875-2320
www.mrtc.org

The Maui Research & Technology Center operated by the

Maui Economic Development Board under a grant from the State of Hawaii's High Technology Development Corporation. This two building complex houses incubator space for start-up businesses, a video conferencing facility, a multi-media production facility, an entry-level computer lab operated by Maui Community College, a small business and technology library, the offices of the UH Hilo Small Business Development Center, and the UH Manoa Office of Technology Transfer and Economic Development.

* The Office of Technology Transfer (OTTED)

Mark J. Andrews, Associate Director
University of Hawaii/OTTED
2800 Woodlawn Dr., Suite 280   808-539-3817
Honolulu, HI 96822   Fax: 808-539-3833
www.mic.hawaii.edu

OTTED represents a link to the scientific, technical, and business development resources of the University of Hawaii. These resources include the University's unique research facilities and faculty expertise which may be used to assist individuals, organizations or businesses with scientific or technical problems.

* Manoa Innovation Center

The High Technology Development Corporation (HTDC)
2800 Woodlawn Drive Suite 100
Honolulu, Hawaii 96822
Executive Office: 808-539-3600
Technology Outreach: 808-539-3814
www.htdc.org/mic/

The High Technology Development Corporation's (HTDC) mission is to facilitate the development and growth of commercial high technology industry in Hawaii. HTDC actively markets and promotes Hawaii as a site for high-technology applications and gives advice on policy and planning. HTDC serves as an advocate for start-up and existing high-technology companies doing business in Hawaii and is a source of information on high technology activity in the State.

* Agribusiness Development Corporation

State Office Tower
235 S. South Beretania St. Room 205   808-586-0186
Honolulu, HI 96813   Fax: 808-586-0189
www.hawaiiag.org/hdoa/adc.htm

The mission of the Agribusiness Development Corporation (ADC) is to provide leadership and advocacy for the conversion of agribusiness into a dynamic growth industry through the use of financial and other tools enabled by the founding legislation for the pursuit of specific projects to achieve the legislative objectives.

* Office of Hawaiian Affairs

711 Kapiolani Boulevard, Suite 500   808-594-1888
Honolulu, HI 96813   Fax: 808-594-1865
www.oha.org

Native Hawaiian Revolving Loan Fund: The Native Hawaiian Revolving Loan Fund (NHRLF) is a lending program for Native Hawaiians whose mission is to increase sustainable, Native Hawaiian-owned businesses by fostering economic independence, commitment and fiscal responsibility through entrepreneurial development.

* Loans For Farmers

Farm Service Agency
U.S. Department of Agriculture
300 Ala Moana Boulevard, Room 5-112   808-541-2600
Honolulu, HI 96850   Fax: 808-541-2648
http://www.fsa.usda.gov/hi/

The Farm Service Agency provides Direct and Guaranteed Loans to farmers through a variety of programs, including:

Farm Ownership Loans: purchase farmland, construct or repair buildings and other fixtures, and promote soil and water conservation. Up to $200,000.

Operating Loans: purchase items needed for a successful farm operation, such as livestock, farm equipment, feed, seed, fuel, farm chemicals, insurance, and other operating expenses. Can also be used to pay for minor improvements. Up to $200,000.

Beginning Farmer and Rancher Loans: provides funds to beginning and farmers and ranchers who are unable to obtain financing elsewhere.

Downpayment Farm Ownership Loans for Beginning Farmers: helps beginning farmers and ranchers purchase a farm or ranch. Also provides a way for retiring farmers to transfer their land to a future generation of farmers and ranchers. Applicant must have a downpayment of 10% and FSA with finance 40%, with the remaining balance from a commercial lender. Purchase price cannot exceed $250,000.

Loans to Socially Disadvantaged Farmers/Ranchers: helps socially disadvantaged applicants buy and operate family-size farms and ranches.

Youth Loans: Made to youths to establish and operate income-producing projects with the participation in 4-H clubs, Future Farmers of America, and similar organizations. Up to $5,000.

Emergency Loan Assistance: provides loans to help producers recover from production and physical losses due to drought, flooding, and other natural disasters, or quarantine. Up to $500,000.

Beginning Farmer and Rancher Land Contract Guarantee Pilot Program: "prompt payment guarantee" from FSA. FSA will provide payment to seller two times if the beginning farmer does not pay. Program is tested in IN, IA, ND, OR, PA and WI.

Farm Ownership and Operating Loan Guarantees: FSA will guarantee loans up to $782,000.

* Small Business Administration (SBA)

Room 2235, Box 50207
300 Ala Moana Blvd.   808-541-2990
Honolulu, HI 96850-4981   Fax: 808-541-2976
www.sba.gov/hi

The Hawaii Small Business Administration Office delivers a variety of programs and services, such as startup and operational assistance through small business training and counseling, financial assistance for startup's, business opportunities and much more

Idaho

* Idaho Department of Commerce
700 West State Street
P.O. Box 83720   208-334-2470
Boise, ID 83720-0093   Fax: 208-334-2631
www.idoc.state.id.us/

Economic Development Division: This office can provide information and expertise in dealing with state, federal, and local agencies. They also have information on financing programs and other services offered by the state government.

Idaho Business Network (IBN): Operated by the Idaho Department of Commerce to help Idaho companies bid on federal, state and large corporation contracts.
- *Opportunity Notices*: Every day bid notices on federal, state and private contracts are entered into the Idaho Business Network computer. These bidding opportunities are matched with the capabilities of Idaho businesses participating in the IBN. When a match occurs the client company is notified with a printed or e-mail version "opportunity notice" alerting them to the opportunity and providing information needed to obtain the bid package.
- *Military and Federal Standards*: Federal bid packages often reference military and federal specifications by name or number without providing the actual documents. The Idaho Business Network maintains a CD-ROM library of all military and federal standards and specifications. Printed copies of required specifications and standards are provided at no charge to businesses participating in the IBN.
- *Federal Acquisition Regulations (F.A.R.)*: Contains the rules and regulations used by federal agencies to purchase products and services. Bid packages often refer to F.A.R. clauses by name or number without providing the text of the document. The IBN maintains the F.A.R. on CD-ROM, and provides printed copies of needed clauses to participating companies at no charge.
- *Trade Missions*: All IBN clients are welcome to attend periodic trade missions to visit large corporations, military sites, and other government agencies. Businesses attending the trade missions have the opportunity to meet with buyers to market their products and services.
- *Workshops and Seminars*: The IBN holds workshops statewide on topics such as selling to Mountain Home Air Force Base, selling to the INEEL, how to package for the military, quality assurance, etc.
- *The Governor's Business Opportunity Conference*: Annually, the IBN hosts the Governor's Business Opportunity Conference with over 60 large private corporations and government agencies sending buyers to meet with representatives of Idaho businesses. Concurrent training workshops are also held during the conference on a wide range of topics, such as introduction to procurement and marketing strategies for small businesses.
- *Electronic Bulletin Board*: Provides computer and modem access to all bid notices obtained by the IBN for the most current ten days.
- *CAGE Code*: All companies wishing to do business with the U.S. Department of Defense must have an identification number known as a Commercial and Government Entity Code, or CAGE Code. Companies applying for a CAGE Code must be sponsored by a government agency. The Idaho Business Network provides CAGE Code application forms and sponsors participating Idaho business applications

- *New Industry Training Program*: Provides customized job training for new and expanding industries.
- *Work Force Training*: Funds are available to provide skilled workers for specific economic opportunities and industrial expansion initiatives.

Industrial Revenue Bonds: Idaho cities and counties are able to form public corporations for the purpose of issuing industrial revenue bonds (IRBs). The IRB program provides for loans of up to $10 million, at tax-exempt interest rates, to finance the improvement or purchase of land, buildings, and machinery or equipment used in manufacturing, production, processing, or assembly.

Rural Economic and Community Development Administration: Offers guarantees up to 90% of loans between $500,000 and $10 million made to small businesses located in areas not within the boundaries of a city of 50,000 or more. Loan proceeds can be used for the purchase, development or improvement of land, buildings and equipment, or a start-up and working capital.

Nonbusiness-Related Contributions: Corporations are allowed credit for certain nonbusiness-related contributions, e.g., education and rehabilitation. Net operating loss carrybacks are limited to $100,000 per tax year. The $100,000 loss limit may be carried back three years and if it is not absorbed by the income in those three years, the rest of the loss may be carried forward 15 years. Instead of carrying a loss back, a taxpayer may choose to carry the loss forward for up to 15 years or until it has been completely absorbed.

The Idaho Department of Commerce's Division of International Business: Provides a variety of services and assistance to all Idaho firms interested in doing business overseas, with special programs for small- and medium-sized firms.

Idaho International Business Development Center (IIBDC): Seeks to coordinate efforts statewide to promote Idaho in the global marketplace. The division, in partnership with the Boise Branch Office of the U.S. Department of Commerce, maintains regular contact with importers, distributors, wholesalers, and retailers in foreign countries and can supply market data and information on foreign packaging, labeling requirements, language barriers, consumer preferences, and other trade factors.

Idaho Department of Agriculture: Offers a broad range of assistance to Idaho companies which export Idaho agricultural commodities and processed and specialty food products. The Department of Agriculture sponsors many special agricultural trade events and participates with the Department of Commerce in joint seminars, workshops, and trade shows.

* Rural Development
Rural Business-Cooperative Service (RBS)
9173 West Barnes, Suite A1
Boise, ID 83709   208-378-5623
www.rurdev.usda.gov/id

The Rural Business-Cooperative Service (RBS) administers programs directed toward increasing rural job opportunities, facilitating development of small and emerging private business enterprises, and improving the economic and environmental climate of rural communities. This service is committed to assisting with economic growth and diversification by providing the following programs to rural businesses:

- Business loans to local private parties and public agencies B&I Direct Loan Program
- Business loan guarantees B&I Guaranteed Loan Program
- Business development grants to public agencies nonprofit corporations Rural Business Enterprise Grants
- Business and community development revolving loan fund loans Intermediary Relending Program
- Helps rural residents form new cooperative businesses and improves the operations of existing cooperatives
- Cooperative Services Technical Assistance
- Business and community development loans and grants to RUS electric/telephone borrowers Rural Economic Development Loan and Grant Program

* Idaho State Department of Agriculture

Division of Marketing and Support Services
P.O. Box 790
2270 Old Penitentiary Road   208-332-8530
Boise, ID 83712   Fax: 208-334-2879
www.agri.state.id.us/marketing/
Services include technical assistance, business workshops, and publications for value-added food processing, specialty foods, traditional and specialty crops, organic production, and ranch recreation; international trade assistance for food and agriculture products; domestic marketing promotions; and start-up and rural rehabilitation.

* Idaho Department of Environmental Quality

Pollution Prevention/Environmental Education
1410 N Hilton   208-373-0502
Boise, ID 83706-1255   Fax: 208-373-0417
www.deq.state.id.us
The Environmental Education section provides assistance to businesses and the public interested in reducing wastes at the source.

* Workforce Development Training

Larry Hertling or Leandra Burns
Idaho Department of Labor
317 Main St.
Boise, ID 83735   208-332-3570
www.idahoworks.com/wrkdev.html

Regional Economic Development Specialists
Idaho Department of Commerce
P.O. Box 83720
Boise, ID 83720-0093   208-334-2470

Dick Winn
Idaho State Division of Professional Technical
  Education
P.O. Box 83720
Boise, ID 83720-0095   208-334-3216
If your company is considering locating or expanding in Idaho, the Workforce Development Training Fund (WDTF) can help. Through the WDTF, your company may be able to receive funds to train new employees or upgrade the skills of current workers who are at risk of being permanently laid off. For information regarding the WDTF program, contact any of the people listed below. Potential applicants are encouraged to seek information and technical assistance on allowable activities prior to submitting a proposal. {www.labor.state.id.us}

* Loans For Farmers

Farm Service Agency
U.S. Department of Agriculture
9173 W. Barnes Drive, Suite B   208-378-5650
Boise, ID 83709-1555   Fax: 208-378-5678
http://www.fsa.usda.gov/id/
The Farm Service Agency provides Direct and Guaranteed Loans to farmers through a variety of programs, including:

Farm Ownership Loans: purchase farmland, construct or repair buildings and other fixtures, and promote soil and water conservation. Up to $200,000.

Operating Loans: purchase items needed for a successful farm operation, such as livestock, farm equipment, feed, seed, fuel, farm chemicals, insurance, and other operating expenses. Can also be used to pay for minor improvements. Up to $200,000.

Beginning Farmer and Rancher Loans: provides funds to beginning and farmers and ranchers who are unable to obtain financing elsewhere.

Downpayment Farm Ownership Loans for Beginning Farmers: helps beginning farmers and ranchers purchase a farm or ranch. Also provides a way for retiring farmers to transfer their land to a future generation of farmers and ranchers. Applicant must have a downpayment of 10% and FSA with finance 40%, with the remaining balance from a commercial lender. Purchase price cannot exceed $250,000.

Loans to Socially Disadvantaged Farmers/Ranchers: helps socially disadvantaged applicants buy and operate family-size farms and ranches.

Youth Loans: Made to youths to establish and operate income-producing projects with the participation in 4-H clubs, Future Farmers of America, and similar organizations. Up to $5,000.

Emergency Loan Assistance: provides loans to help producers recover from production and physical losses due to drought, flooding, and other natural disasters, or quarantine. Up to $500,000.

Beginning Farmer and Rancher Land Contract Guarantee Pilot Program: "prompt payment guarantee" from FSA. FSA will provide payment to seller two times if the beginning farmer does not pay. Program is tested in IN, IA, ND, OR, PA and WI.

Farm Ownership and Operating Loan Guarantees: FSA will guarantee loans up to $782,000.

* Small Business Administration (SBA)

1020 Main St., Suite 290   208-334-1696
Boise, ID 83702-5745   Fax: 208-334-9353
www.sba.gov/id
The Idaho Small Business Administration Office delivers a variety of programs and services, such as startup and operational assistance through small business training and counseling, financial assistance for startup's, business opportunities and much more

* Energy Resources Division

Idaho Department of Water Resources
1301 North Orchard   208-327-7900
Boise, ID 83706   1-800-334-SAVE (7283) in ID

www.idwr.state.id.us/energy   Fax: 208-327-7866
Energy Conservation Loans: Loans to businesses for energy conservation improvements to existing buildings, or new construction. Energy savings must have simple payback of less than 10 years. Interest rate of 4 percent term of 5 years.

* Association of Idaho Cities

3314 Grace   208-344-8594
Boise, ID 83703   Fax: 208-344-8677
www.idahocities.org
Tax Increment Financing: Tax exempt bonds for community development in designated areas. Amount of funding dependent upon increased property values within revenue allocation area. Only available within incorporated cities.

In addition to the government sponsored programs, there are many other financial loan and grant programs available through private institutions and private investors that you may wish to consider. You can obtain details on individual private assistance programs currently being offered by contacting the institutions directly.

Illinois

* Illinois Department of Commerce and Economic Opportunity

Department of Commerce and Economic Opportunity
620 E. Adams   217-782-7500
Springfield, IL 62701   Fax: 217-524-3701
www.illinoisbiz.biz

100 West Randolph St., Suite 3-400   312-814-7179
Chicago, IL 60601   Fax: 312-814-2370
Department of Commerce and Economic Opportunity: Provides information, assistance and advocacy to facilitate and advance the economic development process in partnership with Illinois' communities, businesses, and their network of public and private sector providers.

Small Business Division: Responsible for an environment that supports small business success resulting in increased employment opportunities and prosperous communities throughout Illinois. Provides advocacy, business assistance, training and information resources to help entrepreneurs, small companies and their partners enhance their competitiveness in a global economy. Serves customers through a dynamic, integrated small business assistance delivery system that matches the diversity of their customers' current and future needs.

Workforce Development & Manufacturing Technology Assistance: Provides programs to assist manufacturers to improve employee job skills and manufacturing efficiency. Labor-Management programs are also available.

First Stop Business Information Center: 800-252-2923
Provides individuals with comprehensive information on state business permits and licenses, business startup assistance, regulatory guidance, demographic and census data. Guides them through permitting, licensing and regulatory processes.

Procurement Technical Assistance Centers (PTAC): Provide one-on-one counseling, technical information, marketing assistance and training to existing Illinois businesses that are interested in selling their products and/or services to local, state or federal government agencies. The services are offered through PTACs located at community colleges, universities, chambers of commerce and business development organizations.

Small Business Innovation Research Centers (SBIRC): Provide counseling, technical information and training to Illinois entrepreneurs and small businesses interested in pursuing research and development opportunities available to them through various federal and state programs. These programs provide small businesses with a means of developing new and marketable technologies and innovations and also for enhancing existing products and services.

Participation Loan Program: Through these loan participation programs, the Illinois Department of Commerce and Community Affairs (DCCA) helps small businesses obtain financing through Illinois banks, development corporations, and lending institutions for business start-up, expansion, modernization and competitiveness improvement. Generally, the Department may provide subordinated small business loans up to 25% of the total amount of a project, but not less than $10,000 or more than $750,000.

Title IX Revolving Loan Fund: Provides low-cost supplemental financing to small and medium-sized manufacturers located in areas declared eligible for assistance. Proceeds may be used for the acquisition of land, buildings, machinery and equipment, building construction or renovations, and leasehold improvements.

Rural Development Loan Program: Assists businesses in communities with populations less than 25,000. Proceeds may be used to purchase land, construct or renovate buildings and purchase machinery and equipment.

State Treasurer's Economic Program: Provides companies with access to affordable capital to expand their operations and retain or create jobs in the state. For each permanent full-time job that is created or retained, the Treasurer can deposit $25,000 at well below market rates into the borrower's financial institution. That institution will then lend the money at below prevailing interest rates to the borrower.

Enterprise Zone Financing Program: Designed to encourage businesses to locate within an Illinois Enterprise Zone. DCCA may participate in an eligible loan for no less than $10,000, nor more than $750,000. In no case shall the amount of DCCA's subordinated participation exceed 25% of the total project. Ineligible uses of funds are debt refinancing and contingency funding.

Development Corporation Participation Loan Program: Provides financial assistance through a Development Corporation to small businesses that provide jobs to workers in the region served by the Development Corporation. The state will participate in loans up to 2% of the total amount of a project but not less than $10,000 nor more than $750,000.

Capital Access Program (CAP): Designed to encourage lending institutions to make loans to businesses that do not qualify for conventional financing. CAP is based on a portfolio insurance concept where the borrower and DCCA each contribute a percentage of the loan amount into a reserve fund located at the lender's bank. This reserve fund enables the financial institution to make loans beyond its conventional risk threshold and is available to draw upon to recover losses on loans made under the program.

Technology Venture Investment Program (TVIP): Provides investment capital for young or growing Illinois businesses in cooperation with private investment companies or investors. Program investments will be used for businesses seeking funding for any new process, technique, product or technical device commercially exploitable by Illinois businesses in fields such as health care and biomedical products, information and telecommunications, computing and electronic equipment, manufacturing technology, materials, transportation and aerospace, geoscience, financial and service industries, and agriculture and biotechnology. Program funds shall be used for such costs including, but not limited to, research and development costs, acquisition of assets, working capital, purchase or lease of machinery and/or equipment, and the acquisition and/or improvement or rehabilitation of land and buildings.

Affordable Financing of Public Infrastructure Program: Provides financial assistance to or on behalf of local governments, public entities, medical facilities and public health clinics.

Community Services Block Grant Loan Program: Provides long-term, fixed-rate financing to new or expanding businesses that create jobs and employment opportunities for low-income individuals.

Industrial Training Program: Assists companies in training new workers or upgrading the skills of their existing workers. Grants may be awarded to individual companies, multi-company efforts and intermediary organizations offering multi-company training.

Industrial Revenue Bonds: IDFA issues tax-exempt bonds on behalf of manufacturing companies to finance the acquisition of fixed assets such as land, buildings and equipment. Proceeds may also be used for new construction or renovation.

International Trade Centers/NAFTA Opportunity Centers (ITC/NOC): Provide information, counseling and training to existing, new-to-export Illinois companies interested in pursuing international trade opportunities. The NOCs provide specialized assistance to those firms seeking to take advantage of the trade opportunities in Mexico and Canada made possible by the North American Free Trade Agreement.

Surety Bond Guaranty Program: Designed to provide Illinois' small, minority and women contractors technical assistance, help them receive experience in the industry and assist in obtaining bid, performance and payment bonds for government, public utility and private contracts.

Minority, Women and Disabled Participation Loan Program: The Minority, Women and Disabled Participation Loan Program guidelines differ, in that the program funding may not exceed 50% of the project, subject to a maximum of $50,000.

Community Development Assistance Program (CDAP): CDAP assists smaller Illinois local governments in financing public facilities, housing rehabilitation projects or other economic development needs. Grants are made to governments and may be loaned to businesses for projects that will create and retain jobs in the community. The program is limited to communities with less than 50,000 people.

Employer Training Investment Program (ETIP): The Employer Training Investment Program assists companies in training new workers or upgrading the skills of their existing workers.

Illinois Technology Enterprise Center Program (ITEC): The Illinois Technology Enterprise Centers assist entrepreneurs to locate pre-seed and early stage financing, help entrepreneurs in high growth, high technology fields and assist with new product development and marketing.

Illinois Small Business Energy Program: This program offers energy conservation and energy efficiency information and technical assistance to Illinois businesses.

Illinois Small Business Environmental Assistance Program: The Environmental Assistance Program helps small businesses understand and comply with state and federal pollution regulations. This service is free and confidential.

* Rural Development
2118 West Park Court, Suite A   217-403-6202
Champaign, IL 61821   Fax: 217-403-6243
www.rurdeve.usda.gov/il
The USDA Rural Development in Illinois operates Federal loan programs designed to strengthen rural businesses, finance new and improved rural housing, develop community facilities, and maintain and create rural employment. Direct and/or guaranteed loans are available for housing, water and waste, rural businesses, community facilities, telecommunications and much more.

Direct Rural and Guaranteed Rental Housing Loans: These loans, with rates as low as 1 percent, are available to developers of affordable housing.

Housing Preservation Grants: Housing Preservation Grants provide grants for nonprofit and public organizations to help very low- and low-income homeowners repair and rehabilitate their homes. Rental property owners can use them to repair and rehabilitate their units if they agree to make such units available to low- and very low-income families.

Community Development Programs: These programs help assist rural communities in financing construction, enlargement or improvement of essential community facilities. Programs include: Direct and Guaranteed Community Facility Loans, Community Facilities Grants, Water and Waste Disposal Loans, Technical Assistance and Training, Solid Waste Management Grants, Distance Learning and Telemedicine Loan and Grant Funds and Rural Community Development Initiative Funds.

Business Development Programs: The Rural Development Programs of Illinois promote a dynamic business environment in rural America. They work in partnership with the private sector and community-based organizations to provide financial assistance and business planning. In addition, they provide technical assistance to rural businesses and cooperatives, conduct research into rural economic issues, and provide cooperative education material to the public. The Business and Industry Programs help fund projects that create or preserve quality jobs and/or promote a clean rural environment. The financial resources of Rural Development are often leveraged with those of other public and private credit source lenders to meet business and credit needs in under-served areas. Recipients of these programs may include individuals, corporations, partnerships, cooperatives, public bodies, nonprofit corporations, and private companies. Programs include: Business & Industrial Guaranteed Loans, Intermediary Relending Program, Rural Cooperative Development Grants, Rural Business Enterprise Grants, Rural Economic Development Loans and Grants

Rural Business Opportunity Grants and Cooperative Development Technical Assistance.

* The Illinois Coalition
One East Wacker, Suite 2410
Chicago, IL 60601   312-229-1970
www.ilcoalition.org

The Illinois Coalition is a nonprofit organization of leaders in business, government, academia and labor dedicated to encouraging technology-based economic development. Founded in 1989, the Illinois Coalition seeks to leverage public and private sector support for research and development, to facilitate technology transfer, to foster the commercialization of new technologies, and to advance the deployment of technology modernization services. The Illinois Coalition is responsible for overseeing the affiliate network of private sector experts, comprised of approximately 50 CEO's of technology companies, partners in venture capital and professional service firms, and R&D heads, that reviews applications for financing under the Technology Development Bridge. It makes investment recommendations to the Authority and assists all companies not receiving investment.

* Illinois Development Finance Authority
Technology Development Bridge Program provides seed stage equity financing to small technology companies. The goal is to help the businesses access capital in order to grow and create jobs.
{http://www.idfa.com/products/vc/vc.html}
Chicago office: 312-627-1434
Springfield office: 217-524-1567
Peoria office: 309-495-5959
Carbondale office: 618-453-5566

* Loans For Farmers
Farm Service Agency
U.S. Department of Agriculture
3500 Wabash Ave.
Springfield, IL 62707-8287   217-241-6600
http://w.fsa.usda.gov/il/

The Farm Service Agency provides Direct and Guaranteed Loans to farmers through a variety of programs, including:

Farm Ownership Loans: purchase farmland, construct or repair buildings and other fixtures, and promote soil and water conservation. Up to $200,000.

Operating Loans: purchase items needed for a successful farm operation, such as livestock, farm equipment, feed, seed, fuel, farm chemicals, insurance, and other operating expenses. Can also be used to pay for minor improvements. Up to $200,000.

Beginning Farmer and Rancher Loans: provides funds to beginning and farmers and ranchers who are unable to obtain financing elsewhere.

Downpayment Farm Ownership Loans for Beginning Farmers: helps beginning farmers and ranchers purchase a farm or ranch. Also provides a way for retiring farmers to transfer their land to a future generation of farmers and ranchers. Applicant must have a downpayment of 10% and FSA with finance 40%, with the remaining balance from a commercial lender. Purchase price cannot exceed $250,000.

Loans to Socially Disadvantaged Farmers/Ranchers: helps socially disadvantaged applicants buy and operate family-size farms and ranches.

Youth Loans: Made to youths to establish and operate income-producing projects with the participation in 4-H clubs, Future Farmers of America, and similar organizations. Up to $5,000.

Emergency Loan Assistance: provides loans to help producers recover from production and physical losses due to drought, flooding, and other natural disasters, or quarantine. Up to $500,000.

Beginning Farmer and Rancher Land Contract Guarantee Pilot Program: "prompt payment guarantee" from FSA. FSA will provide payment to seller two times if the beginning farmer does not pay. Program is tested in IN, IA, ND, OR, PA and WI.

Farm Ownership and Operating Loan Guarantees: FSA will guarantee loans up to $782,000.

* Small Business Administration (SBA)
500 West Madison, Suite 1250   312-353-4528
Chicago, IL 60661-2511   Fax: 312-886-5688
www.sba.gov/il

The Illinois Small Business Administration Office delivers a variety of programs and services, such as startup and operational assistance through small business training and counseling, financial assistance for startup's, business opportunities and much more

Indiana

* Indiana Department of Commerce
One North Capitol   317-232-8888
Suite 700   800-463-8081
Indianapolis, IN 46204   Fax: 317-233-5123
www.in.gov/doc

Indiana Department of Commerce: This office can provide information and expertise in dealing with state, federal, and local agencies. They also have information on financing programs and other services offered by the state government.

Energy and Recycling Office: A wide range of assistance in energy efficiency, alternative energy and recycling market development programs.

Enterprise Advisory Group: Counsels emerging and mature businesses.

Government Marketing Assistance Group: Helps companies that wish to sell to federal, state or local governments.

Office of Regulatory Ombudsman: Acts as a mediator, expediter and problem-solver in areas affecting business.

Trade Show Assistance Program (TSAP): Provides reimbursement for a portion of the costs incurred while companies exhibit their products at overseas trade shows.

Loans:
Product Development/Commercialization Funding: Provides loans for businesses in need of financing to support research

and development projects, or to support commercialization of new technology. Loan amounts vary.

Capital Access Program (CAP): Helps financial institutions lend money to Indiana businesses that don't qualify for loans under conventional lending policies. CAP loans may be of any amount

Industrial Development Loan Fund: Revolving loans for industrial growth. Loans up to $1 million are available.

Industrial Energy Efficiency Fund: The Energy Policy Division provides loans for improving energy efficiency in industrial processes. The maximum amount available per applicant is $250,000 or 50% of the total eligible project costs, whichever is less.

Loan Guaranty Programs: Financing for land or building acquisition or improvements, structures, machinery, equipment, facilities and working capital. Loan guaranties are available up to $300,000.

Recycling Promotion and Assistance Fund: Loans to enhance the development of markets for recyclable materials.

Small Business Investment Company Program: Long-term and/or venture capital for small firms.

Certified Development Companies: Loans 1% over Treasury-bond rate for 10 to 20 years for financing fixed-assets including; land, buildings, machinery, equipment and renovations.

Grants:

Industrial Energy Efficiency Fund: The Energy Policy Division provides grant to manufacturers to study energy use in their facilities and recommend ways to reduce energy use and energy costs. Maximum amount available per applicant is $250,000.

Alternative Energy Systems Program: The Energy Policy Division offers grants to businesses to fund eligible alternative-fuel technologies and infrastructure development. The maximum amount available per project is $10,000.

Industrial Development Grant Fund: Grants for nonprofits and local units of government for off-site infrastructure projects in support of new business development. The grant amount is determined based on project needs. However, the program is designed to supplement local funding sources.

National Industrial Competitiveness Through Energy, Environment and Economics Grant: The Energy Policy Division has information about Federal grants, with possible state matching funds, to improve energy efficiency, promote a cleaner production process and improve the competitiveness of industry. The maximum amount of federal grant available per applicant is $500,000.

Tire Market Development Research and Prototype Grant Program: Provides grant to support research on new products or machinery for handling scrap tire recycling. Grant range from $5,000 to $50,000.

Tire-Derived Fuel Testing Grant Program: Provides grants to develop fuel uses for scrap tires. Amount based on project needs.

Trade Show Assistance Program (TSAP): Provides reimbursement for a portion of the costs incurred while companies exhibit their products at overseas trade shows. Reimbursement includes 100% of exhibit space rental or $5,000, whichever is less.

Bonds:

Twenty-First Century Scholars Program Support Fund Credit: Credit for contributions to the fund. A maximum credit of the lesser of (a) $1,000; (b) 50% of the contribution made; or (c) 10% of the adjusted gross income tax is available.

Maternity Home Credit: Credit for maternity-home owners who provide a temporary residence for a pregnant woman (women).

Prison Credit: Credit for investments in Indiana prisons to create jobs for prisoners. The amount is limited to 50% of the inventory in a qualified project plus 25% of the wages paid to the inmates. The maximum credit a taxpayer may claim is $100,000 per year.

Real-Property Abatement Calculation: Real-property abatement is a declining percentage of the increase in assessed value of the improvement based on one of the three following time periods and percentages as determined by the local governing body.

Enterprise Zones: The purpose of the enterprise zone program in the state of Indiana is to stimulate local community and business redevelopment in distressed areas. An enterprise zone may consist of up to three contiguous square miles. There are 18 enterprise zones in Indiana. In order to stimulate reinvestment and create jobs within the zones, businesses located within an enterprise zone are eligible for certain tax benefits. These tax benefits include:

- A credit equal to 100% of property-tax liability on inventory.
- Exemption from Indiana Gross Income Tax on the increase in receipts from the base year.
- State Investment Cost Credit (up to 30% of purchase price) for individuals purchasing an ownership interest in an enterprise zone business.
- State Loan Interest Credit on lender interest income (5%) from qualified loans made in an enterprise zone.
- State Employment Expense Credit based on wages paid to qualified zone-resident employees. The credit is the lesser of 10% of the increase in wages paid over the base year, or $1,500 per qualified employee.
- Tax deduction to qualified zone-resident employees equal to the lesser of 50% of their adjusted gross income or $7,500.

Industrial Recovery Site (Dinosaur Building): Much like the dinosaurs, many large buildings that were once used for mills, foundries and large manufacturers are obsolete for today's new production methods and technologies. Because of this, these buildings now stand vacant. This program offers special tax benefits to offset the cost of adaptive reuse.

Economic Development for a Growing Economy (EDGE): Provides tax credits based on payroll. Individual income tax withholdings for the company's employees can be credited against the company's corporate income tax. Excess withholdings shall be refunded to the company.

Skills Enhancement Fund: Grants are reimbursement of up to 50% of eligible training costs. Awards for retraining have a maximum ceiling of $200,000.

The TECH Fund: Training activities for reimbursement resulting in full-time, Indiana-resident employee receiving certification in systems administration, systems engineering, or software development. Up to 50% of eligible training costs with a maximum of $50,000 or $2,500 per employee, whichever is less.

Incumbent Worker Training Fund (IWTF): Incumbent Worker grants are designed to provide financial assistance to companies committed to expanding the skills of their existing workforce. There are no maximum grant amounts; however, funds are limited. Most grants do not exceed $200,000 and there is no minimum.

Skills Trades Apprenticeship (STA): The STA grants are designed to provide financial assistance to companies expanding the skills of their existing workers through training programs that result in industry-recognized credentials. The maximum grant award is $200,000.

Brownsfields Grant and Loan Fund: This grant program assists in the environmental and remediation of brownsfield sites throughout Indiana. Grants of up to $50,000 per applicant per round are available for environmental site assessment; low-interest loans of up to 10% of the Brownsfield Fund are available for remediation/demolition; and grants of up to $250,000 per applicant per round are available for petroleum remediation.

The Distributed Generation Grant Program (DGGP): The Distributed Generation Grant Program offers grants of up to $30,000 or up to 30% of eligible costs and is designed to enable businesses and institutions to install and study alternatives to central generation such as fuel cells, micro turbines, cogeneration, combined heat & power and renewable energy sources.

Indiana Biomass Grant Program: This program was developed to assist in the research and implementation of Indiana biomass energy systems. Biomass is any organic matter available on a renewable basis for conversion to energy. Eligibility for this program is limited to individuals, businesses, universities or institutions that operate in the state of Indiana.

Indiana Coal Research Grant Program: This program was created to assist businesses in undertaking coal research projects and further develop competitive communities with secure jobs in Indiana. Eligible research projects must use Indiana coal or have direct application to Indiana coal for funding consideration.

Waste Tire Recycling-Civil Engineering Field Reuse: grants for waste tire utilization in an IDEM approved civil engineering reuse project.

Waste Tire Recycling-Recreational Field Reuse: grants for waste tire utilization in an IDEM approved recreational facility beneficial reuse project.

* Indiana Business Modernization and Technology Corporation

10 W. Market St., Suite 450   800-877-5182
Indianapolis, IN 46204   317-635-3058
www.bmtadvantage.org

BMT provides services that include comprehensive business assessments and recommendations, development of action plans and access to cost-effective resources to help you implement your action plans. BMT also helps companies address industry-level concerns such as quality, workforce strategies and technology access through industry-specific programs and company alliances. BMT's can result in increased sales, reduced costs, improved cash flow and access to working capital.

Indiana Micro-Electronics Center (IMC): Assists businesses in using Application Specific Integrated Circuits (ASICs).

The Indiana Quality Initiative: Quality-awareness education, assessments and information

Regional Manufacturing Extension Centers (RMEC): Helps small and medium-sized businesses assess and solve problems related to technology, training, marketing and financing.

* USDA Rural Development

5975 Lakeside Boulevard   317-290-3100, ext. 400
Indianapolis, IN 46278   Fax: 317-290-3095
www.rurdev.usda.gov/in

Program assistance is provided in many ways, including direct or guaranteed loans, grants, technical assistance, research and educational materials. To accomplish its mission, USDA Rural Development often works in partnership with state, local and tribal governments, as well as rural businesses, cooperatives and nonprofit agencies. The Rural Business-Cooperative Service (RBS) provides help to rural areas that need to develop new job opportunities, allowing businesses and cooperatives to remain viable in a changing economy.

Business Program Guaranteed Loans are used to improve, develop, or finance business, industry, and employment, and improve the economic and environmental climate in rural communities, including pollution abatement and control. This objective is achieved through bolstering the existing private credit structure with guarantees of quality loans, which will provide lasting community benefits. This type of assistance is available to business located in rural communities with a population of less than 50,000.

Intermediary Relending Program finances business facilities and community development projects in rural communities with a population of less than 25,000. This is achieved through loans made by USDA to intermediaries that provide loans to ultimate recipients for business facilities and community development in a rural area.

Rural Cooperative Development Grants establish and operate centers for rural technology or cooperative development to carry out activities and generate information useful to rural industries, cooperatives, businesses, and others in the development and commercialization of new products, processes, or services.

Rural Economic Development Loans and Grants make zero interest loans and grants available to rural electric and telephone borrowers to promote rural economic development and job creation projects.

Rural Business Enterprise Grants assist public bodies and nonprofit corporations finance and facilitate development of small and emerging private businesses located in rural areas.

Rural Business Opportunity Grants to promote sustainable economic development in rural communities with exceptional needs. Making grants to organizations to provide for economic development planning, technical assistance, or training accomplishes this.

* Indiana Development Finance Authority (IDFA)

One N. Capitol, Suite 900   317-233-4332
Indianapolis, IN 46204   Fax: 317-232-6786
www.in.gov/idfa

Helps Indiana businesses obtain financial assistance through loan guaranty programs, tax-exempt private activity bonds for industrial development, Ex-Im Bank loan guarantees, insurance and direct loans for export products and flexible lending through case reserve accounts.

* Indiana Economic Development Association (IEDA)

233 McCrea St., Suite 400   317-269-6283
Indianapolis, IN 46225   Fax: 317-269-6276
www.ieda.org

Provides continuity to a statewide community development effort. The organization has two objectives: (1) to utilize the knowledge and resources of the association to make economic development activities in the state more effective, and (2) to cooperate and interact with all state and local organizations engaged in promoting the economic welfare of Indiana.

* Indiana Economic Development Council (IEDC)

One North Capitol, Suite 900   317-234-2371
Indianapolis, IN 46204   Fax: 317-233-0399
www.iedc.org

Helps to shape long-term state goals, strategies and policies on economic development matters through non-partisan planning, evaluation, policy development and coordination. The role of the IEDC includes providing independent performance reviews and recommendations relating to governmental budgets and the economic development support systems of public and private entities, both state and local.

* Indiana Community Business Credit Corporation (ICBCC)

8440 Woodfield Crossing, Suite 315
Indianapolis, IN 46240   317-469-9704

Loans for small to medium-sized businesses that exceed banks' customary limits. Loan amounts range from $100,000 to $750,000, and must be at least matched by a participating lender. Minimum project is $200,000.

* Community Development Action Grant (CDAG)

Community Development Division
Indiana Department of Commerce
One N. Capitol, Suite 600   317-232-8911
Indianapolis, IN 46204   800-824-2476

Grants to help organizations whose missions include economic development to expand administrative capacity and program development by offsetting miscellaneous expenses. In the case of organizations serving at least two counties, the amount of the grant may not exceed one dollar for every one dollar raised by the organization. The maximum grant award for organizations serving two or more counties may not exceed $75,000.

* Tax-Exempt Bonds

Indiana Development Finance Authority
One N. Capitol, Suite 900   317-233-4332
Indianapolis, IN 46204   Fax: 317-232-6786

Provide fixed-asset financing at competitive rates. Limits vary according to the type of project. Most manufacturing facilities are limited to $10 million.

* Foreign Trade Zone or Free Trade Zone

International Trade Division
Indiana Department of Commerce
One North Capitol, Suite 700
Indianapolis, IN 46204   317-233-3762

Foreign Trade Zone or Free Trade Zone: An enclosed, secure area that is located outside U.S. Customs territory. A company located within a Foreign Trade Zone does not pay duties or personal property taxes on goods stored within the zone. Foreign and domestic goods may enter a zone to be stored, processed, distributed, manufactured, assembled or exhibited. Benefits to companies located in a Foreign Trade Zone include the following:

- Duty is deferred on imported goods admitted to the zone, thus improving cash flow for the company.
- No U.S. duty is assessed when exporting goods from the zone.
- Processing goods within the zone can eliminate or lower tariffs.
- Duties can be avoided on defective or damaged goods by inspecting and testing imported goods within a zone.
- Savings may be realized in transport insurance.
- Inventory stored in a Foreign Trade Zone is exempt from local property tax.

* Indiana Workforce Development

10 North Senate
Indianapolis, IN 46204   1-888-WorkOne
www.in.gov/dwd

The Department of Workforce Development (DWD) provides employers with a free labor exchange service designed to help build Indiana's workforce by bringing together qualified job seekers and employers seeking qualified workers. Through a statewide network of One-Stop Employment Centers, job seekers and employers have free access to a variety of information to help make the match between employers and job seekers more effective.

* Loans For Farmers

Farm Service Agency
U.S. Department of Agriculture
5981 Lakeside Boulevard
Indianapolis, IN 46278   317-290-3030
http://www.fs.usda.gov/in/

The Farm Service Agency provides Direct and Guaranteed Loans to farmers through a variety of programs, including:

Farm Ownership Loans: purchase farmland, construct or repair buildings and other fixtures, and promote soil and water conservation. Up to $200,000.

Operating Loans: purchase items needed for a successful farm operation, such as livestock, farm equipment, feed, seed, fuel, farm chemicals, insurance, and other operating expenses. Can also be used to pay for minor improvements. Up to $200,000.

Beginning Farmer and Rancher Loans: provides funds to beginning and farmers and ranchers who are unable to obtain financing elsewhere.

Downpayment Farm Ownership Loans for Beginning Farmers: helps beginning farmers and ranchers purchase a farm or ranch. Also provides a way for retiring farmers to transfer their land to a future generation of farmers and ranchers. Applicant must have a downpayment of 10% and FSA with finance 40%, with the remaining balance from a commercial lender. Purchase price cannot exceed $250,000.

Loans to Socially Disadvantaged Farmers/Ranchers: helps socially disadvantaged applicants buy and operate family-size farms and ranches.

Youth Loans: Made to youths to establish and operate income-producing projects with the participation in 4-H clubs, Future Farmers of America, and similar organizations. Up to $5,000.

Emergency Loan Assistance: provides loans to help producers recover from production and physical losses due to drought, flooding, and other natural disasters, or quarantine. Up to $500,000.

Beginning Farmer and Rancher Land Contract Guarantee Pilot Program: "prompt payment guarantee" from FSA. FSA will provide payment to seller two times if the beginning farmer does not pay. Program is tested in IN, IA, ND, OR, PA and WI.

Farm Ownership and Operating Loan Guarantees: FSA will guarantee loans up to $782,000.

* Small Business Administration (SBA)
Robert Gastineau, Deputy Director
Finance Division
429 N. Pennsylvania, Suite 100 317-226-7272
Indianapolis, IN 46204-1873 Fax: 317-226-7259
www.sba.gov/in
The Indiana Small Business Administration Office delivers a variety of programs and services, such as startup and operational assistance through small business training and counseling, financial assistance for startup's, business opportunities and much more.

* Metro Small Business Assistance Corporation
306 Civic Center Complex
1 NW Martin Luther King Blvd.
Evansville, IN 47708 812-426-5857
Service Area: Vanderburgh, Posey, Gibson, and Warrick counties

SBA Loan Guarantees and Direct Loans: Provides technical assistance to implement SBA finance programs.

Working Capital Loan Pool: Provides short-term, working capital financing for small businesses in the city of Evansville and unincorporated areas of Vanderburg county.

* Indiana Small Business Development Center
James Simpson, Comptroller
One North Capital, Suite 900 317-234-2082
Indianapolis, IN 46204 Fax: 317-232-8872

www.isbdc.org
The Indiana Small Business Development Center helps small businesses throughout Indiana grow, expand, innovate and increase success rates.

Consulting: Free one-to-one service that assists new and existing business owners build better businesses.

Workshops: A variety of low-cost programs are available to meet the small business owner's needs.

Access To Information: All of the Centers in Indiana provide libraries with numerous materials on business topics.

* Minority Business Development
Department of Administration
402 West Washington Street, Room W474
Indianapolis, IN 46204 317-232-3061
http://www.in.gov/idoa/minority/index.html
The Department of Administration administers the state of Indiana's Minority Business Enterprise Program. Some of the services provided include: state purchasing opportunities, workshops on state procurement, monitoring and providing networking assistance and matching majority owned businesses with minority owned businesses.

Iowa

* Iowa Department of Economic Development
200 East Grand Ave. 515-242-4700
Des Moines, IA 50309-1827 800-245-IOWA
www.state.ia.us/ided Fax: 515-242-4809
TTY: 800-735-2942
Workforce Development Fund: Programs under this fund provide training for new and existing employees and include: Jobs Training, Business Network Training, Targeted Industries Training, Innovative Skills Development.

Locating in Iowa: Provides expanding companies with many valuable and unique services, with the end goal of streamlining the site location process. Iowa Department of Economic Development (IDED) confidential services include:
- Working on a confidential basis with companies to determine expansion project needs
- Providing data and information on available buildings, sites and communities
- Coordinating community/site visits
- Packaging appropriate financial assistance and job training programs
- Serving as a liaison with state environmental permitting officials
- IDED Incorporates Information and Technology Into Team Approach

Regulatory Assistance Programs: Provide assistance with environmental permitting, regulations, and compliance with the EPA Clean Air Act.

Community Economic Betterment Account (CEBA): Provides financial assistance to companies that create new employment opportunities and/or retain existing jobs, and make new capital investment in Iowa. The amount of funding is based, in part, on the number of jobs to be created/retained. Funds are provided in the form of loans and forgivable loans. The CEBA program can provide assistance up to $1 million. As an alternative, non-traditional, short-term float loans or interim loans greater than $1 million may be available. The funding level for start-up companies varied depending upon employee wage rates. Assistance through CEBA's "Venture Project" component is provided as an "equity-like" investment, with a maximum award of $250,000. 515-242-4819

Economic Development Set-Aside Program (EDSA): Provides financial assistance to companies that create new employment opportunities and/or retain existing jobs, and make new capital investment in Iowa. The amount of funding is based, in part, on the number of jobs to be created/retained. Funds are provided in the form of loans and forgivable loans. The EDSA program can provide assistance up to $500,000.

Value-Added Products and Processes Financial Assistance Program (VAAPFAP): Seeks to increase the innovative utilization of Iowa's agricultural commodities. It accomplishes this by investing in the development of new agri-products and new processing technologies. The program includes two components:
- Innovative Products and Processes encourages the processing of agricultural commodities into higher-value products not commonly produced in Iowa, or utilizing a process not commonly used in Iowa to produce new and innovative products from agricultural commodities.
- Renewable Fuels and Co-Products encourages the production of renewable fuels, such as soy diesel and ethanol, and co-products for livestock feed.

Any single project may apply for up to $900,000 in assistance. Financial assistance is provided in the form of loans and forgivable loans. Generally, assistance of $100,000 or less is provided as a forgivable loan, while larger awards are usually a combination of loans and forgivable loans, with the forgivable portion decreasing as the award size increases.

Small Business Loan Program and Economic Development Loan Program: Provides financing to new and expanding businesses through the sale of tax-exempt bonds. The maximum loan is $10 million.

USDA Business and Industrial Loan Guarantee Program: Provides guarantees on loans up to $10 million or more made by private lenders for start-up or expansion purposes to for-profit or nonprofit businesses or investors of any size.

Iowa Capital Investment Corporation (ICIC): A for-profit venture capital corporation established with funds provided by the state of Iowa and equity investments by Iowa financial institutions, insurance companies and electric utilities. The corporation's primary purpose is to provide an attractive risk-adjusted rate of return on investment to the corporation's shareholders and advance economic development in Iowa. The corporation provides financing for a broad range of business capital needs. Financing may be in the form of equity participation, loans with stock purchase warrants, royalties, etc. and is tailored to the particular business situation. Investments generally range from $50,000 to $1 million, with the average expected to be approximately $250,000.

Rail Economic Development Program: The Iowa Department of Transportation provides funds for construction or rehabilitation of rail spurs to serve new or existing industries. The rail project must be a key to the creation or retention of jobs.

Revitalize Iowa's Sound Economy (RISE): Administered by the Iowa Department of Transportation for expenditures on city, county and state highways to help attract new development or to support growth with existing developments. Projects are evaluated on economic potential and impact. Funding may be used in conjunction with other sources of federal, state, local and private financing for the purpose of improving area highways and specific access to roads.

Public Facilities Set-Aside Program: Administered by the Iowa Department of Economic Development, provides financial assistance to cities and counties to provide infrastructure improvements for businesses which require such improvements in order to create new job opportunities. The form of assistance is limited to grants to cities under 50,000 population and counties for the provision of or improvements to sanitary sewer systems, water systems, streets and roads, storm sewers, rail lines and airports. Assistance is limited to two-thirds of the total cost of the improvements needed. The emphasis of this program is to increase the productive capacity of the state. Priority will be given to projects that will create manufacturing jobs, add value to Iowa resources and/or export out-of-state.

Venture Capital Resource Fund: A for-profit corporation whose mission is to stimulate economic development and provide an attractive rate of return to shareholders by investing in businesses with significant growth potential.

Targeted Small Business Financial Assistance Program (TSBFAP): Designed to assist in the creation and expansion of Iowa small businesses that have an annual gross sales of $3 million and are at least 51% owned, operated and managed by women, minorities or persons with a disability. The business must be certified as a "Targeted Small Business" by the Iowa Department of Inspections and Appeals before applying for or receiving TSB funds. Awards may be obtained in one of the following forms of assistance:
- Low-interest loans - Loans of up to $25,000 may be provided at interest rates of 0-5 percent, to be repaid in monthly installments over a five- to seven-year period. The first installment can be deferred for three months for a start-up business and one month for an existing business.
- Loan guarantees are available up to $40,000. Loan guarantees can cover up to 75% of a loan obtained from a bank or other conventional lender. The interest rate is at the discretion of the lender.
- In limited cases, equity grants - to be used to leverage other financing (SBA or conventional) - are available in amounts of up to $25,000.
- TSB funds may be used to purchase equipment, acquire inventory, provide operating capital or to leverage additional funding.

Self-Employment Loan Program (SELP): This program is designed to assist in the creation and expansion of businesses owned, operated and managed by women, minorities, or persons with a disability. To qualify for a SELP loan, applicants must have an annualized family income that does not exceed current income guidelines for the program. An applicant is automatically eligible for SELP if he or she is receiving Family Investment Plan (FIP) assistance or other general assistance such as disability benefits. The applicant can also qualify for SELP funds if determined eligible under the Job Training Partnership Act, or is certified as having a disability under standards established by the Iowa Department of Education, Division of Vocational Rehabilitation Services. SELP loans of up to $10,000 are available. The interest rate is 5 percent, and the loan is to be repaid in monthly installments over a five-year period. The first installment can be deferred for three months for a start-up business and one month for an existing business.

Entrepreneurs With Disabilities (EWD): Helps qualified individuals with disabilities establish, acquire, maintain or expand a small business by providing technical and financial assistance. To be eligible for the program, applicants must be active clients of the Iowa Department of Education Division of Vocational Rehabilitation Services or the Iowa Department for the Blind. Technical Assistance grants of up to $10,000 may be used to pay for any specific business-related consulting service such as developing a feasibility study or business plan, or accounting and legal services. Financial Assistance grants of up to $10,000 may be used to purchase equipment, supplies, rent or other start-up, expansion or acquisition costs identified in an approved business plan. Total financial assistance provided to an individual may not exceed 50% (maximum of $10,000) of the financial package. EWD financial assistance must be fully matched by funding from other sources.

Assistive Device Tax Credit: Iowa small businesses can reduce their taxes by buying or renting products or equipment, or by making physical changes to the workplace to help employees with disabilities get or keep a job.

Export Trade Assistance Program (ETPA): ETAP provides financial assistance to eligible Iowa businesses wishing to enter new markets by participating in foreign trade shows and trade missions.

Iowa Department of Economic Development Entrepreneurial Service Team: This Team services the needs of high-growth, value-adding entrepreneurs by offering one-on-one management and technical assistance.

* Cooperative Services
USDA-Rural Development
873 Federal Bldg.
210 Walnut St.   515-284-4663
Des Moines, IA 50309   Fax: 515-284-4821
www.rurdev.usda.gov/ia
Provides free technical assistance to help rural residents form new cooperative ventures and improve operations of existing cooperatives.

Business & Industrial Guaranteed Loans are used to improve, develop or finance business, industry and employment. Their goal is to improve the economic and environmental climate in rural communities, including pollution abatement and control. This type of assistance is available to businesses located in rural communities with a population of less than 50,000.

Intermediary Relending Program finances business facilities and community development projects in rural communities with population of less than 25,000.

Rural Cooperative Development Grant Program provides grants for cooperative development in rural areas. Grants are to be made for the purpose of establishing and operating centers for rural cooperative development.

Rural Economic Development Loans and Grants make zero interest loans and grants available to rural electric and telephone borrowers to promote rural economic development and job creation projects.

Rural Business Opportunity Grants help provide technical assistance for business development and conduct economic development planning in rural areas. Eligible applicants include public bodies, cooperatives and private nonprofit corporations.

Rural Business Enterprise Grants help support the development of small and emerging private businesses located in rural areas. Eligible applicants include public bodies and private nonprofit corporations.

Cooperative Development Technical Assistance is available to help rural residents form new cooperative businesses and improve the operation of existing cooperatives.

* Institute of Social and Economic Development
901 23rd Ave.   319-338-2331
Coralville, IA 52241   Fax: 319-338-5824
www.ised.org
Focuses on minorities, women, persons with disabilities and low-income individuals. Encourages self-sufficiency through the growth of small business and self-employment opportunities, and provides services for any person who wants to start or expand a business employing up to five employees, including the owner(s).

* Center for Industrial Research and Service
ISU Research Park
2272 Howe Hall, Suite 2620   515-294-3420
Ames, IA 50011   Fax: 515-294-4925
www.ciras.iastate.edu
Assists companies with management, production, marketing, engineering, finance, and technology problems and/or contact with resource people, organizations, and agencies that can help provide solutions, and operates as an industrial arm of University Extension, Iowa State University.

* Iowa Manufacturing Extension Partnership
Advanced Technology Center
2701 E. Convenience Blvd., Suite 13   515-289-0600
Ankeny, IA 50021   Fax: 515-289-0601
www.imep.org
Manufacturing Technology Center: A resource for small and mid-sized manufacturers. Helps identify problems and resources, conducts formal needs assessments, and develops strategic plans. Also assists with modernizing facilities, upgrading processes, and improving work force capabilities through the use of effective training and skill development.

* Strategic Marketing Services
University of Northern Iowa
College of Business Administration   800-204-1804
The Cirris Building, Suite 5   319-273-2886
Cedar Falls, IA 50614   Fax: 319-273-6830
www.sms.uni.edu
Provides customized market research, analysis, and strategic planning services to existing businesses, primarily manufacturers.

* Link Investments for Tomorrow (LIFT)
Treasurer of State's Office
LIFT Administration
Hoover State Office Building   515-281-3287
Des Moines, IA 50319   Fax: 515-281-7562
www.treasurer.state.ia.us/investments

Assists with rural small business transfer, and horticulture and alternative agricultural crops.

* Iowa Finance Authority

General Counsel
Iowa Finance Authority   800-432-7230
100 E. Grand, Suite 250   515-242-4990
Des Moines, IA 50309   Fax: 515-242-4957
www.ifahome.com

The Economic Development Loan Program: promotes the development and expansion of family farming, soil conservation, housing and business within the State of Iowa. Iowa's Rural Home Building Initiative ("RHBI"): is seeking to increase the construction of affordable single family homes in eligible rural areas of Iowa. The Iowa Finance Authority ("IFA") and USDA Rural Development ("USDA") are soliciting proposals that specifically address innovative methods to develop new single family residential development in eligible rural areas. The RHBI funds available may be used to mitigate the financial risk of construction lending, to provide gap funding to increase affordability and other direct program costs.

* Iowa Department of Natural Resources

Waste Management Assistance Division
502 E Ninth Street
Wallace State Office Building   515-281-4387
Des Moines, IA 50319-0034   Fax: 515-281-8895
www.iowadnr.com

Landfill Alternatives Financial Assistance Program provides funds to be used for equipment, construction, education, materials, etc.

* Loans For Farmers

Farm Service Agency
U.S. Department of Agriculture
10500 Buena Vista Court
Des Moines, IA 50322   515-254-1540
http://www.fsa.usda.gov/ia/

The Farm Service Agency provides Direct and Guaranteed Loans to farmers through a variety of programs, including:

Farm Ownership Loans: purchase farmland, construct or repair buildings and other fixtures, and promote soil and water conservation. Up to $200,000.

Operating Loans: purchase items needed for a successful farm operation, such as livestock, farm equipment, feed, seed, fuel, farm chemicals, insurance, and other operating expenses. Can also be used to pay for minor improvements. Up to $200,000.

Beginning Farmer and Rancher Loans: provides funds to beginning and farmers and ranchers who are unable to obtain financing elsewhere.

Downpayment Farm Ownership Loans for Beginning Farmers: helps beginning farmers and ranchers purchase a farm or ranch. Also provides a way for retiring farmers to transfer their land to a future generation of farmers and ranchers. Applicant must have a downpayment of 10% and FSA with finance 40%, with the remaining balance from a commercial lender. Purchase price cannot exceed $250,000.

Loans to Socially Disadvantaged Farmers/Ranchers: helps socially disadvantaged applicants buy and operate family-size farms and ranches.

Youth Loans: Made to youths to establish and operate income-producing projects with the participation in 4-H clubs, Future Farmers of America, and similar organizations. Up to $5,000.

Emergency Loan Assistance: provides loans to help producers recover from production and physical losses due to drought, flooding, and other natural disasters, or quarantine. Up to $500,000.

Beginning Farmer and Rancher Land Contract Guarantee Pilot Program: "prompt payment guarantee" from FSA. FSA will provide payment to seller two times if the beginning farmer does not pay. Program is tested in IN, IA, ND, OR, PA and WI.

Farm Ownership and Operating Loan Guarantees: FSA will guarantee loans up to $782,000.

* Small Business Administration (SBA)

210 Walnut, Room 749   515-284-4422
Des Moines, IA 50309   Fax: 515-284-4572

215 4th Ave., SE, Suite 200   319-362-6405
Cedar Rapids, IA 52401-1806   Fax: 319-362-7861
www.sba.gov/ia

The Iowa Small Business Administration Office delivers a variety of programs and services, such as startup and operational assistance through small business training and counseling, financial assistance for startup's, business opportunities and much more.

* Iowa Capital Investment Corporation (ICIC)

Iowa Department of Economic Development
200 E Grand Avenue
Des Moines, IA 50309   515-242-4817
www.state.ia.us/ided/investiowa

The State Legislature created the ICIC to assemble private venture capital for investment targeted enterprises and communities. The ICIC manages the Fund of Funds, which is organized as a private, for-profit, limited partnership to make investments in private venture capital funds. A venture fund must commit to consider equity investments in businesses in Iowa.

* Institute for Physical Research and Technology

311 TASF
Iowa State University   515-294-8849
Ames, IA 50011   877-251-6520
www.iprt.iastate.edu/assistance

The Institute for Physical Search and Technology helps Iowa companies solve technical problems; create new products and increase productivity and quality. They will also help launch start-up companies.

Kansas

* Kansas Department of Commerce

Kansas Department of Commerce
1000 SW Jackson Street, Suite 100   785-296-3481
Topeka, KS 66612-1354   Fax: 785-296-5055
http://kdoch.state.ks.us   TTY: 785-296-3487

First-Stop Clearinghouse: A one-stop Clearinghouse for

general information. It also provides the necessary state applications required by agencies which license, regulate and tax business, and furnishes information about starting or expanding a business.

From the Land of Kansas Trademark Program: Offers marketing opportunities for Kansas produced food, arts, crafts, and plants.

Agricultural Value Added Center: Identifies new technologies and assists companies in commercialization efforts. Both food/feed and industrial related projects are potential candidates for assistance. 785-296-3084

Kansas Match: Promotes economic growth in the state by matching Kansas manufacturers who are currently buying products from outside Kansas with Kansas suppliers of those same products. The benefit to the buyer includes reductions in freight, warehousing, and communication costs. 785-296-3803

Business Retention & Expansion Program: Offered to Kansas communities and counties who wish to sustain existing industry, support its modernization and competitiveness, foster its expansion and provide an environment that encourages new industry creation and recruitment. The Department works with community leaders and volunteers to conduct on-site surveys of local businesses. The information gathered is then analyzed and the results are used to solve immediate short-term problems, as well as to develop long-term local retention and expansion strategies.

Partnership Fund: Provides financial assistance to Kansas cities and counties by making low-interest loans for infrastructure projects needed to encourage and assist in the creation of new jobs either through the relocation of new businesses or the expansion of existing businesses. 785-296-1868

Industrial Training Program (KIT): Provides training assistance primarily to manufacturing, distribution and regional or national service firms in the process of adding five or more new jobs to a new or existing Kansas facility. KIT will pay the negotiated cost of pre-employment, on-the-job and classroom training expenses that include instructor salaries, travel expenses, minor equipment, training aids, supplies and materials, and curriculum planning and development. 785-296-4284

Industrial Retraining Program (KIR): Provides retraining assistance to employees of restructuring industries who are likely to be displaced because of obsolete or inadequate job skills and knowledge. 785-296-8097

Venture Capital & Seed Capital Programs: Instituted to increase the availability of risk capital in Kansas. These programs make use of income tax credits to encourage investment in venture and seed capital pools as a source of early stage financing for small businesses. Businesses demonstrating strong growth potential but lacking the financial strength to obtain conventional financing are the most likely candidates for risk capital funding. The Business Development Division has in operation and continues to develop a network of venture capital resources to assist qualified small businesses in locating potential sources of venture capital financing.

Economic Opportunity Initiatives Fund (KEOIF): A funding mechanism to address the creation/retention of jobs presented by unique opportunities or emergencies. The fund has a

higher level of flexibility than do many of the other state financing programs and allows the State to participate as a funding source when other options have been exhausted. 785-296-1868

Existing Industry Expansion Program (KEIEP): Performance based, with a focus on the expansion/ retention of jobs that are associated with the activities of existing firms.

Investments In Major Projects And Comprehensive Training (IMPACT): A funding mechanism designed to respond to the training and capital requirements of major business expansions and locations in the state. SKILL (State of Kansas Investments in Lifelong Learning) funds may be used to pay for expenses related to training a new work force. MPI (Major Project Investment) funds may be used for other expenses related to the project such as the purchase or relocation of equipment, labor recruitment, or building costs. Individual bond size may not exceed 90% of the withholding taxes received from the new jobs over a 10-year period.

Network of Certified Development Companies: Provides financial packaging services to businesses, utilizing state, Small Business Administration, and private financial sources. The state provides supplemental funding to these organizations in recognition of the service they provide.

Private Activity Bonds (PABs): Tax-exempt bonds (IRBs) for facility and equipment financing for qualifying manufacturers and processors. The reduced financing costs generated through these bonds are passed through to the company.

Training Equipment Grants: Provide area technical schools and community colleges an opportunity to acquire instructional equipment to train or retrain Kansas workers.

Kansas Trade Show Assistance Program: Allows a Kansas company to receive a reimbursement of up to 50% of their international trade show expenses to a maximum of $3,500 per show and $7,000 per state fiscal year.

Foreign Trade Zones: Provide a duty-free and quota-free entry point for foreign goods into specific areas under customs' supervision for an unlimited period of time.

Office of Minority & Women Business Development: Promotes and assists in the development of minority-owned and women-owned businesses in Kansas. The program provides assistance in procurement and contracting, financing resources, business planning, and identification of business opportunities. A directory of minority-owned and women-owned businesses in Kansas is published annually. 785-296-3425

Single Source Certification Program: Responsible for certifying minority-and-women-owned businesses as small disadvantaged businesses for non-highway related firms.

Domestic Agricultural Marketing: This program identifies new markets for Kansas products and helps Kansas agricultural producers market their goods.

Export Assistance: The Trade development provides assistance to Kansas companies wishing to begin or expand their international marketing efforts.

Enterprise Zone: Provides potential Kansas sales tax exemption and Kansas income/privilege tax credits to businesses creating net new jobs in Kansas through major capital investment projects.

Micro-Loans Program: Loans are made to county governments to loan to microenterprise businesses with 5 or fewer jobs.

From the Land of Kansas: This trademark program is designed to help small businesses that manufacture products in Kansas.

* Publications

Kansas Department of Commerce
1000 SW Jackson Street, Suite 100   785-296-3481
Topeka, KS 66612-1354   Fax: 785-296-5055
http://kdoch.state.ks.us   TTY: 785-296-3487

The Kansas Department of Commerce & Housing (KDOC&H) distributes a variety of publications to help Kansas residents, businesses and visitors find the information needed about their state. Here are a few:

Data Book: The information found in the *Data Book* gives a good idea of what Kansas has to offer new and expanding businesses. The book is filled with information about the Kansas economy, labor and workforce training. It briefly describes taxes and incentives for new and expanding businesses. It also includes sections on finance, technology and education, markets and transportation, and the environment.

The Kansas Aerospace Directory: A complete resource for aircraft production, parts, equipment, research and development, etc. *Directory* includes a wide range of aviation products and companies.

Kansas Agribusiness Directory: A complete resource for agriculture-related business, the *Kansas Agribusiness Directory* offers assistance in contacting any firm or business as well as finding specialized products or services.

Steps to Success: A Guide to Starting a Business in Kansas: Created to give entrepreneurs and small business owners all the information needed on licenses, forms, rules and regulations required by State agencies. It discusses the aspects of business development including finance, incentives and taxation. Plus, it has referrals to programs such as Small Business Development Centers, development companies, the Kansas Technology Enterprise Corporation, Inc. and the Small Business Administration.

* Rural Development

1303 First America Place, Suite 100   785-271-2700
Topeka, KS 66604   Fax: 785-271-2708
www.rurdev.usda.gov/ks

Business and Industrial Loan Program: Provides loan guarantees to businesses and industries to benefit rural areas. Loans are made in any area outside the boundary of a city of 50,000 or more and its adjacent urbanized areas with population density of no more than 100 persons per square mile. Any legal entity, including individuals, public and private organizations, and federally recognized Indian tribes may borrow under its program. Priority is given to applications for projects in open country, rural communities and towns of 25,000 and smaller. Primary purpose is to create and maintain employment and improve the economic and environmental climate in rural communities. Guarantees of up to 90 percent of the principal and interest.

Intermediary Relending Program Loans: Intermediary Relending Program loans finance business facilities and community development projects in rural areas, including cities with a population of less than 25,000. RBS lends these funds to intermediaries, which, in turn, provide loans to recipients who are developing business facilities or community development projects. Eligible intermediaries include public bodies, nonprofit corporations, Indian tribes, and cooperatives.

Rural Economic Development Loans and Grants: These programs are available to any Rural Utilities Service electric or telecommunications borrower. Zero–interest loans are made primarily to finance start-up ventures and business expansion projects.

Rural Business Enterprise Grants: Rural Business Enterprise Grants help public bodies, nonprofit corporations, and Federally recognized Indian tribal groups finance and facilitate development of small and emerging private business enterprises located in rural areas (this includes all areas other than cities of more than 50,000 people and their immediately adjacent urban or urbanizing areas). Grant funds can pay for the acquisition and development of land and the construction of buildings, plants, equipment, access streets and roads, parking areas, utility and service extensions, refinancing and fees for professional services.

Rural Business Opportunity Grants: Rural Business Opportunity Grant funds provide for technical assistance, training, and planning activities that improve economic conditions in rural areas. Applicants must be located in rural areas (this includes all areas other than cities of more than 50,000 people and their immediately adjacent urban or urbanizing areas). Nonprofit corporations and public bodies are eligible. A maximum of $50,000 per grant is authorized by the legislation. RBS is designing the program to promote sustainable economic development in rural communities with exceptional needs.

* Mid-America Manufacturing Technology Center

10561 Barkley, Suite 602   800-653-4333
Overland Park, KS 66212   Fax: 913-649-4333
www.mamtc.com

The Mid-America Manufacturing Technology Center .(MAMTC) helps small- and medium-sized manufacturers improve their competitiveness by assisting them in modernizing their operations and adopting appropriate technologies, as well as management, marketing and business practices. MAMTC divides its services into three types: 1) one-on-one client consultations, assessments and information searches; 2) programs for groups of manufacturers, such as seminars/workshops, roundtable discussion groups and cooperative networks; and, 3) equipment and software for demonstration, testing, and developing product prototypes. All services are provided in eight core areas: quality, manufacturing processes, business systems, marketing, information systems, human resources, product development and testing, and company assessment.

* Incubator Centers

Alliance for Technology Commercialization
Pittsburg State University
1501 S. Joplin   620-235-4927
Pittsburg, KS 66762   Fax: 620-235-4030
www.atckansas.com

Enterprise Center of Johnson County
8527 Bluejacket   913-438-2282
Lenexa, KS 66214   Fax: 913-888-6928
www.ecjc.com

The ECJC provides services to entrepreneurs in the

Kansas City metro area. The Kansas Women's Business Center is located at ECJC.

Lawrence Regional Technology Center
1617 St. Andrews Drive, Suite 210   785-832-2110
Lawrence, KS 66047   Fax: 785-832-8234
www.lrtc.biz

Mid-America Commercialization Corporation
1500 Hayes Drive   785-532-3900
Manhattan, KS 66502   Fax: 785-532-3909
www.ksu.edu/tech.transfer/macc/macc.htm

Quest Business Center for Entrepreneurs
Quest Center
One East Ninth   620-665-8468
Hutchinson, KS 67501   Fax: 620-665-7619
www.hutchquest.com

University of Kansas Medical Center Research Institute
Biotechnology Development Center
3901 Rainbow Blvd.   913-588-1495
Kansas City, KS 66160-7702   Fax: 913-588-5242
www.kcbdc.com

Western Kansas Technology Corporation
1922 Main   620-793-7964
Great Bend, KS 67530   Fax: 620-792-4850

Wichita Technology Center
7829 Rockhill Rd., Suite 307   316-651-5900
Wichita, KS 67206   Fax: 316-684-5640
www.wichitatechnology.com

The Mid-America Manufacturing Technology Center strives to improve the technical capabilities of small manufacturers, ensuring they stay competitive. The incubators are public-private partnerships designed to assist companies and transfer new technology to the marketplace. Each incubator also operates a local seed fund.

* Business Tax Bureau

Kansas Department of Revenue
915 SW Harrison St.
Topeka, KS 66625   785-368-8222
www.ksrevenue.org

The Kansas Department of Revenue provides an economic development outreach program that furnishes information about the tax incentives available to individuals and businesses in Kansas. The department visits with cities, counties, chambers, businesses and other groups to promote the Kansas tax incentives. Their goals are to first make our customers aware of the Kansas tax incentives offered and second to provide their customers with the information necessary to understand and qualify for the tax incentives made available through Kansas law. If you are interested in having a representative from the Kansas Department of Revenue speak to your group about Kansas tax incentives, please contact Tax Incentive Department at 785-296-3070 or by Email: {eco@kdor.state.ks.us}.

* Kansas Technology Enterprise Corporation (KTEC)

214 SW 6th Ave., First Floor   785-296-5272
Topeka, KS 66603-3719   Fax: 785-296-1160
www.ktec.com

Through the following programs, KTEC serves inventors, researchers, corporations, investors and entrepreneurs. In addition, they conduct an annual high tech expo.

Applied Research Matching Grants: KTEC funds 60 percent of the cost of industry R&D projects which lead to job creation in Kansas. Industrially-focused Centers of Excellence are operated at several major universities.

Seed Capital Fund: Provides equity financing for high tech product development. Matching funds are provided for the Small Business Innovation Research Program.

KTEC Centers of Excellence: University based research centers providing product development, seminars, research, consulting, networking and training.

Advanced Manufacturing Institute (AMI): Located on the campus of Kansas State University. Purpose is to improve manufacturing practiced by Kansas companies. These include automated and flexible manufacturing and assembly systems, process planning, processing of engineering materials, special developmental efforts, and technology transfer.

Higuchi Biosciences Center (HBC): Located on the campus of the University of Kansas. Serves as a hub of pharmaceutical research and development. Mission is pre-clinical drug delivery, drug development, drug testing and research.

National Institute for Aviation Research (NIAR): Located at the Wichita State University. Integrates higher education, government and business in cooperative efforts to advance the nation's aviation industry. Conducts research and technology transfer to meet industry challenges.

Kansas Polymer Research Center: Located in Pittsburg State University. Helps companies by providing technical assistance and research facilities for design, testing, development of prototypes, products and processing methods.

Information and Telecommunication Technology Center (ITTC): Located at the University of Kansas, ITTC develops technology and advances knowledge in the areas of information technology, telecommunications, radar systems and remote sensing.

Grant Programs

Small Business Innovation Research (SBIR) Grants: Helps small businesses obtain Federal SBIR awards by providing grants to support proposal preparation. Offers a network for SBIR concept evaluation, identification of appropriate SBIR solicitation topics, federal agency contact, and technical assistance.

* Kansas Development Finance Authority

555 S. Kansas Ave., Suite 202   785-357-4445
Topeka, KS 66603-3761   Fax: 785-357-4478
www.kdfa.org

The Authority is authorized to issue bonds for the purpose of financing capital improvements facilities, industrial enterprises, agricultural business enterprises, educational facilities, health care facilities, and housing developments. Several small projects can be combined into one large bond issue.

* Loans For Farmers

Farm Service Agency
U.S. Department of Agriculture
3600 Anderson Avenue   785-539-3531

Manhattan, KS 66503-2511   Fax: 785-537-9659
http://www.fsa.usda.gov/ks/

The Farm Service Agency provides Direct and Guaranteed Loans to farmers through a variety of programs, including:

Farm Ownership Loans: purchase farmland, construct or repair buildings and other fixtures, and promote soil and water conservation. Up to $200,000.

Operating Loans: purchase items needed for a successful farm operation, such as livestock, farm equipment, feed, seed, fuel, farm chemicals, insurance, and other operating expenses. Can also be used to pay for minor improvements. Up to $200,000.

Beginning Farmer and Rancher Loans: provides funds to beginning and farmers and ranchers who are unable to obtain financing elsewhere.

Downpayment Farm Ownership Loans for Beginning Farmers: helps beginning farmers and ranchers purchase a farm or ranch. Also provides a way for retiring farmers to transfer their land to a future generation of farmers and ranchers. Applicant must have a downpayment of 10% and FSA with finance 40%, with the remaining balance from a commercial lender. Purchase price cannot exceed $250,000.

Loans to Socially Disadvantaged Farmers/Ranchers: helps socially disadvantaged applicants buy and operate family-size farms and ranches.

Youth Loans: Made to youths to establish and operate income-producing projects with the participation in 4-H clubs, Future Farmers of America, and similar organizations. Up to $5,000.

Emergency Loan Assistance: provides loans to help producers recover from production and physical losses due to drought, flooding, and other natural disasters, or quarantine. Up to $500,000.

Beginning Farmer and Rancher Land Contract Guarantee Pilot Program: "prompt payment guarantee" from FSA. FSA will provide payment to seller two times if the beginning farmer does not pay. Program is tested in IN, IA, ND, OR, PA and WI.

Farm Ownership and Operating Loan Guarantees: FSA will guarantee loans up to $782,000.

* Small Business Administration (SBA)

271 W. 3rd St. N, Suite 2500   316-269-6616
Wichita, KS 67202-1212   Fax: 316-269-6499

The Kansas Small Business Administration Office delivers a variety of programs and services, such as startup and operational assistance through small business training and counseling, financial assistance for startup's, business opportunities and much more.

Kentucky

* Kentucky Cabinet for Economic Development

2300 Capital Plaza Tower
500 Mero Street   502-564-7670
Frankfort, KY 40601   800-626-2930
www.thinkkentucky.com

Kentucky Cabinet for Economic Development: The Cabinet is the primary state agency responsible for creating new jobs and new investment in the state.
- Job Recruitment, Placement And Training: Provides a package of time-and cost-saving employee recruiting and placement services to Kentucky employers, at no cost to either employers or employees.
- Industrial Location Assistance: Provides a comprehensive package of assistance to large manufacturing, services, and administrative facilities, both before and after their location in Kentucky.

Business Information Clearinghouse: 800-626-2250
Provides new and existing businesses a centralized information source on business regulations, licenses, permits, and other business assistance programs.

Kentucky Economic Development Finance Authority (KEDFA): Provides business loans to supplement other financing. KEDFA provides loan funds at below market interest rates. The loans are available for fixed asset financing (land, buildings, and equipment) for business startup, locations, and expansions that create new jobs in Kentucky or have a significant impact on the economic growth of a community. The loans must be used to finance projects in agribusiness, tourism, industrial ventures, or the service industry. KEDFA may participate in the financing of qualified projects with a secured loan for up to $10,000 per new job created, not to exceed 25% of a project's fixed asset cost. The maximum loan amount is $500,000 and the minimum is $25,000. Small businesses with projects of less than $100,000 may receive loans on fixed assets for up to 45% of the project costs if enough jobs are created. Interest rates are fixed for the life of the loan, and are determined by the length of the loan term. 502-564-4554, ext. 4413

Commonwealth Small Business Development Corporation (CSBDC): Works with state and local economic development organizations, banks, and the SBA to achieve community economic development through job creation and retention by providing long-term fixed asset financing to small business concerns. The CSBDC can lend a maximum of 40% of project cost or $750,000 per project (in certain circumstances $1,000,000).

Linked Deposit Program: Provides loans up to $100,000 for small business and agribusiness. Credit decisions are the responsibility of the lender making the loan. The state will purchase certificates of deposit from participating lenders through the State Investment Commission, at the New York Prime interest rate less four percent, but never less than 2%. 502-564-2064

Local Financial Assistance: Several local governments and area development districts offer loans and other financial incentives for economic development projects. The levels and terms of financial assistance provided generally are negotiable, and are based upon the availability of funds, jobs created, economic viability of the project, and other locally determined criteria.

Bluegrass State Skills Corporation (BSSC): An independent dejure corporation within the Cabinet for Economic Development, provides grants for customized skills training of workers for new, expanding and existing industries in Kentucky.

Industrial Revenue Bonds (IRB): Can be used to finance manufacturing projects and their warehousing areas, major transportation and communication facilities, most health care facilities, and mineral extraction and processing projects. 502-564-4554, ext. 4427

Utility Incentive Rates: Electric and gas utility companies regulated by the Kentucky Public Service Commission (excluding municipal systems) can offer economic incentive rates for certain large industrial and commercial customers.

Kentucky Investment Fund (Venture Capital): Encourages venture capital investment by certifying privately operated venture funds, thereby entitling their investors to tax credits equal to 40% of their capital contributions to the fund. 502-564-0531

Kentucky Tourism Development Act: Provides financial incentives to qualifying tourism projects. Tourism projects are defined as a cultural or historical site, recreation or entertainment facility, or area of natural phenomenon or scenic beauty.

Local Government Economic Development Fund: Grants are made to eligible counties for specific project that enable the counties to provide infrastructure to incoming and expanding business and industry.

Job Development Incentive Grant Program: Grants are made to eligible counties from their coal severance accounts for the purpose of encouraging job development. The grant amount cannot exceed $5,000 per job created.

Kentucky Industrial Development Act (KIDA): Investments in new and expanding manufacturing projects may qualify for tax credits. Companies that create at least 15 new full-time jobs and invest at least $100,000 in projects approved under KIDA may receive state income tax credits for up to 100% of annual debt service costs (principal and interest) for up to 10 years on land, buildings, site development, building fixtures and equipment used in a project, or the company may collect a job assessment fee of 3% of the gross wages of each employee whose job is created by the approved project and who is subject to Kentucky income taxes.

Kentucky Rural Economic Development Act (KREDA): Larger tax credits are available for new and expanding manufacturing projects that create at least 15 new full time jobs in counties with unemployment rates higher than the state average in each of the five preceding calendar years and invest at least $100,000.

Kentucky Jobs Development Act (KJDA): Service and technology related companies that invest in new and expanded non-manufacturing, non-retail projects that provide at least 75% of their services to users located outside of Kentucky, and that create new jobs for at least 15 full-time Kentucky residents may qualify for tax credits.

Kentucky Industrial Revitalization Act (KIRA): Investments in the rehabilitation of manufacturing operations that are in imminent danger of permanently closing or that have closed temporarily may qualify for tax credits. Companies that save or create 25 jobs in projects approved under KIRA may receive state income tax credits and job assessment fees for up to 10 years limited to 50% of the costs of the rehabilitation or construction of buildings and the reoutfitting or purchasing of machinery and equipment. 502-564-4554, ext. 4428

Kentuckyenterprise: This program was developed by the Cabinet for Economic Development to assist new businesses through the maze of start-up questions. They publish a "Kentucky Business Guide" to help you through all the requirements of a new business.

Kentucky Economic Opportunity Zone Program: Provides tax credits to companies that establish new or expand existing manufacturing, service, or technology operations in a qualified zone having high unemployment and poverty levels.

Enterprise Zone Program: Encourages new or renewed development to targeted areas of the state by offering special state and local tax incentives to businesses locating in a zone.

Direct Loan Program: Provides financing for manufacturing, warehousing, distribution, non-retail services, agribusiness, and tourism projects to private firms in participation with other lenders.

Craft Loan Program: Provides direct loans to the craft industry to finance inventory, working capital, up to 50% of eligible operating expenses, and renovation or purchase of equipment or other fixed assets.

Bluegrass State Skills Corporation: An independent corporation that brokers skills training for business and industry, from entry-level to advanced training, and from upgrading present employees to retraining experienced workers. Awards grants to new, expanding and existing companies, providing up to 50% reimbursement of eligible costs. Tax credit is available to existing businesses for skills upgrade and occupational upgrade training. The program works in partnership with other employment and job training resources and programs, as well as economic development activities, to package a program customized to meet the specific needs of a company. 502-564-2021

The Small and Minority Business Division: Coordinates small and minority business activities throughout the state.

One-Stop Business Licensing Program: The One-Stop Business Licensing Program was developed to cut through the 'red tape' by simplifying this process. This program allows users to instantly receive a complete listing of all licenses that could be required at the state level. {www.sos.state.ky.us/ONESTOP/PROGRAM/onestop.asp}

Alliance Program: The Commonwealth Alliance Program helps guide entrepreneurs through an organized process of creating and managing strategic, market-driven business relationships with other companies.

Procurement Assistance: If you want to market your products and/or services to federal, state, and local government agencies then the Kentucky Procurement Assistance Program (KPAP) offers services to assist you.

International Trade Division: The International Trade Division within the Kentucky Cabinet for Economic Development assists business owners with international endeavors. Their programs include: export consulting, export marketing, education and training and representatives in Belgium, Japan, Chile and Mexico.

* Rural Development

771 Corporate Dr., Suite 200   859-224-7300
Lexington, KY 40503-4577   Fax: 859-224-7340

www.rurdev.usda.gov/ky

The Office of Kentucky Rural Development's Rural Business-Cooperative Service promotes economic viability of rural communities through partnerships with public and private community based organizations. Their programs provide financial and technical assistance to rural businesses and cooperatives to create and preserve quality jobs in rural areas. Rural Business-Cooperative Service programs include: Business and Industry Guaranteed Loans, Rural Business Opportunity Grants, Rural Business Enterprise Grants, Intermediary Relending Program, Rural Economic Development Loan and Grants, Rural Cooperative Development Grants and Rural Community Value Added Grants. Contact the office or check their web site for additional information.

FmHA Business and Industrial Guarantee Loan Program: Offers loan guarantees of up to 90 percent of principal and interest on conventional loans to businesses and industries in rural areas of Kentucky. The FmHA designates the eligible rural areas and are in areas with populations of less than 50,000. Priority is given where areas are in open country, rural communities, and cities of 25,000 or fewer. Funds can be used to purchase land, buildings, machinery, equipment, furniture, and fixtures; to finance construction, expansion, or modernization of buildings; and to provide start-up and working capital.

* Kentucky Pollution Prevention Center

KPPC
University of Louisville   800-334-8635
420 Academic Building   502-852-0965 (in Louisville)
Louisville, KY 40292   Fax: 502-852-0964
www.kppc.org

KPPC is a waste management resource center that provides information on how to manage, recycle, procedure or exchange waste even the smallest businesses produce, such as drycleaners or auto body shops. The service is free to all Kentucky businesses. They are located at the University of Louisville and provides a toll-free number for your convenience in calling:

* Business Environmental Assistance Program – Air Quality

Center for Business Development
Business Environmental Assistance Program for Air
  Quality
University of Kentucky
227 Carol M. Gatton College of Business and
  Economics Building   800-562-2327
Lexington, KY 40506-0034   Fax: 859-323-1907
www.kbeap.org

Operated by the Center for Business Development at the University of Kentucky, this non-regulated program offers confidential air quality environmental assistance to businesses while also serving as an advocate for development of environmental regulations which promote economic competitiveness. Services include environmental training seminars, publications to help businesses reduce air emissions through prevention techniques and on-site air quality environmental assessments to individual businesses. The center's reference library and toll-free phone line acts as a clearinghouse for information about techniques, products and equipment that businesses can use to prevent production and release of air pollutants. These services will help businesses comply with federal and state regulations including Title V of the Clean Air Act of 1990.

* Kentucky Tourism Development Cabinet

2200 Capital Plaza Tower
500 Mero Street   502-564-0678
Frankfort, KY 40601   Fax: 502-564-1512
http://tourism.ky.gov

Developers of approved projects will be eligible to recover 25% of their project's cost by having refunded to them the six percent Kentucky sales tax they collect from their visitors. The refund will be paid over a 10-year period. Eligible tourism attractions for Kentucky's incentives are cultural or historic sites, recreation or entertainment facilities, areas of scenic beauty or distinctive natural phenomena, entertainment destination centers, Kentucky crafts and products centers and lodging when built on state or federal parks and recreational land or built with a recreational component that costs more than the lodging facility.

Kentucky Tourism Development Loan Program: The loan program assists smaller tourism facilities obtain financing. The program is targeted to facilities that will attract travelers into the area. Projects approved for funding have included a rock climbing experience, equine shoe facility and a bed & breakfast. Funds are available through this program are for the financing of fixed assets only. The maximum loan amount is $250,000 with an equal amount being provided by another source. The program offers below market interest rates with maximum terms of 15 years.

* Information Technology Resource Center

iTRC-Shelby Campus
9001 Shelbyville Road   502-852-0900
Louisville, KY 40222   Fax: 502-852-4701

iTRC-Downtown
201 East Jefferson St.
Louisville, KY 40202
www.theitrc.com

The iTRC provides incubating facilities for new companies using applications of new technologies. This effort is now being expanded and developed into an international-class offering. The iTRC's incubation program is targeting Information and Telecommunications intensive startup companies or companies less than two years old. They offer an extremely competitive pricing structure for all the facility and infrastructure needs of a new and growing company.

* Loans For Farmers

Farm Service Agency
U.S. Department of Agriculture
771 Corporate Dr., Suite 100   859-224-5971
Lexington, KY 40503-5478   Fax: 859-224-7691
http://www.fsa.usda.gov/ky/

The Farm Service Agency provides Direct and Guaranteed Loans to farmers through a variety of programs, including:

Farm Ownership Loans: purchase farmland, construct or repair buildings and other fixtures, and promote soil and water conservation. Up to $200,000.

Operating Loans: purchase items needed for a successful farm operation, such as livestock, farm equipment, feed, seed, fuel, farm chemicals, insurance, and other operating expenses. Can also be used to pay for minor improvements. Up to $200,000.

Beginning Farmer and Rancher Loans: provides funds to beginning and farmers and ranchers who are unable to obtain financing elsewhere.

Downpayment Farm Ownership Loans for Beginning Farmers: helps beginning farmers and ranchers purchase a farm or ranch. Also provides a way for retiring farmers to transfer their land to a future generation of farmers and ranchers. Applicant must have a downpayment of 10% and FSA with finance 40%, with the remaining balance from a commercial lender. Purchase price cannot exceed $250,000.

Loans to Socially Disadvantaged Farmers/Ranchers: helps socially disadvantaged applicants buy and operate family-size farms and ranches.

Youth Loans: Made to youths to establish and operate income-producing projects with the participation in 4-H clubs, Future Farmers of America, and similar organizations. Up to $5,000.

Emergency Loan Assistance: provides loans to help producers recover from production and physical losses due to drought, flooding, and other natural disasters, or quarantine. Up to $500,000.

Beginning Farmer and Rancher Land Contract Guarantee Pilot Program: "prompt payment guarantee" from FSA. FSA will provide payment to seller two times if the beginning farmer does not pay. Program is tested in IN, IA, ND, OR, PA and WI.

Farm Ownership and Operating Loan Guarantees: FSA will guarantee loans up to $782,000.

* Small Business Administration (SBA)

Room 188
600 Dr. Martin Luther King, Jr. Place   502-582-5671
Louisville, KY 40202   Fax: 502-582-5009
www.sba.gov/ky

The Kentucky Small Business Administration Office delivers a variety of programs and services, such as startup and operational assistance through small business training and counseling, financial assistance for startup's, business opportunities and much more.

* Kentucky Department of Local Government

Division of Community Programs   800-346-5606
1024 Capital Center Dr., Suite 340   502-573-2382
Frankfort, KY 40601   Fax: 502-573-2512
www.dlg.ky.gov

Community Development Block Grant Loan (CDBG): Available to cities and counties for the commercial rehabilitation of existing buildings or structures used for business, commercial, or industrial purposes. The cities and counties loan the grant funds to business to be used for fixed assets and for the creation or retention of jobs. At least 51 percent of the jobs created must be for low-and moderate-income families.

* Community Ventures Corporation

1450 Broadway   800-299-0267
Lexington, KY 40505   859-231-0054
www.cvcky.org   Fax: 859-231-0261

Community Venture Corporation is a community-based, nonprofit organization that strives to help improve the quality of life for urban and rural residents throughout central and northern Kentucky. They offer free Business Orientation classes and a free Small Business Resource Guide. In addition they offer a variety of business classes with a sliding fee scale. The Center for Entrepreneurs provides businesses with highly visible rental space, which includes: conference rooms, computer and faxes, workroom, business training, consultants, and free parking starting at $350 per month.

* Kentucky Highlands Investment Corporation (KHIC)

362 Whitley Road
P.O. Box 1738   606-864-5175
London, KY 40743   Fax: 606-864-5194
www.khic.org

A small business investment company licensed by the SBA, provide both short term and long term financing assistance to small businesses in Southeastern Kentucky. Venture capital loans and equity capital investments for higher-risk projects are available for start-ups, expansions, and relocations of manufacturing and services firms. Participation usually ranges from $50,000 to $500,000. Terms and interest rates are negotiated.

* Mountain Association for Community Economic Development

433 Chestnut St., Suite 9   859-986-2373
Berea, KY 40403   Fax: 859-986-1299
www.maced.org

Private Loans: Appalachian Counties: Loans and financial planning assistance are available to qualifying new and expanding manufacturing businesses in the 49 Appalachian counties of Kentucky. Loans range from $10,000 to $150,000. Funds can be used for working capital or to finance fixed assets.

* Office for the New Economy

702 Capital Avenue, #256   502-564-0531
Frankfort, KY 40601   Fax: 502-564-0963
www.one-ky.com

Created by the Kentucky Innovation Act of 2000, the Office of New Economy facilitates a state-wide strategic development plan to spur the growth of the knowledge-based economy in Kentucky. The Office of the New Economy provides programs for entrepreneurs, science and research, and information technology.

Louisiana

* Louisiana Department of Economic Development

P.O. Box 94185   225-342-3000
Baton Rouge, LA 70804   225-342-5388
www.lded.state.la.us

Quality jobs: Provides an annual refundable credit of up to 6% of payroll for a period of up to 10 years for qualifying companies.

Cost-free training: Louisiana's QuickStart Training Program utilizes the state's vocational-technical institutes to provide cost-free pre-employment training customized to a company's requirements. The Jobs Training Partnership Act Program can help a company find trainees and will also pay a portion of their wages while they are in training.

Workforce development and training: Develops and provides customized pre-employment and workforce upgrade training to existing and prospective Louisiana businesses.

Business Matchmakers: Seeks to pair small and medium-sized suppliers in the state with larger companies which are currently making purchases out of state.

Minority Venture Capital Match Program: Provides for a match investment for qualified minority venture capital funds. The fund must have at least $250,000 of private investment for which LEDC may invest $1.00 for every $2.00 of private capital up to $5 million.

Small Business Loan Program: Provides loan guarantees and participations to banks in order to facilitate capital accessibility for businesses. Guarantees may range up to 75% of the loan amount, not to exceed a maximum of $1.5 million. Loan participations of up to 40% are also available. Applicants must have a business plan and a bank that is willing to fund the loan.

Business Linked Deposit Program: Provides for a 1% to 4% interest rate reduction on a maximum of $200,000 for a maximum of 2 to 5 years on term loans that are funded by banks to Louisiana businesses. Job creation, statistical area employment, and cash flow requirements for underwriting are all criteria, which will effect the percentage and term of the linked deposit.

Micro Loan Program: Provides loan guarantees and participations to banks that fund loans ranging from $5,000 to $50,000 to Louisiana small businesses.

Contract Loan Program: Intended to provide a loan participation and guarantee to a bank for government contract loans. These loans are intended to help businesses finance working capital for contracts with local, state, or federal government agencies. Loans may range from $5000 to $1,000,000 and must be for terms of one year or less.

Exim Bank City/State Program: LEDC has a relationship with the U.S. Export-Import Bank in Washington, DC Under this program, LEDC facilitates export working capital loans for small Louisiana businesses.

Venture Capital Match Program: Provides for a match investment for Louisiana venture capital funds. The fund must have at least $5 million of private investment for which LEDC may provide $5 million.

Venture Capital Co-Investment Program: Provides for a co-investment in a Louisiana business of up to 1/4 of the round of investment, but not more than $500,000, with any qualified venture capital fund with at least $7.5 million in private capital. The venture capital fund may be from outside of Louisiana.

BIDCO Investment Program: Provides for a match or co-investment in certified BIDCOs. BIDCOs are state-chartered, non-depository alternative financing sources for small businesses. BIDCOs frequently provide equity and subordinated debt financing to new and growing companies, as well as to companies requiring turnaround assistance. A BIDCO must have at least $2 million in private capital. LEDC may match the investment $1.00 for $2.00 of private capital up to $2.5 million. Co-investments are considered on a project by project basis and cannot exceed 33% of the total investment.

Specialty BIDCO Investment Program: Provides for a match or co-investment in certified Specialty BIDCOs. Specialty BIDCOs are BIDCOs established with a particular focus on assisting disadvantaged businesses and businesses located in impoverished and economically disadvantaged areas. The BIDCO must have at least $250,000 in private capital. LEDC may match the investment $1.00 for every $1.00 of private capital up to $2.5 million. Co-investments are considered on a project by project basis and cannot exceed 50% of the total investment.

Small Business Bonding Assistance Program: The primary goal of this program is to aid certified Economically Disadvantaged Businesses (EDBs) in acquiring quality bid, performance, and payment bonds at reasonable rates from surety companies. EDBs receive help reaching required bonding capacity for specific projects. Contractors often do not reach these levels on their own due to balance sheet deficiencies and a lack of adequate managerial and technical skills. After certification by the Division and accreditation by LCAI, contractors are eligible to receive bond guarantee assistance to be used as collateral when seeking bonds. The Division will issue a letter of credit to the surety for an amount up to 25% of the base contract amount or $200,000.

Economic Development Award: Provides financial incentives in the form of linked deposit loans, loan guarantees and grants to industrial or business development projects that promote economic development and that require state assistance for basic infrastructure development.

International Trade: The International Trade Division utilizes trade and catalog shows, identifies trade opportunities, offers counseling, matches exporters with markets and encourages participation in their seminars.

Microenterprise Program: The Microenterprise Program assists low income parents of minor children to start or strengthen a small business. The program provides entrepreneurial and economic literacy training and mentoring; financial counseling; and access to capital through micro loans for the participants. In addition, the program provides ongoing assistance to participants to ensure that microentrepreneurs successfully negotiate the challenges new microenterprise businesses face during the initial phases.

Small Business Development Centers: Louisiana Economic Development provides 12 Small Business Development Centers throughout the state.

Louisiana Seed Capital Program: Provides matching funds to be used to provide seed capital for Louisiana small businesses at the early stages.

* Rural Development Office

USDA, Rural Development
Louisiana State Office
3727 Government Street   318-473-7921
Alexandria, LA 71302   Fax: 318-473-7829
www.rurdev.usda.gov/la

USDA Rural Development provides a full range of rural development credit services in rural Louisiana. Programs in the areas of business and industrial development, community facilities, multi-family and single housing and water and waste disposal are administered through Rural Development state and area offices.

* First Stop Shop

Secretary of State
First Stop Shop Division   225-922-2675
P.O. Box 94125   800-259-0001
Baton Rouge, LA 70804-9125   Fax: 225-922-0439

www.sos.louisiana.gov/comm/fss/fss-index.htm
The First Stop Shop is a "licensing information center" for prospective small business owners. The First Stop Shop gives current and potential business owners a single place to go for licensing information needed to start a business in Louisiana.

* Department of Environmental Quality

Small Business Assistance Program
602 N. Fifth Street   225-219-3296
Baton Rouge, LA 70802   Fax: 225-219-3309
www.deq.state.la.us
The mission of the DEQ's non-regulatory Small Business Assistance Program is to provide technical assistance to small business owners in complying with state and federal environmental regulations. The SBAP is dedicated to: interpreting federal and state environmental regulations and giving guidance on how to comply with them; interpreting the rights and obligations of the small businesses, identifying emission sources and compounds; estimating emissions at each source for inventory questionnaires; assisting in the preparation of environmental permit applications and exemptions; developing pollution programs; and providing guidance with multi-media issues.

* Louisiana Department of Agriculture and Forestry

Office of Marketing
5825 Florida Boulevard, Suite 1158
P.O. Box 3334   225-922-1277
Baton Rouge, LA 70821   Fax: 225-922-1289
www.ldaf.state.la.us
The Office of Marketing provides one-on-one counseling assistance to numerous clients for varied marketing services and economic development needs. The staff is capable of providing a wealth of information about Louisiana aquaculture, agriculture and forestry either directly or through extensive professional networks.

* Incumbent Worker Training

Louisiana Department of Labor
1001 North 23rd Street
P.O. Box 94094
Baton Rouge, LA 70804-9094   225-342-3290
www.ldol.state.la.us
Incumbent Worker Training is designed to benefit business and industry by assisting in the skill development of existing employees, increasing employee productivity and the growth of the company. Both are expected to result in the creation of new jobs, the retention of jobs that otherwise may have been eliminated, and an increase in wages for the trained workers.

* Loans For Farmers

Farm Service Agency
U.S. Department of Agriculture
3737 Government Street   318-473-7721
Alexandria, LA 71302-3395   Fax: 318-473-7735
http://www.fsa.usda.gov/la/
The Farm Service Agency provides Direct and Guaranteed Loans to farmers through a variety of programs, including:

Farm Ownership Loans: purchase farmland, construct or repair buildings and other fixtures, and promote soil and water conservation. Up to $200,000.

Operating Loans: purchase items needed for a successful farm operation, such as livestock, farm equipment, feed, seed, fuel, farm chemicals, insurance, and other operating expenses. Can also be used to pay for minor improvements. Up to $200,000.

Beginning Farmer and Rancher Loans: provides funds to beginning and farmers and ranchers who are unable to obtain financing elsewhere.

Downpayment Farm Ownership Loans for Beginning Farmers: helps beginning farmers and ranchers purchase a farm or ranch. Also provides a way for retiring farmers to transfer their land to a future generation of farmers and ranchers. Applicant must have a downpayment of 10% and FSA with finance 40%, with the remaining balance from a commercial lender. Purchase price cannot exceed $250,000.

Loans to Socially Disadvantaged Farmers/Ranchers: helps socially disadvantaged applicants buy and operate family-size farms and ranches.

Youth Loans: Made to youths to establish and operate income-producing projects with the participation in 4-H clubs, Future Farmers of America, and similar organizations. Up to $5,000.

Emergency Loan Assistance: provides loans to help producers recover from production and physical losses due to drought, flooding, and other natural disasters, or quarantine. Up to $500,000.

Beginning Farmer and Rancher Land Contract Guarantee Pilot Program: "prompt payment guarantee" from FSA. FSA will provide payment to seller two times if the beginning farmer does not pay. Program is tested in IN, IA, ND, OR, PA and WI.

Farm Ownership and Operating Loan Guarantees: FSA will guarantee loans up to $782,000.

* Small Business Administration

One Canal Plaza
365 Canal St., Suite 2250   504-589-6685
New Orleans, LA 70130   Fax: 504-589-2339
www.sba.gov/la
The Louisiana Small Business Administration Office delivers a variety of programs and services, such as startup and operational assistance through small business training and counseling, financial assistance for startup's, business opportunities and much more.

Maine

* Department of Economic and Community Development

Office of Business Development   207-624-9804
59 State House Station   Fax: 207-287-5701
Augusta, ME 04333   TTY: 207-287-2656
www.econdevmaine.com/biz-develop.htm
Business Answers: 800-872-3838
Maine's toll-free business information hotline provides rapid responses to questions about doing business in Maine.

One-Stop Business License Center: This central clearinghouse for state regulatory information helps simplify the process of complying with state business regulations. Callers may request business license and permit applications, as well as information on state regulations.

Business Answers/Small Business Advocate: Serves as a central clearinghouse of information regarding business assistance programs and services available to state businesses. Also helps small businesses resolve problems they may be experiencing with state regulatory agencies.

Maine Products Marketing Program: Provides marketing assistance to producers of Maine-made consumer goods. Members of the program promote their message of Maine quality through the use of product tags and labels, literature and package design, which carry the unified theme, "Maine Made America's Best." The program also publishes the "Maine Made" Buyer's Guide, which is sent to more than 25,000 wholesale buyers. {www.mainemade.com}

* Rural Development Administration (RDA)

967 Illinois Ave.
P.O. Box 405   207-990-9160
Bangor, ME 04402-0405   Fax: 207-990-9165
www.rurdev.usda.gov/me

Maine's Rural Business-Cooperative Services Office offers several programs to assist businesses in Maine.

- *Direct Business and Industry Program*: Loans are made to businesses to benefit rural areas. The primary purpose of this program is to create and maintain employment and improve the economic and environmental climate in rural communities.
- *Guaranteed Business and Industry Programs*: Loans made by conventional lender and guaranteed by the Rural Development Office to improve, develop or finance business, industry and employment.
- *Rural Business Enterprise Grants:* Grants are made to facilitate the development of small emerging businesses in rural areas with populations less than or equal to 25,000.
- *Intermediary Relending Program*: The objective of IRP is to finance business facilities and community development projects in rural areas with populations of less than 25,000. Loans are made to intermediaries to relend the funds ultimately to recipients for business facilities or community development.
- *Cooperative Assistance Program*: The cooperative assistance program provides assistance to help recipients form new cooperatives and improve the operations of existing cooperatives.

* Apprenticeship Program

Kenneth L. Hardt
Maine Apprenticeship Program
Maine Department of Labor
55 State House Station   207-624-6390
Augusta, ME 04333-0055   Fax: 207-624-6499
Email: k.skip.hardt@state.me.us

Maine's Apprenticeship Program provides customized training and instruction so workers can obtain professional credentials. Many of Maine's larger firms have taken advantage of this innovative workforce development program, which will underwrite 50% of apprenticeship-related tuition for new and existing employees.

* School-to-Work Initiatives

Susan Brown
Center for Career Development
Maine Technical College System
SMVTC, Fort Road   207-767-5210, ext. 111
South Portland, ME 04106   Fax: 207-767-2542
Email: susan@ccd.mtcs.tec.me.us

www.mtcs.net

School-to-Work Initiatives: This public-private partnership is designed to provide Maine industry with a competitive workforce. The program employs three strategies to train Maine youth. These include:
- Maine Career Advantage: a nationally recognized two-year combination of business internship and integrated academics, including one free year at the technical college level.
- Registered Pre-Apprenticeship: four years of employer-driven high school academics, coupled with two summers of on-the-job training. This culminates in permanent employment and a Registered Apprenticeship upon high school graduation.
- Tech Prep: sequential, industry-driven academic and technical training beginning in eleventh grade and progressing through completion of Certificate, Associate and/or Bachelor Degrees.

* Maine Quality Centers Program

Maine Quality Centers
Center for Career Development
2 Fort Road   207-767-5210, ext. 4107
South Portland, ME 04106   Fax: 207-629-4048
www.mccs.me.edu/mqc.html

This is an economic development initiative of the Maine Technical College System, which provides new and expanding businesses with a trained and ready workforce. New or expanding firms creating at least eight new full-time jobs with benefits may be eligible to receive state financing for 100% of pre-hire classroom training.

* Governor's Training Initiative

Bureau of Employment Services
Maine Department of Labor   207-624-6390
55 State House Station   888-457-8883
Augusta, ME 04333-0055   Fax: 207-624-6499
Email: caroline.p.morgan@state.me.us
www.mainecareercenter.com

This program reimburses training costs when they are required for business expansion, retention or unique upgrading issues. Businesses that meet eligibility requirements may receive reimbursements for on-the-job training, competitive retooling, specialized recruitment, workplace literacy, high-performance skills or customized technical training.

* Safety Education and Training

Safety Works!
Bureau of Labor Standards
Maine Department of Labor   877-SAFE345
45 State House Station   207-624-6400
Augusta, ME 04333-0045   Fax: 207-624-6449
Email: alan.c.hinsey@state.me.us
www.state.me.us/labor/bls/blsmain.htm

At no cost to a company, Maine's Bureau of Labor Standards provides customized health and safety training, site evaluation and technical support. Priority is given to small and mid-sized employers and large employers with documented health and safety problems

* Maine Revenue Services

24 State House Station
Augusta, ME 04333   207-287-2336
www.state.me.us/revenue

Business Equipment Property Tax Reimbursement Program: Program reimbursed, for up to 12 years, all local property taxes paid on eligible business property.

Employee-Assisted Day Care Credit: Provides an income tax credit of up to $5,000. The credit is limited to the lesser of $5,000, 20% of the cost incurred or $100 for each child of an employee enrolled on a full-time basis or for each full-time equivalent throughout the tax year.

Employer Provided Long-term Care Benefits Credit: Provides an income tax credit equal to the lesser of $5,000, 20% of the cost incurred or $100 per employee covered by a long-term care policy as part of a benefits package.

Research and Development Sales Tax Exemption: Sales of machinery and equipment used by the purchaser directly and exclusively in research and development by any business is eligible for a sales tax exemption.

Fuel and Electricity Sales Tax Exemption: Program exempts any business from sales tax 95% of the sales price of all fuel and electricity purchased for use at the manufacturing facility.

Business Property Tax Reimbursement Program: Maine reimburses what companies pay in local property taxes on facilities built after April 1, 1995. Taxes on this property may be reimbursed by the state for a maximum of 12 years. The definition of qualified business property for this program is broad and specified by law.

Maine Seed Capital Tax Credit Program: FAME authorizes state income tax credits to investors in an amount equal to 30% of the cash equity they provide to eligible Maine businesses.

* Maine International Trade Center

Perry Newman, Trade Director
Maine International Trade Center
511 Congress Street   207-541-7400
Portland, ME 04101   Fax: 207-541-7420
Email: newman@ mitc.com
www.mitc.com

Maine offers businesses and organizations international assistance through the Maine International Trade Center. The Trade Center's mission is to expand Maine's economy through increased international trade in goods and services and related activities such as:
- Trade missions
- Training programs in international trade
- Conferences, such as a major Trade Day event
- Publications, including the Trade Center newsletter
- Special member-only programs and one-on-one counseling and technical service assistance
- Comprehensive international library resources

* Finance Authority of Maine (FAME)

David Markovchick, Director of Business Development
5 Community Dr.   800-228-3734
P.O. Box 949   207-623-3263
Augusta, ME 04332-0949   Fax: 207-623-0095
www.famemaine.com

Commercial Loan Insurance Program: Designed to promote economic development by providing business borrowers access to capital that would otherwise be denied by lender due to unacceptable level of credit risk. Must be exhibit responsible ability to repay loan. Insures up to 90 percent or $7,000,000 of a commercial loan. Loan proceeds may be used for purchase of, and improvements to real estate, and machinery and equipment.

SMART-E Bond Program: Tax-exempt, fixed-asset financing for manufacturing facilities. SMART-E will finance up to 90 percent of a loan by grouping it with other similar loans and selling tax-exempt bonds to finance them. Maximum loan is $7 million. Assets that can be financed with loan proceeds include land and depreciable assets.

Potato Marketing Improvement Fund: Provides direct loans to potato growers and packers to construct modern storages, packing lines, and sprout inhibitor facilities. Long-term, fixed-rate loans at below market interest rates are available to help finance construction or improvements to storage and packing facilities. Participating loans can finance between 45 and 55 percent of the costs of eligible construction and improvements.

Linked Investment Program for Agriculture and Small Business: State funds are invested in financial institutions which then lend out funds at reduced interest rates to Maine farmers and small business people.

Occupational Safety Loan Fund Program: Targeted direct loans to Maine businesses seeking to make workplace safety improvements. A business may borrow up to $50,000 for up to 10 years. Interest rate is 3 percent fixed. Funds can be used to purchase, improve, or erect equipment which reduces workplace hazards or promotes health and safety of employees.

Export Financing Services:
- *Working Capital Insurance* provides additional security to bankers.
- *Export Credit Umbrella Insurance* reduces international credit risks, allows an exporter to offer credit terms to foreign buyers in a competitive market, and offers the opportunity to obtain current cash flow against foreign receivables. Provided by the Export-Import bank of the United States (Eximbank).
- Either the Finance Authority of Maine (FAME) or Eximbank is responsible for up to 100 percent of a loan made by a financial institution to the exporter.

Underground Oil Storage Tank Removal and Replacement Program: Provides 100% loan insurance to lenders, or direct loans to business borrowers, for the removal, replacement and disposal of underground tanks for oil, petroleum products or petroleum by-products. Loans must be used for the removal, replacement and/or disposal of storage tanks for oil, petroleum products or petroleum by-products, or for installation of air quality equipment required by state law.

Economic Recovery Loan Program: Direct lending program designed to assist small businesses in their effort to remain viable during difficult economic times. The program is available to assist both existing firms and new business ventures. Borrower requests should be the minimum amount necessary to complete the project under consideration, not to exceed $200,000.

Overboard Discharge Replacement Program: Provides 100% loan insurance to lenders on loans made for the removal, rehabilitation or replacement of certain wastewater disposal systems which result in discharges into fresh or salt water. Maximum insured loan under this program is $1,000,000. Interest rates and loan terms are negotiated between the borrower and lender. Loan term may not exceed 10 years.

Major Business Expansion Program: Provides taxable bond financing of up to $25,000,000 for major industrial or commercial projects.

Waste Reduction and Recycling Loan Program: The Authority will sometimes request that businesses intending to finance projects designed to reduce and recycle waste submit proposals for loans of up to $100,000.

Revenue Obligation Securities Program: FAME is authorized to issue tax-exempt Industrial Revenue Bonds to finance any project authorized under the U.S. Internal Revenue Code, Section 103, including manufacturing facilities, solid waste projects and loans for nonprofit corporations. Proceeds may be used for land, buildings, machinery and equipment, financing and interest charges, engineering, legal services, surveys, cost estimates and studies. Offers low financing rates.

Adaptive Equipment Loan Program: Provides low interest loans to assist disabled persons in becoming more productive member of the community. Businesses may also borrow to make their facilities more accessible to physically challenged individuals. May also be used to enable a business to make physical and structural changes necessary to allow a business to hire disabled workers.

The Agricultural Marketing Loan Program will help natural resource based industries by providing a source of subordinated debt for eligible projects and borrowers. The maximum loan size under this program is $250,000. To be eligible for assistance, projects requesting financing must incorporate new or innovative technology and methodology. For example, it is anticipated that this new loan program will prove helpful to Maine's fledgling cranberry industry and Maine's aquaculture industry.

Maine Seed Capital Tax Credit Program: In order to encourage equity investments in young, dynamic business ventures the Authority may authorize State income tax credits to investors in an amount equal to 30% of the cash equity they provide to certain Maine businesses.

Nutrient Management Program: Eligible Applicant: Any business or individual identified by the State of Maine Department of Agriculture, Food & Rural Resources ("Agriculture") as required by law to upgrade manure and milk room waste containment and handling facilities. Eligible Uses: Proceeds may be used to finance the construction or improvement of livestock manure and milk room waste containment and handling facilities, the associated costs of design and engineering of these facilities, as well as, related equipment that meets the goals of the State's Nutrient Management Plan.

The Plus 1 Computer Loan Program provides lenders with loan insurance on an expedited basis for small business loans for acquisition and installation of computer equipment and software. Since lenders certify that a loan meets specific credit criteria at the time of application and since FAME does not independently underwrite each loan application, all loans meeting the program's credit criteria are promptly approved (within 48 hours). Loans not meeting the credit criteria for the Business Computer Loan Rapid Response Guarantee may be submitted under FAME's Small Business Loan Insurance Program.

Rapid Response Guarantee Program: The Finance Authority of Maine's Rapid Response Guarantee provides lenders with loan insurance on an expedited basis for small business loans

meeting certain minimum credit standards. Since lenders certify that a loan meets specific credit criteria at the time of application and since FAME does not independently underwrite each loan application, all loans meeting the program's credit criteria are promptly approved (within 48 hours). Loans not meeting the credit criteria for the Rapid Response Guarantee may be submitted under FAME's Small Business Loan Insurance Program.

On August 2, 1999, FAME established a Secondary Market for the FAME insured portion of bank loans.

The Small Enterprise Growth Fund was created to provide Maine entrepreneurs with access to "patient" sources of venture capital. Venture capital is typically difficult for Maine small businesses and entrepreneurs to access. This is especially true for smaller projects needing $500,000 or less. Established venture capital firms usually don't invest in increments of less than $500,000.

Waste Oil Furnace Loan Program: an interest rate subsidy to approved lenders who make loans to borrowers to purchase and install an improved waste oil boiler or furnace. Loans may be for up to $5,000 for a term of up to five (5) years. The loan may provide for an interest rate of up to thirteen percent (13%) per annum. The borrower is required to pay an effective interest rate of three percent (3%) per annum on the loan. The Authority will provide a subsidy in an amount which, when invested by the approved lender at an assumed annual return of six percent (6) per annum, will provide the lender with an overall rate of return of thirteen percent (13%).

SMART Bond Program: The Secondary Market Taxable (SMART) Bond Program is similar to the SMART-E Bond Program. It is available (with some exceptions) to those businesses that are not eligible for tax-exempt financing. The process begins when a lending institution provides a business with a loan commitment for acquisition of real estate, equipment or other fixed assets. After reviewing the credit application, FAME may commit to insuring up to 90% of the loan. FAME then helps to place the loan with investors who agree to purchase the insured portion of the loan.

Clean Fuel Vehicle Guarantee: This program provides lenders with loan insurance on loans to businesses for the acquisition or lease of clean fuel vehicles, delivery systems or other clean fuel vehicle components. Funds may be used to cover purchase or lease-related costs.

Dairy Farm Debt Relief Loan Insurance Program: Provides lenders with loan insurance for existing small business loans meeting certain minimum credit standards. The Dairy Farm Debt Relief Program offers up to a 25% leveraged loan insurance. The maximum aggregate insurance is $70,000 per borrower.

Katahdin Loan Insurance Program: Katahdin Loan Insurance Program provides lenders with loan insurance for existing small business loans meeting certain minimum credit standards. The program offers up to a 25% leveraged loan insurance. The maximum aggregate insurance is $50,000 per borrower.

Small Business and Veterans' Small Business Loan Insurance Program: Loan insurance is available for any prudent business activity. This 90% pro-rata or 25% leveraged insurance program is designed to help businesses gain access to commercial credit financing.

Development Fund: This program is designed to provide subordinated financing to businesses. Funds may be used for any prudent business activity that provides a public benefit, including jobs. 5% fixed interest rates for the life of the loan for 40% of project costs up to a maximum loan amount of $200,000.

Energy Conservation Loan Program: This program provides low-interest loans to improve energy efficiency in Maine workplaces.

Intermediary Relending Program: This program is designed to assist qualifying small businesses by providing gap financing for any prudent business activity.

Linked Investments for Commercial Enterprises: The purpose of this program is to reduce borrower's interest expenses.

Regional Economic Development Revolving Loan Program: The Regional Economic Development Revolving Loan program is designed to make loans through Regional Economic Development Agencies for the purpose of creating or retaining jobs. Qualifying businesses must have sales under $5,000,000 or employ fewer than 50 employees.

Regional Economic Development Revolving Loan Program for Daycare: Loans for up to $100,000 for qualifying daycares for physical improvements.

* Department of Agriculture

Food & Rural Resources
Nutrient Management Program Coordinator
State House Station 28
Augusta, ME 04333   207-287-3871
www.state.me.us/agriculture

Eligible Applicant: Any business or individual identified by the State of Maine Department of Agriculture, Food & Rural Resources ("Agriculture") as required by law to upgrade manure and milk room waste containment and handling facilities. Eligible Uses: Proceeds may be used to finance the construction or improvement of livestock manure and milk room waste containment and handling facilities, the associated costs of design and engineering of these facilities, as well as, related equipment that meets the goals of the State's Nutrient Management Plan.

* Maine & Company

P.O. Box 7462
120 Exchange Street   800-871-3485
Portland, ME 04112-7462   Fax: 207-775-6716
www.maineco.org

The State offers several performance based incentives to help attract and retain growing companies. In addition to the statewide incentives outlined below, companies coming to Maine can also take advantage of significant local incentives that may include low priced land, low lease rates, tax increment financing, municipal bond financing, and reimbursement for most personal property tax paid on new machinery and equipment.

Workforce Training: Maine has some of the best training programs in the country. The Maine Quality Centers program provides 100% state-financed education and training for new employees, as well as customized recruitment and guaranteed, fast-track training designed to employer specifications. The Governor's Training Initiative (GTI) offers employers partial reimbursement of training costs for new employees or upgrading existing work force skills.

Property Tax Reimbursement: Companies can be reimbursed for taxes on new machinery and equipment. Through the Business Property Tax Reimbursement program, the state may reimburse a company for as many as 12 years. In addition, companies may be eligible for real and property tax reimbursements from communities through tax increment financing.

Maine Income Tax Reimbursements: Companies hiring 5 or more people can receive as much as 75 percent reimbursement on Maine income tax withholdings from new employees. Those employers who provide benefits and pay above average wages are likely to qualify for this program, known as Employment Tax Increment Financing (ETIF).

Tax Increment Financing: Businesses making significant capital investment in a community may be eligible for partial property tax refunds from the municipality.

Sales Tax Exemptions: Maine sales tax exemptions are available for manufacturing, research and development, custom computer programming and biotechnology.

Investment Tax Credit: Employers can save as much as $500,000 per year for seven years by investing $5 million in personal property and creating at least 100 new jobs. Tax credits apply toward Maine income tax.

Small Enterprise Growth Fund: This venture capital fund provides financing for potential high growth companies with fewer than 50 employees or gross sales of less than $5 million within the past 12 months.

* Loans For Farmers

Farm Service Agency
U.S. Department of Agriculture
967 Illinois Ave.
Bangor, ME 04401   207-990-9100
http://www.fsa.usda.gov/me/me.htm

The Farm Service Agency provides Direct and Guaranteed Loans to farmers through a variety of programs, including:

Farm Ownership Loans: purchase farmland, construct or repair buildings and other fixtures, and promote soil and water conservation. Up to $200,000.

Operating Loans: purchase items needed for a successful farm operation, such as livestock, farm equipment, feed, seed, fuel, farm chemicals, insurance, and other operating expenses. Can also be used to pay for minor improvements. Up to $200,000.

Beginning Farmer and Rancher Loans: provides funds to beginning and farmers and ranchers who are unable to obtain financing elsewhere.

Downpayment Farm Ownership Loans for Beginning Farmers: helps beginning farmers and ranchers purchase a farm or ranch. Also provides a way for retiring farmers to transfer their land to a future generation of farmers and ranchers. Applicant must have a downpayment of 10% and FSA with finance 40%, with the remaining balance from a commercial lender. Purchase price cannot exceed $250,000.

Loans to Socially Disadvantaged Farmers/Ranchers: helps socially disadvantaged applicants buy and operate family-size farms and ranches.

Youth Loans: Made to youths to establish and operate income-producing projects with the participation in 4-H clubs, Future Farmers of America, and similar organizations. Up to $5,000.

Emergency Loan Assistance: provides loans to help producers recover from production and physical losses due to drought, flooding, and other natural disasters, or quarantine. Up to $500,000.

Beginning Farmer and Rancher Land Contract Guarantee Pilot Program: "prompt payment guarantee" from FSA. FSA will provide payment to seller two times if the beginning farmer does not pay. Program is tested in IN, IA, ND, OR, PA and WI.

Farm Ownership and Operating Loan Guarantees: FSA will guarantee loans up to $782,000.

* Small Business Administration (SBA)

Edmund S. Muskie Building
68 Sewall St., Room 512   207-622-8274
Augusta, ME 04330   Fax: 207-622-8277
www.sba.gov/me

Trade Missions: The SBA participates by underwriting private firms and assisting them to enter trade missions with other Federal Agencies. SBA promotes and assists in cost share monies to a limited degree. Trade Shows have been sponsored in Europe, Asia, Mid East, Africa and North America.

The Maine Small Business Administration Office delivers a variety of programs and services, such as startup and operational assistance through small business training and counseling, financial assistance for startup's, business opportunities and much more.

* Maine Technology Institute

2E Mechanic Street   207-582-4790
Gardiner, ME 04345   Fax: 207-582-4772
www.mainetechnology.org

Marine Infrastructure and Technology Fund: The Marine Infrastructure and Technology Fund provides up to $1,000,000 to private nonprofit companies and state agencies that are engaged in marine research.

Marine Biomedical Research Fund: The fund provides grants for capital and expenses for eligible nonprofit biomedical research labs in the state of Maine.

Seed Grant Program: 1:1 matching grants of up to $10,000 are available to support very early stages of product development, commercialization or business planning and development.

Development Awards: 1:1 matching awards of up to $500,000 are available to support research and development of new products or services in Maine's targeted technology regions.

Cluster Enhancement Awards: 1:1 matching awards of up to $500,000 per project to help stimulate and support the formation and growth of eligible technology businesses.

Renewable Resource Matching Funds Award Program (RRMF): Investments of up to $50,000 per project to match funding for approved Cluster Enhancement Awards.

Maryland

* Department of Business and Economic Development

217 East Redwood St.   410-767-6300
Baltimore, MD 21202   888-CHOOSE MD
www.mdbusiness.state.md.us   Fax: 410-333-6792
TDD/TTY: 410-333-6926

This office can provide information and expertise in dealing with state, federal, and local agencies. They also have information on financing programs and other services offered by the state government.

Workforce Resources: Maryland offers several training and grants for training programs to meet a variety of workforce needs. The following are two of their many programs:
1. Maryland Job Service: Provides recruitment and screening services based on the specifications of a company at no costs. It maintains a state/ nationwide data bank of job seekers and acts as the state's labor exchange agent to match qualified workers with available employment opportunities.
2. Partnership for Workforce Quality: Targets training grants to manufacturing firms with 500 or fewer employees to upgrade skills for new technologies.

Industrial Training Program: Provides incentive grants for the development and training of new employees in firms locating or expanding their workforce in Maryland. MITP reimburses companies for up to 100% of the direct costs associated with training programs customized to the work process.

Technology Support: Helps companies diversify into new markets. In addition, the office: provides technical assistance to firms seeking to commercialize new technologies; facilitates collaboration between businesses and universities and federal laboratories; and oversees the Strategic Assistance Fund, which provides matching funds to support the cost of private sector consultants to aid in both strategic plan development and new market strategies.

Investment Financing Programs: Provide for direct investment in technology-driven Maryland-based companies through three programs. All three provide a novel alternative to grants, direct loans or credit enhancements available through other State financing programs. All three involve the use of private sector capital, including venture capital, on a co-investment basis, and while having an underlying economic development agenda, are capital gains and return-on-investment driven.

Enterprise Investment Fund: An investment financing tool that enables DBED to make direct equity investments in "second -stage" technology driven companies located in the state. Investments range from $150,000 to $250,000 per entity. Investment decisions are based on the potential for return on investment, as well as the promotion of broad-based economic development and job creation initiatives.

Day Care Special Loan Fund: Direct loans up to $10,000 for minor renovations and upgrades to meet standards.

Maryland Industrial Development Financing Authority (MIDFA): Available to industrial/commercial businesses except certain retail establishments. Normal project range is $35,000 to $5 million. Insured up to lower of 80% of loan or $1 million. The amount of insurance varies with each loan and is determined after discussing the lender's needs. Typically, MIDFA insures from 20% to 50% of the loan.

Seafood & Aquaculture Loan Fund: Available to individuals or businesses involved in seafood processing or aquaculture. Normal Project Range: $20,000 to $800,000. Maximum Program Participation: The lesser of $250,000 or 80% of the total investment needed.

Contract Financing Program: Eligible applicants are businesses owned 70% or more by socially and economically disadvantaged persons. Normal Project Range: Up to $500,000. Maximum Program Participation: Direct up to $500,000. Loan guarantee up to 90% not to exceed a maximum participation of $500,000. Approved Uses of Funds: Working capital required to begin, continue and complete government or public utility contracts. Acquisition of machinery or equipment to perform contracts. Interest Rates: For guaranteed loans, maximum rate is prime plus 2%. For direct loans, maximum is 15% .

Long Term Guaranty Program: Eligible applicants are businesses owned 70% or more by socially and economically disadvantaged persons. Must have 18 successive months of experience in the trade or business for which financing is sought. Normal Project Range: $50,000 to $1 million. Maximum Program Participation: Loan guarantees may not exceed the lesser of 80% of the loan or $600,000.

Surety Bond Program: Eligible applicants are independently owned small businesses generally employing fewer than 500 full-time employees or those with gross annual sales of less than $50 million. Normal Project Range: Guaranty Program - None. Direct Bonding Program - Up to $750,000. Maximum Program Participation: Guaranty Program - Guarantees up to 90% of face value of the bond not to exceed a total exposure of $900,000. Direct Bonding Program - Can directly issue bonds not to exceed $750,000. Approved Uses of Funds: Guaranty Program - Guarantees reimbursement of losses on a bid, payment or performance bond required in connection with projects where the majority of funds are from government or a regulated public utility. Direct Bonding Program - Issues bid, payment or performance bonds on projects where the majority of funds are from government or a regulated public utility.

Equity Participation Investment Program - Technology Component & Business Acquisition Component: Eligible applicants are technology based businesses and business acquisitions which will be owned 70% or more by disabled, socially or economically disadvantaged persons. Normal Project Range: $100,000 to $3 million. Maximum Program Participation: The lesser of $250,000 or 80% of the total investment needed.

Equity Participation Investment Program - Franchise Component: Eligible applicants are franchises that are or will be owned 70% or more by disabled, socially or economically disadvantaged persons. Must have at least 10% of total project cost in owner's equity. Normal Project Range: $50,000 to $1.5 million. Maximum Program Participation: Equity investments or loans up to 45% of initial investment or $100,000, whichever is less.

Challenge Investment Program: Eligible applicants are technology-driven companies, with principal activity located in Maryland; applicants must have complete business plan as a minimum requirement. Size of Investment: $50,000.

Enterprise Investment Program: Eligible applicants are technology-driven companies, with principal activity located in Maryland; applicants must have complete business plan as a minimum requirement. Size of Investment: $150,000 to $500,000.

Foreign Offices & Representatives: Network of foreign offices and representatives provide exporters with in-country resources and expertise around the globe. These foreign offices in China, Japan, the Netherlands and Taiwan -- and representatives in Argentina, Brazil, Chile, Israel and Mexico -- deliver support in the following areas: agent/distributor searches and business appointments; credit reports, competitor analysis and regulatory information; marketing and logistical support at trade shows; market research and analysis.

Day Care Facilities Guarantee Fund: Eligible applicants are individuals or business entities involved in the development or expansion of day care facilities for infants and children, the elderly, and disabled persons of all ages. Normal Project Range: Up to $1 million. Maximum Program Participation: Loan guarantee up to 80%.

Child Care Facilities Direct Loan Fund: Eligible applicants are individuals, business entities involved in the development of day care facilities for children, either center-based or home-based. Normal Project Range: Minimum $15,000. Maximum Program Participation: Maximum of 50% of fixed assets.

Child Care Special Loan Fund: Eligible applicants are individuals, business entities for expanding or improving child care facilities, meeting state and local licensing requirements and improving the quality of care. Normal Project Range: $1,000 to $10,000. Maximum Program Participation: Direct loans up to $10,000.

Governor's Office of Business Advocacy and Small Business Assistance (GOBA): GOBA helps in the development and growth of small businesses in the state. Small and minority businesses are connected to needed resources, provide information, and offered assistance from permits and licensing to the creation of a business plan. 410-767-0545

Business License Information System (BLIS): This online system quickly connects a business to information on permits and licenses that are needed to start, relocate or expand in Maryland. Instant information on business licenses, occupation licenses, permitting information and business start-up information is also available.

Maryland With Pride: Companies whose products are grown, processed, assembled, manufactured or handcrafted in Maryland can benefit from this program. Those businesses can register to use the Maryland With Pride trademark on product packaging, advertising, web sites, stationery, vehicles and buildings. They are also given exclusive marketing opportunities. 410-767-6519

Department of General Services Small Business Preference Program: With this program, small businesses are able to receive part of the State's total purchases of equipment, materials and supplies. Those businesses that are certified with the program may be eligible to receive a 5% award preference on designated solicitations. 410-767-4621

Smart Growth Economic Development Infrastructure Fund (One Maryland): The fund provides a financial resource in cases where the need to develop industrial sites is not fully met by the private sector. Loans are made to counties or municipalities at below market interest rates and are secured by the full faith and credit of the borrowing government. Loans may be used for the acquisition of land, development of industrial parks, improvements to infrastructure of potential industrial sites, installation of utilities, and the rehabilitation of existing buildings for business incubators. The sites must be in a Priority Funding Area.

Sunny Day Fund: Created to allow the State to take advantage of extraordinary economic development opportunities where assistance from other resources are constrained by program design, timing, or available resources. The fund has been an extremely valuable tool in both business retention and recruiting. Maryland has taken advantage of opportunities with rapid and creative proposals that have assisted in the establishment of several high-profile private sector enterprises, including prized technology and research companies. The project must create employment, especially in those areas of high unemployment. The participants must provide a minimum capital investment of at least five times the amount of the Sunny Day assistance.

Maryland Economic Development Assistance Authority and Fund: This incentive program offers five financing means where the assistance goes to the business community and political jurisdictions. The applicants are restricted to businesses located in a specified area and an industry sector. Assistance cannot generally exceed 70% of the total project costs. If the recipient is a Maryland Economic Corporation (MEDCO), they can receive 100% financing. The funding programs are:
- *Significant Strategic Economic Development Opportunities:* This project provides eligible industries with a significant economic development opportunity on a statewide or regional level. Assistance is provided to a business through a loan where the maximum amount cannot exceed the lesser of $10 million or 20% of the current fund balance.
- *Local Economic Development Opportunity:* Designed for businesses that provide valuable economic development opportunities to the jurisdiction in which it is located and is a priority for the governing body in that area. Loans are for up to $5 million; conditional loans and grants may be up to $2 million. The business must be sponsored by the local jurisdiction and must participate by way of guarantee or a direct loan or a grant equal to 10% of the State's assistance.
- *Direct Assistance to Jurisdiction or MEDCO:* Financial assistance to local jurisdictions for local economic development needs.
- *Regional or Local Revolving Loan Fund:* Grants to local jurisdictions to help capitalize local revolving loan funds.
- *Special Purposes Loans:* Specified funding initiatives that are deemed critical to the States' economic health and development. The special purpose initiatives include: Seafood and Aquaculture, Animal Waste, and Day Care Center programs. 407-767-6353

Strategic Assistance Fund: SAF was originally a grant, which offered assistance to businesses with defense conversion and helped dislocated defense entrepreneurs. SAF is now a state funded program offering businesses marketing assistance with new products, product diversification, new markets, or market expansion. Projects may include defense diversification opportunities, diversification of commercial products into related markets, commercialization of new technologies, expansion into international markets and more. Awards range from $5,000 to $25,000 and can be made to individual businesses or groups. 410-767-0095

Maryland Community Colleges' Business Training Network (MCCBTN): Maryland Community College's Business Training Network is a one-stop for businesses interested in workforce training. {www.marylandtraining.com}

The Maryland Industrial Training Program (MITP): The Industrial training Program works with other state and local agencies to assist in the recruitment, assessment and placement of new employees with participating companies.

Maryland Economic Adjustment Fund (MEAF): The Economic Adjustment Fund assists businesses in the State with the modernization of manufacturing operations, the development of commercial applications for technology and exploring and entering new markets.

* Neighborhood Business Development Program (NBDP)

Maryland Department of Housing and Community
   Development
Neighborhood Business Development Program
100 Community Place   410-514-7288
Crownsville, MD 21032   Fax: 410-685-8270
www.dhcd.state.md.us

Initiative to help stimulate Maryland's established, older communities, NBDP provides flexible, gap financing (up to 50% of total project cost) for many small businesses starting up or expanding in targeted urban, suburban or rural revitalization areas throughout the State. Terms and conditions are established on an individual basis. Financing ranging from $25,000 to $500,000, up to 50% of total project cost, where other funds clearly are unavailable.

* Development Credit Fund, Inc.

2530 N. Charles St., Suite 200   410-467-7500
Baltimore, MD 21218-4627   Fax: 410-467-7988
www.developmentcredit.com

Development Credit Fund Program: Loan guarantees for businesses owned by socially and economically disadvantaged persons. Must show experience in the trade. Projects range from $5,000 to $575,000. Proceeds may be used for working capital, acquisition of machinery and equipment acquisition, and business acquisitions, business real estate. Interest rates are variable, none more than 2 percent over prime rate.

* Community Financing Group

Department of Business and Economic Development
Redwood Tower
217 East Redwood, 22nd Floor
Baltimore, MD 21202   410-767-6352
www.choosemaryland.org

Community Development Block Grant: Available to cities and counties for the commercial rehabilitation of existing buildings or structures used for business, commercial, or industrial purposes. Grants and loans of between $200,000 and $1 million can be made. Every $15,000 of grant funds invested must create at least one full-time job, and at least 51 percent of the jobs created must be for low- and moderate-income families.

* USDA/Rural Development

4607 South DuPont Highway
P.O. Box 400   302-697-4300
Camden, Delaware 19934   Fax: 302-697-4390

Email: Jack.Walls@de.usda.gov
www.rurdev.usda.gov/md

The Community & Business Programs Division consists of the Rural Utilities Service (RUS) and the Rural Business & Cooperative Service (RBS). RUS programs assist rural America in building infrastructure by providing loans and grants for water and wastewater disposal systems, solid waste disposal systems, storm drainage systems and advanced telecommunications. RBS programs help provide financial as well as technical assistance to businesses, nonprofit organizations, educational institutions and cooperatives. The financial assistance is provided in the form of loans, guaranteed loans and grants. It is the intent of the RBS to enhance the quality of life for rural Americans by providing leadership in building competitive businesses and cooperatives.

* Tri-County Council for Western Maryland, Inc.

113 Baltimore St., Suite 302   301-777-2159
Cumberland, MD 21502   Fax: 301-777-2495
www.tccwmd.org

The Tri-County Council Revolving Loan Fund (TCC-RLF) will stimulate and support the development of small to mid-sized businesses in order to diversify the economy and maintain and expand employment opportunities in the Western Maryland-Appalachian area. This will be achieved by providing low cost, flexible financing designed to fill gaps in the local capital market.

* The Dingman Center for Entrepreneurship

Robert H. Smith School of Business
University of Maryland
3570 Van Munching Hall   301-405-9545
College Park, MD 20742   Fax: 301-314-7973
Email: dingman@rhsmith.umd.edu
http://dingham.rhsmith.umd.edu

The Dingman Center for Entrepreneurship facilitates, supports, and encourages entrepreneurship and new enterprise growth in the mid-Atlantic region through outreach, education and research.

* Technology Advancement Program (TAP)

Engineering Research Center
University of Maryland
1105 TAP Building
387 Technology Drive   301-314-7803
College Park, MD 20742   Fax: 301-226-5378
www.tap.umd.edu

Incubator facilities offer space and support services for start up and growing companies. By offering companies a supportive environment, the incubator allows a company to reduce start-up obligations while concentrating its limited resources on product development and bringing its product to the marketplace. Incubators are often best suited for businesses engaged in developing technically-oriented products with commercial potential.

* Maryland Department of the Environment

1800 Washington Blvd.   800-633-6101
Baltimore, MD 21230   410-537-3000
www.mde.state.md.us

The Environmental Permits Service Center, EPSC, which was established in 1994, is a service arm of the Department designed to provide assistance to businesses. The primary responsibility of the EPSC is to track permit applications and streamline the Department's review of permit applications. The EPSC staff work in a multimedia fashion to assist businesses who need environmental permits for a combination of air, water, and waste issues.

The department's Small Business Assistance Program is here to help your small business with environmental permitting and compliance. This free assistance is available to any small business, which means practically any independently owned and operated business with less than 100 employees is eligible. The small business assistance program can help with:
- Understanding environmental requirements
- Getting the proper forms
- Filling out permit applications
- Filling out compliance forms

The Pollution Prevention Program provides information to businesses on how to eliminate potential pollution at the source, which often results in saving businesses money.

* Loans For Farmers

Farm Service Agency
U.S. Department of Agriculture
Rivers Center
8335 Guilford Ave., Suite E   410-381-4550
Columbia, MD 21046   Fax: 10-692-4860
http://www.fsa.usda.gov/md/

The Farm Service Agency provides Direct and Guaranteed Loans to farmers through a variety of programs, including:

Farm Ownership Loans: purchase farmland, construct or repair buildings and other fixtures, and promote soil and water conservation. Up to $200,000.

Operating Loans: purchase items needed for a successful farm operation, such as livestock, farm equipment, feed, seed, fuel, farm chemicals, insurance, and other operating expenses. Can also be used to pay for minor improvements. Up to $200,000.

Beginning Farmer and Rancher Loans: provides funds to beginning and farmers and ranchers who are unable to obtain financing elsewhere.

Downpayment Farm Ownership Loans for Beginning Farmers: helps beginning farmers and ranchers purchase a farm or ranch. Also provides a way for retiring farmers to transfer their land to a future generation of farmers and ranchers. Applicant must have a downpayment of 10% and FSA with finance 40%, with the remaining balance from a commercial lender. Purchase price cannot exceed $250,000.

Loans to Socially Disadvantaged Farmers/Ranchers: helps socially disadvantaged applicants buy and operate family-size farms and ranches.

Youth Loans: Made to youths to establish and operate income-producing projects with the participation in 4-H clubs, Future Farmers of America, and similar organizations. Up to $5,000.

Emergency Loan Assistance: provides loans to help producers recover from production and physical losses due to drought, flooding, and other natural disasters, or quarantine. Up to $500,000.

Beginning Farmer and Rancher Land Contract Guarantee Pilot Program: "prompt payment guarantee" from FSA. FSA will provide payment to seller two times if the beginning farmer does not pay. Program is tested in IN, IA, ND, OR, PA and WI.

Farm Ownership and Operating Loan Guarantees: FSA will guarantee loans up to $782,000.

* Small Business Administration

City Crescent Bldg., 6th Floor
10 S. Howard St.   410-962-4392
Baltimore, MD 21201   Fax: 410-962-1805
www.sba.gov/md

The Maryland Small Business Administration Office delivers a variety of programs and services, such as startup and operational assistance through small business training and counseling, financial assistance for startup's, business opportunities and much more.

* Governor's Office of Minority Affairs

6 Saint Paul Street, Suite 1502   410-767-8232
Baltimore, MD 21202   Fax: 410-333-7568
www.oma.state.md.us

Massachusetts

* Massachusetts Office of Business Development

10 Park Plaza, 3rd Floor   617-973-8600
Boston, MA 02116   800-5-CAPITAL
www.state.ma.us/mobd   Fax: 617-973-8797

Through five regional offices, they will advise and counsel businesses and individuals in utilizing federal, state, and local finance programs established to help businesses with their capital formation needs.

One-Stop Business Centers: Offers a streamlined approach to economic development assistance. Offices located throughout the state are staffed with professionals who know about Massachusetts' programs and opportunities for businesses throughout the state's diverse regions.

Economic Development Incentive Program (EDIP): To stimulate economic development in distressed areas, attract new businesses, and encourage existing businesses to expand in Massachusetts.

Business Finance Specialists: Assists companies with financing targeted to urban and economically disadvantaged areas through the Community Development Finance Corporation and other public funds.

One-Stop Permitting Program: For all construction-related, state-issued permits. Project Managers act as advocates, assisting with identifying all required permits and moving the application through the entire process.

Starting a Business in Massachusetts: A comprehensive guide for business owners available from MOBD.

The Emerging Technology Fund (ETF): A useful tool for economic growth for technology based companies. Targeting the fields of biotechnology, advanced materials, electronics, medical, telecommunications and environmental technologies, the fund provides companies in these industries

with a greater opportunity to obtain debt financing. Loans can be guaranteed for tenant build-out, construction or expansion of facilities and equipment purchased for up to $1.5 million or 50% of the aggregate debt, whichever is less. Loans are also provided for hard asset-owned facilities and equipment, with a maximum amount of $2.5 million or 33 1/3% of the aggregate debt, whichever is less.

State Office of Minority and Women Business Assistance (SOMWBA): Certifies companies as minority or women-owned or controlled, and publishes a directory listing of verified firms. SOMWBA provides management and technical assistance seminars and workshops for minority and women entrepreneurs on a wide variety of business topics.

Minority Business Financing: A MOBD Business Finance Specialist can guide a company to several targeted financing programs including the Community Development Finance Corporation's Urban Initiative Fund, the Economic Development Fund and others.

* Rural Development Administration

USDA Rural Development in Southern New England
451 West Street, Suite 2   413-253-4300
Amherst, MA 01002-2999   Fax: 413-253-4347
www.rurdev.usda.gov/ma

Business Development Programs

This type of assistance is available in rural areas which are outside the boundary of a city or town of 50,000 or more inhabitants and its immediately adjacent urbanized area.

Business and Industry Loans (B&I): Loans are made to improve, develop or finance business, industry and employment and improve the economic and environmental climate in rural communities, including pollution abatement and control. The objective is achieved principally through bolstering a loan made by a private lender with guarantees by the federal government. Direct loans are also available on a limited basis. The funds may be used for real estate purchase or improvement, equipment or capital.

Rural Business Enterprise Grants (RBEG): Grants are made to assist public bodies and nonprofit corporations to finance and facilitate development of small and emerging private business enterprises. Small and emerging businesses have 50 or less employees and less than $1.0 million in gross revenues. Grants are primarily to be used by eligible nonprofits or public entities to provide technical assistance or establish a revolving loan fund. Revolving loan funds can provide micro-loans to small business which may be for the purchase of land, construction of facilities, and other business purposes.

Intermediary Relending Program Loans (IRP): Loans are made to eligible intermediaries (nonprofit or public entities) who in turn provide loans to ultimate recipients for business facilities and community development in a rural area. The interest rate on the loan to the intermediary is one percent with a term of up to 30 years. Eligible applicants must have a record of successfully assisting rural businesses, including experience in making and servicing commercial loans.

* Massachusetts Site Finder Service

Massachusetts Alliance for Economic Development
25 Research Drive   617-247-7800
Westborough, MA 01582   Fax: 617-247-3337
www.massecon.com

Offers confidential, statewide searches for industrial land or buildings to fit defined specifications for expanding businesses. MOBD can also provide up-to-date Community Profiles of communities being considered as a business location. Information provided includes the local tax structure, local permitting requirements, and a demographic profile of area residents.

* Massachusetts Export Center

Massachusetts Export Center
State Transportation Building
10 Park Plaza, Suite 4510   617-973-8664
Boston, MA 02116   Fax: 617-973-8681
www.state.ma.us/export

The Massachusetts Export Center is part of the Massachusetts Small Business Development Center Network (MSBDC). The Export Center operates four offices that are strategically located throughout the state to assist companies locally. The Export Center provides targeted, high-impact services for exporters including: Export Counseling and Technical Assistance, International Market Research and Assessment, International Business Development Assistance, Export Training Programs and Export Publications.

* Massachusetts Department of Food and Agriculture

251 Causeway Street, Suite 500   617-626-1700
Boston, MA 02114   Fax: 617-626-1850
www.state.ma.us/dfa

The Massachusetts Department of Agricultural Resources' mission is to support, promote and enhance the long-term viability of Massachusetts's agriculture. They offer a variety of Technical Assistance and Resource Programs including:

Agriculture Business Training Program: The Agriculture Business Training Program uses several training approaches to help farmers understand their financial situation, plan their operations, track performance and project the effects of anticipated changes. Chief among these is a 10-session, nationally recognized next-level training course for agricultural entrepreneurs entitled "Tilling The Soil of Opportunity".

Agricultural Marketing Grants Program: The Department's Agricultural Marketing Grant Program provides agricultural organizations the opportunity to receive matching grant funds to assist in their promotional efforts. Grants range from $500 to $15,000. All grant recipients are required to acknowledge the Department's support and/or use the "Massachusetts Grown…and Fresher!" or "Mass. Made with Pride" logos in order to receive grant funds. 617-626-1750

Agro-Envronmental Technology Grant Program: The Agro Environmental Technology Grant Program is designed to address agriculturally related environmental concerns and agricultural development needs and opportunities. Through an annual request for proposals, the Department will consider projects which must have practical commercial application involving new or alternative technologies, practices or organizational arrangements which will stimulate expanded agricultural development, economic activity and employment growth.

Agricultural Environmental Enhancement Program: The program grants $150,000 a year to farmers to purchase materials to protect water quality from the potential impacts of agricultural practices. Eligible materials include fencing, culverts, seed and gutters. All interested farmers are encouraged to apply for the next round of this new grant program.

Farm Viability Program: This program is designed to improve the economic bottom line and environmental integrity of participating farms through the development and implementation of farm viability plans developed by teams of agricultural, economic and environmental consultants.

Agriculture Preservation Restriction Program (APR): The APR Program is a voluntary program which is intended to offer a non-development alternative to farmers who are faced with a decision regarding the future use of their farms. The program offers to pay farmers the difference between fair market value and the agriculture value of their land in exchange for a permanent deed restriction which precludes any use of the property that will have a negative impact on its agricultural viability.

Massachusetts Aquaculture Grants Program (MAG): The MAG program encourages environmentally responsible aquaculture projects that can demonstrate public and industry benefit through work that will: result in the development and implementation of new technologies, products, processes or services; reduce aquaculture industry operating costs thereby increasing business profitability; increase the productivity of Massachusetts aquatic cultivation endeavors; and preserve existing jobs and/or result in new employment opportunities for the Commonwealth of Massachusetts.

* Commonwealth Corporation

The Schrafft Center
529 Main Street, Suite 110   617-727-8158
Boston, MA 02129   Fax: 617-242-7660
www.commcorp.org

The Commonwealth Corporation provides services that promote workers, businesses, youth, educators and the entire workforce development system. The Commonwealth Corporation sponsors Entrepreneurial Training and Small Business Assistance Programs. The programs include all aspects of starting and operating a business. There are seminars on marketing research, marketing tools, strategic planning, financial management, sales techniques and much more. The Economic Stabilization Trust Program offers direct loans and guarantees for small and medium-sized manufactures on a $7,500 per employee basis, with a minimum of 12 employees. The financing helps these companies in the areas of modernization and competition in the global marketplace. Another service of the Trust is business consultation and financial guidance.

* MassDevelopment

75 Federal Street, 10th Floor
Boston, MA 02110   617-451-2477
www.massdevelopment.com

Mass Development: Their mission is to promote economic development and job creation that is done in partnership with government, communities, and businesses.

-   *Real Estate Loans:* Loans up to $3 million can be used for facility acquisition, renovation, construction, or permanent financing.
-   *Guarantees*: a portion of private real estate loans are secured thereby providing lenders incentive to extend credit.
-   *Equipment loans*: Below-market-rate financing of

$50,000 to $500,000 can be used for new equipment.

- *Brownsfield Redevelopment Fund:* Interest-free financing up to $50,000 is available for environmental site assessment.
- *Tech Dollars:* Nonprofit organizations with annual revenues of $5 million or less can access 100% financing at below-prime rates for technology equipment purchases and installation.
- *Emerging Technology Fund:* Technology based companies can get loans and guarantees for facilities and specialized equipment.
- *Seafood Loans:* Fixed asset financing can be used to purchase land, building, and equipment for the construction or renovation of seafood-related facilities. Direct loans are also available for facility expansions.
- *Predevelopment Assistance:* Funds are available for early-state economic development projects in communities throughout Massachusetts. Matching fund range between $5,000 and $25,000.
- *Term Working Capital:* Small- and middle-market businesses get help through the replenishing of working capital shortfalls caused by adverse business conditions.
- *Turnaround Management Assistance:* This helps businesses restructure or reposition by funding the services of a turnaround management consultant. A maximum funding of $25,000 is available for the development and implementation of a plan.
- *Tax Exempt Bonds:* Provides very low interest rate financing for capital projects. The four groups eligible for this program are: 501(c)(3) nonprofits for real estate and equipment; exempt facilities for waste recovery and recycling facilities; manufacturers for facilities and equipment; and affordable housing developers for residential housing. All of these businesses must be eligible for tax-exempt financing under the federal tax code.
- *Tax-Exempt Equipment Lease/Purchase Program:* Financing of $300,000 or more is available for manufacturers, nonprofits, and environmental enterprises for equipment needs.
- *Taxable Bonds:* Businesses have access to capital markets for industrial and commercial real estate projects.
- *Capital Financing 501:* Short-term, tax exempt commercial paper financing which can be borrowed and repaid as needed.

* Massachusetts Business Development Corporation

500 Edgewater Drive, Suite 555   781-928-1100
Wakefield, MA 01880   Fax: 781-928-1101
www.mass-business.com

Business Loans: Provides loans to firms which are unable to obtain financing through conventional sources. Loans may be used for purchase or construction of fixed business assets (land, plant, equipment) and for working capital. Can provide up to 100 percent of financing.

* Massachusetts Capital Resource Company

420 Boylston St.   617-536-3900
Boston, MA 02116   Fax: 617-536-7930
www.masscapital.com

Provides unsecured loans in the form of debt and equity financing to small and medium-sized firms that are unable to obtain financing through conventional sources. Maximum loan amount is $5 million.

* Division of Communities Development

Division of Community Services
Department of Housing and Community Development
100 Cambridge St., Suite 300
Boston, MA 02114   617-573-1100
www.state.ma.us/dhcd

Community Development Action Grant: Grants are made to cities and towns for public actions in support of private investments. Projects should create or retain long-term employment and/or housing opportunities and revitalize distressed areas.

Community Development Fund (CDF): CDF is designed to generate and/or retain jobs in small communities. The program provides flexible structured debt financing for businesses which provide, create or retain jobs for low to moderate income residents. CDF can fund up to one third of the total project cost and the loans can be used for purchase of equipment, acquisition of real estate, new construction or rehabilitation, working capital or refinancing.

Massachusetts Downtown Initiative: Seeks to revitalize and strengthen the business and community life or urban centers in cities and towns, while preserving the state's heritage of historic downtown buildings. Funds are offered on a sliding scale for professional staff and technical assistance to nonprofit organizations working on downtown revitalization. Staff funding decreases over the life of the three year program, while technical assistance is focused on different issues each year.

Economic Development Industrial Corporations (EDIC): Enables cities and towns to undertake development projects that will generate jobs and stabilize communities. With EDIC, municipalities can designate economic development areas and shape plans for their development. EDICs have the authority to negotiate payments in-lieu of property taxes and may also issue bonds to finance the development of eligible projects, which very often include industrial parks.

* Loans For Farmers

Farm Service Agency
U.S. Department of Agriculture
445 West Street   413-253-4500
Amherst, MA 01002   Fax: 413-253-4540
http://www.fsa.usda.gov/ma/

The Farm Service Agency provides Direct and Guaranteed Loans to farmers through a variety of programs, including:

Farm Ownership Loans: purchase farmland, construct or repair buildings and other fixtures, and promote soil and water conservation. Up to $200,000.

Operating Loans: purchase items needed for a successful farm operation, such as livestock, farm equipment, feed, seed, fuel, farm chemicals, insurance, and other operating expenses. Can also be used to pay for minor improvements. Up to $200,000.

Beginning Farmer and Rancher Loans: provides funds to beginning and farmers and ranchers who are unable to obtain financing elsewhere.

Downpayment Farm Ownership Loans for Beginning Farmers: helps beginning farmers and ranchers purchase a farm or ranch. Also provides a way for retiring farmers to transfer their land to a future generation of farmers and ranchers. Applicant must have a downpayment of 10% and

FSA with finance 40%, with the remaining balance from a commercial lender. Purchase price cannot exceed $250,000.

Loans to Socially Disadvantaged Farmers/Ranchers: helps socially disadvantaged applicants buy and operate family-size farms and ranches.

Youth Loans: Made to youths to establish and operate income-producing projects with the participation in 4-H clubs, Future Farmers of America, and similar organizations. Up to $5,000.

Emergency Loan Assistance: provides loans to help producers recover from production and physical losses due to drought, flooding, and other natural disasters, or quarantine. Up to $500,000.

Beginning Farmer and Rancher Land Contract Guarantee Pilot Program. "prompt payment guarantee" from FSA. FSA will provide payment to seller two times if the beginning farmer does not pay. Program is tested in IN, IA, ND, OR, PA and WI.

Farm Ownership and Operating Loan Guarantees: FSA will guarantee loans up to $782,000.

* Small Business Administration (SBA)

Boston District Office
10 Causeway St.
2nd Floor, Room 265   617-565-5590
Boston, MA 02222-1093   Fax: 617-565-5598
www.sba.gov/ma

The Massachusetts Small Business Administration Office delivers a variety of programs and services, such as startup and operational assistance through small business training and counseling, financial assistance for startup's, business opportunities and much more.

* The Massachusetts Workforce Training Fund

Division of Employment and Training
19 Staniford Street   800-252-1591
Boston, MA 02114   Fax: 617-727-8671
www.detma.org

Workforce Training Fund Express Program: This program is for businesses with 50 or fewer employees for 50% of training reimbursement. Total grant request cannot exceed $15,000.

Workforce Training Fund General Program: This program is designed for large and small businesses. Matching training grants are available from $2,000 up to $250,000 for training which will occur over a period not to exceed two years.

* Massachusetts Technology Development Corporation

40 Broad Street, Suite 818   617-723-4920
Boston, MA 02109   Fax: 617-723-5983
www.mtdc.com

Massachusetts Technology Development Corporation is a state-owned venture capital firm that offers assistance to Massachusetts's technology-based manufactures whose principal products or services are innovative enough to be competitive. They have made up to one-half million dollars available to qualifying companies. To receive the fund, the applicant company must show that it cannot secure

conventional financing; that funding will produce a significant increase in employment; and that there is a prospect of a high rate of return on investment.

* Massachusetts Trade Office

10 Park Plaza, Suite 3720   617-973-8650
Boston, MA 02116   Fax: 617-227-3488
www.state.ma.us/mobd

This office stimulates export development through an export assistance program and promotes foreign investment and Massachusetts industries. The export assistance programs encompasses the following aspects: product sector marketing, foreign market development, and general export services. Specific services include one-on-one corporate counseling for new-to-export companies, coordination of foreign buying missions to Massachusetts trade, investment, and strategic partnerships, and hosting periodic industry and market seminars on overseas trade opportunities.

* Massachusetts Manufacturing Extension Partnership

100 Grove Street
Worchester, MA 01605   800-MEP-4MFG
www.massmep.org

Small and medium-sized businesses in Massachusetts can get help from over 2,000 manufacturing and business specialists that work through local chapters. They offer assistance in current manufacturing and management technologies such as Lean Manufacturing, plant layout, machinery automation/specification, marketing and business development, and much more. A MEP specialist will visit the business to observe and then sit down with the client and discuss the businesses operations.

* Massachusetts Community Development Finance Corporation (CDFC)

100 City Hall Plaza, Suite 300   617-523-6262
Boston, MA 02108   Fax: 617-523-7676
www.mcdfc.com

One of the goals of the CDFC is to invest in small business, which will result in job growth. They do this through the following programs:

- *Minority & Women Contractor Bond Program*: Technical and financial assistance is available to help contractors to qualify for surety bonds while establishing a relationship with a surety company.
- *Urban Initiative Fund (UIF)*: Minority-owned businesses with less than $500,000 in annual sales can get technical assistance and loans to strengthen their business from the fund. It also provides loans and grants for a variety of innovative economic development and human service projects.
- *Massachusetts Enterprise Loan Fund*: This fund provides debt financing to established businesses for expansion. The investment range is from $100,000 to $300,000 with CDFC providing up to one third of the total financing. The funds can be used for equipment, working capital, and expansion or acquisition costs.
- *Real Estate Fund*: This program offers short-to-medium-term flexible financing for CDC development residential, commercial and industrial real estate projects. Up to $250,000 is provided for the financing of recoverable development expenses. The project must offer a clear public benefit such as job creation or revitalization of blighted commercial properties.
- *CDC Working Capital Fund*: This program fills

pressing capital gaps for CDC's through flexible financing to cover operating expenses.

Michigan

* Michigan Economic Development Corporation

300 North Washington Square   517-373-9808
Lansing, MI 48913   Fax: 517-335-0198
http://medc.michigan.org

Michigan Business Ombudsman: Serves as a "one-stop" center for business permits. Acts as a mediator in resolving regulatory disputes between business and the various state departments and also provides consultation and referral services.

Economic Development Jobs Training: Provides financial assistance to companies that need to train or retrain workers to meet marketplace needs. Grant average: $2,000 per employee.

Economic Development Corporations: Provides a flexible tool to assist in job creation at the local level by acquiring, developing, and maintaining land, buildings, machinery, furnishings, and equipment necessary to complete a project plan.

Michigan Business Development: Assists existing companies with a wide array of business services which are customized to meet the specific needs of the business.

Michigan Technical Assistance Center Network: Assists companies with government contracting and exporting.

Labor Market Information: Detailed information concerning Michigan's economy and business climate. Information is also available regarding various industrial sectors critical to Michigan.

Employee Ownership Program: Provides information, technical assistance, and financing to enhance the establishment of employee-owned companies and Employee Stock Ownership Plans.

Business and Industrial Development Corporations (BIDCOs): Many sound businesses are unable to obtain growth capital because their finances are considered too risky for conventional bank lending, yet they cannot provide the high rates of return required by venture capitalists. BIDCOs are a new type of private institution designed to fill this growth capital gap. BIDCOs offer an array of financing options that can be structured flexibly to suit the needs of individual companies. In addition, they can provide management assistance to help businesses grow. As a privately owned and operated corporation, each BIDCO establishes its own criteria for the kinds of businesses it will finance and for the types of loans and investments it will make. BIDCOs do not normally finance start ups.

Industrial Development Revenue Bond Program (IDRB): Tax-exempt bonds issued on behalf of the borrower by the Michigan Strategic Fund and purchased by private investors. These loans can be made for manufacturing and not-for-profit corporation projects and solid waste facilities. Bond proceeds can only be used to acquire land, building and equipment. Working capital and inventory are not eligible for this type of financing. These bonds are generally used when financing of $1 million and higher is required.

Export Working Capital Program (EWCP): The EWCP was designed to provide short-term working capital to exporters. It is a combined effort of the SBA and the Export-Import Bank. The two agencies have joined their working capital programs to offer a unified approach to the government's support of export financing.

International Trade Loan (ITL): This program provides short- and long-term financing to small businesses involved in exporting, as well as businesses adversely affected by import competition. The SBA can guarantee up to $1.25 million for a combination of fixed-asset financing and working capital. Loans for facilities or equipment can have maturities of up to 25 years. The working capital portion of a loan has a maximum maturity of three years. Interest rates are negotiated with the lender and can be up to 2.25% over the prime rate.

Minority And Women's Prequalification Loan and the Women's Pre-Qualification Loan Program: Use intermediaries to assist prospective minority and women borrowers in developing viable loan application packages and securing loans. The women's program uses only nonprofit organizations as intermediaries; the minority program uses for-profit intermediaries as well.

Disadvantaged Business Enterprise Certification: Insures that firms owned and controlled by disadvantaged individuals, minorities, and women participate in federal-aid contracts and grant entered into and administered by MDOT.

Community Assistance Team (CAT): The Community Assistance Team provides a variety of economic incentives and programs for Michigan communities.

Consultation Education Training (CET): The Consultation Education & Training Division can help your company's safety performance by developing a safety program to meet your needs.

Export Services: The Michigan Economic Development Corporation has trade specialists to help companies gain or expand access to markets in North America, South America and Asia.

* Michigan Rural Development Office

3001 Coolidge Road, Suite 200   517-324-5190
East Lansing, MI 48823   Fax: 517-324-5225
www.rurdev.usda.gov/mi

Rural Development Business Programs works in partnership with the private sector and the community-based organizations to provide financial assistance and business planning. They fund projects that create or preserve quality jobs and/or promote a clean rural environment. Recipients of these programs may include individuals, corporations, partnerships, cooperatives, public bodies, nonprofit organizations, Indian tribes, and private companies.

Business and Industry Loan Guarantees: This program's objective is to create jobs and stimulate rural economics by providing financial backing for rural businesses through a loan guarantee program.

Business and Industry Direct Loans: This program's objective is to create jobs and stimulate rural economics by providing financial backing for rural businesses through a direct loan.

Rural Enterprise Grants: This program finances and facilitates the development of small and emerging private business enterprises through a grant program.

Intermediary Relending Program Loans: This program finances business facilities and community development projects in rural areas through direct loans.

Rural Economic Development Loans and Grants: This program finances economic development and job creation in rural areas for Electric and Telephone Cooperatives.

* Certified Industrial Park Program
Michigan Economic Developers Association
P.O. Box 15096   517-241-0011
Lansing, MI 48901   Fax: 417-241-0089
www.medaweb.org
Industrial park developers and communities have used this identification as a marketing tool to show prospective clients that they are prepared to accept the new client without delay.

ᴬ Alternative Investments Division
Michigan Department of Treasury
Alternative Investments Division
P.O. Box 15128
Lansing, MI 48901   517-373-4330
www.michigan.gov/treasury
Invests in businesses with strong management that show a substantially above-average potential for growth, profitability, and equity appreciation. A typical initial investment is $5,000,000 and up.

* Equipment and Real Property Purchases
Michigan Municipal Bond Authority
Treasury Bldg., 3rd Floor
430 West Allegan   517-373-1728
Lansing, MI 48922   Fax: 517-335-2160
www.michigan.gov/treasury
Municipal Bonds provide streamlined tax-exempt, fixed interest rate financing well suited to equipment purchases.

* Freight Economic Development Project Loans/Grants
Michigan Department of Transportation
Bureau of Urban and Public Transportation
Freight Services and Safety Division
425 W. Ottawa
P.O. Box 30050
Lansing, MI 48909   517-325-2580
www.michigan.gov/mdot
Provides financial assistance to non-transportation companies which promote the development or expansion of new business and industries, by financing freight transportation infrastructure improvements needed to operate a new venture.

* Rail Loan Assistance Program
Michigan Department of Transportation
Bureau of Urban and Public Transportation
Freight Services and Safety Division
P.O. Box 30050
Lansing, MI 48909   517-373-1321
www.michigan.gov/mdot
The Michigan Rail Loan Assistance Program helps preserve and improve rail freight infrastructure. Non-interest bearing loans are available to fund eligible rail infrastructure improvement projects with a repayment period of up to ten years.

* Marketing and Communications Division
Michigan Department of Agriculture   571-241-2178
Office of Agriculture Development   800-292-3939
P.O. Box 30017   517-373-1104
Lansing MI 48909   Fax: 517-335-7071
www.michigan.gov/mda
The Marketing Section is the main contact for Michigan food and agricultural companies who seek assistance in international sales. The division works cooperatively to take advantage of the resources and international expertise of the Michigan Jobs Commission (MJC) and the Mid-America International Agri-Trade Council (MIATCO). Michigan exporters have opportunities to attend trade shows and missions, receive sales leads and market statistics, attend export education programs, and apply for federal Market Promotion Program funds via the MDA/MJC liaison. 517-373-1104.

ᴬ Michigan Department of Consumer & Industry Services
Corporation and Land Development Bureau
2501 Woodlake Circle
P.O. Box 30004   517-241-6470
Lansing, MI 48909   Fax: 571-241-0538
www.michigan.gov/cis
The Corporation Division promotes economic development and growth by facilitating the formation of business entities in Michigan. The Division provides services that enable corporations, limited liability partnerships to be formed, and for foreign entities to obtain a certificate of authority to transact business in the State, as required by Michigan law. The Division also maintains a record of the documents filed by these business entities, and makes this information available to the public.

* Industrial Assessment Center (IAC)
2350 Hayward Street   734-764-7471
Ann Arbor, MI 48109-2125   Fax: 734-647-0079
http://interpro.engin.umich.edu/mfgeng_prog/IAC
IAC is the Industrial Assessment Center with in the Program in Manufacturing at the University of Michigan(UM). There are thirty such university based centers across the country that are supported by the U.S. Department of Energy (DOE). The University of Michigan center serves manufacturers in Michigan and the upper region of Ohio. Small and medium-size manufacturers of all types of products are welcome to take advantage of the free and confidential services offered by the UM IAC.

* Loans For Farmers
Farm Service Agency
U.S. Department of Agriculture
3001 Coolidge Rd., Suite 100   517-324-5110
East Lansing, MI 48823   Fax: 517-324-5120
http://www.fsa.usda.gov/mi/
The Farm Service Agency provides Direct and Guaranteed Loans to farmers through a variety of programs, including:

Farm Ownership Loans: purchase farmland, construct or repair buildings and other fixtures, and promote soil and water conservation. Up to $200,000.

Operating Loans: purchase items needed for a successful farm operation, such as livestock, farm equipment, feed, seed, fuel, farm chemicals, insurance, and other operating expenses. Can also be used to pay for minor improvements. Up to $200,000.

Beginning Farmer and Rancher Loans: provides funds to beginning and farmers and ranchers who are unable to obtain financing elsewhere.

Downpayment Farm Ownership Loans for Beginning Farmers: helps beginning farmers and ranchers purchase a farm or ranch. Also provides a way for retiring farmers to transfer their land to a future generation of farmers and ranchers. Applicant must have a downpayment of 10% and FSA with finance 40%, with the remaining balance from a commercial lender. Purchase price cannot exceed $250,000.

Loans to Socially Disadvantaged Farmers/Ranchers: helps socially disadvantaged applicants buy and operate family-size farms and ranches.

Youth Loans: Made to youths to establish and operate income-producing projects with the participation in 4-H clubs, Future Farmers of America, and similar organizations. Up to $5,000.

Emergency Loan Assistance: provides loans to help producers recover from production and physical losses due to drought, flooding, and other natural disasters, or quarantine. Up to $500,000.

Beginning Farmer and Rancher Land Contract Guarantee Pilot Program: "prompt payment guarantee" from FSA. FSA will provide payment to seller two times if the beginning farmer does not pay. Program is tested in IN, IA, ND, OR, PA and WI.

Farm Ownership and Operating Loan Guarantees: FSA will guarantee loans up to $782,000.

* Small Business Administration (SBA)

Patrick V. MacNamara Bldg.
477 Michigan Ave., Suite 515   313-226-6075
Detroit, MI 48226   Fax: 313-226-4769
www.sba.gov/mi

The Michigan Small Business Administration Office delivers a variety of programs and services, such as startup and operational assistance through small business training and counseling, financial assistance for startup's, business opportunities and much more.

.

* Department of Environmental Quality

Environmental Science and Services Division
P.O. Box 30457   800-662-9278
Lansing, MI 48909   517-241-8280
www.michigan.gov/deq

Small Business P2 Loan Program: The Small Business P2 Loan Program provides loans of up to $100,000 at an interest rate of 5% to businesses with fewer than 100 employees. The loans must be used to implement pollution prevention projects that either eliminate or reduce waste at the point of generation or result in environmentally sound reuse and recycling.

* Michigan Works!

2500 Kerry Street, Suite 210   517-371-1100
Lansing, MI 48912   Fax: 517-371-1140
www.michiganworks.org

Michigan Works! is the state's workforce development resource agency. Michigan Works! fosters quality employment and training programs serving employers and workers.

* Michigan Manufacturing Technology Center

47911 Halyard   888-414-6682
Plymouth, MI 48170   Fax: 734-451-4201
www.mmtc.org

Michigan Manufacturing Technology Centers offer training and consulting services designed for small to midsize manufacturers in Michigan.

Minnesota

* Minnesota Department of Trade and Economic Development (MTED)

500 Metro Square Blvd.   800-657-3858
121 7th Place East   651-297-1291
St. Paul, MN 55101-2146   Fax: 651-296-1290
www.dted.state.mn.us

Minnesota Small Business Assistance Office: Provides accurate, timely, and comprehensive information and assistance to businesses in all areas of start-up, operation, and expansion. They can also provide referrals to other state agencies.

Business Development and Site Location Services: For businesses interested in expanding or relocating to a Minnesota site, it serves as a bridge between government and the resources that businesses are seeking. Business Development Specialists act as liaisons between businesses and state and local government to access financial and technical resources. The program also serves as an important information source, providing businesses with data on topics ranging from the availability of buildings and property or the labor supply in a particular location, to transportation or tax comparisons. The one-on-one nature of this program provides businesses with assistance throughout every phase of their expansion or location projects.

Computer and Electrical Components Industry Services: Exists to foster the growth of jobs, revenues, and investment in Minnesota's computer and electrical components industries. A specialist provides technical review of projects, coordination of statistical analysis, overview of prospect proposals, participation in development efforts with industry associations and other agencies.

Healthcare and Medical Products Industry Services: Exists to seek business investment and job growth in the healthcare industry while promoting Minnesota companies' capabilities in this industry. A specialist provides information to businesses on financial programs, suppliers, business planning, trade opportunities, venture partners and other needed resources. The specialist also works to attract direct investment in existing Minnesota businesses with problems and opportunities involving sources, product development, marketing, financing, site selection, and by marketing Minnesota actively at industry gatherings.

Printing and Publishing Industry Services: Exists to foster the growth of jobs, revenues, and investment in Minnesota's printing and publishing industry. A specialist provides information on resources, markets, technologies, buildings and sites, transportation, and other issues, both in response to inquiries and by marketing Minnesota actively at industry gatherings.

Wood Products, Plastics, and Composites Industry Services: Exists to foster the growth of jobs and added value in Minnesota's wood processing and related businesses and to attract new industry consistent with environmental protection. A specialist represents the industry and the Department of Trade and Economic Development by reviewing projects, organizing statistical data, participating in development efforts with Department of Natural Resources, University of Minnesota, Minnesota Technology, Inc., National Resources Research Institute and other agencies, and by helping to coordinate demonstration projects like model homes. This position has evolved from a primary focus on wood products, to a wider interest in plastics and composite materials that are more frequently used in conjunction with wood.

A Guide to Starting a Business in Minnesota: Provides a current discussion of many of the major issues faced by persons planning to start a new business in Minnesota, including forms or organizations, business name filing, business licenses and permits, business plans, financing, employers' issues, business taxes and small business resources.

Minnesota Investment Fund: To create new and retain the highest quality jobs possible on a state wide basis with a focus on industrial manufacturing and technology related industries; to increase the local and state tax base and improve the economic vitality for all Minnesota citizens. Grants are awarded to local units of government who make loans to assist new expanding businesses. Maximum available: $500,000. Only one grant per state fiscal year can be awarded to a government unit.

Minnesota Job Skills Partnership Board: Awards grants for cooperative education and training projects between businesses and educational institutions.

Small Business Development Loan Program: Provides loans to industrial, manufacturing or agricultural processing businesses for land acquisition, building construction or renovation, machinery and equipment. Maximum available: $500,000 minimum up to a maximum of $6 million.

Rural Challenge Grant Program: Provides job opportunities for low-income individuals, encourage private investment, and promote economic development in rural areas of the state. The Business and Community Development Division has a partnership with each of six regional organizations to provide low-interest loans to new or expanding businesses in rural Minnesota. Eligible projects: Up to 50% of start-up or expansion costs, including property acquisition, site improvements, new construction, building renovation, purchase of machinery and equipment, and working capital. Maximum available: $100,000. Most loans will be smaller due to the high demand for funds compared with the funds available.

Tourism Loan Program: Exists to provide low-interest financing to existing tourism-related businesses providing overnight lodging. Additionally, the program assists with the development of business plans. Businesses with feasible business plans qualify to receive financing for up to half of all eligible costs. Business owners meet with DTED staff to determine project eligibility and receive counseling. Direct loans, or participation loans in cooperation with financial institutions, can be made for up to 50% of total project cost. The maximum state loan may not exceed 50% of the total project cost, or $65,000, whichever is less. Maximum available Septic System Loans: Participation Loans - State funds are used in conjunction with loaned funds from financial institutions. Loans for septic system replacement or upgrade are eligible for an additional $65,000. Direct Loans - Only septic system projects of under $10,000 may receive a direct loan. The borrower must fund 50% of the project with private financing. The maximum direct loan is $5,000.

Certified Community Development Corporation: Certified CDCs may apply for grant funds for several purposes: 1. specific economic development projects within a designated area, 2 dissemination of information about, or taking application for, programs operated by DTED, or 3 developing the internal organizational capacity to engage in economic development activities.

Capital Access Program: To encourage loans from private lending institutions to businesses, particularly small-and medium sized-businesses, to foster economic development. When loans are enrolled in the program by participating lending institutions, the lender obtains additional financial protection through a special fund created by the lender, borrower and the State. The lender and borrower contribute between 3% and 7% of the loan to the fund. The amount of funds contributed by the borrower/lender must be equal; however, the funds contributed by the bank may be recovered from the borrower as additional fees or through interest rates. If the amount of all enrolled loans is less than $2,000,000, the State contribution will be 150% of the borrower/lender contribution. The borrower/lender contribution can be financed as part of the loan.

Contamination Cleanup/Investigation Grant Program: The Department of Trade and Economic Development can award grants towards contamination investigations and the development of a Response Action Plan (RAP) or for the cleanup of contamination on sites which will be redeveloped. The contamination investigation grants will allow smaller, outstate communities to access sites believed to be contaminated which are typically not addressed due to limited financial resources. The Contamination Cleanup grants address the growing need for uncontaminated, developable land. In both cases, grants are awarded to those sites where there is serious, imminent private or public development potential.

Minnesota Pathways Program: Act as a catalyst between business and education in developing cooperative training projects that provide training, new jobs and career paths for individuals making the transition from public assistance to the workforce. Grants are awarded to educational institutions with businesses as partners. Maximum available: $200,000 of Pathway funds per grant can be awarded for a project.

Underground Petroleum Tank Replacement Program: Exists to provide low interest financing to small gasoline retailers for the replacement of an underground petroleum tank. Business owners submit an application on the approved form along with supporting documentation including third party cost estimates from a certified installer, prior year federal tax return, schedule of existing debt and proof of gasoline volume sold in the last calendar year. Loans can only be made to businesses that demonstrate an ability to pay the loan from business cash flow. The maximum loan in $10,000.

Minnesota Trade Office: Acts as an advocate for Minnesota businesses pursuing international markets and to promote, assist and enhance foreign direct investments that contribute to the growth of Minnesota's economy. Services provided for Minnesota companies include information on trade shows and trade missions; education and training; and financial assistance programs for Minnesota companies.

Services for International Companies: Resources, services and direct counseling for all companies interested in international trade.

Minnesota World Trade Center Corporation: An international business resource for Minnesota and the upper Midwest.

Minnesota Export Finance Authority: Assists with the financing of exports through four focus areas: working capital guarantees for purchase orders, receivable insurance for foreign buyers, ExIm bank, and agency liaison.

Minnesota Job Skills Partnership Program: Acts as a catalyst between business and education in developing cooperative training projects that provide training for new jobs or retraining of existing employees. Grants are awarded to educational institutions with businesses as partners. Preference will be given to nonprofit institutions, which serve economically disadvantaged people, minorities, or those who are victims of economic dislocation and to businesses located in rural areas. Maximum available: $400,000 of Partnership funds per grant can be awarded for a project.

Urban Initiative Loan Program: Exists to assist minority owned and operated businesses and others that will create jobs in low-income areas of the Twin Cities. Urban Initiative Board enters into partnerships with local nonprofit organizations, which provide loans and technical assistance to start-up and expanding businesses. Project must demonstrate potential to create jobs for low-income people, must be unable to obtain sufficient capital from traditional private lenders, and must be able to demonstrate the potential to succeed. Eligible projects: Start-up and expansion costs, including normal business expenses such as machinery and equipment, inventory and receivables, working capital, new construction, renovation, and site acquisition. Financing of existing debt is not permitted. Micro-enterprises, including retail businesses, may apply for up to $10,000 in state funds. Maximum available: The maximum total loan available through the Urban Initiative Program is $300,000. The state may contribute 50% of the loan up to $150,000.

* Rural Development State Office

410 Farm Credit Service Building
375 Jackson Street   651-602-7800
St. Paul, MN 55101-1853   Fax: 651-602-7824
Email: a07dirmn@attmail.com
www.rurdev.usda.gov/mn

Their Rural Business Programs offer a variety of options for rural Minnesota.

Business and Industry Guaranteed and Direct Loan Program: This program's goal is to improve, develop, or finance business, industry, and employment and improve the economic and environmental climate in rural communities.

Intermediary Relending Program: The Relding Program is designed to alleviate poverty and increase economic activity and employment in rural communities, through financing targeted primarily toward smaller and emerging business in partnership with other public and private resources.

Rural Business Enterprise Grant Program: The Rural Business Enterprise Grant Program develops small and emerging private business enterprises in rural areas.

Rural Business Opportunity Grant Program: The Rural Business Opportunity Grant Program provides technical assistance to promote sustainable economic development in rural communities.

Rural Cooperative Development Grant Program: This program is designed to facilitate the creation or retention of jobs in rural areas through the development of new rural cooperatives value-added processing, and rural businesses.

Rural Economic Development Loan and Grant Program: The Rural Economic Development Loan and Grant Program promotes rural economic development and job creation.

* Free Workshops - Business Taxes

MN Dept. of Revenue
Mail Station 4410   651-297-4213
St. Paul, MN 55146-4410   800-888-6231
www.taxes.state.mn.us

Practical, real-world business tax information and up-to-the-minute information on state and federal tax laws that apply to your business. 2000 classes are sponsored by the IRS, the Minnesota Department of Revenue, and the Minnesota Department of Economic Security.

* Work Opportunity Tax Credit and the Welfare-To-Work Tax Credit

Minnesota Workforce Center
MN Dept. of Economic Security
5th Floor, 390 N. Robert Street   651-297-2219
St. Paul, MN 55101   888-234-5521
www.mnwfc.org/wotc/index.htm

The Work Opportunity and Welfare-To-Work Tax Credit programs are designed to help individuals from certain target groups secure meaningful employment by providing a federal income tax credit incentive to employers who hire them. These programs cover only new hires. That is, the person may not have worked for that employer in the past.

* Minnesota Rural Finance Authority

Minnesota Department of Agriculture
90 West Plato Boulevard   800-967-2474
St. Paul, MN 55107   651-296-4985
www.mda.state.mn.us/agfinance

The Seller Assisted Farm Ownership Program is a cooperative financing effort involving a buyer, a seller, a local lender, and the Minnesota Rural Finance Authority (RFA).

The Basic Farm Loan Program was established to help people who want to farm in Minnesota. The program offers affordable financing, a reasonable down payment and built-in safeguards, such as farm management training and financial planning to help minimize the risk all farmers face. This is a partnership approach backed by the State's financial participation. You may finance a purchase or possibly refinance an existing farm debt. Funding an improvement may be possible if done in conjunction with the requested financing package.

The Aggie Bond Loan Program is a federal bonding program administered by the State through its Rural Finance Authority. The program offers affordable financing for a qualified beginning farmer. This is accomplished by securing for the applicant a reduced interest rate on the loan they are submitting for approval under the program.

Livestock Expansion Loan Program: A loan program to assist livestock and dairy producers finance the construction of state-of-the-art facilities is offered through the RFA in the Minnesota Department of Agriculture.

Agricultural Improvement Loan Program: The Rural Finance Authority (RFA) in the Minnesota Department of Agriculture is offering a loan participation program to assist eligible farmers to finance capital improvements to their farming operation. The program may help to improve production, efficiency, and increase farm income. Agricultural improvements means improvements to a farm, including the purchase and construction or installation of improvements to land, buildings and other permanent structures. This includes equipment incorporated in or permanently affixed to the land, buildings, or structures which are useful for and intended to be used for the purpose of farming. For this program, agricultural improvements also includes wind energy conversion facilities with an output capacity of one megawatt or less.

Value-Added Stock Loan Program. Helps farmers finance the purchase of stock in a cooperative proposing to build or purchase and operate a facility located in Minnesota to process or produce marketable products from agriculture crops. Stock in certain cooperatives proposing to own and operate livestock processing facilities or farm-generated wind energy production facilities may also be eligible.

Rural Finance Authority (RFA): A Restructure Program for agricultural debt is available through the Rural Finance Authority (RFA) in the Minnesota Department of Agriculture. The Restructure II loan program is designed to help farmers who remain in good credit standing with their local agricultural lender, but are having trouble with cash flow due to adverse events. Only debt of an agricultural nature is eligible for refinancing.

* Minnesota Office of Environmental Assistance (OEA)

520 Lafayette Rd. N, Floor 2   651-296-3417
St. Paul, MN 55155-4100   800-657-3843
www.moea.state.mn.us   Fax: 651-215-0246

The OEA helps start-up and expanding businesses in Minnesota develop uses for recycled materials by offering technical, business, financial, and marketing assistance.

* MnTAP

University of Minnesota
Gateway   800-247-0015 (in MN)
200 Oak St, Suite 350   612-624-1300
Minneapolis MN 55455   Fax: 612-624-3370
www.mntap.umn.edu

The Minnesota Technical Assistance Program (MnTAP) not only helps businesses prevent pollution and better manage waste, we help them save time and money. Located at the University of Minnesota, they provide free technical assistance tailored to individual businesses. MnTAP helps Minnesota companies become more efficient and find alternatives to using hazardous materials. By reducing waste and increasing efficiency, companies save on disposal and raw-material costs and make working conditions healthier and safer for employees.

* Forestry Stewardship Program

Department of Natural Resources
Information Center
500 Lafayette Road   651-296-6157

St. Paul, MN 55155-4040   888-MINNDNR
www.dnr.state.mn.us

The Forest Stewardship Program offers technical assistance and long range planning to landowners. Grants of up to 65% of costs with a maximum of $10,000 per year are available to develop forest plans, tree planting and land stabilization.

* Minnesota Housing Finance Agency

400 Sibley Street, Suite 300   651-296-7608
St Paul MN 55101-1998   800-657-3769
www.mhfa.state.mn.us

Affordable Rental Investment Fund is a statewide program that will provide zero percent interest first mortgages or deferred loans to help cover the costs of the acquisition and rehabilitation or new permanent construction of low-income rental housing.

HOME Rental Rehabilitation Program provides grants to rehabilitate privately-owned rental property to support affordable, decent, safe and energy efficient housing for lower-income families. This program is administered by local housing agencies throughout most of the state.

Low and Moderate Income Rental Program makes mortgage and rehabilitation funds available for the acquisition and rehabilitation or new construction/conversion of rental apartment buildings housing low- and moderate-income Minnesotans. Funds after an initial selection round are generally available on an open pipeline basis.

Low Income Housing Tax Credit Program provides a federal income tax credit to investors who invest in the construction or substantial rehabilitation of rental housing. Housing must meet income and rent restrictions for at least 15 years. Tax credits are awarded in three allocation rounds each year. Call for the application dates.

Rental Rehabilitation Loan Program provides property improvement loans to residential rental property owners. Financing is available only in certain areas of the state.

* Minnesota Technology, Inc.

111 Third Ave. South
Suite 400   800-325-3073
Minneapolis, MN 55401   612-373-2900
www.minnesotatechnology.org   Fax: 612-373-2901

Promotes jobs and economic growth through technology assistance services, and technology information.

* Indian Affairs Council

1819 Bemidji Ave.   218-755-3825
Bemidji, MN 56601   Fax: 218-755-3739
and
161 St. Anthony St., Suite 924   651-296-0041
St. Paul, MN 55103   Fax: 651-296-0132
www.indians.state.mn.us

Provides resources for management and technical assistance for businesses owned by Minnesota-based Indians. A special revolving loan fund disburses funds on a case-by-case basis.

* Loans For Farmers

Farm Service Agency
U.S. Department of Agriculture
375 Jackson Street, Suite 400
St. Paul, MN 55101   651-602-7700

http://www.fsa.usda.gov/mn/
The Farm Service Agency provides Direct and Guaranteed Loans to farmers through a variety of programs, including:

Farm Ownership Loans: purchase farmland, construct or repair buildings and other fixtures, and promote soil and water conservation. Up to $200,000.

Operating Loans: purchase items needed for a successful farm operation, such as livestock, farm equipment, feed, seed, fuel, farm chemicals, insurance, and other operating expenses. Can also be used to pay for minor improvements. Up to $200,000.

Beginning Farmer and Rancher Loans: provides funds to beginning and farmers and ranchers who are unable to obtain financing elsewhere.

Downpayment Farm Ownership Loans for Beginning Farmers: helps beginning farmers and ranchers purchase a farm or ranch. Also provides a way for retiring farmers to transfer their land to a future generation of farmers and ranchers. Applicant must have a downpayment of 10% and FSA with finance 40%, with the remaining balance from a commercial lender. Purchase price cannot exceed $250,000.

Loans to Socially Disadvantaged Farmers/Ranchers: helps socially disadvantaged applicants buy and operate family-size farms and ranches.

Youth Loans: Made to youths to establish and operate income-producing projects with the participation in 4-H clubs, Future Farmers of America, and similar organizations. Up to $5,000.

Emergency Loan Assistance: provides loans to help producers recover from production and physical losses due to drought, flooding, and other natural disasters, or quarantine. Up to $500,000.

Beginning Farmer and Rancher Land Contract Guarantee Pilot Program: "prompt payment guarantee" from FSA. FSA will provide payment to seller two times if the beginning farmer does not pay. Program is tested in IN, IA, ND, OR, PA and WI.

Farm Ownership and Operating Loan Guarantees: FSA will guarantee loans up to $782,000.

* Small Business Administration (SBA)

100 North Sixth St.
Suite 210-C, Butler Square   612-370-2324
Minneapolis, MN 55403-1563   Fax: 612-370-2303
www.sba.gov/mn

The Minnesota Small Business Administration Office delivers a variety of programs and services, such as startup and operational assistance through small business training and counseling, financial assistance for startup's, business opportunities and much more.

* Initiative Funds

Northwest Minnesota Initiative Fund   218-759-2057
4225 Technology Drive, NW   800-659-2328
Bemidji, MN 56601   Fax: 218-759-2328
www.nwmf.org
Area of Operation: Beltrami, Clearwater, Hubbard, Kittson, Lake of the Woods, Mahnomen, Marshall, Norman, Pennington, Polk, Red Lake and Roseau Counties

Northland Foundation
610 Sellwood Building   800-433-4045
202 West Superior Street   218-723-4040
Duluth, MN 55802   Fax: 218-723-4048
www.northlandfdn.org
Area of Operation: Aitkin, Carlton, Cook, Itasca, Koochiching, Lake and St.Louis Counties.

West Central Minnesota Initiative Fund   800-735-2239
1000 Western Avenue   218-739-2239
Fergus Falls, MN 56537   Fax: 218-739-5381
www.wcif.org
Area of Operation: Becker, Clay, Douglas, Grant, Otter Tail, Pope, Stevens, Traverse, and Wilkin Counties.

Southwest Minnesota Foundation
1390 Highway 15 South   320-587-4848
P.O. Box 428   800-594-9480
Hutchinson, MN 55350   Fax: 320-587-3838
www.swmnfoundation.org
Area of Operation: Big Stone, Chippewa, Cottonwood, Jackson, Kandiyohi, Lac Qui Parle, Lincoln, Lyon, McLeod, Meeker, Murray, Nobles, Pipestone, Redwood, Renville, Rock, Swift, and Yellow Medicine Counties.

Minnesota Initiative Fund   320-632-8255
405 First Street Southeast   877-632-9255
Little Falls, MN 56345   Fax: 320-632-9258
www.ifound.org
Area of Operation: Benton, Cass, Chisago, Crow, Wing, Isanti, Kanabec, Mille, Lacs, Morrison, Pine, Sherburne, Stearns, Todd, Wadena, and Wright Counties.

Southern Minnesota Initiative Foundation
525 Florence Avenue   800-590-7759
P.O. Box 695   507-455-3215
Owatonna, MN 55060-0695   Fax: 507-455-2098
www.smifoundation.org
Area of Operation: Blue Earth, Brown, Dodge, Faribault, Fillmore, Freeborn, Goodhue, Houston, LeSueur, Martin, Mower, Nicollet, Olmsted, Rice, Sibley, Steele, Wabasha, Waseca, Watonwan, and Winona Counties.

Private, nonprofit organizations supplemented with funds from various public and private sources. Funds are distributed in grants and loans. The six initiative funds listed above are separate entities, and each has its own programs, funding levels, and guidelines. Call your regional Initiative Fund.

* Midwest Minnesota Community Development Corp. (MMCDC)

832 Washington Ave.
P.O. Box 623   218-847-3191
Detroit Lakes, MN 56501-3042   Fax: 218-847-3192
www.ruralisc.org/mmcdc.htm
Midwest Minnesota Community Development Corp. (MMCDC) receives grants and loans from public and private sources and re-lends these funds to businesses in the form of secured loans. The interest rate charged is normally at or near bank loan rates. The Revolving Loan Fund serves a five county area of Minnesota (Hubbard, Mahnomen, Becker, Clearwater, and Pennington, Polk, and Red Lahr). The Nonprofit National Corporations Loan Program serves rural communities with a population of 20,000 or less.

* Minnesota Rural Partners

P.O. Box 243   507-644-8250
Redwood Falls, MN 56283   Fax: 507-644-8251

www.minnesotaruralpartners.org
Minnesota Rural Partners (MRP) is Minnesota's rural development organization that works to cerate, promote and sustain programs that will help the rural communities throughout the state.

BizPathways: BizPathways is an online tool that matches entrepreneurs to the resources they need to grow based on location, stage of business development and other criteria.

BizPathways-Finance Avenue: This online tool can connect your business with the resources you may need based on your answers to seven questions.

Mississippi

* Mississippi Development Authority
P.O. Box 849   601-359-3499
Jackson, MS 39205-0849   800-927-6378
www.mississippi.org   Fax: 601-359-2832
This office can provide information and expertise in dealing with state, federal, and local agencies. They also have information on financing programs and other services offered by the state government.
- *Training*: Customized industrial training programs provided through the State Department of Education. Job Training Partnership Act assistance provided through the Mississippi Department of Economic and Community Development.
- *Site Finding*: The Mississippi Resource Center in Jackson offers an interactive video for site viewing and detailed data on video, computer disk, or hard copy for later study.
- *One-stop environmental permitting*.

Loan Guarantee Program: Provides guarantees to private lenders on loans made to small businesses allowing a small business to obtain a loan that may not otherwise be possible without the guarantee protection. The maximum guarantee is 75% of the total loan or $375,000, whichever is less.

Industrial Development Revenue Bond Program: Reduces the interest costs of financing projects for companies through the issuance of both taxable and tax-exempt bonds. Additionally, ad valorem and sales tax exemptions are granted in conjunction with this type of public financing. There is a $10 million cap.

Small Enterprise Development Program: Provides funds for manufacturing and processing companies to finance fixed assets. Although a company may qualify for more than one loan under this program, the aggregate amount loaned to any company cannot exceed $2 million.

Mississippi Business Investment Act Program: Through the issuance of State General Obligation Bonds, low-interest loans are provided to counties or cities to finance improvements that complement investments by private companies.

Airport Revitalization Revolving Loan Program: Funds from the issuance of state bonds provide loans to airport authorities for the construction and/or improvement of airport facilities. Maximum loan amount is $500,000.

Port Revitalization Revolving Loan Program: Designed to make loans to port authorities for improvement of port facilities. Maximum is $500,000.

Agribusiness Enterprise Loan Program: Designed to encourage the extension of conventional financing by lending institutions by providing interest-free loans to agribusinesses. Maximum loan is 20% of the total project cost or $200,000, whichever is less. Proceeds may be used to finance buildings and equipment and for costs associated with the purchase of land.

Small Business Assistance Program: Established for the purpose of providing funds to establish revolving loan funds to assist in financing small businesses. Maximum is $100,000.

Energy Investment Program: Provides financial assistance to individuals, partnerships or corporations making energy conserving capital improvements or designing and developing energy conservation processes. This program offers low-interest loans of up to $300,000.

Local Industrial Development Revenue Bonds: Local political entities have the authority to issue tax-exempt and taxable industrial development revenue bonds to finance new or expanding industrial enterprises up to 100% of total project costs.

General Obligation Bonds: Local political entities have the authority to issue general obligation bonds for the purpose of acquiring sites and constructing facilities for lease to new or expanding industries.

Minority Business Enterprise Division (MBED): Provides assistance to businesses in those categories. The division acts as principal advocate on behalf of minority- and women-owned business enterprises and promotes legislation that will help them operate more effectively. Developing funding sources, including state funding, bonding resources, federal and local funds, and others is among the major aims of MBED. But identifying funding sources represents only one aspect of MBED's service to Mississippi's women- and minority-owned firms. The division also attempts to put those businesses in touch with potential customers; MBED maintains an outreach program designed to include them in contracting of goods and services and procurement of contracts. A regional and statewide network of workshops, seminars, and trade shows continually provide training to stimulate the role of entrepreneurship in Mississippi's economic development.

Minority Surety Bond Guaranty Program: Program enables minority contractors, not meeting the surety industry's standard underwriting criteria, to obtain bid and performance bonds on contracts with state agencies and political subdivisions. Maximum bond guarantee is 75% of contract bond amount, or $112,500, whichever is less.

Minority Business Enterprise Loan Program: Designed to provide loans to socially and economically disadvantaged minority-or women-owned small businesses. Loan proceeds may be used for all project costs associated with the establishment or expansion of a minority business, including the purchase of fixed assets or inventory or to provide working capital. The minimum loan is $2,000 and the maximum loan is $25,000. MBFC may fund up to 100% of a total project.

Mississippi Tourism Incentive Program: This is an incentive program for qualified developers for the creation or expansion of family-oriented tourism projects. The types of entertainment enterprises that can receive assistance include: a cultural or historical site; a recreation or entertainment facility; campgrounds; indoor or outdoor play or music shows and more.

Rural Economic Development Assistance Program: Companies financing through the Small Enterprise Development or Industrial Revenue Bond Programs may be eligible to participate in this program. Eligible companies receive credits on Mississippi corporate income taxes. These credits may be used to offset up to 80% of the company's state corporate income tax liability.

* Rural Development

State Director, William Simpson
100 West Capitol St.
Suite 831 Federal Building   601-965-4318
Jackson, MS 39269   Fax: 601-965-5384
Email: wsimpson@rdmail.rural.usda.gov
www.rurdev.usda.gov/ms

The primary goals surrounding these programs are to stimulate economic growth, through the use of several programs administered by the Rural Business & Cooperative Service. The objectives focus on the creation of jobs and cooperatives in rural areas across the State of Mississippi.

Business & Industrial Loan Guarantees: This program encourages commercial financing of rural business, through the use of loan guarantees. This enables lenders the flexibility of maintaining the loan with a percentage guarantee, or sale of the loan on the secondary market. These loans are for the purpose of creating jobs, and improving the economic and environmental climate of rural communities.

Intermediary Relending Program (IRP): The IRP program provides a source of funding for community development, establishment of new businesses, expanding existing businesses and creation of jobs. This is primarily accomplished through the use of a revolving loan fund, which is administered by nonprofit corporations, public bodies, Indian tribes, and cooperatives.

Rural Business Enterprise Grants (RBEG): These grants are primarily used to finance or develop small and emerging private business enterprises. These funds are also administered through nonprofit corporations, public bodies, and Indian tribes. The ultimate recipients of these funds must be small and emerging private businesses.

Cooperative Development Grants: The primary purpose of these funds is for improving the economic condition of rural areas by promoting the development (through technological innovation, cooperative development, and adaptation of existing technology) and commercialization of new services and products that can be produced or provided in rural areas. This includes processes that can be utilized in the production of products in rural areas, and new processes that can be utilized in the production of products in rural areas, and new enterprises that can add value to on-farm production through processing or marketing.

Rural Economic Development Loan And Grants: The basic purpose of this assistance is to promote rural economic development or job creation projects. These funds are administered through private phone and electric companies. The ultimate recipients for these funds will be any type of entity, profit or nonprofit, public or private.

Rural Business Opportunity Grants (RBOG): This grant program is used to promote sustainable economic development in rural communities with exceptional needs.

Funds may be used to pay for the costs of economic planning for rural communities, technical assistance for rural businesses or training for rural entrepreneurs or economic development officials. Grant limits are $50,000.

* Mississippi Department of Agriculture and Commerce

121 North Jefferson Street   601-359-1100
Jackson, MS 39201   Fax: 601-354-6290
www.mdac.state.ms.us
Mailing Address:
P.O. Box 1609
Jackson, MS 39215

The mission of the Mississippi Department of Agriculture and Commerce is to regulate and promote agricultural-related businesses within the state and to promote Mississippi's products throughout both the state and the rest of the world for the benefit of all Mississippi citizens.

* Loans For Farmers

Farm Service Agency
U.S. Department of Agriculture
Mississippi Farm Bureau Building
6311 Ridgewood Rd., Suite W100   601-965-4300
Jackson, MS 39211   Fax: 601-965-4184
http://www.fsa.usda.gov/ms/

The Farm Service Agency provides Direct and Guaranteed Loans to farmers through a variety of programs, including:

Farm Ownership Loans: purchase farmland, construct or repair buildings and other fixtures, and promote soil and water conservation. Up to $200,000.

Operating Loans: purchase items needed for a successful farm operation, such as livestock, farm equipment, feed, seed, fuel, farm chemicals, insurance, and other operating expenses. Can also be used to pay for minor improvements. Up to $200,000.

Beginning Farmer and Rancher Loans: provides funds to beginning and farmers and ranchers who are unable to obtain financing elsewhere.

Downpayment Farm Ownership Loans for Beginning Farmers: helps beginning farmers and ranchers purchase a farm or ranch. Also provides a way for retiring farmers to transfer their land to a future generation of farmers and ranchers. Applicant must have a downpayment of 10% and FSA with finance 40%, with the remaining balance from a commercial lender. Purchase price cannot exceed $250,000.

Loans to Socially Disadvantaged Farmers/Ranchers: helps socially disadvantaged applicants buy and operate family-size farms and ranches.

Youth Loans: Made to youths to establish and operate income-producing projects with the participation in 4-H clubs, Future Farmers of America, and similar organizations. Up to $5,000.

Emergency Loan Assistance: provides loans to help producers recover from production and physical losses due to drought, flooding, and other natural disasters, or quarantine. Up to $500,000.

Beginning Farmer and Rancher Land Contract Guarantee Pilot Program: "prompt payment guarantee" from FSA. FSA will provide payment to seller two times if the beginning farmer does not pay. Program is tested in IN, IA, ND, OR, PA and WI.

Farm Ownership and Operating Loan Guarantees: FSA will guarantee loans up to $782,000.

* Small Business Administration (SBA)

Mississippi District Office
AmSouth Bank Plaza
210 E. Capitol Street, Suite 900 601-965-4378
Jackson, MS 39201 Fax: 601-965-5629

Gulfport Branch Office
Bancorp South Plaza
2909 13th Street, Suite 203 228-863-4449
Gulfport, MS 39501 Fax: 228-864-0179
www.sba.gov/ms

The Mississippi Small Business Administration Office delivers a variety of programs and services, such as startup and operational assistance through small business training and counseling, financial assistance for startup's, business opportunities and much more.

Missouri

* Department of Economic Development

P.O. Box 1157 573-751-4962
Jefferson City, MO 65102-1157 800-523-1434
www.ded.state.mo.us Fax: 573-526-2416

First Stop Shop: Serves to link business owners and state government and provides information on state rules, regulations, licenses, and permits.

Business Assistance Center: 888-751-2863
Provides information and technical assistance to start-up and existing businesses on available state and federal programs. Offers several useful publications.

University Outreach and Extension: Programs to help citizens apply university research knowledge to solve individual and community problems. Working with business owners and managers on a one-to-one basis, B&I specialists help entrepreneurs identify problem areas and find solutions.

Small Business Incubators: Buildings that have been divided into units of space, which are then leased to new small businesses. In addition to low-cost physical space, incubators can help clients with access to necessary office machines, reception and secretarial services, furniture, conference rooms and technical expertise in business management.

Innovation Centers: Provide a wide range of management and technical assistance to businesses. These centers are familiar with up-to-date business management and technology innovations and help businesses apply these innovations to help increase profits.

Action Fund Program: The program provides a subordinate loan to certain types of for-profit companies that need funds for start-up or expansion and have exhausted other sources. The projected growth of the company, economic impact, the risk of failure, and the quality of management are critical factors for approval. DED must determine that the borrower has exhausted other funding sources and only the least amount needed to complete the project may be provided. In any event, an Action Fund Loan would be limited to the

lower of: $750,000 per project; 30% of the total project cost; or $20,000 per new full-time year-round job.

Brownfield Redevelopment Program: The purpose of this program is to provide financial incentives for the redevelopment of commercial/industrial sites owned by a governmental agency that have been abandoned for at least three years due to contamination caused by hazardous substances. The program provides state tax credits for eligible remediation costs. DED may provide a loan or guarantee for other project costs, or a grant for public infrastructure. Also, tax credits may be provided to businesses that create jobs at the facility. The program provides Missouri state income tax credits for up to 100% of remediation costs. Guaranteed loans or direct loans to an owner or operator of the property are limited to $1 million. Grants to public entities are also available up to $100,000 or 50% for feasibility studies or other due diligence costs. Grants can also be issued up to $1 million for the improvement of public infrastructure for the project. The total of grants, loans or guarantees cannot exceed $1 million per project.

CDBG Loan Guarantee Program: The purpose of this program is to provide "gap" financing for new or expanding businesses that cannot access complete funding for a project. "Gap" financing means other sources of financing (including bank loans and owner equity) have been maximized, and a gap exists in the total project cost. The Department of Economic Development (DED) will guarantee 50% to 80% of the principal balance (after liquidation of assets) of a loan made by a financial institution. DED must determine that the borrower has exhausted other funding sources and only the least amount needed to complete the project may be provided. The maximum funding available is based on the lower of: $400,000 per project or $20,000 per new full-time permanent job created or retained. Approval is based on the good character of the owners, sufficient cash flow, adequate management and reasonable collateral.

Certified Capital Companies (CAPCO): Purpose is to induce private investment into new or growing Missouri small businesses, which will result in the creation of new jobs and investment. DED has initiated the formation of private venture capital firms (CAPCOs). These firms have certain requirements to make equity investments in eligible businesses in Missouri. The amount a CAPCO may invest in one Missouri business depends on various factors, however the maximum amount is 15% of the CAPCO's certified capital. Funding decisions are made by each CAPCO based on their evaluation of the return on investment relative to the risk. CAPCO funds may be used for equity investments, unsecured loans or hybrid investments in eligible businesses. Typically, venture capitalists require a projected 25-40% annual ROI, depending on the risk.

Industrial Development Bonds (IDBs): Developed by the US Congress and the Missouri General Assembly to facilitate the financing of business projects. The interest received by the bondholders may be exempt from federal and state income taxes, if the project is eligible.

Urban Enterprise Loan Fund (UEL): A micro lending instrument established by the State of Missouri, Department of Economic Development and administered in Kansas City by the downtown Minority Development Corporation and in St. Louis by the St. Louis Development Corporation. The program is designed to assist Missouri residents with the creation, expansion, and retention of micro-enterprises. Eligible enterprises must be located - or aspire to locate-within the Federally designated Enhanced Enterprise Community and the State Enterprise Zone. One job must be created for every $20,000 in Urban Enterprise Loan proceeds invested. Loans from the State fund range from a minimum of $10,000 up to a maximum of $100,000. The Urban Enterprise Loan Fund also has a matching funds requirement and new job creation criteria.

CDBG Industrial Infrastructure Grant: This program assists local governments in the development of public infrastructure that allows industries to locate new facilities, expand existing facilities or prevent the relocation or closing of a facility. The use of this program is based on the local government exhausting their available resources. DED has targeted a 20% match by the community base upon the availability of unencumbered city or county funds.

Missouri Office Of International Marketing: Services include: International Consulting Service, Competitive Analysis Reports, Trade Show Reports, Trade Exhibitions, Catalog Shows, Missouri International Office Assistance, Foreign Company Background Checks, Rep-Find Service, International Travel Program, Marketing Program, Trade Opportunity Program, Foreign Trade Missions, Strategic Alliance Program, Export Finance Assistance, Made In Missouri Catalogs, Missouri Export Directory, Recognition Program.

Office of Minority Business (OMB): Charged with the responsibility of identifying and developing support systems that assist the minority business community in gaining a foothold in the mainstream of Missouri's economy. This responsibility entails counseling minority small businesses on business start-up, retention, expansion, financing, and procurement; also including but not limited to providing ready access to information regarding current legislation and regulations that affects minority business. The staff of the Office of Minority Business can provide assistance with; administering technical and financial assistance programs; providing new and small businesses with management expertise; business development information; tying minority firms to national and global markets; connecting minority firms to the labor market; accessing research and technology; and other customized assistance.

* Rural Development Administration
601 Business Loop 70 West
Parkade Center, Suite 235   573-876-0976
Columbia, MO 65203   Fax: 573-876-0977
www.rurdev.usda.gov/mo

Business and Industry Loans: Direct loans made by USDA Rural Development and loans made by conventional lenders and guaranteed by USDA Rural Development to help maintain or establish private business and industry enterprises that create employment opportunities. Limited to communities of 50,000 population or less.

Intermediary Relending Program: Loans made to intermediaries at 1% for 30 years. Maximum loan amount $150,000 or 75% of project costs, whichever is less.

Rural Business Enterprise Grants: Grants made to public bodies, not for profits and Indian tribes to support the development of private business enterprise in rural communities of less than 50,000 people.

Rural Business Opportunity Grants: Grants made to public bodies, not for profits, and Indian tribes in rural areas.

Technical Assistance and Training Grants: Grants made to private nonprofit organizations that have been granted tax-exempt status. Grant funds may be used to provide assistance to existing water and water disposal facilities.

Rural Economic Development Grants and Loans: Grants and Loans to rural electric cooperatives and REA telephone borrowers.

* Workforce Development System
Missouri Division of Workforce Development
421 East Durkin Street
P.O. Box 1087   573-751-3999
Jefferson City, MO 65102-1087   Fax: 573-751-4088
www.ded.state.mo.us/employment/workforcedevelopme
nt

Integrates previously fragmented employment and training programs into a comprehensive workforce development system. Services benefit both job seekers and employers through One-Stop Career Centers.

* Missouri First
State Treasurer's Office
P.O. Box 210   573-751-2372
Jefferson City, MO 65102-0210   800-662-8257
www.sto.state.mo.us/link/deposit.htm

The State Treasurer has reserved a portion of available linked deposit funds for small businesses. State funds are deposited with participating lending institutions at up to 3% below the one-year Treasury Bill rate, with the lender passing on this interest savings to the small business borrower. A company must have less than 25 employees, be headquartered in Missouri, and be operating for profit. Small Business MISSOURI FIRST Linked Deposit loans are available for working capital. The maximum loan amount is $100,000.

* Market Development Loans for Recovered Materials
Environmental Improvement and Energy Resources
Authority
P.O. Box 744   573-526-5555
Jefferson City, MO 65102   Fax: 573-635-3486
www.dnr.state.mo.us/eiera/eiera.htm

The Environmental Improvement and Energy Resources Authority funds activities that promote the development of markets for recovered materials. Loans of up to $75,000 are available to companies for equipment used in the production or manufacture of products made from recovered materials. After three years, if all contract obligations are met, the loan is forgiven and repayment is not required.

* Financial Aid for Beginning Farmers
Missouri Agricultural and Small Business Development
Authority
Beginning Farmer Program
P.O. Box 630   800-735-2966
Jefferson City, MO 65102   573-751-2129
www.mda.state.mo.us

Beginning farmers can receive federally tax-exempt loans from commercial lenders at rates 20 to 30% below conventional rates through this program. A qualified borrower can borrow up to $250,000 to buy agricultural land, farm buildings, farm equipment and breeding livestock in Missouri. The borrower must be a Missouri resident, at least 18 years old and whose chief occupation must be farming or ranching after the loan is closed. The borrower's net worth must not exceed $150,000, and he or she must have adequate working capital and experience in the type of farming operation for which the loan is sought. A beginning farmer is one who has not previously owned more than 15% of the medium-sized farm in their county. Land cannot be purchased from a relative.

* Small Corporation Offering Registration (SCOR)

Securities Division
Secretary of State's Office
600 W. Main St., 2nd Floor
Jefferson City, MO 65101   573-751-4136
www.sos.mo.gov/

Missouri's Small Corporate Offering Registration (SCOR) provides a process for entrepreneurs to register their securities. The SCOR process has been designed by state securities regulators to make it easier and less expensive for small companies to raise needed capital from Missouri residents. All securities registered through this process need to complete form U-7 available from the Secretary of State's Office.

* Working Capital, St. Louis

Working Capital
3830 Washington   314-531-4546
St. Louis, MO 63108   Fax: 314-534-1883
http://stlouis.missouri.org/enterprise/about/worcap.htm

Working Capital is a micro-lending program which identifies small business people in the St. Louis area and makes available to them the commercial credit and business support which enables them to expand their business. Working Capital utilizes a peer-lending technique. At required monthly meetings borrowers receive continuing assistance in the marketing of their goods or services. The maximum first-time loan is $500 payable in four to six months; subsequent loans can have increased amounts (up to $5,000) and longer duration. Working Capital gives priority to individuals already in business to minimize loan risk; will consider applications from start-ups.

* Economic Council of St. Louis County

121 South Meramec St., Suite 900   314-889-7663
St. Louis, MO 63105   Fax: 314-615-7666
http://slcec.com

Services include Business Development Fund (BDF), Metropolitan St. Louis Loan Program, Minority/Disadvantaged Contractor Loan Guarantee, Recycling Market Development Loan Program, SBA 504 Loan Program and Minority & Women's Prequalified Loan Program.

* St. Charles County Economic Development Council

St. Charles County Economic
   Development Council
5988 Midrivers Mall Dr., Suite 100   636-441-6880
St. Charles, MO 63304   Fax: 636-441-6881
www.stcc-edc.com

Program assists eligible companies with fixed asset and working capital needs; acts as the certified development company which packages SBA 504 loans.

* St. Louis Development Corporation

1015 Locust St., #1200
St. Louis, MO 63101   314-622-3400
http://stlouis.missouri.org/sldc

St. Louis City Revolving Loan Fund: Provides direct, low interest, subordinated loans for working capital, machinery and equipment, purchasing land and buildings, renovation and constructing facilities and leasehold improvements. Business must be located in the City of St. Louis and be licensed to do business in the City. Must create one full-time job for every $10,000 of funds. Loans can provide up to 1/3 of the project cost to a maximum loan amount of $150,000.

St. Louis Urban Enterprise Loan, St. Louis Development Corporation: Provides loans to businesses located within the Enterprise Community area or the Enterprise Zone within the City of St. Louis. Eligible borrowers must be for profit businesses with current employment of less than 100. Eligible program activities will include fixed asset or working capital needs. Eligible projects must retain existing or create new jobs (one job created for every $20,000 of funding). The UEL can lend up to 50% of the project costs to a maximum loan amount of $100,000.

LDC Micro Loan Program, St. Louis Development Corporation: Microloans are available to start-up companies or businesses less than one year old located within the City of St. Louis; one job, other than the owner's, must be created. Successful applicants must demonstrate a viable business plans and the inability to secure bank financing. Companies must show the ability to start or grow the business with a maximum loan amount of $25,000. Loans may be used to cover start-up costs, working capital and purchase of machinery and equipment.

* First Step Program, Kansas City

First Step Fund
First Step Program
4747 Troost Avenue   816-235-6116
Kansas City, MO 64110   Fax: 816-235-6162
www.firststepfund.org

The First Step Fund (FSF) offers training in business basics such as record keeping, budgeting and marketing; assistance in completing a feasibility study for a business; opportunity to apply for loans of up to $2,500; and ongoing support group. FSF participants must be residents of Jackson, Clay or Platte counties in Missouri and must meet federal guidelines for low to moderate income. During a 10-week business training program, students work on a feasibility study for the proposed business. Potential borrowers receive continuing education at monthly meetings. Participants review each others' feasibility studies and approve loans. The maximum loan amount for first-time borrowers is $2,500 and $5,000 for second-time borrowers.

* Urban Enterprise Loan Fund

Missouri Department of Economic Development
Office of Business Finance
301 W. High Street
PO Box 118   573-751-0295
Jefferson City, MO 65102   Fax: 573-526-1567

The Missouri Department of Economic Development administers a micro-lending program, which provides low interest loans to for-profit businesses in the urban areas in St. Louis and Kansas City. Funds may be used to start a new business; purchase business equipment, inventory, working capital, acquisition of business assets or other expansion purposes of the an existing business. It may also be used to provide an equity match for leveraging a commercial loan, secure lines of credit or secure gap financing from a conventional commercial lender. They may not exceed 50% of the entrepreneurs' total financial need. Interested entrepreneurs may contact the local program administer:

St. Louis Minority Business Council
720 Olive Street, Suite 1630
St. Louis, MO 63101   314-241-1143
www.slmbc.org/

Douglass National Bank
1670 East 63rd Street
Kansas City, MO 64110   816-822-8560

* Community Development Corporation of Kansas City

2420 E. Linwood Blvd., Suite 400   816-924-5800
Kansas City, MO 64109   Fax: 816-921-3350
www.cdcofkc.org

Provides microloan business assistance to small businesses located in a five-county area; assists entrepreneurs whose credit needs are $25,000 and under.

* Thomas Hill Enterprise Center

1714 Prospect Dr., Suite A   660-385-6550
Macon, MO 63552   800-470-8625
www.e-center.org

The Thomas Hill Enterprise Center offers a variety of programs and services to help businesses and communities grow. They provide Community Planning, Business Training, and Computer Training.

* Missouri Export Finance Program

P.O. Box 118   573-526-4967
Jefferson City, MO 65102-0118   Fax: 573-526-1567
www.ded.state.mo.us/business/internationalmarketing

Missouri companies that need financial assistance exporting to foreign markets can use programs of the Export and Import Bank of the United States(Ex-Im Bank) and the Small Business Administration (SBA) through a joint project that provides local access for Missouri businesses. There are primarily two programs available, Working Capital Loan Guarantees and Export Credit Insurance. These programs are designed to help small and medium-sized businesses that have exporting potential but need funds or risk insurance to produce and market goods or services for export.

Export Credit Insurance: The state of Missouri offers assistance in obtaining export credit insurance through the Export/Import Bank of the US to take the risk out of selling to customers overseas. The Missouri program, which insures both commercial and political risks, guarantees an exporter that once his goods are shipped, he will be paid. Insured receivables can enhance an exporter's ability to obtain export financing and allow an exporter to offer more attractive credit terms to foreign buyers.

* Workplace Readiness for Women

Trish Rogers
Central Ozarks Private Industry Council
1202 Forum Drive   800-638-1401 ext. 153
Rolla, MO 65401   Fax: 573-364-7030

This particular program provides skills for employment in manufacturing industries for women living in Camden,

Laclede, and Pulaski Counties. Training includes classroom instruction, one-on-one instruction and tutoring, computer training and work experience assignments with private employers who agree to provide the necessary supervision and work experience to assist participants with skills development and transition into employment in the manufacturing industry.

* Workforce Preparation for Women

Dr. Nancy Wegge, Consortium Director
Jefferson College   573-431-1951
Hillsboro, MO 63050   Fax: 573-431-9397

This program is currently served in two Missouri locations; Mineral Area College in Park Hills and Jefferson College in Hillsboro. These programs focus on self-esteem, foundation skills and competencies as identified by an assessment process, and a workforce preparation plan developed by each student. Experts from education, business, and industry serve as speakers and consultants for the training sessions. Furthermore, the program matches each student with a mentor.

* Capital for Entrepreneurs

4747 Troost Ave.   816-561-4646
Kansas City, MO 64110   Fax: 816-756-1530

Seed capital fund divided into three separate funds of $1 million each: Fund for Women, Fund for Hispanics, and Fund for African-Americans.

* Missouri Enterprise Business Assistance Center

800 West 14th Street, Suite 111   573-364-8570
Rolla, MO 65401   800-956-2682
www.missourienterprise.org   Fax: 573-364-6323

Missouri Enterprise Business Assistance Center is a nonprofit corporation dedicated to helping Missouri business succeed. Their integrated programs provide the resources you need to build a successful enterprise.

* Environmental Improvement and Energy Resource Authority

Missouri Department of Natural Resources
P.O. Box 744
Jefferson City, MO 65102-0744   573-751-4919
www.dnr.state.mo.us/eiera/eiera.htm

The Authority may issue tax-exempt bonds or notes to companies for projects that would reduce, prevent or control the pollution of air or water, or provide for proper methods of solid waste disposal. The Authority also may issue bonds for the construction or installation of energy producing facilities.

* Environmental Improvement and Energy Resources Authority

Market Development Loans
P.O. Box 744
Jefferson City, MO 65102   573-751-4919
www.dnr.state.mo.us/eiera/eiera.htm

Loans of up to $75,000 are available to companies for equipment purchases which enable the recovering and recycling of materials. After three years, if all the loan criteria are met, the loan is forgiven and repayment is not required.

* State Treasurer's Office

Missouri First Linked Deposit Program
P.O. Box 210   573-751-2372
Jefferson City, MO 65102-0210   800-662-8257
www.sto.state.mo.us

The Small Business Program: A portion of these deposits are reserved for small businesses under 25 jobs with the maximum loan amount of $100,000. The interest rate to the borrower is capped at 75% of an average rate typically imposed on small businesses.

* Missouri Women's Council

421 East Durkin Street
Jefferson City, MO 65101
Mailing Address:
P.O. Box 1684   573-751-0810
Jefferson City, MO 65102   877-426-9284
www.womenscouncil.org   Fax: 573-751-8835

This program is designed to help Missouri's women achieve economic self-sufficiency by supporting education, training, and leadership opportunities. Each year the Missouri Women's Council reviews pilot program proposals across the state and selects projects to fund, which promote training, employment and support Missouri women in the work place.

* Loans For Farmers

Farm Service Agency
U.S. Department of Agriculture
Parkade Center
601 Business Loop 70W, Suite 225   573-876-0925
Columbia, MO 65203   Fax: 573-876-0935
http://www.fsa.usda.gov/mo/

The Farm Service Agency provides Direct and Guaranteed Loans to farmers through a variety of programs, including:

Farm Ownership Loans: purchase farmland, construct or repair buildings and other fixtures, and promote soil and water conservation. Up to $200,000.

Operating Loans: purchase items needed for a successful farm operation, such as livestock, farm equipment, feed, seed, fuel, farm chemicals, insurance, and other operating expenses. Can also be used to pay for minor improvements. Up to $200,000.

Beginning Farmer and Rancher Loans: provides funds to beginning and farmers and ranchers who are unable to obtain financing elsewhere.

Downpayment Farm Ownership Loans for Beginning Farmers: helps beginning farmers and ranchers purchase a farm or ranch. Also provides a way for retiring farmers to transfer their land to a future generation of farmers and ranchers. Applicant must have a downpayment of 10% and FSA with finance 40%, with the remaining balance from a commercial lender. Purchase price cannot exceed $250,000.

Loans to Socially Disadvantaged Farmers/Ranchers: helps socially disadvantaged applicants buy and operate family-size farms and ranches.

Youth Loans: Made to youths to establish and operate income-producing projects with the participation in 4-H clubs, Future Farmers of America, and similar organizations. Up to $5,000.

Emergency Loan Assistance: provides loans to help producers recover from production and physical losses due to drought, flooding, and other natural disasters, or quarantine. Up to $500,000.

Beginning Farmer and Rancher Land Contract Guarantee Pilot Program: "prompt payment guarantee" from FSA. FSA will provide payment to seller two times if the beginning farmer does not pay. Program is tested in IN, IA, ND, OR, PA and WI.

Farm Ownership and Operating Loan Guarantees: FSA will guarantee loans up to $782,000.

* Small Business Administration (SBA)

323 West 8th St., Suite 501
Kansas City, MO 64105-1500   816-374-6701

200 N. Broadway, Suite 1500   314-539-6600
St Louis, MO 63102   Fax: 314-539-3785
www.sba.gov/mo

The Missouri Small Business Administration Office delivers a variety of programs and services, such as startup and operational assistance through small business training and counseling, financial assistance for startup's, business opportunities and much more.

Montana

* Department of Commerce

301 S. Park Ave.   406-841-2700
P.O. Box 200501   800-221-8015 (in MT)
Helena, MT 59601-0501   Fax: 406-841-2701
http://commerce.state.mt.us

Economic Development Division: Offers a variety of programs aimed at assisting start-up and existing businesses with the technical and financial assistance necessary for their success. Works closely with other department divisions, state agencies, and federal and private programs, as well as local development groups, chambers and similar organizations.

The Census and Economic Information Center (CEIC): The official source of census data for Montana, the Center maintains a collection of documents and computer-retrievable files that address the economy and population of the state (historical as well as current), including special papers and annual, quarterly and monthly statistical reports from federal agencies and other Montana state agencies.

Montana Health Facility Authority: Issues revenue bonds or notes to finance or refinance projects involving construction, renovation, or equipment purchases for public or private nonprofit health care programs. The MHFA lends its bond proceeds to participating health care facilities at costs below those offered by commercial lending institutions, thereby substantially lowering the facilities' borrowing expenses. In some instances, however, the MHFA includes commercial lending institutions in the financing to provide credit enhancement or private placement for the bonds. The MHFA may issue its notes and bonds, which are not general obligations of the state, for a single entity or a pool of health care facilities. Eligible health facilities may include hospitals, clinics, nursing homes, centers for the developmentally disabled or a variety of other health facilities.

Microbusiness Finance: Montana "micro" business companies with fewer than 10 full-time equivalent employees and annual gross revenues under $500,000 can receive loans of up to $35,000 from the program's network of regional revolving loan funds lending directly to businesses. The loan program is designed to fund economically sound business projects that are unable to obtain commercial financing. Companies must provide a detailed written business plan and may be required to participate in business training classes. In addition to financing, borrowers receive technical assistance and consulting to help assure their success.

Research and Development Financing: Montana Science and Technology Alliance provides $13.1 million in matching capital, from the Permanent Coal Tax Trust Fund, for research and development projects at Montana public universities. 406-444-2778

Growth Through Agriculture: Projects must embody innovative agricultural products or processes. Amounts: $50,000 in any one round, $150,000 to any one firm.

Seed Capital Program: provides funding for early-state entrepreneurial companies. The emphasis for funding is on technological companies but other companies can receive financing as well. The program may loan up to $350,000 in a single financing round, and up to a maximum of $750,000 to any one company over time.

Trade Program: Mission is to identify opportunities for worldwide and domestic trade and to provide representation, information and technical assistance. More specifically, the Trade Program provides: trade consultation, Marketing/Country reports, trade leads, trade show assistance, special promotions for Montana made products and services, tourism promotion services in the Far East.

Made in Montana program: Works to elevate the status of Montana-made products in the marketplace and to educate Montanans about the diversity of products manufactured in their state.

NxLevel: This is an on-line program that prepares business owners with basic business training. It also will walk the business owner through each step of preparing a business plan. {www.nxlevelmontana.org}

Revolving Loan Funds: There are a variety of local and regional revolving loan funds (RFL) in the state, with many of them being co-located. A list of RFL's can be found at {http://mtfinanceonline.com/RLFlist.html}.

Regional Development Office: Montana is divided into five areas with each having a Regional Development Officer (RDO) that serves as a representative for the Department of Commerce. Their primary goal is to provide technical assistance to businesses so they can get funding for start-ups, expansions, and retention projects. {http://commerce.state.mt.us/BRD/BRD_RD.html}

West Regional Development Office
Eric Hanson
15 Depot Park   406-257-2259
Kalispell, MT 59901   Fax: 406-758-2805
Area of Operation: Lincoln, Flathead, Sanders, Lake, Missoula, Mineral and Ravali Counties.

South Central Regional Development Office
Al Jones
2004 Miles Avenue   406-655-1696
Billings, MT 59102   Fax: 406-655-0899
Area of Operation: Meagher, Park, Carbon, Stillwater, Sweet Grass, Yellowstone, Big Horn, Musselshell, Golden Valley, and Wheatland Counties.

Southwest Regional Development Office
Terry Dimock
301 S Park
Helena, MT 59601
Mailing Address:
P.O. Box 200505   406-841-2737
Helena, MT 59620-0505   Fax: 406-841-2731
Area of Operation: Lewis & Clark, Powell, Granite, Deer Lodge, Jefferson, Broadwater, Silver Bow, Beaverhead, Madison, and Gallatin Counties.

Eastern Montana Regional Development Office
Tod Kasten
P.O. Box 520   405-485-3374
Circle, Mt 59215   Fax: 406-485-3376
Area of Operation: Valley, Daniels, Sheridan, Roosevelt, McCone, Richland, Dawson, Prarie, Wibaux, Fallon, Carter, Powder River, Custer, Treasure, Rosebud, and Garfield counties.

North Central Regional Development Office
Randy Hanson
48 2nd Avenue, Room 211
Havre, MT 59501
Mailing Address:
P.O. Box 311   406-262-9579
Havre, MT 59501-0311   Fax: 406-262-9581
Area of Operation: Glacier, Toole, Liberty, Hill, Blaine, Phillips, Petroleum, Fergus, Judith Basin, Choteau, Cascade, Teton, and Pondera Counties.

* USDA Rural Development State Office
P.O. Box 850   406-585-2580
Bozeman, MT 59771   Fax: 406-585-2565
www.rurdev.usda.gov/mt
B&I Guaranteed Loan Program: The Business and Industry (B&I) Guaranteed Loan program provides up to an 80% guarantee on traditional lender loans to businesses. The primary purpose of the program is to create and maintain employment and improve the economic climate of the rural community by providing the financial backing for new and expanding businesses.

Rural Business Enterprise Grant: The Rural Business Enterprise Grant Program provides grants for development of revolving loan funds and to provide technical assistance to small emerging private businesses.

Cooperative Services: Cooperative Services can help rural residents who are trying to form new cooperative businesses or improve the operations of an existing cooperative by providing technical assistance, conducting cooperative research, and producing information products to promote public understanding of cooperatives.

* Montana Manufacturing Extension Center (MMEC)
MSU Advanced Technology Park
960-A Technology Boulevard
Bozeman, MT 59718
Mailing address:
P.O. Box 174255   406-994-3812
Bozeman, MT 59717-4255   Fax: 406-994-3391
www.mmec.montana.EDU
Improves the competitiveness of Montana manufacturers through direct, unbiased engineering and managerial assistance in partnership with public and private resources. MMEC field engineers help companies obtain the highest output from their people, equipment, and capital. They make

"house calls" and provide free initial consultation. Their assistance includes, but is not limited to: productivity and quality audits, facility layouts, materials handling, ISO 9000 and quality assurance, benchmarking, managing growth, capacity planning, feasibility assessment, equipment justification, process design and improvement, cycle time reduction, production management, cost/benefit analysis, cost reduction, product costing, make/buy analysis, inventory analysis, supplier identification and relations, payroll incentive systems, materials requirements planning (MRP), and more.

* Montana Local Technical Assistance Program LTAP

Montana State University-Bozeman
Civil Engineering Department
416 Cobleigh Hall
P.O. Box 173910   800-541-6671
Bozeman, MT 59717-3910   Fax 406-994-1697
Email: mtltap@coe.montana.edu
www.coe.montana.edu/ltap

Each LTAP Center tailors its resources to meet the particular needs of the clients they serve. Basic responsibilities include: Publish a quarterly newsletter; Serve as a clearinghouse for local transportation agencies to obtain publications, video tape and other technology resource materials; Maintain a comprehensive up-to-date mailing list of local officials having transportation responsibilities; Conduct training for local transportation agencies; Provide information on new and existing technology; Conduct program evaluations to assure the needs of local transportation agencies are being met.

* Montana World Trade Center

Gallagher Business Building, Suite 257
The University of Montana   406-243-6982
Missoula, MT 59812-6798   Fax: 406-243-5259
www.mwtc.org

The Montana World Trade Center is a nonprofit organization whose purpose is to help Montana and regional businesses establish or strengthen their international commercial capabilities. The Center works to develop untapped international trade opportunities for the state and region and help businesses capitalize on opportunities to expand their market share around the world.

* One Stop Licensing Center

Montana Department of Revenue
P.O. Box 8003
Mitchell Building   406-444-6900
Helena, MT. 59604   Fax: 406-444-0750
http://discoveringmontana.com/revenue

Here are a few of the benefits of one-stop licensing: One point of contact for obtaining or renewing a majority of the licenses required to operate the business. One master form to obtain or renew these licenses, eliminating the redundancy of filling out multiple forms. Renewal forms may be completed by telephone. One payment (writing one check) rather than making a separate payment for each license. Credit cards will be accepted. A significant reduction in the labor and paperwork involved in licensing the business.

* Family Business Program

College of Business
Montana State University

P.O. Box 173040   406-994-6796
Bozeman, MT 59717-3040   Fax: 406-994-6206
www.montana.edu/wwwdb/FamilyBusiness/FamilyBusiness.html

The purpose of the Family Business Program is to provide educational opportunities and resources to family-owned businesses; in addition, the program provides educational opportunities and resources to service providers of family businesses.

* Montana Capital Companies

The Glacier Springs Company
P.O. Box 2644   406-727-7500
Black Eagle, MT 59403   Fax: 406-454-1085

Southwest Montana Development Corp.
P.O. Box 507
Butte, MT 59703   406-723-4349

Great Falls Capital Corporation
104 2nd Street South, Suite 203
Great Falls, MT 59401   406-761-2000

First Montana Capital Corporation
310 West Spruce St.   406-721-8300
Missoula, MT 59802   Fax: 403-721-6300

The Montana Capital Companies Act is designed to stimulate economic activity in Montana by providing tax credit incentives to investors in Montana capital companies, who in turn provide debt and equity financing to new or expanding qualified Montana Businesses. The Department of Commerce is responsible for oversight of the tax credits, qualified investments, and general operations of Glacier Venture Fund.

* Department of Agriculture

Agriculture/Livestock Building
P.O. Box 200201   406-444-3144
Helena, MT 59620-0201   Fax: 406-444-5409
http://agr.state.mt.us

Junior Agriculture Loan Program: Direct, lower-interest rate financing to active members of rural youth organizations for junior livestock and other agricultural business loans. May also make direct loans to youths unable to participate as members of such organizations. Projects can involve crop and livestock production, custom farming, marketing and distribution processing. Loans shall not exceed $7,000.

Rural Assistance Loan Program: Provides loans to farmers and ranchers with modes financial investments in agriculture. Available to those who are unable to qualify for financing from commercial lenders. Maximum loan amount is $50,000, not to exceed 80 percent of the loan value. Funds can be used to finance agricultural property such as livestock and farm machinery, improvements such as barns and irrigation systems, annual operating expenses, and agricultural land.

Montana Growth Through Agriculture Act (MGTA): Intent of the MGTA is to create jobs and expand small agricultural business opportunities. The Programs receives a level of coal severance tax revenues for the purpose of funding seed capital loans, market enhancement and research grants, agricultural business incubators and foreign trade office activities.

Seed Capital Loans: Funds are specifically intended for the commercialization and marketing of new and innovative agricultural products or processes. Maximum loan amount in any one round of financing is $50,000.

Beginning Farmer/Rancher Loan Program: The Montana Beginning Farmer/Rancher Loan Program is a tax-exempt bond program designed to assist Beginning Farmers/Raanchers in the State of Montana to acquire agricultural property at lower interest rates.

* Resource Development Bureau
Department of Natural Resources and Conservation
P.O. Box 20161
1625 11th Ave.   406-444-2074
Helena, MT 59620-1601   Fax: 406-444-2684
www.dnrc.state.mt.us

Resource Outreach Programs: The state's coal severance tax provides grants, and two bonding authorities fund loans. Loans and grants available for such diverse water development projects as dam and reservoir construction, streambank stabilization and erosion control, development of water conservation measures, and water and sewer projects.

Reclamation and Development Grant Program: Funds projects that protect and restore the environment from damages resulting from mineral development and projects that meet other crucial state needs. Other projects may qualify if they enhance Montana's economy or develop, promote, protect, or otherwise further Montana's total environment and public interest.

State Revolving Fund Program: A loan program for wastewater systems and is proposed to be used for landfills. This allows communities to obtain loans at 4% to finance these types of infrastructure.

Private Water Development Program: This program is made up of loans and grants. The low-interest loans may be used for the development of water-related projects, efficient use of resources, best management practices for the agricultural community, and water and wastewater projects. The grants are made to help private entities to meet regulatory requirements that pertain to water use in Montana. The grants are for up to $5,000.

Range Improvement Loan Program: Low-interest loans to Montana's farmers and ranchers for rangeland improvements and development.

Renewable Resource Loans to Private Entities: Loans for private water development projects up to $200,000 or 80% of fair market value of the security given for the project.

* Loans For Farmers
Farm Service Agency
U.S. Department of Agriculture
P.O. Box 670
Bozeman, MT 59771   406-587-6872
http://www.fsa.usda.gov/mt/

The Farm Service Agency provides Direct and Guaranteed Loans to farmers through a variety of programs, including:

Farm Ownership Loans: purchase farmland, construct or repair buildings and other fixtures, and promote soil and water conservation. Up to $200,000.

Operating Loans: purchase items needed for a successful farm operation, such as livestock, farm equipment, feed, seed, fuel, farm chemicals, insurance, and other operating expenses. Can also be used to pay for minor improvements. Up to $200,000.

Beginning Farmer and Rancher Loans: provides funds to beginning and farmers and ranchers who are unable to obtain financing elsewhere.

Downpayment Farm Ownership Loans for Beginning Farmers: helps beginning farmers and ranchers purchase a farm or ranch. Also provides a way for retiring farmers to transfer their land to a future generation of farmers and ranchers. Applicant must have a downpayment of 10% and FSA with finance 40%, with the remaining balance from a commercial lender. Purchase price cannot exceed $250,000.

Loans to Socially Disadvantaged Farmers/Ranchers: helps socially disadvantaged applicants buy and operate family-size farms and ranches.

Youth Loans: Made to youths to establish and operate income-producing projects with the participation in 4-H clubs, Future Farmers of America, and similar organizations. Up to $5,000.

Emergency Loan Assistance: provides loans to help producers recover from production and physical losses due to drought, flooding, and other natural disasters, or quarantine. Up to $500,000.

Beginning Farmer and Rancher Land Contract Guarantee Pilot Program: "prompt payment guarantee" from FSA. FSA will provide payment to seller two times if the beginning farmer does not pay. Program is tested in IN, IA, ND, OR, PA and WI.

Farm Ownership and Operating Loan Guarantees: FSA will guarantee loans up to $782,000.

* Small Business Administration (SBA)
10 West 15th Street, Suite 1100   406-441-1081
Helena, MT 59626   Fax: 406-441-1090
www.sba.gov/mt

The Montana Small Business Administration Office delivers a variety of programs and services, such as startup and operational assistance through small business training and counseling, financial assistance for startup's, business opportunities and much more.

* Montana Department of Revenue
Office of Research and Information
Sam Mitchell Building
125 N. Roberts
P.O Box 5805
Helena, MT 59604-5805   406-444-6900
www.state.mt.us/revenue

Montana is one of very few states imposing neither a general sales tax nor a use tax. In addition, Montana also offers specific tax incentives to aid businesses with start-up and expansion. These include such topics as: property tax incentives, general individual income tax and corporation license tax incentives, natural resource-related tax incentives, and other significant tax incentives.

Assistance for Business Clinics: The Department of Revenue, in conjunction with the Internal Revenue Service and various state government agencies, offers workshops statewide designed to assist new business start-ups and small businesses. These informative workshops are offered in a variety of locations each summer and cover many employer-related topics, including tax filing obligations.

* Montana Board of Investments

2401 Colonial Drive, 3rd Floor
Helena, MT 59601
Mailing Address:
P.O. Box 200126   406-444-1365
Helena, MT 59620-0126   Fax: 406-449-6579
www.investmentmt.com

The Montana Board cannot make direct loans to businesses; the staff however is able to work with businesses to develop a loan package tailored to the companies needs. The following programs are accessed through banks and approved lending institutions.

Business Loan Participation Program Funded From the Coal Tax Trust: There is fixed-rate financing up to 25 years in this program. The maximum participation is about $64 million, which 10% of the Trust. Job creation credits can reduce the interest by up to 2.5%.

Linked Deposit Business Loan Program Funded From the Coal Tax Trust: Fixed-rate financing for up to 20 years is available. The Board invests in a one year CD with the lender for the life of the loan. The CD amount is reduced annually in line with the loan principal pay-down. The lender will pledge qualifying investments as collateral with the State Treasurer.

Guaranteed Loan Purchase Program Funded From the Coal Tax Trust: Fixed-rate financing is available for up to 30 years. The Board will purchase 100% of the guarantee portion of the loan. The interest rate is reduced up to 2.5% with job creation credits.

Value-Added Business Loan Funded From the Coal Tax Trust: This offers a maximum 15-year loan with 2 ¼% interest rate for the first five years, 6% for the second five years, and the posted rate for the remaining years. If 10-14 jobs are created/retained, the business qualifies for a loan rate at 4% for five years. If 15 jobs are created/retained, the business qualifies for a loan rate of 2% for 5 years. The loan range is from $250,000 to $6.4 million. The borrow's business must add value material and or products.

* Montana Department of Administration

General Services Division
Room 165 Mitchell Building
125 North Roberts Street
P.O. Box 200135   406-444-2575
Helena, MT 59620-0136   Fax: 406-444-2529
www.discoveringmontana.com/doa/gsd

The department develops and administers a cost-effective, professional procurement program for the State of Montana by ensuring fair competition, maximizing the purchasing value of public funds, and providing leadership and services for innovative, responsive and accountable public procurement. In addition, they offer State Procurement Bureau Training on purchasing, through the Professional Development Center on state procurement issues.

Nebraska

* Department of Economic Development

P.O. Box 94666   402-471-3111
301 Centennial Mall South   800-426-6505 (in NE)
Lincoln, NE 68509   Fax: 402-471-3378
www.neded.org   TDD: 402-471-3441

One-Stop Business Assistance Program: Provides assistance on identifying, marketing and finance information; business information and research, regulations, licenses, fees, and other state requirements for business operation.

Skilled Training Employment Program (STEP): Offers a comprehensive, on-the-job training program for new and expanding businesses.

Government Procurement Assistance: Helps create additional markets.

Match Marketing: Assists with matching Nebraska buyers and suppliers.

Technical Assistance: Increases productivity and competitiveness.

Site Location Assistance: Includes facilitating access to programs.

Industrial Revenue Bonds (IRB): All Nebraska counties and municipalities, as well as the Nebraska Investment Finance Authority, are authorized to issue IRBs to finance land, buildings and equipment for industrial projects. The rate of interest is normally lower than on most loans.

Nebraska Investment Finance Authority: Issues IRBs for land, building and equipment for industrial enterprises, as well as provides financing for housing.

Community Improvement Financing: This is Nebraska's version of Tax Increment Financing, a method of financing public improvements associated with a private development project in a blighted and substandard area by using the projected increase in the property tax revenue which will result from the private development.

Local Option Municipal Economic Development Act: Provides the ability for communities to add a sales or property tax for economic development projects.

Nebraska Energy Fund: Provides low-interest loans for energy efficiency improvements.

Nebraska Redevelopment Act: Authorizes Community Improvement Financing for real estate and equipment in a project that adds at least 500 new jobs and $50 million of new investment.

Office of International Trade and Investment (OITI): Works with existing businesses to expand their international marketing efforts, as well as foster international manufacturing investments in the state.

Toolkit for Start-up and Existing Business: The toolkit site has an enormous amount of information covering business needs. From starting a business to finances, taxes, and business law, owners will be connected to resources they need to accomplish their business goals. {http://assist.neded.org}

* Rural Development Administration

Federal Building, Room 308
100 Centennial Mall North   402-437-5551
Lincoln, NE 68508   Fax: 402-437-5408
www.rurdev.usda.gov/ne

The mission of the Rural Business Service is to enhance the quality of life for all rural Americans by providing leadership in building competitive businesses that can prosper in both the domestic and global trading marketplace.

Business and Industry Loan Guarantee: This program provides loan guarantees for business and industrial development to create and maintain employment, expand, and to improve economic climate. Projects include: business/industrial acquisition, construction, enlargement, modernization, real estate, buildings, equipment, working capital, and refinancing. Eligible applicants include traditional lenders, individuals, partnerships, nonprofits, corporations, Indian tribes, and cooperatives.

Rural Economic Development Loan and Grant Program: This program provides for a wide range of rural economic development and job creation projects that will improve the economic condition of rural areas. Loans and grants are made to the Rural Utilities Service (RUS) electric and telephone borrowers who use the funds to provide financing for business and community development projects. Projects may include: business expansion and start-up, community development, incubator, medical, training and technology projects, and revolving loan funds.

Rural Business Enterprise Grant: This program provides grants that facilitate and finance the development of small and emerging private business enterprises in rural areas through establishing small business revolving loan funds, acquisition of land, buildings, and infrastructure to enhance business development or by providing technical assistance. Eligible applicants include public bodies, nonprofits, and Indian tribes.

Rural Business Opportunity Grants: To provide grants for technical assistance for business development and to conduct economic planning in rural areas. Funds may be used to develop project feasibility studies, technical assistance, or for business and economic development, planning and training. Eligible applicants include public bodies, nonprofits, federally recognized tribal groups, and cooperatives.

Intermediary Relending Program: To provide intermediary loans to ultimate recipients for community development projects, establishment and expansion of businesses and creation and/or saving of jobs. Eligible applicants include public bodies/agencies (local/state government), nonprofits, Indian tribes, and cooperatives.

* Dollar and Energy Saving Loans

Nebraska Energy Office
Box 95085
Lincoln, NE 68509
www.nol.org/home/NEO/loan/index.html

402-471-2867
Fax: 402-471-3064

Energy saving loans are offered statewide by the Nebraska Energy Office and the state's lending institutions. The interest rate is 5% or less, but may be adjusted semi-annually. Adjustments do not affect existing loans. Check with a lender or the Nebraska Energy Office for the current rate.

* Rural Business Development Fund

Robert E. Hobbs, Loan Coordinator
16 West 11th Street
P.O. Box 2288
Kearney, NE 68848-2288
www.mnca.net

308-865-5675
308-865-5681

Small Enterprises Economic Development Project, Rural Economic and Community Development, State of Nebraska. LB144, private grants. Provides microenterprise loans, loan counseling, credit analysis, developing business plan and entrepreneurial training.

* Northeast Nebraska Development District

Business Loan Programs
Northeast Nebraska Economic Development District
111 S. 1st St.
Norfolk, NE 68701
www.nenedd.org

402-379-1150
Fax: 402-379-9207

Exists to promote and assist the growth and development of business and industrial concerns within Northeast Nebraska. Priority will be given to fixed asset financing (land, building, equipment); however, working capital can also be financed. Generally, loans will range from $10,000 to $100,000 (maximum).

* Nebraska Department of Revenue

301 Centennial Mall South
P.O. Box 94818
Lincoln, NE 58509-4818
www.revenue.state.ne.us

402-471-5729
800-742-7474

Employment and Investment Growth Act: With a $3 million investment in qualified property and addition of 30 full-time employees, a business qualifies for: direct refund of all sales and use taxes paid on purchases of qualified property; 5% tax credit on the amount of the total compensation paid to employees; 10% tax credit on total investment in qualified property, 5 and 10% tax credits applied to income tax liability or used to obtain refund of sales and use taxes paid on other purchases.

With a $10 million investment in qualified property and addition of 100 full-time employees, a business qualifies for: all of the above plus up to a 15 year personal property tax exemption on newly acquired: turbine-powered aircraft, mainframe computers and peripheral components, equipment used directly in processing agricultural products. Investment in qualified property resulting in a net gain of $20 million with no increased employment qualifies a business for direct refund of all sales and use taxes paid on purchases of qualified property.

Employment Expansions and Investment Incentive Act: Provides tax credits for any business which increase investment by at least $75,000 and increase net employment by an average of two full-time positions during a taxable year. Credits of $1,500 per net new employee and $1,000 per $75,000 net new investment may be used to reduce a portion of the taxpayer's income tax liability or to obtain a refund of sales and use taxes paid.

Enterprise Zones: Within these areas, tax credits are given for qualifying businesses which increase employment and make investments in the area.

* Nebraska Investment Finance Authority (NIFA)

200 Commerce Court
1230 O St.
Lincoln, NE 68508-1402
www.nifa.org

800-204-NIFA
402-434-3900
Fax: 402-434-3921

Beginning Farmer/Rancher Program: The NIFA Beginning Farmer/Rancher Program enables farmers or ranchers to obtain loans at lower interest rates than those available in the conventional farm credit markets. This is made possible by the issuance of a tax-exempt bond by NIFA to the lender, providing the lender with interest that is exempt from federal and Nebraska state income tax. Therefore, the loan can be priced to provide the lender with a desired effective yield due to the tax savings on the bond.

Community Outreach: NIFA provides community outreach and technical assistance services to housing providers, community organizations, community officials, housing advocates, developers, builders and lenders to initiate, facilitate and expedite the development of affordable housing. The technical assistance provided is to better inform the public of the financial resources available in the State; the various programs NIFA has to offer; and the processes by which housing development occurs.

BINGO Bonds: NIFA's loan guarantee program, Building Infrastructure in Nebraska for Greater Opportunities (BINGO), is designed to stimulate the development of eligible projects in rural and targeted areas by leveraging local resources. When using the BINGO Bond program, the original principal balance of any loan to be guaranteed by NIFA may not exceed $250,000 per phase; $500,000 per project and may only finance costs associated with capital improvement funding. Working capital and operating expenses are not eligible for funding. The loan-to-value ratio should be at least 70 percent and any credit-enhancement must be acceptable to NIFA. Eligible developers include individuals, partnerships, communities and limited liability companies, both nonprofit and for-profit, depending on the eligible project, with substantial development experience and/or access to such experience capable of completing the project.

* Commission on Local Government Innovation and Restructuring

521 S. 14th Street, Suite 30   402-471-8697
Lincoln, NE 68508   Fax: 402-471-3079
Email: lwood@mail.state.ne.us
www.state.ne.us/home/clgir

The Goals of the grant program are to stimulate innovation, cooperation, and restructuring of local government in Nebraska; assist in planning innovative, restructuring, or cooperative projects; encourage collaborative or joint use of facilities and capital equipment by local governments; collect evaluations of efforts in government services innovation, restructuring and cooperation; and to identify legislative changes needed to encourage innovation, cooperation and restructuring of local government in Nebraska.

* Nebraska Business Development Center (NBDC)

Nebraska Business Development Center
College of Business Administration
Roskens Hall Room 415
University of Nebraska at Omaha
Omaha, NE 68182-0248   402-554-2521
http://nbdc.unomaha.edu/

NBDC is an educational service designed to help business owners, especially small and medium-sized businesses, compete more evenly with larger firms that have the resources to employ similar consulting services. NBDC works with individuals who wish to start a company, firms that are planning to expand or pursue new business opportunities and firms that are experiencing operations or financial difficulties.

* Nebraska Development Academy

58 Filley Hall
University of Nebraska, Lincoln   800-328-2851
Lincoln, NE 68508-0947   402-472-1724
www.state.ne.us/home/NDN/academy/html

The Nebraska Development Academy committee is the educational arm of the Partnership for Rural Nebraska. The Partnership for Rural Nebraska is a cooperative commitment between the Rural Development Commission, State of Nebraska, University of Nebraska, the United States Department of Agriculture, and the Nebraska Development Network. The Academy provides a systematic way to access education, training and technical assistance in leadership, community, and economic development.

* Nebraska Rural Development Commission

1200 N Street, Suite #610   402-471-6002
Lincoln, NE 68508-2022   877-814-4707
www.rdc.state.ne.us   Fax: 402-471-8690

The Nebraska Cooperative Development Center was created in response to both demand for services and a larger opportunity to create more sustainable rural communities in Nebraska. Cooperative development as a strategy has demonstrated its ability to create economic opportunities that increase the wealth status of its members, improve the economic condition of its area, contribute toward rural community revitalization, and increase the competitiveness of locally owned and operated enterprises. The purpose of the Commission is to foster sustainable community and economic development initiatives. These initiatives should enable Nebraska communities to realize their own goals, thereby contributing to the growth and well-being of the entire state. The Commission is affiliated with National Rural Development Partnership (NRDP). NRDP is a national partnership of states and the national government to support effective development throughout rural America.

Nebraska Rural Partners:
Nebraska Development Network: The Network is a partnership of over 600 public and private organizations committed to supporting community-based development throughout Nebraska.

Nebraska Community Builders: Community Builders is an initiative of the Network and is a process to empower local residents to engage in more effective community building and stimulate regional collaboration through partnerships.

* Nebraska Enterprise Opportunity Network (NEON)

P.O. Box 6605
Lincoln, NE 68506-0605   402-420-9589
Email: neonneb@aol.com
http://neon.neded.org

NEON's mission is to create, expand and support small and micro business opportunities for individuals and communities with limited resources. NEON strives to achieve its mission through networking, training, advocacy, and sharing resources. They are a member-based association of nonprofit organizations and public agencies which provide training, technical services, and micro lending assistance (loans up to $25,000) to Nebraska's micro businesses (five or fewer employees).

* Loans For Farmers

Farm Service Agency
U.S. Department of Agriculture
7131 A Street
Lincoln, NE 68510   402-437-5600
http://www.fsa.usda.gov/ne/

The Farm Service Agency provides Direct and Guaranteed Loans to farmers through a variety of programs, including:

Farm Ownership Loans: purchase farmland, construct or repair buildings and other fixtures, and promote soil and water conservation. Up to $200,000.

Operating Loans: purchase items needed for a successful farm operation, such as livestock, farm equipment, feed, seed, fuel, farm chemicals, insurance, and other operating expenses. Can also be used to pay for minor improvements. Up to $200,000.

Beginning Farmer and Rancher Loans: provides funds to beginning and farmers and ranchers who are unable to obtain financing elsewhere.

Downpayment Farm Ownership Loans for Beginning Farmers: helps beginning farmers and ranchers purchase a farm or ranch. Also provides a way for retiring farmers to transfer their land to a future generation of farmers and ranchers. Applicant must have a downpayment of 10% and FSA with finance 40%, with the remaining balance from a commercial lender. Purchase price cannot exceed $250,000.

Loans to Socially Disadvantaged Farmers/Ranchers: helps socially disadvantaged applicants buy and operate family-size farms and ranches.

Youth Loans: Made to youths to establish and operate income-producing projects with the participation in 4-H clubs, Future Farmers of America, and similar organizations. Up to $5,000.

Emergency Loan Assistance: provides loans to help producers recover from production and physical losses due to drought, flooding, and other natural disasters, or quarantine. Up to $500,000.

Beginning Farmer and Rancher Land Contract Guarantee Pilot Program: "prompt payment guarantee" from FSA. FSA will provide payment to seller two times if the beginning farmer does not pay. Program is tested in IN, IA, ND, OR, PA and WI.

Farm Ownership and Operating Loan Guarantees: FSA will guarantee loans up to $782,000.

* Small Business Administration

11145 Mill Valley Rd.   402-221-4691
Omaha, NE 68154   Fax: 402-221-3680
www.sba.gov/ne

The Nebraska Small Business Administration Office delivers a variety of programs and services, such as startup and operational assistance through small business training and counseling, financial assistance for startup's, business opportunities and much more.

* Center for Rural Affairs

Rural Enterprise Assistance Project (REAP)
145 Main St.
P.O. Box 136   402-687-2100
Lyons, NE 68038   Fax: 402-687-2200
www.cfra.org

REAP begins with a community commitment to raise seed capital funds to be used for small business loans. Loan sizes range from a few hundred to several thousand dollars. A program is set up to provide training for members, who are generally start-up and home-based businesses, in business planning, management and finance.

* Nebraska Center for Productivity and Entrepreneurship

CBA 209, P.O. Box 880487   402-472-3353
Lincoln, NE 68588-0487   Fax: 402-472-5855
www.cba.unl.edu/outreach/ent

The Center provides seminars, workshops, and an annual Productivity and Entrepreneurship Conference which are sponsored by the Center to help new businesses, businesses wishing to increase productivity, and people with ideas for new businesses. Persons involved with the Center are also encouraged to participate in the Young Entrepreneurship Program, which provides internships and mentoring for college students wishing to pursue careers in entrepreneurship.

* Nebraska Diplomats, Inc.

P.O. Box 94666   800-426-6505
Lincoln, NE 68509   402-471-3780
http://nediplomats.org/index.html   Fax: 402-471-3778

The Nebraska Diplomats Inc. is a nonprofit corporation with over 475 business executive and community leaders members. They provide a connection for Nebraska leaders without political, organizational or geographical boundaries.

* Agriculture Promotion and Development Division

Department of Agriculture
P.O. Box 94947   800-422-6692
301 Centennial Mall South   402-471-4876
Lincoln, NE 68509-4847   Fax: 402-471-2759
www.agr.state.ne.us/division/apd/apd.htm

This division supports and promotes the buying, selling, and development of Nebraska agricultural products by linking buyer to seller. The division works closely with other agencies, commodity groups, and public and private institutions to seek new and expanding markets for Nebraska products. These resources can be accessed through the division□s extensive database.

* Bureau of Business Research

Department of Economics
University of Nebraska   402-472-2319
Lincoln, NE 68588   Fax: 402-472-3878
www.bbr.unl.edu

The bureau compiles statistical information on business conditions, produces economic forecasts, and reports economic and demographic information of interest to the business community. The bureau maintains economic and population data files by detailed geographic markets in Nebraska and in the United States.

* Department of Environmental Quality

1200 N St., Suite 400
Box 98922   402-471-2186
Lincoln, NE 68509   Fax: 402-471-2909
www.deq.state.ne.us

Funded primarily from a fee on tire sales, the Waste Reduction and Recycle Grant Program allows businesses to seek grants for solid waste management programs and projects. Emphasis is on tire recycling and tire waste reduction, but other projects may be eligible. Grants are awarded twice each year.

* Midland Venture Forum (MVF)

Scott Technology Center
6825 Pine Street   402-393-0459

Omaha, NE 68106　　　　　Fax: 402-955-1790
www.mvforum.com

This group was put together for the purpose of fostering business development and success of high growth companies; promote economic stability and growth; create jobs and diversify the types of businesses in the midlands. Business owners can get support from resources such as venture capital firms, private investors, educational programs, workshops and more.

* Invest Nebraska Corporation

Invest Nebraska Corporation
4701 Innovation Drive　　　　　402.472.2063
Lincoln, NE 68521　　　　　Fax: 402.472.4203
www.investnebraska.com

Invest Nebraska is a nonprofit partnership that helps new and growth-stage companies succeed. They will help businesses find capital, focus on business plans and identify needed resources.

* Nebraska Microenterprise Partnership Fund

P.O. Box 99
312 Main St., #8　　　　　402-846-5757
Walthill, NE 68067　　　　　Fax: 402-846-5219
www.nebbiz.org

Nebraska Microenterprise Partnership Fund (NMPF) raises money from national, state and local levels and then matches those funds with locally based micro-enterprise programs. There are grantees located throughout Nebraska, which offer training and technical assistance in addition to the loans.

Nevada

* State of Nevada Commission on Economic Development

108 E. Proctor St.　　　　　775-687-4325
Carson City, NV 89710　　　　　800-336-1600
www.expand2nevada.com　　　　　Fax: 775-687-4450

555 E. Washington Avenue
Suite 5400　　　　　702-486-2700
Las Vegas, NV 89101　　　　　Fax: 702-486-2701

Commission on Economic Development: Publishes a pamphlet, *Business Assistance*. Acts as a clearinghouse for information and technical assistance. Operates several business assistance programs and performs advertising and public relations activities on behalf of Nevada business. Maintains a computerized inventory of available manufacturing and warehousing buildings, land and corporate office space, and customized site selection.

Procurement Outreach Program: Assists businesses in successfully tapping into this lucrative market by: introducing firms to federal agencies that purchase the products and services they sell; providing assistance to ensure that companies are prepared with all of the tools, knowledge and skills necessary to meet the federal government's specifications and standards, and properly complete bids; offering seminars, marketing fairs, mailing lists and direct assistance as well as the Automated Bidline which is a fax-on demand system allowing instant access to the latest bid and requests for proposal information.

Venture Capital: A potential source of venture capital is the State Public Employees Retirement System that disperses funds through several venture capital pools.

Rural Business Loans: Companies in rural Nevada have additional avenues for financial assistance designed to: lend money to small businesses in need of expansion or start-up financing; assist small businesses in obtaining gap financing to complete their business expansion projects; provide financing to small businesses which meet job creation requirements. Assistance is available through the Nevada Revolving Loan Fund, Rural Economic and Community Development Services, and Rural Nevada Development Corporation.

Train Employees Now: Grants to training providers up to 75% of the total eligible costs with a cap of $1,000 per trainee.

Business Assistance Program: Helps businesses understand environmental rules and explain the permitting process as well as identify sources of financing for pollution control equipment and provide access to the latest information regarding environmental issues.

Nevada's International Trade Program: Goal is to assist Nevada businesses to begin, or expand, exporting to international markets. Services include: Trade Missions, Export Seminars, Export Counseling, International Trade Database, Foreign Buyers Delegations, International Trade Directories.

Foreign Trade Zones: Two zones allow international importers duty-free storage and assembly of foreign products.

Export Financing: Assistance is available through private sector financial institution, the International Trade Program and the federal Export/Import Bank.

Made in Nevada Program: Companies that are licensed and headquartered in Nevada and have at least 50% of their product(s) manufactured in the state will benefit from this program. In addition to the network support, those businesses will receive marketing assistance and help to find other beneficial business assistance. 702-486-2710.
{www.expand2nevada.com/MadeinNevada2/index.htm}

* Rural Development State Office

1390 S. Curry Street　　　　　702-887-1222
Carson, NV 89703　　　　　Fax: 702-885-0841
www.rurdev.usda.gov/nv

Business And Industry Guarantee And Direct Loans: The guaranteed B&I program provides financial assistance to rural businesses by offering guarantees to lenders as an incentive to extend credit in rural areas. If credit is not available elsewhere, Rural Development may provide direct loans to rural borrowers. Loan funds may be used to support the establishment or expansion of businesses, for working capital, machinery and equipment, buildings and real estate, and certain types of debt refinancing. Businesses involved in forestry, aquaculture, growing of hydroponics and mushrooms and commercial nurseries are eligible for assistance in addition to businesses involved in producing value-added products. The primary purpose is to create and maintain employment and improve the economic climate in rural communities.

Intermediary Relending Program: These loans enable Rural Development to finance business facilities and community development projects in communities of 25,000 or less. This is achieved through loans made by Rural Development to nonprofit intermediaries, which in turn provide loans to businesses in a rural area.

Rural Business Enterprise Grant: Rural Development can make Rural Business Enterprise Grants to tribes, public bodies, and nonprofits to assist small and emerging private business enterprises. Funds may be used to conduct feasibility studies, provide technical assistance, or establish a revolving loan fund.

Rural Business Opportunity Grant: Rural Development can make Rural Business Opportunity Grants to tribes, public bodies, and nonprofits to promote economic development initiatives in rural communities with exceptional needs. This is accomplished by providing planning, technical assistance, and training.

Rural Economic Development Loans: Rural Development can provide zero interest loans to Rural Utilities Service financed telephone utilities to promote rural economic development and job creation projects.

Rural Economic Development Grants: Rural Development can provide grants from the Rural Business-Cooperative Service to rural communities through Rural Utilities Service borrowers. These grants can be used for the revolving loan fund for community facilities and infrastructure, and for assistance in conjunction with the Rural Economic Development Loans.

Cooperative Services: The Cooperative Services program helps rural residents form new cooperative businesses and improve the operations of existing cooperatives. To accomplish this, Cooperative Services provides technical assistance, conducts cooperative-related research, and produces information products to promote public understanding of cooperatives. They provide a wide range of assistance for people interested in forming cooperatives.

* Community Business Resource Center
116 E. 7th St., Suite 1   775-841-1420
Carson City, NV 89701   800-337-4590
www.cbrc.org   Fax: 775-841-2221

A one-stop center for business information designed to enhance the economic self-sufficiency of low-and moderate-income individuals by developing their entrepreneurial skills. Services available include training, technical assistance and access to credit.

* Nevada State Development Corporation (NSDC)
Nevada Development Corporation
6572 South McCarran Blvd.   775-826-6172
Reno, NV 89509   800-726-2494

Southern Nevada Development Corporation
1551 Desert Crossing Rd., Suite 100   702-877-9111
Las Vegas, NV 89114   877-732-7101
www.nsdc-loans.com

A private development fund designed to finance growth opportunities for small, sound Nevada businesses which do not qualify for conventional financing. The financing provided by NDCC includes but is not limited to the following: working capital loans secured by primary or subordinated assets; loans secured by fixed assets with longer terms than could be provided by conventional lending sources; loans for the acquisition of a business or interest in a business; subordinated loans in cases where available bank financing is sufficient; loans to refinance existing debt in cases where existing terms present a hardship for the

business. Most loans will probably be in the $50,000 to $150,000 range.

* Small Business Advocate
Center for Business Advocacy and Services
2501 East Sahara Ave., Suite 100   702-486-4335
Las Vegas, NV 89104   Fax: 702-486-4340

Assistance in cutting bureaucratic red tape. Information and expertise in dealing with state, federal, and local agencies.

* Nevada Housing Division
Department of Business and Industry
Northern Office
Evergreen Center   775-687-4258
1802 N. Carson St., Suite 154   800-227-4960
Carson City, NV 89701   Fax: 775-687-4040

Southern Office
Century Park
1771 East Flamingo, Suite 206-B   702-486-7220
Las Vegas, NV 89119   Fax: 702-486-7226
http://nvhousing.state.nv.us

The Housing Division is the designated issuer of tax-exempt mortgage revenue bonds for Nevada. The multifamily bond program provides a financial mechanism for funding affordable housing projects (apartments) via the use of tax-exempt and taxable mortgage revenue bonds.

* NevadaWorks
5905 South Virginia St., Suite 200   775-337-8600
Reno NV, 89502-6024   877-337-8261
www.nevadaworks.com   Fax: 775-337-9589

The Workforce Investment Act provides workforce development services to employers and job seekers through a seamless One-Stop service delivery system. These services are intended to meet both employer demands for a skilled workforce and to increase the employment, retention and earnings of job seekers.

* Nevada Division of Environmental Protection
333 West Nye Lane, Room 104   775-687-4670
Carson City, NV 89706-0851   Fax: 775-687-5856
http://ndep.nv.gov

The Small Business Assistance Program (SBAP) assists with all aspects of compliance, including permitting, reporting, planning, pollution control and prevention technologies. The technical assistance coordinator (TAC) works cooperatively with local governments and other assistance programs to help small businesses comply with environmental regulations. The ombudsman works to inform businesses of the governmental processes, their appeal rights, and promotes small business participation in the development of regulations. The Air Quality Compliance Advisory Panel (CAP) is a panel of professionals who are involved with or own small businesses.

* Industrial Development Revenue Bonds
Nevada Department of Business and Industry
Office of Business Finance and Planning
788 Fairview Lane, Suite 100   775-687-4246
Carson City, NV 89701   Fax: 775-687-4266
http://dbi.state.nv.us/bfp

A special type of loan to qualified manufacturers who are buying land, building new facilities, refurbishing existing buildings and purchasing new equipment.

* Nevada Microenterprise Initiative

Northern Nevada Office
113 W. Plumb Lane   775-324-1812
Reno, NV 89509   Fax: 775-324-1813

Rural Nevada Office
116 E. 7th Street, Suite 1   775-841-1420 x2
Carson City, NV 89701   Fax: 775-841-2221

Southern Nevada Office
1600 E. Desert Inn Road, Suite 210   702-734-3555
Las Vegas, NV 89109   Fax: 702-734-3530
www.nmimicro.org

Nevada MicroEnterprise Initiative is a private nonprofit community development financial institution. They provide business tools to assist businesses overcome barriers that they may face in starting or in expanding a business. They offer business training, business loans, and networking.

* Loans For Farmers

Farm Service Agency
U.S. Department of Agriculture
1755 E. Plumb Lane, Suite 202   775-784-5411
Reno, NV 89502   Fax: 775-784-5015
http://www.fsa.usda.gov/nv/

The Farm Service Agency provides Direct and Guaranteed Loans to farmers through a variety of programs, including:

Farm Ownership Loans: purchase farmland, construct or repair buildings and other fixtures, and promote soil and water conservation. Up to $200,000.

Operating Loans: purchase items needed for a successful farm operation, such as livestock, farm equipment, feed, seed, fuel, farm chemicals, insurance, and other operating expenses. Can also be used to pay for minor improvements. Up to $200,000.

Beginning Farmer and Rancher Loans: provides funds to beginning and farmers and ranchers who are unable to obtain financing elsewhere.

Downpayment Farm Ownership Loans for Beginning Farmers: helps beginning farmers and ranchers purchase a farm or ranch. Also provides a way for retiring farmers to transfer their land to a future generation of farmers and ranchers. Applicant must have a downpayment of 10% and FSA with finance 40%, with the remaining balance from a commercial lender. Purchase price cannot exceed $250,000.

Loans to Socially Disadvantaged Farmers/Ranchers: helps socially disadvantaged applicants buy and operate family-size farms and ranches.

Youth Loans: Made to youths to establish and operate income-producing projects with the participation in 4-H clubs, Future Farmers of America, and similar organizations. Up to $5,000.

Emergency Loan Assistance: provides loans to help producers recover from production and physical losses due to drought, flooding, and other natural disasters, or quarantine. Up to $500,000.

Beginning Farmer and Rancher Land Contract Guarantee Pilot Program: "prompt payment guarantee" from FSA. FSA will provide payment to seller two times if the beginning farmer does not pay. Program is tested in IN, IA, ND, OR, PA and WI.

Farm Ownership and Operating Loan Guarantees: FSA will guarantee loans up to $782,000.

* Small Business Administration (SBA)

400 South 4th Street, Suite 250   702-388-6611
Las Vegas NV 89101   Fax: 702-388-6469
www.sba.gov/nv

The Nevada Small Business Administration Office delivers a variety of programs and services, such as startup and operational assistance through small business training and counseling, financial assistance for startup's, business opportunities and much more.

New Hampshire

* Department of Resources and Economic Development

State of New Hampshire
172 Pembroke Road
P.O. Box 1856   603-271-2411
Concord, NH 03302-1856   Fax: 603-271-2629
www.dred.state.nh.us

Office of Business and Industrial Development: Provides assistance and publications designed to support and promote business and industry in the state. Information in areas such as licensing and permits, financial counseling, marketing, and exporting, labor markets, and more.

Economic Development Data System: A comprehensive database of all the communities and available industrial properties within the state.

Business Visitation Program: Local volunteers visit businesses to gather information about firms' development issues, economic concerns and opinions about their community as a place to do business. Once aware of these issues, local, state and federal programs can be accessed to assist the firms. A referral network coordinates questions, issues and concerns.

Procurement Technical Assistance Program: Provides the necessary tools to be competitive in the federal marketplace through procurement counseling; contract announcements; specifications and standards; and support databases.

Regional and Local Revolving Loan Funds: Many local and regional revolving loan funds exist throughout New Hampshire. These funds have been capitalized from a variety of services, many with federal monies. The administration of these funds is generally handled by a nonprofit corporation, while the local funds most often are overseen by governing bodies with the help of a loan committee. The loans may be used in conjunction with other sources to leverage additional monies or independently finance the project.

Finance Clearinghouse: Offers companies assistance in obtaining financing. A complete listing of programs can be obtained through the clearinghouse.

International Trade Resource Center: A one-stop location when businesses, both current and potential exporters, can access the assistance and information necessary to effectively explore, develop and penetrate the foreign marketplace. Offers counseling, education and training seminars, automated trade leads, market research, marketing promotion, library and finance assistance. {www.globalnh.org}

Foreign Trade Zones: Provides economic incentives to companies doing business in foreign countries.

* New Hampshire Industrial Research Center

New Hampshire Industrial Research Center
134 Environmental Technology Building
35 Colovos Road   603-862-0123
Durham, NH 03824   Fax: 603-862-0329
www.nhirc.unh.edu

Assistance in basic and applied research, development and marketing through a matching grants program; hands-on training in Design of Experiment methods; and helping inventors develop patent and commercialize their ideas.

* Workforce Opportunity Council, Inc.

New Hampshire Job Training
64 Old Suncook Rd.   603-228-9500
Concord, NH 03301   Fax: 603-228-8557
www.nhworks.org

Provides job training for citizens while helping businesses gain capable workers.

* New Hampshire Export Finance Program

New Hampshire Office of International Commerce
17 New Hampshire Ave.   603-334-6074
Portsmouth, NH 03801   Fax: 603-334-6110
www.globalnh.org/export

To support export sales in providing working capital for the exporter to produce or buy a product for resale; provide political and/or commercial risk insurance in order to provide open account terms to foreign buyers; provide access to funding to qualified foreign buyers who need medium-term financing in order to purchase capital goods and services from New Hampshire Exporters. Rates and premiums arranged per sale or as needed. No dollar limit.

* Rural Development

New Hampshire/Vermont Rural Development
Montpelier Office
City Center, 3rd Floor
89 Main Street   802-828-6010
Montpelier, VT 05602   Fax: 802-828-6076
www.rurdev.usda.gov/vt

Cooperative Services Program: The Cooperative Services Program goal is to promote the understanding and use of the cooperative form of business as a viable organizational option for marketing and distributing agricultural products.

Business and Industry Guaranteed Loans: The Business and Industry (B&I) Guaranteed Loan Program helps create jobs and stimulates rural economies by providing financial backing for rural businesses. Loan proceeds may be used for working capital, machinery and equipment, buildings and real estate, and certain types of debt refinancing. The primary purpose is to create and maintain employment and improve the economic climate in rural communities. The maximum aggregate B&I Guaranteed Loan(s) amount that can be offered to any one borrower under this program is $25 million.

Intermediary Relending Program: The purpose of the Intermediary Relending Program (IRP) is to finance business facilities and community development projects in rural areas. Intermediaries re-lend funds to ultimate recipients for business facilities or community development.

Rural Business Enterprise Grants: The Rural Business-Cooperative Service (RBS) makes grants under the Rural Business Enterprise Grants (RBEG) Program to public bodies, private nonprofit corporations, and Federally-recognized Indian Tribal groups to finance and facilitate development of small and emerging private business enterprises located in areas outside the boundary of a city or unincorporated areas of 50,000 or more and its immediately adjacent urbanized or urbanizing area. Grant funds do not go directly to the business.

Rural Economic Development Loans and Grants: Provides zero-interest loans/or grants to electric and telephone utilities financed by the Rural Utilities Service (RUS), an agency of the United States Department of Agriculture, to promote sustainable rural economic development and job creation projects.

Rural Business Opportunity Grants: The purpose is to promote sustainable economic development in rural communities with exceptional needs. This is accomplished by making grants to pay costs of providing economic planning for rural communities, technical assistance for rural businesses, or training for rural entrepreneurs or economic development officials.

* New Hampshire Housing Finance Authority

32 Constitution Drive
Bedford, NH   800-640-7239 (NH only)
Mailing address:
P.O. Box 5087   603-472-8623
Manchester, NH 03108   Fax: (603) 472-8501
www.nhhfa.org

Tax Exempt Bond Financing: Tax exempt private activity bonds can be issued by the Authority to finance multi-family housing. In return for the reduced interest financing, at least thirty percent of the units must be rented to households earning 50% or less of the median area income or fifty percent of the units must be rented to households earning 60% or less of the median area income. The Authority also adds rent restrictions for the compliance period. The restrictions are in effect for the longer of 15 years or the life of the bond. Any for-profit development entity is eligible to participate.

* New Hampshire Community Technical College System

26 College Drive   603-271-2722
Concord, NH 03301-7400   800-247-3420 (in NH)
www.nhctc.edu   Fax: 603-271-2725

The New Hampshire Community Technical College System is a source of highly skilled personnel for business and industry, both through traditional associate degree programs and through customized professional and skills training. Throughout the state, their seven Centers for Training and Business Development (CTBDs) work with businesses to develop and deliver special classes or entire programs on specific topics to maintain and/or upgrade the skills of their employees. They help employers train their employees to maximize new technologies and increase productivity and competitiveness.

* Business Finance Authority (BFA)

14 Dixon Ave., 2nd Floor   603-271-2391
Concord, NH 03301-6313   Fax: 603-271-2396
www.nhbfa.com

Industrial Development Revenue Bond Financing: Tax exempt revenue bond financing through the Business Finance Authority (BFA). Advantages include 100% financing. Lower interest costs to the company and no dilution of equity. Eligible applicants are manufacturing facilities, facilities for the disposal of waste material; small-scale power facilities for producing electric energy; water-powered electric generating facilities; water facilities for the collecting, purifying, storing or distributing of water for use by the general public. Bond proceeds may be used to finance the cost of land, buildings and equipment, as well as bond counsel fees and the development and financing costs of the project.

Guaranteed Loans

The Guarantee of Loans to Small Business Program: Works in conjunction with the U.S. Small Business Administration (SBA). For businesses seeking guarantees on loan amounts that exceed the SBA's capacity. The BFA guarantees amount shall not exceed 90% of the original principal amount of the loan. The BFA guarantee amount and the SBA guarantee amount shall not exceed $1,500,000. The loan amount used to finance working capital shall not exceed $500,000. There is a non-refundable application fee of $250.

The Capital Access Program (CAP): For small businesses experiencing difficulty obtaining lines of credit and funds for start-up or expansion. Encourages banks to make loans to businesses with more than conventional risk by creating an account designed to protect the lender. The account reduces lender risk by decreasing the bank's exposure on the loan. CAP is available to businesses with annual revenues of less than $5,000,000. Total loan amount may not exceed $100,000.

The Guarantee Asset Program (GAP): Designed to provide assistance to capital intensive businesses experiencing difficulty obtaining normal bank financing. BFA will guarantee up to 90% of a loan made by a bank to a qualifying business. The borrower must have at least 25 full time employees. No more than 40% of the gross proceeds of the loan may used to finance working capital. The maturity of a loan shall not exceed 5 years. The terms of the loan will be determined by the participating financial institution.

Assistance to Local Development Organizations Program: To help LDOs create and maintain employment opportunities, the BFA may lend money to LDOs for the purpose of developing and expanding business opportunities in their market area. By providing LDOs with additional resources for financing, the BFA can effectively foster economic growth through existing organizations dedicated to the development of business. Any local development organization dedicated to the promotion and development of business is eligible for this program. The terms of the loan to the business will determined by the participating LDO.

The Working Capital Line of Credit Guarantee (WAG) program allows participating banks or lending institutions to receive a guarantee of up to 75% for a working capital line of credit, not to exceed $2,000,000.

* Loans For Farmers

Farm Service Agency
U.S. Department of Agriculture
22 Bridge St., 4th Floor   603-224-7941
Concord, NH 03301   Fax: 603-225-1410
http://www.fsa.usda.gov/nh/

The Farm Service Agency provides Direct and Guaranteed Loans to farmers through a variety of programs, including:

Farm Ownership Loans: purchase farmland, construct or repair buildings and other fixtures, and promote soil and water conservation. Up to $200,000.

Operating Loans: purchase items needed for a successful farm operation, such as livestock, farm equipment, feed, seed, fuel, farm chemicals, insurance, and other operating expenses. Can also be used to pay for minor improvements. Up to $200,000.

Beginning Farmer and Rancher Loans: provides funds to beginning and farmers and ranchers who are unable to obtain financing elsewhere.

Downpayment Farm Ownership Loans for Beginning Farmers: helps beginning farmers and ranchers purchase a farm or ranch. Also provides a way for retiring farmers to transfer their land to a future generation of farmers and ranchers. Applicant must have a downpayment of 10% and FSA with finance 40%, with the remaining balance from a commercial lender. Purchase price cannot exceed $250,000.

Loans to Socially Disadvantaged Farmers/Ranchers: helps socially disadvantaged applicants buy and operate family-size farms and ranches.

Youth Loans: Made to youths to establish and operate income-producing projects with the participation in 4-H clubs, Future Farmers of America, and similar organizations. Up to $5,000.

Emergency Loan Assistance: provides loans to help producers recover from production and physical losses due to drought, flooding, and other natural disasters, or quarantine. Up to $500,000.

Beginning Farmer and Rancher Land Contract Guarantee Pilot Program: "prompt payment guarantee" from FSA. FSA will provide payment to seller two times if the beginning farmer does not pay. Program is tested in IN, IA, ND, OR, PA and WI.

Farm Ownership and Operating Loan Guarantees: FSA will guarantee loans up to $782,000.

* Small Business Administration (SBA)

District Office
143 N. Main, Suite 202   603-225-1400
Concord, NH 03301   Fax: 603-225-1409
www.sba.gov/nh

The New Hampshire Small Business Administration Office delivers a variety of programs and services, such as startup and operational assistance through small business training and counseling, financial assistance for startup's, business opportunities and much more.

* Community Development Finance Authority

14 Dixon Avenue, Suite 102   603-271-2170
Concord, NH 03301   Fax: 603-271-1728
www.state.nh.us/osp/cdbg

Community Development Block Grants (CDBG): Grants are awarded to municipalities who in turn loan the funds to help municipalities meet housing and community development needs by alleviating some form of physical or economical distress.

* New Hampshire Port Authority

555 Market St.
Box 369   603-436-8500
Portsmouth, NH 03801   Fax: 603-436-2780
www.state.nh.us/nhport

Foreign Enterprise Zone: Foreign traders can store, mix, blend, repack and assemble various commodities with an exemption from normal custom duties and federal excise taxes. Four areas in New Hampshire have been designated as Foreign Trade Zone 81. They are the Port Authority Terminal, Portsmouth; Portsmouth Industrial Park; Crosby Road Industrial Park, Dover; Manchester Airport (formerly Grenier Air Base, Manchester).

* Industrial Development Manager

Public Service of New Hampshire (PSNH)
1000 Elm St.
P.O. Box 330
Manchester, NH 03105   603-669-4000
www.psnh.com

Development Incentive Rate Contract: PSNH offers an incentive rate to its new or expanding commercial and industrial customers that will provide benefits to all PSNH customers. PSNH negotiates special rate contracts with existing or new customers having incremental load requirements of more than 300 kilowatts.

Small Business Retrofit Program: Through the Small Business Retrofit Program you can get help to improve the efficiency of your businesses electrical appliances. The program can help replace out of date equipment and systems therefore reducing your electric bill.

* NETAAC (New England Trade Adjustment Assistance Center)

600 Suffolk St., 5th Floor North   978-446-9870
Lowell, MA 01854   Fax: 978-446-9820
www.netaac.org

Trade Adjustment Assistance: Manufacturing company must have experienced a decline in production or sales and an actual or threatened decrease in employment, attributable to increased imports of competitive products.

* Manufacturing Management Center

New Hampshire Small Business Development Center
108 McConnell Hall
University of New Hampshire   603-862-2200
Durham, NH 03824   Fax 603-862-4876
www.nhsbdc.org/mmc.htm

The New Hampshire Small Business Development Center is designing a model program and public policy recommendations to help small and medium manufacturers in rural areas of New Hampshire manage growth effectively. In addition, the NH SBDC offers technical, business and financial counseling and training to small manufacturers while enlisting the help of the University's faculty and resources to deliver specialized services on an as-needed basis.

* Merchant Banc

Two Wall Street   603-623-5500
Manchester, NH 03101   Fax: 603-623-3972
www.merchantbanc.com

A nonprofit company in the business of funding loans to small businesses that qualify.

* Micro Credit-New Hampshire

New Hampshire Community Loan Fund   800-432-4110
7 Wall Street   603-224-6669
Concord, NH 03301   Fax: 603-225-7425
www.nhclf.org

This program provides assistance to micro business owners that cannot get traditional funding. Loans start at $500 and have a maximum of $10,000.

New Jersey

* New Jersey Economic Development Authority

P.O. Box 990
Trenton, NJ 08625-0990   609-292-1800
www.njeda.com

Division of Economic Development: Develops and administers comprehensive marketing and support programs. Helps access public and private services which address a broad array of issues, ranging from financial, technical and regulatory concerns to employee training and site location.

Office of the Business Advocate and Business Information: Assists businesses that are having difficulty navigating through State regulations. 609-777-0885

Entrepreneurial Training Institute: An eight week program is offered to help new and aspiring entrepreneurs learn the basics of operating a business.

Small Business Contracts: State law requires that at least 15% of the contracts awarded by the State be given to small businesses. In the first half of 1998, these "set-aside contracts" amounted to more than $425 million.

Doing Business in New Jersey Guidebook: Provides information on starting and operating a business in the state. Topics include requirements and advice for starting a new business, information on tax and employee regulations, state and federal financial information, franchising, procurement opportunities, and exporting.

Selective Assistance Vendor Information Database: A computer database designed especially to assist business owners that wish to do business with the State of New Jersey and the private sector. SAVI-II matches buyers and vendors for public and private contracting opportunities.

Maritime Services: New Jersey offers several services to support businesses engaged in this enterprise. These include advice and assistance with permits and economic development issues, facilitation of dredging-related activities, and assistance in reducing or minimizing the creation of sediment.

New Jersey Economic Development Authority's Trade Adjustment Assistance Center: Can provide technical assistance to manufacturers or certify manufacturers for eligibility for federal government assistance.

Real Estate Development Division: Businesses may be able to lease state-of-the-art, affordable laboratory, production, and research facilities in the Technology Centre of New Jersey. New high-technology businesses may be able to utilize inexpensive lab and office space at one of several technology business incubators throughout the state. These incubators typically offer administrative and consulting services to their tenants.

Technology Transfer Program: Businesses may be able to partner with an academic institution, facilitating the transfer of new technology from research to commercial application.

Technology Help Desk Hotline: 800-4321-TEC
Businesses may take advantage of a one-stop Technology Help Desk Hotline, 1-800-4321-TEC. The hotline offers answers to business and technology questions as well as financial advice, referrals to sources of commercialization assistance, help with research and development grant proposals, and advice on using a statewide and national network of business development resource organizations.

The New Jersey Economic Development Authority's Finance Finder: Helps match companies with appropriate finance programs administered by the NJEDA.

Technology Centre of New Jersey: State-of-the-art, affordable laboratory production and research facilities are available for emerging and advanced technology driven companies.

Consulting Assistance for Manufacturers Impacted By Imports: Manufacturers who can demonstrate that their employment and either sales or production have declined due to foreign competition of a like or similar product may be eligible for consulting assistance.

Bond Financing: Bonds are issued to provide long-term loans at attractive, below-market interest rates for real estate acquisitions, equipment, machinery, building construction, and renovations. Minimum loan size is approximately $1 million. Maximum tax-exempt bond amount for manufacturers is $10 million.

Statewide Loan Pool For Business: Loans from $50,000 up to $5 million for fixed assets and up to $1,000,000 for working capital are available to businesses that create or maintain jobs in a financially targeted municipality or represent a targeted industry such as manufacturing, industrial, or agricultural. Assistance usually will not exceed $35,000 per job created or maintained.

Business Employment Incentive Program (BEIP) Grant: Businesses creating at least 25 new jobs in designated urban areas, or 75 jobs elsewhere, may be eligible to receive a BEIP grant. These grants, which may last for up to 10 years, may be for up to 80% of the value of the income taxes withheld annually from the paychecks of new employees.

Loan Guarantees: Guarantees of conventional loans of up to $1 million for working capital and guarantees of conventional loans or bond issues for fixed assets of up to $1.5 million are available to credit worthy businesses that need additional security to obtain financing. Preference is given to businesses that are either job intensive, will create or maintain tax ratables, are located in an economically distressed area, or represent an important economic sector of the state and will contribute to New Jersey's growth and diversity.

Direct Loans: Loans are made for up to $750,000 for fixed assets and up to $500,000 for working capital for up to 10 years to businesses that are unable to get sufficient bank credit on their own or through the Statewide Loan Pool or with and EDA guarantee. Preference is given to job-intensive enterprises located in economically targeted areas or representing a targeted business sector.

New Jersey Seed Capital Program: Loans are made from $25,000 to $500,000 at a market rate of interest for working capital and fixed assets to technology businesses that have risked their own capital to develop new technologies and need additional funds to bring their products to market.

New Jersey Technology Funding Program: EDA participates with commercial banks to make term loans from $100,000 to $5 million for second stage technology enterprises.

Fund For Community Economic Development: Loans and loan guarantees are made to urban-based community organizations that in turn make loans to micro-enterprises and small businesses which may not qualify for traditional bank financing.

Downtown Beautification Program: Loans ranging from $5,000 - $100,000 are available to existing retail and commercial businesses located in the commercial district of a targeted municipality.

Local Development Financing Fund: Loans ranging from $50,000 to $2 million may be made for fixed assets form commercial and industrial projects located in Urban Aid communities.

Hazardous Discharge Site Remediation Loan and Grant Program: Businesses may qualify for loans of up to $1 million for remediation activities due to a closure of operations or transfer of ownership.

Petroleum Underground Storage Tank Remediation Upgrade and Closure Program: Owners/operators may qualify for 100% of the eligible project costs.

Small Business Loans: Loans and loan guarantees administered by the New Jersey Economic Development Authority's Community Development and Small Business Lending Division.

New Jersey Economic Development Authority's Investment Banking Division: Loans may be available for the purchase of manufacturing equipment.

R&D Excellence Grant Program: Businesses may receive financial support for research and development in critical fields, such as healthcare (especially biomaterials, pharmaceuticals, and biotechnologies), software/information, and environmental and civil infrastructure technologies.

Small Business Innovation Research Grants: Applicants for federal grants may receive technical consulting and bridge loans.

Business Relocation Assistance Grant: Provides grants to relocating companies that create a minimum of 75 new full-time jobs in New Jersey.

International Trade Services: Services include financing assistance, strategic advocacy in foreign markets, opportunities to network and receive information and advice regarding international commerce, and assistance in taking advantage of federal international trade programs and Foreign Trade Zones.

Export Financing: Up to a $1 million one-year revolving line of credit will be provided to finance confirmed foreign orders to assist businesses that want to enter the export market or expand export sales but are unable to do so because they cannot get the financing they need on their own.

Foreign Trade Zones: Within these zones, which are outside U.S. Customs territory, businesses may manufacture, assemble, package, process and exhibit merchandise with a substantial duty and cash flow savings.

* New Jersey Department of Commerce and Economic Growth Commission

Division of Development for Small Businesses and
  Women and Minority Businesses
CN 835   609-292-3860
Trenton, NJ 08625   Fax: 609-292-9145
www.state.nj.us/commerce

Services For Businesses Owned By Women And Minorities: Businesses owned by women and minorities play an important role in the New Jersey economy. New Jersey offers a number of services to help these businesses compete and overcome the special challenges they face. These services include financial assistance, advice and instructional materials, training and education, and certification necessary to receive certain contracts.

Set Aside Contracts: State law requires that 7% of the contracts awarded by the State be given to businesses owned by minorities, and 3% to businesses owned by women. In the first half of 1998, these "set-aside contracts" amounted to more than $180 million.

Women and minorities interested in establishing franchise businesses may receive investments from the Small Business Investment Company, which works in conjunction with the New Jersey Economic Development Authority's Commercial Lending Division.

Contractors Assistance Program: Small contracting businesses owned by women or minorities may receive training courses and consultations with experienced executives of large construction companies designed to make it easier to get performance bonds and successfully bid on major construction projects. This service is provided by the New Jersey Economic Development Authority's Community Development and Small Business Lending Division.

New Jersey Development Authority For Small Businesses, Minorities' And Women's Enterprises: This office offers women and minority-owned small businesses financial, marketing, procurement, technical and managerial assistance. Loans of up to $1 million can be made for real estate, fixed asset acquisition, and working capital. Guarantees to banks are also available for fixed asset acquisition and for working capital. To be eligible, a business must be certified as a small, minority-owned or women-owned enterprise. Most of the funds are targeted to enterprises located in Atlantic City or providing goods or services to customers in Atlantic City, including but not limited to the casinos. Limited monies are available for businesses located in other parts of the state.

Regulatory Assistance: Business assistance with obtaining permits and approvals through state regulations.

One-Stop Permit: Assistance in completing the One-Stop form to becoming a business.

Small Business Environmental Ombudsman/Compliance Assistance: This program can help you business deal with specific technical issues, provide free and confidential visits and refer your business to appropriate agencies as necessary.

Business Information Services: One-stop answers and assistance for many new and existing businesses questions. 609-777-0885

License & Certification Hotline: Information that outlines business and occupation requirements. 800-533-0186

Next Step Workshops: Workshops designed to help you do business with the State of New Jersey.

* Rural Development

New Jersey Rural Development Office
5th Floor North, Suite 500
8000 Midlantic Drive   856-787-7000
Mt. Laurel, NJ 08054   Fax: 856-787-7783
www.rurdev.usda.gov/nj
Commercial Lending
Business and Industry Guarantee Loans: The Business and Industry (B&I) Guarantee Loan Program helps create jobs and stimulates rural economies by providing financial backing for rural businesses.

Revolving Loan Funds And Technical Assistance
Intermediary Relending Program Loans: Intermediary Relending Program loans finance business facilities and community development projects in rural areas, including cities with a population of less than 25,000.

Rural Business Enterprise Grants: Rural Business Enterprise Grants help public bodies, nonprofit corporations, and Federally recognized Indian tribal groups finance and facilitate development of small and emerging private business enterprises located in rural areas (this includes all areas other than cities of more than 50,000 people and their immediately adjacent urban or urbanizing areas).

Rural Business Opportunity Grants: Rural Business Opportunity Grant funds provide for technical assistance, training, and planning activities that improve economic conditions in rural areas. Applicants must be located in rural areas (this includes all areas other than cities of more than 50,000 people and their immediately adjacent urban or urbanizing areas).

Rural Economic Development Loans and Grants: This program finances economic development and job creation projects in rural areas based on sound economic plans. Rural Economic Development Loans and Grants are available to any Rural Utilities Service electric or telecommunications borrower to assist in developing rural areas from an economic standpoint, to create new job opportunities, and to help retain existing employment.

* The New Jersey Redevelopment Authority (NJRA)

New Jersey Redevelopment Authority
50 W. State St.
P.O. Box 790
Trenton, NJ 08625   609-292-3739
www.state.nj.us/njra
An independent state financing agency whose mission is to focus on investing in neighborhood-based redevelopment projects. NJRA offers low and no-interest loans, loan guarantees, equity investment and technical assistance to eligible businesses and municipalities.

* Early Stage Enterprises, LP

103 Carnegie Center, Suite 200   609-921-8896
Princeton, NJ 08540   Fax: 609-921-8703
www.esevc.com

Early Stage Enterprises (ESE) Seed Investment Fund: The Commission was a catalyst in the formation of the Early Stage Enterprises (ESE) Seed Investment Fund, which offers equity financing to qualifying start up companies. ESE offers traditional venture capital funding (never requesting more than 50% equity) to companies in the mid-Atlantic region ranging from $500,000 to $1,000,000. ESE is currently funding 12 companies, expecting to increase its portfolio to 25 - 30 companies in the near future.

* The New Jersey Technology Funding Program

Assistant Director of Commercial Lending
Post Office Box 990   609-292-0187
Trenton, NJ 08625-0990   Fax: 609-633-7751
www.njeda.com/high_tech.htm

The New Jersey Technology Funding Program: This is a financing partnership offered by the New Jersey Economic Development Authority (NJEDA) and area banks to fill the financing gaps in the availability of expansion capital for growing second stage technology-based enterprises. The NJEDA can guarantee a portion of the bank's loan. Funds will be lent for working capital and fixed assets such as buildings and equipment.

* Edison Venture Fund

Mr. John H. Martinson, Managing Partner
1009 Lenox Drive, #4   609-896-1900, ext. 18
Lawrenceville, NJ 08648   Fax: 609-896-0066
www.edisonventure.com

The Edison Venture Fund: This fund provides financing and guidance to growing companies in the mid-Atlantic region. The General Partners have backgrounds in venture capital, management buyouts, banking, acquisitions, technology development, business management, investment banking and entrepreneurial enterprise. The fund's capital pool exceeds $215 million in four independent limited partnerships. The Edison Venture Fund seeks promising enterprises with proprietary products, services and market opportunities which will grow rapidly. The initial investment averages $3 million. Providing more than capital, The Edison Venture Fund contributes specialized knowledge, operating skills and an extensive contact network.

* New Jersey Manufacturing Extension Program (NJMEP)

NJIT University Heights
GITC Suite 3200   973-642-7099
Newark, NJ 07102   Fax: 973-596-6056
www.njmep.org

New Jersey Manufacturing Extension Program (NJMEP): is designed to help improve the performance of small and mid-sized manufacturers in New Jersey. It offers various technical and management solutions to competitive problems and represents a valuable resource for the newly growing manufacturing sector in New Jersey.

* New Jersey Business Incubation Network

Mr. Louis Gaburo
Assistant Director of Enterprise Development
105 Lock Street   973-643-4063
Newark, NJ 07103   Fax: 973-643-4502
www.njbin.org

New Jersey Business Incubation Network: Business incubation is a dynamic process of business enterprise development. Incubators nurture young firms, helping them to survive and grow during the startup period when they are most vulnerable. Incubators provide hands-on management assistance, access to financing and orchestrated exposure to critical business or technical support services. They also offer entrepreneurial firms shared office services, access to equipment, flexible leases and expandable space ó all under one roof. An incubation program's main goal is to produce successful graduates ó businesses that are financially viable and freestanding when they leave the incubator usually in two to three years.

* New Jersey Business & Industry Association

102 West State Street
Trenton, NJ 08608-1199   609-393-7707
www.njbia.org

The New Jersey Business & Industry Association is an employer association providing information, services and advocacy for its member companies in order to build a more prosperous New Jersey.

* Loans For Farmers

Farm Service Agency
U.S. Department of Agriculture
Mastoris Professional Plaza
163 Route 130, Bldg. 2, Suite E
Bordentown, NJ 08505   609-298-3446
Administrative Fax: 609-298-8761
Program Fax: 609-298-8780
http://www.fsa.usda.gov/nj/

The Farm Service Agency provides Direct and Guaranteed Loans to farmers through a variety of programs, including:

Farm Ownership Loans: purchase farmland, construct or repair buildings and other fixtures, and promote soil and water conservation. Up to $200,000.

Operating Loans: purchase items needed for a successful farm operation, such as livestock, farm equipment, feed, seed, fuel, farm chemicals, insurance, and other operating expenses. Can also be used to pay for minor improvements. Up to $200,000.

Beginning Farmer and Rancher Loans: provides funds to beginning and farmers and ranchers who are unable to obtain financing elsewhere.

Downpayment Farm Ownership Loans for Beginning Farmers: helps beginning farmers and ranchers purchase a farm or ranch. Also provides a way for retiring farmers to transfer their land to a future generation of farmers and ranchers. Applicant must have a downpayment of 10% and FSA with finance 40%, with the remaining balance from a commercial lender. Purchase price cannot exceed $250,000.

Loans to Socially Disadvantaged Farmers/Ranchers: helps socially disadvantaged applicants buy and operate family-size farms and ranches.

Youth Loans: Made to youths to establish and operate income-producing projects with the participation in 4-H clubs, Future Farmers of America, and similar organizations. Up to $5,000.

Emergency Loan Assistance: provides loans to help producers recover from production and physical losses due to drought, flooding, and other natural disasters, or quarantine. Up to $500,000.

Beginning Farmer and Rancher Land Contract Guarantee Pilot Program: "prompt payment guarantee" from FSA. FSA will provide payment to seller two times if the beginning farmer does not pay. Program is tested in IN, IA, ND, OR, PA and WI.

Farm Ownership and Operating Loan Guarantees: FSA will guarantee loans up to $782,000.

* Small Business Administration (SBA)

Two Gateway Center, 15th Floor   201-645-2434
Newark, NJ 07102   Fax: 201-645-6265
www.sba.gov/nj

The New Jersey Small Business Administration Office delivers a variety of programs and services, such as startup and operational assistance through small business training and counseling, financial assistance for startup's, business opportunities and much more.

* New Jersey Commission on Science and Technology

28 West State St.
P.O. Box 832   609-984-1671
Trenton, NJ 08625-0832   Fax: 609-292-5920
www.state.nj.us/scitech

The New Jersey Commission on Science and Technology connects university-based innovation with the most vigorous private sector Research & Development facilities in the world, and facilitates financial and technical assistance to high-technology businesses. Programs include:

Research & Development Excellence Program: The Research & Development Excellence Program (R&D Excellence) is intended to create and/or mature new scientific and technology areas with potential for products, services, or processes important to the State's future economic development. The Commission of Science and Technology supports the R&D Excellence Programs listed below:

Business Assistance Programs: The New Jersey Commission on Science and Technology recognizes the significant contributions that small and medium-sized technology-based companies make to technological and economic development. The Commission, working in conjunction with other state agencies, private organizations, and academic institutions, has developed several pioneering programs to assist New Jersey's technology entrepreneurs.

Funding Opportunities:
Technology Transfer & Commercialization Program (TTCP): This competitive investment program, administered by the Commission, is a funding source for small, for-profit technology companies, to conduct produce or process development projects with a near-term commercial outcome. Companies eligible for this funding must be New Jersey-based or plan to relocate in New Jersey. The Program offers direct investments of $50,000 to $250,000 to companies, to conduct product or process development projects with near-term commercial outcome.

SBIR Bridge Loan Program: This is a Commission-sponsored business assistance program for New Jersey companies which helps bridge the time and financial gap between the awarding of Phase I and Phase II Federal SBIR grants.

* Casino Reinvestment Development Authority (CRDA)

1014 Atlantic Avenue
P.O. Box 749
Atlantic City, NJ 08401   609-347-0500
www.njcrda.com

Funnels a portion of casino revenues into state development projects, by mandatory investment in CRDA taxable or tax-free bonds (1.25 percent of casino gross receipts). CRDA pays interest at 2/3rds of market rate, freeing funds for development use. The CRDA then makes loans to designated municipalities at below-market rate financing.

* New Jersey Department of Environmental Protection

401 E. State St.
7th Floor, East Wing
P.O. Box 402   602-292-2885
Trenton, NJ 08625-0402   Fax: 609-292-7695
www.state.nj.us/dep

The Department of Environmental Protection strives to build relationships with the business community that promote both environmental and economic health through cooperation and innovation. These innovative efforts include: issuance of the first facility-wide permit int he nation, which replaces more than five dozen individual permits; amnesty and other programs that encourage compliance without the threat of penalties; and introduction of Alternative Dispute Resolution as a means of resolving permit and other disagreements by mediation rather than litigation.

* New Jersey Technology Council Venture Fund

1001 Briggs Road, Suite 280   856-273-6800
Mt. Laurel, NJ 08054   Fax: 856-273-0990

Roseland Office:
4 Becker Farm Road   973-994-0606
Roseland, NJ 07068   Fax: 973-992-6336
www.njtcvc.com

This program provides funding assistance to emerging high-technology companies in New Jersey. This private enterprise works closely with the State of New Jersey, having been selected through a competitive process to manage certain funds on behalf of the New Jersey Economic Development Authority.

New Mexico

* Economic Development Department

Joseph M. Montoya Bldg.
1100 St. Francis Drive   505-827-0382
Santa Fe, NM 87505-4147   800-374-3061
www.edd.state.nm.us   Fax: 505-827-0407

Business Participation Loans: The State Investment Council may invest a portion of the Severance Tax Permanent Fund in real property related business loans. There is a minimum of $500,000 and a maximum of $2 million.

Industrial Development Training Program: Provides funds for classroom or on-the-job training to prepare New Mexico residents for employment. Trainee wages are reimbursed to the company at 50% during hours of training; 65% in rural New Mexico. Instructional costs involving classroom training will be reimbursed to the educational institution at 100% of all costs outlined in the training contract.

Severance Tax Loan Program: New Mexico can purchase up to $20 million of bonds, notes, debentures or other evidence of indebtedness, excluding commercial paper, whose proceeds are used for the establishment or expansion of business outlets or ventures located in state.

International Trade Division: Provides assistance to manufacturing, agricultural and other production concerns in developing their worldwide export capabilities. Services include:
- Export market development counseling
- Foreign trade shows and missions
- Foreign buying and reverse trade missions
- Identifying and disseminating overseas trade leads
- Attracting foreign businesses
- Developing, maintaining and using a database of potential domestic and international customers for New Mexico goods and services.

New Mexico Communities: {www.edd.state.nm.us/COMMU NITIES/}
This web site offers information in three forms:
- Site and Buildings Database: Search for available land and buildings by size or county.
- Community/County Profile: An overview of each incorporated municipality and its available land and buildings. County statistics are also available.
- State Map: A clickable version that shows where each county and community is located in relation to each other and major intersections.

Industrial Revenue Bonds: Municipalities or counties issue IRBs in order to finance privately operated development projects.

Job Training Incentive Program (JTIP): JTIP is designed to provide fast response training to new and expanding businesses in New Mexico. They offer financial assistance to businesses to help with the expenses associated with employee training.

New Mexico 9000 Program: The New Mexico Economic Development Department has teamed up with area large businesses to provide small businesses technical assistance to achieve ISO 9001:2000 compliance certification at affordable costs.

Office of Mexican Affairs and trade Division: This division provides information pertaining to international trade from New Mexico, major exports, and marketing strategies to businesses.

Trade Division Education Programs: The Trade Division Educational Programs include basic export seminars, advanced trade seminars and assisting trade groups with their educational programming.

Export Library: The Trade Division maintains an international trade research library.

Rural Job Tax Credit: Eligible New Mexico employers may earn the rural job tax credit for each qualifying job created after July 1, 2000.

Welfare-to-Work Credit: The state credit piggybacks onto the federal credit and can be applied to New Mexico personal and corporate income tax.

* Rural Development Office
Rural Development Administration
6200 Jefferson St., NE, Room 255

517 Gold Ave. SW   505-761-4950
Albuquerque, NM 87109   Fax: 505-761-4938

To foster economic development in rural areas, this program offers guarantees to private lenders for projects by healthy, reliable companies that will benefit the community. Loans are for a wide range of rural and industrial purposes, including pollution control and transportation services. Projects should create jobs in areas with populations under 25,000.

The New Mexico Rural Development Office offers a variety of programs including: Business and Industry Direct and Guaranteed Loans, Intermediary Reldending Program, Rural Business Enterprise and Opportunity Grants, and Rural Economic Development Loans and Grants.

* Women's Economic Self-Sufficiency Team
WESST Corp.
414 Silver SW   505-241-4753
Albuquerque, NM 87102   Fax: 505-241-4766
www.wesst.org
Provides consulting, training and support programs as well as financial assistance (loans).

* ACCION
ACCION New Mexico
20 First Plaza NW, Suite 417   505-243-8844
Albuquerque, NM 87102   Fax: 505-243-1551
www.accionnewmexico.org
A private nonprofit organization that extend microloans to small business entrepreneurs designed to help home-based and other self-employed people grow to be self sufficient.

* Cibola Foundation Revolving Loan Fund
Cibola Communities
Economic Development Foundation Inc.
P.O. Box 277   505-285-6604
Grants, NM 87020   Fax: 505-285-6746
http://mttaylor.com/ciboladev/index.htm
A variety of financial incentives offered to encourage economic development in Cibola County.

* Community Development Loan Fund
NM Community Development Loan Fund
P.O. Box 705   505-243-3196
Albuquerque, NM 87103   Fax: 505-243-8803
www.nmcdlf.org
Provides loans to businesses and organizations that have tangible benefits for low-income people. Typical loans are from $5,000 to $25,000.

* Enchantment Land Certified Development Company
625 Silver SW, Suite 210   505-843-9232
Albuquerque, NM 87102   Fax: 505-764-9153
www.elcdc.com
Enchantment Land Certified Development Company (ELCDC) The ELCDC is an SBA licensed, not-for-profit organization, authorized to administer the SBA 504 loan program. A 504 program provides long-term (20 years), low down payment (10%), fixed rate loans for land, buildings and equipment for expanding small businesses. ELCDC sells a debenture with a 100% SBA guarantee for up to 40% of the project, or $750,000 (in some cases $1 million), and the

company provides 10% equity. The remaining 50% is from a first mortgage loan from a private sector lender. Area of Operation: statewide.

* Technology Ventures Corporation
1155 University Blvd. SE 505-246-2882
Albuquerque, NM 87106 Fax: 505-246-2891
www.techventures.org
Technology Ventures Corporation (TVC) TVC was formed by Lockheed Martin to promote the commercialization of technology, particularly in relation to Sandia National Laboratories, TVC serves to link technologies and investment sources with start-up companies and existing business. Also, TVC facilitates technical, business and management assistance for its clients.

* Bureau For Business Research And Services
New Mexico State University
P.O. Box 3001
Las Cruces, NM 88003 505-646-1334
http://bbrs.nmsu.edu
Management training, research services; maintains business and economic data bank.

* NEDA Business Consultants, Inc.
718 Central SW 505-843-7114
Albuquerque, NM 87102 Fax: 505-242-2030
www.nedainc.net
Assists minority entrepreneurs with financing, capital development, marketing, procurement, management, etc.

* Navajo Nation Division of Economic Development
P. O. Box 663 505-871-6544
Window Rock, AZ 86515 Fax: 505-871-7381
www.navajo.org
Provides counseling, financial planning, and loan packaging for small business development

* New Mexico Department of Agriculture
Marketing Development Office
New Mexico State University
P. O. Box 30005, MSC 5600
Las Cruces, NM 88003 505-646-4929
http://nmdaweb.nmsu.edu
Technical assistance to agricultural producers and processors with interstate or international exports.

* New Mexico Entrepreneurs Association
New Mexico Entrepreneurs Association
6416 Glen Oak NE 505-293-3811
Albuquerque, NM 87111 Fax: 505-262-0871
www.edd.state.nm.us/cgi-bin/technoview.cgi
Provides forum for entrepreneurs and support groups; promotes local business development.

* New Mexico Farm and Livestock Bureau
421 N. Water St.
P.O. Box 20004
Las Cruces, NM 88004 505-532-4706
www.nmfb.org
Lobbying organization; business services and insurance for members; publishes New Mexico Farm and Ranch Magazine.

* Rio Grande Minority Purchasing Council, Inc.
7216 Washington Street, NE, Suite B
Albuquerque, NM 87109 505-342-9300
www.rgmpc.org
Supports minority businesses and those owned by women through increased corporate and government purchasing.

* Science And Technology Corporation
University of New Mexico
801 University SE, Suite 101 505-272-7900
Albuquerque, NM 87106 Fax: 505-272-7300
http://stc.unm.edu
Provides business assistance to technology-based companies; transfers technology from publicly funded R&D organizations to commercial markets.

* State Investment Council
2025 South Pacheco St., Suite 100 505-424-2500
Santa Fe, NM 87505 Fax: 505-424-2510
www.state.nm.us/nmsic
The State Investment Council offers a number of programs of interest to developing business in New Mexico.

Venture Capital Investment Program: This program makes investments in qualified New Mexico-based venture capital funds, which are then invested into entrepreneurial businesses. The business must have experienced management; a rapidly growing an d potentially large market; and a competitive advantage where there are barriers to entry for other businesses and significant capital appreciation for investors over a 5 to 7 year period.

The Real Estate Business Loan Participation Program: Allows the Severance Tax Permanent Fund to participate in certain real estate loans up to a total of $2 million. The loan may not exceed 75% of the appraisal and must originate with a New Mexico bank.

The Severance Tax Permanent Fund Policy Governing Purchases of Small Business Administration or Rural Economic and Community Development Service Obligations: Allows the state to use severance tax permanent funds to purchase SBA or RECD loans made to New Mexico businesses.

The New Mexico Venture Capital Fund: Provides capital to venture capital partnerships that already have significant, successful investment experience.

* Department of Finance and Administration
2600 Cerrilos Road 800-432-7108
Santa Fe, NM 87505 505-827-4950
www.nmlocalgov.net Fax: 505-827-4948
This department provides gap financing, often with long term loan amortization, for start-up and expansion projects that address local economic development objectives.

* New Mexico Taxation and Revenue Department
Returns Processing Bureau
P.O. Box 630 505-827-0700
Santa Fe, NM 87504-0630 Fax: 505-827-0331
www.state.nm.us/tax
Investment Tax Credit: Available to manufacturing operations. For each $100,000 of equipment purchased (used

directly and exclusively in a manufacturing process and subject to depreciation) by a company that simultaneously hires one employee, that company may receive credit against its gross receipts taxes or withholding tax due. A business must apply for the credit.

* Loans For Farmers

Farm Service Agency
U.S. Department of Agriculture
6200 Jefferson NE, Room 211   505-761-4900
Albuquerque, NM 87109   Fax: 505-761-4934
http://www.fsa.usda.gov/nm/
The Farm Service Agency provides Direct and Guaranteed Loans to farmers through a variety of programs, including:

Farm Ownership Loans: purchase farmland, construct or repair buildings and other fixtures, and promote soil and water conservation. Up to $200,000.

Operating Loans: purchase items needed for a successful farm operation, such as livestock, farm equipment, feed, seed, fuel, farm chemicals, insurance, and other operating expenses. Can also be used to pay for minor improvements. Up to $200,000.

Beginning Farmer and Rancher Loans: provides funds to beginning and farmers and ranchers who are unable to obtain financing elsewhere.

Downpayment Farm Ownership Loans for Beginning Farmers: helps beginning farmers and ranchers purchase a farm or ranch. Also provides a way for retiring farmers to transfer their land to a future generation of farmers and ranchers. Applicant must have a downpayment of 10% and FSA with finance 40%, with the remaining balance from a commercial lender. Purchase price cannot exceed $250,000.

Loans to Socially Disadvantaged Farmers/Ranchers: helps socially disadvantaged applicants buy and operate family-size farms and ranches.

Youth Loans: Made to youths to establish and operate income-producing projects with the participation in 4-H clubs, Future Farmers of America, and similar organizations. Up to $5,000.

Emergency Loan Assistance: provides loans to help producers recover from production and physical losses due to drought, flooding, and other natural disasters, or quarantine. Up to $500,000.

Beginning Farmer and Rancher Land Contract Guarantee Pilot Program: "prompt payment guarantee" from FSA. FSA will provide payment to seller two times if the beginning farmer does not pay. Program is tested in IN, IA, ND, OR, PA and WI.

Farm Ownership and Operating Loan Guarantees: FSA will guarantee loans up to $782,000.

* Small Business Administration (SBA)

625 Silver SW, Suite 320   505-346-7909
Albuquerque, NM 87102   Fax: 505-346-6711
www.sba.gov/nm
The New Mexico Small Business Administration Office delivers a variety of programs and services, such as startup and operational assistance through small business training and counseling, financial assistance for startup's, business opportunities and much more.

* Small Business Innovation Research

UNM-Los Alamos Small Business Development Center
P.O. Box 715   505-662-0001
Los Alamos, NM 87544   Fax: 505-662-0099
www.nmsbdc.org/losalamos
Small for-profit United States businesses that are able to answer a specific federal governmental research and development need may compete for up to $850,000 in SBIR contracts. Contracts are awarded in phases. Phase I (up to $100,000) for evaluation and analysis of an idea. Phase II (up to $750,000) for further research and development of idea deemed feasible. And Phase III, which require private or non-SBIR governmental funding for the commercialization of the results of Phase II work.

* New Mexico Industry Corporation

700 4th Street, SW   505-244-0574
Albuquerque, NM 87102   Fax: 505-242 – 8666
Small businesses located in eligible counties can get funding for fixed assets and working capital. The loans generally range from $25,000 to $50,000 with lower than market rates interest. Preference is given to existing businesses that develop, manufacturing, or assemble products using local labor. They must have been turned down by at least two lenders.

* Workforce Training Center

5600 Eagle Rock Avenue NE   505-224-5200
Albuquerque, NM 87113   Fax: 505-224-5201
http://planet.tvi.edu/wtc
The Workforce Training Center provides customized training, skill development and business consulting. They also have two small business development centers in Albuquerque and South Valley to provide counseling, assessment, training and other resources to assist entrepreneurs start and grow their own businesses.

New York

* Empire State Development

30 South Pearl Street   518-474-7756
Albany, NY 12245   800-STATE-NY
www.empire.state.ny.us

633 Third Ave.
New York, NY 10017   212-803-3100
www.nylovesbiz.com
Small Business Division: Offers fast, up-to-date information on the State's economic development programs and can help in making contact with appropriate agencies in such areas as financing, job training, technical assistance, etc. {www.nylovessmallbiz.com}

Technical Advisory Services; Provides free, confidential technical assistance concerning compliance to federal and state air quality requirements for small businesses.

Small Business Stationary Source Technical And Environmental Compliance Assistance Program: Provides technical assistance and advocacy services to eligible businesses in achieving environmental regulatory compliance.

Business Ombudsmen Services: Counseling and problem solving assistance to resolve complaints from small businesses concerning interactions with government authorities available to businesses employing 100 or less that are not dominant in their fields.

Entrepreneurial Assistance Program: Referrals of recipients to ESD funded assistance provides classroom instruction and individual counseling, business plan development for minorities, women, dislocated workers, public assistance recipients, public housing recipients and those seeking to start a new business or who have owned a business for five years or less.

Business Development Office: Industrial and manufacturing companies are targeted for a variety of services.

New York State Contract Reporter: Provides listings of contracts made available for bidding by New York State agencies, public benefit corporations, and its public authorities. {www.nyscr.org}

Procurement Assistance: Provides technical assistance to businesses seeking to compete for contracts valued at $1,000,000 or more from the state.

Workforce Training: Empire State Development offers financial support and technical resources to companies to offset the cost of employee training.

Recycling Assistance: New York State has one of the largest concentrations of recycling companies in the world. Works with companies to demonstrate that, in addition to being an important environmental activity, recycling makes good business sense. To this end, they diagnose the research and development, capital, and marketing needs of recycling companies and tailor-make a package of technical and financial assistance. Identifies new markets and assist companies retooling to reach those markets. Assists companies to implement waste prevention practices.

Technical Assistance: New York State has developed a host of business-friendly products ranging from understanding the federal Clean Air Act and its impact on small business to ownership transition plans that can help a company grow and prosper. A hotline (800-STATE NY) puts business people directly in touch with a business ombudsman. The experts staffing this hotline are ready to answer questions. In addition, they serve as advocates for business.

Advanced Controls for Efficiency Program (ACE): Applied research, product design, demonstration and testing, and product commercialization for individuals or enterprises with an innovative, energy-related product.

Financial Incentives: Companies that plan to locate, expand or modernize their facilities in New York State are eligible for financial assistance. Generally, this assistance supports the acquisition of land and buildings or machinery and equipment. It also can help fund construction or renovation of buildings or the infrastructure and working capital required for the establishment or expansion of an eligible company.

Funds may be available through:
- direct loans to business for a portion of the cost of the project;
- interest rate subsidies to reduce the cost of borrowing from private or public sector financial institutions, in the form of a grant or linked deposit with the lending institution;

- loan guarantees for working capital assistance;
- assistance in the form of a loan and grant combination for a portion of the cost of an infrastructure project.

Economic Development Fund:
1. *Industrial Effectiveness Program*: Direct technical assistance for identifying, developing and implementing improved management and production process and grants to pay the cost of feasibility studies up to $60,000.
2. *Employee Training Assistance*: Offers skills training grant from $15,000 to $25,000.
3. *Commercial Area Development*: Loans, loan guarantees, and grants to improve commercial buildings, commercial strips, downtown areas, and business districts from $75,000 to $100,000.
4. *General Development*: Loans and loan guarantees for manufacturers, non-retail service firms, headquarters facilities of retail firms, retail firms in distressed areas, and businesses developing tourist attractions from $75,000 to $2,000,000.
5. *Capital Access*: For small and medium size businesses including minority and women-owned businesses and day care centers, financing from $100,000 to $300,000.
6. *General Development Financing*: Loans and loan guarantees for manufacturing, non-retail service firms, retail headquarters, retail firms located in distressed areas and businesses which develop recreational, cultural or historical facilities for tourist attractions. Amounts are determined case-by-case.
7. *Competitiveness Improvement Services - Global Export Marketing Service*: Grants up to $5,000 for consulting services to assess organizational and product readiness for exporting. Grants up to $25,000 for an individual business or up to $50,000 for a business or industry group to create market development plans.

Environmental Finance Corporation: Grants for resource recovery facilities, solid waste disposal facilities, hazardous waste treatment facilities, Brownfields redevelopment, water supply and management facilities and sewage treatment works. {www.nysefc.org}

Venture Capital Fund: High Tech entrepreneurs, companies with technologies ready for market, and leading-edge enterprises each have different needs for investment capital. New York State has the seed and growth capital that will enable a high tech business to grow. The Small Business Technology Investment Fund program (SBTIF) is a source of early-stage debt and equity funding for high tech companies. Initial investments range as much as $300,000 and later stage investment up to $500,000. New York State is banking on a strong high tech future.

Transportation Capital Assistance Program: Loans up to $500,000 for small business enterprises and NYS-certified minority and women-owned business enterprises that have transportation-related construction contracts. 518-457-1129

Regional Revolving Loan Trust Fund: Loans and loan guarantees up to $80,000 for businesses employing fewer than 100 people.

Small Business Technology Investment Fund: For small technology based companies, financing from $25,000 to $500,000 for seed or capital.

Job Development Authority: Loans to small and medium sized businesses in manufacturing and services from $50,000 to $1,500,000.

Jobs Now Program: Capital loans and grants to private businesses creating at least 300 new full time jobs not to exceed $10,000 per job.

Linked Deposit Program: Interest rate subsidies to a variety of businesses seeking to improve competitiveness and performance up to $1,000,000.

Empire State Development: International market experts help a company enter and expand in the global economy. Offers a step-by-step analysis of a company's capabilities and matches them with the demands of the international marketplace. If a company has what the global marketplace needs, they will work with that company to find the niche, the spot on the globe where they can sell. Then, they will assist them in determining how to reach those markets. They provide information about tariffs, industry specifications and government regulations. They can put a company in touch with representatives, distributors, agents and strategic allies to sell a product or service abroad. Other services include:
- Assistance in identifying foreign sales agent or distributor
- Matching grants of up to $5,000 to assess product sales potential in foreign markets
- Matching grants of up to $25,000 to assist in creating export market development plans
- Low cost participation in international trade shows.

Division of Minority and Women's Business Development: Administers, coordinates, and implements a statewide program to assist the development of M/WBE's and facilitate their access to state contracting opportunities. Through the process of certification, the agency is responsible for verifying minority and women-ownership and control of firms participating in the program.

Division of Minority and Women's Business Development Lending Program: Loans up to $7,000 from the Microenterprise Loan Fund and up to $50,000 from the Minority and Women Revolving Loan Trust Fund.

Semiconductor Manufacturing Initiative: To encourage semiconductor manufacturing, New York has facilitated the pre-permitting of industrial sites solely for chip fabrication. {www.semi-ny.com}

Technology Incubators: New York has over 50 incubator facilities.

Environmental Services Unit: Businesses can get assistance in order to understand and comply with environmental regulations.

* Rural Development
441 S. Salina St.
Suite 357, 5th Floor   315-477-6400
Syracuse, NY 3202-2245   Fax: 315-477-6438
www.rurdev.usda.gov/ny
Rural Business-Cooperative Service supports economic and business development in rural communities.

Guaranteed Business and Industry Loans: Rural Development joins together with local banks and other commercial lenders to provide financing for businesses located in rural areas. Lenders are able to offer larger loans and better terms with a guarantee that may cover up to 80% of the lenders exposure on the loan. B&I guarantees are available in all parts of New York except for cities of more than 50,000 population and the urbanized areas surrounding

them. Eligible Applicants - Individuals, corporations, partnerships, cooperatives, federally recognized Indian Tribes and other legal entities are eligible borrowers.

Intermediary Relending Program: The Intermediary Relending Program makes funds available to community development organizations that will become intermediaries and relend the funds to rural businesses and community development projects. Eligible Applicants - Organizations eligible to become intermediaries include Not-For-Profit Corporations, Public Agencies, Indian Tribal Groups and Cooperatives.

Rural Business Enterprise Grants: Rural communities can receive assistance in promoting the development of small businesses through the Rural Business Enterprise Grant (RBEG) program. Grants are made to public bodies or not-for-profit organizations. Grantees use the funds to promote the development of small private businesses, which are defined as having 50 or fewer new employees and less than $1 million in projected annual gross revenue. Rural communities include cities with up to 50,000 populations and cannot be within the urbanized area of a larger city.
- Eligible Applicants - RBEG grants are made to public bodies and private not-for-profit corporations. Public bodies are States, counties, cities, townships, incorporated towns and villages, boroughs, authorities, districts, and federally recognized Indian Tribes.

Rural Cooperative Development Grants: The program provides grants for establishing and operating centers for cooperative development. The primary purpose is to improve economic conditions in rural areas, including cities of up to 50,000 populations. Grant funds can pay up to 75% of the costs for establishing and operating such centers. Grants may be made to public bodies or not-for-profit institution.

Rural Business Opportunity Grants: Rural Business Opportunity Grants (RBOG) are available to promote sustainable economic development in rural communities with exceptional need. Projects funded by the grants will:
- Promote economic development that is sustainable over the long term without continued need for external support.
- Improve the quality as well as the quantity of economic development activity.
- Act as a catalyst by providing critical investments.
- Serve as examples of "best practices" that merit implementation in rural communities in similar circumstances.
- Eligible rural areas exclude any area that is within the boundaries of a city with a population in excess of 10,000 inhabitants

Rural Cooperative Stock Purchase: The Rural Cooperative Stock Purchase Program works in conjunction with the Guaranteed Business and Industrial loan program allowing loans to be made to producers of agricultural products seeking to join new cooperatives that produce value-added goods. Family farmers can use the B&I loan program to help pay for stock in a start-up cooperative that will process an agricultural commodity into a value-added product.

Cooperative Agreements: The primary objective of this funding is to encourage research through cooperative agreements on critical issues vital to the development and sustainability of user-owned cooperatives as a means of improving the quality of life in America's rural communities. A cooperative agreement is not a grant. Cooperative agreements are to be awarded on the basis of merit, quality, and relevance to advancing the purpose of federally supported rural development programs that increase economic opportunities in farming and rural communities.

Technical Assistance: Rural Business-Cooperative Service (RBS) is developing plans to provide non-financial business advice and assistance to businesses and cooperative enterprises interested in applying for RBS financial assistance. This assistance will include how to complete application forms, acceptable standards for business plans to be used for RBS financing, methods of feasibility analysis, industry statistics, and financial standards generally required by lenders.

Rural Economic Development Loans and Grants: Loans and grants are available to rural electric cooperative or telephone borrowers to help promote economic and community development projects.

Cooperative Development: The office of Cooperative development offers a wide range of assistance for people interested in forming new cooperatives.

* Agricultural Business Development Assistance

New York State Department of Agriculture and Markets
The Winners Circle   800-554-4501
Albany, NY 12235   518-457-3880
www.agmkt.state.ny.us

Technical assistance to help locate public and private funding for food processors and agricultural producers.

* Apprentice Training Program

Long Island Field Office
303 W. Old Country Road   516-934-8525
Hicksville, NY 11801   Fax: 516-934-8557
Area of Operation: Nassau and Suffolk Counties

New York City Field Office
247 W 54th Street, 5th Floor   212-621-0844
New York, NY 10019   Fax: 212-621-0728
Area of Operation: Bronx, Kings, New York, Queens and Richmond Counties.

Albany Field Office
State Office Building Campus
Building 12, Room 436   518-457-4914
Albany, NY 12240   Fax: 518-457-7154
Area of Operation: Albany, Clinton, Columbia, Essex, Franklin, Fulton, Greene, Hamilton, Montgomery, Rensselaer, Saratoga, Schenectady, Schoharie, Warren and Washington Counties.

Utica Field Office
207 Genesee Street, Room 712   315-793-5339
Utica, NY 13501   Fax: 315-793-2514
Area of Operation: Herkimer, Madison, Oneida, and St.Lawrence Counties.

Binghamton Field Office
Glendale Technology Park
2001 Perimeter Road East, Suite 3 607-741-4577
Endicott, NY 13760   Fax: 607-741-4529
Area of Operation: Broome, Chemung, Chenango, Delaware, Otsego, Schuyler, Steuben, Tompkins, and Tioga Counties.

Syracuse Field Office
450 S. Salina Street, Room 203   315-479-3228
Syracuse, NY 13202   Fax: 315-479-3217

Area of Operation: Cayuga, Cortland, Jefferson, Lewis, Onondaga, and Oswego Counties.

Rochester Field Office
130 W. Main Street, Room 202   585-258-8885
Rochester, NY 14614   Fax: 585-258-8882
Area of Operation: Genesee, Livingston, Monroe, Ontario, Orleans, Seneca, Wayne, Wyoming, and Yates Counties.

Buffalo Field Office
290 Main Street, Room 224   716-851-2726
Buffalo, NY 14202   Fax: 716-851-2797
Area of Operation: Allegany, Cattaraugus, Chautauqua, Erie, and Niagara Counties.

Mid-Hudson Field Office
120 Bloomingdale Road   914-997-9534
White Plains, NY 10605   Fax: 914-997-8463
Area of Operation: Dutchess, Orange, Putnam, Rockland, Sullivan, Ulster, and Westchester Counties.

Provides on-the-job training for more than 250 skilled occupations. Contact the Apprentice Training Office that serves your county. {www.labor.state.ny.us/business_ny/apprenticeship_ training/apprenticeship_training.html}

* Rural Employment Program

Room 282, Bldg. 12
State Office Campus
Albany, NY 12240   518-457-6798

Recruits workers for farm, landscaping and food processing industries.

* Division Of Housing And Community Renewal

Hampton Plaza
38-40 State Street
Albany, NY 12207   518-402-3728
and
25 Beaver Street
New York, NY 10004   212-480-6700
www.dhcr.state.ny.us

Low Income Housing Credit Program: The Credit program provides a dollar-for-dollar reduction in federal income tax liability for project owners who develop, rehabilitate and acquire rental housing that serves low-income households. The amount of Credit available to project owners is in direct relation to the number of low-income housing units that they provide.

The Farmworker Housing Program is a low-cost loan program which assists in the improvement of existing housing or construction of new housing for seasonal farmworkers. Under this program loans of up to $100,000 per year are available to agricultural producers who apply to them and demonstrate that these program funds are needed to improve or construct seasonal farmworker housing. DHCR's priority is to provide loan funds for projects which will bring existing seasonal farmworker housing into compliance with applicable building codes

* New York State Office of Science, Technology & Academic Research (NYSTAR)

30 South Pearl Street 11th Floor 518-292-5700
Albany, New York 12207   Fax: 518-292-5780

www.nystar.state.ny.us

NYSTAR makes New York the leader in high-technology academic research and economic development by undertaking a host of new, unprecedented programs and initiatives. These initiatives result in the creation of several world-class, state-of-the-art research centers, the modernization of existing research centers and the rapid transfer of technologies from the research lab to the marketplace. Through programs and other strategic initiatives, NYSTAR strengthens the formation of university-business partnerships to develop and commercialize the most economically promising technologies of tomorrow.

The Technology Transfer Incentive Program is specifically designed to help business make the rapid transfer of new ideas and new technology from the research lab to the marketplace. The Technology Transfer Incentive Program will support a wide array of activities associated with bringing new technologies to the marketplace such as creation of business and marketing plans, obtaining venture capital, filing patent applications and product evaluation and assistance. This program will be structured so that awards may be made several times a year, giving potential applicants greater opportunity to quickly move a product from the research lab to the marketplace.

Science & Technology Law Center Program: As New York's high tech companies bring newly developed technology to market, they need assistance in the business formation and development process. Under NYSTAR's direction, the New York State Science and Technology Law Center will provide low-cost legal consultation and services essential to small and start-up companies as they seek to succeed in a competitive and complex marketplace.

The Centers for Advanced Technology (CAT) Program supports university-industry collaboration in research, education and technology transfer, with a strong focus on helping New York businesses gain a technological edge on their competition. Now this national model for technology transfer will be strengthened to achieve even greater results.

Centers for Advanced Technology:

Center for Advanced Ceramic Technology, Alfred University, Alfred NY 14802, 607-871-2486, {http://cact.alfred.edu}. Research and development of high technology ceramic materials that possess the potential to benefit both the industrial base of New York State and the scientific community.

Center for Ultrafast Photonic Materials & Applications, The City College of CUNY, Dept. of Physics, Room J419, 138th St. & Convent Avenue, New York, NY 10031, 212-650-5531, {http://cunyphotonics.com}. Research and technology development in select areas of photonics that have applications in optical communications, medical diagnostics, laser development, semiconductors, and optical imaging.

Center for Advanced Materials Processing, Clarkson University, Potsdam, Potsdam, NY 13699-5665, 315-268-2336, {www.clarkson.edu/camp/}. Research applied to industrial needs in photocopying and imaging, micro-electronics, pharmaceutical, cosmetic, and environmental control industries, among others.

Center for Advanced Technology in Information Management & Medical Informatics, Columbia University, New York City - Columbia Presbyterian Medical Center, 630 West 168th Street, New York, NY 10032, 212-305-2944, {http://www.cat.columbia.edu}. Specializes in bringing

cutting-edge information science to industry for product development and enhancement.

Center for Biotechnology, Cornell University, Ithaca 130 Biotechnology Building, Ithaca, NY 14853-2703, 607-255-4259, {http://www.research. cornell.edu/Biotech/Biotech. html}. Research and development, education and training, and technology transfer that address the economic development needs of New York industry.

Center for Advanced Technology in Digital Multimedia, New York University, New York City, 719 Broadway, 12th Floor, New York, NY 10003, 212-998-3390, {http://www.cat.nyu.edu/}. Fosters industry growth by developing and licensing new technologies and by providing business assistance to new media companies.

Center for Advanced Technology in Telecommunications, Polytechnic University, Brooklyn 5 MetroTech, Brooklyn, NY 11201, 718-260-3050, {http://catt.poly.edu/catthome. html}. Technology transfer, partnering with both providers and users of telecommunications and information systems to help them turn the latest developments in these technologies into competitive and productive resources.

Center for Automation Technologies, Rensselaer Polytechnic Institute, Troy CII Building, Room 8015, Troy, NY 12180, 518-276-8087, {http://cat.rpi. edu/}. CAT engineers are creating automation solutions that will have a powerful, positive impact on the global economy. Cutting edge research applied to the needs of corporate clients and industry in general.

CAT in Electronic Imaging Systems, University of Rochester/Rochester Institute of Technology, Rochester, Taylor Hall, 260 Hutchison Road, Rochester, NY 14627-0194, 585-275-3999, {http://www.ceis.rochester. edu/}. Basic research in the field of electronic imaging, leveraging the results for economic advantage to New York State and the nation.

Center for Advanced Thin Film Technology, State University of New York, 251 Fuller Road, Albany, NY 12203, 518-437-8686, {http://www.albany. edu/cat}. A research, development, education, and economic outreach resource for industries which manufacture, use, or supply micro-electronics, electronics, optoelectronics, bioelectronics, nanotechnology and telecommunications devices and components.

Integrated Electronics Engineering Center, SUNY at Binghamton, Binghamton Thomas J. Watson School of Engineering, Vestal Parkway East, P.O. Box 6000, Binghamton, NY 13902-6000, 607-777-6880, {/www.ieec.binghamton.edu/ieec/}. Engaged in the process of bringing a semiconductor chip, with its resident circuitry, to a form that can be integrated effectively into a larger microelectronics assembly.

Center for Computer Applications and Software Engineering, Syracuse University, Syracuse 2-212, Center for Science & Technology, Syracuse, NY 13244-4100, 315-443-1060, {http://www.cat.syr.edu/}. Research focused on computer applications and software engineering. Applies traditional university strengths in research and education to economic development.

Center for Biotechnology, State University of New York at Stony Brook, Stony Brook Psychology A, 3rd Floor, Stony Brook, NY 11794-2580, 631-632-8521, {/www.biotech. sunysb.edu/}. Discovery, development, translation and commercialization of promising biotechnology resulting from academic research centers around the state of New York.

CAT in Sensor Systems, State University of New York at Stony Brook, Stony Brook Light Engineering Building, Room 150, Stony Brook, NY 11794-2350, 631-632-1368, {http://www.sensorcat.sunysb.edu}. Magnetic, optical, X-ray, and infrared sensors; signal processing and image recognition; superconducting electronics for sensor applications; DNA sequencing devices; and MEMS-based sensors and actuators.

* New York State Environment Facilities Corporation (EFC)

625 Broadway	518-402-6924
Albany, NY 12207-2997	800-882-9721
www.nysefc.org	Fax: 518-485-8773

Industrial Finance Program (IFP): The Industrial Finance Program (IFP) provides tax-exempt and taxable conduit financing to private entities in New York State for a variety of environmental purposes. The IFP lends the proceeds of tax-exempt bonds to borrowers seeking financing for capital facilities for the following: solid waste handling, disposal and recycling, including brownfield site remediation; sewage treatment, including limited industrial or other wastewater treatment; drinking water supply and management; limited hazardous waste disposal and remediation; and privatization of New York municipal or state environmental facilities. The use of tax-exempt bonds allows IFP clients to borrow funds at a lower rate of interest than would otherwise be available in the market. For projects or portions of projects that do not qualify for tax-exemption under the federal tax code, the IFP can provide taxable conduit financing. The minimum size of an IFP financing is approximately $1.5 million. However, several projects at one or more sites owned by one or more borrowers may be financed with a single IFP bond issue. IFP financing can be used to privatize certain exempt facilities. For More Information about IFP financing contact: Director of Industrial Finance, 518-457-4100 or 1-800-882-9721 (within NY).

Small Business Assistance Program (SBAP): The SBAP provides small businesses, such as printers, metal and wood furniture manufacturers, autobody shops, drycleaners, and various other manufacturers, with free and confidential technical assistance about air emission requirements. The SBAP suggests measures to help businesses achieve compliance, including permitting assistance, pollution prevention, materials substitution, and process modifications. 800-780-7227.

Financial Assistance to Business Program (FAB): The Financial Assistance to Business (FAB) helps businesses cope with the cost of complying with environmental protection mandates. EFC administers this program with the assistance and approval of local governments. EFC is in the process of awarding some of the $60 million of Bond Act funds available under this program.

Dry Cleaner Program: The New York State Environmental Facilities Corporation ("EFC") proposes to provide funding to the owners of certain eligible dry cleaning facilities to defray costs associated with new environmental protection requirements. Contact Laurie A. Allen, Program Manager, 800-200-2200, Fax: 518-486-9246.

The Industrial Finance Program (IFP) provides tax-exempt and taxable conduit financing to private entities in New York State for a variety of environmental purposes. The IFP lends the proceeds of tax-exempt bonds to borrowers seeking

financing for capital facilities for the following: solid waste handling, disposal and recycling, including brownfield site remediation; sewage treatment, including limited industrial or other wastewater treatment; drinking water supply and management; limited hazardous waste disposal and remediation; and privatization of New York municipal or state environmental facilities. Director of Industrial Finance, 518-402-6924 or 800-882-9721.

The Division of Technical Advisory Services (TAS) provides assistance to private- and public-sector clients to help them improve environmental practices and to support management of their environmental projects. Through TAS, EFC offers businesses and government entities a number of pollution prevention, waste reduction and project management services custom-tailored to the needs of the individual client. TAS services are typically provided on a fee-for-service basis, although certain programs are available at no cost to participants. Erick McCandless, Director at 1-800-882-9721.

* New York Business Development Corporation (NYBDC)

New York Business Development Corporation (NYBDC)

50 Beaver Street	800-923-2504
Albany, NY 12207	Fax: 518-463-0240
www.nybdc.com	

The New York Business Development Corporations mission is to promote economic activity within New York state by providing innovative loans to small and medium-size businesses; to assist our partner banks in making such loans; and, particularly, to assist minority and women-owned businesses by offering credit opportunities not otherwise available to them.

Agricultural Business Loan Program: This program is committed to financing the growth of agricultural-related business in New York State.

Mezzanine Loan Program: This program aids in financing emerging technology companies and other growth oriented businesses in need of capital.

Capital Access Program: NYBDC administers a pool of funds that are designed to give banks a flexible and non-bureaucratic tool to make business loans that are somewhat riskier than conventional bank loans.

Linked Deposit Program: This program provides businesses with affordable loans based on interest rates subsidized by state deposits.

Micro Loan Program: The Micro Loan Program was designed to provide an alternative to credit scoring for smaller loan requests.

* Loans For Farmers

Farm Service Agency
U.S. Department of Agriculture

441 S. Salina St., Suite 536	315-477-6300
Syracuse, NY 13202	Fax: 315-477-6323
http://www.fsa.usda.gov/ny/	

The Farm Service Agency provides Direct and Guaranteed Loans to farmers through a variety of programs, including:

Farm Ownership Loans: purchase farmland, construct or repair buildings and other fixtures, and promote soil and water conservation. Up to $200,000.

Operating Loans: purchase items needed for a successful farm operation, such as livestock, farm equipment, feed, seed, fuel, farm chemicals, insurance, and other operating expenses. Can also be used to pay for minor improvements. Up to $200,000.

Beginning Farmer and Rancher Loans: provides funds to beginning and farmers and ranchers who are unable to obtain financing elsewhere.

Downpayment Farm Ownership Loans for Beginning Farmers: helps beginning farmers and ranchers purchase a farm or ranch. Also provides a way for retiring farmers to transfer their land to a future generation of farmers and ranchers. Applicant must have a downpayment of 10% and FSA with finance 40%, with the remaining balance from a commercial lender. Purchase price cannot exceed $250,000.

Loans to Socially Disadvantaged Farmers/Ranchers: helps socially disadvantaged applicants buy and operate family-size farms and ranches.

Youth Loans: Made to youths to establish and operate income-producing projects with the participation in 4-H clubs, Future Farmers of America, and similar organizations. Up to $5,000.

Emergency Loan Assistance: provides loans to help producers recover from production and physical losses due to drought, flooding, and other natural disasters, or quarantine. Up to $500,000.

Beginning Farmer and Rancher Land Contract Guarantee Pilot Program: "prompt payment guarantee" from FSA. FSA will provide payment to seller two times if the beginning farmer does not pay. Program is tested in IN, IA, ND, OR, PA and WI.

Farm Ownership and Operating Loan Guarantees: FSA will guarantee loans up to $782,000.

* Small Business Administration (SBA)

Regional Office
26 Federal Plaza, Room 3100   212-264-4354
New York, NY 10278   Fax: 212-264-4963

111 West Huron St., Suite 1311   ·   716-551-4301
Buffalo, NY 14202   Fax: 716-551-4418

401 S. Salina St., 5th Floor   315-471-9393
Syracuse, NY 13202   Fax: 315-471-9288
www.sba.gov/ny

The New York Small Business Administration Office delivers a variety of programs and services, such as startup and operational assistance through small business training and counseling, financial assistance for startup's, business opportunities and much more.

* Housing and Urban Development (HUD)

Regional Office
26 Federal Plaza, Suite 3541   212-264-8000
New York, NY 10278-0068   Fax: 212-264-3068
                                    TDD: 212-264-0927

Community Development Block Grants: Available to cities and counties for the commercial rehabilitation of existing buildings or structures used for business, commercial or industrial purposes. Grants of up to $500,000 can be made. Every $15,000 of grant funds invested must create at least one

full-time job, and at least 51 percent of the jobs created must be for low- and moderate-income families.

* Power For Jobs

The New York Power Authority
123 Main Street, 10th Floor   888-562-7697
White Plains, NY 10601   Fax: 914-390-8155
www.nypa.gov/economic.htm

Businesses that remain and expand in the state get low cost electricity. The firm must first retain or create a specified number of jobs.

* New York State Energy Research and Development Authority (NYSERDA)

17 Columbia Circle   866-NYSERDA
Albany, NY 12203-6399   518-862-1090
www.nyserda.org   Fax: 518-862-1091

New York State Energy Research and Development Authority's goal is to help all of New York State solve their energy and environmental problems while developing new, innovative products and services that can be manufactured or commercialized by New York businesses.

Economic Development through Greater Energy Efficiency: Grants and technical support for detailed engineering studies of manufacturing operations up to $50,000. Capital financing for demonstrations of energy efficient process technology up to $250,000.

Energy $mart Loan Fund: Interest rate reductions are provided on loans for energy-efficiency projects and renewable technologies.

Energy Efficiency Services: Technical assistance and financial assistance up to $50,000 per project for the following:
- Energy Feasibility Studies
- Energy Operations Management
- Rate Analysis and Aggregation
- Combined Heat & Power Renewable Generation Studies

Industrial Waste Minimization Program: Technical assistance and grants up to $50,000 to assist, develop, and demonstrate energy-efficient methods to reduce, reuse or recycle industrial wastes at the point of generation.

* New York State Banking Department

One State Street   800-522-3330
New York, NY 10004-1417   Fax: 212-709-3582
www.banking.state.ny.us/sbusines/sba.htm

The Banking Department has developed a source book of private, public and nonprofit small business assistance programs in New York State to be used as a resource tool for financial institutions, as well as a referral source for small business entrepreneurs.

North Carolina

* North Carolina Department of Commerce

301 North Wilmington Street
Raleigh, NC 27601
Mailing Address:
4301 Mail Service Center
Raleigh, NC 27699-4301   919-733-4151

www.commerce.state.nc.us

Retention and Expansion Programs: Professional assistance is provided for all aspects of business including environmental consultation, financing alternative, human resources consulting, marketing information, energy process surveys and other issues that impact business and industry.

Business and Industry ServiCenter: Provides technical and industrial management assistance, conducts applied research, advocates industrial use of technology and modern managerial practices, as well as conducts continuing education programs for business, industry, entrepreneurs, engineers and local governments. 866-259-9846

Biotechnology Center: Carries out a variety of programs and activities strengthening North Carolina's biotechnology community. Call 919-541-9366 or contact their website {www.biotech.org}.

Customized Training Program: State funded customized job training programs for new and expanding industries that create 12 or more new jobs in a community within one year.

SBTDC Special Market Development Assistance:

- *Procurement Technical Assistance Program*: The SBTDC provides comprehensive assistance in selling goods and services to the federal government. Services include help in finding out about contracting opportunities, preparing bid and proposal packages, obtaining 8(a) certification, interpreting regulations, and resolving contract administration problems. An integral part of this program is PRO-BID, a computer-based bid matching service that provides accurate and timely information on procurement opportunities.
- *International Business Development*: North Carolina businesses are increasingly looking at exporting as a vehicle to increase sales and profits. The SBTDC helps successful domestic, new-to-export businesses to identify, target and then penetrate foreign markets. SBTDC counselors provide marketing research information, assist with market planning, and then identify implementation procedures.
- *The Technology Group*: Part of the SBTDC's mission is to help emerging businesses commercialize innovative new technologies, and to facilitate the transfer of technology developed within the small business and university communities. Technology Group services include assistance in maritime technology transfer, identifying markets for scientific discoveries, guiding the development of strategies to protect intellectual property and providing referrals to specialized organizations and resources.
- *Marine Trades Program*: The SBTDC's Marine Trades Program provides business development support to marine industry firms. Specific services include assistance in marketing marine products and services, complying with environmental regulations, and maintaining safe operations. The program also provides marine specific training, education and research.

Industrial Revenue Bonds: Revenue Bonds have a variety of names and purposes but essentially three basic types exist. These bonds whose proper name is Small Issue Industrial Development Bonds are referred to as Industrial Revenue Bond's (IRB's). The state's principal interest in these bonds is assisting new and expanding industry while insuring that North Carolinians get good jobs at good wages. The regulations governing bond issuance are a combination of federal regulations and North Carolina statutes. The amount each state may issue annually is designated by population.

There are three types of bond issuances as follows:

- Tax Exempt - Because the income derived by the bondholder is not subject to federal income tax, the maximum bond amount is $10 million in any given jurisdiction. According to federal regulations, the $10 million total includes the bond amount and capital expenditures over a six-year period going both backwards and forwards three years. The maximum any company may have is $40 million nationwide outstanding at any given period.
- Taxable - They are not exempt from federal tax (they are however exempt from North Carolina tax). The essential difference is that the Taxable bond rate is slightly higher to the borrower and not being subject to the federal volume cap, may exceed $10 million in bond amount.
- Pollution Control/Solid Waste Disposal Bond - These bonds are subject to volume cap although there is no restriction on amount, and the interest on these bonds is federally tax exempt.

Industrial Development Fund: Purpose is to provide an incentive for jobs creation in the State's most economically distressed counties, also identified as Tier 1, 2, and 3 areas. Funds for the renovation of manufacturing buildings and the acquisition of infrastructure are made available by the Department of Commerce to eligible counties or their local units of government, which apply for the funds on behalf of their existing or new manufacturing businesses. A commitment to create jobs is executed by the benefiting firm. The amount of funds available to participating firms is determined by multiplying the number of jobs committed to be created times $4,000.00, up to a maximum of $400,000.00 or the cost of the project, whichever is less. Of course, the availability of funds also applies.

Business Energy Improvement: Program provides loans between $100,000 and $500,000 to industrial and commercial businesses located or moving to North Carolina. Loans can be financed for up to seven years at interest rates equal to 50% of the average (high and low) T-bill rate for the past year or five percent, whichever is lower. Current rate is 5%, which is the maximum. Funds are provided from a pool of $2,500,000 designated for energy related capital improvement such as cogeneration, energy saving motors, boiler improvements and low energy use lighting. A participating bank will process loans on a first-come-first-served based upon the date of receipt of a letter of credit.

Partnerships for Regional Economic Development: The counties of North Carolina have been organized into seven regional partnerships for economic development. North Carolina's regional partnerships will enable regions to compete effectively for new investment and to devise effective economic development strategies based on regional opportunities and advantages.

Industrial Access/Road Access Fund: Administered by the Department of Transportation, this program provides funds for the construction of roads to provide access to new or expanded facilities.

The Rail Industrial Access Program: Provides grant funding to aid in financing the cost of constructing or rehabilitating railroad access tracks required by a new or expanded industry which will result in a significant number of new jobs or capital investment.

Export Ready Program: A series of workshops designed to walk a company through every facet of the export process. In cooperation with the North Carolina Community College Small Business Network, the International Trade Division has made this program available in seven regional centers across the state. The Export Outreach Program is a hard-core, intense program where commitment, preparation and action are instilled as the basis for successful exporting. North Carolina is the only state to offer such a program, which increases the quality and competitiveness of North Carolina products.

Trade Events Program: This program consists of Catalog Shows, Trade Fairs and Trade Mission in carefully selected markets worldwide. The Trade Events Calendar is updated periodically to inform North Carolina companies of these opportunities.

International Trade Division: Because North Carolina companies are prepared and committed prior to entering international markets, North Carolina is recognized in the major trading blocs of the world as one of the most aggressive international business development states in the United States. Senior Trade Specialists of the International Trade Division represent the three major trading blocks of the world: Europe/Africa/The Middle East, The Americas, Far East.

* Rural Development
State Director, Rural Development
William A. Tadlock III
4405 Bland Road   919-873-2000
Raleigh, NC 27609   Fax: 919-873-2075
Email: william.tadlock@nc.usda.gov
www.rurdev.usda.gov/nc

Business And Industry Loan Guarantees: The business and industry program provides loan guarantees for expansion and preservation of jobs in rural areas. The guarantees are issued to commercial lenders who make credit available to support business activity in rural areas with populations up to 50,000. Loan funds may be used to purchase land, buildings and equipment; working capital; and refinance debts. The goal of the program is to strengthen the economy of rural communities through the creation of employment opportunities.

Business And Industry Direct Loans: The business and industry program provides for direct loans for expansions and preservation of jobs in rural areas. These loans are made to individuals or corporate businesses to support business activity in rural areas with populations up to 50,000. Loan funds may be used to purchase land, buildings and equipment; working capital; and refinance debts. The goal of the program is to strengthen the economy of rural communities through the creation of employment opportunities.

Intermediary Relending Program: Loans are made to private nonprofit corporations, any state or local government, Indian tribe, or cooperatives who in turn provide credit to finance business facilities and community development projects in rural areas on a revolving loan basis.

Rural Business Opportunity Grants: Rural Business Opportunity Grants provide funding for technical assistance, training, and planning activities that improve economic conditions in rural areas.

Rural Business Enterprise Grants: Rural Business Enterprise Grants finance the development of small and emerging private business enterprises. Public bodies, nonprofit corporations and recognized Indian Tribal Groups may be eligible applicants.

Rural Economic Development Loans And Grants: The purpose of the Rural Economic Development Loan and Grant program is to develop projects that will result in a sustainable increase in economic productivity, job creation, and incomes in rural areas. Projects may include business start-ups and expansion, community development incubator projects, medical and training projects, and feasibility studies.

Cooperative Services Technical Assistance: Cooperative Services (CS) assists rural residents in forming new cooperative businesses and improving the operations of existing cooperatives.

Value-Added Program Grants: Grants for independent producers, eligible agriculture producer groups, and farmer or ranch cooperatives. Grants may also be used for feasibility studies to provide capital to establish alliances or business ventures that allow the producers of the value-added agricultural product to better compete in domestic and international markets.

Renewable Energy Grants: This program enables agricultural producers and small businesses to purchase renewable energy systems and make energy improvements to reduce the cost and consumption of the nation's energy needs.

* SBTDC Minority Business Enterprise Development (SBTDC)
Small Business and Technology
   Development Center
5 West Hargett Street, Suite 600   919-715-7272
Raleigh, NC 27601-1348   800-258-0862 (NC only)
www.sbtdc.org

The Small Business and Technology Development Center is North Carolina's resource for growing companies. Many of the clients counseled are existing businesses. Through their management counseling and educational services, the SBTDC helps owners and managers gain knowledge essential to improving business practices, creating high-value products and services, and enhancing competitiveness. They also provide statewide procurement technical assistance through a partnership with the Defense Logistics Agency. They can help your business export products and services through a partnership with the US Export-Import Bank.

* MCNC
3201 Cornwallis Rd.
P.O. Box 12889   919-248-1800
Research Triangle Park, NC 27709   Fax: 919-248-1455
www.mcnc.org

A private nonprofit corporation that supports advanced education, research and technology programs to enhance North Carolina's technology infrastructure and businesses.

* Sales Tax Exemptions and Discounts
NC Department of Revenue
Box 25000
Raleigh, NC 27640   919-733-3991
www.dor.state.nc.us/

The North Carolina Department of Revenue has information for your business whether you're starting a new business, or have been in business for a while.

* Business License Information

North Carolina Business License Information Office
(BLIO)
Department of the Secretary of State
111 Hillsborough St.,   919-807-2166
Raleigh, NC 27603   800-228-8443 (in NC)
www.secretary.state.nc.us/blio

All BLIO services are free of charge and customized to the individual business concept. Services include: one-on-one client consultations either by phone or in person; customized licensing information including employer forms and business structure information; referrals to state occupational licensing boards; referrals to local government licensing and zoning offices; referrals to the appropriate federal government agencies; and assistance in identifying other business resources.

* Aquaculture and Natural Resources

North Carolina Department of Agriculture & Consumer
Services
2 West Edenton Street
1001 Mail Service Center   919-733-7125
Raleigh, NC 27699-1001   Fax: 919-716-0090
www.ncagr.com

The North Carolina Department of Agriculture & Consumer Services is the lead agency for the aquaculture industry in North Carolina. The Division of Aquaculture and Natural Resources issues the aquaculture license, is a source of general information on aquaculture, and provides farmers with published information on the economics of aquaculture and with one-one-one business counseling. The Division also participates in the National Association of State Aquaculture Coordinators. The Department also maintains seven veterinary diagnostic labs to help farmers maintain healthy fish, and the Agronomic Division does free soil evaluations to help farmers choose the best site for ponds.

* Department of Environment and Natural Resources

Small Business Assistance Program (SBAP)
1640 Mail Service Center   877-623-6748
Raleigh, NC 27699-1640   Fax: 919-715-7468
www.envhelp.org

The mission of the SBAP is to assist small businesses with air quality and other regulatory requirements, encouraging environmental compliance and stewardship.

Small Business Ombudsman (SBO): The state/territory SBOs serve as the small business community's representative where small businesses are impacted by the CAA. The SBO's key responsibilities may include: Review and provide recommendations to EPA and state/local air pollution control authorities regarding development and implementation of regulations impacting small businesses.

Compliance Advisory Panel (CAP): The CAP is created at the state level and is comprised of at least seven members: 2 members who are not owners of small business stationary sources — selected by the Governor to represent the public. 2 members who are owners of small business stationary sources — selected by the lower house of the state legislature. 2 members who are owners of small business stationary sources — selected by the upper house of the state legislature. 1 member from the state air pollution permit program — selected by the head of that agency. The responsibilities of the CAP are to: Render advisory opinions concerning the effectiveness of the SBTCP, difficulties

encountered, and degree and severity of enforcement. Report on the compliance of the SBTCP with the Paperwork Reduction Act, the Regulatory Flexibility Act, and the Equal Access to Justice Act. Submit periodic reports to EPA's SBO. Review information for small business stationary sources to ensure it is understandable to the layperson. Assist in dissemination of information about upcoming air regulations, control requirements, and other matters relevant to small businesses.

Small Business Assistance Program (SBAP): The SBAPs should provide sufficient communications with small businesses through the collection and dissemination of information to the small businesses on matters of: Determining applicable requirements under the Act and permit issuance. The rights of small businesses under the Act. Compliance methods and acceptable control technologies, pollution prevention and accidental release prevention and detection and audit programs.

* North Carolina Department of Transportation

Program Development Branch
Mail Service Center #1534   919-733-2039
Raleigh, NC 27699-1534   Fax: 919-733-3585
www.ncdot.org/planning/development/TIP/TIP/

The TIP Unit develops the Transportation Improvement Program (TIP). The TIP contains funding information and schedules for various transportation divisions including: highways, aviation, enhancements, public transportation, rail, bicycle and pedestrians, and the Governor's Highway Safety Program.

* Carolinas Export Assistance Center

521 E. Morehead Street, Suite 435   704-333-2130
Charlotte, NC 28202   Fax: 704-332-2681

The Center assists clients with information about export finance options. This U.S.E.A.C. consolidates the export promotion and finance services of the U.S. Dept. of Commerce, the U.S. Small Business Administration, and the Small Business and Technology Development Center (SBTDC).

* Crop Production and Marketing Systems

North Carolina Department of Agriculture and
Consumer Services
2 West Edenton Street
Raleigh, NC 27601   919-733-7125
www.agr.state.nc.us

Program goals include helping farmers evaluate alternative production practices and markets; helping part-time and limited-resource producers increase the sustainability of their farms; helping agricultural professionals adopt practices to enhance environmental quality and maintain profitability; helping producers understand and successfully comply with regulations; providing citizens with information about biotechnology; and helping farmers, agribusinesses and related organizations understand how to take advantage of local and global market factors.

* North Carolina Technological Development Authority

2 Davis Dr.
P.O. Box 13169   919-990-8558
Research Triangle Park, NC 27709   Fax: 919-558-0156
www.nctda.org

The North Carolina Technological Development Authority, Inc. (TDA) is a public benefit corporation whose mission is to create jobs and wealth throughout North Carolina using business incubation, venture capital, technology transfer and rural initiatives to commercialize promising business opportunities.

Seed and Incubator Capital: Through the Innovation Research Fund, up to $50,000 in seed money is available for development of new products or services. The Authority funds incubator facilities through its Incubator Facilities Program. It also conducts workshops across the state for those small business interested in the IRF and the Small Business Innovation Research program.

* Loans For Farmers

Farm Service Agency
U.S. Department of Agriculture
4407 Bland Road, Suite 175   919-875-4800
Raleigh, NC 27609   Fax: 919-875-4825
http://www.fsa.usda.gov/nc/

The Farm Service Agency provides Direct and Guaranteed Loans to farmers through a variety of programs, including:

Farm Ownership Loans: purchase farmland, construct or repair buildings and other fixtures, and promote soil and water conservation. Up to $200,000.

Operating Loans: purchase items needed for a successful farm operation, such as livestock, farm equipment, feed, seed, fuel, farm chemicals, insurance, and other operating expenses. Can also be used to pay for minor improvements. Up to $200,000.

Beginning Farmer and Rancher Loans: provides funds to beginning and farmers and ranchers who are unable to obtain financing elsewhere.

Downpayment Farm Ownership Loans for Beginning Farmers: helps beginning farmers and ranchers purchase a farm or ranch. Also provides a way for retiring farmers to transfer their land to a future generation of farmers and ranchers. Applicant must have a downpayment of 10% and FSA with finance 40%, with the remaining balance from a commercial lender. Purchase price cannot exceed $250,000.

Loans to Socially Disadvantaged Farmers/Ranchers: helps socially disadvantaged applicants buy and operate family-size farms and ranches.

Youth Loans: Made to youths to establish and operate income-producing projects with the participation in 4-H clubs, Future Farmers of America, and similar organizations. Up to $5,000.

Emergency Loan Assistance: provides loans to help producers recover from production and physical losses due to drought, flooding, and other natural disasters, or quarantine. Up to $500,000.

Beginning Farmer and Rancher Land Contract Guarantee Pilot Program: "prompt payment guarantee" from FSA. FSA will provide payment to seller two times if the beginning farmer does not pay. Program is tested in IN, IA, ND, OR, PA and WI.

Farm Ownership and Operating Loan Guarantees: FSA will guarantee loans up to $782,000.

* Small Business Administration (SBA)

6302 Fairview Road, Suite 300   704-344-6563
Charlotte, NC 28210   Fax: 704-344-6769
www.sba.gov/nc

The North Carolina Small Business Administration Office delivers a variety of programs and services, such as startup and operational assistance through small business training and counseling, financial assistance for startup's, business opportunities and much more.

* North Carolina Biotechnology Center

15 TW Alexander Dr.
P.O. Box 13547   919-541-9366
Research Triangle Park, NC 27709-3547
www.ncbiotech.org   Fax: 919-990-9544

Supports biotechnology research as a means of improving the state's economy. The center does not actually perform research itself, but supports, coordinates, and educates in the field of biotechnology. Grants are available for academic research, large-scale projects at universities and nonprofit institutions, economic development, and for groups wishing to organize conferences and workshops. These grants total several million dollars per year.

* Industrial Extension Service (IES)

North Carolina Manufacturing Extension Partnership (NCMEP)
IES Technical Services   800-227-0264
Box 7902   919-515-2358
Raleigh, NC 27695-7902   Fax: 919-515-6159
www.ies.ncsu.edu

Through NCMEP, IES delivers services to North Carolina's manufacturing community, offering engineering assistance, problem solving, technical information, continuing education, and demonstration of new technologies and best practices. Extension specialists are linked through electronic communication, industry advisory councils, networking, and state of the art information resources.

North Dakota

* North Dakota Department of Economic Development and Finance

1600 East Century Ave., Suite 2
P.O. Box 2057   701-328-5300
Bismarck, ND 58502   Fax: 701-328-5320
www.growingnd.com   TTY: 800-366-6888

This office can provide information and expertise in dealing with state, federal, and local agencies. They also have information on financing programs and other services offered by the state government.

North Dakota Manufacturing Technology Partnership (MTP): Approximately 400 targeted manufacturers in the state will be able to receive direct assistance from dedicated manufacturing specialists experienced in manufacturing and will be able to access other appropriate assistance through managed referrals. Manufacturers can expect benefits from improved manufacturing processes; enhanced management skills; better business practices; research and development funding and technical assistance; expanded market opportunities; defense conversion assistance; new product development resources; better trained staff; intercompany working relationships; increased revenue; and increased profit.

The North Dakota Development Fund: Provides gap financing for primary sector businesses expanding or relocating in the state. Primary sector is defined as: "an individual, corporation, partnership or association which, through the employment of knowledge or labor, adds value to a product, process or service that results in the creation of new wealth." Primary sector businesses are typically considered to be manufacturing, food processing, and exported services. Types of investments include equity, debt, and other forms of innovative financing up to a limit of $300,000. One of the criteria for dollars invested is projected job creation within 24 months of funding.

Agricultural Products Utilization Commission: Mission is to create new wealth and jobs through the development of new and expanded uses of North Dakota agricultural products. The commission accomplishes its mission through the administration of a grant program.

Basic and Applied Research Grants: This program centers on research efforts that focus on the uses and processing of agricultural products and by-products. Further, consideration is given to products which develop an expanded use of technology for the processing of these products.

Marketing & Utilization Grants: Funds from this category are used for the development or implementation of a sound marketing plan for the promotion of North Dakota agricultural products or by-products.

Farm Diversification Grants: This category focuses on the diversification of a family farm to non-traditional crops, livestock or non-farm value-added processing of agricultural commodities. Traditional crops and livestock are generally defined as those for which the North Dakota Agricultural Statistics Service maintains records. The proposed project must have the potential to create additional income for the farm unit.

International Trade Program: Mission is to increase the number of jobs in North Dakota by helping companies expand their business into foreign markets. Staff counsels companies on export procedures, international marketing, banking and financing. They also provide referrals to translators, customs brokers, consultants and opportunities for participation in international trade show events. Offers a series of international business workshops, titled "Hands-On Training in International Business," to provide North Dakota businesses with the tools to target global markets and expand export opportunities.

* Rural Development Administration

State Director
Federal Building, Room 208
220 East Rosser
P.O. Box 1737   701-530-2037
Bismarck, ND 58502   701-530-2108
www.rurdev.usda.gov/nd

Business and Industrial Loan Programs: Provides loan guarantees to lenders. Proceeds can be used for working capital, equipment, and real property. Interest rates are negotiated between lender and borrower. Maximum terms: 7 years for working capital, 10 years for equipment, and 25 years for real property. Requires 10 percent equity for existing businesses and 20 percent-25 percent for new businesses. Additional funding allowed from any source. Only rural areas and areas with populations under 25,000 are eligible.

Rural Enterprise Grant Program: Provides grants to public or nonprofit agencies to provide loans and/or technical assistance to for-profit enterprises, with the intent of creating jobs for rural residents.

Intermediary Relending Program: Provides loans to rural businesses. The interest rate to the intermediaries is 1%, with repayment terms of up to 30 years. The program is intended to create employment for rural residents.

* Skills and Technology Training Center

1305 19th Ave. North
Fargo, ND 58102   701-231-6900
www.sttc.nodak.edu   Fax: 701-231-6905
Located in Fargo. A partnership between NDSU-Fargo, North Dakota State College of Science, and Wahpeton private sector leaders.

* Job Services North Dakota

P.O. Box 5507   800-732-9787
Bismarck, ND 58506-5507   701-328-3096
www.state.nd.us/jsnd/   Fax: 701-328-1025
Has labor, employment, and other statistical information available.

* One Stop Capital Center

Bank of North Dakota
700 E. Main, 2nd Floor
P.O. Box 5509   701-328-5850
Bismarck, ND 58506   800-544-4674
http://webhost.btigate.com/ ~onestop
Located at the Bank of North Dakota, the One Stop Capital Center offers one-stop access to over twenty financing programs. Together, the five partners work with local financial institutions and economic developers to offer integrated financial packages. The One Stop Capital Center has loan officers available from each of the agencies who jointly work to streamline the financing process and provide timely service.

* Center for Technology & Business/ Women & Technology

P.O. Box 2535   701-223-0707
Bismarck, ND 58502   Fax: 701-223-2507
www.techwomen.org
A partnership funded by the Economic Development and Finance Division and the U.S. Small Business Administration brought about this program, which is designed to serve women in business or about to start a business. It also provides technical assistance and training to help women so they may join the technology revolution.

* Center for Innovation

Bruce Gjovig, Director
University of North Dakota Rural Technology Center
4300 Dartmouth Drive
P.O. Box 8372   701-777-3132
Grand Forks, ND 58202-8372   Fax: 701-777-2339
www.innovators.net
The Center for Innovation offers comprehensive, hands-on assistance to technology entrepreneurs, innovators, and manufacturers interested in starting up new ventures, commercializing new products, and licensing new technologies. They can help your business with Marketing Services, Business Plans, Small Business Innovation Research (SBIR) applications, Commercial Evaluations, and

Patent & Trademark searches. The Center has helped launch hundreds of new products and companies, including several university-developed spinoffs.

* The Rural Technology Incubator

Center for Innovation
4300 Dartmouth Drive
P.O. Box 8372   701-777-3132
Grand Forks, ND 58202-8372   Fax: 701-777-2339
www.innovators.net

The Rural Technology Incubator located in the Center for Innovation is designed to provide a seedbed to help innovators and entrepreneurs grow their businesses. Our highly-diversified staff assists startups by providing them with supportive, creative places in which to work as a team. The Rural Technology Incubator offers university talent, technology, training, and technical assistance to help business startups develop and test market new products, ideas, technologies, and ventures. They also provide tenants with improved exposure to the entrepreneurial enterprise of the greater Grand Forks community. Tenants enjoy a major cost savings due to below-average market prices, flexible rental space, and reduced overhead through shared infrastructure.

* Pride of Dakota

North Dakota Department of Agriculture
Marketing Division   800-242-7535
600 E Boulevard Ave, Dept 602   701-328-2231
Bismarck, ND 58505-0020   Fax: 701-328-4567
Email: ndda@state.nd.us
www.agdepartment.com/Programs/podhp.html

The program was created to develop, improve and expand domestic and foreign markets for North Dakota products. Pride of Dakota products gain exposure through: sharing booth space at trade shows and fairs; listing in North Dakota Products Guide and brochures ; networking with other North Dakota companies Pride of Dakota Day promotions ; and cooperative advertising and magazine advertisements. Pride of Dakota members have access to a marketing staff who can: assist in gaining consumer exposure for their products ; help make sales and distribution contacts in local, regional, national and international markets; assist in design of company brochures, packaging and labels; and develop marketing strategies and promotional planning. Pride of Dakota members can buy these promotional materials at cost: shelf tags; stickers; advertising slicks; and shelf talkers.

* Bank of North Dakota

Bank of North Dakota
P.O. Box 5509
700 East Main Ave.   800-472-2166
Bismarck, ND 58506   Fax: 701-328-5731

PACE (Partnership in Assisting Community Expansion): PACE assists North Dakota communities in expanding their economic base and provide for new job development by reducing the borrower's overall interest rate. The participation by a local lender is a major element, and the borrower must demonstrate that within the first year, there will be a minimum of one job created for every $75,000 of total loan proceeds.

Ag Pace: Provides low-interest financing to on-farm businesses. The program funds are sued to buy down the interest rate on loans which have been approved by a local lender and the Bank of North Dakota. It is available to any business, except traditional agriculture, which is integrated into the farm operation and will be used to supplement farm income.

Oil and Gas Development Loans: Assists North Dakota developers in increasing oil and gas production and job enhancement at existing wells. The Bank's maximum loan participation amount is $100,000.

Small Business Loan Program: Loans of up to $250,000 to any business, through a local lender, for working capital, equipment and real property. Terms are 3-5 years for working capital, 5-7 years for equipment, and 12-15 years for real estate. Equity requirement is 25 percent for new businesses. Local lender is required for 30-40 percent of loan.

Business Development Loans: Available to any business. Local lender is required for up 30 to 40 percent of total loan. BND share is up to $500,000 per project. Fund can be used for working capital, equipment and real property.

Match Program: MATCH is targeted to manufacturing, processing and value-added industries which are financially strong companies and provide interest rates at some of the lowest in the nation.

The SBA Loan Purchase Program is designed to provide low interest rate loans to North Dakota businesses receiving a SBA loan guarantee. This program permits BND to purchase the SBA guaranteed portion of the loan. BND will purchase, at par, the SBA guaranteed portion of any loan. BND's purchase is conditioned upon the borrower receiving the benefit of the lower interest rate. Call 701-328-5670 for further information.

Farm Loan Programs: Agriculture Partnership in Assisting Community Expansion (AG PACE); Beginning Farmer Guaranteed Farm Real Estate Loans; Beginning Farmer Real Estate Loan Program; Value Added Agriculture Equity Program (ENVEST); Established Farmer Real Estate Loan Program; Family Farm Loan Program; Farm Operating Loan Program; Farm Real Estate Loan Rates; FSA Guaranteed Loan Purchase Program; Irrigation Loan Program; and the ND First Time Farmer Finance Program. Call 701-328-5672.

Developmentally Disabled Facility Loan Fund: This fund assists in the construction facilities to house and train the developmentally disabled, the chronically mentally ill, and the physically disabled persons throughout the State. Loans may be made to nonprofit corporations organized in the locality in which a facility is proposed to be located. The proceeds may be used for the cost of real estate, construction, reconstruction, acquisition, furnishing and equipment and administrative costs related to the establishment of facilities for developmentally disabled, chronically mentally ill, and physically disabled persons. The maximum amount of a loan may not exceed 75% of the project costs.

* Grand Forks Region Economic Development Corporation

600 DeMars Ave., Suite 501   701-746-2720
Grand Forks, ND 58201   Fax: 701-746-2725
www.grandforks.org/localprograms.htm

Grand Forks Growth Fund: The fund is intended to provide gap and incentive financing for new or expanding businesses which have capacity to create new primary sector jobs and contribute to the local tax base. Funds can be used to provide temporary or permanent financing for capital costs (land, buildings, and infrastructure), equipment, working capital, seed capital, or other miscellaneous feasibility costs. A minimum 10 percent equity contribution is required. For requests in excess of $25,000, the applicant must obtain some levels of bank participation.

* ND Division of Community Services

1600 East Century Avenue, Suite 2
P.O. Box 2057   701-328-5300
Bismarck, ND 58502-2057   Fax: 701-328-5320
www.state.nd.us/dcs

Community Development Block Grants: Available to cities and counties for the commercial rehabilitation of existing buildings or structures used for business, commercial, or industrial purposes. Grants of up to $300,000 can be made. Every $15,000 of grant funds invested must create at least one full-time job, and at least 51 percent of the jobs created must be for low- and moderate-income families.

* Agricultural Products Utilization Commission

North Dakota Department of Commerce
1600 East Century Avenue, Suite 2
P.O. Box 2057   701-328-5350
Bismarck, ND 58502-2057   Fax: 701-328-5320
www.growingnd.com

Provides funding and assistance to private industry in the establishment of agricultural processing plants for the manufacturing and marketing of agricultural derived fuels, chemicals and other processed products.

* North Dakota Tax Commissioner

600 E. Boulevard Ave.   701-328-2770
Bismarck, ND 58505-0599   Fax: 701-328-3700
www.state.nd.us/taxdpt

Special Tax Incentives for Businesses: Incentives include:
- Five year property and corporation income tax exemptions for new business projects
- Wage and salary income tax credits
- Income tax credit for research expenditures and for investment in a North Dakota venture capital corporation
- Deductions for selling or renting a business to a beginning business person or farmland to a beginning farmer

* Fargo-Cass County Economic Development Corporation

51 Broadway, Suite 500   701-237-6132
Fargo, ND 58102   Fax: 701-293-7819
www.fedc.com

The Fargo-Cass County Economic Development Corporation provides a variety of incentive programs to businesses that locate or expand in Cass County.

* Loans For Farmers

Farm Service Agency
U.S. Department of Agriculture
P.O. Box 3046   701-239-5224
Fargo, ND 58108   Fax: 701-239-5696
http://www.fsa.usda.gov/nd/

The Farm Service Agency provides Direct and Guaranteed Loans to farmers through a variety of programs, including:

Farm Ownership Loans: purchase farmland, construct or repair buildings and other fixtures, and promote soil and water conservation. Up to $200,000.

Operating Loans: purchase items needed for a successful farm operation, such as livestock, farm equipment, feed, seed, fuel, farm chemicals, insurance, and other operating expenses. Can also be used to pay for minor improvements. Up to $200,000.

Beginning Farmer and Rancher Loans: provides funds to beginning and farmers and ranchers who are unable to obtain financing elsewhere.

Downpayment Farm Ownership Loans for Beginning Farmers: helps beginning farmers and ranchers purchase a farm or ranch. Also provides a way for retiring farmers to transfer their land to a future generation of farmers and ranchers. Applicant must have a downpayment of 10% and FSA with finance 40%, with the remaining balance from a commercial lender. Purchase price cannot exceed $250,000.

Loans to Socially Disadvantaged Farmers/Ranchers: helps socially disadvantaged applicants buy and operate family-size farms and ranches.

Youth Loans: Made to youths to establish and operate income-producing projects with the participation in 4-H clubs, Future Farmers of America, and similar organizations. Up to $5,000.

Emergency Loan Assistance: provides loans to help producers recover from production and physical losses due to drought, flooding, and other natural disasters, or quarantine. Up to $500,000.

Beginning Farmer and Rancher Land Contract Guarantee Pilot Program: "prompt payment guarantee" from FSA. FSA will provide payment to seller two times if the beginning farmer does not pay. Program is tested in IN, IA, ND, OR, PA and WI.

Farm Ownership and Operating Loan Guarantees: FSA will guarantee loans up to $782,000.

* Small Business Administration (SBA)

657 2nd Ave. N., Room 219   701-239-5131
Fargo, ND 58102   Fax: 701-239-5645
www.sba.gov/nd

The North Dakota Small Business Administration Office delivers a variety of programs and services, such as startup and operational assistance through small business training and counseling, financial assistance for startup's, business opportunities and much more.

* Marketplace of Ideas/ Marketplace for Kids

Headquarters
411 Main Street West   701-663-0150
Mandan, ND 58554-3164   888-384-8410
www.marketplaceofideas.com   Fax: 701-663-1032

Marketplace of Ideas holds a yearly conference where entrepreneurs can participate in training and technical assistance. Their web site keeps a directory of ideas and other economic development information.

Ohio

* Ohio Department of Development

77 South High Street
Columbus, OH 43215-6140
Mailing Address:
P.O. Box 1001   614-466-3379
Columbus, OH 43216-1001   800-848-1300

www.odod.state.oh.us   Fax: 614-463-1540

Small Business Innovation Research (SBIR) Technical Assistance Services: Increases the number of research contracts won by Ohio companies from eleven participating federal agencies. Provides small businesses with direct, hands-on assistance in identifying research topics; guides businesses through the proposal writing process from design to review; and offers educational and technical services. Also helps companies prepare proposals for SBIR Phase I awards of up to $100,000 and Phase II awards up to $500,000.

Business Development Assistance: Assists domestic and foreign businesses with up-to-date information on sites, buildings, labor, markets, taxes and financing. Development specialists act as liaison between the companies and state/local agencies. Works to maintain and create Ohio jobs through retention and expansion of established businesses and attraction of new businesses; assists local community development organizations and acts as a liaison for communities when dealing with issues under local control.

Labor Market Information: Measurements of economic conditions. Local and national employment/labor-force data to aid in market research, business development and planning. Attracts new employers by identifying skilled workforce. Supplies free information on the training/education available to help workers meet business needs.

Ohio Data Users Center: Census and statistical data; demographic; economic; specific trade, industry and labor analyses. Develops and disseminates population estimates, projections. Provides tools for better coordinated decision-making in public/private sectors.

Ohio Procurement Technical Assistance: Free in-depth counseling, technical resources and historical contracting data, military specifications, financial guidance and advocacy services for federal procurement opportunities. Increases the federal dollars invested in Ohio; increase job and business market opportunities; increase awareness of procurement programs and opportunities.

One-Stop Business Permit Center: Supplies new entrepreneurs with information about licenses and permits required by the State of Ohio; directs callers to proper area for technical, financial and management resources; acts as advocate for licensing and permit problems. 614-446-4232

Edison Technology Centers: Provides businesses with access to state-of-the-art applied research performed in-house or obtained through linkages with universities, federal laboratories and other institutions; education and training programs; plant site assessments; technical problem solving; conferences, seminars and other networking opportunities.

Edison Technology Incubators: Low-cost space that reduces operating costs during start-up phase for technology-based businesses; access to business, technical, and professional services, including legal, accounting, marketing, and financial counseling. 614-466-3887

Federal Technology Transfer Program: "Gateway" organizations to resources of the federal laboratory system including intellectual property, engineering expertise, facilities, and equipment.

166 Regional Loan Program: Land and building acquisition, expansion or renovation, and equipment purchase; industrial projects preferred. Up to 40% of total eligible fixed cost

($350,000 maximum); rate negotiable for 5-15 years; equity minimum 10%, bank minimum 25%. Ohio prevailing wage rate applies.

Direct Loan (166 Loan): Land and building acquisition, expansion or renovation, and equipment purchase; industrial projects preferred. Up to 30% of total eligible fixed cost ($1 million maximum, $350,000 minimum), two-thirds of prime fixed rate for 10-15 years; equity minimum 10%, bank minimum 25%. In distressed areas of the State, preferential rates and terms are available. However, the Director of Development may authorize a higher loan amount or modified terms that address a unique and demonstrated economic development need. Must show repayment and management capabilities; must create one job for every $15,000 received; Ohio prevailing wage rate applies.

Labor/Management Cooperation Program: Enhances relationship between labor and management through regular meetings, seminars, conferences, and work-site labor/management training programs. Creates a stable and positive work environment by nurturing cooperative labor/management relationships and by dispelling negative labor images. Matching grants support community-based area labor/management committees, regional centers for the advancement of labor-management cooperation, and an employee stock ownership assistance program.

Linked Deposit Program: Fixed assets, working capital and refinanced-debt for small businesses, creating or retaining jobs. A similar Agricultural Linked Deposit Program provides funds for Ohio farmers to help meet planning deadlines. 3% below current lending rate fixed for 2 years (possible 2-year extension); bank may then extend term at current rates. (All other sources of funds allowable.) The Agricultural Linked Deposit Program provides up to $100,000 per farm at reduced rate, approximately 4% below borrower's current rate. Must have Ohio headquarters and no divisions out of state, create one job for every $15,000 to $25,000 received, have 150 or fewer employees, be organized for profit, and have bank loan from eligible state depository. 800-228-1102

Ohio Enterprise Bond Fund: Land and building acquisition, construction, expansion or renovation, and equipment purchase for commercial or industrial projects between $1 million and $10 million in size. Long-term, fixed rate for up to 16 years; interest rate based on Standard & Poor's A-minus rating, for up to 90% of total project amount.

Ohio Coal Development Program: Financial assistance for clean coal research and development projects. Advances promising technology into the commercial market. Installed technologies will result in cleaner air, better use of by-products, greater demand for Ohio coal and the jobs associated with its production and use. Strong potential also exists for the export of the technologies. For research: up to $75,000 or two-thirds of total project costs (TPC). Pilot and demonstration scale projects: up to $5 million or one-half of TPC for a pilot project, or one-third TPC for demonstration project. Funds can be issued in the form of a grant, loan, or loan guarantee.

Defense Adjustment Program: Provides assistance to communities and technology-based companies impacted by economic losses because of company and military base drawdowns, realignments and closures. 614-466-3887

Industrial Training Program: Up to 50% funding for orientation, training, and management program; instructional materials, instructor training.

Economic Development Program: Provides funding for development and revitalization of local communities for fixed assets related to commercial, industrial or infrastructure.

Pioneer Rural Loan Program: Provides direct loans for businesses locating or expanding in Ohio's rural areas. Must demonstrate that they will create new jobs.

International Trade Division: Assists Ohio companies to develop export markets worldwide. Ohio's trade staff in Columbus, Tokyo, Hong Kong, Toronto, Mexico City, Sao Paulo, Brussels, and Tel Aviv provide custom-tailored assistance in international marketing and export finance and lead Ohio companies on trade missions and to the world's leading trade shows. Services include:
- Export Counseling
- Trade Shows and Trade Missions
- Electronic Trade
- Export Finance
- Export Incentives
- Japan Trade Program

Minority Management and Technical Services: Provides assistance in management analysis, technical assistance, educational services and financial consulting. Supports overall growth and development of minority firms throughout the State. Counseling is provided at no charge.

Minority Contractor and Business Assistance Program: Provides management, technical, financial, and contract procurement assistance; loan, grant, bond packaging services. Networks with all levels of government, private businesses. Aids in economic growth and development of the minority community; increases awareness of local, state, and federal business assistance programs. Counseling is provided at no charge. Fees may be charged for some programs using federal funding. 614-466-5700

Minority Contract Procurement Services: Assists primarily minority firms in procuring public and private sector contracts. Supports efforts of minority firms to obtain contract awards that will aid in sustaining and developing these firms. Counseling is provided at no charge.

Minority Business Bonding Program: Surety bonding assistance for state-certified minority businesses. Maximum bond pre-qualification of up to $1,000,000 per Minority Business. The bond premium for each bond issued will not exceed 2% of the face value of the bond. 614-644-7708

Minority Direct Loan: Purchase or improvement of fixed assets for state-certified minority-owned businesses. Up to 40% of total project cost at 4.5% fixed for up to 15 years (maximum).

Ohio Mini-Loan Program: Fixed assets and equipment for small businesses. Start-up or existing business expansion. Projects of $100,000 or less. Up to 45% guarantee of an eligible bank loan. Interest rate of the State guarantee of the loan is currently 5.5%, and may be fixed for 10 years. Eligibility: Small business entrepreneurs with fewer than 25 employees, targeted 50% allocation to businesses owned by minorities and women.

Women's Business Resource Program: Assistance for start-up, expansion and management of businesses owned by women; assures equal access to state business assistance and lending programs; direction to purchase and procurement opportunities with government agencies. Researches legislation that may impact businesses owned by women. Increases start-ups and successes of women-owned businesses. No charge. 614-466-4945

Office of Energy Efficiency: Training, technical assistance and partnership programs are available to help businesses become more energy efficient thereby reducing costs and to contribute to a cleaner environment.

Office of Investment Training Program: Companies can receive financial assistance and technical resources for customized training for employees of new and expanding businesses. There is a 50% reimbursement for instructional costs, materials and training-related activities. 614-466-4155

Capital Access Program: Small businesses that have less than $10 million in sales and that have trouble securing a loan may be eligible for funding with this program. Financing is available for working capital and construction of fixed assets and refinancing of existing loans. The maximum loan amount is $250,000 for working capital and $500,000 for fixed assets. 614-644-7708

Technology Action Fund: Grants are awarded on a competitive basis in order to support entrepreneurial activity in technology sectors that enhance the economic development in Ohio. 614-466-3887

Microenterprise Business Development Program: Grants given to cities and counties are used to help with the development of local enterprise businesses and also to create and retain long-term jobs. 614-466-2285

Ohio Qualified Small-Issue Bond Program: Low-interest financing for small manufacturing facilities expanding or relocating in Ohio.

Rural Industrial Park Loan: Provides direct loans and loan guarantees to rural, distressed local communities to create industrial parks.

NxLevel: NxLevel is a community-based training program created to help small-to-medium size businesses through classes and materials.

* USDA, Rural Development
Federal Building, Room 507
200 North High Street
Columbus, OH 43215   614-255-2500
www.rurdev.usda.gov/oh

Business & Industry Loan Guarantees (B&I): The B&I program provides loan guarantees for expansion and preservation of jobs in rural areas. The program can provide development credit in rural areas and towns of 50,000 or less. Jobs produced in this manner will help people stay in their own communities and raise their standard of living in the rural environment. The program provides guarantees to commercial lenders who make credit available to establish or maintain businesses. Loan funds may be used to purchase land, buildings and equipment; working capital; and in some cases to refinance debt. Eligible entities include corporations, partnerships, cooperatives, individuals, federally recognized Indian Tribes and other legal entities.

Intermediary Relending Program (IRP): The purpose of the Intermediary Relending Program is to finance business facilities and community development projects in rural areas. This is achieved through low interest loans made by Rural

Development to intermediaries. The intermediaries relend the funds to ultimate recipients for business purposes or community development projects. Intermediaries establish revolving loan funds, so that collections from loans to ultimate recipients, in excess of necessary operating expenses and debt payments, will be used for more loans to ultimate recipients. Intermediaries may be private nonprofit corporations, public agencies, Indian groups or cooperatives. Any type legal entity, including individuals and public and private organizations, may be an ultimate recipient.

Rural Business Enterprise Grants (RBEG): These grants provide resources which are utilized to develop small and emerging business enterprises in rural areas or cities up to 50,000 population. Qualifying entities include public bodies and nonprofit corporations. Grants are used by third party lenders to create revolving business loan funds. Funds can also be used to install infrastructure to business locations and house business incubators.

Rural Economic Development Loan and Grant (REDLG): This program is utilized to finance rural economic development and rural job creation projects which are based on sound economic and financial analysis. This is done by making zero-interest loans and/or grants to Rural Utilities Service (RUS) electric and telephone borrowers who use the funds to provide financing for business and community development projects. Eligible project costs include project feasibility studies, start-up costs, purchasing facilities and equipment, business incubator projects and other reasonable expenses for the purpose of fostering rural economic development.

* The Clean Air Resource Center (CARC)

Mark R. Shanahan, Executive Director
Clean Air Resource Center   614-224-3383
50 W. Broad Street, Suite 1718   800-225-5051
Columbus, OH 43215   Fax: 614-752-9188
www.ohioairquality.org

CARC seeks to find the most cost-efficient means possible for small businesses to meet these new requirements. They strive to support the critical role played by small business in Ohio's economy and recognize the financial challenges presented by environmental regulations. They are an independent, non-regulatory (no inspection or enforcement, confidential, one-stop shop for finding solutions to air quality problems. State law requires them to keep all information received from businesses seeking assistance strictly confidential.

* Research and Extension Center

Ohio State University Piketon
Research and Extension Center
1864 Shyville Road   740-289-2071
Piketon, OH 45661   Fax: 740-289-4591
http://southcenters.osu.edu/

The South Center provides research based educational resources including: Entrepreneur Program, Small Business Development Center, Manufacturing SBDC, The Ohio Cooperative Development Center, Business Incubator and Training Center, and The Ohio State Learning Center South.

* Ohio Department of Agriculture

Ohio Rural Development Partnership
Family Farm Loan Guarantee Program   614-466-1490

8995 East Main Street   800-282-1955 (in OH)
Reynoldsburg, OH 43068-3399   Fax: 614-466-4346
www.ohioagriculture.gov

The Ohio Family Farm Loan Guarantee Program provides guarantees to conventional lenders that provide loans to persons engaged in agricultural production, which enhances the economic viability of the state's agricultural areas. Through the Family Farm Loan Guarantee Program, the state provides a partial guarantee to an eligible lender, by placing with the lender up to 40 percent of the lender's loan in an interest bearing account. The lender agrees to pay the state one (1%) percent per annum on the amount of the outstanding guarantee. It also agrees to lend the guaranteed portion of the loan to its borrowers at a reduced interest rate that compensates for the state's reduced interest rate. The maximum interest rate allowed on the guaranteed portion of a loan shall be 5 percent. The remaining unguaranteed portion is loaned at the lender's prevailing interest rate. The two rates are then blended and the new blended rate is passed on to the borrower.

* U.S. Export Assistance Center

600 Superior Ave. East, Suite 700   216-522-4731
Cleveland, OH 44114-2650   Fax: 216-522-2235

The Center assists clients with information about export finance options. This U.S.E.A.C. consolidates the export promotion and finance services of the U.S. Dept. of Commerce, the U.S. Small Business Administration, and the Small Business and Technology Development Center (SBTDC).

* Treasurer of the State

30 East Broad St., 9th Floor   614-466-2160
Columbus, OH 43215   800-228-1102 in OH
www.treasurer.state.oh.us   Fax: 614-644-7313

Small Business Linked Deposit Program: Funds are available for fixed assets, working capital, and refinancing for small businesses, creating or retaining jobs. Rates are 3 percent below current lending rate fixed for two years.

Agricultural Linked Deposit Program: Provides funds for Ohio full-time farmers to help meet planning deadlines. Provides up to $100,000 per farm at reduced rate, approximately 4 percent below borrower's current rate.

Access Ohio Program: Small Ohio businesses organized for profit, which have offices and facilities exclusively in Ohio, employ less than 150 people - a majority of who are Ohio residents and, are borrowing money for the specific purpose of becoming ADA compliant and/or more accessible to persons with disabilities may apply for low interest loans through a State Depository Bank. Approved bank loans are submitted to the Treasury which purchases a reduced interest CD with the lender. (Retrofitting work areas and the purchase of adaptive devices are also eligible.)

* Loans For Farmers

Farm Service Agency
U.S. Department of Agriculture
Federal Building
200 North High Street, Room 540   614-255-2441
Columbus, OH 43215   Fax: 614-255-2542
http://www.fsa.usda.gov/oh/

The Farm Service Agency provides Direct and Guaranteed Loans to farmers through a variety of programs, including:

Farm Ownership Loans: purchase farmland, construct or repair buildings and other fixtures, and promote soil and water conservation. Up to $200,000.

Operating Loans: purchase items needed for a successful farm operation, such as livestock, farm equipment, feed, seed, fuel, farm chemicals, insurance, and other operating expenses. Can also be used to pay for minor improvements. Up to $200,000.

Beginning Farmer and Rancher Loans: provides funds to beginning and farmers and ranchers who are unable to obtain financing elsewhere.

Downpayment Farm Ownership Loans for Beginning Farmers: helps beginning farmers and ranchers purchase a farm or ranch. Also provides a way for retiring farmers to transfer their land to a future generation of farmers and ranchers. Applicant must have a downpayment of 10% and FSA with finance 40%, with the remaining balance from a commercial lender. Purchase price cannot exceed $250,000.

Loans to Socially Disadvantaged Farmers/Ranchers: helps socially disadvantaged applicants buy and operate family-size farms and ranches.

Youth Loans: Made to youths to establish and operate income-producing projects with the participation in 4-H clubs, Future Farmers of America, and similar organizations. Up to $5,000.

Emergency Loan Assistance: provides loans to help producers recover from production and physical losses due to drought, flooding, and other natural disasters, or quarantine. Up to $500,000.

Beginning Farmer and Rancher Land Contract Guarantee Pilot Program: "prompt payment guarantee" from FSA. FSA will provide payment to seller two times if the beginning farmer does not pay. Program is tested in IN, IA, ND, OR, PA and WI.

Farm Ownership and Operating Loan Guarantees: FSA will guarantee loans up to $782,000.

* Small Business Administration (SBA)

2 Nationwide Plaza
Suite 1400
Columbus, OH 43215-2592   614-469-6860
    Fax: 614-469-2391

1111 Superior Avenue, Suite 630   216-522-4180
Cleveland, OH 44114-2507   Fax: 216-522-2038
www.sba.gov/oh

The Ohio Small Business Administration Office delivers a variety of programs and services, such as startup and operational assistance through small business training and counseling, financial assistance for startup's, business opportunities and much more.

* Ohio Business Connection

eVantage Program
3155 Research Boulevard, Suite 206
Kettering, OH 45420   937-258-7255 ext. 224
www.evantage-ohio.com   Fax: 937-258-9732

eVantage provides small business owners access to eBusiness techniques that can help their business. For a fee, the eVantage program provides 36 instructional hours and 30 individualized assistance.

Oklahoma

* Oklahoma Department of Commerce

900 North Stiles   405-815-6552
P.O. Box 26980   800-879-6552
Oklahoma City, OK 73126-0980   Fax: 405-815-5199
http://busdev3.odoc5.odoc.state.ok.us

Office of Business Recruitment: Provides comprehensive site location assistance to companies considering new investment in Oklahoma.

Business Development Division: Promotes growth by addressing the needs of existing and start-up businesses. Provides information and seminars directly to businesses. Offers business information and a referral network to assist companies through the maze of regulatory requirements and introduces local resource providers.

Site Location Planner: On CD-ROM and the web at {http://busdev3. odoc.state.ok.us}. Provides comprehensive site location data including available buildings, community information, state incentives, and statistical and other information.

Technology Partnerships: Testing of technologies developed by private business may be performed in partnership with research universities. Such institutions may devote resources such as laboratory usage and faculty time to a particular business's need in return for a portion of business's profits.

Training for Industry: Assists qualifying businesses by paying for training for new employees.

Quality Jobs Program: Provides quarterly cash payments of up to 5% of new taxable payroll directly to a qualifying company, for up to ten years.

Small Employer Quality Jobs Program: Provides annual cash payments of 5% of taxable payroll for new employees to a qualifying company, for up to 5 years.

Enterprise Zones: The enterprise district management authorities created in some enterprise districts are empowered to establish venture capital loan programs and to solicit proposals from enterprises seeking to establish or expand facilities in the zones.

International Trade and Investment Division: Provides diverse services including hands on assistance for companies wishing to learn more about exporting to promoting Oklahoma products at trade shows throughout the world. Also works closely with the international business community to develop top of mind awareness of Oklahoma's business climate advantages. Provide confidential, reliable site location assistance, site selection assistance, tax comparisons, and incentive projections.

International Market Insights (IMI): Commercial specialists also regularly report on specific foreign market conditions and upcoming opportunities for U. S. business.

Customized Market Analysis (CMA): Provides detailed information needed to make the most efficient and beneficial export marketing decisions. CMA will give an accurate assessment of how a product or service will sell in a given market.

Trade Opportunities Program (TOP): Up-to-the-minute sales leads from around the world are prescreened and transmitted every work day to commercial specialists in U. S. embassies and consulates abroad.

Agent/Distributor Service (ADS): Customized search needed to successfully launch an export marketing campaign. Provides pertinent information on up to six prequalified potential representatives per market.

Foreign Trade Zones: Businesses engaged in international trade within these zones benefit from special customs procedures.

Export Finance Program: Assistance is available through a relationship with the Export-Import Bank of the United States to facilitate export financing with working capital guarantees, credit insurance and foreign buyer financing.

Women-owned Business Certification Program: Established to facilitate contracting capabilities for women-owned businesses with public and private sector entities.

Minority Business: Provides a forum to network with banking organizations, utility companies, state agencies and other that can be valuable resources for a business. Each month several business owners are selected to give a brief presentation about their business.

Minority Business Development Centers: A vehicle for small minority-owned businesses that are seeking help in start-up information. The centers provide assistance in business plans, procurement assistance and works with the SBA in the certified lenders program and 8(a) certification.

Oklahoma Business Licensing System: Provides one-stop access to state level licensing requirements for businesses. Links are provided to the agency that issues the license and where the needed forms can be downloaded. This site only handles licensing at the state level, however, it will soon cover city, county and federal levels. 800-TRY-OKLA ext 155 (879-6552)

Business Incubator Certification: Business Incubators are facilities that accelerate the development and success of start-up and existing businesses. They provide lease space and a large variety of on-site managerial administrative and financial services. Tenants are exempt from state tax liability on income earned as a result of activities conducted as an occupant for up to 10 years. There are 25 certified business incubators in Oklahoma. 405-815-5143

Business Incentive Analysis: A confidential analysis of all state incentives and abatements can be gathered pertaining to a business project. 405-855-5182

International Seminars and Workshops: Continuing education seminars and workshops provide hands on training to aid businesses prepare for trade shows, break into international marketing and to stay up-to-date on necessary information.

Oklahoma Small Business Regulatory Review Committee: The Committee reviews new government rules that may have an adverse effect on small businesses and suggest alternatives whenever possible.

Export Assistance: An international business specialist will visit your company to consult with you about your export marketing strategy and goals. Your trade advisor will answer your questions, provide you with research regarding your

target markets and work with you to assess the viability of your product or service in those markets. There is no fee for this service.

Community and County Profiles: Detailed information on Oklahoma communities and counties.

Census, Economic and Demographic Data Analysis: Commerce provides analysis of census, economic, and demographic data to assist businesses and communities in their growth plans.

Business Retention and Expansion: Assistance for communities to retain existing businesses.

Business Incentives Tax Training: This seminar can help you and your CPA learn about the state's business incentives.

Business Financing: This department can help you find information on capital for your business.

Advocacy in Foreign Markets: A service for Oklahoma firms encountering trade problems, including unfair or illegal trade practices in foreign markets.

Agent and Distributor Search: This agency will help your company search for prospective agents and distributors for your products and will initiate a contact. There is no fee for this service.

County Briefs: This office will give you an overview of Oklahoma's top export markets, including current opportunities, an overview of the market and need-to-know information like regulatory issues, freight, market entry advice and business and cultural tips.

Foreign Market Visit Assistance: Arrangement can be made to meet with prescreened contacts whose market interests and objectives match your own.

International Protocol: This office can help you develop a greater awareness of cultural differences. You can find out about business practices, customs, and manners.

Sister State and Cities Program: Commerce promotes international cooperation, business and understanding through community involvement and relationships in education, business, technology, culture, agricultural and youth and other areas exchanges. The agency will assist communities wanting to establish sister cities overseas.

Trade Mission: Commerce organizes trade missions, often led by state officials, to initiate and nurture relationships with potential international business partners.

Trade Show Assistance: Oklahoma Commerce will help your business exhibit at key international trade shows.

Oklahoma Main Street Program: The Oklahoma Main Street Center provides program training, technical assistance, guidance and resources to people, organizations and communities.

Self-Employment Entrepreneurial Development System (SEEDS): The Self-Employment Entrepreneurial Development System uses states funds to provide training, business plan development and start-up financing of micro-businesses started by low-income and unemployed persons.

* Oklahoma Department of Transportation

200 NE 21st Street
Oklahoma City, OK 73105   800-788-4539
www.okladot.state.ok.us/dbeinfo/indexg.htm
The Department of Transportation has a Disadvantaged Business Enterprise certification program for transportation-related projects and facilities.

* Rural Development Administration

100 USDA Agriculture Building
Suite 108   405-742-1000
Stillwater, OK 74074-2654   Fax: 405-742-1005
Business and Industrial Loan Program: Encourages the retention of jobs in rural areas. RDA will guarantee up to 90 percent of a loan from a commercial institution.

Intermediary Relending Program: This program provides 1% loans to intermediaries to establish revolving loan funds for the purpose of relending to small emerging private businesses.

Rural Business Enterprise Grants: USDA makes Rural Business Enterprise Grants to public bodies, nonprofits and Native American tribes to encourage the development of small and emerging private business enterprises in rural areas.

Rural Business Opportunity Grants: Grants from this program provide technical assistance, training and planning activities that improve economic conditions in rural areas.

Rural Economic Development Loans/Grants: These loans/grants are provided to USDA-financed telephone and electric cooperatives to establish revolving loan funds or single purpose loans for businesses/job creation and community development in rural areas. Recipients receive 10 year, zero percent loans.

Value-Added Agricultural Product Market Development Grants

* Oklahoma Capital Investment Board

301 NW 63rd, Suite 520
Oklahoma City, OK 73116   405-848-9456
Facilitates investment in venture capital companies that focus on investing in quality Oklahoma companies.

* Oklahoma Minority Supplier Development Council (OMSDC)

6701 N. Broadway, Suite 216   405-767-9900
Oklahoma City, OK 73116   Fax: 405-767-9901
www.omsdc.org
The mission of the OMSDC is to assist corporations and public sector agencies in creating a business environment that promotes access and increased opportunities for minority-owned businesses. The Council also helps to promote, educate and develop minority-owned businesses.

* Oklahoma Tax Commission

Business Tax Workshops
2501 North Lincoln Boulevard
Connors Building, Capitol Complex
Oklahoma City, OK 73194   405-521-3160
www.oktax.state.ok.us
The Business Tax Workshops offered by the Oklahoma Tax Commission are designed with to meet the needs all business ownership levels from new business owners just starting out

to seasoned business owners needing to brush up on the latest tax changes, and everyone in between. For a new business or an individual thinking about setting up a business in Oklahoma, the workshop offers information on formation, business structures, steps for formation types such as incorporation steps, a step-by-step guide to business registration, bookkeeping techniques, and a line-by-line explanation of the primary business tax forms.

* Business Filing Department

2300 N. Lincoln Blvd., Room 101   405-521-3912
Oklahoma City OK 73105-4897   Fax: 405-521-3771
www.sos.state.ok.us/business/business_filing.htm
The Business Filing Department receives and processes corporation, limited partnership, limited liability company, limited liability partnership, certificate of partnership fictitious name for general partnership and trade name registrations. These include new registrations, amendments, mergers, dissolutions and withdrawals for both domestic and foreign.

Business Records Department: 1-900-555-2424 (A flat fee of $5.00): The Business Records Department provides searches on corporations, limited partnerships, limited liability companies, limited liability partnerships, certificate of partnership fictitious name for general partnerships and trade names. The search includes correct name, status, date of registration, service agent and address, state of domicile, authorized shares and par value, amendments, name changes, mergers, and trade names.

* Oklahoma Agriculture Enhancement and Diversification Program

2800 N. Lincoln Blvd.
Oklahoma City, OK 73105-4298   405-522-5515
www.oda.state.ok.us/gapl.htm
The Oklahoma Agriculture Enhancement and Diversification Program provides funds in the form of loans or grants for the purpose of expanding the state's value added processing sector and to encourage farm diversification. Funds, provided on a cost-share basis, must be used for marketing and utilization, cooperative marketing, farm diversification and basic and applied research. All funding proposals must clearly demonstrate the ability to directly benefit Oklahoma farmers and ranchers.

* The Oklahoma Cooperative Extension Service

Rural Development Program
Oklahoma State University-Oklahoma City
139 Agriculture Hall   405-744-5398
Stillwater, OK 74078   Fax: 405-744-5339
http://www1.dasnr.okstate.edu/oces
Cooperative Extension offers educational and technical assistance to aid rural leaders in promoting economic development and providing quality community services. The programs include economic and business development, community services, and local government education.

* Oklahoma Center for the Advancement of Science & Technology

4545 N. Lincoln Blvd., Suite. 116   405-524-1357
Oklahoma City, OK 73105   866-265-2215
Email: info@ocast.state.ok.us   Fax: 405-521-6501
www.ocast.state.ok.us
The Oklahoma Center for the Advancement of Science and

Technology is the state's only agency focusing solely on technology - its development, transfer, commercialization and impact on Oklahoma's economy. OCAST continues to pursue its legislative mandate to: Support basic and applied research and development (R&D) Facilitate technology transfer and commercialization (SBIR/STTR) Stimulate seed-capital investment in firms commercializing new technologies Encourage manufacturing competitiveness through modernization. OCAST currently has funding to operate the following programs:
- Oklahoma Health Research (OHR)
- Small Business Research Assistance (SBRA)
- Oklahoma Applied Research Support Program (OARS)
- OARS R&D Faculty and Student Intern Partnerships
- Oklahoma Alliance for Manufacturing Excellence, Inc.
- Oklahoma Technology Commercialization Center
- Oklahoma Inventor's Assistance Program
- Technology Business Finance Program

* Oklahoma Technology Commercialization Center

840 Research Parkway, Suite 250
Oklahoma City, OK 73104   800-337-OTCC
www.otcc.org   Tulsa: 918-582-5592
                                 Oklahoma City: 405-235-2305
The Tech Center is the Program Manager for OCAST Technology Business Finance Program. This Oklahoma Center for the Advancement of Science & Technology (OCAST)-funded program is designed to provide Oklahoma-based, high-tech, start-up companies with pre-seed financing and early stage risk capital to stimulate additional investments from private sources.

* Oklahoma Industrial Finance Authority (OIFA)

301 NW 3rd, Suite 225
Oklahoma City, OK 73116   405-842-1145
Loans: Available to manufacturers plus recreational, agriculture processing, livestock processing and conditioning, and mine resource processors. Can loan up to 66 2/3% of the cost of land, buildings and fixed equipment on a secured first mortgage and 33 1/3% on a second mortgage. Maximum loan amount is $2 million per project on a first mortgage, $750,000 on a second mortgage.

* Office of the State Treasurer

Link Deposit Loan Programs
2300 N. Lincoln Blvd., Room 217   405-521-3191
Oklahoma City, OK 73105   Fax: 405-521-4994
Oklahoma Small Business Linked Deposit Program: Loans are available of up to $1 million for small businesses and $5 million for industrial parks. Loan must create new jobs or preserve existing ones. Terms not to exceed two years, but may be renewed for 3 additional terms.

Agricultural Linked Deposit Program: Available for farmers who meet certain criteria. The linked deposit commitment cannot exceed 2 years, but may be renewed. The interest rates are fixed and are calculated based on the current T-note auction rate minus 3 percent.

* Loans For Farmers

Farm Service Agency
U.S. Department of Agriculture
100 USDA, Suite 102   405-742-1130

Stillwater, OK 74074   Fax: 405-742-1177
http://www.fsa.usda.gov/ok/
The Farm Service Agency provides Direct and Guaranteed Loans to farmers through a variety of programs, including:

Farm Ownership Loans: purchase farmland, construct or repair buildings and other fixtures, and promote soil and water conservation. Up to $200,000.

Operating Loans: purchase items needed for a successful farm operation, such as livestock, farm equipment, feed, seed, fuel, farm chemicals, insurance, and other operating expenses. Can also be used to pay for minor improvements. Up to $200,000.

Beginning Farmer and Rancher Loans: provides funds to beginning and farmers and ranchers who are unable to obtain financing elsewhere.

Downpayment Farm Ownership Loans for Beginning Farmers: helps beginning farmers and ranchers purchase a farm or ranch. Also provides a way for retiring farmers to transfer their land to a future generation of farmers and ranchers. Applicant must have a downpayment of 10% and FSA with finance 40%, with the remaining balance from a commercial lender. Purchase price cannot exceed $250,000.

Loans to Socially Disadvantaged Farmers/Ranchers: helps socially disadvantaged applicants buy and operate family-size farms and ranches.

Youth Loans: Made to youths to establish and operate income-producing projects with the participation in 4-H clubs, Future Farmers of America, and similar organizations. Up to $5,000.

Emergency Loan Assistance: provides loans to help producers recover from production and physical losses due to drought, flooding, and other natural disasters, or quarantine. Up to $500,000.

Beginning Farmer and Rancher Land Contract Guarantee Pilot Program: "prompt payment guarantee" from FSA. FSA will provide payment to seller two times if the beginning farmer does not pay. Program is tested in IN, IA, ND, OR, PA and WI.

Farm Ownership and Operating Loan Guarantees: FSA will guarantee loans up to $782,000.

* Small Business Administration (SBA)

District Office
301 NW 6th Street, Suite 116   405-609-8000
Oklahoma City, OK 73102   Fax: 405-609-8990
www.sba.gov/ok
The Oklahoma Small Business Administration Office delivers a variety of programs and services, such as startup and operational assistance through small business training and counseling, financial assistance for startup's, business opportunities and much more.

* HUD Regional Office

500 West Main St.   405-553-7509
Oklahoma City, OK 73102-3202   Fax: 405-553-7588
www.hud.gov/local/index.cfm?state=ok
Urban Development Action Grants (UDAG): Awarded to communities which then lend the proceeds at flexible rates to eligible businesses. Projects whose total costs are less than

$100,000 are not eligible. UDAG funds should leverage at least three to four times their amount in private sector investment.

* Home Based & Micro Business

Oklahoma State University
104 Human Environmental Sciences, Room 336
Stillwater, OK 74078   405-744-9931
www.fcs.okstate.edu/microbiz

If you are thinking about starting a home based business or micro business, this office can help. They can answer questions from "What kind of business should I start?" to "Do I need a license?"

Oregon

* Oregon Economic Development Department

775 Summer St., NE, Suite 200   503-986-0123
Salem, OR 97301   Fax: 503-581-5115
www.econ.state.or.us/

Economic Development Department: This office can provide information and expertise in dealing with state, federal, and local agencies. They also have information on financing programs and other services offered by the state government.

Oregon Downtown Development Association works to revitalize and maintain the heritage and economic health of Oregon's downtowns and older business districts.

Rural Development Initiatives: A nonprofit corporation that builds the capacity of rural communities to make strategic decisions about their futures and to act on those decisions to ensure high quality of life and a vital economy.

Industry Workforce Training: Provides grants to community colleges for the development and implementation of training programs for multiple firms within an industry. Employers must provide matching funds or in-kind services.

Capital Access Program: Offered through the Oregon Economic Development Department, is designed to increase the availability of loans to Oregon small businesses from banks. The program provides loan portfolio insurance so lenders may make loans that carry higher than conventional risks. Borrowers pay a fee of between 3% and 7% of the loan amount, which is matched by the department and contributed to a loan loss reserve account in an enrolled bank. The loans must be within soundness and safety requirements of federal and state banking regulations. A Capital Access Program loan is a private transaction between the borrower and lender. The Oregon Economic Development Department is not a party to loan negotiations or to the loan agreement. The department does not monitor the loan or require reporting from the borrower. Loan may be used for virtually any purpose, except to construct or purchase residential housing, to purchase real property that is not used for business operations of the borrower, or to refinance the principal balance of an existing loan.

Credit Enhancement Fund: Administered by the Oregon Economic Development Department, provides guarantees to enrolled banks to increase capital availability to small Oregon firms, helping them create jobs. The maximum guarantee for a loan is $500,000. The department has authority to guarantee up to $75 million of financial institution loans.

Entrepreneurial Development Loan Funds: Entrepreneurial businesses can receive loans of up to $25,000 through the Oregon Entrepreneurial Development Loan Fund. Additional follow-on loans up to $15,000 are available.

Subordinated and Direct Loans: Subordinated loans usually fill a gap in a financing package, where commercial and private debt financing and equity have been maximized and additional funds are required to complete the financing transaction. Often these loans will "subordinate" or take a lesser security interest in the assets being financed, which will allow the senior lender first priority on project assets in the event of a default. The subordinated loan is often secured with additional assets to help collaterize its position. Direct loans and, in some limited cases, grants are available to finance businesses when the project will further the public objectives of the entity making the loan or grant.

Business Development Fund: Manufacturing, processing and regionally significant tourism projects are eligible for the Oregon Business Development Fund. The fund provides long-term, fixed rate financing for land, buildings, equipment and machinery.

Local Revolving Loan Funds: Many local and regional development groups and local governments throughout Oregon administer revolving loan funds for small business financing. In most cases, funding has been provided by the federal Department of Housing and Urban Development (HUD), the federal Economic Development Administration (EDA), the U.S. Department of Agriculture Rural Economic and Community Development Administration (RECD) or the Oregon Economic Development Department. Loan criteria may reflect some of the objectives of those funding organizations or may have special requirements of those agencies.

Industrial Development Revenue Bonds: The Economic Development Commission may issue industrial development revenue bonds for manufacturing and processing facilities in Oregon. Industrial development bonds can finance fixed assets only, along with some limited transaction costs. If a project qualifies the bonds can be issued on a tax-exempt basis which lowers the overall cost of financing. Revenue bonds are not direct obligations of the State of Oregon. The individual or corporation on whose behalf the bonds are issued is legally obligated to repay them. An eligible company may borrow up to $10 million through the Oregon Industrial Development Revenue Bond Program. Typically, the minimum bond is for $2 million.

Regional Development: Cities, counties and other governmental entities also can obtain loans and grants to help pay for construction projects. The department uses grant and loan funds to support public works, safe drinking water and housing rehabilitation projects. The department also provides funding for community facilities projects to improve or build day care, senior centers, emergency shelters and family counseling facilities, among others.

Business Retention Services: Companies are matched with a consultant based on its specific needs and industry requirements. The maximum benefit for consulting service is $5,000 and the maximum feasibility studies is $30,000. To qualify for a feasibility study, the applicant must contribute 25% of the cost of the study. Consultant fees are treated as an interest-free loan. An application can be downloaded from {www.econ.state.or.us/ businessfinance/brs.htm}.

Targeted Workforce Development: Funds are used for a variety of services that can help businesses organize their workforce needs into affordable initiatives that improve worker skills.

Regulatory Assistance: The state's coordinated environmental and regulatory process allows for a streamlined permitting process without an environmental impact statement. Regulatory experts provide one-stop permitting information and assistance.

Project Sitting Assistance: The Department can provide a custom proposal of available sites to traded sector companies. Once a site requirement form is submitted, a list of qualifying sites with specific community information is created. Assistance with scheduling site visits is also available. This service can be accessed online at {www.econ.state.or.us/usform.htm} or call 503-986-0156.

Business Information Center: Business information from six state agencies is available. Referrals for state licensing, regulatory information and other business needs are provided.

Sustainable Business Liaison: Businesses that are looking to learn more about the "triple bottom line" sustainability, will receive information and networking support from this office. 503-986-0158

* Rural Development
Rural Development Services
Business and Cooperative Programs
101 SW Main, Suite 1410   503-414-3300
Portland, OR 97204-3222   Fax: 503-414-3392
www.rurdev.usda.gov/or

Cooperative Development Assistance: The Cooperative Services program helps residents form new cooperative businesses and improve the operations of existing cooperatives. They provide technical assistance, conduct cooperative-related research, and produce information products to promote public understanding of cooperatives.

Direct Business and Industry Loan Program: The Business and Industry Direct Loan Program provides loans to public entities and private parties who cannot obtain credit from other sources.

Guaranteed Business and Industry Loan Program: The Business and Industry Guarantee Loan Program helps create jobs and stimulates rural economies by providing financial backing for rural businesses. This program guarantees up to 80% of a loan made by a commercial lender.

Intermediary Relending Loan Program: Intermediaries may make loans to private individuals, public or private organizations in cities with population of less than 25,000. The loan must be used for the establishment of new business, the expansion of existing businesses, creation of employment opportunities, saving of existing jobs, or community development projects.

Rural Business Enterprise Grants: The Rural Business Enterprise Grants help public bodies, nonprofits and Indian Tribal groups finance and facilitate development of small and emerging private business enterprises located in rural areas.

Rural Economic Development Loans and Grants: This program finances economic development and job creation projects in rural areas based on sound economic plans. The grants are available to any Rural Utility Service to assist in developing rural areas.

Rural Business Opportunity Grants: Rural Opportunity Grants are provided to promote sustainable economic development in rural communities with exceptional needs.

* Oregon Entrepreneurs Forum
222 NW Fifth Ave., Suite 308   503-222-2270
Portland, OR 97209   Fax: 503-241-0827
www.oef.org

Provides assistance to help companies that are in transition by providing mentoring services.

* Oregon Port Revolving Fund Loans
Ports Division
Oregon Economic Development Department
775 Summer Street NE, Suite 200
Salem, OR 97310   503-986-0153
www.econ.state.or.us/portrevolve.htm

Provides long-term loans to ports at below-market interest rates. Individual loans may be made to a maximum of $700,000 per project. The total outstanding loan amount any individual port can have at any one time cannot exceed $2 million. Funding may be used for port development projects (infrastructure) or to assist port-related private business development projects. The 23 legally formed Port Districts are the only entities eligible for Port Revolving Fund loans. The variety of projects eligible is very broad. These include, but are not limited to, water-oriented facilities, industrial parks, airports and eligible commercial or industrial developments. Projects must be located within port district boundaries.

* Small Scale Energy Loan Program
Oregon Office of Energy   800-221-8035 (in OR)
625 Marion Street NE   503-378-4040
Salem, OR 97301   Fax: 503-373-7806
www.energy.state.or.us

The Small Scale Energy Loan Program (SELP), administered by the Oregon Department of Energy, finances energy conservation and renewable energy projects in Oregon, through the issuance of general obligation bonds. Bond proceeds can be loaned to finance eligible equipment costs, construction, certain design and consultation fees, some reserves, construction interest and most loan closing costs. Eligible costs are those incurred after loan approval. Land and working capital are normally not financed. Costs not part of the energy project also are not eligible. All Oregonians, Oregon businesses, nonprofit organizations, municipal corporations and state agencies can apply for loans. Eligible projects are those which conserve conventional energy, such as electricity and natural gas; or projects which produce renewable energy from geothermal or solar sources or from water, wind, biomass and some waste materials.

* International Division of the Oregon Economic Development Department
One World Trade Center
Suite 205, 121 SW Salmon   503-229-6051
Portland, OR 97204   800-448-7512
www.econ.state.or.us/oregontrade

The international arm of state government. It provides "export ready" Oregon companies assistance in export markets, assists the Governor's Office on protocol and other assignments, and works with public and private organizations to promote Oregon in the international business community.

* Southern Oregon Women's Access to Credit

Southern Oregon Women's Access to Credit (SOWAC)
33 N. Central Avenue   866-608-6094 (toll-free)
Suite #209   541-779-3992
Medford, OR 97501   Fax: 541-779-5195
www.sowac.org

Offers a business development program for new and existing business owners in Jackson, Josephine and Klamath counties. Focuses on training, mentoring and financing.

* Oregon Association of Minority Entrepreneurs

4134 N. Vancouver   503-249-7744
Portland, OR 97217   Fax: 503-249-2027
www.oame.org

A nonprofit, tax exempt organization formed to promote and develop entrepreneurship and economic development for ethnic minorities in the State of Oregon. OAME works as a partnership between ethnic minorities, entrepreneurs, education, government and established corporate business. OAME provides a core of services to start-up and/or existing minority businesses. These services include:
- Technical Assistance
- Access To Capital/Loan Fund
- Capability And Opportunity Matching (OAME's Marketing/ Clearinghouse)
- Administrative Services
- Incubator With & Without Walls Development

* Oregon Department of Environmental Quality

811 SW Sixth Avenue   503-229-5696
Portland, OR 97204   Fax: 503-229-6124
www.deq.state.or.us

Corporate Income Tax Credits; Oregon businesses may be eligible for a number of tax credits allowed under Oregon law. Some of these business-related tax credits include: pollution control tax credit; non-point source pollution control tax credit and clean diesel retrofit tax credits.

* Oregon Department of Revenue

Enterprise Zone Coordinator
955 Center Street NE
Room 256, Revenue Building
Salem, OR 97301   503-945-8318
www.dor.state.or.us

Construction in Progress Exemption: Under Oregon law, new facilities are exempt from property taxes for up to two years while they are under construction and not in use on January 1. The Construction in Progress Exemption also applies to any machinery or equipment installed in the unoccupied facility on January 1. The exemption does not apply to land. The application for this exemption must be filed with the county assessor by April 1 of the taxing year.

* Oregon Advanced Technology Consortium

29353 Town Center Loop East   503-657-6958, ext. 4609
Wilsonville, OR 97070   Fax: 503-682-4494

Technical training, seminars, workshops, one-on-one technical assistance and various course offerings are available through the Oregon Advanced Technology Consortium, which is made up of various community colleges throughout the state. The consortium's primary goal is to help Oregon businesses acquire and implement new technologies and provide workforce training.

* The Performance Center

Performance Center
2459 SE T.V. Highway, PMB #145   503-345-9400
Hillsboro, OR 97123   Fax: 503-345-9409
www.performancecenter.org

To be competitive in the global marketplace, Oregon manufacturers need to meet or exceed applicable international quality standards (ISO 9000). Assistance is available to evaluate whether a product is required to meet these standards. The Performance Center offers a link to a statewide system of total quality training through Oregon's community colleges. The objective is to enable Oregon businesses to acquire the tools to consistently achieve world leadership quality, productivity, service and customer satisfaction.

* ONABEN -- A Native American Business Network

11825 SW Greenburg Road
Suite B-3   800-854-8289
Tigard, OR 97223   503-968-1500
www.onaben.org   Fax: 503-968-1548

ONABEN is a nonprofit public-benefit corporation created by Northwest Indian Tribes to increase the success of private businesses owned by Native Americans. It offers training and support focused on developing entrepreneurship in Native American communities. The network offers courses on starting businesses and small business management. It is a source of micro loans that can be combined with equity to acquire third-party financing. It also provides business owners with technical assistance in completing marketing plans and sponsors various services for Indian businesses.

* Office of Minority, Women, and Emerging Small Business

Department of Consumer & Business Services
350 Winter St. NE, Room 300
Salem, OR 97301-3878   503-947-7922
Mailing Address:
P.O. Box 14480
Salem, OR 97309-0405
Portland Field Office: 503-887-4349
www.cbs.state.or.us/omwesb

The Office of Minority, Women, and Emerging Small Business administers the Disadvantaged Business Enterprise (DBE), Minority Business Enterprise/Women Business Enterprise (MBE/WBE), and Emerging Small Business (ESB) Programs. As the sole certification authority in Oregon for targeted government contracts for disadvantaged, minority-and woman-owned businesses, and emerging small businesses, OMWESB provides "one-stop" certification.

* Business Information Center

Secretary of State Corporation Division
Suite 151
255 Capitol Street NE
Salem, OR 97310-1327   503-986-2200
www.filinginoregon.com

The Business Information Center is a cooperative effort of six state agencies that provides information to the public on state registration and licensing requirements for businesses. The Center handles phone calls and letter inquiries and mails out packets with state business registration information and forms. The packet includes a new publication, the Oregon Business Guide, which provides a consolidated source of information from the participating agencies. The guide also provides a general checklist for starting a business with references to agencies that must be contacted. In addition, the Center's staff provides information on whether a business is required to have a state license, permit or certification and refers the caller to the appropriate regulatory agencies or boards. The Center also offers referrals to business assistance programs available in Oregon.

* Oregon Housing and Community Services (OHCS)

P.O. Box 14508	503-986-2000
Salem, OR 97309-0409	Fax: 503-986-2020
Email: info@hcs.state.or.us	TTY: 503-986-2100
www.hcs.state.or.us	

Tax Exempt Bond Financing: OHCS provides multi-family housing financing, pre-development funds, and other financing options for developing affordable housing to moderate-, low-, and very-low-income Oregonians.

Tax Credits & Grants for Rental Housing Developments: The Housing Resources Section administers OHCS' housing development grant and tax credit programs. Through its activities, the Section provides housing-related technical and financial assistance and carries out the spirit of the OHCS' mission to reach out for opportunities to create partnerships that improve Oregonians' lives and the quality of their communities.

* Oregon Office of Energy

625 Marion St. NE	800-221-8035
Salem, OR 97301	503-373-4040
www.energy.state.or.us	Fax: 503-373-7806

Business Energy Tax Credits: Tax credits for businesses in Oregon that invest in energy conservation, recycling, renewable energy resources and less-polluting transportation fuels. An Oregon business may qualify.

Energy Loan Program: Low-interest, long term loans for businesses and others that invest in energy conservation, produce energy from renewable resources and use recycled materials to create products.

Building Commissioning: Ensuring that the complex equipment providing lighting, heating, cooling, ventilation and other amenities in buildings works together effectively and efficiently. Studies on commissioning show that the process provides average energy savings of 15 to 30 percent.

* Loans For Farmers

Farm Service Agency
U.S. Department of Agriculture

7620 SW Mohawk	503-692-6830
Tualatin, OR 97062	Fax: 503-692-8139
http://www.fsa.usda.gov/or/	

The Farm Service Agency provides Direct and Guaranteed Loans to farmers through a variety of programs, including:

Farm Ownership Loans: purchase farmland, construct or repair buildings and other fixtures, and promote soil and water conservation. Up to $200,000.

Operating Loans: purchase items needed for a successful farm operation, such as livestock, farm equipment, feed, seed, fuel, farm chemicals, insurance, and other operating expenses. Can also be used to pay for minor improvements. Up to $200,000.

Beginning Farmer and Rancher Loans: provides funds to beginning and farmers and ranchers who are unable to obtain financing elsewhere.

Downpayment Farm Ownership Loans for Beginning Farmers: helps beginning farmers and ranchers purchase a farm or ranch. Also provides a way for retiring farmers to transfer their land to a future generation of farmers and ranchers. Applicant must have a downpayment of 10% and FSA with finance 40%, with the remaining balance from a commercial lender. Purchase price cannot exceed $250,000.

Loans to Socially Disadvantaged Farmers/Ranchers: helps socially disadvantaged applicants buy and operate family-size farms and ranches.

Youth Loans: Made to youths to establish and operate income-producing projects with the participation in 4-H clubs, Future Farmers of America, and similar organizations. Up to $5,000.

Emergency Loan Assistance: provides loans to help producers recover from production and physical losses due to drought, flooding, and other natural disasters, or quarantine. Up to $500,000.

Beginning Farmer and Rancher Land Contract Guarantee Pilot Program: "prompt payment guarantee" from FSA. FSA will provide payment to seller two times if the beginning farmer does not pay. Program is tested in IN, IA, ND, OR, PA and WI.

Farm Ownership and Operating Loan Guarantees: FSA will guarantee loans up to $782,000.

* Small Business Administration (SBA)

1515 SW 5th Ave., Suite 1050	503-326-2682
Portland, OR 97201-5494	Fax: 503-326-2808
www.sba.gov/or	

The Oregon Small Business Administration Office delivers a variety of programs and services, such as startup and operational assistance through small business training and counseling, financial assistance for startup's, business opportunities and much more.

* Agricultural Development & Marketing Division

Oregon Department of Agriculture

1207 NW Naito Parkway, Suite 104	503-872-6600
Portland, OR 97209-2832	Fax: 503-872-6601
www.oda.state.or.us	

The Agricultural Development and Marketing Division offers a variety of programs for the producers of Oregon.

Value-added grants: The bill contains $40 million nationally in grants for value-added projects, up to $500,000 per producer, producer organization, cooperative or business venture to assist in developing a business plan, marketing strategies, and marketing efforts.

Small Business Market Development Workshops: These workshops are presented to entrepreneurs developing new value added products.

* Oregon Contract Assistance Program (GCAP)

1144 Gateway Loop, Suite 203   541-736-1088
Springfield, OR 97477   800-497-7551
www.gcap.org   Fax: 541-736-1090

GCAP provides comprehensive assistance and information to Oregon small businesses desiring to enter the government contracting market.

* Lane Community College

Business Development Center & Contract Training
1445 Willamette Street, Suite 1   541-463-5255
Eugene, OR 97401-4087   Fax: 541-686-0096
www.lanebdc.com

Small Business Management: The program is designed for small business owners who have been in business for at least one year, are willing to try new ideas, and are willing to commit to classes and on-site visits. This is a two year program.

Farm Business Management: The program is designed for full-time or pert-time farm operators and managers. The program combines classroom training with on-site visits to achieve the businesses management goals.

Lane MicroBusiness: This program provides free business assistance and training as well as access to capital to Lane County low-income Micro-enterprise entrepreneurs.

Businesswomen's Mentoring Program: Support for women business owners.

Pennsylvania

* Pennsylvania Department of Community and Economic Development

400 North Street, 4th Floor
Commonwealth Keystone Building
Harrisburg, PA 17120   800-379-7448
www.inventpa.com

or

Governor's Action Team
100 Pine Street, Suite 100   717-787-8199
Harrisburg, PA 17101   Fax: 717-772-5419
www.teampa.com

Entrepreneurial Assistance Office: Established to ensure small business owners receive the support and assistance they require. The Entrepreneurial Assistance Office works to build an environment which encourages the creation, expansion and retention of small, women and minority owned businesses.

PAOpen4Business: The single point of contact and hub of information for small businesses, answering state related and general business questions about licenses and permits. The Center has select state forms and applications available as well as other sources of information and technical assistance. {www.paopen4business.state.pa.us}

Environmental Business Advocate: Assists small businesses in complying with requirements of the Federal Clean Air Act and appropriate state regulations. Housed in the PA Department of Environmental Protection, (DEP), the EBA represents the interests of small businesses in matters affecting them with DCED and the U.S. Environmental Protection Agency.

Industrial Resource Centers: Assists companies in solving problems through the deployment of technologies.

Job Centers: Provide employers with a wide array of employment and training services.

Small Business Incubators: Sites where young businesses can start and grow. Offers businesses the opportunity to rent small units of space at a lower than market rate. Provides tenants with business development services that help to reduce costs and increase profits.

PA Industrial Development Authority: Low-interest financing through Industrial Development Corporations for land and building acquisitions, construction and renovation resulting in the creation or retention of jobs. Amounts: Loans up to $1 million (within Enterprise Zones, $1.5 million) no more than 30 to 40% of the total eligible project costs, advanced technology projects and those in an Act 47 or within an Enterprise Zone qualify for lower interest rates.

Machinery and Equipment Loan Fund: Low-interest loan financing to acquire and install new or used machinery and equipment or to upgrade existing machinery and equipment. Amounts: Loans up to $500,000 or 50% of the total eligible project costs, whichever is less.

Small Business First: Funding for small businesses including: low-interest loan financing to small businesses for land and building acquisition and construction; machinery and equipment purchases and working capital; financing to comply with environmental regulations; for businesses involved in municipal or commercial recycling; and for those impacted by defense conversion. Amounts: $200,000 or 50% of the total eligible project costs, whichever is less. Maximum loan amount is $100,000 for working capital.

PA Infrastructure Investment Authority (PennVEST): Low-interest loans for design, engineering and construction of publicly and privately owned drinking water distribution and treatment facilities, storm water conveyance and wastewater treatment systems. Amounts: Loans up to $11 million per project for one municipality, up to $20 million for more than one municipality, up to $350,000 for design and engineering, up to 100% of the total project costs.

PA Capital Access Program: Through participating banks, loan guarantees are provided to support a wide variety of business purposes. Amounts: Loan guarantees up to $500,000.

PA Economic Development Financing Authority: An issuer of tax-exempt and taxable bonds, both in pooled transactions and stand-alone transactions. Bond funds are loaned to businesses and can be used to finance land, building, equipment, working capital and refinances. Amounts: Loans no less them $400,000 and no more than $10 million for manufacturers, no upper limits for other projects, up to 100% of project costs.

Opportunity Grant Program: Provides grant funds to create or preserve jobs within the Commonwealth. Funds may be used for job training, infrastructure improvements, land and building improvements, machinery and equipment, working capital and environmental assessment and redemption. Amounts: No minimum or maximum grant amount.

Infrastructure Development Program: Grant and low-interest loan financing for public and private infrastructure improvements. Amounts: Loans and grants up to $1.25

million, no more than 20% of the annual appropriation for a single municipality.

Industrial Sites Reuse Program: Grant and low-interest loan financing is provided to perform environmental site assessment and remediation work at former industrial sites. Amounts: Grants and loans up to $200,000 for environmental assessment, grants and loans up to $1 million for remediation.

Rail Freight Assistance: Grants to build or repair rail lines and spurs. Amounts: Grants up to $250,000 for maintenance, up to $100,000 for construction.

Enterprise Zone Program: Grants available for loans to businesses: Planning Grant up to $50,000; Basic Grant up to $50,000; Competitive Grant: up to $250,000.

Seed Venture Program: Provides product development and working capital to early-stage venture companies.

Small Business First Export Loan Program: Provides short-term loans to meet the pre and post-export financing needs of small businesses. Amounts: Pre-Export loans: Up to $350,000 or 50% of total eligible project costs, whichever is less. Post-Export loans: Loans not to exceed 80% of the face amount of the contract.

Underground Storage Upgrade Loan: Loans to assist owners of regulated storage tanks in upgrading their underground storage tank systems to meet federal Environmental Protection Agency upgrade requirements. Amounts: $500,000 or 75% of the total eligible project costs, whichever is less.

Challenge Grant Program: Provides grants ranging from $5,000 to $250,000 for research and development, technology transfer, joint research and development.

PA Minority Business Development Authority: Low-interest loan financing to businesses which are owned and operated by minorities. Amounts: Manufacturing, industrial, high-tech, international trade or franchise companies with loans up to $500,000 (within Enterprise Zones, $750,000) or 75% of total eligible project costs, whichever is less, retail or commercial firms loans of up to $250,000 ($350,000 in Enterprise Zones).

Independence Capital Network Fund: Provides grants to small employers to enable them to make special accommodations for workers with disabilities.

Minority Business Advocate: Encourages the development of minority-owned businesses as part of the overall economic development strategy of the Commonwealth. Serves as an advocate for minority owned business owners in resolving issues with state agencies and interacting with other government agencies.

Women's Business Advocate: Works to assist women businesses in the development of their business, specifically assisting in resolving issues with state agencies, exploring marketing options and identifying financing strategies.

Bureau of Contract Administration and Business Development (Formerly the Minority and Women Business Enterprise Office): Benefits small, minority and women businesses. Provides the necessary resources and direction for business owners to compete for and participate in the state contracting process. Furthermore, it is the statewide agency for certification as a Minority Business Enterprise and Women Business Enterprise.

Office of International Business Development: This office is headquartered in Harrisburg but maintains offices all around the world. They support Pennsylvania firms wishing to do business overseas. 888-PA EXPORT

Guaranteed Free Training Program: Funds for basic skills and information technology training for new employees and new or expanding business is available for businesses in manufacturing, technology-based information technology and those other than point of sale/retail. For basic skills, the maximum funding is up to $450 per trainee and $100,000 per company. The maximum for information technology is up to $700 per trainee and $50,000 per company.

Regional Marketing Initiative Grant: Local tourism promotion agencies and nonprofit organizations can get funding to conduct comprehensive destination marketing including research advertising, public relations and other promotional programs that stimulate travel and tourism.

Critical Job Training Grants: Grants to eligible entities for programs that train dislocated workers and other individuals for high-demand jobs or jobs with shortages of skilled workers. A 25% match is required.

Communities of Opportunity: Provides state-funded grants for community revitalization and economic development activities that occur locally.

Community Economic Development Loan Program: Low-interest loans for projects in distressed communities, stimulating self-help initiatives and helping people build assets.

Workforce Leadership Grants: Education programs grants throughout the secondary and post-secondary education system.

Elm Street Program: Grant funds for planning, technical assistance and physical improvements to residential and mixed use areas in proximity to central business districts.

Pollution Prevention Assistance Account (PPAA): Assistance for small businesses that helps implement pollution prevention and energy-efficiency projects, enable these businesses to adopt or install equipment or processes that reduce pollution or energy use.

Customized Job Training (CJT): Grant funds for specialized job training to existing or newly hired employees.

Job Creation Tax Credit Program: The Job Creation Tax Credit Program provides tax credits to eligible businesses that create 25 or more full-time jobs or increase employment by 20% within three years from the start date.

* Bureau of Market Development
Pennsylvania Department of Agriculture
2301 North Cameron Street   717-787-6041
Harrisburg, PA 17110-9408   Fax: 717-783-9115
www.agriculture.state.pa.us

Domestic and International Trade Development Division: The programs provide a platform from which Pennsylvania food, agriculture and wood companies can determine the opportunities available for their products and services beyond the borders of the Commonwealth and present them to the world.

Commodity Promotion Division; Administers programs that provide farmers a means to promote their products or provide funds for production research without the use of public funding; administers a matching grant program that provides public funding for agricultural product promotion by nonprofit agricultural organizations; develops promotional materials and campaigns for Pennsylvania agricultural products.

Division of Aquaculture: The aquaculture program within the is designed to help current and prospective aquaculture farmers to easily access information to help them achieve success. The program provides: Links to information regarding: regulations impacting aquaculture, species production research sales and marketing; Guidance on business development Strategies; Access to local sources for: food fish, ornamental fish, sports fish and bait fish; Marketing initiatives designed to help Pennsylvania fish farmers penetrate new markets and expand current sales. Educational opportunities for aquaculturalists to local venues.

* Tax Credit Program

Manager, Tax Credit Program
Pennsylvania Housing Finance Agency
P.O. Box 8029
Harrisburg, PA 17105-8029
Low Income Housing Tax Credit Program 717-780-3882
www.phfa.org

This program provides owners of and investors in affordable rental housing developments with tax credits that offer a dollar-for-dollar reduction in their tax liability. The credit may be taken for up to ten years. Tax credits are usually sold to investors with the proceeds used to cover project costs.

* Small Business Assistance Program

Department of Environmental Protection
Rachel Carson State Office Building
400 Market Street
Harrisburg, PA 17105   717-787-2814
www.dep.state.pa.us

Act 190 Pollution Prevention (P2)/Energy Efficiency (E2) Grant Program: Grants under the Act 190 P2/E2 Grant Program will be used to fund 80 percent of the total cost of a P2E2 site assessment, up to a maximum of $5,000 for Pennsylvania small businesses with 100 or fewer employees OR up to a maximum of $15,000 for holders of any DEP permit (or holder of an air permit from either the Allegheny County Department of Health or Philadelphia Air Management Services). (6/2/00)

Pennsylvania Environmental Assistance Network (PEAN): PEAN is a partnership of public and private sector service providers offering pollution prevention, energy efficiency, and environmental management systems services.

Small Business Pollution Prevention Assistance Account: The Pollution Prevention Assistance Account is a loan program that helps small Pennsylvania businesses implement pollution prevention and energy-efficiency projects. Go to the Small Business Pollution Prevention Assistance Account web site for more information.

* Keystone Opportunity Zones (KOZ)

Northwest Region:
Northwest Regional Planning & Development
Commission

395 Seneca Street   814-677-4800
Oil City, PA 16301   Fax: 814-677-7663

Southwest Region:
Southwestern Pennsylvania Commission
Regional Enterprise Tower
425 Sixth Avenue, Suite 2500   412-391-5590, ext. 343
Pittsburgh, PA 15219-1819   Fax: 412-391-9160

North Central Region:
North Central Pennsylvania Regional Planning and
Development Commission
651 Montmorenci Avenue   814-773-3162
Ridgway, PA 15853   Fax: 814-772-7045

Southern Alleghenies Region
Planning & Program Management
Southern Alleghenies Planning & Development
Commission
541 58th Street   814-949-6508
Altoona, PA 16602   Fax: 814-949-6505

Northern Tier Region:
Northern Tier Regional Planning & Development
Commission
507 Main Street   570-265-9103
Towanda, PA 18848   Fax: 570-265-7585

Central Region:
Economic Development Programs
SEDA-Council of Governments
201 Furnace Road   570-524-4491
Lewisburg, PA 17837   Fax: 570-524-9190

South Central Region:
South Central Assembly for Effective Governance
777 West Harrisburg Pike   717-948-6324
Middletown, PA 17057   Fax: 717-948-6306

Lackawanna/Luzerne Region:
Redevelopment Authority of Luzerne County
16 Luzerne Avenue, Suite #210   570-655-3329
West Pittston, PA 18643   Fax: 570-655-3287

Urban Workshop
1020 Mellon Bank Center
8 West Market Street   570-822-3166
Wilkes-Barre, PA 18711   Fax: 570-822-3164

Schuykill/Carbon:
Office of Economic Development
401 North Second Street   570-628-1167
Pottsville, PA 17901   Fax: 570-628-1210

Lehigh Valley Region:
Lehigh Valley Economic Development Corporation
2158 Avenue C   610-266-6775
Bethlehem, PA 18017   Fax: 610-266-7623

Southeastern Region:
Bucks Co. Economic Dev. Corp.
2 East Court Street   215-348-9031 ext 12
Doylestown, PA 18901   Fax: 215-348-8829

Philadelphia Region:
Philadelphia Department of Commerce
One Parkway
1515 Arch Street, 12th Floor   215-683-2015
Philadelphia, PA 19102   Fax: 215-557-8538

Keystone Opportunity Zones are defined, parcel-specific

areas with greatly reduced or no tax burden for property owners, residents and businesses. Keystone Opportunity Zones have been designated by local communities and approved by the state–they are, in fact, a partnership between each community and region among state and local taxing bodies, school districts, economic development agencies and community-based organizations.

* Pennsylvania Treasury Department

Linked Deposit Program
129 Finance Building   717-787-2465
Harrisburg, PA 17120-0018   Fax: 717-783-9760
www.treasury.state.pa.us
The Department of Treasury helps small businesses by offering a variety of programs.

State Contract Information: Helps businesses bid for contracts with state agencies by providing information about existing state contracts including: contract descriptions, names of previous bidders, pricing breakdowns and other information that may help an entrepreneur bid for a contract.

Business Referral Service: Helps businesses find resources they need including: publications, web sites, regional lists of professional associations, Small Business Development Centers, consultants, as well as information on how to become a state certified minority or women-owned business.

LowDoc Business Loans: Helps small businesses get fast financing of up to $150,000 through a cooperative effort with the SBA and local banks.

* Revenue Bond and Mortgage Program

Room 466, Forum Building
Harrisburg, PA 17120   717-783-1108
Funds for this program are borrowed through a local Industrial Development Authority, with financing secured from private sector sources. Lenders do not pay taxes on interest earned from the loan and borrowers obtain interest rates lower than conventional ones. Funds may be used for purchase of land, buildings, machinery, or equipment.

* Office of Technology Development

Forum Building, #352   717-787-4147
Harrisburg, PA 17120   Fax: 717-772-5080
Email: tkaufman@doc.state.pa.us
Programs available through the Office of Technology Development include:
-    Ben Franklin Centers
-    Challenge Grants
-    Seed Grants
-    R&D Grants
-    Environmental Technology R&D Fund
-    Technical and Business Assistance

* Ben Franklin Technology Partners

North East Tier BFTP
125 Goodman Dr.
Lehigh University   610-758-5200
Bethlehem, PA 18015   Fax: 610-861-5918

BFTP of Southeastern Pennsylvania
1835 Market St., Suite 1100   215-972-6700
Philadelphia, PA 19103   Fax: 215-972-5588

BFTP of Western Pennsylvania
Innovation Works, Inc.
2000 Technology Dr., Suite 250   412-681-1520
Pittsburgh, PA 15219   Fax: 412-681-2625

BFTP of Central/Northern Pennsylvania
115 Technology Center   814-863-4558
University Park, PA 16802   Fax: 814-865-0960

State Coordinator
200 N. Third St., Suite 400   717-234-1748
Harrisburg, PA 17101   Fax: 717-234-1824
www.benfranklin.org
Seed and Growth Capital: Ben Franklin Technology Partner uses gap financing to help start-up companies by providing a financial bridge between personal assets of entrepreneurs and capital funding from third party investors.

Business and Technical Expertise: Ben Franklin provides ongoing support and mentoring to address business needs.

Resources for Established Manufacturers: Resources to help established manufacturers evaluate processes and operations while implementing solutions.

Ben Franklin Technology Partners: A statewide network that fosters innovation to stimulate Pennsylvania's economic growth.

Technology Company Investment: Flexible financing and investment opportunities are available for technology-oriented businesses.

Technology Development Grants: A grant program to support local initiatives that stimulate the advancement of technology in businesses and communities.

Ben Franklin Venture Investment Forum: This program prepares entrepreneurs to raise equity capital by creating venues in which entrepreneurs and investors can interact.

* Loans For Farmers

Farm Service Agency
U.S. Department of Agriculture
Suite 320, One Credit Union Pl.
Harrisburg, PA 17110-2994   717-237-2113
http://www.fsa.usda.gov/pa/
The Farm Service Agency provides Direct and Guaranteed Loans to farmers through a variety of programs, including:

Farm Ownership Loans: purchase farmland, construct or repair buildings and other fixtures, and promote soil and water conservation. Up to $200,000.

Operating Loans: purchase items needed for a successful farm operation, such as livestock, farm equipment, feed, seed, fuel, farm chemicals, insurance, and other operating expenses. Can also be used to pay for minor improvements. Up to $200,000.

Beginning Farmer and Rancher Loans: provides funds to beginning and farmers and ranchers who are unable to obtain financing elsewhere.

Downpayment Farm Ownership Loans for Beginning Farmers: helps beginning farmers and ranchers purchase a farm or ranch. Also provides a way for retiring farmers to transfer their land to a future generation of farmers and ranchers. Applicant must have a downpayment of 10% and

FSA with finance 40%, with the remaining balance from a commercial lender. Purchase price cannot exceed $250,000.

Loans to Socially Disadvantaged Farmers/Ranchers: helps socially disadvantaged applicants buy and operate family-size farms and ranches.

Youth Loans: Made to youths to establish and operate income-producing projects with the participation in 4-H clubs, Future Farmers of America, and similar organizations. Up to $5,000.

Emergency Loan Assistance: provides loans to help producers recover from production and physical losses due to drought, flooding, and other natural disasters, or quarantine. Up to $500,000.

Beginning Farmer and Rancher Land Contract Guarantee Pilot Program: "prompt payment guarantee" from FSA. FSA will provide payment to seller two times if the beginning farmer does not pay. Program is tested in IN, IA, ND, OR, PA and WI.

Farm Ownership and Operating Loan Guarantees: FSA will guarantee loans up to $782,000.

* Small Business Administration (SBA)

Federal Building - Room 1128
1000 Liberty Avenue   412-395-6560
Pittsburgh, PA 15222   Fax: 412-395-6562

Robert N.C. Nix Federal Building
900 Market Street, 5th Floor   215-580-2SBA
Philadelphia, PA 19107   Fax 215-580-2762
www.sba.gov/pa

The Pennsylvania Small Business Administration Office delivers a variety of programs and services, such as startup and operational assistance through small business training and counseling, financial assistance for startup's, business opportunities and much more.

* Rural Development

U.S. Department of Agriculture
One Credit Union Place, Suite 330   717-237-2299
Harrisburg, PA 17110   Fax: 717-237-2191
www.rurdev.usda.gov/pa

Rural Business Enterprise Grants: Through the Rural Business Enterprise Grant (RBEG) program Rural Development provides grants to public agencies, private nonprofit corporations or Indian groups for financing and facilitating development of small and emerging private business. These grants can be made to public bodies and private nonprofit corporations that serve rural areas.

Business and Industry Loan Guarantee Program: The Business and Industry (B&I) Loan Guarantee program is a lender-driven program that provides a loan guarantee to the bank or other approved lender to finance private businesses located in rural areas of 50,000 population or less.

Rural Business Opportunity Grants: The mission of the Rural Business Opportunity Grant is to provide technical assistance for business development and conduct economic development planning in rural areas. The purpose of this program is to promote sustainable economic development in rural communities.

Rural Economic Development Loan and Grant Program: The Rural Economic Development Loan and Grant Program (REDLG) provides zero-interest loans and grants to Rural Utilities Service (RUS) borrowers, who in turn relend the money as a zero interest loan to local entities to promote rural economic development and job creation projects.

Intermediary Relending Program: The Intermediary Relending Program (IRP) provides a loan to private nonprofit organizations, public entities and others (intermediary) to finance business facilities and community development projects in rural areas of 25,000 population or less. The RBS loan is used to establish or fund a revolving loan program to provide financial assistance to ultimate recipients for community development projects, establishment of new businesses or expansion of existing businesses, and saving and/or creation of jobs in rural areas.

Cooperative Services Technical Assistance: Rural Business - Cooperative Service (RBS) assists rural residents in forming new cooperative businesses and improving the operations of existing cooperatives. Assistance to cooperatives located in rural areas is the primary focus.

Rhode Island

* Rhode Island Economic Development Corporation (RIEDC)

One West Exchange St.   401-222-2601
Providence, RI 02903   Fax: 401-222-2102
www.riedc.com

This office can provide information and expertise in dealing with state, federal, and local agencies. They also have information on financing programs and other services offered by the state government.

Industrial Revenue Bonds: Industrial Revenue Bonds may be used to finance qualified commercial and industrial projects. The bonds offer a competitive interest rate and state sales tax exemption on building materials that may be significant for projects involving new construction. Financing is available through the Rhode Island Industrial Facilities Corporation and covers the entire project cost. The project and the credit of the user provides the security for the bonds which may be issued on the financial strength of the user when the user is appropriately rated. The bonds may also be issued with an enhancement letter of credit from a financial institution.

Tax-Exempt "Small Issue Bonds": Under the small-issue bond provisions of the Omnibus Budget Reconciliation Act of 1993, interest on certain bonds with face amounts of less than $10 million is excluded from income if at least 95% of the bonds' proceeds is used to finance manufacturing facilities. Industrial Revenue Bonds are tax-exempt obligations of the issuer, the interest on which is exempt from federal and state income tax. The interest rate on such obligations is normally below that available for conventional mortgages.

Bond and Mortgage Insurance Program: The Program reduces the capital necessary for new manufacturing facilities, renovation of manufacturing facilities, the purchase of new machinery and equipment in financing projects up to $5,000,000.

The Small Business Loan Fund: The SBLF provides eligible Small Business Fixed Asset Loans from $25,000 to a maximum of $250,000 and Working Capital Loans to a maximum of $30,000.

International Trade Partnership: As the official arm of state government, RIEDC is the principal liaison with foreign governments and hosts in-coming trade delegations from other countries. As the entity charged with developing the state's economic agenda, RIEDC is the partner responsible for providing business services directly to companies. These services include: development and execution of trade shows and trade missions; customized export management training and general trade assistance to Rhode Island companies.

Every Company Counts Network: This program consists of public and private business development organizations, cities and towns and State agencies dedicated to providing expertise and tools for small businesses.

Job Creation Grant Fund: Matching grants to both in-state companies that are expanding their workforce and to out-of-state companies that are relocating or expanding their operations to Rhode Island.

Excellence Through Training Grant Program: Matching grants of up to $30,000 directly to employers for the upgrading and retraining of existing employees to improve the companies competitiveness.

Export Management Training Grant Program: Match grant of up to $5,000 to businesses to address their international training needs.

Employee Investment Grants Reimbursement of up to 50% of the cost of training to a maximum of $10,000 for upgrading and retraining of existing employees.

Urban Enterprise Equity Fund: A revolving loan fund to assist start-up and existing urban businesses.

Urban Ventures: Urban Ventures is a business incubator located in the City of Providence.

Procurement Technical Assistance Center (PTAC): A network of professionals to help small businesses enter into business with the state and federal government.

* Rural Development
Warwick Service Center
David M Delisle, Rural Development Manager
60 Quaker Lane, Suite 44   401-826-0842
Warwick, RI 02886   Fax: 401-828-6042
www.rurdev.usda.gov/ma

Business and Industry Loans (B&I): Loans are made to improve, develop or finance business, industry and employment and improve the economic and environmental climate in rural communities, including pollution abatement and control. The objective is achieved principally through bolstering a loan made by a private lender with guarantees by the federal government. Direct loans are also available on a limited basis. The funds may be used for real estate purchase or improvement, equipment or capital.

Rural Business Enterprise Grants (RBEG): Grants are made to assist public bodies and nonprofit corporations to finance and facilitate development of small and emerging private business enterprises. Small and emerging businesses have 50 or less employees and less than $1.0 million in gross revenues. Grants are primarily to be used by eligible nonprofits or public entities to provide technical assistance or establish a revolving loan fund. Revolving loan funds can provide micro-loans to small business which may be for the purchase of land, construction of facilities, and other business purposes.

Intermediary Relending Program Loans (IRP): Loans are made to eligible intermediaries (nonprofit or public entities) who in turn provide loans to ultimate recipients for business facilities and community development in a rural area. The interest rate on the loan to the intermediary is one percent with a term of up to 30 years. Eligible applicants must have a record of successfully assisting rural businesses, including experience in making and servicing commercial loans.

* Clean Water Finance Agency
Executive Director: Anthony B. Simeone
235 Promenade Street, Suite 119   401-453-4430
Providence, RI 02908   Fax: 401-453-4094
Email: ricwta@doa.state.ri.us
www.ricwf.state.ri.us

All water pollution abatement projects are financed with loans made through the State Revolving Loan Fund with a subsidized interest rate to save the borrowers 1/3 off the market rate for financing these projects.

* First Stop Business Information Center
100 North Main Street,   401-222-2185
Providence, RI 02903   Fax: 401-222-3890
www.faststart.state.ri.us

The First Stop Business Information Center, within the Secretary of State's Office, is designed to make it easier for businesses to deal with federal, state and local requirements. It gives businesses access to the information they need to be competitive by providing quick, accurate information and performing referral assistance services. The Center helps new businesses cut through the red tape and get off the ground, and gives existing businesses the information they need to grow and expand. Services include customized business checklists, resource manuals, and registration assistance.

* Human Resource Investment Council
1511 Pontiac Avenue, Bldg. 72-2   401-462-8860
Cranston, RI 02910   Fax: 401-462-8865
www.rihric.com

The Rhode Island Human Resource Investment Council (HRIC) was established by state law in 1992. Their primary role is to act as a catalyst, initiating inventive programs, funding innovative solutions and building dynamic networks. The HRIC provides grants directly to businesses to help offset the cost of training their workforce which include: Excellence Through Training Grants, Employee Creation Grants, and Export Assistance Grants.

* The Business Development Company of Rhode Island (BDCRI)
40 Westminster Street, Suite 702   401-351-3036
Providence, RI 02903.   Fax: 401-351-3056
www.bdcri.com

The Business Development Company of Rhode Island (BDCRI) is a for-profit, publicly held corporation whose principal stockholders are the Greater Providence Chamber of Commerce, Greater Providence Chamber Foundation and

BDCRI's member banks, which include most Rhode Island banks. Its mission is to provide alternative funding to Rhode Island businesses that require funds and have the ability to repay, but which cannot obtain all necessary funding from traditional sources. BDCRI provides bridge loans, lines of credit and long term loans. BDCRI is an approved Small Business Administration lender for term loans and lender for lines of credit.

* Loans For Farmers

Farm Service Agency
U.S. Department of Agriculture
60 Quaker Lane, Suite 4   401-828-8232
Warwick, RI 02886   Fax: 401-528-5206
http://www.fsa.usda.gov/ri/

The Farm Service Agency provides Direct and Guaranteed Loans to farmers through a variety of programs, including:

Farm Ownership Loans: purchase farmland, construct or repair buildings and other fixtures, and promote soil and water conservation. Up to $200,000.

Operating Loans: purchase items needed for a successful farm operation, such as livestock, farm equipment, feed, seed, fuel, farm chemicals, insurance, and other operating expenses. Can also be used to pay for minor improvements. Up to $200,000.

Beginning Farmer and Rancher Loans: provides funds to beginning and farmers and ranchers who are unable to obtain financing elsewhere.

Downpayment Farm Ownership Loans for Beginning Farmers: helps beginning farmers and ranchers purchase a farm or ranch. Also provides a way for retiring farmers to transfer their land to a future generation of farmers and ranchers. Applicant must have a downpayment of 10% and FSA with finance 40%, with the remaining balance from a commercial lender. Purchase price cannot exceed $250,000.

Loans to Socially Disadvantaged Farmers/Ranchers: helps socially disadvantaged applicants buy and operate family-size farms and ranches.

Youth Loans: Made to youths to establish and operate income-producing projects with the participation in 4-H clubs, Future Farmers of America, and similar organizations. Up to $5,000.

Emergency Loan Assistance: provides loans to help producers recover from production and physical losses due to drought, flooding, and other natural disasters, or quarantine. Up to $500,000.

Beginning Farmer and Rancher Land Contract Guarantee Pilot Program: "prompt payment guarantee" from FSA. FSA will provide payment to seller two times if the beginning farmer does not pay. Program is tested in IN, IA, ND, OR, PA and WI.

Farm Ownership and Operating Loan Guarantees: FSA will guarantee loans up to $782,000.

* Small Business Administration (SBA)

380 Westminster St.
Room 511   401-528-4561
Providence, RI 02903   Fax: 401-528-4539
www.sba.gov/ri

The Rhode Island Small Business Administration Office delivers a variety of programs and services, such as startup and operational assistance through small business training and counseling, financial assistance for startup's, business opportunities and much more.

* Department of Administration

Rhode Island Division of Taxation
1 Capital Hill   800-481-3700
Providence, RI 02908   401-222-3050
www.tax.state.ri.us

Child Daycare Tax Credits: Credits are available against the business corporation tax and other business taxes at 30 percent of amount of day care purchase and of the cost to establish and/or operate a licensed day care facility. Maximum annual credit is $30,000. Certain restrictions apply.

* RI Department of Environmental Management (RIDEM)

235 Promenade St.   401-222-6800
Providence, RI 02908   Fax: 401-222-3810
www.state.ri.us/dem

Hazardous Waste Reduction, Recycling and Treatment Program: Grants are available to companies in four categories for development of hazardous waste reduction, recycling or treatment facilities. The categories are: feasibility study - 90 percent up to $140,000; project design - 70 percent to 90 percent up to $75,000; construction - 50 percent to 90 percent up to $250,000; evaluation - 90 percent to 100 percent up to $50,000.

Office of Technical Assistance: The Office of Technical Assistance provides small business compliance assistance and pollution prevention technical support to businesses, industry, and governmental agencies to help them prevent and minimize pollution at the source of generation. This outreach function includes: on- site technical assistance; training programs, conferences, and workshops; and both regulatory and economic incentives to prevent pollution and to minimize the generation of pollutant wastes associated with industrial processes. These programs work with businesses to reduce regulatory burdens and to develop cost-effective ways to reduce toxic and hazardous material use and waste in the workplace. DEM staff working with the pollution prevention program do not report regulatory violations nor do they issue enforcement actions with penalties for non- compliance. This separation of DEM's assistance and enforcement functions is designed to make the assistance program more attractive to industry.

* Rhode Island MicroEnterprise Association, Inc.

645 Elmwood Avenue   401-383-7940
Providence, RI 02907   Fax: 401-383-7944
www.rimicroenterprise.org

Rhode Island MicroEnterprise Association: The MicroEnterprise Association partners with community-based organizations to provide free microbusiness training and business technical assistance to persons wishing to start their own business.

* Center For Women & Enterprise

55 Claverick Street, Suite 102   401-277-0800
Providence, RI 02903   Fax: 401-277-1122
www.cweprovidence.org

South Carolina

* South Carolina Department of Commerce

1201 Main Street, Suite 1600   803-737-0400
Columbia, SC 29201   877-751-1262
www.callsouthcarolina.com   Fax: 803-737-0418

This office can provide information and expertise in dealing with state, federal, and local agencies. They also have information on financing programs and other services offered by the state government, including Industrial Revenue Bonds, Jobs-Economic Development Authority (JEDA), Small Business Administration, Economic Development Administration, and Farmers Home Administration.

Enterprise Development, Inc.: Develops strategic initiatives and business resources for new capital investments. Initiatives are in the development of finances, technology and human resources.

Taxable Bond Financing Program: Assists commercial business and real estate development firms with affordable long-term debt financing. Proceeds may be used to fund the acquisition, construction or renovation of buildings and land, the purchase of new or used equipment, and for working capital purposes as well as the refinancing of existing debt.

Venture Capital Funding: Loans to businesses for innovative products or processes.

Trade Development Program: Mission is twofold: to increase awareness among South Carolina companies of world market profitability and the valuable export resources available; and to promote South Carolina companies and products to prospective overseas importers, resulting in an increased international market share and direct sales for South Carolina companies.

- Hands-on trade services include such matters as answering export-related inquiries and extending referrals to other export assistance providers. In addition, they regularly co-host trade-related conferences and seminars.
- Promotional activities include assistance to and the recruitment of companies for participation in trade shows and trade missions overseas and the hosting of visiting international trade missions sourcing South Carolina products. These activities are accomplished through staff-organized meetings with South Carolina manufacturers.
- Technological capabilities allow the trade staff to provide the most efficient service through both targeted events scheduling, and the ability to disseminate the most current international sales leads and trade-related reports to South Carolina firms with the push of a button.
- Exporters Database & Directory allows the matching of South Carolina firms with overseas requests for products, and serves as a resource for storing useful promotional information on in-state exporters. South Carolina firms may request their addition to this database, which doubles as the trade programs' mailing list, by completing an Export Questionnaire available from their office.

Export Trade and Finance Program: Assistance through financial counseling, facilitating services and lending/guarantee program.

Foreign Trade Zones: Operating with an FTZ offers several cost benefits: possible reduction or elimination of customs duty, deferral of duty payment, efficiency gains of bypassing customs through direct delivery.

Entrepreneurs/Small Business Assistance: Programs and services to help entrepreneurs and small business owners become successful. They provide *Business One Stop*, an online resource for new businesses and the guide *Starting A Business in South Carolina*.

Recycling Market Development: Technical and economic development assistance to the recycling industry.

Small Business Ombudsman: The Ombudsman serves as an initial contact for entrepreneurs who are looking for assistance or support from business experts.

* USDA Rural Development

Charles Sparks, State Director
Strom Thurmond Federal Building
1835 Assembly Street, Room 1007   803-765-5163
Columbia, SC 29201   Fax: 803-765-5633
Email: Bernie.Wright@sc.usda.gov
www.rurdev.usda.gov/sc

Business and Industry (B&I) Guaranteed Loans: The purpose of this program is to improve, develop, or finance business, industry and employment opportunities in rural communities with a population less than 50,000. Up to an 80% guarantee may be provided on quality loans to lenders with terms ranging from 7 to 30 years.

Intermediary Relending Program (IRP) Loans: Loans are made to intermediaries to establish revolving loan funds for relending to ultimate recipients to finance business facilities and community development projects in rural areas where the population is less than 25,000.

Rural Business Enterprise Grants (RBEG): Public bodies and private nonprofit corporations that serve rural areas can apply for RBEG grantfunds to support the development of small and emerging private business enterprises in rural areas where the population is less than 50,000.

Rural Business Opportunity Grants (RBOG): Public bodies and nonprofit corporations, Indian tribes and rural cooperatives may apply for the Rural Business Opportunity Grant. The purpose of the RBOG program is to promote sustainable economic development in rural communities with exceptional needs. Rural Economic Development Loans and Grants (REDLG): These loans and grants are made to Rural Utilities Service electric or telephone utility borrowers to assist in financing economic development and job creation projects in rural areas, which may include towns/cities with population under 2,500 and any unincorporated areas not adjacent to urbanized areas with population 50,000 or more.

Rural Economic Development Loans and Grants: These loans and grants are made to Rural Utilities Service electric or telephone utility borrowers to assist in financing economic development and job creation projects in rural areas. Loans at zero-interest are passed through to a third party recipient primarily to finance business start-up ventures and business expansion projects.

Cooperative Programs: This program helps rural residents form new cooperative businesses and improve the operations of existing cooperatives. Cooperative Services provides technical assistance to cooperatives and those thinking of forming them.

* Center for Applied Technology

Office of Technology Transfer
Clemson University
P.O. Box 345701
Clemson, SC 29634   864-656-3466

Provides assistance in the formation and development of technology based companies. The Center also offers access to capital, business development, as well as access to federal laboratory technologies.

* South Carolina Research Authority

1330 Lady Street, Suite 503   800-888-0871
Columbia, SC 29201   803-799-4070
www.scra.org

A public, self-funded, nonprofit organization that works to attract and support technology-based companies in South Carolina by: encouraging collaboration between industry, government, and educational institutions; providing unique site locations in specialized research parks; offering technology management specialization.

* Director Of Market Services

South Carolina Department of Agriculture
P.O. Box 11280   803-734-2210
Columbia, SC 29211   Fax: 803-734-2192
www.scda.state.sc.us

Marketing Services provides quality commodity inspection programs, basic and objective market news services to the livestock, fruit and vegetable industry, and to operate regional farmers markets to assist farmers, growers, shippers, processors, receivers and consumers in the effective and efficient marketing of fruits and vegetables.

* Commercial and Industrial Activities

South Carolina Energy Office   800- 851-8899
1201 Main Street, Suite 1010   803- 737-8030
Columbia, SC, 29201   Fax: 803-737-9846
www.state.sc.us/energy/

By promoting energy efficient technologies, the South Carolina Energy Office hopes to increase energy efficiency and promote economic development in the two sectors. Industrial and commercial customers benefit from savings on energy bills, and producers can expect to see an increase in productivity stemming from improvements in production process monitoring and reductions in machine downtime, in addition to energy savings. All of these factors improve a business's ability to compete in the marketplace, leading to job retention and increasing the viability of SC businesses.

Energy Audits: Free Level II energy audits are available for businesses and industry located in South Carolina. Level II audits involve a walk-through review of the facility and a report on the energy efficient opportunities available there. 803-737-8285

How to Reduce Your Energy Costs: The SCEO distributes this book to encourage energy management in commercial and industrial facilities.

Training and Workshops: The South Carolina Energy Office offers a variety of classes for your business.

ConserFund Loan Program: This program provides low cost financing program for energy efficiency improvements in state agencies, public colleges or universities, school districts, local governments and private nonprofit

organizations.{www.state.sc.us/energy/commercial/commercial_index.htm}

* Governor's Office of Small & Minority Business Assistance

1205 Pendleton Street, Room 329   803-734-0657
Columbia, SC 29201   Fax: 803-734-2498
www.govoepp.state.sc.us/osmba

The South Carolina Office of Small & Minority Business Assistance provides a Minority Business Directory to help identify small minority businesses that can help support South Carolina's economic development.

* Business Development Corporation

P.O. Box 21823
Enoree Building, Koger Center
111 Executive Center Dr., Suite 225   803-798-4064
Columbia, SC 29221   Fax: 803-798-1224
www.businessdevelopment.org

Business Development Board (BDB): A source of funds for business development and expansion. The BDB operates as a widely-held stock company made up of bank and savings and loan members. The BDB provides loans for companies which cannot obtain them elsewhere. Terms may range to 10 years or longer, and interest rates are usually comparable to the market rate. The BDB also makes loans under SBA guarantees. Funds are available for any sound business purpose, excluding debt financing or speculative purposes.

* Loans For Farmers

Farm Service Agency
U.S. Department of Agriculture
1927 Thurmond Mall, Suite 100   803-806-3820
Columbia, SC 29201-2375   Fax: 803-806-3839
http://www.fsa.usda.gov/sc/

The Farm Service Agency provides Direct and Guaranteed Loans to farmers through a variety of programs, including:

Farm Ownership Loans: purchase farmland, construct or repair buildings and other fixtures, and promote soil and water conservation. Up to $200,000.

Operating Loans: purchase items needed for a successful farm operation, such as livestock, farm equipment, feed, seed, fuel, farm chemicals, insurance, and other operating expenses. Can also be used to pay for minor improvements. Up to $200,000.

Beginning Farmer and Rancher Loans: provides funds to beginning and farmers and ranchers who are unable to obtain financing elsewhere.

Downpayment Farm Ownership Loans for Beginning Farmers: helps beginning farmers and ranchers purchase a farm or ranch. Also provides a way for retiring farmers to transfer their land to a future generation of farmers and ranchers. Applicant must have a downpayment of 10% and FSA with finance 40%, with the remaining balance from a commercial lender. Purchase price cannot exceed $250,000.

Loans to Socially Disadvantaged Farmers/Ranchers: helps socially disadvantaged applicants buy and operate family-size farms and ranches.

Youth Loans: Made to youths to establish and operate income-producing projects with the participation in 4-H clubs, Future Farmers of America, and similar organizations. Up to $5,000.

Emergency Loan Assistance: provides loans to help producers recover from production and physical losses due to drought, flooding, and other natural disasters, or quarantine. Up to $500,000.

Beginning Farmer and Rancher Land Contract Guarantee Pilot Program: "prompt payment guarantee" from FSA. FSA will provide payment to seller two times if the beginning farmer does not pay. Program is tested in IN, IA, ND, OR, PA and WI.

Farm Ownership and Operating Loan Guarantees: FSA will guarantee loans up to $782,000.

* Small Business Administration (SBA)

Strom Thurman Federal Building.
1835 Assembly St., Room 358   803-765-5377
Columbia, SC 29201   Fax: 803-765-5962
www.sba.gov/sc

The South Carolina Small Business Administration Office delivers a variety of programs and services, such as startup and operational assistance through small business training and counseling, financial assistance for startup's, business opportunities and much more.

South Dakota

* Governor's Office of Economic Development

711 East Wells Ave.   605-773-5032
Pierre, SD 57501-3369   800-872-6190
www.state.sd.us/goed   Fax: 605-773-3256

This office can provide information and expertise in dealing with state, federal, and local agencies. They also have information on financing programs and other services offered by the state government.

Workforce Development Program: Trains new employees, retrains current employees, and upgrades current employee skills.

Economic Development Finance Authority: Allows enterprises to pool tax-exempt or taxable development bonds for the purpose of constructing any site, structure, facility, service or utility for the storage, distribution or manufacturing of industrial or agricultural or nonagricultural products or the purchase of machinery and equipment used in an industrial process. Generally, the Authority will not consider loan requests for enterprises for amounts less than $300,000 and will not pool projects unless the pool volume is $1 million or more.

Revolving Economic Development and Initiative (REDI) Fund: Objective is to create "primary jobs" in South Dakota. Primary jobs are defined as "jobs that provide goods and services which shall be primarily exported from the state, gain market shares from imports to the state or meet an unmet need in the area resulting in the creation of new wealth in South Dakota. Primary jobs are derived from businesses that bring new income into an area, have a stimulative effect on other businesses or assist a community in diversification and stabilization of its economy." All for-profit businesses or business cooperatives are encouraged to apply, whether they are business start-ups, expansions, or relocations from outside South Dakota. The REDI Fund may provide up to 45% of the total project cost and requires the applicant to secure the matching funds before applying to the Board of Economic Development for the REDI Fund, including a 10% minimum equity contribution.

APEX Fund: The Agriculture Processing and Export Loan (APEX) is designed to assist companies in communities with populations of 25,000 or less or which add value to raw agricultural products through processing. The program may provide up to 75% of the total cost up to $150,000.

* Rural Development Administration

200 4th St., SW, Room 210   605-352-1142
Huron, SD 57350-2477   Fax: 605-352-1146
www.rurdev.usda.gov/sd

Guaranteed Business and Industrial Loans: Loans aimed at creating and maintaining employment and improving the economies of rural areas. Local lenders initiate and service the loans, while the RDA guarantees up to 90 percent of the loan. Potential borrowers who want loans of $500,000 or less should apply to the Small Business Administration. Guarantees are limited to $10 million. Interest rates are determined between the borrower and the lender and can be fixed or variable. Eligible projects and costs are business and industrial acquisitions, construction, conversion, enlargement, repair or modernization; purchase of land, machinery and equipment, furniture and fixtures, and certain housing development sites; processing and marketing facilities, start-up and working capital; pollution control; feasibility studies.

Rural Business Enterprise Grant: These grants are available to finance and facilitate development of small and emerging private business enterprises in rural area of cities up to 50,000 with priority given to towns smaller than 25,000.

Rural Business Opportunity Grants: The purpose of the Rural Business Opportunity Grants Program is to promote sustainable economic development in rural communities with exceptional needs. This is accomplished by making grants to public bodies, nonprofit corporations, Indian Tribes or cooperatives to provide for economic development planning, technical assistance, or training activities that improve economic conditions in rural areas.

Rural Economic Development Grant: The purpose of the Rural Economic Development Grant Program is to make available to rural communities through Rural Utility Service borrowers (1) grants to be used for revolving loan funds for community facilities and infrastructure and (2) grant assistance in conjunction with rural economic development loans.

Rural Economic Development Loan: The purpose of the Rural Economic Development Loan Program is to provide zero-interest loans and grants to borrowers to promote rural economic development and job creation projects.

Intermediary Relending Program: The purpose of the Intermediary Relending Program is to alleviate poverty and increase economic activity and employment in rural communities, especially disadvantaged and remote communities, through financing targeted primarily smaller and emerging businesses. This purpose is achieved through loans made to intermediaries that establish programs for the purpose of providing loans to ultimate recipients for business facilities and community developments in a rural area.

Cooperative Service Program: The mission of the Rural Business-Cooperative Service is to enhance the quality of life for all rural Americans by providing leadership in building competitive businesses and cooperatives. Rural Business Service accomplishes this mission by investing its financial resources and/or technical assistance in businesses, cooperatives, and communities, and by building partnerships that leverage public, private, and cooperative resources to stimulate rural economic activity.

* International Trade Directory

Mr. Joop Bollen
South Dakota International Business Institute – NSU
1200 S. Jay Street   605-626-3149
Aberdeen, SD 57401-7198   Fax: 605-626-3004
Email: bollenj@wolf.northern.edu
www.sd-exports.org

Identifies South Dakota traders (i.e. exporters and importers) of manufactured products, agribusiness products, services and technologies. The directory also offers a list of various private companies and public agencies that are available to serve the special needs of South Dakota exporters and importers. *Exporters Directory* is available in hard copy upon request.

* Department of Agriculture

Foss Building, Top Level
523 East Capitol   800-228-5254
Pierre, SD 57501-3182   605-773-3375
www.state.sd.us/doa/doa.html

The Department of Agriculture is responsible for the promotion and enhancement of South Dakota agriculture. They provide a variety of programs including:

Ag Finance Counseling: Ag counselors provide one-on-one assistance to South Dakota farmers and ranchers in financial management, such as completing loan paperwork, financial planning, or handling financial difficulties.

Business Development: This program assists the state's producers in identifying and developing appropriate opportunities. Assistance can be in the form of technical assistance, business plans, pre-feasibility studies or financial reviews.

Farm Loan Mediation: Mediation brings lenders and borrowers together in a confidential setting to resolve their financial disputes.

Livestock Development and Marketing Program: Offers marketing assistance to South Dakota livestock producers.

Ag Loan Programs: There are a wide variety of loan programs available for producers in the state of South Dakota.

Value-Added and Crop Marketing Program: Assists the state's producers and processors in marketing their products both domestically and internationally.

Feed Finder and Harvest Hotline: The feed finder is a computerized listing designed to match buyers and sellers of all types of feed and open pasture land for livestock. Hotline: 800-228-5254

* Housing Tax Credit Program

Housing Development Authority
South Dakota Housing Development Authority
P.O. Box 1237
605-773-3181

Pierre, SD 57501-1237   Fax: 605-773-5154
www.sdhda.org

Projects eligible for housing tax credits involve construction and/or preservation of decent, safe, sanitary and affordable housing in areas of the greatest housing need. A minimum of either 20 percent of the total units must be available to tenants whose incomes do not exceed 50 percent of the area median gross income; or 40 percent of the total units must be available to tenants whose incomes do not exceed 60 percent of the area median gross income. Gross rents on the low-income units, including tenant-paid utilities, cannot exceed 30 percent of the qualifying monthly median income. The project owner must also enter into an agreement to meet the low income occupancy requirements for a minimum of 15 years beyond the initial 15 year compliance period.

* State Investment Council

State Treasurer
Capitol Building, Suite 212
500 East Capitol Ave.   605-773-3378
Pierre, SD 57501-5070   Fax: 605-773-3115
www.sdtreasurer.com

Deals solely with venture capital funds that invest in equity or equity-participating instruments of businesses. The fund can invest only in businesses which have headquarters and the majority of their employees located within the state. The Investment Council's participation in a venture capital fund may not be greater than one-third of the total equity funds invested in the fund.

* Loans For Farmers

Farm Service Agency
U.S. Department of Agriculture
200 Fourth St.
SW Federal Building, Room 308   605-352-1163
Huron, SD 57350   Fax: 605-352-1195
http://www.fsa.usda.gov/sd/

The Farm Service Agency provides Direct and Guaranteed Loans to farmers through a variety of programs, including:

Farm Ownership Loans: purchase farmland, construct or repair buildings and other fixtures, and promote soil and water conservation. Up to $200,000.

Operating Loans: purchase items needed for a successful farm operation, such as livestock, farm equipment, feed, seed, fuel, farm chemicals, insurance, and other operating expenses. Can also be used to pay for minor improvements. Up to $200,000.

Beginning Farmer and Rancher Loans: provides funds to beginning and farmers and ranchers who are unable to obtain financing elsewhere.

Downpayment Farm Ownership Loans for Beginning Farmers: helps beginning farmers and ranchers purchase a farm or ranch. Also provides a way for retiring farmers to transfer their land to a future generation of farmers and ranchers. Applicant must have a downpayment of 10% and FSA with finance 40%, with the remaining balance from a commercial lender. Purchase price cannot exceed $250,000.

Loans to Socially Disadvantaged Farmers/Ranchers: helps socially disadvantaged applicants buy and operate family-size farms and ranches.

Youth Loans: Made to youths to establish and operate income-producing projects with the participation in 4-H clubs, Future Farmers of America, and similar organizations. Up to $5,000.

Emergency Loan Assistance: provides loans to help producers recover from production and physical losses due to drought, flooding, and other natural disasters, or quarantine. Up to $500,000.

Beginning Farmer and Rancher Land Contract Guarantee Pilot Program: "prompt payment guarantee" from FSA. FSA will provide payment to seller two times if the beginning farmer does not pay. Program is tested in IN, IA, ND, OR, PA and WI.

Farm Ownership and Operating Loan Guarantees: FSA will guarantee loans up to $782,000.

* Small Business Administration (SBA)

110 S. Phillips Ave., Suite 200 605-330-4243
Sioux Falls, SD 57104   Fax: 605-330-4215
www.sba.gov/sd

The South Dakota Small Business Administration Office delivers a variety of programs and services, such as startup and operational assistance through small business training and counseling, financial assistance for startup's, business opportunities and much more.

Tennessee

* Department of Economic and Community Development

Rachel Jackson Building, 8th Floor
312 Eighth Avenue North 615-741-1888
Nashville, TN 37243-0405 Fax: 615-741-7306
www.state.tn.us/ecd

Small Business Incubation Centers: Incubation centers offer a low cost way for entrepreneurs to start their businesses in an office/light manufacturing environment. Offering low cost rental rates per square foot, incubators also offer shared resources such as conference rooms, utility hook ups, office copiers, some telephone support. The most valuable commodity they offer is a shared environment in which business owners can discuss common problems and reach solutions.

Small Business Information Guide: A resource manual that assists start-up and existing small businesses with issues like state and federal business taxes, business regulations and government assisted funding programs.

Industrial Training Service: Helps recruit, screen and train new employees, provide job-specific training and overall workforce development. They partner with over 40 community colleges, and technical institutes and technology centers across the state.

Small And Minority Owned Telecommunications Business Assistance Program (Loan Guarantee): Designed to enhance and stimulate the growth, development and procurement opportunities for small, minority, and women owned businesses in the telecommunications industry in Tennessee.

Revolving Loan Funds: Available through nine community development corporations in Tennessee. The revolving loan fund combines funds secured from the Economic Development Administration and Farmer's Home Administration with regional funding sources to provide new

or expanding businesses with financing at below market rates.

Tennessee Child Care Facilities Program: Assists child care providers by enabling them to upgrade facilities, create or expand the number of child care slots. The Program was established to accomplish two main goals: assist child care providers in attaining higher standards of safety and environment; increase the number of child care slots especially in rural and economically distressed areas. The program also assists companies and organizations wishing to establish day care centers for employees or groups of employees. The Program has three components:
- Guarantees to lenders up to $250,000 for new construction
- Direct loans to providers up to $10,000 for upgrade of facilities
- Direct loans to providers up to $25,000 for new or addition of slots

As of spring, 1998, the guarantee portfolio totaled $2.3 million, close to its cap for prudent risk. Direct loans are subject to funding on an annual basis from different sources. Maturities as well as interest rates vary based on uses of the loans.

Rural Electric Administration (REA), Rural Economic Development Revolving Loan Program For Rural Electric And Telephone Cooperatives: Designed to promote rural economic development and job creation by providing zero interest loans to REA borrowers. The program will fund up to $100,000 per project. The maximum term of the loan is ten years at zero interest rate with a two-year deferred payment. For more information, contact your local electric utility company.

Small Business Energy Loan Program: Designed to assist in the identification, installation, and incorporation of approved energy efficiency measures onto, or into, the existing Tennessee located facilities processes, and for operations of approved applicants. The Energy Division currently maintains a loan portfolio of $4,560,000 to 115 borrowers. Approved loan requests average $39,000.

Rural Business & Cooperative Development Service Loan Guarantees: The U.S. Department of Agriculture, through the RBCDS (formerly Farmers Home Administration), guarantees term loans to non-farm businesses in rural areas; that is, localities with populations below 50,000 not adjacent to a city where densities exceed 100 persons per square mile. The Tennessee RBCDS currently maintains a loan portfolio in excess of $40,000,000 (in addition to their relending program with the Development Districts listed above) with 40 industrial borrowers. Approved loan requests average just over $1,000,000.

Small Business Investment Companies: Private investment and loan companies established to serve the small business market. They are funded with a combination of private and federal investment. SBICs assist only businesses below $6,000,000 in net worth and less than $2,000,000 in annual net income. They may prioritize investments in type (equity or loan); dollar amount, location or industry.

Pollution Prevention Loan Program: Loans for the purchase of equipment and/or construction to complete pollution prevention activities at small and medium sized businesses.

Minority Business Development Center: Provides management, marketing, and technical assistance to increase business opportunities for minority entrepreneurs. Each center provides accounting, administration, business planning, construction, and marketing information to minority firms. The MBDC also identifies minority firms for contract and subcontract opportunities with government agencies and the private sector.

The Valley Coalition for Business Development: This coalition promotes the growth and expansion of minority-owned, women-owned and socially and economically disadvantaged businesses.

Business Incubator Loan Fund: Businesses housed within the TVA Business Incubation Network can apply for money from TVA's Business Incubator Loan Fund. Loans of up to $25,000 are available to help young businesses meet their short-term needs for cash flow and operating capital.

* ACCE$$

Nashville Area Chamber of Commerce
211 Commerce Street, Suite 100
Nashville, TN 37201   615-743-3000
www.nashvillechamber.com

The Nashville Area Chamber of Commerce, U.S. Small Business Administration and area banks started a financing program for small businesses. ACCE$$ serves the small business loan market, booking loans of $5000 and up. The program enables entrepreneurs the opportunity to present their business plans orally to a panel of bank loan officers. Panelists can qualify good credit risks immediately, improving the presenter's chances of obtaining an SBA guarantee. Regardless of the decision, small business owners receive valuable outside appraisal of their business plans.

* Rural Development Authority

Department of Agriculture   615-783-1300
3322 W. End Ave., Suite 300   800-342-3149
Nashville, TN 37203   Fax: 615-783-1301
www.rurdev.usda.gov/tn

Business & Industrial Loan Guarantees: This program guarantees loans, which are designed to promote economic growth. Qualifying businesses are eligible for loan note guarantees that better assist the business in obtaining vital credit through a local lender.

Intermediary Relending Program: This program allows the Rural-Business Service to provide loans to local lending authorities, which in turn provide loans to local businesses.

Rural Business Enterprise Grants: These grants provide resources that are utilized to develop small and emerging business enterprises, such as industrial parks. Qualifying entities include public bodies, nonprofit corporations and federally recognized tribal groups.

Cooperative Development Programs: The Rural-Business Service has the responsibility for providing technical and financial assistance to developing existing cooperatives in rural Tennessee. This assistance is targeted to those cooperatives with an emphasis on value-added agricultural products. The goal is to target the technical and financial resources of USDA to cooperatives involved in the development of new products and markets for farmers.

Rural Economic Development Loans and Grants: This program is utilized to finance rural economic development and rural job creation projects that are based on sound economic and financial analyses. Loans and grants are made to Rural Utilities Service electric and telephone borrowers

who use the funds to provide financing for business and community development projects.

* University of Tennessee Center for Industrial Services

193 Polk Avenue, Suite C   888-763-7439
Nashville, TN 37219   615-532-8657
www.cis.utk.edu   Fax: 615-532-4937

Industrial Extension: CIS is a state wide industrial extension program dedicated to helping managers of Tennessee business and manufacturing firms find solutions to technical and managerial problems they face. CIS provides information and counseling services and strives to link resources of higher education with industrial needs.

* Tennessee Technological University Center for Manufacturing Research and Technology Utilization

Tennessee Tech Manufacturing Center
College of Business Administration
TTU Box 5077   931-372-3362
Cookeville, TN 38505   Fax: 931-372-6345
www.tntech.edu/cmr

The Manufacturing Center was created to help improve the manufacturing productivity of state industry and to enhance instructional quality in manufacturing-related areas. The Center seeks to assist industry not only in research and development, but also in integrating manufacturing processes with a systems approach. At any given time in the Manufacturing Center, over 30 separate, but complimentary projects may be in progress.

* Tennessee Valley Authority Special Opportunity Counties Program

Tennessee Valley Authority
400 W. Summit Hill Dr.
Knoxville, TN 37902-1499   865-632-2101
www.tva.gov/econ

Designed to provide capital to finance projects which support the recruitment of new industry, the expansion of existing industry, the growth of small business, and the creation of new companies in the Tennessee Valley.

The Economic Development Loan Fund (EDLF): $20 million per year revolving loan program targeted on low interest loans to established companies relocating or expanding their operations in the Tennessee Valley. Loans are made for buildings, plant equipment, infrastructure, or property based on the capital investment leveraged, the number of jobs created, power load generated and geographic diversity. TVA Economic Development staff market the program, manage the loan review process, and manage the loan portfolio. Primary Focus: Sustained Growth.

Special Opportunities County Fund: $15 million revolving loan program targeted on low interest loans for companies expanding or relocating in the Tennessee Valley's most economically distressed counties. Loans are made for buildings, plant equipment, infrastructure, or property based on the capital investment leveraged and the number of jobs created. TVA Economic Development staff market the program, manage the loan review process, and manage the loan portfolio. Primary Focus: Sustained Growth.

Minority Business Development Loan Fund.: Revolving loan fund targeted to socially and economically disadvantaged businesses in the Valley.

* Office of Minority Business Enterprise

312 8th Ave. North, 11th Floor
Nashville, TN 37243   615-741-1888
www.state.tn.us/ecd/minority.htm

Facilitates the resources needed in assisting minority businesses in growth and business development by identifying sources of capital; linking successful businesses with minority businesses which need help in areas like training, quality control, supplier development or financial management; providing education and training, specialized technical assistance and identification of procurement opportunities in the public and private sectors; and publishing the *Minority and Women Business Directory* profiling minority businesses and their capabilities for public and private organizations which use their services or products.

* Tennessee Technology Development Corporation

1020 Commerce Park Dr.
Oak Ridge, TN 37830   865-220-8832
www.tennesseetechnology.org

Provides seed capital fund for promising technology companies.

* Occupational Safety And Health Grant

Tennessee Department of Labor
Occupational Safety and Health Grant Program
Gateway Plaza, 2nd Floor   800-249-8510
710 James Robertson Parkway   615-741-2793
Nashville, TN 37243   Fax: 615-253-1623
www.state.tn.us/labor-wfd/tosha.html

The goal of this program is to fund the education and training of employees in safe employment practices and conduct in the employer's own business for the employer's own employees; and promote the development of employer - sponsored health and safety programs in the employer's own business for the employer's own employees. Grants average in the $5000 range with some greater amounts.

* Tennessee Department of Agriculture

Division of Marketing
Ellington Agricultural Center
P.O. Box 40627   615-837-5103
Nashville, TN 37204   Fax: 615-360-0194
www.state.tn.us/agriculture

Offers similar services as the Tennessee Export Office, however specifically catering to the Tennessee farmers and agri-business people in the state. Their services include:

- hosting foreign buyer visits from abroad
- participating in trade shows and sales missions to key agricultural market destinations
- identifying foreign import requirements and assistance in obtaining appropriate documentation
- conducting seminars highlighting agricultural exports
- disseminate trade leads and other trade information

* Purchasing Councils

Tennessee Minority Purchasing Council
Metro Center, Plaza 1 Building
220 Athens Way, Suite 105   615-259-4699
Nashville, TN 37228   Fax: 615-259-9480
www.tmsdc.net

Encourages mutually beneficial economic links between ethnic minority suppliers and major purchasers in the public and private sectors.

* The Southern Appalachian Fund

1020 Commerce Park Drive, Suite 5L   865-220-2020
Oak Ridge, TN 37830   865-220-2030
www.southappfund.com

The Southern Appalachian Fund is a venture capital fund focused on investing in technology-based, early-stage, private companies. The Fund is supported by institutional and private investors and is awaiting approval of its license to become a Small Business Investment Company under the Participating Securities Program. Southern Appalachian Fund can make investments throughout the United States but will focus its investments in Tennessee and the surrounding states.

* Environment and Conservation

21st Floor, L&C Tower
401 Church Street   615-532-0104
Nashville, TN 37243-0454   888-891-8332
www.state.tn.us/environment/dco/p2

Pollution Prevention Programs: Provides multimedia pollution prevention assistance to industry, commercial establishments, schools, institutions, homes, government, etc through the preparation and review of pollution prevention plans, onsite visits, market development, general outreach and training.

* Tennessee Department of Labor and Workforce Development

710 James Robertson Parkway
Andrew Johnson Tower, 8th Floor   615-741-6642
Nashville, TN 37243   Fax: 615-741-5078
www.state.tn.us/labor-wfd

The Work Opportunity Tax Credit and the Welfare-to-Work tax credit programs are intended to further the partnership between the employment and training system and the private sector in dealing with problems of the disadvantaged and the unemployed. These two tax credits are significant complements to the welfare reform effort and can be used as incentives for employers to hire regular as well as long-term welfare recipients. 800-432-5268 (in state only) or fax your request to 615-532-1612.

Employment and Training: We are committed to providing employers access to recruitment and training services for both immediate and long-term needs. We help coordinate services through local partners in the state's local workforce investment areas to help connect employers with the well-trained workforce they need to be productive. 800-255-5872

* International Trade Administration (ITA)

U.S. Dept. of Commerce
Nashville Export Assistance Center
Commerce Center Building
211 Commerce St., 3rd Floor, Suite 100   615-259-6060
Nashville, TN 37201   Fax: 615-259-6064

U.S. Dept. of Commerce
Knoxville Export Assistance Center
601 W. Summit Hill Drive, Suite 300   865-545-4637
Knoxville, TN 37902-2011   Fax: 865-545-4435

U.S. Dept. of Commerce
Memphis Export Assistance Center
Buckman Hall
650 East Parkway South, Suite 348   901-323-1543
Memphis, TN 38103-2190   Fax: 901-320-9128

www.state.tn.us/ecd/rg_ch8.htm

These International Trade Centers operate as a division of the Tennessee Small Business Development Center, the state's primary consulting and technical assistance provider for small- and medium-size businesses. Their export assistance efforts focus on exporting firms that are new to the exporting business. Maintaining offices in Memphis and Knoxville, the ITC can offer one-on-one counseling at any SBDC office across the state. ITC counselors can: Assist in evaluating a company's export potential; Assist in market research; Assist with market entry strategies; Advise on market opportunities; Advise on export practices; and Advise on export procedures. In addition to counseling, ITC sponsors continuing-education seminars and workshops across the state.

* Tennessee Department of State

Business Services Division
William R. Snodgrass Tower, 6th Floor`
312 Eighth Avenue North   615-741-2286
Nashville, TN 37243   Fax 615-741-7310
www.state.tn.us/sos/service.htm

The Division of Business Services can assist with corporate filing transactions, issues certifications, responds to corporate telephone inquiries; UCC filing and search transactions ;issues notary- at-large commissions and registers trademarks.

* Loans For Farmers

Farm Service Agency
U.S. Department of Agriculture
579 U.S. Courthouse
801 Broadway   615-277-2600
Nashville, TN 37203-3816   Fax: 615-277-2659
http://www.fsa.usda.gov/tn/

The Farm Service Agency provides Direct and Guaranteed Loans to farmers through a variety of programs, including:

Farm Ownership Loans: purchase farmland, construct or repair buildings and other fixtures, and promote soil and water conservation. Up to $200,000.

Operating Loans: purchase items needed for a successful farm operation, such as livestock, farm equipment, feed, seed, fuel, farm chemicals, insurance, and other operating expenses. Can also be used to pay for minor improvements. Up to $200,000.

Beginning Farmer and Rancher Loans: provides funds to beginning and farmers and ranchers who are unable to obtain financing elsewhere.

Downpayment Farm Ownership Loans for Beginning Farmers: helps beginning farmers and ranchers purchase a farm or ranch. Also provides a way for retiring farmers to transfer their land to a future generation of farmers and ranchers. Applicant must have a downpayment of 10% and FSA with finance 40%, with the remaining balance from a commercial lender. Purchase price cannot exceed $250,000.

Loans to Socially Disadvantaged Farmers/Ranchers: helps socially disadvantaged applicants buy and operate family-size farms and ranches.

Youth Loans: Made to youths to establish and operate income-producing projects with the participation in 4-H clubs, Future Farmers of America, and similar organizations. Up to $5,000.

Emergency Loan Assistance: provides loans to help producers recover from production and physical losses due to drought, flooding, and other natural disasters, or quarantine. Up to $500,000.

Beginning Farmer and Rancher Land Contract Guarantee Pilot Program: "prompt payment guarantee" from FSA. FSA will provide payment to seller two times if the beginning farmer does not pay. Program is tested in IN, IA, ND, OR, PA and WI.

Farm Ownership and Operating Loan Guarantees: FSA will guarantee loans up to $782,000.

* Small Business Administration (SBA)

50 Vantage Way, Suite 201   615-736-5881
Nashville, TN 37228-1500   Fax: 615-736-7232
www.sba.gov/tn

The Tennessee Small Business Administration Office delivers a variety of programs and services, such as startup and operational assistance through small business training and counseling, financial assistance for startup's, business opportunities and much more.

* Tennessee Small Business Development Center (TSBDC)

1415 Murfreesboro Road, Suite 350   615-366-3900
Nashville, TN 37217   877-898-3900
www.tsbdc.org

The TSBDC network is composed of 12 centers and 2 satellite offices throughout the state.

Personalized One-on-One Counseling: A personal consultant is assigned to work with your business for personal attention.

Training: Training on a variety of business subjects are available including: buying and selling abroad, E-commerce, marketing, starting and managing a small business and writing a business plan.

Texas

* Texas Department of Economic Development

P.O. Box 12728   512-936-0100
Austin, TX 78711   800-888-0511
www.tded.state.tx.us   Fax: 512-936-0400

Provides business counseling for both new and established firms. Helps firms locate capital, state procurement opportunities, state certification programs for minority and women-owned businesses, and resources management and technical assistance. An Office of Business Permit Assistance serves as a clearinghouse for permit-related information throughout the state and refers applicants to appropriate agencies for permit and regulatory needs. Publications are available containing information and resources for start-up and existing businesses. Also has a program for corporate expansion and recruitment.

Office of Small Business Assistance: Charged with helping the state's small businesses become more globally competitive. The Office provides information and assistance to establish, operate and expand small and historically underutilized businesses (HUBS). In addition, the Office is charged with being the focal point for comments, suggestions and information regarding HUBS and small businesses to develop and suggest proposals for changes in state and federal policies in response to this information.

Economic Development Clearinghouse: A one-stop center for information about economic development programs and technical assistance offered by state and federal agencies, local governments and other organizations. The clearinghouse's website is {www.edinfo.state.tx.us}.

Office of Defense Affairs: Develops pro-active statewide strategy to prevent future defense closures and realignments and assist defense-dependent communities to prepare for future base realignments or closures.

Linked Deposit Program: Established to encourage lending to historically underutilized businesses, child-care providers, nonprofit corporations, and/or small businesses located in distressed communities by providing lenders and borrowers a lower cost of capital. Minimum loan amount is $10,000; maximum loan amount is $250,000, fixed borrower loan rate.

Small Business Industrial Revenue Bond Program: Designed to provide tax-exempt financing to finance land and depreciable property for eligible industrial or manufacturing projects. The Development Corporation Act allows cities, counties, conservation and reclamation districts to form nonprofit industrial development corporations or authorities on their behalf. Program objective is to issue taxable and tax-exempt bonds for eligible projects in cities, counties, conservation and reclamation districts. The industrial development corporation acts as a conduit through which all monies are channeled. Generally, all debt services on the bonds are paid by the business under the terms of a lease, sale, or loan agreement. As such, it does not constitute a debt or obligation of the governmental unit, the industrial development corporation, or the State of Texas.

Capital Access Fund: Established to increase the availability of financing for businesses and nonprofit organizations that face barriers in accessing capital. Through the use of the Capital Access Fund, businesses that might otherwise fall outside the guidelines of conventional lending may still have the opportunity to receive financing. The essential element of the program is a reserve account established at the lending institution to act as a credit enhancement, inducing the financial institution to make a loan. Use of proceeds may include working capital or the purchase, construction, or lease of capital assets, including buildings and equipment used by the business. There is no minimum or maximum loan amount, only a maximum amount that the state will provide to the financial institution's reserve fund.

Leverage Fund: An economic development bank offering an added source of financing to communities that have passed the economic development sales tax. This program allows the community to make loans to local businesses for expansion or to recruit new industries.

Office of International Business (OIB) helps Texas companies expand their business worldwide. By providing a forum for international business exchange through international trade missions, trade shows, seminars and in-bound buyers missions, OIB gives Texas companies the opportunity to promote their products and services to international buyers and partners. OIB also helps to connect companies with counseling and training available through the International Small Business Development Centers and works with entities such as the U.S. Department of Commerce, the Japan External Trade Organization, the Texas consular corps and its counterparts in the Mexican border states to ensure that Texas business interests are represented

abroad. The State of Texas office in Mexico City is an invaluable resource for facilitating business between Texas and Mexico. Programs include:
- Trade Missions and Trade Shows
- Export Counseling
- Partnerships
- Trade Lead Distribution
- Texas International Center
- Research Publications

State of Texas Mexico Office: Texas businesses and communities receive a variety of services in order to promote Texas tourism and exporting.

Enterprise Zone: This program encourages job creation and capital investment by providing tax incentives to businesses in economically distressed areas.

Defense Zone Program: This program provides tax incentives for businesses in adversely impacted defense-dependent communities.

Business Permit Office: A four-step program to starting a business in Texas.

Texas Marketplace: This is a free online tool that the State of Texas uses to facilitate electronic commerce, including government procurement and private-sector trade opportunities.

* Rural Development Authority
District Office
101 S. Main, Suite 102   254-742-9700
Temple, TX 76501   Fax: 254-942-9709
www.rurdev.usda.gov/tx

Business and Industrial Guaranteed Loans: Commercial loans guaranteed up to 90% for developing improving or financing business, industry and employment in rural areas of less than 50,000.

Business and Industry Direct Loan Program: The Business and Industry Direct Loan Program provides loans to public and entities and who cannot obtain credit from other sources.

Intermediary Relending Program Loans: This program provides assistance to finance business facilities and community development projects in rural areas. These funds are made to intermediaries that ultimately provide loans to recipients for business facilities and community development.

Rural Business Enterprise Grants: This program provides assistance to public and nonprofit corporations to finance and facilitate development of small and emerging private businesses located in rural areas.

Rural Economic Development Loan and Grant Program: Provides uses of loans and grants to promote rural economic development and job creation. These grants can only be made to Rural Utility Service.

Rural Business Opportunity Grants: This program provides grants for technical assistance for business development and economic development planning in rural areas.

* Texas Marketplace
Texas Department of Economic Development
Internet Services Group

P.O. Box 12728
Austin, TX 78711   512-936-0100
www.marketplace.state.tx.us
Offers businesses access to the internet including free web page, daily posting of all major procurement opportunities with the State of Texas, electronic bulletin board for posting information about commodities for sale or to buy, and other resources and government procurement opportunities.

* Business & Industry Data Center (BIDC)
P.O. Box 12728   512-936-2000
Austin, TX 78711   Fax: 512-936-0800
www.bidc.state.tx.us
Provides one-stop access to data, information, and analyses on the Texas economy.

* Texas Agricultural Extension Service
Texas Agricultural Extension Service
112 Jack K. Williams Administration Building
College Station, TX 77843-7101   979-845-7808
http://texasextension.tamu.edu   Fax: 979-845-9542
The Texas Agricultural Extension Service (TAEX) has long been a key element in The Texas A&M University System's effort to reach out to all Texans, from all backgrounds, in all areas of the state. The agency's programs serve all 254 Texas counties providing research-based information and education for agricultural producers, agribusinesses, consumers and families.

* Texas Engineering Extension Service (TEEX)
Texas A&M University
301 Tarrow
College Station, TX 77840   979-458-6800
http://teexweb.tamu.edu
As one of the largest providers of work force training in the nation, the Texas Engineering Extension Service is known for its innovative, customized programs and its hands-on and on-site training. Through a variety of delivery systems, tailored to fit customer needs, TEEX offers technical and vocational work force training, manufacturing and technical assistance and technology transfer services.

* Texas Manufacturing Assistance Center (TMAC)
Technology & Economic Development
Texas A&M University System
College Station, TX 77843-8000   409-862-1670
teex.cy-net.net/TMAC   800-625-4876
www.tmac.org
TMAC's mission is to improve the competitiveness of small Texas manufacturers by helping firms adopt state-of-the-art manufacturing technologies and techniques. TMAC offices are located throughout the region, providing a variety of services to small manufacturers

* Community Reinvestment Fund (CRF)
801 Nicollet Mall   612-338-3050
Suite 1700 West   800-475-3050
Minneapolis, MN 55402   Fax: 612-338-3236
www.crfusa.com/
CRF is a nonprofit organization that provides a secondary market for economic development loans. The fund buys loans from economic development organizations and uses them as collateral to sell bonds to private investors. It tailors each loan purchase to the needs of the client and has auxiliary services like loan servicing portfolio management and training.

* State Grants Team
P.O. Box 12428   512-463-8465
Austin, TX 78711   Fax: 512-936-2681
www.governor.state.tx.us/divisions/stategrants
The Grants Team provides: technical assistance and information about available federal, state and private grants, proposal writing support and review of applications and proposal writing training.

* Texas Business Incubator Association (TBIA)
9600 Long Point Road
Suite 150   713-932-7495, ext. 13
Houston, TX 77055   Fax: 713-932-7498
TBIA's mission is to advance the business incubator industry in Texas; to assist those communities and individuals seeking to open business incubators; to educate managers and operators of business incubators in methods of successfully growing small businesses; to educate those residents in business operations; to influence legislation favorable to small business incubators; and to assist the state of Texas and the United States in economic development and diversification.

* Texas Economic Development Council (TEDC)
1301 Nueces, Suite 101   512-480-8432
Austin, Texas 78701   Fax: 512-472-7907
www.texasedc.org
TEDC provides information, educational and legislative services to its 1,000 members. TEDC's objective is to expand existing industry, recruit new firms to the state and develop strategies that promote a positive business climate in Texas.

* Texas Rural Communities, Inc.
1524 South IH35, Suite 232   512-219-0468
Austin, TX 78704   Fax: 512-219-0416
www.texasrural.org
Texas Rural Communities, Inc. is a nonprofit organization serving rural Texas communities, individuals, groups and support organizations through rural economic development, educational, loan and grant programs.

* Texas Rural Development Council
Cheryl Hinckley, Executive Director
8140 Burnet Road
Suite 218   512-323-6515
Austin, TX 78757-7799   Fax: 512-323-6526
www.trdc.org
The Texas Rural Development Council matches the resources of the federal, state and local governments and the private sector - both profit and nonprofit - with locally conceived and driven development strategies.

* Center for Rural Health Initiatives
Office or Rural Community Affairs
1700 N. Congress Suite 220
Austin, TX 78701

Mailing Address:
P.O. Box 12877   512-936-6701
Austin, TX 78711   800-544-2042
www.orca.state.tx.us   512-936-6776

As the Texas State Office of Rural Health, the Center for Rural Health Initiatives administers programs and services designed to ensure health and well-being in rural communities throughout the state. The Center: provides funding opportunities; serves as a rural information clearinghouse; administers scholarship and loan repayment programs for healthcare professionals; provides a comprehensive service for recruitment and retention of healthcare providers by local communities; assists communities with assessments of health care delivery and availability; develops impact statements and policy development in an advocacy role; collaborates and partners with other state agencies and professional organizations and participates in national leadership roles.

* Texas Agriculture Finance Authority (TAFA)

Department of Agriculture
P.O. Box 12847   512-463-7476
Austin, TX 78711   Fax: 512-463-1104
www.agr.state.tx.us/eco/finance_ag_development

Linked Deposit Program: Available for non-traditional alternative crops, processing facilities for agricultural products, and direct marketing initiatives. Funds can be used to purchase or least land, buildings, equipment, seed, fertilizer, etc. Maximum loan is $100,000 for production, $250,000 for processing and marketing.

Texas Agricultural Finance Authority (TAFA
Loans, loan guarantees or revenue bonds available to small and medium size enterprises that contribute to the diversification of Texas agriculture. Funds can be used for fixed assets and working capital.

Young Farmer Loan Guarantee Program: TAFA provides financial assistance through loan guarantees to eligible applicants from 18 to 39 years of age who wish to establish or enhance their farm and/or ranch operation or establish an agricultural-related business. The program provides up to a 90 percent guarantee to a lender for an eligible applicant, not to exceed $250,000.

* Loans For Farmers

Farm Service Agency
U.S. Department of Agriculture
P.O. Box 2900
College Station, TX 77841-2900   979-680-5150
http://www.fsa.usda.gov/tx/Defaultx.asp

The Farm Service Agency provides Direct and Guaranteed Loans to farmers through a variety of programs, including:

Farm Ownership Loans: purchase farmland, construct or repair buildings and other fixtures, and promote soil and water conservation. Up to $200,000.

Operating Loans: purchase items needed for a successful farm operation, such as livestock, farm equipment, feed, seed, fuel, farm chemicals, insurance, and other operating expenses. Can also be used to pay for minor improvements. Up to $200,000.

Beginning Farmer and Rancher Loans: provides funds to beginning and farmers and ranchers who are unable to obtain financing elsewhere.

Downpayment Farm Ownership Loans for Beginning Farmers: helps beginning farmers and ranchers purchase a farm or ranch. Also provides a way for retiring farmers to transfer their land to a future generation of farmers and ranchers. Applicant must have a downpayment of 10% and FSA with finance 40%, with the remaining balance from a commercial lender. Purchase price cannot exceed $250,000.

Loans to Socially Disadvantaged Farmers/Ranchers: helps socially disadvantaged applicants buy and operate family-size farms and ranches.

Youth Loans: Made to youths to establish and operate income-producing projects with the participation in 4-H clubs, Future Farmers of America, and similar organizations. Up to $5,000.

Emergency Loan Assistance: provides loans to help producers recover from production and physical losses due to drought, flooding, and other natural disasters, or quarantine. Up to $500,000.

Beginning Farmer and Rancher Land Contract Guarantee Pilot Program: "prompt payment guarantee" from FSA. FSA will provide payment to seller two times if the beginning farmer does not pay. Program is tested in IN, IA, ND, OR, PA and WI.

Farm Ownership and Operating Loan Guarantees: FSA will guarantee loans up to $782,000.

* Small Business Administration (SBA)

4300 Amon Carter Blvd.   817-684-5500
Dallas/Fort Worth, TX 76155   Fax: 817-684-5516

10737 Gateway West   915-633-7001
El Paso, TX 79935   Fax: 915-633-7005

222 East Van Buren Street, Suite 500
Harlingen, TX 78550   956-427-8533

8701 S. Gessner Dr., Suite 1200   713-773-6500
Houston, TX 77074-1591   Fax: 713-773-6550

1205 Texas Avenue, Room 408   806-472-7462
Lubbock, TX. 79401-2693   Fax: 806-472-4787

17319 San Pedro, Suite 200   210-403-5900
San Antonio, TX 78232-1411   Fax: 210-403-5933

3649 Leopard Street, Suite 411
Corpus Christi, TX 78408   361-879-0017
www.sba.gov/tx

The Texas Small Business Administration Office delivers a variety of programs and services, such as startup and operational assistance through small business training and counseling, financial assistance for startup's, business opportunities and much more.

Utah

* Business and Economic Development Division

324 South State St., Suite 500   801-538-8700
Salt Lake City, UT 84111   Fax: 801-538-8889
http://dced.utah.gov

Business and Economic Development Division: Provides

information on regulations, sources of assistance, and other important information for starting a business.

Short Term Intensive Training (STIT): Programs are customized and designed to meet full-time job openings. Programs are usually less than one year in length and will be designed to meet the specific training needs of a company while matching needs with people seeking employment. Although potential employees must pay tuition to participate, STIT can provide qualified employees from which a company can hire. STIT gives the option of training at 50% - 70% discount of normal training costs. Funding for this program is distributed to State Colleges.

Job Service: A computerized job matching system that quickly screens applicants to ensure that they meet the qualifications set by a company. Over 16,000 active applicants are presently registered with the Salt Lake Office. Job Service personnel can save countless hours by taking all of company applications and then referring only the most qualified applicants.

Centers of Excellence Program: Supports selected research programs at Utah's universities. Programs are selected based on leading edge research activities that have projected commercial value. The primary objective is to encourage the commercialization of leading edge technologies through licensing patented technologies and by creating new companies. The Centers of Excellence Program impacts Utah's economic development by the creation of jobs, the flow of licensing royalties, the expansion of the tax base, and the leveraged use of matching fund dollars to strengthen research and development at Utah's institutions of higher learning.

Utah Directory of Business and Industry: A listing of more than 9,800 individual employers sorted by Standard Industrial Classification (SIC), which is a standard method for classifying what businesses or other organizations do.

Revolving Loan Funds: In an effort to create jobs and improve the business climate of a community, some cities, counties, and Associations of Governments (geographical regions) will lend money to small businesses located in their areas. The amount available to a business goes from a few thousand dollars to over $100,000. Typically, the money is used for plant and equipment, working capital, inventory or accounts receivable financing. Rates are usually less than or equal to conventional lender financing, and the term for repayment may be either short (6 months) or extended (many years). This type of financing is often used in conjunction with other lender financing since most revolving loan programs will accept a second or third position on financed assets.

Industrial Assistance Fund: Can be used for relocation costs. This incentive loan can be repaid as Utah jobs created meet the IAF requirements resulting in higher quality jobs, and as Utah purchases merit enough earned credits to convert the loan to a grant. Three basic programs exist: 1) rural Utah program with funding up to $100,000 for relocation expenses; 2) Corporate Funding which is dependent on the amount of Utah purchases and wages: 3) Targeted Industries which is primarily aimed at information technology, biomedical and aerospace.

Industrial Development Bonds (IDB's): A financing tool used by private sector developers for manufacturing facilities. The federal tax code places a limit of $10.0 million per project on IDB financing.

International Business Development Office: Programs offered include:
- Trade Representatives
- Country Information
- Market Research Reports
- Trade Lead Resource Center
- Foreign Business Directories
- Trade Shows and Exhibits

Offices of Ethnic Affairs: Recognizing that state government should be responsive to all citizens, and wishing to promote cooperation and understanding between government agencies and its ethnic citizens, these offices were created:
- Office Of Asian Affairs
- Office Of Black Affairs
- Office Of Hispanic Affairs
- Office Of Pacific Island Affairs
- Division of Indian Affairs

Minority and Women Owned Business Source Directory: Offered by the Utah PTAC (Procurement Technical Assistance Center). The directory includes approximately 850 companies, and is the most complete such listing available. However, listings are voluntary, having been obtained through surveys, and this is not to be construed as a comprehensive catalog. There are some 4,400 minority-owned employers in the state, and 46,000 that are women-owned.

Utah Technology Alliance: The Utah Technology Alliance acts as a bridge between the high tech business community and Utah State Government. Its goal is to position Utah as the location of choice to grow and nurture high tech companies.

* Custom Fit Training
Utah College of Applied Technology Central Administration
Board of Regents Building, The Gateway
60 South 400 West   801-321-7183
Salt Lake City, UT 84101-1284   Fax: 801-366-8480
www.ucats.org/aboutcustomfit.html

Provides training for new or expanding companies. A Custom Fit representative will discuss with the company the training needs anticipated and then develop a specific customized training plan to meet those needs. The required training can take place at a variety of locations including the business or a local institution. Often training is provided in both locations. The program can provide instructors from the State's learning institutions, private sector, consultants or instructors within the business. The program is designed to be flexible to meet the specific needs of the company.

* Utah Partners in Education
324 South State St., Suite 500   801-538-8628
Salt Lake City, UT 84111   Fax: 801-538-8888
www.utahpartnership.utah.org

Facilitates business/ education/ government partnerships statewide. Purpose is to find ways in which those three entities can work together to meet common needs and thereby strengthen the economy of Utah.

* Utah Ventures
2755 E. Cottonwood Parkway, Suite 520   801-365-0262
Salt Lake City, UT 84121   Fax: 801-365-0233

www.utahventures.com/

Utah Ventures: a privately financed venture fund focusing on investments in the life sciences and information technology in Utah, other Intermountain states and California. Utah Ventures seeks to identify the best opportunities, secure subsequent coinvestments from other venture funds and corporate investors, and works with the entrepreneur to help build the business.

* Utah Microenterprise Loan Fund

3595 S. Main St.
Salt Lake City, UT 84115   801-269-8408
www.umlf.com   Fax: 801-269-1063

Microenterprise Loan Fund (UMLF) is a tax-exempt, nonprofit corporation. It provides a modestly secured form of financing up to $10,000, with terms up to five years, to owners of startup and existing firms who do not have access to traditional funding sources, especially those who are socially or economically disadvantaged. The interest rate is prime plus 3% fixed, and the business must be located in Salt Lake County.

* Utah Technology Finance Corporation (UTFC)

699 East South Temple
Suite 220   801-741-4200
Salt Lake City, UT 84102   Fax: 801-741-4249
www.utfc.org

The Utah Technology Finance Corporation is an independent corporation of the state that makes debt investments in Utah companies. UTFC leverages state and federal funds as a catalyst in capital formation for the creations, growth, and success of Utah Businesses. UTFC offers various types of debt financing through such programs as Early Technology Business Capital, Utah Rural Loan Program, MicroLoan Program, Utah Revolving Loan Fund, Bank Participation Loan Program, and Defense Conversion Loan Program.

* State Tax Commission

210 North 1950 West   800-662-4335
Salt Lake City, UT 84134   801-297-2200
www.incometax.utah.gov   Fax: 801-297-7574

One-Stop Service Center: You can register a business name, file Articles of Incorporation, obtain application for State Sales Tax License and State and Federal Tax Identification Numbers, file a Status Report with the Department of Employment Security, and apply for State Workers' Compensation Insurance. A *Going Into Business Workbook* is also available which includes all the forms and instructions necessary to do any of these activities.

* Mountain West Venture Group (MWVG)

c/o John M. Knab
6952 South High Tech Drive
Suite A   801-984-5103
Midvale, UT 84047-3756   Fax: 801-566-0880
www.mwvgutah100.org

The Mountain West Venture Group is a nonprofit organization that identifies, monitors, and recognizes "deal flow" within the state of Utah. Through the exchange of ideas, services, and acquaintances, the Group seeks to foster the investment of risk funds. Along with a monthly meeting, a monthly newsletter, and the Utah Deal Flow book, the MWVG hosts an annual awards luncheon that identifies and recognizes Utah's 100 fastest growing companies.

* Utah Information Technologies Association (UITA)

2825 E. Cottonwood Parkway
Suite 460   801-568-3500
Salt Lake City, UT 84121   Fax: 801-568-1072
www.uita.org

UITA is an industry association that represents and provides services to Utah's Information Technology (IT) vendors. UITA assists IT vendors with networking, opportunities to learn and market, saving money through group discounts, and other means.

* Utah Small Cities, Inc.

324 South State Street
Suite 500   801-538-8821
Salt Lake City, UT 84111   Fax: 801-538-8889
http://utahreach.usu.edu/rosie/usci

Aids in the recruitment and expansion of businesses in the rural areas of Utah. Responds to requests for information.

* Utah Supplier Development Council

U of U Purchasing Department
151 Annex Building   801-581-8169
Salt Lake City, UT, 84112   Fax: 801-581-8609
www.usdcutah.com

A purchasing council made up of major Utah firms that specifically look for small businesses owned by minorities and women to be suppliers for the Council. The Council also prints a directory of these businesses.

* Business Information Center

310 South Main Street
North Mezzanine   801-746-2269
Salt Lake City, UT 84101   Fax: 801-746-2273
www.utahbic.org

The Business Information Center (BIC) is a library of electronic and hard copy resources available to existing businesses and individuals seeking information on starting a business. The center provides SCORE counseling, training, and access to computers, business software, and video tapes.

* Utah Business Resource Network (UBRN)

SBDC State Director Michael C. Finnerty
1623 South State Street   801-957-3480
Salt Lake City, UT 84115   888-599-UBRN
www.utah.gov/business

The Small Business Development Center is in partnership with the Utah Business Resource Network. The UBRN provides experts in many fields, including finance, marketing, engineering, manufacturing, contracting, and minority owned businesses. The statewide network makes it easy to put together the team, information and resources that will make your business grow.

* Bureau of Economic and Business Research

David Eccles School of Business
University of Utah
1645 E. Campus Center Drive
Room 401   801-581-6333
Salt Lake City, UT 84112-9302 Fax: 801-581-3354
www.business.utah.edu/BEBR

Maintains a comprehensive and timely information base on the Utah and Rocky Mountain regional economies and uses computer models for data analysis. Periodicals include: Utah

Economic and Business Review, featuring articles on economic development with monthly selected business statistics; Utah Construction Report reporting statistics on construction permits in Utah; Utah Statistical Abstract

* Business Workshops

Taxpayer Education Coordinator
Internal Revenue Service
50 South 200 East
Salt Lake City UT 84111
801-799-6874
800-829-1040
http://tax.utah.gov/business/resources.html

The Utah State Tax Commission, Internal Revenue Service, State Industrial Commission, Worker's Compensation, and the Utah Department of Employment Security jointly sponsor a one day Employment Tax Workshop to provide information and answer questions about employment and other tax requirements for businesses. The seminars are free and scheduled monthly in Salt Lake City. During the summer months, the workshops are available in Ogden, Provo, and St. George. Other specialized education programs are available for partnerships and corporations through the IRS Small Business Tax Education Program (STEP).

* Loans For Farmers

Farm Service Agency
U.S. Department of Agriculture
125 South State Street, Room 3202
Salt Lake City, UT 84138
801-524-4530
Fax: 801-524-5244
http://www.fsa.usda.gov/ut/

The Farm Service Agency provides Direct and Guaranteed Loans to farmers through a variety of programs, including:

Farm Ownership Loans: purchase farmland, construct or repair buildings and other fixtures, and promote soil and water conservation. Up to $200,000.

Operating Loans: purchase items needed for a successful farm operation, such as livestock, farm equipment, feed, seed, fuel, farm chemicals, insurance, and other operating expenses. Can also be used to pay for minor improvements. Up to $200,000.

Beginning Farmer and Rancher Loans: provides funds to beginning and farmers and ranchers who are unable to obtain financing elsewhere.

Downpayment Farm Ownership Loans for Beginning Farmers: helps beginning farmers and ranchers purchase a farm or ranch. Also provides a way for retiring farmers to transfer their land to a future generation of farmers and ranchers. Applicant must have a downpayment of 10% and FSA with finance 40%, with the remaining balance from a commercial lender. Purchase price cannot exceed $250,000.

Loans to Socially Disadvantaged Farmers/Ranchers: helps socially disadvantaged applicants buy and operate family-size farms and ranches.

Youth Loans: Made to youths to establish and operate income-producing projects with the participation in 4-H clubs, Future Farmers of America, and similar organizations. Up to $5,000.

Emergency Loan Assistance: provides loans to help producers recover from production and physical losses due to drought, flooding, and other natural disasters, or quarantine. Up to $500,000.

Beginning Farmer and Rancher Land Contract Guarantee Pilot Program: "prompt payment guarantee" from FSA. FSA will provide payment to seller two times if the beginning farmer does not pay. Program is tested in IN, IA, ND, OR, PA and WI.

Farm Ownership and Operating Loan Guarantees: FSA will guarantee loans up to $782,000.

* Small Business Administration (SBA)

Salt Lake District Office
125 South State St., Room 2227
Salt Lake City, UT 84138-1195
801-524-3209
Fax: 801-524-4160
www.sba.gov/ut

The Utah Small Business Administration Office delivers a variety of programs and services, such as startup and operational assistance through small business training and counseling, financial assistance for startup's, business opportunities and much more.

* Industrial Assistance Fund

324 S. State St., Suite 500
Salt Lake City, UT 84111
801-538-8698
Fax: 801-538-8888
http://dced.utah.gov/iaf/index.html

The Industrial Assistance Fund's mission is to expand the number of high paying jobs and increase in-state purchase of supplies.

* Small Business Assistance Program

Department of Environmental Quality
168 N. 1950 West
P.O. Box 144810-4810
Salt Lake City, UT 84116
800-270-4440
801-536-4400
Fax: 801-536-4401
http://airquality.utah.gov/PERMITS/psba.htm

The Clean Air Act Amendments of 1990 required that all States develop a program to assist small businesses in meeting the requirements of the Act. Since then, these programs have expanded to provide assistance in other environmental areas, including water and waste issues. EPA has established its own Small Business Assistance Program (SBAP) to provide technical assistance to these State small business programs.

* Utah Energy Office

Utah Energy Office
1594 West North Temple, Suite 3610
P.O. Box 146480
Salt Lake City, UT 84114-6480
801-538-5428
800-662-3633

The Utah Energy Office promotes energy efficiency in Utah. They provide businesses with information, research, technical assistance, energy-related policy analysis and access to federal or state programs.

* Venture Capital Programs

Wayne Brown Institute
175 West 200 South, Suite 4002
P.O. Box 2135
Salt Lake City, UT 84110-2135
801-595-1411
Fax: 801-595-1181
www.venturecapital.org

The institute seeks to assist worthy early-state technology based companies raise capital, form partnerships, and strategic alliances for the purpose of creating new wealth, jobs, and tax base.

* Rural Development Office

Wallace F. Bennett Federal Building
125 South State Street, Room 4311   801-524-4320
Salt Lake City, UT 84138   Fax: 801-524-4406
www.rurdev.usda.gov/ut

Business & Industry Loan Guaranteed Loan Program: The Guaranteed Business and Industry loan program guarantee loans to quality businesses that support a diversified economic base and provide or save quality jobs in rural areas.

Intermediary Relending Program: Lenders utilize these funds to obtain low interest capital to make loans up to $250,000 to rural businesses.

Rural Economic Development Loan and Grant Program: his program provides loan to utility companies to promote rural economic development and job creation.

Rural Business Enterprise Grant Program: Funds may be used by rural public bodies, private nonprofit organizations and federally recognized Native American tribes to provide technical assistance to small and emerging businesses, purchase machinery or equipment, construct business incubators or buildings that will be leased to small and emerging businesses.

Rural Business Opportunity Grant: These grants may be used by rural public bodies, nonprofit organizations, cooperatives, and federally recognized Native American tribes to promote economic growth in depressed rural areas.

Value-Added Agricultural Producer Grant Program: These grant funds may be used by eligible producers of agricultural commodities, agricultural producer groups, farmer and rancher cooperatives, and majority-owned producer-based business ventures to plan or implement sales of agricultural products into emerging markets.

Rural Cooperative Development Grants: Rural Cooperative Development Grant funds may be used by selected nonprofit corporations or institutions of higher education to establish and operate centers for rural cooperative development which will facilitate the development of new cooperative, value-added processing and rural businesses that create or retain jobs in rural areas.

Rural Energy Systems & Energy Efficiency Improvements Program: Agricultural producers and small rural businesses with financial need can use these program to obtain matching grant funding up to $500,000 to purchase alternative energy systems or up to $250,000 to make energy efficiency improvements.

Vermont

* Vermont Department of Economic Development

National Life Building, Drawer 20   802-828-3080
Montpelier, VT 05620-0501   800-341-2211
www.thinkvermont.com   Fax: 802-828-3258

A one-stop shop ready to help with businesses to support the economic growth of the state through job creation and retention. Areas in which the Department can assist Vermont businesses are entrepreneurs; international trade; financing; government contracts, marketing; permits; site location; and training.

Regional Development Corporations: Twelve RDCs serve every geographic region of the state serving as satellites of the Department of Economic Development, and provide many of the same services. Their primary function is to coordinate job and business development activities within their geographic region.

Business Assistance Network: An accessible series of resources designed to provide timely and pertinent information to businesses interested in participating in new markets for their products or services, increasing competitiveness, or building "teaming arrangements" with other businesses. The information may be accessed through the Internet at {www.state.vt.us}.

Government Marketing Assistance Center: Exists to design, implement, and maintain resources that promote economic expansion by providing assistance to Vermont businesses' which allow them to pursue and compete in the public procurement process and introduce them to new markets for their goods and/or services. The GMAC can provide a business with a customized search to receive Federal bid opportunities, including bids available through Electronic Data Interchange (EDI). A business must be registered to receive Federal Bids opportunities.

Vermont Business Registry: An on-line registry of businesses throughout Vermont involved in manufacturing, manufacturing support, product distribution, services, research and development, and construction. {www.vermontbusinessregistry.com}

Vermont Bid Opportunities: An electronic resource which provides businesses with a current listing of bid opportunities available through Vermont based federal, state and local governments and by the private sector purchasing organizations. {www.vermontbidsystem.com}

Business Calendar of Events: Lists business assistance seminars, training workshops, trade shows, etc., which are sponsored by various organizations.

The Vermonter's Guide to Doing Business: Provides information relating to public and private institutions that can assist local businesses on any aspect of successful business operation.

Department of Employment and Training: Offers a full range of workforce-related services and information through a network of 12 One-Stop Career Resource Centers. Contact {www.det.state.vt.us).

Regional/Local Revolving Loan Funds: Existing through the state, the administration of these funds is generally a nonprofit development corporation.

Business and Industrial Loan Guarantees: Designed to serve the credit needs of large rural businesses. Emphasis is placed on loan guarantees between $500,000 and $3 million, but may be issued up to $10 million.

Business and Industry Direct Loans: A limited amount of funding is available for direct business loans in designated areas of economic distress. The program is targeting loans in the $100,000 to $250,000 range.

Intermediary Relending Program: Designed to finance small and emerging business and community development projects in rural areas. Loans are made to qualified intermediaries who in turn relend to small businesses and community development organizations. Business or organizations borrowing from the intermediary must be located in a rural area. The maximum loan to an intermediary is $2 million and the maximum loan that the intermediary can relend for a project is $150,000.

Rural Business Enterprise Grant: Provides grants to public bodies and nonprofit corporations for the benefit of small and emerging businesses. Grant funds may be used to establish revolving loan funds, construct facilities, provide planning, or technical assistance.

VEDA Export Financing: In addition to the Export Working Capital Guarantee Program, VEDA offers a number of other loan and insurance programs for Vermont's exporting community. This includes small business credit insurance, and environmental exports program, and export credit insurance short-term multi-buyer policy, and a medium-term single-buyer policy.

Vermont Training Program: The Vermont Training Program promotes industrial expansion and encourages the creation and retention of jobs by providing training for new and existing businesses.

Reach Up Program: This is Vermont's welfare-to-work program which helps welfare recipients access education, vocational training and job placement.

Micro Business Development Program: The Micro Business Development Program promotes self-employment and business opportunities for low income Vermonters. They offer free one-on-one technical assistance, business planning classes, workshops and assistance.

Workplace Literacy and Youth Apprenticeship: Programs provide businesses with the opportunity to update the basic skills of their workforce and to enable vocational/technical students the opportunity to gain work experience.

Women's Small Business Program: Women's Small Business Program through Trinity College offers several services including:
- Getting Serious- A workshop to determine a business idea and whether a business meets personal goals.
- Start-Up: A 15-week intensive course to develop a business plan.
- Working Solutions: Topic specific workshops for micro-business owners.

Vermont Businesses for Social Responsibility: "The Livable Jobs Toolkit" is a hands-on tool for businesses interested in attracting and keeping employees. It features innovative ways to compensate employees and implement workplace practices in businesses.

Direct Loans: VEDA can provide direct loans to eligible facilities for the acquisition of land, buildings and improvements, machinery and equipment.

Financial Access Program: The Vermont Financial Access Program utilizes a "pooled reserve" concept to enhance opportunities for small businesses to access commercial credit.

Small Business Development Corporation: The Vermont Small Business Development Corporation makes loans to low to moderate Vermont business owners.

Industrial Revenue Bonds (IRBs): VEDA issues bonds to businesses eligible for tax-exempt financing. Funds can be used for the acquisition of land, buildings and improvements, or machinery and equipment.

Rural Economic Activity Loans (REAL): REAL provides low interest direct loans for fixed asset financing and for funding inventory and accounts receivable growth through the REAL program. Loan amounts of up to 75% of the fixed projects costs which are under $25,000 and up to 40% of projects which are over $25,000.

Vermont Agricultural Credit Corporation: VEDA provides loans and refinancing for family farms or agricultural facility operators.

Vermont Job Start: Job Start helps develop self-employment opportunities for low and moderate income Vermonters. Loans can be used to start, strengthen or expand small businesses.

* Women's Small Business Program
Trinity College
208 Colchester Ave.
Burlington, VT 05401   802-846-7339
www.trinityvt.edu/WSBP.htm

Offers a continuum of services to women seeking to identify, start, stabilize and expand a small business. Services include: Getting Serious, a workshop to determine a business idea and whether business meets personal goals; Start-Up, a 15 week intensive course to develop a business plan and business management skills; Working Solution, topic specific workshops for micro-business owner; and a graduate association to foster ongoing networking and access to information. They also offer comprehensive skills training and the opportunity to connect with other women entrepreneurs. Grants and scholarships for training are available to income eligible women.

* Vermont Manufacturing Extension Center
VT Technical College
P.O. Box 12   800-MEP-4MFG
Randolph Center, VT 05061-0500   802-728-1432
www.vmec.org   Fax: 802-728-1456

Provides one-on-one support and services through Field Engineers to small and mid-sized manufacturers. Their goal is to assist Vermont manufacturers increase productivity, modernize processes, and improve their competitiveness. Ongoing training opportunities designed specifically for manufacturers are also offered.

* Agricultural Marketing
Department of Agriculture
Development Division
116 State St., Drawer 20   802-828-2416
Montpelier, VT 05620   Fax: 802-828-3831
www.vermontagriculture.com/develop.htm

Provides resource for the promotion of various agricultural projects and works with commodity groups to improve market opportunities. Marketing representatives help with promotion, marketing, packaging, support publications, etc.

* Vermont Economic Development Authority
58 E. State St., Suite 5
Montpelier, VT 05602   802-828-5627
www.veda.org

Small Business Development Corporation: A nonprofit

corporation offering loans up to $100,000 to assist growing Vermont small businesses who cannot access conventional sources of credit. Funds may be used to finance the acquisition of fixed assets or for working capital with restrictions.

Job Start Program: Helps develop self-employment opportunities for low and moderate income Vermonters through loans used to start, strengthen or expand small businesses. Funds may be used to purchase equipment, inventory or for working capital.

Financial Access Program: Designed to enhance opportunities for small businesses to access commercial credit utilizing a pooled reserve concept. Loans must be in an amount up to and including $200,000 made to businesses with sales less than $5 million.

Mortgage Insurance Program: Designed to aid businesses by insuring loans made by commercial banks. Proceeds may be used to insure loans made for the acquisition of land, buildings, machinery and equipment or working capital, for use in an eligible facility. Maximum is $2 million per project.

Local Development Corporation Loans: Loans to nonprofit local development corporations are available through VEDA-s Subchapter 3 program. "Spec" buildings and incubators can provided low cost, flexible leased space for businesses which prefer not to own their own facility. Loan proceeds may be used for the purchase of land for industrial parks, industrial park planning and development, and the construction or improvement of speculative buildings or small business incubator facilities.

Industrial Revenue Bonds: Designed to aid businesses through VEDA's issuance of tax-exempt, low interest bonds to provide funds for the acquisition of land, buildings, and/or machinery and equipment for use in a manufacturing facility.

Direct Loan Program: Designed to finance the establishment or expansion of eligible facilities through the acquisition, construction and installation of fixed assets. Provides attractive variable rate loans to business for the purchase of land, the purchase or construction (including renovation) of buildings, and the purchase and installation of machinery and equipment for use in an eligible facility.

* Vermont Sustainable Jobs Fund, Inc.

61 Elm St.   802-828-5320
Montpelier, VT 05602   Fax: 802-223-2336
www.vsif.org

The goal of the fund is to develop and support projects throughout the State leading to the creation or retention of quality jobs, and the protection and enhancement of Vermont's human and natural resources. Grants and technical assistance will be available for collaborative activity including the development of flexible manufacturing networks, business clusters, and networks. A specific area of focus will be adding value to agricultural products that use the natural resource of grass.

* Vermont World Trade Office

National Life Building
6th Floor, Drawer 20   802-828-1175
Montpelier, VT 05620   Fax: 802-828-3258

60 Main Street, Suite 102   802-865-0493
Burlington, VT 05401   877-VTXPORT

www.vermontworldtrade.org

Assists businesses wishing to export their products and services, to expand by developing sales in new markets, and by encouraging suitable foreign companies to establish operations within the state.

* The Women's Agricultural Network

Women's Agricultural Network
617 Comstock Road, Suite 5   802-223-2389
Berlin, VT 05602   Fax: 802-223-6500
www.uvm.edu/~wagn

The Women's Agricultural Network (WAgN) is a collaborative effort of the UVM Extension System, the Women's Small Business Program (WSBP), and the UVM Center for Sustainable Agriculture. Their mission is to assist individuals interested in starting or expanding a farm or agriculture-related business. WAgN provides education, technical assistance, and networking opportunities for each step along the business development continuum. From developing the idea through the planning and implementation phases, the Women's Agricultural Network has a program to meet client's needs.

* Vermont Telecom Advancement Center

163 South Willard Street   802-865-6448
Burlington, VT 05401   Fax: 802-860-2759
www.vtac.org;

VTAC's mission is to introduce users to workable and achievable solutions designed within the field of telecommunications. The goals are to educate small business owners, entrepreneurs, nonprofit organizations, and educators concerning the latest available technology, products and services available in Vermont; to place interested users in touch with advanced users, vendors and consultants who can aid in facilitating telecom usage, and to provide a neutral source of information serving state government and legislators.

* The North Atlantic Venture Fund II

The Vermont Venture Capital Fund, L.P.
76 St. Paul Street   802-658-7840
Burlington, VT 05401   Fax: 802-658-5757

The North Atlantic Venture Fund II is managed by North Atlantic Venture Capital Corporation, which, through affiliate funds, has a total of $40 million in venture capital under management. The fund is a private enterprise that seeks to invest from $100,000 to $750,000 in high-quality opportunities that have outgrown seed capital resources and are either not ready for or have exceeded the limits of commercial bank lending resources. Investments are made based on estimated return on investment.

* Vermont Community Loan Fund

P.O. Box 827
15 State St.   802-223-1448
Montpelier, VT 05601   Fax: 802-223-1455
Email: VCLF@VCLF.org.
www.vclf.org

Vermont Community Loan Fund is a statewide nonprofit, private community development financial institution. It strengthens Vermont's communities by promoting equitable access to capital through two loan funds:

Enterprise Fund: The Enterprise fund provides critical funding primarily to businesses, which use Vermont's natural resources and/or are agricultural-based.

Building Community Fund: The Building Community Fund provides funding to create or preserve affordable housing and community-based services, such as child and elder care, women's centers, and elderly housing, and community facilities.

Loans are accompanied by technical assistance designed to help borrowers achieve their goals. Through its services and projects, the VCLF serves low and moderate income Vermonters. VCLF also enables individual investors, contributors, corporations and foundations to use their money for positive social purposes.

Building Bright Futures Fund: The Building Bright Future Fund assists new and existing child care and youth programs to expand quality child care. This grant resource is available to start, relocate, expand or improve the physical facility.

Business Loan Program: Loans of up to $250,000 for entrepreneurs, who increase economic opportunities for low-income or underemployed Vermonters, create or save jobs or add value to Vermont's agricultural or natural resources economy.

Child Care Loan Program: The Child Care Loan Program is available to profit and nonprofit childcare providers in Vermont, including home-based facilities. The loans are available to finance major improvements, licensing requirements, renovations and materials or equipment purchases.

* Regional Development Corporations

Addison County Economic Development Corp.
1590 US Route 7S, Suite 3   802-388-7953
Middlebury, VT 05753   Fax: 802-388-0119
www.addisoncountyedc.org

Bennington County Industrial Corp.
P.O. Box 357   802-442-8975
No. Bennington, VT 05257   Fax: 802-477-1101
www.bcic.org

Brattleboro Development Credit Corp.
76 Cotton Mill Hill   802-257-7731
Brattleboro, VT 05301   Fax: 802-257-0294
www.brattleborodevelopment.com

Central Vermont Economic Development Corp.
P.O. Box 1439   802-223-4654
Montpelier, VT 05601   Fax: 802-223-4655
www.central-vt.com/cvedc

Franklin County Industrial Development Corp.
163 N. Main St.
P.O. Box 1099   802-524-2194
St. Albans, VT 05478-1099   Fax: 802-524-6793
www.fcidc.com

Greater Burlington Industrial Corp.
60 Main St., Suite 101
P.O. Box 786   802-562-5726
Burlington, VT 05402-0786   Fax: 802-860-1899
www.vermont.org/gbic

Green Mountain Economic Development Corp.
P.O. Box 246.   802-295-3710
White River Junction, VT 05001   Fax: 802-295-3779
www.gmedc.org

Lake Champlain Island Chamber of Commerce
P.O. Box 213   802-372-8400
North Hero, VT 05474   Fax: 802-372-5107
www.champlainislands.com

Lamoille Industrial Development Corp.
P.O. Box 455   802-888-5640
Morrisville, VT 05661   Fax: 802-888-7612
www.lamoilleeconomy.org

Northeastern Vermont Development Association.
P.O. Box 640   802-748-5181
St. Johnsbury, VT 05819   Fax: 802-748-1223
www.nvda.net

Rutland Economic Development Corp.
110 Merchants Row
4th Floor, Suite 3.   802-773-9147
Rutland, VT 05701-5918   Fax: 802-773-8009
www.rutlandecomony.com

Springfield Regional Development Corp.
14 Clinton St.   802-885-3061
Springfield, VT 05156   Fax: 802-885-3027
www.springfielddevelopment.org

* Northern Community Investment Corporation (NCIC)

P.O. Box 904
347 Portland St.   802-748-5101
St. Johnsbury, VT 05819   Fax: 802-748-1884
www.ncic.org

A private, nonprofit, community-based corporation that assists development in Vermont and northern New Hampshire. The NCIC provides capital and professional assistance to both small and large businesses and community development projects. Some of its services include: personalized technical assistance, direct financing of $500,000 or more, attracting outside capital to supplement its own resources in order to expand its investments, developing industrial space for new or expanding businesses, and investment in residential and commercial development.

* Loans For Farmers

Farm Service Agency
U.S. Department of Agriculture
356 Mountain View Drive, Suite 104   802-658-203
Colchester, VT 05446   Fax: 802-660-0953
http://www.fsa.usda.gov/vt/

The Farm Service Agency provides Direct and Guaranteed Loans to farmers through a variety of programs, including:

Farm Ownership Loans: purchase farmland, construct or repair buildings and other fixtures, and promote soil and water conservation. Up to $200,000.

Operating Loans: purchase items needed for a successful farm operation, such as livestock, farm equipment, feed, seed, fuel, farm chemicals, insurance, and other operating expenses. Can also be used to pay for minor improvements. Up to $200,000.

Beginning Farmer and Rancher Loans: provides funds to beginning and farmers and ranchers who are unable to obtain financing elsewhere.

Downpayment Farm Ownership Loans for Beginning Farmers: helps beginning farmers and ranchers purchase a farm or ranch. Also provides a way for retiring farmers to transfer their land to a future generation of farmers and ranchers. Applicant must have a downpayment of 10% and FSA with finance 40%, with the remaining balance from a commercial lender. Purchase price cannot exceed $250,000.

Loans to Socially Disadvantaged Farmers/Ranchers: helps socially disadvantaged applicants buy and operate family-size farms and ranches.

Youth Loans: Made to youths to establish and operate income-producing projects with the participation in 4-H clubs, Future Farmers of America, and similar organizations. Up to $5,000.

Emergency Loan Assistance: provides loans to help producers recover from production and physical losses due to drought, flooding, and other natural disasters, or quarantine. Up to $500,000.

Beginning Farmer and Rancher Land Contract Guarantee Pilot Program: "prompt payment guarantee" from FSA. FSA will provide payment to seller two times if the beginning farmer does not pay. Program is tested in IN, IA, ND, OR, PA and WI.

Farm Ownership and Operating Loan Guarantees: FSA will guarantee loans up to $782,000.

* Small Business Administration (SBA)

87 State St., Room 205   802-828-4422
Montpelier, VT 05601   Fax: 802-828-4485
www.sba.gov/vt

The Vermont Small Business Administration Office delivers a variety of programs and services, such as startup and operational assistance through small business training and counseling, financial assistance for startup's, business opportunities and much more.

* Northeast Employment and Training Organization (NETO)

P.O. Box 186
17 Center St.   802-748-8935
St. Johnsbury, VT 05819   Fax; 802-748-8936
http://vt-neto.org
or
P.O. Box 584
Ridgeview 91 Bldg.   802-334-7378
Newport, VT 05855   Fax: 802-334-8148

NETO manages the Entrepreneurial Training Program which provides statewide small business management curses to enterprises of all sizes, including individuals interested in self-employment and microbusinesses. Services are available free to certain income eligible persons as well as on a fee basis.

* Micro Business Development Program (MBDP)

Statewide Facilitator, Bruce Whitney
P.O. Box 437   802-387-5029
Putney, VT 05346   Fax: 802-387-5029
www.vtmicrobusiness.org

Central Vermont Community Action Council, Inc.
195 Route 302 Berlin   800-639-1053
Barre, VT 05641   802-479-1053
Email: cflint@cvcac.org   Fax: 802-479-5353

Area of Operation: Orange, Washington and Lamoille Counties

Champlain Valley Office of Economic Opportunity
431 Pine St.   800-287-7971
Burlington, VT 05401   802-860-1417
Email: mbdp@cvoeo.org   Fax: 802-860-1387
Area of Operation: Addison, Chittenden, Grand Isle and Franklin Counties

Community Action in Southwestern Vermont
60 Center St.   800-717-2762
Rutland, VT 05701   802-775-0878
Email: mrock@broc.org   Fax: 802-775-9949
Area of Operation: Rutland and Bennington Counties

Northeast Kingdom Community Action
108 Cherry Street St.   800-639-4065
Johnsbury, VT 05819   802-748-6048
Email: mbdp@nekca.org   Fax: 802-748-0732
Area of Operation: Caledonia, Orleans and Essex Counties

Southeastern Vermont Community Action
91 Buck Drive   800-464-9951
Westminster, VT 05158   802-722-4575
Email: jjuhasz@sevca.org   Fax: 802-722-4509

MBDP promotes self-employment and business expansion opportunities for low income Vermonters. MBDP offers free one-to-one technical assistance and business development workshops for income eligible persons. Specials work in the regional Community Action Program (CAP) agencies listed above.

* Department of Housing and Community Affairs

Vermont Community Development Program (VCDP)
National Life Bldg., Drawer 20   802-828-3211
Montpelier, VT 05620-0501   800-622-4553
www.dhca.state.vt.us   Fax: 802-828-2928

VCDP funds can be used for a wide range of economic development activities such as loans to businesses for capital equipment or real property acquisition, or to assist in the construction of infrastructure improvements such as water and sewer lines.

* Department of Public Service

Utility Demand-Side Management Programs
112 State St., Drawer 20   802-828-2811
Montpelier, VT 05620-2601   Fax: 802-828-2342
www.state.vt.us/psd

Individual Vermont utilities have developed energy efficient and/or energy conservation programs providing technical and financial assistance. In some cases, utilities actually invest along with companies, in energy-saving technology.

* Rural Development Service

89 Main St.
City Center, 3rd Floor   802-828-6010
Montpelier, VT 05602   Fax: 802-828-6076
www.rurdev.usda.gov/vt

Business & Industry Guaranteed Loans: The Business and Industry Guaranteed Loan Program helps create jobs and stimulates rural economies by providing financial backing for rural businesses. This program provides guarantees up to 90 percent of a loan made by a commercial lender. Loan proceeds may be used for working capital, machinery and equipment, buildings and real estate, and certain types of debt refinancing.

Cooperative Services Program: Cooperative Services Program is to promote understanding and use of the cooperative form of business as a viable organizational option for marketing and distributing agricultural products.

Intermediary Relending Program: The purpose of the Intermediary Relending Program is to finance business facilities and community development projects in rural areas. This is achieved through loans made by the Rural Business-Cooperative Service to intermediaries. Intermediaries re-lend funds to ultimate recipients for business facilities or community development.

Rural Business-Cooperative Service: The Rural Business-Cooperative Service makes grants under the Rural Business Enterprise Grants Program to public bodies, private nonprofit corporations, and Indian Tribal groups to finance and facilitate development of small and emerging private business enterprises located in areas with population of less than 50,000. The public bodies, private nonprofit corporations and Indian tribes receive the grant to assist a business. Grant funds do not go directly to the business.

Rural Economic Development Loans: This program provides zero-interest loans to electric and telephone utilities to promote sustainable rural economic development and job creation projects.

Rural Economic Development Grants: This program provides grants to electric and telephone utilities to promote sustainable rural economic development and job creation projects through the operation of a revolving loan fund program.

Rural Business Opportunity Grants: The purpose of this program is to provide sustainable economic development in rural communities with exceptional needs. This is accomplished by making grants to pay costs of providing economic planning for rural communities, technical assistance for rural businesses, or training for rural entrepreneurs or economic development officials.

* Participating Micro Lenders

Economic Dev. Council of Northern Vermont, Inc.
155 Lake Street   802-524-4546
Albans, VT 05478   Fax 802-527-1081
Area of Operation: Chittenden, Franklin, Grand Isle, Lamoille, and Washington counties

Northern Community Investments Corporation
20 Main St.
P.O. Box 904   802-748-5101
St. Johnsbury, VT 05819   Fax: 802-748-1884
Area of Operation: Caledonia, Essex, and Orleans Counties

Vermont Development Credit Union
18 Pearl Street   802-865-3404
Burlington, VT 05401   Fax: 802-862-8971
Area of Operation: Addison, Bennington, Orange, Rutland, Windham Counties

The Microloan Program provides small loans ranging from under $500 to $35,000.

Virginia

* Economic Development Partnership

901 East Byrd Street
P.O. Box 798   804-371-8100
Richmond, VA 23218   Fax: 804-371-8112
www.yesvirginia.org

Helps new and expanding businesses by answering questions about licensing, taxes, regulations, assistance programs, etc. The office can also locate sources of information in other state agencies, and it can identify sources of help for business planning, management, exporting, and financing.

Existing Industry Division (EID): Discovers needs and identifies resources that allow existing businesses and industries to take advantage of opportunities and avoid problems. EID professionals generally call on organizations within geographic territories and discuss business conditions. Information collected is processed and analyzed for further action.

Workforce Services Division (WFS): Works with new and existing businesses and industries to recruit and train qualified workers at all skill levels for newly created jobs. The programs addressing these efforts support State and local Economic Development marketing efforts.

Workforce Services: Mission is to train and retrain Virginians for specific employment opportunities. Offers consulting, video production for training purposes, and funding.

Virginia's Business Development Network: Designed to provide management and technical assistance to small and medium-sized companies. Provides one-on-one counseling and group training on a variety of subjects and assists entrepreneurs with pre-business planning.

Financial Services Division (FSD): Identifies potential financial resources to meet the capital needs of Virginia business clients, and administers loan and guarantee programs designed to foster growth and private financing in Virginia business.

Governor's Opportunity Fund: Supports economic development projects that create new jobs and investment in accordance with criteria established by state legislation. Funds can be used for such things as site acquisition and development; transportation access; training; construction or build-out of publicly owned buildings; or grants or loans to Industrial Development Authorities.

Enterprise Zone Job Grants: Businesses creating new-full-time positions are eligible to receive grants of up to $500 per position ($1,000 if a zone resident fills a position). The maximum grant to any one firm is $100,000 a year for the three consecutive years in the grant period.

International Market Planning: Designed to assist companies developing new export markets and increase sales. Offers international marketing research; current market analyses; specific strategies to access selected markets.

New Jobs Program: Funding and assistance are available to qualified companies that make a capital investment of more than $1 million and create a minimum of 25 new jobs.

Small Business New Jobs Program: Funding and assistance are available to qualified companies that have operated in Virginia for at least one year, are for-profit and have fewer that 250 employees. The company must create 5 to 24 jobs within 12 months and make capital investment of at least $100,000.

Retraining Program: Workforce Services will provide consulting services and funds to eligible Virginia businesses to assist in retraining their existing employees.

Virginia Investment Partnership Grant Fund: The Virginia Partnership Grant Fund is a discretionary performance incentive program in which grants are negotiated and made to selected projects that invest in Virginia and promote employment opportunities

Tobacco Region Opportunity Fund: The Tobacco Opportunity Fund makes grants or loans to localities in Virginia's tobacco producing regions to assist with projects that result in the creation of new jobs.

Loan Guarantee Program: The Loan Guarantee Program is designed to reduce a bank's risk in making loans and increase availability of short-term capital for small businesses.

Small Business Compliance Assistance Fund: The fund is designed to provide Virginia businesses with financing to purchase equipment to comply with federal Clean Air Act, voluntary pollution prevention measures and voluntary agricultural best management practices.

* VWBE Certification Program

Women's Enterprise Program
P.O. Box 446   800-980-VWBE
Richmond, VA 23218   804-371-8200
www.dba.state.va.us/mwbusinesses/wob.asp

Helps Virginia's women-owned and operated companies certify themselves as WBE's to better compete in government and corporate procurement markets. In addition to being listed in the directory, certified companies will be registered in the WBE website, as well as in the Virginia Procurement Pipeline website. Certified WBE's also have the privilege of using the WBE seal on marketing materials and letterhead. They also receive information on other resources available to women-owned businesses regarding government contracting, management issues, and women's ownership.

* Virginia Department of Business Assistance

707 East Main Street
Suite 300
P.O. Box 466   804-371-8200
Richmond, VA 23218   Fax: 804-371-2142
www.dba.state.va.us

A good starting point for new businesses to learn about financial programs, workshops, business planning and more.

* Center for Innovative Technology

2214 Rock Hill Rd, Suite 600   703-689-3000
Herndon, VA 20170   800-383-2482
www.cit.org   Fax: 703-689-3041

Exists to stimulate economic growth by serving technology businesses. Services include: access to 11 technology development centers; assistance with pursuing joint product development with a Virginia university and provide co-funding for projects; entrepreneurship programs designed to help early stage companies bring new products to market; assistance solving manufacturing production problems.

* Virginia Small Business Financing Authority

707 East Main Street, Suite 300
P.O. Box 446   804-371-8200
Richmond, VA 23218   Fax: 804-371-8111
www.dba.state.va.us/financing

Offers financing programs to provide businesses with access to capital needed for growth and expansion. Programs include:

- *Industrial Development Bonds (IDBs) and the Umbrella IDB Program*: VSBFA issues tax-exempt and taxable revenue bonds (IDBs) statewide to provide creditworthy businesses with access to long term, fixed asset financing at favorable interest rates and terms. Tax-exempt IDBs may be used to finance new or expanding manufacturing facilities and exempt projects, such as solid waste disposal facilities. In addition, VSBFA offers an Umbrella IDB Program that provides a cost-effective means for businesses to sell their bonds in the public bond market, particularly for smaller projects with limited access to this market.
- *Virginia Economic Development Revolving Loan Fund*: This fund provides loans of up to $700,000 to bridge the gap between private debt financing and private equity for projects that will result in job creation or retention. Funding is available for fixed asset financing to new and expanding manufacturing companies and other industries that derive 50% or more of their sales outside of Virginia.
- *Virginia Defense Conversion Revolving Loan Fund*: This fund provides loans of up to $700,000 to assist defense dependent companies seeking to expand into commercial markets and diversify their operations. Funding is available for fixed assets and working capital.
- *Loan Guarantee Program*: This program is designed to reduce the risk to banks in making loans thereby increasing the availability of short-term capital for small businesses. Under the program, VSBFA will guarantee up to $250,000 or 50%, whichever is less, of a bank loan. Typical borrowings include revolving lines of credit to finance accounts receivable and inventory, and short-term loans for working capital and fixed asset purchases, such as office or research equipment.
- *Virginia Capital Access Program (VCAP)*: VCAP provides a form of loan portfolio insurance for participating banks through special loan loss reserve accounts which are funded by loan enrollment premiums paid by the bank/borrower and matched by the VSBFA. This allows the banks to exceed their normal risk thresholds for commercial loans of all types and, thereby, accommodate a broader array of loan requests from Virginia businesses.
- *Child Day Care Financing Program*: VSBFA provides small direct loans to child day care providers for quality enhancement projects or to meet or maintain child care standards. Eligible loan uses include infant care equipment or equipment needed to care for children with special needs, playground improvements, vans, and upgrades or minor renovations to kitchens, bathrooms, and plumbing and electrical systems.
- *Small Business Environmental Compliance Assistance Fund*: The Small Business Environmental Compliance Assistance Fund is a revolving low-interest loan fund. It is available to small businesses for the purchase and installation of replacement equipment need to comply with the Clean Air Act or to implement voluntary pollution prevention measures.
- *VSBFA DIRECT*: This program is designed to provide access capital to new and existing small businesses and economic development authorities. These loans from

the Small Business Finance Authority are to facilitate the financing projects that create economic benefit to Virginia's communities through increased revenues and the creation of new jobs.

* Solar Photovoltaic Manufacturing Grants

Virginia Department of Mines, Minerals, and Energy
202 N. Ninth St.
Ninth Street Office Bldg., 8th Floor   804-692-3200
Richmond, VA 23219   Fax: 804-692-3238
www.mme.state.va.us/de/commercialframe.html

Designed to encourage the product development and manufacture of a high technology, renewable energy source in Virginia. Any manufacturer who sells solar photovoltaic panels, manufactured in Virginia, is entitled to receive an annual grant of up to seventy-five cents per watt of the rated capacity of panel sold.

* Virginia Coalfield Economic Development Authority

The Virginia Southwest Promise   800-735-9999
P.O. Box 1060   276-889-0381
Lebanon, VA 24266   Fax: 276-889-1830
www.vaswpromise.com

Designed to enhance the economic base of specific areas. The Authority provides low interest loans or grants to qualified new or expanding industries through its financing program to be used for real estate purchases, construction or expansion of buildings, and the purchase of machinery and equipment.

* Virginia Capital LP

1801 Libbie Avenue, Suite 201   804-648-4802
Richmond, VA 23226   Fax: 804-648-4809
www.vacapital.com

A private venture capital firm. Investments that are attractive include ownership transactions and profitable, growing companies whose needs exceed senior bank debt capacity. Typical investments range between $500,000 and $1,500,000.

* Virginia Resources Authority

707 East Main Street
Suite 1350   804-644-3100
Richmond, VA 23219   Fax: 804-644-3109
www.virginiaresources.org

VRA's Financing Programs:

Virginia Water Facilities Revolving Fund: VRA acts as the financial administrator and manager for the Virginia Water Facilities Revolving Fund (VWFRF). The VWFRF is co-managed with the Department of Environmental Quality (DEQ), Water Division. Funding for the VWFRF is provided by grants from the Environmental Protection Agency along with a state match of twenty percent.

Virginia Water Supply Revolving Fund: The VWSRF was established as a renewing source of funding for improvements to privately and publicly owned community and nonprofit noncommunity waterworks.

Interim Financing: Is available to borrowers whose loans have been approved by VRA's Board of Directors, and to borrowers that have received a loan commitment from either the wastewater or water supply revolving fund. The interim financing program was created to provide approved borrowers with funds for eligible costs incurred before loans can close, including engineering and construction costs.

* eVa

Department of General Services,
Division of Purchases and Supply (DPS).
P.O. Box 644   804-786-3910
Richmond, VA 23218   Fax: 804-371-7841
www.eva.state.va.us

eVa is a one-stop information source about Virginia state government bidding opportunities. The information summarizes opportunities in general and highway construction, data processing, equipment, printing, supplies, surplus property auctions or sealed bid sales, real property and various services: professional, non-professional, individual and consulting. Each listing includes a contact person for more details.

* Department of Environmental Quality

629 East Main Street   804-698-4394
P.O. Box 10009   800-592-5482
Richmond, VA 23240   Fax: 804-698-4510
www.deq.state.va.us

The Virginia Small Business Assistance Program (VA SBAP) is a "non-regulatory," voluntary program within the Department of Environmental Quality. It offers small businesses free technical assistance on air quality and related environmental requirements. It's mission is to help small businesses comply with the Clean Air Act and Virginia's air regulations.

* Virginia Tourism Corporation

901 East Byrd Street   804-786-2051
Richmond, VA 23219   Fax: 804-786-1919
www.vatc.org

The Corporation develops and implements programs beneficial to Virginia travel-related businesses and consumers that no industry component or organization would be expected to carry out on its own. Through its multifaceted national and international marketing programs, the VTC researches and targets specific, highly profitable audience segments in those geographic markets offering the highest potential of travel to Virginia.

* Virginia Department of Forestry

Fontaine Research Park
900 Natural Resources Drive, Suite 800   804-977-6555
Charlottesville, VA, 22903-0758   Fax: 804-296-2369
www.vdof.org

The Conservation Reserve Enhancement Program (CREP) is a State-federal conservation partnership program targeted to address specific State and nationally significant water quality, soil erosion and wildlife habitat issues related to agricultural use. The program uses financial incentives to encourage farmers and ranchers to voluntarily enroll in contracts of 10 to 15 years in duration to remove lands from agricultural production. This community-based conservation program provides a flexible design of conservation practices and financial incentives to address environmental issues.

* Virginia Department of Housing and Community

Development Planning and Development Office
501 North Second Street
Richmond, VA 23219   804-371-7000
www.dhcd.virginia.gov/

The Department of Housing and Community Development has a variety of programs through their Business Assistance Program. They work with business and communities to help foster economic growth and to help stimulate the creation of new businesses.

Virginia Enterprise Initiative Program: This program supports small business development by assisting entrepreneurs in starting new businesses and helping disadvantaged individuals gain business skills and access to credit.

Virginia Enterprise Zone Program: This program encourages new business activity and expansion by providing state and local tax relief and grants, local regulatory flexibility, and local infrastructure development in selected economically depressed areas.

Virginia Individual Development Account Program: This program is designed to encourage savings in the form of cash matching funds. An eligible participant saves into a designated account at a financial institution for a specific purpose, such as home ownership, education, or business start-up and also receives financial training.

* Loans For Farmers
Farm Service Agency
U.S. Department of Agriculture
Culpeper Building
1606 Santa Rosa Rd., Suite 138   804-287-1503
Richmond, VA 23229   Fax: 804-287-1723
http://www.fsa.usda.gov/va/
The Farm Service Agency provides Direct and Guaranteed Loans to farmers through a variety of programs, including:

Farm Ownership Loans: purchase farmland, construct or repair buildings and other fixtures, and promote soil and water conservation. Up to $200,000.

Operating Loans: purchase items needed for a successful farm operation, such as livestock, farm equipment, feed, seed, fuel, farm chemicals, insurance, and other operating expenses. Can also be used to pay for minor improvements. Up to $200,000.

Beginning Farmer and Rancher Loans: provides funds to beginning and farmers and ranchers who are unable to obtain financing elsewhere.

Downpayment Farm Ownership Loans for Beginning Farmers: helps beginning farmers and ranchers purchase a farm or ranch. Also provides a way for retiring farmers to transfer their land to a future generation of farmers and ranchers. Applicant must have a downpayment of 10% and FSA with finance 40%, with the remaining balance from a commercial lender. Purchase price cannot exceed $250,000.

Loans to Socially Disadvantaged Farmers/Ranchers: helps socially disadvantaged applicants buy and operate family-size farms and ranches.

Youth Loans: Made to youths to establish and operate income-producing projects with the participation in 4-H clubs, Future Farmers of America, and similar organizations. Up to $5,000.

Emergency Loan Assistance: provides loans to help producers recover from production and physical losses due to drought, flooding, and other natural disasters, or quarantine. Up to $500,000.

Beginning Farmer and Rancher Land Contract Guarantee Pilot Program: "prompt payment guarantee" from FSA. FSA will provide payment to seller two times if the beginning farmer does not pay. Program is tested in IN, IA, ND, OR, PA and WI.

Farm Ownership and Operating Loan Guarantees: FSA will guarantee loans up to $782,000.

* Small Business Administration (SBA)
Richmond District Office
400 N. 8th St., Suite 1150   804-771-2400
Richmond, VA 23240   Fax: 804-771-2764
www.sba.gov/va
The Virginia Small Business Administration Office delivers a variety of programs and services, such as startup and operational assistance through small business training and counseling, financial assistance for startup's, business opportunities and much more.

* Rural Development Administration
1606 Santa Rosa Rd.
Culpeper Building #238   804-287-1550
Richmond, VA 23229-5014   Fax: 804-287-1718
www.rurdev.usda.gov/va
Business and Industry Loan Guaranteed Loans: The Business and Industry Loan Guarantee Program provides loan guarantees for expansion and preservation of jobs in rural areas in towns of less than 50,000.

Intermediary Re-Lending Program: This program finances business facilities and community development projects in rural areas. This is achieved through loans made by Rural Development to intermediaries. The intermediaries re-lend the funds to ultimate recipients for business facilities or community development. Any type of legal entity, including individuals and public and private organizations may be an ultimate recipient.

Rural Business Enterprise Grants: This program promotes the development and commercialization of new services and products that can be produced in rural areas; new processes that can be produced in rural areas; new processes that can be utilized in the production of products in rural areas; and new enterprises that can add value to on-farm production. Grants may be made to public bodies or nonprofit institutions to pay up to 75% of the costs for establishing and/or operating centers for rural technology and/or cooperative development.

Cooperative Services: The Cooperative Services program helps rural residents form new cooperative businesses and improve the operations of existing cooperatives. To accomplish this, Cooperative Services provides technical assistance, conducts cooperative-related research, and produces information products to promote public understanding of cooperatives.

Rural Cooperative Development Grant Program: Rural Cooperative Development grants are made for establishing and operating centers for cooperative development for the primary purpose of improving the economic condition of rural areas through the development of new cooperatives and improving operations of existing cooperatives.

Rural Business Opportunity Grants: Rural Business Opportunity Grant funds provide for technical assistance, training, and planning activities that improve economic conditions in rural areas. Applicants must be located in rural. Nonprofit corporations and public bodies are eligible. This program is designed to promote sustainable economic development in rural communities with exceptional needs.

Rural Economic Development Loans and Grants: This program finances economic development and job creation projects in rural areas. Loans and Grants are available to any Rural Utilities Service electric or telecommunications borrower to assist in developing rural areas. Loans at zero-interest are made primarily to finance business startup ventures and business expansion projects.

Value-Added Product Market Development Grant: The purpose of the Value-Added Agricultural Product Market Development Grant is to help eligible agricultural producers enter into value-added activities. These grant funds will be used to either develop feasibility studies, business and marketing plans, or other planning activities needed to establish a viable value-added marketing opportunity for an agricultural product.

* Virginia Department of Rail and Public Transportation

1313 E. Main St., Suite 300
P.O. Box 590   804-786-4440
Richmond, VA 23218   Fax: 804-786-7286
www.drpt.state.va.us

The Department of Rail and Public Transportation supports a variety of programs including: Capital Funds, Formula Funds, Rideshare Funds, Technical Assistance Funds, Transportation Efficiency Improvement Funds and more.

* International Trade Division

Director of International Trade
P.O. Box 798
901 East Byrd Street   804-371-0198
Richmond, VA 23218-0798   Fax: 804-371-8860
www.exportvirginia.org

This program provides international business expertise to promote Virginia's products and services in world markets. Services include export counseling, market assistance, educational seminars, international market information and market planning programs.

Washington

* Department of Community, Trade and Economic Development

Raad Building
128 10th Avenue SW
P.O. Box 42525   360-725-4000
Olympia WA 98504-2525   Fax: 360-586-8440
www.cted.wa.gov

One-Stop Licensing Center: A convenient, one-stop system that takes care of basic registration requirements and offers information about any additional licensing.

Business Retention & Expansion Program: Works with at-risk manufacturing and processing firms to reduce the number of business closures, layoffs and failures that result in significant job loss. State and local staff provide technical and problem solving assistance for these companies.

Downtown Revitalization Service: Encourages partnerships between business and government that revitalize a community's economy, appearance and traditional business image.

Education and Training: Works in partnership with local Economic Development Councils to provide businesses and communities with practical application of economic development techniques.

Child Care Advantages: Provides businesses with financial and technical assistance to develop on-site or near-site child care facilities. Qualified businesses are eligible to receive direct loans, loan guarantees, or grants through the Facilities Fund to start or expand their child care facilities.

Coastal Revolving Loan Fund: This fund lends to public agencies and businesses in Jefferson, Clallam, Grays Harbor, Pacific and Wahkiakum counties. Borrowers must demonstrate job creation and private investment to qualify for loans up to $150,000. The program also provides technical assistance loans up to $50,000 for public agencies and $30,000 for businesses for feasibility studies and planning.

Industrial Revenue Bonds: Up to $10 million may be issued to finance a project. Taxable nonrecourse economic development bonds are also available through the Washington Economic Development Finance Authority.

Forest Projects Revolving Loan Fund: Provides financial assistance to small-and medium-sized forest projects companies. Loans up to $750,000 are available for secondary wood product companies and their suppliers.

Community Development Finance: Program is available to help business and industry secure long-term expansion loans. By combining private financial resources with federal and state lending assistance and local leadership, this program focuses on business expansion through community development activities.

Loan programs are available for real estate, new construction, renovation, major leasehold improvements, machinery, equipment, and working capital. Government financing for a start-up business is possible, but more difficult and requires a larger down payment by the business.

Rural Washington Loan Fund: Gap financing for businesses that will create new jobs or retain existing jobs in non-entitlement areas of the state.

International Trade Division: Works to expand future and existing export markets by distributing trade statistics, a bi-monthly newsletter, industry directories, organizing trade missions, participating in trade shows and managing state office in Europe, Japan, Taiwan, Tokyo, and Vladivostock.

Linked Deposit Loan Program: Allows minority or women-owned businesses with 50 or fewer employees to apply at participating banks for reduced rate loans.

Minority and Women-Owned Business Loan: Loans can be available to assist certified minority and woman-owned businesses that are located in non-metropolitan areas.

* Rural Development Administration

Rural Development
1835 Black Lake Blvd. SW, Suite B   360-704-7740
Olympia, WA 98501-5715   Fax: 360-704-7742
www.rurdev.usda.gov/wa

Business and Industry Loans The purpose of the Business and Industry loan program is to improve develop or finance business, industry and employment and improve the economic and environmental climate in rural communities by guaranteeing quality loans, which will provide lasting community benefits.

Rural Economic Development Loans and Grants: This program provides zero interest loans and grants to Rural Utilities Service borrowers and Rural Electrification Administration to promote rural economic development and job creation projects through direct loans or revolving loan funds.

Rural Business Enterprise Grants: Grants made by USDA Rural Development to public bodies, not for profit entities or Indian tribes to support the development of private business enterprises. Limited to communities of 50,000 population or less.

Rural Business Opportunity Grants: Grants to public bodies, nonprofit corporations, Indian tribes, and cooperatives, which will be used to assist in the economic development of rural areas.

Intermediary Relending Program: Loans made by USDA Rural Development to intermediaries (public bodies, not for profit entities or Indian tribes) at 1% interest-30 years. Intermediaries maximum loan is $250,000 or 75% of project cost, whichever is less. Intermediaries establish revolving loan fund accounts and then relend to individuals or public or private organizations to finance business enterprises or community development. This program is limited to communities of 25,000 population or less.

Rural Cooperative Development Grants: Grants made by USDA Rural Development to nonprofit corporations and institutions of higher education for the purpose of establishing and operating centers for rural cooperative development. Grant will be used to facilitate the creation or retention of jobs in rural areas through the development of new rural cooperatives, value-added processing and rural businesses.

Technical Assistance for Cooperative Development: This program provides Assistance for people interested in forming new cooperatives or existing cooperatives facing specific problems or challenges.

* Business Assistance Center

2001 6th Ave., Suite 2600   800-237-1233
Seattle, WA 98121   360-956-3135

Education & Training: Efforts are focused on providing practical application of economic development techniques along with providing a forum for practitioners for the interchange of economic development ideas.

The Business Assistance Center Hotline: A statewide, toll-free information and referral service, provides information regarding state business licensing, registration, technical assistance, other state agencies or one-to-one business counseling. To contact a person from the Business Assistance Hotline, call 800-237-1233; 360-586-4840; TDD 360-586-4852.

* Permit Assistance Center

Department of Ecology   800-917-0043
300 Desmond Dr. SE   360-407-7037
Lacey, WA 98503   Fax: 360-407-6904

Mailing Address:
P.O. Box 47600
Olympia, WA 98504
www.ecy.wa.gov

Regional Staff are available to coordinate permit applications for large, complex projects, and to work with applicants, agencies and regulatory authorities to develop a plan for meeting environmental and land-use requirements.

* Export Finance Assistance Center

Export Finance Assistance Center of Washington
2001 Sixth Ave., Suite 650   206-553-5615
Seattle, WA 98121   Fax: 206-553-7253
www.cymma.com/useac.html

Provides information and guidance on the repayment risk of financing aspects of export transactions.

* Office of Minority and Women's Business Enterprises

406 S. Water St.
P.O. Box 41160   360-753-9693
Olympia, WA 98504   Fax: 360-586-7079
www.omwbe.wa.gov

Mission is to enhance the economic vitality of Washington State by creating an environment which mitigates the effects of race and gender discrimination in public contracting and promotes the economic development and growth of minority and women businesses. Certifies Women's business ventures and publishes a directory.

* Minority & Women Business Development

Washington State Office of Minority & Women's
Business Enterprises
406 South Water Street   866-208-1064
P.O. Box 41160   360-753-9693
Olympia, WA 98504-1160   Fax: 360-586-7079
www.omwbe.wa.gov

The Office of Minority and Women's Business Enterprises help create and sustain the business environment by promoting public procurement by businesses owned by minorities, women and those who are socially and economically disadvantaged.

* Cascadia Revolving Fund

1901 NW Market Street   206-447-9226
Seattle, WA 98107   Fax: 206-682-4804
www.cascadiafund.org

Private, nonprofit community development loan fund which is lent to small businesses that cannot access traditional sources of credit. Maximum loan is $500,000.

* Washington State Department of Agriculture

Agency Operations/Market Development Division
1111 Washington Street SE
P.O. Box 42560   360-902-1800
Olympia, WA 98504-2560   Fax: 360-902-2092
http://agr.wa.gov

Services available include:
Administrative Support Services:
Provides financial services, computer and information technology services, personnel services, communications, administrative procedures guidance, legal services, and safety and emergency management programs for the department's 25 programs.

Agricultural Fairs: 360-902-1809
Provides financial assistance to agricultural fairs and youth shows.

Commodity Commissions: 360-902-2043
Administers agency responsibilities relative to the state's 26 agricultural commodity commissions.

International Marketing: 360-902-1915
Assists food and agriculture companies to sell their products internationally; helps resolve phytosanitary and other trade barriers; organizes and leads companies on trade missions and to major trade shows; and develops and distributes information to buyers on the state's agricultural suppliers.

Small Farm and Direct Marketing: 360-902-1884
The Small Farm and Direct Marketing Program works with small farms, farmers markets, chefs and nonprofit organizations to connect consumers directly to farmers who sell fresh, local products. They partner with public and private organizations to increase the economic viability of small farms and strengthen Washington's local food systems.

"From the Heart of Washington": 360-902-1915
From the Heart of Washington promotes the purchase of local products by Washington consumers, and raises awareness of agriculture's value to the state's economy and its role in sustaining rural communities.

* Washington State Energy Office
925 Plum St., SE, Building 4
P.O. Box 43165 360-956-2000
Olympia, WA 98504-3165 Fax: 360-956-2217
www.energy.wsu.edu
Bioenergy Technical Information: Technical assistance is provided to manufacturing and commercial facilities interested in using biomass for energy production. The Office will also help in identifying funding opportunities, local resources, technology, and conduction environmental assessments.

Commercial Education: Provides training for designers and operators of commercial buildings on energy-efficient technologies and practices.

District Heating and Cooling: This program provides assistance to design or implement district heating or cooling systems for commercial, industrial, or public institutions. Assistance is also provided on obtaining project funding from multiple sources.

Electric Ideas Clearinghouse: 800-872-3568
360-956-2237
Fax: 360-956-2214
Provides a regional resource for professionals involved in commercial building design, construction, operations, and industrial processes. It provides information and technical assistance on products, design, codes, standard, energy programs, training opportunities, job listings, and expert referrals.

* Loans For Farmers
Farm Service Agency
U.S. Department of Agriculture
316 W. Boone Ave., Suite 568 509-323-3000
Spokane, WA 99201-2350 Fax: 509-323-3074
http://www.fsa.usda.gov/wa/

The Farm Service Agency provides Direct and Guaranteed Loans to farmers through a variety of programs, including:

Farm Ownership Loans: purchase farmland, construct or repair buildings and other fixtures, and promote soil and water conservation. Up to $200,000.

Operating Loans: purchase items needed for a successful farm operation, such as livestock, farm equipment, feed, seed, fuel, farm chemicals, insurance, and other operating expenses. Can also be used to pay for minor improvements. Up to $200,000.

Beginning Farmer and Rancher Loans: provides funds to beginning and farmers and ranchers who are unable to obtain financing elsewhere.

Downpayment Farm Ownership Loans for Beginning Farmers: helps beginning farmers and ranchers purchase a farm or ranch. Also provides a way for retiring farmers to transfer their land to a future generation of farmers and ranchers. Applicant must have a downpayment of 10% and FSA with finance 40%, with the remaining balance from a commercial lender. Purchase price cannot exceed $250,000.

Loans to Socially Disadvantaged Farmers/Ranchers: helps socially disadvantaged applicants buy and operate family-size farms and ranches.

Youth Loans: Made to youths to establish and operate income-producing projects with the participation in 4-H clubs, Future Farmers of America, and similar organizations. Up to $5,000.

Emergency Loan Assistance: provides loans to help producers recover from production and physical losses due to drought, flooding, and other natural disasters, or quarantine. Up to $500,000.

Beginning Farmer and Rancher Land Contract Guarantee Pilot Program: "prompt payment guarantee" from FSA. FSA will provide payment to seller two times if the beginning farmer does not pay. Program is tested in IN, IA, ND, OR, PA and WI.

Farm Ownership and Operating Loan Guarantees: FSA will guarantee loans up to $782,000.

* Small Business Administration
Seattle Regional Office
1200 6th Ave., Suite 1700 206-553-7310
Seattle, WA 98101-1128 Fax: 206-553-7099

801 West Riverside Ave., Suite 200 509-353-2800
Spokane WA 99201-0901 Fax: 509-353-2829
www.sba.gov/wa
The Washington Small Business Administration Office delivers a variety of programs and services, such as startup and operational assistance through small business training and counseling, financial assistance for startup's, business opportunities and much more.

West Virginia

* West Virginia Development Office
1900 Kanawha Blvd., East 304-558-2234
Charleston, WV 25305-0311 800-982-3386
www.wvdo.org Fax: 304-558-0449

This office can provide information and expertise in dealing with state, federal, and local agencies. They also have information on financing programs and other services offered by the state government.

Business Counseling: Confidential free service is available to those exploring the option of starting or purchasing a new business and to current owners of small businesses.

Seminars and workshops: Small group training is provided in areas such as starting a business in West Virginia, the basics of business planning, accounting and record keeping, business management techniques, tax law, personnel management techniques, quality customer service, etc. Most seminars and workshops may be attended for a nominal fee.

Site Selection: Industrial specialists assist out-of-state companies, existing state businesses and site location consultants with the identification of suitable locations for their proposed operations utilizing a computerized inventory.

Small Business Work Force Program: Designed to serve businesses with fewer than 20 employees that are established, viable small businesses with demonstrable growth potential. Training programs will be developed based upon a comprehensive needs analysis and the business plan.

Jobs Investment Trust: A $10 million public venture capital fund that uses debt and equity investments to promote and expand the state's economy.

Governor's Guaranteed Work Force Program: Provides training funds to assist new employees in learning their jobs, as well as to improve and expand the skills of existing employees for companies moving to or expanding in West Virginia.

Office of International Development: Offers export counseling and trade promotion opportunities to West Virginia companies. Maintains overseas offices.

Business and Industry Development Division: The Industrial Development Division of the West Virginia Development Office, in cooperation with the Department of Commerce and SBA, cosponsors workshops in international marketing.

West Virginia Export Council: A nonprofit export promotion organization committed to expanding West Virginia exports. The Council assists public sector organizations in planning, promoting, and implementing activities that assist international export efforts.

Minority-owned and Women-owned Business Directory: Each year the West Virginia Small Business Development Center publishes a "Minority-owned and Women-owned Business Directory" This directory is distributed to public and private purchasing agents, Chambers of Commerce, Economic Development Authorities, legislators and many privately owned businesses including contractors and all of the listees. There is no cost for the directory nor is there a charge for being included. The only requirement is that the business be located in West Virginia, be a for profit company and be 51% owned by a minority or woman.

Direct Loan Programs The West Virginia Economic Development Authority provides up to 45% in financing fixed assets by providing low-interest loans to expanding state businesses in West Virginia. Loan proceeds may be used for the acquisition of land, buildings and equipment.

Indirect Loan Programs: The West Virginia Economic Development Authority provides a loan insurance program through participating commercial banks to assist firms that cannot obtain conventional bank financing. This program insures up to 80 percent of a bank loan for a maximum loan term of four years. Loan proceeds may be used for any business purpose except the refinancing of existing debt.

Industrial Revenue Bonds: The Industrial Revenue Bonds program provides for customized financing through federal tax-exempt industrial revenue bonds.

Leveraged Technology Loan Insurance Program: This program expands the loan insurance coverage to 90 percent for those businesses involved in the development, commercialization or use of technology-based products and processes.

West Virginia Infrastructure and Jobs Development Council: The Economic Infrastructure Bond Fund can be used for financial assistance to public utilities, county development authorities and private companies for infrastructure improvements to support economic development projects.

Small Business Development Loans: This program provides capital to entrepreneurs for new or expanded small business with loans from $500 to $10,000. 888-982-7232

Linked Deposit Program: The Linked Deposit program provides low-interest loans to qualified small businesses for amounts up to $150,000 and for terms up to four years.

Competitive Improvement Program: The program targets small (50 or fewer employees) and medium (under 500 employees) sized manufacturers. Grants of up to $1,000 per trainee are available with 50 percent contribution by each employer required.

Workforce Development Initiative Program: The program encourages working partnerships between educational institutions and the business community. To qualify, community and technical colleges must establish their own revolving fund dedicated to work force development initiatives. The program requires a one-to-one match from the private sector.

* Rural Development Administration

75 High Street, Room 320   304-284-4860
Federal Building   800-295-8228
Morgantown, WV 26505   Fax: 304-284-4893
www.rurdev.usda.gov/wv

Guaranteed Business and Industry Loan Program: The Business and Industry program is an incentive program to lenders to make loans to businesses that will result in sustainable jobs in rural areas.

Intermediary Relending Program Loans: The Intermediary Lending Program is a revolving loan program where they lend a nonprofit organization or public entity money at 1% for 30 years. The borrower then relends the funds to eligible businesses at a reduced rate.

Rural Business Enterprise Grants: Rural communities can receive assistance in promoting the development of small businesses through the Rural Business Enterprise Grant Program. Grants are made to public bodies or not-for-profit organizations. Grantees use the funds to promote the development of small private businesses, which are defined as having 50 or fewer new employees and less than $1 million in projected annual gross revenue. Rural communities include cities with up to 50,000 population.

Rural Cooperative Development Grants: The program provides grants for establishing and operating centers for cooperative development. The primary purpose is to improve economic conditions in rural areas, including cities of up to 50,000 population. Grant funds can pay up to 75% of the costs for establishing and operating such centers. Grants may be made to public bodies or not-for-profit institutions.

Rural Business Opportunity Grants: Rural Business Opportunity Grants are available to promote sustainable economic development in rural communities with exceptional need.

Cooperative Stock Purchase Program: The Rural Cooperative Stock Purchase Program works in conjunction with the Guaranteed Business and Industrial Loan Program allowing loans to be made to producers of agricultural products seeking to join new cooperatives that produce value-added goods. Family farmers can use the Business and Industry Loan Program to help pay for stock in a start-up cooperative that will process an agricultural commodity into a value-added product.

Cooperative Development: Cooperative Service's professional staff provides technical assistance, research, statistics, education, and information to agricultural cooperatives and to groups planning to form a cooperative type of organization. Rural-Business Service is expanding its technical assistance role to bring the service closer to the users and to make technical assistance available to all types of rural cooperatives, including consumer cooperatives, housing cooperatives, marketing cooperatives and credit unions.

Rural Economic Development Loans and Grants: Loans or grants under the Rural Economic Development Loans and Grants programs are available only to rural electric cooperative or telephone borrowers. The programs are intended to help these utilities promote economic and community development projects within their service areas.

* Robert C. Byrd Institute

Huntington Manufacturing Technology Center
1050 Fourth Avenue   800-469-RCBI
Huntington, WV 25701   304-696-6275
Fax: 304-696-6277

Charleston Manufacturing Technology Center
100 Angus E. Peyton Drive   800-469-RCBI
South Charleston, WV 25303   304-746-8925
Fax: 304-746-8926

Bridgeport Manufacturing Technology Center
2007 Aviation Way
Benedum Airport   800-469-RCBI
Bridgeport, WV 26330   304-842-0777
Fax: 304-842-0436

Rocket Center Manufacturing Technology Center
410 State Route 956   800-469-RCBI
Rocket Center, WV 26726   304-726-9900
Fax: 304-726-7048
www.rcbi.org

A teaching factory to help small and medium-sized manufacturing companies increase their competitiveness through the adoption of world-class manufacturing technologies and modern management techniques.

* West Virginia Development Office

1900 Kanawha Blvd., East   800-982-3386
Charleston, WV 25305   304-558-2234
www.wvdo.org   Fax: 304-558-0449

Direct Loans: The WVDO can provide up to 45% in financing fixed assets by providing low interest, direct loans to expanding state businesses and firms locating in West Virginia. Loan term is generally 15 years for real estate intensive projects and 5 to 10 years for equipment projects.

Indirect Loans: The WVDO provides a loan insurance program and a capital access program through participating commercial banks to assist firms that cannot obtain conventional bank financing. The program insures up to 80% of a bank loan for a maximum loan term of four years.

Industrial Revenue Bonds: This provides for customized financing through the federal tax exempt industrial revenue bonds. $35 million of the state's bond allocation is reserved for small manufacturing projects.

Leveraged Technology Loan Insurance Program: This program expands the loan insurance coverage to 90% for those businesses involved in the development, commercialization, or use of technology- based products and processes.

West Virginia Capital Company Act: WVDO administers a program that provides for debt and equity venture capital investment to small business.

* Center for International Programs

Dr. Will Edwards, Director
Marshall University
One John Marshall Drive
320 Old Main   304-696-6265
Huntington, WV 25755   Fax 304-696-6353
www.marshall.edu/cip

The Center for International Programs' mission is to assist in globalizing the community.

* Center for Economic Options

214 Capitol St., Suite 200   304-345-1298
Charleston, WV 25301   Fax: 304-342-0641
www.centerforeconomicoptions.org

A nonprofit statewide, community-based organization which promotes opportunities that develop the economic capacity of West Virginia's rural citizens and communities. Working with members of society who traditionally have been excluded from economic decision-making, the Center advocates equity in the workplace, coordinates alternative approaches for economic development, and works to impact the direction of public policy.

* West Virginia Women's Commission

Building 6, Room 850
1900 Kanawha Boulevard, East   304-558-0070
Charleston, WV 25305   Fax: 304-558-5167
www.wvdhhr.org/women/index.asp

Offers women opportunities to learn to be advocates for themselves and to work with others to address systemic change. Projects include leadership and legislative conference like the Women's Town Meeting and Women's Day at the Legislature among others.

* West Virginia Division of Environmental Protection

Pollution Prevention Services
7012 MacCorkle Avenue, South East
Charleston, WV 25304   304-926-3647 Ext 351
www.dep.state.wv.us   Fax: 304-926-3637

The Pollution Prevention (P2) program was established to promote pollution prevention activities among West Virginia's regulated community. P2 activities include such things as adopting new manufacturing processes or materials substitution, both of which can result in less waste being produced. P2 activities can reduce the burden, and cost, of waste treatment and reduce the impact on the environment.

* Regional Contracting Assistance Center

Charleston Regional Contracting Assistance Center
1116 Smith Street, Suite 202   304-344-2546, ext. 4
Charleston, WV 25301   Fax: 304-344-2574

Area of Operation: Barbour, Braxton, Cabell, Calhoun, Clay, Gilmer, Jackson, Kanawha, Lewis, Mason, Putnam, Roane, Upshur, Wirt Counties

Huntington Regional Contracting Assistance Center
1050 Fourth Avenue   304-696-6275
Huntington, WV 25701   Fax: 304-696-4834

Area of Operation: Statewide

Logan Regional Contracting Assistance Center
Southern WV Community & Technical College
P.O. Box 2900
2900 Dempsey Branch Road   304-792-7098 x100
Mt. Gay, WV 25637   Fax: 304-792-7028
www.rcacwv.com/home.html

Area of Operation: Boone, Lincoln, Logan, McDowell, Mingo, Wayne, Wyoming Counties

Princeton Regional Contracting Assistance Center
130 Scott Street, Suite 3   304-487-3104
Princeton, WV 24740   Fax: 304-487-3125

Area of Operation: Fayette, Greenbrier, Mercer, Monroe, Nicholas, Pocahontas, Randolph, Raleigh, Summers, Webster Counties

Ranson Regional Contracting Assistance Center
401 South Fairfax Blvd.   304-724-7547
Ranson, WV 25438   Fax: 304-728-3068
www.rcacwv.com

Area of Operation: Berkeley, Grant, Hampshire, Hardy, Jefferson, Mineral, Monongalia, Morgan, Pendleton, Preston, Tucker Counties

The Regional Contracting Assistance Center (RCAC) is a private nonprofit corporation founded to create information and assistance programs that help West Virginia businesses understand, adapt to, and excel in the evolving business environment. RCAC is dedicated to providing businesses with the direct marketing and technical assistance needed to more fully participate in markets represented by the Department of Defense, other federal agencies, state and local governments, and private corporations. Their aim is to create and retain jobs in the State of West Virginia. All RCAC services are free. They have offices located in Charleston, Beckley, Ranson, and Huntington, WV.

* The Business Information Center

1000 Technology Drive, Suite 1230   304-368-0023
Fairmont, WV 26554   Fax: 304-367-0867
www.sba.gov/wv/wvbic.html

Business Information Centers, or BICs, are one-stop locations for information, counseling and technical assistance designed to help entrepreneurs start, operate and grow their businesses. This center has reference material on almost all areas of business. There are computers with business plan software to assist you in developing your business guidelines. We also have numerous videos and booklets covering what most any business will need.

* Loans For Farmers

Farm Service Agency
U.S. Department of Agriculture
75 High Street, Room 239
P.O. Box 1049   304-284-4800
Morgantown, WV 26507   Fax: 304-284-4821
http://www.fsa.usda.gov/wv/

The Farm Service Agency provides Direct and Guaranteed Loans to farmers through a variety of programs, including:

Farm Ownership Loans: purchase farmland, construct or repair buildings and other fixtures, and promote soil and water conservation. Up to $200,000.

Operating Loans: purchase items needed for a successful farm operation, such as livestock, farm equipment, feed, seed, fuel, farm chemicals, insurance, and other operating expenses. Can also be used to pay for minor improvements. Up to $200,000.

Beginning Farmer and Rancher Loans: provides funds to beginning and farmers and ranchers who are unable to obtain financing elsewhere.

Downpayment Farm Ownership Loans for Beginning Farmers: helps beginning farmers and ranchers purchase a farm or ranch. Also provides a way for retiring farmers to transfer their land to a future generation of farmers and ranchers. Applicant must have a downpayment of 10% and FSA with finance 40%, with the remaining balance from a commercial lender. Purchase price cannot exceed $250,000.

Loans to Socially Disadvantaged Farmers/Ranchers: helps socially disadvantaged applicants buy and operate family-size farms and ranches.

Youth Loans: Made to youths to establish and operate income-producing projects with the participation in 4-H clubs, Future Farmers of America, and similar organizations. Up to $5,000.

Emergency Loan Assistance: provides loans to help producers recover from production and physical losses due to drought, flooding, and other natural disasters, or quarantine. Up to $500,000.

Beginning Farmer and Rancher Land Contract Guarantee Pilot Program: "prompt payment guarantee" from FSA. FSA will provide payment to seller two times if the beginning farmer does not pay. Program is tested in IN, IA, ND, OR, PA and WI.

Farm Ownership and Operating Loan Guarantees: FSA will guarantee loans up to $782,000.

* Small Business Administration

West Virginia District Office   304-623-5631
320 West Pike Street, Suite 330   800-767-8052, #8
Clarksburg, WV 26301   Fax: 304-623-4269
www.sba.gov/wv

The West Virginia Small Business Administration Office delivers a variety of programs and services, such as startup and operational assistance through small business training and counseling, financial assistance for startup's, business opportunities and much more.

* Small Business Development Center

State Capitol Complex
Building 6, Room 652   304-558-2960
1900 Kanawha Blvd. E   888-982-7232
Charleston, WV 25305   Fax: 304-558-0127
www.sbdcwv.org

The SBDC promotes economic development through a program of practical, interrelated services, providing assistance to existing small businesses and the emerging entrepreneurs. The WVSBDC has 14 sub centers throughout the state serving every county.

Wisconsin

* Department of Commerce (COMMERCE)

201 W. Washington Avenue
Madison, WI 53707   608-266-1018
Business Helpline   800-HELP-BUSiness
Fax Request Hotline   608-264-6154
Export Helpline   800-XPORT-WIsconsin
www.commerce.state.wi.us

The Wisconsin Department of Commerce is the state's primary agency for delivery of integrated services to businesses. Services include business financing, technical and managerial services to a wide range of businesses.

Business Development Resources: The Area Development Manager Program assists business expansions, promotes business retention, and helps local development organizations in their respective territories. Area development managers use their knowledge of federal, state, and regional resources to provide a variety of information to expanding or relocating firms. They also mobilize resources to help struggling businesses.

Brownfields Initiative Technical Assistance Program: Provides information and assistance related to brownfields redevelopment. The program can assist in the identification and resolution of regulatory issues, and electronically link prospective buyers with information on available brownfield sites.

Business Development Assistance Center: Provides assistance to small businesses. The office furnishes information on government regulations, and refers businesses to appropriate resources. Call 800-HELP BUSiness.

Assistance with Environmental Regulations and Permits is available to manufacturers. COMMERCE can also expedite regulatory and permit clearance and resolve delays and communications problems. Businesses storing or handling flammable or combustible liquids can receive compliance assistance.

Wisconsin Health Consultation Program: Provides free assistance to employers who request help to establish and maintain a safe and healthful workplace. Health Consultants will conduct an appraisal of physical work practices and environmental hazards, will perform an ergonomics analysis, review various aspects of the employers present occupational safety and health program, and will present occupational health related training.

Manufacturing Assessment Center: Helps small and medium manufacturers improve quality and productivity through professional assessment of operations, systems, and layouts. The center maintains a list of related seminars available throughout the country, and can arrange plant tours of leading-edge manufacturers in the state.

Plan Review Program provides plan review and consultation for structures, plumbing, elevators, HVAC, lighting, erosion control, and private onsite wastewater treatment systems. The services help designers, installers, and owners protect public safety and promote economic efficiency.

Small Business Clean Air Assistance Program: Designed to help small businesses comply with standards established by the federal Clean Air Act.

Small Business Ombudsman: Provides information on government regulations and financing alternatives to small businesses, particularly entrepreneurs. Through its advocacy function, the office promotes special consideration for small businesses in Wisconsin administrative rules.

WiSCon Safety Consultation Program: Assesses current safety programs and suggests improvements; evaluates physical work practices; identifies available assistance; and provides training and education for managers and employees. The consultants do not issue citations, propose penalties, or report possible safety violations to the Occupational Safety and Health Administration.

Wisconsin TechSearch is the fee-based information outreach program of the Kurt F. Wendt Library. TechSearch offers document delivery and reference services to businesses and industry. On-line literature, patent and trademark searches are available. TechSearch provides access to the information resources of the Wendt Library, which contains outstanding collections in science and engineering, and is a US Patent and Trademark Depository Library and more than 40 libraries and information centers on the UW-Madison campus. For more information and a fee schedule, call 608-262-5913/5917 or Email {wtskfw@ doit.wisc.edu}.

Customized Labor Training Fund: Provides training grants to businesses that are implementing new technology or production processes. The program can provide up to 50% of the cost of customized training that is not available from the Wisconsin Technical College System.

Dairy 2020 Initiative: Awards grants and loans for business and feasibility planning to dairy producers and processors considering a modernization or expansion project.

Employee Ownership Assistance Loan Program: Can help a group of employees purchase a business by providing individual awards up to $25,000 for feasibility studies or professional assistance. The business under consideration must have expressed its intent to downsize or close.

Division of Vocational Rehabilitation Job Creation Program: Designed to increase employment opportunities for DVR clients by providing equipment grants, technical assistance grants, and customized assistance to companies that will hire persons with disabilities as part of a business expansion.

Major Economic Development Program: Offers low-interest loans for business development projects that create a significant economic impact.

Rural Economic Development Program: Makes individual awards up to $30,000 for feasibility studies and other professional assistance to rural businesses with fewer than 25 employees. Businesses and farms that have completed their feasibility evaluations are eligible for individual micro loans up to $25,000 for working capital and the purchase of equipment.

Technology Development Fund: Helps businesses finance Phase I product development research. Firms completing Phase I projects can receive Phase II product-commercialization funding.

Tax Incremental Financing: Helps cities in Wisconsin attract industrial and commercial growth in underdeveloped and blighted areas. A city or village can designate a specific area within its boundaries as a TIF district and develop a plan to improve its property values. Taxes generated by the increased property values pay for land acquisition or needed public works.

BDI Micro Loan Program: Helps entrepreneurs with permanent disabilities and rehabilitation agencies finance business start-ups or expansions.

BDI Self-Employment Program: Helps severely disabled DVR clients start micro-businesses.

Industrial Revenue Bonds (IRBs): A means of financing the construction and equipping of manufacturing plants and a limited number of non-manufacturing facilities. The municipality is not responsible for debt service on IRBs, nor is it liable in the case of default. IRBs are also exempt from federal income tax.

Petroleum Environmental Clean-up Fund: Reimburses property owners for eligible clean-up costs related to discharges for petroleum tank systems.

Recycling Demonstration Grant Program: Helps businesses and local governing units fund waste reduction, reuse, and recycling pilot projects.

Recycling Early Planning Grant Program: Awards funds to new and expanding business plans, marketing assistance, and feasibility studies on the start-up or expansion of a recycling business.

Recycling Loan Program: Awards loans for the purchase of equipment to businesses and nonprofit organizations that make products from recycled waste, or make equipment necessary to manufacture these products.

Recycling Technology Assistance Program: Provides low cost loans to fund research and development of products or processes using recovered or recyclable materials. Eligible activities include product development and testing, process development and assessment, specialized research, and technical assistance.

Wisconsin Fund: Provides grants to help small commercial businesses rehabilitate or replace their privately owned sewage systems.

Wisconsin Housing and Economic Development Authority (WHEDA): Offers a program that buys down commercial interest rates, enabling Wisconsin lenders to offer short-term, below-market-rate loans to small, minority- or women-owned businesses. A loan guarantee program is available for firms ramping-up to meet contract demands; for firms in economically-distressed areas; and for tourism and agribusiness projects. The authority also operates a beginning farmer bond program.

Community-Based Economic Development Program: Awards grants to community-based organizations for development and business assistance projects and to municipalities for economic development planning. The program helps community-based organizations plan, build, and create business and technology-based incubators, and can also capitalize an incubator tenant revolving-loan program.

Early Planning Grant: Helps entrepreneurs and small businesses obtain professional services necessary to evaluate the feasibility of a proposed start-up or expansion.

Economic Diversification Loan Program: Low-interest loan to finance a portion of the costs to establish and expand operations.

Wisconsin Small Business Innovative Research (SBIR) Support Program: Coordinates resources to help businesses pursue federal SBIR grants and contracts. The federal SBIR program provides Phase I awards of up to $100,000 for feasibility studies and Phase II awards of up to $750,000 for project development.

Wisconsin Trade Project Program: Can help small export-ready firms participate in international trade shows. The business covers its own travel and lodging expenses. COMMERCE can then provide up to $5,000 in reimbursements to a business for costs associated with attending a trade show, such as booth rental or product brochure translation.

Trade Shows and Trade Missions: Showcase Wisconsin firms and products to prospective international clients. The Department sponsors a Wisconsin-products booth at approximately 12 international trade fairs per year, and also arranges trade and reverse investment missions abroad, many of them led by the Governor.

Economic Impact Loan Program: This program is designed to help Wisconsin businesses that have been negatively impacted by gaming. Loans are for 75% of the cost of modernizing and/or improvements up to $100,000.

Business Employees' Skills Training (BEST) Program: Helps business in industries facing severe labor shortages upgrade the skills of their workforce with tuition reimbursement grants to help cover the costs associated with training employees.

Financial Consulting and Technical Assistance: The bureau counsels individuals who want to start, buy or expand a business. Economic consultants provide information regarding structuring financial plans, preparing loan applications, strategic planning, and guidance for writing business plans.

Enterprise Development Zone Program (EDZ): EDZ provides site specific tax incentives to new or expanding businesses whose projects will affect distressed areas.

Technology Development Fund: The Technology Development Fund program helps Wisconsin businesses research and develop technological innovations that have the potential to provide significant economic benefit to the state.

Agribusiness Guarantee: Agribusiness Guarantee is administered by Wisconsin Housing and Economic Development Authority (WHEDA). This program provides loan guarantees for projects developing products, markets, method of processing or marketing for a Wisconsin-grown commodity. The maximum guarantee of 80% on loans up to $750,000 can be used for equipment, land, buildings, working capital, inventory and marketing expenses. Contact WHEDA at 1-800-334-6873.

Early Planning Grant Program (EPG): EPG helps individual entrepreneurs and small businesses throughout Wisconsin obtain the professional services necessary to evaluate the feasibility of a proposed start up or expansion.

Entrepreneurial Training Grant Program (ETG): ETG provides grants to help cover a portion of the cost of attending Small Business Development Center's (SBDC) new Entrepreneurial Training Course.

Freight Railroad Infrastructure Improvement Program: The Freight Improvement Program awards loans to businesses or communities wishing to rehabilitate rail lines, advance economic development, connect an industry to the national railroad system, or to make improvements to enhance transportation efficiency, safety, and freight movement. Contact the Department of Transportation, 608-267-9284.

Milk Volume Production Program (MVP): MVP is designed to assist dairy producers that are undertaking capital improvement projects that will result in a significant increase in Wisconsin's milk production.

State of Wisconsin Investment Board (SWIB): The State of Wisconsin Investment Board is a large pension fund designed to explore investments in Wisconsin. The Department of Commerce can help your Wisconsin business seek financing to expand your business.

Going into Business in Wisconsin: An Entrepreneur's Guide: This $5 guide covers many issues involved in the planning and starting new business ventures.

Business Wizard: The Business Wizard uses a series of questions-and-answer pages to provide customized information to help you start and operate a Wisconsin-based business.

Trade Show Grant Program: This program is designed to encourage Wisconsin businesses seek out new international markets. Reimbursement grants of up to $5,000 are available for specific expenses for participating in an approved trade show or matchmaker trade delegation event.

Outreach Consultants: These consultants, located throughout the state, will work one-on-one with businesses to solve export problems. This service is free.

* Rural Development Administration

4949 Kirschling Court   715-345-7615
Stevens Point, WI 54481   Fax: 715-345-7669
www.rurdev.usda.gov/wi

Business and Industry Guaranteed and Loans: Business and Industry Guaranteed Loans are loan guarantees where the cost is a one-time, up-front fee of 2% of the amount guaranteed. Loans are made to businesses, which save or create jobs in rural areas (under 50,000 in population). Borrowers may be an individual, partnership, cooperative, for-profit or nonprofit corporation, Indian Tribe, or public body.

Business and Industry Direct Loans: The purpose of the Business and Industry Direct Loan Program is to improve, develop, or finance business, industry, and employment, and improve the economic and environmental climate in rural communities. Loan purposes include purchase and expansion of land, equipment, buildings, and working capital.

Community Facilities Direct Loans and Grants: Community Facilities Direct Loans and Grants provide funding for essential community facilities such as municipal buildings, day care centers, and health and safety facilities. Examples include fire halls, fire trucks, clinics, nursing homes, and hospitals. Community Facility loans and grants may also be used for such things as activity centers for the handicapped, schools, libraries, and other community buildings. Applicant must be unable to borrow money elsewhere at rates and terms to make the project affordable.

Community Facilities Guaranteed Loans: Community Facilities Guaranteed Loans provide funding for essential community facilities such as day care, hospitals, schools, clinics, roads, and fire halls.

Cooperative Development Technical Assistance: Cooperative Development Technical Assistance helps rural residents form new cooperative businesses or to use the cooperative model to address unmet social or economic needs.

Intermediary Relending Program: Intermediary Relending Program money is lent to private nonprofit corporations, any state or local government, an Indian Tribe, or a cooperative that in turn is re-lent by the intermediary to the ultimate recipients. The ultimate recipient must be unable to obtain credit elsewhere at reasonable rates and terms.

Rural Business Enterprise Grants: Rural Business Enterprise Grants are for financing and developing small and emerging private businesses with less than $1 million in revenues, and which will have fewer than 50 new employees. There is no maximum dollar limit for any one project. Funds can be used for technical assistance, revolving loan program, incubator/industrial buildings, and industrial park improvements.

Rural Cooperative Development Grants: Rural Cooperative Development Grants are for establishing and operating centers for cooperative development. The grant program will be used to facilitate the creation or retention of jobs in rural areas through the development of new rural cooperatives and operational involvement of existing cooperatives by the centers. Cooperative development activities by the centers include the startup, expansion, or operational improvement of a cooperative.

Rural Business Opportunity Grants: Rural Business Opportunity Grants provide for technical assistance, training, and planning activities that improve economic conditions in rural areas and cities and villages with a population of 10,000 or less.

Rural Economic Development Loans and Grants: Rural Economic Development Loans and Grants help develop projects that will result in a sustainable increase in economic productivity, job creation, and incomes in rural areas. Projects may include business start-ups and expansion, community development, incubator projects, medical and training projects, and feasibility studies. Ineligible purposes are those that directly benefit the borrower, conflicts of interest, and costs incurred prior to the application.

Value-Added Agricultural Product Market Development Grants: Value Added Agricultural Product Market Development Grants help independent producers and producer organizations enter into value-added activities.

* Bureau of Minority Business Development

Department of Commerce
201 W. Washington Ave.
P.O. Box 7970   608-267-9550
Madison, WI 53707   Fax: 608-267-2829
www.commerce.state.wi.us

Certifies companies to be eligible to participate in state's minority business bid preference. Company must be at least 51% owned, controlled, and managed by minority (being a woman is not considered a minority).

Certification to participate in the state's minority business purchasing and contracting program is available to minority vendors. Interested firms may apply through the department. They are then listed in the *Annual Directory of Minority-Owned Firms*.

Marketing Assistance of various kinds is offered to minority-owned firms. Certified minority vendors are listed in the department's database for access by the purchasing community. Minority-owned firms can receive help developing marketing plans. Each year, the department sponsors the Marketplace Trade Fair to encourage business contacts between minority vendors and state and corporate buyers.

Minority Business Development Fund: Offers low-interest loans for start-up, expansion or acquisition projects. To qualify for the fund, a business must be 51-percent controlled, owned, and actively managed by minority-group members, and the project must retain or increase employment.

Minority Business Early Planning Grant Program: Provides seed capital to minority entrepreneurs for feasibility studies, business plans, and marketing plans.

* Solid and Hazardous Waste Education Center

UW- Green Bay Campus
2420 Nicolet Dr., ES317   920-465-2278
Green Bay, WI 54311   Fax: 920-465-2376
www1.uwex.edu/ces/shwec/index.cfm

Provides technical assistance to businesses and communities on emissions reduction, pollution prevention, recycling, and solid waste management. The Center also offers grants that companies can use for hazardous waste reduction audits.

* Wisconsin Housing and Economic Development Authority

Madison Office   608-266-7884
201 W. Washington Ave., Suite 700   800-334-6873
Madison, WI 53703   Fax: 608-267-1099

Mailing Address:
P.O. Box 1728
Madison, WI 53701-1728

Milwaukee Office   414-277-4039
101 W Pleasant Street, Suite 100   800-628-4833
Milwaukee, WI 53212   Fax: 414-277-4704
www.wheda.com

Business Development Bonds: These are essentially industrial revenue bonds issued by the Wisconsin Housing and Economic Development Authority (WHEDA) on behalf of small businesses. Eligible projects qualify for low-cost fixed-rate financing. Businesses need to supply lenders with a letter of credit from WHEDA to guarantee these bonds. Available to manufacturers and first-time farmers with gross sales of $35 million or less. Project funded must create or retain employment. Proceeds can be used for land, building, or equipment purchase or improvement. Other restrictions apply. BDB's are generally range from $500,000 to $1 million with $10 million maximum.

Agribusiness Guarantee; Qualifying businesses are those located in a municipality with a population under 50,000, that purchase a substantial percentage of its raw agricultural commodities from Wisconsin suppliers, and; 1.) Develop a new product, method of processing, market, or improved marketing method for a Wisconsin product, or; 2.) Produce a specialty cheese product that is new to the business, or; 3.) Commercially harvest whitefish in Lake Superior. Maximum guarantee is 80% on loans up to $750,000. Agribusiness can be used for equipment, land, buildings, permanent working capital, inventory and initial product marketing expenses.

Linked Deposit Loan (LiDL) Subsidy: The purpose of this loan is to assist women- and/or minority-owned and controlled businesses in the start-up or expansion of their business by reducing the interest rate on their bank loans.

Neighborhood Business Revitalization Guarantee: This program helps business owners obtain financing to stimulate economic development in urban neighborhoods.

WHEDA Small Business Guarantee (WSBG): The WSBG program can help your business obtain financing to start a business, acquire land or expand a small business.

Credit Relief Outreach Program (CROP): CROP provides guarantees on agriculture production loans to farmers.

Farm Asset Reinvestment Management (FARM): FARM provides loan guarantees for agricultural expansion and modernization.

Beginning Farmer Bond Loan (BFB): BFB gives beginning farmers below-market interest rates on financing to start an operation.

* Entrepreneurial Training Grant (ETG) Program

P.O. Box 7970
Madison, WI 53707   608-263-7680
www.commerce.state.wi.us

Commerce has partnered with the Small Business Development Center (SBDC) to develop a pilot program designed to help individual entrepreneurs and small businesses throughout Wisconsin. Under the Entrepreneurial Training Grant (ETG) program, Commerce can provide applicants with a grant to help cover a portion of the cost of attending SBDC's new Entrepreneurial Training Course.

* Wisconsin Department of Tourism

P.O. Box 8690   608-266-7621
Madison, WI 53708   Fax: 608-261-8213
http://agency.travelwisconsin.com
Tourism Development
Tourism Communication Program:
Responsible for public information, publication production, media assistance, statewide events publicity, and special projects promotions producing the materials and publicity to ensure that Wisconsin tourism is visible to public.

Joint Effort Marketing (JEM) Program: Department may fund up to 75% of advertising expenses of qualifying projects that help promote the state in coordination with the tourism marketing plan.

JEM Newspaper Program: Businesses can take advantage of special low rates and get greater impact by purchasing advertising space in newspapers under the Wisconsin tourism logo.

Tourism Marketing and Customer Service 101: The Department of Tourism provides a series of basic tourism marketing and customer service educational courses. These courses are designed to provide basic information to assist in the marketing and operational aspects of the tourism business.

Tourism Development Specialist Program: Provides information on funding sources and feasibility assessment to individual businesses and developers. Development consultants advise and help promote the industry in their respective territories.

* Export-Import Bank of the United States

Chicago Regional Office & U.S. Export Center
55 W. Monroe Street, Suite 2440   312-353-8081
Chicago, IL 60603   Fax: 312-353-8098
www.exim.gov
Working Capital Guarantee: Loan guarantees to assist small to medium-sized companies having the potential to export but inability to access working capital lines of credit from their banks to finance operations. Funds can be used for inventory, working capital, materials, labor, marketing activities. Other export credit programs available include medium and long term credit, and various types of export/import insurance.

* Loans For Farmers

Farm Service Agency
U.S. Department of Agriculture
8030 Excelsior Drive, Suite 100   608-662-4422
Madison, WI 53717   Fax: 608-662-9425
http://www.fsa.usda.gov/wi/news/default.asp
The Farm Service Agency provides Direct and Guaranteed Loans to farmers through a variety of programs, including:

Farm Ownership Loans: purchase farmland, construct or repair buildings and other fixtures, and promote soil and water conservation. Up to $200,000.

Operating Loans: purchase items needed for a successful farm operation, such as livestock, farm equipment, feed, seed, fuel, farm chemicals, insurance, and other operating expenses. Can also be used to pay for minor improvements. Up to $200,000.

Beginning Farmer and Rancher Loans: provides funds to beginning and farmers and ranchers who are unable to obtain financing elsewhere.

Downpayment Farm Ownership Loans for Beginning Farmers: helps beginning farmers and ranchers purchase a farm or ranch. Also provides a way for retiring farmers to transfer their land to a future generation of farmers and ranchers. Applicant must have a downpayment of 10% and FSA with finance 40%, with the remaining balance from a commercial lender. Purchase price cannot exceed $250,000.

Loans to Socially Disadvantaged Farmers/Ranchers: helps socially disadvantaged applicants buy and operate family-size farms and ranches.

Youth Loans: Made to youths to establish and operate income-producing projects with the participation in 4-H clubs, Future Farmers of America, and similar organizations. Up to $5,000.

Emergency Loan Assistance: provides loans to help producers recover from production and physical losses due to drought, flooding, and other natural disasters, or quarantine. Up to $500,000.

Beginning Farmer and Rancher Land Contract Guarantee Pilot Program: "prompt payment guarantee" from FSA. FSA will provide payment to seller two times if the beginning farmer does not pay. Program is tested in IN, IA, ND, OR, PA and WI.

Farm Ownership and Operating Loan Guarantees: FSA will guarantee loans up to $782,000.

* Small Business Administration (SBA)

310 West Wisconsin Ave., #400
Milwaukee, WI 53203   414-297-3941

740 Regent St., Suite 100
Madison, WI 53715   608-441-5263
www.sba.gov/wi
The Wisconsin Small Business Administration Office delivers a variety of programs and services, such as startup and operational assistance through small business training and counseling, financial assistance for startup's, business opportunities and much more.

* Wisconsin Business Development Finance Corporation

P.O. Box 2717
100 River Place, Suite 1
P.O. Box 2717   608-819-0390
Madison, WI 53701   Fax: 608-819-0393
www.wbd.org
Wisconsin Business Development (WBD): Offers long-term financing at below conventional rates. Fund can be used for land, building, equipment, and certain soft costs such as architect, accounting, legal fees are also eligible. WBD participation may not exceed 40 percent or a maximum of $750,000 of the project cost.

* Venture Capital

Department of Commerce
P.O. Box 7970
Madison, WI 53707   800-HELP-BUS
www.commerce.state.wi.us
Venture capital firms are interested in investing in businesses with especially high growth potential. Venture capital firms expect to recover three to five times their investment in five to

seven years. They are typically interested in projects requiring an investment of $300,000 to $2,000,000. For more information on Wisconsin venture capital and procedures for obtaining venture capital write or call the Department of Commerce.

* Wisconsin Women's Business Initiative Corporation
2745 N. Dr. Martin Luther King Jr. Dr.   414-263-5450
Milwaukee, WI 53212   Fax: 414-263-5456
www.wwbic.com
The Wisconsin Women's Business Initiative Corporation provides business education, technical assistance and access to capital for entrepreneurs.

Wyoming

* Wyoming Business Council
214 W. 15th St.   307-777-2800
Cheyenne, WY 82002   800-262-3425
www.wyomingbusiness.org   Fax: 307-777-2838
This office can provide information and expertise in dealing with state, federal, and local agencies. They also have information on financing programs and other services offered by the state government.

Science, Technology and Energy Authority: Helps to improve the development of research capability, stimulate basic and applied technological research and facilitate commercialization of new products and processes.

Mid-America Manufacturing Technology Centers: A nonprofit organization that assists small and medium-sized manufacturers in becoming more competitive, improve quality, boost sales and locate production resources.

The state offers a wide spectrum of public sector financial and technical assistance programs.

Wyoming Industrial Development Corporation: Matches resources in both private and public sectors that best fit the needs of business.

Workforce Training: Financial support is available for on-the-job training, classroom training, or a combination of both.

Seed Capital Loan Program: The Seed Capital Loan Program makes direct loans to qualifying businesses that can demonstrate the required capital match, collateral and repayment.

Job Training Grants: Job training grants are available to for-profit businesses that have a need for specially trained employees in their workplace.

Economic Development Technical Assistance Grants: Technical assistance grants are available to for-profit businesses wanting to conduct project-planning research.

Challenge Loan Program: The Challenge Loan Program offers matching funds to a local economic development organization for the benefit of a business.

Business Permitting Assistance Office: This office provides one-stop permitting and licensing information for existing Wyoming businesses and businesses relocating in Wyoming.

Grant Station Database: The Business Council provides a database listing over 5,000 funding sources.

GRO-Biz: Gro-Biz is the Wyoming Procurement Technical Assistance center. The center assists small businesses and entrepreneurs throughout the state in selling their products and services to the government.

Industrial Development Revenue Bonds (IRB): Cities and counties can issue Industrial Development Revenue Bonds to provide financing to promote economic growth in Wyoming and to create jobs for in-state residents.

Market Research Center: The Market Research Center provides marketing information that can improve the ability of Wyoming businesses to thrive.

Tradeshow Incentive Program: The Tradeshow Incentive Program encourages Wyoming businesses promote and sell their products to statewide, national and international buyers.

Wyoming Research Products Center: The technology center helps inventors develop their technology innovations into marketable products.

Wyoming Women's Business Center: The Wyoming Women's Business Center offers a variety services to prospective and current women business owners.

* Rural Development Administration
100 East B Street
Federal Building, Room 1005   307-233-6700
Casper, WY 82601   Fax: 307-233-6727
www.rurdev.usda.gov/wy
Business and Industry Direct and Guaranteed Loans: The business and industry program provides direct and guaranteed loans for expansion and preservation of jobs in rural areas. The program can provide development credit in towns of 50,000 or less. Loan funds may be used to purchase land, buildings, and equipment; working capital; and in certain cases to refinance debts. Priorities place special emphasis on saving existing jobs as well as creating employment opportunities.

Intermediary Relending Program: The purpose of the Intermediary Relending Program is to finance business facilities and community development projects not within the outer boundary of any city having a population of 25,000 or more. This is achieved through loans made by Rural Business-Cooperative Service to intermediaries that provide loans to ultimate recipients for business facilities and community development projects in a rural area.

Rural Business Enterprise Grants: This program provides grants to finance and facilitate development of small and emerging private business enterprises in rural areas or cities up to 50,000 population, with priority to applications for projects in open country, rural communities and towns of 25,000 and smaller and economically distressed communities. Rural Business Enterprise Grants include grants made to third party lenders to establish revolving loan programs. Eligibility is limited to public bodies and private nonprofit corporations.

Rural Economic Development Loan and Grant Program: The Rural Economic Development Loan and Grant Program finances rural economic development and rural job creation projects. Loans and grants are made to Rural Utilities Service electric and telephone borrowers who use the funds to provide financing for business and community development projects.

Rural Cooperative Development Grants: Grants will be made available to nonprofit corporations and institutions of higher education for the purpose of establishing and operating centers for rural cooperative development.

Cooperative Services: Rural Business Service provides a wide range of services including assistance for people interested in forming new cooperatives, technical assistance to existing cooperatives facing specific problems or challenges, and research assistance for cooperatives dealing with changing markets and business trends.

* Department of Environmental Quality

122 West 25th Street,
Herschler Building   307-777-7937
Cheyenne, WY 82002   Fax: 307-777-7682
http://deq.state.wy.us

Small Business Assistance Visits: The Office provides free on-site assistance visits on a rotating basis throughout the state.

* Wyoming Community Development Authority

155 North Beech   307-265-0603
Casper, WY 82601   Fax: 307-266-5414
www.wyomingcda.com

Housing Trust Fund: The WCDA established a Housing Trust Fund for the purpose of financing non-traditional affordable housing other than under its tax-exempt bond program. Loans to projects from the Housing Trust Fund are often combined with other funding sources to accomplish housing goals.

Community Development Block Grant (CDBG) funds: are loaned to applicants for housing-related programs that benefit low-income households. Eligible applicants for these funds are counties and incorporated cities and towns in Wyoming.

Federal Low Income Housing Tax Credits: Housing finance authorities across the county have been designated by federal statute to administer the Federal Low-Income Housing Tax Credit, which was enacted through the Tax Reform Act of 1986. This program provides federal tax credits for developers and contractors as an incentive to develop affordable rental housing projects. An Allocation Plan may be obtained by contacting the WCDA.

* Wyoming Industrial Development Corporation

232 E. Second Street, Suite 300   800-934-5351
Casper, WY 82601   307-234-0501
www.widefrontier.com

Provides non-bank lending through various Small Business Administration programs and other public finance sources for companies with moderately strong credit risks. Funds may be used for acquiring fixed assets, renovation and construction of facilities, financing costs, or working capital. These loans range from $25,000 to $3 million, but most do not exceed $750,000. Some size restrictions and employment requirements apply. Depending on which program is used, the SBA will guarantee between 40 percent-90 percent of a loan. Terms run from between 7 to 10 years, with maturity in 25 years.

SBA 504 Program: Provides loans using 50 percent conventional bank financing, 40 percent SBA involvement through Certified Development Companies, and 10 percent owner equity. A fixed-asset loan in amounts up to $750,000. Loan can be used for land and building, construction, machinery and equipment, and renovation/expansion.

SBA 7(a) Guaranteed and Direct Loan: Guarantees up to 90 percent of a loan made through a private lender, up to 750,000. Can be used for working capital, inventory, machinery and equipment, and land and building. Available only to those unable to obtain a loan from conventional sources. Direct loans are made up to $150,000.

* Loans For Farmers

Farm Service Agency
U.S. Department of Agriculture
951 Werner Court, Suite 130
Casper, WY 82601   307-261-5230
http://www.fsa.usda.gov/wy/

The Farm Service Agency provides Direct and Guaranteed Loans to farmers through a variety of programs, including:

Farm Ownership Loans: purchase farmland, construct or repair buildings and other fixtures, and promote soil and water conservation. Up to $200,000.

Operating Loans: purchase items needed for a successful farm operation, such as livestock, farm equipment, feed, seed, fuel, farm chemicals, insurance, and other operating expenses. Can also be used to pay for minor improvements. Up to $200,000.

Beginning Farmer and Rancher Loans: provides funds to beginning and farmers and ranchers who are unable to obtain financing elsewhere.

Downpayment Farm Ownership Loans for Beginning Farmers: helps beginning farmers and ranchers purchase a farm or ranch. Also provides a way for retiring farmers to transfer their land to a future generation of farmers and ranchers. Applicant must have a downpayment of 10% and FSA with finance 40%, with the remaining balance from a commercial lender. Purchase price cannot exceed $250,000.

Loans to Socially Disadvantaged Farmers/Ranchers: helps socially disadvantaged applicants buy and operate family-size farms and ranches.

Youth Loans: Made to youths to establish and operate income-producing projects with the participation in 4-H clubs, Future Farmers of America, and similar organizations. Up to $5,000.

Emergency Loan Assistance: provides loans to help producers recover from production and physical losses due to drought, flooding, and other natural disasters, or quarantine. Up to $500,000.

Beginning Farmer and Rancher Land Contract Guarantee Pilot Program: "prompt payment guarantee" from FSA. FSA will provide payment to seller two times if the beginning farmer does not pay. Program is tested in IN, IA, ND, OR, PA and WI.

Farm Ownership and Operating Loan Guarantees: FSA will guarantee loans up to $782,000.

* Small Business Administration
100 E. B St., Room 4001
Box 2839   307-261-6500
Casper, WY 82602-2839   Fax: 307-261-6535
www.sba.gov/wy

The Wyoming Small Business Administration Office delivers a variety of programs and services, such as startup and operational assistance through small business training and counseling, financial assistance for startup's, business opportunities and much more.

Free Local Help to Start a Business

Did you know...

- ◆ SBDCs counseled and trained more than 687,000 clients in FY 2003.

- ◆ There are more than 1,100 SBDC service locations in the United States, District of Columbia, Puerto Rico, US Virgin Islands, Guam and American Samoa

- ◆ Since 1980, over 9 million entrepreneurs have received services from SBDCs

- ◆ SBDCs tailor services to the unique needs of local economies - from rural to urban, from marine services to international trade, from government contracting to homebased businesses.

Small Business Development Centers (SBDCs) could be the best deal the government has to offer to entrepreneurs and inventors, and a lot of people don't even know about them! Where else in the world can you have access to a $150 an hour consultant for free? There are over 700 of these offices all over the country and they offer free (or very low cost) consulting services on most aspects of business including:

- ◆ how to write a business plan
- ◆ how to get financing
- ◆ how to protect your invention
- ◆ how to sell your idea
- ◆ how to license your product
- ◆ how to comply with the laws
- ◆ how to write a contract
- ◆ how to sell overseas
- ◆ how to get government contracts
- ◆ how to help you buy the right equipment

You don't even have to know how to spell ENTREPRENEUR to contact these offices. They cater to both the dreamer, who doesn't even know where to start, as well as to the experienced small business that is trying to grow to the next stage of development. In other words, the complete novice or the experienced professional can find help through these centers.

Why spend money on a consultant, a lawyer, an accountant, or one of those invention companies when you can get it all for free at your local SBDC?

Recently, I spoke with some entrepreneurs who used a California SBDC and each of them had nothing but praise for the services. A young man who dropped out of college to start an executive cleaning business said he received over $8,000 worth of free legal advice from the center and said it was instrumental in getting his business off the ground. A woman

who worked in a bank started her gourmet cookie business by using the SBDC to help her get the money and technical assistance needed to get her venture up and running. And a man who was a gymnast raved about how the SBDC helped him get his personal trainer business off the ground. All kinds of businesses being started, and all kinds of compliments for the SBDC's role in assisting these entrepreneurs, in whatever they are attempting. It sounds like a solid recommendation to me.

Can something that is free be so good? Of course it can. Because most of the people who work there are not volunteers, they are paid for by tax dollars. So it's really not free to us as a country, but it is free to you as an entrepreneur. And if you don't believe me that the SBDCs are so good, would you take the word of Professor James J. Chrisman from the University of Calgary in Calgary, Alberta, Canada? He was commissioned to do an independent study of SBDCs and found that 82% of the people who used their services found them beneficial. And the businesses who used SBDCs had average growth rates of up to 400% greater than all the other businesses in their area. Not bad. Compare this to the Fortune 500 companies who use the most expensive consulting firms in the country and only experience growth rates of 5% or less. So, who says you get what you pay for?

The SBDC Program is designed to deliver up-to-date counseling, training and technical assistance in all aspects of small business management. SBDC services include, but are not limited to, assisting small businesses with financial, marketing, production, organization, engineering and technical problems and feasibility studies. Special SBDC programs and economic development activities include international trade assistance, technical assistance, procurement assistance, venture capital formation and rural development. The SBDCs also make special efforts to reach minority members of socially and economically disadvantaged groups, veterans, women and the disabled. Assistance is provided to both current or potential small business owners. They also provide assistance to small businesses applying for Small Business Innovation and Research (SBIR) grants from federal agencies.

Some SBDC Success Stories

- Ron Barillo, owner of EnSwaa Corporation in Pennsylvania, took his hobby of developing skin care products and turned it into a business. His company was doing well, but he needed help with marketing so that he could expand his business. The SBDC was able to help him develop a business plan and obtain a loan. With this assistance, as well as help with his website, Barillo's business increased four fold.

- The Hamilton Horse Cookie company in Groveland, Massachusetts was profitable, but the owners wanted to take their all-natural horse treats overseas. With the help of the SBDC's Export Center, they were able to learn which export shows to attend, how to package, label and ship their product overseas, and which companies should distribute the product. After one year, the Hamilton Horse Cookie can be found in 18 countries, with the goal of 50 countries not too far off.

- Rick Grossman of New Jersey was interested in starting a business. With the help of the local SBDC he was able to determine that the Learning Express was the franchise for him. The Learning Express is a specialty toy store that must compete with the major chains. Rick's trained staff and good news in the press has allowed the store to have better than projected profits.

- Curtis Anderson of Illinois wanted to start his own roofing company after to working for a larger roofer in the area. He and his wife attended classes offered by the local SBDC and developed a business plan. The SBDC helped the Anderson's obtain a loan from a local bank, as well as incorporate his business. He now employs 18 people and is completely out of debt.

- A married couple in Virginia wanted to start a commercial cleaning business after working for a time for a larger firm. The SBDC helped them learn how to start a business and find customers. When their business grew, the SBDC taught them what they needed to do to hire more employees. They now have many regular customers and make a nice profit.

- Kay Snipes and Terri Eager opened a tea shop in a revitalized town in Georgia. The SBDC helped them develop a business plan, examine the financing and helped with expansion. They now have tea rooms in several towns and bed and breakfasts, as well as offer a conference to those wishing to start a business.

These stories were taken from the state SBDC's websites. Check with your state to see what success stories and help they can offer.

To locate the nearest Small Business Development Center, contact your lead SBDC from the list below, contact the Small Business Administration Answer Desk at 800-8-ASK-SBA, or go online at {www.sba.gov/services}. Also see Business Information Centers on page 237.cv

Small Business Development Centers

Alabama

Lead Center:
John Sandefur
Office of State Director
Alabama Small Business
Development Consortium
University of Alabama at
Birmingham
2800 Milan Court, Suite 124

Birmingham, AL 35211-6908
205-943-6750
Fax: 205-943-6752
www.asbdc.org
Email: sandefur@uab.edu

Auburn University
Small Business Development
Center
415 West Magnolia

Room 108B Lowder
Auburn University, AL 36849-5243
334-844-4220
Fax: 334-844-4268
Email: dipofja@auburn.edu

University of Alabama at
Birmingham

Small Business Development
Center
901 South 15th Street, Room 201
Birmingham, AL 35924-2060
205-934-6760
Fax: 205-934-0538
www.business.uab.edu/sbdc
Email: sbdc@uab.edu

University of North Alabama
Small Business Development
Center
UNA Box 5159
Keller Hall, Room 135
Florence, AL 35632-0001
256-765-4629
Fax: 256-765-4813
www.una.edu/sbdc/index.html
Email: clong@unanov.una.edu

North East Alabama Regional
Small Business Development
Center
225 Church Street, NW
Huntsville, AL 35801
256-535-2061
Fax: 256-535-2050
www.hsvchamber.org
Email: egarcia@hsvchamber.org

Jacksonville State University
Small Business Development
Center
700 Pelham Road
114 Merrill Hall
Jacksonville, AL 36265
256-782-5271
Fax: 256-782-5179
www.jsu.edu/depart/sbdc
Email: klowe@jsucc.jsu.edu

University of Alabama
Small Business Development
Center
Station 35
Livingston, AL 35470
205-652-3665
Fax: 205-652-3516
http://sbdc.uwa.edu
Email: kdoggette@uwa.edu

University of South Alabama
Small Business Development
Center
Mitchell College of Business
MCOB, Room 118
Mobile, AL 36688
251-460-6004
Fax: 251-460-6246
www.southalabama.edu/sbdc
Email: sbdc@usouthal.edu

Alabama State University
Small Business Development
Center
915 South Jackson Street
Montgomery, AL 36104
334-229-4138
Fax: 334-269-1102

www.cobanetwork.com/sbdc
Email: lpatrick@asunet.alasu.edu

Troy State University
Small Business Development
Center
102 Bibb Graves
Troy, AL 36082-0001
334-670-3771
Fax: 334-670-3636
http://spectrum.troyst.edu/~sbdc/in
dex.htm
Email: jkervin@troyst.edu

Culverhouse College of Commerce
& Business Administration
University of Alabama
P.O. Box 87037
Tuscaloosa, AL 35487-0396
205-348-7011
Fax: 205-348-6974
http://sbdc.cba.ua.edu
Email: kdavidso@cba.us.edu

Alaska

Lead Center:
Jan Fredericks
University of Alaska
Small Business Development
Center
430 West 7th Avenue, Suite 110
Anchorage, AK 99501-3550
907-274-7232
800-478-7232 (Outside Anchorage)
Fax: 907-274-9524
www.aksbdc.org
Email: anjaf@uaa.alaska.edu

University of Alaska-Anchorage
Small Business Development
Center
Rural Outreach Program
430 West 7th Avenue, Suite 110
Anchorage, AK 99501
907-274-7232
800-478-7232 (Outside Anchorage)
Fax: 907-274-9524
Email: anbas2@uaa.alaska.edu

University of Alaska-Fairbanks
Small Business Development
Center
613 Cushman Street, Suite 209
Fairbanks, AK 99701
907-456-7232
800-478-1701 (Outside Fairbanks)
Fax: 907-456-7233
www.tvc.uaf.edu/sbdc.html
Email: fnsts@uaf.edu

Southeast Alaska
Small Business Development
Center
3100 Channel Drive, Suite 306
Juneau, AK 99801
907-463-3789

Fax: 907-463-3489
Email: anjas3@uaa.alaska.edu

Ketchikan Area
Small Business Development
Center
306 Main Street, Suite 325
Ketchikan, AK 99901
907-225-1388
Fax: 907-225-1385
Email: analc2@uaa.alaska.edu

Matanuska-Susitna Borough
Small Business Development Ctr
P.O. Box 3029
201 North Lucielle Street, Suite 2A
Wasilla, AK 99654
907-373-7232
Fax: 907-373-7234
Email: anamp@uaa.alaska.edu

Kenai Peninsula SBDC
43335 Kalifornsky Beach Road
Suite 16
Soldotna, AK 99669
907-262-7497
Fax: 907-262-6762
Email: inmeg@uaa.alaska.edu

Arizona

Lead Center:
Michael York
Arizona Small Business
Development Center
2411 West 14th Street
Tempe, AZ 85281
480-731-8720
Fax: 480-731-8729
www.dist.maricopa.edu/sbdc
Email:
mike.york@domail.maricopa.edu

Central Arizona College
Small Business Development
Center
1015 East Florence Blvd., Suite B
Casa Grande, AZ 85222
520-426-4341
Fax: 520-876-5966
www.cac.cc.az.us/biz

Coconino Community College
Small Business Development
Center
3000 North 4th Street
Flagstaff, AZ 86004
928-526-7654
Fax: 928-526-8693
www.coconino.edu/sbdc

Northland Pioneer College
Small Business Development
Center
P.O. Box 610
Holbrook, AZ 86025
1001 West Deuce of Clubs
Show Low, AZ 85901
928-532-6170

Fax: 928-532-6171
http://206.207.18.37/SBM/default.htm
Email: npcsbdc@cybertrails.com

Mojave Community College
Small Business Development Center
1971 Jagerson Avenue
Kingman, AZ 86401
928-757-0895
Fax: 928-757-0836
www.mohave.edu/pages/245.asp

Maricopa Community Colleges
Small Business Development Center
2400 North Central Ave., Suite 104
Phoenix, AZ 85004
602-784-0590
Fax: 602-230-7989
www.dist.Maricopa.edu/mccdsbdc
Email: rich.senopole@
domail.maricopa.edu

Yavapai College
Small Business Development Ctr
115 South McCormick St., Suite 4
Prescott, AZ 86301
928-541-1405
Fax: 928-541-1406
www.yavapai.cc.az.us/sbdc.nsf

Cochise College
Small Business Development Center
901 North Colombo, Room 308
Sierra Vista, AZ 85635
520-515-5478
Fax: 520-515-5437
800-966-7943 ext. 5478
www.cochise.cc.az.us
Email: hollism@cochise.edu

Eastern Arizona College
Small Business Development Center
622 College Avenue
Thatcher, AZ 85552-0769
928-428-8590
Fax: 928-428-8591

Pima Community College
Small Business Development Center
401 North Bonita Avenue
Tucson, AZ 85709-1260
520-206-6404
Fax: 520-206-6550
http://cc.pima.edu/sbdc
Email: sbdc@pima.edu

Arizona Western College
Small Business Development Center
281 West 24th Street
Yuma, AZ 85364
928-341-1650
Fax: 928-726-3626
www.yumasbdc.com

Arkansas

Lead Center:
Janet Roderick, State Director
Arkansas Small Business Development Center
University of Arkansas at Little Rock
Little Rock Technology Center Building
2801 S. University
Little Rock, AR 72204
501-324-9043
800-862-2040 (outside Pulaski)
Fax: 501-324-9049
http://asbdc.ualr.edu
Email: jmroderick@ualr.edu

Henderson State University
Small Business Development Center
P.O. Box 7624
Arkadelphia, AR 71999
870-230-5224
Fax: 870-230-5236
www.hsu.edu/dept/sbdc.index.html
Email: jacksol@hsu.edu

University of Arkansas at Fayetteville
Small Business Development Center
140 Reynolds Center
Fayetteville, AR 72701
479 -575-5148
Fax: 479 -575-4013
http://sbdc.waltoncollege.uark.edu/default.asp
Email: lsexton@walton.uark.edu

University of Arkansas-Fort Smith
Small Business Development Center
Fort Smith, AR 72903
479-788-7755
Fax: 479-788-7780
http://asbdc.ualr.edu/fortsmith
Email: vvanzant@uafortsmith.edu

Southern Arkansas University
Small Business Development Center
P.O. Box 9192
Magnolia, AR 71754-9379
870-235-5033
www.saumag.edu/sbd
Email: tpconsidine@saumag.edu

Arkansas State University
Small Business Development Center
P.O. Box 2650
State University, AR 72467
870-972-3517
Fax: 870-972-3678
http://business.astate.edu/sbdc
Email: asusbdc@astate.edu

University of Arkansas-Monticello
College of The-McGehee

1609 East Ash
P.O. Box 747
McGehee, AR 71654
870-222-4900
Fax: 870-222-4900
www.greatriverstech.org/SBDC/SBDChome.htm
Email: peacock@uamont.edu

California

Lead Center:
Nelson Chan, State Director
California Small Business Development Center
California Technology, Trade & Commerce
1102 Q Street, Suite 6000
Sacramento, CA 95814
916-324-5511
916-323-0459
Help Line: 800-303-6600
Fax: 916-324-5791
www.commerce.ca.gov/state/ttca/ttca_htmldisplay.jsp
Email: nchan@commerce.ca.gov

Central Coast Small Business Development Center
c/o Cabrillo College
6500 Soquel Drive
Aptos, CA 95003
831-479-6136
Fax: 831-479-6166
www.businessonline.org
Email:sbdc@businessonline.org

Sierra College
Small Business Development Center
560 Wall Street, Suite J
Auburn, CA 95603
530-885-5488
Fax: 530-823-2831
www.sbdcsierra.org
Email: sbdcinfo@sbdcsierra.org

Weill Institute
Small Business Development Center
2100 Chester Avenue
Bakersfield, CA 93301
661-395-4126
Fax: 661-395-4134
www.weill-sbdc.com

Butte College
Small Business Development Center
19 Williamsburg Lane
Chico, CA 95926
530-895-9017
Fax: 530-566-9851
www.bcsbdc.org
Email: konuwaso@butte.cc.ca.us

Southwestern College
Small Business Development Center

International Trade Center
900 Otay Lakes Road
Building 1600
Chula Vista, CA 91910
619-482-6391
Fax: 619-482-6402
www.sbditc.com
Email: support@sbditc.org

Outreach Center
Commerce Small Business
Development Center
500 Citadel Drive, Suite 213
Commerce, CA 90040
323-887-9627
Fax: 323-887-9670
www.riohondo.edu/ecd/sbdc

Contra Costa Small Business
Development Center
2425 Bisso Lane, Suite 200
Concord, CA 94520
925-646-5377
Fax: 925-646-5299
www.contracostasbdc.com
Email:
bhamile@ContraCostaSBDC.com

Imperial Valley Small Business
Development Center
El Centro, CA 92243
760-312-9800
Fax: 760-312-9838
www.ivsbdc.org

North Coast Small Business
Development Center
520 E Street
Eureka, CA 95503
707-445-9720
Fax: 707-445-9652
www.northcoastsbdc.org
Email: email@northcoastsbdc.org

Central California Small Business
Development Center
3419 West Shaw Avenue, Suite
102
Fresno, CA 93711
559-275-1223
800-974-0064
Fax: 559-275-1499
www.ccsbdc.org
Email: Dennisw@ccsbdc.org

Gavilan College
Small Business Development
Center
8351 Church Street
Building E
Gilroy, CA 95020
408-847-0373
800-847-0373
Fax: 408-847-0393
www.gavilansbdc.org
Email: shannonbishop@verizon.net

Satellite Operation
Glendale Small Business
Development Center

330 North Brand Boulevard, Suite
190
Glendale, CA 91203
818-552-3254
Fax: 818-552-3322
www.sfvsbdc.org
Email: sbdcgln@ibm.net

Outreach Center
Amador Small Business
Development Center
P.O. Box 1077
1500 S Highway 49
Jackson, CA 95642
209-223-0351
Fax: 209-223-2261
www.amador-edc.org

Yuba College Small Business
Development Center
330 9th Street
P.O. Box 262
Marysville, CA 95901
530-749-0153
Fax: 530-749-0155
Email: phpd@aol.com

Satellite Operation
Valley Sierra
Small Business Development
Center
2000 M Street
Merced, CA 95340
209-567-4910
800-323-2623
Fax: 209-383-4959
www.sbdcvalleysierra.org
Email: msoaza@inreach.com

Valley Sierra Small Business
Development Center
1013 11th Street
Modesto, CA 95354
209-567-4910
Fax: 209-567-4955
www.sbdcvalleysierra.org
Email: bearden@scedo.org

Napa Valley College
Small Business Development
Center
1556 First Street, Suite 103
Napa, CA 94559
707-253-3210
Fax: 707-253-3068
www.napasbdc.org
Email: nvcsbdc@napasbdc.org

East Bay Small Business
Development Center
519 17th Street, Suite 210
Oakland, CA 94612
510-893-4114
Fax: 510-893-5532
www.ebsbdc.org
Email: info@ebsbdc.org

North San Diego County Small
Business Development Center
1823 Mission Avenue

Oceanside, CA 92054
760-795-8740
Fax: 760-795-8728
www.sandiegosmallbiz.com
Email: centerinfor@miracosta.edu

Satellite Operation
SFV Financial Development
Corporation
12502 Van Nuys Boulevard, Suite
119
Pacoima, CA 91331
818-834-9860
Fax: 818-897-8007
www.sfvsbdc.org
Email: nevsbdc@vedc.org

Satellite Operation
Coachella Valley Small Business
Development Center
Palm Springs Satellite Center
500 South Palm Canyon Drive,
Suite 222
Palm Springs, CA 92264
760-864-1311
Fax: 760-864-1319

Eastern Los Angeles County
Small Business Development
Center
300 West Second Street, Suite 203
Pomona, CA 91766-1634
909-629-2247
800-450-72323
Fax: 909-629-8310
http://vclass.mtsac.edu/sbdc

Cascade Small Business
Development Center
737 Auditorium Drive, Suite A
Redding, CA 96001
530-225-2770
Fax: 530-225-2769
www.cascadesbdc.org
Email: nheubeck@scedd.org

Inland Empire Small Business
Development Center
1201 Research Park Drive
Riverside, CA 92507
909-781-2345
Fax: 909-781-2353
www.iesbdc.org

Greater Sacramento Small Business
Development Center
1410 Ethan Way
Sacramento, CA 958125
916-563-3210
Fax: 916-563-3266
www.sbdc.net
Email: info@sbdc.net

Satellite Operation
Inland Empire Business Incubator
155 South Memorial Drive, Suite B
San Bernardino, CA 92408
909-382-0065
Fax: 909-382-8543

San Francisco Small Business
Development Center
455 Market Street, 6th Floor
San Francisco, CA 94105
415-908-7501
Fax: 415-974-6035
www.sfsbdc.org
Email: info@sfsbdc.org

Silicon Valley
Small Business Development
Center
84 West Santa Clara, Suite 100
San Jose, CA 95113-1815
408-494-0240
888-726-2712
Fax: 408-494-0245
www.siliconvalley-sbdc.org
Email: sbdc@siliconvalley-
sbdc.org

South Central Coast Small
Business Development Center
3566 South Higuerea St., Suite 100
San Luis Obispo, CA 93401
805-549-0401
877-549-8349
Fax: 805-543-5198
www.smallbusinessinfo.org
Email:
sccsbdc@smallbusinessinfo.org

Orange County Small Business
Development Center
900 North Broadway, 8th Floor
Santa Ana, CA 92701
714-564-5200
Fax: 714-647-1168
www.ocsbdc.com
Email: roessler_michael@rsccd.org

Satellite Operation
Westside Small Business
Development Center
3233 Donald Douglas
Loop South
Santa Monica, CA 90405
310-398-8883
Fax: 310-398-3024
www.sfvsbdc.org

Redwood Empire Small Business
Development Center
606 Healdsburg Avenue
Santa Rosa, CA 95401
707-524-1770
888-346-7232
Fax: 707-524-1772
www.santarosa.edu/sbdc
Email: sbdc@santarosa.edu

San Joaquin Delta College
Small Business Development
Center
445 North San Joaquin Street
Stockton, CA 95202
209-943-5089
Fax: 209-943-8325
http://sbdc.deltacollege.org
Email: gmurphy@deltacollege.edu

Solano County Small Business
Development Center
424 Executive Court North, Suite C
Suisun, CA 94534-4019
707-864-3382
Fax: 707-864-8025
www.solanosbdc.org/index.html
Email: epratt@solano.cc.ca.us

North Los Angeles County SBDC
5121 Van Nuys Boulevard
Van Nuys, CA 91403-2100
818-907-9922
Fax: 818-907-9890
www.sfvsbdc.org
Email: vnsbdc@vedc.org

Satellite Operation
Gold Coast Small Business
Development Center
5700 Ralston Street, Suite 310
Ventura, CA 93003
805-658-2688
Fax: 805-658-2252
www.sfvsbdc.org
Email: gcsbdc@vedc.org

Satellite Operation
Victorville Satellite Center
15490 Civic Drive, Suite 102
Victorville, CA 92392
760-951-1592
Fax: 760-951-8929
www.iesbdc.org
Email: iensbdc@earthlink.net

Satellite Operation
Central California Small Business
Development Center
720 West Mineral King Avenue
Visalia, CA 93279
P.O. Box 787
Visalia, CA 93279-0787
559-625-3051
Fax: 559-625-3053
www.ccsbdc.org
Email: wendi@ccsbdc.org

Outreach Location
EDC of Tuolumne County
39 North Washington Street
Sonora, CA 95370
Contact the Modesto SBDC 209-
567-4910
or the EDC 209-588-0128

Outreach Location
Job Connection Mariposa
5078 Bullion St.
Mariposa, CA 95338
Contact the Merced SBDC 209-
388-9659
or Job Connection 209-966-6700

Northeast Los Angeles SBDC
1576 1/2 Colorado Boulevard
Eagle Rock, CA 90041
323-340-1525
Fax: 323-340-1925
www.sfvsbdc.org

Desert Communities Empowerment
Zone
Enterprise Way, Suite 6
Coachella, CA 92236
760-398-7405
Fax: 760-398-5774
www.iesbdc.org
Email: ezsbdc@earthlink.net

Inland Empire West
Ontario Office
4141 Inland Empire Blvd
Suite 231
Ontario, CA 91764
909-466-6244
Fax: 909-466-6274
www.iesbdc.org
Email: iewsbdc@earthlink.net

Central Los Angeles County SBDC
3375 South Hoover St., Suite 201
Los Angeles, CA 90007
213-821-2100
Fax: 213-746-4587

Eastern Los Angeles County SBDC
300 West Second Street, Suite 203
Pomona, CA 91766
909-629-2244
Fax: 909-629-8310
http://vclass.mtsac.edu/sbdc
Email: sbdcpom@attglobal.net

Colorado

Lead Center:
Kelly Manning, Director
Colorado Small Business
Development Center
Office of Economic Development
1625 Broadway, Suite 1710
Denver, CO 80202
303-892-3840
Fax: 303-892-3848
www.state.co.us/oed/sbdc.
Email: kelly.manning@state.co.us

Alamosa Small Business
Development Center
Adams State College
208 Edgemont Street
Alamosa, CO 81102
719-587-7372
Fax: 719-587-7603
http://sbdc.adams.edu
Email: mchoffman@adams.edu

Aurora Small Business
Development Center
Community College of Aurora
9915 East Colfax
Aurora, CO 80010-2119
303-361-0847
Fax: 303-361-2953
www.ci.aurora.co.us/
Email: businessdev@auroragov.org

Boulder Small Business
Development Center

Boulder Chamber of Commerce
2440 Pearl Street
P.O. Box 73
Boulder, CO 80302
303-442-1044
Fax: 303-938-8837
www.boulderchamber.com/chamber
/sbdc.asp
Email: Sean@boulderchamber.com

Canon City Small Business
Development Center
51320 West Highway, 50
Canon City, CO 81212
719-296-6119
Fax: 719-296-8936
Email:
allan.mconnell@pcc.cccoes.edu

Colorado Springs Small Business
Development Center
815 Eagle Rock Road, Building
202
P.O. Box 7150
Colorado Springs, CO 80933
719-272-7232
Fax: 719-262-3878
http://web.uccs.edu/sbdc
Email: sbdc@uccs.edu

Craig Small Business Development
Center
Colorado Northwestern
Community College
601 Yampa Ave.
Craig, CO 81625
970-824-7078
Fax: 970-824-5004
Email: nwsbdcfdb@springsips.com

Delta Small Business Development
Center
Delta Montrose Vocational Center
1765 U.S. Highway 50
Delta, CO 81416
970-874-7671
Fax: 970-874-8796
www.dmavtc.tec.co.us
Email: info@dmavtc.co.us

Denver Small Business
Development Center
Community College of
Denver/Greater Denver Chamber
of Commerce
1445 Market Street
Denver, CO 80202
303-620-8076
Fax: 303-534-2145
www.coloradosbdc.com
Email: susan.widhalm@den-
chamber.org

Durango Small Business
Development Center
Fort Lewis College
1000 Rim Drive
140 Education Business Hall
Durango, CO 81301-3999
970-247-7009

Fax: 970-247-7205
http://soba.fortlewis.edu/sbdc
Email: sbdc@fortlewis.edu

Fort Collins Small Business
Development Center
125 South Howes Street, Suite 150
Key Tower Building
Fort Collins, CO 80521
970-498-9295
Fax: 970-498-8924
Email: SBDC@frii.com

Fort Morgan Small Business
Development Center
Morgan Community College
300 Main Street
Fort Morgan, CO 80701
970-542-3263
800-622-0216 ext. 3263
Fax: 970-867-3352
www.mcc.cccoes.edu/Educational/
SBDC/sbdc.htm
Email:
merle.rhoades@MorganCC.edu

Glenwood Springs Small Business
Development Center
Colorado Mountain College
817 Colorado Avenue, Suite 306
Glenwood Springs, CO 81602
800-621-1647
970-928-0120
Fax: 970-947-8324
www.ColoradoSBDC.com
Email:
jlivingston@coloradomtn.edu

Lakewood Small Business
Development Center
1667 Cole Boulevard
Building 19, Suite 400
Golden, CO 80401
303-277-1840
Fax: 303-277-1899
Email: sbdcrrcc@rmi.net

Grand Junction Small Business
Development Center
Mesa State College
Western Co. Business
Development
2591 B 3/4 Road
Grand Junction, CO 81503
970-243-5242
Fax: 970-241-0771
www.gjincubator.org
Email: jmorey@giincubator.org

Greeley Small Business
Development Center
Aims Community College/Greeley
and Weld Chamber of Commerce
902 7th Avenue
Greeely, CO 80631
970-352-3661
Fax: 970-352-3572
Email: dcabbott@aims.edu

Lamar Small Business
Development Center

South Eastern C. Enterprise
Development
2401 South Main Street
Lamar, CO 81052
719-336-1586
Fax: 719-336-2448
www.ColoradoSBDC.com
Email:
Cheryl.sanchez@lcc.cccoes.edu

Pueblo Small Business
Development Center
Pueblo Community College
900 West Orman Avenue
Academic Building, Room 154
Pueblo, CO 81004
719-549-3224
Fax: 719-549-3139
www.pueblocc.edu/sbdc
Email:
Allan_McConnell@pueblocc.edu

Trinidad Small Business
Development Center
Trinidad State Junior College
136 West Main Street
Trinidad, CO 81082
719-846-5644
Fax: 719-846-4550
www.tsjc.cccoes.edu/sbdc/sbdc.htm

Westminster Small Business
Development Center
Front Range Community College
3645 West 112th Avenue
Campus Box 6
Westminster, CO 80031
303-460-1032
Fax: 303-469-7143
http://frcc.cc.co.us/pub_index.cfm?
cid=2797
Email: peter.miller@frontrange.edu

South Metro SBDC
South Metro Denver Chamber of
Commerce
6840 South University Boulevard
Centennial, CO 80122
303-540-5300
Fax: 303-795-7520
Email: skristel@bestchamber.com

LaJunta Small Business
Development Center
1802 Colorado Avenue
Humanities Building, Room 108
LaJunta, CO 81050
719-384-6969
www.ColoradoSBDC.com
Email: sbdc@ojc.cccoes.edu

Connecticut

Lead Center:
Connecticut Small Business
Development Center
University of Connecticut
School of Business Administration
2100 Hillside Rd., Unit 1094

Storrs, CT 06269
860-486-4135
Fax: 860-486-1576
www.business.uconn.edu/csbdc
Email: CSBDCInformation@
business.uconn.edu

Small Business Development
Center
10 Middle Street, 1st Floor
Bridgeport, CT 06604-4229
203-330-4813
Fax: 203-335-1297
Email: BridgeportCSBDC@
business.uconn.edu

The Greater Danbury Chamber of
Commerce
Small Business Development
Center
39 West Street
Danbury, CT 06810
203-743-5565
Fax: 203-794-1439
Email: DanburyCSBDC@
business.uconn.edu

Quinebaug Valley Community &
Technical College
Small Business Development
Center
742 Upper Maple Street
Danielson, CT 06239-1440
860-774-1133. ext. 457
Fax: 860-774-6737
www.qvctc.comment.edu/cpl/2SB.
htm
Email: danielsonCSBDC@
business.uconn.edu

Asnuntuck Community College
Continuing Education
Small Business Development
Center
170 Elm Street
Enfield, CT 06082
860-253-3125
Fax: 860-253-3067
Email: enfieldCSBDC@business.
uconn.edu

University of Connecticut
Small Business Development
Center
Administration Bldg., Room 104
1084 Shennecossett Road
Groton, CT 06340-6097
860-405-9002
Fax: 860-405-9041
Email: grotonCSBDC@business.
uconn.edu

Middlesex County Chamber of
Commerce
Small Business Development
Center
393 Main Street
Middletown, CT 06457
860-344-2158
Fax: 860-346-1043

Email: middletownCSBDC@
business. uconn.edu

New Haven Small Business
Development Center
Greater New Haven Chamber of
Commerce
900 Chapel Street, 10th Floor
New Haven, CT 06510
203-782-4390
Fax: 203-782-4329
Email: newhavenCSBDC@
business. uconn.edu

Stamford Small Business
Development Center
c/o Southwestern Area Commerce
and Industry Association
One Landmark Square
Stamford, CT 06901
203-359-3220, ext. 302
Fax: 203-967-8294
Email: stamfordCSBDC@business.
uconn.edu

Greater Hartford Area Small
Business Development Center
1800 Asylum Avenue
West Hartford, CT 06117-2659
860-570-9109
Fax: 860-570-9170
Email: WestHartfordCSBDC@
business.uconn.edu

Eastern Connecticut State
University
Small Business Development
Center
83 Windham Street
Willmantic, CT 06226-2295
860-465-5349
Fax: 860-465-5143
Email: willmanticCSBDC@
business.uconn.edu

CTSBDC
University of Connecticut
1st Floor, 99 East Main Street
Waterbury, CT 06702
203-236-9933
Fax: 203-236-9949
Email: WaterburyCSBDC@
business.uconn.edu

Delaware

Lead Center:
Clinton Tymes, State Director
Delaware Small Business
Development Center
Delaware Technology Park
One Innovation Way, Suite 301
Newark, DE 19711
302-831-1555
Fax: 302-831-1423
www.delawaresbdc.org
Email: tymesc@udel.edu

Delaware State University
1200 N. Dupont Hwy., Suite 108
Dover, DE 19901
302-678-1555
Fax: 302-857-6950
www.dsc.edu/som/entrepreneur/EN
TMAIN.HTM
Email: dover@delawaresbdc.org

Delaware Technical Community
College
Small Business Development
Center
103 West Pine Street
Georgetown, DE 19947
302-856-1555
Fax: 302-854-6979
www.dtcc.edu/owens/ccp/Pages/sb
dc1.html
Email: georgetown@
delawaresbdc.org

New Castle County Center
University of Delaware SBDC
1318 North Market Street
Wilmington, DE 19801
302-571-1555
Fax: 302-571-5222

District of Columbia

Lead Center:
Henry Turner, Executive Director
Howard University
Small Business Development
Center
2600 6th Street, NW, Room 128
Washington, DC 20059
202-806-1550
Fax: 202-806-1777
www.bschool.howard.edu/SBDC
Email: sbdc@bschool.howard.edu

Center for Urban Progress/Office
of Latino Affairs
2000 14th Street, NW, Suite 330
North
Washington, DC 20002
202-671-2828
Fax: 202-671-2597

UDC David Clarke School of Law
Small Business Development
Center
4200 Connecticut Avenue, NW
Building 38, 2nd Floor
Washington, DC 20008
202-274-7363
Fax: 202-274-7363
www.law.udc.edu/clinics/commdev/i
ndex.html

Anacostia Economic Development
Center
Southeastern University
Small Business Development
Center
2021 MLK Avenue, SE
Washington, DC 20020

202-889-5090
Fax: 202-889-9508
www.anacostiacdc.com

Howard University at
Environmental Protection Agency
Office of Small Disadvantaged
Business
Utilization Outreach Center
1200 Pennsylvania Ave., NW,
Suite 1230A
Washington, DC 20020
202-564-4584
Fax: 202-501-0756

Florida

Lead Center:
Jerry Cartwright, State Director
Florida Small Business
Development Center
University of West Florida
Downtown Center
401 East Chase, Suite 100
Pensacola, FL 32502
850-595-6060
Fax: 850-595-6070
www.fsbdc.com
Email: fsbdc@uwf.edu

Central Florida Development
Council
Small & Minority Business
Development Center
300 West Church Street, Suite 130-
A
Bartow, FL 33830
863-534-5943/5941
Fax: 863-534-7521
www.cfdc.org/smb
Email: mstan@cfdc.org

Florida Atlantic University
Small Business Development
Center
777 Glades Road
Building T-9
P.O. Box 3091
Boca Raton, FL 33431
561-297-1140
Fax: 561-297-1141
www.fausbdc.com
Email: sbdc@fau.edu

Daytona Beach Community
College
Small Business Development
Center
Center for Business & Industry
1200 West International Speedway
Boulevard
P.O. Box 2811
Daytona Beach, FL 32120-2811
904-947-5463
Fax: 904-254-4465
htttp://go.dbcc.edu/sbdc/default.ht
ml
Email: burgwil@dbcc.edu

Indian River Community College
Small Business Development
Center
3209 Virginia Avenue
Fort Pierce, FL 34981-5599
772-462-4794
866-866-4722
http://www.ircc.cc.fl.us/atircc/progr
cs/workforce/bdc/bdc.html
Email: bdc@ircc.edu

Okaloosa-Walton
University of West Florida
Small Business Development
Center
1170 Martin Luther King
Boulevard
Fort Walton Beach, FL 32547
850 863 6543
Fax: 850-863-6564
www.sbdc.uwf.com
Email: jbriere@uwf.edu

Gainesville SBDC
Gainesville Technology Enterprise
Center
2153 S.E. Hawthorne Road, Suite
126
Gainesville, FL 32641
352-334-7230
Fax: 352-334-7233
www.sbdc.unf.edu
Email: tll-sbdc@atlantic.net

University of North Florida
Small Business Development
Center
College of Business
12000 Alumni Drive
Jacksonville, FL 32224-2678
904-620-2476
Fax: 904-620-2567
www.sbdc.unf.edu
Email: smallbiz@unf.edu

Gulf Coast Community College
Small Business Development
Center
2500 Minnesota Avenue
Lynn Haven, FL 32444
850-271-1108
800-542-7232
Fax: 850-271-1109
www.northfloridabiz.com
Email: gcccsbdc@knology.net

Brevard Community College
Small Business Development
Center
3865 North Wickham Road
Melbourne, FL 32935
321-632-111 ext. 32760
888-747-2802
www.brevardcc.edu/cpe/pages/mel
bourne_home.html
Email: peakev@brevard.cc.fl.us

Small Business Development
Center
110 East Silver Springs Boulevard

Ocala, FL 34470
352-622-8763
Fax: 352-351-1031
www.sbdc.unf.edu
Email: sbdcoca@atlantic.net

University of Central Florida
Small Business Development
Center
College of Business Administration
315 E. Robinson Street, Suite 100
Orlando, FL 32801
407-420-4850
Fax: 407-420-4862
www.bus.ucf.edu/sbdc
Email: karen.ruiz@bus.ucf.edu

Seminole Community College
Small Business Development
Center
1445 Dolgner Place
Sanford, FL 32771
407-321-3495
Fax: 407-321-4184
http://sbdc.scc-fl.edu
Email: templetr@scc-fl.edu

Florida A&M University
Small Business Development
Center
1363 East Lafayette Street
Tallahassee, FL 32301
850-599-3407
Fax: 850-561-2049
www.mckayw.com/SBDC
Email:
patricia.mcgowan@famu.edu

University of South Florida
Small Business Development
Center
1101 Channelside Drive, Suite 210
Tampa, FL 33602
813-905-5800
Fax: 813-905-5801
www.sbdc.usf.edu

Escambia/Santa Rosa Counties
University of West Florida
401 E. Chase Street
Pensacola, FL 32501
850-595-5480
Fax: 850-595-5487
www.sbdc.uwf.com
Email: lstrain@uwf.edu

Kissimmee Chamber of Commerce
1425 E. Vine St.
Kissimmee, FL 34744
407-847-2452
Fax: 407-847-5971
www.bus.ucf.edu/sbdc
Email: kiss.sbdc@bus.ucf.edu

Largo SBDC
Young-Rainey STAR Center
7887 Bryan Dairy Road, Suite 118
Largo, FL 33777
727-549-6393
Fax: 727-549-6394

Manatee Community College
Small Business Development
Center
8000 South Tamiami Trail
Venice, FL 34293
941-408-1413
Fax: 941-480-3156
www.mccfl.edu/academ/WorkDep/
CorTrain.htm

Florida Gulf Coast University
Small Business Development
Center
12751 Westlinks Drive
Building III, Unit 7
Fort Meyers, FL 33913
239-225-4220
Fax: 239-225-4221

Georgia

Lead Center:
Hank Logan, State Director
Georgia Small Business
Development Center
University of Georgia
Chicopee Complex
1180 East Broad Street
Athens, GA 30602-5412
706-542-6762
Fax: 706-542-6776
www.sbdc.uga.edu
Email: hlogan@sbdc.uga.edu

Small Business Development
Center
University of Georgia Business
Outreach Center
230 South Jackson Street, Suite 333
Albany, GA 31701-2885
229-420-1144
Fax: 229-430-3933
www.sbdc.uga.edu

Small Business Development
Center
University of Georgia
Chicopee Complex
1180 East Broad Street
Athens, GA 30602-5412
706-542-7436
Fax: 706-542-6803
www.sbdc.uga.edu

Small Business Development
Center
University of Georgia Business
Outreach Center
University Plaza, Box 874
Atlanta, GA 30303-3083
404-651-3550
Fax: 404-651-1035
www.gsu.edu/ wwwspd
Email: sbdrec@langate.gsu.edu

Small Business Development
Center
University of Georgia Business
Outreach Center

1054 Claussen Road, Suite 301
Augusta, GA 30907-3215
706-737-1790
Fax: 706-731-7937
www.sbdc.uga.edu

Small Business Development
Center
University of Georgia Business
Outreach Center
501 Gloucester Street, Suite 200
Brunswick, GA 31520
912-264-7343
Fax: 912-262-3095
www.sbdc.uga.edu

State University of West Georgia
Small Business Development
Center
Room 130 Cobb Hall
Carrollton, GA 30118
770-838-3082
Fax: 770-838-3083
www.westga.edu/~busn/sbdc/sbdc.
html
Email: sbdcinfo@westga.edu

Small Business Development
Center
University of Georgia Business
Outreach Center
1030 First Avenue
Columbus, GA 31901-2402
706-649-7433
Fax: 706-649-1928
www.sbdc.uga.edu

Small Business Development
Center
University of Georgia Business
Outreach Center
Technical Building, Room 112
213 North College Drive
Dalton, GA 30260
706-272-2700
Fax: 706-272-2701
www.sbdc.uga.edu

DeKalb Chamber of Commerce
Small Business Development
Center
750 Commerce Drive
Decatur, GA 30030-2622
404-371-7399
Fax: 404-371-7484
www.sbdc.uga.edu

Small Business Development
Center
University of Georgia Business
Outreach Center
604 Washington St., NW, Suite B-2
Gainesville, GA 30501
770-531-5681
Fax: 770-531-5684
www.sbdc.uga.edu
Email: resimmon@sbdc.uga.edu

Small Business Development
Center

University of Georgia Business
Outreach Center
401 Cherry Street, Suite 701
Macon, GA 31201-6592
478-751-6592
Fax: 478-751-6607
www.sbdc.uga.edu

Kennesaw State University
Small Business Development
Center
Busbee Drive
1000 Chastain Rd. #0409
Kennesaw, GA 30144-5591
770-423-6450
Fax: 770-423-6564
http://coles.kennesaw.edu/sbdc
Email: Lydia_Jones@
coles2.kennesaw.edu

Clayton College and State
University
Small Business Development
Center
P.O. Box 285
Morrow, GA 30260
770-961-3440
Fax: 770-961-3428
www.sbdc.uga.edu

Floyd College Small Business
Development Center
P.O. Box 1864
Rome, GA 30720
706-295-6326
Fax: 706-295-6732
www.floyd.edu/sbdc
Email: matthews@floyd.edu

Small Business Development
Center
University of Georgia Business
Outreach Center
111 East Liberty Street, Suite 200
Savannah, GA 31401
912-651-3200
Fax: 912-651-3209
www.sbdc.uga.edu

Small Business Development
Center
University of Georgia Business
Outreach Center
College of Business Administration
P.O. Box 8156
Statesboro, GA30460-8156
912-681-5194
Fax: 912-681-0648
www2.gasou.edu/coba/centers/sbdc
Email: sbdc@ggasou.edu

Valdosta State University
Small Business Development
Center
Thaxton Hall, Room 100
Valdosta, GA 31698
229-245-3738
Fax: 229-245-3741
www.valdosta.edu/sbdc
Email: sbarnett@valdosta.edu

Georgia Southwestern University
SBDC
School of Business
800 Wheatley Street
Americus, GA 31709
229-931-6918
Fax: 229-931-6917

The University of Georgia Business
Outreach Services/SBDC
1000 University Center Lane
Building A, Suite 1520
Lawrenceville, GA 30043
678-407-5385
Fax: 678-407-5386

Georgia Southern University
SBDC Satellite Office
1200 Bellevue Avenue
P.O. Box 818
Dublin, GA 31040
478-274-2496
Fax: 478-275-0811

Clark Atlanta University SBDC
School of Business Administration
223 James P. Brawley Drive, S.W.
Atlanta, GA 30314
404-880-8483

Hawaii

Lead Center:
Darryl Mleynek, State Director
Hawaii Small Business
Development Center
University of Hawaii at Hilo
308 Kamehameha Ave., Suite 201
Hilo, HI 96720-4091
808-974-7515
Fax: 808-974-7683
www.hawaii-sbdc.org
Email: darryl_mleynek@hawaii-
sbdc.org

Small Business Development Park
Maui Research and Technology
Center
590 Liposa Parkway
Kihei, HI 96753-6900
808-875-2402
Fax: 808-875-2452
www.hawaii-sbdc.org/maui.htm
Email: david_fisher@hawaii-
sbdc.org

Small Business Development
Center
Kauai Community College
308 Kamehameha Ave., Suite 201
Lihue, HI 96766-9591
808-246-1748
Fax: 808-245-5102
www.hawaii-sbdc.org/kauai.htm
Email: darryl_mleynek@hawaii-
sbdc.org

East Hawaii Center
100 Pauahi Street, Suite 109

Hilo, HI 96720
808-933-0776
Fax: 808-933-0778
www.hawaii-sbdc.org/
Email: constance_cate@hawaii-
sbdc.org

Small Business Development
Center
O'ahu Center
1041 Nuuanu Avenue, Suite A
Honolulu, HI 96817
808-522-8131
Fax: 808-522-7494
www.hawaii-sbdc.org/
Email: laura_noda@hawaii-
sbdc.org

Idaho

Lead Center:
James Hogge, State Director
Idaho State Business Development
Center
Boise State University
1910 University Drive
Boise, ID 83725
208-426-1640
800-225-3815
Fax: 208-426-3877
www.idahosbdc.org
Email: info@idahosbdc.org

Boise State University
Small Business Development
Center
1021 Manitou Ave
Boise, ID 83725
208-426-1640
Fax: 208-426-3877
www.idahosbdc.org
Email: cchamber@boisestate.edu

Idaho State University
Small Business Development
Center
2300 North Yellowstone
Idaho Falls, ID 83401
208-523-1087
Fax: 208-528-7127
Email: woodrhon@isu.edu
Email: cappmary@isu.edu

Lewis-Clark State College
Small Business Development
Center
500 8th Avenue
Lewiston, ID 83501
208-799-2465
800-933-5272
Fax: 208-799-2878
www.lcsc.edu/isbdc.edu
Email: mfmatson@lcsc.edu

Boise Satellite Office
Small Business Development
Center
P.O. Box 1901
McCall, ID 83638

208-634-2883
Email: klabrum@boisestate.edu

Idaho State University
Small Business Development
Center
1651 Alvin Ricken Drive
Pocatello, ID 83201
208-232-4921
Fax: 208-282-4813
www.isu.edu/departments/respark/
bizdev/sbdc.html
Email: smallbus@isu.edu

North Idaho College
Small Business Development
Center
525 West Clearwater Loop
Post Falls, ID 83854
208-666-8009
Fax: 208-769-3223
www.nic.edu/wft/default.htm

College of Southern Idaho
Small Business Development
Center
Evergreen Building, Room C78
315 Falls Avenue
P.O. Box 1238
Twin Falls, ID 83303-1238
208-733-9554
800-6800-CSI (Idaho & Nevada)
Fax: 208-733-9316
www.csi.edu/support/isbdc/SBDC.
html
Email: info@csi.edu

Illinois

Lead Center:
Mark Petrelli
Illinois Small Business
Development Center
Department of Commerce
620 East Adams Street
Springfield, IL 62701-1696
800-252-3998
www.illinoisbiz.biz/bus/sba.html
Email: sagnew@illinoisbiz.biz
Email:
mpetrill@commerce.state.il.us

Waubonsee Community College
Small Business Development
Center
5 East Galena Boulevard
Aurora, IL 60506
630-906-4143
Fax: 630-892-4668
www.wcc.cc.il.us/business_org/sbd
c.php
Email: sbdc@waubonsee.edu

Southern Illinois University-
Carbondale
Dunn Richard Small Business
Development Center
150 East Pleasant Hill Road
Carbondale, IL 62901-6702

618-536-2424
Fax: 618-453-5040
www.siuc.edu/~sbdc
Email: sbdc@siu.edu

Kaskaskia College
Small Business Development
Center
27210 College Road
Centralia, IL 62801-7878
618-532-2049
Fax: 618-532-4983

Asian American Alliance
222 West Cermak, Suite 303
Chicago, IL 60616-1986
312-326-2200
Fax: 312-326-0399
www.asianamericanalliance.com
Email: megnakano@
asianamericanalliance.com

Back of the Yards Neighborhood
Council
Small Business Development
Center
1751 West 47th Street, 2nd Floor
Chicago, IL 60609-3889
773-523-4419
Fax: 773-254-3525
www.bync.org/small_business/inde
x.cfm
Email: sbdc@bync.org

Chicago State University
Greater Southside Small Business
Development Center
9501 South King Drive, BHS 601
Chicago, IL 60628-1598
773-995-4487
Fax: 773-995-2269
www.csu.edu/CollegeofBusiness
Email: I_conda@csu.edu

Greater North Pulaski
Development Corporation
Small Business Development
Center
4054 West North Ave., 2nd Floor
Chicago, IL 60639
773-384-2262
Fax: 773-384-3850
www.gnpdc.org/sbdc.htm
Email: sbdc@gnpdc.org

North Side Uptown Center Hull
House
4520 North Beacon
Chicago, IL 60640
773-561-3500
Fax: 773-561-3507
www.hullhouse.org
Email: jsierecki@hullhouse.org

South Side Parkway Community
House
500 East 67th Street
Chicago, IL 60637
773-955-8027
Fax: 773-955-8028

www.hullhouse.org
Email: krobbins@hullhouse.org

North Business and Industrial
Council
5353 West Armstrong Avenue
Chicago, IL 60646-6509
773-594-9292
www.norbic.org
Email: info@norbic.org

Women's Business Development
Center
Small Business Development
Center
8 South Michigan, Suite 400
Chicago, IL 60603
312-853-3477
Fax: 312-853-0145
www.wbdc.org
Email: wbdc@wbdc.org

Industrial Council of NW Chicago
Small Business Development
Center
2023 West Carroll Avenue
Chicago, IL 60612
312-421-3941
Fax: 312-421-1871
www.industrygroup.com/icnc/inde
x.html
Email: icnc@industrygroup.com

Latin American Chamber of
Commerce
Small Business Development
Center
3512 West Fullerton Avenue
Chicago, IL 60647
773-252-5211
Fax: 773-252-7065
www.laccl.com/sbdc.html
Email: gbula@yahoo.com

Eighteenth Street Development
Corporation
Small Business Development Ctr.
1839 South Carpenter
Chicago, IL 60608-3347
312-733-2287
Fax: 312-733-8242

Chicago Loop Small Business
Development Center
DCCA/James R. Thompson Center
100 West Randolph, Suite 3-400
Chicago, IL 60601-3219
312-814-6111
Fax: 312-814-5247

McHenry County College
Small Business Development
Center
8900 U.S. Highway 14
Crystal Lake, IL 60012-2761
815-455-6098
Fax: 815-455-9319
www.ccedtraining.mchenry.edu/sb
dc.asp
Email: SBDC@mchenry.edu

Danville Area Community College
Small Business Development
Center
28 West North Street, 1st Floor
Danville, IL 61832-5729
217-442-7232
Fax: 217-442-6228
www.dacc.edu/sbdc
Email: sbdc@dacc.edu

Cooperative Extension Service
Small Business Development
Center
2525 East Federal Dr., Suite 1105
Decatur, IL 62526-2184
217-875-8284
Fax: 217-875-8288
web.extension.uiuc.edu/cie/offices/
index-t.cfm?oid=228
Email: uie-
sbdc@extension.uiuc.edu

Sauk Valley College
Small Business Development
Center
173 Illinois Route #2
Dixon, IL 61021-3188
815-288-5511 ext. 320
Fax: 815-288-5958
Email: sbdc@svcc.edu

Black Hawk College
Small Business Development
Center
301 42nd Avenue
East Moline, IL 61244-4038
309-755-2200 ext. 211
Fax: 309-755-9847
Email: scalfd@outrol.bhc.edu

East St. Louis Small Business
Development Center
601 J. R. Thompson Dr.
Room 2090
East St. Louis, IL 62201-2955
618-482-3833
Fax: 618-482-8341
www.siue.edu/ESL/small_business/
small_business.htm
Email:; tmeehan@siue.edu

Southern Illinois University-
Edwardsville
Small Business Development
Center
Campus Box 1107
Edwardsville, IL 62026-0001
618-650-2929
Fax: 618-650-2607
www.siue.edu/SBA/
Email: jbagent@siue.edu

Elgin Community College
Small Business Development
Center
1700 Spartan Drive, BCC-115
Elgin, IL 60123
847-214-7488
Fax: 847-931-3911
http://elgin.edu/smallbusiness

Email: BusinessResourceCenter@
elgin.edu

The Technology Innovation Center
Small Business Development
Center
1840 Oak Avenue
Evanston, IL 60201-3670
847-866-1817
Fax: 847-866-1808
www.theincubator.com/html_docs/
sbdc.html
Email: sbdcrch@ponymail.com

College of DuPage
Small Business Development
Center
425 Fawell Blvd.
Glen Ellyn, IL 60137-6599
630-942-2771
Fax: 630-942-3789
www.cod.edu/BPI/SBDC.htm
Email: gaydav@cdnet.cod.edu

College of Lake County
Small Business Development
Center
19351 West Washington Street,
Room B201
Grayslake, IL 60030-1198
847-543-2033
Fax: 847-223-9371
www.clcillinois.edu/ddd/dept/sbd.a
sp
ecd384@clcillinois.edu

Southeastern Illinois College
Harrisburg, IL 62946-2125
618-252-5001
Fax: 618-252-0210
www.sic.cc.il.us/web2001/business
/sbdc/index.htm
Email: becky.williams@sic.edu

Rend Lake College
Small Business Development
Center
Student Center, 2nd Floor
Ina, IL 62846-9801
618-437-5321 ext. 335
Fax: 618-437-5677
www.rlc.edu/Academic_Programs/
Community_Services/BusCenter/s
mall_business_center.htm

Joliet Junior College
Small Business Development
Center
Renaissance Center
214 North Ottawa Street
Joliet, IL 60432
815-280-1400
Fax: 815-722-1895
Email: sbdc@jjc.cc.il.us

Kankakee Community College
Small Business Development
Center
Box 888 River Road
Kankakee, IL 60901-7878

815-933-0376
Fax: 815-933-0217
www.kcc.cc.il.us
Email: kcrite@kcc.cc.il.us

Western Illinois University
Small Business Development
Center
214 Seal Hall
Macomb, IL 61455
309-298-2211
TDD: 309-292-4444
Fax: 309-298-2520
www.wiusbdc.org
Email: sb-center@wiu.edu

Maple City Business and
Technology
Small Business Development
Center
620 South Main Street
Monmouth, IL 61462-2688
309-734-4664
Fax: 309-734-8579

Illinois Valley Community College
Small Business Development
Center
815 North Orlando Smith Avenue
Oglesby, IL 61348-9692
815-224-2720 Ext.212
Fax: 815-224-3033
www.ivcc.edu/conted/Small_Busin
ess_Development_Center/index.ht
ml
Email: bpalmer@ivcc.edu

Illinois Eastern Community
College SBDC
702 West High Street
Olney, IL 62450-2119
618-395-3011
Fax: 618-395-1922
www.ieccsbdc.com
Email: sbdc@iecc.edu

Moraine Valley College
Small Business Development
Center
10900 South 88th Avenue
Palos Hills, IL 60465-0937
708-974-5468
708-974-8412
www.morainevalley.edu/SBDC/def
ault.htm
Email: sbdc@morainevalley.edu

Bradley University
Small Business Development
Center
141 North Jobst Hall, 1st Floor
1501 West Bradley Avenue
Peroria, IL 61625-0001
309-677-2992
Fax: 309-677-3386
www.bradley.edu/turnercenter/sbdc
.html
Email: sbdc@bradley.edu

Triton College
2000 Fifth Avenue
River Grove, IL 60171-1995
708-456-0300 ext. 3593
www.triton.edu/community/cbpd/s
bdc.html
Email: gbarnes@triton.cc.il.us

Rock Valley College
Small Business Development
Center
3301 N. Mulford Rd, Room 277
Rockford, IL 61101
815-921-2081
Fax: 815-921-2057
http://www.rockvalleycollege.edu/s
how
Email: C.Klotz@rvc.cc.il.us

Lincoln Land Community College
Small Business Development
Center
1300 South 9th
Springfield, IL 62703-1002
217-789-1017
Fax: 217-522-3512
www.llcc.cc.il.us/bti/sbdc
Email: sbdc@llcc.cc.il.us

Shawnee College
Small Business Development
Center
8364 Shawnee College Road
Ullin, IL 62992-2206
618-634-9618
1-800-481-2242 ext. 3284
Fax: 618-634-9028.
www.shawneecc.edu/communit/sb
dc.asp
Email: benm@shawneecc.edu

Governors State University
Small Business Development
Center
1 University Parkway
University Park, IL 60466
708-534-4929
Fax: 708-534-1646
www.centerpointgsu.com
Email: h_gereg@govst.edu

Cooperative Extension Service
Small Business Development
Center
1817 South Neil Street, Suite 201
Champaign, IL 61820
217-378-8535
Fax: 217-359-1809
web.extension.uiuc.edu/cie/offices/
index-t.cfm?oid=228
Email: uie-
sbdc@extension.uiuc.edu

The Chicagoland Entrepreneurial
Center
330 N. Wabash, Suite 2800
Chicago, Illinois 60611-3605
312-494-6777
www.wehaveanswers.org/
Email: dweinstein@
chicagolandchamber.org

University of Illinois at Chicago
Small Business Development
Center
College of Business Administration
601 South Morgan St.
Suite B4UH
Chicago, IL 60607
312-413-8130
Fax: 312-355-3604
Email: freidac@uic.edu

Illinois Hispanic Chamber of
Commerce
Westside Technical Institute SBDC
2800 South Western Avenue
Chicago, IL 60608
773-843-4500

Kishwaukee College
Small Business Development
Center
21193 Malta Road
Malta, IL 60150-9699
815-825-2086 ext. 205
kish.cc.il.us/bid/small-
business.shtml
Email: bid@kougars.kish.cc.il.us

Black Hawk College
Small Business Development
Center
4703 16th Street, Suite G
Moline, IL 61265
309-764-2213
Fax: 309-797-9344
Email: scalfd@bhc1.bhc.edu

1200 West Algonquin Road
Palatine, IL 60067-7398
847-925-6000/2969
www.harpercollege.edu/learning/ce
/program/pd/sb.shtml
Email: brichter@harper.cc.il.us

Kaskaskia College
Small Business Development
Center
206 West Main
Salem, IL 62881
618-548-9001
618-548-9007
http://www.kc.cc.il.us/BusinessSer
viceCenter/SmallBusinessDevelop
mentCenter.asp
Email: dcsbdc@kaskaskia.edu

Indiana

Lead Center:
Debbie Bishop-Trocha
Indiana Small Business
Development Center
Small Business Development
Center Corporation
One North Capitol, Suite 900
Indianapolis, IN 46204
317-234-2082
888-ISBD-244
Fax: 317-232-8872

www.isbdc.org
Email: dbishop@isbdc.org

South Central Indiana Small
Business Development Center
216 Allen Street
Bloomington, IN 47403
812-339-8937
Fax: 812-335-7352
www.sbdcbiz.com
Email: southcentral@isbdc.org

Columbus Satellite Office
Columbus Enterprise Development
Center
4920 North Warren Drive
Columbus, IN 47203
800-282-7232

Southwestern Indiana Small
Business Development Center
Evansville Chamber of Commerce
100 NW Second Street, Suite 200
Evansville, IN 47708
812-425-7232
Fax: 812-421-5883
Email: southwestern@isbdc.org

Northeastern Indiana Small
Business Development Center
1830 Wayne Trace
Fort Wayne, IN 46803
260-426-0040
877-676-6160
Fax: 260-424-0024
www.neisbdc.org
Email: neisbdc@isbdc.org

Small Business Development
Center
212 North Main St.
Kokomo, IN 46901
765-454-7922
www.wdsi.org/SBDC_home.htm
Email: sstreet@isbdc.org

Greater Lafayette Area Small
Business Development Center
337 Columbia Street
PO Box 311
Lafayette, IN 47902-0311
765-742-2394
Fax: 765-742-6276
www.glpi.org/sbdc.asp
Email: grlafayette@isbdc.org

Southeastern Small Business
Development Center
975 Industrial Drive
Madison, IN 47250
812-265-3127
800-595-3127
Fax: 812-265-5544
www.madisonchamber.org/sbdc.ht
ml
Email: southeastern@isbdc.org

Northwest Indiana Small Business
Development Center
6100 Southport Road

Portage, IN 46368
219-762-1696
Fax: 219-763-2653
www.nwisbdc.org
Email: northwest@isbdc.org

East Central Indiana Small
Business Development Center
33 South 7th Street, Suite 3
Richmond, IN 47374-5462
765-962-2887
Fax: 765-966-0882
www.rwchamber.org/chamber_pro
grams.htm
Email: eastcentral@isbdc.org

Indiana State University/Wabash
Valley
Small Business Development
Center
School of Business
Ninth & Sycamore Streets
Terre Haute, IN 47809-5402
812-237-7676
800-227-7232
Fax: 812-237-7675
www.indstate.edu/schbus/sbdc
Email: SBDC@indstate.edu

Merrillville Small Business
Development Center
1919 West 81st Avenue
Merrillville, IN 46410
219-762-1696 (Portage Office
contact)
Fax: 219-763-2653
www.nwisbdc.org

Michigan City Small Business
Development Center
200 East Michigan Boulevard
Michigan City, IN 46360
219-874-6221
www.nwisbdc.org

Valparaiso Small Business
Development Center
150 Lincolnway
Valparasio, IN 46383
219-462-1105
www.nwisbdc.org

Satellite Office
Tri-State University
1 University Avenue
Angola, IN 46703
877-676-6160

Bedford Satellite Office
1116 16th Street
Bedford, IN 47421
812-275-4493

Satellite Office
Wells County Chamber of
Commerce
WorkOne Office
3156 E. State Rd 124
Buffton, IN. 46714
877-676-6160

Southern Indiana SBDC
1613 E. Eighth St.
Jeffersonville, IN 47130
812-288-645
Fax: 812-284-8315
southern@isbdc.org

Satellite Office
Kendallville Chamber of
Commerce
122 S. Main Street
Kendallville, IN 46755
877-676-6160

Linton Satellite Office
159 1st Street NW
Linton, IN 47441
812-847-4846

Central Indiana SBDC
One North Capitol, Suite 900
Indianapolis, IN 46204
317-233-SBDC
Fax: 317-232-8872
www.isbdc.org
centralindiana@isbdc.org

Nashville Satellite Office
37 W. Main St.
Nashville, IN 47448
812-988-6647

South Bend Area SBDC
401 East Colfax Avenue
Suite 120
South Bend, IN 46617
574-282-4350
Fax: 574-236-1056
southbend@isbdc.org

Spencer Satellite Office
205 East Morgan Street, Suite D
Spencer, IN 47460
812-829-3245

Iowa

Lead Center:
Ronald Manning
Iowa Small Business Development
Center
Iowa State University
College of Business Administration
Chamblynn Building
137 Lynn Avenue
Ames, IA 50014-7126
515-292-6351
800-373-7232
Fax: 515-292-0020
www.iabusnet.org/sbdc/index
Email: jonryan@iastate.edu

Iowa State University
Small Business Development
Center
2501 North Loop Drive
Building 1, Suite 1615
Ames, IA 50010-8283
515-296-7828

Fax: 515-296-6714
www.iabusnet.org

Des Moines Area Community
College
Small Business Development
Center
Circle West Incubator
P.O. Box 204
Lot 3, Industrial Park
Audubon, IA 50025
712-563-2301
Fax: 712-563-2301
www.iabusnet.org
Email: circlew@netins.net

Eastern Iowa Community College
District
Small Business Development
Center
320 W. 3rd St
Davenport, IA 52801
563-336-3401
800-462-3255, ext. 3401
Fax: 563-336-3479
www.eicc.edu/proser/biznind.html
Email: eiccdinfo@eicc.edu

Drake University
Small Business Development
Center
Drake Business Center
2507 University Avenue
Des Moines, IA 50311-4505
515-271-2655
Fax: 515-271-1899
www.cbpa.drake.edu/aspx/SBDC/de
fault.aspx
Email: drakesbdc@drake.edu

Northeast Iowa Community
College
Small Business Development
Center
300 Main Street, Suite 200
Dubuque, IA 52001
563-588-3350
Fax: 563-557-1591
www.dubuquechamber.com/Public/
Business_Assistance.cfm
Email: tsullivan@neiasbdc.org

Iowa Central Community College
Small Business Development
Center
330 Avenue M
VocTech - Room 302
Fort Dodge, IA 50501
515-576-5090
800-362-2793 ext. 2732
Fax: 515-576-0826
www.iccc.cc.ia.us/btech

University of Iowa-Oakdale
Campus
Small Business Development
Center
108 Pappajohn Business
Administration Bldg., Suite S-160
Iowa City, IA 52242-1000

319-335-3742
Fax: 319-335-2445
www.iowajpec.org/entreps/smallbu
s.html
Email: paul-heath@uiowa.edu

Kirkwood Community College
Small Business Development
Center
3375 Armar Drive
Marion, IA 52302
319-377-8256
Fax: 319-398-5698
www.iabusnet.org
Email: sspragu@kirkwood.cc.ia.us

North Iowa Area Community
College
Small Business Development
Center
500 College Drive
Mason City, IA 50401
614 -422-4342
888-GO NIACC ext. 4342
Fax: 614 -422-4129
www.niacc.cc.ia.us/pappajohn/smb
usdev.html
Email: peterric@niacc.cc.ia.us

Indian Hills Community College
Small Business Development
Center
623 Indian Hills Drive, Building 12
Ottumwa, IA 52501
641-683-5127
800-726-2585 ext. 5127
Fax: 641-683-5263
www.ihcc.cc.ia.us/ihbirc/sbdc.asp
Email: bziegler@ihcc.cc.ia.us

Western Iowa Tech Community
College
Small Business Development
Center
4647 Stone Avenue, Building B
P.O. Box 5199
Sioux City, IA 51102-5119
712-274-6418
Fax: 712-274-6429
www.iabusnet.org

Iowa Lakes Community College
Small Business Development
Center
1900 North Grand Avenue, Suite 8
Spencer, IA 51301
712-262-4213
Fax: 712-262-4047
www.iabusnet.org
Email: kmccarty@ilcc.cc.ia.us

University of Northern Iowa
Small Business Development
Center
212 East 4th Street
Waterloo, IA 50703
319-236-8123
Fax: 319-236-8240
www.uni.edu/rbc
Email: info@unirbc.org

Southeastern Community College
Small Business Development
Center
P.O. Box 180
1500 West Agency Road
West Burlington, IA 52655-0180
319-752-2731 ext. 8103
Fax: 319-752-3407
www.secc.cc.ia.us/workforce/small
bus.html
Email: jclover@secc.cc.ia.us

Kansas

Lead Center:
Wally Kearns
Kansas Small Business
Development Center
Fort Hays State University
214 SW 6th Street, Suite 301
Topeka, KS 66603-3719
785-296-6514
Fax: 785-291-3261
www.fhsu.edu/ksbdc
Email: ksbdc.wkearns@fhsu.edu

Colby Community College
Small Business Development
Center
1255 South Range
Colby, KS 67701
785-462-3984 ext. 239
www.fhsu.edu/sbdc
Email: bob@Katie.colby.cc.ks.us

Emporia State University
Small Business Development
Center
1320 Cof E Drive
Emporia, KS 66801
620-341-5308
Fax: 620-341-5418
www.emporia.edu/sbdc
Email: brumbaul@emporia.edu

Garden City Community College
Small Business Development
Center
801 Campus Drive
Garden City, KS 67846
620-276-9632
Fax: 620-275-3249
www.westernkansas.net/sbdc
Email: sbdc@gcnet.com

Barton County Community College
Small Business Development
Center
245 NE 30th Road
Great Bend, KS 67530
316-792-9214
www.fhsu.edu/sbdc
Email: simmonse@barton.cc.ks.us

Fort Hays State University
Small Business Development
Center
109 West 10th Street
Hays, KS 67601

785-628-6786
Fax: 785-628-0533
Email: sbdc@fhsu.edu

University of Kansas
Small Business Development Ctr.
734 Vermont, Suite 104
Lawrence, KS 66044
785-843-8844
Fax: 785-843-8878
www.kusbdc.net
Email: office@kusbdc.net

Johnson County Community
College
Small Business Development
Center
12345 College Boulevard
Carlsen Center, Room 223
Overland Park, KS 66210-1299
913-469-3878
Fax: 913-469-2547
www.centerforbusiness.org/progra
m.asp?ksbdc
Email: cstreet@jcc.net

Pittsburg State University
Small Business Development
Center
Shirk Hall
1501 South Joplin
Pittsburg, KS 66762
620-235-4920
Fax: 620-235-4919
www.pittstate.edu/bti
Email: drichard@pittstate.edu

Salina Area Chamber of Commerce
Small Business Development
Center
120 West Ash
Salina, KS 67401
785-827-9301
Fax: 785-827-9758
www.salinakansas.org/SBDC/Sbdc
.htm
Email: gaines@informatics.net

Washburn University
Small Business Development
Center
120 SE 6th Street, Suite 1100
Topeka, KS 66603
785-234-3235
Fax: 785-234-8656
www.washburn.edu/sbdc/index.ht
ml
Email: sbdc@wasburn.edu

WSU CCCC Outreach Center
Small Business Development
Center
Cloud County Community College
2221 Campus Drive
P.O. Box 1002
Concordia, KS 66901
785-243-1435 ext. 324
800-729-5101 ext.324
www.webs.wichita.edu/ksbdc
Email: lsutton@cloud.edu

WU MACC Outreach Center
SBDC
Manhattan Area Chamber of
Commerce (MACC)
501 Poyntz Avenue
Manhattan KS 66502-6605
785-587-9917
Email: susie.pryor@washburn.edu

Wichita State University
Small Business Development
Center
1845 Fairmount, Campus Box 248
Wichita, KS 67260-0148
316-978-3193
Fax: 316-978-3647
www.webs.wichita.edu/ksbdc
Email: wsusbdc@wichita.edu

Kentucky

Lead Center:
Becky Naugle
Kentucky Small Business
Development Center
University of Kentucky
225 Gatton College of Business
and Economics
Lexington, KY 40506-0034
859-257-7668
888-475-SBDC
Fax: 859-323-1907
www.ksbdc.org
Email: lrnaugo@uky.edu

Ahsland Small Business
Development Center
Moorehead State University
1401 Winchester Avenue, Suite
305
Ashland, KY 41101
606-329-8011
Fax: 606-324-4570
www.morehead-st.edu/sbdc
Email: k.jenkin@moorehead-st.edu

Bowling Green Small Business
Development Center
Western Kentucky University
2355 Nashville road
Bowling Green, KY 42101
270-745-1905
Fax: 270-745-1931
www.wku.edu/Dept/Support/Acad
Affairs/IED/SBDC
Email: rick.horn@wku.edu

Elizabethtown Small Business
Development Center
1105 Julianna Court, #6
Elizabethtown, KY 42701
270-765-6737
Fax: 270-769-5095
www.ksbdc.org
Email: pksbdc@kvnet.org

North Kentucky Small Business
Development Center
Northern Kentucky University

BEP Center, Room 463
Highland Heights, KY 41009-0506
859-572-6524
Fax: 859-572-6177
www.nku.edu/~sbdc
Email: landrys@nku.edu

Hopkinsville Small Business
Development Center
Murray State University
5221 Ft. Campbell Boulevard
Hopkinsville, KY 42240
270-886-8666
Fax: 270-886-3211
www.ksbdc.org
Email:
mike.carter@murraystate.edu

Lexington Areas Small Business
Development Center
4th Floor Central Library Building
140 East Main Street
Lexington, KY 40507-1376
859-257-7666
Fax: 859-257-1751
www.ksbdc.org
Email: dharbut@uky.edu

Greater Louisville Small Business
Development Center
123 East Main Street
Louisville, KY 40202
502-625-0123
Fax: 502.625.1181
www.louisvillesmallbiz.org/site/ho
me.asp
Email:
SBDCInfo@greaterlouisville.com

Southeast Kentucky Small
Business Development Center
Southeast Community College-Bell
County Campus
1300 Chichester Avenue
Middlesboro, KY 40965-2265
606-242-2145 ext. 2021
888-225-7232
Fax: 606-242-4514
www.secc.kctcs.edu/cbdc/sbdc
Email: John.Moore@kctcs.net

Moorehead Small Business
Development Center
Moorehead State University
203 Combs Building
Moorehead, KY 40351
606-783-2895
Fax: 606-783-5020
www.morehead-st.edu/sbdc

West Kentucky Small Business
Development Center
Murray State University
Business Bldg. South, Room 253
Murray, KY 42071
270-762-2856
Fax: 270-762-3049
www.ksbdc.org
Email:
rosemary.miller@murraystate.edu

Owensboro Small Business
Development Center
Murray State University
3860 U.S. Highway 60 West
Owensboro, KY 42301
270-926-8085
Fax: 270-684-0714
www.ksbdc.org
Email: mickeyjohnson@gradd.com

West Kentucky Small Business
Development Center
MSU-Harry L. Crisp Sr. Regional
Higher Ed Campus
3000 Irvin Cobb
Paduch, KY 42001
270-442-3897
Fax: 270-762-5473
www.ksbdc.org
Email:
loretta.daniel@murraystate.edu

Pikeville Small Business
Development Center
Moorehead State University
3455 North Mayo Trail #4
Pikeville, KY 41501
606-432-5848
Fax: 606-432-8924
www.morehead-st.edu/sbdc
Email: m.morley@moorehead-
st.edu

South Central Small Business
Development Center
Eastern Kentucky University
The Center for Rural Development
2292 South Highway 27, Suite 260
Somerset, KY 42501
606-677-6120
859-622-1384 (Richmond)
877-EKU-SBDC
Fax: 859-622-1413
www.centertech.com
Email: kmoats@centertech.com

Paintsville SBDC
340 Main Street Suite #200
Paintsville, KY 41240
606-788-7331
www.morehead-st.edu/sbdc

Louisiana

Lead Center:
Mary Lynn Wilkerson
Louisiana Small Business
Development Center
University of Louisiana at Monroe
College of Business Administration
Room 2-57
Monroe, LA 71209-6435
318-342-5506
Fax: 318-342-5510
www.lsbdc.org/index.htm
Email: brwilkerson@ulm.edu

Capital Small Business
Development Center

1933 Wooddale Boulevard
Baton Rouge, LA 70806
225-922-0998
Fax: 225-922-0024
Email: grspa@yahoo.com

Louis State University
Small Business Development
Center
South Stadium Drive
Baton Rouge, LA 70803-6100
225-578-4842
Fax: 225-578-3975
www.bus.lsu.edu/lbtc
Email: lsu-sbdc@lsu.edu

Southeastern Louisiana University
Small Business Development
Center
College of Business
SLU 10522
Hammond, LA 70402
985-549-3831
Fax: 985-549-2127
www.selu.edu/Academics/Business
/SBDC
Email: sbdc@selu.edu

University of Louisiana at
Lafayette
Acadiana Small Business
Development Center
P.O. Box 43732
Lafayette, LA 70504
337-262-5344
Fax: 337-262-5296
www.louisiana.edu/Research/SBD
C
Email: sbdc@louisiana.edu

McNeese State University
Small Business Development
Center
Burton Business Center, Room 423
P.O. Box 90508
Lake Charles, LA 70609
318-475-5529
Fax: 318-475-5528
www.mcneese.edu/colleges/bus/sbdc/
sbdc.htm
Email:
msusbdc@mail.mcneese.edu

University of Louisiana at Monroe
College of Business Administration
Monroe, LA 71209
318-342-1224
Fax: 318-342-1209
ele.ulm.edu/esc/sbdc.htm
Email: esc@ulm.edu

Northwestern State University
Small Business Development
Center
Russell Hall, Room 114A
Natchitoches, LA 71497
318-357-5611
Fax: 318-357-6810
www.nsula.edu/nsusbdc
Email: sbdc@alpna.nsula.edu

University of New Orleans
Small Business Development
Center
LA International Trade
2926 World Trade Center
New Orleans, LA 70130
504-568-8222
Fax: 504-568-8228
www.uno.edu/~litc
Email: litc@uno.edu

Loyola University
Small Business Development
Center
Box 134
New Orleans, LA 70118
504-864-7942
Fax: 504-864-7070
www.cba.loyno.edu
Email: sbdc@loyno.edu

Southern University
Small Business Development
Center
College of Business Administration
Room 114
New Orleans, LA 70126
504-286-5308
Fax: 504-284-5512
www.suno.edu/college_bus/progra
m%20info.htm
Email: ktousant@suno.edu

University of New Orleans
Small Business Development
Center
UNO Technology Enterprise
Center
1600 Canal Street, Suite 620
New Orleans, LA 70112
504-539-9292
Fax: 504-539-9295
www.uno.edu/~coba/sbdc

Louisiana Tech University
Small Business Development
Center
College of Administration and
Business
Box 10318, Tech Station
Ruston, LA 71272
318-257-3537
Fax: 318-257-4253
www.cab.latech.edu/public/DEPTS
/sbdc/index.htm
Email: sbdc@latech.edu

Louisiana State University
Shreveport
Small Business Development
Center
One University Place
Business/Education Bldg.
Room 103
Shreveport, LA 71115
318-797-5144
Fax: 318-797-5208
www.lsus.edu/sbdc
sbdc@pilot.lsus.edu

Nicholls State University
Small Business Development
Center
105 White Hall
P.O. Box 2015
Thibodaux, LA 70310
985-448-4242
Fax: 985-448-4922
www.nich.edu/sbdc
Email: sbdc@nicholls.edu

Maine

Lead Center:
John Massaua
Maine Small Business
Development Center
University of Southern Maine
68 High Street, 2nd Floor
Mailing Address:
    96 Falmouth Street
    P.O. Box 9300
Portland, ME 04104-9300
207-780-4420
TTY: 207-780-5646
Fax: 207-780-4810
www.mainesbdc.org
Email: mainesbdc@usm.maine.edu

Androscoggin Valley Council of
Governments (AVCOG)
Small Business Development
Center
125 Manley Road
Auburn, ME 04210
207-783-9186
Fax: 207-783-5211
www.avcog.org/business_home.php
Email: mdubois@avcog.org

Coastal Enterprises, Inc
Small Business Development
Center
Weston Building
7 North Chestnut Street
Augusta, ME 04330
207-621-0245
Fax: 207-622-9739
www.ceimaine.org/business.htm/m
sbdc/home.htm
Email: wbs@ceimaine.org

Eastern Maine Development
Corporation
Small Business Development
Center
One Cumberland Place, Suite 300
P.O. Box 2579
Bangor, ME 04401
207-942-6389
800-339-6389
Fax: 207-942-3548
www.emdc.org
Email: tgallant@emdc.org

Satellite Operation
Brunswick Small Business
Development Center
11 Cumberland Street

Brunswick, ME 04011-1903
207-373-0851
Email: jburbank@gwi.net

MidCoast Council for Business
Development & Planning
49 Pleasant Street
Brunswick, ME 04011
207-729-0144
Fax: 207-725-0989
www.mcbdp.org/sbdc.htm
Email: sgill@mcbdp.org

Satellite Operation
Calais Small Business
Development Center
Washington County Technical
College
RR1, Box 22C, River Road
Calais, ME 04619
207-454-1066
Email: srichard@emdc.org

Northern Maine Regional Planning
Commission
Small Business Development
Center
11 West Presque Isle Road
P.O. Box 779
Caribou, ME 04736
207-498-8736
800-427-8736
Fax: 207-493-3108
www.nmdc.org/bus/sbdchome.html
Email: rthompson@nmdc.org

Satellite Operation
Dover-Foxcroft Small Business
Development Center
Penquis Higher Education Center
50 Mayo Street
Dover-Foxcroft, ME 04426
800-339-6389
207-942-1744
Fax: 207-942-3548
Email: srichard@emdc.org

Satellite Operation
East Millinocket Small Business
Development Center
KATEC Center
1 Industrial Drive
East Millinocket, ME 04430
800-339-6389 (ME)
207-942-1744
Fax: 207-942-3548
Email: mballesteros@emdc.org

Fairfield Small Business
Development Center
Kennebec Valley Council of
Governments
17 Main Street
Fairfield, ME 04937
207-453-4258 ext. 16
Fax: 207-453-4264
www.ceimaine.org/business/msbdc/
home.htm
Email: trw@ceimaine.org

Satellite Operation
Fort Kent Small Business
Development Center
Aroostook County Register of
Deeds
2 Hall Street Suite 201
Fort Kent, ME 04743
207-498-8736
800-427-8736 (ME)
Fax: 207-493-3108
Email: dspooner@nmdc.org

Satellite Operation
Houlton Small Business
Development Center
39 Bangor Street
Houlton, ME 04730
207-498-8736
800-427-8736 (ME)
Fax: 207-493-3108
Email: rthompson@nmdc.org

Satellite Operation
Kittery Small Business
Development Center
Gateway of Maine Chamber of
Commerce
306 US Route 1
Kittery, ME 03904
207-439-7545

Satellite Operation
Lewiston Small Business
Development Center
Lewiston Career Center
5 Mollison Way
Lewiston, ME 04240
207-783-9186 (Auburn Office)
Fax: 207- 783-5211
Email: ggould@avcog.org

Satellite Operation
Machias Small Business
Development Center
Career Center
15 Prescott Drive, Suite 2
Machias, ME 04654
800-339-6389 (ME)
207-255-1919
Fax: 207-255-4778
Email: srichard@emdc.org

Small Business Development
Center
University of Southern Maine
68 High St, 2nd Floor
P.O. Box 9300
Portland, ME 04104-9300
207-780-4949
Fax: 207-780-4810
www.usm.maine.edu/sbdc
Email: entwstle@maine.edu

Satellite Operation
Portland Small Business
Development Center
Portland Resource Hub
441 Congress Street
Portland, ME 04101
207-756-8180

Fax: 207-780-4810
Email: burwell@usm.maine.edu

Satellite Operation
Rockland Small Business
Development Center
Key Bank of Maine
331 Main Street
Rockland, ME 04841
207-882-4340 (Wiscasset Office)
207-882-4456
Email: cfm@ceimaine.org

Satellite Operation
Biddeford-Saco Small Business
Development Center
Biddeford-Saco Chamber of
Commerce
110 Main Street
Saco, ME 04072
207-282-1567
Fax: 207-282-3149
Email: gplatt@usm.maine.edu

Southern Maine Regional Planning
Commission
Small Business Development
Center
21 Bradeen Street, Suite 304
Springvale, ME 04083
207-324-0316
Fax: 207-324-2958
www.smrpc.org/businesseconomicf
rameset.htm
Email: gplatt@usm.maine.edu

Coastal Enterprises, Inc.
Small Business Development
Center
36 Water Street, Box 268
Wiscasset, ME 04578
207-882-4340
Fax: 207-882-4456
www.ceimaine.org/business.htm/m
sbdc/home.htm
Email: drhill@ceimaine.org

Satellite Operation
York Small Business Development
Center
York Chamber of Commerce
449 Route 1
York, ME 03909
207-363-4422
Fax: 207-324-2958

Maine Small Business
Development Center Outreach
Office
Hutchinson Center
80 Belmont Avenue
Belfast, ME 04915
207-621-0245
Fax: 207-622-9739
Email: drhill@ceimaine.org

Bingham SBDC Outreach Office
Municipal Building, Town of
Bingham
13 Murray Street

P.O. Box 652
Bingham, ME 04920-0652
207-453-4258 ext. 16
207-672-5519
Email: trw@ceimaine.org

Ellsworth SBDC Outreach Office
248 State Street, Suite 3A
Ellsworth, ME 04605
207-664-2317
Fax: 207-667-4789
Email: srichard@emdc.org

Coastal Aracadia Economic
Development
Small Business Development
Center
217 High Street
P.O. Box 554
Ellsworth, Maine 04605
207-664-7457
Fax: 207-664-0902
www.acadia.net/cadc
Email: cdavisems@yahoo.com

The Thomas M. Teaque
Biotechnology Center of Maine
Maine's Applied Technology
Development Centers
P.O. Box 149
50 Eskelund Drive
Fairfield, ME 04537
207-423-4283 ext.16
Fax: 207-453-4264
Email: trw@ceimaine.org

Franklin SBDC Outreach Office
Aquaculture and Marine Science
33 Salmon Farm Road
Franklin, ME 04634
207-664-7457
207-460-4467
Email: cdavisems@yahoo.com

Maine Technology Institute
Small Business Development Ctr
2E Mechanic Street Above the Log
Cabin Fuel Building
Gardiner, ME 04345
207-582-4790
Fax: 207-582-4772
www.mainetechnology.org
Email: meriby@usm.maine.edu

Limestone SBDC Outreach Office
Loring Applied Technology Center
191 Development Drive
Limestone, ME 04750
207-498-8736
Email: rthompson@nmdc.org

Orono SBDC Outreach Office
Maine Aquaculture Incubators
Maine Aquaculture Innovation
Center
5717 Corbett Hall, Room 438
Orono, ME 04469
207-882-4340
Fax: 207-882-4456
Email: drhill@ceimaine.org

Orono SBDC Outreach Office
Target Technology Center
20 Godfrey Drive
Orono, ME 04473
207-942-1744
Fax: 207-942-3548
Email: dneuman@emdc.org

Rumford SBDC Outreach Office
River Valley Business Resource
Center
34 River Street
Rumford, ME 04276
207-363-0062
Fax: 207-363-0062
Email: bkasputes@avcog.org

Outreach Office
River Valley Precision
Manufacturing Incubator
P.O. Box 559
60 Lowell Street
Rumford, ME 04276
207-781-9186
Fax: 207-783-5211
Email: bkasputes@avcog.org

Sanford Outreach Office
P.O. Box 508
60 Community Drive
Sanford, ME 04073
207-324-0316
Fax: 207-324-2958
Email: gplatt@usm.maine.edu

South Paris SBDC Outreach Office
218 Main Street
South Paris, ME 04281
207-743-5297
Fax: 207-783-5211
Email: clogan@avcog.org

Wilton SBDC Outreach Office
862 US Route 2E
Wilton, ME 04234
207-645-5824
Fax: 207-783-5211
Email: ggould@avcog.org

Maryland

Lead Center:
Renee Sprow
University of Maryland
Small Business Development Ctr.
Administrative Offices
7100 Baltimore Avenue, Suite 401
College Park, MD 20740-3627
301-403-8300
877-787-SBDC
Fax: 301-403-8303
www.mdsbdc.umd.edu
Email: rsprow@sbdc.umd.edu

Central Small Business
Development Center
3 West Baltimore Street #170
Baltimore, MD 21201
888-898-2073

Charles County Community
College
Southern Region Small Business
Development Center
P.O. Box 910
Mitchell Road
LaPlate, MD 20646-0910
301-934-7583
800-762-7232
Fax: 301-934-7681
www.sbdchelp.com

Satellite Operation
Calvert County Department of
Economic Development
Small Business Development
Center
Courthouse Annex, Suite 101
175 Main Street
Prince Frederick, MD 20678
301-934-7583 (appointments)
www.sbdchelp.com

Eastern Shore Small Business
Development Sub-Center
Salisbury State University
PP171
Salisbury, MD 21801
410-548-3991
800-999-7232
Fax: 410-548-5389
www.salisbury.edu/community/sbd
c

Towson University
Small Business Development
Center
8000 York Road
Towson, MD 21252-0001
877-421-0830
410-704-5001
Fax: 410-704-5009
wwwnew.towson.edu/sbdc/aboutsb
dc.asp
Email: SBDC@towson.edu

Satellite Operation
Small Business Development
Center
Wye Mills Campus
PO Box 8
1000 College Drive
Wye Mills, MD 21679
888-852-6712
www.salisbury.edu/community/sbd
c

St. Mary's SBDC Satellite
CSM Training Center
21795-D1 North Shangi-La Drive
Lexington Park, MD 20653
301-866-1923
Fax: 301-934-7681
www.sbdc.help.com

Satellite Operation
Dorchester County Chamber of
Commerce
528 Poplar St.
Cambridge, MD 21613

410-228-3715
www.salisbury.edu/community/sbd
c

SBDC - Western Region, Inc
957 National Highway Suite 3
LaVale, MD 21502-7328
301-729-2400
800-457-7232
Fax: 301-729-8700
www.hagerstownmd.org/html/smal
l_business.html

Massachusetts

Lead Center:
Georgiana Parkin
Massachusetts Small Business
Development Center
University of Massachusetts
Amherst
227 Isenberg School of
Management
121 Presidents Drive
Amherst, MA 01003-9310
413-545-6301
Fax: 413-545-1273
http://msbdc.som.umass.edu
Email: gep@msbdc.umass.edu

Procurement Technical Assistance
Center
Small Business Development
Center
University of Massachusetts
Amherst
227 Isenberg School of
Management
121 Presidents Drive
Amherst, MA 01003
413-545-6303
Fax: 413-545-1273
msbdc.som.umass.edu/ptac
Email: info@msbdc.umass.edu

Satellite Operation
Massachusetts Export Center
State Transportation Building
10 Park Plaza, Suite 4510
Boston, MA 02116
617-973-8664
Fax: 617-973-8681
www.state.ma.us/export
Email: pmurphy@massport.com

Satellite Operation
Minority Business Assistance
Center
Small Business Development
Center
100 Morrissey Boulevard
Boston, MA 02125-3393
617-287-7750
Fax: 617-287-7767
www.sbdc.umb.edu

Boston College
Small Business Development
Center

142 Beacon Street
Chestnut Hill, MA 02467
617-552-4091
Fax: 617-552-2730
www.bc.edu/centers/sbdc
Email: sbdcmail@bc.edu

University of Massachusetts at
Dartmouth
Southeastern Massachusetts
Regional Small Business
Development Center
200 Pocasset Street
Fall River, MA 02772
508-673-9783
Fax: 508-674-1929
www.umassd.edu/sbdc
Email: cornwell@msbdc.umass.edu

Satellite Operation
Chamber of Commerce of the
Berkshires
Small Business Development
Center
75 N Street, Suite 360
Pittsfiled, MA 01201
413-499-0933
Fax: 413-499-0933

Salem State College
Northeast Region Small Business
Development Center
Enterprise Center
121 Loring Avenue, Suite 310
Salem, MA 01970
978-542-6343
Fax: 978-542-6345
www.salemsbdc.org

University of Massachusetts
Western Regional Small Business
Development Center
One Federal Street
Springfield, MA 01105-1160
413-737-6712
Fax: 413-737-2312
msbdc.som.umass.edu/wmass
Email:
ddoherty@msbdc.umass.edu

Clark University
Small Business Development
Center
5 Maywood Place
Worcester, MA 01610
508-793-7615
Fax: 508-793-8890
www.clarku.edu/offices/sbdc
Email: lmarsh@clarku.edu

Michigan

Lead Center:
Carol Lopucki
Michigan Small Business and
Technology Development Centers
Seidman School of Business
Grand Valley State University
510 W. Fulton

Grand Rapids, MI 49504
616-331-7480
Fax: 616-331-7485
www.misbdc.org
Email: sbtdchq@gvsu.edu

Satellite Operation
Lenaweee County Chamber of
Commerce
Small Business Development
Center
128 E. Maumee Street
Adrian, MI 49221
517-266-1488
Fax: 517-265-2432
www.misbtdc.org/region12
Email: spin@wccnet.org

Satellite Operation
Ottawa County Economic
Development Office, Inc.
Small Business Development
Center
6676 Lake Michigan Drive
P.O. Box 539
Allendale, MI 49401-0539
616-892-4120
Fax: 616-895-6670
www.misbtdc.org/region7
Email: ken@ocedo.org

Alpena Community College
666 Johnson Street
Alpena, MI 49707
989-358-7383
Fax: 989-358-7554
www.misbtdc.org-region3
Email: bourdelc@alpena.cc.mi.us

Satellite Operation
Huron County Economic
Development Center
Small Business Development
Center
Huron County Building, Suite 303
250 East Huron
Bad Axe, MI 48413
989-269-6431
Fax: 989-269-7221
www.misbtdc.org/region6
Email: carl@huroncounty.com

Satellite Operation
Mecosta County Area Chamber of
Commerce
246 North State Street, Suite B
Big Rapids, MI 49307
231-796-7649
Fax: 231-796-1625
www.misbtdc.org/region4
Email: anja@mecostacounty.com

Satellite Operation
Tuscola County Economic
Development
Small Business Development
Center
157 North State Street
Caro, MI 48723
989-673-2849

Fax: 989-673-2517
www.misbtdc.org/region6

Metropolitan Center for High
Technology
Small Business Development
Center
2727 Second Avenue, Suite 113
Detroit, MI 48201
313-967-9295
Fax: 313-967-9296
www.misbtdc.org/region9
Email: emu.sbdc@emich.edu

1st Step, Inc.
Small Business Development
Center
2415 14th Avenue, S
Escanaba, MI 49829
906-786-9234
Fax: 906-786-4442

Grand Valley State University
MI-SBTDC Region 7
401 West Fulton Street, 4th Floor
DeVos Center, 318C
Grand Rapids, MI 49504
616-331-7370
Fax: 616-331-7195
www.misbtdc.org/region7
Email: sbtdcinfo@gvsu.edu

Satellite Operation
Oceana Economic Development
Corporation
Small Business Development
Center
P.O. Box 168, 314 State Street
Hart, MI 49420-0168
231-873-7141
Fax: 231-873-5056
www.misbtdc.org/region4
Email: edcoceana1@chartermi.net

Satellite Operation
Jackson Business Development
Center
414 North Jackson Street
Jackson, MI 49201
517-787-0442
Fax: 517-787-3960
www.misbtdc.org/region12
Email:
vweaver@enterprisegroup.org

Kalamazoo College
Small Business Development
Center
MI-SBTDC Region 11
Stryker Center
1327 Academy Street
Kalamazoo, MI 49006
269-337-7350
Fax: 269-337-7352
www.misbtdc.org/region11
Email: sbdc@kzoo.edu

Lansing Community College
Small Business Development
Center

MI-SBTDC Region 8
P.O. Box 40010
520 Seymour Street
Lansing, MI 48901
517-483-1921
Fax: 517-483-1675
www.misbtdc.org/region8
Email; sbtdc@email.lcc.edu

Satellite Operation
Lapeer Development Corporation
Small Business Development
Center
449 McCormick Drive
Lapeer, MI 48446
810-667-0080
Fax: 810-667-3541
www.misbtdc.org/region6

Satellite Operation
Midland Economic Development
Council
Small Business Development
Center
300 Rodd Street, Suite 201
Midland, MI 48640
989-839-0340
Fax: 989-839-7372
www.misbdtc.org/region5
Email: kat@midlandedc.org

Satellite Operation
Monroe County IDC
PO Box 926
2929 E. Front Street
Monroe, MI 48161
734-241-8754
Fax: 734-241-0813
www.misbtdc.org/region9
Email:
mail@monroecountyidc.com

MI-Regional Small Business
Technology and Development
Center
1 South Main Street, 7th Floor
Mt. Clemens, MI 48043
586 -469-5118
Fax: 586 -469-6787
www.co.macomb.mi.us/planning/e
conomic_development.htm
www.misbtdc.org/region10
Email; SBDC@co.macomb.mi.us

Satellite Operation
Ontonagon County Economic
Development Corporation
725 Greenland Road
Ontonagon, MI 49953
906-884-4188
Fax: 906-884-6788
www.misbtdc.org/region1
Email: ontcoedc@jamadots.com

Satellite Operation
Economic Development Alliance
of St. Clair Shores
Small Business Development
Center
735 Erie Street, Suite 250

Port Huron, MI 48060
810-982-9511
Fax: 810-982-9531
www.misbtdc.org/region10
Email:
sbtdc@edaofstclaircounty.com

Satellite Operation
Saginaw County Minority Business
Development Center
PO Box 1993
Saginaw, MI 48605-1993
989-755-7630
www.misbtdc.org/region5
Email: katw@concentric.net

Satellite Operation
Saginaw Future, Inc.
Small Business Development
Center
301 East Genessee, Suite 300
Saginaw, MI 48607
989-754-8222
Fax: 989-754-1715
www.misbtdc.org/region5
Email: info@saginawfuture.com

Satellite Operation
Downriver Community Conference
15100 Northline Road
Southgate, MI 48195
734-362-3477
Fax: 734-281-0276
www.misbtdc.org/region9
Email: paulab@dccw.org

Satellite Operation
Sterling Heights Chamber of
Commerce
12900 Hall Road, Suite 110
Sterling Heights, MI 48313
586-731-5400
Fax: 586-731-3521
www.misbtdc.org/region10
Email: ladams@suscc.com

Satellite Operation
Northwestern Michigan College
1701 East Front Street
Traverse City, MI 49686
231-946-1596
Fax: 231-946-2565
www.misbtdc.org/region2
Email: tbedc@gtii.com
Email: info@tcchamber.org

Travers Bay Economic
Development Corporation
Traverse City Small Business
Development Center
202 East Grandview Parkway
Traverse City, MI 49684
231-995-2023
Fax: 231-995-2022
www.misbtdc.org/region2
Email: khornburg@nmc.edu

Northwest Michigan Council of
Governments
1209 South Garfield Ave., Suite C

P.O. Box 506
Traverse City, MI 49685-0506
231-922-3780
Fax: 231-929-5042
www.nwm.org/business/sbtdc
Email: bpalladi@nwm.cog.mi.us

Satellite Operation
Warren/Centerline/Sterling Heights
Chamber of Commerce
30500 Van Dyke Ave., Suite 118
Warren, MI 48093
586-751-3939
Fax: 586-751-3995
www.misbdtc.org/region10
Email:
jmillhench@wcschamber.com

MI-SBTDC Regional Center
Small Business Development
Center
301 West Michigan Ave., Suite 101
Ypsilanti, MI 48197
734-547-9170
Fax: 734-547-9178
www.misbtdc.org/region12
Email: sbtdc@wccnet.org

Albion Economic Development
Corporation
309 N. Superior St.
PO Box 725
Albion, MI 49224
517-629-3926
Fax: 517-629-3929
www.misbtdc.org/region 11
Email: psindt@albionedc.org

Allegan County Economic Alliance
2891 116th Avenue
M-222 East
PO Box 2777
Allegan, MI 49010
269-673-8442
Fax: 269-686-2232
www.misbtdc.org/region11
Email: aceda.accn.org

USDA Rural Development-Lake
County, Baldwin
P.O. Box 220
Baldwin, MI 49304
231-745-8364
Fax: 231-745-8493
www.misbtdc.org/region4
Email: reggie.magee@mi.usda.gov

Keweenaw Bay Indian Community
Baraga Village Office
100 Hemlock Street
Baraga, MI 49908
906-353-6237
Fax: 906-353-6100

Battle Creek Area Chamber of
Commerce
77 E. Michigan Avenue, Suite 200
Battle Creek, MI 49017
269-962-8996
Fax: 269-962-3692

www.misbtdc.org/region11
Email: Larry@battlecreek.org

MI-SBTDC Region 11
Lake Michigan College
M-TEC
400 Klock Road
Benton Harbor, MI 49022
269-926-4047
Fax: 269-926-1956
www.misbtdc.org/region11

Northern Lakes Economic Alliance
PO Box 8
1313 Boyne Avenue
Boyne City, MI 49712
231-582-6482
Fax: 231-582-3213
www.misbtdc.org/region2
Email: tom@northernlakes.net

Glen Oaks Community College
Center for Business Services
62249 Shimmel Rd.
Centreville, MI 49072
269-467-9945 ext.296
Fax: 269-467-7912
www.misbtdc.org/region11
Email: showell@glenoaks.cc.mi.us

Branch County Economic Growth
Alliance
20 Division St.
Coldwater, MI 49036
517-278-4146
Fax: 517-279-8936
www.misbtdc.org/region11
Email: bcega@bcega.com

Iron County EDC
2 South 6th Street, Suite 8
Crystal Falls, MI 49920
906-875-6688
Fax: 906-875-0657
Email: edc@iron.org

Michigan SBTDC - East Detroit
Jefferson East Business
Association
14628 E. Jefferson
Detroit, MI 48215
313-331-7939
Fax: 313-331-0311
www.misbtdc.org/region9
Email: Dinist@aol.com

MI-SBTDC Region 6
University of Michigan, Flint
432 North Saginaw St., Suite 805
Flint, MI 48502-1950
810-767-7373
Fax: 810-767-7183
www.misbtdc.org/region6
Email: hblecker@umflint.edu

Newaygo County EDC, Fremont
4747 W. 48th Street, Suite 108
Fremont, MI 49412
231-924-8890
Fax: 231-924-9250

www.misbtdc.org/region4
Email: alofgren@ncisd.net

Otsego County Economic Alliance
225 West Main Street, Room 209
Gaylord, MI 49735
989-732-6484 ext. 337
Fax: 989-732-7764
www.misbtdc.org/region3
Email: ratclifj@msue.msu.edu

Business Information Center
233 East Fulton Street, Suite 101
Grand Rapids, MI 49503
616-771-6880
Fax: 616-771-8021
www.misbtdc.org/region7
Email: garnere@kamls.org

Grayling Regional Chamber of
Commerce
P.O. Box 406
City Park/213 North James Street
Grayling, MI 49738
989-348-2921
Fax: 989-348-7315
www.misbtdc.org/region3
Email: visitor@grayling-mi.com

Finlandia University
601 Quincy Street
Hancock, MI 49930
906-487-7344
Fax: 906-487-7290
Email:
Joanne.macinnes@finlandia.edu

Hastings Industrial Incubator
1035 E. State Street
Hastings, MI 49058
269-945-2468
Fax: 269-962-6309
www.misbtdc.org/region11

Mid Michigan Community College
M-TEC Building
1375 South Clare Avenue
Harrison, MI 48625
989-802-0993
Fax: 989-802-0971
www.misbtdc.org/region4
Email: melliott@midmich.edu

Holland Area Chamber of
Commerce
272 East 8th Street
Holland, MI 49432
616-392-9719
www.misbtdc.org/region7
Email: sbdc@chamber-holland.org

Houghton Lake Chamber of
Commerce
1625 West Houghton Lake Drive
Houghton Lake, MI 48629
989-366-5644
Fax: 989-366-9472
www.misbtdc.org/region3
Email: hlcc@iserve.net

Satellite Office
Lansing Community College
Howell Center
1600 Pinckney Rd
Howell, MI 49943
517-545-3522
Fax: 517-545-3525
www.misbtdc.org/region8
Email: dennisw@brightoncoc.org

Dickinson Area Partnership
600 South Stephenson Avenue
Iron Mountain, MI 49801
906-774-2002
Fax: 906-774-2004

Greater Gratiot Development, Inc.,
Ithaca
136 South Main
Ithaca, MI 48847
989-875-2083
Fax: 989-875-2990
www.misbtdc.org/region4
Email: don.schurr@gratiot.org

Michigan SBTDC
Western Wayne Co.
Schoolcraft College
18600 Haggerty
Livonia, MI 48152
734-462-4438
Fax: 734-462-4439
www.misbtdc.org/region9
Email:
vmathur@schoolcraft.cc.mi.us

Manistee Economic Council &
Chamber Alliance
50 Filer Street, Suite 224
Manistee, MI 49660
231-723-4325
Fax: 231-723-1515
Email: tkubanek@manistee.com

Schoolcraft County EDC
PO Box 277
Manistique, MI 49854
906-341-5126
Fax: 906-341-5555

Lake Superior Community
Partnership
501 South Front Street
Marquette, MI 49855
906-226-6591
Fax: 906-226-2099

Marshall Chamber of Commerce
424 E. Michigan Ave.
Marshall, MI 49068
269-781-5163
Fax: 269-781-6570
www.misbtdc.org/region11
Email: mea@voyager.net

River Cities Regional Chamber of
Commerce
1005 Tenth Avenue
Menominee, MI 49858
906-863-2679
Fax: 906-863-3288

Mid Michigan Community College,
Mt. Pleasant Campus
5805 E. Pickard Street
Mt. Pleasant, MI 48858
989-773-6622
Fax: 989-772-2386
www.misbtdc.org/region4
Email: pfairchi@midmich.edu

Muskegon Area Chamber of
Commerce
900 Third Street, Suite 200
Muskegon, MI 49440
231-722-3751
Fax: 231-728-7251
www.misbtdc.org/region7
Email: sbdcinfo@gvsu.edu

Luce County EDC
401 W. Harrie Street
Newberry, MI 49868
906-293-5982
Fax: 906-293-2904
Email: mclaren@up.net

Southwestern Michigan College
Business Development
2229 US 12 East
Niles, MI 49120
269-687-5640
Fax: 269-687-5655
www.misbtdc.org/region11
Email: jcousins@skyenet.net

Alpena Community College/Huron
Shores Campus
5800 Skeel Avenue
Oscoda, MI 48750
989-358-7375
Fax: 989-358-7554
www.misbtdc.org-region3
Email: mehargk@alpenacc.edu

MSU Extension Center - Van
Buren
226 East Michigan Ave.
Paw Paw, MI 49079
269-655-8308
Fax: 269-655-8307
www.misbtdc.org/region11
Email: thomasm@msue.msu.edu

Michigan SBTDC - Northern
Oakland Co.
Oakland University, School of
Business Administration
238H Elliott Hall
Rochester, MI 48309-4493
248-370-2726
Fax: 248-370-4963
www.misbtdc.org/region9
Email:
oaklanduniversity.sbdc@emich.edu

Presque Isle County EDC
658 South Bradley Highway
Rogers City, MI 49779
989-734-8446
Fax: 989-734-2577

www.misbtdc.org/region3
Email: heidemam@msue.msu.edu

Higgins Lake-Roscommon
Chamber of Commerce
P.O. Box 486
701 Lake Street
Roscommon, MI 48653
989-275-8760
Fax: 989-275-2029
www.misbtdc.org/region3
Email: hlrcc@voyager.net

MI-SBTDC Region 5
Delta College Corporate Services
310 Johnson Street, Suite 245
Saginaw, MI 48607
989-686-9597
Fax: 989-667-2222
www.misbtdc.org/region5
Email: sbtdc@corpserv.delta.edu

Biz Resource Center
Michigan Works! Service Center
3875 Bay Road, Suite 7
Saginaw, MI 48603
989-249-5232
www.misbtdc.org/region5

Sault Area Chamber of Commerce
2581 I-75 Business Spur
Sault Ste. Marie, MI 49783
906-632-3301
Fax: 906-632-2331
Email:
saultchamber@30below.com

Mackinac County EDC
100 South Marley
St. Ignace, MI 49781
906-643-0356
Fax: 906-643-6581
Email: edc@mackinaccounty.net

Ogemaw County EDC
205 South Eight Street
West Branch, MI 48661
989-345-0692
Fax: 989-345-1284
www.misbtdc.org-region3
Email: zoiay@msue.msu.edu

MI-SBTDC Regional Center
Eastern Michigan University
306 Gary M. Owen Building
300 West Michigan Avenue
Ypsilanti, MI 48197
734-487-0355
734-481-3354
www.misbtdc.org/region9
Email: emu.sbdc@emich.edu

Minnesota

Lead Center:
Mary Kruger
Minnesota Small Business
Development Center

Department of Trade and Economic
Development
500 Metro Square Building
121 7th Place East
St. Paul, MN 55101-2146
651-297-5773
Fax: 651-296-1290
www.dted.state.mn.us
Email: mary.kruger@state.mn.us

Central Lakes College
Small Business Development
501 West College Drive
Brainerd, MN 56401
218-855-8142
Fax: 218-855-8141
www.clcmn.edu/smallbusiness
Email: gbergman@clcmn.edu

University of Minnesota at Duluth
Small Business Development
Center
11 East Superior Street, Suite 210
Duluth, MN 55802
218-726-6192
888 387 4594
Fax: 218-726-6338
www.umdced.com
Email: lbujold@umdced.com

Vermillion Community College
Small Business Development Sub-
Center
1900 East Camp Street, Room PE
140
Ely, MN 55731
218 365 7295
Fax: 218 365 2248
www.umdced.com
Email: jzigich@umdced.com

Itasca Development Corporation
Small Business Development Sub-
Center
12 NW 3rd Street
Grand Rapids, MN 55744
218-327-2241
Fax: 218-327-2242
www.umdced.com
Email: mikea@itascadv.org

Hibbing Community College
Small Business Development Sub-
Center
1515 East 25th Street
Hibbing, MN 55746
218-262-6703
Fax: 218-262-6717
www.umdced.com
Email: jtolan@umdced.com

Small Business Development
Center
Rainy River Community College
1501 Highway 71
International Falls, MN 56649
218-285-2255
Fax: 218-285-2239
www.umdced.com

Copyright © 2004 Matthew Lesko, Information USA, Inc., 12081 Nebel Street, Rockville, MD 20852 • 1-800-955-7693 • www.lesko.com

Region Nine Development
Commission
Small Business Development
Center
P.O. Box 3367
410 Jackson Street
Mankato, MN 56002-3367
507-387-5643
800-450-5643
Fax: 507-387-7105
www.rndc.org/programs/sbdc

Southwest State University
Small Business Development
Center
ST #105, 1505 State Street
Marshall, MN 56258
507-537-7386
Fax: 507-537-6094
www.southwest.msus.edu
Email:
struve@ssu.southwest.msus.edu

University of St. Thomas
Small Business Development
Center
Graduate School of Business
1000 LaSalle Avenue, TMH
#100LL
Minneapolis, MN 55403
651-962-4500
800-328-6819 ext. 2-4500
Fax: 651-962-4508
www.stthomas.edu/sbdc
Email: smallbus@stthomas.edu

Moorhead State University
Small Business Development
Center
Box 132
1104 7th Avenue South
Moorhead, MN 56563
218-477-2289
www.mnstate.edu/cbi
Email: sliwoski@mnstate.edu

Pine Technical College
Small Business Development Sub-
Center
1000 4th Street
Pine City, MN 55063
320-629-7340
Fax: 320-629-7603

Rochester Community and
Technical College
Small Business Development
Center
Riverland Hall
851 30th Avenue, SE
Rochester, NN 55904
507-285-7536
Fax: 507-280-5502
www.roch.edu/rctc/workforce/CE
WEDIndex/business.html
Email:
michelle.pyfferoen@roch.edu

St. Cloud State University
Small Business Development Ctr

Business Resource Center
720 4th Avenue, South
St. Cloud, MN 56301-3761
320-255-4842
Fax: 320-255-4957
Email: djensen@stcloudstate.edu

North Shore Business Enterprise
Center
Small Business Development Sub-
Center
1313 Fairgrounds Road
P.O. Box 240
Two Harbors, MN 55616
218-834-3494
888-387-4594
www.umdced.com
Email: hhelgen@umdced.com

Bemidji State University
Center for Research and Innovation
3801 Bemidji Avenue North
Bemidji, MN 56601
218-755-4900
www.cri-bsu.org/SBDC/index.html
Email: cfalk@bemidjistate.edu

University of Minnesota Duluth
Center for Economic Development
Natural Resources Research
Institute
5013 Miller Trunk Highway
Hermantown, MN 55611
218-726-7298
888-387-4594
Fax: 218-726-6338
Email: www.umdced.com

Mesabi Range Community &
Technical College
1001 Chestnut Street West
Virginia, MN 55792
218-749-7752
888-387-4594
www.umdced.com
Email: rbraun@umdced.com

Mississippi

Lead Center:
Walter Gurley, Jr.
Mississippi Small Business
Development Center
University of Mississippi
P.O. Box 1848
B19 Jeanette Phillips Drive
University, MS 38677-1848
662-915-5001
800-725-7232 (MS)
Fax: 662-915-5650
www.olemiss.edu/depts/mssbdc
Email: msbdc@olemiss.edu

Northeast Mississippi Community
College
Small Business Development
Center
Holliday Hall 303
Cunningham Boulevard

Booneville, MS 38829
662-720-7448
Fax: 662-720-7464

Delta State University
Small Business Development
Center
P.O. Box 3235 DSU
Cleveland, MS 38733
662-846-4236
Fax: 662-846-4235
www.deltastate.edu/sbdc/online
Email: dsusbdc@deltastate.edu

East Central Community College
Small Business Development
Center
P.O. Box 129
275 Broad Street
Decatur, MS 39327
601-635-2111 ext. 297
Fax: 601-635-4031
www.eccc.edu/PROGRAMS/onest
op/#F
Email: rwestbrook@eccc

Jones Jr. College
Small Business Development
Center
900 Court Street
Ellisville, MS 39437
601-477-4235
Fax: 601-477-4166
www.jcjc.cc.ms.us/depts/crc/sbdc.h
tml
Email: greg.butler@jcjc.cc.ms.us

Mississippi Gulf Coast Community
College
Small Business Development
Center
P.O. Box 100
2300 Highway 90
Gautier, MS 39553
228-497-7723
Fax: 228-497-7788
Email:
janice.mabry@mgccc.cc.ms.us

Delta Community College
Small Business Development
Center
P.O. Box 5607
1656 East Union
Greenville, MS 38704-5607
662-378-8183
Fax: 662-378-5349
Email: mdccsbdc@tecinfo.com

Pearl River Community College
Small Business Development
Center
Highway 49 South
Forrest County Center, Building 1
Hattiesburg, MS 39401
601-544-5533
Fax: 601-544-5549
www.prcc.edu/fcc/smallbusiness.ht
m
Email: sbdc@prcc.cc.ms.us

Jackson State University
JSU Small Business Development
Center
JSU Mississippi E-Center
1230 Raymond Road, Box 500
Jackson, MS 39204
601-979-2795
Email: hthomas@jsums.edu

University of Southern Mississippi
Small Business Development
Center
136 Beach Park Place
Long Beach, MS 39560
228-865-4578
Fax: 228-865-4581
www.gp.usm.edu/sbdc/index.html
Email: Jill.Scafide@usm.edu

Alcorn State University
Small Business Development
Center
1000 ASU Drive #90
Alcorn State, MS 39096-7500
601-877-3901
601-877-6450
Fax: 601-877-3900
www.alcorn.edu/Outreach/Sbdc.htm
Email:
gpurohit@lorman.alcorn.edu

Co-Lin Community College
Small Business Development
Center
11 Co-Lin Circle
Natchez, MS 39120
601-445-5254
Fax: 601-446-1221
www.colin.edu/communityservi/W
orkforce_Dev_Center/small_busine
ss_development_cente.htm
Email: RobertRuss@colin.edu

Hinds Community College
Small Business Development
Center
International Trade Center
PMB 11263
1500 Raymond Lake Rd, 3rd Flr
PO Box 1100
Raymond, MS 39154-1100
601-857-3536
Fax: 601-857-3474
www.hindscc.edu/Departments/RC
U/Small_Business_Development_
Center
Email: mhwall@hindscc.edu

Mississippi State University
Small Business Development
Center
Mississippi Research &
Technology Park
The Technology Center, Suite 201
Starkville, MS 39760
662-325-8684
Fax: 662-325-4016
www.cbi.msstate.edu/cobi/sbdc/sbd
c.html
Email: sfisher@cobilan.msstate.edu

Southwest MS Community College
Small Business Development
Center
College Drive
Summit, MS 39666
601-276-3890
Fax: 601-276-3883
www.smcc.cc.ms.us/support/ccente
r/webdoc6.htm
Email: waller@smcc.cc.ms.us

University of Mississippi
Small Business Development
Center
P.O. Box 1848
B19 Jeanette Phillips Drive
University, MS 38677-1848
662-234-2120
662-951-1291
Fax: 662-951-5650
www.olemiss.edu/depts/umsbdc
Email: sbdc@olemiss.edu

Greenville Higher Education
Center
Small Business Development
Center
DSU Office Suite 332
2900 A Hwy 1 South
Greenville, MS 38701
662-378-8589
www.deltastate.edu/sbdc/online
Email: dsusbdc@deltastate.edu

Missouri

Lead Center:
Max Summers
Missouri Small Business
Development Center
University of Missouri-System
1205 University Avenue, Suite 300
Columbia, MO 65211
573-882-0344
Fax: 573-884-4297
www.mo-sbdc.org
Email: sbdcmso@missouri.edu

Southeast Missouri State
University
Small Business Development Ctr
Rovert A Dempster Hall
One University Plaza MS-5925
Cape Girardeau, MO 63701
573-986-6084
Fax: 573-986-6083
www2.semo.edu/sesbdc/homepage.
html
Email: c402sbi@semovm.semo.edu

Satellite Operation
Small Business Development
Center
Chillicothe City Hall
715 Washington Street
Chillicothe, MO 64601-2229
660-646-6920
Fax: 660-646-6811
Email: lkturner@greenhills.net

University of Missouri at Columbia
Small Business Development
Center
306 Cornell Hall
Columbia, MO 65211
573-882-7096
Fax: 573-882-9931
http://business.missouri.edu/sbdc/
Email: eastinb@missouri.edu

Missouri Southern State College
Small Business Development
Center
3950 Newman Road
Joplin, MO 64801-1595
417-625-3128
Fax 417-625-9782
www.msscsbdc.com
Email: krudwig-j@mssu.edu

Truman State University
Small Business Development
Center
100 East Normal
Kirksville, MO 63501-4221
660-785-4307
www.sbdc.truman.edu
Email: sbdck@missouri.edu

Northwest Missouri State
University
Small Business Development
Center
McKmey Center for Lifelong
Learning
800 University Drive
Maryville, MO 64468
660-562-1701
Fax: 660-562-1890
www.nwmissouri.edu/sbdc
Email: sbdcm@missouri.edu

Southwest Missouri State
University
Small Business Development Ctr
Center for Business Research
901 South National
Springfield, MO 65804-0089
417-836-5685
Fax: 417-836-7666
www.sbdc.smsu.edu
Email: sbdcs@missouri.edu

Satellite Operation
St. Joseph Satellite Center
3003 Frederick Avenue
St. Joseph, MO 64506
816-232-4461
Fax: 816-364-4873
www.nwmissouri.edu/sbdc
darnellsbdc@saintjoseph.com

St. Louis Enterprise Center
315 Lemay Ferry Road, Suite 131
St. Louis, MO 63125
314-631-5327
Fax: 314-631-7996
http://mo-
sbdc.org/stlouis/index.html
Email: RichteA@missouri.edu

Central Missouri State University
Small Business Development
Center
Dockery Suite 102
Warrensburg, MO 64093-5037
660-543-4402
Fax: 660-543-8159
www.cmsu.edu/sbdc
Email: sbdc@cmsu1.cmsu.edu

Southwestern Missouri State
University-West Plains
Small Business Development
Center
128 Garfield
West Plains, MO 65775-2715
417-255-7966
Email: sbdc@wp.smsu.edu

University of Missouri-Kansas City
Small Business Development
Center
4747 Troost, Suite 113B
Kansas City, MO 64110
816-235-6063
Fax: 816-235-5754
www.bloch.umkc.edu/sbdc/index.h
tm
Email: sbdckc@missouri.edu

Kansas City Satellite Center
1901 NE 48th Street
Kansas City, MO 64118
816-792-7720
Email:
reuben.siverling@rockhurst.edu

SBA St. Louis District Office
200 N Broadway, Suite 1500
St. Louis, MO 63102
314-539-6600 ext. 227
Fax: 314-539-3785
www.mo-
sbdc.org/stlouis/index.html
Email:
JakubovskisA@missouri.edu

St. Louis Empowerment Zone
100 N Tucker Blvd, Suite 530
St. Louis, MO 63101
314-241-1511
Fax: 314-241-4099
http://www.mo-
sbdc.org/stlouis/index.html
Email: williamsand@missouri.edu

5988 Mid Rivers Mall Drive
St. Charles, MO 63304-7119
636-928-7714
www.mo-
sbdc.org/stlouis/index.html
Email: muellerrf@missouri.edu

Montana

Lead Center:
Ann Desch
Montana Small Business
Development Center
Department of Commerce

301 S. Park Ave.
Helena, MT 59620
406-841-2747
Fax: 406-841-2728
http://commerce.state.mt.us/brd/brd
_sbdc.html

Billings Small Business
Development Center
Big Sky Economic Development
Authority
222 North 32nd Street
Billings, MT 59101
406-256-6871
Fax: 406-256-6877
www.bigskyeda.org/SBDC/index.h
tm
Email: langman@bigskyeda.org

Bozeman Small Business
Development Center
Gallatin Development corporation
222 East Main, Suite 102
Bozeman, MT 59715
406-587-3113
Fax: 406-587-9565
www.bozeman.org/cgi-
bin/gdc/small_biz_dev_center
Email: askus@bozeman.org

Butte Small Business Development
Center
Headquarters RC&D
305 West Mercury, Suite 211
Butte, MT 59701
406-782-7333
Fax: 406-782-9675
http://hosts4.in-tch.com/www.headw
atersrcd.org/redisbdc.htm
Email:
jdonovan@headwatersrcd.org

Colstrip Small Business
Development Center
Southeastern Montana
Development Corporation
P.O. Box 1935
6200 Main Street
Colstrip, MT 59323
406-748-2990
Fax: 406-748-2990
www.semdc.org
Email: semdc.org@mcn.net

Great Falls Small Business
Development Center
High Plains Development
Authority
710 1st Avenue North
P.O. Box 2568
Great Falls, MT 59403-2568
406-453-8834
Fax: 406-454-2995
www.gfdevelopment.org/smallbiz.
htm
Email: suzie@gfdevelopment.org

Havre Small Business
Development Center

Bear Paw Development
Corporation
P.O. Box 170
48 2nd Avenue
Havre, MT 59501
406-265-4945
Fax: 406-265-5602
www.bearpaw.org/
small_business_development_cente
r.htm
Email: tjette@bearpaw.org

Helena Small Business
Development Center
Gateway Economic Development
Corporation
225 Cruise Ave
Helena, MT 59601
406-447-1512
Fax: 406-447-1514
www.gatewayedc.org/sbdc.htm
Email: hlnsbdc@mt.net

Kalispell Area Chamber of
Commerce
Small Business Development
Center
15 Depot Park
Kalispell, MT 59901
406-758-2802
Fax: 406-758-2805
www.kalispellsmallbusiness.com
Email: kalsbdc@centrurytel.net

Missoula Community Development
Corporation
Small Business Development
Center
110 East Broadway, Second Floor
Missoula, MT 59802
406-728-9234
Fax: 406-542-6671
www.mtcdc.org/sbdc.html
Email: mcdc@mtcdc.org

Wolf Point Small Business
Development Center
233 Cascade Street
Wolf Point, MT 59201
406-653-2590
Fax: 406-653-1840
www.gndc.org/sbdc.htm

Nebraska

Lead Center:
Robert Bernier
Nebraska Business Development
Center
University of Nebraska at Omaha
College of Business Administration
Roskens Hall, Room 415
Omaha, NE 68182
402-554-2521
Fax: 402-554-3473
http://nbdc.unomaha.edu
Email:
robert_bernier@unomaha.edu

University of Nebraska at Kearney
Nebraska Business Development
Center
1917 W. 24th Street
West Center Bldg, Room 135
Kearney, NE 68849-3035
308-865-8344
Fax: 308-865-8153
www.unk.edu/departments/NBDC
Email: ingersollo@unk.edu

Nebraska Business Development
Center
1135 M Street, Suite 200
Lincoln, NE 68508
402-472-3358
Fax: 402-472-3363
NBDCLincolnNE@aol.com

Northeast Community College
Lifelong Learning Center
801 East Benjamin Avenue
Norfolk, NE 68702-0469
402-844-7234
Email: rheld@mail.unomaha.edu

Nebraska Business Development
Center
Mid Plains Voc. Tech. Campus
1101 Halligan Drive, Room 409B
North Platte, NE 69101
308-534-5115
Email: dkurth@mail.unomaha.edu

Entrepreneur Shop
10868 West Dodge Road
Omaha, NE 68154
402-595-1158
Fax: 402-595-1194

Nebraska Business Development
Center
Omaha Business and Technology
Center
2505 North 24th Street, Suite 101
Omaha, NE 68110
402-595-3511
MaryGraffNEPTAC@netscape.net

Nebraska Business Development
Center
Peter Kiewit Conference Center
1313 Farnam, PKCC Suite 230
Omaha, NE 68182-0164
402-595-2381
Fax: 402-595-2385
Email:
dmuellerfichepain@mail.unomaha.e
du

Nebraska Business Development
Center
US Bank Building
1620 Broadway, Room 201
Scottsbluff, NE 69361
308-635-7513

Wayne State College
Nebraska Business Development
Center

Gardner Hall
1111 Main Street
Wayne, NE 68787
402-375-7575
Fax: 402-375-7574
www.wsc.edu/nbdc
Email: nbdc@wsc.edu

Nevada

Lead Center:
Sam Males
Nevada Small Business
Development Center
University of Nevada Reno
College of Business Administration
Business Building, Room 411
Reno, NV 89577-0100
702-784-1717
Fax: 702-784-4337
www.nsbdc.org
Email: nsbdc@unr.nevada.edu

Great Basin College
Small Business Development
Center
723 Railroad St
Elko, NV 89801
775-753-2245
Fax: 775-753-2242
www.nsbdc.org/offices/elko
Email: judye@gbcnv.edu

University of Nevada at Las Vegas
Small Business Development
Center
851 E Tropicana, Building 700
Mailing Address:
    UNLV
    4505 Maryland Parkway
    Box 456011 (mail)
Las Vegas, NV 89154
www.nsbdc.org/offices/lasvegas
Email: nsbdc@nevada.edu

Carson City Chamber of
Commerce
Small Business Development
Center
1900 South Carson Street, #100
Carson City, NV 89701
775-882-1565
Fax: 775-882-4179
www.nbdc.org/offices/carson_city
Email: ccchamber@semp.net

Ely Small Business Development
Center
Rural Nevada Development
Corporation
740 Park Avenue
Ely, NV 89301
775-289-8519
www.nsbdc.org/offices/ely
Email: rbart@idsely.com

Fallon Small Business
Development Center

Churchill County Economic
Development Authority
448 West Williams Street
Fallon, NV 89406
775-423-8587
Fax: 775-423-0381
www.nsbdc.org/offices/fallon
Email: rlattin@sci-nevada.com

Carson Valley Small Business
Development Center
Carson Valley Chamber of
Commerce
1512 Highway 395 North, Suite 1
Gardnerville, NV 89410
775-782-8144
Fax: 775-782-1025
www.nsbdc.org/offices/carson_vall
ey
Email: rhalbard@prodigy.net

Henderson Small Business
Development Center
112 Water Street
Henderson, NV 89015
702-992-7208
Fax: 702-992-7245
www.nsbdc.org/offices/henderson
Email: bernief@nevada.edu

Hi-Desert Economic Development
Authority
Small Business Development
Center
90 West Fourth Street
P.O. Box 820
Winnemucca, NV 89445
775-623-1064
Fax: 775-623-1664
www.nsbdc.org/offices/winnemucca
Email: sbdc@desertlink.com

Safety and Environmental
Assistance
Business Environmental Program
PO Box 15225
Las Vegas, NV 89114
702-866-5962
Fax: 702-866-6800
http://nsbdcbep.org

Safety and Environmental
assistance
Business Environmental Program
Sierra Pacific Power Company
6100 Neil Road, Suite 400
Reno, NV 89511
775-689-6688
800-882-3233
Fax: 775-689-6689
http://nsbdcbep.org

New Hampshire

Lead Center:
Mary Collins
New Hampshire Small Business
Development Center
University of New Hampshire

The Whittemore School of
Business
108 McConnell Hall
15 College Road
Durham, NH 03824-3593
603-862-2200
Fax: 603-862-4876
www.nhsbdc.org
Email: mary.collins@unh.edu

Keene State College
Small Business Development
Center
Mail Stop 2101
Keene, NH 03435-2101
603-358-2602
Fax: 603-358-2612
www.nhsbdc.org/keene.htm
Email: gchabot@keene.edu

Small Business Development
Center
120 Main Street
Littleton, NH 03561
603-444-1053
Fax: 603-444-5463
www.nhsbdc.org/littleto.hmt
Email: eaward@ncia.net

Small Business Development
Center
670 N. Commercial Street
4th Floor, Suite 1
Manchester, NH 03101
603-634-2000
Fax: 603-647-4410
www.nhsbdc.org/manchest.htm
Email:
bob.ebberson@verizonesg.net

Plymouth State College
Small Business Development
Center
101 Samuel Read Hall
Plymouth, NH 03264-1595
603-535-2526
Fax: 603-535-2850
www.nhsbdc.org/plymouth.htm
Emaill: eburt@mail.plymouth.edu

Small Business Development
Center
Rivier College, Sylvia Trottier Hall
420 Main St.
Nashua, NH 03060
603-897-8588
Fax: 603-897-8884
www.nhsbdc.org/nashua.htm
Email: dnelson@rivier.edu

International Trade Resource
Center
17 New Hampshire Avenue
Peace International Tradeport
Portsmouth, MH 03801-2838
603-334-6074
Fax: 603-334-6110
www.nhsbdc.org/itrc.htm
Email: nh.sbdc@unh.edu

New Hampshire Small Business
Development Center
c/o Rochester Chamber of
Commerce
18 South Main Street, Suite 2A
Rochester, NH 03867
603-330-1929
Fax: 603-330-1948
www.nhsbdc.org/rocheste.htm
Email: wdaniel@cisunix.unh.edu

Seacoast Satellite Office
Pease Tradeport
320 Corporate Drive
Portsmouth, NH 03801
603-330-1929
www.nhsbdc.org/rocheste.htm

New Jersey

Lead Center:
Brenda Hopper
New Jersey Small Business
Development Center
Rutgers Business School
49 Bleeker Street
Newark, NJ 07102-1993
973-353-1927
800-432-1565
Fax: 973-353-1110
www.njsbdc.com
Email: bhopper@njsbdc.com

Rutgers University Campus at
Camden
Small Business Development
Center
School of Business
325 Cooper Street, 3rd Floor,
Room 334
Camden, NJ 08102
856-225-6221
Fax: 856-225-6621
http://camden-sbc.rutgers.edu/rsbdc
Email:
hcharles@camden.rutgers.edu

Brookdale Community College
Small Business Development
Center
765 Newman Springs Road
Lincroft, NJ 07738
732-224-2751
www.brookdale.cc.nj.us/staff/sbdc

Rutgers University Campus at
Newark
Small Business Development
Center
University Heights
Bleeker Street
Newark, NJ 07102
973-353-5950
Fax: 973-353-1030
www.njsbdc.com/newark
Email: tndoro@njsbdc.com

Paterson Small Business
Development Center

131 Ellison Street
Paterson, NJ 07505
973-754-8695
Fax: 973-754-9153

Kean University
Small Business Development
Center
East Campus, Room 242
Union, NJ 07083
908-737-5950
Fax: 908-527-2960
Email: mkostak@kean.edu

Warren County Community
College
Skylands Small Business
Development Center
475 Route 57 West
Washington, NJ 07882
908-689-9620
Fax: 908-689-2247
www.warren.edu/ssbdc/aboutus.ht
ml
Email: sbdc@warren.edu

Small Business Development
Center
5100 Harding Highway
Mays Landing, NJ 08330
609-909-5339
Fax: 609-909-9671
Email: jmolineaux@njsbdc.com

Bergen Community College
Small Business Development
Center
Ciarco Learning Center
355 Main Street
Hackensack, NJ 07601
201-489-8670
Fax: 201-489-8673
www.bergen.edu/SBDC
Email: jtenuto@bergen.edu

Raritan Valley Community College
Small Business Development
Center
Route 28 & Lamington Road
Information Center, South Building
Mailing address:
    Corporate and Continuing
    Education
    P.O. Box 3300
    Somerville, NJ 08876-1265
Regional
    North Branch, NJ 08876
908-526-1200 ext.8515
Fax: 908-725-9687
www.sbdcrvcc.com
Email: sjohnson@raritanval.edu

New Jersey City University
SBDC
20 College Street
Jersey City, NJ 07301
201-200-2156
Fax: 201-200-3404
Email: boneal@njcu.edu

Ocean County College
SBDC
Center For Lifelong Learning
College Drive
Toms River, NJ 08754
732-255-0468
www.ocean.edu/conted/small_busi
ness_development_center.htm
Email: jpeterson@ocean.edu

Mercer/Middlesex Small Business
Development Center
36 South Broad Street
Trenton, NJ 08608
609-989-5232
Fax: 609-989-7638
Email: lallen@tcnj.edu

William Paterson University
Small Business Development
Center
300 Pompton Road
Wayne, NJ 07470
973-754-8695
Email: mirabeaul@wpunj.edu

New Mexico

Lead Center:
J. Roy Miller
New Mexico Small Business
Development Center
Santa Fe Community College
6401 Richards Avenue
Santa Fe, NM 87508
505-428-1362
800-281-7232
Fax: 505-438-1469
www.nmsbdc.org
Email: info@nmshbdc.org

New Mexico State University at
Alamogordo
Small Business Development
Center
2230 Lawrence Boulevard
Alamogrodo, NM 88310
505-434-5272
Fax: 505-434-1432
www.alamosbdc.org
Email: director@alamosbdc.org

South Valley Small Business
Development Center
700 4th Street, SW
Albuquerque, NM 87102
505-248-0132
Fax: 505-248-0127
Email: svsbdc.org@abq.com

New Mexico State University at
Carlsbad
Small Business Development
Center
221 South Canyon Street
Carlsbad, NM 88220
505-885-9531
Fax: 505-885-1515
Email: lcoalson@cavern.nmsu.edu

Clovis Community College
Small Business Development
Center
417 Schepps Boulevard
Clovis, NM 88101
505-769-4136
Fax: 505-769-4135
www.clovis.cc.nm.us/BusinessCom
munity/SBDC/index.asp
Email: sbdc@clovis.edu

Northern New Mexico Community
College
Small Business Development
Center
921 Paseo de Onate
Espanola, NM 87532
505-747-2235/2236/2237
Fax: 505-747-2234
http://nnmcc.edu/www/pages/sbdc.
htm
Email: rprather@nnmcc.edu

San Juan College
Small Business Development
Center
5101 College Blvd
Farmington, NM 87402
505-566-3528
Fax: 505566-3698
www.sjc.cc.nm.us/qcb/sbdc.html
Email:
armstrongl@sanjuancollege.edu

University of New Mexico at
Gallup
Small Business Development
Center
103 West Highway 66
Gallup, NM 87301
505-722-2220
Fax: 505-863-6006
Email: sbdc@gallup.unm.edu

New Mexico State University at
Grants
Small Business Development
Center
709 East Roosevelt
Grants, NM 87020
505-287-8221
Fax: 505-287-2125
www.grants.nmsu.edu/gr_general/s
bdc.html
Email: sbdcgrant@7cities.net

New Mexico Junior College
Small Business Development
Center
5317 Lovington Highway
Hobbs, NM 88240
505-392-5603 ext. 651
Fax: 505-492-1493
www.nmjc.edu/sbdc

Dona Ana Branch Community
College
Small Business Development
Center
Box 30001, Department 3DA

2345 East Nevada Street
Las Cruces, NM 88003-8001
505-527-7601
505-527-7676/7606
Fax: 505-528-7432
http://dabcc-
www.nmsu.edu/comm/sbdc
Email: fowensby@nmsu.edu

Luna Community College
Small Business Development
Center
P.O. Box 1510
Las Vegas, NM 87701
505-454-2582
800-588-7232 ext. 1759
Fax: 505-454-5326
www.nmsbdc.org/lasvegas
Email:
lvtisbdc@nmhu.campus.mci.net

University of New Mexico at Los
Alamos
Small Business Development
Center
P.O. Box 715
190 Central Park Square
Los Alamos, NM 87544
505-622-0001
Fax: 505-662-0099
www.losalamos.org/lacdc/unmla.ht
ml
Email: sbdc@losalamos.org

University of New Mexico at
Valencia
Small Business Development
Center
280 La Entrada
Los Lunas, NM 87031
505-925-8980
Fax: 505-925-8981
www.unm.edu/loslunas

Eastern New Mexico University at
Roswell
Small Business Development
Center
20 West Mathis
P.O. Box 6000
Roswell, NM 88201-6000
505-624-7133
Fax: 505-624-7132
www.nmsbdc.org/roswell
Email: eugene.simmons@
roswell.enmu.edu

Santa Fe Community College
Small Business Development
Center
6401 Richards Road
Santa Fe, NM 87505
505-428-1343
Fax: 505-428-1469
www.nmsbdc.org/santafe

Western New Mexico University
Southwest Small Business
Development Center
P.O. Box 2672

Silver City, NM 88062
505-538-6320
Fax: 505-538-6341

Mesalands Community College
Small Business Development
Center
911 South 10th
Tucumcari, NM 88401
505-461-4413 ext. 133 or 140
Fax: 505-461-1901/4318
www.nmsbdc.org/Tucumcari
Email: sbdc@mesalands.edu

Albuquerque SBDC
TVI Workforce Training Center
5600 Eagle Rock Ave NE
Suite 201
Albuquerque NM 87113
505-224-5250
Fax: 505-224-5256
http://planet.tvi.cc.nm.us/wtc/abqsb
dc
Email: sbdc@tvi.edu

Taos Satellite Office
1332 Gusdorf Road Suite B
Taos, NM 87571
505-737-5651

New York

Lead Center:
James L. King
New York Small Business
Development Center
State University Plaza
41 State Street
Albany, NY 12246-0001
518-443-5398
800-732-7232
Fax: 518-443-5275
www.nyssbdc.org
Email: kingjl@nyssbdc.org

State University of New York at
Albany (SUNY)
Small Business Development
Center
1 Pinnacle Place, Suite 218
Albany, NY 12203-3439
518-453-9567
Fax: 518-453-9572
Email: albsbdc@nycap.rr.com

Binghamton University
Small Business Development
Center
Binghamton, NY 13902-6000
607-777-4024
Fax: 607-777-4029
http://sbdc.binghamton.edu
Email: sbdc@binghamton.edu

State University College at
Brockport
Small Business Development
Center
350 New Campus Drive

Morgan III, Room 3205
Brockport, NY 14420
585-395-2334
Fax: 585-395-2467
http://cc.brockport.edu/~smallbus/i
ndex.html
Email: sbdc@brockport.edu

Lehman College
Bronx Small Business
Development Center
250 Bedford Park Boulevard, West
Bronx, NY 10468
718-960-8806
Email: bxsbdc@binc.org

Boricua College
9 Graham Avenue
Brooklyn, NY 11206
718-963-4112
718-960-8697
Fax: 718-963-2031
Email:
boricuasbdc@mindspring.com

Buffalo State College
Small Business Development
Center
Buffalo State College , GC206
Buffalo, NY 14222
716-878-4030
Fax: 716-878-4067
www.nyssbdc.org
Email: buffalosbdc@yahoo.com

SUNY Canton
Canton Small Business
Development Center
Faculty Office Building, Room 202
Cornell Drive
Canton, NY 13617
315-386-7312
Fax: 315-379-3814
www.nyssbdc.org

Corning Community College
Small Business Development
Center
24 Denison Parkway West
Corning, NY 14830-2607
607-962-9461
Fax: 607-936-6642
www.nyssbdc.org
Email: gestwicki@corning-cc.edu

Mercy College Outreach Center
Small Business Development
Center
555 Broadway
Dobbs Ferry, NY 10522-1189
914-674-7845
Fax: 914-693-4996
www.nyssbdc.org/centers/centers.c
fm?centid=16

SUNY Geneseo
Small Business Development
Outreach Center
South Hall 111
1 College Circle

Geneseo, NY 14454
716-245-5429
Fax: 716-245-5430
www.sunyniagara.cc.ny.us/sbdc/in
dex.html
Email: SBDC@uno.cc.geneseo.edu

EOC Hempstead Outreach Center
Small Business Development Ctr
269 Fulton Avenue
Hempstead, NY 11550
516-564-8672
Fax: 516-564-1895
www.nyssbdc.org/centers/centers.c
fm?centid=17
Email: schwarjf@farmingdale.edu

York College, The City University
of New York
Small Business Development
Center
94-20 Guy R. Brewer Blvd
Jamaica, NY 11451
718-262-2880
Fax: 718-262-2881
www.nyssbdc.org/centers/centers.c
fm?centid=22
Email: atitone@york.cuny.edu

Jamestown Community College
Small Business Development
Center
Community Services Center
525 Falconer Street
Jamestown, NY 14701
716-665-5754
800-522-7232
Fax: 716-665-6733
www.sunyjcc.edu/sbdc/sbdc.html
Email:
dobiesia@jccw22.cc.sunyjcc.edu

Mid-Huron Small Business
Development Center
Business Resource Center
1 Development Court
Kingston, NY 12401
845-339-0025
Fax: 845-339-1631
www.nyssbdc.org/centers/centers.c
fm?centid=15
Email: hardingf@sunyulster.edu

Midtown Outreach Center
Small Business Development
Center
Baruch College
Field Center
55 Lexington Avenue
New York, NY 10010
646-312-4790
Fax: 646-312-4781
www.nyssbdc.org/centers/centers.c
fm?centid=24
Email:
patrice_tombline@baruch.cuny.edu

Pace University
Small Business Development
Center

163 William Street, 16th Floor
New York, NY 10038
212-346-1900
Fax: 212-346-1613
www.nyssbdc.org/centers/centers.c
fm?centid=21
Email: sbdc@pace.edu

International Trade Center
Niagara Falls Small Business
Development Center
Niagara Office Building
345 Third Street
Niagara, Falls, NY 14303-117
716-285-4793
Fax: 716-285-4797
www.sunyniagara.cc.ny.us/sbdc/in
dex.html
Email: sbdc@niagaracc.suny.edu

Plattsburgh State University of
New York
Small Business Development
Center
Ward Hall 118
101 Broad Street
Plattsburgh, NY 12901
518-564-2042
Fax: 518-564-2043
www.nyssbdc.org/centers/centers.c
fm?centid=8
Email: SBDC@plattsburgh.edu

Small Business Development
Outreach Center-SUNY Brockport
55 St. Paul St., Riverside Entrance
Rochester, NY 14604
716-232-7310
Fax: 716-232-7274
http://cc.brockport.edu/~smallbus/i
ndex.html

Niagara County Community
College at Sanborn
Small Business Development
Center
3111 Saunders Settlement Road
Sanborn, NY 14132
716-614-6480
Fax: 716-614-6825
www.sunyniagara.cc.ny.us/sbdc/in
dex.html

Southampton Outreach Small
Business Development Center
Long Island University
Abney Peak, Montauk Highway
Southhampton, NY 11968
631-287-0059
Fax: 631-287-8287
http://naples.cc.sunysb.edu/CEAS/s
mallbusiness.nsf

The College of Staten Island
Small Business Development
Center
2800 Victory Boulevard
Building 2A
Staten Island, NY 10314
718-982-2560

Fax: 718-982-2323
www.nyssbdc.org/centers/centers.c
fm?centid=23
Email:
schwartzm@postbox.csi.cuny.edu

SUNY at Stony Brook
Small Business Development
Center
Harriman Hall, Room 101
Stony Brook, NY 11794-3775
516-632-9070
Fax: 516-632-7176
http://naples.cc.sunysb.edu/CEAS/s
mallbusiness.nsf

Onondaga Community College at
Syracuse
Small Business Development
Center
Whitney Applied Technology
Center, Suite 106
Syracuse, NY 13215-2099
315-498-6070
Fax: 315-492-3704
www.nyssbdc.org/centers/centers.c
fm?centid=6
Email: SBDC@SUNYOCC.EDU

Brookhaven National Laboratory
Small Business Development
Outreach Center
Building 179B, Bell Avenue
Upton, NY 11973
631-344-2393
Fax: 631-344-3543

SUNY Institute of Technology at
Utica/Rome
Small Business Development
Center
Route 12 North
P.O. Box 3050
Utica, NY 13504-3050
315-792-7547
Fax: 315-792-7554
www.sbdc.sunyit.edu
Email: sbdc@sunyit.edu

Jefferson Community College
Small Business Development
Center
Coffeen Street
Watertown, NY 13601
315-782-9262
Fax: 315-782-0901
www.nyssbdc.org/centers/centers.c
fm?centid=4
Email: sbdc@sunyjefferson.edu

The Small Business Resource
Center
Small Business Development
Center
222 Bloomingdale Road, Suite 400
White Plains, NY 10605-1500
914-948-4349/4450
www.nyssbdc.org/centers/centers.c
fm?centid=16

Outreach Office
Centro Civico of Amsterdam Inc.
143-145 East Main Street
Amsterdam, NY 12010
518-842-3762

36 South Street
Auburn, NY 13021
315-498-6070

Madison County Industrial
Development Agency
Canastota Business Center
Canastota, NY 13032
315-697-9817

Delaware County Chamber of
Commerce
97 East Main Street
Delhi, NY 13753
607-746-2281

Outreach Office
Jamestown Community College
10807 Bennett Road
Dunkirk, NY 14048
800-522-7232

Cortland County Chamber of
Commerce
34 Tompkins Street
Cortland, NY 13045
607-756-2814

Farmingdale State University of
New York
Campus Commons
Farmingdale, NY 11735-1006
631-420-2765
631-370-8888
Fax: 631-370-8895
www.nyssbdc.org/centers/centers.c
fm?centid=17
wesnofl@farmingdale.edu

Marist College Extension
400 Westage Business Center
Fishkill, NY 12524-2947
845-897-3945
Fax: 845-897-4653

Outreach Office
5 Warren Street
Glens Falls, NY 12801-2801
518-453-9567

LI Business and Technology Center
3500 Sunrise Highway
Great River, NY 11739
631-859-8929
Fax: 631-859-8929

Herkimer County Community
College
Offices of Community Education
Herkimer, NY 13350
315-866-0300

Outreach Office
Akwesasne Mohawk Reservation
412 State Route 37
Hogansburg, NY 13655-3109
315-386-7312
Fax: 315-379-3814

Essex City Business Council
216 Main Street at Lake Placid
Visitor's Bureau
Lake Placid, NY 12946
518-523-4906
518-564-2042

8015 Oswego Road
(Rte. 57)
Liverpool, NY 13090
315-498-6070

LaGuardia Community College
SBDC
29-10 Thomson Avenue, 9th Floor
Long Island City, NY 11101
718-482-5303
www.nyssbdc.org/centers/centers.c
fm?centid=95
Email: sbdc@lagcc.cuny.edu

Outreach Office
LCIDA
7642 State Street, Box 106
Lowville , NY 13367
315-782-9262

One Work Source Center
158 Finney Blvd.
Malone, NY 12953
518-481-5755
518-564-2042

SUNY Canton Education Center
St. Lawrence Centre Mall
Massena , NY 13662
315-386-7312
315-764-5321
Fax: 315-379-3814

IBIG
Orange County Community
College
Middletown, NY 10940-6437
845-341-4771
Fax: 845-341-4921

Sullivan Co. Comm. Coll.
196 Broadway
Monticello, NY 12701-9998
845-791-8338
Fax: 845-791-5287

Outreach Office
Stewart Airport
33 Airport Center Drive
New Windsor, NY 12553
845-567-2702
Fax: 845-567-6085

Chenango County Chamber of
Commerce
The Eaton Center

19 Eaton Avenue
Norwich, NY 13815
607-334-1400

Otsego County Chamber of
Commerce
12 Carbon Street
Oneonta, NY 13820
607-432-4500

Tioga County Chamber of
Commerce
188 Front Street
Owego, NY 13827
607-687-2020

Outreach Office
Oswego State University
100 Sheldon Hall
Oswego , NY 13126-3599
315-312-5696
Fax: 315-312-3374

BOSS Project Incubator
32 Front Street
Port Jervis, NY 12771
845-856-3830
845-856-2169

Chamber of Commerce
One Civic Center Plaza
Poughkeepsie , NY 12601-3117
845-454-1700
Fax: 845-454-1702

Rome Industrial Development
Corporation
139 West Dominick Street
Rome, NY 13440
315-337-6360
www.sbdc.sunyit.edu

Outreach Office
28 Clinton Street
Saratoga Springs, NY 12866-2866
518-453-9567

1201 East Fayette Street
Syracuse, NY 13210-1953
315-498-6070

PRIDE of Ticonderoga, Inc
111 Montcalm Street, Suite 2
Ticonderoga, NY 12883
518-585-6366
518-564-2042

Outreach Office
The Rice Building
216 River Street
Troy, NY 12180
518-453-9567
Email: albsbdc@nycap.rr.com

Outreach Office
257 Ranger School Road
Wanakena, NY 13695-0048
315-386-7312

Mercy College Small Business
Development Center
Westchester 1

Park Building 3
Yonkers, NY 10701-2752
914-375-2107
Fax: 914-375-9276
www.nyssbdc.org/centers/centers.c
fm?centid=16
Email: tmorley@mercy.edu

North Carolina

Lead Center:
Scott Daugherty
North Carolina Small Business and
Technology Development Center
5 W. Hargett St., Suite 600
Raleigh, NC 27601
919-715-7272
800-258-0862
Fax: 919 715-7777
www.sbtdc.org
Email: info@sbtdc.org

Asheville Office
Western Region Small Business
and Technology Development
Center
P.O. Box 2510
Bank of America Building
68 Patton Avenue, Suite 1
Asheville, NC 28801
828-251-6025
Fax: 828-232-5126

Appalachian State University
Small Business and Technology
Development Center
Walker College of Business
P.O. Box 32114
Boone, NC 28608
828-262-2492
Fax: 828-262-2027

Small Business and Technology
Development Center
608 Airport Road, Suite B
Chapel Hill, NC 27514
919-962-0389
800-815-8906
Fax: 919-962-3291

Small Business and Technology
Development Center
The Ben Craig Center
8701 Mallard Creek Road
Charlotte, NC 28262
704-548-1090
Fax: 704-548-9050

Western Region Small Business
and Technology Development
Center
Western Carolina University
WCU School of Business
204 Forsyth Building
Cullowhee, NC 28723
828-227-3504
Fax: 828-227-7422

Elizabeth City State University
Small Business and Technology
Development Center
Northeastern Region
K.E. White Graduate Center
Box 874
Elizabeth City, NC 27909
252-335-3247
800-258-0862
Fax: 252-335-3648

Fayetteville State University
Small Business and Technology
Development Center
Continuing Education Center
P.O. Box 1334
Fayetteville, NC 28302
910-672-1727
Fax: 910-672-1949

NC A&T University/
Small Business and Technology
Development Center
2007 Yanceyville Street
Suite 300
Greensboro, NC 27405
336-334-7005
Fax: 336-334-7073

East Carolina University
Small Business and Technology
Development Center
300 1st Street
Greenville, NC 27858-4353
252-328-6157
Fax: 252-328-6992

Appalachian-Foothills Small
Business and Technology
Development Center
905 Highway 321 NW, Suite 354
Hickory, NC 28601
828-345-1110
Fax: 828-326-9117

University of North Carolina at
Pembroke
P.O. Box 1510
Pembroke, NC 28272-1510
910-521-6611
Fax: 910-521-6550
www.uncp.edu/rc/sbtdc

University of North Carolina at
Wilmington
Small Business and Technology
Development Center
5051 New Centre Drive, Suite 122
Wilmington, NC 28403
910-962-3744
Fax: 910-962-3014
www.uncw.edu/dpscs/sbtdc
Email: llanger@sbtdc.org

Winston-Salem University
Small Business and Technology
Development Center
Northern Piedmont Region
P.O. Box 19483
Winston-Salem, NC 27110

306-750-2030
Fax: 306-750-2031

Durham SBTDC
School of Business
15 Alexander-Dunn Building
North Carolina Central University
Durham, NC 27707
919.530.7386

Raleigh SBTDC
5 West Hargett Street, Suite 212
Raleigh, NC 27601-1348
919-715-0520

Rocky Mount SBTDC
100 Coastline Street, Suite 309
Rocky Mount, NC 27804-0100
252-467-0338

North Dakota

Lead Center:
Christine Martin
North Dakota Small Business
Development Center
University of North Dakota
118 Gamble Hall
P.O. Box 7308
Grand Forks, ND 58202-7308
701-777-3700
800-445-7232
Fax: 701-777-3225
www.ndsbdc.org
Email: ndsbc@und.edu

Small Business Development
Center
Bismarck Regional Center
700 East Main Avenue, 2nd Floor
Bismarck, ND 58502
701-328-5865
800-596-6622
Fax: 701-250-4304
Email: rnewman@minotstateu.edu

Small Business Development
Center
Minot Regional Center
1925 South Broadway
Minot, ND 58701
701-852-8861
Fax: 701-839-3889
Email: anderson@minotstateu.edu
Email: votava@minotstateu.edu

Willston Regional Center
Small Business Development
Center
Box 1326, Creighton Building
Williston, ND 58802-1326
701-774-4235
Fax: 701-774-4201
Email: gsukat@minotstateu.edu

Small Business Development
Center
Devils Lake Regional Center
417 5th Street

Devils Lake, ND 58301
701-662-8131
Fax: 701-662-8132
Email: denisencpc@stellarnet.com

Small Business Development
Center
Fargo Regional Center
51 Broadway, Suite 505
Fargo, ND 58102
701-235-1495
800-698-5726
Fax: 701-237-9734
Email: linda_liebert_hall@und.edu

Small Business Development
Center
Grand Forks Regional Center
1501 28th Avenue South
Grand Forks, ND 58201
701-795-3734
Fax: 701-772-9238
Email: dwadholm@state.nd.us

Small Business Development
Center
Grafton Regional Center
516 Cooper Avenue, Suite 101
Grafton, ND 58237
701-352-3550
Fax: 701-352-3015
Email: dkeeley@state.nd.us

Small Business Development
Center
Jamestown Regional Center
210 10th Street SE
Jamestown, ND 58402
701-252-8060
Fax: 701-252-4930
Email: scdrc@csicable.net
Email: sbdc@csicable.net

Ohio

Lead Center:
Ohio Small Business Development
Center
77 South High Street, 28th Floor
Columbus, OH 43216-0101
614-466-2711
800-848-1300
Fax: 614-644-5167
www.odod.state.oh.us/edd/osb/sbdc/
Email: sbdc@odod.state.oh.us

Greater Akron Chamber of
Commerce
Akron Regional Development
Board
Small Business Development Ctr
One Cascade Plaza, 17th Floor
Akron, OH 44308-1192
330-237-1258
800-621-8001
Fax: 330-379-3164
www.greaterakronchamber.org/cgi-
bin/content/content.pl?id=25

Southeast Ohio SBDC
Ohio University
Small Business Development
Center
Enterprise & Technology Building
20 East Circle Drive, Suite 174
Athens, OH 45701
740-593-1797
Fax: 740-593-1795
www.voinovichcenter.ohio.edu
Email:
abdella@voinovichcenter.ohio.edu

Small Business Development
Center
Bowling Green State University
40 College Park
Bowling Green, OH 43403
419-372-9536
877-650-8165
Fax: 419-372-8667

Kent State University Geagua
Campus
14111 Claridon-Troy Road
Burton, OH 44021
440-834-4187
Fax: 440-834-8846
www.geauga.kent.edu
Email: smarshall@geauga.kent.edu

Kent Stark Small Business
Development Center
Office of Corporate and
Community Services
6000 Frank Avenue, NW
Canton, OH 44720
330-244-3279
Fax: 330-494-6121
http://yourcorporateu.kent.edu/Busi
nessDevelopment/index.cfm
Email: sbdc@stark.kent.edu

Wright State University Lake
Campus
Small Business Development
Center
7600 State Route 703
Celina, OH 45822
419-586-0355
800-237-1477 ext. 8355
Fax: 419-586-0358
www.wright.edu/lake/webpages/sb
dc.html

Cincinnati Small Business
Development Center
University of Cincinnati
7162 Reading Road, Suite 725
Cincinnati, OH 45237-3844
513-556-2072
Fax: 513-556-2074
www.cba.uc.edu/cbainfo/sbdc
Email: kennesn@email.uc.edu

Greater Cleveland Growth
Association
Small Business Development
Center
200 Tower City

50 Public Square
Cleveland, OH 44113-2291
216-621-3300
Fax: 216-621-6013
www.clevelandgrowth.com
Email: jkroeger@clevegrowth.com

Columbus Ohio ITAC
Columbus Chamber of Commerce
37 North High Street
Columbus, OH 43215-3065
614-225-6949
Fax: 614-469-8250
www.columbus-
chamber.org/sbdc.html
Email:
mercedes_moore@columbus.org

Ohio Small Business Development
Center at Wright State University
College of Business
120 Rike Hall
3640 Colonel Glenn Highway
Dayton, OH 45435
937-775-3503
Fax: 937-775-3545
www.sbdcwsu.org
Email: michael.bodey@wright.edu

Maumee Valley Planning
Organization
Northwest Small Business
Development Center
197-2-B1 Park Island Avenue
Defiance, OH 43512
419-782-6270
Fax: 419-782-6273
Email: nwsbdc@defiance-
county.com

Small Business Development
Center
Fremont Office
Terra Community College
2830 Napoleon Road
Freemont, OH 43420-9967
419-334-8400
800-826-2431
Fax: 419-334-9414
Email: baxter@terra.cc.oh.us

Greater Hamilton Chamber of
Commerce
Small Business Development
Center
201 Dayton Street
Hamilton, OH 45011
513-844-1500
Fax: 513-844-1999
www.hamiltonohio.org/chamber/sb
dc.asp

Satellite Small Business
Development Center
36 West Walnut Street
Jefferson, OH 44047
216-576-9134
Fax: 216-576-5003

The Ohio Manufacturing, Defense,
& Technology SBDC
Kent State University
NEOH Manufacturing Small
Business Development Center
Van Deusen Hall
School of Technology
P.O. Box 5190
Kent, OH 44242-0001
330-672-2892
Fax: 330-672-2894
www.tech.kent.edu/pages/outreach.
asp
Email: tsouthards@tech.kent.edu

Kent-Portage Small Business
Development Center
Kent State University Partnership
College of Business
Administration, Room 300A
Kent, OH 44242
330-672-1279, ext. 21279
Fax: 330-672-9338
http://business.kent.edu/SBDC/inde
x.htm
Email: lyost@bsa3.kent.edu

Dayton PTAC Supersite
Edison Materials Technology
Center
3155 Research Park, Suite 206
Kettering, OH 45420
937-259-1321
Fax: 937-252-9314
Email: dwallace@emtec.org

Region 3 Lead Center
The Ohio SBDC at Rhodes State
College
Small Business Development
Center
545 West Market Street, Suite 305
Lima, OH 45801-4717
419-224-0396
Fax: 419-229-5424
Email: hyter.j@rhodesstate.edu

Lorain County Chamber of
Commerce
Small Business Development
Center
6100 South Broadway, Suite 201
Lorain, OH 44053
440-233-6500
Fax: 440-246-4050
www.lorcham.org/sbdc
Email: djones@lorcham.org

Mid-Miami Valley
Small Business Development
Center
1500 Central Avenue
Middletown, OH 45044
513-422-4551
Fax: 513-422-6831
www.mmvchamber.org/SBDC.htm
craig@mmvchamber.org

Lake Erie College
Lake County Economic
Development Center
391 West Washington Street
Painesville, OH 44077
440-357-2293
Fax: 440-357-2296
www.lcedc.org/sbdc/Default.htm
Email: lcedc@lcedc.org

East Central Region SBDC
Kent State University Tuscarawas
Campus
Small Business Development Ctr
300 University Drive, NE
New Philadelphia, OH 44663-9447
330-308-7479
Fax: 330-339-2637
www.tusc.kent.edu/ServicesforBusi
ness/small_business.cfm
Email: pcomanitz@tusc.kent.edu

Lawrence EDC
Small Business Development
Center
P.O. Box 488
216 Collins Avenue
Southpoint, OH 45680
800-408-1334
Email: klawhorn@zoomnet.net

Springfield Small Business
Development Center
300 East Auburn Avenue
Springfield, OH 45505
937-322-7821
Fax: 937-322-7824
www.smbusdev.org
Email: smichaels@smbusdev.org

Toledo Chamber of Commerce
Small Business Development
Center
Enterprise Suite 200
300 Madison Avenue
Toledo, OH 43604-1575
419-243-8191
Fax: 419-241-8302
www.toledochamber.com/small_bu
siness_development_center.htm
Email: joinus@toledochamber.com

Small Business Development
Center
241 Federal Plaza West
Youngstown, OH 44503
330-746-3350
Fax: 330-746-3324
www.ohiosbdc-ysu.com

Akron MCBAP
Safe Harbor Incubator
1046 South Arlington Street
Akron, OH 44306
330-773-2598
Email: IKUMAH1@aol.com

Region 6 Lead Center
The Ohio SBDC at Ashland
University

19 West Main Street, Suite 9
Ashland, OH 44805
877-289-1468
Email: msynorac@ashland.edu

Satellite Office
4536 Main Avenue
Ashtabula, OH 44004
440-998-6998
800-487-GROW (4769)
Fax: 440-992-8216
www.ohiosbdc-ysu.com

PTAC of Ohio at Bowling Green
State University/Toledo
Jerome Library, Room 140B
Bowling Green, OH 43403
419-372-9257
Email: rarcher@bgnet.bgsu.edu

The Ohio SBDC at Ohio Mid-
Eastern Government Association
326 Highland Avenue
P.O. Box 130
Cambridge, OH 43725
740-439-4471
www.omega-ldd.org/page4.htm
Email: cvoorhies@omega-ldd.org

The Ohio Manufacturing, Defense
& Technology SBDC at TechSolve
6705 Steger Drive
Cincinnati, OH 45237
800-345-4482
513-948-2064
www.techsolve.org
Email: jacobson@techsolve.org

Cincinnati MCBAP
Cincinnati B.D.S., Inc.
7165 Reading Road, Suite 630
Cincinnati, OH 45237
513-631-7666
Email:
omartin@ohiostatewidembdc.org

Cleveland MCBAP
David N. Myers University
112 Prospect Avenue
Cleveland, OH 44115
216-523-1190
Email: csbaemcap@aol.com

Region 1 Lead Center
The Ohio SBDC at the Greater
Columbus Chamber of Commerce
37 N. High Street
Columbus, OH 43215
614-225-6910
www.columbus-
chamber.org/a/services/sbdc.htm
Email:
michael_bowers@columbus.org

Central Ohio ITAC
Greater Columbus Chamber of
Commerce
37 North High Street
Columbus, OH 43215
614-225-6949

Email:
mercedes_moore@columbus.org

The Ohio Manufacturing, Defense,
& Technology SBDC at Central
Ohio
1214 Kinnear Road
Columbus, OH 43212
614-688-4018
Email: jshick@stcc.org

Columbus MCBAP
Central Ohio Minority Business
Association
1000 East Main Street
Columbus, OH 43205
614-252-8005
Email: kimknights@comba.com

Central Ohio PTAC Supersite
1214 Kinnear Road
Columbus, OII 43212
614-365-3200
Email: coptac@netwalk.com

Dayton MCBAP
City of Dayton MCBAP
201 Riverside Drive, Suite 1E
Dayton, OH 45405
937-223-2164
Email: mcbaphrc@dayton.net

PTAC of Ohio at KRBA, Inc.
Kent State University
College of Business
Administration, Room 300
Kent, OH 44242
330-672-9448
Email: ktarbett@bsa3.kent.edu

The Ohio Manufacutring, Defense
& Technology SBDC at Wright
State University
3155 Research Blvd., Suite 106
Kettering, OH 45420
937-259-1307
Email: cbaumhauer@emtec.org

Dayton PTAC Supersite
Edison Materials Technology
Center
3155 Research Blvd., Suite 106
Kettering, OH 45420
937-259-1321
Email: dwallace@emtec.org

The Ohio SBDC at Washington
State Community College
710 Colgate Drive
Marietta, OH 45750
740-374-8716
Fax: 740-376-0257
www.wscc.edu/workforce/default.h
tm
Email: sberry@wcss.edu

The Ohio SBDC at Clermont
County Chamber of Commerce

553 Chamber Drive
Milford, OH 45150
513-576-5000
www.clermontchamber.com
Email: john.melvin@
clermontchamber.com

North Coast ITAC & PTAC
Supersite
Lake County Economic
Development Center
391 West Washington Street
Painesville, OH 44077
440-357-2290 Ext. 29
www.lcedc.org
Email: itac@lcedc.org

Region 7 Lead Center
Ohio SBDC at The Ohio State
University South Center Enterprise
Center
1864 Shyville Road
Piketon, OH 45661
800-860-7232
740-289-3727
www.sbdc.osu.edu
Email: fox.264@osu.edu

The Ohio Manufacturing, Defense,
& Technology SBDC at The Ohio
State University Enterprise Center
1864 Shyville Road
Piketon, OH 45661
800-297-2072
740-289-2071
www.sbdc.osu.edu
Email: boulay.1@osu.edu

Portsmouth MCBAP
Portsmouth Inner City
Development Corporation
P.O. Box 847
1206 Waller Street
Portsmouth, OH 45662
740-354-6626
Email: pidc@zoominternet.net

PTAC of Ohio at South Point
Lawrence Economic Development
Corporation
P.O. Box 488
South Point, OH 45680
800-408-1334
Email: klawhorn@zoominternet.net

The Ohio Manufacturing, Defense,
& Technology SBDC at Edison
Industrial Systems Center
2600 Dorr Street
Toledo, Ohio 43607
877-668-3472
419-535-6000
Email: greg.stewart@eisc.org

Northwest ITAC
Toledo Area Chamber of
Commerce
300 Madison Avenue, Suite 200
Toledo, Ohio 43604
419-243-8191

Email:
joe.loeffler@toledochamber.com

Toledo MCBAP
Economic Opportunity Planning
Association
505 Hamilton Street
Toledo, Ohio 43602
419-242-7304
Email: jpowell@eopa.org

Youngstown/Warren Satellite
418 South Main Avenue
Warren, OH 44481
330-841-2566
Fax: 330-841-2738
www.ohiosbdc-ysu.com

Oklahoma

Lead Center:
Dr. Grady Pennington
Oklahoma Small Business
Development Center
Southeastern Oklahoma State
University
1405 N. 4th Ave. PMB 2584
Durant, OK 74701
580-745-7577
800-522-6154
Fax: 580-745-7471
www.osbdc.org/osbdc.html
Email: gpennington@sosu.edu

East Central State University
Small Business Development
Center
1036 East 10th St.
Ada, OK 74820
580-436-3190
Fax: 580-436-3190
www.ecok.edu/dept/osbdcecu
Email: aritter@mailclerk.ecok.edu

Northwestern State University
Small Business Development
Center
709 Oklahoma Boulevard
Alva, OK 73717
580-327-8608
Fax: 580-327-8408
www.nwosu.edu/osbdc/index.html
Email: BWGregory@nwosu.edu

Southeastern State University
Small Business Development
Center
517 University
Durant, OK 74701
580-745-7577
Fax: 580-745-7471
www.osbdc.org
Email: hmanning@sosu.edu

Northwestern State University
Enid Satellite Center
2929 East Randolph
Enid, OK 73701
580-213-3197

Fax: 580-213-3196
www.nwosu.edu/osbdc/index.html
Email: BWGregory@nwosu.edu

Northwestern State University
Goodwell Satellite
Small Business Development
Center
301 Sewell Hall
Goodwell, OK 73939
580-349-2611
Fax: 580-349-2302
Email: osbdc@opsu.edu

Lawton Satellite Center
Small Business Development
Center
711 SW "D", Suite 203
Lawton, OK 73501
580-248-4946
Fax: 580-357-4964
Email: jveal@sbcglobal.net

Northeastern State University
Miami Satellite
NEO A&M College
Dyer Hall, Room 306
Miami, OK 74354-0985
918-540-0575
Fax: 918-540-0575
Email: clcox@neoam.cc.ok.us

Rose State College
Procurement Specialty Center
6420 SE 15th Street
Midwest City, OK 73110
405-733-7348
Fax: 405-733-7495
www.rose.edu/commfriend/bizdev
Email: sbdc@rose.edu

University of Central Oklahoma
Small Business Development Ctr
115 Park Avenue
Oklahoma City, OK 73102
405-232-1968
Fax: 405-232-1967
www.osbdc.org
Email: osbdc@osbdc.org

Langton University
Minority Assistance Center
4205 North Lincoln Boulevard
Oklahoma City, OK 73105
405-962-1628
Fax: 405-962-1639
Email: jmbowers@lunet.edu

Eastern Central University
Poteau Satellite Center
Small Business Development
Center
1507 South McKenns
Poteau, OK 74953
918-647-4019
Fax: 918-647-4019
Email: dqualls@casc.cc.ok.us

Northeastern State University
Tulsa Satellite

Small Business Development
Center
Williams Towers II, Suite 150
2 West 2nd St.
Tulsa, OK 74103
918-5813-2600
Fax: 918-599-6173
Email:
johnblue@tulsachamber.com

Southwestern State University
Small Business Development
Center
100 Campus Drive
Weatherford, OK 73096
580-774-7095
Fax: 580-774-7096
Email: balchs@swosu.edu

Oregon

Lead Center:
Edward Cutler
Oregon Small Business
Development Center
99 W. 10th Ave., Suite 390
Eugene, OR 97401
541-463-5250
Fax: 541-345-6006
www.bizcenter.org
Email: carterb@lanecc.edu

Linn-Benton Community College
Small Business Development
Center
6500 Pacific Boulevard SW
Albany, OR 97321
541-917-4923
Fax: 541-917-4445
www.lbcc.cc.or.us/bdc
Email: albany@bizcenter.org

Central Oregon Community
College
Small Business Development Ctr
The Welcome Center
The Center for Business and
Industry
2600 NW College Way
Bend, OR 97701
541-383-7290
Fax: 541-317-3445
http://daedalus.cocc.edu/cbi/
Email: cbi@cocc.edu

Lane Community College
Small Business Development
Center
1445 Williamette Street, Suite 1
Eugene, OR 97401-4087
541-463-5255
Fax: 541-686-0096
www.lanecc.edu/cc_gen/bdc/busdc.
htm
Email: scheideckerj@lanecc.edu

Rogue Community College
Small Business Development
Center

214 SW 4th Street
Grants Pass, OR 97526
541-956-7494

Mount Hood Community College
Small Business Development
Center
323 NE Roberts Street
Gresham, OR 97030
503-491-7658
Fax: 503-666-1140
www.mhcc.cc.or.us/center/bizcente
r/main.htm
Email: loomisd@mhcc.edu

Oregon Institute of Technology
Small Business Development
Center
3201 Campus Drive
Boivin Hall 119
Klamath Falls, OR 97601-8801
541-885-1760
Fax: 541-885-1761
www.oit.edu//sbdc
Email: sbdc@oit.edu

LaGrande Small Business
Development Center
Eastern Oregon University
One University Boulevard
LaGrande, OR 97850
541-962-1532
www.eoni.com/sbdc
Email; sbdc@eoni.com

Small Business Development
Center
Oregon Coast Community College
North County Center
1206 SE 48th Street
Lincoln City, OR 97367
541-994-4166
Fax: 541-996-4958
www.occc.cc.or.us/sbdc/index.html
Email: gfaust@occc.cc.or.us

Small Business Development
Center
322 West 6th Street
Medford, OR 97501
541-772-3478
Fax: 541-776-2224
www.sou.edu/business/SBDC.htm

Clackamas Community College
Small Business Development
Center
7736 SE Harmony Road
Milwaukie, OR 97222
503-656-4447
Fax: 503-650-7358
depts.clackamas.cc.or.us/bdc
Email: bizcenter@clackamas.edu

Treasure Valley Community
College
Small Business Development
Center
650 College Road
Ontario, OR 97914

541-881-8822, ext. 256
Fax: 541-881-2743
www.tvcc.or.us/del/page38.htm
Email: ontario@bizcenter.org

Blue Mountain Community
College
Small Business Development
Center
2411 N.W. Carden Avenue
Morrow Hall Room M-11
Pendelton, OR 97801
541-276-6233
888-441-7232
Fax: 541-276-6819
www.bluecc.edu/programs/sbdc/in
dex.html
Email: Pendelton@bizcenter.org

Portland Community College
Small Business Development
Center
2025 Lloyd Center Mall
Portland, OR 97232
503-978-5080
Fax: 503-288-1366
www.pcc.edu/pcc/pro/sbdc/default.
htm
Email: yjohnson@pcc.edu

Umpqua Community College
Small Business Development
Center
2555 NE Diamond Lake Boulevard
Roseburg, OR 97470
541-672-2535
Fax: 541-672-3679
www.umpqua.cc.or.us/commed/sbd
c.htm
Email: swagert@umpqua.edu

Chemeketa Community College
Small Business Development
Center
365 Ferry Street, SE
Salem, OR 97301
503-399-5088
Fax: 503-581-6017
Email: salem@bizcenter.org

Columbia Gorge Community
College
Small Business Development
Center
400 East Scenic Drive, Suite 257
The Dalles, OR 97058
541-298-3118
Fax: 541-298-3119
www.cgcc.cc.or.us/SBDC/SBDC.h
tm
Email: sbdc@cgcc.or.us

Tillamook Bay Community
College Service District
Small Business Development
Center
401 B Main Street
Tillamook, OR 97141
503-842-8222 ext. 101
Fax: 503-842-2555

www.tbcc.cc.or.us/prgms/sbdc.html
Email: tillamook@bizcenter.org

Southwestern Oregon Community
College
The Brookings BizCenter
420 Alder Street
Brookings, OR 97415
541-469-5017
Email: Brookings@bizcente.org

The Coos Bay/North Bend
BizCenter
2455 Maple Leaf Lane
North Bend, OR 97459
541-756-6866
Email: coosbay@bizcenter.org

The Seaside BizCenter
1761 North Holladay Drive
Seaside, OR 97138
503-738-3347
Email: seaside@bizcenter.org

Pennsylvania

Lead Center:
Pennsylvania Small Business
Development Center
University of Pennsylvania
The Wharton School
409 Vance Hall, 4th Floor
3733 Spruce Street
Philadelphia, PA 19104-6374
215-898-1219
Fax: 215-573-2135
www.pasbdc.org
Email: pasbdc@wharton.upenn.edu

Lehigh University
Small Business Development
Center
Rauch Business Center
621 Taylor Street, Room 390
Bethlehem, PA 18015-3117
610-758-3980
Fax: 610-758-5205
www.leigh.edu/~insbdc
Email: insbdc@lehigh.edu

Clarion University of Pennsylvania
Small Business Development
Center
102 Dana Still Business
Administration Bldg.
Clarion, PA 16214-1232
814-393-2060
Fax: 814-393-2636
www.clarion.edu/sbdc/index.html
Email: yearney@clarion.edu

Gannon University
Small Business Development
Center
120 West 9th Street
Erie, PA 16501
814-871-7232
877-258-6648
Fax: 814-871-7383

www.gannon.edu/resource/other/or
g/sbdc
Email: gusbdc@gannon.edu

Kutztown University
Small Business Development
Center
Dixon University Center SSHE
2917 North Front Street
Harrisburg, PA 17110
717-346-2029
Fax: 717-346-2038
www.kutztownsbdc.org/default1.ht
m
Email: mckowen@kutztown.edu

St. Vincent College
Small Business Development
Center
Center for Global Competitiveness
300 Fraser Purchase Road
First Floor, Benedict Hall
Latrobe, PA 15650
724-537-4572
866-SBDC-CGC (Toll free)
Fax: 724-537-0919
http://sbdc.stvincent.edu
Email: sbdc@stvincent.edu

Bucknell University
Small Business Development
Center
125 Dana Engineering building
Lewisburg, PA 17837
570-577-1249
866-275-6010
Fax: 570-577-1768
www.departments.bucknell.edu/sbd
c
Email: sbdc@bucknell.edu

Lock Haven University of
Pennsylvania
Small Business Development
Center
105 Annex Building
Lock Haven, PA 17745
570-893-2589
www.lhup.edu/sbdc

St. Francis College
Small Business Development
Center
117 Evergreen Drive
Loretto, PA 15940
814-472-3200
Fax: 814-472-3202
www.sfcpa.edu/sbdc
Email: brc@francis.edu

Temple University
Small Business Development
Center
1510 Cecil B. Moore Avenue
Philadelphia, PA 191221
215-204-7282
Fax: 215-204-4554
www.temple.edu/sbdc
Email: sbdc@sbm.temple.edu

University of Pennsylvania
Small Business Development
Center
The Wharton School, Vance Hall
3733 Spruce Street
Philadelphia, PA 19104-6374
215-898-4861
Fax: 215-898-1063
http://whartonsbdc.wharton.upenn.
edu
Email:
mail@sbdc.wharton.upenn.edu

Chrysler Corporation Small
Business Development Center
Duquesne University
108 Rockwell Hall
600 Forbes Avenue
Pittsburgh, PA 15282-0103
412-396-6233
Fax: 412-396-5884
http://srv02a.sbdc.business.duq.edu
/sbdc/default.cfm
Email: duqsbdc@duq.edu

University of Pittsburgh
Small Business Development
Center
First Floor, Wesley W. Posvar Hall
Pittsburgh, PA 15620
412-648-1542
Fax: 412-648-1636
http://iee.katz.pitt.edu/sbdc
Email: ieeinfo@katz.pitt.edu

University of Scranton
Small Business Development
Center
Fl 2, Estate Building
200 Monroe Ave
Scranton, PA 18510-4639
570 -941-7588
800-829-7232
Fax: 570 -941-4053
http://sbdc.scranton.edu
Email: sbdc@scranton.edu

Pennsylvania State University
Small Business Development
Center
117 Technology Center
University Park, PA 16802-7000
814-863-4293
www.research.psu.edu/sbdc
Email: sbdc@psu.edu

Wilkes College
Small Business Development
Center
Hollenback Hall
192 South Franklin Street
Wilkes-Barre, PA 18766
570-408-4340
800-945-5378 ext. 4340
Fax: 570-824-2245
www.sbdc.wilkes.edu

Outreach Center
Small Business Development
Center

McDade Trust & Transit Centre
100 West 3rd Street
Willliamsport, PA 17701
570-326-1971
www.lhup.edu/sbdc

Rhode Island

Lead Center:
Robert Hamlin
Rhode Island Small Business
Development Center
Bryant College
1150 Douglas Pike
Smithfield, RI 02917-1284
401-232-6111
Fax: 401-232-6933
www.risbdc.org
Email: rhamlin@risbdc.org

Northern Rhode Island Chamber of
Commerce
Small Business Development
Center
6 Blackstone Valley Pl., Suite 301
Lincoln, RI 02865-1105
401-334-1000
Fax: 401-334-1009
Email: djobling@bryant.edu

East Bay Office
Small Business Development
Center
Newport County Chamber of
Commerce
45 Valley Road
Middletown, RI 02842-6377
401-849-6900
Fax: 401-841-0570
www.newportchamber.com
Email: dcotham@bryant.edu

Rhode Island Small Business
Development Center
Enterprise Community Office
550 Broad Street
Providence, RI 02907-1445
401-272-1083
Fax: 401-272-1186
www.risbdc.org
Email: mencucci@bryant.edu

Bryant College
Small Business Development
Center
30 Exchange Terrace, 4th Floor
Providence, RI 02903-1793
401-831-1330
Fax: 401-454-2819
www.bryant.edu/BUSINESS.HTM
Email: djobling@bryant.edu

Verizon Telecommunications
Center
Small Business Development
Center
Bryant College Koffler Technology
Center
1150 Douglas Pike

Smithfield, RI 02917-1284
401-232-0220
Fax: 401-232-0242
www.risbdc.org
Email: sbrigido@bryant.edu

Export Assistance Center
Bryant Colllege EAC
1150 Douglas Pike
Smithfield, RI 02917-1284
401-232-6407
Fax: 401-232-6416
www.rieac.org
Email: postoffice@rieac.org

East Bay Chamber of Commerce
654 Metacom Avenue, Suite 2
Warren, RI 02885-0250
401-245-0750
Fax: 401-245-0110

Central Rhode Island Chamber of
Commerce
3288 Post Road
Warwick, RI 02886-7151
401-732-1101
Fax: 401-732-1107
Email: dfournar@bryant.edu

Center for Women and Enterprise
Office
55 Claverick Street
Providence, RI 02903
401-277-0800
Fax: 401-277-1122

South Carolina

Lead Center:
John Lenti
South Carolina Small Business
Development Center
The Frank L. Roddey SBDC of
South Carolina
University of South Carolina
Moore School of Business
1705 College Street
Columbia, SC 29208
803-777-4907
Fax: 803-777-4403
http://scsbdc.moore.sc.edu
Email: sbdc@moore.sc.edu

University of South Carolina-Aiken
Small Business Development
Center
471 University Parkway, Box 9
School of Business
Aiken, SC 29801
803-641-3646
Fax: 803-641-3647
www.usca.edu/sbdc
Email: sbdc@usca.edu

University of South Carolina at
Beaufort
Small Business Development
Center
801 Carteret Street

Beaufort, SC 29902
843-521-4143

Clemson University
Small Business Development
Center
425 Sirrine Hall
Clemson, SC 29634-1392
864-656-3227
Fax: 864-656-4869
http://business.clemson.edu/sbdc
Email: jillb@clemson.edu

University of South Carolina
Small Business Development
Center
Moore School of Business
Columbia, SC 29208
803-777-5118
Fax: 803-777-4403
http://scsbdc.moore.sc.edu

Columbia Manufacturing Field
Office
1136 Washington Street, Suite 300
Columbia, SC 29201
803-252-6976 ext. 237

Coastal Carolina University
Small Business Development
Center
School of Business Administration
P.O. Box 261954
Wall Building, Suite 111
Conway, SC 29528-6054
843-349-2170
Fax: 803-349-2445
http://cba.winthrop.edu/sbdc
Email: sbdcweb.badm.sc.edu

Florence/Darlington Technical
College
Small Business Development
Center
P.O. Box 100548
Florence, SC 29501-0548
843-661-8256
Fax: 843-661-8041
http://cba.winthrop.edu/sbdc
Email: lowdert@flo.tec.sc.us

Upper Savannah Area Small
Business Development Center
600 Monument Street, Suite 106
Greenwood, SC 29648
864-943-8028
Fax: 864-942-8592
http://business.clemson.edu/sbdc

University of South Carolina at
Hilton Head
Small Business Development
Center
1 College Center Drive
Hilton Head Island, SC 29928
843-785-3995
Fax: 843-785-7730
Email: Pcameron@sc.edu

Charleston Area Small Business
Development Center
5900 Core Drive, Suite 104
North Charleston, SC 29406
843-740-6160
Fax: 843-740-1607
Email: Lenr@Infoave.net

South Carolina State College
Small Business Development
Center
School of Business
Algernon S. Belcher Hall
300 College Street
Campus Box 7176
Orangeburg, SC 29117
803-536-8445
Fax: 803-536-8066
www.sbdc.scsu.edu
Email: zs_sthomas@scsu.edu

Winthrop University
Small Business Development
Center
118 Thurmond Building
Rock Hill, SC 29733
803-323-2283
Fax: 803-323-4281
http://cba.winthrop.edu/sbdc
Email: sbdctech@winthrop.edu

Spartanburg Office
Small Business Development
Center
142 South Dean Street, Suite 216
P.O. Box 5626
Spartanburg, SC 29304-5626
864-316-9162
864-586-3602
http://business.clemson.edu/sbdc
Email: Dtinsel@clemson.edu

Sumter Area Small Business
Development Center
University of South Carolina at
Sumter
200 Miller Road
Sumter, SC 29150-2498
803-938-3833
Email:
Leron@uscsumter.uscsu.sc.edu

Greenville Office
1200 Woodruff Road, Suite C-38
Greenville, SC 29607
864-297-1016
Fax: 864-329-0453
http://business.clemson.edu/sbdc

Conway Area SBDC
Myrtle Square Mall #11
2501 North Kings Hwy.
Myrtle Beach, SC 29577
843-913-7883
843-913-7884
Fax: 843-913-7888
http://cba.winthrop.edu/sbdc
Email: nniles@coastal.edu

South Dakota

Lead Center:
Belinda Engelhart and Mark Slade,
Acting co-State Directors
South Dakota Small Business
Development Center
University of South Dakota
414 East Clark
Vermillion, SD 57069-2390
605-677-5287
Fax: 605-677-5427
www.sdsbdc.org
Email: sbdc@dailypost.com

Aberdeen Small Business
Development Ctr.
416 Production Street North
Aberdeen, SD 57401
605-626-2565
Fax: 605-626-2667
Email: kweaver@midco.net

Pierre Small Business
Development Center
221 South Central
Pierre, SD 57501
605-945-1661
Fax: 605-224-8320
Email: hughsobolik@csded.org

Small Business Development
Center
444 North Mount Rushmore Rd.,
Room 204
Rapid City, SD 57701
605-394-5311
Fax: 605-394-6140
Email: bmadden@tie.net

Small Business Development
Center
1000 North West Avenue, #230
Sioux Falls, SD 57104
605-367-5757
Fax: 605-367-5755
Email: mslade@usd.edu

Watertown Small Business
Development Center
124 First Avenue, NW
P.O. Box 1207
Watertown, SD 57201
605-882-5115
Fax: 605-882-5049
Email: sbdc@dailypost.com

Yankton Small Business
Development Center
1808 Summit Avenue
P.O. Box 687
Yankton, SD 57078
605-665-0751
Fax: 605-665-0303
www.districtiii.org/SBDC.html
Email: sbdc@districtiii.org

Tennessee

Lead Center:
Albert Laabs
State University and Community
College
Tennessee Small Business
Development Center
1415 Murfreesboro Rd, Suite 350
Nashville, TN 37217
615-366-3900
877-898-3900
Fax: 615-366-4464
www.tsbdc.org
Email: alaabs@mail.tsbdc.org

Chattanooga State Technical
Community College
Small Business Development
Center
100 Cherokee Boulevard, Suite 202
Chattanooga, TN 37405
423-756-8668
Fax: 423-756-6195
www.chattanoogastate.edu/TSBDC
/default.htm
Email: rtawil@mail.tsbdc.org

Cleveland State Community
College
Small Business Development
Center
P.O. Box 3570
Cleveland, TN 37320-3570
423-614-8707
Fax: 423-478-6251
www.clscc.cc.tn.us/sbdc/SbdcPage/
Email: rplatz@clevelandstatecc.edu

Small Business Development
Center
Maury County Alliance
106 West Sixth Street
P.O. Box 8069
Columbia, TN 38402
931-388-5674
Fax: 931-867-3344
Email:
gosekowsky@mail.tsbdc.org

Tennessee Technological
University
Small Business Development
Center
College of Business Administration
P.O. Box 5023
Cookeville, TN 38505-0001
931-372-3638
Fax: 931-372-6534
Email: mreel@mail.tsbdc.org

Dyersburg Community College
Small Business Development
Center
1510 Lake Road
Dyersburg, TN 38024
731-286-3201
Fax: 731-286-3271
Email: jfrakes@mail.tsbdc.org

Four Lakes Regional Industrial
Development Authority
Small Business Development
Center
P.O. Box 63
Hartsville, TN 37074-0063
615-374-4607
Fax: 615-374-4608

Jackson State Community College
Small Business Development
Center
210 East Chester Street
Jackson, TN 38301-3797
731-424-5389
800-355-5722 ext. 627
Fax: 731-425-2641
http://conted.jscc.edu/sbdc.htm
Email: croth@jscc.cc.tn.us

East Tennessee State University
Small Business Development
Center
College of Business
2109 West Market Street
Johnson City, TN 37604
423-439-8505
Fax: 423-461-7080
http://business.etsu.edu/Tsbdc
Email: bjustice@mail.tsbdc.org

Kingsport Small Business
Development Center
1501 University Boulevard
Kingsport, TN 37660
432-392-8017
http://business.etsu.edu/Tsbdc
Email: rgraham@mail.tsbdc.org

International Trade Center
601 West Summit Hill Drive
Knoxville, TN 37915
423-632-2990
Fax: 423-521-6367
www.tsbdc.org/itm.htm

Pellissippi State Technical
Community College
Small Business Development
Center
601 W. Summit Hill Dr., Suite 300
Knoxville, TN 37902-2011
865-632-2980
Fax: 865-971-4439
www.pst.no.cc.cc.tn.us/bcs/TNsbdc
.html

Small Business Development
Center
320 South Dudley Street
Memphis, TN 38101-3206
901-527-1041
Fax: 901-527-1047
www.tsbdc.memphis.edu

University of Memphis
Small Business Development
Center
976 W. Park Loop, Room 101
Memphis, TN 38152

901-678-4041
Fax: 901-678-4072
Email: jmalloy@mail.tsbdc.org

Middle Tennessee State University
Small Business Development
Center
Chamber of Commerce Building
501 Memorial Boulevard
Murfreesboro, TN 37129
615-898-2745
Fax: 615-893-7089
www.tsbdc.org/mtsu/sbdc.html
Email: pgeho@mail.tsbdc.org

Tennessee State University
Small Business Development
Center
330 10th Avenue, North
Nashville, TN 37203-3401
615-963-7179
Fax: 615-963-7160
www.tnstate.edu/
Email: wlatham@tnstate.edu

Austin Peay State University
420B Madison Street, Suite 2
Clarksville, TN 37044
931-647-2331 ext. 261
931-221-1370
Fax: 931-503-0984
www.apsu.edu/ext_ed/small_busin
ess/
Email: tsbdc@apsu.edu

Satellite Office of MTSU
149 Public Square
Lebanon, TN 37087
615-444-5503
Fax: 615-443-0596

Satellite Office of University of
Memphis
Business Information Center
555 Beale Street
Memphis, TN 38103
901-526-9300
Fax: 901-525-2357

Satellite Office of PSTCC
201 South Washington Street
Maryville, TN 37804
865-983-2241

Technology 2020 Office
Affiliate Office of PSTCC
1020 Commerce Park Drive
Oak Ridge, TN 37830-8026
865-483-2668
Fax: 865-220-2030
Email: dcollier@mail.tsbdc.org

Satellite- Rogersville Chamber of
Commerce
107 E. Main Street, Suite 100
USBANK Building
Rogersville, TN 37857
423-439-8505
Email: bjustice@mail.tsbdc.org

Satellite Office
1227 Ninth Avenue North
Nashville, TN 37208
615-963-7179 (TN State contact)
www.tnstate.edu

Texas

Lead Centers:
North Texas Small Business
Development Center
Dallas County Community College
1402 Corinth Street
Dallas, TX 75215
214-860-5835
800-350-7232
Fax: 214-860-5813
www.tded.state.tx.us/guide
www.ntsbdc.org
ntsbdc@dcccd.edu

Texas Economic Development
Office of Small Business
Assistance
1700 North Congress Avenue
Austin, TX 78711
512-936-0297
Fax: 512-936-0440
www.tded.state.tx.us/SmallBusiness

Small Business Development
Center
500 Chestnut, Suite 601
Albilene, TX 79602
325-670-0300
www.abilene-sbdc.org/
Email: b.Anderson@nwtsbdc.org

Small Business Development
Center
2300 North Western
Amarillo, TX 79124
806-372-5151
Fax: 806-372-5261
http://www.amarillo-sbdc.org/
Email: ppronger@mail.wtamu.edu

Coastal Plains SBDC
2200 7th Street, Suite 300
Bay City, TX 77414
979-244-8466
Fax: 979-244-8463
Email: sbdc@wcnet.net

Best Southwest SBDC
207 N. Cannady Drive
Cedar Hill, TX 75104
972-860-7894
Fax: 972-291-1320
Email: bswcvcc@airmail.net

The Government Contracting
SBDC
1402 Corinth Street
Dallas, TX 75215
214-860-5889
www.ntsbdc.org/NTGovernment.ht
m
Email: cpw9421@dcccd

Denton Chamber of Commerce
Bldg.
414 Parkway
Denton, TX 76201
940-380-1849
Fax: 940-382-0040
www.nctc.cc.tx.us/Continuing_edu
cation/sbdc.html
Email: nctcsbdc@denton-
chamber.org

Kingsville Chamber of Commerce
635 E King
Kingsville, TX 78363
361-592-6438
Fax: 361-661-1119
www.delmar.edu/sbdc
Email: ruralsbdc@sdcglobal.net

University of Houston
Small Business Development
Center
2302 Fannin, Suite 200
Houston, TX 77002
713-752-8444
www.sbdc.uh.edu/offices.html
Email: rskebo@uh.edu

San Jacinto College District
5800 Uvalde, S209C
Houston, TX 77049
281-459-7643
Fax 281-459-7694
www.sjcd.edu/sbdc

Small Business Development
Center
4901 East University Boulevard
Odessa, TX 79762
915-552-2455
Fax: 915-552-3455
http://www.midland-odessa-
sbdc.org/
Email: Connor_a@utpb.edu

San Jacinto College District
2006 East Broadway, Suite 101
Pearland, TX 77581
281-485-5214
Fax: 281-485-6978
www.sjcd.edu/sbdc

Austin Community College SBDC
202 North C M Allen Parkway
San Marcos, TX 78666
512-393-5912

Small Business Development
Center
Box T-0650
Stephenville, TX 76402
254-968-9330
Fax: 254-968-9329
www.stephenville-sbdc.org
Email: beck@tarleton.edu

North Harris Montgomery
Community College
5000 Research Forest Drive
The Woodlands, TX 77381-4399

832-813-6674
Fax: 832-813-6662
http://www.cbed.org/sbdc/

Middle Rio Grande Development
Council
209 North Getty Street
Uvalde, TX 78801
830-758-5025
Fax: 830-278-2929

Small Business Development
Center
3410 Taft Boulevard
Wichita Falls, TX 76308
940-397-4373
Fax: 940-397-4374
www.wichita-falls-sbdc.org
Email: jeannie.hilbers@mwsu.edu

Texas Gulf Coast Small Business
Development Center
University of Houston
2302 Fannin
Houston, TX 77002
713-752-8444
Fax: 713-756-1500
www.sbdc.uh.edu
Email: gshelton@uh.edu

Northwest Texas Small Business
Development Center
2579 South Loop 289, Suite 210
Lubbock, TX 79423
806-745-3973
800-992-7232
Fax: 806-745-6207
http://nwtsbdc.org
Email: SBDCweb@nwtsbdc.org

South Texas Border Small Business
Development Center
University of Texas at San Antonio
Downtown
Institute for Economic
Development
UT San Antonio SBDC
145 Duncan Drive Suite 200
San Antonio, TX 78226
210-458-2460
Fax: 210-458-2464
www.iedtexas.org
Email: MWOODS@UTSA.EDU

SUL Ross State University
Big Bend Region Minority and
Small Business Development
Center
Room 319, Briscoe Administration
Building
P.O. Box C-47
Alpine, TX 79832
432-837-8694
Fax: 432-837-8104
www.sulross.edu/~sbdc
Email: lgarcia@sulross.edu

Trinity Valley Small Business
Development Center

100 Cardinal Drive
Athens, TX 73751
903-675-7403
Fax: 903-675-5199
www.ntsbdc.org
Email: jloden@tvcc.edu

Lee College
Small Business Development
Center
P.O. Box 818
Baytown, TX 77522-0818
281-425-6309
Fax 281-425-6307
www.lee.edu/sbdc
Email: thatthawa@lee.edu

John Gray Institute/Lamar
University
Small Business Development
Center
855 Florida Avenue, Suite 101
Beaumont, TX 77705
409-880-2367
800-722-3443
Fax: 409-880-2201
http://hal.lamar.edu/~sbdc
Email: arnolde@hal.lamar.edu

Blinn College
Small Business Development
Center
902 College Avenue
Brenham, TX 77833
409-830-4137
Fax: 409-830-4135
www.blinn.edu/sbdc
Email: sbdc@blinncol.edu

Brazos Valley Small Business
Development Center
4001 East 29th Street, Suite 175
Bryan, TX 77802
979-260-5222
Fax: 979-260-5229
www.bvsbdc.org

Del Mar College, East Campus
Small Business Development
Center
101 Baldwin Boulevard
Corpus Christi, TX 78404-3897
361-698-1021
888-698-6111
Fax: 361-698-1024
www.delmar.edu/sbdc
Email: lfarr@delmar.edu

Navarro Small Business
Development Center
120 North 12th Street
Corsicanna, TX 75110
903-874-0658
Fax: 903-874-4187
www.ntsbdc.org
Email: torte@nav.cc.tx.us

Dallas Small Business
Development Center
1402 Corinth

Dallas, TX 75215
214-860-5865
Fax: 214-860-5867
www.ntsbdc.org/dallas.htm
Email: dsbdc@dcccd.edu

International Small Business
Development Center
2050 Stemmons Freeway
World Trade Center, Suite 156A
P.O. Box 20451
Dallas, TX 75342
214-747-1300
800-337-7232
Fax: 214-748-5774
www.iexportimport.com
Email:
information@iExportImport.com

Grayson Small Business
Development Ctr
6101 Grayson Drive
Denison, TX 75020
903-463-8787
Fax: 903-463-5437
www.ntsbdc.org
Email: stidhamk@grayson.edu

University of Texas/Pan American
Small Business Development
Center
2412 S. Closner
Edinburg, TX 78539-2999
956-316-2610
Fax: 956-316-2612
http://coserve1.panam.edu/sbdc/loca
tion.html
Email: sbdc@panam.edu

El Paso Community College
Small Business Development
Center
1359 Lomaland Drive, Suite 535
El Paso, TX 79902-1423
Fax: 915-831-7734
www.elpasosbdc.biz
dannyn@epcc.edu
Email: roques@epcc.edu

Small Business Development
Center for Excellence, ARRI
7300 Jack Newell Boulevard
Fort Worth, TX 76118
817-272-5930
Fax: 817-272-5952
http://arri.uta.edu/sbdc/home.htm
Email: jweddle@arri.uta.edu

Tarrant Small Business
Development Center
1150 South Freeway, Suite 229
Fort Worth, TX 76104
817-871-6028
Fax: 817-332-6417
web.tccd.net/ce/ce_sbdc.asp
Email: tcc_sbdc@fwbac.com

North Central Texas Small
Business Development Center
1525 West California

Gainesville, TX 76240
940 -668-4220
Fax: 940 -668-6049
www2.nctc.cc.tx.us/user/continuing
_education/SBDC/index.html
Email: nctc_sbdc@lists.nctc.edu

Galveston College
Small Business Development
Center
4015 Avenue Q
Galveston, TX 77550
409-762-7380
888-743-7380
Fax: 409-762-7898

Sam Houston State University
Small Business Development
Center
College of business Administration
2424 Sam Houston Avenue
Huntsville, TX 77340
936-294-3737
Fax: 936-294-3738
www.shsu.edu/~sbd_www
Email: sbd_rab@shsu.edu

Brazosport College
Small Business Development
Center
500 College Drive, Room K-201
Lake Jackson, TX 77566
979-230-3380
Fax: 979-230-3482
www.brazosport.cc.tx.us/~sbdc

Laredo Development Foundation
Small Business Development
Center
616 Leal Street
Laredo, TX 78041
956-722-0563
800-820-0564
Fax: 956-722-6247
www.laredo-ldf.com/page6.html
Email: lozano@laredo_ldf.com

Kilgore College
Small Business Development
Center
911 Loop 281, Ste. 209
Longview, TX 75604
903-757-5857
Fax: 903-753-7920
www.kilgore.edu/sbdc.html
Email: bradbunt@aol.com

Texas Tech University
Small Business Development
Center
2579 South Loop 289
Lubbock, TX 79423
806-745-1637
Fax: 806-745-6717
www.lubbock-sbdc.org
Email: s.caldwell@nwtsbdc.org

Angelina Community College
Small Business Development
Center

3500 South First Street
P.O. Box 1768
Lufkin, TX 75902
936-633-5400
Fax: 936-633-5478
www.angelina.cc.tx.us/
SBDC/CS%20SBDC%20.INDEX.
htm
Email: dbrowning@agelina.edu

Northeast/Texarkana Small
Business Development Center
P.O. Box 1307
Mt. Pleasant, TX 75455
903-897-2956
800-357-7232
Fax: 903-897-1106
www.bizcoach.org
Email: sbdcnetcc@aol.com

Paris Small Business Development
Center
2400 Clarksville Street
Paris, TX 75460
903-782-0224
Fax: 903-782-0219
www.paris.cc.tx.us/sbdc
Email: pbell@paris.cc.tx.us

San Jacinto College District
Small Business Development
Center
8060 Spencer Highway B105E
Pasadena, TX 77501
281-542-2024
Fax: 281-478-3610
www.sjcd.edu/sbdc

Collin County Small Business
Development Center
Courtyard Center for Professional
and Economic Development
4800 Preston Park Boulevard
Suite A126
Plano, TX 75093
972-985-3770
Fax: 972-985-3775
www.cccd.edu/sbdc
Email: sbdc@cccd.edu

Lamar State College
Small Business Development
Center
1401 Proctor Street
Port Arthur, TX 77640
409-984-6531
Fax 409-984-6063
www.portarthur.com/sbdc/main.ht
m
Email: Linda.Tait@lamarpa.edu

Angelo State University
Small Business Development
Center
P.O. Box 10910, ASU Station
San Angelo, TX 76909
325-942-2098
Fax: 325-942-2096
www.angelo.edu/services/sbdc
Email: SBDC@angelo.edu

Kelly Small Business Assistance
Center
1222 North Main, Suite 450
San Antonio, TX 78212
210-458-2470
Fax: 210-458-2464

Tyler Small Business Development
Center
1530 South SW Loop 323, Suite
100
Tyler, TX 75701
903-510-2975
903-510-2972
www.tjc.edu/sbdc/
Email: dpro@tjc.tyler.cc.tx.us

University of Houston-Victoria
Small Business Development
Center
700 Main Center, Suite 102
Victoria, TX 77901
512-575-8944
Fax: 512-575-8852
www.vic.uh.edu/sbdc
Email: parksc@viptx.net

McLennan Small Business
Development Center
401 Franklin
Waco, TX 76701
254-714-0077
Fax: 254-714-1668
http://mcweb.mcc.cc.tx.us/sbdc/sbd
c.html

Utah

Lead Center:
Mike Finnerty
Salt Lake Community College
Small Business Development
Center
1623 South State Street
Salt Lake City, UT 84115
801-957-3493
Fax: 801-957-3488
www.slcc.edu/sbdc
Email: holtlu@slcc.edu

College of Eastern Utah
Small Business Development
Center
639 West 100 South
Blanding, UT 84511
435-678-2201 ext. 173
Fax: 435-678-2220
Email:
Bill_olderog@sanjuan.ceu.edu

Southern Utah University
Small Business Development
Center
351 West Center
Cedar City, UT 84720
435-586-5400
Fax: 435-586-5493
www.suu.edu/business/sbdc/

Snow College
Small Business Development Ctr
345 West 100 North
Ephraim, UT 84627
435-283-7372
Fax: 435-283-6913
Email: wheelwright@snow.edu

Utah State University
Small Business Development Ctr
East Campus Building, Room 24
1330 East 700 North
Logan, UT 84322-8330
435-797-2277
Fax: 435-797-3317
Email: fprante@ext.usu.edu

Moab Higher Education Center
125 West 200 South
Moab, UT 84532
435-259-3622
Email: BrianD@ext.usu.edu

Weber State University
Small Business Development
Center
School of Business and Economics
3806 University Circle
Ogden, UT 84408-3806
801-626-7051
Fax: 801-626-7423
http://community.weber.edu/sbdc
Email: sbdc@weber.edu

College of Eastern Utah
Utah Valley State College
800 West University Parkway
Orem, UT 84058
801-222-8230
801-764-7071
http://www.uvsc.edu/sbdc/
riggsle@uvsc.edu

Small Business Development
Center
375 East Carbon Avenue
Price, UT 84501
435-637-5444
Fax: 435-637-7336
www.seualg.dst.ut.us/econdev/sbdc/
sbdc.htm
Email: dpaletta@seualg.dst.ut.us

Salt Lake Community College
9750 South 300 West Suite 205
Sandy, UT 84070-3264
801-957-5200
Fax: 801-957-5333
Email: bartleba@slcc.edu

Salt Lake Community College
1623 South State Street
Salt Lake City, UT 84115
801-957-3480
Fax: 801-957-3489
Email: huntpa@slcc.edu

Dixie College
Small Business Development
Center

225 South 700 East
St. George, UT 84770
435-652-7741
Fax: 435-652-7870
www.dixiebusinessalliance.com/sb
dc.htm
Email: carter@dixie.edu

Utah State University Extension
Small Business Development
Center
1680 West Highway 40
Vernal, UT 84078
435-789-6100
Fax: 435-789-3916
Email: markh@ext.usu.edu

Vermont

Lead Center:
Don Kelpinski
Vermont Small Business
Development Center
Vermont Tech. College
P.O. Box 188
Randolph, VT 05061-0188
802-728-9101
800-464-7232 (in Vermont)
Fax: 802-728-3026
www.vtsbdc.org
Email: dkelpins@vtsbdc.org

Greater Burlington Industrial
Corporation
P.O. Box 786
60 Main Street
NW VT SBDC
Burlington, VT 05402-0786
802-658-9228 ext. 13
Fax: 802-860-1899
Email: dcohen@vtsbdc.org

Brattleboro Dev. Credit Corp.
Small Business Development
Center
76 Cotton Mill Hill, C-1
Brattleboro, VT 05301-1177
802-257-7731
Fax: 802-258-3886
Email: scasabon@vtsbdc.org

Addison Co. Econ. Dev. Corp
Small Business Development
Center
RD#4, Box 1309A
Middlebury, VT 05753
802-388-7953
Fax: 802-388-8066
www.addisoncountyedc.org/index.
html
Email: spaddock@vtsbdc.org

Central VT Econ. Dev. Center
Small Business Development
Center
P.O. Box 1439
Montpelier, VT 05601-1439
802-223-4654
Fax: 802-223-4655

www.central-vt.com/cvedc/sbdc.htm
Email: ptravers@vtsbdc.org

Lamoille Econ. Dev. Center
Small Business Development
Center
P.O. Box 455
Morrisville, VT 05661-0455
802-888-4542
Fax: 802-888-5640
Email: mjohnson@vtsbdc.org

Bennington Co. Industrial Corp.
Small Business Development
Center
P.O. Box 357
No. Bennington, VT 05257
802-442-8975
Fax: 802-442-1101
Email: wmook@vtsbdc.org

Lake Champlain Islands
Chamber of Commerce SBDC
P.O. Box 213
North Hero, VT 25474-0213
802-372-5683
802-372-8400 ext. 12
Fax: 802-372-6104
Email: sbourgeois@vtsbdc.org

Franklin County Industrial Dev.
Corp.
Small Business Development
Center
P.O. Box 1099
St. Albans, VT 05478-1099
802-524-2194
Fax: 802-527-5258
www.fcidc.com/sbdc.htm

Northeastern VT Dev. Assn.
Small Business Development
Center
P.O. Box 630
St. Johnsbury, VT 05819
802-748-1014
Fax: 802-748-1223
www.nvda.net/NVDAasRDC/sbdc.
html
Email: jfreeman@vtsbdc.org

Rutland Economic Development
Corporation
110 Merchants Row
4th Floor, Suite 3
Rutland, VT 05701
802-773-9147
www.rutlandeconomy.com/key_ass
oc.asp
Email: wwilton@vtsbdc.org

Springfield Regional Development
Corporation
14 Clinton Square, Suite 7
Springfield, VT 05156
802-257-7731
www.springfielddevelopment.org/s
rdcmore.htm
Email: scasabon@vtsbdc.org

Virginia

Lead Center:
Bob Wilburn
Department of Business Assistance
Virginia Small Business
Development Center
4031 University Drive, Suite 200
Fairfax, Virginia 22030
703-277-7700
Fax: 703-277-7730
www.virginiasbdc.org
Email: jkeenan@gmu.edu

VA Highland Community College
Small Business Development
Center
P.O. Box 828
Abingdon, VA 24212
276-739-2474
www.vhcc.edu/cbi

Alexandria Small Business
Development Center
801 N. Fairfax Street, Suite 402
Alexandria, VA 22314
703-778-1292
Fax: 703-778-1293
www.alexandriasbdc.org
Email: info@alexandriasbdc.org

Community Business Partnership
Northern VA SBDC
6911 Richmond Hwy., Suite 290
Alexandria, VA 22306
703-768-1440
www.cbponline.org
aschrief@gmu.edu

George Mason
University/Arlington Campus
Small Business Development
Center
3401 N. Fairfax Drive, Room #224
Arlington, VA 22201
703-993-8128
Fax: 703-993-8130
www.arlingtonsbdc.org
Email: mail@arlingtonsbdc.org

Mountain Empire Community
College
Small Business Development
Center
PO Drawer 700, Route 23S
Big Stone Gap, VA 24219
276-523-6529
Fax: 276-523-8139
www.me.cc.va.us/dept/sbdc
Email:
tblankenbecler@me.vccs.edu

Central Virginia Small Business
Development Center
308 East Market Street
Charlottesville, VA 22902
434-295-8198
Fax: 434-295-7066
http://avenue.org/sbdc
Email: sbdc@cstone.net

Fairfax Small Business
Development Center
4031 University Drive
Fairfax, VA 22030
703-277-7700
Fax: 703-277-7730
www.sbdc.org
Email: info@sbdc.org

Longwood Small Business
Development Ctr.
515 Main Street
Farmville, VA 23909
434-395-2086
Fax: 434-395-2359
www.longwood.edu/sbdc
Email: kcopelan@longwood.edu

Rappahannock Region Small
Business Development Center
The James Monroe Center
121 University Boulevard
Fredericksburg, VA 22406
540-286-8060
Fax: 540-286-8042
www.jmc.mwc.edu/sbdc
Email: rrsbdc@mwc.edu

Small Business Development
Center
600 Butler Farm Road, Suite
A1105
Hampton, VA 23666
757-865-3127/3128
Fax: 757-865-5885
www.hrsbdc.org
Email: jcarroll@hrccva.com

James Madison University
Small Business Development
Center
College of Business
1598 South Main Street
MSC 5502
Harrisonburg, VA 22807
276-632-4462
Fax: 276-632-5059
www.jmu.edu/sbdcenter
Email: sbdc@jmu.edu

Lynchburg Regional Small
Business Development Center
147 Mill Ridge Road
Lynchburg, VA 24502
434-582-6170
800-876-7232
Fax: 434-582-6106
www.lbdc.com
Email: sbdcinfo@lbdc.com

Martinsville Small Business
Development Center
115 Broad Street
Martinsville, VA 24114
540-632-4462
Fax: 540-632-5059
www.longwood.edu/sbdc
Email: jtberry@neocomm.net

Crater Small Business
Development Center
1964 Wakefield Street
Petersburg, VA 23805
804-518-2003
Fax: 804-518-2004
Email: dhowerton@cpd.state.va.us

Radford University
Business Assistance Center
P.O. Box 6953
Radford, VA 24142
540-831-6056
http://btp.radford.edu/ba/sbdc.html
Email: bac@radford.edu

Southwest Virginia Community
College
Small Business Development
Center
P.O. Box SVCC
Richlands, VA 24641
540-964-7345
Fax: 540-964-7575
www.sw.vccs.edu/sbdc/svccsbdc.ht
m
Email: Jim.boyd@sw.cc.va.us

Greater Richmond Small Business
Development Center
201 East Franklin Street
Richmond, VA 23241-2280
804-648-1234
Fax: 804-783-9366
www.grsbdc.com
Email: mike.leonard@grcc.com

Regional Chamber Small Business
Development Center
212 South Jefferson Street
Roanoke, VA 24011
540-983-0717
Fax: 540-983-0723
www.rrsbdc.org

South Boston Small Business
Development Center
820 Bruce Street
South Boston, VA 24592
434-572-5484
Fax: 434-572-5462
www.longwood.edu/sbdc
Email: lharris@longwood.edu

Loudoun County Small Business
Development Center
21145 Whitfield Place
Suite 104
Sterling VA 20165
703-430-7222
Fax: 703-430-7258
www.loudounsbdc.org
Email: sbdc@loudounsbdc.org

Lord Fairfax Small Business
Development Center
6480 College Street
Warrenton, VA 20187
540-351-1595
Fax: 540-351-1597

www.lfsbdc.org/fauquier/index.html
Email: bpoffenberger@lfsbdc.org

Warsaw Small Business
Development Center
P.O. Box 490
479 Main Street
Warsaw, VA 22572
804-333-0286
800-524-8915
http://homepages.sylvaninfo.net/sb
dcwar
Email:
sbdcwarsaw@sylvaninfo.net

Wytheville SBDC
300 Gordondale Road
Atkins, VA 24311
276-783-1777
Fax: 276-783-8335
www.wcc.vccs.edu/sbdc
Email: wcedwar@wcc.vccs.edu

Hampton Roads Chamber of
Commerce
400 Volvo Parkway
Chesapeake, VA 23320
757-664-2592
Fax: 757-548-1835
www.hrsbdc.org

Dan River Small Business
Development Center
300 Ringgold Industrial Parkway
Danville, VA 24540
434-793-9100
Fax: 434-793-9200
www.danriversbdc.org/contact.html
Email: dfunkhouser@
danriverincubator.com

Eastern Shore SBDC - Hampton
Roads SBDC
P.O. Box 133
Melfa, VA 23410-0133
757-789-3418
Fax: 757-787-7579
www.hrsbdc.org/contact/eshore.ht
ml
Email: sbdc@esva.net

Lord Fairfax Small Business
Development Center
173 Skirmisher Lane, Suite 317
Lord Fairfax Community College
Middletown, VA 22645
540-868-7093
Fax: 540-868-7095
www.lfsbdc.org/lord_fairfax/
Email: bsirbaugh@lfsbdc.org

Blue Ridge Community College
Box 80
Weyers Cave, VA 24486
540-213-7037
540-941-3757
888-750-2722 (VA)
www.jmu.edu/sbdcenter/SBDC/ho
me.html
Email: sbdc@br.vccs.edu

Williamsburg SBDC
T.N.C.C Historic Triangle Office
161-C John Jefferson Place
Williamsburg, VA 23185
757-253-4322
Fax: 757-253-4335
www.hrsbdc.org/contact/williamsb
urg.html
Email: rileys@tncc.vccs.edu

Washington

Lead Center:
Jim Kraft
Washington Small Business
Development Center
Washington State University
601 West First Ave.
Spokane, WA 99201-3899
509-358-7765
Fax: 509-358-7764
www.wsbdc.org
Email: kraft@wsu.edu

Bellevue Community College
North Campus
Small Business Development
Center
10700 Northup Way, Bellevue,
WA
Bellevue, WA 98007-6484
Mailing:
3000 Landerholm Circle SE
Bellevue, WA 98007-6484
425-564-2888
Fax: 425-564-4023
www.conted.bcc.ctc.edu/sbdc/sbdc.
asp
Email: wsbdc@bcc.ctc.edu

Western Washington University
Small Business Development
Center
College of Business and Economics
119 North Commercial Street,
Suite 195
Bellingham, WA 98225
360-733-4014
Fax: 360-733-5092
www.cbe.www.edu/SBDC
Email: sbdc@www.edu

Edmonds Community College
Small Business Development
Center
728 134th Street SW, Suite 128
Everett, WA 98204
425-640-1435
Fax: 425-640-1371
www.btc.edcc.edu/sbdc
Email: rbattles@edcc.edu

Big Bend Community College
Small Business Development
Center
7662 Chanute Street
Building 1500
Moses Lake, WA 98837-3299
509-762-5351 ext. 906

Fax: 509-762-6289
Email: stephani@bbcc.ctc.edu

Skagit Valley College
Small Business Development
Center
204 W. Montgomery
P.O. Box 40
Mt. Vernon, WA 98273
360-336-6114
Fax: 360-336-6116
Email: ryan@skagit.org

South Puget Sound Community
College
Small Business Development
Center
665 Woodland Square Loop SE
Suite 201
Lacey, WA 98503
360-753-5616
Fax: 360-586-5493
Email:
DouglasHammel@olywa.net

Port Angeles Small Business
Development Center
102 East Front Street
P.O. Box 1085
Port Angeles, WA 98362
360-417-5657
Fax: 360-452-9618
Email: kpurdy@clallam.org

Seattle Small Business
Development Center
Parkplace Building
1200 6th Avenue, Suite 1700
Seattle, WA 98101
206-553-7328
Fax: 206-553-7044
Email:
mfranz@connectexpress.com

Community College of Spokane
Small Business Development
Center
SIRTI Building
665 North Riverpoint Boulevard,
Suite 201
Spokane, WA 99202
509-358-7890
Fax: 509-358-7896
ccs.spokane.cc.wa.us/TECC/small_
business.htm
Email: spokesbdc@wsu.edu

Washington State University
Small Business Development
Center
12000 NE 95th Avenue, Suite 504
Vancouver, WA 98682
360-260-6372
Fax: 360-260-6369
www.columbian.com/SBDC/sbdc.h
tml
Email: harte@vancouver.wsu.edu

Yakima Valley Community
College

Small Business Development
Center
P.O. Box 1647
113 South 14th Avenue
Yakima, WA 98902
509-574-4935
Fax: 509-574-4943
www.yvcc.edu/academics/Workforc
eEd/business%20development%20c
enter/smallbus.asp
Email: arice@yakima.edu

Columbia Basin College
Tri-Cities Small Business
Development Center
901 North Colorado
Kennewick, WA 99336
509-735-6222
Fax: 509-735-6609
www.cbc2.org/instruct/bus/sbdc.ht
m
Email: BlakesCafe@3-cities.com

Walla Walla Community College
Small Business Development
Center
500 Tausick Way
Walla Walla, WA 99362
509-527-4681
Fax: 509-525-3101
www.portwallawalla.com/smbcenter
/info.htm
Email: rm@portwallawalla.com

Green River Community College
108 South Division St. Suite A
Auburn, WA 98001
253-333-1600
Fax: 253-333-8635
www.greenriver.edu/businesscenter
Email: dburnett@grcc.ctc.edu

Small Business Development
Center
1611 North National Avenue
Chehalis, WA 98532
360-748-0114
Fax: 360-748-1238
Email: dbaria@localaccess.com

Highland Community College
Small Business Development
Center
PO Box 98000 M/S Omni 3-3
Des Moines, WA 98198
206 878-3710 ext. 5151
Fax: 206- 870-5915
http://flightline.highline.edu/cel/sbd
c.htm
Email: jshelton@highline.edu

Enumclaw Small Business
Assistance Center
1414 Griffin Avenue
Enumclaw, WA 98022
253-288-3400
www.greenriver.edu/businesscenter

Okanogan County SBDC
P.O. Box 626

320 Omak Avenue #400
Omak, WA 98841
509-826-5107
Fax: 50-826-7425
Email: blakeney@methow.com

Olympic Peninsula SBDC
Port Townsend Office
540 Water Street
P.O. Box 1849
Port Townsend, WA 98368
360-344-3078
Fax: 360-344-3079
Email: kpurdy@clallam.org

Community Capital Development
SBDC
PO Box 22283
1437 S Jackson
Seattle, WA 98122
206-324-4330 ext. 107
Fax: 206-324-4322
www.seattleccd.com/sbdc/index.ht
m
Email: lindak@seattleccd.com

Seattle SBDC
3600 -15th Avenue West, Suite 303
Seattle, WA 98119
206-298-4402
Fax: 206-298-4423
Email: wwong@wolfenet.com

Tacoma SBDC
Bates Technical College
1101 South Yakima Avenue, Room
M-123
Tacoma, WA 98405
253-680-7768
Fax: 253-680-7771
Email: dyoung@bates.ctc.edu

Small Business Development
Center
Columbia Station, 3rd Floor
300 S. Columbia
Wenatchee, WA 98801
509-662-8016
509-662-3256
Email: SBDC@wenatchee.org

West Virginia

Lead Center:
Conley Salyer
West Virginia Small Business
Development Center
West Virginia Development Office
1900 Kanawha Boulevard East
Building 6 Room 652
Charleston, WV 25305
304-558-2960
888-WVA-SBDC
Fax: 304-558-0127
www.sbdcwv.org
Email: csalyer@wvsbdc.org

Charleston Small Business
Development Sub Center

State Capitol Complex
1900 Kanawha Blvd. East
Building 6, Room 652
Charleston, WV 25305
304-558-2960
Fax: 304-558-0127
www.sbdcwv.org

Elkins Satellite Small Business
Development Center
1 Station Square
Room 202 Railroad Avenue
Elkins, WV 26241
304-637-7205
Fax: 304-637-4902
Email: jrjm@westvirginia.com

Fairmont State College
Small Business Development
Center
3000 Technology Drive, Suite 200
Fairmont, WV 26554
304-367-2712
Fax: 304-367-2717
www.fscwv.edu/fsctc/sbdc
Email: mgamble1@mail.fscwv.edu

Marshall University
Small Business Development Ctr
2000 Seventh Avenue
Cabell Hall, Suite 304
Huntington, WV 25703-1527
304-696-6246
Fax: 304-696-4835
www.marshall.edu/ibd/sbdc.htmlx
Email: emcclain@marshall.edu

Eastern WV Community and
Technical College
Small Business Development Ctr
HC 65, Box 402
Moorefield, WV 26836
304-434-8000
Fax: 304-434-7003
www.eastern.wvnet.edu/sbdc.htm
Email: kellyj@eastern.wvnet.edu

West Virginia University
Small Business Development
Center
3040 University Ave. Suite 2008
Morgantown, WV 26505
304-293-5839
Fax: 304-293-8905

West Virginia University at
Parkersburg
Small Business Development
Center
300 Campus Drive
Parkersburg, WV 26101
304-424-8277
Fax: 304-424-8266
www.wvup.wvnet.edu/www/BIDS/
Sbdc.htm
Email: greg.hill@mail.wvu.edu

Flatwoods Outlet Mall, Suite 249
Small Business Development
Center

249 Skidmore Lane
Sutton, WV 26601-9272
304-765-7300
Fax: 304-765-7724
Email: cook@glenville.wvnet.edu

West Virginia Northern
Community College
Small Business Development
Center
1704 Market Street
Wheeling, WV 26003
304-233-5900 ext. 4355
Fax: 304-232-3819
http://techctr1.northern.wvnet.edu/
northern/ CBDS_sbdc.htm
Email:
daberegg@northern.wvnet.edu

Region I Workforce SBDC -
Beckley
921 W. Neville Street, Suite 200
Beckley, WV 25801
304-55-4022
800-766-4556
Fax: 304-252-9584
Email:
tparrish@r1workforcewv.org

Southern WV Community &
Technical College
300 Main Street
Logan, WV 25601
304-792-7234 ext. 27
Fax: 304-792-7239
www.southern.wvnet.edu/wd/Econ
Dev/Maindefault.htm
Email: raye@southern.wvnet.edu

Community & Technical College
of Shepherd
400 West Stephen Street
Martinsburg, WV 25401
304-260-4385
Fax: 304-260-4384
www.shepherd.edu/sbdcweb
Email: clundberg@shepherd.edu

Region I Workforce SBDC -
Summersville
812 Northside Drive, Suite 7J
Summersville, WV 26651
304-872-0020
Fax: 304-872-0020
Email: jepling@r1workforcewv.org

Wisconsin

Lead Center:
Erica Kauten
Wisconsin Small Business
Development Center
University of Wisconsin
432 North Lake Street, Room 423
Madison, WI 53706
608-263-7794
800-940-SBDC
Fax: 608-263-7830
www.wisconsinsbdc.org

University of Wisconsin at Eau
Claire
Small Business Development
Center
P.O. Box 4004
210 Water Street
Eau Claire, WI 54702-4004
715-836-5811
866-UWEC4CE
Fax: 715-836-5263
Email: ce@uwec.edu

University of Wisconsin at Green
Bay
Small Business Development
Center
835 Potts Ave
Green Bay, WI 54304
920-496-2115
Fax: 920-496-6009
www.uwgb.edu/outreach/sbdc
Email: dgjerde@titletown.org

Kenosha County Small Business
Development Center
c/o Job Center/Human Services
Building
8600 Sheidan
Kenosha, WI 53141
262-697-4525
Fax: 262-697-4563
http://oldweb.uwp.edu/admin/com
munity.partnerships/sbdc
Email: dschacht@co.kenosha.wi.us

University of Wisconsin at
LaCrosse
Small Business Development
Center
120 W. Carl Wimberly Hall
La Crosse, WI 54601
608-785-8782
Fax: 608-785-6919
www.uwlax.edu/sbdc
Email: gallaghe.jani@uwlax.edu

University of Wisconsin at
Madison
Small Business Development
Center
School of Business
975 University Ave., Room 3260
Madison, WI 53706
608-263-7680
Fax: 608-263-0818
www.uwsbdc.org
Email: sbdc@bus.wisc.edu

University of Wisconsin at
Milwaukee
Small Business Development
Center
161 West Wisconsin Ave., Suite
6752
Milwaukee, WI 53203
414-227-3142
http://cfprod.imt.uwm.edu/sce/dci.c
fm?id=15
Email: lucyh@csd.uwm.edu

University of Wisconsin at
Oshkosh
Small Business Development
Center
347 Park Plaza
Oshkosh, WI 54901
920-424-1453
800-232-8939
Fax: 920-424-2005
www.ccp.uwosh.edu/services/
services_smallbusiness.html
Email: nigl@uwosh.edu

University of Wisconsin at
Platteville
Southwest Wisconsin Small
Business Development Center
Room 710/711
Pioneer Tower Building
UW-Platteville
Plateville, WI 53818
608-342-1038
Fax: 608-342-1599
www.uwplatt.edu/~swsbdc/index.h
tml
Email: swsbdc@uwplatt.edu

University of Wisconsin at River
Falls
Small Business Development
Center
410 South Third Street, 128 SH
River Falls, WI 54022
715-425-0620
Fax: 715-425-0707
www.uwrf.edu/cbe/sbdc
Email: Kathy.bartelt@uwrf.edu

University of Wisconsin at Stevens
Point
Small Business Development
Center
2100 Main Street
103 Main Building
Stevens Point, WI 54481
715-346-3838
800-898-9472
Fax: 715-346-4045
www.uwsp.edu/extension/sbdc
Email: vloberme@uwsp.edu

University of Wisconsin at
Superior
Small Business Development
Center
Belknap & Catlin
P.O. Box 2000
Superior, WI 54880-2898
715-394-8351
Fax: 715-394-8592
www2.uwsuper.edu/bdc/index.htm
Email:
mpekklal@staff.uwsuper.edu

University of Wisconsin at
Whitewater
Small Business Development
Center
2000 Carlson Hall
Whitewater, WI 53190
262-472-3217
800-621-7235
Fax: 262-472-5692
www.uww.edu/sbdc

2320 Renaissance Boulevard
Sturtevant, WI 53177
262-898-7414
Fax: 262-898-7401
www.racine-sbdc.com
Email: info@racine-sbdc.com

Wyoming

Lead Center:
Diane Wolverton
University of Wyoming
Small Business Development
Center
P.O. Box 3922
Laramie, WY 82071-3922
307-766-3505
800-348-5194
Fax: 307-766-3406
http://uwadmnweb.uwyo.edu/sbdc
Email: ddw@uwyo.edu

Wyoming Small Business
Development Center
300 South Wolcott, Suite 300

Casper, WY 82601
307-234-6683
800-348-5207
Fax: 307-577-7014
Email: sbdc@trib.com

Laramie County Community
College
Small Business Development Ctr
1400 East College Drive
Cheyenne, WY 82007-3298
307-632-6141
800-348-5208
Fax: 307-632-6061
Email: sewsbdc@wyoming.com

Region 5 Small Business
Development Center
First Interstate Bank Building
222 South Gillette Ave., Suite 402
Gillette, WY 82716
307-682-5232
888-956-6060
Fax: 307-686-5792
Email: sbdc@vcn.com

Region 2 Small Business
Development Center
143 South Bent Street, Suite A
Powell, WY 82435
307-754-2139
800-383-0371
Fax: 307-754-0368
Email: director@wir.net

Fremont County Satellite Office
Riverton Branch Public Library
1330 West Park Avenue
Riverton, WY 82501-1790
307-857-1174
Fax: 307-857-1175
Email: wsbdc@tcinc.net

Region 1 Small Business
Development Center
1400 Dewar Drive, Suite #205
Rock Springs, WY 82901
307-352-6894
800-348-5205
Fax: 307-352-6876
Email: bellis@uwyo.edu

Business Information Centers

The Business Information Center (BIC) is administered by the US Small Business Administration (SBA) and provides a one-stop center for current and future small business owners. Entrepreneurs can obtain books, publications, and videotapes to help plan, or expand their businesses. BIC's also contain computers for clients' use with an array of business software. SCORE, Service Corps of Retired Executives, provides on-site counseling to help small business owners make a plan of action for their future business needs.

Arkansas
Arkansas State University
2007 E. Aggie Road, Room 117A
P.O. Box 310
State University AR 72467
870-910-8063
Fax: 870-972-3678

Arkansas Women's Business
Development Center
2304 W. 29th Avenue
Pine Bluff, AR 71603
870- 535-6233
Fax: 870- 535-0741

California
U.S. Small Business Administration
3600 Wilshire Blvd. Suite L100
Los Angeles, CA 90010
213- 251-7253
Fax: 213-251-7255

U.S. Small Business Administration
San Diego District Office
San Diego, CA 92101-3500
619- 557-7250 ext. 1126
Fax: 619-557-5894

Southwestern College
900 Otay Lake Road, Building 1600
Chula Vista, CA 91910
619- 482-6393
Fax: 619-482-6402

The Entrepreneur Center
U.S. Small Business Administration
455 Market Street, 6th Floor
San Francisco, CA 94105-2420
415- 744-4244
Fax: 415-744 6812

The Entrepreneur Center
U.S. Small Business Administration
Attn: Bonnie Austin
84 W. Santa Clara
San Jose, CA 95113
408- 835-9228
Fax: 408-494-0214

Mission/SBA Business Information
Center
3566 S. Higuera Street, Suite 100

San Luis Obispo, CA 93401
805- 549-0401

Connecticut
Connecticut Small Business
Information Center
330 Main Street, 2nd Floor
Hartford, CT 06103
860- 251-7000
Fax: 860-251-7006

Delaware
Delaware Small Business Resource
& Information Center
1318 N. Market Street
Wilmington, DE 19801
302-571-5225
Fax: 302-571-5668

District of Columbia
e-Business Information Center
King Memorial Library
901 G St. NW
Washington, DC 20001
(202) 727-2244
www.dclibrary.org/ebic

Florida
Jacksonville Business Service Center
5000-3 Norwood Avenue
Jacksonville, FL 32208
904- 924-1100

Disney/SBA National Entrepreneur
Center
315 East Robinson Street
Orlando, FL 32801
407- 420 4848
Fax: 407-420-4849 fax
www.floridanec.org

Georgia
U.S. Small Business Administration
Atlanta District Office
233 Peachtree St., NE, Suite 1900
Atlanta GA 30303
404- 331-0100 Ext 704
Fax: 404-529-9853

Hawaii
Business Information and
Counseling Center

1041 Nuuanu Avenue, Suite A
Honolulu, HI 96817
808-522-8130
Fax: 808-522-7494

Idaho
Idaho Business Information Center
1020 Main Street, Suite 290
Boise, ID 83702-5745
208-334-1696 ext. 234
Fax: 208-334-9353

Illinois
U.S. Small Business Administration
500 W. Madison Street, Suite 1250
Chicago, IL 60661-2511
312- 886-0710
Fax: 312-886-5688

Indiana
SBA Business Information Center
2126 N. Meridian St.
Indianapolis IN 46204
317-226-1212
Fax: 202-481-0851

Iowa
University of Northern Iowa
Business Center
212 Fourth Street
Waterloo, IA 50703
319-236-8123
Fax: 319-236-8240

Southern Community College
335 Messenger Road
Keokuk, IA 52632-6007
319-524-3221 Ext. 8441

Kentucky
Business Resource Center
NIA Center
2900 W. Broadway
Louisville, KY 40211
502-582-5971 Ext 224

Maine
Business Information Center of
Maine Career Center
5 Mollison Way
Lewiston, ME 04240
207-622-8275

207-783-2770
Fax: 207-783-7745

Portland Economic Development Center
The Resource Hub
441 Congress St.
Portland ME 04101
207-756-8180
Fax: 207-756-8178

The Anderson Learning Center
Business Information Center
21 Bradeen Street
Springvale ME 04083
207-324-2952

Maryland
Baltimore City Small Business
Resource Center
3 West Baltimore St.
Baltimore, MD 21201
410-605-0990
Fax: 401-605-0995

Western MD Business Resource
Center
113 Baltimore St.
Cumberland, MD 21502
301-722-9300

Massachusetts
Boston Business Information Center
10 Causeway Street, Room 265
Boston, MA 02222-1093
617- 565-5615
Fax: 617-565-5598

Business Information Center of Cape
Cod
Cape Cod Community College
Learning Resource Center
2240 Iyanough Road
West Barnstabl, MA 02668-1599
508-362-2131 Ext. 4487
Fax: 508-375-4020
www.metrosouthchamber.com

Berkshire Enterprises Business
Information Center
1 Fenn St., Suite 301
Pittsfield, MA 01201
413-448-2755
Fax: 413-448-2749
www.berkshireenterprises.com

South Coast Business Information
Center
c/o Fall River Chamber of
Commerce
200 Pocasset Street
Fall River, MA 02721-1585
508-673-9783
Fax: 508-674-1929

Lynn Small Business Assistance
Center
39 Central Square
Lynn, MA 01901
781-477-7222

Fax: 781-592-6104
www.lynnsbac.org

Worcester Business Information
Center
237 Chandler St.
Worcester, MA 01609
508-363-0303
Fax: 508-363-2814

Metro South Business Assistance
Center
Metro South Chamber of Commerce
60 School Street
Brockton, MA 02301-4087
508-586-0500 ext 233
508-586-1340

Lawrence Small Business
Information Center
276 Essex St.
Lawrence, MA 01840
978-686-2072 Ext. 10
Fax: 978-686-2182

Minnesota
Business Information Center
Midtown Commons Bldg., Suite 112
2324 University Ave. W.
St. Paul, MN 55114-1843
651-209-1884
Fax: 651-209-8785

Mississippi
MS Technology Alliance Innovation
Center
1230 Raymond Road
Jackson, MS 39204
601-979-5050

Missouri
U.S. Small Business Administration
323 West 8th Street, Suite 104
Kansas City, MO 64105
816-374-6675
Fax: 816-74-6692

U.S. Small Business Administration
Business Information Center
200 North Broadway, Suite 1500
St. Louis, MO 63102
314-539-6600 ext. 252

Economic Development Center of
St. Charles County
Satellite Business Information
Center
5988 Mid Rivers Mall Drive
St. Charles, MO 63304
636-441 6880

University of Missouri – Columbia
Small Business Development Center
306 Cornell Hall
Columbia MO 65211
573-882-7096

Southeast Missouri State University
Satellite Business Information
Center

One University Plaza MS 5925
Cape Girardea, MO 63701
573-986-6084

Montana
Business Information Center
347 N. Last Chance Gulch
Helena, MT 59626
406-443-0800
Fax: 406-441-1090

Big Sky Business Information Center
Big Sky Economic Development
Authority
222 N. 32nd St.
Billings MT 59101
406-256-6871
406- 256-6042

Business Information Center
Bozeman Chamber of Commerce
2000 Commercial Way
Bozeman MT 59715
406-586-5421
Fax: 406-388-6592

Nebraska
U.S. Small Business Administration
Business Information Center
11141 Mill Valley Road
Omaha, NE 68154
402-221-3606
Fax: 402-221-3680

Nevada
Vegas Business Information Center
1951 Stella Lake Street, Suite 5
Las Vegas, NV 89106
702-338-6683

New Hampshire
Business Information Center
151 Main Street
Nashua, NH 03060
603-225-1400 Ext. 113
603-598-1164

NH Business Information Center
Satellite
Monadnock Economic Development
Corporation
39 Central Square, Suite 201
Keene, NH 03431
603-352-4939

NH Business Information Center
Satellite
North Country Council
107 Glessner Road
Bethlehem, NH 03574
603-444-6303

NH Business Information Center
Satellite
The Amoskeag Small Business
Incubator
33 S. Commercial
Manchester, NH 03101
603-629-9511

NH Business Information Center
Satellite
Belknap County Economic
Development Council
2 Airport Road
Gilford, NH 03249
603-524-3057

NH Business Information Center
Satellite
Southern Maine Regional Planning
Commission
21 Bradeen Street, Suite 304
Springvale, ME 04083
207-524-3057

NH Business Information Center
Satellite
Mt. Washington Valley Economic
Council
P.O. Box 1066
Conway, NH 03818
603-447-2516

New Jersey
U.S. Small Business Administration
2 Gateway Center, 15th Floor
Newark, NJ 07102
973-645-3968
Fax: 973-645-6265

Rutgers Small Business
Development Centers
325 Cooper Street
Camden, NJ 08102-1566
856-225-6634
Fax: 856-225-6621

New Mexico
New Mexico Business Information
Center
1309 Fourth SW, Suite A
Albuquerque, NM 87102
505-346-7830
Fax: 505-346-7831

New York
The Capital Resource Center
1 Computer Drive South
Albany, NY 12205
518-446-1118 ext. 231
Fax: 518- 446-1228

North Dakota
Business Information Center
Grand Forks Chamber of Commerce
1501 28th Avenue S.
Grand Forks, ND 58203
701-746-5160
Fax: 701-746-5748

Business Information Center
2201 15th Street SW
Minot, ND 58701
701-857-8227
Fax: 701-839-3889

Oklahoma
Terry Neese Center for
Entrepreneurial Excellence
2709 West I-44 Service Road

Oklahoma City, OK 73112
405-601-1929
Fax: 405-601-1935

Oregon
SBA/Confederated Tribes of the
Warm Springs
Economic Development Office
1134 Paiute Street
P.O. Box 849
Warm Springs, OR 97761
541-553-3592
Fax: 541-553-3593

SBA/The Klamath Tribes
501 Chiloquin Blvd.
P.O. Box 436
Chiloquin, OR 97624
541 783-2219
800-524-9787
Fax: 541-783-2029

U.S. Small Business Administration
Business Information Center
1515 SW Fifth Avenue, Suite 1050
Portland, OR 97201-5494
503-326-5209
Fax: 503-326-2808

Pennsylvania
Business Information Center River
Commons
700 River Avenue, Suite 510
Pittsburgh, PA 15212
412-322-6441
Fax: 412-322-3513

Rhode Island
Central Rhode Island Chamber of
Commerce
Business Information Center
3288 Post Road
Warwick, RI 02886
401-732-1100
Fax: 401-732-1107

Enterprise Community Center
550 Broad Street
Providence, RI 02907
401-272-1086
Fax: 401-272-1186

South Carolina
South Carolina Business Information
Center
2750 Speissegger Drive
North Charleston, SC 29405
843-805-3092
Fax: 843-805-3112

South Dakota
West River Service Center
444 North Mt. Rushmore Road,
Suite 204
Rapid City, SD 57701
605-394-1707
Fax: 605-394-6140

Business Information Center
1000 N. West Avenue, Suite 400
Sioux Falls, SD 57l04

605-367-5757
Fax: 605-367-5755

Business Information Center
1808 Summit Avenue
P.O. Box 687
Yankton, SD 57078
605-665-4408
Fax: 605-665-0303

Tennessee
Tennessee State University
Avon Williams Campus
330 10th Avenue N., Room 314
Nashville, TN 37203-3401
615-963-7253
Fax: 615-963-7160

Memphis Technical Assistance &
Resource Center
555 Beale Street
Memphis, TN 38103
901-526-9300
Fax: 901-544-3201

Jackson Business Information Center
Madison County Chamber of
Commerce
210 E. Chester Avenue
Jackson, TN 38301
731-427-7900
Fax: 731-427-3942

Murphreesboro Small Business
Resource Center
Rutherford Chamber of Commerce
501 Memorial Boulevard
Murfreesboro, TN 37129
615-898-2734
Fax: 615-893-7089

Texas
Greater El Paso Chamber of
Commerce
Business Information Center
10 Civic Center Plaza
El Paso, TX 79901
915-534-0541
Fax: 915-534-0513

Fort Worth Business Assistance
Center
1150 South Freeway, Suite 134
Fort Worth, TX 76104
817-871-6002
Fax: 817-332-6465

U.S. Small Business Administration
Houston District Office
8701 S. Gessner Drive, Suite 1200
Houston, Texas 77074
Fax: 713-773-6550

Utah
Business Information Center
310 S. Main Street, North Mezzanine
Salt Lake City, UT 84191
801-746-2269
Fax: 801-746-2273

Business Information Center
2444 Washington Boulevard
Ogden, UT 84401
801-629-8604
Fax: 801-392-0604

Vermont
Burlington Business Information
Center
149 Bank Street
Burlington VT 05401
802-828-4580
Fax: 802-828-4485

Virginia
Dr. Wm. E.S. Flory Small Business
Development Center
10311 Sudley Manor Drive
Manassas, VA 20109
703-335-2500
Fax: 703-335-1700

Virginia Hispanic Chamber of
Commerce

10700 Midlothian Turnpike, Suite
200
Richmond, VA 23235
804-379-1727
Fax: 202-481-4235

Washington
U.S. Small Business Administration
Seattle District Office
1200 Sixth Avenue, Suite 1700
Seattle, WA 98101-1128
206-553-7311
Fax: 206-553-6264

Spokane Chamber of Commerce
Business Information Center
801 W. Riverside
Spokane, WA 99201
509-353-2800
Fax: 509-353-2600

Tacoma Business Assistance Center
Bates Technical College

1101 South Yakima Avenue, Room
M-123
Tacoma, WA 98402
253-680-7770

Business Resource Center
Skagit Valley College
204 W. Montgomery Street
Mt. Vernon, WA 98273
360-416-7873

Auburn Business Resource Center
Green River Community College
108 S. Division
Auburn, WA 98001
253-333-1600 ext 18

Wyoming
Business Information Center
100 East B Street, Room 4001
Casper, WY 82601
307-261-6566
Fax: 307-261-6561

Tribal Business Information Centers

Tribal Business Information Centers (TBIC) are funded by the SBA and provide culturally appropriate business development assistance to prospective and current small business owners. The TBIC offers business related computer software, management and technical assistance, guidance, free counseling and many other resources.

Arizona
TBIC: The Navajo Nation
P.O. Box 663
Window Rock, AZ 86515
520-871-6486
Fax: 520-871-6476

TBIC: The Navajo Nation
P.O. Box 565
Chinle, AZ 86503
520-674-2240
Fax: 520-674-2244

California
TBIC: Karuk Tribe of Indians
P.O. Box 1148
Happy Camp, CA 96039
530-493-5135
Fax: 530-493-5378
Email: tburcell@karukcdc.com

Minnesota
TBIC: Minnesota Chippewa Tribe
P.O. Box 217
Cass Lake, MN 56633
218-547-2676
Fax: 218-547-2173

Montana
TBIC: Blackfeet Community
College
P.O. Box 819
Browning, MT 59417
406-338-5441
Fax: 406-338-3272

TBIC: Crow Tribe of Indians/Little
Big Horn
1 Forestry Lane
Crow Agency, MT 59022
406-638-2228
Fax: 406-638-2229

TBIC: Fort Belknap College
Highway 2 & 66

Harlem, MT 59526
406-353-4672
Fax: 406-3532774
Email: fbsbdc@hotmail.com

TBIC: Fort Peck Community
College
P.O. Box 398
Poplar, MT 59255
406-768-3155
Fax: 406-768-3581
Email: marks@fpcc.cc.mt.us

TBIC: Northern Cheyenne
Tribe/Dull Knife
One College Drive
Lame Deer, MT 59043
406-477-6215
Fax: 406-477-6219
Email: peppers@dkmc.cc.mt.us

TBIC: Salish & Kootenai College
P.O. Box 117
Pablo, MT 59855
406-675-4800
Fax: 406-675-4801
Email: nancy_warneke@skc.edu

TBIC: Stone Child College/Rocky
Boy
RR1 Box 1082
Box Elder, MT 59521
406-395-4313
Fax: 406-395-4836/4138

North Carolina
TBIC: Eastern Band of Cherokee
Indians
P.O. Box 1200
Cherokee, NC 28719
828-497-9335
Fax: 828-497-9009
Email: cnabdc@yahoo.com

North Dakota
TBIC: Fort Berthold Community
College
P.O. Box 490
New Town, ND 58763
701-627-4738
Fax: 701-627-3609

TBIC: Sitting Bull College
1341 92nd Street
Fort Yates, ND 58538
701-854-3861 ext 212
Fax: 701-854-7139
Email: lodeea@sbci.edu

TBIC: Spirit Lake Sioux Tribe
P.O. Box 359
Fort Totten, ND 58335
701-766-1214
Fax: 701-766-1267

South Dakota
TBIC: Cheyenne River Sioux Tribe
P.O. Box 590
Eagle Butte, SD 57625
605-964-8242
Fax: 605-964-8243
Email: crsttbic@rapidnet.com

TBIC: Sinte Gleska
University/Rosebud Sioux
P.O. Box 8
Mission, SD 57555
605-856-4039
Fax: 605-856-4051
Email: bryanlisa@hotmail.com

TBIC: The Lakota Fund/Oglala
Sioux
P.O. Box 340
Kyle, SD 57752
605-455-2500
Fax: 605-455-2585
Email: olntbic@gwtc.net

Federal Money Programs for Business

Millions of dollars are available to small businesses, entrepreneurs, inventors, and researchers. This information is derived from the *Catalog of Federal Domestic Assistance* which is published by the U.S. Government Printing Office in Washington, DC. The number next to the title description is the official reference for this federal program. Contact the office listed below the caption for further details. The following is a description of the terms used for the types of assistance available:

Loans: money lent by a federal agency for a specific period of time and with a reasonable expectation of repayment. Loans may or may not require a payment of interest.

Loan Guarantees: programs in which federal agencies agree to pay back part or all of a loan to a private lender if the borrower defaults.

Grants: money given by federal agencies for a fixed period of time and which does not have to be repaid.

Direct Payments: funds provided by federal agencies to individuals, private firms, and institutions. The use of direct payments may be "specified" to perform a particular service or for "unrestricted" use.

Insurance: coverage under specific programs to assure reimbursement for losses sustained. Insurance may be provided by federal agencies or through insurance companies and may or may not require the payment of premiums.

Federal Money Programs for Business
Success Stories

The following examples are excerpted from the web sites of Federal agencies listed in this chapter. Contact the agencies for more information on how they can help you.

Thousands of Dollars for the Younger Generation!

You're (almost) never too small to run a small business. The Youth Loan Program of the Farm Service Agency (FSA) provides thousands of dollars for young people age 10-20 who are ready to turn a profit. The FSA office in Nevada boasts a number of success stories:

At age eleven, Rusty attends a one-room schoolhouse with three other students. He already has a dream of going to college, and is working on saving for the tuition. He applied for a FSA loan to buy three pairs of first calf heifers. He had experience with cattle, as he worked with his parents on their ranch, and was also involved with the local 4H. The loan was approved, and he now owns four bred cows and is showing in the county fair. With the help of the loan, Rusty is on his way to making his dream come true.

Moira had already owned and raised her own sheep for ten years by the time she approached the FSA at the age of 16. She and her mother met with a loan officer, who put the stamp of approval on her project. Moira got a loan to purchase British White cattle, which allowed her to own one of the first certified British White herds in the state. She also experimented with cross breeding in order to see the effects on tenderness, marbling and performance, and is now doing very well with her specialty breed. She also purchased three bred heifers, two young cows and a yearling bull.

Josh, a resident of the Pyramid Lake Reservation, obtained a loan of $5,000 to buy 20 heifers and increase his beginning beef cattle herd. Though the terms of the loan required it to be repaid in four years, Josh fulfilled his obligation in two. He also increased his base number of breeding cows from 15 to 24, and replaced some of his older cows. Josh now has a debt free herd and a good financial position, and is on the road to future success.

Ben had a different idea for a youth loan when he came into the FSA office. He wanted to start a lawn care business. Ben was 16, and had been mowing lawns every summer since he was nine years old. He wanted to purchase new equipment and increase his clientele. His loan was approved and a supervised bank account was set up for his purchases. Now in college, Ben still operates his successful lawn care business.

More Than Half a Million to Expand a Seaside Business

After 15 years as a graphic artist and saleswoman, Reasa Pabst wanted to start her own business. She used the equity in her home to get things rolling, and since she was located on the coast in Jacksonsville, FLA, she called her outfit Surfside Printing & Blueprints, Inc.

Reasa accepted any project, no matter how big or how small. She worked with competitors as friends, and was always willing to help another printer in town or to refer a customer to other printers when their services were more appropriate. She also had a hand in every project, all the way to the finished product. After three years of business, these services and traits earned her a profitable, growing business, and she needed to move to a bigger building.

Reasa attempted to secure financing to expand the business, but, despite her proven track record, she ran into barriers from conventional lenders. She then pursued funding through the Small Business Administration (SBA), focusing on the 504 Loan Program. She worked directly with the Jacksonville Economic Development Company (JEDCO), an SBA licensed Certified Development Company, and secured a $794,000 loan.

The SBA loan enabled Reasa to move into a new building, which nearly doubled her office space. She then purchased additional equipment, attracting more customers. This, in turn, allowed Reasa to hire additional staff, providing twice as many jobs as she had before the expansion.

The SBA loan allowed Reasa to make the leap, and provided more jobs along the way. Success like this deserves a day at the beach!

Government Funding to Go Back in Time

While many people find success by looking forward, Thomas and Cheryl Etheredge created a profit by looking back – and bringing hundreds of people along for the experience.

Thomas and Cheryl left a high powered income to "get back to the land" on a family ranch in Kansas. The reality of operating a profitable cattle ranch was challenging – but Thomas and Cheryl turned lemons into lemonade when they envisioned the ranch as a vacation destination. They thought the romantic heritage of cowboys might draw city folk to their ranch.

They called it the Prairie Rose Chuckwagon Supper, and started to draw up a business plan. But where could they get the financial backing for such a unique idea? They turned to the SBA, and secured a 504 Loan that allowed them to turn the ranch into a unique restaurant and entertainment complex. Now, tens of thousands of guests from around the world enjoy the grounds and attractions year-round. They are treated to a real chuckwagon supper, served family-style in the Prairie Rose Chuckwagon Opera Hall, and then sit back to enjoy country western music.

Once they saw the success of their idea, Thomas and Cathy continued to grow, expanding into a museum and souvenir shop. Their success was due in part to the original 504 Loan, which has allowed Thomas and Cathy to create jobs and share the cowboy way of life. The company was awarded the "2004 Small Business of the Year" for the State of Kansas.

The SBA was the first to believe in Thomas and Cathy's idea. With the SBA loan – and innovation and hard work – Thomas and Cathy turned one piece of property that was one among hundreds into a business that's one in a million.

Commercials in a Taxi Cab? Uncle Sam Helped Give the Idea a Ride

If you have a product to advertise, you must compete against other ads to win your customer's attention. Magazines, tv, radio and billboards are already crowded with messages. Is there anyplace left to promote your goods?

If you are Innovative Media in Miami, FLA, you know the answer to that question: yes! It's in the back seat of a taxi cab. Innovative Media's founder, Matari Howard, offers a patent pending innovation called "Mobilmercials." He installs a high-resolution screen in view of the taxi's passengers, hooks it up to a DVD in the trunk, and his customers' advertisements are presented to passengers en route.

It's a great idea – but where was the evidence that Matari could sell ads in the first place? Traditional lenders are often hesitant to provide loans for untested ventures. Mitari approached the Ft. Lauderdale Minority Business Development Center (MBDC), which is funded by the U.S. Department of Commerce. His contacts there led him to the Miami-Dade Empowerment Trust, Inc., where Mitari was able to get $200,000 in investment financing.

"The MBDC was instrumental in walking us through this process, both in the development of our business plan and assisting to introduce and present us to the funding source," said Matari.

Go Global! Your Country Provides the Guarantee for International Success

Go global! American businesses are able to sell to customers around the world, but how

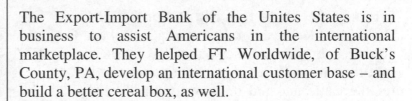
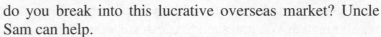

do you break into this lucrative overseas market? Uncle Sam can help.

The Export-Import Bank of the Unites States is in business to assist Americans in the international marketplace. They helped FT Worldwide, of Buck's County, PA, develop an international customer base – and build a better cereal box, as well.

FT Worldwide exports paperboard from U.S. paper mills to companies overseas, where it is made into packaging such as Tylenol cartons, KFC chicken boxes and cereal boxes. Michael Shragher, the company founder, wanted the business to grow south of the border. He obtained an Ex-Im Bank insurance policy for his company's foreign receivables, which helped to lower the risk associated with extending terms. The insured receivables served as collateral for a line of credit, which in turn enabled FT Worldwide to pay its suppliers and others in a timely fashion.

The plan has paid off. Since FT Worldwide began participating in this program, its business has grown 56% in its first year and 324% in its second year. There are new plans in the works for expanding the product portfolio as well as the customer base.

As a kid, you may have looked for the surprise toy hidden in a box of cereal. Now you know where to find the real prize – by manufacturing or selling those boxes, along with thousands of other needed goods, overseas!

Federal Money Strengthens Rural Businesses

America needs farmers and ranchers, and sometimes these business owners face hardships that go beyond the ups and downs of commercial endeavors. Their profits do not just depend on sales, but on unpredictable forces such as weather, natural predators and other threats. The Farm Services Agency (FSA) provides loans to help farmers and ranchers get started, to expand, and to endure the tough times. Some say America is the breadbasket to the world – if that's the case, the FSA helped to make a lot of sandwiches!

Hired Man Buys Land with FSA Loan

Newlyweds Raymond and Anne Smith were each raised in ranch families, and wanted to continue the tradition with their own land. Being young, they had no money saved up and had no credit established to secure the major funding needed.

"No bank was going to loan to a hired man, making very little a month," said Raymond. They contacted the FSA and received a $60,000 loan to purchase three sections, a house and outside buildings. Since that original purchase, the Smiths have added more land to their existing place and have paid off three FSA operating loans. Raymond and Anne have always had outside jobs to make ends meet.

"It has been a struggle," Raymond and Anne said. "Sometimes we didn't know if we were going to make it, but we've worked hard and never had to borrow more money than was budgeted. Without the FSA loan we would not be doing what we love to do: ranch."

From Foreclosure to a Big Dollar Ranch

For the first ten years of their marriage, Bill and Corky French leased land and ran cattle on shares. In addition, they put up hay on shares, sold their part of the hay when it wasn't needed for the cattle and fed the cows for half of the calves.

They were then able to purchase their own "home place." After almost a decade, they had the opportunity to double the size of the home place and had enough funding available when hard times hit. Interest rates soared and the drought of the late 1970's took a toll.

To get through the drought years, the Bill and Corky secured FSA disaster loans with machinery and livestock. After the drought, they faced another challenge. The bank that supplied their operating loans shifted hands, which changed their loan status. Bill and Corky turned to FSA for financial assistance. Utilizing FSA's operating loans for three years, they were able to keep their same number of cattle while buying feed. This enabled them to sell cattle when the price was higher.

"With the help of the FSA loan program, we went from being foreclosed on in 1986 to purchasing a $750,000 ranch in 1991," Bill said.

In 1999, conditions were on their side, as Corky and Bill were blessed with an abundance of Western wheatgrass seed. They sold all the seed they could and raised enough to seed their own 3400 acres of CRP instead of buying seed for planting.

In 2000 they "graduated" from the FSA Farm Loan Program and are now able to secure funding from banking facilities without FSA's assistance.

"FSA loans help a lot of people. They helped us a lot. We were glad to graduate," both Bill and Corky said with a smile. "We were able to just stay alive and operate. When no one else would lend us money, FSA believed in us and gave us a chance."

Keeping the Support Through Thick and Thin

Freeman and Barb Peabody got their first FSA loan in 1958. Thanks to the support of the agency, they have stayed in business since then. The Peabodys have endured the drought years of the late 1980's, and have witnessed their livestock lost overnight to predators.

"When you see baby lambs packed off by a predator and there's nothing you can do about it, you better get out of that line of the ranching business," said Freeman.

The FSA has been there to help them throughout it all. Now, the Peabodys produce hay from 2000 acres once enrolled in the FSA's Conservation Reserve Program.

"I would have lived a lot different life without FSA's assistance," Freeman, now 76, says.

Federal Money Programs

Loans to Producers of Cotton, Rice, Soybeans, Canola, Flaxseed, Mustard Seed, Rapeseed, Safflower, Sunflower Seed, Feed Grains, Wheat, Rye, Peanuts, Tobacco, Sugar, and Crambe

(10.051 Commodity Loans and Loan Deficiency Payments)
U.S. Department of Agriculture
Farm Service Agency
Price Support Division
Stop 0512, 1400 Independence Ave., SW
Washington, DC 20250-0512   202-720-7901
www.fsa.usda.gov
This program is designed to improve and stabilize farm income, to create a better balance between supply and demand of the commodities and to assist farmers in the marketing of their crops. Types of assistance: direct payments with unrestricted use; direct loans. Range of money available: $162 to $1,006,400; Average: $22,959.

Grants to Dairy Farmers Whose Milk is Contaminated Because of Pesticides

(10.053 Dairy Indemnity Program)
U.S. Department of Agriculture
Farm Service Agency
1400 Independence Av., SW
Washington, DC 20250-0512   202-720-7641

www.fsa.usda.gov
This program provides money to dairy farmers and manufacturers of dairy products who are forced to remove their products from commercial markets due to contamination. Fair market value is paid for the milk and dairy products as long as the contamination was not caused by negligence or failure to follow procedures set forth by the Federal government. Possible sources of contamination include pesticides approved for use by the Federal government, chemicals, toxic substances, and nuclear radiation or fallout. Types of assistance: direct payments with unrestricted use. Range of money available: $88 to $95,000; Average: $40,000.

Grants to Producers of Wheat, Corn, Grain Sorghum, Barley, Oats, Upland Cotton and Rice

(10.055 Production Flexibility Payments for Contract Commodities)
Philip W. Stronce
U.S. Department of Agriculture
Farm Service Agency
Economic and Policy Analysis Staff
Stop 0508, 1400 Independence Ave., SW
Washington, DC 20250-0508   202-720-2711
www.fsa.usda.gov

This program provides financial assistance to farmers in order to ensure a steady supply of food, while maintaining the flexibility necessary to adjust to the condition of the economy while complying with farm conservation and wetland protection requirements. Type of assistance: direct payment with unrestricted use. Range of money available: up to $40,000.

$200,000 To Operate a Farm or Ranch

(10.406 Farm Operating Loans)
U.S. Department of Agriculture
Farm Service Agency
Director, Loan Making Division
Ag Box 0522
Washington, DC 20250   202-720-1632
www.fsa.usda.gov
Through the extension of credit and supervisory assistance, this program helps the operators of family size farms to make more efficient use of their land, labor, and other resources. It also helps to establish and maintain financially stable farming and ranching operations. Types of assistance: direct loans; guaranteed/insured loans. Range of money available: Direct Loans up to $200,000; average: $47,365. Guaranteed/Insured Loans up to $731,000; average: $157,339.

Money to Implement Emergency Conservation Programs

(10.054 Emergency Conservation Program)
U.S. Department of Agriculture
Farm Service Agency
Stop 0513, 1400 Independence Ave., SW
Washington, DC 20250-0513   202-720-6221
www.fsa.usda.gov
Any agricultural producer who, as owner, landlord, tenant or sharecropper on a farm or ranch, bears a part of the cost of an approved conservation practice in a disaster area is eligible to apply for cost-share assistance. This program enables farmers to perform emergency conservation measures to control wind erosion on farmlands, to rehabilitate farmlands damaged by wind erosion, floods, hurricanes or other natural disasters and to carry out emergency water conservation or water enhancing measures during periods of severe drought. Type of assistance: direct payments for specified use. Range of money available: $50 to $64,000; average: $2,681.

Loans to Purchase and Construct On-Farm Storage Facilities

(10.056 Farm Storage Facility Loans)
U.S. Department of Agriculture
Farm Service Agency
Director, Price Support Division
1400 Independence Ave., SW
Washington, DC 20250   202-720-7935
www.fsa.usda.gov/dafp/psd/FSFL.html
The purpose of this program is to support the construction of on-farm grain storage facilities and to help farmers adapt to identity preserved storage and handling requirements for genetically enhanced production. Funding from this program can be used for the purchase and construction of new storage structures, handling equipment, drying equipment, and to finance the remodeling of existing storage structures. Type of assistance: direct loans. Range of money available: $1,000 to $100,000.

Grants to Livestock Producers

(10.066 Livestock Assistance Program)
U.S. Department of Agriculture
Farm Service Agency

Production, Emergencies and Compliance Division
Emergency Preparedness and Program Branch
Stop 0517, 1400 Independence Ave., SW
Washington, DC 20250-0517   202-720-7641
www.fsa.usda.gov
This program provides grants to eligible livestock producers who suffered grazing losses due to drought, hot weather, disease, insect infestation, fire, hurricane, flood, earthquake, severe storm or other disasters occurring after January 1, 2000. Benefits are provided to producers who suffered 40% or greater grazing loss for three or more months. Eligible livestock producers must be in a county where a severe natural disaster occurred and said county must have been approved as a primary disaster area under a Secretarial or Presidential disaster declaration. Type of assistance: direct payment with unrestricted use. Range of money available: up to $40,000; average: $875.

$500,000 Low Interest Loan to Apple Producers

(10.075 Special Apple Program)
Department of Agriculture
Farm Service Agency
Director, Loan Making Division
Ag Box 0522, 1400 Independence Ave., SW
Washington, DC 20250   202-720-1632
www.fsa.usda.gov
This program is available to producers of apples that are suffering from economic loss due to low prices for apples. Loan funds may be used for payment of costs associated with reorganizing a farm to improve its profitability, payment of annual farm expenses, purchase of farm equipment or fixtures or any other approved purposes related to the production or marketing of apples. Type of assistance: direct loans. Range and average of money available: program is new; this information is not available at this time

Loans for Seed Producers

(10.076 Emergency Loans for Seed Producers)
Department of Agriculture
Farm Service Agency
Director, Loan Making Division
AgBox 0522, 1400 Independence Ave., SW
Washington, DC 20250   202-720-1632
www.fsa.usda.gov
The aim of this program is to assist seed producers who were adversely impacted by the bankruptcy filing of AgriBiotech. To be eligible, an applicant must have filed a valid proof of claim for seed produced under contract to AgriBiotech in 1999 in the United States or a United States Territory. Type of assistance: direct loans. Range and average of money available: program is new; this information is not available yet.

Grants to Producers of Cattle, Sheep, Goats, Buffalo, and Catfish

(10.077 Livestock Compensation Program)
U.S. Department of Agriculture
Farm Service Agency
Production Emergency and Compliance Division
Washington, DC 20250   202-720-7641
www.fsa.usda.gov
This program provides financial compensation to livestock producers in counties that received primary disaster designation due to drought in 2001 and 2002. Type of assistance: direct payments with unrestricted use. Range of money available: up to $40,000.

Grants to Bioenergy Producers

(10.078 Bioenergy Program)
U.S. Department of Agriculture
Farm Service Agency
Kansas City Commodity Office
Contract Reconciliation Division
P.O. Box 419205, Stop 8758
Kansas City, MO 64141-6205   816-926-6525
www.fsa.usda.gov/daco/bio_daco.htm

This program provides financial assistance to producers of Bioenergy. The money is to be used to increase purchases of eligible commodities for the purpose of expanding production of Bioenergy, such as ethanol and biodiesel, and to support new production capacity for Bioenergy. Producers must be able to show an increase in their purchase of eligible commodities and the resulting increase of production as compared to the previous fiscal year. Type of assistance: direct payments for specified use. Range of money available: information not available.

Money to Farmers, Ranchers, and Aquaculture Businesses

(10.407 Farm Ownership Loans)
U.S. Department of Agriculture
Farm Service Agency
Director, Loan Making Division
AgBox 0522
Washington, DC 20250   202-720-1632
www.fsa.usda.gov

This program assists eligible farmers, ranchers, and aquaculture operators, including farming cooperatives, corporations, partnerships, and joint operations, through the extension of credit and supervisory assistance to become owner-operators of not larger than family farms; make efficient use of the land, labor, and other resources; carry on sound and successful farming operations; and enable farm families to have a reasonable standard of living. Loan funds may be used to enlarge, improve, and buy family farms; provide necessary water and water facilities; provide basic soil treatment and land conservation measures; construct, repair, and improve essential buildings needed in the operation of a family farm; construct or repair farm dwellings; or provide facilities to produce fish under controlled conditions. Types of assistance: direct loans; guaranteed/insured loans. Range of money available for direct loans: up to $200,000; average: $111,762. Range of money available for guaranteed/insured loans: up to $731,000: average: $250,421.

$200,000 in Low Interest Loans For Small Farmers and Ranchers

(10.437 Interest Assistance Program)
U.S. Department of Agriculture
Farm Service Agency
Director, Loan Making Division
Ag Box 0522
Washington, DC 20250   202-720-1632
www.fsa.usda.gov

This program provides a 4% interest subsidy to farmers and ranchers who do not qualify for standard commercial credit. Operating loans obtained through the Interest Assistance Program can be used to finance livestock or farm equipment; to pay annual operating expenses or family living expenses; or to refinance debts under certain conditions. Type of assistance: guaranteed/insured loans. Range of money available: $1 to $731,000; average: $158,000.

Grants to Market Food Related Products Overseas

(10.600 Foreign Market Development Cooperation Program)
U.S. Department of Agriculture
Foreign Agricultural Service
Deputy Administrator
Commodity and Marketing Programs
1400 Independence Ave., SW
Washington, DC 20250   202-720-4761
www.fas.usda.gov/mos/programs/fmd.html

The purpose of this program is to develop, maintain and expand long-term export markets for U.S. agricultural products. This is to be achieved through cost-share assistance and the opportunity to work closely with the Foreign Agricultural Service and its overseas offices. Funding from this program may be used for trade servicing, market research and technical assistance to actual or potential foreign purchasers of U.S. commodities. Type of assistance: direct payments for specified use. Range of money available: $11,000 to $7,000,000; average: $1,243,000.

Grants to Sell Food Related Products Overseas

(10.601 Market Access Program)
Deputy Administrator
Commodity and Marketing Programs
Foreign Agricultural Service
U.S. Department of Agriculture
1400 Independence Ave., SW
Washington, DC 20250   202-720-4761
www.fas.usda.gov/mos/programs/mapprog.html

This program encourages the creation, maintenance, and expansion of commercial export markets for U.S. agricultural commodities through cost-share assistance to eligible trade organizations that implement programs to develop foreign markets. Program funds may be used for consumer advertising, point of sale demonstrations, public relations, trade servicing activities, participation in trade fairs and exhibits, market research and technical assistance. Type of assistance: direct payments for specified use. Range of money available: $22,000 to $9,611,000; average: $1,375,000.

Technical Assistance for Farming Cooperatives

(10.350 Technical Assistance to Cooperatives)
Deputy Administrator
Rural Business-Cooperative Service
U.S. Department of Agriculture
Box 3250
Washington, DC 20250-3250   202-720-8460
www.rurdev.usda.gov

This program provides technical assistance, research, and advisory services to farmer cooperatives and to groups of farmers interested in forming cooperatives. It also provides educational programs on the financial, organizational, management, legal, social and economic aspects of farmer cooperatives. Types of assistance: advisory services and counseling; dissemination of technical information.

Emergency Loans for Farmers, Ranchers and Aquaculture Businesses Hurt by Natural Disasters

(10.404 Emergency Loans)
Department of Agriculture
Farm Service Agency
Director, Loan Making Division
Ag Box 0522
Washington, DC 20250   202-720-1632

www.fsa.usda.gov
The Farm Service Agency provides emergency loans to help farmers, ranchers, and aquaculture businesses recover from production and physical losses due to drought, flooding, other natural disasters, or quarantine. These loan funds may be used to restore or replace essential property; pay all or part of production costs associated with the disaster year; pay essential family living expenses; reorganize the farming operation; or refinance certain debts. Type of assistance: direct loans. Range of money available: $500 to $500,000; average: $58,000.

Loans and Grants to Build Housing for Farm Laborers

(10.405 Farm Labor Housing Loans and Grants)
Multi-Family Housing Processing Division
Department of Agriculture
1400 Independence Ave., SW
Washington, DC 20250   202-720-1604
www.rurdev.usda.gov
The purpose of this program is to insure decent, safe, and sanitary low-rent housing and related facilities for domestic farm laborers. Funds from this program can be used for construction, repair, or purchase of year-round or seasonal housing; land acquisition and the improvements necessary to build; and developing related support facilities such as central cooking and dining areas, small infirmaries, laundry facilities, day care centers, and other essential equipment and facilities or recreation areas. Types of assistance: project grants; guaranteed/insured loans. Range of money available for grants: $135,000 to $2,300,000; average $1,104,120. Range of money available in loans to individuals: $20,000 to $200,000; average $34,500. Range of money available in loans to organizations: $165,000 to $670,000; average $292,753.

Money to Local Communities Near National Forests to Help Businesses Grow or Expand

(10.670 National Forest-Dependent Rural Communities)
Deputy Chief
State and Private Forestry
Forest Service
U.S. Department of Agriculture
P.O. Box 96090
Washington, DC 20090-6090   202-205-1657
www.fs.fed.us/links/stateandprivate.shmtl
Through this program, eligible economically disadvantaged rural areas can request assistance in identifying opportunities that will promote economic improvement, diversification, and revitalization of their community. To be eligible, the community must be located in or near a national forest and be economically dependent on forest resources. Assistance is coordinated through a community action plan and team. Programs may include the upgrading of existing businesses, technical assistance, and training and education directed towards meeting the community action plan. Types of assistance: project grants; direct loans; use of property, facilities, and equipment; training. Range of money available: $1,000 to $30,000.

$600,000 Grant to Organizations in Small Towns Who Lend to Local Small Businesses

(10.767 Intermediary Relending Program)
Rural Business-Cooperative Service
Room 6867, South Agriculture Building, Stop 3225
Washington, DC 20250-3225   202-690-4100
www.rurdev.usda.gov

This program provides loans to Intermediary Lenders who in turn re-lend the money to finance community development and business facilities in rural areas. Type of assistance: direct loans. Range of money available: $3,000 to $615,000; average $19,684.

$25,000,000 For Businesses in Small Towns

(10.768 Business and Industry Loans)
Administrator
Rural Business-Cooperative Service
U.S. Department of Agriculture   202-690-4730
Washington, DC 20250-3201   Fax: 202-690-4737
www.rurdev.usda.gov
In order to improve the economic and environmental climate, including pollution abatement and control, in rural communities, this program helps public, private, or cooperative organizations (profit and nonprofit) obtain quality loans to improve, develop or finance business, industry and employment. These loans may be used in many ways including modernization or developing costs; purchasing and developing land, easements, rights-of-way, buildings, facilities, leases or materials; purchasing equipment, leasehold improvements, machinery and supplies; and pollution control and abatement. Types of assistance available: direct loans; guaranteed/insured loans. Range of money available for direct loans: $35,000 to $10,000,000; average: $559,471. Range of money available for guaranteed/insured loans: $35,000 to $25,000,000; average: $1,836,853.

$500,000 In Grants to Nonprofits to Lend Money to New Businesses

(10.769 Rural Business Enterprise Grants)
Director, Specialty Lenders Division
Rural Business-Cooperative Service
U.S. Department of Agriculture
Washington, DC 20250-3222   202-720-1400
www.rurdev.usda.gov
The goal of this program is to increase employment and the development of small and new private business and industry to improve the economy in rural communities. The grant funds may be used for learning networks or programs that provide educational or job training instruction; to establish revolving loan funds; or refinancing services and fees. Funds may also be used to develop, construct or purchase land, buildings, plants, equipment, access streets and roads, parking areas, utility extensions, or necessary water supply and waste disposal facilities. Television Demonstration Grants (TDG) may be used for television programming to provide information on agriculture and other topics of importance to farmers and rural residents. All uses must assist a small or emerging private business enterprise except for the TDG Program. Type of assistance: project grants. Range of money available: $2,000 to $500,000; average: $83,309.

Money to Run a Teenage Business

(10.406 Farm Operating Loans)
U.S. Department of Agriculture
Farm Service Agency
Director, Loan Making Division
Ag Box 0522
Washington, DC 20250   202-720-1632
www.fsa.usda.gov
The FSA makes loans to individual rural teens to establish and operate an income-producing business. To be eligible, teens must be associated with a 4-H Club, Future Farmers of America or a similar organization. The business project must be planned and operated under the supervision of the

organization advisor, produce enough income to repay the loan, and provide the youth with practical business and educational experience. Loan funds may be used to buy livestock, equipment or supplies; to buy, rent or repair needed tools and equipment; and to pay operating expenses for running the project. Type of assistance: direct loans. Range of money available: up to $5,000.

Loans to Companies That Provide Electricity to Small Towns

(10.850 Rural Electrification Loans and Loan Guarantees)
Administrator, Rural Utilities Service
U. S. Department of Agriculture
Washington, DC 20250-1500   202-720-9540
www.rurdev.usda.gov
This program provides loans to qualified organizations to supply or improve electric services on a continuing basis in rural areas. Its goal is to assure that people in eligible areas have access to electric services comparable in reliability and quality to the rest of the nation. Types of assistance: direct loans. Range of money available in direct loans: $443,000 to $103,000,000; average: $8,167,383. Range of money available in guaranteed FFB; $698,000 to $269,940,000; average $17,000,000.

Loans to Companies That Provide Telephone Service to Small Towns

(10.851 Rural Telephone Loans and Loan Guarantees)
Administrator
Rural Utilities Service
U.S. Department of Agriculture
Washington, DC 20250   202-720-9554
www.rurdev.usda.gov
This program provides loans to qualified organizations to finance the improvement, expansion, construction, acquisition and operation of telephone lines, facilities or systems to furnish and improve telecommunications service in rural areas. Its goal is to assure that people in eligible rural areas have access to telecommunications services comparable in quality and reliability to the rest of the nation. Types of assistance: direct loans; guaranteed/insured loans. Range of money available in direct loans: $289,000 to $61,567,000: average: $9,375,000. Range of money available in guaranteed/insured loans: $4,476,000 to $59,389,000; average: $13,333,333.

Extra Loans to Companies That Provide Telephone Services to Small Towns

(10.852 Rural Telephone Bank Loans)
Assistant Governor
Rural Telephone Bank
U.S. Department of Agriculture
Washington, DC 20250   202-720-9554
www.rurdev.usda.gov
This program provides supplemental financing to qualified organizations to extend and improve telecommunication services in rural areas. Type of assistance: direct loans. Range of money available: $169,050 to $35,918,400; average: $5,468,728.

$650,000 In Grants and Loans to Telephone Companies That Then Provide Financing to Small Businesses

(10.854 Rural Economic Development Loans and Grants)
Director, Specialty Lenders Division
Rural Business-Cooperative Service
  U.S. Department of Agriculture
Washington, DC 20250   202-720-1400
www.rurdev.usda.gov

The goal of this program is to fund rural economic development and job creation projects through electric and telephone utility companies. Program grants and loans may be used for project feasibility studies, start-up costs, incubator projects and other reasonable expenses incurred while promoting rural development. The maximum term for loans is ten years at an interest rate of zero. Type of assistance: direct loans and project grants. Range of money available for loans: $10,000 to $450,000; average: $375,000. Range of money available for grants: $10,000 to $200,000; average: $ 160,000.

Free Plants for Conservation Studies

(10.905 Plant Materials for Conservation)
Deputy Chief for Science and Technology
Natural Resources Conservation Service
U. S. Department of Agriculture
P.O. Box 2890
Washington, DC 20013   202-720-4630
www.nrcs.usda.gov
This program is limited to conservation co-op properties in conjunction with soil conservation districts. Its goal is to develop technology for land management and restoration with plant materials by promoting the use of new and improved plant materials for soil, water, and related resource conservation and environmental improvement programs. Breeder and foundation quality seed or propagules are provided to commercial seed growers. Type of assistance: provision of specialized services.

Grants to Communities That Provide Money and Help to Small Business Incubators

(11.300 Grants for Public Works and Economic
  Development)
David L. McIlwain, Director
Public Works Division
Economic Development Administration
Room H7326, Herbert C. Hoover Building
U.S. Department of Commerce
Washington, DC 20230   202-482-5265
www.doc.gov/eda
The EDA provides funding for special projects to support long-term economic development in areas experiencing substantial economic distress. Eligible projects must fulfill a pressing need in the area; improve the opportunities for the successful establishment or expansion of industrial or commercial businesses, assist in the creation of long term employment or benefit the unemployed/ underemployed or low-income residents of the area. Such projects could include water and sewer system improvements, industrial access roads, industrial and business parks, port facilities, railroad sidings, distance learning facilities, skill training facilities, business incubator facilities, eco-industrial facilities and telecommunications infrastructure improvements needed for business retention and expansion. Type of assistance: project grants. Average grant amount: $1,201,991.

Grants to Communities to Help Small Businesses Start or Expand

(11.302 Economic Development Support for Planning
  Organizations)
Anthony Meyer
Acting Director, Planning and Development Assistance
  Division
Economic Development Administration
Room H7317, Herbert C. Hoover Bldg.   202-482-2121
Washington, DC 20230   Fax: 202-482-0466
www.doc.gov/eda

The purpose of this program is to help States, Indian Tribes and/or local governments strengthen their economic development planning, and to formulate and establish comprehensive economic development strategies designed to reduce unemployment and increase income. Grants are used to help defray the cost of economic development and the administrative expenses necessary to carry out the planning. Type of assistance: project grants. Range of money available: $500 to $175,000; average $56,000.

Grants to Communities That Help Finance New or Old Businesses Due to Military Base Closings

(11.307 Economic Adjustment Assistance)
David F. Witschi, Director
Economic Development Administration
Room H7327, Herbert C. Hoover Building
U.S. Department of Commerce
Washington, DC 20230   202-482-2659
www.doc.gov/eda
The goal of this program is to assist state and local areas in the development and/or implementation of strategies designed to address structural economic adjustment problems resulting from sudden and severe economic dislocation such as plant closings, military base closures and defense contract cutbacks, and natural disasters, or from long term economic deterioration in the area's economy. Funded activities may include, but are not limited to, the creation or expansion of business development and financing programs such as revolving loan funds, infrastructure improvements, organizational development, and market or industry research and analysis. Type of assistance: project grants. Range of money available: no specific minimum or maximum.

Grants to Fisherman Hurt by Oil and Gas Drilling on the Outer Continental Shelf

(11.408 Fishermen's Contingency Fund)
Michael Grable
Chief, Financial Services Division
National Marine Fisheries Service
1315 East-West Highway   301-713-2396
Silver Spring, MD 20910   Fax: 301-713-1306
www.noaa.gov
This program compensates U.S. Commercial fishermen for damage/loss of fishing gear and 50% of resulting economic loss due to oil and gas related activities in any area of the Outer Continental Shelf. Type of assistance: direct payments with unrestricted use. Range of money available: $500 to $54,000; average: $6,000.

$3,000,000 Grant To Commercialize Science & Related Ideas

(11.612 Advanced Technology Program)
Barbara Lambis
Advanced Technology Program
National Institute of Standards and Technology
100 Bureau Drive, Stop 4700   301-975-4447
Gaithersburg, MD 20899-4700   Fax: 301-869-1150
Email: Barbara.lambis@nist.gov
www.atp.nist.gov/atp
To receive application kits:
ATP customer service staff   800-ATP-FUND
Working in partnership with industry, the Advanced Technology Program provides funding for development of new, high-risk technologies that offer the potential for significant, broad based economic benefits for the entire country. ATP funding may not be used to fund product development, or existing or planned research programs that

would otherwise be conducted in the same time period. Type of assistance: project grants. Range of money available: $434,000 to $31,478,000; average: $3,043,374.

Grants to Organizations That Help Minorities Start Their Own Businesses

(11.800 Minority Business Development Centers)
Barbara Curry
Business Development Specialist
Room 5071, Minority Business Development Agency
U.S. Department of Commerce
14th and Constitution Ave., NW
Washington, DC 20230   202-482-1940
www.mbda.gov
The Minority Business Development Agency provides funding for Minority Business Development Centers. For a nominal fee, these centers provide a wide range of services from initial consultations, to the identification and resolution of specific business problems. The goal of this program is to provide electronic and one-on-one business development services to minority firms or individuals interested in entering, expanding, or improving their efforts in the marketplace. Type of assistance: project grants. Range of money available: $155,000 to $385,750.

Grants to Organizations That Help Native Americans Start Their Own Businesses

(11.801 Native American Program)
Barbara Curry
Business Development Specialist
Room 5071, Minority Business Development Agency
U.S. Department of Commerce
14th and Constitution Ave., NW
Washington, DC 20230   202-482-1940
www.mbda.gov
This program provides funding for eight Native American Business Development Centers that provide electronic and one-on-one business development service to Native Americans interested in entering, expanding, or improving their efforts in the marketplace. These centers provide advice and counseling in areas such as preparing financial packages, business counseling, business information and management, accounting guidance, marketing, business/industrial site analysis, production, engineering, construction assistance, procurement, and identification of potential business opportunities. Type of assistance: project grants. Range of money available: $155,000 to $287,500.

Grants to Help Minority Businesses Enter New Markets

(11.802 Minority Business Development)
Barbara Curry
Room 5071, Minority Business Development Agency
U.S. Department of Commerce
14th and Constitution Ave., NW
Washington, DC 20230   202-482-1940
www.mbda.gov
This Program supports minority business development through indirect business assistance programs that identify and develop private markets and capital sources; expand business information and business services through trade associations; promote and support the utilization of Federal, State and local government resources; and assist minorities in entering new and growing markets. Type of assistance: project grants. Average amount of financial assistance: $300,000.

Grants to Organizations That Will Help You Sell to the Department of Defense

(12.002 Procurement Technical Assistance for Business Firms)
Defense Logistics Agency
Office of Small and Disadvantaged Business Utilization (DDAS)
8725 John J. Kingman Road, Suite 2533
Fort Belvoir, VA 22060-6221   703-767-1650
www.dla.mil/db
The purpose of the Procurement Technical Assistance Program is to generate employment and to improve the economy of an area by assisting business firms in obtaining and maintaining Federal, State, and local government contracts. Recipients of project funds are to provide marketing and technical assistance to businesses in selling their goods and services to the Department of Defense, other Federal agencies, and local and State governments. Type of assistance: project grants. Range of money available: $30,000 to $300,000; average: $160,185.

$500,000 For Native Americans to Start or Expand a Business

(15.124 Indian Loans-Economic Development)
Woodrow Sneed
Office of Economic Development
Bureau of Indian Affairs
1849 C Street, NW, MS-4640
Washington, DC 20240   202-208-4796
www.doi.gov/bia/ecodev/loanpgm.html
This program assists Federally Recognized Indian Tribal Governments, Native American Organizations, and individual American Indians in obtaining financing from private sources in order to promote business development on or near Federally Recognized Indian Reservations. Funding may be used to finance commercial, industrial, agricultural, or business activities organized for profit. Types of assistance: guaranteed/insured loans. Range of money available for individuals and tribal enterprises: $2,500 to $500,000; average: $125,000. Range of money available for Federally Recognized Tribal Governments and Native American Organizations: $10,000 to $7,000,000; average: $1,500,000.

Grants to Small Coal Mine Operators to Clean Up Their Mess

(15.250 Regulation of Surface Coal Mining and Surface Effects of Underground Coal Mining)
Chief, Division of Regulatory Support
Office of Surface Mining Reclamation and Enforcement
U.S. Department of the Interior
1951 Constitution Ave., NW
Washington, DC 20240   202-208-2651
www.osmre.gov
This program provides grants to develop permanent programs that protect society and the environment from the adverse effects of surface coal mining, while maintaining the coal supply necessary to meet the Nation's energy needs. Coal mining operators that have total annual production of less than 300,000 tons at all locations can apply for assistance in meeting certain technical permit application requirements. Types of assistance: project grants; direct payments for specified use. Range of money available: $2,500 to $500,000; average: $125,000.

Money to Fisherman Who Have Their Boats Seized by a Foreign Government

(19.204 Fisherman's Guaranty Fund)
Mr. Stetson Tinkham

Office of Marine Conservation
Bureau of Oceans and International Environmental and Scientific Affairs
Room 5806
U.S. Department of State   202-647-3941
Washington, DC 20250-7818   Fax: 202-736-7350
www.state.gov
The Fisherman's Guaranty Fund is an insurance program that provides reimbursement for losses incurred as a result of the seizure of U.S. commercial fishing vessels by a foreign country on the basis of rights or claims in territorial waters or on the high seas, which are not recognized by the U.S. Effective November 28, 1990, the United States acknowledges the authority of coastal states to manage highly migratory species, thus reducing the basis for valid claims under the Fishermen's Protective Act. Type of assistance: insurance. Range of money available: up to $500,000.

$35,000,000 In Grants to Build or Improve an Airport

(20.106 Airport Improvement Program)
Federal Aviation Administration
Office of Airport Planning and Programming
Airports Financial Assistance Division, APP-500
800 Independence Avenue, SW
Washington, DC 20591   202-267-3831
www.faa.gov
Using grants, advisory services, and counseling, this program's goal is to assist owners or operators of public airports in the development of a nationwide system of airports sufficient to meet needs of civil aeronautics. Grants can be made for integrated airport system planning in a specific area, airport master planning, construction, or rehabilitation of a public-use airport. Eligible work at airports includes airport master plans; airport noise compatibility plans; land acquisition; site preparation; construction, alteration, and rehabilitation of runways, taxiways, aprons, and certain roads within airport boundaries; construction and installation of airfield lighting, navigational aids, and certain offsite work; safety equipment required for certification of the airport facility; required security equipment ; snow-removal equipment; terminal development; aviation-related weather reporting equipment; equipment to measure runway surface friction; burn area training structures and land for that purpose, on or off airport; agency-approved noise compatibility projects; relocation of air traffic control towers and navigational aids ; land, paving, drainage, aircraft deicing equipment and structures for centralized deicing areas; and projects to comply with the Americans with Disabilities Act of 1990, Clean Air Act, and Federal Water Pollution Control. Types of assistance: project grants; advisory services, and counseling. Range of money available: $12,000 to $35,000,000; average: $1,250,000.

Grants to Bus Companies

(20.509 Formula Grants for Other Than Urbanized Areas)
Federal Transit Administration
Office of Program Management
Office of Capital and Formula Assistance
400 Seventh Street, SW
Washington, DC 20590   202-366-2053
www.fta.dot.gov
In order to improve, introduce or continue public transportation service in rural areas, this program provides technical and financial assistance to rural transportation providers. Funding may be used for operating and administrative expenses, and for the acquisition, construction, and improvement of facilities and equipment. Type of assistance: formula grants.

Grants to Become a Women-Owned Transportation Related Company

(20.511 Human Resources Program)
Director, Office of Civil Rights
Federal Transit Administration
U.S. Department of Transportation
400 Seventh Street, SW, Room 9102
Washington, DC 20590   202-366-4018
www.fta.dot.gov
This program provides financial assistance to national, regional, and local initiatives that address human resource needs in the area of public transportation. Projects may include employment training programs; outreach programs to increase minority and women's employment in public transportation activities; research on training and public transportation manpower needs; and training and assistance for minority businesses that meet Section 120 program criteria. Types of assistance: project grants (cooperative agreements), dissemination of technical information.

Money for Airlines to Fly to Small Towns and Make a Profit

(20.901 Payments for Essential Air Services)
Director, Office of Aviation Analysis, X-50
U.S. Department of Transportation
400 Seventh Street, SW
Washington, DC 20590   202-366-1030
www.ost.dot.gov
The purpose of this program is to assure that air transportation services are provided to eligible communities. When necessary, subsidy payments are made to air carriers providing air services to eligible locations in order to ensure the continuation of service. Subsidies are paid to cover the carrier's prospective operating loss plus an element of profit. Type of assistance: direct payment for specified use. Range of money available: $297,636 to $1,871,825 annually per point; average $858,599 annually per point.

Grants to Women-Owned Businesses to Help Get Contracts from the Department of Transportation

(20.903 Support Mechanisms for Disadvantaged Businesses)
Office of Small and Disadvantaged Business Utilization, S-40
Office of the Secretary
400 Seventh Street, SW   800-532-1169
Washington, DC 20590   202-366-1930
www.dot.gov
This program is designed to help small businesses (minority and non-minority), socially and economically disadvantaged persons, and businesses owned and operated by women increase their participation in Department of Transportation programs and funded projects. Financial assistance may be given to develop support mechanisms, such as liaison and assistance programs, that provide outreach and referrals for technical assistance, information dissemination, and communication networks with government offices. Type of assistance: project grants (cooperative agreements). Average amount of financial assistance: $134,000.

Loans to Start a Credit Union

Mr. Anthony Lacreta
(44.002 Community Development Revolving Loan Program for Credit Unions)
Community Development Revolving Loan Program for Credit Unions
National Credit Union Administration
1775 Duke Street
Alexandria, VA 22314-3428   703-518-6610

www.ncua.gov
The Community Development Revolving Loan Program for Credit Unions provides funding to support low-income credit unions' efforts to provide a variety of financial and related services designed to meet the needs of their community. Funds from this program may be used to support and stimulate economic development and revitalization efforts in the community; provide member services such as financial counseling; and for programs to increase the membership and capitalization base. Type of assistance: direct loans. Range of money available: $25,000 to $300,000.

Money if Your Business Was Hurt by a Natural Disaster or Drought

(59.002 Economic Injury Disaster Loans)
Herbert Mitchell
Office of Disaster Assistance
Small Business Administration
409 3rd Street, SW
Washington, DC 20416   202-205-6734
Email: disaster.assistance@sba.gov
www.sba.gov/DISASTER
This program provides assistance to small businesses, agricultural cooperatives, and nurseries that suffered economic injury as a result of a disaster declared by the President, Small Business Administration, and/or the Secretary of Agriculture. These loans can be used to pay liabilities which the business could have paid if the disaster had not occurred, or as working capital to keep the business in operation until conditions return to normal. Funds are not available for lost income or profits, equipment repair or acquisition. Types of assistance: direct loans; guaranteed/insured loans (including immediate participation loans). Range of money available: up to $1,500,000; average: $76,200.

Money for Businesses Hurt by Physical Disaster or Drought

(59.008 Physical Disaster Loans)
Herbert Mitchell
Office of Disaster Assistance
Small Business Administration
409 3rd Street, SW
Washington, DC 20416   202-205-6734
Email: disaster.assistance@sba.gov
www.sba.gov/DISASTER
Businesses that have suffered uninsured losses due to a declared physical-type disaster may qualify for loans through this program. Funds may be used to repair or replace damaged or destroyed real property to its pre-disaster condition. Types of assistance: direct loans; guaranteed/insured loans. Range of money available: up to $1,500,000; average: $51,160.

Money to Start a Venture Capital Company

(59.011 Small Business Investment Companies)
Associate Administrator for Investment
Investment Division
Small Business Administration
409 Third Street, SW
Washington, DC 20416   202-205-6510
www.sba.gov
This program provides funding to establish privately owned and managed investment companies, which are licensed and regulated by the U.S. Small Business Administration. These companies, in turn, provide equity capital, long term loan funds, and advisory services to small businesses. Range of money available: $50,000 to $90,000,000: average: $14,323,000.

$500,000 to Start or Expand Your Own Business

(59.012 Small Business Loans)
Director, Loan Policy and Procedures Branch
Small Business Administration
409 Third Street, SW
Washington, DC 20416
202-205-6510
800-8ASK-SBA
www.sba.gov

The Small Business Loans program provides guaranteed loans to small businesses that are unable to obtain financing elsewhere, but have shown the ability to repay their debts. These loans are made to low-income business owners, businesses located in areas of high unemployment, nonprofit sheltered workshops and similar organizations that produce goods or services, small businesses started, acquired or owned by handicapped individuals, and to enable small businesses to manufacture , design, market, install, or services specific energy measures. Loans may be used to construct, expand, or convert facilities, to purchase building equipment or materials, and for working capital. The SBA's 7(a) Lending Authority includes: the Cap Line Program, the Low Documentation Loan Program (Low Doc), Fa$ Trak Program (formerly the Small Loan Express), the Women's Prequalification Program, and the Minority Prequalification Program. Types of assistance: guaranteed/insured loans (including immediate participation loans). Range of money available: up to $500,000; Average: $226,521.

Help for Contractors and Others to Get Bonded to Obtain Contracts

(59.016 Bond Guarantees for Surety Companies)
Associate Administrator, Robert J. Moffitt
Office of Surety Guarantees
Small Business Administration
409 Third Street, SW
Washington, DC 20416
202-205-6540
www.sba.gov

Under this program, small contractors unable to obtain a bond are guaranteed surety bonds issued by commercial surety companies. Guarantees are for up to ninety percent of the losses incurred and are paid by participating sureties when conditions are met. Types of assistance: insurance (guaranteed surety bonds). Range of money available: up to $500,000; average: $226,521.

Money to Local Organizations to Finance Small Businesses

(59.041 Certified Development Company Loans [504 loans])
Office of Financial Assistance
Small Business Administration
409 Third Street, SW
Washington, DC 20416
202-205-6490
www.sba.gov/financing/sbaloan/cdc504.html

The CDC/504 loan program is a long-term financing tool for economic development within a community. The 504 loan program provides growing businesses with long-term fixed rate financing for major fixed assets. A Certified Development Company (CDC) is a nonprofit corporation set up to contribute to the economic development of its community. CDC's work with private sector lenders and the SBA to provide financing to small businesses. These loans have either a 10 or 20 year term, and may be used for the acquisition of land and buildings; the construction, expansion, renovation or modernization of buildings; or the acquisition and/or installation of machinery and equipment. Type of assistance: guaranteed/insured loans. Range of money available: up to $1,000,000; average: $350,000.

Grants to Local Organizations That Help Women Start Their Own Businesses.

(59.043 Women's Business Ownership Assistance)
Sally Murrell
Office of Women's Business Ownership
Small Business Administration
409 Third Street, SW
Washington, DC 20416
202-205-6673
www.sba.gov/womeninbusiness

Private, non profit organizations can receive funding through this program to provide training and counseling to small businesses owned and operated by women in an effort to eliminate discriminatory barriers women may encounter in obtaining credit and promoting their businesses. Type of assistance: project grants (cooperative agreements or contracts). Range of money available: $75,000 to $150,000.

Free Services and Money for Veterans to Receive Entrepreneurial Training

(59.044 Veteran's Entrepreneurial Training and Counseling)
Reginald Teamer
Office of Veteran Affairs
Small Business Administration
5th Floor, 409 Third Street, SW
Washington, DC 20416
202-205-6773
www.sba.gov

This program establishes Veteran Business Outreach Centers to provide long term training, counseling, and mentoring to small businesses and potential small businesses owned and operated by eligible U.S. Veterans. Type of assistance: cooperative agreements. Range of money available: $350 to $1,500 per client.

$25,000 For Small Businesses

(59.046 Micro-loan Demonstration Program)
Small Business Administration
Office of Financial Assistance
Micro Enterprise Development Branch
409 Third Street, SW, Eighth Floor
Washington, DC 20416
202-205-6490
www.sba.gov

The Micro Loan program provides very small loans to start up, newly established or growing small businesses. Its objective is to help business owners, especially women, low-income entrepreneurs, minorities, potential entrepreneurs, and those located in areas with a lack of credit due to economic conditions. To achieve this, the Small Business Administration makes loans and loan guarantees to intermediary lenders, who in turn make short term, fixed interest rate micro loans to start-up, newly established, and growing businesses. These micro-loans can only be used for working capital, supplies, furniture, fixtures, inventory, equipment and/or machinery. The SBA makes grants to participating intermediary lenders to provide marketing, management and technical assistance to micro-loan recipients. The SBA also provides training for the lenders and non-lenders participating in the program, and makes grants to nonprofit organizations to provide marketing, technical and managerial assistance to low-income individuals seeking private financing for their businesses. Types of assistance: formula grants; direct loans. Range of money available: up to $35,000; average: $10,500.

Free Help for Disabled Veterans to Start New Businesses

(64.116 Vocational Rehabilitation for Disabled Veterans)
Veterans Benefits Administration
Vocational Rehabilitation and Counseling Service (28)
U.S. Department of Veteran Affairs
Washington, DC 20420
202-273-7419

www.va.gov

This Vocational Rehabilitation Program provides services and assistance to help disabled veterans get and keep a suitable job. The program also provides the needed services and assistance to help individuals achieve the necessary skills to maximize independence in daily living. Veterans who meet certain requirements may receive an initial supply of goods and commodities to start a small business. Types of assistance: direct payments with unrestricted use; direct payments for specified use; direct loans; advisory services and counseling. Range of money available: information is not available at this time.

Grants For Veterans to Learn Entrepreneuring

(64.123 Vocational Training for Certain Veterans Receiving VA Pension)
Veterans Benefits Administration
Vocational Rehabilitation and Counseling Service (28)
U.S. Department of Veterans Affairs
Washington, DC 20420   202-273-7419
www.va.gov

This program provides vocational and counseling to recipients of VA pensions so they may get and keep a suitable job. Veterans who meet certain eligibility requirements may be provided with the goods or commodities to start a small business. Type of assistance: direct payments for specified use; advisory services and counseling. Range of money available: information is not available at this time.

Money to Invest in Companies Overseas

(70.002 Foreign Investment Financing)
Information Officer
Overseas Private Investment Corporation
1100 New York Ave, NW   202-336-8799
Washington, DC 20527   Fax: 202-336-8700
Email: info@opic.gov
www.opic.gov

The Overseas Private Investment Corporation provides financing for investments in developing countries for projects that contribute to the social and economic development of the host country and at the same time have a positive impact on the U.S. economy. OPIC disqualifies projects that may have a negative effect on the environment, U.S. employment, the host country's development, or would violate internationally recognized worker rights. Direct loans can only be made for private sector projects where there is significant involvement by a U.S. small business. Types of assistance: Guaranteed insured loans; direct loans. Range of money available: $10,000,000 to $400,000,000; average: $9,000,000.

Money to Privately Owned Community Drinking Water Utilities for Security Improvements

(66.477 Vulnerability Assessments and Related Security Improvements as Large Privately Owned Drinking Water Utilities)
U.S. Environmental Protection Agency
Private Water Utility Security Grant Program
Room 2104A, EPA East Building
1201 Constitution Avenue, NW   202-564-3750
Washington, DC 20004   800-426-4791
www.epa.gov

Large privately owned community drinking water utilities that serve 100,000 or more people are eligible to apply for this funding. The money may be used to conduct a vulnerability assessment, develop or revise an emergency response operating plan, enhance security plans, or a combination of these efforts. Type of assistance: project grants. Range of money available: up to $115,000.

Grants for Security Improvements at Drinking Water Utilities

(66.476 Vulnerability Assessments and Related Security Improvements at Large Drinking Water Utilities)
U.S. Environmental Protection Agency
Public Water Utility Security Grant Program
1201 Constitution Ave., NW
Washington, DC 20004   800-426-4791
www.epa.gov

Large publicly owned community drinking water utilities that serve at least 100,000 people are eligible to apply for this funding. Recipients of these grants may use the money to conduct a vulnerability assessment, develop or revise an emergency response operating plan, enhance security measures, or any combination of these efforts. Grant money may not be used for construction or other physical improvements. Type of assistance: project grants. Range of money available: up to $115,000.

Insurance Against Currency Fluctuations When Investing Overseas

(70.003 Foreign Investment Insurance)
Information Officer
Overseas Private Investment Corporation
1100 New York Avenue, NW   202-336-8799
Washington, DC 20527   Fax: 202-336-8700
Email: info@opic.gov
www.opic.gov

To encourage private U.S. investment in developing countries, OPIC provides insurance to protect against the risks of inconvertibility, expropriation and political violence. Insurance is available for contractors and exporters against arbitrary drawings of letters of credit posted as bid, performance or advance payment guaranties; petroleum exploration, development and production; leasing operations; and debt financials, including securities. Type of assistance: insurance. Range of insurance available: up to $250,000,000.

Free Patent Licenses to Develop and Market Energy Saving Inventions

(81.003 Granting of Patent Licenses)
Robert J. Marchick
Office of the Assistant General Counsel for Patents
U.S. Department of Energy
Washington, DC 20585   202-586-2802
www.doe.gov

The Department of Energy grants nonexclusive, revocable patent licenses to qualified applicants with plans to develop and/or market one of the more that 1,200 DOE owned U.S. Patents. Type of assistance: dissemination of technical information. Range of money available: not applicable.

$500,000 Grant to Work on an Energy Related Invention

(81.036 Invention and Innovations)
Lisa Barnett
Office of Industrial Technologies (EE-23)
U.S. Department of Energy
Weatherization and Intergovernmental Programs
1000 Independence Avenue, SW
Washington, DC 20585   202-586-2212
www.eere.energy.gov/inventions

The U.S. Department of Energy's Inventions and Innovation program provides financial and technical support to inventors and businesses to develop energy saving concepts and technologies. Grant recipients are selected through a competitive process. Types of assistance: project grants, advisory services and counseling, and dissemination of technical information. Range of money available for projects in early stage development: up to $40,000. Range of money available for technology near the point of prototype: up to $250,000. Range of money available for technology demonstrations: up to $500,000. Average amount of assistance: $83,000.

Counseling to Help Women and Minority Owned Businesses Get Department of Energy Contracts

(81.082 Management and Technical Assistance for Minority Business Enterprises)
Sterling Nichols
Office of Economic Impact and Diversity
U.S. Department of Energy
ED-1, Forrestal Building, Room 5B-110
Washington, DC 20585   202-586-8698
www.hr.doe.gov/ed/index.html
This program strives to support increased participation of minority and women owned and operated small businesses; to develop energy related minority small business assistance programs; to encourage public/private partnerships to provide technical assistance to MBE's; to transfer applicable technology from national Federal laboratories to MBE's; and to increase the Department of Energy's high technology research and development contracting activities. Services provided by this program include identification and compilation of DOE procurement opportunities; technical assistance; dissemination of DOE energy technology opportunities; financial proposal and bid assistance; and matching business opportunities in public and private organizations with minority businesses and educational institutions. Type of assistance: advisory services and counseling. Range of money available: not applicable.

Help for Farmers to Control Plant and Animal Diseases

(97.003 Agricultural Inspections)
Department of Homeland Security
245 Murray Drive, SW
Washington, DC 20528   202-282-8000
www.dhs.gov
This program's objective is to protect U.S. agriculture from harmful plant and animal diseases and pests. It provides for inspections to detect and evaluate infestations and carries out regulatory actions to prevent the interstate spread of diseases and infestations. Type of assistance: project grants (cooperative agreements). Range of money available: not applicable.

Grants for Commercial Fisheries Failing Due to a Natural Disaster

(11.477 Fisheries Disaster Relief)
Alicia Jarboe
Financial Services Division (F/CS2)
National Marine Fisheries Service
1315 East-West Highway   301-713-2358
Silver Spring, MD 20910   Fax: 301-713-1939
Email: Alicia.jarboe@noaa.gov
www.fakr.noaa.gov/omi/grants/default.htm (Alaska)
http://caldera.sero.nmfs.gov/grants/programs/disaster.htm (Southeast)
This program provides assistance to fishing vessel owners, operators, and crew, and fish processors that are facing failure due to a fishery resource disaster. Disasters may be natural, man-made, or by undetermined causes. Funds may be used to assist affected communities, assess the effect of

commercial fishery failures, restore fisheries, or prevent future failures. Type of assistance: project grants (cooperative agreements). Range of money available: $343,500 to $7,000,000: average: $2,781,167.

Money for Small, Minority, and Women Owned Businesses to Develop an AIDS Prevention Activity

(93.118 Acquired Immunodeficiency Syndrome (AIDS) Activity)
Division Contact:
Ron VanDuyne
Division of HIV/AIDS Prevention
Centers for Disease Control and Prevention
Department of Health and Human Services
1600 Clifton Road, A43
Atlanta, GA 30333   404-639-0930

Grants Management Contact:
Lynn Mercer
Grants Management Branch
Procurement and Grants Office
Centers for Disease Control and Prevention
Department of Health and Human Services
2920 Brandywine Road
Atlanta, GA 30341   770-488-2810
www.cdc.gov
Through this program, small and minority businesses, and businesses owned by women are eligible to apply for funds to develop and implement public information and education programs on HIV prevention and awareness. Type of assistance: project grants. Range of money available: $45,000 to $2,000,000; average: $390,174.

Grants to Develop Energy Saving Products

(81.086 Conservation Research and Development)
Office of Energy Efficiency and Renewable Energy (EERE)
Mail Stop EE-1
Department of Energy   202-586-9220
Washington, DC 28585   800-DOE-3732
www.eere.energy.gov
This program offers grants to conduct research in the areas of buildings, industry and transportation. Grants are also offered to develop and transfer conservation technology to the non-federal sector. The Department of Energy EERE offices involved in this program are the Office of Building Technology, Office of Freedom CAR and Vehicle Technologies, Office of Industrial Technologies, and the Office of Hydrogen, Fuel Cells and Infrastructure. Type of Assistance: project grants. Range of money available: $50,000 to $500,000.

Grants to Work on Solar Energy Products

(81.087 Renewable Energy Research and Development)
Office of Energy Efficiency and Renewable Energy (EERE)
Mail Stop EE-1
Department of Energy   202-586-9220
Washington, DC 28585   800-DOE-3732
www.eere.energy.gov
The Department of Energy provides funding to conduct research and development efforts in the following energy technologies: distributed energy and electric reliability, solar, hydrogen, biomass, fuel cells and infrastructure, geothermal, wind and hydropower. Grants are also offered to develop and transfer these renewable energy technologies to the scientific and industrial communities, and state and local governments. Type of assistance: project grants. Range of money available: $10,000 to $100,000.

$2,000,000 Grant To Work On Fossil Energy Ideas

(81.089 Fossil Energy Research and Development)
Mary J. Roland
Fossil Energy Program
Mail Stop FE-3
19901 Germantown Road
Department of Energy
Germantown, MD 20874   301-903-3514
www.fe.doe.gov
The focus of the Fossil Energy Research and Development program is to promote the development and use of environmentally and economically advanced technologies for supply, conversion, delivery and utilization of fossil fuels. Cooperative agreements will involve industry, DOE laboratories, universities and States. The successes of this program will benefit everyone through lower energy costs, reduced environmental impact, increased technology exports, and reduced dependence on foreign energy sources. Type of assistance: project grants, cooperative agreements. Range of money available: $10,000 to $25,000,000.

$22,000,000 In Grants to Businesses That Employ People with Disabilities

(89.234 Projects with Industry)
Lavanna Kia Weems and Lois Vaughan
Rehabilitation Services Administration
U.S. Department of Education
400 Maryland Avenue, SW
OSERS, Room 3332   202-205-8749 (Vaughan)
Washington, DC 20202   202-205-8922 (Weems)
Email: lavanna.weems@ed.gov
Email: lois.vaughan@ed.gov
www.ed.gov/offices/OSERS/RSA/Programs/Discretionary/pwi.html
Projects with Industry grants are awarded to employers, labor unions, profit and nonprofit organizations and State vocational rehabilitation agencies. Funds may be used to support projects that create and expand job and career opportunities in the competitive labor market for individuals with disabilities. Type of assistance: project grants, cooperative agreements. Average continuation award: $205,000. Average new award: $230,000.

Grants to Telecommunications Companies to Provide Services to Schools

(84.203 Star Schools)
Joseph Wilkes
U.S. Department of Education
Office of Innovation and Improvement
Technology in Education Programs
555 New Jersey Ave., NW
Washington, DC 20208-5645   202-219-2186
Email: joseph.wilkes@ed.gov
www.ed.gov/offices/OII
This program provides grants to telecommunications companies to provide facilities and equipment, educational and instructional programming, and necessary technical assistance to elementary and secondary schools. Priority is given to companies that provide services to schools in traditionally underserved areas, individuals excluded from careers in math and science due to discrimination or economic disadvantages, areas with scarce resources, and areas with limited access to courses in math, science, and foreign languages. Type of assistance: project grants. Range of money available: information not available at this time.

Money to Develop Health and Safety Programs for Construction Workers

(93.955 Health and Safety Programs for Construction Workers)
Grant Management Contact:
Mildred Garner
Grants Management Branch
Procurement and Grants Office
Centers for Disease Control and Prevention
2920 Brandywine Road
Atlanta, GA 30341   770-488-2745

Program Management Contact:
Office of Extramural Programs
National Institute for Occupational Safety and Health
Centers for Disease Control and Prevention
1600 Clifton Road
Mail Stop E-74
Atlanta, GA 30333   404-498-2530
www.cdc.gov
The purpose of this program is to develop health and safety programs for construction workers in order to reduce occupational injuries and illnesses. Funds may be used for salaries of personnel employed specifically for the project, consultant fees, supplies and equipment necessary to conduct the project, essential travel expenses, and other project related expenses. Type of assistance: project grants. Range of money available: up to $5,000,000.

Grants to Improve Emergency Medical Service in Rural Areas

(93.952 Improving EMS/Trauma Care in Rural Areas)
Richard J. Smith III
Chief, Injury/EMS Branch
Maternal and Child Health Bureau
Health Resources and Services Administration
Public Health Service
Department of Health and Human Services
Parklawn Building, Room 18A-38
5600 Fishers Lane
Rockville, MD 20857   301-443-0324

Grants Management Contact:
Grants Management Branch
Maternal and Child Health Bureau
Health Resources and Services Administration
Public Health Service
Department of Health and Human Services
Parklawn Building, Room 18-12
5600 Fishers Lane
Rockville, MD 20857   301-443-1440
www.mchb.hrsa.gov
This program makes grants for research and demonstration projects designed to improve the quality and availability of emergency medical services in rural areas. Funds may be used to develop and use new, innovative communications technologies; develop model curricula for training emergency medical services personnel; make training, certification, and continuing education more accessible; develop increased access to pre-hospital care and improve the availability of emergency transportation services; and evaluate the effectiveness of current emergency medical services and systems. Type of assistance: project grants. Range of money available: $50,000 to $150,000; average: $100,000.

Pension Plan Termination Insurance for Small Businesses

(86.001 Pension Plan Termination Insurance)
Pension Benefit Guaranty Corporation

1200 K Street, NW
Washington, DC 20005-4026   202-326-4000
www.pbgc.gov

This program encourages the continuation and maintenance of voluntary private pension plans, provides for timely and uninterrupted payment of pension benefits to participants and beneficiaries in plans covered by the PBGC, and maintains premiums at the lowest possible level. Type of assistance: insurance. Range of monthly benefit available: $10 to $3664.77; average: $383.

Crop Insurance for Owners or Operators of Farmlands

(10.450 Crop Insurance)
Department of Agriculture
Administrator, Risk Management Agency
Ag Box 0801
Washington, DC 2050   202-690-2803
www.fsa.usda.gov

The Federal Crop Insurance Corporation (FCIC) is a government owned corporation created to provide comprehensive crop insurance nation wide. Catastrophic crop insurance protection (CAT) is fully subsidized except for administrative fees paid by the producer. This coverage compensates the producer for yield losses greater than 50% at a price equal to 55% of maximum price. Additional protection is offered at higher levels of coverage and variable levels of premium subsidy. Owners or operators of farmland, who have an insurable interest in a crop in a county where insurance is offered on that crop, are eligible for insurance. Type of assistance: insurance. Range of assistance available: level of assistance varies according to policy, crop, and indemnities paid.

Crop Loss Assistance for Uninsured Producers of Commercial Crops

(10.451 Noninsured Assistance)
Department of Agriculture
Farm Service Agency
Production, Emergency and Compliance Division
Noninsured Assistance Program Branch
Mail Stop 0517
1400 Independence Avenue, SW
Washington, DC 20250-0526   202-720-5172
www.fsa.gov

This program provides crop loss assistance to producers of commercial crops and other agricultural commodities where crop insurance at the catastrophic risk protection level is not available. Crops that are produced for food or fiber are eligible including: floricultural, ornamental nursery, and Christmas tree crops, turf grass sod, seed crops, aquaculture (including ornamental fish) and industrial crops. To be eligible, producers must be an owner, tenant, sharecropper, or landlord who shares in the risk of producing the crop, must be entitled to share in the crop available for marketing or would have shared had the crop been produced, and whose qualifying gross revenue for the preceding tax year was less than $2 million. Type of assistance: Direct payments with unrestricted use. Range of money available: not applicable.

Money for Livestock Owners Hurt by a Natural Disaster

(10.452 Disaster Reserve Assistance)
Department of Agriculture
Farm Service Agency
Emergency and Noninsured Assistance Program Division
Mail Stop 0526
1400 Independence Avenue, SW
Washington, C 20250-0526   202-720-3168

www.fsa.usda.gov

This program provides emergency assistance to eligible livestock owners in an area, county or state where an official emergency has been declared due to insect infestation, disease, fire, drought, flood, hailstorm, hurricane, earthquake, hot weather, c old weather, ice, snow, freeze, winter kill, or other natural disaster. Type of assistance: direct payments for specified use. Range of money available: not applicable.

Health and Safety Education and Training for Mine Operators

(17.602 Mine Health and Safety Education and Training)
Director, Educational Policy and Development
Mine Safety and Health Administration
Department of Labor
4015 Wilson Blvd.   703-235-1515 (Jeffrey Duncan)
Arlington, VA 22203   304-256-3201 (Jack Spadaro)
www.msha.gov

The Mine Safety and Health Administration provides initial and advanced Mine Safety and Health Training for Federal Mine Inspectors, Mine Operators, miners, States, and labor organizations. Assistance is also provided through written and audiovisual training materials dealing with health and mining safety issues. Type of assistance: training. Range of money available: not applicable.

Money for U.S. Fishermen Whose Vessels are Seized by a Foreign Country

(19.210 Protection of Ships from Foreign Seizure)
Mark A. Clodfelter
Assistant Legal Adviser for International Claims and
    Investment Disputes
Office of the Legal Advisor
Suite 203, South Building
2430 E Street, NW
Washington, DC 20037-2800   202-776-8360
www.state.gov

U.S. Fishermen whose vessels are seized by a foreign country may be eligible for reimbursement by the State Department. Claims for reimbursement can be filed for fines, license or registration fees, levies, any direct charges paid to a foreign government to secure the prompt release of the vessel and crew, and for fees charged by the government of a foreign country to engage in transit between points in the United States. Seizures made by a country at war with the U.S., or a seizure made in accordance with the provisions of any convention or treaty made with the U.S. and in force at the time of seizure are not eligible for reimbursement. Type of assistance: insurance (reimbursement). Range of money available: dependent on Congressional authorizations.

Help for Farmers and Ranchers on Indian Lands

(15.034 Agriculture on Indian Lands)
Mark Bradford
Office of Trust Responsibilities
Division of Water and Land Resources
Branch of Agriculture and Range
Bureau of Indian Affairs
1849 C Street, NW
Mail Stop 4513 MIB
Washington, DC 20240   202-208-3598
www.doi.gov/bia/otrhome.htm
www.doi.gov/bureau-indian-affairs.html

This program helps Indian farmers, ranchers and landowners manage and develop their land for farming and grazing. It also provides for noxious weed eradication by means of chemical, mechanical, cultural, and biological control methods. Funds may be used for farmland improvements such as farm drainage, land leveling, crop varieties, cropping patterns, stock water engineering, range inventories, inventories to identify vegetation, range conditions, precipitation zones and current forage utilization; rangeland pest control, livestock control, maintenance of readiness conditions for fire suppression; leasing and permitting support, and performance evaluations. Types of assistance: direct payments for specified use, advisory services and counseling, provision of specialized services. Range of money available for agricultural assistance: $200 to $575,000; average: $50,000. Range of money available for noxious weed eradication: $500 to $300,000; average: $20,000.

Money to Indian Tribes for Economic Development

(15.032 Indian Economic Development)
Woodrow Sneed
Office of Economic Development
Bureau of Indian Affairs
1849 C Street, NW
Mail Stop 4640
Washington, DC 20240   202-208-4796
www.doi.gov/bia/ecodev/index.htm
www.doi.gov/bureau-indian-affairs.html
Funds from this program can be used to administer revolving loan and guaranty loan programs to promote economic development on tribal lands. Assistance is provided to American Indian owned businesses in obtaining financing from private sectors. Type of assistance: direct payments for specified use. Range of money available: $5,000 to $300,000; average: $215,000.

Grants to Market Food Related Products to Emerging Markets Overseas

(10.603 Emerging Markets Program)
Director
Marketing Operations Staff
Foreign Agricultural Services
Department of Agriculture
Washington, DC 2020   202-720-4327
www.fas.usda.goc/mos/em-markets/em-markets.html
The Emerging Markets Program's goal is to promote, enhance, or expand the export of U.S. agricultural commodities in low to middle income counties that are likely to emerge as promising export markets in the near future. U.S. agricultural and agribusiness firms, especially those that need assistance in obtaining or maintaining access to overseas markets, may be eligible for cost-share assistance to implement an Emerging Markets Program. Program funds may be used to finance activities such as feasibility studies, market research, sectorial assessments, orientation visits, specialized training, and business workshops. Type of assistance: direct payments for specified use. Range of money available: $5,000 to $500,000.

Help for Farmers and Ranchers to Conserve Natural Resources

(10.912 Environmental Quality Incentives Program)
Deputy Chief for Natural Resource Conservation Programs
Natural Resources Conservation Service
U.S. Department of Agriculture
P.O. Box 289   202-720-1845
Washington, DC 20013   Fax: 202-72-4265
www.nrcs.usda.gov
This program provides technical, educational and financial assistance to eligible farmers and ranchers to address soil, water and other natural resource concerns on their lands through the implementation of structural, vegetative, and land management practices. Technical assistance is provided for conservation planning measures. Educational and financial assistance is provided for the implementation of structural, vegetative and land management practices. Cost-share payments may be used to implement one or more eligible structural or vegetative practices. Incentive payments can be used to implement one or more land management practices. To be eligible, farmers and ranchers must face serious threats to soil, water and related natural resources or need assistance in complying with Federal and State environmental laws. Type of assistance: direct payments for specified use. Range of money available in cost-share and incentive payments: up to $10,000 per year, $50,000 over the length of the contract; average: $15,000.

Money for Great Plains Farmers and Ranchers to Conserve Soil and Water

(10.900 Great Plains Conservation)
Deputy Chief
National Resources Conservation Programs
Natural Resources Conservation Services
Department of Agriculture
P.O. Box 2890
Washington, DC 20013   202-720-1873
www.nrcs.usda.gov
In order to conserve and develop the Great Plains water and soil resources, technical and financial assistance is provided to farmers and ranchers to plan and implement conservation practices. Cost-share funds are available for many of the soil and water conservation measures necessary to protect and stabilize a farm or ranch against the effects of climate and erosion in the Great Plains area. Applicants must have control of the land for the period of the contract, between 3 to 10 years. Land must be located in one of the 556 designated counties in Colorado, Kansas, Montana, Nebraska, New Mexico, Oklahoma, South Dakota, Texas or Wyoming. Types of assistance: direct payments for specified use; advisory services and counseling. Range of money available: up to $35,000 per farm operating unit over a contract period of 3 to 10 years.

Money for Businesses to Reduce High Energy Costs in Rural Communities

(10.859 Assistance to High Energy Cost-Rural Communities)
Administrator
Rural Utilities Service
Department of Agriculture
Washington, DC 20250-1500   202-720-9540
www.rurdev.usda.gov
This program provides assistance to rural communities with extremely high energy costs. Funds must be used to acquire, construct, extend, upgrade, or otherwise improve the energy generation, transmission, or distribution facilities in these communities. Types of assistance: direct loans, project grants. Range of money available: not established yet.

Grants to Agricultural Producers and Rural Small Businesses to Conserve Energy

(10.775 Renewable Energy Systems and Energy Efficiency Improvements Program)
Rural Business-Cooperative Services
Department of Agriculture
1400 Independence Avenue, SW
Washington, DC 20013   202-720-1400
www.rurdev.usda.gov/rbs
The Rural Business-Cooperative Service provides direct loans, loan guarantees and grants to farmers, ranchers, and rural small businesses for measures to help reduce the cost and consumption of energy. Funds must be used to purchase

renewable energy systems or energy efficiency improvements. Types of assistance: direct loans, loan guarantees, and grants. Range of money available: not applicable.

Money to Enhance Production and Marketing in the Sheep and Goat Industries

(10.774 National Sheep Industry Improvement Center)
National Sheep Industry Improvement Center
U.S. Department of Agriculture
1400 Independence Avenue, SW
Room 2117   202-690-0632
Washington, DC 20250   Fax: 202-236-6576
www.rurdev.usda.gov/coops/cssheep.htm
The National Sheep Industry Improvement Center provides financial assistance to the U.S. Sheep and Goat Industries to strengthen and enhance the production and marketing of sheep, goats, and their products within the United States. Funds may be used for increasing production or improving production efficiency; improving product quality or marketing efficiency; coordinating marketing systems and industry participants; improving communication between the industry, public, and the center; and taking actions that will keep the center viable. Types of assistance: direct loans, guaranteed/insured loans, direct payments for specified use, and project grants. Range of money available: each program or project loan may not exceed $1,000,000.

$615,000 Grant To Organizations Who Help Small Businesses In Small Towns

(10.773 Rural Business Opportunity Grants)
Rural Business-Cooperative Service
U.S. Department of Agriculture
Specialty Lenders Division
Mail Stop 3225, Room 6767
1400 Independence Avenue, SW
Washington, DC 20250-1521   202-720-1400
www.rurdev.usda.gov
Grant funds from this program can be used to improve the economic development of rural areas by providing technical assistance for rural businesses, training for rural entrepreneurs and economic development officials, or planning for business and economic development. Type of assistance: project grants. Range of money available: $3,000 to $615,000; average $98,684.

Money for U.S. Businesses to Train Foreign Interns

(11.114 Special American Business Internship Training Program)
SABIT Program
U.S. Department of Commerce
FCB, Fourth Floor, 4100W
1401 Constitution Avenue, NW
Washington, DC 20230   202-482-2443
www.ita.doc.gov/sabit/sabit.html
The SABIT Program awards funding to qualified U.S. Companies for training scientists and business executives form the New Independent States (NIS) of the former Soviet Union. Recipient firms will be reimbursed up to $13,700 per intern for airline travel, stipends and housing. This program exposes NIS managers and scientists to American methods of management and innovation, and also benefits U.S. businesses who gain business associates and customers in the NIS. Type of assistance: project grants, cooperative agreements. Range of money available: $8,400 to $40,400; average: $18,000.

Loans to Fishermen and Fisheries

(11.415 Fisheries Finance Program)
Michael Grable
Financial Services Division
National Marine Fisheries Service
Department of Commerce
1315 East-West Highway   301-713-1306
Silver Spring, MD 20910   Fax: 301-713-1306
www.noaa.gov
This program provides loans for certain fisheries costs. Loans are made for up to 80% of the actual cost, for the reconstruction or reconditioning of fishing vessels, and the renovation, repair, or construction of shore side fishery facilities (including aquaculture facilities). Funds from this program may not be used for purposes which could lead to the over capitalization of the fishing industry. Type of assistance: direct loans. Range of money available: $10,000 to $100,000,000; average: $1,000,000.

Grants to Improve and Extend Public Telecommunications Services in the U.S.

(11.550 Public Telecommunications Facilities-Planning and Construction)
William Cooperman
Director, Public Telecommunications Facilities Program
Office of Telecommunications and Information Application/NTIA
Room 4625
Department of Commerce
1401 Constitution Avenue, NW
Washington, DC 20230   202-482-5802
www.ntia.doc.ov/ptfp
This program's purpose is to assist in the planning, acquisition, installation and modernization of public telecommunication facilities. Grants are given to extend public telecommunications service by the most efficient and economical means; including the use of broadcast and non-broadcast technologies; increasing public telecommunications services and facilities owned and operated by women and minorities; and strengthening the capability of existing public television and radio stations to provide public telecommunications service to the public. Planning grants are awarded for the construction of public telecommunications facilities. Matching grants are given for the equipment needed for the production and distribution of programming, and for the reception of non-commercial educational and cultural radio and television programs. Type of assistance: project grants. Range of money available: $15,073 to $1,800,000; average: $362,575.

Money to Help Bus Operators Comply With "Transportation for Individuals with Disabilities" Requirements

(20.518 Capital and Training Assistance Program for Over-the Road Bus Accessibility)
Brenda Younger
Program Coordinator
Federal Transit Administration
Office of Program Management
Office of Resource Management and State Programs
400 7th Street, SW
Washington, DC 20590   202-366-2053
www.fta.dot.gov
This program provides funding to private operators of over-the-road buses to assist with the costs and training necessary to comply with the Department of Transportation's "Transportation for Individuals with Disabilities" rule. Capital projects eligible for funding include adding wheelchair lifts and other accessibility equipment to new

vehicles, and purchasing lifts to retro-fit existing vehicles. Eligible training costs include sensitivity training, boarding assistance, securement, handling and storage of mobility devices, and training in the proper operation and maintenance of equipment. Type of assistance: project grants. Range of money available: $10,000 to $50,000; average: $20,000.

Loans to U.S. Shipowners and Shipyards

(20.802 Federal Ship Financing Guarantees)
Associate Administrator for Shipbuilding
Office of Ship Financing
Maritime Administration
Department of Transportation
400 7th Street, SW
Washington, DC 20590   202-366-5744
www.marad.dot.gov
The purpose of this program is to promote the growth and modernization of the U.S. Merchant Marine and U.S. Shipyards. It provides competitive financing, through loan guarantees, to fund the construction, re-construction, or re-conditioning of vessels built in U.S. Shipyards. It also guarantees loans for general shipyard facilities located in the U.S. in order to stimulate commercial ship construction for domestic and export sales, encourage shipyard modernization, and support increased productivity. Loans may be used to finance advanced shipbuilding technology and modern shipbuilding technology of general shipyard facilities located in the U.S. and for vessels which are designed for research or commercial use. Type of assistance: guaranteed/insured loans. Range of money available: past projects have ranged from less than one million to several hundred million dollars.

Firefighting, Safety and Marine Operations Training for Seafarers

(20.810 Supplementary Training)
Bruce J. Carlton
Associate Administrator for Policy and International Trade
Maritime Administration
Department of Transportation
400 7th Street, SW
Washington, DC 20590   202-366-5755
www.marad.dot.gov
Marad provides supplemental training for seafarers in marine firefighting, safety, marine operations, and defense readiness. Type of assistance: training. Range of money available: fee-paid basis.

Help for Minority, Women-owned and Disadvantaged Businesses to Get Bonded to Obtain Transportation Related Contracts

(20.904 Bonding Assistance Program)
Bonding Manager
Office of Small and Disadvantaged Business Utilization
S-40, Office of the Secretary
Department of Transportation
400 7th Street, SW   800-532-1169
Washington, DC 20590   202-366-2852
http://osdbuweb.dot.gov
Through this program, small and disadvantaged businesses can get assistance in obtaining bid, performance and payment bonds for transportation related contracts emanating from the DOT. The bonds are issued to support contracts for maintenance, rehabilitation, restructuring, improvement or revitalization of any mode of transportation in the U.S. with any public or commercial provider of transportation or any Federal, State or local transportation agency. Only certified minority, women-owned and disadvantaged businesses are

eligible for this assistance. Type of assistance: insurance. Range of money available: average dollar amount of bonds issued is $330,000.

$500,000 For Women-Owned and Minority Businesses to Get Government Contracts

(20.905 Short Term Lending Program)
Office of Small and Disadvantaged Business Utilization
S-40, Office of the Secretary
Department of Transportation
400 7th Street, SW   800-532-1169
Washington, DC 20590   202-366-2852
http://osdbuweb.dot.gov
Short term working capital is provided in the form of a revolving line of credit in support of transportation related contracts through the DOT. Transportation related means a contract for the maintenance, rehabilitation, restructuring, improvement, or revitalization of any mode of transportation in the U.S. with any public or commercial provider of transportation, or any Federal, State, or local transportation agency. Businesses can borrow against the line of credit to meet the short term costs of performing the contract being financed. Loans are repaid as the contracts are completed and paid for. Lines of credit are for one year periods and may be renewed for up to five years. Only certified Disadvantaged Business enterprises, minority owned businesses, or women owned businesses are eligible. Type of assistance: direct loans. Range of money available: up to $750,000.

Help to Establish and Operate a Credit Union

(44.001 Credit Union Charter, Examination, Supervision, and Insurance)
Chairman
NCUA Board
National Credit Union Administration
1775 Duke Street
Alexandria, VA 22314-328   703-518-6300
www.ncua.gov
NCUA staff will explain Federal Credit Union chartering requirements to any group interested in forming a credit union. They also help with the preparation of the charter application, assist newly chartered credit unions begin operation, and will assist credit unions and their members in consumer matters. Grant of a Federal Charter will provide $100,000 depositor insurance on individual accounts. State chartered credit unions are eligible to apply for depositor insurance in accordance with applicable State laws. Type of assistance: insurance, provision of specialized services, advisory services and counseling. Range of money available: not applicable.

Money to Improve Services at Art, History, Natural History, Children's, General and Specialized Museums, Aquariums, Zoological Parks, Botanical Gardens, Arboretums, Nature Centers, Science and Technology Centers, and Planetariums

(44.301 Institute of Museum and Library Services, Learning Opportunity Grants)
Christine Henry
Institute of Museum and Library Services
1100 Pennsylvania Avenue, NW
Room 510
Washington, DC 20506   202-606-8687
Email: chenry@imls.gov
www.imls.gov
The Institute of Museum and Library Services supports the efforts of museums to conserve the country's historic, scientific, and cultural heritage by maintaining and

expanding the educational roles of museums and libraries, and easing their financial burden as well. Funds from this program may be used for building public access, expanding educational services, reaching families and children, and using technology more effectively in support of these goals. Art, history (including historic buildings and sites), children's, general and specialized museums, aquariums, zoological parks, botanical gardens, arboretums, nature centers, science and technology centers, and planetariums are considered museums and are eligible for assistance through the IMLS. Types of assistance: project grants, direct payments for specified use. Range of money available: $5,000 to $150,000.

Institutional, Collections Management, Public Dimension and Governance Assessments for Museums, Nature Centers, Science and Technology Centers and Botanical Gardens

(45.302 Museum Assessment Program)
Jeannette Thomas
Institute of Museum and Library Services
1100 Pennsylvania Avenue, NW
Room 510   202-606-8458 (Jeanette Thomas)
Washington, DC 20506   202-606-8339 (Public Affairs)
Email: imlsinfo@imls.gov
www.imls.gov
The Museum Assessment Program (MAP) is funded by the Institute of Museum and Library Services and administered by the American Association of Museums. It is designed to help museums assess their strengths and weaknesses and plan for the future. The program provides non-competitive grants of technical assistance for four types of assessments: Institutional, Collections Management Public Dimension, and Governance. In all Map assessments, members of the museum staff and governing authority complete a self-study and receive a site visit by one or more museum professionals who tour the museum and meet with the staff, governing officials, and volunteers. The surveyors work with MAP staff and the museum to produce a report on the museum's operations, suggesting resources and making recommendations. Museums include art, history (including historic buildings and sites), natural history, children's, general and specialized museums, science and technology centers, planetariums, aquariums, zoological parks, botanical gardens, arboretums, and nature centers. Types of assistance: direct payments for specified use, cooperative agreements Rage of money available: $1775 to $2970.

Grants to Museums, Aquariums, Zoological Parks, and Planetariums for Conservation Programs

(45.304 Conservation Assessment Program)
Noelle Giguere
Institute of Museum and Library Services
1100 Pennsylvania Avenue, NW
Room 510   202-606-8550 (Noelle Giguere)
Washington, DC 20506   202-606-8339 (Public Affairs)
Email: imlsinfo@imls.gov
www.imls.gov
The Conservation Assessment Program (CAP) supports a two day site visit by conservation professional to perform the assessment and up to three days to write the report. The general conservation survey or assessment provides an overview of all the museum's collections, as well as its environmental conditions, policies and procedures relating to collections care. The report aids the museum by providing recommendations and priorities for both immediate and long term conservation actions; facilitating the development of

long range institutional plans for the care and preservation of the collection; and serving as a fundraising tool for future conservation projects. CAP helps institutions with living animal collections that do not have an assessment of the animal's physical conditions and habitats. Institutions with fully surveyed living animal collections may use the grant to assess the conservation needs of their non-living collections only. Botanical gardens and arboreta may use the grant to asses the conservation needs of both their living and non-living collections. Museums that have received a grant for a general conservation survey through the Conservation Project Support Program are not eligible for the Conservation Assessment Program. Art, history (including historic buildings and sites), natural history, children's, general and specialized museums, science and technology centers, planetariums, aquariums, zoological parks botanical gardens, arboretums and nature centers are eligible for this program. Types of assistance: direct payments for specified use, cooperative agreements. Average grant amount: $6,000.

Grants to Museums, Botanical Gardens, Arboretums, and Nature Centers for Conservation Projects

(45.303 Conservation Project Support)
Steven Shwartzman
Institute of Museum and Library Services
1100 Pennsylvania Avenue, NW
Room 510   202-606-4641 (Steven Shwartzman)
Washington, DC 20506   202-606-8339 (Public Affairs)
Email: imlsinfo@imls.gov
www.imls.gov
The IMLS Conservation Project Support program awards matching grants to help museums identify conservation priorities and needs, and perform activities to ensure the safekeeping of their collections. The primary goal of each project must be conservation care and not collection management or maintenance. Conservation Project Support also funds exceptional projects with far reaching effects that benefit multiple institutions. Applicants may receive additional funding if their project has a directly related education component. Collections may be in one of four categories: non-living, systemic/natural history, living plants, and living animals. Grants are available for five broad areas of conservation activities: surveys, training, research, treatment, and environmental improvements. Aquariums, zoological parks, botanical gardens, arboretums, nature centers, science and technology centers, planetariums, and art, history (including historic buildings and sites), natural history, children's and specialized museums are eligible for this program. Types of assistance: project grants, direct payments for specified use. Range of money available: up to $50,000; up to $75,000 for exceptional projects; up to $10,000 in additional funds for an education component; average: $35,148.

Business Development Help for Small Businesses

(59.005 Business Development Assistance to Small Business)
Associate Administrator for Business Initiatives
Small Business Administration
409 3rd Street, SW   800-8ASK-SBA
Washington, DC 20416   202-205-6665
www.sba.gov
This program provides assistance to prospective, as well as present, small business persons to improve the skills necessary to manage and operate a business. The assistance includes workshops for prospective small business owners; management counseling including assistance from the

Service Corps of Retired Executives (SCORE) and other volunteer groups; management courses, conferences, and seminars; and educational materials to assist in the management of a small business. Types of assistance: advisory services and counseling, dissemination of technical information, and training. Range of money available: not applicable.

Help in Obtaining Federal Contracts for Small Businesses

(59.009 Procurement Assistance to Small Businesses)
Associate Administrator for Government Contracting
Small Business Administration
409 3rd Street, SW   202-205-6460
Washington, DC 20416   800-8ASK-SBA
www.sba.gov
This program helps small business obtain a "fair" share of contracts and sub-contracts for Federal government supplies and services, and a "fair" share of property sold by the government. Assistance includes: the application of small business set-asides to increase the Federal procurement and disposal requirements awarded to small business; consultations to optimize small business participation in procurement activities; review and analysis of small firms in order to certify competence as a prime contractor; review of large prime contractors' sub-contracting plans and programs to insure sub-contracting opportunities for small, disadvantaged, and women owned businesses; consultation and advice for small firms regarding government procurement and property sales matters; assistance in specific contract administration problems; and determination of small business eligibility for SBA's procurement financial programs. Existing and potential small businesses are eligible for assistance through this program. Type of assistance: provision of specialized services. Range of money available: not applicable.

$3,000,000 In Venture Capital

(59.051 New Markets Venture Capital)
Director
New Markets Venture Capital Program
409 3rd Street, NW   202-205-6510
Suite 6300   800-8ASK-SBA
Washington, DC 20416   Fax: 202-205-6013
www.sba.gov/INV/venture.html
The goal of this program is to promote economic development and job opportunities in low-income geographic areas through developmental venture capital investments in smaller businesses located in such areas. The SBA designates New Markets Venture Capital companies which are eligible to receive guaranteed loans and project grants. The guaranteed loan funds are used to make equity capital investments in smaller businesses located in low-income geographic areas. Grant funds are used to provide management and technical assistance to these smaller enterprises in connection with the capital investments. Types of assistance: project grants, guaranteed/insured loans. Range of money available: minimum grant award is $1,500,000.

Short-Term, Working-Capital Loans for Small Businesses

(59.012 Small Business Loans)
Office of Financial Assistance
CAPLines Program
Small Business Administration
409 Third Street, SW   202-205-6490
Washington, DC 20416   800-UASK-SBA
www.sba.gov/financing/loanprog/caplines.tml

CAPLines is a SBA loan program that helps small businesses meet their short term and cyclical working capital needs. Under the CAPLine program, there are five short term working capital loans: Seasonal line, Contract line, Builders line, Standard asset-based line, and Small asset-based line. The Seasonal line is an advance against anticipated inventory and accounts receivable during peak seasons when businesses experience seasonal sales fluctuations. The loan can be revolving or non-revolving. A Contract line finances the material cost and direct labor associated with performing assignable contracts. It can be revolving or non-revolving. A Builders' line is for small general contractors or builders who are constructing or renovating commercial or residential buildings. The building project serves as collateral, and loans can be revolving or non-revolving. A Standard asset-based line is a revolving line of credit for businesses unable to meet credit requirements for long term credit. It provides financing for cyclical growth and recurring and/or short term needs. A Small asset-based line is a revolving line of credit up to $200,000. It operates like a standard asset-based line except that some of the stricter requirements are waived providing the business demonstrates repayment ability. Type of assistance: direct loans. Range of money available: up o $1,000,000.

$1,000,000 For Companies Hurt By Defense Cuts

(59.012 Small Business Loans)
Office of Financial Assistance
DELTA Program
Small Business Administration
409 Third Street, SW   202-205-6490
Washington, DC 20416   800-UASK-SBA
www.sba.gov/financing/loanprog/military.html
The Defense Economic Transition Assistance Program (DELTA) provide technical and financial assistance to defense dependent small businesses that have been negatively affected by defense reductions. The goal of the program is to help those businesses diversify into the commercial market while remaining part of the defense industrial base. Loans must be used to retain jobs of defense workers, create new jobs in impacted communities, or to retool and expand in order to remain available to the Department of Defense. Type of assistance: direct loans. Range of money available: up to $1,250,000.

$1,000,000 To Sell Your Goods and Services Overseas

(59.012 Small Business Loans)
Office of Financial Assistance
International Trade Loan Program
Small Business Administration
409 Third Street, SW   202-205-6490
Washington, DC 20416   800-UASK-SBA
www.sba.gov/financing/loanprog/tradeloans.tml
The International Trade Loan program helps businesses that are preparing to engage in or are already engaged in international trade, or are adversely affected by competition from imports. Applicants must establish that the loan will significantly expand or develop an export market, currently be adversely affected by import competition, upgrade equipment or facilities to improve competitive position, or be able to provide a business plan that reasonably projects sufficient export sales to cover the loan. Loan funds may be used to acquire, construct, renovate, modernize, improve or expand facilities and equipment to be used in the U.S. in order to produce goods or services involved in international trade, and to develop and penetrate foreign markets. International Trade Loan funds cannot be used to repay debt.

Type of assistance: guaranteed loans. Range of money available: up to $1,250,000.

$750,000 For Businesses Hurt By North American Free Trade Agreement

(59.012 Small Business Loans)
Office of Financial Assistance
CAIP Program
Small Business Administration
409 Third Street, SW   202-205-6490
Washington, DC 20416   800-UASK-SBA
www.sba.gov/financing/loanprog/caip.html
The U.S. Community Adjustment and Investment Program (CAIP) was established to aid communities that suffered job losses due to changing trade patterns with Canada and Mexico after the North American Free Trade Agreement (NAFTA). CAIP increases the availability of credit to encourage business development and expansion in impacted areas. Through CAIP, credit is available to businesses in eligible communities to create new, sustainable jobs or to preserve existing jobs. CAIP works with the SBA in both the 7(a) loan program and 504 programs to reduce borrower costs and increase the availability of funds. Eligible businesses must be located in, or relocating to, a specific geographic area designated as eligible for funding under the CAIP by the U.S. Treasury and the NAD Bank. Type of assistance: guaranteed loans. Range of Money Available: up to $750,000.

$1,250,000 To Sell Your Goods and Services Overseas

(59.012 Small Business Loans)
Office of Financial Assistance
Special Purpose Loans
Export Working Capital Program
Small Business Administration
409 Third Street, SW   800-UASK-SBA
Washington, DC 20416   202-205-6490
www.sba.gov/financing/loanprog/ewcp.html
The Export Working Capital Program (EWCP) is designed to provide short term working capital to exporters who have been in business for at least one full year. The EWCP supports export financing to small businesses when other financing is not available on reasonable terms. The program encourages lending by guaranteeing loans up to $1,000,000 or 90% of a loan amount, whichever is less. The EWCP is a combined effort of the SBA and the Export-Import Bank. The SBA handles loan requests of $1,111,111 or less, and the Export-Import Bank processes loans for more than $1,111,111. Loans through the EWCP must be used to finance the working capital needs associated with single or multiple transactions of the exporter. Type of assistance: guaranteed/insured loans. Range of money available: up to $1,250,000.

$750,000 To Start or Expand a Small Business

(59.012 Small Business Loans)
Office of Financial Assistance
7(a) Loan Program
Small Business Administration
409 Third Street, SW   202-205-6490
Washington, DC 20416   800-UASK-SBA
www.sba.gov/financing/sbaloa/7a.html
7(a) loans are the most basic and the most used of the SBA's business loan programs. The loans are from commercial lenders, but are guaranteed by the SBA. Small businesses are considered for eligibility based on size, type of business, use of proceeds, and the availability of funds from other sources. 7(a) loan funds may be used to establish a new business, or to

assist in the operation, expansion or acquisition of an existing business. Eligible uses include the purchase of land or buildings, new construction as well as expansion or conversion of existing facilities; to acquire equipment, machinery, furniture, fixtures, supplies or materials; long-term working capital including the payment of accounts payable and/or the purchase of inventory; to purchase an existing business; and to refinance existing business debts which are not already structured with reasonable terms and conditions. Type of assistance: guaranteed loans. Range of money available: $2,000,000.

$250,000 For Women and Minority Entrepreneurs

(59.012 Small Business Loans)
Office of Financial Assistance
Prequalification Program
Small Business Administration
409 Third Street, SW   202-205-6490
Washington, DC 20416   800-UASK-SBA
www.sba.gov/financing/sbaloan/prequalification.html
The Prequalification Loan Program uses intermediary organizations to assist prospective borrowers in developing viable loan application packages and securing loans. This program is primarily for rural and specialized industries, veterans, exporters, new and emerging businesses, disabled business owners and low income borrowers. The intermediaries work with applicants to ensure business plans are complete and that the application is eligible and has credit merit. Qualified loan packages are submitted to the SBA for approval. If approval is granted, the SBA will issue a pre-qualification letter on behalf of the applicant that indicates the SBA's willingness to guarantee a loan. The intermediary then helps the borrower to locate an appropriate commercial lender. Type of assistance: guaranteed loans, counseling. Range of money available: up to $250,000.

$150,000 With a One Page Application

(59.012 Small Business Loans)
Office of Financial Assistance
LowDoc Loan Program
Small Business Administration
409 Third Street, SW   202-205-6510
Washington, DC 20416   800-UASK-SBA
www.sba.gov/financing/lendinvest/lowdoc.html
The Low Documentation Loan Program (LowDoc) streamlines the process of making small business loans. Once a small business borrower is approved for credit by a lender, the lender can request a loan guarantee from the SBA. The borrower completes the front of the one page form and the lender completes the back. The lender submits the completed application to the SBA and receives an answer within 36 hours. LowDoc loan funds can be used to start or expand a business. Type of assistance: guaranteed loans. Range of money available: up to $150,000.

Technical and Financial Assistance to Small Businesses to Develop an Export Market

(59.012 Small Business Loans)
Director
Office of Financial Assistance
Specialty Loan Programs
Small Business Administration
409 Third Street, SW   202-205-6720
Washington, DC 20146   800-UASK-SBA
www.sba.gov/financial/loanprog/exportexpress.html
The SBA Export Express program combines lending assistance and technical assistance to help small businesses that have traditionally has difficulty in obtaining export

financing. Export Express helps small businesses that have exporting potential, but need funds to buy or produce goods and/or to provide services for export. Loan funds nay be used to finance export development activities such as: participation in a trade show; general lines of credit for export purposes; translation of product brochures or catalogues for use in overseas markets; service contracts from buyers located outside the U.S.; transaction-specific financing needs associated with completing actual export orders; purchase real estate and/or equipment to be used in the expansion of services and the production of goods; provide loans and other financing to allow small businesses, export trading companies, and export management companies to develop foreign markets; acquire, purchase, renovate, expand, modernize, or improve production facilities or equipment used in the U.S. to produce goods or services for international trade. The Export Express program also offers technical assistance in the form of marketing, management and planning assistance. The Technical assistance is provided by the SBA's U.S. Export Assistance Centers, Small Business Development Centers (SBDC's), and the Service Corps of Retired Executives (SCORE). On approval of an SBA Export Express Loan, a representative from a U.S. Export Assistance Center will contact the borrower to offer appropriate assistance. This assistance may include training offered through the Export Trade Assistance Partnership, SBDC International Trade Center, SCORE, the District Export Council, or the Export Legal Assistance Network. Types of assistance: Guaranteed loans, technical assistance. Range of money available: up to $250,000.

Help to Start or Expand a Microenterprise
(59.050 Micro-enterprise Development Grants)
Judy Raskind
Office of Financial Assistance
Small Business Administration
409 Third Street, SW   202-205-6497
Washington, DC 20416   800-UASK-SBA
www.sba.gov/INV
The PRIME program was created to help the smallest of small businesses, those with fewer than six employees, at the beginning stage of starting a business when the greatest amount of service and guidance is needed. Under the Program for Investment in Micro-entrepreneurs (PRIME), the SBA provides federal funds to community based organizations that in turn offer training and technical assistance to low-income and very low-income micro-entrepreneurs. Type of assistance: training and technical assistance. Range of money available: not applicable.

Free Counseling and Mentoring Services for Potential and Existing Small Businesses
(59.026 Service Corps of Retired Executives Association)
W. Kenneth Yancey
National SCORE Association Office
Small Business Administration
409 Third Street, SW   800-634-0245
Washington, DC 20025   202-205-6762
www.score.org
www.sba.gov
SCORE uses the management experience of retired and active business professionals to counsel and train potential and existing small business owners. SCORE members volunteer their counseling and mentoring services to the public free of charge, though small business training workshops are offered for a low fee. Confidential counseling is offered face-to-face or through Email. SCORE is a resource partner with the SBA. Types of assistance: advisory services and counseling, training. Range of money available: not applicable.

Business Development Help for Asian American, African American, Hispanic American, Native American and Asian Pacific American Businesses
(59.006 8(a) Business Development)
Associate Administrator for 8(a) Business Development
Small Business Administration
409 Third Street, SW   202-205-6421
Washington, DC 20416   800-UASK-SBA
www.sba.gov/8abd
This program offers business development assistance to business owners who are both socially and economically disadvantaged. The assistance provided includes: management and technical assistance, access to capital and other forms of financing, business training and counseling, and access to sole source and limited competition Federal Contract opportunities. Socially and economically individuals and businesses owned and operated by such individuals, economically disadvantaged Indian tribes, Alaskan Native corporations, and Native Hawaiian organizations may be eligible for assistance through this program. Type of assistance: provision of specialized services. Range of money available: not applicable.

Loans to Small Businesses to Plan, Design or Install a Pollution Control Facility
(59.012 Small Business Loans)
Office of Financial Assistance
Special Purpose Loan Programs
Small Business Administration
409 Third Street, SW   202-205-6490
Washington, DC 20416   800-UASK-SBA
www.sba.gov/financing/lanprog/pollution.html
Pollution Control Loans are SBA 7(a) loans with the special purpose of pollution control. The program provides financing to eligible small businesses for the planning, installation or design of a pollution control facility. This facility must control, abate, reduce or prevent any form of pollution; this also includes recycling. Loan funds can only be used for fixed assets. Type of assistance: direct loans for a specified purpose. Range of money available: up to $2,000,000.

$10,000,000 To Help Sell Overseas
(Medium and Long Term Loan Guarantee Program)
Jeffrey Miller
Export Finance Department
Export-Import Bank of the United States
811 Vermont Avenue, NW   202-565-3946
Washington, DC 20571   800-565-3946
www.exim.gov/products/loan_guar.html
Ex-Im Bank assists U.S. Exporters by guaranteeing financing to credit worthy international buyers for purchase of U.S. goods and services, and exports to large scale projects. Financing may also be available for refurbished equipment, software, certain banking and legal fees, and certain local costs and expenses. The benefits of this program include flexible financing options and repayment terms, no limits on transaction size, medium and long term financing, 100% coverage of commercial and political risks, and it enables buyers to obtain loans from lenders. To qualify for Ex-Im support, the product or services must be made up of at least 50% U.S. content, and must be shipped from the U.S. to an international buyer. Military or defense items are not eligible, nor are sales to military buyers. The loans are available for up to 85% of the U.S. export value. The buyer must make a cash payment of at least 15% of the U.S. export value. Type of assistance: loan guarantees. Range of money available: There is no minimum or maximum limit to the size of the

export sale that may be financed with Ex-Im Bank's loan guarantee.

$200,000,000 To Help Exporters With Cash Flow Problems

(Project and Structured Finance)
Barbara O'Boyle
Project and Structured Finance Division
Export-Import Bank of the United States
811 Vermont Avenue, NW
800-565-3976 ext. 3690
Washington, DC 20571
202-565-3377
Email: structuredfinance@exim.gov
www.exim.gov/products/guarantee/proj_finance.html
Ex-Im Bank's Project Finance program is an arrangement in which Ex-Im Bank lends to newly created project companies and looks to the project's future cash flow as the source of repayment of the debt. Eligible project candidates include significant facility or production expansions and Greenfield projects. Ex-Im Bank has no dollar limits on project size, sector, or country. While there is no minimum transaction size, applicants should consider carefully the costs associated with a limited recourse project financing approach. The Ex-Im Bank uses seven major guidelines to determine eligibility of costs related to a project finance transaction. They are foreign content, reach-back, related parties, capital cost, contingencies, local cost and progress payments. This program allows for flexible loan repayment terms to match a project's revenue flow. Project finance transactions can be structured with tailored repayment profiles, more flexible grace periods, and more flexibility on total repayment terms. Through "Structured Finance", Ex-Im Bank considers existing overseas companies as potential borrowers based on their credit worthiness as reflected on heir balance sheet, and other sources of collateral or security enhancements. Type of assistance: direct loans. Range of money available: there is no minimum or maximum dollar amount associated with this program.

$50,000,000 To Help Ship Building Companies Sell Overseas

(Transportation Loan Guarantees- Ship Exports)
Robert Morin
Transportation Division
Export-Import Bank of the United States
811 Vermont Avenue, NW
800-565-3976 ext. 3787
Washington, DC 20571
202-565-3550
www.exim.gov/products/transportation/ship.html
The Export-Import Bank of the United States offers a variety of financing options, through its direct loan, loan guarantee, and insurance programs, to assist U.S Manufacturers in the sale of new and used ships. Ships are defined as self-propelled sea going vessels of more than 1000 gross tons. The OECD governs the terms and conditions of Ex-Im Bank's financing support for ship exports. For sales of new ships, Ex-Im Bank can provide financing for the lesser of 85% of the contract price or 100% of the U.S. content. Ex-Im also supports the export of used ships from the United States. A Used Equipment Questionnaire must be completed and an inspection may be required in order to determine the terms of Ex-Im Bank's financing support. Type of assistance: loan guarantees. Range of money available: up to $50,000,000.

$50,000,000 To Help Railroad Companies Sell Overseas

(Transportation Loan Guarantees- Railroad Equipment)
Robert Morin
Transportation Division
Export-Import Bank of the United States
811 Vermont Avenue, NW
800-565-3946 ext. 3787

Washington, DC 20571
202-565-3550
www.exim.gov/products/transportation/rail.html
Ex-Im Bank offers financing support to assist U.S. Manufacturers in the sale of new and used, commercial and general railroad equipment to foreign purchasers through its direct loan, insurance and loan guarantee programs. Terms and conditions of the financing support of railroad equipment exports are established by the OECD. Railroad equipment includes locomotives, passenger and freight cars (rolling stock) and infrastructure equipment such as tracks, and switching and signaling equipment. Ex-Im Bank bases its credit decision on the creditworthiness of the borrower, and may require additional security provided by a mortgage on the equipment. For government owned or controlled borrowers a sovereign guarantee may be required. Generally, Ex-Im Bank can support up to 85% of the contract price, but not more than 100% of the U.S. content of the equipment. For new rolling stock equipment, support is usually provided through a medium or long term guarantee program where the Ex-Im Bank guarantees 100% of the principle and interest of a loan extended by a financial institution. Used rolling stock may also be eligible for support provided the equipment meets Ex-Im bank's used equipment criteria. These criteria specify that the equipment must have been manufactured in the U.S., has been used in the U.S. for at least one year, and must be exported from a U.S. port. A Used Equipment Questionnaire must be completed when the application is submitted and will be reviewed by the Ex-Im Bank to determine eligibility. Type of assistance: loan guarantees. Range of money available: up to $50,000,000.

$50,000,000 To Help U.S. Businesses Sell Used Aircraft Overseas

(Transportation Loan Guarantees- Aircraft Equipment)
Robert Morin
Transportation Division
Export-Import Bank of the United States
811 Vermont Avenue, NW
800-565-3946 ext. 3787
Washington, DC 20571
202-565-3550
www.exim.gov/products/transportation/aircraft.html
Ex-Im Bank offers financing support, through its direct loan, insurance and loan guarantee programs, to foreign purchasers of new and used U.S. Made commercial and general aviation aircraft, including helicopters. The OECD governs the terms and conditions of the Ex-Im Bank's financing support under this program. Credit decisions are based on the credit worthiness of the airline/lessee and the additional security provided by the aircraft. New, large, commercial aircraft (those with passenger seating for 70 or more) are usually financed using an asset-based finance lease structure. New, small aircraft (fewer than 70 seats) are typically financed by other methods. The maximum amount of Ex-m Bank supported financing for a new aircraft is 85% of the U.S contract price net of all manufacturer and supplier memoranda, but not more than 100% of the U.S. content of the aircraft. Spare parts, related ground equipment, training costs, and transaction expenses may be included in sovereign guaranteed large aircraft transactions. Ex-Im Bank considers the financing support of pre-owned or used aircraft on a case by case basis. A Used Equipment Questionnaire must be completed and submitted as part of the application. The amount of financing support granted by the Ex-Im Bank will be based on the net invoice price of the used aircraft, an appropriate advance rate determined by Ex-Im Bank, and an inspection/appraisal performed by an independent third party appraiser. Ex-Im Bank is prohibited from financing the export of military aircraft or the export of civilian aircraft to a foreign military unit. Type of assistance: guaranteed loans. Range of money available: up to $50,000,000.

$10,000,000 To Financial Institutions Who Lend to Exporters

(Credit Guarantee Facility Program)
Wayne Gardella
Export-Import Bank of the United States
822 Vermont Avenue, NW   800-565-3976 ext 3787
Washington, DC 20571   202-565-3900
www.exim.gov/products/credt_guar.html
This program facilitates the sale of U.S. goods and services by establishing lines of credit between a U.S. bank and a foreign bank, or occasionally a large foreign buyer. Ex-Im Bank guarantees the repayment of the foreign bank's obligation and the foreign bank then makes credit available to the end user of the U.S. exports and takes the repayment risk of that local company. Standard guarantee coverage is available: 100% of principle and interest up to 85% of the U.S. export value. The buyer must make a 15% cash payment to the exporter. Type of assistance: loan guarantees. Range of money available: $10,000,000.

$10,000,000 For Exporters of Architectural, Industrial and Engineering Design Services

(Engineering Multiplier Program)
Wayne Gardella
Export-Import Bank of the United States
811 Vermont Avenue, NW   800-565-3976 ext. 3787
Washington, DC 20571   202-565-3380
www.exim.gov/ebd-m-03.html
This program finances feasibility studies, pre-construction design, and engineering and architectural services that involve projects that have the potential of generating substantial U.S. export orders. The Engineering Multiplier Program offers fixed rate loans and guarantees to foreign buyers of project related feasibility studies and pre-construction engineering services. In the long term, the program is designed to generate additional overseas sales of U.S. goods and services (the "multiplier effect") since the foreign buyer is more likely to order U.S. equipment and services for a construction project on which U.S. engineers, designers and architects did the feasibility and design work. Type of assistance: loans, loan guarantees. Range of money available: up to $10,000,000.

$200,000,000 For Foreign Buyers to Purchase From U.S. Companies

(Direct Loan Program)
Jeffrey Miller
Export Finance Department
Export-Import Bank of the United States
811 Vermont Avenue, NW   202-565-3946
Washington, DC 20571   800-565-3946
www.exim.gov/products/directloan.html
Ex-Im Bank assists U.S. Exporters by guaranteeing financing to credit worthy international buyers for purchase of U.S. goods and services, and exports to large scale projects. Financing may also be available for refurbished equipment, software, certain banking and legal fees, and certain local costs and expenses. The benefits of this program include flexible financing options and repayment terms, no limits on transaction size, medium and long term financing, 100% coverage of commercial and political risks, and it enables buyers to obtain loans from lenders. To qualify for Ex-Im support, the product or services must be made up of at least 50% U.S. content, and must be shipped from the U.S. to an international buyer. Military or defense items are not eligible, nor are sales to military buyers. The loans are available for up to 85% of the U.S. export value. The buyer must make a cash payment of at least 15% of the U.S. export value. Type

of assistance: direct loans. Range of money available: There is no minimum or maximum limit to the size of the export sale that may be financed with direct loan from Ex-Im Bank, though most transactions are over $10,000,000.

$10,000,000 In Working Capital Money For Exporters and Foreign Purchasers

(Working Capital Guarantee Program)
Pamela Bowers
Export-Import Bank of the United States   800-565-3946
811 Vermont Avenue, NW   202-565-3780
Washington, DC 20571   Fax: 202-565-3793
www.exim.gov/products/work_cap.html
Ex-Im Bank's working capital financing allows U.S. exporters to obtain loans to produce or buy goods or services for export. Exporters may use the financing to purchase finished products for export, pay for raw materials, equipment, supplies, labor and overhead to produce goods and/or provide services for export, cover standby letters of credit serving as bid bonds, performance bonds or payment guarantees, or to finance foreign receivables. Eligible exporters must be located in the U.S., have been in business for at least one year, and have a positive net worth. Eligible exports must be shipped from the U.S., services must be performed by U.S. personnel, and products must have at least 50% U.S. content. Military or defense items are not eligible, nor are sales to military buyers. Ex-Im Bank assumes 90% of the bank loan, including principal and interest. For qualified loans to minority, woman-owned, or rural businesses, Ex-Im Bank can increase its coverage to 100%. Type of assistance: loan guarantees. Range of money available: There is no minimum or maximum transaction amount for this program.

Insurance to Protect Letters of Credit for Exporters

(Bank Letter of Credit Insurance Policy)
Richard Maxwell
Trade, Finance and Insurance Division
Export-Import Bank of the United States   202-565-3633
811 Vermont Avenue, NW   800-565-3946
Washington, DC 20571   Fax: 202-565-3684
www.exim.gov/products/insurance/loc.html
The Ex-Im Bank's Letter of Credit Insurance Policy reduces a bank's risks on irrevocable letters of credit issued by foreign banks to support U.S. Exports. The policy provides coverage against losses caused by war, revolution, expropriation or confiscation by a governmental authority, cancellation of export or import licenses, foreign exchange inconvertibility, and commercial losses due to insolvency of the foreign issuing bank and failure to pay or reimburse for other reasons. Terms up to 180 days may be extended for consumer goods, spare parts, and raw materials. Agricultural commodities, fertilizer and capital equipment may be insured up to 360 days on a case by case basis. Type of assistance: insurance. Range of coverage available: up to $10,000,000.

Insurance For Leasing Companies With Special Problems

(Financing Lease Policy)
Richard Maxwell
Trade, Finance and Insurance Division
Export-Import Bank of the United States   800-565-3946
811 Vermont Avenue, NW   202-565-3633
Washington, DC 20571   Fax: 202-565-3684
www.exim.gov/products/insurance/leasing,html
The Financing Lease insurance policy is designed to provide protection to leasing companies where the lease contract stipulates there will be little residual value in the leased product and ownership is to be transferred to the lessee at the

end of the lease. Ex-Im Bank considers this type of lease structure to be similar to a medium term sale transaction, and requires a 15% advance payment from the lessee to the lessor before delivery of the leased product. Ex-Im Bank will insure the remaining 85% of the lease transaction. Should the lessee default, coverage for the insured percentage of each lease payment is provided to the lessor as it falls due, until the end of the lease term. The Financing Lease policy covers only single transactions. A separate policy is issued for each lease insured by Ex-Im Bank. Type of assistance: insurance. Range of coverage available: up to $10,000,000.

Insurance For Leasing Companies Who Export

(Operating Lease Policy-Coverage for Stream of Payments)
Richard Maxwell
Trade, Finance and Insurance Division
Export-Import Bank of the United States   800-565-3946
811 Vermont Avenue, NW   202-565-3633
Washington, DC 20571   Fax: 202-565-3684
www.exim.gov/products/insurance/leasing,html
The Operating Lease Insurance Policy was designed to provide coverage for leases where payments total less than the full value of the lease products, there is no intention on the part of the lessor to transfer title of the leased product to the lessee at the end of the lease period, and the lessor keeps the risk that the leased products will decline in market value at a greater rate than expected. Stream of Payments is one of two types of coverage under the Operating Lease Policy. It provides coverage for the "stream of payments" falling due during a repossession effort period after a default on the part of the lessee. This part of the overall coverage maintains the insured will receive a stream of payments while action is taken to repossess the leased products. The length of repossession efforts period is underwritten on a case by case basis, and usually covers periodic and non-periodic payments which fall due for up to five months. Periodic payments represent the rental portion of the lease, and non-periodic payments include service or maintenance payments. Coverage for the stream of payments is provided at a maximum of 100% for sovereign lessees and 90% for all others. Type of assistance: insurance. Range of coverage available: $10,000,000.

Insurance For Leasing Companies Who Export

(Operating Lease Policy-Government Prevention of
   Repossession)
Richard Maxwell
Trade, Finance and Insurance Division
Export-Import Bank of the United States   800-565-3946
811 Vermont Avenue, NW   202-565-3633
Washington, DC 20571   Fax: 202-565-3684
www.exim.gov/products/insurance/leasing,html
Coverage against Governmental Prevention of Repossession (GPR) is one of two types of coverage provided by Ex-Im Bank's Operating Lease Policy. This policy is designed to support leasing companies involved in the export of goods by providing coverage in cases where government actions may prevent the repossession, expropriation, or confiscation of leased products, or lead to the cancellation of export licenses. This coverage, usually 100% for all lessee types, comes into effect only after the end of the repossession-efforts period. It is limited to the fair market value of the leased product at the time of the claim. Type of assistance: insurance. Range of coverage available: up to $10,000,000.

$10,000,000 To Pay Exporters' Bad Debts From Foreign Buyers

(Medium Term Insurance Credit Program)
Richard Maxwell
Trade, Finance and Insurance Division
Export-Import Bank of the United States   800-565-3946
811 Vermont Avenue, NW   202-565-3946
Washington, DC 20571   Fax: 202-565-3684
www.exim.gov/products/insurance/medium_term.html
Exporters and Financial Institutions supporting the credit sale of U.S. capital equipment, its installation, and/or spare parts can insure their foreign receivables against losses with Ex-Im Bank's medium term insurance policy. Documentary policies are issued to financial institutions, and non-documentary policies are issued to exporters. These medium term policies cover two types of losses. Commercial losses resulting from non-payment for such reason's as a buyer's insolvency or failure to pay an obligation within six months of the date due, and Political losses from certain specifically defined risks such as war, revolution, cancellation of import or export licenses, and currency inconvertibility. Ex-Im Bank's medium term policies cover credit sales in which payment terms range from 1 to 5 years after the goods arrive at the port of importation. Two types of transaction are covered under these policies: single sales or one time transactions; and repetitive sales in which there is an ongoing relationship between the exporter and a dealer or distributor. All medium term policies require the buyer to pay the insured party a 15% cash payment before delivery of the goods. The remaining financed portion is then insured at 100%. Type of assistance: insurance. Range of coverage available: up to $10,000,000.

Insurance To Help Businesses Sell Environmental Equipment Overseas

(Environmental Exports Program)
James A. Mahoney Jr.
Engineering and Environment Division
Export-Import Bank of the United States
811 Vermont Avenue, NW   800-565-3946
Washington, DC 20571   202-565-3946
www.exim.gov/products/special/environment.html
Ex-Im Bank's Environmental Exports Program has several policies to support U.S. Exporters of renewable energy and environmentally beneficial goods and services, and exporters participating in foreign environmental projects. The Short-term Environmental Export Insurance Policy provides short-term, multi-buyer, and single-buyer insurance coverage for small business environmental exporters. The policy enables the exporter to offer credit terms to its foreign customers for up to 180 days. The medium-term export credit insurance policy allows U.S. exporters to offer both technology and financing to their international buyers of capital goods and environmental services. Ex-Im Bank also offers enhanced medium and long term loans and loan guarantees in support of environmental projects, products and services. Exports qualifying for support under this program include products or services for foreign environmental or renewable energy projects or facilities; the export of products or services specifically used to aid in the prevention, abatement, control or mitigation of air, water and ground pollution or contamination; and the export of products and services which provide protection in the handling of toxic substances and waste. Types of assistance: insurance, loans, and loan guarantees. Range of money available: $10,000,000.

Insurance To Cover Risky Foreign Customers

(Short-Term, Single-Buyer, Export Credit Insurance)
Richard Maxwell
Trade, Finance and Insurance Division
Export-Import Bank of the United States   800-565-3946
811 Vermont Avenue, NW   202-565-3633
Washington, DC 20571   Fax: 202-565-3684
www.exim.gov/products/insurance/single_buyer.html

Exporters of U.S. goods and services can reduce their risks when selling on credit terms internationally by insuring specific, foreign receivables with Ex-Im Bank's Short-term, Single-Buyer, Export Credit Insurance Policy. This policy insures receivables against non-payment by international buyers, extends competitive credit terms to foreign buyers, and uses insured foreign receivables as additional collateral to get better financing terms with the exporter's lender. This policy covers exports of U.S. goods and services with at least 51% U.S. content, single or multiple shipments to one buyer on credit terms, in an eligible country, and repayment terms of up to 180 days. Confirmed letters of credit, cash-in-advance sales and military or defense related items are not covered. This policy covers losses due to commercial reasons (insolvency, default) and political events (war, revolution, seizure of goods, foreign exchange inconvertibility, and revocation of import/export licenses). Type of assistance: insurance. Range of coverage available: up to $10,000,000.

Short Term Insurance to Cover Political and Commercial Risks For Small Business Exporters

(Multi-Buyer Export Credit Insurance)
Richard Maxwell
Trade, Finance and Insurance Division
Export-Import Bank of the United States   800-565-3946
811 Vermont Avenue, NW   202-565-3633
Washington, DC 20571   Fax: 202-565-3684
www.exim.gov/products/insurance/multi_buyer.html
Exporters of U.S. goods and services can reduce their risk of selling on credit terms by insuring their export accounts receivable with Ex-Im Bank's Short-term, Multi-buyer, Export Credit Insurance. This policy covers exports of U.S. goods and services with at least 51% U.S. content, sold to multiple buyers, on credit terms of up to 180 days. Commercial losses such as bankruptcy and protracted default, and losses due to political events such as war, revolution, seizure of goods, revocation of import license and foreign exchange inconvertibility are covered under this policy. Two coverage options are available: Split coverage (90% for commercial losses, 100% for political losses) and Equalized coverage (95% for both commercial and political losses). For an additional premium, the exporter can choose pre-shipment coverage in cases where goods are special ordered or there is a long manufacturing wait. This policy does not cover confirmed letters of credit, cash-in-advance sales, and military or defense related items. Type of assistance: insurance. Range of coverage available: up to $10,000,000.

Insurance To Cover Political and Commercial Risks For Small Business Exporters

(Small Business Multi-Buyer Export Credit Insurance)
Richard Maxwell
Trade, Finance and Insurance Division
Export-Import Bank of the United States   800-565-3946
811 Vermont Avenue, NW   202-565-3633
Washington, DC 20571   Fax: 202-565-3684
www.exim.gov/products/insurance/small_bus_multi_buyer.html
This policy is a special product for small, financially viable businesses that export occasionally, or are new to exporting. It can help increase international sales by extending competitive credit terms while minimizing risks. To be eligible, the exporter must be a small business as defined by the Small Business Administration, have export credit sales of not more than $5 million, have at least a one year operating history, and a positive net worth. Commercial losses caused by insolvency, bankruptcy and/or default are

covered at 95%. Political losses due to war, revolution, cancellation of import/export licenses or currency inconvertibility are covered at 100%. There is no first-loss deductible. Confirmed letters of credit, cash in advance sales and military or defense related items are excluded from coverage. Type of assistance: insurance. Range of coverage available: up to $10,000,000.

Foreign Currency Guarantees for Banks on Export Credits

(Foreign Currency Guarantee)
Export-Import Bank of the United States
811 Vermont Avenue, NW   800-565-3946
Washington, DC 20571   202-565-3946
www.exim.gov/products/guarantee/foreign_curr.html
The Ex-Im Bank Foreign Currency Guarantee policy (FCG) is designed to help buyers control certain risks associated with export credits by taking the full political and commercial risk of the credit. All lenders are eligible to use the program as long as they enter into a standard Master Guarantee Agreement with Ex-Im Bank. Under the FCG, a commercial bank extends an export credit to a buyer of U.S. goods and/or services, and Ex-Im Bank extends to the commercial bank 100% guarantee of all principal and regular interest. Ex-Im Bank issues guarantees in such currencies as the Australian Dollar, Dutch Guilder, Italian Lira, Austrian Schilling, Euro, Japanese Yen, British Pound, French Franc, Swedish Krona, Canadian Dollar, German Mark, Swiss Franc, CFA Franc, Egyptian Pound, Indian Rupees, Mexican Peso, and South African Rand. Type of assistance: loan guarantees. Range of coverage available: up to $10,000,000.

Help for U.S. Exporters to do Business in Africa

(Special Initiatives- Africa)
Export-Import Bank of the United States 800-565-3946 ext. 3900
811 Vermont Avenue, NW   202-565-3839 ext. 390
Washington, DC 20571   Fax: 202-565-3839
Email: eximAfrica@exim.gov
www.exim.gov/prodcuts/special/africa/index.html
Ex-Im Bank has several programs to help U.S. exporters compete for business in all regions of Africa, including high-risk and emerging markets. These programs include the working Capital Guarantee Program, Export Credit Insurance, Direct Loans and Guarantees, and the Project Finance Program. These programs offer exporters increased access to working capital, protection against political and commercial risk, and the ability to offer buyers competitive financing. Types of assistance: insurance, loans, loan guarantees. Range: up to $10,000,000.

Working Capital Loans for Small Business Exporters

(Special Initiatives- Underserved Exporters)
Pamela Bowers
Small and Medium Enterprises Division
Export-Import Bank of the United States
811 Vermont Avenue, NW   800-565-3946
Washington, DC 20571   202-565-3792
www.exim.gov/products/special/underserved.html
Ex-Im Bank offers eligible underserved exporters coverage of 100% of their working capital financing needs with their enhanced working capital guarantee, compared to 90% under their regular working capital guarantee. This program is designed to help small businesses that have not been able to obtain financing for their exports in the traditional market, especially those that are owned by women or minorities, located in an economically depressed or rural area, or specialize in environmentally beneficial goods and services.

To be eligible, the borrower must be new to Ex-Im Bank, have total annual sales under $10,000,000, have fewer than 100 employees, and qualify as a small business under Small Business Administration guidelines. Type of assistance: guaranteed loans. Range of money available: up to $2,000,000.

Insurance for Lenders Who Finance the Export Receivables of Small Business Exporters

(Financial Institution Supplier Credit Multi-Buyer Insurance Policy)
Richard Maxwell
Trade, Finance and Insurance Division
Export-Import Bank of the United States   800-565-3946
811 Vermont Avenue, NW   202-565-3633
Washington, DC 20571   Fax: 202-565-3684
www.exim.gov/products/insurance/supplier.html
The Financial Institution Supplier Credit Multi-Buyer Insurance Policy protects lenders who finance the export receivables of small businesses on a non-recourse basis. It is available in documentary and non-documentary formats. Eligible financial institutions must have a minimum of 3 years financing or purchasing export or domestic receivables; a minimum short term debt rating of Standard & Poors "A" or better, or Moody's "P-2" or better; and a written business plan to finance or purchase export receivables including identifying sufficient credit management and staffing resources to process large transaction volumes. Type of assistance: insurance. Range of coverage available: up to $10,000,000.

Insurance for Lenders Who Make Reimbursement and Short Term Direct Buyer Credit Loans to Foreign Buyers

(Financial Institution Buyer Credit Export Insurance)
Richard Maxwell
Trade, Finance and Insurance Division
Export-Import Bank of the United States   800-565-3946
811 Vermont Avenue, NW   202-565-3633
Washington, DC 20571   Fax: 202-565-3684
www.exim.gov/proucts/insurance/buyercredit.html
Financial Institutions can lower their risks on a short term direct buyer credit loan or reimbursement loan made to a foreign buyer for the financing of U.S. exports through an Ex-Im Bank Financial Institution Buyer Credit Insurance Policy (FBIC) also call a Bank Buyer Credit Policy. The policy provides coverage against political risks such as war, revolution, expropriation or confiscation by a government authority, cancellation of import or export licenses after shipment, and foreign exchange inconvertibility, and commercial losses due to protracted default, insolvency of the buyer or failure to reimburse for other reasons. Devaluation is not considered a political risk. The policy is issue in two formats: a documentary policy for buyer credits and certain supplier credits when the supplier is a small business; and a non-documentary policy for supplier credits when the supplier is not a small business or otherwise does not meet the criteria. Type of assistance: insurance. Range of coverage available: up to $10,000,000.

Grants to Museums for Projects that Sustain Our Cultural Heritage and Support Life Long Learning in the Community

(Museums for America)
Christine Henry
Senior Program Officer
Office of Museum Services, Room 609
Institute of Museum and Library Services

1100 Pennsylvania Avenue, NW   202-606-8687
Washington, DC 20506   Fax: 202-606-0010
Email: chenry@imls.gov
www.imls.gov/grants/museum/mus_mfa.htm
Museums for America Grants support projects and activities that strengthen museums as active resources and centers of community engagement. These grants may be used to fund ongoing museum activities; purchase equipment or services; research and scholarships; upgrading and integration of new technology; improve institutional infrastructure; or to plan new programs or activities. Grants are available to all types and sizes of museums. Funding falls into one of three categories: $5,000 to $24,999; $25,000 to $74,999; and $75,000 to $150,000. A 1:1 funding match is required in each category. All applications must show evidence of strategic planning and the relationship between the museum's plan and the funding applied for. Projects should be investments for the future, not one-time activities with no long term impact. Type of assistance: grants. Range of money available: $5,000 to $150,000.

Grants to Nonprofit Museums for Innovations in Public Services and Meeting Community Needs

(45.312 National Leadership Grants for Museums)
Dan Lukash
Senior Program Officer
Office of Museum Services, Room 609
Institute of Museum and Library Services
1100 Pennsylvania Avenue, NW   202-606-4644
Washington, DC 20506   Fax: 202-606-0010
Email: dlukash@imls.gov
www.imls.gov/grants/museum/mus_nlgm.asp
National Leadership Grants support innovation in providing public service and meeting community needs through the creative use of new technologies; model projects to be replicated though out the field; increased public access to museum collections; and collaborative projects to extend the impact of funding. Funding falls into one of three grant categories. Museum Online Grants address the technological needs and issues of museums. They are designed to make technology resources available to all types of museums. Projects should address the challenges and potential application of new technology and/or demonstrate the educational impact of connecting museums and communities through technology. Museums in the Community Grants support museum and community partnerships that enhance the quality of community life. Projects should focus on developing long term relationships between museums and community organizations with an emphasis on how the project meets documented community needs. Professional Practise Grants support projects that improve the professional practises in the museum field. This includes projects that use research to improve museum operations, projects to collect, assess or develop information and research that will serve the field, and projects that create opportunities to improve professional practises through training or the development of new materials. Museums of all disciplines are eligible including youth, children's, art, natural history, history, anthropology, science, technology and nature centers, zoos, arboreta, aquariums, botanical gardens, planetariums, historic houses and sites, general, specialized, museum agencies and museum consortia. Federal and For-Profit museums are not eligible. Type of assistance: grants. Range of money available: $15,000 to $500,000.

Grants to Improve Native American Libraries

(45.311 Native American Library Services)
Alison Freese
Senior Program Specialist
Office of Library Services, Room 802

Institute of Museum and Library Services
1100 Pennsylvania Avenue, NW   202-606-5408
Washington, DC 20506   Fax: 202-606-1077
Email: afreese@imls.gov
www.imls.gov/grants/library/lib_nat.asp
This program offers three types of grants to support libraries for Native Americans. Basic Grants are non-competitive and are distributed in equal amounts among eligible applicants. They are used to support core library operations and ensure a minimum level of public library service. Professional Assistance Grants are also non-competitive and can be used to support professional assessments of library operations. Consultants provide advice on a full range of library services including staffing, financial management, types and levels of services, and collections development and management. Enhancement Grants are competitive grants that fund projects to enhance existing library services, or implement new library services. Type of assistance: grants. Range of money available: up to $150,000.

Grants to Libraries that Serve Native Hawaiians

Alison Freese
Senior Program Specialist
Office of Library Services, Room 802
Institute of Museum and Library Services
1100 Pennsylvania Avenue, NW   202-606-5408
Washington, DC 20506   Fax: 202-606-1077
Email: afreese@imls.gov
www.imls.gov/grants/library/lib_nhls.asp
Grants from the Native Hawaiian Library Services Program can be used to support improvements in library services to Native Hawaiians. Funds may be used to establish or enhance electronic links between libraries; link libraries electronically with social, educational or information services; help libraries access information through electronic networks; encourage libraries in different areas, and different types of libraries to establish consortia and share resources; pay costs for libraries to acquire or share computer systems and telecommunications technologies; and target library and information services to persons having difficulty using a library and to underserved urban and rural communities. Type of assistance: grants. Range of money available: up to $150,000.

Help for Manufacturers and Producers Hurt by Increased Imports

(Trade Adjustment Assistance Program)
David A. Sampson
Economic Development Administration
Department of Commerce
1401 Constitution Avenue, NW
Washington, DC 20230   202-482-5081
www.eda.gov/InvestmentsGrants/Investments.xml
The EDA provides assistance to manufacturers and producers injured by increased imports. A network of 12 Trade Adjustment Assistance Centers (TAAC) help affected firms complete and submit an eligibility petition to the EDA. Once approved, the TAAC helps the firm to prepare an adjustment proposal that includes an objective analysis of the firm's weaknesses, strengths, and opportunities. After the EDA approves the adjustment plan, the firm can receive cost share assistance from the TAAC. Types of assistance provided through this program include; market research; development of new marketing materials such as e-commerce; completion of a quality assurance program; and identification of technology, software and computer systems to meet the specific needs of the firm. Types of assistance: technical

assistance; cost-share assistance. Range of money available: up to $75,000.

Help for Marine Suppliers and Owners and Operators of U.S. Shipbuilding and Repair Facilities to Improve Their Competitiveness in International Markets

(National Maritime Resource and Education Center)
Joseph Byrne
Director, Office of Shipbuilding and Marine Technology
Maritime Administration
U.S. Department of Transportation   800-99-MARAD
400 7th Street, SW   202-366-1931
Washington, DC 20590   Fax: 202-366-7197
www.marad.dot.gov/NMREC/index.html
The Maritime Administration (MARAD) established the National Maritime Resource and Education Center to assist marine suppliers, and the owner/operators of U.S. shipbuilding and repair facilities in improving their international competitiveness. Some of the services provided by NMREC include conferences and workshops; information on the Title XI Federal Ship Financing Program; energy technologies information; Standards Organizations and Information; MARAD Guideline Specifications for Merchant Ship construction; Maritime Industry Standards Library; the ISO 9000 family of standards for quality management and assessment handbook and training courses; and environmental information. Type of assistance: technical assistance and training. Range of money available: not applicable.

Help for Owners and Operators of U.S. Flag Ships to Construct, Reconstruct or Acquire New Vessels

(Capital Construction Fund, CCF)
Office of Ship Financing
Maritime Administration
U.S. Department of Transportation
400 7th Street, SW, Room 8122   202-366-5744
Washington, DC 20950   800-99-MARAD
www.marad.dot.gov/TitleXI/ccf.html
The CCF Program was established to help owners and operators of U.S. Flag vessels accumulate the capital necessary to modernize and expand the U.S. Merchant Marine. The program promotes the construction, reconstruction or acquisition of vessels by deferring Federal Income Taxes on money or property placed into a Capital Construction Fund. CCF vessels must be built in the U.S., and be documented under U.S. laws for operation in the Nation's foreign, Great Lakes, or noncontiguous domestic trade or its fisheries. The CCF program can lower the effective cost to a company of replacing or adding new vessels, and hasten the time frame for accumulating the necessary capital. CCF funds may also be used to pay existing indebtedness on vessels if it is a part of an overall building program. Type of assistance: financial assistance through tax deferrals. Range of money available: not applicable.

Help for Owners of U.S. Flag Ships to Buy, Build or Purchase Vessels

(Construction Reserve Fund, CRF)
Director, Office of Ship Financing
Maritime Administration
U.S. Department of Transportation
400 7th Street, SW, Room 8122   800-99-MARAD
Washington, DC 20590   202-366-5744
www.mrad.dot.gov/TitleXI/crf.html

The CRF is a financial assistance program that provides tax deferral benefits to owners of U.S. Flag Ships. Eligible owners can defer the gain from the sale or loss of a vessel as long as the proceeds are used to expand or modernize the U.S. Merchant fleet. The main goal of the Construction Reserve Fund is to promote the construction, re-construction, or acquisition of merchant vessels which are necessary to the development of U.S. commerce and national defense. Type of assistance: financial assistance through tax deferrals. Range of money available: not applicable.

Help for Exporters of U.S. Dairy Products

(Dairy Export Incentive Program, DEIP)
Operations Division, Export Credits
Foreign Agricultural Service, USDA
Mail Stop 1035   202-720-3224
1400 Independence Avenue, SW   202-720-6211
Washington, DC 20250-1035   Fax: 202-720-0938
www.fas.usda.gov/excredits/deip.html
The Dairy Export Incentive Program helps exporters of U.S. dairy products meet world prices for certain dairy products and destinations. Through this program, the USDA pays cash bonuses to exporters, allowing them to sell certain U.S. dairy products at prices lower that their acquisition costs. The goal of this program is to develop export markets for dairy products where U.S. products are not competitive due to the presence of subsidized products from other countries. Eligible products include milk powder, butter fat and various cheeses. Type of assistance: cash bonuses. Range of money available: bonus values vary with each agreement.

Cash Bonuses to Exporters of U.S. Agricultural Products

(Export Enhancement Program, EEP)
Operations Division, Export Credits
Foreign Agricultural Service, USDA
Mail Stop 1035   202-720-3224
1400 Independence Avenue, SW   202-720-6211
Washington, DC 20250-1035   Fax: 202-720-0938
www.fas.usda.gov/excredits/eep.html
The main objectives of the program are to expand U.S. agricultural exports and to challenge unfair trade practices. The EEP helps products produced by U.S. farmers meet competition from subsidized products from other countries, and especially the European Union. To achieve these objectives, the USDA pays cash bonuses to exporters, allowing them to sell U.S. agricultural products in targeted countries at prices below their cost of acquiring them. Type of assistance: financial assistance in the form of cash bonuses. Range of money available: bonus values vary with each agreement.

Loan Guarantees for Exporters of U.S. Agricultural Products

(Export Credit Guarantee Program, GSM-102, GSM-103)
Program Planning, Development, and Evaluation Division
Export Credits
Foreign Agricultural Service, USDA
1400 Independence Avenue, SW   202-720-4221
Washington, DC 20250-1034   Fax: 202-690-0251
www.fas.usda.gov/excredits/exp-cred-guar.html
The USDA's Export Credit Guarantee Programs help ensure that credit is available to finance commercial exports of U.S. agricultural products, while at the same time providing competitive credit terms to buyers. Credit guarantees support exports to buyers, mainly in developing countries, where credit is needed to increase or maintain U.S. sales, but may not be available without such guarantees. The Export Credit Guarantee Program (GSM-102) covers credit terms p to 3 years, and the Intermediate Export Credit Guarantee Program (GSM-103) covers credit terms up to 10 years. Both

programs are administered by the Foreign Agricultural Service on behalf of the Commodity Credit Corporation (CCC), which issues the credit guarantees. The CC guarantees payments due from approved foreign banks to exporters of banks in the U.S. The CCC only provides the guarantees; financing must be obtained through normal commercial sources. Usually, 98% of principal and a portion of the interest are covered by a guarantee. Type of assistance: loan guarantees. Range of money available: not applicable.

Short Term Credit Guarantees for Exporters of U.S. Agricultural Products to Offer to their Foreign Buyers

(Supplier Credit Guarantee Program, SCGP)
Program Planning, Development, and Evaluation Division
Export Credits
Foreign Agricultural Service, USDA
1400 Independence Avenue, SW   202-720-4221
Washington, DC 20250-1034   Fax: 202-690-0251
www.fas.usda.gov/excredits/scgp.html
This program reduces the financial risk to exporters by guaranteeing a large portion of the payments due from importers, where financing has been arranged for a 180 day period. The direct credit extended by the exporter to the importer must be for the purchase of U.S. agricultural products and secured by a promissory note signed by the importer. The USDA's Foreign Agricultural Service administers this program on behalf of the Commodity Credit Corporation (CCC). The CCC issues credit guarantees only, the exporter or the exporter's bank provides the financing. SCGP guarantees 65% of the value of the exports. Type of assistance: credit guarantees. Range of money available: not applicable.

Money for Farmers to Incorporate Conservation into their Farming Operations

(Agricultural Management Assistance)
David B. Mason
National AMA Program Manager
Natural Resources Conservation Service, USDA
1400 Independence Avenue, SW
Room 5242-S
Washington, DC 20250   202-720-1873
Email: dave.mason@usda.gov
www.nrcs.usda.gov/programs/ama
Agricultural Management Assistance (AMA) provides cost share assistance to agricultural producers to voluntarily incorporate conservation efforts, such as water management, water quality and erosion control, into their farming operations. AMA provides the personnel and resources needed to conduct conservation planning, conservation practice surveys, layout design, installation and certification, quality assurance and assessment of the program. Cost-share payments are 75% of the cost of eligible installed conservation practices. Producers may construct or improve water management structures or irrigation systems, plant trees to provide windbreaks or to improve water quality, practice resource conservation, control soil erosion, practice product diversification, integrate pest management or transition to organic farming. Types of assistance: cost-share financial assistance; technical assistance. Range of money available: up to $50,000 for any fiscal year, no more than $150,000 over the course of the contract.

Money for Farmers and Ranchers to Conserve Soil and Water

(Soil and Water Conservation Assistance, SWCA)
Walley Turner
National Program Manager

Natural Resources Conservation Service, USDA
1400 Independence Avenue, SW
Washington, DC 20250   202-720-1875
Email: walley.turner@usda.gov
www.nrcs.usda.gov/programs/swca
The SWCA program helps farmers and ranchers address threats to water, soil and other related natural resources, including grazing land, wetlands and wildlife habitat, by providing cost share and incentive payments. SWCA also helps landowners comply with Federal and state environmental laws, and make cost effective changes to nutrient management, irrigation, grazing management and cropping systems. NRCS will work with the landowner to develop a conservation plan which will become the basis of the SWCA contract. Contracts are for 5 to 10 years and the landowners must agree to maintain cost shared practices for the length of the contract. Eligible land includes cropland, hay land, pasture, rangeland, land used for subsistence purposes and land that produces crops or livestock where there is a serious threat to soil, water or related natural resources. Cost share payments are 75% of the cost of an eligible conservation practice. Type of assistance: cost share financial assistance. Range of money available: up to $50,000.

Grants to Convert Military Airfields for Civilian Use
(Military Airport Program)
Oliver Murdock
Office of Airport Planning and Programming
Federal Aviation Administration
Military Airport Branch (APP-420)
800 Independence Avenue, SW
Washington, DC 20591   202-267-8244
www.faa.gov/planning/MAP
The Military Airport Program (MAP) provides financial assistance to civilian sponsors who are converting or have already converted a military airfield for civilian or joint military/civilian use. Eligible projects include utility work, building or rehabilitating surface parking lots, access roads, hangars, fuel farms, passenger terminal facilities, and projects to construct, improve or repair building facilities with up to 50,000 square feet of floor space. Type of assistance: grants. Range of money available: up to $7,000,000.

$3,000,000 Grant To Train Your Employees
(H-1B Technical Skills Training Grant)
Mindy Feldbaum
Program Officer
U.S. Department of Labor
Employment and Training Administration
Room 4659
200 Constitution Avenue, NW   202-693-3382
Washington, DC 20210   Fax: 202-693-2982
Email: Feldbaum.Mindy@dol.gov
www.doleta.gov/h-1b/h-1b_index.cfm
The goal of the H-1B Technical Skills Training Grant Program is to raise the technical skill levels of American workers so firms can lessen their dependence on highly skilled foreign workers. Grants are awarded to local Workforce Investment Boards and business partnerships made up of at least two businesses or a businesses related nonprofit organization. The grants are to be used for training workers in high technology, information technology and biotechnology skill areas, including software and communications services, telecommunications, systems installation and integration, computers and communication hardware, advanced manufacturing, health care technology, biomedical research and manufacturing, and innovation

services. Type of assistance: matching grants. Range of money available: $10,000 to $3,000,000.

Loans and Technical Assistance for Small Businesses in New Market Areas
(Community Express Loans)
Office of Financial Assistance
Special Purpose Loan Programs
Small Business Administration
409 Third Street, SW   800-UASK-SBA
Washington, DC 20416   202-205-6490
www.sba.gov/financing/lendinvest/comexpress.html
Community Express is a SBA loan program with the National Community Reinvestment Coalition (NCRC). It is offered in pre-designated geographic areas that primarily serve low and moderate incomes and New Market small businesses. The program also includes hands-on technical and management assistance. Loan funds may be used for start-up, working capital, expansion, real estate acquisitions or equipment purchases. Types of assistance: loans and technical assistance. Range of money available: up to $250,000.

Loans to Locate a Business at an Army Industrial Facility
(Armament Retooling and Manufacturing Support (ARMS) Loan Guarantee Program)
Ms. Donnetta Rigney
United States Department of Agriculture
Rural Business Cooperative Service
Business Programs
Room 5045-S, Mail Stop 3201
1400 Independence Avenue, SW
Washington, DC 20250-3201   202-720-9812
Email: donnetta.rigney@usa.gov
www.rurdev.usda.gov/rbs/bp-arms.htm
This program is a cooperative effort between the U.S. Department of Agriculture and the U.S. Army. The ARMS Asset Management program offers mature infrastructure and services to businesses looking for manufacturing, warehouse, office and other industrial park resources. The ARMS Loan Guarantee Program provides tenants with money for working capital, equipment acquisition, building modification and other business resources to locate at an eligible Army Industrial facility. Type of assistance: guaranteed loans. Range of money available: up to $10,000,000.

$100,000 In Loans to Beginners to Make a Down Payment on a Ranch or Farm
(Down Payment Farm Ownership Loan Program)
Carolyn Cooksie
Farm Loan Programs
Farm Service Agency
U.S. Department of Agriculture
1400 Independence Avenue, SW
Washington, DC 20250   202-720-4671
www.fsa.usda.gov/pas/services.htm
The Farm Service Agency helps beginning farmers and ranchers purchase a farm or ranch. with its Down Payment Farm Ownership Loan Program. A beginning farmer or rancher is a person who has not operated a farm or ranch for more than ten years and substantially participates in the operation. Applicants must make a cash down payment of at least 10% of the purchase price. FSA can provide up to 40% of the appraised value or purchase price whichever is less. The purchase price/appraised value can not be greater than $250,000. FSA also acquires property from retiring farmers and ranchers and offers it to beginning ranchers and farmers first. Type of assistance: direct and guaranteed loans. Range of money available: up to $100,000.

$782,000 For First Time Farmers or Ranchers

(Loans for Beginning Farmers and Ranchers)
Carolyn Cooksie
Farm Loan Programs
Farm Service Agency
U.S. Department of Agriculture
1400 Independence Avenue, SW
Washington, DC 20250   202-720-4671
www.fsa.usda.gov/daf/deafult.htm
The Farm Service Agency has several loan programs to help beginning farmers and ranchers who are unable to get financing from commercial credit sources. Included are direct and guaranteed loans for farm ownership (FO) and farm operation (OL). A beginning farmer or rancher is a person who has not operated a farm or ranch for more than 10 years, participates significantly in the operation, and owns a farm less than 30% of the average size farm in the county. Type of assistance: direct and guaranteed loans. Range of money available: for direct FO or OL loans- up to $200,000; for guaranteed FO or OL loans- up to $782,000.

$782,000 For Women and Minorities To Buy Farms or Ranches

(Loans for Socially Disadvantaged Persons)
Carolyn Cooksie
Farm Loan Programs
Farm Service Agency
U.S. Department of Agriculture
1400 Independence Avenue, SW
Washington, DC 20250   202-720-4671
www.fsa.usda.gov/daf/deafult.htm
The Farm Service Agency makes and guarantees loans to qualified socially disadvantaged applicants to purchase and operate family size farms and ranches. For this program's purposes, socially disadvantaged persons include women, Pacific Islanders, African Americans, Asian Americans, Alaskan Natives, Hispanics, and American Indians. Direct loans are made by FSA and may be farm operating (OL) or farm ownership (FO) loans. Guaranteed loans are made by commercial lenders and guaranteed by FSA. They also can be used for farm ownership or operating purposes. Farm Ownership loans can be used to purchase easements or rights of way necessary to the farm's operation, erect or improve buildings, promote soil and water conservation and development, pay closing costs, and to purchase or enlarge a farm or ranch. Direct farm operating loans can only be used to purchase a farm or ranch, guaranteed loan funds may also be used to refinance debt. Farm Operating Loans (OL) may be used for hail and other crop insurance, hired labor, medical care, food, clothing, livestock, poultry, chemicals, farm equipment, fuel, fertilizer, seed and feed. Funds may also be used to refinance debt, to install or improve water systems for home use, irrigation or other improvements. Type of assistance: direct and guaranteed loans. Range of money available: for direct FO or OL loans- up to $200,000; for guaranteed FO or OL loans- up to $782,000.

$782,000 To Operate a Farm or Ranch

(FSA Guaranteed Loans)
Carolyn Cooksie
Farm Loan Programs
Farm Service Agency
U.S. Department of Agriculture
1400 Independence Avenue, SW
Washington, DC 20250   202-720-4671
www.fsa.usda.gov/daf/guaranteed.htm
This program provides lenders with a FSA guarantee for up 95% of the loss of principal and interest on a loan. Farmers and ranchers apply to an agricultural lender which then arranges for the guarantee. FSA guaranteed loans are for both farm ownership and operating purposes. Guaranteed Farm Ownership Loans (FO) may be used to purchase farmland, refinance debt, construct or repair buildings and other fixtures, or to develop farmland to promote soil and water conservation Guaranteed Operating Loans (OL) may be used for operating expenses, livestock, farm chemicals, fuel, feed, seed, farm equipment, and insurance. Under certain conditions, they can also be used to pay for minor improvements to buildings, family living expenses, costs associated with land and water development, and to refinance debt. Type of assistance: loan guarantees. Range of money available: up to $782,000.

Money for Agricultural Land Owners to Establish Long-Term Resource Conserving Covers on Eligible Farmland

(Conservation Reserve Program)
Robert Stephenson
Conservation and Environmental Programs Division
Farm Service Agency
U.S. Department of Agriculture
1400 Independence Avenue, SW
Washington, DC 20250   202-720-6221
www.fsa.usda.gov/dafp/cepd/crp.htm
The Conservation Reserve Program (CRP) is a voluntary program for agricultural producers to help them protect environmentally sensitive land. Producers taking part in CRP plant long term, resource conserving, ground covers to improve the quality of water, control soil erosion, and enhance wildlife habitats. In return, FSA provides participants with rental payments and cost share assistance. CRP contracts are for ten to fifteen years. To be eligible for the CRP program, land must be cropland or pasture land, have a weighted average erosion index of 8 or higher, be expiring CRP acreage, or be located in a state/national CRP conservation priority area. FSA provides participants in the CRP program with annual rental payments, maintenance incentive payments and cost share assistance. Rental rates are based on the relative productivity of the soils within each county and the average dry-land cash rent or cash rent equivalent. In addition CRP may include an additional amount, not more than $5.00 per acre per year, to perform maintenance obligations. Cost share assistance is up to 50% of the participant's cost to establish an approved cover on eligible cropland. FSA may offer additional financial incentives of up to 20% of the annual payment for certain continuous sign up practices. Type of assistance: cost sharing, rent, incentive payments. Range of money available: not applicable.

$750,000 In Grants for Small Businesses to Research and Develop High-Tech Innovations

(Small Business Innovation Research Program)
Robert Connolly
SBIR/STTR Program
Office of Technology
U.S. Small Business Administration
409 Third Street, SW
Mail Code: 6540   202-205-6450
Washington, DC 20416   Fax: 202-205-6390
Email: robert.connolly@sba.gov
www.sba.gov/sbir
The Small Business Innovation Research Program encourages small businesses to conduct research and development on high-tech innovation. Many small businesses lack the resources to conduct serious research and development efforts. The SBIR is able to help by reserving a

portion of their Federal research and development funds just for small businesses enabling them to compete on the same level as larger firms. SBIR funds the start up and development stages of the technology, product or service and encourages its commercialization. Small businesses must be American owned and independently operated, for-profit, have less than 500 employees, and the principal researcher must be employed by the business to be eligible for this program. The Departments of Agriculture, Commerce, Defense, Education, Energy, Health and Human Services and Transportation, Environmental Protection Agency, National Aeronautics and Space Foundation and the National Science Foundation participate in the SBIR Program. They designate the Research and Development topics and accept the proposals. Awards are based on small business qualification, degree of innovation, technical merit, and future market potential. Small businesses that receive awards or grants then enter into a three phase program. The start-up phase is Phase I. Awards, up to $100,000, are given for six months to explore the technical merit or feasibility of an idea or technology. Phase II consists of up to $750,000 for as long as 2 years to expand Phase I results. Research and development is completed and the developer evaluates commercial potential. Only Phase I award winners are eligible for Phase II. Phase III is where the innovation moves from the lab into the marketplace. There are no SBIR funds to support this phase. The small business must acquire funding from the private sector or other non-SBIR federal agencies. Type of assistance: grants. Range of money available: Phase I- up to $100,000; Phase II- up to $750,000.

Program Contacts

Department of Agriculture
Charles Cleland PhD.
Director, SBIR Program
Cooperative State Research, Education & Extension Service
U.S. Department of Agriculture
Stop 2243, Waterfront Centre, Suite 2312
1400 Independence Avenue, SW   202-401-6852
Washington, DC 20250-2243   Fax: 202-401-6070
Email: CCLeland@reeusda.gov
www.reeusda.gov/sbir

Department of Commerce
Joseph Bishop, Ph.D.
Director, Office of Research and Technology Applications
U.S. Department of Commerce/NOAA
1335 East-West Highway, Room 106   301-713-3565
Silver Spring, MD 20910   Fax: 301-713-4100
Email: Joseph.Bishop@NOAA.GOV
www.ofa.noaa.gov/~amd/sbir/sbir.html

Department of Defense
Jeff Bond
Acting SBIR/STTR Program Coordinator
OSD/SADBU
U.S. Department of Defense
1777 North Kent Street, Suite 9100   703-588-8616
Arlington, VA 22209   Fax: 703-588-7561
Email: Jeff.Bond@osd.mil
www.defenselink.mil

Department of Education
Joseph G. Teresa, Ph.D.
U.S. Department of Education
Institute of Education Sciences
Room 620, 555 New Jersey Avenue, SW   202-219-2046
Washington, DC 20208   Fax: 202-501-3005
Email: Joe.teresa@ed.gov
www.ed.gov/programs/sbir/index.html

Department of Energy
Arlene M. DeBlanc, J.D.
SBIR/STTR Program
Office of Science
U.S. Department of Energy
100 Independence Avenue, SW
SC-32, Germantown Building   301-903-3199
Washington, DC 20585-1290   Fax: 301-903-5488
Email: Arlene.deblanc@science.doe.gov
www.science.doe.gov/sbir

Department of Health and Human Services
Debbie Ridgely
Director
OSBDU, Office of the Secretary
U.S. Department of Health and Human Services
200 Independence Avenue, Room 360G   202-690-7235
Washington, DC 20201   Fax: 202-260-4872
Email: Debbie.ridgely@hhs.gov
www.hhs.gov/osdbu

Department of Transportation
Joseph D. Henebury
SBIR Program Director
U.S. Department of Transportation
Volpe Center
55 Broadway, Kendall Square   617-494-2712
Cambridge, MA 02142-1093   Fax: 617-494-2370
Email: Henebury@volpe.dot.gov
www.volpe.dot.gov/sbir

Environmental Protection Agency
James Gallup, Ph.D.
Office of Research and Development
U.S. Environmental Protection Agency
ORD/NCER (8722R)
1200 Pennsylvania Avenue, NW   202-564-6823
Washington, DC 20460   Fax: 202-565-2447
Email: Gallup.James@epa.gov
http://es.epa.gov/ncer/sbir

NASA
Robert L. Norwood, Ph.D.
Director, Commercial Development and Technology Transfer
National Aeronautics and Space Administration-HQ
300 E Street, SW
Code XC   202-358-2320
Washington, DC 20546-0001   Fax: 202-358-3878
http://sbir.gsfc.nasa.gov/SBIR/SBIR.html

National Science Foundation
Kesh S. Narayanan
Director
Industrial Innovation Programs
U.S. National Science Foundation
SBIR Program
4201 Wilson Boulevard, Room 550   703-292-7076
Arlington, VA 22230   Fax: 703-292-9057
Email: knarayan@nsf.gov
www.eng.nsf.gov/sbirspecs

$500,000 Grant For Small Business to Work on Scientific Research With Nonprofit Organizations
(Small Business Technology Transfer Program)
Robert Connolly
SBIR/STTR Program
Office of Technology
U.S. Small Business Administration

409 Third Street, SW
Mail Code: 6540   202-205-6450
Washington, DC 20416   Fax: 202-205-6390
Email: robert.connolly@sba.gov
www.sba.gov/sbir

The Small Business Technology Transfer Program (STTR) is a competitive program that sets aside a certain percentage of federal research and development funds for awards to small business and nonprofit research institution partnerships. To be eligible, small businesses must be American owned and independently operated, for profit, and have fewer than 500 employees. The principal researcher does not need to be employed by small business. The nonprofit research center must be located in the U.S, and be either a nonprofit college or university, a domestic nonprofit research organization, or a federally funded research and development center (FFRDC). The Department of Defense, Department of Energy, Department of Health and Human Services, the National Aeronautics and Space Administration, and the National Science Foundation all participate in the STTR Program. These departments and agencies designate research and development topics and accept proposals for the program. STTR awards are based on the qualifications of the small business/nonprofit research institution, degree of innovation, and future market potential. Small businesses that receive awards or grants enter into a three phase program. Phase I is the start up phase. It consists of awards up to $100,000 for one year to fund the exploration of the technical, scientific and commercial feasibility of an idea or technology. Phase I consists of awards up to $500,000 for two years to expand on Phase I results. Research and development work is performed and commercial potential considered, Phase I must be completed in order to be considered for Phase II. During Phase III, the innovation moves from the laboratory into the marketplace. This phase is not supported by STTR funds. The small business must acquire funding from the private sector or other non-STTR federal agencies. Type of assistance: grants. Range of money available: Phase I -up to $100,000; Phase II- up to $500,000.

Program Contacts:

National Science Foundation
Kesh S. Narayanan
Director
STTR Program
National Science Foundation
4201 Wilson Boulevard, Room 550   703-292-7076
Arlington, VA 22230   Fax: 703-292-9057
Email: knarayan@nsf.gov
www.nsf.gov

National Aeronautics and Space Administration
Robert L. Norwood, Ph.D.
Director, STTR Program
National Aeronautics and Space Administration-HQ
300 E Street, SW
Code-XC   202-358-232
Washington, DC 20546-0001   Fax: 202-358-3878
www.nasa.gov

Department of Health and Human Services
Debbie Ridgely
Director, STTR Program
OSBDU, Office of the Secretary
U.S. Department of Health and Human Services
200 Independence Avenue, Room 360G   202-690-7235
Washington, DC 20201   Fax: 202-260-4872
Email: Debbie.ridgely@hhs.gov
www.hhs.gov/osbdu

Department of Energy
Arlene M. DeBlanc, J.D.
STTR Program
Office of Science
U.S. Department of Energy
1000 Independence Avenue, SW
SC-32, Germantown Building   301-903-3199
Washington, DC 20585-1290   Fax: 301-903-5488
Email: Arlene.deblanc@science.doe.gov
www.science.doe.gov/sbir

Department of Defense
Jeff Bond
Acting STTR Program Coordinator
OSD/SADBU
U.S. Department of Defense
1777 North Kent Street, Suite 9100   703-588-8616
Arlington, VA 22209   Fax: 703-588-7561
Email: jeff.bond@osd.mil
www.defenselink.mil

Venture Capital to Start a Water Related Business in an Emerging Market County

(Aqua International Partners Fund)
John Sylvia
Chief Operating Officer
Texas Pacific Group
345 California Street, Suite 3300   415-743-1570
San Francisco, CA 94104   Fax: 415-743-1504
Email: jlyvia@texpac.com
www.opic.gov/investmentfunds

This fund supports equity investments in operating and special purpose companies involved in the treatment, bulk supply and distribution of water in emerging market countries. The Aqua International Partners Fund is a privately owned, privately managed investment fund supported by the Overseas Private Investment Corporation. It is designed to promote and facilitate U.S. investment in emerging markets by working with private capital to make direct equity and equity related investments. This investment fund is designed to complement OPIC's insurance and loan products. Each investment fund must meet OPIC policy requirements, including impact on the U.S. economy and employment. Type of assistance: venture capital. Range of money available: $5,000,000 to $40,000,000.

$30,000,000 In Venture Capital For Starting Infrastructure in the Baltic Region

(AIG Brunswick Millennium Fund)
Peter Yu
American International Group
175 Water Street, 24th Floor   212-458-2156
New York, NY 10038   Fax: 212-458-2153
www.opic.gov/investmentfunds

This fund provides equity investments in the Baltic, Russia, and NIS for large infrastructure projects including transportation, power, natural resource development and related industries. The AIG Brunswick Millennium Fund is a privately owned, privately managed investment fund supported by the Overseas Private Investment Corporation. It is designed to promote and facilitate U.S. investment in emerging markets by working with private capital to make direct equity and equity related investments. This investment fund is designed to complement OPIC's insurance and loan products. Each investment fund must meet OPIC policy requirements, including impact on the U.S. economy and employment. Type of assistance: venture capital. Range of money available: $5,000,000 to $30,000,000.

$15,000,000 In Venture Capital For Starting Businesses in Emerging Market Countries

(Russia Partners Fund, A)
Drew Guff
Managing Director
Siguler, Guff & Company
630 Fifth Avenue, 16th Floor   212-332-5108
New York, NY 10111   Fax: 212-332-5120
www.opic.gov/investmentfunds
This program supports equity investments in Russia in natural resource related companies, telecommunications, light manufacturing, and consumer services and products. This fund may also invest in other OPIC covered NIS states. The Russia Partners Fund, A is a privately owned, privately managed investment fund supported by the Overseas Private Investment Corporation. It is designed to promote and facilitate U.S. investment in emerging markets by working with private capital to make direct equity and equity related investments. This investment fund is designed to complement OPIC insurance and loan products. Each investment fund must meet OPIC policy requirements, including impact on the U.S. economy and employment. Type of assistance: venture capital. Range of money available: $4,500,000 to $15,000,000.

$20,000,000 In Venture Capital For Starting Businesses in Ukraine, Russia and Other Countries

(New Century Capital Partners LP Fund)
George Rohr
Chief Executive Officer
NCH Advisors
712 Fifth Avenue, 46th Floor   212-641-3229
New York, NY 10019-4018   Fax: 212-641-3201
www.opic.gov/investmentfunds
This fund provides equity investment in consumer products, financial and service industries, and diversified manufacturing in the following target areas: Latvia, Ukraine, Lithuania, Russia, Estonia, Kazakhstan, Moldova, Armenia, Bulgaria, Romania, Belarus, and Georgia. The direct equity investments of this OPIC supported fund complement OPIC's insurance and loan products. By supplementing the capital of privately owned, privately managed investment funds, OPIC can help profit oriented enterprises in emerging market areas gain access to venture capital, management guidance and financial expertise. Type of assistance: venture capital. Range of money available: $7,000,000 to $20,000,000.

$18,000,000 In Venture Capital For Starting Businesses in Thailand, India, Korea, and Others

(Asia Development Partners LP Fund)
Daniel Mintz
Managing Director
Olympus Capital Holdings, Asia
153 East 53rd Street, 43rd Floor   212-292-6531
New York, NY 10022   Fax: 212-292-6570
Email: dmintz@zbi.com
www.opic.gov/investmentfunds
This program funds equity investment in consumer products, financial services and telecommunication in the emerging market areas of Bangladesh, India, Vietnam, Thailand, Indonesia, Korea, Sri Lanka, Laos and the Philippines. The direct equity investments of this OPIC supported fund complement OPIC's insurance and loan products. By supplementing the capital of privately owned, privately managed investment funds, OPIC can help profit oriented businesses in emerging market areas gain access to venture capital, management guidance, and financial expertise. Type

of assistance: venture capital. Range of money available: $450,000 to $18,000,000.

$18,000,000 In Venture Capital to Start a Business in South America

(South American Private Equity Growth Fund)
Varel D. Freeman
Vice President and Managing Director
Baring Latin American Partners, LLC
230 Park Avenue   212-309-1795
New York, NY 10169   Fax: 212-309-1794
www.opic.gov/investmentfunds
This program supports equity investments in South America, with emphasis on Argentina, Brazil, Chile and Peru, for diversified manufacturing, service and financial services. The direct equity investments of this OPIC supported fund complement OPIC's insurance and loan products. By supplementing the capital of privately owned and managed investment funds, OPIC can help profit oriented enterprises in emerging market areas gain access to venture capital, management guidance and financial expertise. Type of assistance: venture capital. Range of money available: $1,000,000 to $18,000,000.

$14,000,000 In Venture Capital to Start a Business in Southern Africa

(New Africa Opportunity Fund)
Thomas C. Barry
Chief Executive Officer
Zephyr Management, LP
320 Park Avenue   212-508-9410
New York, NY 10022-6815   Fax: 212-508-9494
Email: info@opic.gov
www.opic.gov/investmentfunds
This fund provides equity investment in South Africa and regional SADC countries for financial and service industries and diversified manufacturing. The direct equity investments of this OPIC supported fund complement OPIC's insurance and loan products. By supplementing the capital of privately owned and managed investment funds, OPIC can help profit oriented businesses in emerging market areas gain access to venture capital, management guidance, and financial expertise. Type of assistance: venture capital. Range of money available: $3,600,000 to $14,000,000.

$16,000,000 In Venture Capital to Start a Manufacturing or Computer Business in India

(India Private Equity Fund)
Michele J. Buchignani
Managing Director
CIBC Oppenheimer & Company
Oppenheimer Tower
World Financial Center   212-667-8190
New York, NY 10281   Fax: 212-667-4468
Email: Michele.buchignani@us.cibc.com
www.opic.gov/investmentfunds
This fund supports equity investment in India for basic manufacturing, consumer goods, computer, banking and related industries. The direct equity investments of this OPIC supported fund complement OPIC's insurance and loan products. By supplementing the capital of privately owned and managed investment funds, OPIC can help profit oriented enterprises in emerging market areas gain access to venture capital, management guidance and financial expertise. Type of assistance: venture capital. Range of money available: $4,200,000 to $16,800,000.

$16,000,000 In Venture Capital to Start a Business in Latin America

(Newbridge Andean Partners LP Fund)
Bernard Aronson
ACON Investments, LLC
1133 Connecticut Avenue, NW
Suite 700   202-861-6060 ext. 103
Washington, DC 20036   202-861-6061
Email: infp@opic.gov
www.opic.gov/investmentfunds
This program funds equity investments in Belize, Bolivia, Brazil, Columbia, Ecuador, Peru, Argentina, Venezuela, El Salvador, Costa Rica, Honduras, Guatemala, Uruguay, Panama, Paraguay, Nicaragua and Chile for diversified manufacturing, financial and service industries. The direct equity investments of this OPIC supported fund complement OPIC's insurance and loan products. By supplementing the capital of privately owned, privately managed investment funds, OPIC can help profit oriented businesses in emerging market areas gain access to venture capital, management guidance and financial expertise. Type of assistance: venture capital. Range of money available: $4,800,000 to $16,000,000.

$6,000,000 In Venture Capital to Start an Environment Related Business in an Emerging Market

(Global Environment Emerging Markets Fund I)
H. Jeff Leonard
President
GEF Management
1225 Eye Street, NW, Suite 900   202-789-4500
Washington, DC 20005   Fax: 202-789-4508
Email: info@opic.gov
www.opic.gov/investmentfunds
This fund provides equity investments in all OPIC eligible countries for environment oriented sectors relating to the development, financing, operating or supplying of infrastructure relating to clean water and energy. The direct equity investments of this OPIC supported fund complement OPIC's insurance and loan products. By supplementing the capital of privately owned, privately managed investment funds, OPIC can help profit oriented enterprises in emerging market areas gain access to venture capital, management guidance and financial expertise. Type of assistance: venture capital. Range of money available: $2,000,000 to $6,000,000.

$15,000,000 In Venture Capital to Start a Business in Southeast Europe

(Soros Investment Capital Ltd)
David Matheson
Manager
Soros Private Funds Management, LLC
888 Seventh Avenue   212-333-9727
New York, NY 10106   Fax: 212-397-0139
Email: info@opic.gov
www.opic.gov/investmentfunds
This program provides equity investments in Albania, Bosnia, Bulgaria, Croatia, Herzegovina, FYR Macedonia, Montenegro, Romania, Slovenia, Turkey, and should they become eligible, Serbia and Kosovo. The direct equity investments of this OPIC supported fund complement OPIC's insurance and loan products. By supplementing the capital of privately owned, privately managed investment funds, OPIC can help profit oriented businesses in emerging market areas gain access to venture capital, management guidance and financial expertise. Type of assistance: venture capital. Range of money available: $4,000,000 to $15,000,000.

$14,000,000 In Venture Capital to Start an Agriculture Business in the Baltic Region

(Agribusiness Partners International)
Robert Peyton
President
Agribusiness Management Company
c/o America First Companies
11004 Farnam Street   402-930-3060
Omaha, NE 68102   Fax: 402-930-3007
Email: bpeyton@am1st.com
www.opic.gov/investmentfunds
This program provides equity investments in the NIS/Baltic region for agriculture, food firms, infrastructure projects, privatizations, and food storage and distribution facilities. The direct equity investments of this OPIC supported fund complements OPIC's insurance and loan products. By supplementing the capital of privately owned, privately managed investment funds, OPIC can help profit oriented enterprises in emerging market areas gain access to venture capital, management guidance and financial expertise. Type of assistance: venture capital. Range of money available: $2,945,000 to $14,915,000.

$14,000,000 In Venture Capital to Start an Environment Related Business in an Emerging Market

(Global Environment Emerging Markets Fund II)
H. Jeff Leonard
President
GEF Management
1225 Eye Street, NW, Suite 900   202-789-4500
Washington, DC 20005   Fax: 202-789-4508
Email: info@opic.gov
www.opic.gov/investmentfunds
This fund provides equity investments in all OPIC eligible countries for environment oriented sectors relating to the development, financing, operating or supplying of infrastructure relating to clean water and energy. The direct equity investments of this OPIC supported fund complement OPIC's insurance and loan products. By supplementing the capital of privately owned, privately managed investment funds, OPIC can help profit oriented enterprises in emerging market areas gain access to venture capital, management guidance and financial expertise. Type of assistance: venture capital. Range of money available: $3,600,000 to $14,400,000.

$11,000,000 In Venture Capital to Start a Business in a Sub-Sahara Country

(Modern Africa Growth and Investment Fund)
Steve Cashin
Managing Director
Modern Africa Fund Managers
1100 Connecticut Avenue, NW
Suite 500   202-887-1772
Washington, DC 20036   Fax: 202-887-1788
Email: info@opic.gov
www.opic.gov/investmenfunds
This fund supports equity investments in all sub-Saharan countries, except South Africa, with a focus on telecommunications, natural resources and manufacturing. The direct equity investments of this OPIC supported fund complement OPIC's insurance and loan products. By supplementing the capital of privately owned, privately managed investment funds, OPIC can help profit oriented businesses in emerging market areas gain access to venture capital, management guidance and financial expertise. Type of assistance: venture capital. Range of money available: $3,000,000 to $11,000,000.

$9,500,000 In Venture Capital to Start a Business in Central Europe

(Bancroft Eastern Europe Fund)
Fred Martin
President
Bancroft UK, LTD
7/11 Kensington
High Street   44-20-7368-334
London W8 5NP   Fax: 44-20-738-3348
Email: martin@bancroftgroup.com
www.opic.gov/investmentfunds

This fund supports equity investments in basic manufacturing, distribution networks, consumer goods and related services networks. Eligible countries include Central Europe/Baltic Republics, Albania, Bulgaria, Croatia, the Czech Republic, Estonia, Hungary, Latvia, Lithuania, Poland, Romania, Slovakia and Slovenia. The direct equity investments of this OPIC supported fund complement OPIC's insurance and loan products. By supplementing the capital of privately owned, privately managed investment funds, OPIC can help profit oriented enterprises in emerging market areas gain access to venture capital, management guidance and financial expertise. Type of assistance: venture capital. Range of money available: $2,850,000 to $9,500,000.

$9,200,000 In Venture Capital to Start a Telecommunications Business in Armenia, Georgia or Azerbaijan

(Caucasus Fund)
Irakli Rukhadze
CEO
Caucasus Advisors
Suite 901, 31 Milk Street   617-646-4512
Boston, MA 02109   Fax: 617-646-4512
Email: info@opic.gov
www.opic.gov/investmentfunds

This fund provides equity investments for telecommunications projects in Georgia, Armenia and Azerbaijan. The direct equity investments of this OPIC supported fund complement OPIC's loan and insurance products. By supplementing the capital of privately owned, privately managed investment funds, OPIC can help profit oriented enterprises in emerging markets gain access to venture capital, management guidance and financial expertise. Type of assistance: venture capital. Range of money available: $2,850,000 to $9,200,000.

$7,500,000 In Venture Capital to Start a Business in Southeast Asia

(Asia Pacific Growth Fund)
Ta-Lin Hsu
Chairman
Hambrecht & Quist Asia Pacific
156 University Avenue   650-838-8098
Palo Alto, CA 94104   Fax: 650-838-0801
Email: info@opic.gov
www.pic.gov/investmentfunds

This program supports equity investments in financial, construction, high tech, light manufacturing and telecom services in Indonesia, Singapore, Taiwan, Malaysia, Thailand and the Philippines. The Asia Pacific Growth Fund is a privately owned, privately managed investment fund supported by the Overseas Private Investment Corporation. It is designed to promote and facilitate U.S. investment in emerging markets by working with private capital to make direct equity and equity related investments. This investment fund is also designed to complement OPIC's insurance and loan products. Each investment must meet OPIC policy requirements, including impact on the U.S. economy and

employment. Type of assistance: venture capital. Range of money available: @2,250,000 to $7,500,000.

$6,500,000 In Venture Capital to Start a Business in West Bank/Gaza and Jordan

(West Bank/Gaza & Jordan Fund)
Scott Stupay
International Capital Advisors
6862 Elm Street, Suite 720   703-847-0870
McLean, VA 22101   Fax: 703-847-3068
E-ail: info@opic.gv
www.opic.gov/investmentfunds

This program provides equity investments in West Bank/Gaza and Jordan for basic services and manufacturing companies. The West Bank/Gaza & Jordan Fund is a privately owned, privately managed investment fund supported by the Overseas Private Investment Corporation. It promotes and facilitates U.S. investment in emerging markets by working with private capital to make direct equity and equity related investments. This fund is designed to complement OPIC's insurance and loan products. Each investment must meet OPIC policy requirements, including impact on the U.S. economy and employment. Type of assistance: venture capital. Range of money available: $1,200,000 to $6,500,000.

$6,000,000 In Venture Capital to Start a Business in Central and Eastern Europe

(Emerging Europe Fund)
Jamie Halper
Managing Director
TDA Capital Partners, Inc
15 Valley Drive   203-625-4525
Greenwich, CT 06831   Fax: 203-625-4525
Email: jhalper@templeton.com
www.opic.gov/investmentfunds

This program supports equity investments in Central and Eastern Europe for sustainable development industries. Eligible countries include Poland, Czech Republic, Slovakia, Romania, Bulgaria, Hungary and Slovenia. Investments are capped at 40% of commitments in any single country. The direct equity investments of this OPIC supported fund complement OPIC's insurance and loan products. By supplementing the capital of privately owned, privately managed investment funds, OPIC can help profit oriented enterprises in emerging market areas gain access to venture capital, management guidance and financial expertise. Type of assistance: venture capital. Range of money available: $1,800,000 to $6,000,000.

$5,500,000 In Venture Capital For Starting a Business in India

(Draper International India Fund)
Robin Richard Donohoe
Draper International
50 California Street, Suite 2925   415-616-4056
San Francisco, CA 94111   Fax: 415-616-4060
Email: rarichards@draperintl.com
www.opic.gov/investmentfunds

This program supports equity investments in India for information technology, telecommunications and consumer goods. Draper International India Fund is a privately owned, privately managed investment fund supported by the Overseas Private Investment Corporation. It promotes and facilitates U.S. investment in emerging markets by working with private capital to make direct equity and equity related investments. This fund is designed to complement OPIC's insurance and loan products. Each investment must meet OPIC policy requirements, including impacts on the U.S.

economy ad employment. Type of assistance: venture capital. Range of money available: $1,650,000 to $5,500,000.

$5,000,000 In Venture Capital for Starting a Business in Poland

(Poland Partners LP Fund)
Landon Butler
President
Landon Butler & Company
700 Thirteenth Street, NW, Suite 1150   202-737-7360
Washington, DC 20005   Fax: 202-737-7604
Email: info@opic.gov
www.opic.gov/investmentfunds
This program provides equity investments in Poland for consumer goods, manufacturing, distribution networks, merchandising, and related service networks. The Poland Partners LP Fund is a privately owned, privately managed investment fund supported by the Overseas Private Investment Corporation. OPIC promotes and facilitates U.S. investment in emerging markets by working with private capital to make direct equity and equity related investments. This fund is designed to complement OPIC's insurance and loan products. Each investment must meet OPIC policy requirements, including impact on the U.S. economy and employment. Type of assistance: venture capital. Range of money available: $1,500,000 to $5,000,000.

$4,500,000 In Venture Capital for Starting a Business in Oman, Jordan and West Bank/Gaza

(Inter-Arab Investment Fund)
Dr. Fuad S. Abu Zayyad
Chairman
Inter-Arab Management, Inc
2468 Embarcadero Way   650-917-0390
Palo Alto, CA 94303   Fax: 650-856-9864
Email: info@opic.gov
www.opic.gov/investmentfunds
This program supports equity investments in Oman, Jordan and West Bank/Gaza for basic industries that create intra/inter-regional synergies. The direct equity investments of this OPIC supported fund complement OPIC's insurance and loan products. By supplementing the capital of privately owned and managed investment funds, OPIC can help profit oriented enterprises in emerging market areas gain access to venture capital, management guidance and financial expertise. Type of assistance: venture capital. Range of money available: $1,000,000 to $4,500,000.

$4,000,000 In Venture Capital to Start a Business in Israel

(Israel Growth Fund)
Allan Barkat
General Manager
Apax-Leumi Partners, Inc
Herzliya Business Park
2 Maskit Street, 6th Floor
P.O. Box 2034   972-3-696-5992
Herliza, Israel 46120   Fax: 972-9-958-8366
Email: allan@apax.co.il
www.opic.gov/investmentfunds
This program supports equity investment in Israel for technology, telecommunications, consumer retail and consumer products. The Israel Growth Fund is a privately owned, privately managed investment fund supported by the Overseas Private Investment Corporation. OPIC promotes and facilitates U.S. investment in emerging markets by working with private capital to make direct equity and equity related investments. This fund is designed to complement

OPIC's insurance and loan products. Each investment must meet OPIC policy requirements, including impact on the U.S. economy and employment. Type of assistance: venture capital. Range of money available: $1,000,000 to $4,000,000.

$3,000,000 In Venture Capital for Starting a Mining or Manufacturing Business in Sub-Sahara Africa

(Africa Growth Fund)
Joe Jandreau
Managing Director
Equator Overseas Services, LTD
45 Glastonbury Boulevard   860-633-9999
Glastonbury, CT 06033   Fax: 860-633-6799
Email: info@opic.gov
www.opic.gov/investmentfunds
This program provides equity investments in Sub-Sahara Africa for mining, manufacturing and financial services. The Africa Growth Fund is a privately owned, privately managed investment fund supported by the Overseas Private Investment Corporation. OPIC promotes and facilitates U.S. investment in emerging markets by working with private capital to make direct equity and equity related investments. This fund is designed to complement OPIC's insurance and loan products. Each investment must meet OPIC policy requirements, including impact on the U.S. economy and employment. Type of assistance: venture capital. Range of money available: $750,000 to $3,000,000.

$2,000,000 In Venture Capital to Start a Small Business Overseas

(Allied Small Business Fund)
Cabell Williams
Allied Capital Corporation
1919 Pennsylvania Avenue, NW   202-973-6319
Washington, DC 20006-3434   Fax: 202-659-2053
Email: info@opic.gov
www.opic.gov/investmentfunds
This program supports equity investments for basic manufacturing and service industries sponsored by qualifying U.S. small businesses in any OPIC eligible country. The Allied Small Business Fund is a privately owned, privately managed investment fund supported by the Overseas Private Investment Corporation. OPIC promotes and facilitates U.S. investment in emerging markets by working with private capital to make direct equity and equity related investments. This fund is designed to complement OPIC's insurance and loan products. Each investment must meet OPIC policy requirements, including impact on the U.S. economy and employment. Type of assistance: venture capital. Range of money available: $^00,000 to $2,000,000.

$2,000,000 In Medium Term Loans for Small Businesses to Invest Overseas

(Corporate Finance Loans)
Robert Drumheller
Vice-President, Finance Department
Overseas Private Investment Corporation
1100 New York Avenue, NW   202-336-8400
Washington, DC 20527   Fax: 202-408-9866
Email: info@opic.gov
www.opic.gov/Finance
This program is designed to promote U.S. investment in emerging market economies by providing medium term loans to OPIC eligible U.S. small or medium sized businesses or the overseas subsidiary of such a business. The loans may be used to fund an overseas investment, including fixed assets, permanent working capital, and expansion of facilities. This type of loan is intended to provide long term support for

credit worthy U.S. small businesses that desire to make overseas investments when the overseas project is not intended to be the sole source of repayment. Borrowers should own at least 25% of the investment overseas. Type of assistance: loans. Range of money available: $100,000 to $2,000,000.

Loans to Start a Franchise Business Overseas

(Franchise Loans)
Robert Drumheller
Vice-President, Finance Department
Overseas Private Investment Corporation
1100 New York Avenue, NW   202-336-8400
Washington, DC 20527   Fax: 202-408-9866
Email: info@opic.gov
www.opic.gov/Finance

This program s designed to promote U.S. investment in emerging market economies by providing franchise loans to U.S. small businesses that have a 25% ownership in the franchisee or significant involvement of the small business U.S. franchiser in the project. The franchise projects must be financially sound, foster private initiative and competition in the host country, and promise significant benefits to the social and economic development of the host country. Type of assistance: loans. Range of money available: $100,000 to $4,000,000.

$2,000,000 In Medium and Long Term Loans for Businesses to Invest Overseas

(Hybrid Loans)
Robert Drumheller
Vice-President, Finance Department
Overseas Private Investment Corporation
1100 New York Avenue, NW   202-336-8400
Washington, DC 20527   Fax: 202-408-9866
Email: info@opic.gov
www.opic.gov/Finance

This program is designed to promote U.S. investment in emerging market economies by providing hybrid loans to qualified businesses. Hybrid loans combine features of the Corporate Finance Loan and the Project Finance Loan. Hybrid loans use the cash flow and collateral from the domestic parent company and the project company to create an acceptable loan structure. These loans may be used when the domestic partner has already pledged assets to its existing bank. OPIC may be able to see sufficient value in the cash flow and collateral overseas to consider the loan, whereas a local bank may not. OPIC can lend up to 50% of the cost of the start up operation, or up to 75% of the costs for the expansion of a successful existing business. Loan funds may be used for feasibility studies, organizational expenses, land, construction, machinery, equipment, training, market development, interest payments during construction, and start up expenses including initial losses and adequate working capital. Type of assistance: loans. Range of money available: $100,000 to $200,000,000.

$250,000,000 In Medium Term Loans for Businesses to Invest Overseas

(Project Finance Loan)
Robert Drumheller
Vice-President, Finance Department
Overseas Private Investment Corporation
1100 New York Avenue, NW   202-336-8400
Washington, DC 20527   Fax: 202-408-9866
Email: info@opic.gov
www.opic.gov/Finance

This program is designed to promote U.S. investment in emerging market economies by providing medium term loans and guarantees. OPIC provides financing for overseas investments that are completely owned by U.S. companies, or joint ventures where the U.S. sponsoring firm is a participant. The U.S. investor must have at least 25% equity in the project. Projects must be financially and commercially sound and must be able to repay the loan from the project cash flow. Projects that are owned or controlled by governments, or have a negative impact on U.S. employment, the U.S. economy, or the host country are not eligible. OPIC can lend up to 50% of the cost of the start up operation, or up to 75% of the costs for the expansion of a successful existing business. Loan funds may be used for feasibility studies, organizational expenses, land, construction, machinery, equipment, training, market development, interest payments during construction, and start up expenses including initial losses and adequate working capital. Type of assistance: loans and guarantees. Range of money available: loans-$100,000 to $1,000,000; guarantees up to $250,000,000.

Insurance Coverage for Overseas Contractors and Exporters

(Contractors and Exporters Insurance Coverage)
Michael T. Lempres
Vice President
Insurance Department
1100 New York Avenue, NW   202-336-8400
Washington, DC 20527   Fax: 202-408-9866
Email: info@opic.gov
www.opic.gov/Insurance

This program offers coverage to companies and investors that are acting as contractors pursuant to international construction, sales, or services contracts. It also covers companies that export heavy machinery, turbines, computers, medical equipment, and other goods. This program protects against the wrongful calling of bid, performance, advance payment guaranties, custom bonds and other guaranties. Coverage is provided against the loss of physical assets and bank accounts due to confiscation or political violence, inconvertibility of proceeds from the sale of equipment used at a site, and losses due to certain breaches by foreign buyers of contractual disputes resolution procedures. Type of assistance: insurance. Range of coverage available: up to$250,000,000.

Insurance Protection for Overseas Financial Transactions

(Capital Markets Insurance Program)
Michael T. Lempres
Vice President
Insurance Department
1100 New York Avenue, NW   202-336-8400
Washington, DC 20527   Fax: 202-408-9866
Email: info@opic.gov
www.opic.gov/Insurance

This program insures capital market transactions including new bond financing of existing ventures, Rule 144A bond issuances, and Private Placements. This coverage protects U.S. based bond holders who provide 50% of the funding for at least 40 days, and companies in developing countries and emerging markets with strong underlying credit that can pierce the sovereign ceiling and move from sub investment to investment rating by insuring their foreign currency denomination bonds against inconvertibility. Type of assistance: insurance. Range of coverage available: up to $250,000,000.

Insurance Coverage for Financial Institutions Who Make Loans in Emerging Market Economies

(Financial Institution Insurance Program)
Michael T. Lempres
Vice President
Insurance Department
1100 New York Avenue, NW   202-336-8400
Washington, DC 20527   Fax: 202-408-9866
Email: info@opic.gov
www.opic.gov/Insurance

This program protects financial institutions engaged in activities that result in financial exposure in developing countries or emerging markets. Coverage may be tailored to reflect the specific nature of the project. Activities insured by this program include loans made or arranged by banks, Capital Market transactions, cross-border leases, debt for equity investments, commodity price or interest rate swaps, and gold loans. Type of assistance: insurance. Range of coverage available: up to $250,000,000.

Insurance Protection for Overseas Leasing Arrangements

(Leasing Coverage Insurance Program)
Michael T. Lempres
Vice President
Insurance Department
1100 New York Avenue, NW   202-336-8400
Washington, DC 20527   Fax: 202-408-9866
Email: info@opic.gov
www.opic.gov/Insurance

This program provides protection for capital leases, operating leases and coverage against unlawful host government actions that prevent a lessor from enforcing its right to repossess, re-export and de-register leased equipment. Capital leases, where ownership of the asset is expected to be transferred to the lessee at the end of the lease, are protected against default on lease payments due to inconvertibility, expropriation, and/or political violence. Operating leases, where the lessor expects to recover the leased asset at the end of the lease, are insured for the value of the asset including installation, transportation costs, and for inconvertibility resulting in default on lease payments. Type of assistance: insurance. Range of coverage available: up to $250,000,000.

Insurance Coverage for Overseas Mineral Exploration

(Natural Resources Insurance, other than oil or gas)
Michael T. Lempres
Vice President
Insurance Department
1100 New York Avenue, NW   202-336-8400
Washington, DC 20527   Fax: 202-408-9866

Email: info@opic.gov
www.opic.gov/Insurance

Natural Resources Insurance protects investors from risks involved in large scale natural resource projects. Coverage is provided to protect against traditional political risks, and may also insure against unlawful withdrawal or breach by the host government involving mineral exploitation rights and other types of risk. Type of assistance: insurance. Range of coverage available: up to $250,000,000.

Insurance Coverage for Overseas Gas and Oil Projects

(Oil and Gas Insurance Program)
Michael T. Lempres
Vice President
Insurance Department
1100 New York Avenue, NW   202-336-8400
Washington, DC 20527   Fax: 202-408-9866
Email: info@opic.gov
www.opic.gov/Insurance

The Oil and Gas Insurance Program offers coverage to any large or small U.S. investor involved in oil and gas exploration and/or production. This program provides enhanced and special protection with expropriation coverage designed especially for oil and gas projects. Expropriation includes losses caused by material change in project agreements unilaterally imposed by the host government. Coverage is also available for confiscation of tangible assets and bank accounts, and interference with operations as a result of political violence that cases the cessation of operations for 6 or more months. Type of assistance: insurance. Range of coverage available: up to $250,000,000.

Insurance Coverage for Technical Assistance Companies Doing Business Overseas

(Technical Assistance Insurance Program)
Michael T. Lempres
Vice President
Insurance Department
1100 New York Avenue, NW   202-336-8400
Washington, DC 20527   Fax: 202-408-9866
Email: info@opic.gov
www.opic.gov/Insurance

This policy provides insurance coverage for U.S. investors who provide only technology or services, or provide technology or services as part of the financing plan for a project in which it has other equity and/or debt investment. This program protects investments in the form of technology and "know-how", or services, pursuant to technical assistance agreements between the U.S and foreign companies. Coverage is provided for 90% of payment accrued but unpaid as a result of inconvertibility, expropriation or political violence. Type of assistance: insurance. Range of coverage available: up to $250,000,000.

City And County Money
To Start A Business

The Federal and your state government offer a wide variety of loans, loan guarantees, and more, but those are not the only places to look. Help can be as close as your back door. City and county governments provide a wide variety of programs to help local businesses start or expand. Most of these are part of city or county economic development councils or programs. In addition, don't forget to check  neighboring cities and counties. By locating your business across city lines, you may open up a wealth of programs at your disposal. So what if you have to commute ten minutes more. It may be worth your time by allowing you access to loans or grants not available at your initial location.

We cannot possibly begin to list every city and county program. The grand total would be over 10,000 programs, and you would have to own a forklift to even begin to move the book. You can go to {www.govengine.com} to find the cities and counties that you may want to explore. You just need to find the place that gives you the most money to help you get your business off the ground.

Obviously programs and services vary from city to city and county to county, so this section is designed to give you a feel for the possibilities. Some programs offered include:

- Site location assistance
- Industrial Revenue Bonds
- Property Tax Abatement
- Gap financing
- Job Training Tax Credit
- Create new jobs and a get a great tax credit worth up to $3,000
- Some areas offer Downtown Revitalization programs.

Many places have microloans available for up to $35,000 for deserving businesses to start or expand. For instance:

- Savannah, Georgia offers an Entrepreneurial Center for technical assistance, training, access to loans and workshops.
- Business Incubators can be a great place to get low rent, services, and help in getting your business started. Erie, Pennsylvania and Santa Fe, New Mexico each offer incubators.
- Buffalo, New York has gap financing for minority construction businesses.

- There is a $5,000 mini grant available in Alameda County, California for recycling programs.
- Thornton, Colorado offers small grants to local businesses to upgrade their buildings or to help fund special promotions such as grand openings.
- New Haven, Connecticut has a microloan fund for childcare facilities.

Remember that these are just the beginning. Look to your local cities and counties to find out what they offer and how they can assist you in becoming an entrepreneurial success story!

Alabama

Conecuh County Programs
Conecuh County Economic Development Authority
100 Depot Square
Evergreen, AL 36401
251-578-1000
www.conecuheda.com/index.php
The Department of Housing and Urban Development (HUD) has designated certain counties in Alabama to be a Renewal Community. More than half of the county has been designated as such. Through the Renewal Community Incentive Program, they are able to offer the following incentives to existing and new businesses.

Increased Section 179 Deduction: Businesses can deduct the cost of property acquired up to a maximum amount, which is $35,000 higher than non-renewal community businesses. It also allows for full cost deduction of equipment in the year it was purchased.

Commercial Revitalization Deduction: Businesses that construct or rehabilitate commercial property can deduct a portion of the costs over a shorter time period than the standard depreciation period. As such, they can deduct one-half the costs in the year the building is placed in service; or deduct all costs ratably over a 10-year period.

Environmental Cleanup Cost Deduction: Businesses can deduct the costs to clean up hazardous substances at certain contaminated sites.

Zero Percent Capital Gains Rate: Capital gains on Renewal Community business assets held for five years are not taxed.

Renewal Community Employment Credit: Businesses that hire or retain employees that live and work in Renewal Community zones can receive a credit of $1,500 per employee per year against their federal taxes.

Jefferson County Programs
Planning and Community Development
805 North 22nd Street
Birmingham, AL 35203
205-325-5761
www.jeffcointouch.com
Jefferson County Business Loan Fund: The loan can be used to purchase real estate, construction, working capital or machinery and equipment. The maximum amount is for up to 50% of the amount of the contract. There are requirements for location, job creation, and those eligible to apply.

Economic Development Loan Program: Provides loans through several programs ranging from short-term construction financing, infrastructure loans and GAP financing to long-term financing loan guarantees. All loans are dependent upon the creation of jobs aimed at low and moderate-income persons.

Workshops and Seminars: The Office of Planning and Community Development puts on workshops annually for the purpose of enhancing minority enterprise development. The workshops are provided at no cost.

Jefferson County Economic and Industrial Development Authority
500 Beacon Parkway West
Birmingham, AL 35209
205-325-5761
www.jeffcoeida.com/index.html
The Jefferson County Economic and Industrial Development Authority is a public corporation formed to take on the solicitation and promotion of industry, industrial development and other concerns, and to convince enterprises to locate, expand, improve their operations or remain in Jefferson County. Some of the services provided to businesses that wish to locate or expand in the county are, site and facility selection, workforce recruitment and screening, workforce training, and project financing and incentive packages.

Sumter County
Sumter County Chamber of Commerce
128 Franklin Street
Livingston, AL 35470
205-652-9303
Greeene-Sumter Enterprise Community Program: This program was created to provide economic opportunity through the creation of jobs in the community and region. Grants are available for seed money and matching funds for infrastructure development in the Enterprise Community area. They provide assistance for engineering and pre-development costs for water, sewer, roads, bridges, and other infrastructure projects related to business development and expansion for new job development.

Alabama-Tombigbee Loan Administrative Board
107 Broad Street
Camden, AL 36726
334-682-4234
Fax: 334-682-4205
Alabama Tombigbee Revolving Loan Fund: This is a locally controlled source of capital that is used to finance start-up and expanding businesses with projects that will create

permanent jobs and influence private sector investments. Interests are generally below prime loans.

Talladega County

Talladega County Economic Development Authority
P.O. Box 867
Sylacauga, AL 35150
256-245-8332
Fax: 256-245-8336
www.tceda.com

Talladega County offers a strategic location at the center of the country's fastest growing economy, a nationally recognized work force training program, and a business friendly atmosphere with one of the nation's lowest operating costs, a skilled and dedicated labor force with a strong work ethic. As a site for business and industry Talladega County has significant advantages.

Sylacauga's Industrial Land Purchase Incentive Program: Businesses are eligible for a $1,000 per job credit for every job created averaging $10.00 per hour on the purchase of land controlled by the City of Sylacauga Industrial Development Board. Job creation credits will never exceed the sale price of the land needed for a project. To qualify, a company must create a minimum of twenty jobs within an eighteen-month period from the date of the land purchase and must realistically project the total number of jobs to be created and have an average payroll cost per hour rate of at least $10.00.

Revolving Loan Fund: To complement a conventional bank loan, this Fund can be used to finance up to $125,000, or 1/3 of project needs, including working capital. Rates and terms are negotiable depending upon credit and need; the interest rate can be as low as two percent below prime, and the term can be as long as the conventional loan or the life of the assets financed, whichever is longer.

Industrial Revenue Bonds: The Industrial Development Board of local municipalities will issue industrial revenue bonds to finance fixed asset needs. This can result in a net interest cost savings of approximately two percent compared to a conventional loan at prime for a 15-year amortization period. A related benefit is the ability to fix the rate long term.

Atmore City

Atmore City Hall
201 East Louisville Avenue
Atmore, AL 36502
251-368-2253

Atmore Industrial Park has been designated an Enterprise Zone. In addition to the incentives provided by the state, the city also offers these additional incentives:
-   10-year exemption from Business License Fee; and
-   2-cent sales tax exemption on building materials purchased within the city limits.

Atmore City Gas & Water Department
Atmore Utilities Board
412 East Ridgeley Street
Atmore, AL 36502
251-368-2207

The Utilities Board of the City of Atmore provides other incentives to the Atmore Industrial Park, such as:
-   Provide gas, water, and sewage utility services to the building of any qualifying industry at no cost to the user;
-   Deliver and sell gas, water and sewage services for the first year of operation at the providers cost; and

-   Provide services to any area of the Park that is not currently served within 90 days, to serve a new or expanding industry.

Bessemer City

Bessemer Industrial Development Board
1800 Third Avenue North
Bessemer, AL 35020
205-424-4060
www.bessemeral.org/bdb.html

The City of Bessemer has evolved into a major small business, tourist, light manufacturing, and distribution center for the State of Alabama. An advanced transportation network, access to business assistance programs, an abundance of power resources capable of meeting any energy demand, a small business incubator program housed in two facilities and the services of outstanding medical facilities, have contributed to a local economy that is diverse and vibrant.

Revolving Loan Fund: Funding is available to credit-worthy firms or developers for up to 40% financing of a project's total fixed-asset costs, in amounts ranging from $20,000 to $200,000. Generally, the term is in the range of ten to fifteen years, with a fixed rate of interest at or below prime lending rate. Restrictions apply to the types of businesses that can qualify under this program.

Bessemer IBD Revolving Loan Fund: This fund provides up to 25% financing of a project's total costs, in amounts ranging from $10,000 to $75,000. Loans from this fund are generally used for small business start-ups or small equipment purchases. These loans carry a below prime rate of interest fixed for the duration of the loan term, but amortized over a five to ten year period. Restrictions apply for assistance under this loan program.

Lot Financing: In certain cases, the Board may hold a mortgage on a Board-owned industrial site, and lower its position on the property to a private lender. This form of lot financing permits a credit-worthy firm or developer to finance, generally over a ten-year period, the land cost at a fixed rate of interest. For a business seeking financing for building construction, the program preserves equity, resulting in less money needed from the primary lender.

Business License Cap for Distributors: Firms meeting the classification of "general merchandise wholesalers" can take advantage of a cap provision on the amount of business license fees paid to the city. Instead of basing licenses upon total gross receipts with no cap, the City charges only a percentage of gross sales earned within the State of Alabama. This does not apply to out-of-state sales. The maximum amount for the wholesalers' business license is capped at $2,500 a year.

Non-Educational Tax Abatements: Firms that meet certain SIC code restrictions may be eligible for an abatement from that portion of local and state property tax and sales and use tax on construction-related materials not levied for educational purposes. There are job creation requirements and capital investment requirements attached to this program.

Microloan Lending Program: In partnership with the city of Bessemer and the city of Birmingham, the Board administers a lending program for small, minority and women-owned businesses. Loan amounts are up to $10,000 and may be used for working capital and small capital equipment acquisition.

Downtown Building Rehabilitation Program: The City works with the Bessemer Downtown Redevelopment Authority and offers financial assistance to owners or property located within the designated downtown historic district. The funds can be used to improve the exterior appearance of building facades. The term of the loan is five years with an interest rate of 5%.

Birmingham City
Operation New Birmingham
505 20th Street, Suite 150
Birmingham, AL 35203
205-324-8797
205-324-8799
www.onb.org/index.htm
City "Float" Loan (Interim Financing): This is a short-term loan that is available for economic development projects in downtown Birmingham. The funds may be used for real estate acquisition and renovation, construction, purchase of machinery, equipment, and working capital. The maximum term is 30 months.

Tax Increment Financing: Cities are allowed to create tax increment financing districts that set aside the district's property tax increases in a separate Tax Increment Financing fund. Businesses, developers and others that demonstrate a viable redevelopment plan that contributes to the urban renewal of the City Center may request support for their projects from TIF funds.

Brewton City
City of Brewton
1010A Douglas Avenue
Brewton, AL 36426
251-809-1770
Fax: 251-809-1775
www.cityofbrewton.org
Brewton Industrial Park has been declared an Enterprise Zone (EZ). In addition to the state EZ incentives, the city has created the following benefits to businesses located in the Park:
-    -All City of Brewton utilities (natural gas, water, and sewerage) at the City's cost for the first year of operation; and
-    Exemption of City license fees on the following scale:
     -    100% for the first year in the city
     -    50% for the second year in the city
     -    25% for the third year in the city

Intermediary Relending Program: This financing program provides below market fixed rate loans for development projects in the rural areas of Barbour, Coffee, Covington, Dale, Geneva, Henry and Houston counties. The funds may be used for fixed asset financing. The maximum loan amount is $150,000. The loan cannot exceed $15,000 per job created or retained with this program.

MicroLoan Program: This source of capital is used to finance startup and expanding businesses or entrepreneurial projects in eligible rural areas. The funds can be used for construction, expansion, renovation, modernization or development costs; purchase of machinery, equipment & supplies; and provide for permanent working capital.

Alaska

Kenai Peninsula Borough
Community and Economic Development Division
Red Diamond Center

43335 K-Beach Road, Suite 16
Soldotna, AK 99669
907-262-6355
Fax: 907-262-6762
www.borough.kenai.ak.us/CEDD/default.htm
The Business Development Manager encourages businesses to locate on the Kenai Peninsula, promote economic development projects, network at trade shows and workshops, and assist new businesses. Businesses can take advantage of the free publications and web documents that cover local markets and developing plans.

Ketchikan Borough
344 Front Street
Ketchikan, AK 99901
907-228-6625
www.borough.ketchikan.ak.us
Property Tax Exemption: Real or personal property that is used in a manufacturing business that has not previously been taxed as real or personal property by the borough and is used in a trade or business, can apply for an exemption. The business must create employment in the borough and generate sales outside of the borough of goods produced in the borough, or must materially reduce the importation of goods from outside the borough. There must not be more than 100 annual full-time employees and the business value must not exceed 5,000,000.00. The exemption begins with 0% in year one and increases by 20% each year until the sixth year at 100%.

Northwest Arctic Borough
P.O. Box 1110
Kotzebue, AK 99752
907-442-2930
800-478-1110
Fax: 907-442-2930
www.northwestarcticborough.org/edc
Small Business Grant Program: A total of $50,000 is currently available for grants to small businesses for expansion or start-up costs. These grants can be a maximum of $5,000 to organizations serving many people or up to $1,500 for individuals. Grants are for the purpose of purchasing tools, equipment, and supplies, acquiring training, or assisting with various start up costs. The application can be downloaded from the website listed above.

Revolving Small Business Loan Program: Interest-free loans of up to $1,500 are available with this program. Repayment of the loan is based on assignment of a portion of the Permanent Fund Dividend. The loan provides an opportunity for "self-investment" and can be used for the purchase of inventory for resale, raw materials for the production of commercially sold products, or other costs associated with operating a business for profit.

Arts and Crafts Marketing Program: As a means of promoting traditional Native arts and crafts as a reliable source of income for residents, the borough takes an active role in assisting artists sell their products. A revolving art purchase fund has been established that enables the borough to actually purchase crafts directly from artists. This program is exclusively for residents who are dedicated to producing work on a large scale, on a regular basis, as a means of producing a reliable source of continuing income.

City of Anchorage
Anchorage Economic Development Corporation
900 West 5th Avenue, Suite 300
Anchorage, AK 99501
907-258-3700

800- 462-7275
Fax: 907-258-6646
www.aedcweb.com

Property Tax Exemption: Property that has not been previously taxed by the municipality and that is used in a trade or business is eligible for an exemption. The business must create employment in the municipality and generate sales outside of the municipality of goods and services that are produced in the municipality, or materially reduce the importation of goods and services from outside the municipality. The exemption is for up to $7,500 annually for up to five years for each job created and sustained by the business, not to exceed 50% of the tax due in each year; or no tax in the first full year of operation, up to $7,500 annually for up to two additional years for each job crated and sustained by the business up to 100% of the tax due in each year.

Inventory Tax Exemption: Inventory held for shipment outside of Alaska may be exempted from local inventory taxes. Evidence that an exemption is necessary to the operation of the business and the creation of employment or eligible must be shown.

City of Juneau

Juneau Economic Development Council (JEDC)
612 West Willoughby Avenue, Suite A
Juneau, AK 99801-1732
907-463-3662 907
Fax: 907-463-3929
www.jedc.org

The JEDC works to enhance quality of life by actively promoting economic diversity and sustainable development in Juneau, Southeast Alaska and through specific statewide programs.

Southeast Alaska Revolving Loan Fund (RLF): Created by the Juneau Economic Development Council in 1997, the RLF bridges the financial gap between what banks will finance and what the business community needs. The goal is to provide financing for viable projects that will create and retain quality jobs and help to diversify local economies in Southeast Alaska. Fixed rate loans between $35,000 and $350,000 are available to eligible businesses at market rates and terms.

City of Wrangell

Economic Development Department
P.O. Box 531
Wrangell, AK 99929
907-874-2381
Fax: 907-874-3952
www.wrangell.com/business/economy/incentives

For the most part, business incentives need to be voted on or renewed in Wrangell. Below are a few programs that they have administered in the past and may be available again.

Property Tax Relief: Property tax relief may be available for economic development projects that create jobs within the community. Tax relief currently takes a vote of the people, but the voters approved a five-year tax incentive package in 1999 for a company creating over 35 jobs.

Financing participation: The City participates in the Southeast Alaska Revolving Loan Fund which can assist directly with financing of a project or work in cooperation with a local bank. The Fund may help with modifying payment schedules or amounts to ease the start-up/expansion efforts for the business.

Loan Participation: The City Council has in the past approved a loan participation through an interest buy down program. Such a program would need to be reviewed specific to any project.

Power Rate Reduction: Industrial oriented projects may be able to negotiate a lower interruptible power rate with the Project Management Committee with the support and assistance of the City of Wrangell.

City of Sitka

Sitka Economic Development Association
329 Harbor Drive, Suite 212
Sitka, AK 99835
907-747-2660
www.sitka.net

There are no specific incentives in Sitka. Sitka will provide incentives from time to time on specific projects. For example, if it involves a lease of land or building at the City's industrial park, there may be a forgiveness of lease for a period of time to help the tenant recover a portion of the improvements they might have to make to the leasehold. The City also has the capacity to make small loans. There is no particular formula for the loans with the exception of the small business loan guarantee program. In this program, the City will provide up to $37,000 in loan guarantees but only with bank participation.

Arizona

Apache County

Economic Development Apache County (EDAC)
75 West Cleveland
St. Johns, AZ 85936
928-337-2644
www.apachecounty.com

EDAC facilitates site selection, assists businesses in identifying incentive programs, and provides introductions to government and financial institutions for new and expanding businesses in the region.

Wood Products Development Grants: Matching funds are available for entrepreneurial start-up businesses. Assistance is also available in grant application and grant management.

Enterprise Zone: The entire Southern Apache County has been designated an Enterprise Zone. In addition to the state incentives, there are also local incentives that can benefit businesses located in an Enterprise Zone.

Maricopa County

Department of Planning and Development
301 West Jefferson Street, Floor 3
Phoenix, AZ 85003
602-506-3301

The County offers superior business/industry location assistance, statistics and strategic data for business locations and expansion (domestic and international). They also market and recruit desirable new business and industry in key economic clusters.

Industrial Development Bonds: Funding assistance is available in the form of Industrial Development Bonds, which are free from state or local income tax.

Capital Access Program (CAP): CAP is a credit enhancement program for small businesses that involves a

50% guarantee. The maximum loan amount is $250,000 that can be used for working capital.

City of Chandler

Office of Economic Development
City of Chandler
P.O. Box 4008
Chandler, AZ 85244
480-782-3035
http://chandleraz.gov

Chandler Industrial Development Authority: CIDA offers businesses the ability to finance new manufacturing projects with tax-exempt industrial revenue bonds. Eligible projects include new, improved or expanded manufacturing facilities, and manufacturing equipment. The interest rates tend to be significantly lower than prime, and the interest on the bond is exempt from federal and state income tax.

Foreign Trade Zones: The City of Chandler may request a foreign trade sub zone on the behalf of a company. A sub zone is site specific, and businesses that are activated in the sub zone can receive the benefit of deferring duty on imported goods. The advantage of the foreign trade zone is that imported goods are allowed to be manufactured within the zone and commingled with domestic and other foreign goods, and the businesses pay the lesser of the duty on the goods as imported or as a component of the final product. In addition, goods that never enter the US customs territory, such as waste or defects, never pay duty. State law also provides for an 80% property tax reduction on both real and personal property for business activated within a foreign trade zone sub zone.

Downtown Improvement Fund (DIF): The (DIF) program is intended to provide financial assistance to viable small and medium-sized firms who locate or expand in Historic Downtown Chandler. The program will reimburse property owners or tenants for implementing construction projects that will influence additional capital investment, business investment or create jobs for Chandler residents. Up to $35,000 in reimbursement matching funds is available to assist property or business owners for the renovation or improvement of Downtown properties for retail or restaurant use.

Historic Facade Improvement Program: This program is intended to provide financial assistance to viable firms whose relocation, expansion or rehabilitation will preserve part of Chandler's historic character. Funding is available in the form of loans or recoverable grants to assist in the acquisition and rehabilitation of Downtown Chandler's Historic Buildings. The goal is to leverage long-term capital investment from private lenders and investors while preserving Chandler's unique historic assets. Structures to be considered historic must be eligible for listing on the National Register of Historic Place, either individually or as part of a larger district.

Colonnade Signage Program: In order to recapture the effectiveness of the colonnade signs, the City of Chandler is encouraging downtown businesses to install signs on the front of the colonnade facing the street. To help business owners to meet this goal, grants of up to $650 per business are available for the creation and installation per sign. The money can be used for design fees, materials, and/or installation of the sign. The sign must conform to the Downtown Sign Code and receive a permit to be considered for the program.

City of Glendale

Economic Development Department
City of Glendale
5850 West Glendale Avenue
Glendale, AZ 85301
623-930-2983
Fax: 623-931-5730
www.glendaleaz.com/EconDev

The City publishes the *Guide to Operating a Business* and also helps businesses with site analysis as well as other development services.

Economic Development Opportunity Fund: The city of Glendale has created a $2,000,000 opportunity fund to assist qualified projects. These projects include: high quality new buildings, high quality new employment for Glendale, target wages of at least $14 per hour, and increases in the city's retail sales tax base. The Economic Development Opportunity Fund can be used to: reimburse construction sales tax, reimburse development fees, provide grant funding for workforce development, and develop off-site infrastructure.

Economic Development Bond Financing: The city of Glendale has bonding capacity of up to $50,000,000 to assist development projects with public infrastructure. Qualified projects will need to meet the same criteria as the Opportunity Fund, and must provide a net return to the city's property tax base.

Industrial Development Bonds: Through the city of Glendale Industrial Development Authority, IDB bonds can be issued and are free from state or local income tax. This provides the borrower lower interest rate financing.

City of Phoenix

Department of Economic and Community Development
200 West Washington Street, 20th Floor
Phoenix, AZ 85003-1611
602-262-5040
Fax: 602-495-5097
TTY: 602-534-3476
www.phoenix.gov/ECONDEV/index.html

Besides the financial programs available to assist small businesses in Phoenix, there are also programs that provide technical assistance. They publish a guide to operating a business in the city that will help a business to be successful. {www.ci.phoenix.az.us/BUSINESS/guide.html}

Business Customer Service Center: The BCSC serves as a one-stop service center for businesses and customers seeking development information and/or are interested in developing property in Phoenix. It also serves as a customer consultant in navigating the City development process and assists in resolving problems with start-up and expanding businesses. The BCSC provides information and referrals on development process, fee estimates, plan review time frames, and steps necessary for City approval and permits.

Annual Facilities Permit Program: This program simplifies the permitting and inspection process by maintaining inspectors who are familiar with a specific facility's construction and can review related plans. Participating facilities are exempt from conventional permits for work regulated by the construction code when that work does not increase the floor area and is performed on the facility's existing buildings, structures and utilities. The facility must be engaged in manufacturing, processing or service and contain specialized buildings and service equipment that require full-time maintenance staff.

Management Technical Assistance (MTA): Access to private business consultants is available to small businesses without a charge. MTA consultants provide expertise in general business and marketing, financing and loan packaging, business needs assessment and workforce development.

Technology Office: This office is dedicated to attracting technology and biotech companies. They can help those companies with expansion or relocation information through a variety of resources.

Phoenix Industrial Development Authority (PIDA) Bonds: This program can provide tax-exempt financing through industrial revenue bonds up to $10 million for the acquisition, construction, equipping or improvement of qualified manufacturing projects located within the city of Phoenix. Non-profit organizations may finance larger amounts. The interest rate on these bonds generally ranges from one to three points below the prime interest rate. The interest earned on these bonds is exempt from federal and state income taxation, resulting in a lower overall cost of financing a project.

Redevelopment Area Tax Abatement: Property tax incentives are available in designated central city redevelopment areas in Phoenix. Under qualifying conditions, real property may be subject to an excise tax, which is significantly lower than a traditional property tax. In certain redevelopment areas this tax is abated for the first eight years of a qualified project. This program may also be available outside of redevelopment area, however, the excise tax rate would be 1.5 times the rate applied within redevelopment areas and there is no abatement period.

Assistance to Businesses Affected By Light Rail Transit (LRT): The City of Phoenix and partner agencies can provide assistance to businesses affected by LRT construction. This includes marketing and promotional services, no charge consulting services, business plan preparation assistance, and guidance with loan applications. Networking and educational opportunities are available through City-sponsored events. Courtesy and traffic guidance signs will be made available to help direct customers to businesses.

Expansion Assistance and Development Program (EXPAND): The EXPAND program encourages lender participation by reducing their risk through collateral enhancement. EXPAND reserve deposits are pledged in amounts from 25% to 50% of a loan with a ceiling of $150,000.

Capital Access Program (CAP): The City's Capital Access Program encourages lenders to make loans that present a moderately higher risk than normally considered. Eligible businesses are commercial enterprises in the City's Enterprise Community, smaller manufacturers, wholesalers, and distributors. CAP loans are made directly through a bank and qualifying businesses will pay a market rate of interest, plus a premium up to 6 percent of the loan amount. The loan premium is matched by the City of Phoenix Industrial Development Authority to reduce lender risk

Foreign Trade Zones: Foreign Trade Zone #75 is administered by the City of Phoenix. As the zone administrator, the City of Phoenix can also create Foreign Trade Zone sub zones for qualifying projects throughout metropolitan Phoenix. Foreign trade zones are used by companies to reduce, eliminate, or defer payment of customs duties on products that are imported into the United States. Additionally, companies operating in the Phoenix Foreign

Trade Zone can benefit from an 80 percent reduction in real and personal property taxes.

City of Tucson

Economic Development Office
City Hall 3rd Floor
255 West Alameda
Tucson, AZ 85701
520-791-5093
Fax: 520-791-5413
www.ci.tucson.az.us/oed
The City of Tucson has established a number of Revolving Loan Funds that provide loans to businesses located within city limits. These loans are available for any legitimate business purpose, such as the purchase of real estate, fixed assets, inventory, working capital, and start-ups. The Business Development Finance Corporation (BDFC) manages most of those Funds.

Business Development Finance Corporation (BDFC)
186 East Broadway Boulevard
Tucson, Arizona 85701
520-623-3377
www.bdfc.com
Small Loan Program: The loan amount ranges from $10,000 to $100,000 that can be used for any business purpose. A major advantage of the Small Loan Program is that it offers affordable fixed interest rates with no prepayment penalty.

Mini- 504 Program: This program is for smaller real estate projects, which offers a typical financing structure of 10% borrower contribution, 50% bank financing in first lien position on the commercial property and 40% BDFC financing in second position behind the bank.

Community Economic Development Opportunities (CEDO): CEDO provides small loans to assists businesses that are at least 51% owned by a minority or woman. For these businesses, Business Development Finance Corporation provides specialized support in the loan application process and assistance after loan approval.

Tucson Industrial Development Authority
186 East Broadway Boulevard
Tucson, AZ 85701
520-882-5591
Fax: 520-624-1728
www.tucsonida.com
The Industrial Development Authority of the City of Tucson (Tucson IDA) is a quasi-public enterprise, which provides a range of financing alternatives for community projects.

Community Investment Fund: This program actively seeks to fund Tucson-based projects that have economic development, affordable housing, or downtown, neighborhood or community development objectives. Loans can be made between $5,000 and $75,000. Larger size loans may also be made in participation with other lenders. The term of the loans can be for up to five years, with up to 20-year amortizations and competitive interest rates.

The Tucson IDA is also seeking projects for private activity bond financing. Such financing is available for certain eligible projects, including but not limited to manufacturing facilities (with qualifications), multi-family rental apartments, certain assisted living facilities, and various nonprofit 501(c)(3) projects. Taxable bond financing is available for a wide range of projects and can provide below market interest rates, financing up to 100% of project costs and amortizations up to 25 years. Bond financing is generally available for projects over $1,500,000.

Chicanos por la Causa (CPLC)
1112 East Buckeye Road
Phoenix, AZ 85034-4043
520- 882-0018
The City of Tucson has also established Small Business Loan Programs with another agency, Chicanos por la Causa. These programs were established to address the problems encountered by small business entrepreneurs seeking financing and provide alternatives for existing and emerging micro-enterprises in the Tucson community.

The Tucson Revolving Loan Fund: Long-term loan capital is available to small local businesses for investments that create, maintain, or enhance employment opportunities for low-income persons. Loan funds may be used for working capital or the purchase of equipment, machinery, furniture, fixtures, supplies and/or inventory. This is a revolving loan fund because loan payments are deposited back into the fund and become the lending capital for future loans. Loan amounts range from $10,000 to $40,000.

Besides the financial assistance, the city of Tucson offers a great amount of business resources.

Small Business Commission: It is the mission of this group to advise the Mayor and the Council on current and proposed City policies affecting small business and facilitate communication between the City and small business.

Business Community Calendar: It lists not only the events sponsored by the city, but also by various business groups.

Guide to Operating a Business in the City of Tucson: The Small Business Commission has created this free publication for new and relocating businesses. The information it provides is designed to explain the various steps, requirements and resources available to those starting and operating a business in the City.

Other available publications are: *Guide to Promoting a Business in the City of Tucson, 17 Step Checklist to Obtaining Your Business License, OED Newsletter*.

Arkansas

City of Little Rock
Little Rock Regional Chamber of Commerce
1 Chamber Plaza
Little Rock, AR 72201
501-374-2001
Fax: 501-374-6018
www.littlerock.dina.org/business/default.html
PILOT (Payment in Lieu of Taxes) Program: This program is offered by the City of Little Rock. Under Arkansas' Constitution, property taxes cannot be negotiated or forgiven unless an industrial revenue bond is used. However, any project financed by an industrial revenue bond (taxable or non-taxable), can see their property taxes reduced by 65% over the life of the bond issue. This reduction can be structured by the company to maximize their advantage.

City of Magnolia
Magnolia Economic Development Corporation
P.O. Box 2262
Magnolia, AR 71754-2262

870-234-0800
800-206-0889
Fax: 870-234-9291
www.medc.cc/medc.htm
Business Park Location Program: The Magnolia Business Park consists of 280 acres of gently sloping and well-drained land. Bounded on the south by US highway 82, US highway 79 is approximately 2 miles to the east and US highway 371 is 1 mile to the west. Rail transportation is located in the park with sites available for rail spur construction. Qualifying industries will receive assistance in purchasing prime sites in the Magnolia Business Park. Qualifying industries will have all deposits and hook up fees waived by Entergy Corporation and the City of Magnolia City.

MEDC Cash Incentive: A financial rebate is available to qualifying businesses hiring specified net new full-time permanent employees and capital investment within 24 months after completion of a new location or plant expansion.

City of Searcy
The Searcy Chamber of Commerce
2323 South Main Street
Searcy, AR 72143
501-268-2458
Fax: 501-268-9530
www.searcyarkansas.org
Quality First Training Program: This program involves a variety of training programs. Quality First can operate at the business location or off-site. The program is designed to fit the business' work plan with a highly efficient and convenient training schedule. This customized approach ensures the best return on a training investment. A wide range of subjects and course work is offered. Since its inception, the program has saved participating businesses over $60 million dollars.

Arkansas Community of Excellence (ACE): Searcy has received ACE classification from the State of Arkansas. This means that the community is recognized as being a prime area for potential economic development. The ACE designation indicates to prospects that the community has what it takes to be a future industry location. The city is fully prepared to take a pro-active approach to economic development and the recruitment of jobs.

Cross County
P.O. Box 234
500 North Falls Boulevard
Wynne, AR 72396
870-238-2601
Fax: 870-238-7844
www.crosscountychamber.com
Cross County has passed a countywide sales tax for economic development. The Cross County Economic Development Corporation is committed to assisting industries with their needs when locating their facilities in Cross County. Assistance is available with local tax incentives, construction of infrastructure, such as rail spurs, roads, etc. and with training and educating the workforce. The type of assistance available depends on the project that requires funding.

Workforce Training: The Cross County Economic Development Corporation is in the process of forming a partnership with the University of Arkansas Engineering Department and East Arkansas Community College, which will create The East Arkansas Technology Center for The Delta. The technology center will have the ability to provide technology training for the workforce as well as deliver technology assistance to industries.

West Central Arkansas Planning and Development District, Inc.

1820 Higdon Ferry Road, Suite "D"
P.O. Box 21100
Hot Springs, AR 71903
501-525-7577
Fax: 501-525-7677
www.wcapdd.dina.org/RLF.html

Revolving Loan Fund: The District administers this program that may be used as a business development financing tool in eligible areas of the District. This fund is designed to provide "gap financing" to small businesses by assisting the borrower to leverage private sector funds. The RLF is intended to provide low interest loans to small businesses. The program has flexible financing options and working capital loans, fixed assets and inventory projects may be financed for eligible projects.

Financial Assistance for Clark and Hot Spring Counties' Small Business: The district administers this loan program to assist small businesses in Clark and Hot Spring Counties with post-disaster long-term economic recovery efforts. The fund is designed to provide financing to businesses by working with borrowers and banks to design financing packages that assist business to expand and create jobs for the local economy. The program is flexible and loans for most small business operating and expansion needs are eligible.

East Arkansas Planning and Development District

2905 King Street
P.O. Box 1403
Jonesboro, AR 72403
870-932-3957
Fax: 870-932-0135
www.eapdd.com

EAPDD was incorporated as a nonprofit, regional planning and development agency in 1967, serving a 12 county area of northeast Arkansas. The District's purpose is to promote and support the economic development of the region. It does this by providing technical assistance to the cities, counties, businesses, and other development organizations in the area, and by networking extensively with state and federal resource agencies.

EDA Revolving Loan Programs: The District administers this business loan designed for financing new business expansion opportunities that will result in the creation of one new job for every $10,000 borrowed. Eligible activities for investments are business acquisitions, construction, conversion, enlargement, repair, modernization and development costs; purchase and development of land, easements, rights-of-way, buildings, facilities, leases or materials; purchase of equipment, leasehold improvements, machinery or supplies; pollution control and abatement; transportation services; start-up operating costs and working capital; interest on interim financing; feasibility studies; reasonable fees related to the project; and aquaculture. The maximum loan amount is 33% of project costs, or $200,000, whichever is less.

RDA Revolving Loan Programs: The District administers this business loan designed for financing new business expansion opportunities that will result in the creation of one new job for every $10,000 borrowed. Eligible activities for investments are business acquisitions, construction, conversion, enlargement, repair, modernization and development costs; purchase and development of land, easements, rights-of-way, buildings, facilities, leases or materials; purchase of equipment, leasehold improvements, machinery or supplies; pollution control and abatement; transportation services; start-up operating costs and working capital; interest on interim financing; feasibility studies; reasonable fees related to the project; and aquaculture. The maximum loan amount is 50% of project costs, or $150,000, whichever is less. The service area for this loan is in communities with fewer than 25,000 people.

The two loan programs can be used in combination to jointly fund an eligible project, up to a maximum combined loan of $350,000.

California

San Bernardino County

Economic Development Division
290 North D Street, 6th Floor
San Bernardino, CA 92415
909-388-0838
Fax: 909-388-0844
www.co.san-bernardino.ca.us/ecd/economic

The Economic Development Division provides a variety of programs and services designed to attract new industry to the County while retaining existing businesses. The ultimate objective is to maximize employment opportunities and increasing capital investment in the area. The Division offers a variety of incentives financing programs, demographic and statistical information, provides technical assistance and referral services, and financing programs to businesses.

Microloan Program: Microenterprise businesses that have been operational for at least two years and are looking to expand their business within the County can apply for this loan guarantee. The loan minimum is $5,000 and the maximum amount is $25,000. Applicants must demonstrate 20% equity injection into the expansion of their business. Matching financing from other sources is encouraged. Loan proceeds may be used to finance the purchase of equipment, machinery and inventory, refinancing of business-related debt, working capital and property improvement. This program requires the creation of at least one job, per $35,000 of County funds borrowed.

Small Business Enhancement Loan Program (SBEL): Small businesses that are expanding their operations within the County are eligible for this program. A loan guarantee is available for a loan in the range of $25,000 to $50,000. Applicants must demonstrate 20% equity injection into the expansion of their business. The funds may be used to finance acquisition of equipment, machinery and inventory, refinancing of business-related debt, working capital and property improvement. The loan requires the creation of at least one job, per $35,000 of County funds borrowed. Matching financing from other sources is encouraged but not required.

Business Expansion Loan Program (BusEx): Direct financing is available for businesses that would like to expand or relocate in the County. This program is designed to "fill the financing gap" between private lending sources and the owner's equity participation in the project. Applicants will be able to obtain below-market-rate financing which can be used for land acquisition, building acquisition or construction, capital equipment purchases and, in some cases, working capital. The loan ranges from $50,000 to $500,000 with the

County's participation not exceeding 40%. County funds must be fully secured by real property, personal property and/or a Letter of Credit from an acceptable bank. Loan requires the creation of at least one job, per $35,000 of County funds borrowed.

Grow America Fund Program: Long-term, fixed-rate loans for up to $1 Million dollars are available to eligible businesses that have been successfully operational for over 3 years. The funds may be used for property acquisition, construction, building renovations or leasehold improvements, debt refinancing, capital equipment and working capital. Repayment ability from cash flow of the business is a primary criteria in the loan evaluation, but good character, management capability, and collateral are also important considerations.

County Float Loan Program: Businesses and developers can apply for interim financing to be used for real estate acquisition, construction, machinery and equipment purchases, and working capital. This program will reduce the cost of interest during construction, reducing the risk during a lease-up period, providing a bridge loan for equity, or allowing a business to become established. Projects must lead to the creation of one new job per $35,000 of County loan funds over a 2.5-year period. In special situations, projects that eliminate "slums and blight" may not be required to meet the job creation requirement.

Borrower must obtain a Letter of Credit from a qualified financial institution in the full amount to be financed. The borrowing limit is $1 million to $5 million.

Agua Mansa Enterprise Zone: Businesses expanding or relocating in this Enterprise Zone are eligible for State tax credits and various local government incentives.

Shasta County
Economic Development Council of Shasta County
410 Hemsted Drive, #220
Redding, CA 96002
530-224-4920
800-207-4278
Fax: 530-224-4921
www.shastaedc.org/incentives.asp
Shasta Metro Enterprise Zone: Businesses that are located in the Metro Enterprise Zone in Shasta County can receive a hiring tax credit of $29,500 per qualified employee for a five-year period, tax credits for qualified machinery, qualified property may be expensed in one year, 100% of net operating losses and tax credits may be carried over, bid preference of 5%-9% on State of California contracts, and other incentives.

Targeted Employment Areas: Employees that work in an Enterprise Zone and live in Targeted Employment Area, can qualify their employers for substantial hiring credits.

Shasta Metro Recycling Market Development Zone: Companies considering locating or expanding in the RMDZ can take advantage of a number of incentive programs such as personal property tax rebates, job credits, fee deferrals, traffic impact fee waivers, revolving loan funds, electric incentive rates, industrial development bonds, and redevelopment and financing incentives. Eligible applicant may borrow 50% of project costs to $1,000,000 with low fixed rates.

Job Credits and Fee Deferrals: Each jurisdiction in Shasta County offers some type of "Job Credit" program that benefits new or outstanding manufacturers. Depending on the location these "Job Credits" could be used to lower development fees or offset other development costs.

Personal Property Tax Rate: Companies located in the County of Shasta may apply for a rebate of personal property taxes paid on qualified manufacturing process property. To be eligible, the business must create and maintain at least 10 new jobs paying $10.00 per hour or more for a period of 5 years.

Electric Rate Discount: Local municipal utilities offer their commercial/industrial customers discounted and negotiated rates.

Madera County
Madera County Economic Development Commission
2425 West Cleveland Avenue, Suite 101
Madera, CA 93637
800-357-5231
www.maderaindustry.org
The Commission provides a full range of financing and consulting services for businesses of all types and sizes.

EDC Small Business Loan Program: This loan program provides gap financing to new and existing businesses that will be creating new jobs and can obtain matching private capital. Interest rates are generally below market and the loan terms are set on a case-by-case basis, and generally match the asset being financed.

Valley Small Business Development Corporation
7035 North Fruit Avenue
Fresno, CA 93711
559-438-9680
Fax: 559-438-9690

1706 Chester Avenue, #200-27
Bakersfield, CA 93309
661-322-7889
Fax: 661-322-7892
www.vsbdc.com
Valley Small Business Development Corporation is a private, nonprofit corporation that administers a variety of small business financing programs, including various loan guaranty programs, and direct loan programs.

Capital E RLF: Participants of the Entrepreneurial Resource Center can apply to this program for a loan guarantee that can be used for equipment acquisition, plant improvements, inventory and permanent working capital. The maximum loan amount is $5,000 for a term of 5 years.

CEDLI Intermediary Relending Program: Small businesses that are unable to find conventional financing are eligible to apply for this market rate loan. The loan funds are to be used for equipment acquisition, plant improvements, inventory, permanent working capital or refinancing of debt. The maximum loan amount is $50,000 for a term of 7 years.

I-5 RLF Program: Business located in Kerman, Firebaugh, San Joaquin, Mendota, or Tranquility are eligible for loans to be used for equipment acquisition, plant improvements, inventory, permanent working capital or refinancing of debt when hire or retain employees in rural area. Loan amounts are for $20,000 per borrower for a term of five years with an interest rate at 1% below prime.

Orange Cove RLF Program: Business located in Orange Cove are eligible for loans to be used for equipment acquisition, plant improvements, inventory, permanent working capital or refinancing of debt when hire or retain employees in rural area. Loan amounts are for $95,000 per borrower for a term of five years with an interest rate at 1% below prime.

Alameda County

General Services Agency
Purchasing Department
1401 Lakeside Drive, Suite 907
Oakland, CA 94612
510-208-9600
www.co.alameda.ca.us/gsa/sleb/index.shtml
Small Local and Emerging Business Program: In its desire to promote growth for the County's small, local, and emerging businesses, they created this program. It has been designed to assure that all local businesses are given an opportunity to contract with the County and will promote the economic growth of the community.

Surety Bond and Insurance Procurement Program: To ensure that those businesses have the same opportunities as larger financially established businesses, they made the resources available to them to help in procuring surety bonds and insurance that meets the County standard requirements. Assistance is available for the small contractor that lacks the capital that is necessary to meet surety-underwriting requirements for bid, performance and miscellaneous bonds.

First Source Program: This is a pilot program that links those looking for employment with employers, through the County's relationship with businesses, including vendors. Vendors who are awarded contracts for goods and services for $100,000 and over are required to provide the County with 10 working days to refer potential employees to the vendor. Some of the incentives to the vendor to participate with this program include tax credits for the employees hired, Enterprise Zone credits/vouchers for businesses located in an eligible zone, Fidelity bond program, on-the-job training subsidy, reduction in recruitment and hiring costs, and more.

Alameda County Waste Management Authority

Alameda County Source Reduction and Recycling Board
777 Davis Street, Suite 100
San Leandro, CA 94577
510-614-1699
Fax: 510-614-1698
www.stopwaste.org
The Authority manages a long-range program for development of solid waste facilities and offers a wide variety of programs in the areas of waste reduction, market development, technical assistance and public education. With the Stop Wa$te program The Alameda County Waste Management Authority and the Alameda County Source Reduction & Recycling Board offer funding assistance private businesses, nonprofit organizations, and other qualified parties. Funding is generally available for innovative projects that promote source reduction, decrease the amount of waste disposed in Alameda County landfills, and encourages the development, marketing and use of recycled content products.

Mini-Grants: With this program, small amounts of money are available for a specific and limited purpose. The proposed project must be in the area of source reduction, reuse, recycling and market development. Funds may also be requested for educational programs that promote source reduction, reuse, recycling and buy recycled. The minimum grant amount is $1,000 and the maximum amount is $5,000.

Business Waste Prevention Fund: This program was designed for waste prevention projects, those that reduce, avoid, or eliminate waste before it is produced. Waste prevention projects might include redesigning a manufacturing process to reduce scrap waster, better estimating food supplied to avoid spoilage or redesigning to reduce shipping waste. Proposals may be made in the range of $10,000 to $100,000.

Market Development Assistance: The program supports and funds business expansion and attraction efforts aimed at establishing or expanding value-added processors or end-use manufacturing facilities in the County. Assistance to technically viable projects is in the form of siting assistance, feedstock sourcing, and market research.

Revolving Loan Fund: Low interest loans are available to encourage businesses to reduce the amount of waste going to Alameda County landfills. Funding is in the range of $10,000 to $200,000 and can be used for source reduction, recycling, composting, processing or recycled market development efforts.

Stop Wa$te Partnership Incentive: Businesses in Alameda County that have the potential to divert at least 50 tons of discards per year from the landfill are eligible to participate in this incentives pilot program. Up to $10,000 of incentive payments, based on tons diverted, are available per business and are distributed in increments.

City of Eureka

Eureka Redevelopment Agency
531 K Street
Eureka, CA 95501
707-441-4209
Fax: 707-441-4138
www.eurekaredevelopment.com/index.cfm
The agency receives primary funding from tax increment revenues as a result of the establishment of three redevelopment project areas. Their primary goal is to revitalize project areas and improve the economic base of the community by facilitating both redevelopment and economic development activities.

Owner Participation Agreement: Approved commercial or industrial/manufacturing projects can receive gap financing from the Eureka Redevelopment Agency. The structure must be a rehabilitation of an existing structure that is located within the Redevelopment Project Area. Projects eligible for consideration include rehabilitation of existing structures, capital equipment and off-site improvements (if the off-site improvements are to be owned by the City/Agency upon completion, such as public parking lots, sewer/water lines, street improvements, etc.). Approved projects will be reimbursed for project costs, from 10 to 20% of the increase in assessed value upon completion, in the form of a 15-year low interest loan at 3% per annum.

Revolving Business Loan Fund: Qualifying small businesses may apply for a secured loan from $5,000 up to $50,000 for inventory, equipment, property, or working capital. Preference is given to small businesses and projects that have the greatest potential for long-term job creation and retention, especially jobs created and retained for economically disadvantaged workers.

Façade Grants: This program helps commercial property owners and business tenants in targeted downtown areas to improve the exterior of their buildings. Eligible projects include Facade renovation; sign renovation, replacement and repainting; exterior wall repair and painting; window replacement or modification; door replacement; handicap accessibility modifications; planter box installation and permanent landscaping; decorative lighting; or other improvements that will increase the attractiveness of the building. Approved projects will receive 50% of costs with a maximum grant of $7,500. Buildings must have at least one wall facing the main street.

Seismic Upgrade Loan Program: This loan allows property owners to bring their unreinforced masonry buildings up to current safety standards. The owner must hold title to a City-designated "high hazard" structure within a targeted redevelopment area. Gap financing is provided to complete the retrofit project. Developers can be reimbursed for up to 50% of the cost of the project with a maximum grant amount of $100,000.

Eureka Enterprise Zone: Some of the incentives available for businesses in Enterprise Zones are a reduction in state income or franchise tax liability with the purchase of certain types of machinery or equipment for use at their location. The hiring of an employee from a designated economically disadvantaged group can bring a tax savings of more than $31,000 per each employee over a five year period. Also, lenders can deduct additional lending expenses when they lend to businesses in an Enterprise Zone, which may lead to additional savings for the business.

Eureka Foreign Trade Zone: Businesses located within a Foreign Trade Zone can avoid customs duties on qualifying imported materials. Benefits ranging from inverted tariffs for manufacturers and duty deferral for high volume importers are also available.

City of Sacramento

Economic Development Department
1030 15th Street, Second Floor
Sacramento, CA 95814-4009
916-808-7948
www.cityofsacramento.org/econdev/msc/incentive_programs.html
The priority of the Department is to market and facilitate private investment within the City in accordance with established economic development priorities.

Grow Sacramento Fund: With this program, small businesses located in the City can receive guaranteed loans. Lending is targeted both to businesses that are expanding and growing their employment base, and to energy related ventures. Loans range in size from $25,000 to $1,000,000 with a maximum term of 25 years with competitive rates. Grow Sacramento Fund loans may be used for a wide range of business purposes, including real estate acquisition, leasehold improvements, machinery and equipment purchases, and permanent working capital. Presently, Grow Sacramento is unable to finance start-up companies or provide venture capital, fund research and development, or satisfy equity needs.

Commercial Revitalization Program: Financial assistance is provided for physical improvements to commercial properties located in designated areas. Eligible uses of funds include improvements to exterior building facades including storefronts, awnings, lighting, decorative trim and security items; and renovations to correct code violations and handicapped accessibility. Tenants or property owners can receive up to $50,000 in rebates for eligible physical improvements to the exterior of their buildings. Loans of up to $500,000 are available at below-market rates to help with physical and structural improvements to commercial

properties can also be used for building expansions up to 20%.

EnterFund Micro Loan Program: Direct loans are available to small businesses that are unable to get financing through conventional lenders. The business may be a start-up, newly established or growing. This program also provides business training, consultation, and skill development. Clients are also encouraged to build assets through an Individual Development Account (IDA), with matching contributions from *EnterFund*, as a means to achieve economic independence.

California Capital Loan Guarantee: California Capital provides loan guarantees on loans to those businesses that cannot find conventional financing. The maximum guarantee is for 85% of a loan or $350,000 whichever is less. The loan funds may be used may be used for equipment purchases, inventory, working capital, business purchases, lines of credit, contract financing, and to refinance existing debt. Additional services provided by California Capital include business plan analysis, entrepreneurial and small business education services, and referrals to lenders.

Sacramento Brownsfield Loan Program: Through a partnership, the city is providing loans to property owners or developers for the cleanup and removal of hazardous materials (with the exception of petroleum) from Brownsfield sites prior to development. Any owner or developer of a site in the City of Sacramento is eligible to apply. Applicant should have strong financial capacity and a credible re-use plan.

Enterprise Zones/LAMBRA: State tax credits, deductions and employment incentives are available for businesses located within any of Sacramento's state-designated Enterprise Zones or LAMBRA areas. Some of the incentives are sales tax credits on qualified property, hiring wage tax credits for a period of five years, 100% Net Operating Loss Carryovers that are available for 15 years, financing assistance, and much more.

Redevelopment Funds: The Economic Development Department, in partnership with other local agencies, has funds available to offer financial assistance for development projects that meet the revitalization goals and criteria within any of the eleven redevelopment project areas in Sacramento.

Recycling Market Development Zone Program: Businesses located in one of Sacramento's Recycling Market Development Zones can receive financial, technical, and marketing incentives. Eligible projects must result in diversion of solid waste from a landfill. Recycling-based manufacturers in the SRRMDZ are eligible to apply for low-interest loans of up to $1,000,000 per applicant.

Economic Development Treatment Capacity Bank: The City of Sacramento's Economic Development Treatment Capacity Bank program can assist commercial and industrial users in reducing their sewer connection fees. This program is available to those users who meet the City's guidelines and criteria for receiving credits through the Economic Development Treatment Capacity Bank. Depending upon the area in which a project is located, commercial and industrial users who qualify for the program will save between 59% and 79% on their sewer connection fees.

City of San Jose

Office of Economic Development
60 South Market Street, Suite 470

San Jose, CA 95113
408-277-5880
Fax: 408-277-3615
www.sjeconomy.com
The Office is committed to a vital, competitive San Jose economy that increases prosperity for people and companies and enhances City revenues. Their three core services are Economic Strategy and Information, Assistance for Business, and Workforce Development.

Development Enhancement Special Fund (DESF): Businesses in San Jose that would not otherwise qualify for commercial credit, can assistance through this loan guarantee program. DESF will also supplement bank loans through gap financing on a case-by-case basis. The loans range from $50,000 to $350,000 and can be used for expansion, inventory, working capital, and other reasonable expenses.

Lenders for Community Development: This program offers small businesses loans up to $50,000 and lines of credit up to $15,000. Technical assistance is also available at no cost.

Revolving Loan Fund: Small businesses can apply for loans in the range of $5,000 to $40,000 from this fund. It can be used for working capital, tenant improvements, equipment and other business expenses.

Recycling Market Development Zone: Manufacturers in San Jose that use recycled feedstock (glass, paper, plastic, used tires, etc.) may be eligible for low-interest loans up to $2 million and technical, marketing and location assistance.

Special Incentive Program: This program provides incentives to developers to further tenant improvement projects in vacant buildings. Incentives include construction tax suspension, plan check fee deferrals, phased project building permit fee payment plans, one stop permit process, expedited plan check, and enhanced inspection services.

Historic Landmark Tax Deduction: The City is allowed to enter into a Historic Property Contract with the owner of a City Landmark. That allows the owner to obtain property tax reductions for agreeing to maintain the City Landmark.

San Jose Enterprise Zone: State tax credits, deductions and employment incentives are available for businesses located in the San Jose Enterprise Zone.

City of Escondido
Economic Development Department
City Hall, Second Floor
201 North Broadway
Escondido, CA 92025
760-839-4563
Fax: 760-739-7004
http://www.ci.escondido.ca.us/econdev/index.html
Besides the many business incentives available through the City, there are numerous business services to benefit a business. The Business Retention and Expansion Program offers a variety of technical assistance, location assistance, help in finding funding, and much more. The Department also publishes a monthly newsletter and a Business Resource Guide filled with important information.

Façade Property Improvement Program (FPIP): All commercially or industrial zoned properties within the City that are permitted uses, may be eligible to participate with this grant program. Eligible improvements include structural façade improvements, paint, awnings, signs, addition of architectural detail to façade, façade tile or stone accents, decorative entry walkway area, outside dining with decorative fencing, irrigated landscape/flower planters or pots, outside decorative lighting, and new windows. Grant amounts range from $5,000 to $10,000. Funding is dependent on the type of improvements to be made.

City of Escondido Fee Deferrals: The purpose of the City's fee deferral policy is to provide an incentive, on a case-by-case basis, to reduce the up-front cost of development for businesses that encourage beneficial economic development in Escondido. To be eligible, the business must be expanding it's floor area or constructing a new building within the City. Connection and development fees of $50,000 or more will be considered for deferral. Businesses locating in targeted areas or those businesses providing a significant community benefit other than jobs or revenue may also be a candidate for a fee deferral.

Business Enhancement Zone (BEZ): This Zone was created to encourage private investment and positive quality development/redevelopment in older commercial areas of the City. Incentives are made on a case-by-case basis and include fee reductions or waivers, creative use of public improvement projects, minor adjustments in certain codes, and expedited plan and permit processing.

Restaurant Incentives: Restaurants that are located in the downtown central core can receive 100% fee reductions for sewer, water and traffic. Major quality restaurants/dinner houses citywide may be eligible for incentives determined on a case-by-case basis.

Waiver of Impact Fees for the First 25% of Non-Residential Building Expansion: All existing non-residential buildings may expand up to 25% of their building floor area without being charged fees for water, sewer, traffic, public facilities, public art and drainage facilities.

Changes in Use for Existing Buildings: This program was developed to encourage revitalization of existing building stock. Tenant improvement permits will not be charged for water, sewer or traffic fees unless the project requires a larger water meter, a larger sewer line or significant additional parking.

Building Demolition Fee Credit: A business may receive a fee credit for connection and development fees for demolished buildings if they are used on the same property.

Fee Waivers for Targeted Commercial Areas: Certain processing and permit fees will be waived, up to $500, to encourage the improvement of existing and expanding businesses in the South Escondido Boulevard and East Valley Parkway Commercial Corridors and the Downtown Revitalization Area. Eligible improvements are for the exterior of the building only. Waivers for new construction are limited to additions and expansions to existing businesses.

Downtown Special Plan Incentive: Properties in the Specific Plan Area are eligible to receive development incentive bonuses when they provide pedestrian amenities, lot consolidation and/or mixed uses.

1% Sales Tax Credit of Local Vendors: The City has a purchasing practice that authorizes a 1% sales tax credit on the amount of a local bid when determining who is the lowest bidder. Your business may be eligible to become a City vendor.

Colorado

Colorado Cities

Mayor's Office of Economic Development and International
 Trade
201 W. Colfax, 10th Floor
Denver, CO 80202
720-913-1640
Fax: 720-913-1802
http://www.denvergov.org/moedit/default.asp
Mayor's Office of Economic Development and International
Trade can provide information on a variety of business
development services such as demographic data, financial
assistance, real estate searches, tax credit information,
marketing research, and more. They offer:

- Enterprise Zone: tax credits for creating jobs, providing
  employee health insurance, investing in equipment and
  research and development, providing training programs,
  and for rehabilitating older vacant building.
- Site Job Training and Recruitment Programs: link
  companies needing to recruit or train employees to
  public and private organization. There are also grant
  and reimbursement options through the Colorado First
  program and the Mayor's Office of Workforce
  Development.
- Private Activity Bonds: tax exempt bonds, up to
  $10,000,000 are available to construct and expand
  manufacturing facilities and to purchase equipment.
- Small Business/Financing and Start-Up Assistance:
  offers gap financing through Revolving Loan Fund and
  neighborhood Business Revitalization programs, and
  provides links to other sources of capital.
- Brownfields: The EPA has funding available for site
  assessment and clean-up activities on Brownfield sites.
- Foreign Trade Zone: allows manufacturers using
  imported parts and materials in their products to
  expedite customs and reduce or eliminate some fees and
  tariffs.

Lafayette-Louisville Downtown Revitalization (LLDR)
901 Main Street
Louisville, CO 80027
303-666-1895
Loans to businesses in downtown Lafayette. Highest priority
is given to exterior renovation. Loans are not for capital or
inventory purposes.

City of Thornton
Business Development Division
9351 Grant St., Suite 200
Thornton, CO 80229-4358
303.538.7605
Fax: 303.538.7244
www.cityofthornton.net
Economic Development Incentive Program is a grant funded
by the city of Thornton to encourage small business owners
to upgrade their buildings and sites. Funds can be used to
reduce the costs of improvements to their buildings by
providing matching grants. Businesses can upgrade doors and
windows, roofing, landscaping, parking lots, and more. The
Promotion Grant Program provides funds to small businesses
to allow them to conduct promotion programs such as grand
openings, special events, sports promotions, and musical
programs.

Englewood Small Business Development Corporation
3400 So. Elati St.
Englewood, CO 80110
Darren Hollingsworth

303-762-2300
Makes loans to small businesses in the Englewood area
which have been turned down for conventional financing.
Administers a revolving loan fund, providing business
financing and gap financing. Loans are made to businesses
which offer good potential and benefit the community.

Colorado Counties

Colorado Capital Initiatives
Richard Davidson
San Luis Valley Development Resources Group
P.O. Box 300
626 Fourth St.
Alamosa, CO 81101
719-589-6099
Fax: 719-589-6299
www.slvdrg.org
This loan program is only available in Conejos County. Low
income persons can borrow money to help with business start
up or expansion expenses. Loans are from $500 $19,000.
Loans are made through the First Western Bank in La Jara or
through the Christian Community Services in Alamosa.

The Prairie Development Corporation
128 Colorado Ave., Box 202
Stratton, CO 80836
719-348-5562
800-825-0208
Fax: 719-348-5887
www.prairiedevelopment.com
Loan programs available to businesses in the following
counties: Cheyenne, Elbert, Kit Carson and Lincoln
Counties. Loan programs include;

- Direct Loan: up to $150,000 to purchase real estate,
  equipment, inventory, furniture and fixtures, and
  working capital.
- Micro-Enterprise Loan: for businesses with five or
  fewer employees. Businesses can borrow up to $25,000.
- Guaranteed Loan; guarantees loans made by banks to
  businesses.
- Disaster Loan: Assists businesses affected by man-
  made or natural disaster. Help available in 48 hours.
- PDC Revolved Loan: similar to PDC Direct Loan but
  can only be used of Direct Loan funds are unavailable
  or business is ineligible.
- PDC Mini-Loan: similar to Micro Enterprise Loan, but
  can only be used if Micro Enterprise Loan funds are
  unavailable or business is ineligible.

Adams County Economic Development, Inc.
12050 Pecos Avenue, Suite 200
Westminster, CO 80234
303-450-5106
Fax: 303-252-8230
E-Mail: info@adamscountyed.com
www.adamscountyed.com
Property Tax Rebates; can negotiate up to 50% rebate of
corporate property taxes over four years.

- Adams County Community Development Block
  Grants: can be used for business finance projects,
  including loans, loan guarantees, equity investments or
  infrastructure grants. For more information contact
  Adams County's Community Development Department
  at (303) 286-4160.
- Adams County Enterprise Zone Program: businesses
  located in the Enterprise zone can qualify for state
  income tax credits. Investment tax credit of 3% of
  qualified equipment purchases. Job training credit of
  10% of qualified cost. New Jobs Credit of $500 for

each new job. Health Insurance Credit of $200 per new job. New Jobs Agricultural Processing Credit of $500 per new job. Research and Development Credit of 3% or qualified expenses, and Vacant Building Rehabilitation Credit of 15% of qualified expenses.

Upper Arkansas Area Development Corporation
P.O. Box 1212
Buena Vista, CO 81211
719-395-2602
http://www.uaacog.com/uaadevelop.htm
Offers assistance to businesses in Chaffee, Custer, Fremont, Lake, Park, and Tellar counties. The Gap Financing program provides 1/3 to 1/2 of the financing needed for a business. Loans range from $5,000 to $125,000 with the creation of a new job being required for every $20,000 loaned. A Direct Loan is from $5,000 to $30,000.

Connecticut

MetroHartford Alliance
31 Pratt St.
Hartford, CT 06103
860-525-4451
Fax: 860-493-7499
www.metrohartford.com
The MetroHartford Alliance provides a wealth of programs and services to businesses located in or thinking of locating in the greater Hartford area. Businesses can receive assistance with site search, professional services, international affairs, incentive opportunities and more. They also offer the MetroHartford Growth Fund, which is revolving loan program providing below-market rate financing for companies who are adding employees to help their businesses grow. Businesses in the greater Hartford area who are planning to create new jobs within the next three years and are in the business of manufacturing, financial services, health care, information technology, distribution, tourism/entertainment, and environmental technologies/recycling/pollution prevention are eligible. Money can be used for building rehabilitation and construction, utility upgrades, land acquisition, machinery and equipment purchase, site remediation and preparation, workforce training, and more. Loans up to $350,000 per project are available, with the creation of one new job for every $20,000 loaned.

Northeast Alliance
83 Windham Street
ECSU / Beckert Hall
Willimantic, CT 06226
860 465-5141
Fax: (860) 465-5143
http://www.nealliance.com/
The Alliance offers loans to business who have been denied funding from banks. These businesses must have 50 or fewer employees, and loans range from $5,000 to $50,000. The Revolving Loan fund covers 21 towns in the Northeast Alliance service region. The Small cities Loan Fund may be used with the ten towns of Ashford, Chaplin, Columbia, Coventry, Hampton, Killingly, Mansfield, Putnam, Thompson, and Windham. The Alliance also offers th northeast Technology Enterprise Fund for new businesses located in the Windham Mills Technology Center.

SouthEastern Connecticut Enterprise Region
190 Governor Winthrop Blvd., Suite 300
New London, CT 06320

860-437-4659
888-6-SECTER
Fax: 860-437-4662
www.secter.org
The SouthEastern Connecticut Enterprise Region offers a regional revolving loan fund to support manufacturing and processing businesses in the area. Loans are available from $25,000 to $300,000. Special consideration is given to defense diversification projects, dislocated works, and women and minority owned businesses. The Fisherman's Loan Fund lends up to $10,000 for every job created. Businesses can be in aquaculture, marine resource redevelopment, vessel or equipment conversion, and more. A non-fishing related business may qualify if it is from a dislocated commercial fishermen.

Connecticut Community Investment Corporation
100 Crown Street
New Haven, CT 06510
866-776-6172
Fax: 302-776-6837
http://www.ctcic.org/About_us.htm
The Child Care Facilities MicroLoan Fund can offer up to $25,000 fixed rate loan to help with the availability of child care in the region. Funds can be used for furniture, permits, licensing, zoning, professional fees, marketing and lease and/or improvements in the facility. In addition, the CCIC offers a Direct Loan Fund to help with the creation, expansion and modernization of businesses. Businesses must be located in: Bethany, Branford, East Haven, Guilford, Hamden, Madison, Meriden, Milford, New Haven, North Branford, North Haven, Orange, Wallingford, West Haven, and Woodbridge. The TIF Near Equity Financing is a program offer to technology based businesses as well as manufacturers. This if for companies with growth potential and who have innovative products or processes. This program is like a venture capital fund, where there is an expected return on the investment.

Empower Newhaven
59 Elm St.
New Haven, CT 06510
203-776-2777
www.empowernewhaven.org
The Enterprise Community Revolving Loan Fund provides micro-loans up to $10,000 to residents who live or own businesses in any of the Empowerment Zone neighborhoods. The money can be used to help with start-up or expansions of businesses.

Small Business Initiative
City of New Haven
165 Church St., 6th Floor
New Haven, CT 06510
203-946-7093
Fax: 203-946-7687
www.cityofnewhaven.com/govt/citydepartments
The city of New Haven offers several different loan programs. The Small Business Revolving Loan Program makes funds up to $40,000 available for start-up or existing businesses located within the City of New Haven. Loan funds must be used for economic development activities which result in job creation or retention, including acquisition of real estate renovations or repairs, purchase of inventory, equipment or other goods, working capital, or purchase of existing business. The Small Business Initiative Loan Program offers from $10,000 to $250,000 to businesses not located in the Enterprise Community/Enterprise Zone. The HUD 108 Loan Program offers up to $250,000, but requires a one-for-one match with private financing. Businesses must

be existing businesses located within, or willing to relocate into the City of New Haven.

Hartford Economic Development Corporation
15 Lewis St. Suite 204
Hartford, CT 06103
860-527-1301
Fax: 860-727-9224
http://www.hedco-ghbdc.com/who.htm

Greater Hartford Business Development Center Inc.
15 Lewis Street, Suite 204
Hartford, CT 06103

Hartford Economic Development Corporation (HEDCo) and The Greater Hartford Business Development Center (GHBDC) have joined together to help businesses start and expand in the Hartford metropolitan area. HEDCo provides support for businesses, such as technical assistance, loan packaging, problem solving, location assistance and regulatory assistance. GHBDC is the alternative lender of choice and seeks out under-served and diverse customer base.

Loans From Greater Hartford Business Development Center
- Metro-Hartford Revolving Loan Fund: Loan may be used for purchase or renovation of commercial or industrial real estate, purchase of machinery and equipment, acquisition of inventory, and more. The goal is to stimulate growth and retain and create jobs. Loans may be up to $100,000. Businesses in 29 Capital Region Towns, Middlesex county and Central Connecticut Regional Planning Area are eligible.
- Non-Profit Revolving Loan Fund: Available to nonprofits to help manage cash flow, and to assist in site improvement and purchase of equipment. Loans up to $75,000 are available to those in 40 Town Area, Capital Region and Tolland County.
- Middlesex County Revitalization Commission Revolving Loan Fund: Loan may used for purchase and renovation of commercial or industrial real estate, purchase of machinery and equipment, acquisition of inventory, and more. The goal is to stimulate growth and retain and create jobs. Loans are for up to $50,000 and available to those in Cromwell, Portland, East Hampton, Middletwon, Middlefield, Durham, Higganum, Haddam, Killingworth, Chester, Deep River, Centerbury, Clinton, East Haddam, Westbrook, Essex, and Old Saybrook.
- Central Connecticut Revolving Loan Fund: Loan may used for purchase and renovation of commercial or industrial real estate, purchase of machinery and equipment, acquisition of inventory, and more. The goal is to stimulate growth and retain and create jobs. Loans are for up to $100,000 and are available to those in Berlin, Bristol, Burlington, New Britain, Plainville, Plymouth, and Southington.

Loans from Hartford Economic Development Corporation
- *Merchants Revolving Loan Fund: Loan may used for purchase and renovation of commercial or industrial real estate, purchase of machinery and equipment, acquisition of inventory, and more. The goal is to stimulate growth and retain and create jobs. Loans can be for up to $30,000. Eligible applicants must be in the following areas: Upper-Albany Merchants Association Loan Pool, Hartford Enterprise Zone Business Association Loan Pool, Franklin Avenue Merchants Association Loan Pool, and Spanish-American Merchants Associates Loan Pool.

- Neighborhood Economic Development Revolving Loan Fund: Loan may used for purchase and renovation of commercial or industrial real estate, purchase of machinery and equipment, acquisition of inventory, and more. The goal is to stimulate growth and retain and create jobs. Loans may be for up to $250,000. Eligible applicants must be located in the following areas: Urban League Pool, Asylum Hill/West End Pool, or Park Street/SAMA.
- Umbrella Revolving Loan Fund: Loan may used for purchase and renovation of commercial or industrial real estate, purchase of machinery and equipment, acquisition of inventory, and more. The goal is to stimulate growth and retain and create jobs. Loans may be up to $150,000 and are for businesses located in Hartford.
- Fleet CDC/SAMA Revolving Loan Fund: Loan may used for purchase and renovation of commercial or industrial real estate, purchase of machinery and equipment, acquisition of inventory, and more. The goal is to stimulate growth and retain and create jobs. Loans may be up to $72,500 and are for business in Hartford in the Frog Hollow and Parkville Neighborhood, new Britain, and Meriden.
- Nuisance Abatement Loan Fund: Loan may used for purchase and renovation of commercial or industrial real estate, purchase of machinery and equipment, acquisition of inventory, and more. Loans can be for up to $100,000 for businesses in Hartford with a emphasis on encouraging socially acceptable business practices.

City of Middletown
Department of Planning, Conservation and Development
245 deKoven Dr.
Middletown, CT 06457
860-344-3425
Fax; 860-344-3593
www.cityofmiddletown.com
The city of Middletown offers two loan programs. REINVEST Loan Program are low-interest loans up to $25,000 that can be used for improvements to buildings. Businesses must be in the city of Middletown. JOBS Loan Program provides loans of up to $50,000 for new or expanding firms in the fields of manufacturing, high technologies, and research and development. A new job must be created for every $10,000 loaned.

Naugatuck Valley Development Corporation (NVDC)
156 West Main St., 2nd Floor
Mattatuck Museum
Waterbury, CT 06702
203-756-2719
Fax: 203-756-9077
http://www.nvdc.org/
Naugatuck Valley Development Corporation was created to help businesses start and grow and to help with the economic development in the city of Waterbury and the Naugatuck Valley Region. NVDC has several different loan funds:
- Regional Business Investment Fund: Businesses must be located in Beacon Falls, Bethlehem, Cheshire, Middlebury, Naugatuck, Oxford, Prospect,Southbury, Thamston, Waterbury, Woodbury, Wolcott, Watertown, or Oakville. Loans are available for up to $350,000, and are designed to help create and retain jobs.
- Waterbury Non-Profit Revolving Loan Fund: This fund is available to businesses in the city of Waterbury and can be used to improve buildings and construction, for the purchase of machinery and equipment and for capital.

- Downtown Development Incentive Fund: This is for businesses located in downtown Waterbury. The loan may be used to purchase property and equipment, working capital, job training, property improvements, and more. Loans area available up to $250,000.
- Information Technology Zone Incentive Fund: Applicants must be in downtown Waterbury, and must be an information technology business.

Delaware

Wilmington Economic Development Corporation
100 W. 10th St., Suite 706
Wilmington, DE 19801
302-571-9088
www.wedco.org
The Wilmington Economic Development Corp. helps business in the city of Wilmington by providing financing when businesses are denied help elsewhere. Priority is given to businesses who will create or retain jobs. Programs include:

- Gap Financing; Loans range from $2,500 to $100,000 to be used for machinery, equipment, improvements, inventory, or working capital.
- SBA 504 Program: Provides financing for up to 40% of the project's cost. Loans from $50,000 to $1,000,000.
- Microloans and Short-term contract Financing: Loans for up to $25,000 and short-term contract financing for up to 50% of the contract amount.
- SBA Women, Minorities and Veterans Loan Guarantee Pre Qualification: Business can receive pre-qualification for a loan guarantee of up to 80%. Staff works with individuals to prepare a business plan and to streamline the application process for amounts up to $250,000.

City of Wilmington
Office of Economic Development
800 French St., Third Floor
Wilmington, DE 19801
302-576-2120
www.ci.wilmington.de.us
The city of Wilmington offers several different programs to help businesses in the area. The Micro Loan Training Program is a business training program for persons interested in developing small businesses. It provides core instruction to the elements needed to produce a business plan and also covers finances, advertising, market research, cash flow projections and business management. They offer a Micro Loan Lending with loans ranging from $500-$5,000. The City's Retail Incubator Program offers low cost rent and a wide-range of development services. The Minority Business Enterprise Office provides assistance to disadvantage businesses and offers a Disadvantage Business Enterprise Program which offers certification for procurement opportunities. City Tax Incentives include: Christiana Gateway Tax Incentive Program, Real Property Tax Exemption, Head Tax, Enterprise Zone, Blue Collar Tax Program, and Brownfields. They also offer a Micro Biz Business Development competition for New Businesses (under 2 years), Emerging Businesses (2-5 years), and Existing businesses (over 6 years). Winners receive matching grants between $500-$2,500.

Sussex County Office of Economic Development
P.O. Box 589
9 S. Dupont Hwy.
Georgetown, DE 19947

302-855-7770
www.sussexcounty.net/depts/econdev/index.html
Operates an Industrial Revenue Bond program with a cap of $15 million each year for industrial projects in the county. Project review requires a letter of commitment for placement of the bond before a project recommendation is made by the Industrial Revenue Bond Review Committee.

New Castle County
C/o Ronald A. Morris, Chief Financial Officer
87 Reads Way
Finance Division
New Castle, DE 19720
302-395-8383
Manufacturing projects located in New Castle County may qualify for financing at tax-exempt rates through the county's Economic Development Revenue Bond Program administered by New Castle County. The purchasers of the bonds provide the funds for the revenue bond financing. The County's annual volume limit is $39.4 million.

District of Columbia

Latino Economic Development Corporation
2316 18th Street, NW
Washington, D.C. 20009
202-588-5102
Fax: 202-588-5204
www.ledcdc.org
The Latino Economic Development Corporation (LEDC), originally established to help the Latino community of DC's Mount Pleasant neighborhood, delivers an array of programs, services and funding opportunities to low- and moderate-income individuals of all cultures and ethnicities who looking to start or expand their small businesses. LEDC touts 22 different business technical assistance services available to DC entrepreneurs, aimed at assisting with start-up practicalities, the development of business plans, basic accounting practices, marketing and strategic planning, tax and legal responsibilities, and management skills. Through the LEDC's MicroLoan Fund Program, new and existing entrepreneurs in the District of Columbia can take out loans ranging from $2,000 to $25,000; benefits of the program include individualized attention, financial planning assistance, and flexible repayment schedules. A Peer Lending Program, featuring a free 12-week business training program followed by small loans of up to $6,000, is administered in collaboration with the Foundation for International Community Assistance (see Regional Listings for more about FINCA). Those hoping to start a business in the near future can count on LEDC as well: the organization offers Individual Development Accounts, where each dollar deposited into an account whose funds are to be used for a commercial enterprise is matched by LEDC and deposited into the person's account. Finally, the LEDC runs a small business incubator which provides its clients with commercial space to develop a business, as well as hands-on technical assistance and training.

Marshall Heights Community Development Organization
3939 Benning Road, NE
Washington, DC 20019
202-396-1200
Fax: 202-396-4106
www.mhcdo.org
Prospective business owners looking to set up shop in Washington DC's Ward 7/Marshall Heights area have strong support from the Marshall Heights Community Development

Organization (MHCDO). As part of its effort to foster the economic prosperity of the community, the MHCDO provides, often at no cost, entrepreneurial and business training, one-on-one small business counseling in its Business Information Resource Center, technical assistance with loans, legal, accounting and other business-related areas, and special loan packaging. The First Step Program supplies entrepreneurs unable to secure funding for their small businesses with loans ranging from $10,000 to $25,000. The group will also perform market research and assist with the development of print advertisements and other materials to promote the entrepreneur's business. A listing in the MHCDO's Ward 7 Directory is free.

Florida

Gainesville Department of Economic Development
200 E. University Ave., Suite 402
P.O. Box 490, Station 6
Gainesville, FL 32602
352-334-5012
www.cityofgainesvile.org
This Department is a central resource for business issues in the city of Gainesville. It administers the city's Enterprise Zone Program. Tax savings are offered to businesses located in the Enterprise zone. Companies can receive credits on state sales tax, corporate income tax, and property tax. There is also a discount on building permits, development fees, and occupational licenses. The Local Minority Business Enterprise (LMBE) and Local Small Business Enterprise (LSBE) Procurement Program helps minority and small businesses in Gainesville. Free workshops are available and assistance in city procurement contracts can be obtained. Businesses can also be certified a Minority Business Enterprise to help with state contracts. City's Procurement Coordinator can be reached at 352-334-5027.

Pasco County Economic Development Council
4111 Land O' Lakes Blvd., Suite 305
Land O'Lakes, FL 34639
888-607-2726
813-996-4075
www.pascocdc.com
Pasco County Economic Development Incentive is a reimbursement of all or part of the impact fees for transportation and or water/sewer in unincorporated areas of Pasco County. This can be used for businesses either relocating or expanding into the county or for businesses already located in the county but wants to expand. There are size and employment requirements that need to be met. Industrial Development Bonds are issued by the county for the purchase of land and or buildings, construction of buildings and equipment for use by private industry.

Mom and Pop Small Business Grant
Commissioners
Miami-Dade County
111 NW 1st St., Suite 2910
Miami, FL 33128
305-375-5071
www.miamidade.gov/commiss
The Mom and Pop Small Business Grant Program is operated by each of the County's 13 Commissioners. Applicants must contact their commissioner directly to learn how to apply. Grants can be for up to $10,000 to be used to help start or expand a new small business.

Miami-Dade Empowerment Trust
3050 Biscayne Blvd., Suite 300
Miami, FL 33137
305-372-7620
Fax: 305-372-7629
www.ezonetrust.org
The Community Development Revolving Loan Fund helps businesses in need of funds for start-up or expansion. The loans can be up to $250,000. The goal of the fund is to help reduce unemployment, raise income levels and help improve distressed areas of the city. Micro Loan Program offers loans up to $5,000 and are available to businesses located in Enterprise Zones. Loan funds can be used for working capital, inventory or fixed asset acquisition. Bond Financing is available to Enterprise Zone businesses. The borrower must borrow at least $1,000,000. Funds can be used for new construction, purchase of existing property, or substantial renovation of existing property.

Black Business Investment Fund
315 E. Robinson St., Suite 222
Orlando, FL 32801
www.bbif.com
The Black Business Investment Fund provides financial assistance to African American Businesses in the Central Florida area. Programs include Loan Guarantee Programs, allowing funds to be used for equipment, assets, or working capital. Contract Financing Program helping business in the area of construction contracting. Direct Loan Program is for businesses borrowing $25,000 or less. International Business Development Program helping those businesses interested in international development. Management and Technical Assistance is available to businesses. The Black Business Investment Fund also operates the SBA Women and Minority Pre-Qualification loan program.

Ybor City Development Corporation
2105 N. Nebraska Ave.
Tampa, FL 33602
813-274-7936
Fax: 813-274-7935
www.tampagov.net/dept_YCDC/
Ybor City is part of the Tampa Enterprise Community District and the State Enterprise Zone. These designations allow businesses to take advantage of a variety of incentives, such as jobs tax credits, property tax credits, sales tax refund, and more. There is also an Historic Preservation Incentive, offering a 10 year ad valorem tax exemption and federal preservation tax credit assistance to certain properties in the Ybor City Historic District.

Economic Development
City of Cape Coral
P.O. Box 150027
Cape Coral, FL 33915
239-574-0445
Fax: 239-574-0452
www.capecoral.net
The city offer the Cape Coral Revolving Loan Program designed to provide "gap" financing between the needs of a business and bank financing. Funds can be used for land, building, or new construction. Minimum loan about in $10,000 and maximum cannot exceed 25% of entire project cost.

Lee County
Economic Development Office
2180 W. First St., Suite 306
Fort Myers, FL 33901
800-330-3161

239-338-3161
Fax: 239-338-3227
www.LeeCountyBusiness.com
Lee County offers Industrial Development Revenue Bonds that provide a source of long-term financing of capital requirements for new and expanding manufacturing facilities. Bond size can range from $3 million to $10 million. Proceeds from the bonds may be used to finance fixed assets and qualified costs associated with the project. The Economic Development Office can also help with permitting, licenses, employee training, state and local incentives, referrals for financial assistance, and more. Women and minority owned businesses can be certified to assist in business contracting with state and county governments. This is done through the Lee County Office of Equal Employment at 239-335-2267.

Clearwater Neighborhood Housing Services
608 N. Garden Ave.
Clearwater, FL 33755
727-442-4155
The Clearwater Neighborhood Housing Services operates a Micro Enterprise Loan Program offering loans from $2,500-$35,000. They provide business training and technical assistance to low-income persons who are interested in starting a business.

Pinellas County Community Development
14 South Fort Harrison Ave., Suite 3050
Clearwater, FL 34616
717-464-8210
www.pced.org
Pinellas County Community Development operates a commercial building façade improvement program. You may receive a grant of up to 50% of the cost of the building improvement with a maximum of $2,000. You may also receive a non-matching grant of up to $1,000 for exterior work needed for compliance with ADA requirements. Pinellas County also offers Industrial Revenue Bonds to finance land, building, and equipment. Project size can vary from $1 million to $10 million.

Targeted Business Pilot Program
Tallahssee Economic Development Council
100 N. Duval St.
P.O. Box 1639
Tallahassee, FL 32302
850-224-8116
www.taledc.com
The Targeted Business Pilot Program provides incentives to new and existing business that create new jobs in the city and Leon County. Businesses may be reimbursed up to 100% of the cost of development fees and a portion of the capital investment of business project based on ad valorem taxes paid. This is a means to reimburse a part of the capital investment cost required to relocate or expand a business.

Georgia

Georgia City Economic Development Councils

City of Atlanta Economic Development
55 Trinity Avenue
Atlanta, GA 30303
404-330-6000
Fax: 404-658-7673
www.ci.atlanta.ga.us/EconomicDevelopment
The Economic Development Office provides information for doing business with the City of Atlanta and information for Minoritics/Womcn in business. This office also is involved in the Atlanta Development Authority which focuses on community development programs.

- *Tax-exempt Bonds*: below market interest rate mortgage loans to developers for rental units for low and moderate income renters.
- *Business Improvement Loan Fund*: The Business Improvement provides direct loans for eligible projects in targeted Business Improvement Districts. The maximum loan amount is $50,000.
- *The Phoenix Fund*: this Fund assists small and medium-sized businesses with affordable loans. It provides assistance for the construction or renovation of privately-owned commercial buildings; equipment purchases need to operate a business and sometimes working capital. Loan amounts range from $10,000 to $100,000 at a rate below prime.
- *Industrial Revenue Bonds*: The Atlanta Development Authority issues taxable and tax-exempt industrial revenue bonds in the City of Atlanta.

City of Alpharetta Economic Development
Two South Main Street
Alpharetta, GA 30004
678-297-6075
http://alpharetta.ga.us
Low interest loans are available for building improvement in the historic downtown district. The Department also offers a brochure *How To Start a Business in Alpharetta* which provides information to small businesses.

The City of Savannah Economic Development Department
2 E. Bay Street
Savannah, GA 31401
912-651-3653
Fax: 912-651-7616
www.ci.savannah.ga.us

- *Martin Luther King Jr. Revolving Loan Fund (MLK/RLF)*: Loans are available for land & building acquisition, construction, equipment/inventory and working capital. Loans range in amounts from $10,000 to $150,000.
- *Micro-Loan Funds*: Loans are available for working capital, equipment/inventory, supplies and fixed assets. Loan amounts range from $500 to $25,000.
- *Individual Development Account*: Through this program you can start your own business by establishing a savings account. For every dollar you contribute towards the program, $4 will be added to the account for you up to $50 per month. If two people in the household both apply and are accepted into the program, the program will contribute $8 for every $2 invested by your family.
- *Savannah Entrepreneurial Center*: This center provides technical assistance, training and access to loans for small business development. They offer classes related to business start-up and expansion.
- *Minority/Women Business Enterprise*: This program offers a variety of workshops and services for Minority/Women Business Owners including the City of Savannah's procurement process.

Georgia Counties Economic Councils

Albany/Dougherty Economic Development Commission
225 West Broad Street
Albany, GA 31701
229-434-0044
800-475-8700
Fax: 229-434-8716

www.albanyga.com
The Albany/Dougherty Economic Development offers economic information for businesses in the area. The Albany area is designated a Enterprise Zone and businesses in the community are eligible for incentives which include:
- *Facility Bonds*: up to $3 million in tax free bonds
- *Working Opportunity Tax Credits*: up to $2,100 per employee
- *Low Interest Loans*: loans at 75% of Prime rate

Barnesville-Lamar County Economic Development
100 Commerce Place
P.O. Box 505
Barnesville, GA 30204
770-358-2732
Fax: 770-358-0006
www.barnesville.org
Local incentives are offered on an individual basis determined by expected local economic impact. Usually incentives may include infrastructure improvements, discounted real estate costs, tax abatement, and financial assistance through the Barnesville Lamar County Industrial Development Authority.

Dooly County Economic Development
402 Hawkinsville Road
Vienna, GA 31092
229-268-4554
Fax: 229-268-4500
www.doolyedc.org
The Dooley County Economic Development Office can provide you with a variety of information to help you start your business. They have a list of industrial sites and buildings available, local demographics, a Training Center and Empowerment Zone Incentives.

Hawaii

Hawaii City and County Economic Development Councils
County of Kauai
Office of Economic Development
4444 Rice Street, Suite 200
Lihue, HI 96766-1300
808-241-6390
Fax: 808-241-6399
www.kauaigov.org/OED
This County Office serves the islands of Kauai and Nihau. The Office of Economic Development provides technical and financial support for both large and small businesses as well as new or existing industries.

City and County of Honolulu
Economic Development Office
Honolulu Hale, Suite 305
530 S. King Street
Honolulu, HI 96813
808-547-7820
Fax: 808-547-7808
www.co.honolulu.hi.us
The Economic Development Office can provide you with information on a variety of information that can help you start or expand your business.
- *Enterprise Zone Program:* offers state and county tax reduction and other benefits for up to seven years.
- *High Tech Tax Incentives:* provides Qualified High Technology Businesses (QHTB) with 100% return on cash investments on a front-loaded basis over 5 years.

- *Foreign Trade Zone (FTZ):* provides duty-free treatment for items processes in a FTZ and then re-exported.

Maui County Office of Economic Development
Mayor's Office
200 South High Street. 9th Floor
Wailuku, HI 96793-2155
808-270-7710
Fax: 808-270-7870
www.co.maui.hi.us
This County Office serves the islands of Kaho`olawe, Lanai, Maui and Molokai. Their Small Business Division publishes *Starting a Business In Maui Count*, which can help you get started. The Office supports projects through grants and assistance in the follow areas: visitor; small business; agriculture; aquaculture; film; technology; manufacturing; cultural arts; education; and other special events.

County of Hawaii
Research and Development
25 Aupuni Street, Room 219
Hilo, HI 96720
808-961-8366
Fax: 808-935-1205
www.hawaii-county.com/links/economic_dev_links.html
The Department of Research and Development is responsible for economic development in the areas of tourism, agriculture, new and existing industry, energy and film.
- *Tourism*: contracts available for such activities as visitor greeting, marketing, festivals and other special events.
- *Agriculture*: Research and Development Grants are available as well as workshops.

Idaho

E.D.G.E.
Economic Development Grows Economies
Morris D. Huffman
Economic Development Specialist
109 South McKinley Ave.
Emmett, ID 83617
208-365-4743
Fax: 208-365-2499
http://www.economicdevelop.org
E.D.G.E. works with companies in Boise and Gem Counties and with the cities of Horseshoe Bend, Emmett, and Idaho City to help businesses and communities grow. They would like to create economic growth while maintaining the wonderful atmosphere of the towns.

Gem County Chamber of Commerce
127 E. Main Street
Emmett, ID 83617
208-365-3485
http://www.emmettidaho.com/
The County Chamber of Commerce offers customized services for businesses wishing to start up or expand in the area. There are investment tax credits, workforce development training funds, and some rural infrastructure allowances. Sometimes there are local incentives based on your industry, size of building needed, and more.

Eastern Idaho Economic Development Council
151 N. Ridge, Suite 260
Idaho Falls, ID 83402
800-900-2014

208-522-2014
Fax: 208-522-3824
www.estidaho.org/EIEDC
The Eastern Idaho Economic Development Council manages a $3 million dollar enterprise fund which provides equity capital for businesses. They also have access to other revolving loan funds, private investors, venture capital and more. They will loan money to businesses who are or will be located in Eastern Idaho and will help the economy by maintaining or creating jobs.

Regional Development Alliance Inc.
2300 North Yellowstone
Idaho Falls, ID 83401
208-528-9400
www.regalliance.org
The mission of the Regional Development Alliance (RDA) is to assist the Governor of the state of Idaho in the utilization of the Idaho National Engineering and Environmental Laboratory (INEEL) Settlement Fund program as a catalyst to affect and enhance quality job creation opportunities, activities and efforts in Bannock, Bingham, Bonneville, Butte, Custer, Jefferson, and Madison counties. A total of $19.5 million has been received under this program.

Clearwater Economic Development Association
1626 6th Ave.
Lewiston, ID 83501
208-746-0015
www.clearwater-eda.org
The Clearwater Economic Development Association offers loans (sometimes in partnership with area banks) to help create and retain jobs in the north central area of Idaho. The goal is to help the economic growth of these rural communities. The EDA Revolving Loan Fund is for expansion or start-up of businesses with a maximum loan amount of $100,000. SEED Joint Development Loan Fund offers loans of up to $50,000 for expansion or start-up business located in 5 counties in north central Idaho. This loan is available to borrowers unable to obtain conventional bank loans. SEED Micro Loans are for up to $5,000 for start up business in 5 counties in north central Idaho. The IRP Revolving Loan Fund is for start up and expansion of businesses in a rural area of 25,000 population or less and must be outside Lewiston city limits. The maximum loan amount is $150,000.

Bannock Development Corporation
1651 Alvin Ricken Drive
Pocatello, ID 83201
866-395-3500
208-233-3500
Fax: 208-233-0268
www.bannockdevelopment.org
The Bannock Development Corporation offers a wide range of services to help businesses start and expand in the area. They can assist with economic and demographic data, help secure financing, train employees, and more. There are a number of incentives to lower costs for businesses looking to grow in southeastern Idaho. Industrial Revenue Bonds, Rural Business Development Grants, and Tax Increment Financing are available to offer support. New jobs credits and job training credits are available to businesses and the Bannock Development Corporation can help businesses take advantage of these offerings.

Southern Idaho Economic Development Organization
1731 W. Lincoln
Jerome, ID 83338
866-768-8443

208-324-7408
Fax: 208-324-7449
www.southernidaho.org
The Southern Idaho Economic Development organization provides assistance to the Southern Idaho region in helping businesses grow and expand in the area. Industrial Revenue Bonds are available for businesses wishing to borrow at least $1 million. The S.I.E.D. can help businesses apply for other types of grants and loans to help improve the economy of the region.

Illinois

Illinois City Economic Development
City of Kankakee Economic Development
385 E. Oak Street
Kankakee, IL 60901
815-933-0462
Fax: 815-933-0482
www.ci.kankakee.il.us/economic.html
The City of Kankakee offers a wide range of information for small business owners. They offer information on the following programs: Small Business Micro Loans, Property Tax Abatement, Permit and Fee Waivers, Community Development Block Grants and Utility Tax Relief.

Mt. Vernon Economic Development Commission
200 Potomac Boulevard
Mt. Vernon, IL 62864
618-244-3554
Fax: 618-244-7533
www.mtvernon.com/edc_mtvernon/edc_frame_page.htm
The Mt. Vernon Economic Commission provides assistance in the development of incentive programs to new and existing businesses.
- *Enterprise Zone:* Enterprise Zone incentives include: state and local sales tax exemption on purchase of building materials, state income tax deductions, additional investment tax credits, job tax credits and property tax abatement.
- *City Revolving Loan Fund*: The purpose of this program is to make low interest loans for new investments and expansions which result in the creation of new jobs and retention of existing jobs as well as enhance future investment opportunities within the community.
- *Training Programs*: Employee training programs are available through the State of Illinois and the local community college, Rend Lake College. A complete training package would include: screening of applicants, testing and possible reimbursement of part of the employer generated training costs.
- *Employee Relocation Assistance Program*: A mortgage program has been created by local lending institutions to provide loans to current employees of prospective companies that may be moving into the Mt. Vernon community.

St. Charles Economic Development Department
2 E. Main Street
St. Charles, IL 60174
630-443-4093
www.stcharles.org/departments/edd/index.asp
The St. Charles Economic Development Department strives to create a business-friendly environment so that existing businesses will choose to expand in St. Charles and new businesses will locate there.
- *Small Business Classes and Counseling*: A variety of classes and counseling is available.

- *Corridor Improvement Grants Program*: The Corridor Improvement Grant Program is designed to help property owners on highly visible corridors with landscape improvements.

Illinois County Economic Development

Cook County
69 West Washington Street, Suite 1422
Chicago, IL 60602
312-603-0140
Fax: 312-603-9803
www.enterpriz.org
Enterpiz Cook County has business specialists that provide custom assistance to businesses. Business services may include economic data, market research, technical assistance with incentive and financing programs, site selection assistance, international trade assistance, industry sector profiles, and professional referral service.

Property Tax Incentives:
- *Industrial Development*: Up to 50% reduction in a manufacturing, warehouse, or distribution company's total tax bill for 12 years.
- *Environmental Cleanup and Industrial Development*: Up to 50% reduction in property taxes for 3 to 5 years.
- *Commercial Development*: Up to 50% reduction in a company's total bill for 12 years. For projects in Redevelopment Areas.
- *Industrial or Commercial Development*: Up to 50% reduction in a company's total property tax bill for 12 years. For facilities in severely blighted areas.
- *Multifamily Residential Development*: Over 50% reductions in a company's total property tax bill for up to 30 years. For rental buildings in low and moderate income levels.
- *Industrial or Commercial Development*: Up to 50% reduction in property taxes for 10 years. For commercial or industrial rehabilitation of landmark buildings.

Financing and Grants:
- *Business Loan Fund*: Low-interest business loans from $25,000 to $300,000. One half of prime rate. No points. A minimum 51% of the jobs must be filled by low and moderate income persons.
- *Industrial Revenue Bonds*: Below market financing for industrial expansion. Projects from $1 million to $10 million.
- *Infrastructure Grants*: Municipalities request grants for public improvements to support private development.
- *No Cash Bid/Tax Reactivation*: An incentive to redevelop tax delinquent commercial, industrial or residential property by eliminating all back taxes, interest and penalties.
- *Job Training*: Vocational on-the-job and customized training.

Data:
- *Chicago-Cook County CD-ROM*: Interactive CD with market trends, trade statistics, business programs, internet links and aerial photos of available industrial real estate.

Champaign County Economic Development Corporation
1817 S. Neil Street, Suite 201
Champaign, IL 61820
217-359-6261
Fax: 217-359-1809
www.cupartnership.org
The Champaign Economic Development Corporation assists businesses with establishing new and expanding operations in the county and providing start-up businesses with information about the marketplace.
The Champaign County Economic Development Corporation efforts include:
- marketing the community to new and prospective business as well as relating business opportunities to local companies
- assembling and disseminating community market data for analyzing the community's business environment
- maintaining a database of available office and industrial properties in the community
- providing assistance in identifying financing alternatives through local financial institutions as well as low interest loans available from local, state and federal government
- maintaining relationships with area builders, developers and realtors to provide expertise in facility identification and development
- working with business and community leaders to identify and provide insight on issues affecting the economic growth and stability of the area

DeKalb County Economic Development Corporation
421 N. California Street, Suite 200
Sycamore, IL 60178
815-895-2711
Fax: 815-895-8713
www.dcedc.org
The DeKalb County Economic Development Corporation provides economic and demographic information about the county and its communities.

Indiana

Indiana City Economic Councils

Connersville Economic Development Group
The Commerce Center
504 North Central Avenue
Connersville, IN 47331
765-827-1366
800-943-2432
www.edgconnersville.com
- *Site Location*: The Connersville Economic Development Group offers businesses room to grow by listing commercial and industrial buildings and sites.
- *Connersville Urban Enterprise Zone*: Provides tax incentives and credits.
- *Main Street Revolving Loan Fund*: Assists business owners to make necessary repairs and/or improvements to properties located on Main Street.

Lafayette-West Lafayette Economic Development
  Corporation
337 Columbia Street
P.O. Box 311
Lafayette, IN 47902-0311
765-742-0095
Fax: 765-742-6276
http://glpi.org
- *Site Location*: Lafayette and West Lafayette has a wide range of office space, industrial buildings and sites available for new and expanding businesses.
- *Greater Lafayette Progress, Inc.*: A one-stop business assistance resource for new or existing businesses. They provide free, confidential help in many areas of business.

- *Tax Incentives*: Local tax incentives include: *Tax Abatement, Tax increment Financing, Economic Development Income Tax,* and *Urban Enterprise Zone.*

Michigan City Economic Development Corporation
2 Cadence Park Plaza
Michigan City, IN 46360
219-873-1211
Michigan City Economic Development Corporation uses a one-stop-shop approach to easily accommodate the area businesses.

- *Site Location*: Assistance to help you find the perfect industrial sites and buildings, commercial sites and buildings as well as office/retail sites for your business.
- *Business Assistance*:
- *Financial*: A variety of lending options including: venture capital, Michigan City Revolving Loan Fund, Industrial Revenue Bonds and a listing of local lenders.
- *Nx Entrepreneurial Training Program*: A 12-session program for business owners to help enhance their entrepreneurial skills and assist them in the creation of a quality business plan.

Indiana County Economic Councils

Allen County Economic Development
Department of Planning Services
630 City-County Building
One East Main Street
Fort Wayne, IN 46802
260-449-7607
Fax: 260-449-7682
www.co.allen.in.us

- *Tax Abatement Development Fund*: Funds to encourage industrial development.
- *Site Location*: Information is available on industrial site locations.

Clinton County Economic Development
259 East Walnut Street
Frankfort, IN 46041
765-654-5507
Fax: 765-654-9592
www.clintoncountyeconomicdevelopment.com

- *Site Location*: Listings for industrial buildings and sites available in the county.
- *Revolving Loan Fund*: Small loans are available for new business start-ups or business expansions.

Knox County Development Corporation
102 N 3rd Street
P.O. Box 701
Vincennes, IN 47591
812-886-6993
Fax: 812-886-0888
www.kcdc.com

- *EDIT Funds*: Over $500,000 per year available from Vincennes/Knox County for Industrial Development.
- *Tax Abatement*: Offered by local government units on real property and equipment.

Iowa

Iowa City Economic Development

Mason City Economic Development Corporation
25 West State Street, Suite B
P.O. Box 1128
Mason City, IA 50402-1128
800-944-1708
Fax: 641-423-5725
www.masoncityedc.com

- *Site Location*: Assistance to help you find the perfect industrial sites and buildings or commercial sites and buildings for your business.
- *Mason City Revolving Loan Fund*: Funds to promote economic activity and growth through new industry and expansion.
- *Tax Increment Financing*: Money to pay the cost of public improvements and utilities which will serve private development.

Cedar Falls Industrial & Technology Park
City of Cedar Falls Economic Development
220 Clay Street
Cedar Falls, IA 50613
319-273-8606
Fax: 319-273-8610
www.cedarfallsitp.com

- *Site Location*: Assistance to help you find space in for your business in Cedar Falls.
- *Financial Incentives*: Cedar Falls custom-designs their incentives for your business which may include: land incentives, tax incentives, grants and loans.
- *Exempted and Abated Taxes*: The city's industrial and technology tax abatement program is designed to lower your property taxes over a five-year period, beginning with a 75% exemption the first year.
- *Iowa Industrial Job Training Program*: This program can help new and expanding businesses pay for job-related employee education, training facilities, training materials, reimbursement of travel expenses and trainers' salaries.

Webster City Association of Business and Industry
628 Second Street
P.O. Box 310
Webster City, IA 50595-0310
800-535-8341
Fax: 515-832-5130
www.webstercity-iowa.com/iowa_economic_development.php

- *Tax Increment Financing*: Public Improvement financing for eligible businesses located in one of the designated urban renewal areas.
- *Industrial Revenue Bonds*: City-issued bonds for some economic development projects.
- *Webster City Business and Industry revolving Loan Fund*: Loans usually at zero percent interest for up to ten years for new or expanding businesses located in Webster City. There is no minimum or maximum for these loans.
- *Webster City Economic Development Set-Aside Revolving Loan Fund*: Locally controlled funds that can be used for a variety of purposes. The funds are distributed on a case-by-case basis.

Iowa County Economic Development

Fayette County Economic Development Commission
101 North Vine
West Union, IA 52175
563-422-5073
Fax: 563-422-6322
www.fayettecountyia.com

- *Site Location*: Assistance to help you find industrial sites and buildings for your business.
- *Fayette County Revolving Loan Fund (Job Creation)*: $8,000 to $9,000 per job created is available for small businesses.

- *Fayette County Revolving Loan Fund*: Fayette County offers a non-job related revolving loan fund.

Wright County Economic Development
115 North Main
P.O. Box 214
Clarion, IA 50525
515-532-6422
Fax: 515-532-2348
www.wrightcounty.org/economic_development.htm
- *Site Location*: Assistance to help you find the perfect industrial sites and buildings or commercial sites and buildings for your business.
- *Wright County Economic Development Revolving Loan Fund*: This loan identifies business opportunities, provides technical assistance, and makes loans to existing or start-up businesses to improve the quality of life in the county through job creation.

Union County Development Association
208 W. Taylor
P.O. Box 471
Creston, IA 50801
641-782-2003
Fax: 641-782-9927
www.ucda.us
- *Iowa Jobs Training Program*: This program provides for tax-aided training for new employees.
- *Union County Development Association*: Eligible businesses in Enterprise Zones qualify for a variety of incentives.
- *Economic Development Set-Aside Program*: This program is based on the number of jobs created and financial need. Funding limits are generally $1,000 to $3,000 per job.
- *Community Economic Betterment Account*: This program can help you if you have an existing business. Funds are usually limited to $2,000 to $4,000 per job.
- *Revitalize Iowa's Sound Economy*: Forgivable loans to cities and companies to improve or replace streets and roads. Funding limits are $2,000 to $5,000 per job.
- *Revolving Loan Fund*: This program can be used to locate or develop a business.

Kansas

Kansas City Economic Developments
City of Abilene Economic Development Council
City Hall
419 North Broadway
Abilene, KS 67410
785-263-2550
www.abilenecityhall.com/develop.htm
Abilene's public officials can help your new or expanding business in site packaging, development and financing.
- *Site Location*: Industrial sites are available from one to fifty acres and are serviced by municipal utilities.
- *Revolving Loan Funds*: Flexible low-interest loans are available through the City of Abilene.
- *Industrial Revenue Bonds*: These bonds are issued by the City of Abilene and may be used to finance land, buildings, equipment and construction. Building materials are exempt from sales tax.

City of Hiawatha
Economic Development Administrator
723 Oregon St.
Hiawatha, KS 66434

785-742-2254
Fax: 785-742-4504
www.cityofhiawatha.org/EconDevelop.htm
- *Site Location*: The City of Hiawatha has developed commercial and industrial park sites for businesses in the City.
- *Local Incentives*: Local incentives are negotiated on a case-by-case basis with each business.

Pittsburg Economic Development
201 West 4th
Pittsburg, KS 66762
620-231-4100
www.pittks.org/department/economic
Pittsburg Economic Development provides incentives which include two local revolving loan funds, property tax incentives, income tax credits and state training programs. The City of Pittsburg has created two heavy industrial parks, one airport light industrial park, and a research and development park in conjunction with the Kansas Technology Center at Pittsburg State University.

Kansas County Economic Developments
Butler County Economic Development
121 S. Gordy
El Dorado, KS 67042
316-322-4242
800-794-6907
Fax: 316-322-4245
www.bucoks.com/bced
- *Industrial Revenue Bonds*: These bonds are offered by Butler County as a low cost tool to help finance business projects.
- *Local Property Tax Abatement*: Each city in Butler County has adopted their own property tax abatement policy based on the number of new jobs created and the amount of new capital investment.
- *Community Development Block Grant*: You can apply for financial assistance for your business through Butler County Economic Development.
- *Enhanced Enterprise Zone Benefits*: Butler County is a non-metro enhanced county. This means that your business can receive a $2,500 income tax credit per new job created verses a state allowed $1,500 tax credit.
- *Training Programs*: Butler County supplies access to the state training funds through the Butler County Community College. The college will work to develop custom programs to meet business owner's needs.
- *Micro-Loan Program*: Funds are available fro small start-up and existing businesses in Butler County.

Coffey County Economic Development Department
110 S. 6th Street
Burlington, KS 66839
620-364-8780
800-947-4796
Fax: 620-364-8643
www.coffeycountyks.org/econdevo/index.html
- *Enterprise Zone*: Credits available for qualifying businesses located in the Enterprise Zones.

Hutchinson/Reno County Economic Development
117 N. Walnut
Hutchinson, KS 67501
800-691-4262
620-662-3391
www.hutchchamber.com/economic /eco_dev.shtml
- *Neighborhood Revitalization Plan (City of Hutchinson)*: The City of Hutchinson offers property owners a ten-

year incremental rebate on the increase in property tax incurred as a result of new construction or renovation to a property. Residential, commercial, and industrial properties are eligible.

- *Incremental Tax Rebate*: An incremental tax rebate in industrial/commercial property.
- *Enterprise Zone*: Manufacturing and non-manufacturing businesses are eligible for all Enterprise Zone incentives in Hutchinson/Reno Counties.
- *Property Tax Exemption*: Hutchinson/Reno County has approved a property tax exemption policy for businesses engaged in manufacturing, distribution, or research and development.

Kentucky

Kentucky City Economic Development Councils

Greater Louisville Inc.
614 West Main Street, Suite 6000
Louisville, KY 40202
502-625-0072
www.greaterlouisville.com
- *Manufacturing Tax Moratorium*: New and expanding manufacturing operations located within Louisville Metro may qualify for a five-year moratorium on all assessed property and real estate taxes.

Greater Paducah Economic Development Council
401 Kentucky Avenue
P.O. Box 1155
Paducah, KY 42002-1155
270-575-6633
800-788-0110
Fax: 270-575-6648
www.gpedc.com
- *Site Location*: Assistance to help you find the perfect industrial sites and buildings or commercial sites or buildings for your business.

Jeffersontown Economic Development
10416 Watterson Trail
Jeffersontown, KY 40299
502-267-8333
Fax: 502-267-0547
www.jeffersontownky.com
- *Jeffersontown Facade Improvement Program*: The Jeffersontown Facade Program is an opportunity for industrial and property owners to improve the exterior of their buildings. The program will provide up to $500 for architectural assistance and low fixed rate loans up to $20,000.

Kentucky County Economic Development Councils

Hopkinsville-Christian County Economic Development Council
2800 Fort Campbell Boulevard
P.O. Box 1382
Hopkinsville, KY 42241-1382
270-885-1499
800-842-9959
Fax: 270-886-2059
www.commercecenter.org/edc/index.thm
- *Site Location*: Assistance to help you find the perfect industrial sites and buildings for your business.

Madisonville-Hopkins County Economic Development Corporation
755 Industrial Road
Madisonville, KY 42431
270-821-1939
Fax: 270-821-1945
www.kymtec.org
- *Site Location*: The Madisonville-Hopkins County Economic Development Corporation can assist your business in finding an industrial site or industrial building.

Mount Sterling-Montgomery County
51 North
Maysville, KY 40353
859-498-5343
859-498-3947
www.mtsterlingchamber.com/industry.asp
- *Local Incentives*: The Chamber will develop local incentives for companies offering to employ local men and women.

Louisiana

Louisiana City Economic Development

Lafayette Economic Development Authority
221 East Devalcourt Street
Lafayette, LA 70506-1421
337-593-1400
Fax: 337-234-3009
www.lafayette.org
- *Micro-Business Development Center*: The Micro-Business Development Center is located at the University of Louisiana at Lafayette. The Center helps new and existing businesses in marketing, management and financing.

City of New Iberia Economic Development
457 East Main Street, Room 300
New Iberia, LA 70560-3700
337-373-3120
Fax: 337-373-3113
www.cityofnewiberia.com
- *Economic Development Team*: The Team works with businesses to help them with grant opportunities, economic development sources, capital and other business needs.

City of Shreveport Economic Development
505 Travis Street
P.O. Box 31109
Shreveport, LA 71130
318-673-7503
www.ci.shreveport.la.us
- *Economic Development Loan Program*: Long-term low-interest financing is available to businesses to help stimulate growth, retain jobs, provide management training and increase general business activity.
- *Shreveport Inner City Economic Development Initiative*: This program is designed to provide businesses with funding for machinery, equipment, furniture, fixtures, vehicles, land, building, construction and rehabilitation of new and existing real property.
- *Technical Assistance Program*: This program assesses the needs of needs of businesses and offers management and administrative support to participants.

Louisiana County (Parish) Economic Development

Jeff Davis Parish
100 Rue de L'Acadie
P.O. Box 1207
Jennings, LA 70546
337-821-5534
www.jeffdavis.org/econdev.htm
The Office of Economic Development collectively provides professional assistance to current expanding businesses, as well as, prospective new business opportunities for the entire parish. A wide-range of planning and economic research data that tracks regional statistical trends for the five-parish region is also available.

Jefferson Parish Economic Development Commission
3445 N. Causeway Boulevard, Suite 300
Metairie, LA 70002
504-833-1881
Fax: 504-833-7676
www.jedco.org
- *Jefferson Economic Future Fund (J.E.F.F.)*: The Jefferson Economic Future Fund is a parishwide incentive fund designed to help Jefferson Parish compete for new jobs and investments. Projects are negotiated on a case-by-case basis, depending on the number of new jobs and payroll to be generated, location, and deal structure.
- *Incubator Centers*: Jefferson County offers two business incubators for local entrepreneurs.

St. Tammany Parish Economic Development Foundation (STEDF)
21454 Koop Drive, Suite 2E1
Mandeville, LA 70471
888-868-3830
985-809-7874
Fax: 985-809-7596
www.stedf.org
- *Business Assistance*: The department will help your business with securing state tax incentives, the zoning and rezoning process, and the promotion of business opportunities.
- *Site Location*: Assistance to help you find the perfect industrial sites and buildings or commercial sites and buildings for your business.
- *Free Business Counseling*: STEDF offers free business counseling to new and existing businesses through an outreach program through the Small Business Development Center at Southeastern Louisiana University.
- *Revolving Loan Fund*: Short-term low interest financing is available to qualified businesses that use the funds to create or retain jobs.

Maine

Maine City Economic Development

Lewistown Auburn Economic Growth Council
95 Park Street
P.O. Box 1188
Lewiston, ME 04243-1188
207-784-0161
Fax: 207-786-4412
www.economicgrowth.org
- *Site Location*: The Growth Council can help you locate buildings and/or land that meet your business specifications.

- *Commercial Financing*: The Council can help your business explore traditional and nontraditional financing to meet your need.

Madison Economic Community Development
P.O. Box 190
26 Western Avenue
Madison, ME 04950
207-696-3334
www.madison-maine.org
The Madison Economic Community Development Office offers a variety of programs for their local businesses that include: three different loan grants, development fund loan, downtown revitalization program, facade loan program, planning grant and several other services.

City of Portland Economic Development Center
389 Congress Street
Portland, ME 04101
800-874-8144
207-874-8683
Fax: 207-756-8217
www.portlandedc.com
- *The Portland Business Fund*: Loans up to $150,000 for 20 years for building renovation, equipment purchase, leasehold improvements, façade renovation and building acquisition for business located in Downtown Portland.
- *The Downtown Micro*: Low rate loans up to $20,000 for 7 years for first floor retail/service businesses in Downtown Portland. The money may be used for renovation, working capital, building facades, inventory, equipment purchase, leasehold improvements and ADA renovations.
- *The Portland Micro*: Loans up to $15,000 for 4 years for businesses outside of Downtown Portland. Applicants participate in 1-hour business technical assistance per $1,000 borrowed.
- *Free Counseling*: Free and confidential counseling on how to plan and launch a business, market what you are selling, manage, obtain finances and more.
- *Seminars & Workshops*: Seminars and workshops that address critical issues of businesses.

Maine County Economic Development

Piscataquis County Economic Development Council
50 Mayo Street
Dover-Foxcroft, ME 04426
207-564-3638
800-539-0332
www.pcedc.org
- *Incubator Without Walls*: This program provides businesses with business training, marketing assistance, individual counseling, networking opportunities and access to scholarships and loans.
- *Government Procurement*: Businesses in Piscataquis County can receive Federal contracting preferences because the County is recognized as a HUB Zone.

Sunrise County Economic Council
P.O. Box 679
1 Stackpole Road
Machias, ME 04654
207 255 0983
Fax: 207-255-4987
www.sunrisecounty.org
- *Sunrise Loan Fund*: Gap financing for business start-up and expansion.

- *Sunrise County Business Support Center*: Business services that include lending, technical assistance and web based resources and data.

Somerset Economic Development Corporation
41 Court Street
Skowhegan, ME 04976
207-474-0166
Fax: 207-474-0465
www.somersetcountymaine.org
The Somerset Economic Development Corporation encourages growth in the county by helping businesses find programs to meet their needs.

Maryland

Maryland City Economic Development
Annapolis Office of Economic Development
160 Duke of Gloucester Street
Annapolis, MD 21401
410-263-7940
Fax: 410-263-1129
www.ci.annapolis.md.us/government/depts/econdev
The City's Office of Economic Development assists in the recruitment of new businesses and employers as well as the retention, assistance in the growth and competitiveness of existing business and industry.

Baltimore City Development Corporation
36 S. Charles Street, Suite 1600
Baltimore, MD 21201
410-837-9305
Fax: 410-837-6363
www.baltimoredevelopment.com
The Baltimore City Development Corporation provides a variety of assistance for businesses: one-stop business resources, demographic and economic analysis, site-selection assistance, financial assistance and fast-track permitting.

Havre de Grace Department of Economic Development and Planning
711 Pennington Avenue
Havre de Grace, MD 21078
410-939-1800
Fax: 410-939-7632
www.havredegracemd.com
The Havre de Grace Economic Development Office promotes and administers development grants, loans and incentive programs.
Technical Assistance: Assistance is provided to businesses and potential businesses.
Site Location: A database of commercial property is maintained for businesses.

Maryland County Economic Development
Allegany County Economic Development
701 Kelly Road
Cumberland, MD 21502
800-555-4080
301-777-5967
Fax: 301-777-2194
www.alleganyworks.org
- *Allegany County Revolving Building Fund Program*: The Allegany County Economic Development office can offer firms a partner in the development of a project.
- *Work Force Preparation*: The Western Maryland Consortium can provide wage reimbursements to companies for hiring economically disadvantaged or unemployed persons.

Carroll County Department of Economic Development
225 N. Center Street, Suite 101
Westminster, MD 21157
410-386-2070
Fax: 410-876-8471
www.carrollbiz.org
- *Carroll County Development Corporation*: Carroll County Development Corporation is a source of investment and debt financing to support local small business and economic growth in the county.
- *Industrial Revenue Bonds*: Carroll County can authorize the use of IRB's to help finance eligible projects.
- *Economic Development Trust Fund*: The Department can offer grants and low-interest loans for a variety of projects.
- *Job Training*: Job training funds may be available to help employers train and hire Carroll County workers.
- *Business & Employment Resource Center*: The Business & Resource Center is a one-stop workforce development center.

Howard County Economic Development Authority
6751 Columbia Gateway Drive
Suite 500   410-313-6500
Columbia, MD 21046 Fax: 410-313-6525
www.hceda.org
Customized services and programs are available to start-up businesses through the Howard County Economic Development Authority (EDA), a private group whose mission is to improve the economic well-being and independence of county residents. The Business Resource Center is home to EDA's financial and technical assistance specialists. The Business Funding Advisory Office advises entrepreneurs of funding opportunities; the Franchise Advisory Office offers advice, guidance, and seminars on the business aspects of franchising; the Intellectual Property Advisory Office offers workshops on the patent application process, trade and service marking, and intellectual property issues; the International Trade Center helps companies to develop international business opportunities through one-on-one counseling and workshops; and the Proposal Development Office focuses on the basics of creating business proposals and responses to Requests for Proposals (RFP). Low cost seminars cover business plans, the basics of starting a business, and other pertinent topics.

Somerset County Economic Development Commission
11916 Somerset Avenue, Suite 202
Princess Anne, MD 21853
410-651-0500
888-651-0500
Fax: 410-651-3836
www.skipjack.net/le_shore/somerset
- *Small Business Expansion Program (SBEP)*: A local Revolving Loan Program operated by the Somerset County Economic Development Commission.
- *Site Location*: The Somerset County Economic Development Commission operates a number of industrial sites for businesses.

Massachusetts

Massachusetts City Economic Development
City of Boston Office of Business Development
2201 Washington Street
Roxbury, MA 02119

617-989-9100
Fax: 617-989-9125
www.cityofboston.gov/dnd/OBD

- *Boston Local Development corporation (BLDC)*: The BLDC provides loans between $15,000 and $150,000 for qualifying businesses in the City of Boston. These loans can be used to buy new business property, purchase equipment, enlarge and existing plant or to make leasehold improvements.
- *Boston Industrial Development Financing Authority (BIDFA)*: The BIDFA issues bonds to finance the capital needs of Boston's businesses and institutions. Bonds may be used to finance construction, capital expenses and working capital needs resulting from expansion. The minimum is generally $750,000.
- *ReStore Boston*: This is a city wide program that provides grants and loans up to $7,000 per storefront to help neighborhood business and property owners complete storefront renovation projects. In addition to funding, ReStore Boston provides professional architectural design services at no cost to the business.
- *Business Technical Assistance*: The Office of Business Development provides technical assistance grants to businesses that demonstrate the financial need for services. Technical assistance can include financial management, bookkeeping, inventory management and control, marketing and design assistance.
- *Boston Main Streets*: This program provides technical assistance and matching grants to 19 local Main Streets commercial districts.

City of Cambridge Economic Development Division
Community Development Department
344 Broadway
Cambridge, MA 02139
617-349-4637
Fax: 617-349-4638
www.cambridgema.gov/~CDD/econdev

- *Counseling and Technical Assistance*: The Cambridge Economic Development Division offers one-to-one counseling and technical assistance to small businesses and individual entrepreneurs in developing businesses.
- *Cambridge Minority and Women-Owned Business Directory*: A directory listing the Minority and Women-Owned Businesses in Cambridge offering a variety of services. It also includes information on how to do business with the City of Cambridge.
- *Cambridge Business Development Center*: The Center is dedicated to helping start and grow successful businesses. It offers a mentoring program to pair less experienced entrepreneurs with experienced mentors.
- *Site Locator*: The Cambridge Economic Development Division maintains a listing of available commercial real estate for businesses seeking space in Cambridge.

Fitchburg Economic Development Office
718 Main Street
Fitchburg, MA 01420
978-345-9602
Fax: 978-345-9604
www.discoverfitchburg.com

- *Fitchburg Downtown Urban Revitalization and Development Plan*: The Fitchburg Downtown Urban Revitalization Development Plan provides several incentives for new and existing businesses.

Massachusetts County Economic Development

Berkshire Chamber of Commerce
6 West Main Street

North Adams, MA 01247
413-662-3735
Fax: 413-664-1049
www.berkshirechamber.com

- *Small & Micro Business Committee*: The Small & Micro Committee plans events and programs to strengthen and support the small and micro business community.
- *Business-to-Business*: Members of the Berkshire Chamber of Commerce receive exclusive discount offers or other incentives from other Chamber members.

Cape Cod Economic Development Council
Barnstable County
3225 Main Street
P.O. Box 226
Barnstable, MA 02630
508-362-8051
www.capecodedc.org

- *Large Grant Program*: Grants to nonprofits and municipalities to improve economic development.
- *Small Grant Program*: The Small Grant Program focuses on creating and maintaining artistic and intellectual capital.

Economic Development Council of Western Massachusetts
1441 Main Street
Banknorth Center
Springfield, MA 01103
888-593-6421
Fax: 413-593-5126
www.ecdev-wma.com

- *Community Capital Fund*: If your business is located in a qualifying community, you may be eligible for this fund. Loans may be used for the purchase of equipment, acquisition of real estate, new construction, working capital and refinancing.
- *Venture Capital*: Qualifying technology-based companies are eligible for assistance for early stage development.
- *Technical Assistance*: Technical assistance is available for first-time entrepreneurs.
- *Site Location*: The Council provides a data base of available properties for sale or lease for your business.

Michigan

Michigan City Economic Development

City of Bay City
301 Washington Avenue
Bay City, MI 48708
989-894-8200
Fax: 989-894-0704
www.baycitymi.org

- *Land Assembly*: Professionals employed by the City, assist businesses with locating, assembling and purchasing land for residential, commercial and industrial purposes.
- *Industrial Property Tax*: Incentives are available for eligible businesses to renovate or expand aging manufacturing plants or to build new ones.
- *Obsolete Property Rehabilitation Act*: The Act provides an exemption from ad valorem property taxes to commercial property and commercial housing property within qualifying districts.

Charlotte City Economic Development
111 E. Lawrence Avenue
Charlotte, MI 38813
517-543-8853
Fax: 517-543-8851
http://development.charlotte-mi.com

- *Industrial Facilities Tax Exemptions*: The Industrial Facilities Tax Exemption is an abatement that reduces both real and personal tax liability by 50% for new facilities and 100% for the new value of a rehabilitation of existing property.
- *Community Development Block Grants*: The City may use these federal funds for eligible projects with private businesses including land acquisition, construction, demolition and rehabilitation.
- *Local Development Finance Authority*: The Local Development Finance Authority at Combs Industrial Park can assist industry with construction and installation of public infrastructure.
- *Workforce Training Programs*: The Eaton County Intermediate School District offers training programs for local industries. Funds may be available from the Michigan Jobs Commission to pay for employee training for qualifying industries.
- *Michigan Economic Growth Authority (MEGA)*: The Michigan Economic Growth Authority can provide exemptions from the Single Business Tax and sales taxes on purchase of goods for their own use.

The City of Novi, Michigan
45175 West 10 Mile Road
Novi, MI 48375
248-347-3284
www.ci.novi.mi.us/Business/EconomicDevelopment.htm
The City of Novi provides a variety of services for businesses. Contact them at the above address if you are thinking of relocating your business in Novi.

Michigan County Economic Development

Berrien County Economic Development
701 Main Street
St. Joseph, MI 49085-1392
269-983-7111 ext 8786
www.berriencounty.org/econdev

- *Brownfield Redevelopment*: A developer of a contaminated property can be reimbursed for eligible environmental activities in Berrien County.
- *Revolving Loan Fund*: The Berrien County Revolving Loan Fund is used to promote the growth of small, entrepreneurial businesses that have no other options for financial assistance. Although they are typically loans, funds can also be grants.

Delta County Economic Development Alliance
230 Ludington Street
Escanaba, MI 49829
906-786-2192
888-DELTAMI
Fax: 906-786-8830
www.deltami.org/eda.html

- *Information*: The Alliance will customize information as need by your business including: demographics, workforce data, education and training, and business climate. They also have a library of pamphlets, magazines, books, and computer programs to assist you in your research.
- *Site Visits*: The Alliance has a team that visits existing businesses to determine how the community can help

maintain and improve the businesses current levels of workforce, management and physical equipment.

- *New Business Assistance*: New business assistance and counseling is available for those entrepreneurs just starting out.

Wayne County Department of Jobs & Economic Development
323 Wayne County Building
600 Randolph
Detroit, MI 48226
313-224-0756
Fax: 313-224-8458
www.waynecounty.com

- *Urban Loan Fund*: The Urban Loan Fund is for any small or minority-owned business in Detroit, Ecorse, Hamtramck, Highland, Park, Inkster, River Rouge or other qualifying community. Loans of up to 30% of projects under $200,000 are eligible.
- *Job Training & Job Placement*: The Education and Job Training Division coordinates job training and placement for businesses in Wayne County.
- *Wayne County HealthChoice*: This program offers affordable Healthcare coverage for businesses located in Wayne County.

Minnesota

Minnesota City Economic Development

City of Detroit Lakes Economic Development
1025 Roosevelt Avenue
P.O. Box 647
Detroit Lakes, MN 56502
218-847-5658
Fax: 218-847-8969
www.ci.detroit-lakes.mn.us
The City of Detroit Lakes Economic Development offers a variety of programs including: business incentives, low interest loans, tax increment financing and tax abatements.

Moorhead Economic Development
500 Center Avenue
P.O. Box 779
Moorhead, MN 56561
218-299-5442
877-833-6667
www.ci.moorhead.mn.us/eda

- *Property Tax Exemptions*: Property Tax Exemptions for up to five years and negotiated payments are available for all types of businesses that increase building value by more than $150,000.
- *Income Tax Credit*: A refundable state tax credit equal to 5% of a completed new building value in a qualifying target area.
- *Border City enterprise Zone Program*: Tax credit based on a percentage of the business's annual workers compensation expenses.
- *Moorhead Community Loan Program*: Gap financing for qualifying businesses. Loans up to $50,000 are available for land and building, machinery and equipment, or working capital.

New Ulm Economic Development Corporation
1 North Minnesota Street
P.O. Box 384
New Ulm, MN 56073
507-233-4305
Fax: 507-354-1504

www.newulm.com/ed

Site Location: New Ulm Economic Development Corporation will conduct a custom search of available land and buildings to meet your needs.

- *Finance Packaging*: Assistance in developing financial packages accessing local revolving loans, Chamber Incentive Programs, business plans and financial projections.
- *Access to Information*: New Ulm can provide your business the information about labor markets, community profiles, suppliers, technology and other business statistics to make an informed decision.

Minnesota County Economic Development

Ramsey County Economic Development
250 Ramsey County Courthouse
15 West Kellogg Boulevard
Saint Paul, MN 55102
561-266-8004
Fax: 651-266-8039
www.co.ramsey.mn.us/cm/ced

- *Ramsey County Business Loan Program*: This program is for new and expanding businesses creating head-of-household jobs. Loans are typically below-market rates for acquisition of land, buildings or machinery and equipment.

Renville County Economic Development Commission
500 East DePue Avenue
Olivia, MN 56277
320-523-3656
www.renville.com/businesses.htm

- *Southwest Minnesota Foundation*: Financial support for start-up and expanding businesses that will create employment by generating new wealth and diversifying the economy.
- *Business Finance Program*: Gap financing to qualifying businesses.

Wright County Economic Development Partnership
P.O. Box 525
6800 Electric Drive
Rockford, MN 55373
763-477-3086
Fax: 763-477-3054
www.wrightpartnership.org

- *Wright County Enterprise Revolving Loan Fund*: Gap financing to new and expanding industrial businesses that create quality jobs with good wages.
- *Site Location*: You can search the County web site for land or buildings available and sort for a variety of criteria.
- *Technical Assistance*: Free assistance for businesses including marketing plan creation, cash-flow analysis through the Small Business Development Center.
- *Workshops*: Business-oriented workshops and seminars are available.

Mississippi

Mississippi City Economic Development

City of Biloxi Department of Economic & Community Development
676 Martin Luther King Boulevard
Biloxi, MS 39530
Mailing address:
P.O. Box 588
Biloxi, MS 39533

228-435-6280
Fax: 228-435-6188
http://biloxi.ms.us/communitydevelopment

- *Renovated Building Tax Exemption*: Businesses who renovate existing structures in the City of Biloxi's designated Central Business District can apply for an ad valorem tax exemption that would waive city/county taxes on the value of the improvements.
- *Historic Building Tax Credit Program*: Restoration of buildings listed on the National Register of Historic Places or are designated as Mississippi Landmarks are eligible for a 20% federal tax credit.

The City of Jackson
218 South President Street
Jackson, MS 39205
601-960-1055
Fax: 601-960-2403
www.city.jackson.ms.us/economdev.htm
The city of Jackson's Office of Economic Development has several objectives. These include business recruitment and retention, business development, minority business development, the Equal Business Opportunity Program, and the implementation of programs aimed at downtown revitalization.

Town of Walnut Grove
P.O. Box 236
Walnut Grove, MS 39189-0236
601-253-2321
Fax: 601-253-2385
www.walnutgrove-ms.com/econdev.htm

- *Renewal Community Employment Credit*: Businesses located in the federally designated Renewal Community are eligible for up to $1,500 for every existing employee and new hire that lives and work in the Renewal Community.
- *Welfare-to-Work Credits*: tax credits for businesses of up to $3,500 in the first year and $5,000 in the second year for newly hired long-term welfare recipients.

Mississippi County Economic Development

Hinds County Economic Development District
P.O. Box 248
909 N. President Street
Jackson, MS 39205
601-353-6056
www.hcedd.com

- *Training*: The Hinds Community College Workforce Development Center provides industry-specific training and services for businesses, government agencies and community organizations.
- *Tax Credits*: Hinds County can exempt as Valorem (property) taxes for manufacturers who apply soon after they locate or expand in Hinds County.
- *Renewal Community Employment Credit*: Businesses located in the federally designated Renewal Community are eligible for up to $1,500 for every existing employee and new hire that lives and work in the Renewal Community.
- *Foreign Trade Zones*: These zones allow imports to enter into the United States without custom duties.

Jackson County Economic Development Foundation, Inc (JCEDF)
3033 Pascagoula Street
P.O. Drawer 1558
Pascagoula, MS 39568-1558
228-769-6263

800-362-0103
Fax: 228-762-8431
www.jcedf.org
- *Site Location*: JCEDF can help you find the perfect location for your new or expanding business.

Tupelo/Lee County Community Development Foundation
300 West Main Street
Tupelo, MS 38804
Mailing address:
P.O. Box A
Tupelo, MS 38802-1210
662-842-4521
Fax: 800-523-3463
www.cdfms.org/ed_overview.cfm
- *P3*: This initiative unites businesses, industry and education to create a prepared workforce.
- *Business Assistance*: One-on-one consultation on how to start a business, how to write a business plan and where to get financing.
- *Site Location*: The Business development division will help you locate the perfect location or building for your business.

Missouri

Missouri City Economic Development

City of Blue Springs Economic Development
City Hall
903 W. Main Street
Blue Springs, MO 64015
816-228-0208
Fax: 816-228-0204
www.bluespringsgov.com/ecodevo
- *Brownfield Redevelopment*: Financial incentives for the redevelopment of commercial/industrial sites in blighted areas.
- *Utility Incentives*: Two utilities servicing Blue Springs offer financial incentives to qualifying customers.
- *Site Location*: A data base of available site locations is available.

Kansas City Economic Development Corporation
10 Petticoat Lane, Suite 250
Kansas City, MO 64106-2103
800-889-0636
816-221-0636
Fax: 816-221-0189
www.edckc.com
- *Site Location*: Kansas City EDC provides listings of available properties and buildings for your business.
- *Governmental Ombudsman* This program provides guidance through permitting and regulatory processes.
- *Export Programs*: EDC can help your company with export financing, trade leads, export credit insurance and overseas agents.
- *Real Property Tax Abatements*: Kansas City provides real property tax abatement in targeted areas on improvements made for periods ranging from 10 to 25 years and in amounts ranging from 50-100%.
- *Greater Kansas City Foreign Trade Zone*: Kansas City Foreign Trade Zone benefits companies involved in international commerce by providing U.S. Customs duty-fee.

City of Liberty Economic Development
101 E. Kansas Avenue
Liberty, MO 64068

816-792-6011
www.ci.liberty.mo.us
- *Tax Abatement*: The City may approve tax abatements on real and personal property up to 50% for up to ten years.
- *Financial Incentives*: The City of Liberty will consider financial incentives to new or expanding businesses to provide significant public benefit.

Missouri County Economic Development

Jackson County Economic Development
200 S. Main
Independence, MO 64505
816-881-4440
www.jacksongov.org
The Jackson County Economic Development department promotes economic development in Jackson County (primarily outside the City of Kansas City) through attraction of new business, and expansion and retention of existing business with three broad initiatives: marketing, alliances, and research.

Macon County Development Corporation
510 N. Missouri, Suite C
Macon, MO 63552
660-385-5627
Fax: 660-385-3972
www.maconcounty.org
- *Business Assistance*: One-stop-shop for local businesses, permitting assistance, relocation services and a personal community ambassador for businesses.
- *Financial Assistance*: Low-interest loans at reduced rate financing for qualifying businesses.

St. Charles County Economic Development Center
5988 Mid Rivers Mall Drive, Suite 100
St. Charles, MO 63304
636-441-6880
Fax: 636-441-6881
www.stcc-edc.com
- *Mini-Bond Program*: The mini-bond loan program provides low interest rates to qualifying businesses.
- *Revolving Loan Fund*: The revolving Loan Fund provides short-term loans to qualified small businesses that cannot obtain financing from conventional sources.
- *Saint Louis Business Development Fund*: The Fund is a financial resource for businesses that need financing for growth capital.

Montana

Montana City Economic Development

City of Billings Economic Development
210 N 27th
P.O. Box 1178
Billings, MT 59101
406-658-8364
http://ci.billings.mt.us/development.php
- *Business Assistance*: The Economic Development Office provides information on starting a new business including requirements for new businesses.

City of Kalispell
284 Third Avenue East
Kalispell, MT 59901
406-758-7740
Fax: 406-758-7742
www.kalispell.com/community

- *Tax Increment Financing*: Low-interest loans for interior and exterior renovation of exiting commercial or retail structures in an Urban Renewal District.
- *Grants*: Economic Development Grants are available for the creation of well paying jobs in the city.

City of Missoula
Missoula Redevelopment Agency
123 West Spruce Street
Missoula, MT 59802
406-258-4608
Fax: 406-258-4710
www.ci.missoula.mt.us

- *Code Compliance Program (CCP)*: The CCP program subsidizes private businesses efforts in life-safety compliance regulations efforts in rehabilitating commercial properties.
- *Commercial Rehabilitation Loan Program (CRLP)*: Commercial loans to foster voluntary rehabilitation of eligible commercial properties.
- *Tax Increment Financing (TIF)*: Financing for public improvements related to urban renewal projects.

Montana County Economic Development

Big Sky Economic Development Authority
Yellowstone County
222 North 32nd Street
Billings, MT 59101
406-256-6871
Fax: 406-256-6877
www.bigskyeda.org

- *Training*: Training programs include regularly scheduled seminars and workshops on a wide variety of business topics.
- *Assistance*: The Authority provides free individual in-depth assistance to SBDC clients.

Flathead County Economic Development Authority
129 Main Street
Kalispell, MT 59901
406-257-7711
Fax: 406-257-7772
www.flatheadport.org

- *Jobs Now, Inc.*: This program provides relocation information to companies considering relocating to Flathead County. They also assist local companies wishing to expand. www.jobs-now.org
- *Flathead Business Resource Development Center*: This Center provides counseling to small business owners and start up businesses. 406-758-2802
- *Loans*: Local low-interest funds are available through Community Development Block Grants.
- *Tax Assistance*: Tax increment assistance may be used for certain types of economic development assistance within a tax increment district.
- *Site Location*: A database of available site locations is available.

PhillCo Economic Growth Council, Inc.
Phillips County
10 ½ South 4th East
P.O. Box 1637
Malta, MT 59538
406-654-1776
www.maltachamber.com/phillco

- *Phillips County Revolving Loan Fund*: Funds available to county businesses that either create or retain jobs.
- *Microbusiness Loan Fund*: Loans to small businesses of up to $35,000.

- *Individual and Business Technical Assistance*: PhillCo maintains a small resource library on business start-ups and funding. One-on-one assistance is also available.

Nebraska

Nebraska City Economic Development

City of Blair Economic Development
One Blair Place
1526 Washington Street
Blair, NE 68008
402-533-4455
www.blairchamber.org/econdevindex.htm

- *Site Location*: The Office of Business Development offers a list of available properties in the City.
- *Business Assistance*: Information is available on tax incentives, training programs and funding assistance for local businesses.

City of Central City Economic Development
1515 17th Street
Central City, NE 68826
308-946-2386
Fax: 308-946-2387
www.centralcity.org/econ.htm

- *Sales Tax Funds*: The Department of Economic Development uses sales tax funds to assist local businesses in the form of direct financial assistance. The assistance may be low interest loans, purchase/lease back of buildings, assistance with moving and new equipment costs.
- *Utilities*: The City owns and operates all utilities making a one-stop for businesses coordinating all of their business utility needs.
- *Tax Increment Financing*: The City can assist new or expanding businesses with the use of Tax In cement Financing.

Omaha Economic Development Council
Greater Omaha Chamber of Commerce
1301 Harney Street
Omaha, NE 68102
800-852-2622
402-346-5905
Fax: 402-346-7050
www.omahachamber.net/Busienss/business.html

- *Site Location*: The Omaha Economic Development Council offers a customized search of properties available in the area.
- *Business Assistance*: Information is available for state and local programs that provide assistance to new and expanding businesses.

Nebraska County Economic Development

Box Butte County Development Corporation
204 East Third
P.O. Box 802
Alliance, NE 69301
308-762-1800
Fax: 308-762-4268
www.bbc.net/bbdc/home.htm

- *Business Activities*: The Box Butte County Development Corporation offers a coordination of business and industry, confidential business consultation and small business support groups.
- *Business Assistance Center*: The Business Assistance Center creates an environment where small and new businesses can be successful. They offer technical

assistance, Internet access, light clerical access and computer time.

Fillmore County Development Corporation
1032 G Street
Geneva, NE 68361
402-759-4910
Fax: 402-759-4455
http://fillmorecounty.org/development/Development1.html
- *Site Location*: Fillmore County offers a list of available industrial and building locations to meet the need of your business.
- *Micro Business Energizers*: The local business development organization that works to build and support small self-employed & home-based businesses in the County.
- *Revolving Loan Fund*: The communities of Geneva and Exeter have access to Revolving Loan Funds. These low interest loans are available to new and expanding businesses.

York County Development Corporation
116 S. Lincoln Avenue, Suite 1
York, NE 68467
402-362-3333
888-733-9675
Fax: 402-362-5953
www.yorkchamber.org/ycdc.html
- *Revolving Loan Fund*: Low interest loans are available for capital related expenses that provide jobs for the low-middle income person.
- *Tax Increment Financing*: Funding available for public improvements associated with private development in designated areas.

Nevada

Nevada City Economic Development
City of Carlin Economic Development
101 South 8th Street
Carlin, NV 89822
775-754-6354
Fax: 775-754-6912
http://explorecarlinnv.com
- *Business Assistance*: The City of Carlin Economic Office proves information for businesses on a variety of topics that include: utilities, workforce, taxes and state incentives.

City of Henderson Economic Development
240 Water Street, 4th Floor
P.O. Box 95050
Henderson, NV 89009-5050
702-267-1650
Fax: 702-267-1651
www.cityofhenderson.com/ecodev/php/ecodevbody.php
- *Utility Franchise Fee Waiver*: The City of Henderson can provide partial exemption from the payment of the Public utilities License Fee tax for gas and/or electricity for qualifying businesses.
- *Site Location*: The City of Henderson provides a listing of available industrial sites and buildings to fit your businesses needs.
- *Business Workshops*: The City offers a wide variety of workshops, seminars, courses and events to help local businesses.

City of Las Vegas Office of Business Development
400 Steward Avenue
Las Vegas, NV 89101
702-229-6551
Fax: 702-385-3128
www.ci.las-vegas.nv.us/obd
- *New Business Assistance*: The City of Las Vegas offers a "New Business Checklist" to help new businesses get off to a great start.
- *Business & Industry/Business Parks*: Business Parks offer excellent locations, services and utilities as well as government cooperation. Companies located in these Parks pay no corporate, earnings, inventory, unitary or in-transit goods taxes; and their employees pay no personal income taxes.

Nevada County Economic Development
Churchill County Economic Development Authority
446 W. Williams Avenue
Fallon, NV 89406
775-423-8587
Fax: 775-423-1759
www.ceda-nv.org
- *Site Location*: Churchill County provides a listing of available land, building and business opportunities in the County.
- *Small Business Development Center*: The Center is staffed with professionals to help your company with any aspect of your business.

Elko County Economic Diversification Authority
723 Railroad Street
Elko, NV 89801
775-738-2100
866-YES-ELKO
Fax: 775-738-7978
www.eceda.com
- *Customized Industrial Training*: Customized Industrial Training provides job assistance to new businesses. The funds can help your company quickly train workers in the specialized skills your company needs.
- *International Trade Program*: This program offers assistance to begin or expand their international markets.
- *Sales & Use Tax Deferment*: New and Expanding businesses can defer sales and use taxes without interest for up to 5 years on certain capital goods purchased.

Lyon County Economic Development Authority
227 South Main Street
Yerington, NV 89447
775-463-2245
Fax: 775-577-5094
www.lceda.info
- *Business Information*: The Lyons County Economic Development office provides state economic information to businesses and how they can be utilized in Lyons County.
- *Business Assistance*: Lyons County offers a fast track approval system for businesses.

New Hampshire

New Hampshire City Economic Development
Town of Bow Economic Development
10 Grandview Road
Bow, NH 03304
603-225-3008
Fax: 603-225-5428

www.ci.bow.nh.us
- *Site Location*: The Town of Bow has six areas zoned for business development.

City of Concord Community Development
41 Green Street
Concord, NH 03301
603-225-8595
Fax: 603-228-2701
www.ci.concord.nh.us
The Business Development Division works to help current companies grow by assisting them in expansion efforts and by attracting new businesses to the Concord area.
- *Business Assistance*: The Concord Business Development Division provides a listing of financial institutions, industrial and professional space available other city programs.

City of Portsmouth Economic Development
1 Junkins Avenue
Portsmouth, NH 03801
603-431-2006 ext. 218
Fax: 603-427-1593
www.cityofportsmouth.com/economic
- *Portsmouth Economic Development Loan Program (PEDLP)*: The Portsmouth Economic Development Loan Program provides Portsmouth-based small businesses with long-term, low-interest financing.
- *Business Assistance*: The City of Portsmouth provides the "Economic Development Relocation Pages". This information can be found online to help businesses interested in starting or relocating to Portsmouth.

New Hampshire County Economic Development

Belknap County Economic Development Council
Southern New Hampshire University-Laconia Center
2 Airport Road
Gilford, NH 03249
603-524-3057
Fax: 603-524-0314
www.bcedc.org
- *Intermediary Relending Program*: These funds are to be used to supplement capital that could not be obtained through conventional sources and can be used for acquisition, expansion of small businesses, revitalization of downtowns, preservation and creation of employment opportunities.
- *Enterprise Loan Fund*: This is a flexible program designed to assist micro-enterprise businesses in Belknap County.
- *Lakes Region Job Start Fund*: The Lakes Region Job Start Fund is designed to develop and enhance self-employment opportunities. Priority is given to low and moderate income residents to start, strengthen or expand small businesses.
- *Community Development Grant Loan Program*: Projects that directly benefit low and moderate income residence through job creation.
- *Visitation Program*: The Grafton County Outreach program provides assistance to area businesses.

Grafton County Economic Development Council
20 Highland Street, Suite 2-5
Plymouth, NH 03264
603-536-1273
Fax: 603-536-1291
www.graftoncountyedc.org
- *The White Mountain Investor Alliance (WMIA)*: The White Mountain Investor Alliance provides equity capital for business startup, expansion or recruitment opportunities in Grafton County.
- *Business Finance Program*: The Grafton County Economic Development Council offers business assistance to develop and structure a financing package when quality jobs are retained or created.

Rockingham Economic Development Corporation
2 Center Street
P.O. Box 465
Exeter, NH 03833
603-772-2655
Fax: 603-772-0213
www.redc.com
The Rockingham Economic Development Corporation works to create jobs for low to moderate income people, by accessing alternative financing for business and industrial expansion/relocations, which in turn provides tax relief for the community.

New Jersey

New Jersey City Economic Development
Bayonne Economic Development Corporation
630 Avenue C, Room 4A
Bayonne, NJ 07002
201-339-0052
Fax: 201-339-0744
www.bayonnenj.org
- *One-Stop-Shop*: The One-Stop-Shop provides access to a wide range of financial assistance available to help your business.
- *Consultation Services*: In cooperation with Kean University, free one-on-one consultation is available for new and existing businesses.
- *Commercial Loan Program*: Short-term, below market rate loans to businesses unable to obtain conventional financing for job creating projects.
- *Site Location*: The Economic Development Corporation offers up-to-date listings of available industrial, commercial, office and storefront property in the City.

City of Camden Economic and Industrial Development
520 Market Street
City Hall, 13th Floor
P.O. Box 95120
Camden, NJ 08181-5120
856-968-4788
Fax: 856-968-4787
www.ci.camden.nj.us/economic.html
- *Cooperative Business Assistance Corporation (CBAC)*: The Cooperative Business Assistance Corporation provides business loans and technical assistance to small businesses in the City of Camden.
- *First Camden Business Center*: A business incubator designed to support both disadvantaged and established businesses. Retail and office tenants that are disadvantaged are offered discounts on rent, technical assistance and training seminars.

City of Vineland
640 E. Wood Street
Vineland, NJ 08360
856-794-4000 ext. 4619
www.vinelandbusiness.com
- *Five Year Real Estate Tax Exemption*: The City of Vineland five-year tax exemption program is applicable

to all new real property improvements. The plan offers 100%

- real estate tax exemption on the improved assessment for the first year after issuance of the final certificate of occupancy for the building, 80% exemption for the second year, 60% exemption for the third year, 40% exemption for the fourth year, and 20% exemption for the fifth year. Applies to improvements only. Taxes on land are not eligible.
- *Vineland Revolving Loan Fund*: The Vineland Revolving Loan Fund provides financial assistance to new and existing businesses with below market interest rate loans for qualifying equipment and improvements. Loan amounts range from $25,000 to $4 million.
- *Cumberland County College Mobile Learning Center Grants*: The Mobile Learning Center is a 10-station computer classroom offering instruction to your employees at you business location. The program is free to certified Urban Enterprise Zone businesses.

New Jersey County Economic Development

Cumberland County Department of Planning & Development
800 East Commerce Street
Bridgeton, NJ 08302
856-453-2175
Fax: 856-453-9138
www.co.cumberland.nj.us
- *Cumberland County Revolving Fund and Cumberland County Loan Assistance*: These five-year loans may be used for fixed assets and property acquisition.

Hudson County Economic Development Corporation
601 Pavonia Avenue, Suite 302
Jersey City, NJ 07306
201-222-1900
Fax: 201-222-6350
www.hudsonedc.org
- *MicroLoan Program*: The MicroLoan Program offers loans to businesses with five or fewer employees. Loan amounts range from $5,000 to $25,000.
- *Site Location*: The Economic Development Corporation maintains an extensive database of commercial and industrial properties available in the County.
- *Ombudsman Services*: The Ombudsman Service provides help to your business questions and problems.

Monmouth County Department of Economic Development & Tourism
31 E. Main
St. Freehold, NJ 07728
732-431-7470
Fax: 732-294-5930
www.visitmonmouth.com/econdev
- *Monmouth County Small Business Loan Program*: The Monmouth County Small Business Loan Program provides low-interest business loans and technical assistance.
- *County Planning Board's Report and Data Section*: A wealth of statistical information is available on Monmouth County including: building permits, Census, demographics and more.

New Mexico

New Mexico City Economic Development

Albuquerque Economic Development
851 University Boulevard SE, Suite 203
Albuquerque, NM 87106

800-451-2933
505-246-6200
Fax: 505-246-6219
http://abq.org
- *Business Assistance*: The Albuquerque Economic Development can provide your company with the following services: site-selection, labor market and business incentive analysis, workforce recruitment and job-training assistance.

Rio Rancho Economic Development Corporation
1700 Grando Court, Suite 222
Rio Rancho, NM 87124
800-544-8373
Fax: 505-891-4297
www.rredc.org
- *Site Location*: The Rio Rancho Economic Development Office offers a list of available business sites including: industrial parks, land, buildings and a Build-to-Suite Program.

Santa Fe Economic Development, Inc.
P.O. Box 8184
Santa Fe, NM 87504-8184
505-984-2842
Fax: 505-989-8614
www.sfedi.org
- *Santa Fe Direct Revolving Loan Fund*: Funds are available for businesses in Santa Fe and Extra Territorial Zone that target low to moderate income employees and create at least one job.
- *Tri-County Regional Revolving Loan Fund*: Businesses must create or retain one job for each $25,000 of federal funding.
- *Santa Fe Business Incubator*: The business facility supports new and growing businesses by offering affordable rent, shared support services and equipment and access to professional, technical and financial programs.

New Mexico County Economic Development

Bernalillo County Economic Development
One Civic Plaza NW
Albuquerque, NM 87102
505-768-4185
www.berno.gov
- *Bernalillo County International Trade*: Bernalillo County is working to bring businesses new and unique phases of international trade.
- *Economic Development Team*: The Economic Development Team can assist your business in locating or expanding in Bernalillo County. The team can also expedite permitting for quality development and assisting you in the development process.

Otero County Economic Development Council, Inc.
1301 N White Sands Boulevard
Alamogordo, NM 88310-6659
505-434-5882
Fax: 505-437-7139
www.ocedc.com
- *City of Alamogordo Incentives*: Otero County Economic Development Council manages this local development plan that allows the city to provide land, building and infrastructure resources at below market values.
- *Site Location*: The Council provides a list of available sites and buildings for area businesses.

Taos County Economic Development Corporation
P.O. Box 2830
Taos, NM 87571
505-758-4104
- *Business Assistance*: Consultation for new and existing small businesses.
- *Business Incubator*: Taos County provides a business incubator to help your business succeed.

New York

New York City Economic Development

Buffalo Economic Renaissance Corporation
920 City Hall
Buffalo, NY 14202
716-842-6923
Fax: 716-842-6942
www.growbfo.org
- *Small Business Resource Center*: A "first-stop" for new and existing business owners in the City of Buffalo where you can receive technical support, marketing assistance, internet access, money management skills, credit counseling and tax assistance.
- *Bond Readiness Program*: This program assists minority construction businesses through the bonding process.
- *Buffalo Economic Renaissance Council Business Loan Program*: Gap financing up to $300,000 to businesses in the City of Buffalo for renovation or acquisition of real estate, purchase of furniture and for permanent working capital.
- *Micro Loan Program*: Financing of up to $25,000 for businesses in the City of Buffalo particularly for start-up and minority and women businesses. Minimum loan $2,500.
- *Neighborhood Micro Loan Program*: Financing for City of Buffalo businesses that have been in operation for a year or more to encourage expansion. Loan amounts from $2,500 to $25,000.
- *Minority Contractor Loan Program*: Gap financing for minority construction businesses up to $300,000.

Ogdensburg Economic Development
330 Ford Street
City Hall, Room 10
Ogdensburg, NY 13669
315-393-7150
www.ogdensburg.org/econ.html
- *Real Property Tax Exemption*: New and expanding businesses in the Empire Zone are eligible for certain exemptions from real property taxes.
- *Local Sales Tax Credit*: A refund or credit of local sales taxes paid on building materials used in the construction, improving or rehabilitating industrial and some commercial property.
- *Ogdensburg Growth Fund Development Corporation*: Low-interest loans for acquisition, renovation equipment and working capital. A special program for construction assistance may allow for short-term borrowing at 0% when permanent financing has been arranged.

Syracuse Department of Economic Development
233 East Washington Street
219 City Hall
Syracuse, NY 13202
315-448-8100
Fax: 315-448-8036

www.syracuse.ny.us/deptEcoDev.asp
- *Urban Business Opportunity Center*: The Urban Business Opportunity Center focuses on increasing the participation of minorities and women with small business opportunities. They also offer a ten-week entrepreneurial training program twice a year.

New York County Economic Development

Delaware County Department of Economic Development
97 Main Street
Delhi, NY 13753
607-746-8595
Fax: 607-746-8836
www.co.delaware.ny.us/depts/ecodev/ecodev.htm
- *Agri-Business Loan Fund*: 6% loans for small businesses in Delaware County with 5 or fewer employees. It is expected that 1 new job will be created for each $5,000 of requested loan funds.
- *Microenterprise Business Training Program*: Free fourteen three hour classes for qualifying entrepreneurs to help in the business planning process.
- *Main Street Revitalization Loan Program*: Low-interest loans of up to $25,000 are available to new and existing main street businesses.
- *Site Location*: The Economic Development Office will help your business find the perfect site for your new or expanding business.

Genesee County Economic Development
One Mill Street
Atavia, NY 14020
877-343-4866
585-343-4866
Fax: 585-343-0848
www.gdedc.com
- *Sale Lease Back*: The Sale Lease Back Program can provide real estate tax abatement and tax exemptions related to capital investment projects.
- *Genesee County Revolving Loan Fund*: Low cost gap financing for Genesee County business owners for local development projects.

Warren County Economic Development Corporation
234 Glen Street
Glen Falls, NY 12801
518-761-6007
Fax: 518-761-9053
www.warrencounty.org
- *Training Grants*: Reimbursement of up to 50% of training costs for new employees with a maximum of $1,000 per person.
- *Local Tax Incentives*: 50% abatement on real property taxes for the first year, decreasing 5% each year for a nine year period.
- *Niagara Mohawk Power Corporation*: Incentives to reduce initial utility costs.

North Carolina

North Carolina City Economic Development

Farmville Development Partnership
3725 North Main Street
P.O. Box 150
Farmville, NC 27828
252-753-4670
Fax: 252-753-7313
www.farmvillenc.com

- *Business Incubator*: Farmville offers a Small Business Incubator to help new businesses get a great start.

Greensboro Economic Development Partnership
342 North Elm Street
Greensboro, NC 27401
336-691-6480
888-693-6939
Fax: 336-230-1867
www.forwardgreensboro.com
- *City of Greensboro Economic Development Investment Policy*: The City of Greensboro offers economic development incentives on a case by case basis.
- *Site Location*: The Greensboro Economic Development Partnership assists businesses with the selection of available properties.

Raleigh Economic Development Program
222 W. Hargett Street, 4th Floor
Raleigh, NC 27602
919-890-3125
www.raleigh-
   nc.org/planning/Economic/economic_program.htm
- *Business Assistance Program*: The City of Raleigh offers a Small Business Success Program and a Minority and Women-Owned Business Enterprise Program to help the businesses of Raleigh thrive.
- *Design Assistance Program*: The City of Raleigh helps businesses and property owners in older commercial areas upgrade and improve their building's exterior appearance.

North Carolina County Economic Development
Columbus County Economic Development Commission
111 Washington Street
P.O. Box 456
Whiteville, NC 28472
910-640-6608
Fax: 910-642-1876
www.columbusforindustry.com
- *Business Development Centers*: Centers are located in Tabor City and Whiteville and are intended to help start-up and emerging small businesses.
- *Job Creation Tax Credit*: Credit is available up to $4,000 per job and $8,000 within a Development Zone.
- *Investment Tax Credit*: 7% credit on all investment in machinery and equipment over $100,000.
- *Training Tax Credit*: $500 per job tax credit for each person trained.
- *Economic Development Zone*: Enhanced benefits for locating a new facility in the zone.

Orange County economic Development Commission
110 East King Street
P.O. Box 1177
Hillsborough, NC 27278
919-245-2325
www.co.orange.nc.us/ecodev
- *Orange County Small Business Loan Program*: Loans to existing and start-up companies in Orange County. Loan amounts range from $5,000 to $50,000 with a maximum 5 year term.
- *Small Business Resource Guide*: The Orange County Small Business Resource Guide was developed to help existing small business owners and those considering a start-up business find answers to their business questions.

Wake County Economic Development
800 South Salisbury Street
Raleigh, NC 27601
919-664-7000
Fax: 919-664-7099
www.raleigh-wake.org
- *Investment Tax Credit*: The investment tax credit equals 4% of the excess value of machinery and equipment placed in service by eligible businesses in Wake County.
- *Jobs Tax Credit*: Businesses with at least 5 full-time employees working at least 40 hours per week during a taxable year can take a $500 credit for each new job created in Wake County.
- *Worker training Tax Credit*: Eligible firms can take up to $500 credit against eligible training expenses.

North Dakota

North Dakota City Economic Development
FORWARD Devils Lake Corporation
P.O. Box 879
Devils Lake, ND 58301
701-662-4933
Fax: 701-662-2147
www.forwardd.com
- *Lake Region Growth Fund*: Local funds to be used for interest buy downs reduce interest loans, direct grants, equity positions and other financial incentives.
- *North Central Planning Council Revolving Fund*: The Revolving Loan Fund may be used for a variety of business needs. Terms of the loans are based on need. Funds are available for up to $150,000 and require a match from another source.
- *Micro-Loans*: Short-term loans of up to $15,000, $25,000 with a bank turndown.
- *Devils Lake Loan Pool*: Local lending to businesses for economic development of up to $400,000.
- *Start-up Entrepreneur Program (STEP)*: This program is designed to provide financing for small business activities including home-based businesses, retail services, manufacturing and tourism related businesses. The net worth of the business is limited to $150,000.

Grand Forks Region Economic Development Corporation
600 DeMars Avenue, Suite 501
Grand Forks, ND 58201
701-746-2720
Fax: 701-746-2725
www.grandforks.org
- *Grand Forks Growth Fund*: Gap and incentive financing for qualifying new and expanding businesses. Funds may be used to provide bridge and longer-term financing for initial construction costs, capital equipment, and working capital or seed rounds.
- *Site Location*: Grand Forks Economic Development offers a listing of available commercial buildings and sites in the area.

Linton Industrial Development Corporation
P.O. Box 433
Linton, ND 58552
701-254-4267
Fax: 701-254-4382
www.lintonnd.org/edc.htm
The Linton Industrial Development Corporation offers a variety of programs including: property and income tax

exemptions, job training assistance, Revolving Loan Fund and other incentives.

North Dakota County Economic Development

Divide County Jobs Development Authority
P.O. Box 297
Crosby, ND 58730
www.dividecounty.org
- *Divide County Revolving Loan Fund*: Low-interest loans to businesses with fewer than 50 employees and less than $1 million in sales. Loan amounts range from $2,500 to $25,000.
- *Spirit Fund*: Funds are targeted for job development; retention and capital expenses to businesses that want to expand or relocate in Crosby County which includes all of Divide County.

Stark County Development Corporation
P.O. Box 765
Dickinson, ND 58602-0765
701-225-5997
Fax: 701-227-8647
www.starkdev.com
- *Site Location*: Stark County maintains a listing of industrial sites and buildings available in Stark County.
- *West River Business Center*: Funding is available to provide customized training for your selected or potential employees.
- *Low Cost Capital & Siting Grants*: The Stark County Development Corporation provides a variety of programs to reduce the cost of capital necessary to stat, expand or relocate your business.
- *Business Counseling*: The Small Business Development Center provides free individual counseling to small business owners.

Traill County Economic Development Commission
330 Third Street NE #1856
Mayville, ND 58257-1299
701-788-4746
www.tcedc.com
- *Site Location*: The Traill County Economic Development Commission provides businesses with up-to-date commercial and industrial site information.
- *Loans*: Limited 0% interest loans are available for start-ups, expansions and transfer of ownership for local businesses of all types.
- *Micro-Loan Program*: Loans of up to $35,000 are available to qualifying businesses.

Ohio

Ohio City Economic Development

City of Painesville Economic Development Division
7 Richmond Street
P.O. Box 44077
Painesville, OH 44077
440-392-5795
Fax: 440-639-4831
www.painesville.com/development.htm
- *Site Location*: The Painesville Department of Economic Development maintains a list of vacant land sites in the City and can assist your business in finding a building or site that meets your needs.
- *PLEDGE Linked Deposit Low-Interest Loan Program*: The City assists new businesses in the City with loans at up to 3% below the conventional loan rate.

- *Community Reinvestment Area Tax Incentive*: The City has four Community Reinvestment Areas that provide business with real property tax exemptions of up to 100% for ten years.
- *Questline: Technical Assistance Hotline*: Questline is a free technical information and research hotline available to all Painesville city businesses.

City of Springfield Economic Development
City Hall
76 East High Street
Springfield, OH 45502
937-324-7300
Fax: 937-328-3497
www.springfield.oh.us/depts/ed
- *Site Location*: Springfield Economic Office maintains a listing of available properties in the City.
- *City Jobs Credits*: City Jobs Credits can be applied toward acquisition costs of land at the City's industrial parks.
- *Microloan Program*: Loans are available to eligible start-up or newly formed small businesses with loan amounts of $500 to $5,000.
- *Springfield City Revolving Loan Program*: Direct loans of up to 33% of the project costs are available to manufacturers, retail and service companies. Companies must demonstrate need and verify the creation/retention of one job for every $10,000 received.
- *Springfield Targeted Investment Loan Fund*: Direct loans to manufactures, wholesalers and large scale retail projects in targeted areas of the City of Springfield.

City of Toledo Economic Development
626 Jackson Boulevard, Suite 1710
Toledo, OH 43604
419-245-1470
Fax: 419-245-1462
www.ci.toledo.oh.us
- *Core City Façade Grant Program*: Businesses located in Downtown Overlay District may apply for one-third reimbursement grants for investments of up to $75,000 to improve the exterior of existing buildings in the designated project areas.
- *Downtown Employment Incentive Program*: Funds are available to encourage private businesses to expand and remain within the Downtown Overlay District.

Ohio County Economic Development

Franklin County Department of Community & Economic Development
373 South High Street, 25th Floor
Columbus, OH 43215
614-462-5631
Fax: 614-462-5549
www.co.franklin.oh.us/commissioners/ced/economic_development.htm
- *Tax Increment Finance Districts*: The County provides tax incentives in special designated districts to encourage industrial, commercial or residential development.
- *Grow Franklin County Fund*: This revolving loan fund is designed to provide loans to larger scale businesses to be used for the purchase of equipment, capital expenditures or working capital.
- *Micro-Enterprise Program*: Loans of up to $15,000 are available to individuals and small businesses for the purpose of creating or expanding their business.

Hamilton County Development Company
Economic Development Office
1776 Mentor Avenue
Cincinnati, OH 45212
513-631-8292
Fax: 513-631-4887
www.hcdc.com
- *Business Incubator*: The Hamilton County Business Center Incubator assists entrepreneurs by providing flexible space, administrative services, business counseling and assistance and a supportive environment.
- *Microloans*: Loans are available for up to $20,000 for qualifying start-ups and $35,000 for qualifying existing businesses in Hamilton County.

Monroe County Office of Economic Development and Tourism
101 North Main Street, Room 11
Woodsfield, OH 43793
740-472-0169
877-456-2737
Fax: 740-472-0490
www.monroecountyohio.net/
- *Monroe County Revolving Loan Fund*: Financing available for qualifying businesses in Monroe County.
- *Site Location*: Monroe County offers a variety of development sites for businesses in the County.

Oklahoma

Oklahoma City Economic Development

Ardmore Development Authority
P.O. Box 1585
Ardmore, OK 73402
580-223-7765
www.ardmoredevelopment.com
- *Ardmore Build-to Suit Program*: Low-construction cost building program and favorable tax treatment can provide you business with a new industrial or commercial building.
- *Business Programs*: The Ardmore Development Authority coordinates business assistance programs and networking for businesses in the community.

Norman Economic Development Coalition
710 Asp Avenue, Suite 100
Norman, OK 73069
405-573-1900
Fax: 405-573-1999
http://etecok.com/nedc
- *eTec*: The Emerging Technical Entrepreneurial Center (eTec) is a business accelerator designed to help new technology companies grow.
- *Site Location*: Norman maintains a list of available sites and buildings to meet the needs of your business.
- *Ombudsman Service*: The Ombudsman service provides information for businesses to state and local government incentives.

Ponca City Development Authority
012 S. Fifth, Suite 3
Ponca City, OK 74601
580-765-7070
www.goponca.com
- *New Business Information*: The City of Ponca publishes "Starting a Business" with information on starting a business in the City of Ponca.

- *Site Location*: The City maintains information of available sites and buildings in the City to meet your businesses needs.
- *Business Incentives*: The Ponca City Development Authority can design incentive packages based on your business needs.
- *Cost Analysis*: Ponca City can provide your business with up-to-date cost analysis on a variety of topics.

Oklahoma County Economic Development

Enid/Garfield County Economic Development Alliance
P.O. Box 5616
Enid, OK 73702
580-233-4232
Fax: 580-237-2497
www.enidchamber.com
- *Site Location*: The Alliance maintains a listing of available buildings and sites in the County to meet the needs of your business.
- *Small Business Linked Deposit Program*: This program provides below-market interest rates for qualifying small businesses and certified industrial parks.

Pawnee County Economic Development Foundation
P.O. Box 177
Cleveland, OK 74020
918-358-2245
www.pawneecounty.org
- *Site Location*: The Pawnee County Economic Development Foundation maintains a listing of current available properties to meet the need of your business.

Rogers County Industrial Development Authority
P.O. Box 606
Claremore, OK 74018
918-343-8959
http://rcida.com
- *Business Incubator*: The Rogers County Business Incubator nurtures business development for new and expanding companies.

Oregon

Oregon City Economic Development

Albany-Millersburg Economic Development Corporation
435 1st Avenue W
P.O. Box 548
Albany, OR 97321
541-926-1519
Fax: 541-926-7064
www.albany-millersburg.com
- *Site Location*: Albany-Millersburg Economic Development Corporation maintains a listing of industrial buildings and land to meet the needs of your business.
- *Management Assistance*: Albany-Millersburg Economic Development Corporation offers free, confidential counseling in business planning, financial management, marketing and other areas of business for all sizes and stages of business.

Grants Pass Economic Development
101 NW "A" Street
Grants Pass, OR 97526
541-474-6360
Fax: 541-479-0812
www.visitgrantspass.org/econdev

- *Grants Pass Industrial Development Revolving Loan Program*: Low-interest gap financing to expand your business.
- *Downtown Grants Pass Building Renovation Loan Fund*: The City's Building Renovation Loan Fund can provide financing for the restoration and or renovation of buildings within the Central Business District.

Portland Development Commission
1900 SW Fourth Avenue, Suite 7000
Portland, OR 97201-5348
503-823-3200
Fax: 503-823-3368
www.pdc.us
- *Site Location*: Portland Development Commission maintains a listing of available real estate locations that meet the needs of your business.
- *Seismic Loan Program*: A renovation loan program intended to upgrade the safety and use of Class B and Class C commercial buildings in the Central City.
- *Finance Guide*: Portland Economic Commission publishes "Quick Guide to Business Finance Programs" and is available online at their web site.

Oregon County Economic Development
Corvallis-Benton County Economic Development
  Partnership
1600 SW Western Boulevard
Corvallis, OR 97333
541-757-1507
Fax: 541-757-2556
www.corvallisedp.com
- *Site Location*: Corvallis-Benton County Economic Development Partnership maintains a current listing of industrial sites available to meet the needs of your business.
- *Import/Export Assistance*: Assistance is available through the Willamette International Trade Center, the World Trade Center in Portland and the Oregon International Trade Division.
- *Access to Finances*: Access to "Angel" investment through the Corvallis Venture Forum.

Harney County Economic Development
450 N. Buena Vista
Burns, OR 97720
541-573-6356
Fax: 541-573-8387
www.harveycountyeconomicdevelopment.com
- *Business Classes*: Low cost classes to help you learn how to write a business plan, apply for financing, and other business topics.
- *Site Location*: Harvey County Economic Development maintains a listing of available retail, industrial and commercial sites to meet the needs of your business.

Union County Economic Development Corporation
1119 Washington Avenue
P.O. Box 1208
La Grande, OR 97850
www.ucedc.org
- *Business Incubator*: The incubator provides assistance to early stage companies. They offer a variety of opportunities including: flexible office space leases, access to office equipment, technical assistance, clerical support and training sessions.
- *Site Location*: The Union County Economic Development Corporation maintains a current listing of available sites to meet the needs of your business.

Pennsylvania

Pennsylvania City Economic Development
Bensalem Economic Development Corporation
Bensalem Township Municipal Building
2400 Byberry Road
Bensalem, PA 19020
215-633-3681
Fax: 215-633-3609
www.bensalem-edc.com
- *Enterprise Zone Competitive Grant (Loan)*: Low-interest loans for up to 30% of total project costs.
- *Enterprise Zone Tax Credit Program*: Provides tax credits to EX businesses making investments in the rehabilitation, expansion or improvement of existing buildings or land eligible activities.
- *Small Business Capital Fund*: Loans of up to$500,000 for small businesses located in the Enterprise Zone for working capital or bridge financing.

Greater Scranton Chamber of Commerce Economic
  Development
222 Mulberry Street
Scranton, PA 18503
570-342-7711
Fax: 570-347-6262
www.scrantonchamber.com/economic
- *Site Location*: The Greater Scranton Chamber of Commerce Economic Development maintains a current listing of available sites to meet the needs of your business.
- *Business Incubator*: A business incubator facilities is available to assist entrepreneurs get their businesses started.
- *Scranton Industrial Development Company Loan Program*: Scranton Industrial Development Company Loan Program provides short-term working capital loans of up to $75,000 to local businesses that are unable to obtain conventional financing.

Lehigh Valley Economic Development Corporation
P.O. Box 21750
Lehigh, PA 18002
610-266-6775
800-581-7483
Fax: 610-266-7623
www.leighvalley.org
- *Site Location*: The Lehigh Valley Economic Development Corporation maintains a current listing of available sites to meet the needs of your business.
- *Downtown Façade Program*: The program is designed to improve the appearance, safety and energy efficiency of downtown retail properties and to provide for interior renovations and equipment purchases for retail operators.

City of Pittsburgh Economic Development
City-County Building
414 Grant Street
Pittsburgh, PA 15219
412-255-2626
www.city.pittsburgh.pa.us/ed/home.html
- *One-Stop Assistance*: Businesses in Pittsburgh are assigned an Economic Development Coordinator who will serve as a single point of contact to your businesses throughout the development process.
- *Site Location*: The City of Pittsburgh Economic Development maintains a current listing of available sites to meet the needs of your business.

Pennsylvania County Economic Development

Adams County Economic Development Corporation
1300 Proline Place
Gettysburg, PA 17325
717-334-0042
Fax: 717-337-1628
www.aceds.org

- *Site Location*: The Adams County Economic Development Corporation maintains a current listing of available sites to meet the needs of your business.
- *Small Business First Fund*: Funds available for businesses of 100 employees or fewer.

Economic Development Corporation of Erie County
5240 Knowledge Parkway
Erie, PA 16510-4658
814-899-6022
Fax: 814-899-0250
www.connectforsuccess.org

- *Erie Technology Incubator*: Four area incubators available for start-up businesses.
- *Site Location*: The Economic Development Corporation of Erie County maintains a current listing of available sites to meet the needs of your business.
- *Small Business First (SBF)*: The Small Business First Funding Program provides businesses with low-interest loan financing for land and building acquisition and construction, machinery and equipment purchase and working capital.
- *Enterprise Development Fund of Erie County*: This is a revolving loan fund to provide a stable interest rate and credit enhancement through second-lien lending for small businesses in Erie County.

Washington County Chamber of Commerce
20 East Beau Street
Washington, PA 15301
724-225-3010
Fax: 724-228-7337
www.washcochamber.com

- *Site Location*: The Washington County Chamber of Commerce maintains a current listing of available sites to meet the needs of your business.

Rhode Island

Rhode Island City Economic Development

City of East Providence Economic Development Office
145 Taunton Avenue
East Providence, RI 02914
401-435-7500
Fax: 401-435-7501
www.eastprovidence.com

- *Site Location*: The City of East Providence Economic Development Office maintains a current listing of available sites to meet the needs of your business.
- *Commercial Loan Program*: Low interest loans are available for commercial or industrial businesses to finance acquisition, construction and improvements of land or buildings and for the purchase of capital equipment located in East Providence.
- *Commercial Microloan Program*: Financing for start-up expenses, operating expenses and to purchase assets for businesses with five or fewer employees which are unable to obtain a loan through conventional sources. Loans are available from $1,000 to $10,000.

- *Site Location*: The City of East Providence Economic Development Office maintains a current listing of available sites to meet the needs of your business.

Providence Department of Planning and Development
400 Westminster Street
Providence, RI 02903
401-351-4300
www.providenceri.com/government/planning/planning-index.html
The Providence Department of Planning and Development works to attract and retain businesses to Providence. They achieve this through a variety of programs.

Woonsocket Economic Development
169 Main Street
Woonsocket, RI 02895
401-762-6400
www.ci.woonsocket.ri.us/ecnmc_dv.htm

- *Woonsocket Job Creation Incentive Program*: Financial incentive for new and existing businesses to construct and/or renovate industrial and commercial facilities.
- *Small Business Loan Program*: Woonsocket offers a Small Business revolving Loan Program to assist marginal businesses which may otherwise not qualify for conventional financing.

South Carolina

South Carolina City Economic Development

Charleston Regional Development Alliance
5300 International Boulevard, Suite 103A
North Charleston, SC 29418
843-767-9300
Fax: 843-760-4635
www.charleston-for-business.com
Charleston Regional Development Alliance assists businesses with information, workforce development, market access and state taxes and incentives.

City of Greenville Economic Development
P.O. Box 2207
Greenville, SC 29602
864-467-4401
www.greenville.com/development/eco_dev.asp

- *Façade Improvement Program*: Grants of up to 20% of total renovation and new construction costs with a $10,000 maximum for façade improvements within the Pleasantburg Drive Corridor Plan Overlay District.
- *Upper Story House Loan*: Low interest loans to create or rehabilitate residential units in the upper stories of buildings in the Central Business District or the West End Tax Increment District.
- *Business License Tax Abatement*: A graduated 3-year abatement of the City business license fee for new corporate offices, manufacturing, research and development and technology services on a city-wide basis.

Town of Mount Pleasant Office of Economic Development
100 Ann Edwards Lane
P.O. Box 745
Mount Pleasant, SC 29465
843-856-2504
Fax: 843-856-2180
http://townofmountpleasant.com/EconDev

- *Site Location*: The Town of Mount Pleasant Office of Economic Development maintains a current listing of available sites to meet the needs of your business.

Rock Hill Economic Development Corporation
155 Johnson Street
Rock Hill, SC 29730
803-329-7090
Fax: 803-329-7007
www.ci.rock-hill.sc.us
- *Free Training*: Training is available through York technical College.
- *Site Location*: The Rock Hill Economic Development Corporation maintains a current listing of available sites to meet the needs of your business.

South Carolina County Economic Development

Barnwell County Economic Development Commission
P.O. Box 898
Barnwell, SC 29812
803-259-1263
Fax: 803-259-0030
www.barnwellcountysc.com
- *Barnwell County Revolving Loan Fund*: Financial assistance and guidance are available to qualifying new and existing businesses located in one of the three industrial parks.
- *Site Location*: The Barnwell County Economic Development Commission maintains a current listing of available sites to meet the needs of your business.

Hampton County Economic Development Commission
P.O. Box 672
Courthouse Annex
10 Elm Street East
Hampton, SC 29924
803-943-7521
Fax: 803-943-7538
www.hamptoncountyedc.com
Hampton County has a variety of economic incentives and will work with businesses on a case-by-case basis.
- *Site Location*: The Hampton County Economic Development Commission maintains a current listing of available sites to meet the needs of your business.

Union County Economic Development
207 S. Herndon Street
Union, SC 29379
864-319-1097
Fax: 864-319-1099
www.unioncountydevelopment.com
- *Site Location*: The Union County Economic Development maintains a current listing of available sites to meet the needs of your business.

South Dakota

South Dakota City Economic Development

Brookings Economic Development Corporation
2308 6th Street
Brookings, SD 57006
605-697-8103
www.swiftel.net/brkecon
- *Business Incubator*: A business incubator facilities is available to assist entrepreneurs get their businesses started.

- *Site Location*: The Brookings Economic Development Corporation maintains a current listing of available sites to meet the needs of your business.

Rapid City Economic Development
444 North Mount Rushmore Road
Rapid City, SD 57701
800-956-0377
605-343-1880
Fax: 605-343-1916
www.rapiddevelopment.com
- *Site Location*: The Rapid City Economic Development maintains a current listing of available sites to meet the needs of your business.

Yankton Office of Economic Development
P.O. Box 588
Yankton, SD 57087
888-YANKTON (926-5866)
www.yanktonsd.com
- *Site Location*: The Yankton Office of Economic Development maintains a current listing of available sites to meet the needs of your business.
- *Property Tax Abatement*: Tax abatements are available to qualifying new commercial or industrial construction.
- *Financing*: Financing is available to qualifying businesses for approved projects.

South Dakota County Economic Development

First District Association of Local Governments
P.O. Box 1207
124 1st Avenue NW
Watertown, SD 57201
605-882-5115
800-981-9092 (in-state only)
Fax: 605-882-5049
www.1stdistrict.org
First District serves the counties of Brookings, Clark, Codington, Deuel, Grant, Hamlin, Kingsbury, Lake, Miner, Moody and Roberts.
- *Revolving Loan Fund*: Two revolving loan funds are available to eligible businesses located in one of the First District Counties.
- *Deuel, Hamlin, and Kingsbury Revolving Loan Fund*: Funds available to qualifying businesses in these counties.

Hamlin County Development
17852 447th Avenue
Hayti, SD 57241-0237
605-783-3201
Fax: 605-783-3201

Northeast South Dakota Economic Corporation (NESDEC)
414 Third Avenue East
Sisseton, SD 57262
605-698-7654
Fax: 605-698-3038
www.nesdcap-nesdec.org
Northeast South Dakota Economic Corporation serves the counties of Beadle, Brown, Buffalo, Clark, Codington, Day, Edmunds, Faulk, Grant, Hand, Jerald, Marshall, Kingsbury, Miner, McPherson, Roberts, Campbell, Walworth, Potter, Sully, Hughes, Sanborn, Stanley, Hyde, Spink and Walworth.
- *CD Pledge Program*: NESDEC can pledge a CD of up to 50 % of a small business loan with a maximum of $20,000.

- *Technical Assistance*: Free technical assistance program assists with requirements of loan processes, business planning, cash flow projections, start-up procedures, and state/federal requirements.

Tennessee

Tennessee City Economic Development

City of Bartlett Economic Development
City Hall
6400 Stage Road
Bartlett, TN 38134
901-385-6417
Fax: 901-385-6419
www.cityofbartlett.org/subdepts/econdev.htm
- *Free Guide*: A step-by-step guide *Opening a Business in Bartlett* is available on their web site.
- *Tax Abatement*: Incentives are available for qualifying businesses.

City of Burnet Economic Development
P.O. Box 1369
Burnet, TN 78611
512-756-6093
Fax: 512-756-8560
www.cityofburnet.com
- *Site Location*: The City of Burnet Economic Development maintains a current listing of available sites to meet the needs of your business.
- *Tax Abatement*: The City provides tax abatement and other incentives within the "Reinvestment Zone".

Oak Ridge Economic Development
1400 Oak Ridge Turnpike
Oak Ridge, TN 37830
865-483-1321
Fax: 865-483-1678
www.orcc.org/economicdev
- *Oak Ridge Economic Partnership's Existing Business Development (EBD)*: EBD was created to help existing businesses develop and succeed. They will visit and work with your company to connect you with resources.

Tennessee County Economic Development

Benton County Economic Development
202 West Main Street
Camden, TN 38320
731-584-8395
Fax: 731-584-5544
www.bentoncountynet.com
- *Site Location*: The Benton County Economic Development Office maintains a current listing of available sites to meet the needs of your business.
- *Incentives*: Benton County offers incentives to local businesses. Contact the Benton County Economic Development Office to apply.

Campbell County Chamber of Commerce
P.O. box 305
Jacksboro, TN 37757
423-566-0329
Fax: 423-562-0535
http://co.campbell.tn.us
- *Site Location*: The Campbell County Chamber of Commerce maintains a current listing of available sites to meet the needs of your business.

Giles County Economic Development Commission
203 South First Street
P.O. Box 633
Pulaski, TN 38478
931-363-9138
Fax: 931-363-3408
www.gilescountyedc.com
- *Site Location*: The Giles County Economic Development Commission maintains a current listing of available sites to meet the needs of your business.

Texas

Texas City Economic Development

Amarillo Economic Development Corporation
Bank One Center, Suite 1503
600 South Tyler
Amarillo, TX 79101
806-379-6411
Fax: 806-397-0112
www.amarillo-tx.com
- *Site Location*: The Amarillo Economic Development Corporation maintains a current listing of available sites to meet the needs of your business.
- *Business Incentives*: Amarillo offers business incentives in the form of cash grants and interest-free loans to companies creating new jobs in Amarillo.
- *Tax Abatement*: Businesses constructing new industrial facilities may be eligible for local tax abatement.

City Development Corporation of El Campo
201 E Jackson
P.O. Box 446
El Campo, TX 77437
979-578-0066
Fax: 979-543-5495
www.elcampoeco.org
- *Site Location*: The City Development Corporation of El Campo maintains a current listing of available sites to meet the needs of your business.
- *Business Services*: CDC of El Campo provides many services including: Small Business Center, Business and Retention Services, and a Education and Training Center.

Taylor Economic Development Corporation
P.O. Box 975
316 N Main
Taylor, TX 76574
888-828-5678
512-352-4321
Fax: 512-352-4318
www.tayloredc.com
- *Financial Incentives*: The Taylor Development Corporation offers funds to qualifying businesses in Taylor on a case-by-case basis.
- *Tax Abatement*: The City of Taylor offers tax abatements designed to encourage the creation of jobs, capital investment and to implement the city's master plan.

Texas County Economic Development

Goliad County Economic Development
P.O. Box 519
Goliad, TX 77963
361-645-3540
www.goliad.org

- *Goliad Sales Tax Development Corporation*: Funds are available to qualifying new and existing businesses that create jobs and impact the County of Goliad.
- *Reinvestment Zone*: Four areas in Goliad County are designated as reinvestment zones.
- *Tax Abatement Program*: The Tax Abatement Program is based on job creation by local businesses.

Harris County Community & Economic Development
  Department
8410 Lantern Point Drive
Houston, TX 77054
713-578-2000
www.cedd.hctx.net

Johnson County Economic Development Commission
P.O. Box 1657
Cleburne, TX 76033-1657
817-558-3900
Fax: 817-641-6059
www.jc-edc.com
- *Tax Abatement*: Tax abatements are available to qualifying businesses on a case-by-case basis in Johnson County.
- *Enterprise Zones*: Businesses located in Alvarado, Burleson and Cleburne are eligible for local and state business benefits.

Utah

Utah City Economic Development

Cedar City Utah
10 North Main Street
P.O. Box 249
Cedar City, UT 84720
435-586-2950
www.cedarcity.org
- *Small Business Development Center*: Personal consultation is available to small businesses on management, marketing and planning.
- *Site Location*: Cedar City Utah maintains a current listing of available sites to meet the needs of your business.
- *Custom Fit Training*: Custom Fit Training is available through Southern Utah University.

Commission for Economic Development Orem
777 South State Street
Orem, UT 84058
801-226-1521
Fax: 801-226-2678
www.cedo.org
- *Business Incubator*: A business incubator facilities is available to assist entrepreneurs get their businesses started.
- *Revolving Loan Fund*: Financing is available to Orem qualifying businesses that show potential for significant growth.

West Jordan City Economic Development Office
8000 Redwood Road
West Jordan, UT 84088
801-569-5000
www.wjordan.com/EconDev/ed.cfm
West Jordan Economic Development offers incentive programs to businesses on a case-by-case basis.

Utah County Economic Development

Emery County Economic Development
P.O. Box 297
Castle Dale, UT 84513
435-381-5576
www.emerycounty.com
- *Business Incubator*: A business incubator facilities is available to assist entrepreneurs get their businesses started.

Uintah County and Vernal City Economic Development
State and County Building
147 East Main
Vernal, UT 84078
435-781-6731
http://utahreach.usu.edu/uintah/govt/econ.htm

Weber County Economic Development Corporation
2484 Washington Boulevard, Suite 400
Ogden, UT 84401
888-621-8306 ext. 3013
Fax: 801-392-7609
www.webergrowth.com
- *Site Location*: The Weber County Economic Development Corporation maintains a current listing of available sites to meet the needs of your business.

Vermont

Vermont City Economic Development

Burlington Community & Economic Development Office
Room 23- City Hall
149 Church Street
Burlington, VT 05401
802-865-7144
Fax: 802-865-7024
www.cedoburlington.org
- *Business Loan Program*: This gap financing is available to eligible small businesses located in Burlington.
- *Site Location*: The Burlington Community & Economic Development Office maintains a current listing of available sites to meet the needs of your business.
- *Burlington's Designated Downtown District*: There are benefits available to property or business owners in the district.
- *Government Contracting*: The Burlington Community & Economic Development Office
- provides information about available programs to help your business with government contracting.

Montpelier Community & Economic Development
City Hall
39 Main Street
Montpelier, VT 05602-2950
802-223-9506
Fax: 802-223-9524
www.montpelier-vt.org/dca/index.cfm
- *Montpelier Business Loan Fund*: The Montpelier Community & Economic Development Office offers funds for eligible businesses.

Springfield Development Corporation
14 Clinton Street
Springfield, VT 05156
802-885-3061
Fax: 802-885-3027
www.springfielddevelopment.org

- *Site Location*: The Springfield Development Corporation maintains a current listing of available sites to meet the needs of your business.
- *Financial Assistance*: The Springfield Development Corporation will help your business sort through the programs available to meet your individual needs.

Vermont County Economic Development

Bennington County Industrial Corporation
P.O. Box 357
109 Water Street
N. Bennington, VT 05257
802-442-8975
Fax: 802-447-1101
www.bcic.org

The Central Vermont Economic Development Corporation
P.O. Box 1439
Montpelier, VT 05601-1439
802-223-4654
Fax: 802-223-4655
www.central-vt.com/cvedc

- *Free Information Packet*: A free information packet is available to businesses looking to start a business in Central Vermont that includes information on tax credits, incentives, workforce and financing.
- *Site Location*: The Central Vermont Economic Development Corporation maintains a current listing of available sites to meet the needs of your business.

Town and Village of Waterbury, Vermont
P.O. Box 9
51 South Main Street
Waterbury, VT 05676
802-244-7033
www.waterburyvt.com

- *Site Location*: The Town and Village of Waterbury, Vermont maintains a current listing of available sites to meet the needs of your business.
- *Waterbury Village Revolving Loan Fund*: The fund is designed to attract businesses to the village or assist existing businesses to expand.

Virginia

Virginia City Economic Development

City of Hampton Department of Economic Development
One Franklin Street, Suite 600
Hampton, VA 23669
800-555-3930
757-6237
Fax: 757-727-6895
www.hamptonva.biz

- *Business Incubators*: The City of Hampton has three business incubator facilities that can assist entrepreneurs get their businesses started.
- *Hampton Rehab Credit*: Commercial and industrial structures that are 25 years or older are eligible for a 6-year exemption of the increased assessed value of property after rehabilitation.

Roanoke Economic Development
111 Franklin Plaza, Suite 200
Roanoke, VA 24011
540-853-2715
Fax: 540-853-1213
www.roanokegov.com

- *Business Assistance*: The Roanoke Economic Development Office serves as an ombudsman for business concerns. They also provide Site visits to work with your business on an individual basis to improve your company.
- *Site Location*: The Roanoke Economic Development Office maintains a current listing of available sites to meet the needs of your business.

The City of Virginia Beach Economic Development
222 Central Park Avenue, Suite 1000
Virginia Beach, VA 23462
800-989-4567
Fax: 757-499-9894
www.vbgov.com/dept/econdev
The City of Virginia Beach Economic Development Office implements strategies to help new and existing businesses.

Norfolk Redevelopment and Housing Authority
201 Granby Street, 6th Floor
Norfolk, VA 23510
757-314-1646
Fax: 757-314-1304
www.ccdi-va.net/
Future business owners of the Hampton Roads, VA community can benefit from the Cottage Industry Microenterprise Program administered by the Center for Community Development, Inc. (CCDI). Designed to serve as a catalyst for low income persons, women and minorities to achieve success through business ownership, program highlights include an 8-week MicroBusiness Development course on business planning, one-on-one practical counseling with a Microenterpise Specialist, and access to loan funding. Three loan types are available to entrepreneurs who have completed the CCDI training course: term loans of up to $35,000; contract loans up to $15,000, based on contract assignment; and participation loans, in which CCDI partners with an area bank to lend amounts up to $105,000. Collateral is not required in all cases. Counselors assist applicants through each step of the application process. The organization remains active with its business clients during the term of the loan, extending counseling services and making on-site visits. Detailed instructions and sample outlines for a business plan are also available for all prospective business owners on CCDI's website.

Virginia County Economic Development

Henrico County Economic Development Authority
4300 E. Parham Road
Richmond, VA 23228
804-501-7654
Fax: 804-501-7890
www.henricobusiness.com

- *Site Location*: The Henrico County Economic Development Authority maintains a current listing of available sites to meet the needs of your business.

James City County Office of Economic Development
101-C Mounts Bay Road
P.O. Box 8784
Williamsburg, VA 23187
757-253-6607
www.jccecondev.com

- *Site Location*: The James City County Office of Economic Development maintains a current listing of available sites to meet the needs of your business.
- *Incentives*: The James City County Office of Economic Development considers incentive for qualifying new and existing businesses based on a case-by-case basis.

Orange County Economic Development Office
105 East Main Street
Orange, VA 22960
540-672-1238
800-672-4778
Fax: 540-672-4762
www.orangevirginiawelcomebusiness.com
- *Site Location*: The Orange County Economic Development Office maintains a current listing of available sites to meet the needs of your business.
- *Business Incubator*: Business office space for new businesses in Orange County at reduced costs. www.orangebusinessincubator.com

Washington

Washington City Economic Development

Port of Olympia
915 Washington Street NE
Olympia, WA 98501
360-528-8000
Fax: 360-528-8090
www.portolympia.com
- *Foreign Trade Zone*: Land and infrastructure improvements are provided to encourage business development.

Port of Port Townsend
333 Benedict Street
P.O. Box 1180
Port Townsend, WA 98368
360-385-0656
www.portofpt.com/edc.html

City of Richland Office of Business and Economic Development
505 Swift Boulevard
P.O. Box 190
Richland, WA 99352
509-942-7582
Fax: 509-942-5665
www.ci.richland.wa.us
- *Hotel and Motel Tax Fund*: Funds are available for eligible tourism-related programs in the City of Richland.
- *Business License Reserve Fund*: This fund provides grants to organizations for business activities which support business development, tourism, economic development, capital expenditures and community improvements.
- *Citywide Improvements Grants*: These grants are available to help business owners improve the exterior appearance of buildings in the City.
- *Rental Rehabilitation Program*: The Rental Rehabilitation Program assists investors or property owners to rehabilitate residential properties.

Washington County Economic Development

Grays Harbor Economic Development Council
506 Duffy Street
Aberdeen, WA 98520
360-532-7888
800-553-6618
Fax: 360-532-7922
www.ghedc.com
- *Fast Track Permitting*: The Gray Harbor Economic Development Council acts as an ombudsman for local businesses to help them with the roadblocks and paperwork with permits and licenses.
- *Site Location*: The Grays Harbor Economic Development Council maintains a current listing of available sites to meet the needs of your business.

Skamania County Economic Development Council
P.O. Box 436
Stevenson, WA 98648
509-427-5110
Fax: 509-427-5122
www.skamania-edc.org
- *Business Counseling*: The Skamania County Economic Development Council provides business counseling and business planning assistance to new and existing businesses.
- *Workshops*: The Skamania County Economic Development Council sponsors workshops for local businesses and maintains a business information center.
- *Micro-loan Programs*: Skamania County Economic Development Council operates two micro-loan programs for area businesses.

Economic Development Council of Thurston County
665 Woodland Square Loop SE, Suite 201
Lacey, WA 98503
360-754-6320
Fax: 360-407-3980
www.thurstonedc.com
- *Site Location*: The Economic Development Council of Thurston County maintains a current listing of available sites to meet the needs of your business
- *Free Counseling*: Thurston County provides free counseling through their business resource Center Manager.

West Virginia

West Virginia City Economic Development

Bridgeport Economic Development
515 W. Main Street
Bridgeport, WV 26330
304-842-8200
Fax: 304-842-8201
www.bridgeportwv.com
- *Site Location*: The Bridgeport Economic Development maintains a current listing of available sites to meet the needs of your business.
- *Tax Credits*: Bridgeport offers tax credits including: New Business Incentives, Business Expansion Incentives, Annexed Business Incentives, Business Enterprise Zone, and Façade Improvement Incentives.
- *City Economic Development Grants/Loans*: The Bridgeport City Economic Development Committee can provide grants and loans to area businesses at their discretion.

Huntington Area Development Council
916 Fifth Avenue, Suite 400
Huntington, WV 25701
304-525-1161
Fax: 304-525-1163
www.hadco.org
- *Site Location*: The Huntington Area Development Council maintains a current listing of available sites to meet the needs of your business.

- *Business Incentives*: The Huntington Area Development Council offers incentive packages to companies that establish new facilities.

Terra Alta Economic Development Corporation
P.O. Box 295
Terra Alta, WV 26764
304-879-2455
www.taedc.com

West Virginia County Economic Development

Morgan County Economic Development Authority
83 Fairfax Street
Berkeley Springs, WV 25411
304-258-8540
www.morgancountyeda.com

- *Site Location*: The Morgan County Economic Development Authority maintains a current listing of available sites to meet the needs of your business.
- *Financial Assistance*: Morgan County Economic Development Authority can help you find tax credits and financial assistance to locate in Morgan County.

Putnam County Development Authority, Inc.
P.O. Box 167
Scott Depot, WV 25560
304-757-0318
Fax: 304-757-7748
www.pcda.org/pcda
The Putnam County Development Authority serves as a one-stop information resource for business and industry in the county.

- *Site Location*: The Putnam County Development Authority, Inc.maintains a current listing of available sites to meet the needs of your business.

Upshur County Development Authority
2 WBUC Road
P.O. Box 109
Buckhannon, WV 26201
304-472-1757
Fax: 304-472-4998
www.wvlink.com/ucda
Upshur County Has a full time development staff to assist new businesses in the county. They also assist existing businesses in their retention and expansion.

Wisconsin

Wisconsin City Economic Development

City of Appleton Department of Economic Development
100 N. Appleton Street
Appleton, WI 54911
920-832-6468
Fax: 920-832-5994
www.appleton.org

- *E-Seed Program*: The E-Seed Program offers a 12-week entrepreneur training program to assist you in the business planning process.
- *Business Start-Up Guide*: The guide is provided by the Wisconsin Department of Commerce and available at the Appleton Department of Economic Development.
- *Free Business Counseling*: Free business counseling is available in conjunction with SCORE.

The City of Eau Claire's Economic Development Division
203 South Farwell Street
Eau Claire, WI 54702-5148

715-839-4914
Fax: 715-839-4939
www.ci.eau-claire.wi.us

- *Site Location*: The City of Eau Claire maintains a current listing of available sites to meet the needs of your business.
- *Eau Claire Revolving Loan Fund*: Business in manufacturing or service industries that create new jobs are eligible for funds.
- *Eau Claire Economic Development Fund*: Local funding for projects which create jobs in the City.

Milwaukee Department of City Development
809 N. Broadway
Milwaukee, WI 53202
414-286-5840
Fax: 414-286-5778
www.mkedcd.org
www.medconline.com

- *Emerging & Technology Business Planning Assistance*: Assistance is available to early stage technology companies in feasibility assessment, market research and business plan development.

Wisconsin County Economic Development

Barron County Economic Development
P.O. Box 71
Barron, WI 54812
800-529-4148
715-637-3755 ext. 23
Fax: 715-637-3061
www.co.barron.wi.us

- *Barron County Revolving Loan Fund*: The Revolving Loan Fund offers funds for commercial and industrial projects for the creation of jobs and to increase the tax base.
- *Site Location*: The Barron County Economic Development Corporation maintains a current listing of available sites to meet the needs of your business.

Columbia County Economic Development Corporation
311 East Wisconsin Street, Suite 108
Portage, WI 53901
608-742-6161
Fax: 608-742-3582
www.ccedc..com

- *Site Location*: The Columbia County Economic Development Corporation maintains a current listing of available sites to meet the needs of your business.
- *Columbia County Revolving Loan Fund*: This fund is designated to make direct business loans for the creation of permanent jobs, retention or expansion of existing businesses and leveraging of new private investment in Columbia County.

Columbia Job Center: A center to assist employers and job seekers in Columbia County.

Lincoln County Economic Development Corporation
1106 E. Eighth Street
Merrill, WI 54452
715-536-0383
Fax: 715-536-0386
www.co.lincoln.wi.us

- *Free Assistance*: The Lincoln County Economic Development Corporation offers free and confidential assistance in the areas of financial packaging, business planning and workforce development to businesses located in Lincoln County and those seeking to do business there.

- *Site Location*: The Lincoln County Economic Development Corporation maintains a current listing of available sites to meet the needs of your business.

Wyoming

Wyoming City Economic Development

Evanston Economic Development
1200 Main Street
Evanston, WY 82930
866-783-6300
Fax: 307-783-6390
www.evanstonwy.org/economic_dev/default.asp
The Evanston Economic Development office offers business a variety of information and statistics about the City of Evanston.

City of Laramie Business Services
406 E Ivinson
P.O. Box C
Laramie, WY 82073
307-721-5200

Thermopolis Economic Development Council
420 Broadway
P.O. Box 603
Thermopolis, WY 82443
307-864-2348
800-501-6708
Fax: 307-864-9353
http://server1.thermopedc.com

City of Torrington Economic Development
P.O. Box 250
Torrington, WY 82240-0250
307-532-5666
www.city-of-torrington.org/economic_development.htm

Wyoming County Economic Development

Campbell County Economic Development Corporation
222 Gillette Avenue, Suite 402

Gillette, WY 82717
307-686-2603
800-376-0848
Fax: 307-868-7268
www.ccedc.net

- *Site Location*: The Campbell County Economic Development Corporation
- maintains a current listing of available sites to meet the needs of your business.
- *Trade Show Grants*: Up to $1,000 annually is available to Wyoming based companies to attend trade shows.
- *Campbell County Economic Development Revolving Loan Fund*: This fund is available to businesses with at least two years of business in manufacturing value-added processing, export product or service.

Cheyenne-Laramie County Corporation for Economic Development
One Depot Square
121 W 15th Street, Suite 304
Cheyenne, WY 82001
307-638-6000
www.cheyenneleads.org

- *Site Location*: The Cheyenne-Laramie County Corporation for Economic Development
- maintains a current listing of available sites to meet the needs of your business.
- *Business Incentives*: The Corporation for Economic Development customizes incentive packages to each companies individual needs.

Sweetwater County Economic Development Association
1400 Dewar Drive, Suite 205A
Rock Springs, WY 82901
307-352-6874
800-803-6362
Fax: 307-352-6876
www.sweda.net

- *Site Location*: The Sweetwater County Economic Development Association maintains a current listing of available sites to meet the needs of your business.
- *Grants*: Sweetwater County offers a variety of grants and loans programs.

Get Money From Nonprofit Organizations to Start a Business

Nonprofit organizations come in all shapes and sizes and offer a wide range of services to help those who want to start or expand a business. Some like the Community Development Financial Institutions Fund give money to banks, who in turn loan it to those who want to become entrepreneurs. In addition, many of these banks also provide technical assistance and training to help you become a success. Other nonprofits provide unconventional loans. These are loans to low and moderate income individuals who don't qualify for credit through conventional methods. The aim is to help individuals become self-sufficient and stimulate growth in the economy. Nonprofits also offer 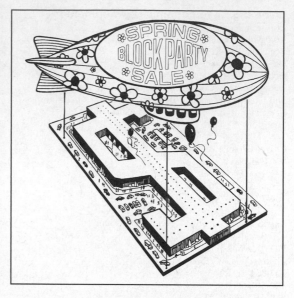 business assistance in the form of training, counseling, mentoring, support, and more. This kind of help can be the difference between success and failure. Sometimes businesses only need a small amount of money to get off the ground and that is when a microloan can be of help. Whereas other times a larger loan may be needed and that is when you might turn to a Certified Development Company for assistance. If all that weren't enough, many nonprofits operate business incubators where you can find low rent, technical support, and more to help nurture your company during the beginning phase of operation. The Business Information and Tribal Information Centers provide a one-stop center for books, publications, software, and other help to get your business up and running. Read through the following sections to see what kinds of help are available to you. You will be surprised at what you find!

Millions For Those In Communities In Need

Been turned down for a loan to start a business or buy a house? Want money to expand your business or fix up your house? The government supports certain banks and credit unions who help people who have trouble getting loans elsewhere, so they can make their dreams come true. These banks have special programs to helpthose in need. The banks work with people who have poor credit histories or little savings. They can provide you with the loans you need, as well as teach you how to manage the money.

It is often the case for those who live in poor communities that finding funding to buy a house or start a business is impossible. Banks and other financial institutions are not willing to take the risks necessary to lend money in poorer neighborhoods. Individuals who live in these neighborhoods do not have a relationship with a traditional bank or depend on the services of places such as pawnshops, check cashers and payday lenders. Many of these individuals live in neighborhoods where no bank branches are found, or cannot buy a home or start a business because they lack the credit history or collateral needed. Some people become victims of predatory mortgage lenders, whose excessive interest rates, fees and prepayment penalties may lead to foreclosure and loss of the home.

Not only individuals and businesses suffer from the lack of financial services and financing, but community service suffers as well. Nonprofit developers have limited alternatives for financing new affordable housing units. Low-income communities in great need of childcare centers, hospitals, or charter schools find these services in short supply. Capital needed to revitalize these areas is difficult to obtain.

The U.S. Department of Treasury's Community Development Financial Institutions (CDFI) Fund is designed to award money to banks in support of their activities benefiting needy communities across the country. These banks provide a range of financial products and services including: mortgage financing for first-time-home-buyers, financing for needed community facilities, commercial loans and investments to start or expand small businesses, loans to rehabilitate rental housing and financial services needed by low-income households and local businesses. CDFIs include community development banks, credit unions, loan funds, venture capital funds, and microenterprise loan funds.

To help keep their investments safe, CDFIs provide technical assistance and training to their borrowers. Through credit counseling, business training and first-time homebuyer training, individuals learn how to manage debt and how to recognize predatory lending practices; entrepreneurs learn how to grow their businesses responsibly; and first-time homebuyers learn the importance of budgeting and home-repair to maintain the value of their homes.

The following examples are excerpted from the websites of the U.S. Department of Treasury's Community Development Financial Institutions Fund (CDFI) and lending institutions listed in this chapter. Contact CDFI and lenders in your area for more information on how they can help you.

Do you dream of starting a business, but don't have the start-up funds you need to stock the shelves? North, South, East, West - there is money all over the USA to help people just like you. In this case, the funds are available through local banks, and granted to individuals, businesses and organizations. The money is available through the U.S. Department of Treasury's Community Development Financial Institutions (CDFI) Fund.

The CDFI Fund does not make loans directly to individuals. Instead, it directs funds to local banks, as they know their community best. The banks receive enough funds to make a number of loans available to their community. For example:

- In the Snow Belt, the University Bank of St. Paul, Minnesota received an award of $795,969.

- In rural Mississippi, the Delta Southern Bank of Ruleville received an award of $401,521.

- On the East Coast, the Harbor Bank in Baltimore, Maryland, received $663,818.

- And, out West, the Northern Trust Bank in Phoenix, Arizona, received $354,506.

Once the banks receive the funds, they can use the money to assist individuals who want to start their own businesses, and can also help owners of existing businesses. When banks help businesses grow, this means more jobs and stability for the community.

If the bank in your area is a certified community development financial institution, that means they receive funds from the federal government that are earmarked to help people like you. If you are thinking about starting a business and need a loan to get the office up and running, if your firm is ready to grow and you need a boost of capital, or if you need help with the nuts and bolts of operating your business, contact a community development financial institution. That is what individuals from every corner of the country have done – and here are their success stories:

A Support Team for Financial and Technical Help

In 1991, Margaret Quenemoen was living in her car. As a last ditch effort to make ends meet, she began making and selling headbands for skiers – and the headbands sold like hot cakes. She now sells thousands of vests, jackets and other outerwear throughout the country, earning millions of dollars in sales every year. Quenemoen credits her leap to success with the help she received from her local CDFI, the Utah Microenterprise Loan Fund (UMLF).

Quenemoen had been turned down for bank loans, but the UMLF recognized her drive to succeed and awarded her a $10,000 loan. They also helped her with technical assistance, so she could make the best decisions for her business. "The information was new to me," she explained. "The UMLF helped get me through the processes needed to comply with the regulations. The people there were my support team!"

Springboard to Success

When Digital Equipment Corporation shut their doors, one of their employees saw an opportunity to open doors of his own. Tony Dolphin proposed to buy out the division that repaired hard drives, and go into business for himself. Dolphin knew that he would have to grow to stay competitive, so he secured funding from the Boston Community Ventures Fund. More than ten years later, his firm – Springboard Technologies - provides services to large computer manufacturers, and also offers a jumpstart for local students through community college training programs.

Pick the Outcome to Your Story

Imagine going to the office – in your own garage! That is where Joe and Bambi Serna once operated their Colorado-based print brokering service. Along the way, they learned enough about the printing business to open their own plant, but needed funds to help them expand. Their local CDFI, the Colorado Enterprise Fund, helped them meet their goals.

According to Joe Serna, "Small companies don't always need millions to get started. Sometimes a few thousand is all you need to get the ball rolling."

Joe says he owns a business because he wants the opportunity to make his own destination. "By owning your own business, you pick the outcome to your story."

A River of Dreams

We all have dreams. For Don Hasch, it was to turn his love for canoeing and recreational activities into a business. When the owner of a local canoe rental company retired, Don saw his chance. Like so many would-be entrepreneurs in rural areas, however, he could not raise the capital he needed. He approached a Pennsylvania-based CDFI called The Progress Fund, and secured a loan that made his dream a reality. Now he is the owner of Hazelbaker's Recreational Services, which offers canoe, kayak and fishing trips - and for

those who prefer their recreation on dry land, Don rents out bikes and provides space for picnics.

Cooking Up Good Business

Sha-Dee's Kountry Kettle is known as having the best food in Salisbury, Maryland. Before Shelvia and Delores Donohue opened the restaurant, they had 40 years of restaurant experience between them – so they knew how to make a delicious meal. But, a restaurant needs to offer more than what's on the menu. – so with a loan from Maryland Capitol Enterprises, they were also able to enhance operations and help their business grow.

When A Traditional Bank Won't Help

Charles Leseman and Philip Mahler met in a hardware store – and decided to go into the contracting business. They came upon a project that was good business, and also helped their community. They planned to develop a hotel into apartments, and to partner with a social service agency that worked with homeless individuals who needed efficiency units. Finding funding through traditional banks for the project was difficult. When Leseman and Mahler contacted their local CDFI – the Community Capital Bank of New York City – they secured the money required.

"Compared to other institutions, Community Capitol Bank is the best I've ever worked with," Leseman says. "You never felt like you were small when you were dealing with them."

For more information contact
Community Development Financial Institutions Fund
601 13th St., NW, Suite 200
Washington, DC 20005
202-622-8662
Fax: 202-622-7754
www.cdfifund.gov

Certified Community Development Financial Institutions

Alabama
Canaan Baptist Federal Credit Union
824 15th Street North
Bessemer, AL 35020-5669
205-428-5572

Birmingham Community
Development Corporation, Inc.
110 12th Street North, Suite 110
Birmingham, AL 35203-1537
205-250-6380

New Hope Community Development
Federal Credit Union
P.O. Box 110339
Birmingham, AL 35211-0339
205-941-1800

Prichard Federal Credit Union
P.O. Box 10576
Prichard, AL 36610
251-456-7079

Stevenson Federal Credit Union
P.O. Box 587
Stevenson, AL 35772-0587
256-437-2181

Tuscaloosa Community Federal
Credit Union (TCFCU)
P.O. Box 3148
Tuscaloosa, AL 35403-3148
205-391-0690

Alaska
Alaska Growth Capital BIDCO, Inc.
3900 C Street, Suite 302
Anchorage, AK 99503
888-315-4904
907-339-6760
Fax: 907-339-6771
Email: info@alaskagrowth.com
www.alaskagrowth.com

Anchorage Neighborhood Housing
Service, Inc.
480 West Tudor Road

Anchorage, AK 99503-6614
907-677-8490
Email: info@akanhs.org
www.akanhs.org/lpos.shtml

Rural Alaska Investments & Finance
1577 C Street, Suite 304
Anchorage, AK 99501-5133
907-274-5400

Fairbanks Neighborhood Housing
Services
534 10th Avenue
P.O. Box 71168
Fairbanks, AK 99701-1168
907-451-7230
Fax: 907-451-7236
www.fnhs.org/index.html

Haa Yakaawu Financial Corporation
P.O. Box 32237
Juneau, AK 99803
907-780-6868

Arizona
Hopi Credit Association
P.O. Box 1259
Keams Canyon, AZ 86034-1259
928-738-2205

Neighborhood Economic
Development Corporation
635 East Broadway Road
Mesa, AZ 85204-2023
480-833-9200

Arizona Multibank, CDC
101 North 1st Avenue, Suite 1880
Phoenix, AZ 85003-1910
602-643-0030
Fax: 602-643-0031
www.multibank.org

Neighborhood Housing Services of
Phoenix, Inc.
320 East McDowell Road, Suite 120
Phoenix, AZ 85004

602-258-1659
www.nhsphoenix.org/Services.htm

Prestamos CDFI, LLC
1112 East Buckeye Road
Phoenix, AZ 85034
602-257-0700

Raza Development Fund, Inc.
111 West Monroe, Suite 1610
Phoenix, AZ 85003-1736
602-417-1409

Self-Employment Loan Fund, Inc.
(SELF)
1601 North 7th Street, Suite 340
Phoenix, AZ 85006-2231
602-340-8834
Fax: 602-340-8953
TDD: 800-367-8939
www.selfloanfund.org

Navajo Partnership for Housing, Inc.
P.O. Box 1370
St. Michaels, AZ 86511-1370
928-810-3112
www.navajopartnershipforhousing.org

PPEP Microbusiness and Housing
Development Corporation
901 East 46th Street
Tucson, AZ 85713-5008
800-376-3553
520-806-9513
www.ppep.org/main.html

Arkansas
Elk Horn Bank & Trust
P.O. Box 248
605 Main Street
Arkadelphia, AR 71923-0248
870-246-5811
www.ehbt.com

Southern Development
Bancorporation
605 Main Street, Suite 202

Arkadelphia, AR 71923
870-246-3945
Fax: 870-246-2182
Email: info@southerndevelop
mentbancorp.com
www.southerndevelopmentbancorp.c
om

Southern Financial Partners
605 Main Street, Suite 203
Arkadelphia, AR 71923-6037
870-246-9739
Email:
info@southernfinancialpartners.org
www.southernfinancialpartners.org

College Station Community Federal
Credit Union
P.O. Box 599
College Station, AR 72053
501-490-0646

Community Resource Group, Inc.
P.O. Box 1543
Fayetteville, AR 72702-1543
479-443-2700

First National Bank of Phillips
County
502 Cherry
P.O. Box 160
Helena, AR 72342-3304
870-816-1111
Email: mainoffice@fnbpc.com
www.fnbpc.com

Phillips County Self-Help Federal
Credit Union
420 Elm Street
P.O. Box 356
Helena, AR 72342-3553
870-338-3798

California

Neighborhood Housing Services of
Orange County, Inc.
198 West Lincoln Avenue, 2nd Floor
Anaheim, CA 92805-2901
714-490-1250

Vernon/Commerce Credit Union
P.O. Box 911227
5720 E. Washington Blvd.
Commerce, CA 90091
323-890-4500 x103
www.vc-cu.org

Century Community Development,
Inc.
1000 Corporate Pointe, Suite 200
Culver City, CA 90230-7694
310-258-0700

Oregon Trail Corporation
8361 E. Florence Ave., Suite 201
Downey, CA 90240
562-861-3325

Valley Small Business Development
Corporation

7035 North Fruit Avenue
Fresno, CA 93711
559-438-9680
Fax: 559-438-9690
Email: valleysb@vsbdc.com
www.vsbdc.com

California Community Reinvestment
Corporation
225 West Broadway, Suite 120
Glendale, CA 91204
818-550-9801
Fax: 818-550-9806
www.e-ccrc.org

Hoopa Development Fund
P.O. Box 1307
Hoopa, Ca 95546-1307
530-625-5565 x 11

Inglewood Neighborhood Housing
Services, Inc.
335 east Manchester Boulevard
Inglewood, CA 90301
310-674-3756 x103
Email:
info@homeownershipcenter.com
www.homeownershipcenter.com

The Clearinghouse CDFI
23861 El Toro Road, Suite 401
Lake Forest, CA 92630-4732
800-445-2142
949-859-3600
Fax: 949-859-8534
Email: info@clearinghousecdfi.com
http://sites.wsupdate.com/cdfi

Asian Pacific Revolving Loan Fund
of Los Angeles
1541 Wilshire Blvd., Suite 310
Los Angeles, CA 90017-2211
877-988-LOAN
213-353-9400
Email: info@asianloanfund.com
www.asianloanfund.com

Communidades Federal Credit
Union
1107 South Alvarado St., Suite 107
Los Angeles, CA 90006
213-251-2190
www.cfcu.freeservers.com

Community Commerce Bank
5444 East Olympic Blvd.
Los Angeles, CA 90022
323-888-8777

Episcopal Community Federal Credit
Union
840 echo Park Ave.
Los Angeles, CA 90026
213-482-2040
Fax: 213-977-9762
Email: creditunion@ladiocese.org
www.ladiocese.org/creditunion

Fame Assistance Corporation/Fame
Renaissance

2241 South Hobart
Los Angeles, Ca 90018
323-730-9180

Community Financial Resources
Center
4060 South Figueroa Street
Los Angeles, CA 90037-2042
323-233-1900
Fax: 323-235-1686
Email: info@cfrc.org
www.cfrc.net

Los Angeles LDC, Inc.
1055 West 7th Street, Suite 2840
Los Angeles, CA 90017-2677
213-362-9113
Fax: 213-362-9119
www.losangelesldc.com

NHS Neighborhood Lending
Services
3926 Wilshire Boulevard, Suit 200
Los Angeles, CA 90010-3303
213-381-2862

TELACU Community Capital
5400 East Olympic Boulevard, Suite
300
Los Angeles, CA 90022
323-721-1655
Fax: 323-724-3372
Email: info@telacu.com
www.telacu.com

Vermont Slauson Local
Development Corporation, Inc.
5918 South Vermont Avenue
Los Angeles, CA 90044-3714
323-753-2335

Food Processors Credit Union
2504 Tenaya Drive
P.O. Box 3026
Modesto, CA 95353-3026
800-350-FPCU
209-521-6015
Fax: 209-521-0407
www.foodprocessorscu.com

Neighborhood Bancorp
1727 Sweetwater Road, Suite J
National City, CA 91950-7649
619-789-4416

Neighborhood National Bank
3511 National Avenue
San Diego, CA 92113
619-789-4400
Fax: 619-696-7732
www.neighborhoodnationalbank.com

Community Bank of the Bay
1750 Broadway
Oakland, CA 94612-2106
510-433-5400
Fax: 510-433-5431
Email:
info@communitybankbay.com
www.communitybankbay.com

KO-AM Federal Credit Union
339 14th Street
Oakland, CA 94612
510-663-1004

Low Income Investment Fund
1330 Broadway, Suite 600
Oakland, CA 94612
510-893-3811

Neighborhood Housing Services of
America;
Community Development Financing
1970 Broadway, Suite 470
Oakland, CA 94612-2216
404-373-5669

People's Community Partnership
Federal Credit Union
900 Market Street, Suite L
Oakland, CA 94607-3100
510-267-0450
Fax: 510-267-0452
www.pcpfcu.org

Pasadena Development Corporation
1015 North Lake Avenue, Suite 209
Pasadena, CA 91104
626-398-9971
Fax: 626-398-9307
Email: info@pdcloans.org
www.pdcloans.org/default.htm

Enterprise Funding Corporation
101 East Redlands Blvd., Suite 219
Redlands, CA 92373
909-792-3803
Fax: 909-792-3813
www.efundinglandempire.com

Community Investment Corporation
4250 Brockton Avenue, Suite 100
Riverside, Ca 92501
909-786-1370
www.cicontheweb.com

Inland Empire Lenders Community
Development Corporation
10370 Hemet Street, Suite 360
Riverside, CA 92505
909-352-5736
Fax: 909-358-2830

California Capital Small Business
Development Corporation
926 J Street, Suite 1500
Sacramento, CA 95814-2708
916-326-5225
Fax: 916-326-5226
Email: cerf@ca-cerf.com
www.ca-cerf.com

California Environmental
Redevelopment Fund
1812 J Street, Suite 21
Sacramento, CA 95814
916-326-5225
Fax: 916-326-5226
www.ca-cerf.com

Sacramento Neighborhood Housing
Services, Inc.
3453 5th Avenue
Sacramento, CA 95817-3102
916-452-5361 x 11

California Coastal Rural
Development Corporation
221 Main Street, Suite 301
Salinas, CA 93901-0479
831-424-1099
Fax: 831-424-1094
www.calcoastal.org

ACCION San Diego
1250 6th Avenue, Suite 500
San Diego, CA 92101
619-685-1380
Fax: 619-685-1470
Email: info@accionsandiego.org
www.accionsandiego.org

Banker's Small Business CDC of
San Diego
925 Fort Stockton Drive
San Diego, CA 92103-1817
619-291-3594

Mission Area Federal Credit Union
2940 16th Street, Suite 305
San Francisco, CA 94103
415-431-2268

Northeast Community Federal Credit
Union
19 Walter U. Lum Place
San Francisco, CA 94108-1801
415-434-0738
Fax: 415-434-0715
Email: info@necfcu.org
www.necfcu.org

Northern California Community
Loan Fund
870 Market Street, Suite 677
San Francisco, CA 94102-3024
415-392-8215
Fax: 415-392-8216
Email: info@ncclf.org
www.ncclf.org

Pacific Community Ventures
Investment Partners I, LLC
539 Bryant Street, Suite 302
San Francisco, Ca 94107
415-442-4300
Fax: 415-442-4313
Email: info@pcvmail.org
www.pacificcommunityventures.org

Lenders for Community
Development
111 West St. John Street, Suite 710
San Jose, CA 95113
408-297-0204
Fax: 408-297-4599
www.l4cd.com

Neighborhood Housing Services
Silicon Valley, Inc.

1136 N. Fourth Street
San Jose, CA 95112
408-272-2878
408-279-2600
www.nhssv.org/overview.htm

Mission Community Bancorp
581 Higuera Street
San Luis Obispo, CA 93401-3834
805-782-5000

Mission Community Bank
581 Higuera Street
San Luis Obispo, CA 93401-3834
805-782-5000
www.missioncommunitybank.com

Banker's Small Business CDC of
Orange County
2323 North Broadway, Suite 340
Santa Ana, CA 92706
714-550-5444

Women's Economic Ventures of
Santa Barbara
1136 E. Montecito Street
Santa Barbara, CA 93103
805-962-4288
Fax: 805-962-9622
Email: info@wevonline.org
www.wevonline.org

Santa Cruz Community Credit Union
324 Front Street
P.O. Box 1877
Santa Cruz, CA 95061-1877
831-425-7708 x 232
Fax: 831-425-4824
www.scruzccu.org

Rural Community Assistance
Corporation
3120 Freeboard Drive, Suite 201
West Sacramento, CA 95691-5010
916-447-2854
Fax: 916-447-2878
Email: rcac@rcac.org
www.rcac.org

Colorado

Valley Educators Credit Union
415 Ross Avenue
Alamosa, CO 81101-2454
719-589-6535
Fax: 719-589-8852
Email: vecu@fone.net
http://slv.math.adams.edu/vecu

Colorado Enterprise Fund
1888 Sherman Street, Suite 530
Denver, CO 80203-1159
303-860-0242
Fax: 303-860-0409
Email: microloans@
coloradoenterprisefund.org
www.coloradoenterprisefund.org

Colorado Housing Assistance
Corporation
670 Santa Fe Drive

Denver, CO 80204-4427
303-572-9445
Fax: 303-573-9214
Email: colohac@aol.com
www.coloradohousingassistance.org

Denver Community Development
Credit Union
3305 Downing Street
Denver, CO 80205
303-292-3910
Fax: 303-296-2378
Email: info@dcdcu.com
www.dcdcu.com

Mercy Loan Fund
601-East 18th Avenue, #150
Denver, CO 80203-1492
303-830-3386
Fax: 303-830-3301
Email: loanfund@mercyhousing.org
www.mercyhousing.org

Mile High Fund, Inc.
P.O. Box 181103
Denver, CO 80218-1103
303-585-4333

Mutual Financial Services, Inc.
1550 Park Avenue, Suite 200
Denver, CO 80218
303-863-8651

Zion United Credit Union
6700 East Colfax Avenue
Denver, CO 80220-1704
303-333-2910
www.zionunitedcreditunion.com

Funding Partners for Housing
Solutions, Inc.
2000 South College Ave., Suite 220
Fort Collins, CO 80525
970-494-2021
Fax: 970-494-2022
www.fundingpartners.org

Native American Bank, N.A.
165 South Union Blvd., Suite 1000
Denver, CO 80228
303-988-2727
Fax: 303-988-5533
www.nabna.com

Saguache County Credit Union
P.O. Box 337
Moffat, CO 81143-0337
719-256-4899
Fax: 719-256-4458

Colorado Housing Enterprise, LLC
3621 West 73rd Avenue, Suite C
Westminster, CO 80030
303-428-1448

Connecticut
Bridgeport Neighborhood Fund
177 State Street, 5th Floor
Bridgeport, CT 06604-4872
203-332-7977

Family Assets, LLC
475 Clinton Avenue
Bridgeport, CT 06605-1700
203-368-4291 x730
Email: cmiklos@fsinc.org

Grow Bridgeport Fund I, LLC
10 Middle Street, 1st Floor
Bridgeport, CT 06604-4229
203-335-1562

Community Economic Development
Fund Corporation 1, LLC
50-G Weston Street
Hartford, CT 06120
860-249-3800

Connecticut Housing Investment
Fund, Inc. (CHIF)
121 Tremont Street
Hartford, CT 06105
800-992-3665 (in CT)
860-233-5165
Fax: 860-920-2038
Email: info@chif.org
www.chif.org

South Hartford Initiative
434 Franklin Avenue
Hartford, CT 06114-1220
860-296-7005
Fax: 860-296-7064

Neighborhood Housing Services of
New Britain, Inc.
223 Broad Street
New Britain, CT 06053-4107
860-224-2433
Fax: 860-225-6131
Email: info@nhsnb.org
www.nhsnb.org

Greater New Haven Community
Loan Fund, Inc.
171 Orange Street, 3rd Floor
New Haven, CT 06510
203-789-8690
Fax: 203-865-6475

New Haven Home Ownership
Center, Inc.
333 Sherman Avenue
New Haven, CT 06511-3107
203-777-6925

Housing Development Fund of
Lower Fairfield County, Inc.
100 Prospect Street, Suite S-201
Stamford, CT 06901-3001
203-969-1830
Fax: 203-969-2356
Email: info@hdt-ct.org
www.hdf-ct.org/main

Need Action Federal Credit Union
106 Grove Street
P.O. Box 1168
Waterbury, CT 06721-1168
203-756-2185

Waterbury Housing Fund, Inc.
1 Exchange Place, 1st Floor
Waterbury, CT 06702
203-753-3017

Delaware
Delaware Community Investment
Corporation (DCIC)
Three Mill Road, Suite 105
Wilmington, DE 19806-2153
302-655-1420
Fax: 302-655-1419
www.dcicnet.org

First State Community Loan Fund
100 West 10th Street, Suite 1005
Wilmington, DE 19801
800-652-4779
302-652-6774
Fax: 302-656-1272
Email: fsclf@firststateloan.org
www.firststateloan.org

District of Columbia
CFBanc Corporation
2400 14th Street, N.W., Suite B
Washington, DC 20009-4530
202-745-4489

City First Bank of D.C., N.A.
2400-B 14th Street, N.W., Suite B
Washington, DC 20009-4530
202-332-5002

Community Development
Transportation Lending Services
1341 G Street, N.W., 10th Floor
Washington, DC 20005-3116
202-661-0210
Fax: 202-737-9197
www.ctaa.org

Cornerstone, Inc.
1828 Jefferson Place, N.W.
Washington, DC 20036
202-347-7808
Fax: 202-347-7803
Email:
cornerstone@cornerstonedc.org
www.cornerstonedc.org

Faithworks
1400 16th Street, N.W., Suite 101
Washington, DC 20036-2219
202-328-1625 x 689

FINCA USA, Inc.
1101 14th Street, N.W., Suite 1100
Washington, DC 20005
202-682-1510

H Street Community Development
Corporation
501 II Street, N.E.
Washington, DC 20002
202-544-8353
Fax: 202-544-3051
www.hstreetcdc.org

Hospitality Community Federal
Credit Union
1114 H Street, N.E.
Washington, DC 20002-4443
202-397-4131

Housing Assistance Council
1025 Vermont Avenue, NW
Suite 606
Washington, DC 20005-3516
202-842-8600
Fax: 202-347-3441
Email: hac@ruralhome.org
www.ruralhome.org

Latino Economic Development
Corporation (LEDC)
2316 18th Street, N.W.
Washington, DC 20009
202-588-5102
Fax: 202-588-5204
www.ledcdc.org

National Fund for Enterprise
Development
777 North Capitol Street, NE
Suite 800
Washington, DC 20002-4291
202-408-9788

National Housing Trust Community
Development Fund
1101 30th Street, N.W.
Washington, DC 20007-3708
202-333-8931
Fax: 202-833-1031
www.nhtinc.org/nhcdf.asp

Partners for the Common Good, Inc.
1030 15th Street, NW, Suite 325
Washington, DC 20005-1529
202-289-5353
Fax: 202-289-2638
www.pcg21.org

Washington Area Community
Investment Fund
3624 12th Street, NE
Washington, DC 20017-2546
202-529-5505
Fax: 202-529-5525
Email: info@wacif.org
www.wacif.org/success.html

Florida

Community Trust Federal Credit
Union
P.O. Box 1023
Apopka, FL 32704-1023
407-880-4300

Metro Broward Economic
Development Corporation
3800 West Broward Blvd.
Fort Lauderdale, FL 33312
954-587-3755
Fax: 954-587-3703
Email: info@metrobroward.org
www.metrobroward.org

Neighborhood Housing and
Development Corporation
633 N.W. 8th Avenue
Gainesville, FL 32601
352-380-9119
Fax: 352-580-9170

Jacksonville Affordable Mortgage,
Inc.
4401 Emerson Street, Suite 1
Jacksonville, FL 32207
904-398-4424

BAC Funding Corporation
6600 N.W. 27th avenue
Miami, FL 33147
305-693-3550
Fax: 305-693-7450
Email: info@bacfunding.com
www.bacfunding.com

Camacol Loan Fund, Inc.
1401 West Flagler Street
Suite 209
Miami, FL 33135
305-642-7472
Email: info@camacol.org
www.camacol.org/html/loan-
fund.html

Little Haiti-Edison Federal Credit
Union
6201 Northeast Second Avenue
Miami, FL 33138
305-756-6581

Miami Dade Neighborhood Housing
Service
181 NE 82nd Street
Miami, FL 33138
305-751-5511

Miami-Dade Affordable Housing
Foundation, Inc.
25 West Flagler Street, #750
Miami, FL 33130
305-372-7990
Fax: 305-371-9152

North Dade Community
Development Federal Credit Union
18951 N.W. 27th Avenue
Miami, FL 33056-3154
305-620-5569
Fax: 305-621-0207

Partners for Self-Employment, Inc
d/b/a/ Micro-Business, USA
3000 Biscayne Blvd., Suite 102
Miami, FL 33137-4139
877-722-4505
305-438-1407
Fax; 305-438-1411
Email:
success@microbusinessusa.org
www.microbusinessusa.org

Community Fund of North Miami-
Dade, Inc.
490 Opa-Locka Blvd., Suite 20

Opa-Locka, FL 33054-3563
305-687-3545 x 223

Black Business Investment Fund of
Central Florida, Inc.
315 East Robinson Street, Suite 222
Orlando, Fl 32801
407-649-4780
Fax: 407-649-8688

Florida Community Capital
Corporation
3100 Clay Avenue, Suite 220
Orlando, FL 32804-4020
407-898-1661
Fax: 407-898-1414
www.floridacommunitycapital.org

Florida Community Loan Fund, Inc.
3107 Edgewater Drive, Suite2
Orlando, FL 32804
888-578-2030
407-246-0846
Fax: 407-246-0856
www.fclf.org

Minority Women Business
Enterprise Alliance, Inc.
625 East Colonial Drive
Orlando, FL 32803
407-428-5860
Fax: 407-428-5860
Email: alliamwbe@aol.com
www.allianceflorida.com

Community Enterprise Investments,
Inc.
302 North Barcelona Street
Pensacola, Fl 32501
850-595-6234
Fax: 850-595-5254
Email: ceii2234@aol.com
www.ceii.pensacola.com

Neighborhood Lending Partners of
West Florida, Inc.
2002 North Lois Avenue, Suite 150
Tampa, FL 33607
813-879-4525
Fax: 813-873-9767
www.nlp-inc.com

Tampa Bay Black Business
Investment Corporation, Inc.
2105 North Nebraska Avenue
Tampa, FL 33602
813-274-7923
Fax: 813-274-7927
www.tampabaybbic.com

The Business Loan Fund of the Palm
Beaches, Inc.
1016 North Dixie Hwy, 2nd Floor
West Palm Beach, FL 33401-3332
561-838-9027
Fax: 561-838-9029
www.businessloanfund.org

Community Financing Consortium
1016 North Dixie Highway

West Palm Beach, FL 33401-3332
561-833-8503

Georgia

Capitol City Bank & Trust Company
562 Lee Street
Atlanta, GA 30310-1928
404-752-6067

Citizens Bancshares Corporation
75 Piedmont Avenue, N.E.
Atlanta, GA 30303-2508
404-653-2800

Citizens Trust Bank
75 Piedmont Avenue, N.E.
Atlanta, GA 30303-2508
404-653-2881

Community Redevelopment Loan
and Investment Fund, Inc.
100 Peachtree Street, NW, Suite 700
Atlanta, GA 30303
404-522-2637 x 19
Fax: 404-523-4359
Email:andpi@andpi.org
www.andpi.org

Enterprise Funding Corporation
241 Peachtree Street, Suite 200
Atlanta, GA 30303-1423
404-659-5955
Fax: 404-880-9561

Georgia Affordable Housing
Corporation
1475 Peachtree Street, Suite 120
Atlanta, GA 30309
404-888-8237

Carver State Bank of Savannah
701 Martin Luther King, Jr. Blvd.
Savannah, GA 31401-5507
877-489-2434
912-233-9971
Fax: 912-232-8666
Email: info@carverstatebank.com
www.carverstatebank,com

United Singers Federal Credit Union
P.O. Box 64t
Thomasville, GA 31799
912-226-5010

Hawaii

North Hawaii Community federal
Credit Union
P.O. Box 24945
Honoka'a, HI 96727-0249
808-775-0887

Hawaii Community Loan Fund
677 Ala Moana Boulevard, Suite 702
Honolulu, HI 96813
866-525-4253
808-523-0075
Fax: 808-534-1199
Email: hifund@hclf.org
www.hclf.org

Hawaii Community Reinvestment
Corporation
1001 Bishop Street, Pauahi Tower,
Suite 2395
Honolulu, HI 96813-3403
808-532-3115
Fax: 803-524-1069
www.hcrc.hawaii.org

Pacific Gateway Center
720 North King Street
Honolulu, HI 96817-4511
808-845-3918
Fax: 808-842-1962
www.pacificgateway.org

Word of Life Federal Credit Union
550 Queen Street
Honolulu, Hi 96813-5016
808-441-1732

First Hawaiian Homes Federal Credit
Union
P.P. Box 220
Hoolehua, HI 96729
808-567-6107
Email: fhhfcu@mobettah.net

Kahuku Federal Credit Union
P.O. Box 245
Kahuku, HI 96731-0245
808-293-9063

Molokai Community Federal Credit
Union
135 Puali Place
P.O. Box 1888
Kaunakakai, HI 96748-1888
808-553-5328
Fax: 808-553-3830
www.molokaicommunityfcu.com

Ka'u Federal Credit Union
P.O. Box 347
Na'alehu, HI 96772-0347
808-929-7334
Fax: 808-929-8766
Email: manager@kaufcu.org
www.kaufcu.org

Onomea Federal Credit Union
P.O. Box 19
Papaikou, HI 96781
808-964-1031

Schofield Federal Credit Union
P.O. Box 860669
Wahiawa, HI 96786
808-624-9884

Kulia Ohana Federal Credit Union
240 Lepoko Place
Wailuku, HI 96793-1213
808-244-9191

MEO Business Development
Corporation
99 Mahalani Street
Wailuku, HI 96793
808-249-2990 x 237

Fax: 808-249-2991
www.meoinc.org

Lokahi Pacific
1935 Main Street, Suite 204
Wailuku, Maui, HI 96793-1706
808-242-5761
Fax: 808-244-2057
Email: lokahi@tiki.net

Idaho

Neighborhood Housing Services
Lending, Inc.
416 South 8th Street
P.O. Box 8223
Boise, ID 83707
208-343-4065
Email: info@boisenhs.org
www.boisenhs.org

The Rural Collaborative
2816 North 26th Street
Boise, ID 83702-0313
208-345-1919

Pocatello Neighborhood Housing
Services, Inc.
206 North Arthur Avenue
P.O. Box 1146
Pocatello, ID 83204-1146
208-232-9468
Fax: 208-232-3155
www.pnhs.org

Idaho-Nevada Community
Development Financial Institution
P.O. Box 5079
Twin Falls, ID 83303-5079
208-732-5727

Illinois

ACCION Chicago
3245 West 26th Street, 2nd Floor
Chicago, IL 60623-4034
773-376-9004
Fax: 773-376-9048
Email: info@accionchicago.org
www.accionchicago.org

Austin/West Garfield Federal Credit
Union
4909 West Division Street, Suite 100
Chicago, IL 60651-3161
773-287-2943

CEDA Community Development
Fund
208 South LaSalle Street, Suite 1900
Chicago, IL 60604-1001
312-795-8980
Fax: 312-795-0240

Chicago Community Loan Fund
29 East Madison Street, Suite 1700
Chicago, IL 60602-4415
312-252-0440
Fax: 312-252-0419
Email: info@cclfchicago.org
www.cclfchicago.org

Chicago Community Ventures
700 N. Sacramento, Suite 130
Chicago, IL 60612
773-822-0320
Fax: 773-822-0308
Email: info@chiventures.org
www.chiventures.org

Community Bank of Lawndale
1111 South Homan Avenue
Chicago, IL 60624-4398
773-533-6900
Fax: 773-533-8215
www.cblbank.com

Community Investment Corporation
222 South Riverside Plaza
Suite 2200
Chicago, IL 60606-6109
312-258-0070
www.cicchicago.com

Connections for Community
Ownership
C/o Center for Neighborhood
Technology
2125 W. North Avenue
Chicago, IL 60647-5415
773-278-4800
Fax: 773-278-3840
Email: info@cnt.org
www.cnt.org

FBA Bancorp Inc.
1715 West 47th Street
Chicago, IL 60609
773-523-3145
Fax: 773-523-6038

First Bank of the Americas, S.S. B.
1715 West 47th Street
Chicago IL 60609
773-523-3145
Fax: 773-523-6038

Greater North Pulaski Development
Corporation
4054 West North Avenue
Chicago, IL 60639-5223
773-384-7074
Fax: 773-384-3850
Email: info@gnpdc.org
www.gnpdc.org

IBC Bancorp, Inc.
5069 North Broadway
Chicago, IL 60640-3005
773-769-2899

IBC Community Development
Corporation
5069 North Broadway
Chicago, IL 60640-3005
773-769-2899

Illinois Facilities Fund
300 West Adams, Suite 431
Chicago, IL 60606-5174
312-629-0060
Fax: 312-629-0065

Illinois Services Federal Savings and
Loan Association
4619 South Martin Luther King, Jr.
Dr.
Chicago, IL 60653
773-624-2000

International Bank of Chicago
5069 North Broadway
Chicago, IL 60640-3005
773-769-2899
Fax: 773-769-2686
Email: cust-service@inbk.com
www.inbk.com

Latino Economic Development
Assistance Corporation
205 West Wacker Drive, Suite 2300
Chicago, IL 60606-2300
312-443-1360

Mayan Financial, Inc.
1440 North Dayton, Suite 207
Chicago, IL 60622-2604
312-915-0592

NAB Bank
222 West Cermack Road
Chicago, IL 60616-1997
201-868-3973

Neighborhood Housing Services of
Chicago, Inc.
1279 North Milwaukee Ave
5th Floor
Chicago, IL 60622
773-329-4010
Fax: 773-329-4120
www.nhschicago.org

Neighborhood Lending Services,
Inc.
747 North Mat Street
Chicago, IL 60622-5854
312-491-5101

Nonprofit Financial Center
29 East Madison, Suite 1700
Chicago, IL 60602-4415
312-252-0420
Fax: 312-252-0099
www.NFConline.org

North Side Community Federal
Credit Union
4138 N. Sheridan Road
Chicago, IL 60613
773-549-6790
Fax: 773-549-8279
Email: nosidefcu@aol.com
http://collaboratory.nunet.net/itr/ncfc
u/index.html

Pan American Bank
2627 West Cermack Road
Chicago, IL 60608
773-254-9700

Partners in Community Investment
1525 East 53rd Street, Suite 504

Chicago, IL 60615
773-493-0102

Sable Bancshares, Inc
1111 South Homan Avenue
Chicago, IL 60624
773-533-7079

Seaway National Bank of Chicago
645 East 87th Street
Chicago, IL 60619-6183
800-461-5134
773-602-4153
www.seawaynb.com

ShoreBank
7054 South Jeffrey Boulevard
Chicago, IL 60649-2095
800-669-7725
773-288-1000
Fax: 773-493-6609
www.sbk.com/livesite/main

Shorebank Corporation
7054 South Jeffrey Boulevard
Chicago, IL 60649-2096
773-420-4960
Email: inof@shorebankcorp.com

Women's Self-Employment Project
(WSEP)
11 South LaSalle, Suite 1850
Chicago, IL 60603
312-606-8255
Email: info@wsep.com
www.wsep.net/WSEPhome2.htm

Neighborhood and Family
Investment Fund
16333 South Halsted Street
Harvey, IL 60426-5918
708-333-1471

Illinois Ventures for Community
Action
3301 Constitution Drive, Suite B
P.O. Box 9285
Springfield, IL 62791-9285
217-522-4553
Email: info@ilventures.org
www.ilventures.org

Indiana

Fort Wayne Neighborhood Housing
Partnership, Inc.
525 Oxford Street
P.O. Box 6123
Fort Wayne, IN 46896-6123
219-744-1587

Community Choice Federal Credit
Union
2811 East 10th Street, Suite A
Indianapolis, IN 46201-2471
317-633-3100

Indianapolis Neighborhood Housing
Partnership, Inc.
3550 North Washington Blvd.
Indianapolis, IN 46205-3719

317-925-1400
Fax: 317-925-1408
www.inhp.org

Lafayette Neighborhood Housing
Services, Inc.
1119 Ferry
P.O. Box 252
Lafayette, IN 47902-0252
765-423-1284
www.nhslaf.org

Iowa
Homeward, Inc.
P.O. Box 98
Allison, IA 50602-0098
319-267-2726

Covenant Financial Services Co.
1202 West Third Street
Davenport, IA 52802
563-322-3751
Fax: 563-323-3782

Mississippi Valley Neighborhood
Housing Services, Inc.
1817 LaClaire Street
Davenport, IA 52801
563-324-1556
Fax: 563-324-3540

Iowa Community Capital
1111 9th Street, Suite 200
Des Moines, IA 50314
319-338-2331

Neighborhood Finance Corporation
1912 Sixth Avenue
Des Moines, IA 50314-3331
515-246-0010
Fax: 515-246-0012

Grow Iowa Foundation, Inc.
P.O. Box 212
3264 Nevada Avenue
Orient, IA 50858-8051
641-345-2281
Fax: 641-345-2284
www.southwestiowa.org

Kansas
Douglass Bancorp
1314 North 5th Street
Kansas City, KS 66101-2310
913-321-7200

Douglass National Bank
1314 North 5th Street
Kansas City, KS 66101-2310
913-321-7200

Communities United Credit Union
212 North Hillside, Suite A
Wichita, KS 67214-4904
316-684-1500

Kentucky
Central Appalachian Peoples Federal
Credit Union

P.O. Box 504
Berea, KY 40403
859-986-1651 x 20

Federation of Appalachian Housing
Enterprises, Inc.
P.O. Box 908
Berea, KY 40403
859-986-2321 x 103
Fax: 859-986-5836
Email: fahe@mis.net
www.fahe.org

Human/Economic Appalachian
Development Corporation (HEAD
Corp.)
106 Pasco Street
Berea, KY 40402-0504
859 986 2321 x 121

Mountain Association for
Community Economic Development,
Inc.
433 Chestnut Street
Berea, KY 40403-1510
859-986-2373
Fax: 859-986-1299
Email: info@maced.org
www.maced.org

Pine Mountain Community
Development Corporation
700 College Road, 113 Chrisman
Hall
Cumberland, KY 40823-1046
606-589-2145

Community Ventures Corporation,
Inc.
1450 North Broadway
Lexington, KY 40505-3162
800-299-0267
859-231-0054
Fax: 859-231-0261
Email: info@cvcky.org
www.cvcky.org

LexLinc Community Development
Federal Credit Union
436 Georgetown Street
Lexington, KY 40058
859-381-0076
Fax: 859-381-0133
www.lcdfcu.com

Kentucky Highlands Investment
Corporation
P.O. Box 1738
London, KY 40743-1738
606-864-5175
Fax: 606-864-5194
Email: khicnet@khic.oeg
www.khic.org

Louisville Central Development
Corporation
1407 West Jefferson Street
Louisville, KY 40203
502-589-1173

Louisville Community Development
Bank
2901 West Broadway
Louisville, KY 40211-9982
502-775-2500
Fax: 502-775-5232

Louisville Development Bancorp,
Inc.
2901 West Broadway
Louisville, KY 40251
502-778-4000

The Housing Foundation, Inc.
P.O. Box 442
Marion, KY 42064
270-965-2233

Southern Kentucky Economic
Development Corporation
2292 South Highway 27, Suite 340
Somerset, KY 42501-2905
606-677-6100
www.southernkentucky.com/incentiv
es.htm

Mountain Economic Development
Fund, Inc.
201 South Main Street
P.O. Box 187
Winchester, KY 40391
859-745-5739

Louisiana
Louisiana Community Development
Capital Fund, Inc.
350 Third Street, Suite 125
Baton Rouge, LA 70801
504-343-1050
Fax: 504-343-6200

ASI Federal Credit Union
5508 Citrus Boulevard
Harahan, LA 70123
800-749-6193
504-733-1733
www.asifcu.org

Southern Mutual Financial Services,
Inc.
3602 Old Jeanerette Road
New Iberia, LA 70563
337-367-3277
Email:
smha@southernmutualhelp.org
www.southernmutualhelp.org/smfs_
1.html

Business Resource Capital Specialty
BIDCO, Inc.
650 Poydras Street, Suite 1220
New Orleans, LA 70130
504-524-6172

Dryades Bancorp, Inc.
233 Carondelet Street, Suite 200
New Orleans, LA 70130
504-598-7200
Fax: 504-598-7283

Dryades Savings Bank, FSB
231 Carondelet Street, Suite 200
New Orleans, LA 70130-3002
504-581-5891
Fax: 504-598-7288
www.dryadesbank.com

Liberty Bank and Trust Company
6600 Plaza Dr., Suite 310
P.O. Box 60131
New Orleans, LA 70160-0131
504-240-5115
www.libertybank.net

Neighborhood Housing Services of
New Orleans, Inc.
4700 Freret Street
New Orleans, LA 70115-6321
504-899-5900
Fax: 504-899-6190
Email: info@nhsnola.org
www.nhsnola.org

New Orleans Community
Development Fund
P.O. Box 61540
Attn: NEW/MOB 18
New Orleans, LA 70161-5545
504-533-5846

NEWCORP Business Assistance
Center
1600 Canal Street, Suite 601
New Orleans, LA 70112-2731
504-539-9340
Fax: 503-539-9343
Email:
newcorpinfo@newcorpbac.net
www.newcorpbac.net/about.htm

United Bank and Trust Company
2714 Canal Street
New Orleans, LA 70119-5548
504-827-0060

Red River Valley BIDCO, Inc.
5210 Hollywood, Avenue
P.O. Box 37005
Shreveport, LA 71133-7005
318-632-2022
Fax: 318-632-2099

Northeast Louisiana Delta
Community Development Corp.
P.O. Box 1149
Tallulah, LA 71284-1149
318-574-0995

Maine

MaineStream Finance
262 Harlow Street
P.O. Box 1162
Bangor, ME 04402-1162
207-973-3663
Fax: 207-973-3699
Email: mst@penquiscap.org
www.mainestreamfinance.org

Genesis Fund Inc.
P.O. Box 609

Damariscotta, ME 04543
207-563-6073
Fax: 207-563-6055
Email: info@genesisfund.org
www.genesisfund.org

LaVallee Federal Credit Union
90 Main Street
Madawaska, ME 04756-1500
207-728-4121
Fax: 207-728-7029
Email: lvfcu@lavalleefcu.org
www.lavalleefcu.org

NorState Federal Credit Union
78 Fox Street
Madawaska, ME 04756
207-728-7555
www.norstatefcu.org/ffcu_eng.htm

Four Directions Development
Corporation
20 Godfrey Drive
Orono, ME 04473
207-866-6546

Coastal Ventures II, LLC
2 Portland Fish Pier, Suite 201
Portland, ME 04101
207-772-5356
Fax: 207-772-5503
Email: thd@ceimaine.org
www.ceimaine.org/venturecapital

Biddeford-Saco Area Economic
Development Corporation
110 Main Street, Suite 1202
Saco, ME 04072
207-282-1748
Fax: 207-282-3149
Email: info@bsaedc.org
www.bsaedc.org

Community Concepts Financial
Corporation
P.O. Box 278
South Paris, ME 04281
207-743-7716

Western Maine Finance
150 Main Street, Suite 2
South Paris, ME 04281-1650
207-743-8830
Fax: 207-743-5917

Coastal Enterprises, Inc.
36 Water Street
P.O. Box 268
Wiscasset, ME 04578
207-882-7552
Fax: 207-882-7308
Email: cei@ceimaine.org
www.ceimaine.org

Maryland

Baltimore Community Development
Financing Corporation
36 South Charles Street, Suite 1510
Baltimore, MD 21201
410-727-8590

Fax: 410-752-1396
www.bcdfc.com

Community Capital of Maryland,
Inc.
2700 Lighthouse Point E., Suite 310
Baltimore, MD 21224
410-732-9571
Email: contact@mmgroup.com
www.mmgroup.com

Community Development Ventures,
Inc.
826 East Baltimore Street, Suite 203
Baltimore, MD 21202-4702
410-333-2550
Fax: 410-333-2552
Email: contact@mmgroup.com
www.mmgroup.com

Development Credit Fund, Inc.
(DCF)
2530 North Charles Street, Suite 200
Baltimore, MD 21218
410-467-7500
Fax: 410-467-7988
Email: dcfinc@erols.com
www.developmentcredit.com

Faith Fund, Inc.
4301 Roland Avenue
Baltimore, MD 21210-2703
410-366-1324

Harbor Bank of Maryland
25 West Fayette Street
Baltimore, MD 21201-3794
888-833-7920
410-528-1800
www.theharborbank.com

Harbor Bankshares Corporation
25 West Fayette Street
Baltimore, MD 21201-3794
410-528-1800

Calvert Social Investment
Foundation
4550 Montgomery Avenue
Suite 1000N
Bethesda, MD 20814-3384
800-248-0337
301-951-4895
Fax: 310-654-7820
www.calvertfoundation.org

Enterprise Housing Financial
Services, Inc.
10227 Wincopin Circle, Suite 500
Columbia, MD 21044-3313
410-772-2447
Fax: 410-964-1918
Email:
mail@enterprisefoundation.org
www.enterprisefoundation.org

First Combined Community Federal
Credit Union
7800 Central Avenue, Suite 205
Landover, MD 20785

301-333-8442
Fax: 301-333-0370

Prince George's Financial Services
Corporation
1400 McCormick Drive, Suite 240
Largo, MD 20774-5313
301-883-6900
Fax: 301-883-6160
www.pgfsc.com

Maryland Capital Enterprises, Inc.
300 East Main Street
P.O. Box 1844
Salisbury, MD 21801
866-MARYCAP
410-546-1900
Fax: 410-546-9718
www.marylandcapital.org/news.html

Salisbury Neighborhood Housing
Service
513 Camden Avenue
Salisbury, MD 21801-5801
410-543-4626
Fax: 410-543-9204
www.salisburynhs.org

McAuley Institute
8380 Colesville Road, Suite 420
Silver Spring, MD 20910-6263
301-588-8110
Fax: 301-588-1890
www.mcauley.org

National Community Investment
Fund
1441 Crestridge Drive
Silver Spring, MD 20910
773-420-4910

Unitarian Universalist Affordable
Housing Corporation (UUAHC)
8730 Georgia Avenue, Suite 306
Silver Spring, MD 20910
301-588-5533
Fax: 310-588-5272
Email: uuahc@uuahc.org
www.uuahc.org

Massachusetts
ACCION USA
56 Roland Street, Suite 300
Boston, MA 02129
617-625-7080
Fax: 617-625-7020
Email: info@accionusa.org
www.accionusa.org/massachusetts

BCLF Ventures I, LLC
56 Warren Street
Boston, MA 02119
617-427-8600
Fax: 617-427-9300
www.bostoncommunitycapital.org

BCLF Ventures II, LLC
56 Warren Street, 3rd Floor
Boston, MA 02119
617-427-8600

Fax: 617-427-9300
www.bostoncommunitycapital.org

BCLF Ventures, Inc. d/b/a Boston
Community Venture Fund
56 Warren Street, Palladio Hall
Boston, MA 02119
617-427-8600
Fax: 617-427-9300
www.bostoncommunitycapital.org

Boston Bank of Commerce
133 Federal Street
Boston, MA 02110-1703
617-457-4400
Fax: 617-457-4430

Boston Community Loan Fund
56 Warren Street, Suite 300
Boston, MA 02119-3236
617-427-8600
Fax: 617-427-9300
www.bostoncommunitycapital.org

The Housing Partnership Fund
160 State Street, 5th Floor
Boston, MA 02109
617-720-1999
Fax: 617-720-3939
Email:
information@housingpartnership.net
www.nahp.net

Massachusetts Housing Investment
Corporation
70 Federal Street, Sixth Floor
Boston, MA 02119-1906
617-850-1000
Fax: 617-850-1103
Email: loandept@mhic.com
www.mhic.com

MHIC, LLC
70 Federal Street, 6th Floor
Boston, MA 02110-1906
617-850-1000
Fax: 617-850-1103
Email loandept@mhic.com
www.mhic.com

South End Federal Credit Union
P.O. Box 180216
Boston, MA 02118-0003
617-247-1673
Fax: 617-247-9503

Local Enterprise Assistance Fund
One Harvard Street, Suite 200
Brookline, MA 02445-7948
617-232-1551
Fax: 617-232-9545
Email: leaf@leaffund.org
www.leaffund.org

Working Capital Fund
99 Bishop Allen Drive
Cambridge, MA 02139
617-625-7080
Fax: 617-576-8623

NOAH Community Development
Fund, Inc.
22 Paris Street
East Boston, MA 02128-3045
617-657-5882
Fax: 617-657-7563
Email: info@noahcdc.org
www.noahcdc.org

Jobs for Fall River, Inc.
One Government Center
Fall River, MA 02722
508-324-2620
Fax: 508-677-2840
Email: frodema@aol.com

Western Massachusetts Enterprise
Fund, Inc.
P.O. Box 1077
Greenfield, MA 01302-1077
413-774-4033
Fax: 419-739-6800
www.wmef.org

Cape and Islands Community
Development, Inc.
307 Main Street, Suite 2
P.O. Box 790
Hyannis, MA 02601-0790
508-790-2921
Fax: 508-790-1889

New Bedford Economic
Development Council, Inc.
700 Pleasant Street, Suite 410
New Bedford, MA 02740-6254
877-AT-NBEDC
508-991-3122
Fax: 508-991-7372
www.ci.new-
bedford.ma.us/ECONOMIC/ECON
OMIC/devassis.htm

UECDF Corporation
2010 Columbus Avenue
Roxbury, MA 02119-1106
617-541-2571

Institute for Community Economics,
Inc.
57 School Street
Springfield, MA 01105-1331
413-746-8660 x 115
Fax: 413-746-8862
Email: info@iceclt.org
www.iceclt.org

Springfield Neighborhood Housing
Service
111 Wilbraham Road
Springfield, MA 01109-3127
413-739-4737

New Markets Entrepreneurial Fund
237 Chandler Street
Worcester, MA 01609-2935
508-798-2007

WCHR Securities, Inc.
11 Pleasant Street, Suite 300

Worcester, MA 01609
508-799-0322 x 106

Michigan

Neighborhood Inc. of Battle Creek
47 North Washington Avenue
Battle Creek, MI 49017-3025
269-968-1113 x 30
Fax: 616-963-7022
Email: info@nibc.org
www.nibc.org

First Independence National Bank of
Detroit
44 Michigan Avenue
Detroit, MI 48226-2601
313-256-8419

Community Capital Development
Corporation
316 West Water Street
Flint, MI 48503-5612
810-239-5847
Fax: 810-239-5575

Kalamazoo Neighborhood Housing
Service, Inc.
802 South Westnedge Avenue
Kalamazoo. MI 49008
616-385-2916
Fax: 616-385-9912
Email: info@knhs.org
www.knhs.org

Michigan Housing Trust Fund
1000 South Washington Avenue,
Suite 100
Lansing, MI 48910-1647
517-372-6001
Fax: 517-372-6004
www.mhtf.org

Northern Economic Initiatives
Corporation
228 West Washington Street
Marquette, MI 49855-4330
800-254-2156
906-228-5571
Fax: 906-228-5572
Email: info@niupnorth.org
www.northerninitiatives.com

Shorebank BIDCO, Inc.
228 West Washington Street
Marquette, MI 49855-4330
906-228-6080
Fax: 906-228-5572

Minnesota

Northwest Minnesota Foundation
4225 Technology Drive, N.W.
Bemidji, MN 56601
800-659-7859 (MN only)
218-759-2057
Fax: 218-759-2328
Email: mwmf@nwmf.org
www.nwmf.org

Minnesota Chippewa Tribal Housing
Corporation
15542 State Highway 371 NW
P.O. Box 217
Cass Lake, MN 56633
218-335-8582
Fax: 218-335-6925
Email: mcthl@paulbunyan.net
www.mnchippewathribe.org/housing
.htm

Anoka Sherburne County Capital
Fund
299 Coon Rapids Blvd., Suite 12
Coon Rapids, MN 55433
763-786-0869

Midwest Minnesota Community
Development Corporation
P.O. Box 623
Detroit Lakes, MN 56502-0623
218-847-3191
Fax: 218-847-3192
Email: mmcdc@telstar.com
www.ruralisc.org/mmcdc.htm

Iron Range Ventures (IRV)
202 West Superior Street, Suite 747
Duluth, MN 55802
218-722-9915

Neighborhood Housing Services of
Duluth, Inc.
224 East 4th Street
Duluth, MN 55805
218-727-8604
Fax: 218-727-9368
www.nhsduluth.org

Northeast Ventures Corporation
202 West Superior Street
747 Sellwood Bldg.
Duluth, MN 55802
218-722-9915
Fax: 218-722-9871
Email: ventures@neventures.com
www.nwventures.com

Northland Foundation
202 West Superior Street, Suite 610
Duluth, MN 55802-1944
800-433-4045
218-723-4040
Fax: 218-722-4048
Email: info@northlandfdn.org
www.northlandfdn.org

Initiative Foundation
405 1st Street, S.E.
Little Falls, MN 56345-3007
320-632-9255
Fax: 320-632-9258
Email: info@ifound.org
www.ifound.org

Community Loan Technologies
2801 21st Avenue South, Suite 210
Minneapolis, MN 55407-1229
612-278-7182
Fax: 612-278-7181

Email:
info@communityl;oantech.org
www.communityloantech.org

Development Corporation for
Children
212 3rd Avenue North, Suite 310
Minneapolis, MN 55401-1400
612-338-3023
Fax: 612-338-4596
www.dcc-corner.com

Milestone Growth Fund, Inc.
401 2nd Avenue South, Suite 1032
Minneapolis, MN 55401-2310
612-338-0090
Fax: 612-338-1172
Email:
inquirymgf@milestonegrowth.com
www.milestonegrowth.com

Minneapolis Consortium of
Community Developers
2308 Central Avenue, N.E.
Minneapolis, MN 55418-3710
612-789-7337
Fax: 612-789-8448
www.mccdmn.org

Northcountry Cooperative
Development Fund, Inc.
219 Main Street, S.E., #500
Minneapolis, MN 55414
612-331-9103
Fax: 612-331-9145

Northside Neighborhood Housing
Services
1501 Dupont Avenue North
Minneapolis, MN 55411
612-521-3581
Fax: 612-522-1963

Arrowhead Community Economic
Assistance corporation
8880 Main Street
Bank Bldg, Box 406
Mt. Iron, MN 55768
218-735-8201
Fax: 218-735-8202
Email: aceac@rangenet.com
www.northspan.org/finance/aceac.as
p

Community Development Bank,
FSB
516 Main Street West
P.O. Box 38
Ogema, MN 56569-0038
218-983-3241

Habitat for Humanity of
Minneapolis, Inc.
3001 4th Street, S.E.
Minneapolis, MN 55414
612-331-4439
Fax: 612-331-1540
www.hfhmn.org

Community Neighborhood Housing
Services
35 West Water Street
St. Paul, MN 55107-2046
651-292-8701 x 201
Fax: 651-292-0473
www.communitynhs.org

Minnesota Indian Economic
Development Fund
2380 Wycliff Street, Suite 200
St. Paul, MN 55114
651-641-0819

Minnesota Investment Network
Corporation
1600 University Avenue West
Suite 401
St. Paul, MN 55104
651-632-2140
Fax: 651-632-2145
Email: info@mincorp.org
www.mincorp.org

Neighborhood Development Center
651 ½ University Avenue
St. Paul, MN 55104
651-291-2480
Fax: 651-291-2597
Email: windndc@windndc.org
www.windndc.org/ndc

University Financial Corporation
200 University Avenue West
St. Paul, MN 55103-2043
651-265-5627
Fax: 651-298-6759

University National Bank
200 University Avenue West
St. Paul, MN 55103-2043
651-265-5627
Fax: 651-298-6759

Women Venture
2324 University Avenue, Suite 200
St. Paul, MN 55114-1854
651-656-3808
Fax: 651-641-7223
www.womenventure.org

Northeast Entrepreneur Fund, Inc.
820 Ninth Street North, Suite 200,
Olcott Plaza
Virginia, MN 55792
800-422-0374
218-749-4191
Fax: 218-749-5213
Email: info@entrepreneurfund.org
www.entrepreneurfund.org

Mississippi
Delta Foundation, Inc.
P.O. Box 588
Greenville, MS 38702
662-335-5291
Fax: 662-335-5295

ECD Investments, LLC
308 east Pearl Street, Suite 400

Jackson, MS 39201-3407
601-944-1100
Fax: 601-944-0808
Email: web@ecd.org
www.ecd.org

Enterprise Corporation of the Delta
308 East Pearl Street, Suite 400
Jackson, MS 39201
601-944-1100
Fax: 601-944-0808
Email: web@ecd.org
www.ecd.org

First American Bank
200 South Lamar Street
Jackson, MS 39225-3518
601-355-3300

Hope Community Credit Union
308 Pearl Street, Suite 400
P.O. Box 9401
Jackson, MS 39286-9401
601-713-0974
Fax: 601-713-0975
www.hopecu.org

Minority Capital Fund of
Mississippi, Inc.
2530 Bailey Avenue
P.O. Box 11305
Jackson, Ms 39201-1200
877-713-3322
601-969-5339
Fax: 601-948-6004
www.mincap.org

Quitman Tri County Federal Credit
Union
P.O. Box 277
Marks, MS 38646
662-326-4000
Fax: 662-326-3904
www.qcdo.org

East Mississippi Development
Corporation
910 Highway 19 North
P.O. Box 790
Meridian, MS 39307
601-696-1306
Fax: 601-693-5638
Email: info@embdc.org
www.embdc.org

Delta Southern Bank
P.O. Box 99
117 West Floyce Street
Ruleville, MS 38771-3923
662-756-4343
Fax: 662-759-2425

Shelby/Bolivar County Federal
Credit Union
P.O. Box 790
1009 Broadway Street
Shelby, MS 38774
662-398-7091
Fax: 662-398-7009
Email: shelbycu@tecinfo.com

Missouri
Central Bancshares of Kansas City,
Inc.
2301 Independence Blvd.
Kansas, City, MO 64124
816-483-1210

Central Bank of Kansas City
2301 Independence Blvd.
Kansas City, MO 64124-2396
816-483-1210
Fax: 816-483-2586
www.centralbankkc.com

EDC Loan Corporation
10 Petticoat Lane, Suite 250
Kansas City, MO 64106-2103
800-889-0636
816-221-0636
Fax: 816-221-0189
Email: edckc.com
www.edckc.com

Growth Opportunity Connection,
Inc.
4747 Troost Avenue
Kansas, MO 64110-1727
816-235-6146
www.goconnection.org

Housing & Economic Development
Financial Corporation
600 Broadway, Suite 450
Kansas, MO 64105
816-472-3008

Kansas City Metro Fund
1055 Broadway, Suite 130
Kansas City, MO 64105-0388
816-842-0388

Great Rivers Community Capital
5031 Northrup Avenue
St. Louis, MO 63110-2029
314-664-5051
Fax: 314-664-5364

Montana
Fallon County Federal Credit Union
P.O. Box 1101
16 Sewall Avenue
Baker, MT 59313-1101
406-778-2920

Native American Development
Corporation
2722 3rd Avenue North
Suite 310
Billings, MT 59101
406-259-3804

Butte Local Development
Corporation
305 West Mercury
Butte, MT 59701-1692
406-723-4349
Fax: 406-723-4672
www.buttemontana.org

Tri-Valley Community Federal
Credit Union
704 East Main Street
P.O. Box 760
East Helens, MT 59635-0760
406-227-5831
Fax: 406-227-6339
Email: tvcfcu@in-tch.com
www.trivalleyfcu.com

Carter County Federal Credit Union
P.O. Box 292
Ekalaka, MT 59324-0292
406-775-8748

Montana Credit Unions for
Community Development
1236 Helena Avenue
Helena, MT 59601
406-442-9081

Kootenai Valley Federal Credit
Union
P.O. Box 636
Libby, MT 59923-0636
406-293-6421

Gateway Community Federal Credit
Union
2300 Great Northern Way
Missoula, MT 59808
406-728-4475
Fax: 406-728-0257
Email: gateway@gateway
communityfcu.com
www.gatewaycommunityfcu.com

Montana Community Development
Corporation
110 East Broadway, 2nd Floor
Missoula, MT 59802
406-728-9234 x 205
Fax: 406-542-6671
Email: mcdc@mtcdc.org
www.mtcdc.org

Sovereign Leasing & Financing, Inc.
P.O. Box 478
Polson, MT 59860
406-883-4317

Heritage Capital Fund
218 Third Avenue S., Suite C
Wolf Point, MT 59201
406-653-2988
Fax: 406-653-1627
www.heritageinstitute.org

Wolf Point Federal Credit Union
217 Third Avenue South
P.O. Box 426
Wolf Point, MT 59201-0426
406-653-2880
Fax: 406-653-2884
Email: wpfcu@nemontel.net
www.wpfcu.com/home.asp

Nebraska

Self Employment Loan Fund of
Lincoln

1135 M Street, 3rd Floor, Suite 116
Lincoln, NE 68508-2196
402-436-2386
Fax: 402-436-2387
Email: info@self-lincoln.org
www.self-lincoln.org

Northeast Economic Development
Inc.
111 S. 1st Street
Norfolk, NE 68701
402-379-1836
Fax: 402-379-9207
www.nedinc.org

Midwest Housing Development
Fund LLC
13057 West Center Road, Suite 20
Omaha, NE 68144-3723
402-334-8899
www.mheginc.com

Omaha 100, Incorporated
2414 Lake Street
Omaha, NE 68111
402-738-5412

Nebraska Microenterprise
Partnership Fund
312 Main Street, #8
P.O. Box 99
Walthill, NE 68067
402-685-6866
Fax: 402-846-5219
Email: nmpf@nebbiz.org
www.nebbiz.org

Nevada

Pahranagat Valley Federal Credit
Union
169 North Main Street
P.O. Box 419
Alamo, NV 89001-0419
775-725-3586
Fax: 775-725-3585
Email: pvfcu@lcturbonet.com
www.pahranagat.net

Nevada Microenterprise
Development Corporation
116 East 7th Street
Carson City, NV 89701
775-841-1812

Rural Nevada Development
Corporation
1320 East Aultman Street
Ely, NV 89301-1645
775-289-8519
Fax: 775-289-8214
Email: mdc@the-onramp.net
www.rndcnv.org

New Hampshire

Business Enterprise Development
Corporation (BEDCO)
177 Main Street
P.O. Box 628
Berlin, NH 03570-0628

603-752-3319
Fax: 603-752-4421
Email: bedco@ncia.net
www.bedco.org

New Hampshire Community Loan
Fund, Inc.
7 Wall Street
Concord, NH 03301
603-224-6669
Fax: 603-225-7425

New Jersey

Cooperative Business Assistance
Corporation
328 Market Street
Camden, NJ 08102
856-966-8181
Fax: 856-966-0036
Email: info@cbaclenders.com
www.cbaclenders.org

City national Bancshares
Corporation
900 Broad Street
Newark, NJ 07102-2611
973-624-0865

City National Bank of New Jersey
900 Broad Street
Newark, NJ 07102-2611
973-624-0865
Fax: 973-643-5717
Email:
CustomerService@citynabank.com
www.citynabank.com

La Casa Federal Credit Union
39 Broadway
Newark, NJ 07104
973-485-0701

New Community Federal Credit
Union
233 West Market Street
Newark, NJ 07103
973-623-2800
www.newcommunity.org/main.htm

Renaissance Community
Development Credit Union
P.O. Box 328
Somerset, NJ 08875-0328
732-247-6883

Community Loan Fund of New
Jersey, Inc.
16-18 West Lafayette Street
Trenton, NJ 08608-2088
609-989-7766
Fax: 609-393-9401
Email:njclf@bellatlantic.net
www.njclf.com

Regional Business Assistance
Corporation (RBAC)
247 East Front Street
Trenton, NJ 08611
609-396-2595
Fax: 609-396-2598

Email: info@rbacloan.com
www.tbacloan.com

Union County Economic
Development Corporation
Liberty Hall Corporate Center
1085 Morris
Union, NJ 07083-7150
908-527-1166
Fax: 908-527-1207
Email: info@ucedc.com
www.ucedc.com

New Mexico

ACCION New Mexico
20 First Plaza, N.W., Suite 417
Albuquerque, NM 87102-3391
800-508-7624
505-243-8844
Fax: 505-243-1551
Email: accion@accionnm.org
www.accionnewmexico.org

New Mexico Community
Development Loan Fund
700 4th Street SW
P.O. Box 705
Albuquerque, NM 87103
505-243-3196
Fax: 505-243-8803
Email: nmcdlfgen@aol.com
www.nmclf.org

Women's Economic Self-Sufficiency
Team
414 Silver, S.W.
Albuquerque, NM 87102
800 Go WESST
505-241-4758
Fax: 505-241-4766
Email: wesst@swcp.com
www.wesst.org

Neighborhood Housing Services of
Santa Fe, Inc.
1570 Pacheco Street
Suite A-1
Santa Fe, NM 87505-3980
505-983-6214
Fax: 505-983-4655

Santa Fe Community Housing Trust
P.O. Box 713
Santa Fe, NM 87504-0713
505-989-3960
Fax: 505-982-3690

New York

Albany Community Development
Federal Credit Union
185 Clinton Avenue
Albany, NY 12210-2401
518-432-9881

Capital District Community Loan
Fund, Inc.
255 Orange Street, #103
Albany, NY 12210
518-436-8586

Fax: 518-689-0086
www.cdclf.org

Allegany Community Development
Service, Inc.
P.O. Box 117
Belmont, NY 14813
585-268-7605

Binghamton Housing Authority
Residents Community FCU
P.O. Box 1906
Binghamton, NY 13901
607-723-9491
Fax: 607-722-5031

Bethex Federal Credit Union
20 East 179th Street, Basement
Bronx, NY 10453-4770
718-299-9100 x 19
Fax: 718-294-4950
Email: info@bethexfcu.org
www.bethexfcu.org

Credit, Inc.
370 East 149th Street
Bronx, NY 10455
718-292-3113
Fax: 718-292-3115
www.creditinc.org

New York National Bank
369 East 149th Street
Bronx, NY 10455-3906
718-401-6100
Fax: 718-401-1280

University Neighborhood Housing
Program
2751 Grand Concourse
Bronx, NY 10468
718-933-3101
Fax: 718-933-3624
Email: mail@unhp.org
www.unhp.org

ACCION New York
235 Havemeyer Street, 3rd Floor
Brooklyn, NY 11211-6238
718-599-5170
Fax: 718-387-9686
Email: info@accionnewyork.org
www.accionnewyork.org

Boc Capital Corporation
85 South Oxford Street, 2nd Floor
Brooklyn, NY 11217
718-624-9115
Fax: 718-246-1881
Email: info@bocnet.oeg
www.bocnet.org

Brooklyn Ecumenical Federal Credit
Union
67 Hanson Place
Brooklyn, NY 11217
718-858-8803 x 28
Fax: 718-852-5997

Bushwick Cooperative Credit Union
1475 Myrtle Avenue

Brooklyn, NY 11237-5157
718-418-8232
Fax: 718-418-8252

CAMBA Economic Development
Corporation
1720 Church Avenue
Brooklyn, NY 11226-2630
718-282-2500
Fax: 718-287-0857
www.camba.org

Community Capital Bank
111 Livingston Street
Brooklyn, NY 11201-5078
718-802-1212
Fax: 718-243-0213
www.communitycapitalbank.com

First American International Bank
5503 8th Avenue
Brooklyn, NY 11220-3515
718-871-8338
Fax: 718-686-0969

New York City Financial Network
Action Consortium
237 Garfield Place
Brooklyn, NY 11215-2208
718-638-2061
www.nycfnac.org

Regional Economic Development
Assistance Corporation
175 Remsen Street, Suite 350
Brooklyn, NY 11201
718-522-4600

Restoration Capital Fund, Inc.
1368 Fulton Street
Brooklyn, NY 11216-2630
718-636-6930

Buffalo Economic Renaissance
Corporation
920 City Hall
Buffalo, NY 14202
716-842-6923
Fax: 716-842-6942
www.growbfo.org

CDCLI Funding Corporation
2100 Middle Country Road, Suite
300
Centereach, NY 11720
631-471-1215
Fax: 631-471-1210
www.cdcli.org

Westchester Housing Fund, Inc.
14 Saw Mill River Road, Suite 3
Hawthorne, NY 10532
914-592-3244
Fax: 914-592-2549
Email: vcpino@bestweb.net

Housing Resources of Columbia
County, Inc.
605 State Street
Hudson, NY 12534-2513

518-822-0707
Fax: 518-822-0367
Email: hroc@housingresources.org
www.housingresources.org

Alternatives Federal Credit Union
301 West State Street
Ithaca, NY 14850
607-273-3582
Fax: 607-277-6391
Email: afcu@alternatives.org
www.alternatives.org

Ithaca Neighborhood Housing
Services, Inc.
115 West Clinton Street
Ithaca, NY 14850
607-277-4500
Fax: 607-277-4536
Email: info@ithacanhs.org
www.ithacanhs.org

Greater Jamaica Local Development
Company, Inc.
90-04 161st Street
Jamaica, NY 11432-6154
718-291-0282
Fax: 718-658-1405
www.gjdc/GreaterJamaicaLocalDev
elopmentCompany.HTML

Long Island Fund for Sustainable
Development
28 Woodmont Road
Melville, NY 11747
631-491-1388

AAFE Community Development
Fund
111 Division Street
New York, NY 10002
212-964-2288
Fax: 212-964-6003
Email: info@aacfecd.org
www.aafecdf.org

Audubon Partnership for Economic
Development LDC
513 West 207th Street
New York, NY 10034-2645
212-544-2400

Carver Federal Savings Bank
75 West 125th Street
New York, NY 10027
212-876-4747
Email:
customer.service@carverbank.com
www.carverbank.com

The Community Development Trust,
LP
1350 Broadway, Suite 700
New York, NY 10018
212-271-5087

Community Development Venture
Capital Alliance
330 Seventh Avenue, 19th Floor
New York, NY 10001

212-594-6747
Fax: 212-594-6717
Email: cdvca@cdcva.org
www.cdvca.org

Community Partnership
Development Corporation
1 Battery Park Plaza, 4th Floor
New York, NY 10004
212-493-7437

Corporation for Supportive Housing
50 Broadway, 17th Floor
New York, NY 10004-3618
212-986-2966
Fax: 212-986-6552
Email: ny@csh.org
www.csh.org

East Harlem Business Capital
Corporation
2261-63 First Avenue, 3rd Floor
New York, NY 10035
212-427-6590
Fax: 212-427-6537
Email: ehbcc@aol.com

Fund for the City of New York
121 Avenue of the Americas
New York, NY 10013
212-925-6675
Fax: 212-925-5675
Email: info@fcny.org
www.fcny.org

Grow America Fund
51 east 42nd Street, Suite 300
New York, NY 10017-5404
212-682-1106
Fax: 212-573-6118
www.ndc-online.org

Homesteaders Federal Credit Union
P.O. Box 1512
New York, NY 10268-1512
212-222-0328

Local Initiatives Support
Corporation
733 Third Avenue, 8th Floor
New York, NY 10017-3204
212-455-9800
Fax: 212-682-5929
www.liscnet.org

Lower East Side People's Federal
Credit Union
37 Avenue B
New York, NY 10009-7441
212-529-8197
Fax: 212-529-8368
www.lespfcu.org

National Federation of Community
Development Credit Unions
120 Wall Street, 10th Floor
New York, NY 10005
212-809-1850
Fax: 212-809-3274
Email: info@natfed.org
www.natfed.org

Neighborhood Housing Services of
New York City, Inc.
121 West 27th Street, Suite 404
New York, NY 10001
212-519-2503
Fax: 212-727-8171
Email: info@nhsnyc.org
www.nhsnyc.org

Neighborhood Trust Federal Credit
Union
4211 Broadway
New York, NY 10033-3747
212-927-5771
Fax: 212-543-9120

New York Community Investment
Company, LLC
110 William Street, 32nd Floor
New York, NY 10038-3920
212-693-0870
Fax: 212-693-0949
Email: info@NYCIC.com
www.nycic.com

Nonprofit Finance Fund
70 West 36th Street, 11th Floor
New York, NY 10018-8031
212-868-6710
Fax: 212-268-8653
www.nonprofitfinancefund.org

The Parodneck Foundation for Self-
Help Housing and Community
Development, Inc.
121 Sixth Avenue, Suite 501
New York, NY 10013
212-431-9700
Fax: 212-431-9783

Primary Care Development
Corporation
291 Broadway, 17th Floor
New York, NY 10007
212-693-1850
Fax: 212-693-1860
Email: info@pcdcnyc.org
www.pcdcnyc.org

Project Enterprise
144 West 125th Street, 4th Floor
New York, NY 10027-4423
212-678-6734 x 6
Fax: 212-678-6737
Email: pe@projectenterprise.org
www.projectenterprise.org

Renaissance Economic Development
Corporation
1 Pike Street
New York, NY 10002
212-964-6022 x 208
Fax: 212-964-6003
Email: info@renaissance-ny.org
www.renaissance-ny.org

Seedco
915 Broadway, Suite 1703
New York, NY 10010
212-473-0255

Fax: 212-473-0357
Email: info@seedco.org
www.seedco.org

The Community Preservation
Corporation
5 West 37th Street, 10th Floor
New York, NY 10018
212-869-5300
Fax: 212-719-9374
www.communityp.com

Union Settlement Federal Credit
Union
237 East 104th Street
New York, NY 10029
212-828-6063
Fax: 212-828-6064
www.unionsett.org/credit.htm

Washington Heights & Inwood
Development Corporation
57 Wadsworth Avenue
New York, NY 10033
212-795-1600
Fax: 212-781-4051
Email: whidc@aol.com
www.members.aol.com/whidc

Women's Venture Fund Inc.
240 West 35th Street, Suite 201
New York, NY 10001
212-563-0499
Fax: 212-868-9116
Email: info@wvf-ny.org
www.womensventurefund.org

Long Island Small Business
Assistance Corporation
255 Executive Drive
Suite 400
Plainview, NY 11803
516-349-7800
Fax: 516-349-7881
www.lidc.org

Genesee Co-op Federal Credit Union
741 South Avenue
Rochester, NY 14620
585-461-2230
Fax: 585-461-3189
Email: msr@gencoopfcu.com
www.gencoopfcu.com

Greater Rochester Housing
Partnership
183 East Main Street, Suite 900
Rochester, NY 14604-1621
585-423-6320
Fax: 585-423-6322
Email: GRHP@frontiernet.net

Neighborhood Housing Services of
Rochester Inc.
570 South Avenue
Rochester, NY 14620-1337
585-325-4170
Fax: 585-325-2587
www.nhsrochester.org

Progressive Neighborhood FCU
470 West Main Street
Rochester, NY 14608-1945
585-328-5410
Fax: 585-328-6510
Email: kstiokas@pnfcu.org

Rural Opportunities Enterprise
Center, Inc.
400 East Avenue
Rochester, NY 14607
585-340-3388
Fax: 585-340-3326
www.ruralinc.org

Worker Ownership Resource Center
104 Scio Street
Rochester, NY 14621
585-338-7822
Fax: 585-338-1232
www.atworc.net

Adirondack Economic Development
Corporation
60 Main Street, Suite 200
P.O. Box 747
Saranac Lake, NY 12983-0747
888-243-AEDC
518-891-5523
Fax: 518-891-9820
Email: info@aedconline.com
www.aedconline.com

Commercial and Industrial Capital
Corporation
900 South Avenue, Suite 402
Staten Island, NY 10314-3425
718-983-8800

Home Headquarters, Inc.
124 East Jefferson Street
Syracuse, NY 13202
315-474-1939 x 226
Fax: 315-474-0637
Email: info@homehq.org
www.homehq.org

Syracuse Cooperative Federal Credit
Union
723 Westcott Street
Syracuse, NY 13210
315-471-1116 x 201
Fax: 315-476-0567
www.syrcoopfcu.org

Utica Neighborhood Housing
Services, Inc.
1611 Genesee Street
Utica, NY 13501-4737
315-724-4197
Fax: 315-724-1415

Leviticus 25:23 Alternative Fund,
Inc.
928 McLean Avenue
Yonkers, NY 10704
914-237-3306
Fax: 914-237-3916
Email: info@leviticusfund.org
www.leviticusfund.org

North Carolina

Tri County Credit Union
P.O. Box 754
Ahoskie, NC 27910-0754
252-332-4413

Mountain Microenterprise Loan
Fund, Inc.
29 ½ Page Avenue
Asheville, NC 28801
888-389-3089
828-253-2834
Fax: 828-255-7953
www.mtnmicro.org

Neighborhood Housing Services of
Asheville North Carolina, Inc.
135 Cherry Street
Asheville, NC 28801-2223
828-251-5054

East Carolina Community
Development Inc.
315 Turner Street
Beaufort, NC 28516
252-504-3996
Fax: 252-504-2248
Email: info@eccdi.com
www.eccdi.com

Charlotte-Mecklenburg Housing
Partnership, Inc.
1201 Greenwood Cliff, Suite 300
Charlotte, NC 28204-2822
704-342-0933
Fax: 704-342-2745
Email: info@cmhp.org
www.cmhp.org

School Workers Federal Credit
Union
431 Beatties Ford Road
Charlotte, NC 28297
704-375-5781
Fax: 704-343-0823
Email: info@schoolworkersfcu.org
www.schoolworkersfcu.org

Latino Community Credit Union
201 West Main Street
Durham, NC 27702-5360
919-530-8800
Fax: 919-530-8802
www.cooperativalatina.org

Mechanics and Farmers Bank
116 West Parrish Street
Durham, NC 27701
919-683-1521
Fax: 919-687-7821
Email: inof@mfbonline.com
www.mfbonline.com

Mutual Community Savings Bank,
Inc. SSB
315 East Chapel Hill Street
P.O. Box 3827
Durham, NC 27702-3827
916-688-1308
Fax: 919-682-1380

North Carolina Minority Support
Center
123 West Main Street
P.O. Box 2086
Durham, NC 27702-2086
919-530-1683
Fax: 919-530-1684
www.ncmsc.org

Self-Help Credit Union
P.O. Box 3619
Durham, NC 27702-3619
919-956-4400
Fax: 919-956-4600
www.self-help.org

Self-Help Ventures Fund
P.O. Box 3619
Durham, NC 27702-3619
919-956-4400
Fax: 919-956-4600
www.self-help.org

Sustainable Jobs Corporation (SJC)
400 West Main Street, Suite 604
Durham, NC 27701-3241
919-530-1177
Fax: 919-530-1178
www.sjfund.com

Sustainable Jobs Fund, L.P.
400 West Main Street, Suite 604
Durham, NC 27701-3241
919-530-1177
Fax: 919-530-1178
www.sjfund.com

Generation Credit Union
P.O. Box 627
Edenton, NC 27932
919-530-1683

College Heights Credit Union
1503 Murchinson Road
Fayetteville, NC 28301
910-488-7634
Fax: 910-488-0343
www.uncfsu.edu/MurchDev/chcu.htm

Generations Community
Development Credit Union
314 South Garnett Street
P.O. Box 755
Henderson, NC 27536-4538
252-492-5854
Fax: 252-492-7832
www.gencomcu.org

Perquimans Credit Union
306 Dodds Street
P.O. Box 102
Hertford, NC 27944-0102
252-426-5098
Fax: 252-426-5965

Greater Kinston Credit Union
901 North Queen Street
Kinston, NC 28501
252-527-4002
Fax: 252-527-7785

Chatham-Lee Credit Union
69 Cornwallis Street
P.O. Box 321
Pittsboro, NC 27312-0321
919-542-2106
Fax: 919-545-0786

North Carolina Community
Development Initiative Capital, Inc.
2209 Century Drive, 2nd Floor
P.O. Box 98148
Raleigh, NC 27624
919-828-5655
Fax: 919-834-8018
Email: ncinitiative@ncinitiative.org
www.ncinitiative.org

MAY Coalition, Inc.
167 Locust Street
P.O. Box 704
Spruce Pine, NC 28777-2977
828-765-8880
Fax: 828-765-9655
Email: mayloan@bellsouth.net
www.maycoalition.org

Metropolitan Community Credit
Union
327 North Market Street
P.O. Box 2661
Washington, NC 27889-4933
252-946-1128
Fax: 252-946-4020
www.metroploitancommunity.org

South East Community Credit Union
4713 Market Street
P.O. Box 2677
Wilmington, NC 28402-2677
910-799-6622
Fax: 910-799-5349
Email: seccu@bellsouth.net
www.southeastccu.org

St. Luke Credit Union
302 Granville Street
Windsor, NC 27983
252-794-3240
Fax: 252-794-4206

Caswell Credit Union
P.O. Box 186
Yanceyville, NC 27379-0186
336-694-1544
Fax: 336-694-9938

North Dakota
Lake Agassiz Regional Development
Corporation
417 Main Street
Fargo, ND 58103-1956
701-235-1197
Fax: 701-235-6706

Renaissance Ventures, LLC (Dakota
Renaissance Ventures)
51 Broadway, Suite 500
Fargo, ND 58102
701-237-6132
Fax: 701-293-7819

First Community Credit Union
P.O. Box 2180
Jamestown, ND 58402-2180
701-253-5140
Fax: 701-253-5133

Ohio
Enterprise Community Fund
550 South Arlington Street
Akron, OH 44306
330-773-6838
Fax: 330-773-0345

ACEnet Ventures, Inc.
94 Columbus Road
Athens, OH 45701-1312
888-422-3638
740-592-3854
Fax: 740-593-5451
Email: info@acenetworks.org
www.acenetworks.org

Cincinnati Development Fund
1100 Walnut Street
Cincinnati, OH 45202
513-721-7211
Fax: 513-721-7214

Cornerstone Homesource Regional
Loan Fund
1115 Pendleton Street, Suite 2 N.W.
Cincinnati, OH 45210-4104
513-369-0114

Greater Cincinnati Microenterprise
Initiative, Inc.
1501 Madison, Road
1st Floor Rear
Cincinnati, OH 45206
513-569-4816
Fax: 513-569-0075
www.gcmi.org

The Home Ownership Center of
Greater Cincinnati, Inc.
2820 Vernon Place
Cincinnati, OH 45219
513-961-2800
Fax: 513-961-8222
www.hometoday.cc

Faith Community United Credit
Union
3550 East 93rd Street
Cleveland, OH 44105
216-271-7111
Fax: 216-271-7488
Email: faithcu@prodigy.net
www.faithcommcu.com

Neighborhood Capital Corporation
2530 Superior Avenue, Sixth Floor
Cleveland, OH 44114
216-771-0805
Fax: 216-771-0822

Shorebank Cleveland
540 East 105th Street
Cleveland, OH 44108-4301
216-268-6100

Fax: 216-268-6107
www.shorebankcleveland.com

Village Capital Corporation
1956 West 25th Street, Suite 200
Cleveland, OH 44113-3450
216-830-2770
Fax: 216-830-2767
Email:
bah@neighborhoodprogress.oeg
www.neighborhoodprogress.org

The Columbus Growth Fund Inc.
900 Michigan Avenue
Columbus, OH 43215
614-645-6287

Ohio Capital Finance Corporation
88 East Broad Street, 18th Floor
Columbus, OH 43215-3526
614-224-8446
Fax: 614-224-8452
Email: info@occh.org
www.occh.org

CountyCorp
40 West Fourth Street
Suite 1600
Dayton, OH 45402-1828
937-225-6328
Fax: 937-225-5089
Email: countycorp@countycorp.com
www.countycorp.com

Neighborhood Housing Services of
Hamilton, Inc.
100 South Martin Luther King, Jr.
Blvd.
Hamilton, OH 45011-2824
513-737-9301
Fax: 513-737-9304

J.C.C. Federal Credit Union
102 Broadway Street
P.O. Box 322
Jackson, OH 45640-0322
740-286-5168
Fax: 740-288-9834
Email: jccfcu@bright.net

Marion Federal Credit Union
409 Davids Street
Marion, OH 43302-4798
740-383-6765
Fax: 740-382-2900

Appalachian Development Federal
Credit Union
54 West Washington Street
Nelsonville, OH 45764-1135
740-753-9122

Portage Area Development
Corporation
218 West Main Street
Ravenna, OH 44266-2714
330-297-6400
Fax: 330-297-5303
http://padcorp.org

Neighborhood Housing Services of
Toledo, Inc.
704 Second Street
P.O. Box 8125
Toledo, OH 43605
419-691-2900
Fax: 419-691-2980
www.nhstoledo.org

Northwest Ohio Development
Agency
1000 Monroe Street, Suite 4
Toledo, OH 43624
419-243-3734
Fax: 419-243-3924
www.nodatloedo.org

Toledo Urban Federal Credit Union
1339 Dorr Street
P.O. Box 3344
Toledo, OH 43607
419-255-8876
Fax: 419-255-4390

Oklahoma

First National Bank
227 East Main Street
P.O. Box 750
Davis, OK 73030
580-369-2325

Rural Enterprises of Oklahoma, Inc.
P.O. Box 1335
Durant, OK 74702
800-658-2823
580-924-5094
Fax: 580-920-2745
www.ruralenterprises.com

Fort Gibson State Bank
P.O. Box 130
Fort Gibson, OK 74434
918-456-3900

MetaFund Corporation
2225 North May Avenue
Oklahoma City, OK 73107
405-949-0001
Fax: 405-949-9005
Email: info@metafund.org
www.metafund.org

Neighborhood Housing Services of
Oklahoma City, Inc.
P.O. Box 60327
Oklahoma City, OK 73146-0327
405-231-4663
Fax: 405-231-5137

Oklahoma City Northeast, Inc.
1500 N.E. 4th Street, Suite 204
Oklahoma City, OK 73117
405-235-0415
Fax: 405-272-033
Email: okcne@tetpath.com

Adair County Indian Credit
Association
916 West Cedar
P.O. Box 602

Stilwell, OK 74960-3406
918-969-7095
Fax: 918-696-7095

Bank of Cherokee County, Inc.
125 East 1st Street
Tahlequah, OK 74467-4834
918-456-3900
Fax: 918-458-5417
www.bankofcherokeecounty.net

Cherokee Nation Economic
Development Trust Authority, Inc.
P.O. Box 948
Tahlequah, OK 74464
918-456-0671

Greenwood Community
Development Corporation
131 North Greenwood Ave, 2nd Floor
Tulsa, OK 74120-1444
918-585-2084
Fax: 918-585-9628

Security State Bank of Wewoka,
Oklahoma
210 South Mekusukey
P.O. Box 749
Wewoka, OK 74884
405-257-5411

Oregon

Harney County Federal Credit Union
743 Hines Blvd.
Burns, OR 97720
541-573-7501
Fax: 541-573-5740

O.U.R. Federal Credit Union
P.O. Box 11922
Eugene, OR 97440
541-485-1190
Fax: 541-685-1651

Community & Shelter Assistance
Corporation dba CASA of Oregon
212 East First Street
Newberg, OR 97132-2904
503-537-0319
Fax: 503-537-0558

Albina Community Bancorp
2002 N.E. Martin Luther King, Jr.
Blvd.
Portland, OR 97212-3722
503-288-7280
Email: info@albinabank.com
www.albinabank.com

Albina Community Bank
2002 N.E. Martin Luther King, Jr.
Blvd.
Portland, OR 97212-3722
800-814-6088
503-288-7280
Email: info@albinabank.com
www.albinabank.com

Hacienda Community Credit Union
6736 NE Killingsworth, Suite 102

Portland, OR 97218-3318
503-249-5559

Homestead Community Financing,
LLC
222 S.W. Columbia Street, Suite 200
Portland, OR 97201-6601
503-288-1555
Fax: 503-276-1563
Email: info@homesteadcap.com
www.homesteadcap.com

Mercy Enterprise Corporation
936 S.E. Ankeny Street, Suite 1
Portland, OR 97214-1303
503-236-1580 x 6
Fax: 503-236-3615
Email: contact@mercyenterprise.org
www.mercyenterprise.org

Network for Oregon Affordable
Housing
1020 S.W. Taylor Street, Suite 585
Portland, OR 97205
503-223-3211
Fax: 503-223-0663
Email: info@noah-housing.org
www.noah-housing.org

Portland Housing Center
3233 NE Sandy Blvd.
Portland, OR 97232-2557
503-282-7744
www.portlandhousingcenter.org

Pennsylvania

Rising Tide Community Loan Fund
651 East Broad Street
Bethlehem, PA 18018-6332
610-691-5620

Rural Enterprise Development
Corporation
105 West Main Street
P.O. Box 276
Bloomsburg, PA 17815-0276
570-784-7003
Fax: 570-784-7030
Email: help@redc-leap.org
www.redc-leap.org

The Progress Fund
105 Zee Plaza
P.O. Box 565
Hollidaysburg, PA 16648-0565
814-696-9380
Fax: 814-696-9569
www.progressfund.org

Mon Valley Initiatives
303/305 East Eight Avenue
Homestead, PA 15120-1517
412-464-4000

USSCO Federal Credit Union
522 Central Avenue
Johnstown, PA 15902-2699
814-535-4646
Fax: 814-535-2969
www.usscofcu.org

Community First Fund
P.O. Box 524
Lancaster, PA 17608-0524
717-393-2351
Fax: 717-393-1757
www.communityfirstfund.org

Lancaster Housing Opportunity
Partnership
30 West Orange Street, Suite 150
Lancaster, PA 17603-3841
717-291-9945
Fax: 717-291-9850
Email: info@lancasterhousing.org
www.lancasterhousing.org

Housing Opportunities, Inc.
P.O. Box 9
McKeesport, PA 15134
412-664-1590

Community Financial Resources,
Inc. (CFR)
4200 Crawford Avenue, Suite 200
Northern Cambria, PA 15714
814-948-4444

American Street Financial Services
Center
2530 North Second Avenue, Second
Floor
Philadelphia, PA 19133
215-426-3882

Berean Federal Savings Bank
5228 Chestnut Street
Philadelphia, PA 19139-3491
215-472-4545
Fax: 215-472-4549

Borinquen Federal Credit Union
629-31 West Erie Avenue
Philadelphia, PA 19140
215-228-4180
Fax: 215-228-5110

Ceiba, Inc.
147 West Susquehanna Avenue
Philadelphia, PA 19122-1719
215-634-7245

Community Capital Works, Inc.
1334 Walnut Street, 7th Floor
Philadelphia, PA 19107-5314
215-546-3100
Fax: 215-546-8055

Economic Opportunities Fund, Inc.
2010 Chestnut Street
Philadelphia, PA 19103-4411
215-564-5500

Impact Loan Fund, Inc.
1952 East Allegheny Avenue
Philadelphia, PA 19134-3122
215-739-0243

Murex Investments, Inc.
4700 Wissahickon Avenue
Suite 126

Philadelphia, PA 19144
215-951-7200
Fax: 215-951-9228
www.murexinvests.com

North Philadelphia Financial
Partnership
1522 West Girard Avenue, Suite 100
Philadelphia, PA 19130
215-787-9540
Fax: 215-787-9165
Email: info@npfp.org
www.npfp.org

Philadelphia Neighborhood Housing
Services, Inc.
121 North Broad Street, Suite 502
Philadelphia, PA 19107-1913
215-988-9879

The Reinvestment Fund
718 Arch Street, Suite 300 North
Philadelphia, PA 19106-1591
215-925-1130
Fax: 215-923-4764
Email: contact@trfund.com
www.trfund.com

The Triumph Baptist Federal Credit
Union
1538 West Wingohocking Street
P.O. Box 9848
Philadelphia, PA 19140-0848
215-455-2282
Fax: 215-324-8086
Email: tbfcu@aol.com
www.charityadvantage.com/tbfcu/H
ome.asp

United Bank of Philadelphia
300 North Third Street
Philadelphia, PA 19106-1101
215-351-4638
www.unitedbankofphiladelphia.com

Universal Capital Investment Fund,
Inc.
800 South 15th Street
Philadelphia, PA 19146-2105
215-732-6518

West Philadelphia Financial Services
Institution
5200 Warren Street
Philadelphia, PA 19131
215-452-0100
Fax: 215-452-0101
Email: info@wpfsi.com
www.wpfsi.com

Citizens East Community
Development Federal Credit Union
7249 Frankstown Avenue, Suite 103
Pittsburgh, PA 15208
412-247-5600

Community Loan Fund of
Southwestern Pennsylvania, Inc.
1920 Gulf Towers
707 Grant Street

Pittsburgh, PA 15219-1908
412-201-2450 x 13
Fax: 412-201-2451
www.clfund.com

Northside Community Development
Fund
415 East Ohio Street
Pittsburgh, PA 15212
412-231-4714
Fax: 412-231-5306

Neighborhood Housing Services of
Reading, Inc.
383 Schuylkill Avenue
Reading, PA 19601
610-372-8433
Fax: 610-374-2866
Email: nhsread@ix.netcom.com

MetroAction, Inc.
P.O. Box 431
Scranton, PA 18501
570-342-7711

Washington County Council on
Economic Development
40 South Main Street, Lower Level
Washington, PA 15301
724-225-8241
Fax: 724-225-8202
www.washingtoncountypa.org

Puerto Rico

Comerciantes Unidos para el
Desarrollo Comunitario de Camuy,
Inc.
P.O. Box 945
Camuy, PR 00627-2629
787-262-3722

Cooperativa de Ahorro Y Credito
Nuestra Senora de la Candelaria
P.O. Box 3249
Manati, PR 00674-5032
787-854-1620

Ponce Neighborhood Housing
Services, Inc.
P.O. Box 0223
Ponce, PR 00733-0223
787-841-5055

Pueblo Coop
P.O. Box 363288
San Juan, PR 00936-3288
787-769-0206

San Juan Neighborhood Housing
Service, Inc.
P.O. Box 13926
San Juan, PR 00908-3926
787-721-8833

Cooperativa de Ahorro y Credito
Empleado Pepsi Cola
P.O. Box 2600
Tao Baja, PR 09512
787-251-2809

Rhode Island

Minority Investment Development
Corporation
216 Weybosset Street
Providence, RI 02903-3734
401-351-2999
Fax: 401-351-0990
Email: MDC_loans@efortress.com
www.midcri.com

West Elmwood Housing
Development Corporation
392 Cranston Street
Providence, RI 02907-2703
401-453-3220
Fax: 401-453-3222
www.westelmwoodhousing.com

South Carolina

Charleston Citywide Local
Development Corporation (LDC)
75 Calhoun Street, 3rd Floor
Charleston, SC 29401
843-724-3796
Fax: 843-724-7354
Email: economicdev@charleston.net
www.ci.charleston.sc.us

Business Carolina, Inc.
1441 Main Street, Suite 900
P.O. Box 8327
Columbia, SC 29202
803-461-3801
Fax: 803-461-3826
http://businesscarolina.net

Native Island Business and
Community Affairs Association, Inc.
P.O. Box 23452
Hilton Head, SC 29925
843-689-9314

South Dakota

Neighborhood Lending Services,
LLC
817 ½ Main Street
Deadwood, SD 57732-1003
605-578-1401

Four Bands Community Fund, Inc.
101 South Main Street
P.O. Box 932
Cheyenne River Lakota Nation
Eagle Butte, SD 57625
605-964-3687
Fax: 605-964-3689
Email: 4bands@lakotanetwork.com
www.fourbands.org

Consumer's Federal Credit Union
301 West Highway18
P.O. Box 69
Gregory, SD 57533-0069
605-835-8749
Fax: 605-835-9413
Email: consfcu@gwtc.net
www.sdcw.com/fcus/consumersfcu/c
omsuners.htm

Dakotaland Federal Credit Union
1371 Dakota South
Huron, SD 57350
800-440-6573
605-352-2845
Fax: 605-352-2852
Email:
helpdesk@dakotalandfcu.com
http://site.dakotalandfcu.com

The Lakota Fund
Suite 201 Lakota Trade Center
P.O. Box 340
Kyle, SD 57752-0340
605-455-2500
Fax: 605-455-2696
Email: inof@lakotafund.org
www.lakotafund.org

Rural Electric Economic
Development, Inc.
P.O. Box 227
Madison, SD 57042-0227
605-256-4536

Fort Randall Federal Credit Union
340 Lewis Avenue
P.O. Box 110
Pickstown, SD 57367-0110
888-244-9009
605-487-7641
Fax: 605-487-7944
www.ftrandallfcu.com

South Dakota Rural Enterprises, Inc.
P.O. Box 802
Sioux Falls, SD 57101-0802
605-978-2804
Fax: 605-978-2805
Email: info@sdrei.org
www.sdrei.org

Northeast South Dakota Economic
Corporation (NESDEC)
414 3rd Avenue East
Sisseton, SD 57262-1598
605-698-7654
Fax: 605-698-3038
Email: nesdcap@nesdec.htm
www.onida.org/nesdec.htm

Sisseton Co-op federal Credit Union
212 West Hickory
Sisseton, SD 57262
605-698-7481
Fax: 605-698-7481
Email: scfcu@tnics.com
www.sdcul.com/fcus/sissetoncoopfc
u/sissetoncoop.htm

Tennessee

Bethlehem Community Development
Credit Union
P.O. Box 2131
Chattanooga, TN 37409-0131
423-266-2384

Chattanooga Community
Development Financial Institution
1301 Market Street, Suite 100

Chattanooga, TN 37402-4098
423-756-6201

Chattanooga Neighborhood
Enterprise, Inc.
535 Chestnut Street, Suite 100
Chattanooga, TN 37402-4927
423-756-6201
Fax: 423-756-3851
www.cneinc.org

Church Koinonia Federal Credit
Union
2319 East Third Street
Chattanooga, TN 37404-2718
423-629-5400

East Tennessee Enterprise
Partnership, Inc.
3503 Baker Hwy.
P.O. Box 186
Huntsville, TN 37756
423-286-9090

Imani Federal Credit Union
3034 Austin Peay Highway,
Building GIC-3
Memphis TN, 38128
901-454-9248

MemphisFirst Community Bank
4230 Elvis Presley Boulevard
Memphis, TN 38116-6438
901-346-1111
www.memphisfirstbank.com

MemphisFirst Corporation
4230 Elvis Presley Boulevard
Memphis, YN 38116-6438
901-346-1111

Tennessee Capital & Development,
LLC
802 Walker Avenue, Suite 5
Memphis, TN 38126-6736
901-942-6265
Fax: 901-942-6448

United Housing, Inc.
51 North Cooper Street
Memphis, TN 38104-6511
901-272-1122
www.uhinc.org

Affordable Housing Resources, Inc.
1011 Cherry Avenue
Nashville, TN 37203-4755
615-251-0025
Fax: 615-256-9836
www.ahrhousing.org

Citizen's Savings Bank & Trust
Company
1917 Heiman Street
Nashville, TN 37208-2409
615-327-9787 x 209

Nashville Housing Fund, Inc.
806 South Sixth Street
Nashville, TN 37206-3812

615-780-7000
Email:
mail@nashvillehousingfund.org
www.nashvillehousingfund.org

Southeast Community Capital
Corporation
1020 Commerce Park Drive
Suite 5L
Oak Ridge, TN 37830-8099
865-220-2025
Fax: 865-220-2024
Email: info@SECapitalPartners.com
www.secapitalpartners.com

Texas

Austin Community Development
Corporation
207 Chalmers Avenue
P.O. Box 15331
Austin, TX 78761-5331
512-472-8087
Fax: 512-472-8191
Email: auscdc@austincdc.org
www.austincdc.org

Business Invest in Growth
4100 Ed Bluestein, Suite 207
Austin, TX 78721-2301
512-928-8010
Fax: 512-926-2997

Corporation for the Development of
Community Health Centers
2301 South Capital of Texas
Highway
Austin, TX 78746-7700
512-329-5959
www.tach.org/cdchc.htm

Greater Brownsville Community
Development Corporation
901 East Levee
Brownsville, TX 78520
956-686-0263

Brazos Valley CDC, Inc.
1706 East 29th Street
P.O. Box 4128
Bryan, TX 77805-4128
979-775-4244

Neighborhood Housing Services of
Dimmit County, Inc.
301 Pena Street
Carrizo Springs, TX 78834
830-876-5295
Fax: 830-876-4136
Email: nhsdc@brushco.net

Dallas Affordable Housing Coalition
3103 Greenwood Street
Dallas, TX 75204-6011
214-946-3500

Southern Dallas Development
Corporation
351 West Jefferson Blvd., #800
Dallas, TX 75208
214-948-7800

Texas Mezzanine Fund, Inc.
351 West Jefferson Blvd.
Suite 750
Dallas, TX 75208
214-943-5900
Fax: 214-943-5905
Email: kcross@tmfund.com
www.tmfund.com

Women's Southwest Federal Credit
Union
4301 Bryan, Suite 120F
P.O. 720207
Dallas, TX 75204
214-887-0700
Fax: 214-887-0099
Email: wsfcudallas@aol.com
www.wsfcudallas.org

El Paso Collaborative for
Community and Economic
Development
616 Virginia Avenue, Suite D
El Paso, TX 79901-2695
915-532-7788
Fax: 915-532-7340

William Mann, Jr. Community
Development Corporation
1150 South Freeway, Suite 118
Fort Worth, TX 76104
817-871-6267

Corporation for Economic
Development of Harris County, Inc.
11703 ½ Eastex Freeway
Houston, TX 77039
281-590-5600
Email: info@cedhc.com
www.cedhc.com

Covenant Community Capital
Corporation
P.O. Box 15398
Houston, TX 77219
713-223-1864

Laredo-Webb Neighborhood
Housing Services, Inc.
216 Bob Bullock Loop
Laredo, TX 78046
956-712-9100

Pineywoods Community
Development Financial Institution
P.O. Box 190
Lufkin, TX 75902-0190
936-559-0883

PRAXIS Corporation
P.O. Box 1050
Manor, TX 78653-1050
512-278-1455
www.faith-
based.org/PraxisIntro.html

Community Development
Corporation of South Texas
(CDCST)
1420 Erie Avenue

McAllen, TX 78501
956-664-0158

Inter National Bank
1801 South 2nd Street
McAllen, TX 78503-1266
956-664-8400
Email: inb@inbweb.com
www.internationalbank.net

McAllen Affordable Homes, Inc.
600 South 11th Street
McAllen, TX 78501
956-687-6263
Fax: 956-682-9751
Email: mahi1@flash.net
www.mcallenaffordablehomes.com

Midland Community Development
Corporation
P.O. Box 11134
Midland, TX 79703-5408
915-687-2500

Tejas Community Credit
Opportunities, Inc.
1303 Matamoros
Mission, TX 78572
956-424-7477

Permian Basin Business
Development Center
1609 West 10th Street
Odessa, TX 79763-3433
915-580-8661
Fax: 915-337-6266

ACCION Texas
2014 South Hackberry
San Antonio, TX 78210
888-215-2373
210-226-3664
Fax: 210-533-2940
Email: info@acciontexas.org
www.acciontexas.org

Bexar County Teachers Federal
Credit Union
220 Connelly Street
San Antonio, TX 78203-1708
210-226-7789

Community Development Loan
Corporation (CDLC)
100 West Olmos Drive, Suite 104
San Antonio, TX 78212-1954
210-738-0312
Fax: 210-738-0330

Community Development Loan
Fund (CDLF)
225 West Poplar
San Antonio, TX 78212
210-738-0312
Fax: 210-738-0330
Email: info@cdlf.neyt
www.cdlf.net

Neighborhood Housing Services of
San Antonio

851 Steves Avenue
San Antonio, TX 78210-3923
210-533-6673

Rural Development and Finance
Corporation
711 Navarro Street, Suite 104
San Antonio, TX 78205-1721
210-212-4552
Fax: 210-212-9159
Email: webmaster@rdfc.org
www.rdfc.org

Unitarian Universalist Housing
Assistance Corporation
2015 North Main Street
San Antonio, TX 78212
210-731-8203
Email: uuhac@aol.com

Azteca Community Loan Fund
P.O. Box 27
San Juan, TX 78589-0027
956-702-3307

Neighborhood Housing Services of
Waco, Inc.
922 Franklin Avenue
Waco, TX 76703
254-752-1647

Utah
Neighborhood Housing Services of
Provo, Inc.
91 West 200 South
Provo, UT 84601
801-375-5820

Salt Lake Neighborhood Housing
Services, Inc.
622 West 500 North
Salt Lake City, UT 84116
801-539-1590
Fax: 801-539-1593
Email: info@slnhs.org
www.slnhs.org

Utah Microenterprise Loan Fund
(UMLF)
3595 South Main Street
Salt Lake City, UT 84115
801-269-8408
Fax: 801-269-1063
www.umlf.com

Vermont
Vermont Development Credit Union
18 Pearl Street
Burlington, VT 05401-4330
800-865-8328
802-865-3404 x 106
Fax: 802-862-8971
Email: info@vdcu.org
www.vdcu.org

Vermont Development Ventures,
Inc.
18 Pearl Street

Burlington, VT 05401-4330
802-865-3404

Vermont Community Loan Fund
15 State Street
P.O. Box 827
Montpelier, VT 05601-0827
802-223-1448
Fax: 802-223-1455
www.vclf.org

RNA Community Builders, Inc.
27 Center Street
Rutland, VT 05701
802-776-7000

Northern Community Investment
Corporation
347 Portland Street
P.O. Box 904
St. Johnsbury, VT 05819
802-748-5101
Fax: 802-748-1884
Email: ncic@ncic.org
www.ncic.org

Rutland West Neighborhood
Housing Services, Inc.
P.O. Box 541
West Rutland, VT 05777-0541
802-438-2303
rwnhs@vermontel.net

Virgin Islands
Virgin Islands Capital Resources,
Inc.
#7A Crystal Grade
St. Thomas, VI 00802-6623
340-776-0677
www.seslia.com/vi_cap/html

Virginia
Southwest Virginia Community
Development Financing, Inc.
1173 West Main Street
Abingdon, VA 24210-4703
276-623-9000

Shiloh of Alexandria Federal Credit
Union
1323 Duke Street
P.O. Box 25853
Alexandria, VA 22314-3509
703-739-0652
Fax: 703-739-5940
Email: shilohfcu@aol.com
www.shilohfcu.com

ECDC Enterprise Development
Group
1038 South Highland Street
Arlington, VA 22204-4311
703-685-0510
Fax: 703-685-0529

Piedmont Housing Alliance
2000 Holiday Drive, Suite 200
Charlottesville, VA 22901
434-817-2736

Fax: 434-817-0664
Email: pha@avenue.org
http://avenue.org/pha

New Enterprises Fund, Inc.
930 Cambria Street
Christiansburg, VA 24073-1602
540-382-2002
Fax: 540-382-1935

First Nations Oweesta Corporation
2300 Fall Hill Avenue
Suite 412
Fredericksburg, VA 22401
540-371-5615
Fax: 540-371-3505
Email: info@firstnations.org
www.firstnations.org

Newport News Neighborhood
Federal Credit Union
P.O. 37
Newport News, VA 23607
757-247-0379

NCP Community Development
Federal Credit Union
530 South Main Street
P.O. Box 4767
Norfolk, VA 23523
757-543-2400
Fax: 757-543-2600

Neighborhood Housing Services of
Richmond
2712 Chamerlayne Avenue
Richmond, VA 23222
804-329-2500
Fax: 804-329-2100
www.nhsrichmond.org

Richmond Economic Development
Corporation (REDC)
501 East Franklin Street
Suite 358
Richmond, VA 23219-2325
804-780-3013
Fax: 804-788-4310
www.redcfinance.org

Virginia Community Development
Loan Fund
1624 Hull Street
Richmond, VA 23224
804-233-2014
Fax: 804-233-2158
www.vcdlf.org

Virginia Community Development
Fund
114 East Cary Street, Suite 101
Richmond, VA 23219-3735
804-343-1200
Fax: 804-343-1043

Virginia Foundation for Housing
Preservation
601 South Belvidere Street
Richmond, VA 23220-6504
804-343-5605

Southeast Rural Community
Assistance Project, Inc.
145 West Campbell Avenue, S.W.
P.O. Box 2868
Roanoke, VA 24011-2868
866-928-3731
540-345-1184
Fax: 540-342-2932
Email: xyz@microsoft.com
www.sercap.org

Washington
The Lending Network
1611 North National Avenue
P.O. Box 916
Chehalis, WA 98532
360-740-6960

NEWRIZONS Federal Credit Union
120 Firman Street
Hoquiam, WA 98550-2006
86-NEWRIZON
360-533-4760
Fax: 360-532-0280
www.newrizonsfcu.com

Shorebank Enterprise Pacific
203 Howerton Way, S.E.
P.O. Box 826
Ilwaco, WA 98624-0826
360-642-4265
Fax: 360-642-4078
www.sbpac.com

Timber Country Community Federal
Credit Union
P.O. Box 400
Morton, WA 98356
360-496-5420

People Working Together Federal
Credit Union
P.O. Box 96
Ridgefield, WA 98642-0096
360-887-4876

Cascadia Revolving Fund
1901 NW Market Street
Seattle, WA 98107
206-447-9226 x 104
Fax: 206-682-4804
Email: info@cascadiafunding.org
www.cascadiafunding.org

Homesight
5117 Rainier Avenue South
Seattle, WA 98118-1929
888-749-4663
206-723-4355
Fax: 206-760-4210
www.homesightwa.org

Impact Capital
401 Second Avenue South, Suite301
Seattle WA 98104
800-336-0679
206-507-3200
Fax: 206-587-3230
Email: info@impactcapital.org
www.impavtcapital.org

Northwest Baptist Federal Credit
Union
1604 19th Avenue
Seattle, WA 98122-2849
206-322-1604

Seattle Economic Development Fund
d/b/a Community Capital
Development
P.O. Box 22283
Seattle, WA 98122-0283
206-324-4330

Washington Assistance Technology
Foundation
3670 Stone Way North
Seattle, WA 98103
206-826-1038

Washington Cash
1912 East Madison Street
Seattle, WA 98122
206-352-1945
Fax: 202-352-1899

Washington Community
Reinvestment Association
1200 5th Avenue, Suite 1406
Seattle, WA 98101
800-788-6508
206-292-2922
Email: info@wcra.net
www.wcra.net

Spokane Neighborhood Economic
Development Alliance
715 East Sprague, Suite 101
Spokane, WA 99202
509-484-6733
www.sneda.org

Rural Community Development
Resources
24 South Third Avenue
P.O. Box 9492
Yakima, WA 98909-0492
509-453-5133
Fax: 509-453-5165

West Virginia
The Center for Rural Health
Development, Inc.
500 Westmoreland Office Center
Suite 201 A
Dunbar, WV 25064
304-766-1591
Fax: 304-766-1597
www.wvruralhealth.org/home.cfm

Randolph County Federal Credit
Union
1200 Harrison Avenue
Randolph Center
Elkins, WV 26241
304-636-5488

Community Works in West Virginia,
Inc.
P.O. Box 890
Elkview, WV 25071-0890
304-965-2241

Lightstone Community Development
Corporation
HC63 Box 73
Doe Hill Road
Moyers, WV 26815-9502
304-249-5200
Fax: 304-249-5310
Email: contact@lightstone.org
www.lightstone.org

Natural Capital Investment Fund,
Inc.
Rt. 1, Turner Road
P.O. Box 1889
Shepardstown, WV 25443-1889
304-876-2815
Fax: 304-870-2205
Email:
wvncif@freshwaterinstitute.org
www.wvncif.org

Valley Health Care Federal Credit
Union
2000 Eoff Street
Wheeling, WV 26003
304-234-8616

Wisconsin

Impact Seven, Inc.
147 Lake Almena Drive

Almena, WI 54805-7004
715-357-3334
Fax: 715-357-6233
Email: impact@impactseven.org
www.impactseven.org

Lac Courte Orielles Federal Credit
Union
9790 North County Road K
LCO Box 1710
Hayward, WI 54843-1710
715-634-7772

The Dane Fund, Inc.
211 South Peterson Street, Suite 160
Madison, WI 53703-4530
608-257-3863

Legacy Bancorp, Inc.
2102 West Fond du Lac Avenue
Milwaukee, WI 53206
414-343-3000

Legacy Bank
2102 West Fond du Lac Avenue
Milwaukee, WI 53206-1533
414-343-3500

Partners Advancing Values in
Education (PAVE)

1841 North Martin Luther King
Drive
Milwaukee, WI 53212-3639
414-263-2970
www.PAVE.org

Ways to Work
11700 West Lake Park Drive
Milwaukee, WI 53224
414-359-1040 x 3658

Wisconsin Women's Business
Initiative Corporation
2745 N. Dr. Martin Luther King, Jr.
Milwaukee, WI 53121
414-263-5450
Fax: 414-263-5456
www.wwbic.com

Community Assets for People
5499 Highway 10 East
Stevens Point, WI 54481-9113
715-343-7509

Wyoming

Elk Basin Federal Credit Union
207 North Bent Street
P.O. Box 454
Powell, WY 82435-0454
307-754-0633

Unconventional Loan Programs

The following is a description of loan programs available to low and moderate income individuals, minorities, Native Americans, Hispanics, refugees, unemployed individuals, welfare recipients, youths, and low and moderate income individuals who don't qualify for credit through conventional methods.

Most of these programs allow individuals (depending on the situation) to roll closing costs and fees into the amount of the loan. So you actually go to the closing with NO money in your pocket.

The aim of these programs is to stimulate economic growth through small businesses or microenterprises. Helping individuals become self-sufficient is the main focus, and also to challenge conventional methods of providing credit. All of the programs hope to demonstrate that persons with limited incomes are responsible, will repay, and can become successful if given access to knowledge and resources.

Some programs are designed just for youths, (15-21 years old), to develop their own businesses, avoid drugs and crime, sharpen academic skills and form positive attitudes about themselves and their communities. This is accomplished by utilizing the leadership, communication, management and business skills they may have acquired through affiliation with the illegal drug trade and other street activities. Loan amounts can range from $50 to $2,000 with terms from six months to two years.

The following examples are excerpted from the websites of the microenterprise and technical assistance organizations listed in this chapter. Contact the organizations listed in your area for more information on how they can help you.

Susanna Rodriquez started making ceramic figurines for children's parties. Susanna is a former teacher's assistant who presently works in the kitchen of her small apartment. Her creations fill every free corner. She was constantly looking for ways to expand her business. One day she was in a store where the owner sold similar products. As they were comparing notes, the owner mentioned ACCION New York. After four loans as a result of working with that organization, Susanna's monthly revenue from her ceramics business has increased from $350 a month to $800 a month. In time, she hopes to open her own store. She feels that if it were not for ACCION, she would not be at the advanced stage of business that she is enjoying now.

Jeff Hess of Virginia had fished and hunted with his father since the age of five. He earned his associates degree in business and was working in an assembly plant for a moderate hourly wage, but wanted more. At the age of 24 he didn't see opportunity coming to call on him because he had no money and no credit. He and his wife, Cherylanna enrolled in the BusinessStart class at People, Inc. With this training, assistance in small business planning and a small loan, Jeff and Cherylanna were able to buy a bait shop in Honaker and turn it into Bucks and Bass, a full service hunting and fishing store. Located in prime hunting and fishing country, Bucks and Bass has nearly doubled its sales in its first year alone. Both Jeff and Cherylanna have left their jobs and run Bucks and Bass full time.

Making it in Miami

Can two recent immigrants begin anew in the competitive business world of Miami, Florida?

If they combine hard work with the support of an ACCION loan, the answer is yes. When Claudia, Javier, and their daughter arrived in Florida, they were fleeing the violence of their native Columbia – and were forced to leave a thriving architectural practice behind. Javier found work as a handyman, and Claudia studied for the General Contractors' Exam. When she passed the exam, the couple was ready to open a remodeling business – but with no credit history, they could not secure the commercial credit they needed.

They turned to ACCION USA for working capital to pay for the labor and supplies for their first remodeling job. Now the couple is managing various projects, and employing 15 subcontractors. The ACCION loan helped them get started, and they built the business from there!

A Rocky Mountain Success Story

What would you do if you found yourself divorced and facing bankruptcy after 33 years of marriage and raising children? That was what happened to Kathy Cowgill. It was "the most humiliating time of my life," she says, but then she decided to pick up the pieces and start her own business.

Kathy decided to start a window-blind cleaning and repair business. A friend agreed to co-sign a loan through MicroBusiness Development Corporation's BusinessWorks! Program with the MicroBusiness Development Corporation in Denver, Colorado, and Kathy was on her way.

She and her son-in-law – who worked for free – built a shop in the garage. Within two years Kathy added a mobile unit for on-site cleaning and an office behind the shop. She also hired two full-time employees.

Kathy recently closed on her second BusinessWorks! loan, which she will use to further expand the business.

The Fastest Plumber in the USA

Tino Rodriguez is no ordinary plumber. He once entered a contest and won first prize – a 1957 cherry red T-Bird convertible – for being the fastest plumber in the nation.

Rodriguez saw more in the T-Bird than a flashy car, however. He also knew it might be the ticket to his own plumbing business.

Rodriquez contacted the Santa Cruz Community Credit Union, which provides a variety of loans to entrepreneurs in the Santa Cruz, CA, area, and offered his prize as collateral for a loan. The credit union agreed. They gave him enough money to launch Tino's Plumbing – and ten years later, the firm has a fleet of vans, an office, a showroom and 13 full-time employees.

Rodriquez still works with the credit union – and they call him for their plumbing needs!

Turning a Profit with Lullabyes

Elizabeth Baez is redecorating the living room in her Chicago apartment - with cribs, rocking chairs and teddy bears. In an effort to get off of welfare, Baez opened a child care center in her home. She soon discovered an unfilled niche: many parents work the night

shift, with no place to bring their young ones. Her nighttime childcare service will meet that need.

Baez launched the center because she did not want to leave her own children in daycare. She took a class to get licensed – but then she needed a loan for equipment. But who would lend money to a recent welfare recipient? She heard about ACCION Chicago, and within a few days, she had a loan of $5,000 for highchairs, tables, playpens and a washer and dryer.

As with many small business owners, Baez is taking it one step at a time. Offering daytime care got her back on her feet – thanks to the ACCION loan. Now that she has steady customers and can expand to overnight hours, she will begin to see a profit.

Baez says the home-based business is good for her family, and for her peace of mind. "It stabilized me in my home," she explains. "I don't have to wake up and wonder if a welfare check is going to be there at the agency or not."

You Are Never Too Young to Succeed!

Got the energy and dreams of youth? You may as well profit from it! The Prudential Young Entrepreneur Program (PYEP) helps young people in the Newark, New Jersey and Philadelphia who want to start a business and need a loan, business skills and technical assistance to get the ball rolling.

Jamila Payne of Philadelphia started her high-end, on-line boutique, Mila by Mail Direct in May 2003 after receiving a microloan through PYEP. Her designs have created a buzz in the industry, and she is mentoring student interns who want to launch their own businesses.

In Newark, Joseph Cambell launched a network of African-American professionals called BLACKNJ with the help of PYEP. BLACKNJ is a thriving network of over 2,000 members connected by a website, an e-news-letter, and networking events. The network allows members to establish professional contacts and support each other.

PYEP graduates Natasha Haughton and Nevea Van Wright, also of Newark, started another community organization, Integrated Vision for Youth (IVY). IVY empowers urban youth through environmental awareness, leadership training, and life skills coaching.

A Last-Minute Loan to Open the Doors

Jocelyn Tejada arrived in Boston from the Dominican Republic with a limited knowledge of English and a great big dream. She was a talented hairdresser, and wanted to operate her own beauty salon. Jocelyn and her husband both found jobs and worked on renovating a salon after hours – and then, just before the opening day, the faced a problem that needed a lot of money to fix. They could not install the right air conditioning system, and that was crucial to attracting customers in the hot summer months.

This is the kind of barrier that can put the brakes on opening a small business, as many lenders are hesitant to provide a loan when there is no track record to back it up. And, they needed the money quickly in order to open on time. The Tejadas approached ACCION USA, and the salon welcomed its first customers on a steamy day in June.

"ACCION USA was just great," says Francisco. "They loaned to us when no one else would."

The salon was soon bustling with customers. With the success of the business, the Tejadas can look forward to a secure future for their three children – and a cool place to work every summer!

Loan Programs

National Programs

The Abilities Fund

332 S. Linn St., Suite 15   866-720-3863
Iowa City, IA 52240   319-338-2521
http://www.abilitiesfund.org   Fax: 319-338-2528

The Abilities Fund is a nationwide developer targeted exclusively to advancing entrepreneurial opportunities for Americans with disabilities. They deliver a combination of training, technical assistance services, and advisory supports to individuals with disabilities and the organizations that support them. They also assist entrepreneurs to obtain the funding they need to launch or grow a small business by linking entrepreneurs to a variety of lending programs that best match the needs and situations of the borrower.

Association for Enterprise Opportunity

1601 North Kent St., Suite 1101   703-841-7760
Arlington, VA 22209   Fax: 703-841-7748
http://www.microenterpriseworks.org/

The Association for Enterprise Opportunity is committed to microenterprise development. It primarily assists organizations to promote opportunities for people with limited access to economic resources. They do have a wide variety of resources and a list of organizations in your area.

FIELD (Microenterprise Fund for Innovative, Effectiveness, Learning and Dissemination)

The Aspen Institute
One Dupont Circle, NW, Suite 700   202-736-1071

Washington, DC 20036 Fax: 202-467-0790
http://fieldus.org/home/index.html

FIELD's mission is to identify, develop and disseminate the best practices throughout the United States about microenterprise programs as an anti-poverty intervention. They offer publications, access to information as well as a directory of microenterprise organizations.

Community Express: Entrepreneurial Loans and Business Assistance

National Community Reinvestment Coalition
733 15th Street, Suite 540 202-628-8866
Washington, DC 20005 Fax: 202-628-9800
www.ncrc.org/

The goal of the National Community Reinvestment Coalition's CommunityExpress program is to provide financing and technical assistance to entrepreneurs who have been under-served by financial institutions. The national initiative is administered jointly by the NCRC and the U.S. Small Business Administration, with local banks and nonprofits providing support and resources. How it works: SBA guarantees business loans, community-based organizations provide the technical support, and lenders compensate these groups for the cost of support. Eligible small businesses must be located in low-income areas, or owned by women, minorities or veterans. The average size of a CommunityExpress loan is approximately $75,000, with the maximum allowable loan set at $250,000. Interest rates on loans do not exceed 2.75% over prime rate. The CommunityExpress Program also includes pre- and post-loan assistance in the form of marketing, financial, management and planning assistance. To qualify, a business should be owned by or serve low-income populations, women or minorities.

Low Interest Finance Options With A New Kind of Bank

FINCA International, Inc.
1101 14th Street, NW, 11th Floor
Washington, DC 20005 202-682-1510
www.villagebanking.org

Though its development efforts extend beyond US borders, the Foundation for International Community Assistance (FINCA) works hard to help metropolitan Washington DC entrepreneurs achieve economic and personal success. FINCA offers self-employment loans to business founders through its unique Village Banking program. The program offers market-rate loans and savings products to those who could not otherwise obtain them. Loans typically range from $500 to $6,000, with participants able to benefit from a five loan "cycle." FINCA's Village Banking program has a communal aspect, with groups of participants who meet to discuss their businesses and financial issues; group members may guarantee loans for each other. Services in the DC area also include monthly training classes in entrepreneurship that help clients master such skills as developing business plans and marketing strategies, managing time, and improving credit records. To date, over 250 DC-area entrepreneurs have benefited from the local outreach efforts of this international development star.

Grameen Foundation/USA

1029 Vermont Avenue NW
Suite 400 202-628-3560
Washington, DC 20005-3517 Fax: 202-628-3880
www.gfusa.org/

Very low-income individuals can start their own businesses with the assistance of a loan from the Grameen Foundation USA. This international organization dedicated to stopping

poverty administers a microcredit program for poor Americans looking to start a small or home-based commercial business. Targeted borrowers include women, minorities, and those living below the poverty line who have no hope of receiving funding from traditional lenders. Loan amounts are typically very small, under $5,000 and require no financial collateral on the part of the borrower.

Environmentalists Take StEPPs Toward New Business Success

The StEPP Foundation
P.O. Box 468 303-277-0932
Golden, CO 80402-0468 Fax: 303-384-3636
www.steppfoundation.org

Entrepreneurs with a focus on environmental and energy conservation have a source of business funding in the Strategic Environmental Project Pipeline (StEPP) Foundation. StEPP specializes in finding loans and grants for renewable energy, energy efficiency or pollution prevention projects to be undertaken by emerging businesses. How it works: A new business submits a proposal to the Foundation for evaluation. If accepted, the proposal is entered into a database system, which regularly searches for a "match" – a government entity, nonprofit or other organization that has either a need for a particular project or a need to provide funding whose requirements match the characteristics of an entrepreneur's proposal, skills and business plan. StEPP looks at a number of characteristics in business owners and their proposed ventures to determine eligibility for funding. These include a proven capability for successful project completion on the part of the entrepreneur; the immediacy with which a project can be implemented; a demonstrated ability to complete and plan for the operation, maintenance and management of projects; and the potential positive impact of a venture on a local community, region or state. The program is primarily designed for businesses that have past the start-up stage and are looking to expand. Businesses throughout the country are eligible for funding services. StEPP also provides assistance with all application steps and also provides technical assistance and project oversight to chosen ventures.

$700 Grant to Start Your Business

Trickle Up
104 W. 27th St., 12th Floor 212-255-9980
New York, NY 10001 866-246-9980 (toll-free)
www.trickleup.org Fax: 212-255-9974

Trickle Up provides grants of $700 (in two installments) to people wishing to start a business. Frequently these businesses are based in the home. They provide business training and seed capital to low income individuals who want to become entrepreneurs. Trickle Up works with 250 different coordinating agencies to provide the business training necessary to receive this grant. The first $500 is given once a business plan has been completed, and the second $200 is given after the business has been operational for 3 months. Contact Trickle Up to learn if a program is available near you.

$8,000 For a Car, School, Business or House Down Payment

IDA Network
Corporation for Enterprise Development
777 N Capitol St NE, Suite 800
Washington, DC 20002   202-408-9788
http://www.idanetwork.org/index.php?section=state&page=state_pages.html

Over 500 programs run by nonprofit organizations will give you up to $5 for every $1 you place into a savings account that is used to complete a life goal like education, housing , start a business, or even transportation. They are called Individual Development Accounts and they are designed for people with little money to save. You can make up to $60,000 and still qualify. To find a program near you contact the IDA Network.

Prudential Young Entrepreneur Program

240 Dr. Martin Luther King Jr. Boulevard
Newark, NJ 07102   973-643-4063
http://www.njit-edc.org/PYEP.htm

Young entrepreneurs can learn skills that can be translated into successful business ventures, better job opportunities, and enhanced real-world skills. They can also meet other entrepreneurs and successful business-people, have access at PYEP facilities to office space and computers, and may be eligible for $15,000 in loans to assist the launching of a business. PYEP covers such topics as Recognizing a Business Opportunity, Marketing Your Idea, Effective Sales Strategies, Understanding Your Costs, Choosing a Structure for Your Business, Building a Work Team, Using Cutting-Edge Computer Technology, Raising Capital, and Developing a Business Plan. There is a $25 fee for each participant upon acceptance into the program.

Alabama

Community Development Metro Loan Fund

Community Service Program of West Alabama
601 17th Street   205-752-5429
Tuscaloosa, AL 35401   Fax 205-758-7229
http://www.cspwal.com/comdev-new-1.htm

Loans are made to open or expand small businesses owned by minorities, women and low-income individuals. Loan Amounts range from $1,000 to $25,000 for up to 5 years with a 10% interest rate. Loans are made only to businesses located within the City of Tuscaloosa.

Alabama Microenterprise Network

110 12th St., North   205-250-6380
Birmingham, AL 35203   Fax: 205-250-6384

Help is available in a variety of ways for entrepreneurs who wish to start or expand their business.

Birmingham Business Resource Center

110 12th St., North   205-250-6380
Birmingham, AL 35203   Fax: 205-250-6384
www.bbrc.biz

The Birmingham Business Resource Center offers a variety of loan programs to help new or expanding businesses in the area. In addition they offer seminars, entrepreneurial training, support groups, one on one counseling and a learning center.

Central Alabama Women's Business Center

110 12th St., North   205-250-6380
Birmingham, AL 35203   Fax: 205-250-6384
www.cawbc.org

The Central Alabama Women's Business Center offers educational scholarships and loans through the Schlarb Foundation for Women Entrepreneurs. They also offer classes, resources, newsletters and more to help women businesses in the area.

Human Resource Development Corp.

100 Wallace Dr.
P.O. Box 311407   334-347-0881 ext. 22
Enterprise, AL 36331   Fax: 334-393-0048

Help is available in a variety of ways for entrepreneurs who wish to start or expand their business.

Huntsville Revitalization

700 Adventist Blvd.   256-726-7139
Huntsville, AL 35896   Fax: 256-726-8329

Huntsville Revitalization is working towards helping to revitalize the downtown area by offering a variety of programs and incentives.

Tuskegee/Macon County Community Development Corp.

P.O. Box 831134
Tuskegee, AL 36083   334-724-9662

The Tuskegee/Macon County Community Development Corp. offers a variety of incentives to help improve the economic and employment opportunities in the region.

Alaska

Southeast Alaska Revolving Loan Fund

Juneau Economic Development Council
612 W. Willoughby Ave., Suite A   907-463-3662
Juneau, AK 99801-1732   Fax: 907-463-3929
www.jedc.org

If you have a project that will create or retain jobs in Southeast Alaska, the Revolving Loan Fund might be the lender you've been looking for. Its purpose is to bridge the financial gap between what banks will finance and what the business community needs. Their goal is to provide financing for viable projects that will create and retain quality jobs and help to diversify local economies in Southeast Alaska. Loan amounts range from $35,000 - $350,000.

Microloan Fund

Kenai Peninsula Economic Development District
14896 Kenai Spur Hwy., Suite 103A   907-283-3335
Kenai, AK 99611   Fax: 907-283-3913
www.kpedd.org

This fund is designed for the home-based entrepreneur who is primarily producing an Alaskan craft or artwork or is involved in a trade within the Kenai Peninsula. Applicants have to live in a rural area or, if in a city, a city of less than 5,000 in population. Applicants have to be financially challenged. Traditional financing sources have either denied or are under serving the applicant. Loan amounts range from $250-$1,000.

Revolving Loan Fund

Kenai Peninsula Economic Development District
14896 Kenai Spur Hwy., Suite 103A   907-283-3335
Kenai, AK 99611   Fax: 907-283-3913
www.kpedd.org

The Kenai Peninsula Economic Development District's Revolving Loan Fund provides alternative financing options to small businesses. Financing is available to support the startup and expansion of businesses within the borough; which create long-term employment and diversify. Loan amounts range from $5,000-$50,000. Projects that are financed with

Revolving Loan Fund proceeds must be located within the Kenai Peninsula Borough and stay within the Borough until paid off.

KAWERAK CED

P.O. Box 948   907-443-9231
Nome, AK 99762   Fax: 907-443-4452
www.kawerak.org

KAWERAK provides technical assistance to Bering Strait communities in small business start-up and expansion, and economic development planning. CED's mission is to promote economic growth thru increased employment and income in the Bering Strait Region; and to create an economic climate that promotes businesses development.

Arizona

MicroBusiness Advancement Center

P.O. Box 42108   520-620-1241
Tucson, AZ 85733   Fax: 520-622-2235
www.mac-sa.org

Offers a variety of loan programs, one on one counseling, business classes and more to help new and expanding businesses succeed.

PPEP Microbusiness and Housing Development Corp.

901 E. 46th St.   520-806-9513
Tucson, AZ 85713   Fax: 520-806-9515
www.azsmallbusinessloans.com

The PPEP Microbusiness and Housing Development Corp. provides business and housing loans designed to help with community development. Loans offered include a Microenterprise loan of up to $25,000, A Bridge Loan of up to $75,000, and a Small Business Loan of up to $250,000. They also provide business assistance in the form of business planning, bookkeeping referrals, grant writing, technical assistance, training, and more.

Self Employment Loan Fund, Inc.

1601 N. 7th St., Suite 340   602-340-8834
Phoenix, AZ 85006   Fax: 602-340-8953
www.selfloanfund.org

The Self Employment Loan Fund offers a variety of services to help new or expanding entrepreneurs. A 10 week course on how to run a business, which covers topics such as writing a business plan, bookkeeping, marketing and more. Technical assistance includes networking, counseling, and business assistance. Two loan programs are offered. Peer Lending can be for up to $5,000 and can be sued for equipment, materials, and more. You receive continual peer support and encouragement for your business. The Individual Lending Program loans funds for up to $15,000 and you must have been in business for at least one year.

Gila River Entrepreneurship Program

P.O. Box 97   520-562-6138
Sacation, AZ 85247   Fax: 520-562-6125
http://www.gilariverdevelopment.com/entrepreneurship.htm

The Gila River Entrepreneurship Program is designed to assist those in the Gila River Indian Community to start and run businesses to help improve the local economy. A variety of microloans, loan guarantees, and other loan programs are available. In addition, business counseling covers topics such as financing, marketing, accounting, and business planning. Classes are offered on how to run a business, as well as computer classes on different computer programs.

Workshops, seminars, and artisan's cooperative are also available to entrepreneurs.

Arkansas

Good Faith Fund

2304 W. 29th Ave.   870-535-6233
Pine Bluff, AK 71603   Fax: 870-535-7883
www.goodfaithfund.org

Help is available in a variety of ways for entrepreneurs who wish to start or expand their business.

Beacons and Bridges Business Development Center

231 S. Fisher St.   870-931-1707
Jonesboro, AR 72401   Fax: 870-910-3516

Help is available in a variety of ways for entrepreneurs who wish to start or expand their business.

Central Arkansas Development Council

722 Gaunt St.
P.O. Box 580   501-315-1121
Benton, AR 72018   Fax: 501-778-9120
www.cadconline.net

The Central Arkansas Development council makes small loans available to those wishing to start or expand a business. In addition would be entrepreneurs can take education and training classes to learn how to best run a successful business.

California

California Association for Microenterprise Opportunity (CAMEO)

655 13th Street   510-238-8260
Oakland, CA 94612   Fax: 510-238-8361
http://www.microbiz.org/members.htm

CAMEO is a statewide membership organization designed to build the capacity of microbusiness organizations. CAMEO provides referrals to microbusiness owners seeking assistance. Use the site above or call to find a member service provider or for entrepreneur information in your area.

Micro Loan

ACCESS San Diego
2612 Daniel Ave   858-560-0871
San Diego, CA 92111   Fax: 858-560-8135
www.access2jobs.org

ACCESS has created a micro loan program with funding from the San Diego Foundation. This micro loan program provides small loans to local entrepreneurs to help them "jump start" their small businesses.

Home Based and Small Business Loans

ACCION San Diego
World Trade Center San Diego
1250 6th Avenue, Suite 500   619-685-1380
San Diego, CA 92101   Fax: 619-685-1470
http://www.accionsandiego.org/

As a community lender, this program provides low- to moderate-income small business owners loans ranging from $300-$25,000. The program is particularly geared to those businesses which are home-based, whose efforts not only support their families but, create jobs and contribute to the revitalization of their neighborhoods. First loans are usually termed between 9 and 24 months, which can enable an entrepreneur to grow their business and succeed. Serving San Diego County.

Micro Loan Program

California Coastal Rural Development Corporation
Cal Coastal Micro Loan Program
221 Main Street   831-424-1099
Salinas, CA 93901   Fax: 831-424-1094
www.calcoastal.org/indexnew.html

Cal Coastal is a California chartered Financial Development Corporation which provides loan capital and other financial services to businesses and farms located on the Central Coast. They serve the counties of Monterey, Santa Cruz, San Benito, Santa Clara, San Luis Obispo, Santa Barbara and Ventura.

Micro Loans

California Capital Small Business Development
Corporation
926 J Street, Suite 1500   916-442-1729
Sacramento, CA 95814   Fax: 916-442-7852
cwilliams@capital.com

Serving ethnic minorities, immigrants, and women to provide counseling and individual development accounts in the Sacramento area.

Industrial Development Bonds

City of Los Angeles Community Development Department
215 West 6th Street, 10th Floor   213-473-0311
Los Angeles, CA 90014   Fax: 213-485-8151
www.cityofla.org/cdd

City of Los Angeles Industrial and Commercial Division offers loans for projects in low to moderate-income communities in the LA and area. Loan amounts range from $500,000 to $10 million.

Micro Enterprise Loan Program

City of Long Beach California Business Development
Center
200 Pine Avenue, Suite 400   562-570-3800
Long Beach, CA 90802   Fax: 562-570-3897
www.ci.long-beach.ca.us/bdc/index.htm

The City of Long Beach Micro Enterprise Loan program provides up to $25,000 to start-up and existing businesses. The purpose for these programs is to make capital available to underserved and disadvantaged businesses, specifically those unable to obtain financing from conventional sources. Businesses must be located within the City of Long Beach.

Community Development Financial Institute

Clearinghouse CDFI
23861 El Toro Rd, #401   949-859-3600
Lake Forest, CA 92630   Fax: 949-859-8534
http://clearinghousecdfi.com

The Clearinghouse CDFI, Community Development Financial Institution, is a corporation that is addressing unmet credit needs in Southern California. The CDFI provides direct loans for small business.

Capital Partners, SEED Loan Program, Small Expansion Loan Program

Community Financial Resource Center
4060 So. Figueroa St.   323-233-1900
Los Angeles, CA 90037   Fax: 323-235-1686
www.cfrc.net

Community Financial Resource Center offers a variety of financial loan options for the LA area. The Capital Partners Program provides self-employed business owners and entrepreneurs access to working capital. Loans range from $500-$5,000. Start-ups as well as existing businesses are eligible. The SEED Loan program provides low cost commercial loans for businesses in operation for one year or more. SEED loans range from $5,000 to $30,000. The Small Expansion Loan Program is for businesses ready to expand. Loans range from $30,000 to $250,000.

Micro-Enterprise Loan Fund

East Bay Asian Local Development Corporation
310 8th Street, Suite 200   510-287-5353
Oakland, CA 94607   Fax: 510 763-4143
http://www.ebaldc.com/

The East Bay Asian Local Development Corporation is a community economic development organization dedicated to the betterment of the East Bay community, particularly the low-income and Asian and Pacific Islander population. East Bay Asian Local Development Corporation provides business planning and marketing assistance to small businesses located in its commercial properties. A revolving micro-loan fund is available to commercial tenants and others seeking small business loans.

Emergency Interest Free Loans

Jewish Free Loan Association
6505 Wilshire Boulevard, Suite 715   323-761-8830
Los Angeles, CA 90048   Fax: 323-761-8841
www.jfla.org

The Jewish Free Loan Association of Los Angeles offers interest-free loans on a non-sectarian basis to individuals, families and businesses whose needs are urgent and who may not qualify through normal financial resources. They serve the residents of Los Angeles and surrounding communities. A satellite office operates in West Hills, providing service to residents of the San Fernando and Conejo Valleys.

Community Development Loan

Lenders for Community Development
111 West St. John Street, 10th Floor 408-297-0204
San Jose, CA 95113   Fax: 408-297-4599
www.L4CD.org

Lenders for Community Development (LCD), is a nonprofit, community development financial institution whose mission is to increase the flow of capital into low-income communities throughout the Silicon Valley. LCD provides small business loans of between $5,000 and $50,000.

Financial Assistance

Madera County Economic Development Commission
413 W. Yosemite Ave., Suite 103   559-675-7768
Madera, CA 93637   800-357-5231
www.maderaindustry.org   Fax: 559-675-3252

The Madera County Economic Development Commission provides a full range of financing and consulting services for businesses in the Madera area. This assistance could include: financial assistance through grants, loan packaging assistance, and bond funding.

Revolving Loan Fund

Micro-Entrepreneurs Support Association
MESA Governing Council
C/O Merced County CAA
P.O. Box 2085   209-723-4565
Merced, CA 95344-0085   Fax: 209 725-8574
www.mercedcaa.org

Merced County members of the Micro-Entrepreneurs Support Association are eligible for loans for start-up or expansion of their business. Loan preference is given to micro-enterprise loans that create or retain local jobs, are to State certified women and minority owned businesses, to previous borrowers with an excellent payment record, and to finance projects that improve business by upgrading micro-enterprise employee(s) skills and wages. Loans will be for as little as $500 but no more than $10,000.

Start-up Loans

MicroEnterprise Assistance Program
2118 K Street   916-492-2591
Sacramento, CA 95816   Fax: 916-492-2603
www.mapsac.org

Microenterprise Assistance Program (MAP) empowers underserved individuals in the Sacramento area to become self-employed by providing financial assistance. MAP manages a loan pool and works with other financial agencies in Sacramento to secure funding for clients' start-up businesses.

Loan Fund

Northern California Community Loan Fund
870 Market Street, Suite 677   415-392-8215
San Francisco, CA 94102   Fax: 415-392-8216
www.ncclf.org

The Northern California Community Loan Fund (NCCLF) was founded to help revitalize the economy of low-income communities by providing nonprofit loans to create healthier communities. NCCLF estimates that more than 61% of the clients served by NCCLF borrowers are ethnic minority and more than 40% are women. NCCLF's geographic focus is Northern California with a majority of the current portfolio focused in the San Francisco Bay Area. Loans range from $10,000 to $450,000.

Financial Resource Center

Renaissance Entrepreneurship Center
275 5th Street   415-541-8580
San Francisco, CA 94102   Fax: 415-541-8589
www.rencenter.org

The Financing Resource Center assists San Francisco Bay Area new and established small business owners in understanding their company's financial position and growth options. A major component of the FRC is helping small business owners access needed capital to start or grow their businesses. The FRC helps entrepreneurs to package and secure loans. Loans range in size from $1,500 to $250,000.

Micro Enterprise Loan Program

Riverside County Community Investment Corporation
4250 Brockton Avenue, Suite 100   909-786-1370
Riverside, CA 92501   Fax: 909-786-0050
www.cicontheweb.com

Community Investment Corporation extends credit to start-ups and established businesses as part of their Micro Enterprise Loan Program in the low-income areas throughout the Inland Empire. Maximum loan amounts are $25,000

North Coast Microloan Program

SAFE-BIDCO
1211 N. Dutton Ave, Suite D   707-577-8621
Santa Rosa, CA 95401-4638   Fax: 707-577-7348
www.safe-bidco.com

SAFE-BIDCO is a catalyst for economic development of the North Coast Region, serving as a non-traditional financing source. This program is open to small businesses that are looking for financing to start-up or expand operations. Loan amounts range from $1,000-$25,000.

Revolving Loan

Silicon Valley Economic Development Corporation
City of San Jose Revolving Loan Fund
1155 N. First Street, Suite 107   408-298-8455

San Jose, CA 95112   Fax: 408-971-0680
www.sved.org/dsp_main.htm

The Revolving Loan Fund was established to advance the economic development of San Jose by creating jobs in the community. Businesses must be in San Jose and be able to create jobs in order to obtain the loan. Loans range from $5,000 to $40,000 with no loan fees and competitive fixed rates.

Lenders for Community Development

Start Up EPA
1395 Bay Road
East Palo Alto, CA 94303
For East Palo Alto/ East Menlo Park   650-321-2548
For Santa Clara or San Mateo counties   408-297-4554
www.startupepa.org

Start Up is a private, nonprofit organization whose mission is to promote economic development in and around East Palo Alto, California by providing training, capital, and other assistance to help establish and support locally-owned and operated small businesses. Lenders for Community Development provide fixed-rate term loans to small businesses ranging from $5,000 to $50,000. The program is targeted to women and minority-owned businesses, low-income-owned businesses, and businesses located in low-income communities.

Business Development Loan Program

Superior California Economic Development District
737 Auditorium Dr.   530-225-2760
Redding, CA 96001   Fax: 530-225-2769
www.scedd.org

Superior California Economic Development District (SCEDD) is a four county economic development district with its main office in Redding. SCEDD offers communities and businesses in Modoc, Shasta, Siskiyou and Trinity counties loans for start-up and established businesses. Loan amounts range from $5,000 to $250,000.

Community Capital

TELACU
5400 E. Olympic Blvd., Suite 300   323-721-1665
Los Angeles, CA 90022   Fax: 323-724-3372
www.telacu.com

TELACU Community Capital works closely with the Los Angeles Community Development Bank, serving as one of the Bank's micro-loan intermediaries. TELACU makes micro-loans on behalf of the Bank ranging from $5,000 to $25,000. The micro-loan program assists clients in gaining entry to the mainstream of the business world.

Microenterprise Resource for Medocino County

West Company: Ukiah Office
367 N State St., Suite 201   707-468-3553
Ukiah, CA 95482   Fax: 707-468-3555
info@westcompany.org

West Company: Coast Office
306 E. Redwood Ave., Suite 2   707-964-7571
Fort Bragg, CA 95437   Fax: 707-964-7576
www.westcompany.org

If you live in Mendocino County and are interested in starting or growing a micro business the West Company may be able to help you. Recognizing that access to capital has been the most restrictive barrier to low-income people who seek self-employment, West Company makes small loans from the West Company Loan Fund to people enrolled in their program. West Company particularly strives to empower low-income persons, women and minorities by helping them to build financial stability, self-confidence, and social and personal responsibility. Opportunity Loans provide short-term access to capital to individuals needing immediate financial assistance for a discrete business use. Loan amounts range from $100 to $250. Graduate Loans are also available in the $5,001 to $10,000 range for clients who have successfully paid back a West Company loan and are in an expansion stage.

Loan Fund

Women's Economic Ventures
Small Business Fund of Santa Barbara
1136 E. Montecito Street   805-965-6073
Santa Barbara, CA 93103   Fax: 805-962-9622
http://www.wevonline.org/

The goal of the Loan Fund is to diversify and expand the local economy and create new jobs by providing start-up and expansion capital to small businesses that do not qualify for conventional bank financing. SBLF loans are targeted to low and moderate-income men and women, minorities and others who have been traditionally underserved by lenders. Applicants must have resided within Santa Barbara for at least one year. Loans range from $1,000 to $25,000.

Loans for Women

Women's Initiative for Self-Employment
1390 Market Street, Suite113   415-247-9473
San Francisco, CA 94102   Fax: 415-247-9471
www.womensinitiative.org

Women's Business Center
1611 Telegraph Avenue, Suite 702   415-247-9473
Oakland, CA 94612   Fax: 510-451-3428
www.womensinitiative.org/Revolving_Loan_fund.htm

Women's Initiative for Self Employment is a private, nonprofit agency providing comprehensive business training, on-going technical assistance and financing to San Francisco Bay Area low-income women. Women's Initiatives lends money to women who have graduated from their "Managing Your Small Business," are starting or growing their businesses, and who show the cash-flow capacity to pay back the loan. Loans are made to businesses located in Alameda, Contra Costa, Marin, San Francisco and San Mateo Counties. The loan limit is $10,000.

Revolving Loan

Yuba-Sutter Enterprise Zone   530-741-6463
1364 Sky Harbor Drive   530-742-6280
Marysville, CA 95901   Fax: 530-742-7835
www.yubacounty.org
www.yubasutterez.com

Yuba County, Sutter County, Yuba City, and Marysville have established revolving loan fund programs to assist businesses and industries in satisfying capital needs. These loans are often used as "gap" financing to complete a financing package. The maximum loan amount available is $150,000.

Micro Loans

Yuba-Sutter Enterprise Zone   530-741-6463
1364 Sky Harbor Drive   530-742-6280
Marysville, CA 95901   Fax: 530-742-7835
www.yubacounty.org
www.yubasutterez.com

If you are just getting started in business and are from the Yuba County, Sutter County, Yuba City, and Marysville area this type of fund may be for you. The loan amount begins at $150 to a maximum of $25,000. Designed for the individual

just starting out. Applicants must complete the 12-hour Micro enterprise Training Program.

Anew America Community Corp.

2974 Adeline St.   510-540-7785
Berkeley, CA 94703   Fax: 510-540-7786
www.anewamerica.org

Anew American provides training and coaching to people wishing to start of expand a business. They help with marketing and planning, and provide access to capital by linking entrepreneurs with funding sources.

Economic and Employment Development Center

2200 W. Valley Blvd., Suite A   626-281-3792
Alhambra, CA 91803   Fax: 626-281-8064

Help is available in a variety of ways for entrepreneurs who wish to start or expand their business.

Santa Cruz Credit Union

Community Ventures
P.O. Box 1877   831-425-7708
Santa Cruz, CA 95061   Fax: 831-425-4824
www.scruzccu.org

Provides a variety of loans to entrepreneurs.

Vermont Slauson Economic Development Corp.

5918 S. Vermont Ave.   323-753-2335
Los Angeles, CA 90044   Fax: 323-753-6710
www.vsedc.org

Vermont Slauson provides a variety of programs and services to help improve the economic environment of the community.

Arcata Economic Development Corporation

100 EricsonCr., Suite 100   707-822-4616
Arcata, CA 95521   Fax: 707-822-8982

The Arcata Economic Development Corporation offers a variety of loan and business service assistance to those interested in starting or expanding a business.

CHARO Communnity Development Corp.

4301 East Valley Blvd.   323-269 0751
Los Angeles, CA 90032   Fax: 323-343-9485
www.charocorp.com

CHARO provides a business incubator, business training, technical assistance, and loan information to the Latino community in the area.

Jacobs Center for Non-profit Innovation

P.O. Box 740650   619-527-6161
San Diego, CA 92174   Fax: 619-527-6162
www.jacobscenter.org

The Jacobs Center for Non-profit Innovation uses a variety of financial strategies, such as equity investments, loans, loan guarantees, and more to help the people of the Diamond Neighborhoods. They work together with the residents to help make the community stronger and more vital.

Tulare County Redevelopment Agency

5961 S. Mooney Blvd.   559-733-6291
Visalia, CA 93277   Fax: 559-730-2591
www.co.tulare.ca.us

The Tulare County Redevelopment Agency woks to help improve the economy of the area. They offer incentives to businesses and have an entrepreneur training program to help new businesses.

Valley Economic Development Center

5121 Van Nuys Blvd., 3rd Floor   818-907-9977
Van Nuys, CA 91403   Fax: 818-907-9720
www.vedc.org

The Valley Economic Development Center offers training, consulting, technical assistance and financing to small and medium-sized businesses. They offer several different types of loan and loan guarantee programs, as well as an extensive entrepreneurial training program.

Colorado

Colorado Alliance for Microenterprise Initiatives

3003 Arapahoe St., Suite 110   303-996-0045
Denver, CO 80205   Fax: 303-996-4939
www.coloradoalliance.org

Colorado Alliance for Microenterprise Initiatives (CAMI) is a coalition of microenterprise development organizations dedicated to providing entrepreneurs in under-served communities the opportunity and resources to become self-sufficient through private enterprise. Check with them frequently because members are added regularly.

Initiative Loans for Small Businesses

Business Capital of Colorado, Inc.
1410 Grant St., Suite B-203   303-832-8647
Denver, CO 80203   Fax: 303-832-8649
www.bcc-colorado.com

Business Capital of Colorado, Inc. (BCC) provides loans to eligible small businesses located in Denver Metro and Boulder, Colorado. Business Capital of Colorado, Inc. serves small businesses that cannot qualify for conventional bank financing due to lack of collateral, personal credit issues, or length of time in business. Loans range from $100 up to $50,000.

Business Loans

Colorado Lending Source   877-852-6799
730 17th Street, #1A   303-657-0010
Denver, CO 80202-3580   Fax: 303-657-0140
http://coloradolendingsource.org

Colorado Lending Source is a private, nonprofit community based organization dedicated to assisting diverse small businesses within the Denver community. Loans from $10,000 are available.

MicrocreditWorks! And BusinessWorks!

MicroBusiness Development Corporation
3003 Arapahoe St., Suite 112A   303-308-8121
Denver, CO 80205   Fax: 303-308-8120
www.microbusiness.org

Microbusiness Development Corporation is a Colorado organization that provides many services for area business owners. The Direct Lending Peer Loan Program called MicrocreditWorks! Makes small loans without credit checks or collateral for business start-up and expansion. They also provide Small Business Loans for access capital. Loans range from $500 to $30,000.

San Juan 2000 Development Association

P.O. Box 722
1315 Snowden   970-387-5101
Silverton, CO 81433   Fax: 970-387-5104
www.sanjuan2000.org

San Juan 2000 Development Association tries to improve the community and the economy of the Silverton area by providing loans and technical assistance to new or expanding businesses. Loans can range for $500-$5,000 to help businesses grow and prosper. Technical assistance can be had in the form of bookkeeping help, marketing and planning.

Youth Works

MicroBusiness Development Corporation
3003 Arapahoe St., Suite 112A   303-308-8121
Denver, CO 80205   Fax: 303-308-8120
www.microbusiness.org

YouthWorks helps the youth of Denver enter into the business world. Youth Works Management helps coach and support youth run businesses. They also manage the youth loan process and create opportunities for the young adults to start businesses. YouthWorks Enterprise is an entrepreneurial training program, where youth learn what it takes to run a successful business.

Christian Community Services

Entrepreneur Loan Center
P.O. Box 984
309 San Juan Ave.   719-589-5192
Alamosa, CO 81101   Fax: 719-589-4330

Small loan is available to residents in the area for new or expanding businesses.

Connecticut

Loaves and Fishes Ministries

360 Farmington Ave.   860-524-1730
Hartford, CT 06105   Fax: 860-249-2871

Loaves and Fishes Ministries offers a Business Initiative$ Program for low to moderated income entrepreneurs. There is a 14-week business training course and access to capital for new businesses.

Delaware

Microloan and Business Growth Fund

First State Community Loan Fund   800-652-4779
100 West 10th Street, Suite 1005   302-652-6774
Wilmington, DE 19801   Fax: 302-656-1272
www.firststateloan.com

The First State Community Loan Fund (FSCLF) is a not-for-profit Community Development Financial Institution (CDFI) that supports small businesses and micro-enterprises particularly for the underserved populations. They have created a micro enterprise program to lend $300 to $15,000 to small businesses to be repaid with interest over a 4-month to 3-year period. For larger amounts they have a Business Growth Fund where business owners can borrow $15,001 to $50,000 to be repaid with interest over a 1-5 year period.

District of Columbia

The Dingman Center for Entrepreneurship

3570 Van Munching Hall   301-405-9545
College Park, MD 20742   Fax: 301-314-7973
www.rhsmith.umd.edu/

Entrepreneurs from Maryland, Virginia and DC can turn to the Dingman Center for Entrepreneurship for assistance with starting up and expanding a small business. The Capital Access Network (CAN) administered by Dingman connects area start-up companies established with private equity investors in the DC area. The program is especially designed for early-stage companies seeking smaller amounts of capital not generally available from traditional sources of funding.

New businesses in DC, MD, VA and DE that are seeking between $250,000 and $1,500,000 of equity financing are eligible for CAN. An initial application, or "circulation," fee of $100 is charged; an additional $250 is assessed if an applicant is invited to present his proposal. Detailed application instructions and a list of materials required for processing are available online. The Center offers a Mentoring Program in which an experienced professional will provide a variety of assistance services to new and fledgling business owners. Mentors help entrepreneurs formulate business plans, locate and obtain financing, understand legal and tax issues, create successful marketing strategies, explore expansion and/or partnerships and joint venture opportunities, and undertake many additional projects and task to ensure a business attains success. Three mentoring programs are available: VentureAdvisor ($590), for those requiring assistance from several industry groups; Cohort Mentor ($350), an 8-week program based on an entrepreneur's specific goals; and Custom, in which Dingman staff will work to set up an individualized mentoring agenda. Dingman's programs are open to early-stage DC, MD and VA businesses; to apply, an owner must submit a business plan. Dingman also offers a three-hour consultation session to review a start-up business plan.

Ethiopian Community Development Council, Inc.

1038 South Highland Street   703-685-0510
Arlington, VA 22204   Fax: 703-685-0529
www.ecdcinternational.org

Initially formed to assist Ethiopian refugees achieve professional success, the Microenterprise Development Program of the Ethiopian Community Development Council (ECDC; also known as Group Enterprise Development) has extended its services to new businesses started by minorities, women and low- to moderate-income individuals in the DC metropolitan area. The program offers entrepreneurial training and assistance with business start-up matters, loans up to $35,000, and technical assistance in business operations. The ECDC offers funding to many unable to receive it from other sources, with flexible application and credit requirements. Loan recipients continue to receive support and training through the organization after loan inception; follow-up assistance includes lessons in how to expand a business, cash management, bookkeeping and accounting, strategic planning, and marketing.

Florida

Florida Community Loan Fund

3107 Edgewater Drive, Suite 2   407-246-0846
Orlando, FL 32804   888-578-2030
www.fclf.org   Fax: 407-246-0856

The Florida Community Loan Fund provides capital to qualifying organizations with insufficient access to capital, from conventional lending sources. In addition, the fund has bridge loans for job training programs in Florida. At least one job must be created or retained for each $10,000 borrowed. Projects must be located in a low-income area and must employ low-income people

Business Loan Fund of the Palm Beaches Inc.

1016 N. Dixie Hwy.   561-838-9027
West Palm Beach, FL 33401   Fax: 561-838-9029
www.businessloanfund.org

The Business Loan Fund offers several different types of funds for new or expanding businesses in the area Microloans range from $500-$7,500. Generally these loans are used to

buy a new piece of equipment. Small Business Loans range from $5,000- $50,000. Typically the loans are used for new equipment, inventory or expansion. The Rural Development Intermediary Re-lending Program offers loans to those in rural areas in Palm Beach County. Loans range from $25,000- $150,000. The business Loan Fund also offers classes to train entrepreneurs in bookkeeping, marketing, planning, and more.

Florida WWINS,Inc.

Doris Reeves-Lipscomb
3318 San Pedro St.
Clearwater, FL 33759   727-723-7714

Florida WWINS Inc. helps women entrepreneurs in a variety of areas.

Minority/Women Business Enterprise Alliance, Inc.

625 East Colonial Drive   407-428-5860
Orlando, FL 32803   Fax: 407-428-5869
www.allianceflorida.com

The Minority/Women Business Enterprise Alliance, Inc., provides assistance to small and medium sized business in the Orlando and Orange County area, focusing on the needs of minority and women businesses. The Alliance offers a variety of loan programs. Most are available to those located in Brevard, Hillsborough, Lake, Marion, Orange, Osceola, Polk, Seminole, Sumter and Volusia counties. The Alliance Micro Loan provides loans from $1,000-$35,000 for inventory, supplies, and equipment. The Contracts/Accounts Receivable Program loans up to $10,000 based on accounts receivable financing. The Walt Disney Micro Loan program loans up to $50,000 for start-up, expansion, inventory and more for women and minority businesses. SOHO (Small Office Home Office) Community Express Loan Program offers loan of $5,000, $10,000 and $15,000 for start up, inventory, business purchase, equipment, and more. The Alliance Community Express Loan Program is a loan program of up to $5,000 for start-up, expansion, equipment, and more. Most of these loan programs come with technical assistance.

Georgia

ACCION USA

100 Peachtree Street, Suite 700   404-521-0594
Atlanta, GA 30303   Fax: 404-521-0597
http://www.accionatlanta.org/

ACCION USA's lending methodology is character-based. Unlike traditional lenders, they don't make loans based on credit history or collateral alone. Instead, they focus on a potential borrower's initiative and desire to succeed, knowledge of his or her business and market, as well as on references from customers and neighbors. Loans range from $500 to $50,000 with terms of 3 to 36 months. They offer loans designed to match the credit needs of each business, the borrower's character and the business/family income and expenses. ACCION USA serves the following counties in Georgia: Clayton, Cobb, DeKalb, Douglass, Fulton, Gwinnett, Henry, the northern portion of Fayette county and the southern portion of Cherokee county and the Atlanta metro area.

Mountain Partnership Loan Fund

Appalachia Community Enterprises, Inc.
1727 Turner's Corner Road   706-348-6609
Cleveland, GA 30528   877-434-6609 toll free
www.acenorthgorgia.org   Fax: 706-219-4976

The Mountain Partnership Loan Fund is a loan source for residents of Fannin, Lumpkin, White, Franklin, Hart, Stephens, Rabun, Towns, Union, Habersham, Banks, and Elbert counties who want to start or grow a small enterprise and are not able to secure traditional financing. Loans are provided to businesses for working capital as well as business asset purchases. Maximum loan amounts are $5,000.

Loan Fund

Business NOW
Goodwill Industries of North Georgia, Inc.
2201 Glenwood Ave., SE   404-486-8400
Atlanta, GA 30316   Fax: 404-486-8500
www.biznow.org

BusinessNOW assists women of low and moderate income who want to achieve economic self-sufficiency through self-employment. They assist women living in the Crim, Douglass and Harper Clusters of The Atlanta Project and metropolitan Atlanta who want to start and grow their own businesses. Loans range from $50 to $5,000 to qualified participants.

Micro Loan Funds

Cobb Microenterprise Center
Kennesaw State University
Small Business Development. Center
1000 Chastain Rd - BB423   770-499-3228
Kennesaw, GA 30144   Fax: 770-423-6564
www.cobbmicro.org

The services provided by the Cobb Microenterprise Center are for low-to-moderate-income individuals who have an "entrepreneurial spirit" and need development and capital to start or grow a business. If you are on welfare, unemployed, underemployed, disable, elderly, and you have a good business idea, you can participate in this opportunity. During a 12-week training program participants will have access to credit through microloan funds, revolving loan funds, financial institutions and asset building accounts with the microenterprise Individual Development Accounts (IDA).

East Athens Development Corporation

410 McKinley Drive   706-208-0048
Athens, GA 30601   Fax: 706-208-0015
www.eadcinc.com

The East Athens Development Corporation, Inc. (EADC) is a nonprofit community based development organization. They provide loans to micro enterprise businesses in Athens that do not yet qualify for conventional loans. The program targets businesses owned by low to moderate income, minority, and women entrepreneurs and businesses located in underserved areas. To be eligible, businesses must be located in Athens and must be for-profit. Priority will be given to low-to-moderate income, minority, and women business owners and businesses creating jobs for low-to-moderate income individuals. Loan maximums are $3,500 for terms of up to 3 years.

Atlanta Micro Fund

AHAND
P.O. Box 11387   404-586-0808
Atlanta, GA 30310   Fax: 404-586-0805
http://ahand.org

Atlanta Micro Fund offers first-time loans for up to $1,500 for low-income people interested in starting a business. Once that loan is repaid, the business can request a larger loan.

Refugee Women's Network

4151 Memorial Dr., Suite 103-F
Decatur, GA 30032   404-299-0180
www.riwn.org

The Refugee Women's Network helps women start and expand their own businesses by assisting them with their microenterprise and microloans.

Hawaii

Hawaii Community Loan Fund

677 Ala Moana Blvd., Suite 702   808-523-0075
Honolulu, HI 96813   Fax: 808-534-1199
www.hclf.org

The Hawaii Community Loan Fund (HCLF) is a certified Community Development Financial Institution that provides capital to businesses, nonprofit organizations and projects that create jobs, build wealth, and improve the quality of life for disadvantaged communities and people. HCLF's provides loans to individuals and organizations whose work and success benefits low-income individuals and communities across the state of Hawaii. Maximum loans are $25,000 that can be used for start-up or growth of microbusinesses generally defined as businesses with five or fewer employees.

Micro Lending

Maui Economic Opportunity, Business Development
Corporation
99 Mahalani Street   808-249-2990
Wailuku, HI 96793   Fax: 808-249-2991
www.meoinc.org

Maui Economic Opportunity, Business Development Corporation is a private, nonprofit Community Action Agency that helps low-income entrepreneurs start and expand their businesses. They provide funding for low-income entrepreneurs who do not have access to traditional lending. They serve the residents of Maui and Kauai counties.

Illinois

ACCION Chicago

3245 W. 26th Street   773-376-9004
Chicago, IL 60623   Fax: 773-376-9048
http://www.accionchicago.org/

ACCION Chicago's lending methodology is character-based. Unlike traditional lenders, they don't make loans based on revenue, collateral or credit alone. Instead, they focus on a client's commitment to their business, as well as references from customers and suppliers. ACCION Chicago offers a variety of loan products for the small business owner including individual and group loans, start-up loans and lines of credit. Loans range from $500 to $35,000. If you live in the greater Chicago area, can't qualify for conventional bank loans or have a poor credit history, ACCION may be able to help.

LCP and IDFA Micro Loans

Lake County Partners
28055 Ashley Circle, Suite 212   847-247-0137
Libertyville, IL 60048   Fax: 847-247-0423
www.lakecountypartners.com

Have you always wanted to start a business or expand your existing one, but have been unable to access capital? You may be eligible to acquire a small business loan through the Lake County Integrated Financing Program for Small Business Micro Loan Program. They help people start or expand a small business within Lake County, Illinois. Lake Count Partners Micro Loan program loans range from $500 to $50,000 with terms of 3 to 5 years. The Illinois Development Finance Authority Micro Loan assists start-up and existing small business with access to capital of up to $25,000 and terms of up to 3 years.

Community Development Publications

Woodstock Institute
407 S. Dearborn, Suite 550   312-427-8070
Chicago, IL 60605   Fax: 312-427-4007
www.woodstockinst.org

The Woodstock Institute offers a variety of business related publications including descriptions of community development banks, community development loan funds, community development credit unions, and microenterprise funds.

Jewish Vocational Service - Chicago

Duman Microenterprise Center & Loan Fund
One South Franklin Street   312-357-4548
Chicago, IL 60606   Fax: 312-553-5544
www.jvschicago.org

The Duman Microenterprise Center and Loan Fund helps those wishing to start or expand a small business. You can apply for zero or low interest loans up to $15,000, business assistance, seminars, mentoring, network opportunities, and more.

Tri-County Opportunities Council

405 Emmons Avenue
Rock Falls, IL 61071   800-323-5434
www.tcochelps.com/

The Tri-County Opportunities Council offers assistance to small businesses to help increase employment opportunities. The loan program is coordinated with banks and other financial organizations. Training is also provided to those wishing to start or expand their business.

Indiana

Community Action Program, Inc. of Western Indiana

418 Washington St.
P.O. Box 188   765-793-4881
Covington, IN 47932   Fax: 765-793-4884
www.capwi.org

The Community Action Program of Western Indiana offers a revolving loan of $10,000 (or possibly more) for people wishing to start or expand a business. Funds can be used for working capital, inventory, or even fixed assets. Funds cannot be used for construction or the purchase of real estate.

Neighborhood Self-Employment Initiative

Concord Community Development Corporation
324 W. Morris   317-917-3266
Indianapolis, IN 46225   Fax: 317-917-1447
http://concordindy.org

Neighborhood Self-Employment Initiative (NSI) is a program targeting low to moderate income people wishing to start or expand their business in urban Indianapolis. The NSI offers business assistance, which includes training, mentoring, financing, and more. They offer a 20 hour business course for those wishing to start a business.

Louisiana

Acadiana Regional Development District

601 Loire Ave., Suite C
P.O. Box 90070   337-886-7782
Lafayette, LA 70507   Fax: 337-886-7081

www.ardd.org

Acadiana Regional Development District provides small business loans through the Revolving Loan Fund Program for businesses based in Acadia, Evangeline, Iberia, Lafayette, St. Landry, St. Martin, St. Mary and Vermilion Parishes. Financing is provided on a mid-level scale, ranging from $10,000 up to $150,000.

Louisiana Department of Economic Development

Mailing address:
P.O. Box 94185
Baton Rouge, LA 70804
Physical address:
Capital Annex
1051 N. 3rd Street   225-342-3000
Baton Rouge, LA 70802   Fax: 225-342-5389
www.lded.state.la.us

The Louisiana Economic Development Corporation (LEDC) administers several loan programs for small Louisiana businesses. The Micro Loan Program provides loan guarantees and participations to banks that fund loans ranging from $5,000 to $50,000 to Louisiana small businesses.

Micro Loans for Women

Microenterprise Development Alliance of Louisiana
1200 S. Acadian Thruway, Suite 204 225-387-1166
Baton Rouge, LA 70806   Fax: 225-343-6935
www.microenterprisela.org

The MicroEnterprise Development of Alliance Louisiana (MEDAL) is a statewide not for profit alliance committed to helping entrepreneurs through the establishment of microenterprises, particularly by women and youth. MEDAL will provide loans as well as other financial services to women microentrepreneurs.

Maine

Penquis C.A.P., Inc.

262 Harlow Street   207-973-3612
Bangor, ME 04401   Fax: 207-973-3699
www.penquiscap.org

Penquis Community Action Program primarily serves low- and moderate-income individuals in Penobscot and Piscataquis Counties. Their Economic Development Department provides assistance to individuals interested in starting or expanding a microenterprise, a business with five or fewer employees. Small Business Loans are available to low-income residents who want to start or expand a business and who are unable to receive financing from traditional sources, such as a bank or other lending institutions.

Women, Work, and Community

Administrative Office
46 University Drive
Augusta, ME 04330-9410   800-442-2092
http://www.womenworkandcommunity.org/

Women, Work, and Community was begun to help women re-enter the job market, but has since expanded to include a variety of programs to improve the lives of women in Maine. They offer assistance in business planning development, access to financing, and other programs to help women-owned businesses succeed. Services include workshops, training courses, and a mentoring. Self-employment Assistance for TANF is a program to help those on welfare start a business and run it successfully.

Maryland

Garrett County Community Action MicroWorks

104 E. Center Street   301-334-9431
Oakland, MD 21550   Fax: 301-334-8555
www.garrettcac.org

Garrett County Community Action Corporation is a not for profit corporation committed to improving the quality of life for persons with needs by helping them become more self sufficient. The Microenterprise Loan offers a variety of options for the small business owners of Garrett County, Maryland. Loan amounts range from $500 to $15,000.

Maryland Capital Enterprises, Inc.

P.O. Box 1844   866-MARY-CAP
Salisbury, MD 21802   410-546-1900
www.marylandcapital.org   Fax: 410-546-9718

Maryland Capital Enterprises work to build economically distressed communities by supporting micro businesses. They offer many small community-based businesses the resources they need to grow. The loan program is solely based on the individual. Loan amounts range from $2,000 to $15,000.

Business Loan Fund, Inc.

99 Maryland Avenue
Rockville, MD 20850   240-777-2000
www.montgomerycountymd.gov/content/ded/

A nonprofit formed by a collaboration between Montgomery County and area banks works solely to provide loans and financial assistance to new businesses who could not otherwise obtain proper funding for their venture. The Business Loan Fund, Inc. specializes in flexible loans of $2,500 to $200,000 for small businesses located in and serving Montgomery County, MD. Loans are intended to be used to purchase fixed assets and equipment, finance contracts, and provide working capital. Partner lending institutions commit $1 million per year to the Fund to subsidize the loan program.

Community Ministry Micro-Enterprise, LLC

620-M E. Diamond Avenue   240-361-0858
Gaithersburg, MD 20877   Fax: 301-977-0687
www.communityministrymc.org

Community Ministry Montgomery County Micro-Enterprise (CMMC-E) was founded in 2001 with the sole purpose of providing business mentoring, technical assistance, and low interest loans to low-income individuals thinking of starting their own business and to recently formed small businesses. CMMC-E staff and volunteers work with new entrepreneurs to help write business plans, understand payroll, accounting and tax responsibilities, and establish credit. The participant is then ready to approach the group for a new business loan. CMMC-E's technical assistance and mentor relationship will continue after the loan is made. The organization actively seeks out potential beneficiaries of its programs, with volunteers looking for and identifying low-income entrepreneurs in the community.

Jim Rouse Entrepreneurial Fund, Inc.

9250 Bendix Road North
Columbia, MD 21045
410-313-6170
Fax: 410-313-7515
www.jref.org

Ambitious entrepreneurs hoping to turn valuable ideas into successful commercial ventures can look to the Jim Rouse Entrepreneurial Fund (JREF) for funding and supportive services. New businesses located in Howard County, MD who are unable to secure financing from traditional sources can receive loans ranging from $5,000 to $100,000 to meet start-up costs. Loans are also available to small business looking to expand. The maximum loan term is seven years. To qualify, a business must be a full-time, for-profit venture and an owner must have received loan decline letters from two separate area banks. Applications need to be accompanied by detailed financial statements of owner(s); business plans; projections; resumes; and other related documentation. JREF partners with the Howard County Business Resource Center to provide all applicants with assistance in preparing loan documents. Application fees vary by loan amount, with a $350 maximum; an origination fee of one percent is due at closing. The approval process generally takes about one to two months. Loan recipients receive additional education, hands-on monitoring and mentoring and other assistance aimed at successful business growth. Since 1992, the Jim Rouse Entrepreneurial Fund has provided over $1 million in loans to 21 Howard County businesses.

The Dingman Center for Entrepreneurship

3570 Van Munching Hall   301-405-9545
College Park, MD 20742   Fax: 301-314-7973
www.rhsmith.umd.edu/

Entrepreneurs from Maryland, Virginia and DC can turn to the Dingman Center for Entrepreneurship for assistance with starting up and expanding a small business. The Capital Access Network (CAN) administered by Dingman connects area start-up companies established with private equity investors in the DC area. The program is especially designed for early-stage companies seeking smaller amounts of capital not generally available from traditional sources of funding. New businesses in DC, MD, VA and DE that are seeking between $250,000 and $1,500,000 of equity financing are eligible for CAN. An initial application, or "circulation," fee of $100 is charged; an additional $250 is assessed if an applicant is invited to present his proposal. Detailed application instructions and a list of materials required for processing are available online. The Center offers a Mentoring Program in which an experienced professional will provide a variety of assistance services to new and fledgling business owners. Mentors help entrepreneurs formulate business plans, locate and obtain financing, understand legal and tax issues, create successful marketing strategies, explore expansion and/or partnerships and joint venture opportunities, and undertake many additional projects and task to ensure a business attains success. Three mentoring programs are available: VentureAdvisor ($590), for those requiring assistance from several industry groups; Cohort Mentor ($350), an 8-week program based on an entrepreneur's specific goals; and Custom, in which Dingman staff will work to set up an individualized mentoring agenda. Dingman's programs are open to early-stage DC, MD and VA businesses; to apply, an owner must submit a business plan. Dingman also offers a three-hour consultation session to review a start-up business plan.

Massachusetts

ACCION USA

56 Roland Street
Suite 300, South Lobby   617-625-7080
Boston, MA 02129   Toll-free: 866-245-0783
www.accionusa.org/boston/   Fax: 617-625-7020

ACCION USA's lending methodology is character-based. Unlike traditional lenders, they don't make loans based on credit history or collateral alone. Instead, they focus on a potential borrower's initiative and desire to succeed, knowledge of his or her business and market, as well as on references from customers and neighbors. Loans range from $500 to $50,000 with terms of 3 to 36 months. If you are an entrepreneur who lives in the greater Boston area, can't qualify for conventional bank loans or have a poor credit history, ACCION may be able to help.

ACCION USA

450 Essex Street, 2nd Floor	978-725-5934
Lawrence, MA 01840	Fax: 978-794-7600

www.accionusa.org/lawrence/
Serving greater Lawrence area.

ACCION USA

One Federal Street	
Building 101	413-734-6679
Springfield, MA 01105	Fax: 413-755-6101

www.accionusa.org/springfield/
Serving greater Springfield area.

ACCION USA

11 Pleasant Street, Suite 300	508-799-0029
Worcester, MA 01609	Fax: 508-799-7771

www.accionusa.org/worcester/
Serving greater Worcester area.

Day Care Business Loans

Acre Family Day Care Corporation	
14 Kirk Street	978-937-5899
Lowell, MA 01852	Fax: 978-937-5148

www.acrefamily.org
The Acre Family Day Care not for profit organization that helps low-income women in Greater Lowell become financially independent by providing child care training and assistance in setting up licensed child care businesses in their own homes. Acre can offer business loans for start-up or expansion of family day cares.

Michigan

Renaissance MicroLoan Development Fund

Cornerstone Alliance	
P.O. Box 428	
38 W. Wall Street	269-925-6100
Benton Harbor, MI 49023	Fax: 269-925-4471

www.cstonealliance.org
The Renaissance Development Fund was created by the Cornerstone Alliance to promote economic development in the most distressed region of the Twin Cities area of Benton Harbor and St. Joseph, Michigan. The fund provides credit to small businesses in the service area that do not have access to traditional financing. They offer a Neighborhood Venture Loan for entrepreneurs who are facing start-up costs. Loans range from $500 to $3,000 with terms of 6 months to two years. The Commercial Micro Loan program is for small businesses that have been in business for at least 6 months. Loan amounts range from $500 to $25,000 with terms from 6 months to 5 years. The Renaissance Development Fund also offers larger loan for more established businesses.

Detroit Entrepreneurship Institute, Inc.

455 W. Fort St., 4th Floor	313-961-8426
Detroit, MI 48226	Fax: 313-961-8831

www.deibus.org
The Detroit Entrepreneurship Institute (DEI) provides entrepreneurship training to those interested in starting or expanding a business. The DEI provides an incredible number of programs and services, almost all of which are free. Business consultants and assigned to help you with your business. A computer center is available and has accountants on duty to help with bookkeeping. For those who complete the training program, DEI has several loan funds to help with business needs. A library and graphic design services as also available. The Self-Employment Initiative offers workshops, training, consultations, business cards, and more. The Enterprise Development Initiative offers consultations, training, design services, and a loan fund. The Young CEO & Investor Program teaches children ages 14-17 how to operate a business.

Kent Area MicroBusiness Loan Services

Masonic Temple Building	
233 E. Fulton, Suite 101	616-771-6880
Grand Rapids, MI 49503	Fax: 616-771-8021

www.kamls.org
KAMLS offers loans and assistance to new or expanding companies in the Grand Rapids or Kent County Area. Microloans are available for up to $3,000. Money can be used for working capital, inventory, furniture, or equipment. You may not purchase real estate or pay off debt. In addition, KAMLS offers support to help your business succeed.

Minnesota

Neighborhood and Small Business Loans

Neighborhood Development Center, Inc	
651-½ University Avenue	651-291-2480
St. Paul, MN 55104	Fax: 651-291-2597

www.windndc.org
The Neighborhood Development Center, Inc (NDC) is a community-based nonprofit organization that works with entrepreneurs in the inner city of Minneapolis and St. Paul develop successful businesses and stronger neighborhoods. NDC provides access to credit for start-up businesses and other entrepreneurs who do not qualify for traditional financing. The Neighborhood Entrepreneurs Fund is available to graduates of NDC's training programs. Loan amounts range from $500 to $10,000. NDC's Small Business Loan Fund makes loans available up to $30,000 to established small businesses in the St. Paul inner city neighborhoods.

Child Care Business Loan

Tri-County Community Action Program, Inc.	
501 LeMieur St.	
P.O. Box 368	320-632-3691
Little Falls, MN 56345	Fax: 320-632-3695

www.tccaction.com
The Tri-County Community Action Program is a not for profit corporation committed to creating opportunities for self-sufficiency for citizens in Crow Wing, Morrison and Todd Counties. The Child Care Business Loan Program is exclusively for Family Day Care Providers. Loans can be used to start or expand a business. In addition, loan recipients are eligible for business skills training. Loan amounts range from $300 to $3,000.

MEDA

250 Second Ave., South, Suite 106	612-332-MEDA
Minneapolis, MN 55401	Fax: 612-317-1002

www.meda.net
MEDA provides assistance to new and expanding businesses owned by ethnic minorities. MEDA offers a loan program to help those who typically are denied financing through traditional lenders. Loans can be for up to $300,000 and are

for working capital, equipment, capital expenditures, and more.

Arrowhead Community Economic Assistance Corporation

8880 Main Street Bank Building, POB 406   218-735-8201
Mountain Iron, MN 55768   Fax: 218-735-8202
Email: aceac@rangenet.com

Arrowhead Community Economic Assistance Corporation (ACEAC) is a community-based nonprofit providing primary service to Cook, Lake and St. Louis counties, excluding the City of Duluth. ACEAC also provides service to Aitkin, Carlton, Itasca, and Koochiching counties in cooperation with individual communities, other agencies and organizations. Services include community development and business planning, technical assistance, business loans and other types of financial assistance that will benefit low-and moderate-income persons. This includes providing technical assistance coupled with small business loans, a micro-business loan and TA project and a peer group-lending project. Loans can range up to $50,000. Money can be used for assets, equipment, and capital expenditures. New or expanding businesses are eligible, as well as home based businesses

North Star Community Development Corporation

301 West 1st Street, Suite 604   218-727-6690
Duluth, MN 55802   Fax: 218-723-7120
www.nstarcdc.org

North Star Community Development Corp. helps local businesses by providing financing, training, seminars, workshops, and other forms of assistance to help them succeed. Many of those served are low-income individuals wishing to start or expand a business. Business located in Duluth are eligible for assistance. Loans are available up to $20,000 and businesses must be located in Duluth. Businesses must also agree to hire low to moderate income people to fill new jobs created at their business.

Initiative Foundation

405 First Street Southeast   320-632-9255
Little Falls, MN 56345   Fax: 320-632-9258
Email: info@ifound.org
http://www.ifound.org/

The Initiative Foundation helps promote economic development throughout the state. They offer four different types of loan funds to help improve the job environment and increase wages by providing assistance to businesses. The Microenterprise Loan Guarantee Program offers loans up to $50,000 for women, minorities, and young adults who generally lack the needed capital. Seed Capital Fund has money for up to $50,000 for new businesses. The Direct Business Loan Program offers up to $250,000 for new or expanding companies that will increase the number of jobs available. The Technology Capital Fund has $500,000 to support new technology ventures.

Southeastern MN Development Corporation

P.O. Box 684   507-864-7557
Rushford, MN 55971   Fax: 507-864-2091
Email: mthein@acegroup.cc
www.semdc.com/

The Southeastern Minnesota Microenterprise Fund makes available up to $35,000 to new or expanding businesses in the area. Money can be used for capital expenditures, inventory, equipment, real estate, and renovation. Business must exist in any of eight communities in the Southeastern part of the state.

Mississippi

Micro Loan

Minority Business Enterprise Division
Mississippi Development Authority
501 North West Street
P. O. Box 849   601-359-3448
Jackson, MS 39205   Fax: 601-359-5290
www.mississippi.org

The Mississippi Development Authority administers the state Minority Business Loan Program as a source of financing for small businesses. A minority business is an economically disadvantaged small business with at least on minority or female owner. Loan amounts range from $2,000 to $15,000 with terms up to 5 years.

Micro Loan

Quitman County Development Organization, Inc.
201 Humphrey Street
PO Box 386   662-326-4000
Marks, MS 38646   Fax: 662-326-3904
www.qcdo.org

The Quitman County Development Organization (QCDO) Micro-Enterprise Loan and Business Development Program is dedicated to assisting women, minority and small businesses in Quitman County and surrounding areas. The Micro Loan Program provides loans for all types of businesses start-ups and expansions. Loan are reviewed and determined on a per loan basis, with loan amounts typically ranging from $500 to $25,000.

Minority Capital Fund of Mississippi

2530 Bailey Ave.   601-713-3322
P.O. Box 11305   877-713-3322
Jackson, MS 39283   Fax: 601-713-3610
www.mincap.org

The Minority Capital Fund of Mississippi provides financing and other types of assistance to minority and women owned businesses located in Mississippi. This is designed to help with the disparity between the minority owned and majority owned businesses. The goal of all is to help improve the economic and employment opportunities in the area. Loans are available up to $150,000, and money can be used for equipment, working capital, inventory, and other capital expenditures. In addition, the Fund provides technical assistance with marketing, accounting, business planning, and more.

Missouri

Micro Loans

Growth Opportunity Connection
4747 Troost Avenue   816-235-6146
Kansas City, MO 64110   Fax: 816-235-6177
Email: acorbet@goconnection.org
www.goconnection.org

The Growth Opportunity Connection is a nonprofit organization, specializing in assisting small businesses prepare and obtain financing. The Micro Loan Program provides funds for micro-entrepreneurs who do not qualify for conventional lending. They help both start-up and expanding businesses. Loan amounts are up to $35,000 with terms of up to 5 years.

International Institute

3654 S. Grand Blvd.   314-773-9090
St. Louis, MO 63118   Fax: 314-773-6047
http://www.intlinst.org/

The Micro Enterprise Development Program is designed to assist refugees in the St. Louis area. The program offers business planning, training, marketing, technical, and other types of assistance to those not yet citizens. The services are offered free of charge.

Montana

Small Business Loans

Montana Department of Commerce
301 S Park Ave
Helena, MT 59601
Mailing address:
P.O. Box 200501   406-841-2751
Helena, MT 59620-0501   Fax: 406-841-2701
www.commerce.state.mt.us

The Montana Department of Business Resources provides small businesses with 10 or fewer employees and gross revenue of less than $500,000 the opportunity to apply for a revolving loan of up to $35,000. They have a close relationship with resource providers to help low-to-moderate income people interested in self-employment

District 7 Human Resources Development Council

7 North 31st St.   406-247-4732
Billings, MT 59101   Fax: 406-248-2943
www.hrdc7.org

The Human Resources Development Council offers a revolving loan program to business wishing to start or expand. The loans are for up to $35,000 and can be used for working capital, inventory, and more.

Nebraska

Micro Loan Fund

Lincoln Action Program
210 "O" Street   402-471-4515
Lincoln, NE 68508   Fax: 402-471-4844
www.lincoln-action.org

The Microenterprise Program is designed to help low-to-moderate incomes establish their own small businesses. Access to small loans through peer lending are available. Loan Funds are provided by the Nebraska Microenterpriese Development Partnership Fund and Union Bank and Trust Company.

Micro Business Directory

Nebraska Department of Economic Development
Nebraska Micro Business Resource Directory
P.O. Box 6605
Lincoln, NE 68506-0605   402-420-9589
http://neon.neded.org/mbrd/index.html

The Nebraska Micro Business Resource Directory provides a wide variety of loan options available to micro businesses in Nebraska.

Small Business Loans

Community Development Resources
1135 M Street
3rd Floor, Suite 116   402-436-2386
Lincoln, NE 68508-3169   Fax: 402-436-2360
http://www.self-lincoln.org/about.html

SELF provides business loans for small and home-based businesses in the City of Lincoln, Nebraska. Loan amounts range from $250-$25,000.

New Hampshire

Microbusiness Loans

MicroCredit-NH
7 Wall Street   603-224-2069
Concord, NH 03301   Fax: 603-225-7425
http://www.microcreditnh.org/

MicroCredit-NH provides small loans to microbusinesses in New Hampshire. Loan amounts range from $500 to $5,000.

New Jersey

Small Business Loans

New Jersey Economic Development Authority
PO Box 990
Trenton, NJ 08625-0990   609-292-1800
http://www.njeda.com/

The New Jersey Economic Development Authority offers direct loans for small businesses, minority-owned and women-owned businesses. Generally loans are available to enterprises located in Atlantic City although monies are available for other areas.

Microbusiness Loans

Prudential Young Entrepreneur Program
NJIT-Enterprise Development Center
105 Lock Street
Newark, NJ 07103   973-643-4063
www.njit-edc.org/PYEP.htm

The program assists entrepreneurs between 18-30 years of age starting businesses. Microloans are available to qualified young adults establishing businesses in targeted urban areas.

Micro Loan Fund

Tri-County Community Action Agency
River's Edge Community Campus
110 Cohansey Street   856-451-6330
Bridgetown, NJ 08302   Fax: 856-455-7288
http://www.tricountycaa.org/

Tri-County Community Loan Fund provides loans to small businesses in Cumberland, Gloucester and Salem counties. Loans amounts range from $5,000 to $30,000.

Bergen County Economic Development Corporation

One Bergen County Plaza
Suite 440   201-336-7500
Hackensack, NJ 07601   Fax: 201-336-7513
www.bergen4business.com

The Bergen County Economic Development Corporation (BCEDC) wants to help businesses succeed in the area. They have partnered with many different agencies to offer assistance and training to business owners. The Bergen County Small Business Loan Program provides loans for people to open new or expand their businesses.

Elizabeth Development Company

288 North Broad St., 3rd Floor
P.O. Box 512   908-289-0262
Elizabeth, NJ 07207   Fax: 908-558-1142
http://www.edcnj.org/

The Elizabeth Development Company offers a variety of programs to help new or expanding business in the city of Elizabeth. Business financing, site location, and an Urban Enterprise Program are just some of the ways businesses can start and grow in the area.

Hudson County Economic Development Corporation

601 Pavonia Ave., Suite 302   201-222-1900
Jersey City, NJ 07306   Fax: 201-222-6350
http://www.hudsonedc.org/

The Hudson County Economic Development Corporation helps businesses in a variety of ways including loan programs. The Business Loan Program offers funds up to $100,000 that can be used for capital, inventory, equipment, real estate purchase, and more. The MicroLoan Program offers funds up to $25,000 to business in East Newark, Guttenberg, Harrison, Hoboken, Kearney, Secaucus, Weehawken, and West New York. The HCEDC also has a bonding program.

New Mexico

ACCION Loan

ACCION New Mexico   505-243-8844
20 First Plaza NW, Suite 417   800-508-7624
Albuquerque, NM 87102   Fax: 505-243-1551
http://www.accionnewmexico.org/

ACCION is a community-based organization that provides loans to entrepreneurs in targeted counties of New Mexico. Loan amounts range from $200 to $20,000.

Loan Fund

New Mexico Community Development Loan Fund
Mailing Address:
PO Box 705
Albuquerque, NM 87103
Street Address:
700 Fourth Street, SW   505-243-3196
Albuquerque, NM 87102   Fax: 505-243-8803
http://www.nmcdlf.org/

The New Mexico Community Development Loan Fund provides loans for small businesses in New Mexico. Particular emphasis is placed on helping low-income people; minority and women based businesses that are unable to obtain traditional financing.

New York

ACCION New York

235 Havemeyer St.   718-599-5170
Brooklyn, NY 11211   Fax: 718-387-9686
http://www.accionnewyork.org/

ACCION New York provides loans for businesses to expand or start a new business. ACCION serves all 5 boroughs of New York City. Loan amounts range from $500 to $25,000.

Start-up Loan

Appleseed Trust
220 Herald Place, 2nd Floor   315-424-9485
Syracuse, NY 13202   Fax: 315-424-7056
http://www.appleseedtrust.org/

Appleseed Trust is a not for profit organization that is committed to assisting low- to moderate-income residents of Syracuse to start or expand their own business. Entrepreneurs with an idea for a product or service can pay a small monthly fee to participate in an eight-week training program. The process includes applying for an initial loan.

Community Loan Fund

Capital District Community Loan Fund
255 Orange Street
Albany, NY 12210   518-436-8586

http://www.cdclf.org/1024.html

The Community Loan Fund provides loans to small businesses and micro businesses in the New York State Capital region. Loans of up to $10,000 are available for business start-ups and up to $25,000 for business expansions.

Loan Fund

Chautauqua Microenterprise Loan Fund
Chautauqua Opportunities for Development
402 Main Street   716-366-2334
Dunkirk, NY 14048   Fax 716-366-7407
http://www.codi-wny.com

The Chautauqua Microenterprise Loan Fund provides loans to small businesses with fewer than 5 employees in Chautauqua County. Loans must have a positive impact on low-income to moderate-income individuals. Loan amounts range from $1,000 to $15,000.

Micro-Loans

Homesteaders Federal Credit Union
2052 Adam Clayton Powell Jr. Blvd   212-222-0328
New York, NY 10027   Fax: 212-222-1035
http://www.homesteadersfcu.org/

The Homesteaders Federal Credit Union is a not-for-profit financial institution that provides affordable financing for people in the Harlem and New York City areas. Loans of up to $25,000 are available.

Peer Micro Lending

Project Enterprise
144 West 125th St., 4th Floor   212-678-6734
New York, NY 10027   Fax: 212-678-6737
http://www.projectenterprise.org/

Project Enterprise lending practices provides business credit to New York's low-income individuals. It is a comprehensive program delivering microcredit, business training and networking opportunities to entrepreneurs in New York City's economically disadvantages communities. Members interested in credit may access loans starting at a maximum of $1,500. After each successful loan repayment, the member may increase their available credit in steps up to a maximum of $12,000.

Loans

Rural Opportunities, Inc
400 East Avenue   716-340-3387
Rochester, NY 14607-1910   Fax: 716-340-3326
www.ruralinc.org

Rural Opportunities, Inc is a not-for-profit community development organization providing services to low to moderate-income people and economically depressed communities throughout New York and Ohio. The aim is to promote self-sufficiency and economic independence through the creation and expansion of microenterprises. Loan amounts of up to $50,000.

Trickle Up

104 W. 27th Street, 12th Floor   212-255-9980
New York, NY 10001   Fax: 212-255-9974
www.trickleup.org

Over 75% of the recipients of this program either have no credit and cannot even apply for a microloan. Entrepreneurs are given $700 in grant money, not loans for start-up capital. Grants are awarded in two installments with requirements, which are required of the recipient. Most of the businesses are home based with grants being used to buy supplies such as flour for baking or yarn for sewing products to sell.

Loans for Women

Women's Venture Fund, Inc
240 West 35 Street, Suite 201   212-563-0499
New York, NY 10001   Fax: 212-868-9116
www.womensventurefund.org

The Women's Venture Fund relies on character-based lending principles in approving loans to low-income women who lack business experience. Women applicants must establish their skills of business concepts submit a business plan and possess a willingness to comply with program requirements. The Assessment Committee identifies businesses that can implement growth plans with loans up to $15,000.

Washington Heights and Inwood Development Corporation

57 Wadsworth Ave.   212-795-1600
New York, NY 10033   Fax: 212-781-4051
www.members.aol.com/whidc

The Washington Heights and Inwood Development Corporation offers a variety of programs to help new and expanding businesses in the area. The Business Operating Success System offers a micro loan program, as well as a business assistance center. They also offer a mentoring program and a street vendor program.

ACCORD Corp.

84 Schuyler Street   585-268-7605
Belmont, NY 14813   Fax: 585-268-7241
www.accordcorp.org/

The Allegany County Community Opportunities and Rural Development offers entrepreneurial assistance through 120 hours of classroom instruction and mentoring. Topics covered include business planning, bookkeeping, marketing, finances, and more. They also offer a Micro Enterprise Revolving Loan Fund of up to $3,500.

North Carolina

Loans for Crafts People

HandMade in America
P.O. Box 2089   828-252-0121
Asheville, NC 28802   Fax: 828-252-0388
www.handmadeinamerica.org

HandMade in America works closely with financial institutions in Western North Carolina that understand craft businesses and offer alternative lending programs. Contact their office for additional information on loan options.

Individual Development Account

Mountain Microenterprise Fund
29 ½ Page Avenue   828-253-2834
Asheville, NC 28801   Fax: 828-389-3089
www.mtnmicro.org

Mountain Microenterprise Fund (MMF) provides entrepreneurs with the option to set up an Individual Development Account. The fund matches your $1,000 for capitalizing your business with matches as large as $2,000, which means you triple your savings. Members of MMF also receive assistance in obtaining loans.

Group and Individual-Based Lending

North Carolina Microenterprise Loan Program
4021 Carya Drive   919-250-4314
Raleigh, NC 27610   Fax 919-250-4325
ckperry@ncruralcenter.org
http://www.ncruralcenter.org/grants/micro.htm

The North Carolina Microenterprise Program provides rural people with small business loans to help them become self-sufficient through business ownership. The program helps low-income and rural area individuals who have sound business ideas but do not qualify for traditional financing. Loan amounts are up to $25,000.

Ohio

ASSETS Toledo

333 14th St.   419-381-2721
Toledo, OH 43624   Fax: 419-720-0079
http://www.assetstoledo.com/

ASSETS Toledo assists individuals in Lancaster County who strive for self-employment but have limited resources. They provide capital through their Loan Fund to graduates of their business course.

Food and Technology Loans

ACEnet –Appalachian Center for Economic Networks
94 Columbus Road   740-592-3854
Athens, OH 45701   Fax: 740-593-5451
www.acenetworks.org

The fund works with the food and technology sectors, including start-ups that have the potential to create wealth for low-income entrepreneurs. The fund provides capital for any business activities not served by conventional financial institutions. Loans are awarded packaged with technical assistance provided by ACEnet's staff to increase the likelihood of business success.

Revolving Loan Funds

Community Action Committee of Pike County
MicroEnterprise/Business Development Department
941 Market Street
P.O. Box 799   740-289-2371
Piketon, OH 45661   Fax: 740-289-4291
www.pikecac.org

The Community Action Committee of Pike County administers three revolving loan funds available to those clients who successfully complete the Business Training program. The fund offers financial assistance to potential entrepreneurs who are not able to get loans through traditional lenders. Rates and terms are based upon each business's ability to repay. Loans range from $200 to $100,000, which cannot exceed 8 years.

Greater Cincinnati Microenterprise Initiative

1501 Madison Rd., 1st Floor Rear   513-569-4816
Cincinnati, OH 45206   513-569-4816
www.gcmi.org   Fax: 513-569-0075

Greater Cincinnati Microenterprise Initiative (GCMI) provides access to microloans to individual business owners who are low to moderate income. Loans may be used to start or expand a small business. Microloan amounts range from $500 to $10,000 with a repayment period of 36 months.

Oklahoma

Micro-Enterprise Development Program

Cherokee Nation
P. O. Box 948   918-456-0671
Tahlequah, OK 74465   800-256-0671 (in OK)
http://www.cherokee.org

Loans are available to Native American entrepreneurs residing and operating their business in rural area of the Cherokee Nation. Loans of up to $25,000 with a maximum term of 7 years.

Oregon

Micro Loans

Mercy Enterprise
936 SE Ankeny, Suite 1
Portland, OR 97214   503-236-1580
http://www.mercyenterprise.org/

Mercy is a nonprofit organization, which provides financing to entrepreneurs in the Portland area who may not have perfect credit but have the "entrepreneurial spirit". Loans from $500 to $25,000 with terms up to 36 months and competitive rates.

Childcare Neighborhood Network Loan Fund

ROSE Community Development
5215 SE Duke Street
Portland, OR 97206   503-788-0826 ext. 109
http://www.rosecdc.org/childcare.htm

Through community based micro enterprise development, ROSE Community Development Corporation helps to increase the character of childcare and secure providers' businesses. These loans are established in order to help the childcare providers who have difficulty getting conventional loans. Loan amounts range from $500 to $5,000 for child care business expenses such as equipment, education, and minor facility renovations.

Shorebank Enterprise Pacific

429 Spruce Street
P. O. Box 56   541-572-5172
Myrtle Point, OR 97458   Fax: 541-572-5261
http://www.sbpac.com/index.cfm

Shorebank Enterprise is a nonprofit rural economic development corporation assisting entrepreneurs build business and market ventures, which improve the social and environmental conditions of rural communities. Loan amounts range from $3,000 to $350,000 for new business start-up or new equipment for existing businesses.

Pennsylvania

Community Capital Works

Philadelphia Development Partnership
1334 Walnut Street, 7th Floor   215-545-3100
Philadelphia, PA 19107   Fax: 215-546-8055
http://www.pdp-inc.org/

Community Capital Works' mission is to increase self-employment, employment and income-generating opportunities through microenterprise activities with a focus on entrepreneurs from socially and economically distressed communities in the City of Philadelphia and the City of Chester. Loan amounts range from $500 to $5,000.

Prudential Young Entrepreneur Program (PYEP)

The Enterprise Center
4548 Market Street
Philadelphia, PA 19139   215-895-4000
www.theenterprisecenter.com/forentre/start_business/pyep.asp

The Prudential Young Entrepreneur Program (PYEP) is an innovative microenterprise initiative funded by The Prudential Foundation to help provide young adults with the skills and resources they need to make their entrepreneurial dreams a reality. The PYEP is an extensive, multi-year business development and job creation program for young adults between the ages of 18-30. It combines business training, technical assistance and microloans to qualified young adults establishing businesses in targeted urban areas.

Revolving Loan Fund

Rural Enterprise Development Corp.
10 East Main Street
P.O. Box 276   570-784-7003
Bloomsburg, PA 17815   Fax: 570-784-7030
http://www.redc-leap.org/

The Local Enterprise Assistance Program through the Rural Enterprise Development Corporation loans funds for new business startups as well as business expansions. Loan amounts range from $500 to $25,000.

Rhode Island

ACCION USA

775 Mineral Spring Avenue   401-722-5558
Pawtucket, RI 02860   Fax: 401-722-0629
http://www.accionusa.org/rhodeisland/
Serving all of Rhode Island

South Dakota

Loan Fund

Four Bands Community Fund, Inc.
Cheyenne River Lakota Nation
101 South Main Street
P.O. Box 932   605-964-3687
Eagle Butte, SD 57625   Fax: 605-964-3689
http://www.fourbands.org/loan_fund.htm

Four Bands Community Fund, Inc., is a nonprofit corporation, which assists entrepreneurs of the Cheyenne River Indian Reservation by providing access to capital, encouraging economic development and enhancing the quality of life for all communities and residents of the reservation. They offer a MicroLoan that of $100 to $1,000 and Small Business Loans of $1,000 to $25,000.

Tennessee

Central Appalachian Microenterprise Program (CAMP)

East Tennessee Community Partnership Center
300 East Main Street, Suite 301   423-232-5730
Johnson City, TN 37601   Fax: 423-232-5760
http://www.etsu.edu/keystone/microenterprise.html

Microenterprise loan funds are structured to make loans to individuals much like traditional bank lending model.

Texas

ACCION Texas

2014 S. Hackberry   888-215-2373
San Antonio, TX 78210   Fax: 210-533-2940
http://www.acciontexas.org/
    210-226-3664 (San Antonio inquiries)
Serving San Antonio, Austin, Brownsville, Dallas, El Paso, Fort Worth, Harlingen, Houston and McAllen

Loan Program

Alliance for Multicultural Community Services
6440 Hillcroft, Suite 411   713-776-4700
Houston, TX 77081   Fax: 713-776-4730
http://www.allianceontheweb.org

The Alliance's mission is to assist refugees, immigrants, and other low-income residents of Harris County. They offer an

Individual Development Account, which provides matching funds for entrepreneurs in addition to small business workshops. Through their newly established Multicultural Community Development Corporation (MCDC), they have added a microenterprise loan program.

PLAN Fund

2008 Didsbury Rd., Apt. B   214-942-6698
Dallas, TX 75224   Fax: 214-942-5430
www.planfund.org

The PLAN Fund (Peer Lending Action Network) is a micro-lending program for low-income people, especially women, who would like to start a new business. Anyone interested in a loan will be part of a group of people similarly driven to become entrepreneurs. The group works together reviewing business plans and training. You are accountable to the group. There are three different loan types: General loans of up to $1,500; Short Term Loans payable over ten weeks; and Technology Loans for computer equipment. For more information contact PLAN.

Utah

Micro-Loan, Childcare and "Under 3-Step" Loan Programs

Utah Microenterprise Loan Fund
3595 South Main St   801-269-8408
Salt Lake City, UT 84115   Fax 801-269-1063
http://www.umlf.com/

The Utah Microenterprise Loan Fund is a private, nonprofit, multi-bank community development financial institution, whose mission is to provide financing to entrepreneurs in start-up and existing firms that do not have access to traditional funding sources; especially those who are socially and economically disadvantaged. UML offers three loan products for businesses. Their Traditional Micro-Loan is available for start-up and existing businesses in Boxelder, Davis, Morgan, Salt Lake, Summit, Tooele, Utah or Weber counties. Loan amounts of up to $10,000 for 5 years at a fixed 5% interest rate. Childcare Provider Loan's are available for working capital and construction of day care facilities in Salt Lake County. "Under 3 Step Loan" program is designed businesses needing even smaller loans between $0-$3,000. The "stepped" program means that borrowers receive a small first loan (0-$500) for short terms with follow-up loans offered in progressively larger amounts. Businesses must be located in Salt Lake County.

Vermont

Vermont Job Start

58 E. State Street, Suite 5   802-828-5466
Montpelier, VT 05602   Fax: 802-828-5474
http://www.vermontjobstart.org

Vermont Job Start 's mission is to help develop self-employment opportunities for low to moderate-income entrepreneurs of Vermont. Loan amounts up to $20,000 are available with terms of up to 5 years at a fixed 8% interest rate.

Community Economic Development Program

Central Vermont Community Action
195 US Rt. 302   800-639-1053
Barre, VT 05641   802-479-1053

The Community Economic Development Program provides financing, support, and assistance to low income individuals who would like to start or expand a business. The community

Capital of Central Vermont offers up to $50,000 loans and other assistance to help small businesses.

Virginia

Micro-Loan Program

Community Business Partnership
6911 Richmond Hwy., Suite 290   703-768-1440
Alexandria, VA 22306   Fax: 703-768-0547
http://www.cbponline.org

Community Business Partnership was formed in response to an identified need for small business financing services, particularly to low-moderate income and disadvantaged individuals, including minorities, women and the disabled. Loans are available from $3,500 to $25,000 to benefit low to moderate-income individuals in Fairfax County. Loan recipients do not have to be low-moderate income to qualify, however all loans must in some way benefit low-moderate income individuals

New Enterprise Fund

Community Housing Partners Corporation
930 Cambria Street, NE   540-382-2002
Christiansburg, VA 24073   Fax: 540-382-1935
http://www.communityhousingpartners.org/

The New Enterprise Fund provides entrepreneurs with microloans from $1,000 to $25,000 with terms of one to four years at 8% interest rate. Individual Development Accounts are available with a matching 3:1 program for income qualifying individuals. They serve low to moderate-income individuals. Women, minorities and youth are encouraged to apply. Businesses must be located in the counties of Floyd, Giles, Montgomery, Pulaski, and the City of Radford.

Micro Loans

New Visions, New Ventures, Inc.
801 East Main Street, Suite 1100   804-643-1081
Richmond, VA 23219   Fax: 804-643-1085
http://nvnv.org/index.html

New Visions, New Ventures supports women in difficult life situations, striving to become independent by providing microenterprise development. They provide clients access to capital through Individual Development Accounts that match savings accounts. New Visions, New Ventures works closely with community micro lenders to provide loans to clients.

Valley Microenterprise Alliance

1251 Virginia Avenue
Harrisonburg, VA 22802   540-433-5624
http://www.vmalliance.org/

Valley Microenterprise Alliance offers microloans to encourage underemployed and low to moderate-income individuals to start or expand a microenterprise in the Shenandoah Valley Region. Valley Microenterprise Alliance offers character-based microloans for small business purposes to graduates of the Blueprint for Business Success training class

Middle Peninsula Business Development Partnership

125 Bowden St.
P.O. Box 286   804-758-4917
Saluda, VA 23149   Fax: 804-758-3221
www.mppdc.com

The Business Development Partnership helps small businesses start or expand in the Middle peninsula of Virginia. They offer up to $25,000 loans to help your business. In order to be eligible for the loan, you must complete an 8 course business training program and have five or fewer employees.

Business Seed, Inc.

145 Campbell Avenue, SW
P.O. Box 2868
Roanoke, VA 24001   540-345-6781
www.businessseed.org/

Business SEED, Inc. caters to the needs of disadvantaged entrepreneurs in Virginia. A founding member of the Virginia Microenterprise Network, the organization furnishes loans and offers business classes and one-on-one counseling to those looking to start or expand a business in the Commonwealth. SEED financial products include five-year loans and lines of credit of $500 to $35,000. Loan funds can be used for working capital, inventory or equipment. To be eligible, an entrepreneur must be a US citizen over age 18 who runs, or plans to run, a business in the Roanoke, VA area, must be low-income (or agree to hire 51% low-income employees) or unable to secure traditional credit products, and have no unsettled or unexplained credit or legal problems. To receive an application, a prospective business owner first meets with a SEED Loan Officer; fee for applying for a SEED financial product is about $30. Applications are reviewed by committee; a client has the opportunity to revise a declined application using specific recommendations made by the reviewers. Anyone thinking of starting or expanding a business can partake of SEED's counseling services and Small Business Management classes.

Community Business Partnership

7001 Loisdale Road, Suite C   703-768-1440
Springfield, VA 22150   Fax: 703-768-0547
www.cbponline.org/

The Micro-Loan Program administered by the Community Business Partnership provides direct and guaranteed loans business owners and entrepreneurs that provide a benefit to low- or moderate-income residents of Fairfax County. Three to five-year loan amounts range from $3,500 to $25,000, with interest rates typically under prime rate plus five percent. The funds may be used by business owners to purchase computers, supplies and equipment, hire employees, buy inventory and pay for marketing expenses. Loan recipients do not have to be of low or moderate income to qualify, however all loans must in some way benefit that market segment. Those with viable business ideas are encouraged to apply and submit a business plan along with a three-year cash projection. The initial application fee is $8, to cover the cost of a credit report. An additional assessment ranging from $50 to $150, depending on loan amount, is due only if a loan application is accepted. A networking breakfast is useful to accepted participants… as well as mandatory. The Community Business Partnership, a nonprofit organization, also features a Business Development Center, where new and existing small business owners can receive marketing assistance and have access to networking opportunities and referral services that will increase their chances for success.

The Dingman Center for Entrepreneurship

3570 Van Munching Hall   301-405-9545
College Park, MD 20742   Fax: 301-314-7973
www.rhsmith.umd.edu/

Entrepreneurs from Maryland, Virginia and DC can turn to the Dingman Center for Entrepreneurship for assistance with starting up and expanding a small business. The Capital Access Network (CAN) administered by Dingman connects area start-up companies established with private equity investors in the DC area. The program is especially designed for early-stage companies seeking smaller amounts of capital not generally available from traditional sources of funding. New businesses in DC, MD, VA and DE that are seeking between $250,000 and $1,500,000 of equity financing are eligible for CAN. An initial application, or "circulation," fee of $100 is charged; an additional $250 is assessed if an applicant is invited to present his proposal. Detailed application instructions and a list of materials required for processing are available online. The Center offers a Mentoring Program in which an experienced professional will provide a variety of assistance services to new and fledgling business owners. Mentors help entrepreneurs formulate business plans, locate and obtain financing, understand legal and tax issues, create successful marketing strategies, explore expansion and/or partnerships and joint venture opportunities, and undertake many additional projects and task to ensure a business attains success. Three mentoring programs are available: VentureAdvisor ($590), for those requiring assistance from several industry groups; Cohort Mentor ($350), an 8-week program based on an entrepreneur's specific goals; and Custom, in which Dingman staff will work to set up an individualized mentoring agenda. Dingman's programs are open to early-stage DC, MD and VA businesses; to apply, an owner must submit a business plan. Dingman also offers a three-hour consultation session to review a start-up business plan.

Ethiopian Community Development Council, Inc.

1038 South Highland Street   703-685-0510
Arlington, VA 22204   Fax: 703-685-0529
www.ecdcinternational.org

Initially formed to assist Ethiopian refugees achieve professional success, the Microenterprise Development Program of the Ethiopian Community Development Council (ECDC; also known as Group Enterprise Development) has extended its services to new businesses started by minorities, women and low- to moderate-income individuals in the DC metropolitan area. The program offers entrepreneurial training and assistance with business start-up matters, loans up to $35,000, and technical assistance in business operations. The ECDC offers funding to many unable to receive it from other sources, with flexible application and credit requirements. Loan recipients continue to receive support and training through the organization after loan inception; follow-up assistance includes lessons in how to expand a business, cash management, bookkeeping and accounting, strategic planning, and marketing.

BusinessStart / Southwest Virginia Community Development Financing, Inc.

1173 West Main Street   276-619-2228
Abingdon, VA 24210   Fax: 276-628-2931
www.businessstart.org/

Southwest Virginia Community Development Financing and its parent organization People, Inc. run a comprehensive microenterprise program for existing small businesses and those looking to start a new business. Known as BusinessStart, the program provides entrepreneurs with business education, technical assistance and access to capital by way of a revolving loan fund. Loans of up to $35,000 are available to planned and existing businesses in a number of cities and counties in southwestern Virginia; interest rates are set at 3% above prime rate. To be eligible, an applicant must have a low- to moderate-income, or plan to hire at least 50% low-income employees. Applications are reviewed weekly by an internal review committee; requests for amounts over $10,000 are forwarded on to an external committee. Free individual technical assistance and counseling from Business Development Managers is provided to all program participants; assistance with loan applications is also free of charge. Also affiliated with People, Inc. is Ninth District Development Financing, Inc., which has a similar microenterprise assistance and loan program for start-up nonprofits and tourism businesses serving the ninth congressional district of Virginia (see www.nddf.org).

Loans, Training, and Technical Assistance for Central Virginians

Total Action Against Poverty/MicroEnterprise Loan
Program
151 Campbell Avenue, SW
Roanoke, VA 24011   540-982-3859
www.korrnet.org/tap/rprogram.html

Training classes, new business counseling and low interest business loans are all elements of the Entrepreneur Training and Microenterprise Loan program run by Total Action Against Poverty (TAP). Part of TAP's This Valley Works project, the program serves entrepreneurs who lack access to business start-up knowledge, business training, or traditional credit markets, and who reside in Alleghany, Bath, Botetourt, Craig or Roanoke county, Virginia. For $15, prospective business owners can enroll in a 12-hour class series that covers initial business research, financing, marketing, personnel and time management, legal issues, business location, inventory, equipment, time management, tax requirements, cash flow projections, and business plan development. Free one-on-one technical assistance is available from TAP staff and volunteers to assist with writing business plans, filling out loan applications and accompanying documentation, and conducting market research. The organization's microloan program provides loans to cover the business start-up expenses. Minimum loan amount is $500; all loans carry an interest rate of prime plus 3%. All applicants must first complete the 12-hour educational program. Applications cost $15 and must be accompanied by a business plan (prepared with the assistance of TAP). Free continuous counseling services are available to all participating new businesses.

Washington

Microloan Program

Center for Economic Opportunity
202 North Tacoma Avenue   253-591-7026
Tacoma, WA 98402   Fax: 253-593-2744
http://www.mdc-tacoma.org/page26.html

The Center for Economic Development provides low-income adults in Tacoma Pierce County access to loans in support of their microenterprise development.

Shorebank Enterprise Pacific

203 Howerton Way SE
P.O. Box 826   360-642-4265
Ilwaco, WA 98624   Fax: 360-642-4078
http://www.sbpac.com/index.cfm

Shorebank Enterprise is a nonprofit rural economic development corporation assisting entrepreneurs build business and market ventures, which improve the social and environmental conditions of rural communities. Loan amounts range from $3,000 to $350,000 for new business start-up or new equipment for existing businesses.

Microenterprise Loan

Spokane Neighborhood Action Program
212 South Wall Street   509-456-7174
Spokane, WA 99201   Fax: 509-456-7170
http://www.snapwa.org/microent.html

The Microenterprise Development Program is designed to assist low to moderate-income individuals and families to realistically enter into business, expand an existing small or home-based business. They offer a term loan from $500 to $10,000 in conjunction with technical support.

West Virginia

Micro Loans Fund

Unlimited Future, Inc.
1650 Eighth Avenue
Huntington, WV 25703   304-697-3007
http://www.unlimitedfuture.org

Unlimited Future, Inc. offers access to micro loans for graduates of their Business Basic Training Course.

Free Business Assistance Programs

A helping hand is just a phone call away for individuals who want to enter into a small business or microenterprise. If you fall into any of the following categories: low to moderate income, Native American, minorities, women, welfare recipients, or have little or no money, you may be eligible for a wide range of assistance. These programs are aimed to assist individuals toward self-sufficiency.

Imagine getting training, counseling, peer support and exchange, and mentoring for free to help you get the knowledge you need to start your own business. Learn how to prepare a business plan and get guidance from the best instructors in the country. One such program is NOVA, located in Arkansas. Their program has four major components: Group Training; Individual Sessions; Business Start-Up; and Networking and Mentoring.

Imagine youths able to receive effective business course training. One such program is Kidpreneur Enterprises, located in Michigan. This program is available to all youths who express an interest in owning and operating their own small business. Kidpreneur is designed to provide and instill concepts and experiences in the minds of youths.

Doors can open for entrepreneurs, like Adina Rosenthal, owner of Threadbearer, a fabric and accessory shop located on Capitol Hill. At a very young age, Adina knew she wanted to work with fabrics. At age 17, she lost the use of her right arm when she was hit by a logging truck. After receiving her degree from the Fashion Institute of Design and Merchandising she attempted to get work at various design companies only to be passed over time and time again. A friend suggested she join the Black Dollar Days' program for entrepreneurs. After completing their entrepreneurial program, Adina opened Threadbearer. She accredits her success to the assistance she received, and is still receiving, from the Black Dollar Days Task Force.

Daryl Anderson an experienced roofer, lacked the necessary skills to run a business of his own. In 1994, Daryl began his involvement with the Cottage Industry Programs offered by the Portsmouth Community Development Group (PCDG) in Montana. After a year of technical assistance, the use of an office, and hours of encouragement, Daryl and his wife Karen were able to open Quality Roofing and Siding. Daryl admits he never would have made it without PCDG's commitment to business counseling and training.

The aim of these programs is to develop a participant's confidence and skills in understanding business enterprise and to further the development of viable business ideas.

The following examples are excerpted from the websites of microenterprise organizations and lending institutions listed in this chapter. Contact organizations and institutions in your area for more information on how they can help you.

A High School Drop-Out Becomes a Role Model of Success

Sonja Thornsberry dropped out of high school to marry her high school sweetheart. She had four children, and felt she was living the American Dream. Then, her husband was injured, and Sonja became the family breadwinner overnight.

Without training or a fancy resume, what could she do? Sonja thought that owning her own business was the answer, and decided to become a used car dealer. She researched the industry, bought a used car at an auction and sold it for a profit. The experience was an eye-opening event that changed her life. She was now convinced that there was money to be made and she could carve out a future for her family.

Despite her enthusiasm, Sonja had empty pockets within the first six months of her business. For the next two years, she worked in a sewing factory to make ends meet, and then ran her car lot in the evenings. But even with all the hours she put in, the business was not as successful as she had hoped. She knew that something needed to change if she was going to succeed.

Sonja contacted BusinesStart, a microenterprise program operated by People, Inc of Southwest Virginia. After taking the Business Basics class, she put together a business plan and applied for a loan. This allowed her to increase her inventory and to generate cash flow while getting a new financing program into action.

Sonja's company now grosses over $250,000 a year. Her children are involved in the business, and look to her as their role model for success. After watching her "drop out" mom become a successful business owner, Sonja's daughter became the valedictorian of her high school graduating class.

A Plan to Get Started

Francisco Ramos wanted to run his own gardening business, but needed help with getting it started. He enrolled in a course with the California Association for Microenterprise Opportunity (CAMEO), which offered a Spanish-language Entrepreneur Training class. The class taught Francisco to structure his business plan in a way that allowed him to cover his startup costs.

Francisco is now the proud owner of Ramos General Gardening, which provides home and business gardening services from basic maintenance to landscape design and execution. Since taking the class, his success has allowed him to purchase two trucks and upgraded his equipment. CAMEO helped Francisco plant the seeds – and he is making the business bloom.

Stick With Your Dream!

What do you do when your employer closes the doors, and no one else is hiring? If you ask Jequita Stutts, she'll tell you to hold onto your dream.

Jequita, a single mother of two, lost her job and became dependent on food stamps and assistance from social services. She was about to leave her hometown in rural Virginia to try her luck in Florida – but she had a dream. She knew of a small cinder block building along the road to a popular fishing and boating destination, and wanted to open a convenience store there create a job for herself and others in her community.

It remained a dream, however, until Jequita heard about BusinesStart, the microenterprise program operated by People, Incorporated. She enrolled in BusinesStart's twelve-hour Business Basics class to learn more. Although she knew it was going to be hard work, she was encouraged enough to develop a business plan and go forward for a loan. Three months after taking the class, her dream became a reality. She opened The Gap Grocery, which features convenience foods, kerosene, and fishing supplies.

During the first four years, sales slowly but steadily increased, even during bad winter months. The business now grosses well over $200,000 a year, making it possible for Jequita to employ three part time people in addition to herself. She has paid off her BusinesStart loan completely and now owns both the building and the business. As Jequita will tell you, dreams can come true!

Discover an Untapped Market

Scott Sordahl worked in the timber industry until back injuries forced him to seek a new way to support his family. When a friend mentioned that he couldn't find a place within miles to have his boat repaired, Scott realized there might be an untapped market of boat owners who would pay for his mechanical expertise.

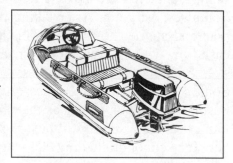

Before he hung out a shingle, Scott wanted to make sure his intuition was right. He signed up for a class entitled, It's Your Business, through the Jefferson Economic Development Institute (JEDI) in Mt Shasta, CA.. His research through these classes showed him that there were about three thousand boat owners in his county. He ran the numbers and determined that if he could earn just five percent of that market, he could build a viable business, and Mt. Shasta Specialty Marine opened its doors.

After five years into the business, Scott plans to start a boat dealership, selling boats and motors as well as repairing them. And it all started through a casual conversation with a friend!

Homemaker's Hobby Hits the Big Time

Carol Willoughby wanted to add to the family's income, but she lacked the confidence to ask for a job. Instead, she used her interest in art to start a small sign and banner business. Seven years later, sales were 20 times what they were when she hung her first sign.

Carol began by making wedding and church banners in her living room. A turning point came when she wanted to display her wedding banners at a bridal show in a local convention center, but did not have enough money for exhibitor's fee. She offered to make signs for the show's producers in exchange for the fee, and when the staff at the convention center saw her work, they hired her to make signs for them.

The business was about to take off, but Carol still needed the confidence to make it successful. She found a mentor at the Northeast Entrepreneur Fund in Minnesota, and now credits the organization with teaching her about business ownership and coaching her through the growth and development of her company.

"I had no experience with self-employment," she said. "My mentor kept saying, 'Of course you can do this!' I still check with her on every important step I take."

Today, her business provides convention, sporting event and special promotion signage for the upper Midwest. As the business grew, so did Carol's confidence. Now, she sets new business goals each year – and has what it takes to achieve them.

Take the First Step

Blake Eames is an artist and a small business owner. She wanted to open a studio and to sell her artwork, but with no collateral and no financial backing, how could she get started?

"I went to the bank first," Blake she said. "They had no interest at all in financing an artist."

One day she drove past Community Ventures Corporation (CVC) in her home town of Lexington, Kentucky, and decided to go inside. That was her first step toward success. She found someone willing to listen to her dream and help her figure out how to make it happen. Blake says working with CVC helped her learn how to focus her business, implement a marketing strategy, be realistic about who her customers might be and the income she could expect to generate.

Though she is miles past her first step, Blake continues to use the resources at CVC assistance with marketing and networking. The journey continues!

Technical Assistance Programs

National Programs

The Abilities Fund

332 S. Linn St., Suite 15	866-726-3863
Iowa City, IA 52240	319-338-2521
http://www.abilitiesfund.org	Fax: 319-338-2528

The Abilities Fund is a nationwide developer targeted exclusively to advancing entrepreneurial opportunities for Americans with disabilities. They deliver a combination of training, technical assistance services, and advisory supports to individuals with disabilities and the organizations that support them. They also assist entrepreneurs obtain the funding they need to launch or grow a small business by linking entrepreneurs to a variety of lending programs that best match the needs and situations of the borrower.

Association for Enterprise Opportunity

1601 North Kent Street, Suite 1101	703-841-7760
Arlington, VA 22209	Fax: 703-841-7748
http://www.microenterpriseworks.org/	

The Association for Enterprise Opportunity is committed to microenterprise development. It primarily assists organizations to promote opportunities for people with limited access to economic resources. They do have a wide variety of resources and a list of organizations in your area.

FIELD (Microenterprise Fund for Innovative, Effectiveness, Learning and Dissemination)

The Aspen Institute

One Dupont Circle, NW, Suite 700	202-736-1071
Washington, DC 20036	Fax: 202-467-0790
http://fieldus.org/home/index.html	

FIELD's mission is to identify, develop and disseminate the best practices throughout the United States about microenterprise programs as an anti-poverty intervention. They offer publications, access to information as well as a directory of microenterprise

Hobbies into Cash

http://www.make-stuff.com/home_business/index.html
Make-Stuff.com is an on-line resource for crafters, hobbyist and entrepreneurs. They provide information in turning your craft or hobby into a marketable business.

Free On-Line Training

My Own Business Inc.
13181 Crosswoods Parkway North

Suite 190	562-463-1800
City of Industry, CA 91746	Fax: 562-463-1802
http://www.myownbusiness.org/	

My Own Business Inc. is a nonprofit organization dedicated to educating entrepreneurs by giving them access to vital information about business. They provide a free 12-session business course intended for both start-up and established businesses.

ONABEN

11825 SW Greenburg Rd., Suite B-3	800-854-8289
Tigard, OR 97223	503-968-1500
http://www.onaben.org/	Fax: 503-968-1548

ONABEN is a nonprofit organization created by Northwest Indian Tribes to increase the success of private businesses owned by Native Americans regardless of tribe. They offer free workshops on a variety of topics including: Website Planning and Development and Website Building Computer-Based Workshop. Their business classes: Financial Literacy and Starting a Successful Business are available for a fee. ONABEN is available to Native Americans living in Oregon, Washington, Idaho, or Northern California.

FastTrac National Headquarters

4747 Troost	800-689-1740
Kansas City, MO 64110	Fax: 816-235-6216

Looking for an organization that focuses on educating and producing successful new business owners? FastTrac is a comprehensive entrepreneurship-educational program that provides entrepreneurs with business and leadership skills and professional connections needed to create a new business or expand an existing enterprise. The FastTrac program includes practical, hands-on business development programs and workshops for existing and aspiring entrepreneurs. Separate tracts are available depending on the needs of the entrepreneur. They include: New Venture (which supplies the vitals for all prospective businesses), Planning, Tech, Manufacturing, FirstStep, and many others. The national program is administered locally by partner agencies; costs vary by administering organization. See {http://www.fasttrac.org/search_event.cfm} to find out who is currently offering FastTrac programs. FastTrac is affiliated with Ewing Marion Kauffmann Foundation, a leading provider of entrepreneurial grants to nonprofit organizations.

Loads of Grant Opportunities To Start or Expand Your Business

www.businessownersideacafe.com/
The Business Owners' Idea Café, a website dedicated to the needs of prospective business owners, provides lists of current available grant money on its BizGrant pages. Included are up-to-the minute listings of grants available from government sources, nonprofit organizations, and corporations. The offerings are often offbeat, including competitions and questionnaire applications, with awards ranging from full business financing for a year, to free website hosting, to training courses. The website provides a description of grant application procedures for each listing, deadlines [usually in the upcoming month(s)], the exact nature of the grant award, and a link to the grantor. The Idea Café itself also awards grants to entrepreneurs to aid in business start-up. A brief information page must be filled out in exchange for free log-in access to the BizGrant site.

You're Never Too Young to Discover Business

Discover Business
http://www.sba.gov/young/indexyoung.html
The curriculum provided on the website is designed to enhance a semester course in small business ownership or entrepreneurship. Each lesson includes a teaching guide and a topic outline, black-line print masers for overheads, paper-based activities, answer-keys for the activities, and worksheets. The worksheets can be used in conjunction with the Business Basics, which outlines the steps to starting a business. Self-assessment quizzes and an extensive glossary of business terms are also provided on the website.

Small Business Training Network

United States Small Business Administration
http://www.sba.gov/training/
The Small Business Training Network is an Internet-based environment that operates like a virtual campus. It offers

online courses, workshops, publications, information resources, learning tools, direct access to electronic counseling, and other forms of technical assistance. The Network offers courses in such areas as E-Commerce, Risk Management, Government Contracting, Marketing and Advertising, Financing, Business Management, Employee Management, International Trade, Franchising, and Starting a Business. As well as providing links to other small business resources, the Network provides information about national training events, programs, and other training opportunities offered by the SBA Administration.

Young Biz

Young Biz, Inc.
P.O. Box 7987
Atlanta, GA 30357   888-543-7929
http://www.youngbiz.com

The mission of Young Biz is to provide youth with skills in entrepreneurship, business, and finance through innovative experience in both education and the real world. Young Biz Media produces an entrepreneurship-only magazine and develops content and design online for organizations that are interested in the entrepreneurship and financial literacy education of youth. Young Biz Youth Programs include instructor-led classes both in school and after school as well as camps, special events, conferences, and rallies, offering methods that are both exciting and engaging to gain experience in the real world and to develop basic business skills. The Young Biz catalogue is a source of business education and resourced for financial literacy. Young Biz Professional Development Workshops provide training for educators to teach entrepreneurship, business, and financial literacy in classrooms, camps, and after-school programs to youth.

Alabama

Birmingham Business Resource Center

110 12th St., North   205-250-6380
Birmingham, AL 35203   Fax: 205-250-6384
www.bbrc.biz

The Birmingham Business Resource Center offers a variety of loan programs to help new or expanding businesses in the area. In addition they offer seminars, entrepreneurial training, support groups, one on one counseling and a learning center.

Central Alabama Women's Business Center

110 12th St., North   205-250-6380
Birmingham, AL 35203   Fax: 205-250-6384
www.cawbc.org

The Central Alabama Women's Business Center offers educational scholarships and loans through the Schlarb Foundation for Women Entrepreneurs. They also offer classes, resources, newsletters and more to help women businesses in the area.

The Women's Business Center, Inc.

1301 Azalea Road
Suite 201 A
Mobile, AL 36693   251-660-2735
http://ceebic.org/~wbac/

The Women's Business Center is a nonprofit organization. Qualified trainers and counselors work with women at every level of business, from those living in public housing to those owning and managing million-dollar companies. The Center conducts workshops and events on useful topics to help entrepreneurs of both existing businesses and startup businesses. Some of the classes offered are Be Your Own

Boss, Home Based Business Conference, Marketing and Sales, and Women and Wealth.

Center for Entrepreneurial Excellence

Business Innovation Center
1301 Azalea Road   251-660-7002
Mobile, AL 36693   Fax: 251-660-7004
www.ceebic.org

The mission of the Business Innovation Center is to help start new small businesses through its small business incubator and outreach programs. Training programs include business opportunities, market research, marketing, forms of legal organization, accounting, raising capital, strategic planning, balance sheets and How to Write a Business Plan.

Self Employment Assistance

Department of Industrial Relations
649 Monroe Street
Montgomery, AL 36131   334-242-8025
http://dir.alabama.gov/

The Self-Employment Assistance Program is a great program if you are a dislocated worker and interested in starting your own small business. The program allows states to pay a self-employed allowance, instead of regular unemployment insurance benefits to any unemployed worker to create their own job by starting their own small business. Participants receive weekly allowances while they are getting their businesses off the ground. If you are interested in this program you must meet the requirements to receive regular unemployment benefits under state law. You may be eligible even if you are engaged in full-time self-employment activities - including entrepreneurial training, business counseling, and technical assistance. Currently, only about 9 states have established the Self-Employment Assistance Program. Check with your state Unemployment Insurance Office to see if your state has implemented this entrepreneurial program.

Alaska

Business Innovation Center

Kenai Peninsula Economic Development District
14896 Kenai Spur Hwy., Suite 103A   907-283-3335
Kenai, AK 99611   Fax: 907-283-3913
www.kpedd.org

The mission of the Kenai Peninsula Economic Development Center is to serve the Kenai Peninsula Borough residents by enhancing their quality of life through responsible and sustainable regional economic and workforce development. The Business Innovation Center (BIC) is a small business incubator designed to provide assistance for new and expanding businesses in the Kenai Peninsula Borough.

Sitka Business Resource Center

Work Force Development Center
303 Lincoln Street, Suite 3   907-966-3066
Sitka, AK 99835   Fax: 907-966-3055
http://sitkaworks.org/index.shtml

The Sitka Business Resource Center promotes the growth and development of small and emerging businesses in the Sitka area. They provide technical assistance and support services to start-up businesses, existing businesses that are experiencing growth or change, new owners of existing businesses, businesses at risk of failure, out of town businesses that want a local office and resources, businesses that want to move to Sitka, or anyone who wants to learn more about starting or buying a businesses. The Center offers an eight week businesses start up class called Smart Steps to

Business Success. It is a hands on program that consists of lectures and workshops where participants learn how to plan, start, and operate a small business. Cost of the class is $195. The Center staff provides free business counseling and office equipment is available to make copies, send and receive faxes, make phone calls, check e-mail or access the internet.

Women$ Fund

245 West Fifth Avenue
P.O. Box 102059   907-274-1572
Anchorage, AK 99501   Fax: 907-272-3146
http://www.alaskabizbuilders.org/women$fund/training.ht
m

The main goal of the Women$ Fund entrepreneurial training is to encourage women and ethnic minorities to start, grow, or rebalance their own small or micro businesses. Courses include a Description of Business, Marketing, and Financial Statements, covering Insurance, Accounting, Market Analysis, Customer Service, and other subjects.

Alaska Women's Network

Membership Goddess
P.O. Box 240165
Anchorage, AK 99524-0165   Fax: 907-780-4203
(the above address is the one to which a membership form should be mailed)

The Alaska Women's Network's goal is to further the empowerment of women in Alaska by sharing information, education, and support and, by encouraging the development of skills that will enable women to assume leadership roles, the Network maintains a statewide communications network between women in Alaska and women's organizations. The Network also helps women identify job training opportunities.

Self Employment Assistance

Department of Labor and Workforce Development
Employment Security Division
P.O. Box 25509
Juneau, AK 99802-5509   907-465-2712
www.labor.state.ak.us/esd/home.htm

The Self-Employment Assistance Program is a great program if you are a dislocated worker and interested in starting your own small business. The program allows states to pay a self-employed allowance, instead of regular unemployment insurance benefits to any unemployed worker to create their own job by starting their own small business. Participants receive weekly allowances while they are getting their businesses off the ground. If you are interested in this program you must meet the requirements to receive regular unemployment benefits under state law. You may be eligible even if you are engaged in full-time self-employment activities - including entrepreneurial training, business counseling, and technical assistance. Currently, only about 9 states have established the Self-Employment Assistance Program. Check with your state Unemployment Insurance Office to see if your state has implemented this entrepreneurial program.

Arizona

Self Employment Loan Fund, Inc.

1601 N. 7th St., Suite 340   602-340-8834
Phoenix, AZ 85006   Fax: 602-340-8953
www.selfloanfund.org

This program provides a variety of services to help those in the area who wish to start or expand a business.

Enterprise Network, Inc.

7225 West Oakland Street   480-496-4408
Chandler, AZ 85226   Fax: 480-858-1802
www.en.org/

The Enterprise Network is a nonprofit corporation established to foster and support entrepreneurship in Arizona. Programs include Business Forums that provide contacts, ideas, education and information to help entrepreneurs gain insight into the challenges many entrepreneurs experience; Business Showcase Programs featuring management of entrepreneurial success stories sharing the difficulties they experienced and the methods they used to overcome them; Business Seminars consisting of discussion groups on entrepreneurial issues and solutions; and other programs including informal forums that unite start up businesses with experienced entrepreneurs who offer guidance and insight in solving specific issues faced by small businesses.

Self Employment Assistance

Department of Economic Security
Unemployment Insurance
P.O. Box 28880
Tucson, AZ 85726   602-364-2722
www.de.state.az.us/esa/

The Self-Employment Assistance Program is a great program if you are a dislocated worker and interested in starting your own small business. The program allows states to pay a self-employed allowance, instead of regular unemployment insurance benefits to any unemployed worker to create their own job by starting their own small business. Participants receive weekly allowances while they are getting their businesses off the ground. If you are interested in this program you must meet the requirements to receive regular unemployment benefits under state law. You may be eligible even if you are engaged in full-time self-employment activities - including entrepreneurial training, business counseling, and technical assistance. Currently, only about 9 states have established the Self-Employment Assistance Program. Check with your state Unemployment Insurance Office to see if your state has implemented this entrepreneurial program.

Arkansas

Business Assistance

Alt.Consulting
Delta Region Office:
6210 Dollarway Road, Suite 5-1   870-267-1725
Pine Bluff, AR 71602   Fax: 870-267-1726
www.altconsulting.org/

Alt.Consulting is a nonprofit, economic development organization that operates like a management-consulting firm but is driven by a passion for economic justice. They provide on-site business assistance for the clients they serve.

MicroEnterprise Development and Training

Central Arkansas Development Council
P.O. Box 580   501-315-1121
Benton, AR 72018   Fax: 501-778-9120
http://www.cadconline.net/

This initiative helps make credit accessible to the low-income through a combination of education, training, mentoring, and resource development. Economic Literacy classes gives persons in all areas the tools needed to get out of debt and to build sound financial futures. Pre-Business Classes helps individuals develop plans to become entrepreneurs in their communities. Serving Calhoun, Clark, Columbia, Dallas, Hot

Spring, Lonoke, Montgomery, Ouachita, Pike, Pulaski, Saline, Union counties.

Arkansas Enterprise Group

Good Faith Fund's Arkansas Women's Business Center
2304 W. 29th   870-535-6233
Pine Bluff, AR 71603   Fax: 870-535-0741
The Good Faith Fund provides business skills training, including special modules for childcare providers, a mentoring program, loan packaging assistance, and training on the Internet. The Arkansas WBC organizes monthly regional peer support groups.

Self Employment Assistance

Employment Security Department
#1 Pershing Circle
North Little Rock, AR 72114   501-682-3201
www.state.ar.us/esd/
The Self-Employment Assistance Program is a great program if you are a dislocated worker and interested in starting your own small business. The program allows states to pay a self-employed allowance, instead of regular unemployment insurance benefits to any unemployed worker to create their own job by starting their own small business. Participants receive weekly allowances while they are getting their businesses off the ground. If you are interested in this program you must meet the requirements to receive regular unemployment benefits under state law. You may be eligible even if you are engaged in full-time self-employment activities - including entrepreneurial training, business counseling, and technical assistance. Currently, only about 9 states have established the Self-Employment Assistance Program. Check with your state Unemployment Insurance Office to see if your state has implemented this entrepreneurial program.

California

California Association for Microenterprise Opportunity (CAMEO)

655 13th Street   510-238-8260
Oakland, CA 94612   Fax: 510-238-8361
http://www.microbiz.org/members.htm
CAMEO is a statewide membership organization designed to build the capacity of microbusiness organizations. CAMEO provides referrals to microbusiness owners seeking assistance. Use the site above or call to find a member service provider or for entrepreneur information in your area.

Micro Business Training

ACCESS San Diego
2612 Daniel Ave   858-560-0871
San Diego, CA 92111   Fax: 858-560-8135
www.access2jobs.org
ACCESS offers microenterprise training and development to prepare low-income individuals especially those in low-income communities impacted by immigrants. Clients are taught how to start and operate a small business in fields where they have expertise including handcrafts or cultural or ethnic services

One-On-One Training

ACCION San Diego
World Trade Center San Diego
1250 6th Avenue, Suite 500   619-685-1380
San Diego, CA 92101   Fax: 619-685-1470
http://www.accionsandiego.org/

ACCION helps clients build favorable credit histories and improve their business skills with one-on-one training in bookkeeping, preparation of financial statements and credit repair. They support the leadership and entrepreneurial spirit of their clients energy in San Diego's low-income neighborhoods.

Micro Loans

California Capital Small Business Development Corporation
926 J Street, Suite 1500   916-442-1729
Sacramento, CA 95814   Fax: 916-442-7852
cwilliams@capital.com
Serving ethnic minorities, immigrants, and women to provide microloans in the Sacramento area.

Business Development Center

Central California Small Business Development Center
Fresno Office
3419 W. Shaw, Suite 102   559-275-1223
Fresno, CA 93711   800-974-0664

Visalia Office
720 West Mineral King
P.O. Box 787
Visalia, CA 93279   559-625-3051
www.ccsbdc.org
The mission of the Central California Small Business Development Center (CCSBDC) is to enhance economic growth by making the Central Valley's small businesses more competitive through entrepreneurial assistance. The CCSBDC provides one-on-one counseling, business training and a variety of workshops.

Child Care Home Business

Chicano Federation of San Diego County, Inc
Southeastern Regional Resource Center.
610 22nd Street
San Diego, CA 92102-2909   619-236-1228, ext. 315
www.chicanofederation.org
The Southeastern Regional Resource Center builds child care capacity in unserved and underserved communities in San Diego, Orange and Imperial Counties through training and technical assistance for small private child care centers, community based organizations, ethnic organizations and family child care providers to increase and enhance quality child care centers. Provides family child care home (FCCH) training, accelerated child development training, subsidized child care for infants and toddlers (birth to 36 months), center-based child care and development for pre-school children (3 to 5 years old), financial reimbursements for meals provided to children in licensed child care homes.

Technical Assistance

Community Financial Resource Center
4060 So. Figueroa St.   323-233-1900
Los Angeles, CA 90037   Fax: 323-235-1686
www.cfrc.net
The Center offers technical assistance in English and Spanish to help entrepreneurs in the LA area prepare loan packages and develop business plans.

Business Training for Women

Creating Economic Opportunities for Women (CEO)
971 Regal Road
Berkeley, CA 94708   510-526-3258
www.ceowomen.org
CEO Women is an organization dedicated to helping immigrant women create economic opportunities for

themselves and their families. They offer micro-enterprise business training, technical assistance, and asset education to women who are planning to start or expand their own business. CEO Women concentrates its efforts on assisting low to moderate-income women within the San Francisco Bay Area but also assists the broader population of women in need of micro-enterprise support services. All CEO Women programs are offered on a sliding scale basis.

East Bay Small Business Development Center

519 17th Street, Suite 210   510-893-4114
Oakland, CA 94612-1528   Fax: 510-893-5532
www.ebsbdc.org

The East Bay Small Business Development Center (EBSBDC) provides training, one-on-one counseling and workshops throughout Alameda County. All of the programs are designed to assist business owners in developing the critical tools needed for long-term success. Consulting services and most training events are available at no cost.

Small Business Development Center

Eastern Los Angeles County Small Business Development Center

363 S. Park Ave., Suite 101   909-629-2247
Pomona, CA 91766   Fax 909-629-8310
Email: sbdcpom@ibm.net
www.companyhelp.org

The Eastern Los Angeles County Small Business Development Center provides management and business technical assistance at no cost to small businesses and entrepreneurs in Eastern Los Angeles County.

Business Assistance

El Pájaro Community Development Corporation
23 East Beach Street, #209   831-722-1224
Watsonville, CA 95076   Fax: 831-722-3128
www.elpajarocdc.org

El Pájaro Community Development Corporation has more than twenty years of experience in the provision of bilingual/bicultural small business assistance and job creation for primarily minority and low-income entrepreneurs. Serving the El Pájaro community.

Business Programs

Fresno West For Economic Development
Fresno Street, Suite 212   559-485-1273
Fresno, CA 93706   Fax: 559-485-1276
www.fwced.org

The Fresno West Coalition for Economic Development's (FWCED) overall mission and goal is to improve the physical and socio-economic condition of the Southwest Fresno area and its residents. They develop programs for small businesses located in or desiring to locate within the Fresno area.

Training and Technical Assistance

Jefferson Economic Development Institute
711 Pine Street
P.O. Box 1586   530-926-6670
Mt. Shasta, CA 96067   Fax: 530-926-6676
www.e-jedi.org

The Jefferson Economic Development Institute (JEDI), is located in Mt. Shasta, California, and serves all of Siskiyou County. They offer free and low-cost services to Siskiyou County residents who would like to receive help to grow or start a business along with individualized technical assistance.

BusinesStarts Program

Job Starts, Inc.
3010 West 48th Street

Los Angeles, CA 90043
www.jobstarts.org

BusinesStarts Program targets the poorest of the economically active persons in south Los Angeles communities to assist emerging entrepreneurs start or improve a business enterprise in order to help families improve their economic well being. The Program consists of Business Design and Management Training Workshops, Volunteer Mentors, Technical Assistance, and Access to Credit Classes.

Legal Assistance

Legal Aid Foundation of Los Angeles
8601 South Broadway   231-640-3968
Los Angeles, CA 90003   Fax: 231-640-3988
www.lafla.org

Legal Aid Foundation of Los Angeles provides legal help for low-income people; they promote access to justice, strengthen communities, combat discrimination, and provide community education.

Los Angeles Business Assistance Program

City of Los Angeles Community Development Department
216 West 6th Street, 10th Floor   231-473-0311
Los Angeles, CA 90014   Fax: 231-485-8151
www.cityofla.org/cdd

Los Angeles Business Assistance Program (LABAP) provides technical assistance, support and growth for area entrepreneurs and microenterprises in the LA area. Training is provided for microenterprises and start-ups using high quality, reasonably priced technical services.

Training and Technical Assistance

Madera County Economic Development Commission
413 W. Yosemite Ave., Suite 103   559-675-7768
Madera, CA 93637   800-357-5231
www.maderaindustry.org   Fax: 559-675-3252

The Madera County Economic Development Commission (MCEDC) provides counseling and guidance for small businesses and assists in their development and expansion in the Madera area. Resources include the business and marketing plans, finance analysis, access to capital and technical assistance.

Business and Technical Assistance

Micro-enterprise Assistance Program
2118 K Street   916-492-2591
Sacramento, CA 95816   Fax: 916-492-2603
www.map-srm.org

Micro-enterprise Assistance Program (MAP) empowers underserved individuals in the Sacramento area to become self-employed by providing business and technical assistance. MAP has developed and continues to refine a program of training and assistance specifically tailored to meet the needs of our clients.

Technical Assistance

Mission Economic Development Association
3505 20th Street   415-282-3334
San Francisco, CA 94110   Fax: 415-282-3320
www.medasf.org

The Mission Economic Development Association is a community-based corporation located in the Mission District of San Francisco. MEDA targets minority and women-owned businesses and provides them with technical assistance and business training.

Micro Business Incubation

Technical Assistance
The New America Foundation

2974 Adeline St.   510-540-7785
Berkeley, CA 94703   Fax: 510-540-7786
www.anewamerica.org

The New America Foundation offers a 3-year holistic program of asset building for families and communities. The current programs serve Latino and Indo-Chinese communities in the San Francisco Bay Area through micro business incubation, networking and technical assistance.

Business Assistance

North Coast Small Business Development Center (NCSBDC)
520 E Street   707-443-5057
Eureka, CA 95501   Fax: 707-445-9652
www.northcoastsbdc.org

North Coast Small Business Development Center provides business assistance, education and resources not available in isolated rural communities to small business owners. They serve new and established businesses in the Del Norte and Humboldt Counties. Free services include general information, referrals and consulting assistance. Low cost services include troubleshooting, problem solving and technical support.

Business Resource Center

North San Diego County
1823 Mission Avenue   760-795-8740
Oceanside, CA 92054   Fax: 760-795-8728
www.sandiegosmallbiz.com

The Small Business Development and Resource Center serves North San Diego County providing business assistance. They offer one-on-one business consulting, workshops, training, referral resources and a business resource center.

Business Assistance

PACE Business Development Center
1541 Wilshire Blvd., Suite 310   213-353-9400
Los Angeles, CA 90017   213-353-4665
www.pacela.org

The Pacific Asian Consortium in Employment (PACE) was founded in 1975 to address the employment and job training needs of the Asian Pacific Islander communities. There are a variety of business assistance programs for entrepreneurs in the LA area.

Outreach

Planada Community Development Center
9167 East Stanford Avenue
P.O. Box 1045   209-382-2321
Planada, CA 95365   Fax: 209-82-2316
www.planadacdc.org/abcd.htm

Planda CDC goals are to provide low-income entrepreneurs, especially women, minorities and immigrants with support through increased outreach.

One-On-One Counseling

Redwood Empire Small Business Development Center
606 Healdsburg Avenue   707-524-1770
Santa Rosa, CA 95401   Fax: 707-524-1772
www.santarosa.edu/sbdc

The Redwood Empire Small Business Development Center, hosted by Santa Rosa Junior College, is a valuable resource for the small business communities in Marin, Sonoma, and Mendocino Counties of California. The program assists small businesses by providing one-on-one, no cost, business consulting, low-cost workshops and technical assistance.

Business Training

Renaissance Entrepreneurship Center
275 5th Street   415-541-8580
San Francisco, CA 94102   Fax: 415-541-8589

www.rencenter.org

Training classes and workshops provide hands-on practical experiences that teach you what you need to know to start and grow your own business. The business incubator provides office space, consultation and support services for growing businesses. There is also a Women's Business Center offering programs to help women succeed in business.

Investment Corporation

Riverside County Community Investment Corporation
4250 Brockton Ave., Suite 100   909-786-1370
Riverside, CA 92501   Fax: 909-786-0050
www.cicontheweb.com

Community Investment Corporation provides mentoring and coaching to help entrepreneurs in low-income areas throughout the Inland Empire overcome obstacles of business ownership.

Business Training and Childcare Provider Services

Silicon Valley Economic Development Corporation
1155 N. First Street, Suite 107   408-298-8455
San Jose, CA 95112   Fax: 408-971-0680
www.sved.org/dsp_main.htm

Silicon Valley Economic Development Corporation provides opportunities for low-income persons, and other disadvantaged individuals in Santa Clara County to become entrepreneurs. Services are offered through a variety of programs, including: Entrepreneur training, business assistance center, childcare provider services and classes for developmentally disabled entrepreneurs.

One-On-One Counseling

Business Resource Center
Small Business Development and International Trade Center
Southwestern College (SBDITC)
900 Otay Lakes Road
Building 1600   619-482-6393
Chula Vista, CA 91910   Fax: 619-482-6387
www.sbditc.org

The Small Business Development and International Trade Center provides, free of charge, many resources to assist potential and existing entrepreneurs in the San Diego and Imperial counties. Their small business services include: one-on-one counseling, seminars, classes, import/export assistance, and a business resource center.

Capital Access Initiative

Start Up EPA
1395 Bay Road   650-321-2193 ext. 15
East Palo Alto, CA 94303   Fax: 650-321-1025
www.startupepa.org

Start Up is a private, nonprofit organization whose mission is to promote economic development in and around East Palo Alto, California by providing training, capital, and other assistance to help establish and support locally-owned and operated small businesses. Start Up's Capital Access (CAP) initiative aims to help clients' access a broad array of financing resources and technical assistance needed to launch and sustain viable enterprises.

MicroEnterprise Development Program

Superior California Economic Development District
737 Auditorium Dr.   530-225-2760
Redding, CA 96001   Fax: 530-225-2769
www.scedd.org

Superior California Economic Development District (SCEDD) is a four county economic development district with its main office in Redding. SCEDD offers communities and businesses in Modoc, Shasta, Siskiyou and Trinity counties economic, technical and business assistance.

Technical Assistance

Vermont Slausen Economic Development Corporation
VSEDC Headquarters
5918 S. Vermont Avenue   323-753-2335
Los Angeles, CA 90044   Fax: 323-753-6710
http://vsedc.org/

VSEDC Business Enterprise Center
6109 S. Western Avenue   323-789-4515
Los Angeles, CA 90047   Fax: 323-789-4524
http://vsedc.org/

The VSEDC facilitates community development of the Vermont Slauson area by providing programs structured to revitalize the community. VSEDC has developed and implemented a comprehensive approach to community economic development that includes business development, technical assistance and training,

Microenterprise Resource for Medocino County

West Company: Ukiah Office
367 N State St., Suite 201   707-468-3553
Ukiah, CA 95482   Fax: 707-468-3555

West Company: Coast Office
306 E. Redwood Ave., Suite 2   707-964-7571
Fort Bragg, CA 95437   Fax: 707-964-7576
www.westcompany.org

If you live in Mendocino County and are interested in starting or growing a microbusiness the West Company may be able to help you. West Company delivers Technical Assistance to business owners through consultations. Technical Assistance is conducted on a one-on-one basis with clients.

Business Cooperative

Women's Action to Gain Economic Security (WAGES)
1214 Webster St. Suite B
P.O. Box 71885   510-272-0564
Oakland, CA 94612   Fax: 510-272-0384
www.wagescooperatives.org

WAGES is designed to help women move out of poverty through cooperative ownership. They use the cooperative model to allow women to pool their skills and work together to succeed. A cooperative is a business owned and controlled by those who work in it. WAGES is currently helping Latina women establish environmentally sound housecleaning cooperatives in the greater San Francisco Bay Area.

Business Training for Women (And Men Too)

Women's Economic Ventures
1136 E. Montecito Street   805-965-6073
Santa Barbara, CA 93103   Fax: 805-962-9622
www.wevonline.org

Women's Economic Ventures (WEV) is a local, nonprofit organization dedicated to helping women become economically self-sufficient through entrepreneurship development. Although they primarily target women, business counseling and loans are available to men, especially minority and low-income men who have not had access to traditional job opportunities, training and business capital. Training opportunities include: self-employment training, mentoring programs, business consulting and business owner roundtables.

Business Classes

Women's Enterprise Development Corp.
235 East Broadway, Suite 506   562-983-3747
Long Beach, CA 90802   Fax: 562-983-3750
www.wedc.org

Women's Enterprise Development Corporation (WEDC) is a private, nonprofit, community supported organization providing a broad range of training and support programs to help entrepreneurs from all cultures and economic levels successfully start, manage, expand and diversify their businesses. Classes are available in "Starting Your Own Business", "Starting you Own Home Based Childcare Business", "Managing Your Business", and "Manage Your Business for Growth". Course fees vary and scholarships are available.

Microenterprise Training Program

Yuba-Sutter Enterprise Zone   530-741-6463
1364 Sky Harbor Drive   530-742-6280
Marysville, CA 95901   Fax: 530-742-7835
www.yubacounty.org
www.yubasutterez.com

The training program is a 14-week training session that includes a comprehensive reference book, hands-on assistance and instruction from real practitioners. This program includes the areas of Yuba County, Sutter County, Yuba City, and Marysville.

Asian Pacific Islander Small Business Program

231 E. 3rd St.   213-473-1605
Los Angeles, CA 90013   Fax: 213-473-1601
www.apisbp.org

This program provides a variety of services to help those in the area who wish to start or expand a business.

Center for Community Futures

6621 Elverton Dr.   510-339-3801
Oakland, CA 94611   Fax: 510-339-3803
www.cencomfut.com

The Center for Community Futures provides information on how to start and run a business.

Economic and Employment Development Center

2200 W. Valley Blvd., Suite A   626-281-3792
Alhambra, CA 91803   Fax: 626-281-8064

This program provides a variety of services to help those in the area who wish to start or expand a business.

Mayfair Improvement Initiative

2342 Alum Rock Ave.   408-251-6900
San Jose, CA 95116   Fax: 408-251-6987
www.mayfairneighborhood.org

This program provides a variety of services to help those in the area who wish to start or expand a business.

Arcata Economic Development Corporation

100 Ericson Cr., Suite 100   707-822-4616
Arcata, CA 95521   Fax: 707-822-8982

The Arcata Economic Development Corporation offers a variety of loan and business service assistance to those interested in starting or expanding a business.

Bay Area Entrepreneur Association

1714 Franklin St., #100-134   510-663-0656
Oakland, CA 94612   Fax: 510-663-0657

This association provides a variety of programs and services to those wishing to start or expand a business.

CHARO Community Development Corp.

4301 East Valley Blvd.   323-269-0751
Los Angeles, CA 90032   Fax: 323-343-9485
www.charocorp.com
CHARO provides a business incubator, business training, technical assistance, and loan information to the Latino community in the area.

Southeast Asian Community Center

875 O'Farrell St.   415-885-2743
San Francisco, CA 94019   Fax: 415-8853253
The Community center works with the Southeast Asian population to help them pursue their goals.

Tulare County Redevelopment Agency

5961 S. Mooney Blvd.   559-733-6291
Visalia, CA 93277   Fax: 559-730-2591
www.co.tulare.ca.us
The Tulare County Redevelopment Agency woks to help improve the economy of the area. They offer incentives to businesses and have an entrepreneur training program to help new businesses.

Valley Economic Development Center

5121 Van Nuys Blvd., 3rd Floor   818-907-9977
Van Nuys, CA 91403   Fax: 818-907-9720
www.vedc.org
The Valley Economic Development Center offers training, consulting, technical assistance and financing to small and medium-sized businesses. They offer several different types of loan and loan guarantee programs, as well as an extensive entrepreneurial training program.

Fame Renaissance Center

1968 West Adams Boulevard   323-730-7700
Los Angeles, CA 90018   Fax: 323-737-5717
www.famerenaissance.com
Fame Renaissance operates several business development programs in impoverished communities in Los Angeles County. The center offers two training programs. StartUp!! 101 is a four week course for those who want to start a business but don't know where to begin. Classes cover business planning, financing, accounting, marketing, and sales. Students also have the opportunity to network with business professionals and other entrepreneurs. StartUp!! 102 consists of 14 classes over a 7 week period designed to help existing businesses increase sales and profit. It provides assistance with developing a marketing plan, one-on-one strategic planning, and access to a business library, meeting room spaces and computers.

Women's Initiative for Self-Employment

450 Mission Street, Suite 402   415-247-9473
San Francisco, CA 94105   Fax: 415-247-9471
The Women's Initiative for Self-Employment provides training and technical assistance in establishing a business. There are two programs, one in English and one in Spanish. The English-language program consists of a two-week business assessment workshop, a fourteen-week workshop on business skills, and a four-week workshop on writing a business plan. The Spanish program follows the English program but is in a modular format. The WI also offers business support services, including one-on-one consultations, peer networking, support groups, and special seminars.

North Coast Opportunities, Inc.

413 North State Street   707-462-1954
Ukiah, CA 95482   Fax: 707-462-8945

http://www.ncoinc.org
North Coast Opportunities, Inc. is an agency serving Mendocino County to provide low-income women with job training and placement, self-employment training, and other services necessary for them to achieve self-sufficiency. The program integrates personal development, life skills training, and case management into a program of employment and micro enterprise development training.

Self Employment Assistance

Employment Development Office
800 Capitol Mall, MIC 83
Sacramento, CA 95814   800-300-5616
www.edd.ca.gov/
The Self-Employment Assistance Program is a great program if you are a dislocated worker and interested in starting your own small business. The program allows states to pay a self-employed allowance, instead of regular unemployment insurance benefits to any unemployed worker to create their own job by starting their own small business. Participants receive weekly allowances while they are getting their businesses off the ground. If you are interested in this program you must meet the requirements to receive regular unemployment benefits under state law. You may be eligible even if you are engaged in full-time self-employment activities - including entrepreneurial training, business counseling, and technical assistance. Currently, only about 9 states have established the Self-Employment Assistance Program. Check with your state Unemployment Insurance Office to see if your state has implemented this entrepreneurial program.

Colorado

Colorado Alliance for Microenterprise Initiatives

3003 Arapahoe St., #35   303-996-0045
Denver, CO 80205   Fax: 303-996-4939
www.coloradoalliance.org
Colorado Alliance for Microenterprise Initiatives (CAMI) is a coalition of microenterprise development organizations dedicated to providing entrepreneurs in under-served communities the opportunity and resources to become self-sufficient through private enterprise. Check with them frequently because members are added regularly.

One-Stop Center

Colorado Business Assistance Center
2413 Washington St.   800-333-7798 (Nationwide)
Denver, CO 80205   303-592-5920 (Denver)
www.state.co.us/oed/sbdc/bac.html
The Colorado Business Assistance Center is a one-stop center for new and existing business owners in Colorado.

Training for Women

Colorado Women's Business Office
1625 Broadway, Suite 1700   303-892-3840
Denver, CO 80202   Fax: 303-892-3848
www.state.co.us/oed/wbo
The Colorado Women's Business Office offers a variety of services for the women business owners of Colorado. They have training and counseling for start-ups and expansions along with internet resources.

Business Incubator

Denver Enterprise Center
3003 Arapahoe St.   303-296-9400

Denver, CO 80205   Fax: 303-296-5542
www.thedec.org

The Denver Enterprise Center is a small business incubator. The incubator provides new and existing companies affordable light manufacturing and office space. Business can also share office and administrative services that include: copier, fax, business library, consulting services technical assistance and the newly added commercial kitchen.

Business Center

Denver Minority Business Development Center
1011 West 45th Ave.   303-455-3099
Denver, CO 80211   Fax: 303-455-3076
www.denvermbdc.com

The Denver Minority Business Development Center (DMBDC) provides consulting services in the areas of business plan development, financial planning and loan packaging.

Entrepreneurial Training for Latinas

Mi Casa Resource Center for Women, Inc.
360 Acoma   303-573-1302
Denver, CO 80223   Fax: 303-595-0422
Http://miscasadenver.org

Mi Casa strives to advance self-sufficiency for primarily low-income Latinas and youth. Mi Casa Resource Center offers a free 3-hour business workshop to help you decide if becoming a business owner is for you. The center also offers classes for entrepreneurs to learn more about their business. Classes offered include: Secrets to Becoming a Successful Small Business Owner, Legal and Tax Matters, Marketing and many more. They also have a computer lab for clients to work on technical aspects of their business.

Technical Assistance

MicroBusiness Development Corporation
3003 Arapahoe St., Suite 112A   303-308-8121
Denver, CO 80205   Fax: 303-308-8120
www.microbusiness.org

MicroBusiness Development Corporation offers PACEWorks!, a technical assistance program for entrepreneurs. They offer workshops on a variety of topics, usually at no or low cost to the client. In addition, they offer fee based one-to-one services and a mentoring program. They offer loans from $500-$50,000 and business training and development.

Counseling and Technical Assistance

SCORE Denver
721 19th Street, 4th Floor
Denver, CO 80202   303-844-3985
www.scoredenver.org

Counselors to America's Small Business (SCORE) is a nonprofit organization that provides entrepreneur education to form, grow and succeed in small business. They conduct free counseling and low-cost workshops in addition to a business information center and speakers bureau.

San Juan 2000 Development Association

P.O. Box 722
1315 Snowden   970-387-5101
Silverton, CO 81433   Fax: 970-387-5104
www.sanjuan2000.org

San Juan 2000 Development Association tries to improve the community and the economy of the Silverton area by providing loans and technical assistance to new or expanding businesses. Loans can range for $500-$5,000 to help businesses grow and prosper. Technical assistance can be had in the form of bookkeeping help, marketing and planning.

Colorado Women's Chamber of Commerce

2150 West 29th Avenue, Suite 325   303-458-0220
Denver, CO 80211   Fax: 303-458-0222
http://www.cwcc.org/

The Colorado Women's Chamber of Commerce creates an economic community for women through education and training, partnerships and alliances and information exchange. Their programs include business roundtables, newsletters, a resource library, a membership directory, government assistance, and many activities and functions that change monthly.

Youth Works

Micro Business Development Corporation (MBDC)
3003 Arapahoe St., Suite 112A   303-308-8121
Denver, CO 80205   Fax: 303-308-8120
www.microbusiness.org/content.asp?CID=30

MBDC supports teens who are interested in developing their entrepreneurial potential through their Youthworks Management and Youthworks Enterprise programs. Youthworks Management is a youth committee made up of teens who want to focus on business management. This committee guides the Youthworks program, mentors other youth interested in business, manages the youth loan process, supports fundraising efforts, and creates youth run business opportunities. The Youthworks Enterprise program is a self-paced skills development program. Enrollees work through a variety of assignments and activities designed to build their general business knowledge along with industry specific expertise.

Self Employment Assistance

Department of Labor & Industry
1515 Arapahoe
Tower 2, Suite 400   800-388-5515
Denver, CO 80202   303-318-9000
www.coworkforce.com/UIB/

The Self-Employment Assistance Program is a great program if you are a dislocated worker and interested in starting your own small business. The program allows states to pay a self-employed allowance, instead of regular unemployment insurance benefits to any unemployed worker to create their own job by starting their own small business. Participants receive weekly allowances while they are getting their businesses off the ground. If you are interested in this program you must meet the requirements to receive regular unemployment benefits under state law. You may be eligible even if you are engaged in full-time self-employment activities - including entrepreneurial training, business counseling, and technical assistance. Currently, only about 9 states have established the Self-Employment Assistance Program. Check with your state Unemployment Insurance Office to see if your state has implemented this entrepreneurial program.

Connecticut

Aid to Artisans, Inc.

331 Wethersfield Avenue   860-947-3344
Hartford, CT 06114   Fax: 860-947-3350
http://www.aidtoartisans.org/

The mission of Aid to Artisans, Inc. is to create employment opportunities for disadvantaged artisans worldwide. They provide assistance with business training, product development, marketing and small grants. Their plans are to develop relationships between American and foreign artisans worldwide.

The Entrepreneurial Center at Hartford College for Women

50 Elizabeth Street 860-768-5681
Hartford, CT 06105 Fax: 860-768-5622
http://uhaweb.hartford.edu/entrectr

The mission of The Entrepreneurial Center is to help women and men achieve financial independence through self-employment. Entrepreneurs of all income levels are encouraged to participate. They provide a self-assessment workshop for Connecticut entrepreneurs to discover what's involved in starting a Connecticut small business. They provide a 16-week program "Comprehensive Small Business Training. In addition they provide one-on-one counseling, business workshops and special events for women from start-up to established business owner. Services are available on a sliding scale to eligible individuals.

Women's Business Development Center

400 Main Street, Suite 410 203-353-1750
Stamford, CT 06901-3004 Fax: 203-353-1084

The WBDC serves women from all social and economic backgrounds throughout southwest Connecticut and it collaborated with other community agencies to target clients who are disadvantaged either socially or economically. The training courses include one-on-one counseling, Finance a Business, Launch a Business, The Business Toolbox, the Experienced Entrepreneur: Leveraging Growth, Government Procurement and Camp Entrepreneur: A Mother/Daughter Experience. The WBDC is developing an innovative program for girls between the ages of 11 and 14 by collaborating with the YWCA of Greenwich and the Urban League of Southwestern Connecticut, Inc.

Access Entrepreneurial Center

1315 Main St. 860-450-7146
Willimantic, CT 06226 Fax: 860-450-7477

The Access Entrepreneurial Center serves New London, Tolland and Windham Counties. The Center's small business development program includes classroom business training, one on one business and credit counseling, economic literacy training, technical assistance in business and marketing plans and financing, and a resource center.

The Family Business Program

University of Connecticut
2100 Hillside Road, Unit 1041 860-486-5628
Storrs, CT 06269-1041 Fax: 860-486-9116
http://sbweb.business.uconn.edu/page.asp?id=1.8.6

The Family Business Program at UCONN is a place where family businesses can gain insight into the unique problems experienced by family businesses. Members have access to consultants, faculty, staff, sponsors, and other members.

Self Employment Assistance

Department of Labor
200 Folly Brook Boulevard
Wethersfield, CT 06109 860-263-6074
www.ctdol.state.ct.us/

The Self-Employment Assistance Program is a great program if you are a dislocated worker and interested in starting your own small business. The program allows states to pay a self-employed allowance, instead of regular unemployment insurance benefits to any unemployed worker to create their own job by starting their own small business. Participants receive weekly allowances while they are getting their businesses off the ground. If you are interested in this program you must meet the requirements to receive regular unemployment benefits under state law. You may be eligible even if you are engaged in full-time self-employment activities - including entrepreneurial training, business counseling, and technical assistance. Currently, only about 9 states have established the Self-Employment Assistance Program. Check with your state Unemployment Insurance Office to see if your state has implemented this entrepreneurial program.

Delaware

YWCA of New Castle County

233 King Street 302-658-7161
Wilmington, DE 19801 Fax: 302-658-7547

The YWCA uses lessons and materials from the Working Capital Program as well as offering peer and individual lending, career counseling, childcare services, and a group savings program for low-income families.

New Castle County Chamber of Commerce

630 Churchmens Road
P.O. Box 11247 302-368-5700, ext 235
Wilmington, DE 19850-1247 Fax: 302-737-8450
www.ncccc.com

The Small Business Department of the New Castle County Chamber of Commerce is a vital resource for small businesses in the community. They provide networking breakfasts, executive roundtables, seminars, one-on-one counseling and business publications to their member businesses to help them grow, successfully.

Self Employment Assistance

Department of Labor
4425 North Market Street 302-761-6576
Wilmington, DE 19802 800-794-3032
www.delawareworks.com/

The Self-Employment Assistance Program is a great program if you are a dislocated worker and interested in starting your own small business. The program allows states to pay a self-employed allowance, instead of regular unemployment insurance benefits to any unemployed worker to create their own job by starting their own small business. Participants receive weekly allowances while they are getting their businesses off the ground. If you are interested in this program you must meet the requirements to receive regular unemployment benefits under state law. You may be eligible even if you are engaged in full-time self-employment activities - including entrepreneurial training, business counseling, and technical assistance. Currently, only about 9 states have established the Self-Employment Assistance Program. Check with your state Unemployment Insurance Office to see if your state has implemented this entrepreneurial program.

District of Columbia

Get Paid To Save For Your New Business

Capital Area Asset Building Corporation
1801 K Street, NW, Suite M100 202-419-1440
Washington, DC 20006 Fax: 202-419-1447
http://www.caab.org

Have a great idea and want to turn it into a successful business in the future? Capital Area Asset Building can double a client's money, enabling a swifter transition from idea to money-maker. The nonprofit specializes in establishing individual development accounts (IDAs) for lower income Washington DC residents. IDAs are matched savings accounts – every dollar deposited by a participant is matched by the organization. One of the approved purposes of the account is starting a new business or microenterprise.

Columbia Heights Community Supports and Services Area Businesses

Columbia Heights Community Supports and Services
  Area Businesses
Development Corporation of Columbia Heights
3419 14th Street, NW
Washington, DC 20010   202-483-4986
www.dcch.org

Through the Advanced Business Learning and Entrepreneurship (ABLE) program, small businesses in the Columbia Heights area of Washington, DC hoping to expand their business have the tools and resources to do just that. ABLE is administered by the Development Corporation of Columbia Heights (DCCH). It is a free seminar series that provides training and related services on business financing, marketing, accounting, business plan development, technology know-how, loan and investor resources, and business expansion strategies. Working alongside DCCH to service area businesses is the Columbia Heights Association of Merchants and Professionals (CHAMPS). CHAMPS provides low-cost website design and hosting to neighborhood enterprises, and also makes available business services such as accounting, bookkeeping, legal assistance and representation, technology support, and insurance coverage at extremely low group rates. {www.champs-dc.org/}

FREE Business Assistance and Training for Entrepreneurs in DC

Georgia Avenue Business Resource Center
7408 Georgia Avenue, NW
Washington, DC 20012   202- 545-0220
www.brc.dc.gov/gabrc/

The Georgia Avenue Business Resource Center offers technical assistance, access to computers and other equipment, and training programs to DC-based small businesses and nonprofit organizations, with a particular eye towards neighborhood-based businesses run by minorities and women. Almost all services are free of charge. Services include providing access to and assistance with start-up financing, one-on-one counseling on the basics and intricacies of starting and running a small business, and a mentoring project to connect entrepreneurs with veteran business professionals in their field. The organization established the Small Business Technology Learning Center, which includes a computer lab and reference library for use by business owners. The lab offers computer training courses and access to high-tech equipment. The library provides materials and information on federal and local government small business programs, private contracting opportunities, and incentives for operating a business in the District of Columbia. The center is an initiative of the DC Chamber of Commerce.

Help Finding Capital in the Capital Area

North Capitol Neighborhood Development, Inc.
1330 North Capitol Street, NW   202-483-2100
Washington, D.C. 20001   Fax: 202-483-2107
www.ncnd.org

The North Capital Neighborhood Development Corporation runs free and low-cost programs for prospective and existing small businesses in Washington DC's Wards 2 and 5. Offerings for local start-up and existing businesses include free entrepreneurial workshops and seminars, one-on-one counseling and technical assistance, and an 8-week business plan development course (administered in partnership with

Georgetown University Law Center). Under a partnership with the DC Department of Employment Services, clients can use the Department's extensive Business Resource Center. Also available are loan packaging services and a limited microloan program. Approximately 200 businesses annually benefit from the organization's small business initiatives.

Women's Business Center, Inc.

1001 Connecticut Avenue, NW
Suite 312   202-785-4WBC
Washington, D.C. 20036   202-785-4110
http://www.womensbusinesscenter.org

The Women's Business Center, Inc. provides excellent and affordable business training and creates opportunities for clients to participate in business-to-business networking. Entrepreneurs are introduced to the business uses of technology, including the Internet and the World Wide Web. Mentor partnerships are developed to enhance the capabilities of each individual entrepreneur as their businesses grow. Special outreach efforts are made to attract and serve women who are socially and/or economically disadvantaged.

The Entrepreneurial Development Institute (TEDI)

2025 I Street, NW, Suite 905
Washington, DC 20006   202-822-8334
www.bedrock.com/tedi/tedi.htm

TEDI is a nonprofit organization that helps minority youth between the ages of 7 and 21. They have a 26 week extensive training program that prepares them to develop and start up a community based business.

Florida

Business Development Center and Disadvantaged Business Enterprise Assistance

City of Petersburg Economic Development
P.O. Box 2842   800-874-9026
St. Petersburg. FL 33731   727-893-7146
www.stpete.org/bdc.htm   Fax: 727-551-3360

The Business Development Center (BDC) is a one-stop center that helps current and future small business owners research ideas and receive technical assistance and training in business development. It provides a comprehensive array of financial and technical information, training, services, and follow up. Technical and financial assistance, workshops, seminars and training programs are available through the Business Development Center for Disadvantaged Business Enterprises.

Florida Community Loan Fund

3107 Edgewater Drive, Suite 2   407-246-0846
Orlando, FL 32804   888-578-2030
www.fclf.org   Fax: 407-246-0856

The Florida Community Loan Fund provides technical assistance to qualifying organizations with insufficient access to capital from conventional lending sources. They provide assistance with: design development, budgeting, finances, management and needs assessment. The services may also include the assignment of a Technical Assistant Consultant to work with your organization.

Center for Urban Redevelopment and Empowerment

111 E. Las Olas Blvd., Suite 604   954-762-5270
Fort Lauderdale, FL 33301   Fax: 954-762-5278
www.cure.fau.edu/Programs/microbusiness.htm

FAU-CURE provides entrepreneurial training twice a year in the form of a 15-week microbusiness training course. Topics covered include bookkeeping, marketing, taxes, planning, financing, and more. Courses are offered in English, Spanish and Haitian Creole.

Miami Urban Ministries

2850 SW 27th Ave.   305-442-8306
Miami, FL 33133   Fax: 305-442-9726
www.mum-umc.org

ASSETS Miami is an entrepreneur training program offered through the Miami Urban Ministries. This is an eleven week training program for those who want to start or expand a business. The program includes classroom work, coaching, computer lab, and assistance in securing loans.

Women's Business Development Center

11205 S. Dixie Highway, Suite 101   305-971-9446
Pinecrest, FL 33156   Fax: 305-921-7061
http://www.womensbusiness.info/index.html

The WBDC provides services such as special events, including expos, trade fairs, and even a golf tournament, business forums for the free exchange of ideas among members, seminars, workshops, one-on-one counseling, and a mentoring program.

Women Business Owners of North Florida

P.O. Box 551434
Jacksonville, FL 32255-1434   904-278-9270
http://www.jaxwbo.org/

The Women Business Owners of North Florida's goal is to create and recognize opportunities to lift up the successes of women in the business world. The WBO will support a vision of practical educational opportunities with mentors that will offer encouragement, advice, and networking assistance.

Jacksonville Chamber of Commerce

Small Business Center
5000-3 Norwood Avenue
Jacksonville, FL 32208   904-924-1100
www.myjaxchamber.com

The goal of the Jacksonville Small Business Center (SBC) is to provide training, assistance and comprehensive support to small businesses in the area. Entrepreneurs and business owners can attend business workshops covering such topics as Business Start-Up, Marketing Like a Pro, Managing your Money, How to Start a Childcare Business, Feasibility Planning, Selling to the Government, Writing a Business Plan and many more. They also offer business research facilities, core city business recruitment and access to capital.

Self Employment Assistance

Unemployment Claims and Benefits
Post Office Drawer 5350
Tallahassee, FL 32314-5350   866-778-7356
www.floridajobs.org/unemployment/

The Self-Employment Assistance Program is a great program if you are a dislocated worker and interested in starting your own small business. The program allows states to pay a self-employed allowance, instead of regular unemployment insurance benefits to any unemployed worker to create their own job by starting their own small business. Participants receive weekly allowances while they are getting their businesses off the ground. If you are interested in this program you must meet the requirements to receive regular unemployment benefits under state law. You may be eligible even if you are engaged in full-time self-employment activities - including entrepreneurial training, business counseling, and technical assistance. Currently, only about 9

states have established the Self-Employment Assistance Program. Check with your state Unemployment Insurance Office to see if your state has implemented this entrepreneurial program.

Georgia

Technical Support for Atlanta Union Mission Alumni

Atlanta Mission Entrepreneur Network (AMEN)
P.O. Box 76956   707-952-0862
Atlanta, GA 30358   Fax: 707-984-8627
www.ameninc.org

AMEN is designed with the purpose to help overcome the resource barriers faced by men and women who have completed the Atlanta Union Mission program and who exhibit strong interest in starting their own businesses. Additionally, AMEN will provide the tools and the support necessary to help these startup businesses to be successful.

Technical Assistance

Appalachia Community Enterprises, Inc.
1727 Turner's Corner Road   706-348-6609
Cleveland, GA 30528   877-434-6609 toll free
www.acenorthgorgia.org   Fax: 706-219-4976

The Appalachia Community Loan Fund provides ongoing support, technical assistance and business education to loan recipients by the loan fund through partner organizations.

Athens-Clarke Microenterprise Program for Women

UGA-School of Environmental Design
609 Caldwell Hall
Athens, GA 30602   706-542-0936
http://www.sed.uga.edu/pso/athensmicro/default.htm

The Athens-Clarke Microenterprise Program for Women is a public service program of the University of Georgia School of Environmental Design. The program's mission is to assist women with minimum income levels achieve economic self-sufficiency through microenterprise development. They provide a 12-week program of intensive business and personal effectiveness training for women who have viable business ideas or who are engaged in some business activity. The program is open to women residents in Athens-Clarke County whose income does not exceed $47,950. If your income exceeds the limit, please contact the director to discuss your options.

Micro Business Center

BusinessNOW- Neighborhood Organization for Women
Goodwill Industries of North Georgia, Inc.
2201 Glenwood Ave., SE   404-486-8400
Atlanta, GA 30316   Fax: 404-486-8500
www.biznow.org

Entrepreneurs living in the Atlanta Metropolitan Area have a Micro Business Center to help them bridge the gap between a great idea and a successful business. The Center provides many resources to assist the small business owner with business strategies, from designing business cards to technical assistance to legal advice the center is a one-stop-center. The Micro-Business Center offers: computers with internet access, business resources, fax and phone services, copiers, meeting facilities and training workshops. Daily admission for the Center is $3.00.

Center for Black Women's Wellness, Inc.

477 Windsor St., SW, Suite 309   404-688-9202
Atlanta, GA 30039   Fax: 404-880-9435

www.cbww.org

The Center for Black Women's Wellness, Inc. (CBWW) is a nonprofit community-based, family-service center. CBWW assists low-to-moderate income women who are starting micro businesses by providing personal and business development training, counseling, business-to-business networking sessions, and access to financial resources They offer 19 workshop sessions that include: How to Conduct Market Research; Marketing and Advertising Strategies; Pricing Your Product/Service; Legal Structure; Record Keeping; and more.

Business Training Program

Cobb Microenterprise Center
Kennesaw State University
Small Business Development Center
1000 Chastain Rd - BB423   770-499-3228
Kennesaw, GA 30144   Fax: 770-423-6564
www.cobbmicro.com

The services provided by the Cobb Microenterprise Center are for low-to-moderate-income individuals who have an "entrepreneurial spirit" and need development and capital to start or grow a business. If you are on welfare, unemployed, underemployed, disable, elderly, and you have a good business idea, you can participate in this opportunity. Cobb Microenterprise offers a 12-week training program in business development, technical assistance, access to its business incubator and many other services.

Technical Assistance

East Athens Development Corporation
410 McKinley Drive   706-208-0048
Athens, GA 30601   Fax: 706-208-0015
www.eadcinc.com

The East Athens Development Corporation, Inc.(EADC) is a nonprofit community based development organization. EADC manages and collaborates with other agencies to provide technical assistance and training to businesses in the East Athens Community. Some services include: business plan development, cooperative marketing and advertising, micro loans, micro enterprise development, business incubator and adult and youth entrepreneurial training.

Partnership for Community Action

3597 Covington Hwy.   404-929-2415
Decatur, GA 30088   Fax: 404-508-9330
www.pcaction.org

The Microenterprise Initiative is a 12-week curriculum which helps those wanting to develop a business plan and are in need of financing. Many of those who attend are refugees.

Women's Economic Development Agency

675 Ponce de Leon Avenue, N.E.   404-856-7680
Atlanta, GA 30308   Fax: 404-853-7677
http://www.weda-atlanta.org/

The WEDA offers training in starting and growing small businesses, researching and writing a business plan, financial management, banking fundamentals, credit managing, and retirement planning. Also provided are one-on-one assistance and counseling and focused networking.

Greater Atlanta Small Business Project (GRASP)

241 Peachtree Street NE
Suite 200   404-659-5955
Atlanta, GA 30303   Fax: 404-880-9561
http://www.graspnet.org/

GRASP provides entrepreneurial training to prepare and empower individuals to become owners of small businesses

and to achieve economic self-sufficiency through the ownership of a small business, business consulting, and incubator office suites.

Southwest Atlanta Youth Business Organization (SWAYBO)

3687 Dover Blvd., SW
Atlanta, GA 30331   404-691-4111

SWAYBO is a nonprofit volunteer organization that teaches African-American children, age 7 to 18 years, how to operate a business. Classroom training is provided covering economics and entrepreneurship. SWAYBO also conducts community service projects and travels as a group.

Self Employment Assistance

Department of Labor
Unemployment Insurance
Appeals Tribunal Suite 150
148 Andrew Young International Boulevard, NE
Atlanta, GA 30303-1751   404-232-3755
www.dol.state.ga.us

The Self-Employment Assistance Program is a great program if you are a dislocated worker and interested in starting your own small business. The program allows states to pay a self-employed allowance, instead of regular unemployment insurance benefits to any unemployed worker to create their own job by starting their own small business. Participants receive weekly allowances while they are getting their businesses off the ground. If you are interested in this program you must meet the requirements to receive regular unemployment benefits under state law. You may be eligible even if you are engaged in full-time self-employment activities - including entrepreneurial training, business counseling, and technical assistance. Currently, only about 9 states have established the Self-Employment Assistance Program. Check with your state Unemployment Insurance Office to see if your state has implemented this entrepreneurial program.

Hawaii

Hawaii Community Loan Fund

677 Ala Moana Blvd., Suite 702   808-523-0075
Honolulu, HI 96813   Fax: 808-534-1199
www.hclf.org

The Hawaii Community Loan Fund (HCLF) is a certified Community Development Financial Institution that provides technical assistance to their clients. The objective of technical assistance is to build healthy businesses that result in better internal management and to increase employment within local neighborhoods. Programs include: organizational assessment, management training, one-to-one counseling and loan packaging.

Business Training

Maui Economic Opportunity
Business Development Corporation
99 Mahalani Street   808-249-2990
Wailuku, HI 96793   Fax: 808-249-2991
www.meoinc.org

Maui Economic Opportunity, Business Development Corporation is a private, nonprofit Community Action Agency that helps low-income entrepreneurs start and expand their businesses. They provide a FastTrac New Venture, an 11-week course that teaches entrepreneurs the tools needed to write a feasibility study for any business they may be thinking of starting.

Hawaii Women's Business Center

Attn: Oliv'e
1041 Nuuanu Avenue, Suite A   808-522-8136
Honolulu, HI 96817   Fax: 808-522-7494
http://www.hawaiiwbc.org

The WBC's mission is to provide the resources for women to develop and grow successful businesses. Some of the services provided include one-on-one counseling, Intro to Numbers and Computerized Bookkeeping workshops and Fast Trac training. There is a resource library with an extensive list of resource books, manuals, and periodicals and a computer lab that offers the latest business software versions to assist the development of businesses.

Business Action Center

1130 North Nimitz Highway
Second level, Suite A-220
Honolulu, HI 96817   808-586-2545
www2.hawaii.gov/dbedt/index.cfm?section=start_and_gro
w_a_business_188

The Business Action Center has everything an entrepreneur needs to start a small business in Hawaii. They provide information and forms for getting a tax license, registering a trade name, employer registration, State, County and Federal permits, counseling, workshops, and financing programs.

Self Employment Assistance

Unemployment Insurance Division
Department of Labor and Industrial Relations
830 Punchbowl Street, Room 325
Honolulu, HI 96813   808-586-9069
www.dlir.state.hi.us/

The Self-Employment Assistance Program is a great program if you are a dislocated worker and interested in starting your own small business. The program allows states to pay a self-employed allowance, instead of regular unemployment insurance benefits to any unemployed worker to create their own job by starting their own small business. Participants receive weekly allowances while they are getting their businesses off the ground. If you are interested in this program you must meet the requirements to receive regular unemployment benefits under state law. You may be eligible even if you are engaged in full-time self-employment activities - including entrepreneurial training, business counseling, and technical assistance. Currently, only about 9 states have established the Self-Employment Assistance Program. Check with your state Unemployment Insurance Office to see if your state has implemented this entrepreneurial program.

Idaho

Women's Business Center

119 N. 9th Street
Lower Level
Boise, ID 83702   208-336-5464
http://www.wemswbc.org/WNET.asp

The WBC provides services such as business counseling, classes on how to start and continue small businesses and writing a business plan, networking opportunities, and round tables.

Business Information Center (BIC)

1020 Main Street, Suite 290   508-334-1696, ext. 236
Boise, ID 83702-5745   Fax: 208-334-9353

The BIC is a free resource center for the start up and expansion of small businesses. They have the latest computer equipment, software, CD-Rom databases, video tapes and over 250 business start-up guides for use on-site. The BIC also offers an extensive business reference library, counseling and training classes.

Self Employment Assistance

Department of Labor
Unemployment Insurance Division
317 West Main Street
Boise, ID 83735-0001   208-332-3570 ext. 3437
www.labor.state.id.us/

The Self-Employment Assistance Program is a great program if you are a dislocated worker and interested in starting your own small business. The program allows states to pay a self-employed allowance, instead of regular unemployment insurance benefits to any unemployed worker to create their own job by starting their own small business. Participants receive weekly allowances while they are getting their businesses off the ground. If you are interested in this program you must meet the requirements to receive regular unemployment benefits under state law. You may be eligible even if you are engaged in full-time self-employment activities - including entrepreneurial training, business counseling, and technical assistance. Currently, only about 9 states have established the Self-Employment Assistance Program. Check with your state Unemployment Insurance Office to see if your state has implemented this entrepreneurial program.

Illinois

Small Business Development Center

Jane Adams Hull House Association
Uptown Center Development
4520 N. Beacon   773-561-3500
Chicago, IL 60640-5519   Fax: 773-561-3507
www.hullhouse.org/sbdu.asp

The Jane Adams Hull House Small Business Development Center operates on the north and south sides of Chicago to help revitalize local neighborhoods. They work with new and expanding businesses to find the resources to operate a successful business venture. A variety of small business programs to available for entrepreneurs, including: individual counseling, small business workshop series, small business training programs and networking opportunities.

Financial and Technical Assistance

Lake County Partners
28055 Ashley Circle, Suite 212   847-247-0137
Libertyville, IL 60048   Fax: 847-247-0423
www.lakecountypartners.com

The Financial and Technical Services Committees help all businesses in Lake County have access to loans and capital for starting and growing their business. They can help your business thrive.

Project Now

418 19th St.
Rock Island, IL 61201   309-793-6391
www.projectnow.org   Fax: 309-793-6352

Project Now offers and eight week Self-Employment Training Program. The program provides information on how to write a business plan, bookkeeping, marketing, sales, and more. A Revolving Loan Fund can provide you with a $15,000 loan for each job created. This service targets the unemployed or low-income persons.

Women's Self-Employment Project

11 S. La Salle Street
Chicago, IL 60603   312-606-8255
http://www.wsep.net/WSEP.htm

The WSEP provides classes including The Business Concept, Competition, Marketing, Pricing, Operation and Management, and Development and Design of a Self-Employment Action Plan. Class fees and based on income and range from $30 to $375 per series. Graduates of the program are eligible to participate in WSEP's loan program and free tuition in the Financial ProForma series as well as receiving a one-year membership to WSEP.

Women's Business Development Corporation

8 South Michigan Avenue, Suite 400   312-853-3477
Chicago, IL 60603   Fax: 312-853-0145
http://www.wbdc.org

The WBDC's goal is to strengthen and accelerate the growth of women owned businesses. The services provided include workshops and one-on-one counseling on aspects of business development such as marketing, finance, technology integration, and business management.

Women in Franchising, Inc.

53 W. Jackson Boulevard, Suite 205   312-431-1467
Chicago, IL 60604   Fax: 312-431-1469
http://www.infonews.com/wif/

WIF's goal is to educate women, minorities, and the physically challenged about franchising. It offers business training seminars and workshops as well as one-on-one assistance with special emphasis on the 'Business Review of a Franchise Offering Circular.'

The Springfield Employment and Training Center

1300 South Ninth   217-782-3846
Springfield, IL 62703   TTY: 217-558-3530
www.ietc.org/index.html

The Springfield Employment and Training Center offers many services, among them are professional workshops, seminars, and entrepreneur training. They also have computers, printers, fax machines and copies available for participant use.

Urban Options

1830 South Springfield Avenue, Unit C   773-762-2814
Chicago, IL 60623   Fax: 773-762-2815
www.urbanoptions.net

Urban options is a community based youth development organization that offers a multi-level entrepreneurship program. Classes include Entrepreneurship One, an introduction to basic entrepreneurship skills; Entrepreneurship Two, the development of life action and business plans; Entrepreneurship Three focuses on the development of a student owned business; and Kids Invent Toys, which guides students through the entire inventing process.

Self Employment Assistance

Department of Employment Security
33 South State Street
Chicago, IL 60603   312-793-5700
www.ides.state.il.us/

The Self-Employment Assistance Program is a great program if you are a dislocated worker and interested in starting your own small business. The program allows states to pay a self-employed allowance, instead of regular unemployment insurance benefits to any unemployed worker to create their own job by starting their own small business. Participants receive weekly allowances while they are getting their businesses off the ground. If you are interested in this program you must meet the requirements to receive regular unemployment benefits under state law. You may be eligible even if you are engaged in full-time self-employment activities - including entrepreneurial training, business counseling, and technical assistance. Currently, only about 9 states have established the Self-Employment Assistance Program. Check with your state Unemployment Insurance Office to see if your state has implemented this entrepreneurial program.

Indiana

Community Action of Southern Indiana

1613 E. 8th Street   812-288-6451 ext. 123
Jeffersonville, IN 47130   Fax: 812-284-8314
www.casijeff.net/

The Community Action of Southern Indiana offers assistance to small businesses in planning, marketing, training, and more. The Micro Enterprise Business Development Program targets small businesses with less than five people.

Fort Wayne Women's Bureau, Inc.

303 E. Washington Boulevard   219-424-7977
Fort Wayne, IN 46805   Fax: 219-426-7576

The FWWBI reaches out to low-income, Hispanic, and disabled women. FWWBI training includes financial, management, and marketing assistance as well as workshops. Bilingual services are offered for all programs, signing interpreters are provided for the hearing impaired, and transportation is supplied for the disabled.

Northeast Indiana Innovation Center

Center for Entrepreneurial Excellence (CEE)
1410 Production Rd.   260-407-6442
Fort Wayne, IN 46808   Fax: 260-407-6448
www.niic.net

CEE serves prospective entrepreneurs, existing small business owners, post secondary students, postsecondary education institutions, service providers, and lifelong learners. Programs and activities of the center include the Entrepreneurial Resource Center, an Entrepreneurial Leadership Development Program, workshops and classes.

Entrepreneurship Training for Practicing Business Owners

Purdue University, Calumet
Entrepreneurship Center, A-351   219-989-2746
Hammond, IN 46323-2094   Fax: 800-937-2101

The Entrepreneurship Training for Practicing Business Owners is a community based university program for entrepreneurs who may not have had the chance to receive specific training on how to manage or develop their business. It is a 22 month program offered in 3 segments. The first segment lasts 6 months and takes place in a conference room setting. It covers the "how-to" aspects of management and entrepreneurship, focusing on cash flow management, strategic planning, creative funding sources, hiring, and break even analysis. The second segment lasts 4 months and consists of participants applying their new found management skills as consultants to other small businesses. The third segment is spread out over a 12 month period. It involves monthly round table mentoring focused on business improvement.

Self Employment Assistance

Department of Workforce Development
Indiana Government Center South
10 North Senate Avenue
Indianapolis, IN 46204   800-WORKONE
www.in.gov/dwd

The Self-Employment Assistance Program is a great program if you are a dislocated worker and interested in starting your own small business. The program allows states to pay a self-employed allowance, instead of regular unemployment insurance benefits to any unemployed worker to create their own job by starting their own small business. Participants receive weekly allowances while they are getting their businesses off the ground. If you are interested in this program you must meet the requirements to receive regular unemployment benefits under state law. You may be eligible even if you are engaged in full-time self-employment activities - including entrepreneurial training, business counseling, and technical assistance. Currently, only about 9 states have established the Self-Employment Assistance Program. Check with your state Unemployment Insurance Office to see if your state has implemented this entrepreneurial program.

Iowa

Institute of Social and Economic Development

910 23rd Avenue   319-335-2331
Coralville, IA 52241   Fax: 319-338-5824
http://www.ised.org

ISED's mission is to strengthen the social and economic well being of both individuals and communities. It offers assistance in Organizational Structure, Vision, Mission, Strategic Planning, Governance, Personnel Management, Financial Management, Resource Development, Program Management, Technology, Evaluation, Collaboration, and other organizational development issues and processes. ISED also offers micro-enterprise training and technical assistance to help low-income entrepreneurs start, expand, and strengthen small businesses.

John Pappajohn Entrepreneurial Center

21 East Market Street
John Pappajohn Business Building, Suite S160
Iowa City, IA 52242-1000   319-335-1022

The John Pappajohn Entrepreneurial Center (JPEC) provides a wide range of learning opportunities for persons who want to start a business venture, learn the entrepreneurial process, or update their skills and knowledge in order to grow their business, JPEC offers a nine session program for new entrepreneurs. The class covers personal and business criteria, market research, financing and financial documents, and how to conduct a feasibility study on a business idea. For small business owners, there is an eleven session program that deals with strategic planning, legal issues, cash flow management and financial documents, market research and analysis, and growth strategies for small business owners.

Self Employment Assistance

Workforce Development Center
Unemployment Insurance Service Center
P.O. Box 10332   877-891-5344
Des Moines, IA 50306-0332   515-281-4199
www.iowaworkforce.org/ui

The Self-Employment Assistance Program is a great program if you are a dislocated worker and interested in starting your own small business. The program allows states to pay a self-employed allowance, instead of regular unemployment insurance benefits to any unemployed worker to create their own job by starting their own small business. Participants receive weekly allowances while they are getting their businesses off the ground. If you are interested in this program you must meet the requirements to receive regular unemployment benefits under state law. You may be eligible even if you are engaged in full-time self-employment activities - including entrepreneurial training, business counseling, and technical assistance. Currently, only about 9 states have established the Self-Employment Assistance Program. Check with your state Unemployment Insurance Office to see if your state has implemented this entrepreneurial program.

Kansas

The First Step Fund

4747 Troost Ave.
Kansas City, MO 64110   816-235-6116
www.firststepfund.org

The First Step Fund's mission is to serve low- to moderate-income individuals; there are income requirements for all class participants. First Step Fund offers two types of business training classes: general business and child care entrepreneurship. The general business class they offer is a 36-hour course to help entrepreneurs with their businesses, called First Step FastTrac. The Family Child Care Entrepreneur Course is an interactive 54-hour course. In addition to training, First Step students receive assistance with personal challenges and referrals. Child Care reimbursement and transportation assistance is also available.

Huck Boyd National Institute for Rural Development

Kansas State University
216 Call Hall   785-532-7690
Manhattan, KS 66506-1604   Fax: 785-536-7036
http://www.oznet.ksu.edu/huckboyd

The mission of the Huck Boyd Institute is to enhance rural development by helping rural people help themselves. The institute offers presentations encouraging grass-roots community self-help throughout the state as well as conducting rural policy studies. The Institute has compiled and broadcast over 200 profiles of entrepreneurs and others who have created hundreds of jobs in more than 89 of Kansas' 105 counties to encourage entrepreneurship.

Youth Entrepreneurs of Kansas

1845 Fairmount, Box 157
Wichita, KS 67260-0157   316-978-7959
www.yeks.org

Youth Entrepreneurs of Kansas (YEK) is a non profit organization dedicated to helping young people learn business skills that can help them be self-sufficient, productive adults. YEK encourages students to pursue higher education, provides the knowledge for students to start and maintain their own business, and helps students understand how to apply that knowledge and be a better employee for others.

Self Employment Assistance

Department of Human Resources
Division of Employment Security
401 SW Topeka Boulevard
Topeka, KS 66603   785-296-0295
www2.hr.state.ks.us/ui/html/EnUI.htm
www.kansasjoblink.com

The Self-Employment Assistance Program is a great program if you are a dislocated worker and interested in starting your own small business. The program allows states to pay a self-employed allowance, instead of regular unemployment insurance benefits to any unemployed worker to create their own job by starting their own small business. Participants receive weekly allowances while they are getting their businesses off the ground. If you are interested in this program you must meet the requirements to receive regular unemployment benefits under state law. You may be eligible even if you are engaged in full-time self-employment activities - including entrepreneurial training, business counseling, and technical assistance. Currently, only about 9 states have established the Self-Employment Assistance Program. Check with your state Unemployment Insurance Office to see if your state has implemented this entrepreneurial program.

Kentucky

Business Training and Business Center

Community Ventures Corporation   859-231-0054
1450 North Broadway   800-299-0267
Lexington, KY 40505   Fax: 859-231-0261
www.cvcky.org

The Community Ventures Corporation (CVC) is a community-based, nonprofit organization that exists to improve the quality of life for urban and rural residents throughout central and northern Kentucky. CVC's mission is to provide individuals and families with the skills, income, and assets; they need to achieve financial independence. They offer a variety of classes including: computer courses, business planning, and a free business orientation. The Business Center offers entrepreneurs: copiers, faxes, computer access, conference rooms, work rooms and office space with lease rates starting at $350 per month.

Center for Microenterprise Development

Jewish Family and Vocational Services
3587 Dutchmans Lane   502-452-6341
Louisville, KY 40205   Fax: 502-452-6718
www.jfvs.com

The Jewish Family and Vocational Services help immigrants start their own small businesses by providing economic training, business planning and technical assistance.

Mountain Association for Community Economic Development

433 Chestnut St.   859-986-2373
Berea, KY 40403   Fax: 859-986-1299
www.maced.org

The Mountain Association for Community Economic Development provides an accessible clearinghouse of information, access to training, and opportunities to learn from other entrepreneurs. Their program called Business First Stop provides these resources for communities in Kentucky and Central Appalachia.

Midway College

Center for Women, Diversity, and Leadership
512 East Stephens Street   606-846-5811
Midway, KY 40347-1120   Fax: 606-846-5787

The Center reaches out to welfare-to-work, low-income, and minority populations. It offers online training programs including 'Taking Off: Launching Your Small Business,' 'Advancing Your Business,' and technical workshops on sources of capital, selling to the government, mentoring, and team building and discussion groups.

Jackson County Entrepreneurship Center

Easton Kentucky University, College of Business and Technology
Center for Economic Development, Entrepreneurship and Technology (CEDET)
P.O. Box 1080
McKee, KY 40447   606-287-4184
E-mail: jcec@prtcnet.org

The Jackson County Entrepreneurship Center provides residents of Jackson County with instruction and technical assistance that provide the knowledge and skills needed to startup and be successful in business. Services include classroom instruction, individual business consultation, resource materials, computer access and clerical support. The Center provides formal training and ongoing technical support for starting new businesses and expanding existing operations. 12-week small business training classes are held in the spring and fall of each year.

Self Employment Assistance

Department for Employment Services
275 East Main Street
Frankfort, KY 40621   502-564-4761
www.des.ky.gov/des/ui/ui.asp

The Self-Employment Assistance Program is a great program if you are a dislocated worker and interested in starting your own small business. The program allows states to pay a self-employed allowance, instead of regular unemployment insurance benefits to any unemployed worker to create their own job by starting their own small business. Participants receive weekly allowances while they are getting their businesses off the ground. If you are interested in this program you must meet the requirements to receive regular unemployment benefits under state law. You may be eligible even if you are engaged in full-time self-employment activities - including entrepreneurial training, business counseling, and technical assistance. Currently, only about 9 states have established the Self-Employment Assistance Program. Check with your state Unemployment Insurance Office to see if your state has implemented this entrepreneurial program.

Louisiana

Entrepreneurial Training

Acadiana Regional Development District
601 Loire Ave., Suite C
P.O. Box 90070   337-886-7782
Lafayette, LA 70507   Fax: 337-886-7081
www.ardd.org

The Acadiana Regional Development District Small Business Entrepreneurial Training Program (SBET) is available to assist individuals interested in starting their own small business. SBET is designed to assist those with little or no experience in running a business. The program focuses on three training models in the areas of business plan preparation, loan packaging, and finding financial resources. The District serves the eight parishes of Region Four: Acadia, Evangeline, Iberia, Lafayette, St. Landry, St. Martin, St. Mary and Vermilion.

Louisiana Department of Economic Development

Mailing address:
P.O. Box 94185
Baton Rouge, LA 70804
Physical address:
Capital Annex

1051 N. 3rd Street   225-342-3000
Baton Rouge, LA 70802   Fax: 225-342-5389
www.lded.state.la.us

The Louisiana Economic Development Department provides a variety of programs for beginning and existing small businesses. The Microenterprise Program assists low- income parents of minor children to start or strengthen a small business. The program provides entrepreneurial and economic literacy training and mentoring; financial counseling; and access to capital through micro loans for the participants. The Small and Emerging Business Development Program (SEBD) offers workshops to small business owners with assistance in marketing, technical training, and management. These programs are offered through statewide Small Business Development Centers (SBDC).

Microenterprise Development Alliance of Louisiana

1200 S. Acadian Thruway, Suite 204   225-387-1166
Baton Rouge, LA 70806   Fax: 225-343-6935
www.microenterprisela.org

The MicroEnterprise Development of Alliance Louisiana (MEDAL) is a statewide not for profit alliance committed to helping entrepreneurs through the establishment of microenterprises, particularly by women and youth. MEDAL provides technical assistance in the areas of marketing, recruiting, program design, evaluation design, technology, sector service and start-up.

Women Entrepreneurs for Economic Development, Inc. (WEED)

1683 North Clairborne Avenue, Suite 101   504-947-8522
New Orleans, LA 70116   Fax: 504-949-8885

WEED provides business training and counseling, one-on-one Internet and computer training, basic life skills training, housing and family services, and the only inner-city business incubator in the area. It also provides low-interest loans to graduates living in public housing and microloans to residents with small businesses.

Acadiana Regional Development District

Small Business Entrepreneurial Training
601 Loire Avenue, Suite C
P.O. Box 90070
Lafayette, LA 70507   337-886-7081
www.ardd.org/index.htm

The Acadiana Regional Development District Small Business Entrepreneurial Training Program (SEBT) is designed to help those with little or no experience in running a business. The program consists of three training sections: business planning, management, and loan processing. Training is provided in a classroom setting and covers all areas of business development and operation.

Self Employment Assistance

Department of Labor
1001 North 23rd Street
P.O. Box 94094
Baton Rouge, LA 70804-9094   225-342-3111
www.ldol.state.la.us

The Self-Employment Assistance Program is a great program if you are a dislocated worker and interested in starting your own small business. The program allows states to pay a self-employed allowance, instead of regular unemployment insurance benefits to any unemployed worker to create their own job by starting their own small business. Participants receive weekly allowances while they are getting their businesses off the ground. If you are interested in this program you must meet the requirements to receive regular unemployment benefits under state law. You may be eligible even if you are engaged in full-time self-employment activities - including entrepreneurial training, business counseling, and technical assistance. Currently, only about 9 states have established the Self-Employment Assistance Program. Check with your state Unemployment Insurance Office to see if your state has implemented this entrepreneurial program.

Maine

Penquis C.A.P., Inc.

262 Harlow Street   207-973-3612
Bangor, ME 04401   Fax: 207-973-3699
www.penquiscap.org

Penquis Community Action Program primarily serves low- and moderate-income individuals in Penobscot and Piscataquis Counties. Their Economic Development Department provides assistance to individuals interested in starting or expanding a microenterprise, a business with five or fewer employees. One-On-One Technical Assistance for Entrepreneurs offers assistance to low-income individuals starting or expanding a business. After completing a business plan class, participants meet with a business coach to determine their needs and goals. Areas of assistance may include: business plan completion, marketing, technical assistance, and general supporting services.

Coastal Enterprises, Inc.

36 Water Street
P.O. Box 268   207-882-7552
Wiscasset, ME 04578   Fax: 207-885-7308
http://www.ceimaine.org

Coastal Enterprises, Inc. provides services such as one-on-one confidential consultation, on-site consultation for select, experienced business owners, networking and peer support opportunities, assistance in obtaining financing, workshops on important business issues, and research, information and referrals.

Portland Resource Hub

441 Congress Street   207-756-8180
Portland, ME 04101   Fax: 207-756-8178

The Portland Resource Hub is a one-stop help center serving businesses in the greater Portland area. The Hub offers assistance through business counseling, workshops, seminars, and technology.

Self Employment Assistance

Department of Labor
P.O. Box 259
Augusta, ME 04332-0259   207-624-6400
www.state.me.us/labor

The Self-Employment Assistance Program is a great program if you are a dislocated worker and interested in starting your own small business. The program allows states to pay a self-employed allowance, instead of regular unemployment insurance benefits to any unemployed worker to create their own job by starting their own small business. Participants receive weekly allowances while they are getting their businesses off the ground. If you are interested in this program you must meet the requirements to receive regular unemployment benefits under state law. You may be eligible even if you are engaged in full-time self-employment activities - including entrepreneurial training, business counseling, and technical assistance. Currently, only about 9 states have established the Self-Employment Assistance Program. Check with your state Unemployment Insurance

Office to see if your state has implemented this entrepreneurial program.

Maryland

Garrett County Community Action MicroWorks

104 E. Center Street   301-334-9431
Oakland, MD 21550   Fax: 301-334-8555
www.garrettcac.org

Garrett County Community Action Corporation is a not for profit corporation committed to improving the quality of life for persons with needs by helping them become more self sufficient. They provide training and technical assistance to small business owners in Garrett County, Maryland that have microloans with the Action Corporation and those not seeking loans. Their program includes: training, seminars, product design, tax issues, marketing, financial counseling, a lending library and many other services.

Maryland Capital Enterprises, Inc.

P.O. Box 1844   410-546-1900
Salisbury, MD 21802   866-MARY-CAP
www.marylandcapital.org   Fax: 410-546-9718

Maryland Capital Enterprises work to build economically distressed communities by supporting micro businesses. They offer many small community based businesses the resources they need to grow. The Enterprise also offers business skills workshops, business networks, and business support groups.

Entrepreneurial Training and Merchant Development Initiative

Microenterprise Development Center, Inc.
2401 Liberty Heights Ave., Suite 310   410-669-5782
Baltimore, MD 21215   Fax: 410-669-8348
http://microdc.homestead.com

Microenterprise Development Center, Inc. is a not for profit corporation dedicated to promoting self-sufficiency of distressed communities through entrepreneurial training activities. The Center offers an Entrepreneurial Training class with over 64 hours of classroom instruction. The students will visit successful businesses, receive technical assistance and prepare a business plan. They also offer a 12-week Merchant Development Initiative for retail clients to educate themselves in customer service, marketing, sales and other retail issues.

Technical Training

Women Entrepreneurs of Baltimore, Inc.
1118 Light St., Suite 202   410-727-4921
Baltimore, MD 21230   Fax: 410-727-4989
www.webinc.org

Women Entrepreneurs of Baltimore, Inc (WEB) is a nonprofit organization that provides entrepreneurial training, technical assistance and follow-up services for microbusiness start-ups in the Baltimore metro area. WEB screens potential entrepreneurs with a viable business idea to participate in their Business Skills Training Course, a 12-week class. Graduates of the training class are eligible to receive free technical assistance, resources and support for the 12 months following graduation. WEB has a large variety of programs to offer including but not limited to: internet training, mentoring, networking, financial strategies, and business consultation.

Garrett Information Enterprise Center

685 Mosser Road
P.O. Box 151   301-387-3167
McHenry, MD 21541   Fax: 301-387-0307
www.giecworks.com

The Garrett Information Enterprise Center and the GIEC Works Resource Center provide supportive services to small information technology businesses. These services include access to Internet based training, CD-ROMs, video and audiotapes, seminars and traditional classroom training. The Center also has a networking and technical resources database.

Women Entrepreneurs of Baltimore, Inc. (WEB)

1118 Light Street, Suite 202   410-727-4921
Baltimore, MD 21230   Fax: 410-727-4989
http://www.webinc.org

Participants must attend twelve weeks of training, write a business plan, and plan to start a business before or within nine months after completing training. The main services and business skills training, financing strategies, resource sharing, Internet training, mentoring, community networking, Government certification and procurement, information and referral, and business consultation.

Women's Business Institute, Inc.

10 S. Howard Street, 6th Floor
Baltimore, MD 21201   410-266-8746

The WBI serves both start-up and established businesses. Services include one-one-one counseling, Internet training, 'First Step' for welfare-to-work clients, 'Premier FastTrac' parts I and II, 'Contracting Dollar$ and Sense' and 'Entrepreneurship 101' as well as loan packaging and mentoring. Each participant will receive a mentoring manual and booklet.

Youth Entrepreneur Academy

Baltimore City Office of Employment Development
417 E. Fayette St., Suite 468   410-396-1910
Baltimore, MD 21202   Fax: 410-752-6625

The Youth Entrepreneur Academy is a Saturday program for Baltimore city youth age 12 to 21. Career awareness presentations are made from October through December by successful adult role models to interest youths in entrepreneurship. Students who are interested are invited to attend the Youth Entrepreneur Academy. The Academy consists of a series of business skills and self-enhancement seminars that give participants the practical skills and basic knowledge to start up and manage a small business. Faculty is comprised of both business leaders and educators. The Academy is made up of ten sessions held weekly from January to March. During this time, student teams create business plans which are entered into a competition. The top 5 rated teams receive priority enrollment into the Launching Entrepreneurs into Action Program. The students in this program receive the financial and advisory support to implement their plans during June and July. In addition, they will earn wages through the city's summer jobs program.

Self Employment Assistance

Department of Labor, Licensing and Regulation
Division of Workforce Development
1100 North Eutaw Street   410-949-0022
Baltimore, MD 21201   800-827-4839
www.dllr.state.md.us/employment/

The Self-Employment Assistance Program is a great program if you are a dislocated worker and interested in starting your own small business. The program allows states to pay a self-employed allowance, instead of regular unemployment insurance benefits to any unemployed worker to create their own job by starting their own small business. Participants receive weekly allowances while they are getting their businesses off the ground. If you are interested in this program you must meet the requirements to receive regular unemployment benefits under state law. You may be eligible even if you are engaged in full-time self-employment activities - including entrepreneurial training, business counseling, and technical assistance. Currently, only about 9 states have established the Self-Employment Assistance Program. Check with your state Unemployment Insurance Office to see if your state has implemented this entrepreneurial program.

Massachusetts

Day Care Training

Acre Family Day Care Corporation
14 Kirk Street   978-937-5899
Lowell, MA 01852   Fax: 978-937-5148
www.acrefamily.org

The Acre Family Day Care not for profit organization that helps low-income women in Greater Lowell become financially independent by providing child care training and assistance in setting up licensed child care businesses in their own homes. Family Day Care Businesses in Lowell can benefit from continued support of day care training and business support.

Business Training

Center for Women and Enterprise
1135 Tremont St., Suite 480   617-536-0700 ext. 248
Boston, MA 02120   Fax: 617-536-7373
www.cweboston.org

The Center for Women and Enterprise (CWE) is a nonprofit organization dedicated to the mission of empowering women in the Boston and Worcester areas, to become economically self-sufficient through entrepreneurship. Training programs are offered in Business Planning, Business Basics: Starting a Retail Business Community Entrepreneur Programs and many more. All fees are on a sliding scale.

Business and Technical Training, Incubator

Commonwealth Corporation   617-727-8158
529 Main Street, Suite 110   800-439-0183
Boston, MA 02129   Fax: 617-242-7660
www.commcorp.org

The Commonwealth Corporation administers a variety of training for the entrepreneurs of Massachusetts. For the beginning small business owner, they offer a 10-week Entrepreneurial Training Program and a 20-week Starting Your Own Business class. In addition, they offer classes in marketing, business plan writing, preparing financial documents and even a business incubator.

Berkshire Enterprises

One Fenn St., Suite 301   413-448-2755
Pittsfield, MA 01201   Fax: 413-448-2749
www.berkshireenterprises.com

Berkshire Enterprises offer a variety of classes to help people wishing to start or expand their business. They have a Daytime Dislocated Worker Program designed to teach the skills necessary to run a successful business. Marketing, financing, business planning and more are covered in the course. Berkshire Enterprises offers a fee based evening program as well.

Lowell Business Assistance Center

169 Merrimack St.
Lowell, MA 01852   978-441-1889
www.comteam.org

For businesses located in Lowell, the Lowell Business Assistance Center is a wonderful resource. They offer workshops, seminars, and more to help with starting or expanding a business. They also provide support and other resources to help your business succeed.

This Neighborhood Means Business!

Dorchester Center for Adult Education
269 East Cottage St.
Dorchester, MA 02125   617-474-1170
www.fdnh.org/Programs/adults.htm

This Neighborhood Means Business! is a program designed to help improve the community by offering assistance to businesses to help them succeed. Workshops are offered that cover topics necessary to operating a business. such as marketing, bookkeeping, and more. Additional workshops cover important computer programs with a business focus.

M.A.D.E. for Business

Commonwealth Corp.
529 Main St., Suite 110
Boston, MA 02129   617-727-8158
www.weiu.org

M.A.D.E. for Business (Manufacturers, Artisans, Designers, Entrepreneurs) is a micro enterprise program begun by the Women's Union. The focus was on helping women artisans start their own business. participants in the program can attend workshops on business planning, financing, selling, and more. Services also include lectures, referrals, and business counseling.

Women's Business Opportunity Program

The Elizabeth Stone House
P.O. Box 59
Jamaica Plain, MA 02130   617-522-3659
www.elizabethstonehouse.org

The Elizabeth Stone House is a program run for women and provides services necessary for women to take control of their lives. Transitional housing, mental health services and more are provided. In addition, they run a Community Education for Economic Development Program to help improve the communities in the area. Women can take classes in personal finances, and participate in the Women's Business Opportunity program where they learn how to create and run a business.

State Office of Minority and Women Business Assistance (SOMWBA)

10 Park Plaza, Suite 3740   617-973-8692
Boston, MA 02116   Fax: 617-973-8367
http://www.state.ma.us/mobd

The SOMWBA offers technical assistance as well as certifying companies as minority or women-owned or controlled and publishing a directory of verified firms. It provides management seminars and workshops for minority and women business owners on many important topics.

Entrepreneurial Institute

Springfield Technical Community College
One Armory Square
Springfield, MA 01105   413-755-6107
www.eship.org

The Entrepreneurial Institute provides a "one stop" approach to educating entrepreneurs who need start-up or growth information and knowledge. Courses are offered on a credit and non-credit basis by a team of professionals on all topics relevant to ongoing small businesses and new business start ups. The Entrepreneurial Institute also offers interdisciplinary programs involving cooperative, experiential learning, and internships which enable prospective entrepreneurs to learn first hand the joys and hardships of starting and growing their own business.

Entrepreneur For a Day Program

The Entrepreneurial Institute
Springfield Technical Community College
One Armory Square, Suite 1 413-755-6143
P.O. Box 9000 Springfield, MA 01102-9000
Fax: 413-755-6141
http://www.ei.stcc.edu

The Entrepreneur For a Day Program, organized by the Springfield Technical Community College, is designed to teach students from kindergarten to eighth grade the principles of starting a business. Presentations in a classroom setting explain the basic concepts of economics and entrepreneurship. Students then have the opportunity to come to SCC and practise what they've learned, which includes borrowing from a bank, paying loans, rent, and utilities, and other business-related expenses. Only students within the Springfield public elementary schools are eligible for this program.

Self Employment Assistance

Division of Unemployment Assistance
Charles F. Hurley
19 Staniford Street
Boston, MA 02114 617-626-6560
www.detma.org

The Self-Employment Assistance Program is a great program if you are a dislocated worker and interested in starting your own small business. The program allows states to pay a self-employed allowance, instead of regular unemployment insurance benefits to any unemployed worker to create their own job by starting their own small business. Participants receive weekly allowances while they are getting their businesses off the ground. If you are interested in this program you must meet the requirements to receive regular unemployment benefits under state law. You may be eligible even if you are engaged in full-time self-employment activities - including entrepreneurial training, business counseling, and technical assistance. Currently, only about 9 states have established the Self-Employment Assistance Program. Check with your state Unemployment Insurance Office to see if your state has implemented this entrepreneurial program.

Michigan

Technical Assistance

Cornerstone Alliance
P.O. Box 428
38 W. Wall Street 269-925-6100
Benton Harbor, MI 49023 Fax: 269-925-4471
www.cstonealliance.org

Cornerstone Alliance is committed to economic growth and civic development in the cities of Benton Harbor and St. Joseph, the charter townships of Benton, St. Joseph, Lincoln and Royalton. The technical assistance program provides business and financial technical assistance to low-income entrepreneurs. Programs include: entrepreneurial support, pre-loan and loan packaging classes.

Small Business and Entrepreneurial Training

Grand Rapids Opportunities for Women
25 Sheldon Blvd., SE, Suite 210 616-458-3404
Grand Rapids, MI 49503 Fax: 616-458-6557
www.growbusiness.org

(GROW) is a not for profit economic development organization which provides women, many who face economic barriers, with the skills to be achieve economic independence. GROW focuses on small businesses with training and counseling plus several support services to start or expand a business. The "Minding Your Own Business" class is offered on a sliding fee scaled based on income and up to two hours of counseling if free. Seminars vary in cost but no one is turned away solely on their ability to pay.

Women's Initiative for Self-Employment (WISE)

2002 Hogback Road, Suite 12 734-677-1400
Ann Arbor, MI 48105 Fax: 734-677-1465

WISE provides low-income women with the resources and tools needed to start up and expand businesses. The WISE program includes business training, personal development workshops, credit counseling, start-up and expansion financing, peer group support, mentoring, and business counseling. The program's mission is to fight poverty, raise self-esteem, increase incomes, develop skills, stabilize families, and renew communities.

The Enterprise Group of Jackson

Business and Technology Development Center
33 West Michigan Avenue
Jackson, MI 49201 517-788-4680
www.entreprisegroup.org

The Enterprise group of Jackson offers a full range of business development services for entrepreneurs, start-up companies and existing businesses.

Detroit Entrepreneurship Institute, Inc. (DEI)

455 W. Fort Street, 4th Floor 313-961-8426
Detroit, MI 48226 Fax: 313-961-8831

DEI serves businesses that are owned by welfare recipients, dislocated workers and other low- to moderate-income women who are seeking to be self-sufficient through business ownership. Two of the DEI's classes, both eleven weeks long, are "Self-Employment Initiative," which is open to welfare recipients, and "Enterprise Development Initiative," which is open to low- to moderate-income general public, dislocated workers, and disabled women. A partnership between the Corporation for Enterprise Development and the state of Michigan secured a two-year waiver to protect the welfare benefits of DEI participants by allowing them to earn business income and accumulate assets while still receiving their grants and medical benefits during the start-up phase of their businesses.

Alliance for Women Entrepreneurs (AWE)

P.O. Box 1201
Grand Rapids, MI 49501-1201 616-975-0134

AWE is an important resource for West Michigan women business owners and provides educational meetings for women at all levels of entrepreneurship, from start-up businesses to mature ones. Members of AWE receive a solid support base for networking with other business owners and AWE works to provide current information of legislation, political issues, and trends at both the state and national levels that impact small businesses. AWE has the support of the state and community officials and leaders.

Self Employment Assistance

Unemployment Insurance Agency
P.O. Box 169
Grand Rapids, MI 49501-0169 800-638-3995
www.michigan.gov/uia

The Self-Employment Assistance Program is a great program if you are a dislocated worker and interested in starting your own small business. The program allows states to pay a self-employed allowance, instead of regular unemployment insurance benefits to any unemployed worker to create their own job by starting their own small business. Participants receive weekly allowances while they are getting their businesses off the ground. If you are interested in this program you must meet the requirements to receive regular unemployment benefits under state law. You may be eligible even if you are engaged in full-time self-employment activities - including entrepreneurial training, business counseling, and technical assistance. Currently, only about 9 states have established the Self-Employment Assistance Program. Check with your state Unemployment Insurance Office to see if your state has implemented this entrepreneurial program.

MInnesota

Neighborhood Development Center, Inc

651 ½ University Avenue	651-291-2480
St. Paul, MN 55104	Fax: 651-291-2597

www.windndc.org

The Neighborhood Development Center, Inc (NDC) is a community-based nonprofit organization that works with entrepreneurs in the inner city of Minneapolis and St. Paul develop successful businesses and stronger neighborhoods. NDC provides training programs to applicants living in some of the lowest income neighborhoods in the Twin Cities. Neighborhood Entrepreneur Training, Ethnic Entrepreneur Training, and RECIPE for Business Success are the three training programs currently available. After initial training, technical assistance is available for business owners in marketing, management, legal issues, and accounting.

Self Employment Program

Tri-County Community Action Program, Inc.
501 LeMieur St.

P.O. Box 368	320-632-3691
Little Falls, MN 56345	Fax: 320-632-3695

www.tccaction.com

The Tri-County Community Action Program is a not for profit corporation committed to creating opportunities for self-sufficiency for citizens in Crow Wing, Morrison and Todd Counties. The Self-Employment Program provides training to citizens to help them start their own business. Eligibility is based on income.

WomenVenture

2324 University Avenue West	651-646-3808
Saint Paul, MN 55114	Fax: 651-641-7223

WomenVenture helps participants identify career directions, make career changes, enter or reenter the workforce, or find that perfect job as well as assist with the start-up and expansion of businesses. Orientation is free and career development services are on a sliding fee scale and include individual counseling, Strong Interest Inventory, and Myers-Briggs Type Indicator. Career and Life Planning for Women, How to Ace an Interview, and Career and Employment Transition Group for Women are some of the classes offered. WomenVenture offers training in resume development, personal empowerment, sexual harassment prevention, interviewing techniques, job search strategies, job placement, job retention support, and library and computer access.

Minnesota Women's Business Center

A division of The People Connection

Bonnie Stewart, Director	
226 East 1st Street	218-435-2134
Fosston, MN 56542	Fax: 218-435-1347

The MWBC provides technical assistance to new and existing businesses. The services provided include one-on-one counseling, classroom training, an annual regional women's business conference, and several networking organizations.

Self Employment Assistance

Department of Employment and Economic Development
Unemployment Insurance Program
390 Robert Street N, 2nd Floor

Saint Paul, MN 55101-1812	877-898-9090

www.uimn.org/ui/index.htm

The Self-Employment Assistance Program is a great program if you are a dislocated worker and interested in starting your own small business. The program allows states to pay a self-employed allowance, instead of regular unemployment insurance benefits to any unemployed worker to create their own job by starting their own small business. Participants receive weekly allowances while they are getting their businesses off the ground. If you are interested in this program you must meet the requirements to receive regular unemployment benefits under state law. You may be eligible even if you are engaged in full-time self-employment activities - including entrepreneurial training, business counseling, and technical assistance. Currently, only about 9 states have established the Self-Employment Assistance Program. Check with your state Unemployment Insurance Office to see if your state has implemented this entrepreneurial program.

Mississippi

Technical Assistance

Minority Business Enterprise Division
Mississippi Development Authority
501 North West Street

P. O. Box 849	601-359-3448
Jackson, MS 39205	Fax: 601-359-5290

minority@mississippi.org

The Minority Business Enterprise Division provides business and educational assistance to minority and women-owned businesses to promote entrepreneurship in Mississippi. Assistance includes: business start-up and expansion training, counseling, referrals and outreach. The Minority Business Enterprise Division also has several publications that may be of assistance to businesses.

Technical Assistance

Quitman County Development Organization, Inc.
201 Humphrey Street

P.O. Box 386	662-326-4000
Marks, MS 38646	Fax: 662-326-3904

www.qcdo.org

The Quitman County Development Organization (QCDO) provides technical assistance through the Micro-Enterprise Loan Program to promote and grow successful businesses before and after loans are made. They offer business development workshops, seminars for women and cooperative groups.

Virtual Entrepreneurial Education and Training Project

Mississippi State University Extension Service
P.O. Box 9642

Mississippi State, MS 39762	662-325-2160

E-mail: bethd@ext.msstate.edu
www.muscares.com

The focus of this program is to teach adult and youth entrepreneurs business and E-commerce skills. Adult training includes an Entrepreneurship 101 course which consists of 4 workshops: Basic Business Start-up; Marketing Products and Services; Small Business Record keeping and Taxes; and Writing a Business Plan. A one day "Electronic Retailing: Selling on the Internet" conference was developed for new and existing businesses that want to utilize a retail web site. An in depth E-Commerce training course, E-BIZ, consists of 4 hands on classes including: Small Business E-Commerce overview and site analysis; Web Store Development I and II; and web site Marketing. The Entrepreneurship Corps (E-corps) is a youth group that meets twice a month on a regular basis. They learn technology and entrepreneurial skills that enable them to publish a newsletter, design and create web sites, attend web page development and product development training, and present youth entrepreneurship training workshops for other groups.

Mississippi Action for Community Education (MACE)

119 South Theobald Street 662-335-3506
Greenville, MS 38701 Fax: 662-334-2939
http://www.deltamace.org

MACE oversees the Mid-Delta Women's Entrepreneurial Training and Technical Assistance Program (WE-TAP) and creates non-traditional means of economic support for low-income women. Participants may benefit from programs such as Project New, a business incubator project, or Jump Start, the women's entrepreneurial program. MACE's goal is to create self-sufficiency and build wealth particularly for low-income women living in the Mississippi Delta.

Self Employment Assistance

Employment Security Commission
1520 West Capitol Street
P.O. Box 1699
Jackson, MS 39215-1699 601-354-8711
www.mesc.state.ms.us

The Self-Employment Assistance Program is a great program if you are a dislocated worker and interested in starting your own small business. The program allows states to pay a self-employed allowance, instead of regular unemployment insurance benefits to any unemployed worker to create their own job by starting their own small business. Participants receive weekly allowances while they are getting their businesses off the ground. If you are interested in this program you must meet the requirements to receive regular unemployment benefits under state law. You may be eligible even if you are engaged in full-time self-employment activities - including entrepreneurial training, business counseling, and technical assistance. Currently, only about 9 states have established the Self-Employment Assistance Program. Check with your state Unemployment Insurance Office to see if your state has implemented this entrepreneurial program.

Missouri

Technical Assistance

Economic Opportunity Corporation Community Action Agency
817 Monterey St.
P.O. Box 3068
St. Joseph, MO 64503 816-223-8281
www.eoccaa.org Fax: 816-233-8262

The EOC Community Action Agency serves the needs of low-income families in Andrew, Buchanan, Clinton and DeKalb Counties in Northwest Missouri. They have created a micro-enterprise program that includes the First Step FastTrac training program with follow-up technical assistance for two years. Participants must meet income guidelines, live in the ABCD area and be ready to start or expand a business. Tuition waivers and scholarships are available to persons of low-to-moderate income.

General Business and Child Care Training

First Step Fund
4747 Troost Avenue 816-235-6116
Kansas City, MO 64110 Fax: 816-35-6177
www.firststepfund.org

The First Step Fund is a nonprofit agency providing business training and support to low-to-moderate-income entrepreneurs in the metro Kansas City area. The agency uses the First Step FastTrac curriculum to offer general business and childcare training classes. The business training class is a 36-hour course covering marketing, budgeting, finances and other concepts for $20. The Family Child Care Entrepreneur course trains individuals on childhood development and business skills. This 54-hour course costs $25.

Community Development Corporation of Kansas City

2420 E. Linwood Blvd., Suite 400 816-924-5800
Kansas City, MO 64109 Fax: 816-921-3350
www.cdcofkc.org

The Community Development Corp. Small Business Technical Assistance Program provides help to those wishing to start or expand a business in the Kansas City area. The program offers assistance in business planning, financing, bookkeeping, marketing, and more. All of this is free of charge.

Grace Hill Neighborhood Services

2600 Hadley 314-539-9506
St. Louis, MO 63106 Fax: 314-214-8938

Grace Hill Neighborhood Services serves areas that consist entirely of impoverished neighborhoods that have residents that are at or below poverty level, high crime or high school dropout rates, drug and gang presence, and deteriorating properties. The GHNS's main concern is outreach and marketing to make women aware of their services. GHNS runs a business incubator and provides a listing of local suppliers who offer discounts to women business owners as well as providing long-term training for start-up and existing businesses, subcontracted through a Small Business Development Center. GHNS also maintains a listing of women's businesses, so that they can patronize one another's companies. GHNS also holds a monthly online chat group of disadvantaged clients from around the country because of their special focus on welfare-to-work participants and low-income women.

National Association of Women Business Owners (NAWBO)-St. Louis Branch

7165 Delmar, Suite 204 314-863-0046
St. Louis, MO 63130 Fax: 314-863-2079

NAWBO offers one-on-one counseling, mentoring, monthly educational and networking meetings, an educational program, and referrals to women-owned businesses. The program, "SUCCESSavvy," consists of a series of classes designed to help women start and expand a successful business. "Do I Really Want To Be In Business?" "Writing a Business Plan," "Basic Accounting for Your Business," "Writing a Marketing Plan," and "When and How to Use

Professionals" are some of the course topics. Also included in the program is a "Smart Business" conference, with seminars to educate women in the various stages of business ownership.

Self Employment Assistance

Division of Employment Security
421 East Dunklin Street
P.O. Box 59
Jefferson City, MO 65102-0059   573-751-3215
www.dolir.state.mo.us/es/

The Self-Employment Assistance Program is a great program if you are a dislocated worker and interested in starting your own small business. The program allows states to pay a self-employed allowance, instead of regular unemployment insurance benefits to any unemployed worker to create their own job by starting their own small business. Participants receive weekly allowances while they are getting their businesses off the ground. If you are interested in this program you must meet the requirements to receive regular unemployment benefits under state law. You may be eligible even if you are engaged in full-time self-employment activities - including entrepreneurial training, business counseling, and technical assistance. Currently, only about 9 states have established the Self-Employment Assistance Program. Check with your state Unemployment Insurance Office to see if your state has implemented this entrepreneurial program.

Montana

Microbusiness Technical Assistance

Montana Department of Commerce
301 S Park Ave
Helena, MT 59601
Mailing address:
P.O. Box 200501   406-721-3663
Helena, MT 59620-0501   Fax: 406-841-2701
www.state.mt.us

The Montana MicroBusiness Technical Assistance Program focuses on providing technical assistance to low and moderate-income individuals to assist them in obtaining financing of up to $35,000 to start or expand a small business. The focus of the Montana program is to provide business management training through a combination of traditional classroom and Internet training. The NxLevel Online Training Program is offered at various locations throughout the state to offer in-depth training for entrepreneurs.

Career Training Institute

347 North Last Chance Gulch   406-443-0800
Helena, MT 59601   Fax: 406-442-2745

The Career Training Institute targets 12 counties, extending from the Helena area north to the Canadian border and encompassing a total area of 30,403 square miles. The CTI offers training classes in four strategically located areas: Lewistown, Great Falls, Browning, and Helena.

Montana Community Development Corporation

127 North Higgins   406-543-3550
Missoula, MT 59802   Fax: 406-721-4584

The Montana Community Development Corporation provides counseling to clients in western Montana. Its professional staff has worked with hundreds of large and small businesses.

Human Resource Development Council of Bozeman (HRDC)

32 South Tracy   406-587-4486
Bozeman, MT 59715   Fax: 406-585-3538
http://www.thehrdc.org

The HRDC offers Microbusiness training and technical assistance to low-income entrepreneurs. A community action agency for Gallatin County has developed as partnership to improve an existing Microbusiness incubator program.

Self Employment Assistance

Unemployment Insurance Division
Department of Labor and Industry
P.O. Box 8020
Helena, MT 59604-8020   406-444-3783
http://uid.dli.state.mt.us/

The Self-Employment Assistance Program is a great program if you are a dislocated worker and interested in starting your own small business. The program allows states to pay a self-employed allowance, instead of regular unemployment insurance benefits to any unemployed worker to create their own job by starting their own small business. Participants receive weekly allowances while they are getting their businesses off the ground. If you are interested in this program you must meet the requirements to receive regular unemployment benefits under state law. You may be eligible even if you are engaged in full-time self-employment activities - including entrepreneurial training, business counseling, and technical assistance. Currently, only about 9 states have established the Self-Employment Assistance Program. Check with your state Unemployment Insurance Office to see if your state has implemented this entrepreneurial program.

Nebraska

Microbusiness Training

Lincoln Action Program
210 "O" Street   402-471-4515
Lincoln, NE 68508   Fax: 402-471-4844
www.lincoln-action.org

The Microenterprise Program is an economic development program designed to help low-to-moderate incomes entrepreneurs establish their own small businesses. The program provides self-assessment, business training and technical support. They also have a Computer Microenterprise Development (CDM) to help very low-income people start a business from their home by providing services using computers. After training, the graduates work from home on their very own home-based computer business.

Microbusiness Technical Assistance

Nebraska Department of Economic Development
Nebraska Micro Business Resource Directory
P.O. Box 6605
Lincoln, NE 68506-0605   402-420-9589
http://neon.neded.org/mbrd/index.html

The Nebraska Micro Business Resource Directory provides a wide variety of technical assistance options available to microbusinesses in Nebraska.

Technical Training

Nebraska EDGE Program
University of Nebraska   402-472-4138
58 Filey Hall   800-328-2851
Lincoln, NE 68583-0947   Fax: 402-472-0688

The Nebraska EDGE (Enhancing, Developing and Growing Entrepreneurs) is an organization for rural entrepreneurial training programs hosted by local communities and organizations. They offer a variety of classes and training programs, including some online.

Technical Assistance

Community Development Resources
1135 M Street
3rd Floor, Suite 116   402-436-2386
Lincoln, NE 68508-3169   Fax: 402-436-2360
http://www.self-lincoln.org/about.html
SELF offers one-on-one technical assistance in many areas of business including: financing, planning, marketing and advertising. The services are free.

Nebraska Business Development Center

Entrepreneur Shop
10868 West Dodge Road   402-595-1158
Omaha, NE 68154   Fax: 402-595-1194
www.nbdc.unomaha.edu/about/eshop.cfm
The Entrepreneur Shop is a consulting/training center and retail outlet for small business owners. Business support services include businesses consulting and mentoring, management and computer training, office resource, administrative support and networking opportunities. Seminar and workshop topics include business start-up, finance, marketing and sales, and child care business management.

Nebraska Center for Entrepreneurship

CBA 209
University of Nebraska-Lincoln
PO Box 880487   402-472-3353
Lincoln, NE 68588-0487   Fax: 402-475-5885
http://www.cba.unl.edu/outreach/ent/
The mission of the NCE is to enable and inspire entrepreneurs by exceeding their needs through both traditional and non-traditional learning strategies. The Center hosts a Global Conference on Creative Entrepreneurship (GCCE) that brings together talented entrepreneurial students from all over the world to study entrepreneurship, to promote international understanding and cultural awareness, and to create an international business network of entrepreneurs. The International Business Plan Competition encourages new ventures by college students who present their business plans to prominent business leaders and venture capitalists who serve as judges. Opportunities for college students to be matched with successful entrepreneurs with interests similar to theirs are provided by the internship program. Internships also allow students to earn college credit while they are working for a successful company in a practical entrepreneurial environment.

Self Employment Assistance

Workforce Development
550 S. 16th Street
P.O. Box 94600
Station House Station
Lincoln, NE 68509   402-471-9835
www.dol.state.ne.us
The Self-Employment Assistance Program is a great program if you are a dislocated worker and interested in starting your own small business. The program allows states to pay a self-employed allowance, instead of regular unemployment insurance benefits to any unemployed worker to create their own job by starting their own small business. Participants receive weekly allowances while they are getting their businesses off the ground. If you are interested in this program you must meet the requirements to receive regular unemployment benefits under state law. You may be eligible even if you are engaged in full-time self-employment activities - including entrepreneurial training, business counseling, and technical assistance. Currently, only about 9 states have established the Self-Employment Assistance Program. Check with your state Unemployment Insurance Office to see if your state has implemented this entrepreneurial program.

Nevada

Southern Nevada Certified Development Company

The Nevada Women's Business Resource and Assistance Center
2770 S. Maryland Parkway, Suite 212   702-732-3998
Las Vegas, NV 89109   Fax: 702-732-2705
NWBRAC targets low- to moderate-income women. In its six-week pre-startup course, participants can assess their skill levels and the feasibility of their ideas, determine startup costs, pricing, and break-even points, and address licensing and other startup issues. A following eight-week course helps participants develop a solid business plan. An additional course helps existing businesses address the challenges of growth. Also, an alumni program develops leaders and mentors from graduates as well as providing ongoing educational opportunities.

Northern Nevada:
Nevada Microenterprise Initiative
113 W. Plumb Lane   775-324-1812
Reno, NV 89509   Fax: 775-324-1813

Rural Nevada:
Nevada Microenterprise Initiative
116 E. 7th St., Suite 1   775-841-1420, ext. 2
Carson City, NV 89701   Fax: 775-841-2221

Southern Nevada:
Nevada Microenterprise Initiative
1600 E. Desert Inn Road, Suite 210   702-734-3555
Las Vegas, NV 89109   Fax: 702-734-3530
www.4microbiz.org/default.asp
The Nevada Microenterprise Initiative (NMI) is a private, nonprofit, community development, financial institution dedicated to helping entrepreneurs to start or expand a business. NMI staff and volunteers provide business technical assistance by means of one-to-one counseling to develop a loan request, trouble shoot your business, perfect your business plan, or to identify local resources for your business. Specialized business courses are offered that address child care businesses, cosmetics marketing training, and a business plan writing class taught in Spanish. A 3-part Core Business Course teaches the basics of business ownership. Part one, Feasibility Study, covers entrepreneurship, creating a 30 second commercial, time management, costs associated with starting and operating a business, and conducting a market study. Part two, Business Foundation, addresses small business taxes and recordkeeping, legal issues, business operation, and basic marketing. Part three, Business Plan, focuses on developing a business plan, creating financial projections, getting financing, and discussions with local experts on marketing, financing, and financial projections. The Business Tune-up course is designed for business owners with two years experience and a written business plan. The class addresses the growing pains of small business, creating a more efficient management plan, and fine-tuning your business plan.

Self Employment Assistance

Department of Employment Training & Rehabilitation
500 East Third Street
Carson City, NV 89713   775-684-3849
http://detr.state.nv.us/

The Self-Employment Assistance Program is a great program if you are a dislocated worker and interested in starting your own small business. The program allows states to pay a self-employed allowance, instead of regular unemployment insurance benefits to any unemployed worker to create their own job by starting their own small business. Participants receive weekly allowances while they are getting their businesses off the ground. If you are interested in this program you must meet the requirements to receive regular unemployment benefits under state law. You may be eligible even if you are engaged in full-time self-employment activities - including entrepreneurial training, business counseling, and technical assistance. Currently, only about 9 states have established the Self-Employment Assistance Program. Check with your state Unemployment Insurance Office to see if your state has implemented this entrepreneurial program.

New Hampshire

Women's Business Center, Inc.

150 Greenleaf Avenue, Unit 8   603-430-2892
Portsmouth, NH 03801-5341   Fax: 603-430-3706
http://www.womenbiz.org/

The Women's Business Center, a nonprofit organization, promotes the ownership of businesses by women as a means to maximize personal potential and achieve economic independence. Services include monthly roundtable meetings in Portsmouth, Concord, and Manchester, twice monthly e-mail updates on WBC programs, roundtables, courses, and special events, quarterly WBC connections round the state of New Hampshire and many courses, seminars, and other programs.

Dartmouth Entrepreneurial Network

14 South Main Street, Suite 2F
Hanover, NH 03755   603-646-0290
www.den.dartmouth.edu

The Dartmouth Entrepreneurial Network serves people in the Dartmouth community helping them learn and implement entrepreneurship. DEN works with a variety of business teams at every stage of development assisting in areas such as team building, business plans, idea generation, market research, funding, articles of incorporation, space and office infrastructure, sales and marketing plan implementation, and management and organizational behavior.

Self Employment Assistance

Employment Security Division
32 South Main Street   603-224-3311
Concord, NH 03301   800-852-3400
www.nhes.state.nh.us/

The Self-Employment Assistance Program is a great program if you are a dislocated worker and interested in starting your own small business. The program allows states to pay a self-employed allowance, instead of regular unemployment insurance benefits to any unemployed worker to create their own job by starting their own small business. Participants receive weekly allowances while they are getting their businesses off the ground. If you are interested in this program you must meet the requirements to receive regular unemployment benefits under state law. You may be eligible even if you are engaged in full-time self-employment

activities - including entrepreneurial training, business counseling, and technical assistance. Currently, only about 9 states have established the Self-Employment Assistance Program. Check with your state Unemployment Insurance Office to see if your state has implemented this entrepreneurial program.

New Jersey

New Jersey Economic Development Authority

P.O. Box 990
Trenton, NJ 08625-0990   609-292-0187
http://www.njeda.com/finance_mstr.htm

The New Jersey Economic Development Authority offers an eight-week program for small businesses, minority-owned and women-owned businesses. The program helps entrepreneurs learn the basics of operating a business. Sessions are held bi-annually throughout the state.

Business Training for Young People

Prudential Young Entrepreneur Program
NJIT-Enterprise Development Center
105 Lock Street
Newark, NJ 07103   973-643-4063
www.njit-edc.org/PYEP.htm

Interested entrepreneurs 18-30 years old may enroll for a 9-week course that provides them with the fundamentals needed to run a small business. Examples of the topics covered include: marketing, sales, financial statements, and how to write a business plan. Students are encouraged to write a business plan, and set it into motion.

Tri-County Community Action Agency

River's Edge Community Campus
110 Cohansey Street   856-451-6330
Bridgetown, NJ 08302   Fax: 856-455-7288
http://www.tricountycaa.org/

Tri-County Community Loan Fund provides a six-week Entrepreneurial Training Program to small businesses in Cumberland, Gloucester and Salem counties. The class provides training in 16 areas including: marketing, credit, financing and other areas of business.

Middlesex County Economic Opportunities Commission

1215 Livingston Ave.   732-846-6600
North Brunswick, NJ 08902   Fax: 732-846-3728
www.mceoc.org

The Middlesex County Economic Opportunities Commission helps microenterprises in a variety of ways. They have a 12 hour business course for those interested in starting or expanding their businesses. They also operate a print shop offering lower prices to help new businesses

New Jersey Association of Women Business Owners (NJAWBO) EXCEL

225 Hamilton Street   732-560-9607
Bound Bank, NJ 08805-2042   Fax: 732-560-9687
http://www.njawbo.org

The center provides courses for all phases of business development: 'Start Right' for start-up businesses, 'Grow Smart' for established businesses, and 'Profit-Savvy Financial Management' to help businesses develop a solid financial foundation. The 'SUCCESS' course offers goal setting and career guidance in addition to an introduction to entrepreneurship for low-income and welfare-to-work women. Other courses offer Internet and procurement training. An interactive developmental personal assessment helps women to determine their directions as entrepreneurs or in other career areas. NJAWBO helps women enhance their self-confidence, develop public-speaking skills, and make and use business contacts.

Kean University
Admissions, Continuing Education
1000 Morris Avenue
Union, NJ 07083-7133   908-737-5840
http://www.kean.edu/
The Kean Office of Continuing Education offers vocational interest testing (Strong and Myers-Briggs), resume consultation, career counseling, and workshops on starting your own business and job enhancement. Fees range from $25-$75.

Self Employment Assistance
Division of Unemployment Insurance
Technical Support Unit
P.O. Box 058
Trenton, NJ 08625-0058   609-292-7162
www.nj.gov/labor/ui/uiindex.html
The Self-Employment Assistance Program is a great program if you are a dislocated worker and interested in starting your own small business. The program allows states to pay a self-employed allowance, instead of regular unemployment insurance benefits to any unemployed worker to create their own job by starting their own small business. Participants receive weekly allowances while they are getting their businesses off the ground. If you are interested in this program you must meet the requirements to receive regular unemployment benefits under state law. You may be eligible even if you are engaged in full-time self-employment activities - including entrepreneurial training, business counseling, and technical assistance. Currently, only about 9 states have established the Self-Employment Assistance Program. Check with your state Unemployment Insurance Office to see if your state has implemented this entrepreneurial program.

New Mexico

Free Technical Training
New Mexico Community Development Loan Fund
Mailing Address:
P.O. Box 705
Albuquerque, NM 87103
Street Address:
700 Fourth Street, SW   505-243-3196
Albuquerque, NM 87102   Fax: 505-243-8803
http://www.nmcdlf.org/
The New Mexico Community Development Loan Fund provides free personalized pre-loan and post-loan technical training.

Center for Entrepreneurship
New Mexico Council for Economic Education
1009 Bradbury Dr. SE   505-272-7677
Albuquerque, NM 87106-4302   Fax: 505-843-8223
The Center for Entrepreneurship is a nonprofit organization that provides community based on entrepreneurship education. Educational activities are designed for students, young entrepreneurs, teachers, practitioners and potential entrepreneurs.

Women's Economic Self-Sufficiency Team (WESST Corp.)
(headquarters)
414 Silver SW   505-241-4753
Albuquerque, NM 87102   Fax: 505-241-4766
http://www.wesst.org

Regional Locations:
WESST Corp.
700 4th Street SW   505-241-0794
Albuquerque, NM 87102   Fax: 505-241-0707
http://www.wesst.org
Counties served: Bernalillo, Socorro, Torrance, Valencia

WESST Corp.
410 West Broadway   505-325-0678
Farmington, NM 87401   Fax: 505-325-0695
http://www.wesst.org
Counties served: Cibola, McKinley, Rio Arriba, San Juan

WESST Corp.
410 Gusdorf Road, Suite B   505-758-3099
Taos, NM 87571   Fax: 505-751-1575
http://www.wesst.org
Counties served: Colfax, Guadalupe, Harding, Mora, Quay, San Miguel, Taos, Union

WESST Corp.
3900 Paseo del Sol, Suite 322   505-474-6556
Santa Fe, NM 87507   Fax: 505-474-6687
http://www.wesst.org
Counties served: Rio Arriba, Sandoval, Santa Fe

WESST Corp.
200 W. First Street, Suite 527   505-624-9850
Roswell, NM 88203   Fax: 505-624-9845
http://www.wesst.org
Counties served: Chaves, Curry, De Baca, Eddy, Lea, Lincoln, Roosevelt

WESST Corp.
2907 East Idaho, Suite A   505-541-1583
Las Cruces, NM 88011   Fax: 505-647-5524
Mailing Address:
PO Box 444
Las Cruces, NM 88004
http://www.wesst.org
Counties served: Catron, Doña Ana, Grant, Hidaldo, Luna, Otero, Sierra

WESST Corp. provides workshops and seminars ranging from one or two hour small group workshops to multi-part series spanning several weeks. Workshops include Evaluating Your Business Readiness, Setting Business Goals, Cost-Effective Marketing Strategies, Customer-Driven Enterprise, Business Plan Writing, Forging Alliances for Profit, and Should You Incorporate. Experienced business consultants work with participants that are interested in starting or expanding a business. Consultations take place in a series of one-on-one hour-long sessions. Those looking to start a new business will learn to assess new business ideas, do market research, price products or services, develop effective marketing strategies, build income and cash flow projections, determine financial options, and develop a business plan. Existing business owners may obtain assistance with growth planning, marketing strategies, and financing.

Self Employment Assistance
Department of Labor
Employment Security Division
401 Broadway NE
Albuquerque, NM 87102   505-841-8429
www.dol.state.nm.us/

The Self-Employment Assistance Program is a great program if you are a dislocated worker and interested in starting your own small business. The program allows states to pay a self-employed allowance, instead of regular unemployment insurance benefits to any unemployed worker to create their own job by starting their own small business. Participants receive weekly allowances while they are getting their businesses off the ground. If you are interested in this program you must meet the requirements to receive regular unemployment benefits under state law. You may be eligible even if you are engaged in full-time self-employment activities - including entrepreneurial training, business counseling, and technical assistance. Currently, only about 9 states have established the Self-Employment Assistance Program. Check with your state Unemployment Insurance Office to see if your state has implemented this entrepreneurial program.

New York

Business Training
Appleseed Trust
220 Herald Place, 2nd Floor
Syracuse, NY 13202   315-424-9485
http://www.appleseedtrust.org/
Appleseed Trust is a not for profit organization that is committed to assisting low- to moderate-income residents of Syracuse to start or expand their own business. Entrepreneurs with an idea for a product or service can pay a small monthly fee to participate in an eight-week training program. The process includes applying for an initial loan.

Technical Assistance
Capital District Community Loan Fund
255 Orange Street
Albany, NY 12210   518-436-8586
http://www.cdclf.org/1024.html
The Community Loan Fund provides technical assistance to its small businesses and micro businesses clients in the New York State Capital region.

Loan Fund Technical Assistance
Chautauqua Microenterprise Loan Fund
Chautauqua Opportunities for Development
402 Main Street   716-366-2334
Dunkirk, NY 14048   Fax 716-366-7407
http://www.codi-wny.com
The Chautauqua Microenterprise Loan Fund provides technical assistance to loan applicants and recipients of small businesses with fewer than 5 employees in Chautauqua County.

Technical Assistance
Homesteaders Federal Credit Union
2052 Adam Clayton Powell Jr. Blvd   212-222-0328
New York, NY 10027   Fax: 212-222-1035
http://www.homesteadersfcu.org/
The Homesteaders Federal Credit Union is a not-for-profit financial institution that provides affordable financing and technical assistance for people in the Harlem and New York City areas. Members may receive technical assistance for their small business.

Ongoing Training and Technical Assistance
Project Enterprise
144 West 125th St., 4th Floor   212-678-6734
New York, NY 10027   Fax: 212-678-6737
http://www.projectenterprise.org/

Project Enterprise lending practices provides business credit to New York's low-income individuals. It is a comprehensive program delivering microcredit, business training and networking opportunities to entrepreneurs in New York City's economically disadvantages communities. All clients receive ongoing, personalized business training and technical assistance.

Technical Assistance and Training
Rural Opportunities, Inc
400 East Avenue   716-340-3387
Rochester, NY 14607-1910   Fax: 716-340-3326
www.ruralinc.org
Rural Opportunities, Inc is a not-for-profit community development organization providing services to low to moderate-income people and economically depressed communities throughout New York and Ohio. The aim is to promote self-sufficiency and economic independence through the creation and expansion of microenterprises. Technical assistance is available for small business entrepreneurs.

Family Day Care Training
Women's Housing and Economic Development Corporation
50 E. 168th, Suite 702   718-839-1100
Bronx, NY 10452   Fax: 718-839-1170
www.whedco.org
The Women's Housing and Economic Development Corporation (WHEDCO) offers microenterprise support for individuals to be their own boss by opening or expanding a Family Day Care Program from their home. They offer a bilingual training program, which exceeds state requirements. Members receive continuing education, access to a resource library, loan application assistance and other programs to help them become successful business owners.

Training Services
Women's Venture Fund, Inc
240 West 35 Street, Suite 201   212-563-0499
New York, NY 10001   Fax: 212-868-9116
www.womensventurefund.org
The Women's Venture Fund provides entrepreneurs with a comprehensive offering of business classes necessary to build the essential building blocks for an aspiring business owner, as well as the established business owner. All classes are open to the public and there is a nominal fee for classes. Contact them for a current listing of classes, workshops and seminars.

Micro Technical Training Programs
Worker Ownership Resource Center
104 Scio Street   585-338-7822
Rochester, NY 14604   Fax: 585-338-1232
www.atworc.net
Worker Ownership Resource Center, Inc (WORC) is a nonprofit organization that helps refugees and economically disadvantaged people in the Southern Tier of New York State start their own microbusinesses. WORC has developed training and technical assistance programs that provide a comprehensive package of classes for the disadvantaged entrepreneur. The package includes assessment, workshops, one-on-one technical assistance, business planning and other support services.

American Woman's Economic Development Corporation
216 E. 45th Street   917-368-6100
New York, NY 10017   Fax: 212-956-7114
http://www.awed.org/

The American Woman's Economic Development Corporation is the premier nonprofit organization that is committed to helping women entrepreneurs start and grow their own businesses. The services provided include formal course instructions, one-to-one business counseling, seminars, special events, and peer group support. AWED's goal is to increase the start-up, survival, and expansion rates of small businesses.

Excellence Center for Entrepreneurship Leadership (EXCEL)

Broome Community College
907 Upper Front Street   607-778-5341
Binghamton, NY 13901   Fax: 607-778-5535
www.sunybroome.edu/~commed/excel

The goal of EXCEL is to provide resources, referrals, and education to facilitate the establishment, growth and success of small businesses in the Southern Tier. EXCEL helps both new and established businesses in being competitive and serves as a clearinghouse for resources and services offered by other agencies. The EXCEL program provides business training classes; publishes a newsletter and resource guide; maintains a resource library; offers business related curriculum in customer service, sales/sales management, business start-up, and operating a business.

Workshop in Business Opportunities

220 East 23rd, Room 309   212-648-0854 ext. 105
New York, NY 10010   Fax: 212-681-1096
www.wibo.org

The Workshop in Business Opportunities is a nonprofit operation with the mission to enable small business owners and entrepreneurs in under served communities achieve financial success in starting and operating businesses that will in turn develop economic power, create jobs, and improve their communities. WIBO's workshop, "How to Build a Growing Profitable Business", consists of 16 three hour classroom sessions. Each session deals with a different phase of running a business. Each phase of your business is covered in the 318-page WIBO workbook. The workbook is designed to help you create a complete step by step book of directions for carrying out every aspect of your business plan.

Brooklyn Economic Development Corporation

175 Remsen St. Suite 350   718-522-4600
Brooklyn, NY 11201   Fax: 718-797-9286
www.bedc.org

BEDC's Entrepreneur Training Program is a hands-on 14 week classroom program that stresses the development of a working business plan and covers topics essential to starting and operating a profitable and successful business. The program is designed for the novice entrepreneur as well as experienced business people who want to hone their skills. Program Topics include business and marketing plans; financial statements and credit review; accounting, bookkeeping and taxes; business certification; site selection and real estate, insurance and financing options.

Rochester Women's Network

1530 East Avenue   585-271-4182
Rochester, NY 14610   Fax: 585-271-7159
http://www.rwn.org

RWN's mission is to promote the growth and advancement of women in the workplace. RWN membership offers challenging, stimulating programs; many valuable benefits; and continuing support, both professionally and personally.

Entrepreneurial Assistance Program

633 Third Avenue
New York City, NY 10017-6706   800-782-8369
http://www.empire.state.ny.us

The typical EAP center provides counseling on the feasibility of starting a business, assistance in refining a business concept and developing a business plan, education in establishes management principals and practises, in-depth business counseling in product development and marketing, guidance in exporting, contract procurement and licensing, one-on-one counseling in identifying and accessing capital and credit, access to business support networks, ongoing and continue technical assistance to program graduates including linkages to other small business services.

Self Employment Assistance

New York State Department of Labor
State Office Building Campus, Room 500
Albany, NY 12240-0003   518-457-9000
www.labor.state.ny.us/

The Self-Employment Assistance Program is a great program if you are a dislocated worker and interested in starting your own small business. The program allows states to pay a self-employed allowance, instead of regular unemployment insurance benefits to any unemployed worker to create their own job by starting their own small business. Participants receive weekly allowances while they are getting their businesses off the ground. If you are interested in this program you must meet the requirements to receive regular unemployment benefits under state law. You may be eligible even if you are engaged in full-time self-employment activities - including entrepreneurial training, business counseling, and technical assistance. Currently, only about 9 states have established the Self-Employment Assistance Program. Check with your state Unemployment Insurance Office to see if your state has implemented this entrepreneurial program.

North Carolina

Construction, Child Care and General Business Assistance

Good Work, Inc.
115 Market Street, Suite 470   919-682-8473
Durham, NC 27701   Fax: 919-687-7033
www.goodwork.org

Good Works is a nonprofit organization, which provides entrepreneurs with business and technical assistance. Entrepreneurs in the Chapel Hill, Durham and Raleigh area may learn more about becoming a member of this organization by attending a free information session. Nearly all of the members are businesses owned by women, minorities, and/or low-income individuals. Good Work offers three types of classes for entrepreneurs starting or expanding a small business: Building Your Business, Building Your Child Care Business, and Managing Your Construction Trade Business.

Craft Business Assistance

HandMade in America
P.O. Box 2089   828-252-0121
Asheville, NC 28802   Fax: 828-252-0388
www.handmadeinamerica.org

HandMade in America works with organizations in Western North Carolina to provide learning opportunities about business issues for craftspeople. Topics include business planning, marketing, sales techniques, and others.

Training Programs

Mountain Microenterprise Fund
29 ½ Page Avenue   828-253-2834
Asheville, NC 28801   Fax: 828-389-3089
www.mtnmicro.org

Mountain Microenterprise Fund offers programs in everything you need to know to start a new business: marketing, cash flow, budgeting, and sales forecasting. They also offer a 21-hour course for businesses ready to expand.

Technical Training

North Carolina Rural Economic Development Center
4021 Carya Drive   919-250-4314
Raleigh, NC 27610   Fax 919-250-4325
http://www.ncruralcenter.org/grants/micro.htm

The North Carolina Microenterprise Program provides North Carolina rural residence with small business loans to help them become self-sufficient through business ownership. They provide their clients with technical assistance in conjunction with their loan program.

Entrepreneurship Education Training

REAL Enterprises
115 Market Street, Suite 320   919-688-7325
Durham, NC 27701   Fax: 919-682-7621
www.realenterprises.org

REAL Enterprises (Rural Entrepreneurship through Action Learning) makes entrepreneurial training accessible to rural communities through hands-on education. Programs for youth and adult are available.

North Carolina Center for Women Business Owners

230 Hay Street   910-323-3377
Fayetteville, NC 28301   Fax: 910-323-8828
http://www.wcof.org

The center's mission is a first-step resource and referral agency for women. It has a variety of programs of empowerment for women, high local credibility, and strong local partnerships. The center runs an enterprise that provides ongoing training on product development and marketing and support through its retail outlet for home-based women's businesses.

The Small Business Center

Central Piedmont Community College
P.O. Box 35009
Charlotte, NC 28235   704-330-4651
www.cpcctraining.org/small_business

The Small Business Center helps people who want to start a small business and those who need help with an existing business. The Center offers advice, information, one-on-one counseling, additional training, and business contracts. They will also help you develop solid business and marketing plans. Services include: small business classes; international business courses; classes and seminars on "How to Start a Business" in Spanish; counseling and assessments; a Resource Center; free library seminars; and The Business and Entrepreneurial Skills Training Program (BEST).

The Council for Entrepreneurial Development (CED)

104 T.W. Alexander Dr., Building 1   919-549-7500
Research Triangle Park, NC 27709   Fax: 919-549-7405
www.cednc.org

The Council for Entrepreneurial Development provides services and programs in 4 major areas: mentoring, communications, capital formation and education. Their business training program, Fast Trac, is designed to help current and prospective entrepreneurs grow and star their businesses successfully. The program utilizes comprehensive work books, peer learning, guest speakers, interactive instruction and one-on-one coaching. Fast Trac is offered in three formats to completely and effectively meet the needs of businesses at all levels and stages of development.

Self Employment Assistance

The Employment Security Commission of North Carolina
700 Wade Avenue
Raleigh, NC 27605   866-278-3822
www.ncesc.com/

The Self-Employment Assistance Program is a great program if you are a dislocated worker and interested in starting your own small business. The program allows states to pay a self-employed allowance, instead of regular unemployment insurance benefits to any unemployed worker to create their own job by starting their own small business. Participants receive weekly allowances while they are getting their businesses off the ground. If you are interested in this program you must meet the requirements to receive regular unemployment benefits under state law. You may be eligible even if you are engaged in full-time self-employment activities - including entrepreneurial training, business counseling, and technical assistance. Currently, only about 9 states have established the Self-Employment Assistance Program. Check with your state Unemployment Insurance Office to see if your state has implemented this entrepreneurial program.

North Dakota

Technology Transfer, Inc.

Women and Technology Program
1833 East Bismarck Expressway   701-258-2251
Bismarck, ND 58504   Fax: 701-258-7514

Women and Technology Program provides a support structure within North Dakota to provide business-development and technical assistance, financial advice, business education, and market planning, mainly through distance learning, to Native American and welfare-to-work participants. The program addresses such areas as home-based businesses, international trade, franchising, and legal issues. Available through BICs and Tribal BICs are distance learning, video conferencing, workshops and seminars. The program reaches women in rural areas and on Indian reservations as well as disabled women through modern technology.

Center for Innovation

4300 Dartmouth Drive   701-777-3132
Grand Folks, ND 58203   Fax: 701-777-2339
www.innovators.net

The Center for Innovation offers business plan development and review services, market research and analysis, market feasibility studies, market plans Export and Import services, and workshop and one on one consulting for nonprofit organizations.

Women's Business Institute

320 North Fifth Street, Suite 203
PO Box 2043   701-235-6488
Fargo, ND 58107-2043   Fax: 701-235-8284
http://www.rrtrade.org/women/wbi

The Women's Business Institute's mission is to improve the opportunities for economic and business growth for the women in North Dakota, Minnesota, and the surrounding area. Many programs and services are available to women who are interested in improving their business and career skills. Services offered by the WBI include monthly training classes, activities such as 'Women Mean Business' networking events, coaching, and counseling (including 'Business Success' mentoring teams) as well as marketing and purchasing opportunities. Also, the WBI hosts annual events such as the Business Technology Expo and a home-based business conference and trade show. Some of the regular activities include computer classes and courses in management, marketing, financing and entrepreneurial confidence.

Self Employment Assistance

Job Service North Dakota
P.O. Box 5507   800-732-9787
Bismarck, ND 58506-5507   701-328-3096
www.jonsnd.com

The Self-Employment Assistance Program is a great program if you are a dislocated worker and interested in starting your own small business. The program allows states to pay a self-employed allowance, instead of regular unemployment insurance benefits to any unemployed worker to create their own job by starting their own small business. Participants receive weekly allowances while they are getting their businesses off the ground. If you are interested in this program you must meet the requirements to receive regular unemployment benefits under state law. You may be eligible even if you are engaged in full-time self-employment activities - including entrepreneurial training, business counseling, and technical assistance. Currently, only about 9 states have established the Self-Employment Assistance Program. Check with your state Unemployment Insurance Office to see if your state has implemented this entrepreneurial program.

Ohio

ASSETS Toledo

333 14th St.   419-381-2721
Toledo, OH 43624   Fax: 419-720-0079
http://www.assetstoledo.com/

ASSETS Toledo assists individuals in Lancaster County who strive for self-employment but have limited resources. They provide hands-on training, peer mentoring and a support network.

Food Venture Assistance

ACEnet –Appalachian Center for Economic Networks
94 Columbus Road   740-592-3854
Athens, OH 45701   Fax: 740-593-5451
www.acenetworks.org

Food Ventures assists small specialty food businesses in southeastern Ohio. They provide information to businesses including a Community Kitchen incubator. The aim is to transform relationships within communities to allow people with low-incomes to successfully enter the economic mainstream.

Technical Assistance

Community Action Committee of Pike County
MicroEnterprise/Business Development Department
941 Market Street
P.O. Box 799   740-289-2371
Piketon, OH 45661   Fax: 740-289-4291
www.pikecac.org

Community Action Committee of Pike County offers technical assistance in developing business plans and marketing strategies, as well as advertisements and basic

business counseling. In addition they offer one-on-one assistance to small business owners in Pike, Ross, Jackson and Scioto Counties.

Technical Assistance

EnterpriseWorks
88 East Broad Street, Suite 1770   614-228-1043
Columbus, OH 43215   Fax: 614-621-9222
www.enterpriseworksinc.org

EnterpriseWorks is designed to identify entrepreneurship as an employment option, to improve the success rate of business start-ups and to generate new jobs. They provide Ohioans two types of classes and technical assistance: self-assessment and Business Plan Development. Programs are offered throughout the state.

Greater Cincinnati Microenterprise Initiative

1501 Madison Rd.
PNC Building, 1st Floor Rear   513-569-4816
Cincinnati, OH 45206   Fax: 513-569-0075
www.gcmi.org

The Greater Cincinnati Microenterprise Initiative provides Business Coaches who guide their clients through the steps to start and operate their own small business. The Coach will customize a training program to meet your specific needs. Training is provided through a variety of settings including classroom training, small business workshops, one-to-one coaching and technical assistance. If you already have a business they will work with you to achieve your expansion plans.

Ohio Women's Business Resource Network

77 South High Street, 28th Floor   614-466-2682
Columbus, OH 43215-6108   800-848-1300 ext. 62682
    Fax: 614-466-0829

The Ohio Women's Business Resource Network is an effort to help women business owners and to promote the ownership of businesses by women. It also promotes the sharing of information, technical assistance and education among its member organizations.

The following Centers are all graduated members of OWBRN:

1. Women's Organization for Mentoring, Entrepreneurship and Networking, (WOMEN) and Women's Network, Inc.
   526 South Main Street, Suite 235   330-379-9280
   Akron, OH 44311-1058   330-379-2772
   http://www.womennet.org   Fax: 330-379-9283

2. Women's Business Resource Program of Southeastern Ohio
   20 East Circle Drive, Suite 155
   Technology and Enterprise Building   740-593-1797
   Athens, OH 45701   Fax: 740-593-1795

3. Pyramid Career Services
   2400 Cleveland Avenue North   330-453-3767
   Canton, OH 44709   Fax: 330-453-6079

4. Glenville Development Corporation Micro-Enterprise Program
   10640 St. Clair Avenue   216-851-8724
   Cleveland, OH 44108   Fax: 216-854-8941

5. Central Ohio Women's Business Development Center
   317 North High Street   614-225-6910
   Columbus, OH 43215-3065   Fax: 614-469-8250
   http://www.columbus.org/busi/sbdc/index.htm

6. Ohio Women's Business Development Council, Inc.
462 W. Broad Street — 614-621-0881
Columbus, OH 43215 — 877-238-6081
Fax: 614-621-2633

7. Women's Development Center
42101 Griswold Road — 440-324-3688
Elyria, OH 44035 — Fax: 440-324-3689

8. Women's Entrepreneurial Network
1605 Holland Road, Suite A3 — 419-897-9799
Maumee, OH 43537-1630 — Fax: 419-897-9776

9. Women Entrepreneurs, Inc.
36 East Fourth Street, Suite 925
Cincinnati, OH 45202 — 513-684-0700

Women's Business Center

1864 Shyville Road — 740-289-3727
Piketon, OH 45661 — 800-860-7232
http://www.ag.ohio-state.edu/~prec/ — Fax: 740-292-1953
The Women's Business Center is part of an Enterprise Center sponsored by Ohio State University Extension. The WBC focuses on rural transition issues and alternative income sources. This Center is one of the international trade assistance centers.

Northwest Ohio Women's Entrepreneurial Network

5555 Airport Highway, Suite 210 — 419-381-7555
Toledo, OH 43615 — Fax: 419-381-7573
The Northwest Ohio Women's Entrepreneurial Network sponsors training for start-up businesses and seminars for existing women business owners. An 'Expert Team Review' program is being developed that will allow women-owned businesses to meet with a panel of successful women business owners to discuss problems with their business plans.

Byesville Area Entrepreneur Development Partnership

P.O. Box 268
Byesville, OH 43723 — 740-685-8625
The Byesville Area Entrepreneur Development Partnership's goal is to enhance entrepreneurial development through education, mentorship, and student scholarships and projects. Programs include a series of 12 workshops for small business entrepreneurs; financial support for growing, new firms; scholarships for students with promising business proposals; a youth mentorship program; a Small Business Education and Resource Center; Business and Services Directory; and a Small Business Expo.

Entrepreneur Training and Support

Columbia County Career Center
9364 State Route 45 — 330-424-9561
Lisbon, OH 44432 — 330-424-4046
The Columbia County Career Center provides classroom training, financial contacts, and personal consulting for current and potential entrepreneurs in Columbiana, Carroll, Jefferson and Mahoning Counties. The classroom training program consists of two levels. Level one is geared towards entrepreneurs who want to start a small business. The development of a working business plan is stressed. Level two is designed for those who have already started a business. Both levels cover taxes, finances, insurance, pricing and advertising.

Self Employment Assistance

The Ohio Department of Job and Family Services
30 E. Broad Street, 32nd Floor
Columbus, OH 43215-3414 — 614-466-6282
http://jfs.ohio.gov/
The Self-Employment Assistance Program is a great program if you are a dislocated worker and interested in starting your own small business. The program allows states to pay a self-employed allowance, instead of regular unemployment insurance benefits to any unemployed worker to create their own job by starting their own small business. Participants receive weekly allowances while they are getting their businesses off the ground. If you are interested in this program you must meet the requirements to receive regular unemployment benefits under state law. You may be eligible even if you are engaged in full-time self-employment activities - including entrepreneurial training, business counseling, and technical assistance. Currently, only about 9 states have established the Self-Employment Assistance Program. Check with your state Unemployment Insurance Office to see if your state has implemented this entrepreneurial program.

Oklahoma

Technical Assistance

Cherokee Nation
P. O. Box 948 — 918-456-0671
Tahlequah, OK 74465 — 800-256-0671 (in OK)
http://www.cherokee.org
Technical assistance is available to help Native American entrepreneurs living and running their business in the Cherokee Nation with writing a business plan.

Women's Business Center

Working Women's Money University
(WWMU) — 405-232-8257
234 Quadrum Drive — 405-842-5067
Oklahoma, City, OK 73108 — Fax: 405-947-5388
The Women's Business Center is an 'entrepreneurial training camp' where a team of small business supporters are committed to help those who want to help themselves and their businesses. WBC offers a complete one-stop resource toolbox. Entrepreneur-led educational experiences will empower participants with knowledge and develop every aspect of small business skills. Opportunities to build business-support networks and connect their community's entrepreneurs with one another are created. Through its alliance with the Small Business Administration and the First National Bank of Bethany, the WBC can provide participants with access to capital once they are in the program. Monthly programs include Connections-Building Business Networks, Quest for Capital, Intro to the Internet and Entrepreneur 101. Bi-monthly programs are Camp Cash Flow and Jungle Marketing. Premier FastTrac I and Premier FastTrac II are offered each Spring and Fall term.

Western Technology Center

Business Development
621 Sooner Drive
Burns Flat, OK 73624 — 580-562-3181
www.wtc.tec.ok.us
WTC's Business Development Program provides assistance to entrepreneurs who are starting or want to expand a business. They offer one-on-one consulting, and classroom/seminar training on business plan development, product and Food Development and manufacturing, loan

packaging, cash flow management, human resources management, marketing plans and e-commerce development.

Self Employment Assistance

Will Rogers Memorial Office Building
2401 N. Lincoln Boulevard
P.O. Box 52003
Oklahoma City, OK 73152-2003   405-557-7100
www.oesc.state.ok.us

The Self-Employment Assistance Program is a great program if you are a dislocated worker and interested in starting your own small business. The program allows states to pay a self-employed allowance, instead of regular unemployment insurance benefits to any unemployed worker to create their own job by starting their own small business. Participants receive weekly allowances while they are getting their businesses off the ground. If you are interested in this program you must meet the requirements to receive regular unemployment benefits under state law. You may be eligible even if you are engaged in full-time self-employment activities - including entrepreneurial training, business counseling, and technical assistance. Currently, only about 9 states have established the Self-Employment Assistance Program. Check with your state Unemployment Insurance Office to see if your state has implemented this entrepreneurial program.

Oregon

Mercy Enterprise

936 SE Ankeny, Suite 1
Portland, OR 97214   503-236-1580
http://www.mercyenterprise.org/

Mercy offers a 7 week Business Basics class for its clients which address a variety of topics including: market research, taxes, writing a business plan and many others. Mercy Enterprise also offers a yearly training called Business Seminars Series on a variety of business topics.

Neighborhood Pride Team

9117 SE Foster Rd.   503-774-4880
Portland, OR 97266   Fax: 503-774-4832
http://www.neighborhoodpride.org/

The Neighborhood Pride Team offers a variety of technical and business classes to entrepreneurs to realize their dreams by making concrete business plans.

Food Innovation Center

Oregon State University
1207 NW Naito Parkway
Portland, OR 97209   503-872-6680
http://fic.oregonstate.edu/

The Food Innovation Center offers one-stop access to important services for food entrepreneurs. They have a staff of technologists, engineers, economists, and business professional which have a breath of real-world experience and depth of technical understanding.

Child Care Neighbor Network

ROSE Community Development
5215 SE Duke Street
Portland, OR 97206-6839   503-788-0826 ext. 109
http://www.rosecdc.org/childcare.htm

The Child Care Neighbor Network brings together home-based family child care providers in order to improve quality of care. Technical assistance is also available to help providers run their home-based business.

Shorebank Enterprise Pacific

429 Spruce Street
P O Box 56   541-572-5172
Myrtle Point, OR 97458   Fax: 541-572-5261
http://www.sbpac.com/index.cfm

Shorebank Enterprise is a nonprofit rural economic development corporation assisting entrepreneurs build business and market ventures, which improve the social and environmental conditions of rural communities. Development services are specifically designed for small rural businesses. Their staff's services include financial planning, business strategy, deal structuring, business plan preparation assistance, and management assistance.

Southern Oregon Women's Access to Credit (SOWAC)

33 North Central Avenue, Suite 211   541-779-3992
Medford, OR 97501   Fax: 541-779-5195
http://www.sowac.org

The Southern Oregon Women's Access to Credit provides business training, mentoring and financing services for women and men with barriers including low-income Hispanic entrepreneurs and very rural entrepreneurs. More than 288 students have participated in their training program and SOWAC has assisted more than 65 businesses to start up and expand. Graduates may apply to SOWAC's Mentor Program to receive help from an experienced person who volunteers expertise over a six-month period.

Bolt Mountain

P.O. Box 4   541-471-0658
Grants Pass, OR 97528   Fax: 541-471-0658

Bolt Mountain trains, consults, and offers professional technical assistance to current and aspiring businesses in Jackson and Josephine counties. Classes are offered in 4, 8, and 12 week durations. Participants in the 12 week course will produce a bank worthy business plan. Bolt Mountain also offers marketing and technical assistance. Marketing assistance trains students in presentations, advertising, on-line marketing, and low-cost marketing techniques appropriate to their industry. One-to-one technical assistance is offered to interested students outside of class. It covers such topics as web page design and marketing, the creation of brochures, business cards, and packaging assistance.

Self Employment Assistance

Employment Department
875 Union Street NE   800-237-3710
Salem, OR 97311   503-947-1394
www.emp.state.or.us

The Self-Employment Assistance Program is a great program if you are a dislocated worker and interested in starting your own small business. The program allows states to pay a self-employed allowance, instead of regular unemployment insurance benefits to any unemployed worker to create their own job by starting their own small business. Participants receive weekly allowances while they are getting their businesses off the ground. If you are interested in this program you must meet the requirements to receive regular unemployment benefits under state law. You may be eligible even if you are engaged in full-time self-employment activities - including entrepreneurial training, business counseling, and technical assistance. Currently, only about 9 states have established the Self-Employment Assistance Program. Check with your state Unemployment Insurance Office to see if your state has implemented this entrepreneurial program.

Pennsylvania

ASSETS Lancaster

1821 Oregon Pike, Ste. 201   717-560-6546
Lancaster, PA 17601-6466   Fax: 717-560-6549
http://www.geocities.com/AssetsL/

ASSETS Lancaster is dedicated to serving the low to moderate-income entrepreneurs of Lancaster County. They offer a Business Design and Management Course in English and in Spanish. In addition, they provide technical assistance and mentors for their clients.

ASSETS Montco Inc (A Service for Self-Employment Training Support)

3 East Marshall Street   610-275-3520
Norristown, PA 19401   Fax: 610-272-7802
http://www.assetsmontco.org/index.html

ASSETS offers business training and peer lending groups to entrepreneurs. Volunteers teach a 13-week training course that teaches the basics of setting up and running a small business. Participants are later matched with volunteer mentors who encourage and counsel participants as they develop or grow their business. During monthly contacts over a six-month period, mentors help participants learn the practical realities of the business world and ways to solve problems.

Market Access for Neighborhood Enterprises (MANE)

Philadelphia Development Partnership
1334 Walnut Street, 7th Floor   215-545-3100
Philadelphia, PA 19107   Fax: 215-546-8055
http://www.pdp-inc.org/

MANE is a marketing and growth management service for small neighborhood businesses. Their mission is to promote neighborhood economic development to help business succeed and grow.

Prudential Young Entrepreneur Program (PYEP)

The Enterprise Center
4548 Market Street
Philadelphia, PA 19139   215-895-4000
www.theenterprisecenter.com/forentre/start_business/pyep.asp

Interested entrepreneurs enroll for a 9-week course that provides them with the fundamentals needed to run a small business. Examples of the topics covered include: marketing, sales, financial statements, and how to write a business plan. Students are encouraged to write a business plan, and set it into motion.

Local Enterprise Assistance Program (LEAP)

Rural Enterprise Development Corp.
10 East Main Street
P.O. Box 276   570-784-7003
Bloomsburg, PA 17815-0276   Fax: 570-784-7030
http://www.redc-leap.org/

The Rural Enterprise Assistance Program provides introductory and intermediate level business training classes - specifically designed for LEAP participants. These non-credit classes usually include 48 hours of instruction. Principles of marketing, management, finance, accounting, taxes, insurance, and business law are topics, which are covered. Technical assistance and peer networking are also provided through LEAP.

Trehab Center Inc.

P.O. Box 366
10 Public Avenue   570-278-5227
Montrose, PA 18801   Fax: 570-278-1889
http://www.trehab.org/

The ASSETS-TREHAB Program is a training, mentoring and technical support program for entrepreneurs, with emphasis on serving low- to-middle income participants. They provide a six-week, three-hour long Business Design and Management course twice a year. Serving Susquehanna, Bradford, Sullivan, Tioga and Wyoming counties.

The Business Center

New Covenant Campus
Elders Hall, Suite 113
7500 Germantown Avenue   215-247-2477
Philadelphia, PA 19119   Fax: 215-247-2477
www.TheBizCtr.com

The Business Center is a community based entrepreneurship education program. They provide ongoing business development resources, office space, workshops, consulting, and technical resources through the support of community organizations and in-house consultants. The Center offers many courses and programs, including Pre-Assessment of Business Needs; Before You Start; Business Plan Workshop; Young Urban Entrepreneurs; and an After-school Youth Program.

Women's Business Network

PMB#12
2400 Oxford Drive
Bethel Park, PA 15102   412-835-4566
http://www.wbninc.com

The WBN has been a networking organization of enthusiastic women business owners and professionals committed to integrity of performance and service and the creative exchange of business since 1989. Over 300 members of the network belong to local chapters that meet twice a month throughout Pennsylvania. These meetings provide members with time to network, to market her business, and to learn and discuss various aspects of running a successful business. As well as regular chapter meetings, the WBN sponsors many social and educational activities throughout the year that give members the opportunity to network within the entire organization, not just their chapter. Some of these events are the annual holiday breakfast in December, the annual dinner in May, the annual meeting in June, an annual retreat, educational seminars and other organization-wide networking events. WBN also co-sponsors special events with other professional organizations.

Self Employment Assistance

Department of Labor and Industry
7th and Foster Streets, Room 1700
Harrisburg, PA 17120   707-787-5279
www.dli.state.pa.us

The Self-Employment Assistance Program is a great program if you are a dislocated worker and interested in starting your own small business. The program allows states to pay a self-employed allowance, instead of regular unemployment insurance benefits to any unemployed worker to create their own job by starting their own small business. Participants receive weekly allowances while they are getting their businesses off the ground. If you are interested in this program you must meet the requirements to receive regular unemployment benefits under state law. You may be eligible even if you are engaged in full-time self-employment activities - including entrepreneurial training, business counseling, and technical assistance. Currently, only about 9 states have established the Self-Employment Assistance Program. Check with your state Unemployment Insurance Office to see if your state has implemented this entrepreneurial program.

Rhode Island

Rhode Island MicroEnterprise Association

8 Abbott Park Place   401-598-2256
Providence, RI 02903   Fax: 401-598-2257
http://www.rimicroenterprise.org/
The Rhode Island MicroEnterprise Association provides free microbusiness training and business technical assistance to persons wishing to start their own small business. Their services are available to microbusinesses and home-based businesses in Rhode Island. They offer a four-week Microbusiness Training Program; all worksheets, planning guides, and other written materials are provided free of charge.

Center for Women and Enterprise, Inc.

55 Claverick Street, Suite 102   401-277-0800
Providence, RI 02903   Fax: 401-277-1122
http://www.cweboston.org
CWE helps women access financing through banks and SBA loan-guaranty programs. Entrepreneurial courses include Fast/Trac, GROW (Getting Right On With It Groups), TEAM (The Executive Advisory Meeting), workshops, seminars, networking groups, plus one-on-one counseling. CWE is a national clearinghouse for women and financing and provides technical assistance on SBA loan programs and directs women business owners to local SBA resource partners. CWE offers 'Turbo Day' once a year. Turbo Day is a day-long program of high-impact workshops, each of which is geared to a specific level of business experience. Workshops include Shoestring Marketing, Power Negotiating, Super Sales Strategies, Show Me the Money, and Personnel: Everything You Wanted to Know But Were Afraid to Ask.

Self Employment Assistance

Department of Labor and Training
Center General Complex
1511 Pontiac Avenue
Cranston, RI 02920   401-243-9100
www.dlt.ri.gov/ui/
The Self-Employment Assistance Program is a great program if you are a dislocated worker and interested in starting your own small business. The program allows states to pay a self-employed allowance, instead of regular unemployment insurance benefits to any unemployed worker to create their own job by starting their own small business. Participants receive weekly allowances while they are getting their businesses off the ground. If you are interested in this program you must meet the requirements to receive regular unemployment benefits under state law. You may be eligible even if you are engaged in full-time self-employment activities - including entrepreneurial training, business counseling, and technical assistance. Currently, only about 9 states have established the Self-Employment Assistance Program. Check with your state Unemployment Insurance Office to see if your state has implemented this entrepreneurial program.

South Carolina

Center for Women Entrepreneurs

Columbia College of South Carolina   800-277-1301
1301 Columbia College Drive   803-786-3582
Columbia, SC 29203   803-786-3871
http://www.colacoll.edu   Fax: 803-786-3375
The Center for Women Entrepreneurs at Columbia College of South Carolina's mission is to expand economic opportunities for women by advancing entrepreneurship and providing resources to assist in successful business start-ups, maintenance of growth, and exploration of new business opportunities. Participants can benefit from services that include individual consultations, management and technical assistance, annual women's conference, round table luncheon series, resource guides, seminars, workshops, and internships. The Center's focus on communications online enables toe project to serve not only mature women who are ready to start businesses or women who are already involved in business, but young female entrepreneurs in high schools.

Tate Center for Entrepreneurship

College of Charleston
66 George Street   843-953-5628
Charleston, SC 29424   www.cofc.edu
Fax: 843-953-7633
The Tate Center hosts a wide range of activities such as conferences and seminars. They offer entrepreneurship courses to students and are committed to strengthening entrepreneurial education.

Self Employment Assistance

Employment Security Commission
P.O. Box 995
1550 Gadsen Street
Columbia, SC 29202   803-737-3071
www.sces.org
The Self-Employment Assistance Program is a great program if you are a dislocated worker and interested in starting your own small business. The program allows states to pay a self-employed allowance, instead of regular unemployment insurance benefits to any unemployed worker to create their own job by starting their own small business. Participants receive weekly allowances while they are getting their businesses off the ground. If you are interested in this program you must meet the requirements to receive regular unemployment benefits under state law. You may be eligible even if you are engaged in full-time self-employment activities - including entrepreneurial training, business counseling, and technical assistance. Currently, only about 9 states have established the Self-Employment Assistance Program. Check with your state Unemployment Insurance Office to see if your state has implemented this entrepreneurial program.

South Dakota

Four Bands Community Fund, Inc.

Cheyenne River Lakota Nation
101 South Main Street
P.O. Box 932   605-964-3687
Eagle Butte, SD 57625   Fax: 605-964-3689
http://www.fourbands.org/loan_fund.htm
Four Bands Community Fund, Inc., is a nonprofit corporation which assists entrepreneurs of the Cheyenne River Indian Reservation by providing training and business incubation encouraging economic development and enhancing the quality of life for all communities and residents of the reservation. They offer the CREATE Program (Cheyenne River Entrepreneurial Assistance, Training & Education), a 10-week class which meets two times a week for two hours.

Essential Networking and Training for Entrepreneurship Program

Engineering Resource Center
South Dakota State University
Box 2220, Harding Hall

Brookings, SD 57007-0199   605-688-4184
www.engineering.sdstate.edu/~erc/uits/entrepage.html
Essential Networking and Training for Entrepreneurship (ENTRE) provides training and support for entrepreneurs. The ENTRE program is made up of two training courses and follow-up networking. ENTRE I is a multi session course that helps entrepreneurs determine the feasibility of their prospective business. ENTRE II is an intensive multi session program that focuses on creating business and operating plans for start-up and existing businesses.

Entrepreneur's Network for Women

100 South Maple
P.O. Box 81
Watertown, SD 57201-0081   Fax: 605-882-5069
http://www.network4women.com
The Entrepreneur's Network for Women offers toll-free phone counseling, training seminars in management, marketing, financing, government contracting, and entrepreneurial confidence. At many locations in the state, networking sessions, group mentoring programs, and Business Success Teams and offered.

Self Employment Assistance

Department of Labor
Unemployment Insurance
420 S. Roosevelt Street
P.O. Box 4730
Aberdeen, SD 57402-4730   605-626-2452
www.state.sd.us/dol/dolui/ui_tables/UI-home.htm
The Self-Employment Assistance Program is a great program if you are a dislocated worker and interested in starting your own small business. The program allows states to pay a self-employed allowance, instead of regular unemployment insurance benefits to any unemployed worker to create their own job by starting their own small business. Participants receive weekly allowances while they are getting their businesses off the ground. If you are interested in this program you must meet the requirements to receive regular unemployment benefits under state law. You may be eligible even if you are engaged in full-time self-employment activities - including entrepreneurial training, business counseling, and technical assistance. Currently, only about 9 states have established the Self-Employment Assistance Program. Check with your state Unemployment Insurance Office to see if your state has implemented this entrepreneurial program.

Tennessee

Central Appalachian Microenterprise Program (CAMP)

East Tennessee Community Partnership Center
300 East Main Street, Suite 301   423-232-5730
Johnson City, TN 37601   Fax: 423-232-5760
http://www.etsu.edu/keystone/microenterprise.html
Technical assistance and individual counseling are available to entrepreneurs.

Community Kitchen

Jubilee Project, Inc.
123 N. Jockey St.
P.O. Box 657   423-733-4195
Sneedville, TN 37869   Fax: 423-733-1624
http://jubileeproject.holston.org
Clinch-Powell Community Kitchens can help you turn a good idea or a great recipe into a successful food product business. Entrepreneurs renting the kitchens have access to a variety of

assistance at no additional cost, which include food safety and equipment training, recipe development, product testing and business assistance. Consulting and technical assistance are also available on a fee-for-service basis for businesses not renting space in the kitchen.

Alt.consulting

P.O. Box 40210   901-312-9797
Memphis, TN 38104   Fax: 901-312-9798
www.altconsulting.org
alt.consulting is a nonprofit that will help all businesses grow and develop. They offer a wide variety of services at a below market rate.

Women's Resource Center

1112 8th Avenue South   615-248-3474
Nashville, TN 37203   Fax: 615-256-2706
The Women's Resource Center offers on-site business counseling services, training programs, and technical assistance to women business owners. The Centre provides training programs statewide through satellite, two-way interactive videoconferences and the Internet.

Renaissance Business Center

555 Beale Street
Memphis, TN 38103   901-526-9300
The Renaissance Business Center offers a wide range of services for individuals interested in starting their own business. These services include marketing and financial assistance, counseling, training, workshops and seminars.

Self Employment Assistance

Department of Labor & Workforce Development
Andrew Jackson Tower, 8th Floor
Nashville, TN 37243-0655   615-253-4809
www.state.tn.us/labor-wfd
The Self-Employment Assistance Program is a great program if you are a dislocated worker and interested in starting your own small business. The program allows states to pay a self-employed allowance, instead of regular unemployment insurance benefits to any unemployed worker to create their own job by starting their own small business. Participants receive weekly allowances while they are getting their businesses off the ground. If you are interested in this program you must meet the requirements to receive regular unemployment benefits under state law. You may be eligible even if you are engaged in full-time self-employment activities - including entrepreneurial training, business counseling, and technical assistance. Currently, only about 9 states have established the Self-Employment Assistance Program. Check with your state Unemployment Insurance Office to see if your state has implemented this entrepreneurial program.

Texas

MicroEnterprise Assistance

Alliance for Multicultural Community Services
6440 Hillcroft, Suite 411   713-776-4700
Houston, TX 77081   Fax: 713-776-4730
http://www.allianceontheweb.org/
The Alliance's mission is to assist refugees, immigrants, and other low-income residents of Harris County. They offer an Individual Development Account that provides matching funds for entrepreneurs in addition to small business workshops. Through their newly established Multicultural Community Development Corporation (MCDC), they have added microenterprise training.

Urban Business Initiative

2223 North Main Street, Suite 203   713-222-8085
Houston, TX 77009   Fax: 713-222-8097
http://www.urbanbusiness.org

The Urban Business Initiative believes a good foundation is needed for any business to succeed. That foundation is a well-written business plan. Their volunteers provide assistance in the development of this key business component. They assist the client with the consulting, research, and analysis needed to compile the plan.

Texas Center for Women's Business Enterprise

Two Commodore Plaza, 13th Floor
206 East 9th Street, Suite 13.140
Austin, TX 78701
Mailing Address:
PO Box 2044   512-472-8522
Austin, TX 78768   888-352-2525
http://www.txcwbe.org   Fax: 512-472-8513

The TCWBE is a public/private initiative dedicated to the entrepreneurial success of Texas women. Participants will be prepared for business success by dealing with topics including certification information, internet training for small businesses, business plans, loan assistance referral program, women's construction network, and consortium and contributing partners.

Target Texas Business

Texas Agricultural Extension Service
Route 3, Box 213AA   806-746-4055
Lubbock, TX 79403   Fax: 806-746-4057
http://fcs.tamu.edu/entrepreneurship

The Extension's Entrepreneurship Program provides training for Target Texas Business, home based and micro business, youth entrepreneurs, and family businesses. Ca$hing in on Business Opportunities is designed to help the development of small businesses, especially micro and home-based businesses. Training includes economic development, identification of resources, market analysis, and visits to active small businesses, with a focus on small community/urban needs with agriculture and non-farm applications.

Greater Dallas Hispanic Chamber of Commerce

Business Assistance Center
4622 Maple Avenue, Suite 407   214-521-6007
Dallas, TX 75219   Fax: 214-520-1987
or
351 W. Jefferson, Suite 210   214-224-2960
Dallas, TX 75208   Fax; 214-943-7725
www.gdhcc.com

The Greater Dallas Hispanic Chamber of Commerce (GDHCC) offers a series of seminars designed to help develop, train, and educate Hispanic Business Owners. All seminars are taught in Spanish and English. Topics covered include inventory control, administration, bookkeeping, investments, marketing, presentations, personnel, internet, office management, web pages, computer software, leasing, office equipment and more. The Chamber also offers free one-on-one counseling, a legal seminar series, a one day start-up business clinic, IRS workshops, and loan seminars.

Self Employment Assistance

Workforce Commission
101 E. 15th Street
Austin, TX 78761   512-463-0735
www.twc.state.tx.us

The Self-Employment Assistance Program is a great program if you are a dislocated worker and interested in starting your own small business. The program allows states to pay a self-employed allowance, instead of regular unemployment insurance benefits to any unemployed worker to create their own job by starting their own small business. Participants receive weekly allowances while they are getting their businesses off the ground. If you are interested in this program you must meet the requirements to receive regular unemployment benefits under state law. You may be eligible even if you are engaged in full-time self-employment activities - including entrepreneurial training, business counseling, and technical assistance. Currently, only about 9 states have established the Self-Employment Assistance Program. Check with your state Unemployment Insurance Office to see if your state has implemented this entrepreneurial program.

Utah

Technical Assistance

Utah Microenterprise Loan Fund
3595 South Main St   801-269-8408
Salt Lake City, UT 84115   Fax: 801-269-1063
http://www.umlf.com/

The Utah Microenterprise Loan Fund is a private, nonprofit, multi-bank community development financial institution, whose mission is to provide management support to entrepreneurs in start-up and existing firms that do not have access to traditional funding sources; especially those who are socially and economically disadvantaged. They offer free Business Counseling and low-cost training, workshops and seminars

Women's Business Center

175 East 400 South, Suite 600   801-328-5075
Salt Lake City, UT 84111   Fax: 801-328-5098
http://www.saltlakechamber.org

The WBC supports the success of women business owners throughout the state of Utah with counseling, training and loan packaging assistance. The center provides participants with unique networking opportunities and a full service export assistance program. The onsite high-tech center offers access to the internet and all types of business software. Women business owners can access assistance with marketing, management, finance, and procurement. There may be a small fee for some of the services, but scholarships and specialized training are available for socially or economically disadvantaged women.

Center for Entrepreneurship Training

Salt Lake Community College
8811 South 700 East   801-255-5878
Sandy, UT 84070   Fax: 801-255-6393

The Center for Entrepreneurship Training (CET) targets adults age 30 to 65 and provides skill training to help them grow or start a business. CET serves residents and company personnel in Salt Lake and Tooek counties. The Center sponsors classes in financing, credit repair, business planning, accounting, valuation, marketing, and financial management. CET also has developed programs called Jump Start Entrepreneurship for Single Parents and Managing Business Growth.

Self Employment Assistance

Department of Workforce Services
P.O. Box 45249
Salt Lake City, UT 84145-0249

http://jobs.utah.gov/ui/ 801-526-WORK (9675)

The Self-Employment Assistance Program is a great program if you are a dislocated worker and interested in starting your own small business. The program allows states to pay a self-employed allowance, instead of regular unemployment insurance benefits to any unemployed worker to create their own job by starting their own small business. Participants receive weekly allowances while they are getting their businesses off the ground. If you are interested in this program you must meet the requirements to receive regular unemployment benefits under state law. You may be eligible even if you are engaged in full-time self-employment activities - including entrepreneurial training, business counseling, and technical assistance. Currently, only about 9 states have established the Self-Employment Assistance Program. Check with your state Unemployment Insurance Office to see if your state has implemented this entrepreneurial program.

Vermont

BROC Community Action in Southwestern Vermont

60 Center Street 802-775-0878
Rutland, VT 05701 800-717-BROC (2762)
http://www.broc.org/

BROC's Micro Business Development Program provides technical assistance and training for low to moderate income residents of Vermont interested in starting or expanding a small business. Programs offered include a comprehensive training course, computer class, virtual incubator program as well as a child care business initiative program. All classes are free for income eligible entrepreneurs. BROC also offers an Individual Development Account savings plan. Program participant's savings are matched while saving for their business.

Micro Business Development Program

P.O. Box 437
Putney, VT 05346 802-387-5029
http://www.vtmicrobusiness.org/

The Micro Business Development Program provides counseling and education to low to moderate income Vermont entrepreneurs striving to start or expand small businesses. Micro Business Development Program services include: one-on-one counseling, classroom training, seminars, loan packaging, and market research.

Women's Agricultural Network

590 Main Street, UVM
Burlington, VT 05405 802-656-3276
http://www.uvm.edu/~wagn/

Women's Agricultural Network (WAgN) offers several educational and assistance opportunities that help individuals develop and/or further expand an ag-based enterprise. They offer workshops in all aspects of business development, from starting to expanding projects. There is a cost for the workshops however; grants are available for eligible participants.

Trinity College of Vermont

Women's Small Business Program/Vermont Women's Center
208 Colchester Avenue 802-846-7164
Burlington, VT 05401 Fax: 802-685-7435

The WBC focuses on economically disadvantaged women, including welfare recipients, and ensures access for people who have special needs or disabilities, those living in rural areas, and women who are interested in agriculture. The training offered ranges from basic to advanced and services include management and marketing assistance and working with individual women business owners. WNET mentoring round tables meet monthly. A six-hour seminar on wholesale tradeshows is also available and the center holds an annual business showcase and conference. Internet training and assistance are provided through a subcontract with Cyberskills Vermont. Vermont's Interactive Television Network also offers programs.

Self Employment Assistance

Department of Employment and Training
P.O. Box 488
5 Green Mountain Drive
Montpelier, VT 05601-0488 802-828-4000
www.det.state.vt.us

The Self-Employment Assistance Program is a great program if you are a dislocated worker and interested in starting your own small business. The program allows states to pay a self-employed allowance, instead of regular unemployment insurance benefits to any unemployed worker to create their own job by starting their own small business. Participants receive weekly allowances while they are getting their businesses off the ground. If you are interested in this program you must meet the requirements to receive regular unemployment benefits under state law. You may be eligible even if you are engaged in full-time self-employment activities - including entrepreneurial training, business counseling, and technical assistance. Currently, only about 9 states have established the Self-Employment Assistance Program. Check with your state Unemployment Insurance Office to see if your state has implemented this entrepreneurial program.

Virginia

Business Development Assistance Group

George Mason University Enterprise Center
3401 N. Fairfax Drive, #225 703-993-8127
Arlington, VA 22201 Fax: 703-993-8130
http://www.bdag.org/index.html

Business Development Assistance Group's mission is to help small and minority-owned businesses become more viable in American economic life through educational programs, workshops and training seminars. Most of the services to individuals are provided free of charge if they meet certain income levels.

Community Business Partnership

6911 Richmond Hwy., Suite 290 703-768-1440
Alexandria, VA 22306 Fax: 703-768-0547
http://www.cbponline.org

Community Business Partnership was formed in response to an identified need for small business technical assistance, particularly to low-moderate income and disadvantaged individuals, including minorities, women and the disabled. A variety of workshops are available for entrepreneurs in Fairfax County.

New Enterprise Fund

Community Housing Partners Corporation
930 Cambria Street, NE 540-382-2002
Christiansburg, VA 24073 Fax: 540-382-1935
http://www.communityhousingpartners.org/enterprise/me.html

The New Enterprise Fund requires training for applicants. Scholarships are available to attend training to qualified entrepreneurs. After small business training, counseling services or a loan has been funded, on-going technical assistance is provided to those entrepreneurs participating in the Micro-Enterprise Program.

New Visions, New Ventures, Inc.

801 East Main Street, Suite 1100   804-643-1081
Richmond, VA 23219   Fax: 804-643-1085
http://nvnv.org/index.html

New Visions, New Ventures supports women in difficult life situations, striving to become independent by providing microenterprise development. They provide entrepreneurial training, technical assistance, peer networking and a technology resource center.

Valley Microenterprise Alliance

1251 Virginia Avenue
Harrisonburg, VA 22802   540-433-5624
http://www.vmalliance.org/

Valley Microenterprise Alliance offers training and business assistance to encourage underemployed and low to moderate-income individuals to start or expand a microenterprise in the Shenandoah Valley Region. Valley Microenterprise Alliance offers a wide variety of classes, workshops and counseling for every aspect of entrepreneurial process.

Matchmaking Service for Entrepreneurs

MBA Tech Connection, Inc.
P.O. Box 5769   434-295-5599
Charlottesville, VA 22905   Fax: 434-295-0293
www.mbatechconnect.org

Entrepreneurs with great business skills, or with a great new product or business idea, who are looking for like-minded individuals can use the MBA Tech Connection to find a partner and forge a successful new enterprise. The organization specializes in forming management teams and start-up businesses through an internet-based screening and matching service. How it works: Inventors and those with innovative and viable business ideas submit detailed information on their proposed idea, product or service to MBA Tech. The information is reviewed, categorized and entered into an Innovation Database; current categories range from biotech and high-tech, to real estate and retail, to pet products and printing services. Entrepreneurs looking to apply their highly tuned business skills and expertise to a start-up commercial venture similarly provide MBA Tech with information on their area of expertise and interests. Participants on both sides of the equation receive detailed personal reports that will enable them to search the databases for potential partners. MBA Tech works with participants to find a "match," using background research and testing results to build partnerships that are likely to succeed. The fee for using the program is $350.

FREE Job Skills Training and Counseling for Low-Income Entrepreneurs

United Community Ministries of Virginia / Workforce Development Center
7842 Richmond Highway   703-360-9088
Alexandria VA 22306   Fax: 703-360-4895
www.ucmagency.org/

Among the employment services offered by United Community Ministries of Virginia are training and assistance programs geared towards low-income individuals who want to start or sustain their own businesses. Courses in entrepreneurship and business skills, training sessions and computer classes are offered at the organization's Workforce Development Center. Most are free for qualifying individuals. The Center also offers free goals and planning

counseling and technical assistance to prospective and existing small business owners.

How To Get Your Business Noticed...

Virginia's Business Pipeline
P.O. Box 7035   540-831-6392
Radford, VA 24142   Fax: 540-831-6397
www.virginiabusiness.org

For a minimal fee, members of the Virginia Business Pipeline (VBP) can let the organization market their product or service to a huge audience. Dedicated to establishing competitive advantages and increasing the profits of businesses in the Commonwealth, VBP serves as a mass marketing tool through innovative internet and database vehicles. Members submit their company profile, logo and any photographs or visual tools to VBP, who in turn will advertise the business and use internet technology to attract large numbers of viewers (and prospective clients) to the profile. New businesses can pay a bit extra to be billed as a "Recommended Company" or to be featured on VBP's home pages. Members have access to VBP's complete searchable database as well and can purchase detailed website analyses to monitor activity for their posted profile. Memberships range in price and duration, starting at $29.95 for a two-week logo posting on the VBP website.

BusinesStart

People, Incorporated of Southwest Virginia
1173 West Main Street   276-619-2228
Abingdon, VA 24210   Fax: 276-628-2931
www.businesstart.org

BusinesStart offers Business Basics Workshops and Core Four Training programs to adult entrepreneurs and potential business owners. The Business Basics Workshop is a formal 12 hour class taught in every county in the area. Core Four Training programs focus on the four main business topics of marketing, cash flow, operation and planning. Other services include classroom training, technical assistance, incubator without walls, a newsletter, individual development accounts, loan capitol, and marketing services. BusinesStart serves eighteen counties and two cities of Southwestern Virginia, with further expansion planned.

Entreprep

605-9 Pine Street
Hillsville, VA 24343   540-728-3191

The Entreprep program is designed to introduce entrepreneurship to high school seniors. It is comprised of a week long training session, quarterly meetings, and 150 hours spent working with a mentor. Students are allowed to choose their own mentors and those who satisfy all the requirements will receive a $1,000 scholarship for the college of their choice.

Center for Innovative Technology

2214 Rock Hill Road
CIT Tower, Suite 600   703-689-3000
Herndon, VA 20170-4200   Fax: 703-689-3041
http://www.cit.org/

Virginia's Center for Innovative Technology provides a full range of services for technology application, process and product development, and commercialization. CIT-funded Entrepreneurship centers provide advances services for market analysis, market and business planning, and financial investment consultation. Participants have access to scientific, technical, and marketplace documentation and analysis. CIT also assists clients with website and e-commerce development. The center has developed many educational events and electronic publications as well as the one-day seminar, TechStart Boot camp. This seminar covers such topics as assessing a technology's commercial potential, legal aspects of new business formation, IP protection, developing a successful business plan, high-tech marketing, financing a business and an overview of regional support services for technology entrepreneurs. Networking opportunities are offered monthly in the form of Breakfasts with Experts.

Regional offices of the Center for Innovative Technology are:

Applied Research Center
12050 Jefferson Avenue, Suite 247   757-249-0884
Newport News, VA 23606   Fax: 757-249-0738
http://www.cit.org

Lynchburg Business Development Center
147 Mill Ridge Road, Suite 122   434-582-6154
Lynchburg, VA 24502   Fax: 434-582-6106
http://www.cit.org

308 East Market Street   434-817-3000
Charlottesville, VA 22902   Fax: 703-467-3957
http://www.cit.org

1701 East Parham Road, Suite 210
Richmond, VA 23228
Mailing address:
PO Box 85622   804-371-3433
Richmond, VA 23285-5622   Fax: 804-371-3621
http://www.cit.org

1872 Pratt Drive, Suite 1750   540-231-3880
Blacksburg, VA 24060   Fax: 540-231-3922
http://www.cit.org

355 Crawford Street, Suite 200   757-397-7016
Portsmouth, VA 23704   Fax: 757-397-7062
http://www.cit.org

530 Main Street, Suite 204   434-791-5376
Danville, VA 24541   Fax: 434-791-5378
http://www.cit.org

Mezzanine Level
212 S. Jefferson Street   540-857-7304
Roanoke, VA 24011   Fax: 540-857-7302
http://www.cit.org

One College Avenue
Resource Center, Room 130
Wise, VA 24293
Mailing address:
Mezzanine Level
212 S. Jefferson Street   276-376-4514
Roanoke, VA 24011   Fax: 276-376-4516
http://www.cit.org

Self Employment Assistance

Employment Commission
703 East Main Street
Richmond, VA 23219   804-786-1485
www.vec.state.va.us/vccportal/
The Self-Employment Assistance Program is a great program if you are a dislocated worker and interested in starting your own small business. The program allows states to pay a self-employed allowance, instead of regular unemployment insurance benefits to any unemployed worker to create their own job by starting their own small business. Participants

receive weekly allowances while they are getting their businesses off the ground. If you are interested in this program you must meet the requirements to receive regular unemployment benefits under state law. You may be eligible even if you are engaged in full-time self-employment activities - including entrepreneurial training, business counseling, and technical assistance. Currently, only about 9 states have established the Self-Employment Assistance Program. Check with your state Unemployment Insurance Office to see if your state has implemented this entrepreneurial program.

Washington

Technical Assistance

Center for Economic Opportunity
202 North Tacoma Avenue   253-591-7026
Tacoma, WA 98402   Fax: 253-593-2744
http://www.mdc-tacoma.org/page26.html
The Center for Economic Development provides low-income adults in Tacoma Pierce County with technical assistance in support of their microenterprise development.

Shorebank Enterprise Pacific

203 Howerton Way SE
P.O. Box 826   360-642-4265
Ilwaco, WA 98624   Fax: 360-642-4078
http://www.sbpac.com/index.cfm
Shorebank Enterprise is a nonprofit rural economic development corporation assisting entrepreneurs build business and market ventures, which improve the social and environmental conditions of rural communities. Development services are specifically designed for small rural businesses. Their staff's services include financial planning, business strategy, deal structuring, business plan preparation assistance, and management assistance.

Microenterprise Assistance

Spokane Neighborhood Action Program
212 South Wall Street   509-456-7174
Spokane, WA 99201   Fax: 509-456-7170
http://www.snapwa.org/microent.html
The Microenterprise Development Program is designed to assist low to moderate-income individuals and families to realistically and successfully enter into business, or expand an existing very small or home-based business. They offer a variety of assistance from Business Training to Counseling.

Business Information Center

801 W. Riverside Avenue, Suite 240   509-353-2800
Spokane, WA 99201   Fax: 509-353-2600
www.spokanebic.org/bic/bicinfo.htm
The BIC is a free resource center for the start up and expansion of small businesses. They have the latest computer equipment, software, CD-Rom databases, video tapes and over 250 business start-up guides for use on-site. The BIC also offers an extensive business reference library, counseling and training classes.

Northwest Entrepreneur Network

10700 Northup Way
P.O. Box 40128   425-564-5701
Bellevue, WA 98015-4128   Fax: 425-564-5702
www.nwen.org
The Northwest Entrepreneur Network is a nonprofit organization dedicated to helping entrepreneurs to be successful. They sponsor Entrepreneur University, which is a 2 day seminar focused on how to obtain financing and build a

successful business. They hold free educational seminars dealing with specific business challenges. Other programs and services include Venture Breakfast meetings, early stage investment forums, coaching clubs and executive round tables.

Community Capital Development Program

PO Box 22283
1437 South Jackson Street, Suite 302
Seattle, WA 98122-0283   206-324-4330

The Community Capital Development Program is distinguished by its approach to three general categories of assistance: the seasoned entrepreneur (in business 3 to 5 years), the business owner (in business 3 years or less), and the start-up (including refugee and immigrant women on welfare, and welfare-to-work participants). The center has strong local partnerships and its own in-house loan fund as well as substantial funding from the city of Seattle.

Self Employment Assistance

Employment Security Department TeleCenter-King County
P.O. Box 47076
Seattle, WA 98146-7076   206-766-6000
http://fortress.wa.gov/esd/portal/

Employment Security Department TeleCenter-Pierce County
P.O. Box 112601
Tacoma, WA 98411-2601   253-396-3500
http://fortress.wa.gov/esd/portal/

Employment Security Department TeleCenter-Spokane
P.O. Box 14857
Spokane, WA 99214-0857   509-893-7000
http://fortress.wa.gov/esd/portal/

The Self-Employment Assistance Program is a great program if you are a dislocated worker and interested in starting your own small business. The program allows states to pay a self-employed allowance, instead of regular unemployment insurance benefits to any unemployed worker to create their own job by starting their own small business. Participants receive weekly allowances while they are getting their businesses off the ground. If you are interested in this program you must meet the requirements to receive regular unemployment benefits under state law. You may be eligible even if you are engaged in full-time self-employment activities - including entrepreneurial training, business counseling, and technical assistance. Currently, only about 9 states have established the Self-Employment Assistance Program. Check with your state Unemployment Insurance Office to see if your state has implemented this entrepreneurial program.

West Virginia

Appalachian by Design

208 South Court Street
Lewisburg, WV 24901   304-647-3455 ext. 14
http://www.abdinc.org

Appalachian by Design provides a training program which teaches Appalachian women the technical and business aspect of hand loomed knitwear.

Business Development Center

Unlimited Future, Inc.
1650 Eighth Avenue

Huntington, WV 25703   304-697-3007
http://www.unlimitedfuture.org/

Unlimited Future, Inc. provides small business and entrepreneurial classes and training. Classes are free of charge to eligible clients. They also provide one-on-one counseling free of charge.

Center for Economic Options Inc.

West Virginia Microbusiness Center
601 Delaware Avenue   304-345-1298
Charleston, WV 25302   Fax: 304-342-0641
http://www.centerforeconoptions.org

The center is a statewide, nonprofit, community-based organization. It promotes opportunities to develop the economic capacity of West Virginia's rural citizens, women in particular. The center creates alternative approaches to economic development, including networks of home-based business entrepreneurs, and helps build support for small and micro-businesses.

Entrepreneurship Center

University of Charleston
2300 MacCorkle Avenue, SE
Charleston, WV 25304   800-995-4682
www.ucwv.edu/ec

The Entrepreneurship Center offers counseling and information services to entrepreneurs. They also unite start-up ventures with an extensive network of specialists, business owners and professionals throughout the state and region. The EC also has programs of study, internships and special projects so the challenges and opportunities of entrepreneurship can be experienced first hand.

Self Employment Assistance

Charleston Unemployment Compensation
P.O. Box 2573
Charleston, WV 25330-2753   304-558-2624
www.state.wv.us/bep/

There are many Unemployment Compensation offices throughout the state. Check the web site for the location nearest you.

Wisconsin

Wisconsin Women's Business Initiative Corporation (WWBIC)

2821 North Fourth Street   414-263-5450
Milwaukee, WI 53212   Fax: 414-263-5456
or
217 South Hamilton Street
Suite 201   608-257-7409
Madison, WI 53703   Fax: 608-257-7429
http://www.wwbic.com
http://www.onlinewbc.org

The WWBIC is an economic development corporation that provides quality business education, technical assistance and access to capital. WWBIC consults with, educates, and mentors small and micro-business owners throughout the state of Wisconsin. Participants benefit from over 200 business courses and workshops offered throughout the state annually. Course topics include business planning, entrepreneurship, management, marketing, finances, and the Internet. Also, participants who are women, people of color, or are low-income individuals who own or can demonstrate the ability to operate a small business, WWBIC can provide access to loans of $100 to $25,000 to help.

The Institute for Entrepreneurship

P.O. Box 26191
9722 Watertown Plank Road   414-302-9922
Milwaukee, WI 53226   Fax: 414-302-9944
www.theEplace.org

The Institute for Entrepreneurship provides real assistance for actual businesses run by young people. Through the E Place, young people actually start businesses, earn money, and contribute to the community. The Institute for Entrepreneurship provides start-up funds, student conferences, business assistance, teacher training, grants and curriculum to help you start a personal business, school store, classroom business or educational fund raising program.

Wisconsin Learning Center

5501A Vern Holmes Drive   715-343-2700
Stevens Point, WI 54481-9791   866-343-2700
www.wlc.info/index.html   Fax: 715-343-2701

The Wisconsin Learning Center offers a variety of business seminars and customized training programs. The Entrepreneurship Training Program teaches how to prepare a well-researched business plan, and covers topics such as market research, management skills, legal issues, marketing planning, cash flow, financial management, financing and revenue and expensive projections.

Self Employment Assistance

Department of Workforce Development
201 E. Washington Avenue
Madison, WI 53701
Mailing address:
P.O. Box 7946
Madison, WI 53707-7946   608-266-3131
www.dwd.state.wi.us

The Self-Employment Assistance Program is a great program if you are a dislocated worker and interested in starting your own small business. The program allows states to pay a self-employed allowance, instead of regular unemployment insurance benefits to any unemployed worker to create their own job by starting their own small business. Participants receive weekly allowances while they are getting their businesses off the ground. If you are interested in this program you must meet the requirements to receive regular unemployment benefits under state law. You may be eligible even if you are engaged in full-time self-employment activities - including entrepreneurial training, business counseling, and technical assistance. Currently, only about 9 states have established the Self-Employment Assistance Program. Check with your state Unemployment Insurance Office to see if your state has implemented this entrepreneurial program.

Wyoming

Fremont County

Board of Cooperative Education Services (BOCES)
2660 Peck Avenue   307-855-2297
Riverton, WY 82501   Fax: 307-855-2041
www.fcboces.org/default.asp

The BOCES EntrePrep program is designed for high school students, in transition from their junior to senior year, who are motivated and ambitious. EntrePrep provides the building blocks for students to start their own businesses. The program consists of a one week residential camp, along with a 72 hour internship and two booster workshops to provide both formal instruction and real business experience for each student. Upon successful completion of all program components, each student will receive a $500 scholarship for college tuition and the designation as a Kauffman Center for Entrepreneurial Leadership Scholar.

Wyoming Business Council

214 West 15th Street   307-777-2800
Cheyenne, WY 82002-0240   800-262-3425
www.wyomingbusiness.org   Fax: 307-777-2838

The Wyoming Business Council connects Entrepreneurs with available services and programs. The Business Council offers a wide range of services including consulting, help finding financing and assistance in creating a business plan. The Wyoming Business Council office staff works with you directly to determine what resources are available to best suit your needs.

Wyoming Women's Project of the Wyoming Coalition Against Domestic Violence and Sexual Assault

P.O. Box 236   307-745-3059
Laramie, WY 82703   Fax: 307-755-5482

The WWP serves all women throughout the state of Wyoming, especially those who are economically and socially disadvantages, seeking referrals from churches and the Wyoming Department of Family Services. The project started with the first statewide women's conference held in Wyoming in 25 years from a resolution to set up a micro-credit program for women with low and moderate incomes to help them start their own businesses. Micro-credit loan peer groups and women mentors provide ongoing support, and some training is subcontracted to the state SBDC.

CANDO Youth Entrepreneurship Camp

CANDO Youth Tech Center
131 West Center Street   307-358-2000
Douglas, WY 82633   Fax: 307-358-3299
http://www.candotechcenter.org

Wyoming's Converse Area New Development Organization holds three camps for youth each summer. The Camps are designed to provide the next generation of the area with entrepreneurship skills and the keep young business people in the state of Wyoming. The website offers information on the camps as well as a schedule of guest speakers, applications, a list of available positions, and information on scholarships for the camps.

Self Employment Assistance

Department of Employment
Unemployment Insurance Division
100 W. Midwest
P.O. Box 2760
Casper, WY 82602   307-235-3253
http://wydoe.state.wy.us/

The Self-Employment Assistance Program is a great program if you are a dislocated worker and interested in starting your own small business. The program allows states to pay a self-employed allowance, instead of regular unemployment insurance benefits to any unemployed worker to create their own job by starting their own small business. Participants receive weekly allowances while they are getting their businesses off the ground. If you are interested in this program you must meet the requirements to receive regular unemployment benefits under state law. You may be eligible even if you are engaged in full-time self-employment activities - including entrepreneurial training, business counseling, and technical assistance. Currently, only about 9 states have established the Self-Employment Assistance Program. Check with your state Unemployment Insurance Office to see if your state has implemented this entrepreneurial program.

Microloans

The U.S. Small Business Administration's (SBA) Microloan Program was developed for those times when just a small loan can make the real difference between success and failure. Under this program, loans range from less than $100 to a maximum of $35,000.

SBA has made these funds available to nonprofit organizations for the purpose of lending to small businesses. These organizations can also provide intense management and technical assistance. A microloan must be repaid on the shortest term possible — no longer than six years, depending on the earnings of the business. The interest rates on these loans will be competitive and based on the cost of money to the intermediary lender.

This program is currently available in 44 states. To learn which nonprofit organizations in your area offer this program, contact U.S. Small Business Administration, 409 3rd St., SW, Suite 8300, Washington, DC 20416; 800-8-ASK-SBA; 202-205-6490; {www.sba.gov}.

What can you accomplish with a small loan? Just as every journey begins with the first step, most businesses begin with an initial influx of cash. Without the funds to cover start-up expenses, it's tough for a business to open its doors. Microloans are designed to help people launch a business and get beyond the start-up stage, or to get past a bumpy road along the way. The following stories are examples of people who used microloans for just that – to get the ball rolling, or to keep it moving when the business got a little stuck.

And - while money is critical, it isn't worth much without the know-how to put behind it. Many of the organizations listed here provide technical training – as well as a loan - to give business owners the tools they need for success. These stories include people who worked with teachers, experts and support groups to help make their dreams come true.

A Jump Start for the Business

Alternate Care Services provides an important function. If someone who is elderly or has limited mobility needs assistance with shopping, light housekeeping or transportation to the doctor or any appointment, they can call the company and hire someone to help them out. When she opened the business, according to owner Barbara Hammack, demand grew faster than she expected. She wanted to keep up with sales, but did not have the cash flow to hire the help she needed to respond to her customers.

Hammack turned to the Center for Community Development in Portsmouth, VA, and secured a microloan. "This was a real 'jump start' for my business," she says. "I moved from a small bedroom in my son's house to a small suite for office space, and hired more caregivers. This money gave us something to work with and helped us to look towards the future."

Calm the Fears of Opening a Business

Dena Baldwin owns a "dollar store" in International Falls, Wisconsin. She knew she wanted to operate her own business, but was worried about the risk involved. The Northeast Entrepreneur Fund in Superior, WI offered a CORE FOUR® Business Planning Course, so she attended to upgrade her skills. She also found the confidence she needed in order to overcome her fears.

"It's important to talk about the risk one takes in starting a business and CORE FOUR® really covered that topic well."

Baldwin launched the business with a celebration. The night before the doors opened, everyone who had a hand in helping her was invited to a first look at the store, and received a hearty thanks from Baldwin and employees.

Expanding a Business with a Microloan

As long as people drive cars, there will be business for tow trucks. But what if roadside recovery does not allow for the kind of growth a business owner is working towards?

Scott and Mary Hess, owners of R.H. Towing in Fairfax, Ohio, were ready to bring their company to the next level. They applied for a microloan to expand their services, and purchased a U-Haul dealership, which works along side the towing service. Now, their customer base has expanded to include a large variety of accounts. Their success earned them the 2002 Microenterprise of the Year Award.

Dancing her Way to Success

As a girl, Rhonda Auten excelled in gymnastics and dance. As an adult, these interests became her ticket to success. When her marriage ended and she faced the reality of supporting her young son, she decided to open a dance studio – but knew that it took more than tap shoes to turn a profit. She completed a business plan with the help of the Institute of Social and Economic Development in Coralville, Iowa, and soon opened Showtime Dance Studio. Five years later, Auten traveled to Washington, DC to accept a Presidential Award for Excellence in Microenterprise Development.

Build a Better Mousetrap

Imagine that you have invented something that all of your friends want to use, and you know it would fly off the shelves – but you do not have the money to produce your product.

This is what happened to Victor Valdez of Nogales, Arizona. In the middle of an afternoon of raking leaves, he came up with a product that his family and neighbors considered a great idea: a frame for leaf bags, to get leaves into the bag without having to hold it open. The invention allowed him to hold the bag with one hand and rake leaves with the other.

When family and friends saw Valdez effortlessly gathering leaves while they struggled, they'd plead with him to make them one of his frames. Eventually, he got a patent for his idea, and was ready to start a business – but he needed help to make the leap into mass production.

Vadez approached PPEP Microbusiness and Housing Development Corp., a Tucson-based nonprofit organization that administers loans for microenterprises. It granted him a $3,000 low interest loan that he used to make plastic prototypes of his frames. Two years later, he had 40,000 injection-molded units ready to ship.

Valdez credits the microloan with making the difference between a good idea to share with neighbors and a successful production business. Now he is "raking in" the profits!

The Art of Turning a Profit

Laura Matson wanted to stay home and help to care for her brother, whose health was in decline. When she was laid off in October 2001, Laura thought about going back to work and putting her brother in a long-term healthcare facility. But Matson is an artist, so she decided to combine her skill for creating hand-pleated silk scarves with her desire for a flexible, home-based schedule.

Matson began selling her handcrafted scarves at the Pike Place Market in Seattle. The scarves were beautiful, and she did have active sales – but after a year, Matson realized that she hadn't turned a profit.

"I'd put tons of thought into the product," she explained, "but nothing into marketing or bookkeeping - and I hadn't made any money."

Matson signed up for a business course at Washington Cash. After just a few weeks of attending the classes, she understood why she had not turned a profit, and learned what she needed to do to make the business viable. She shifted her focus from creating scarves to planning, marketing, and bookkeeping. She then secured a wholesale account, which took some of the risk out of sales, and increased her marketing efforts by displaying the scarves at high-end art shows throughout the year. By taking the course, these and other ideas put Matson on the track to profitability – and she still has the flexibility she wants.

Keeping the Business Afloat

It was not too long ago that Cheryl Lynn Fields picked up jobs as a painting subcontractor. Now, she runs a full service construction firm. She credits her success in part to the assistance she received from Micro-Business USA in Miami, Florida – and to making the right phone call.

A friend told Fields about the loans and training available through Micro-Business. When she called for information, she learned about a meeting that was scheduled for that night, and decided to attend.

Within a few months, she received a loan for $500.00 for a fax machine. With a second loan of $1,500, she purchased tools so she no longer had to bear the cost of renting. She then took out a third microloan to get her through a cash flow crunch when a client was delinquent on a payment.

The lender has also provided support along the way, Fields says. "All of the staff members have always been very helpful and encouraging. They keep small business owners afloat."

Technical Assistance Teaches MBA Grad to Succeed

Prism Imaging Inc.'s founders were initially among the masses of small business owners struggling to get their ideas off the ground. Now, they are flying high.

The company began in 1993, when a trio of University of Texas grads wanted to break into the business of converting paper files into archives on CD-ROMs. In its first year in business, Prism generated $17,000 in revenue. Six years later, revenue surpassed $1.27 million. Prism now employs more than 60 people and is opening a second location in Chicago. How did the company make the leap? The secret to success was technical assistance.

After the first year, CEO George Francis, who had earned a Masters in Business Administration (MBA), knew he needed to learn more. He contacted Austin's Business Invest In Growth, or BIG, for help.

BIG suggested their 12-week training course, and provided a loan that enabled him to purchase necessary office equipment. Francis says that the most important thing he gained from the BIG training course was how to apply the business theory he had learned in MBA courses.

Every Business Needs the Basics

How much training do you need just to sell a cup of coffee from a tiny booth?

There are certain things you need to know to run a profitable business, no matter what your product. Just ask Antoinette Gonzales, owner of the successful Zoombaz Double Drive-Thru Espresso Bars in Austin, Texas. She credits the growth in her bottom line to training she received at BIG, where she learned how to write a marketing plan; design cash flow, income, and balance statements; and perform industry analyses.

After taking the course, she knew the nuts and bolts of managing a business. For example, she says, "I was able to figure out my break-even point - the amount of sales needed on a daily basis to pay back the loan, rent, supplies, and other costs associated with running a business."

Don't forget the milk and sugar!

Participating Intermediary Lenders and Non-Lending Technical Assistance Providers

Intermediary Lenders
Alabama
Community Equity Investments, Inc.
302 N. Barcelona St.
Pensacola, FL 32501
850-595-6234
888-605-2505
Fax: 850-595-6264
Email: bigdanfla@aol.com
www.ceii.pensacola.com
Executive Director: Dan Horvath
Microloan Contact: Elbert Jones
Service Area: Baldwin, Mobile, Washington, Clarke, Monroe, Escambia, Conecuh, Covington, Geneva, Coffee, Dale, Henry, and Houston counties

Birmingham Business Resource Center
110 12th Street North
Birmingham, AL 35203
205-250-6380
Fax: 205-250-6384
Email: BBRC@Inlinenet.net
www.bbrc.biz/
Executive Director: Robert Dickinson, Jr.
Microloan Contact: Rodney E. Evans
Service Area: Jefferson County

Southeast Community Capital
1020 Commerce Park Drive
Oak Ridge, TN 37830
865-220-2020
Fax: 865-220-2030
Email: hortonw@tech2020.org
http://www.tech2020.org
Executive Director: Don Welty
Microloan Contact: David Bradshaw
Service Area: Bibb, Blount, Calhoun, Chambers, Chilton, Colbert, Coosa, Cullman, De Kalb, Elmore, Etowah, Fayette, Franklin, Hale, Jackson, Lauderdale, Lawrence, Limestone, Macon, Madison, Marion, Marshall, Morgan, Pickens, Randolph, St. Clair, Shelby, Talladega, Tallapoosa, Tuscaloosa, Walker, and Winston

Alaska
Alaska Village Initiatives
1577 C St., Suite 104
Anchorage, AK 99501
907-274-5400
Fax: 907-263-9971
Email: avi@ruralak.org
www.akvillage.com/index.html
Executive Director: Tom Harris
Microloan Contact: Tom Harris
Service Area: State of Alaska.

Arizona
Prestamos CDFI, LLC
1112 E. Buckeye Rd.
Phoenix, AZ 85034-4043
602-252-0483
Fax: 602-252-0484
Executive Director: Pete Garcia
Microloan Contact: Joe Martinez
www.cplc.org
Service Area: Urban Maricopa and Pima counties, Graham and Gila counties (including Point of Pines Reservation and the Southwestern area of Fort Apache Reservation), Coconino and Mohave counties (including the Kaibab, Havasupai, and Hualapai Reservations and western portions of the Navajo and Hopi Reservations), Yavapai and LaPaz counties

PPEP Housing Development Co.
Micro Ind. Credit Rural Org.
802 E. 46th St.
Tucson, AZ 85713
520-806-9513
Fax: 520-806-9515
Email: gballesteros@ppepruralinst.org
www.ppep.org
Exec. Director: Frank Ballesteros
Microloan Contact: Frank Ballesteros
Service Area: Cochise, Santa Cruz, Pinal, Yuma, rural Pima, and rural Maricopa counties including the Fort McDowell, Gila River, Maricopa, Papago, Salt River, and San Xavier Indian Reservations.

Self-Employment Loan Fund, Inc.
1601 North 7th St., Suite 340
Phoenix, AZ 85006
602-340-8834
Fax: 602-340-8953
Email: self@uswest.net
www.selfloanfund.org
Executive Director: Caroline Newsom
Microloan Contact: Caroline Newsom
Service Area: Maricopa County

Arizona Council for Economic Conversion
10 East Broadway, Suite 210
P.O. Box 42108
Tucson, AZ 85701
520-620-1241
Email: bmurphy@acec-az.org
Pimawbe.vstone.com/
Executive Director: Rosalyn Boxer
Microloan Contact: Bart T. Murphy
Service Area: Tucson, and Pima Counties

Arkansas

White River Planning and Development District, Inc.
1652 White Drive
P.O. Box 2396
Batesville, AR 72501
870-793-5233
Fax: 870-793-4035
Email: billray@wrpdd.org
www.arkplan.org/WRPDD.html
Executive Director: Van C. Thomas
Microloan Contact: Bill Ray
Service Area: Cleburne, Fulton, Independence, Izard, Jackson, Sharp, Stone, Van Buren, White, and Woodruff counties

Southern Financial Partners
605 Main Street
Pine Bluff, AR 71923
870-246-9739
Fax: 870-246-2182
Email: slinn@ehbt.com
www.southernfinancialpartners.org
Executive Director: Penny Penrose
Microloan Contact: William Matthews or Sandy Linn
Service Area: Southern and extreme northeast areas of the State including Arkansas, Ashley, Bradley, Calhoun, Chicot, Clark, Clay, Cleveland, Columbia, Craighead, Dallas, Desha, Drew, Garland, Grant, Greene, Hempstead, Hot Spring, Howard, Jefferson Lafayette, Lawrence, Lincoln, Little River, Lonoke, Miller, Mississippi, Montgomery, Nevada, Ouachita, Phillips, Pike, Poinsett, Polk, Prairie, Pulaski, Randolph, Saline, Sevier, and Union Counties

Forge-Financing Ozarks Rural Growth and Economy
208 East Main P.O. Box 1138
Huntsville, AR 72740
501-738-1585
Fax: 501-738-6288
Email: forgein@madisoncounty.net
Executive Director: Alva C. West
Microloan Contact: Charlie Stockton
Service Area: Crawford, Baxter, Yell, Perry, Conway, Boone, Madison, Marion, Carroll, Franklin, Pope, Benton, Washington, Searcy, and Newton

California

Arcata Economic Development Corporation
100 Ericson Court, Suite 100
Arcata, CA 95521
707-822-4616
Fax: 707-822-8982
Email: arianek@reninet.com
www.aedc1.org
Executive Director: Jim Kimbrell
Microloan Contact: Arianne Knoeller or Kelly Denny
Service Area: Del Norte, Humboldt, Lake, Mendocino, Siskiyou, and Trinity counties

California Coastal Rural Development Corporation
221 Main St., Suite 300
P.O. Box 479
Salinas, CA 93906
831-424-1099
Fax: 831-424-1094
Email: rey_hidalgo@calcoastal.org
www.calcoastal.org/
Executive Director: Herb Aarons
Microloan Contact: Ray Hidalgo
Service Area: Santa Cruz, Monterey, San Benito, San Luis Obispo, Santa Barbara, and Ventura

Southeast Asian Community Center
875 O'Farrell St.
San Francisco, CA 94109
415-885-2743
Fax: 415-885-3253
Email: seaccphilip@juno.com
Executive Director: Philip Tuong Duy Nguyen
Microloan Contact: Victor Hsi
Service Area: Alameda, Contra Costa, Marin, Merced, Sacramento, San Francisco, San Joaquin, San Mateo, Santa Clara, and Stanislaus counties

Valley Small Business Development Corporation
3417 W. Shaw, Suite 100
Fresno, CA 93711
559-438-9680
Fax: 559-438-9690
Email: valleysb@psnw.com
www.vsbdc.com/
Executive Director: Michael E. Foley
Microloan Contact: Lee Takikawa
Service Area: Fresno, Kings, Kern, Stanislaus, Madera, Mariposa, Merced, Tuolumne, and Tulare counties

CDC Small Business Finance Corp.
925 Ft. Stockton Dr.
San Diego, CA 92110
619-291-3594
Fax: 619-291-6954
Email: arobinson@cdcloans.com
www.cdcloans.com/
President: Kurt Chilcott
Microloan Contact: Alex Robinson
Service Area: San Diego

Oakland Business Development Corporation
519 17th Street Suite 100
Oakland, CA 94612
510-763-4297
Fax: 510-763-1273
Email: mike@obdc.com robert@obdc.com
www.obdc.com/
Executive Director: Micheal McPherson
Microloan Contact: Robert Gebauer
Service Area: Alameda and Contra Costa counties

PCR Small Business Development
3255 Wilshire Blvd.
Los Angeles, CA 90010
213-739-2999, ext. 222
Fax: 213-739-0639
Email: mark.robertson@pcrcorp.org
www.pcrcorp.org/
President: R. D. Lottie, Jr.,
Microloan Contact: Mark Robertson, Jr.
Service Area: South Los Angeles County

Sierra Economic Development District
560 Wall Street Suite F
Auburn, CA 95603
530-823-4703
Fax: 530-823-4142
Email: betty@sedd.org dillc@scdd.org
www.sedd.org/
Executive Director: Betty Riley
Microloan Contact: Tom Dille
Service Area: Modoc, El Dorado, Lassen, Nevada, Plumas, Sierra, and Placer counties

Valley Economic Development Corp.
5121 Van Nuys Blvd. 3rd Floor
Van Nuys, CA 91403
818-907-9977
Fax: 818-907-9720
Email: roberto@vedc.org
www.vedc.org
Executive Director: Roberto Barragan
Microloan Contact: Rebecca Haas
Service Area: Los Angeles and Orange County

Colorado

Colorado Enterprise Fund
1888 Sherman St. Suite 530
P.O. Box 2135
Denver, CO 80203
303-860-0242
Fax: 303-860-0409
Email: microloans@coloradoenterprisefund.org
www.coloradoenterprisefund.org
Executive Director: Cecilia H. Prinster
Microloan Contact: Angela Valdez
Service Area: City of Denver, and Adams, Arapahoe, Boulder, Denver, and Jefferson counties

Region 10 LEAP for Economic Development
P.O. Box 849
300 N. Cascade St., Suite 1
Montrose, CO 81401
970-249-2436
Fax: 970-249-2488
Email: region10@rmii.com
www.region10.net
Executive Director: Leslie Jones
Microloan Contact: Bob Bolt
Service Area: West Central area including Delta, Gunnison, Hinsdale, Montrose, Ouray, and San Miguel counties

Connecticut

Community Economic Development Fund
50-G Weston Street
Hartford, CT 06120
860-249-3800
Fax: 860-249-2500
Email: donnwertenbach@cedf.org
www.cedf.com/
Executive Director: Donna Wertenbach
Microloan Contact: Thomas Holloway
Service Area: Statewide

Connecticut Community Investment Corp.
100 Crown St.
New Haven, CT 06510
203-776-6172
Fax: 203-776-6837
Email: mcousineau@ctcic.org
Email: bmcmanus@ctcic.org
www.ctcic.org
Executive Director: Salvatore J. Brancati, Jr.
Microloan Contact: Mark Cousineau
Service Area: Statewide

Delaware

Wilmington Economic Development Corporation
100 W. 10th St., Suite 706
Wilmington, DE 19801
302-571-9088
Fax: 302-652-5679
Email: wedco@wedcode.org

www.wedco.org/
Executive Director: Constance McCarthy
Microloan Contact: Constance McCarthy
Service Area: New Castle county, in the cities of Wilmington, Newark, New Castle, Middletown, Odessa, and Townsend

District of Columbia

ARCH Development Corporation
1227 Good Hope Rd., SE
Washington, DC 20020
202-889-5023
Fax: 202-889-5035
Executive Director: Duane Gautier
Microloan Contact: Teina Linthicum
Service Area: Portions of the District of Columbia commonly referred to as Adams Morgan, Mount Pleasant, and Anacostia, Congress Heights, Columbia Heights, and 14th Street Corridor

H Street Development Corp.
501 H Street, NE
Washington, DC 20002
202-544-8353
Fax: 202-544-3051
Email: yulonda.queen@hstreetcdc.org
www.cdsc.org/404.html
Executive Director: William Barrow
Microloan Contact: Yulonda Queen
Service Area: West-the Anacostia River; East-7th Street, NW; North-Benning Road to K Street; and South-the Southeast/ Southwest Freeway: Servicing Capitol Hill, H Street, NE, Lincoln Park, Mt. Vernon Square, Judiciary Square, Benning Road-West of the Anacostia River, Union Station, Stadium Armory, and Lower North Capitol. Eastern border of North Capitol to Rhode Island to 7th Street NW; West-Anacostia River; North-Eastern Avenue to North Capitol; and Southeast/Southwest Freeway: Servicing Eckington, Catholic University, Michigan Park, Edgewood, Brookland, Ft. Lincoln, New York Avenue, Florida Avenue, Brentwood-DC, Woodridge, Trinidad, and NE Rhode Island Avenue, Silver Springs, Takoma Park, Hyattsville, Riverdale, Bladensburg, Seat Pleasant, Capitol Heights, District Heights, Cheverly, Landover, Suitland, Hillcrest Heights, Marlow Heights, Oxon Hill, Mt. Ranier, and Coral Hills.

East of the River Community Development Corporation
3101 Martin Luther King, Jr. Ave., SE
Washington, DC 20032
202-561-4974
Fax: 202-561-4978
Email: gilliam@ercdc.org
www.ercdc.org/
Exec. Director: W. Retta Gilliam
Microloan Contact: W. Retta Gilliam
Service Area: Portion of southeast Washington DC commonly known as Ward 8. Westernmost boundary of the Anacostia River; Oxon Creek, Oxon Run Drive to Southern Avenue, SE; Northeast to Naylor Road, SE; Southwest of Altamont Place, SE; Pearson Street, SE to Erie Street, SE; West of Erie to Morris Street, SE; North of Chicago Street, SE to Interstate 295; North of Interstate 295 to the 11th Street bridge southeast to the Anacostia River

Florida

Community Equity Investments, Inc.
302 North Barcelona St.
Pensacola, FL 32501
850-595-6234

Fax: 850-595-6264
Email: bigdanfla@aol.com
www.ceii.pensacola.com/
Executive Director: Dan Horvath
Microloan Contact: Elbert Jones
Service Area: Florida Panhandle including Bay, Calhoun, Escambia, Gadsden, Gulf, Jackson, Holmes, Liberty, Leon, Franklin, Wakulla, Walton, Wasington, Okaloosa, and Santa Rosa counties

United Gainesville Community Dev. Corp., Inc.
505 NW 2nd Avenue
P.O. Box 2518
Gainesville, FL 32602
352-334-0943
Fax: 352-334-0947
Email: vian@ugcdc.org
Email: lyndah@ugcdc.org
Executive Director: Appie L. Graham
Microloan Contact: Appie L. Graham
Service Area: Alachua and Marion counties

Central Florida Community Development Corporation
P.O. Box 15065
Daytona Beach, FL 32115
368-258-7520
Fax: 368-238-3428
Email: geraldc@n-jcenter.com
www.cfcdc.com/
Executive Director:
Microloan Contact: Gerald O. Chester
Service Area: Brevard county

Clearwater Neighborhood Housing Services, Inc.
608 North Garden Avenue
Clearwater, FL 33755
727-442-4155
Fax: 727-446-4911
Executive Director: Isay M. Gulley
Microloan Contact: John J. Moloney
Service Area: City of Clearwater and Pinellas County

Minority/Women Business Enterprise Alliance, Inc.
625 E. Colonial Drive
Orlando, FL 32803
407-428-5860
Fax: 407-428-5869
www.allianceflorida.com/
Executive Director: Geovanny Sepulveda
Microloan Contact: Geovanny Sepulveda
Service Area: Orange, Osceola, Lake, Seminole, Polk, Hillsborough, Sumter, Brevard, Volusia, and Marion counties

Partners for Self-Employment, Inc./ d.b.a./Micro-Business, USA
3000 Biscayne Boulevard Suite 102
Miami, FL 33137
877-722-4505
Fax: 305-438-1411
www.microbusinessusa.org/
Executive Director: Diane Silverman
Microloan Contact: Diane Silverman
Service Area: Miami-Dade, Broward, Palm Beach and Pinellas counties

Tampa Bay Economic Development Corporation
2105 N. Nebraska Avenue 2nd Floor
Tampa, FL 33602
813-274-7969
Fax: 813-274-7551

www.tampagov.net/dept_TEDCO/
Executive Director:
Microloan Contact: George Guida
Service Area: Hillsborough county

The Business Loan Fund of the Palm Beaches, Inc.
1016 North Dixie Highway, 2nd Floor
West Palm Beach, FL 33401
561-838-9027
Fax: 561-838-9029
Email: blfpb@evcom.net
www.businessloanfund.org/index.html
Executive Director: John B. Brown
Microloan Contact: John B. Brown
Service Area: Palm Beach County, Hendry, Indian River, Martin, Palm Beach County Development Regions and St. Lucie

Georgia
Enterprise Funding Corp/GRASP Enterprises
241 Peachtree Street, Suite 200
Atlanta, GA 30303
404-659-5955
Fax: 404-880-9561
Email: tscott@graspnet.org
www.grasp.net
Executive Director: Maurice Coakley
Microloan Contact: Tim Scott
Service Area: Fulton, Dekalb, Cobb, Gwinnett, Fayette, Clayton, Henry, Douglas, and Rockdale counties

Small Business Assistance Corporation
111 E. Liberty St., Suite 100
P.O. Box 10750
Savannah, GA 31412-0716
912-232-4700
Fax: 912-232-0385
Email: toreilly@sbacsav.com
www.sbacsav.com/
Executive Director: Tony O'Reilly
Microloan Contact: Tony O'Reilly/Stephen George
Service Area: Appling, Atkinson, Brooks, Bacon, Berrien, Ben Hill, Bryan, Bulloch, Bleekly, Brantley, Coffee, Charlton, Camden, Clinch, Candler, Cook, Chatham, Dodge, Emanuel, Echols, Effingham, Evans, Glynn, Irwin, Johnson, Jeff Davis, Laurens, Liberty, Long, Lowndes, Lanier, McIntosh, Montgomery, Pierce, Tift, Turner, Telfair, Truetlen, Toombs, Tattnall, Ware, Wilcox, Wayne, and Wheeler counties

Southeast Community Capital
1020 Commerce Park Drive
Oak Ridge, TN 37830
865-220-2020
Fax: 865-220-2030
Email: hortonw@tech2020.org
Executive Director: Don Welty
Microloan Contact: David Bradshaw
Service Area: Barrow, Bartow, Carroll, Cherokee, Dade, Elbert, Fannin, Floyd, Franklin, Gordon, Gwinnett, Hall, Hart, Heard, Paulding, Pickens, Polk, Stephens, Union, Walker, and Whitfield

Hawaii
Pacific Gateway Center
720 N. King St.
Honolulu, HI 96817
808-845-3918
Fax: 808-842-1962
Email: pgcmyaing@hotmail.com

www.pacificgateway.org
Exec. Dir.: Tin Myaing Thein
Microloan Contact:
Service Area: Statewide

Idaho

Sage Community Resources
10624 W. Executive Dr.
Boise, ID 83713
208-322-7033
Fax: 208-322-3569
Email: pmchoate@ida-ore.com
www.sageidaho.com/
Executive Director: Robert Barber
Microloan Contact: Bob Richards
Service Area: Payette, Washington, Adams, Valley, Gem, Boise, Elmore, Ada, Canyon and Owhyee counties

Panhandle Area Council
11100 Airport Dr.
Hayden, ID 83835-9743
208-772-0584
Fax: 208-772-6196
Email: pacbus@nidlink.com or ksmith@pacni.org
www.pacni.org/
Exec. Dir.: James Deffenbaugh
Microloan Contact: kay Kitchel
Service Area: Northern Panhandle including Benewah, Bonner, Boundary, Kotenai, and Shoshone counties

Illinois

Accion Chicago, Inc.
3245 W. 26th
Chicago, IL 60623
773-376-9004
Fax: 773-376-9048
Email: lpacheco@accionchicago.org
www.accionchicago.org/
President: F. Leroy Pacheco
Microloan Contact: Jonathan Brereton
Service Area: Cook County (including parts of Chicago), Lake, McHenry, Dekalb, Kane, Dupage, Kendall, Grundy, Kankanee, Will, and Lasalle counties

Justine Petersen Housing & Reinvestment Corporation
5031 Northrup Avenue
St. Louis, MO 63110
314-664-5051 ext. 117
Fax: 314-644-5364
Email: sflanigan@justinepetersen.org
http://justinepetersen.org/
Executive Director: Robert Boyle
Microloan Contact: Sheri Fannigan-Vasquez
Service Area: Clinton, Jersey, Madison, and St. Clair counties

Neighborhood Inst./Women's Self Employment Project
11 South LaSalle Street, Suite 1850
Chicago, IL 60603
312-606-8255
Fax: 312-606-9215
Email: wsepaa@wsep.com
www.wsep.net
Executive Director: Wanda White
Microloan Contact: Wanda White
Service Area: Portions of the City of Chicago

Indiana

Seed-Corp
216 W. Allen Street
Bloomington, IN 47403

812-323-7827
Fax: 812-335-7352
Email: tbrown@thestarcenter.com
www.seed-corp.org
Executive Director: Terri Brown
Microloan Contact: Charlotte Zietlow, Beth Kuebler
Service Area: Morgan, Owen, Greene, Lawrence, Monroe, Brown, and Jackson Bartholomew, Decatur, Jennings counties

Iowa

Siouxland Economic Development Corporation
428 Insurance Center
507 7th St.
P.O. Box 447
Sioux City, IA 51102
712-279-6286
Fax: 712-279-6920
Email: glenda@simpco.org
www.siouxlandedc.com
Executive Director: Ken Beekley
Microloan Contact:
Service Area: Cherokee, Ida Monona, Plymouth, Sioux, and Woodbury counties

Kansas

South Central Kansas Economic Development District, Inc.
209 East William Street, Suite 300
Wichita, KS 67214
316-262-7035
Fax: 316-262-7062
www.sckedd.org/
Exec. Dir.: William Bolin
Microloan Contact: Christie Henry
Service Area: Butler, Chautauqua, Cowley, Elk, Greenwood, Harper, Harvey, Kingman, Marion, McPherson, Reno, Rice, Sedgwick, and Sumner counties

Growth Opportunity Connection (Go Connection)
4747 Troost Ave.
Kansas City, MO 64110
816-235-6146
Fax: 816-756-1530
Email: info@goconnection.org
www.goconnection.org
Executive Director: Alan Corbet
Microloan Contact: Rebecca Gubbels
Service Area: Wyandotte, Johnson, Douglas, and Leavenworth counties

Kentucky

Community Ventures Corporation
1450 N. Broadway
Lexington, KY 40505
816-231-0054
Fax: 816-231-0261
Email: cvccorp@prodigy.net
www.cvcky.org/
Executive Director: Kevin Smith
Microloan Contact: Tyrone Tyra/David Collins
Service Area: Anderson, Bourbon, Boyle, Clark, Estill, Fayette, Franklin, Garrard, Harrison, Jessamine, Lincoln, Madison, Mercer, Nicholas, Powell, Scott, and Woodford counties

Kentucky Highlands Investment Corporation
362 Whitley Rd.
P.O. Box 1738
London, KY 40743-1738
606-864-5175

Fax: 606-864-5194
Email: cbowles@khic.org
www.khic.org/default.htm
Executive Director: Jerry Rickett
Microloan Contact: Edgar Davis/Cindy Bowles
Service Area: Bell, Clay, Clinton, Harlan, Jackson, McCreary, Rockcastle, Wayne, and Whitley counties

Louisville Central Development Corporation/Business Plus
1407 W. Jefferson St., Suite 200
Louisville, KY 40203
502-583-8821
Fax: 502-583-8824
Email: swatkins@louisvillecentralcenters.org
www.lcccnews.org
Executive Director: Sam Watkins Jr.
Microloan Contact: Kirk Bright
Service Area: Jefferson County/Primary focus Enterprise Empowerment Zone

Purchase Area Development District
1002 Medical Drive
P.O. Box 588
Mayfield, KY 42066
502-247-7171
Fax: 502-251-6110
Email: henry.hodges@mail.state.ky.uw
www.purchaseadd.org/
Executive Director: Henry Hodges
Microloan Contact: Norma Reed-Drouin
Service Area: Ballard, Calloway, Carlisle, Fulton, Graves, Hickman, McCracken and Marshall counties

Louisiana
NewCorp Business Assistance Center
1600 Canal Street, Suite 601
New Orleans, LA 70112
504-539-9340
Fax: 504-539-9343
Email: newcorpinfo@newcorpbac.net
www.newcorpbac.net
Executive Director: Vaughn R. Fauria
Microloan Contact: Romona D. Summers
Service Area: State of Louisiana

Maine
Coastal Enterprises, Inc.
P.O. Box 268
36 Water Street
Wiscasset, ME 04578
207-882-7552
Fax: 207-882-7308
Email: efg@cei.maine.org or jgs@cei.maine.org
www.ceimaine.org/
Executive Director: Ronald Phillips
Microloan Contact: Ellen Golden
Service Area: Statewide excluding Aroostock, Piscataquis, Washington, Oxford, Penobscot and Hancock counties

Northern Maine Development Commission
302 S. Main St.
P.O. Box 779
Caribou, ME 04736
207-498-8736
Fax: 207-493-3108
Email: rclark@nmdc.org
www.nmdc.org/indexv1.cfm
Executive Director: Robert Clark
Microloan Contact: Duane Walton
Service Area: Aroostook

In consortium with
Eastern Maine Development Corporation
One Cumberland Pl., Suite 300
Bangor, ME 04401
207-942-6389
Fax: 207-942-3548
Email: dmetzler@emdc.org
Executive Director: David Cole
Microloan Contact: Debbie Metzler
Service Area: Hancock, Penobscot, Piscataquis, and Washington counties

Community Concepts, Inc.
19 Market Sq.
P.O. Box 278
South Paris, ME 04281
207-743-7716
Fax: 207-743-6513
Email: wriseman@community-concepts.org
www.community-concepts.org/
Executive Director: Charleen Chase
Microloan Contact: Walter Riseman
Service Area: Oxford county

Androscoggin Valley Council of Government
125 Manley Road
Auburn, ME 04210
207-783-9186
Fax: 207-783-5211
Email: gwhitney@avcog.org
www.avcog.org/
Executive Director: Robert J. Thompson
Microloan Contact: Julie Sherman
Service Area: Androscoggin, Franklin and Oxford counties

Maryland
The Development Credit Fund
2526 N. Charles St. Suite 200
Baltimore, MD 21218
410-235-8100
Fax: 410-235-5899
Email: ejohnson@developmentcredit.net
www.developmentcredit.com/
Executive Director: Acknell M. Muldrow, II
Microloan Contact: Erik Johnson
Service Area: Statewide Maryland excluding Montgomery and Prince Georges counties

H Street Community Development Corporation
501 H Street, NE
Washington, DC 20002
202-544-8353
Fax: 202-544-3051
Email: oomhscdc@aol.com
www.hstreetcdc.org/
Exec. Director: William Barrow
Microloan Contact: Yulonda Queen
Service Area: Montgomery and Prince George's counties

Massachusetts
Economic Development Industrial Corp. of Lynn
37 Central Square, 3rd Floor
Lynn, MA 01901
617-581-9399
Fax: 617-581-9731
Email: pdeveau@shore.net
Exec. Director: Peter M. DeVeau
Microloan Contact: Peter M. DeVeau/Mary Smalley
Service Area: City of Lynn

Jewish Vocational Service, Inc.
105 Chauncy St., 6th Floor
Boston, MA 02111
617-451-8147
Fax: 617-451-9973
Email: ekorsh@jvs-boston.org
www.jvs-bosten.org/
Exec. Dir.: Barbara Rosenbaum
Microloan Contact: Erik Korsh
Service Area: Greater Boston with special emphasis on businesses in the Boston Enterprise Zone/Boston Empowerment Zone, and businesses in Mattapan, Dorchester, Roxbury, Hyde Park, and Jamaica Plain

Jobs for Fall River, Inc.
One Government Center
Fall River, MA 02722
508-324-2620
Fax: 508-677-2840
Email: kenfiolajn@aol.com
Executive Director: Kenneth Fiola
Microloan Contact: Stephen Parr
Service Area: City of Fall River

Greater Springfield Entrepreneurial Fund
1176 Main St.
Springfield, MA 01103
413-781-6900
Fax: 413-736-0650
Email: hcetc@javanet.com
Executive Director: Jim Krzytofik
Microloan Contact: James Asselin
Service Area: Hampden County excluding the towns of Chester and Chicopes.

Western Massachusetts Enterprise Fund
P.O. Box 1077
Greenfield, MA 01302
413-774-4033
Fax: 413-773-3673
Email: info@wmef.org
www.wmef.org/
Exec. Director: Christopher Sikes
Microloan Contact: Moon Morgan
Service Area: Berkshire, Franklin counties, the towns of Chester and Chicopes within Hampden county, the towns of Athol, Petersham, Phillipston and Royalston within Worcester county, and Hampshire county.

Community Development Transportation Lending Services
1341 G Street, NW, Suite 600
Washington, DC 20005
202-661-0210
Fax: 202-737-9197
Email: Kellogg@ctaa.org
www.ctaa.org/transitfunding/
Executive Director: Dale J. Marsico
Microloan Contact: Patrick Kellogg
Service Area: North Central Massachusetts - county subdivisions of Athol, Winchendon, Gardner, Templeton, Phillipston, Orange, Erving, Wendell, Montague, Gill, and Greenfield counties

South Eastern Economic Development Corp/SEED
80 Dean Street
Taunton, MA 02780
508-822-1020
Fax: 508-880-7869
Email: SEEDCORP@aol.com
www.seedcorp.com/

Executive Director: Maria Gooch-Smith
Microloan Contact: Janice Johnson Plumer
Service Area: SE Massachusetts – Norfolk, Bristol, Plymouth,Barnstable, Dukes, and Nantucket counties

Michigan

Center for Empowerment and Economic Development (CEED)
2002 Hogback Rd., Suite 12
Ann Arbor, MI 48105
734-677-1400
Fax: 734-677-1465
Email: mrichards@wwnet.net
www.miceed.org/
Exec. Director: Michelle Richards
Microloan Contact: Michelle Richards
Service Area: Washtenaw, Oakland, Wayne and Livingston counties.

Community Capital Development Corp.
The Walter Reuther Center
316 W. Water St.
Flint, MI 48503
810-239-5847
Fax: 810-239-5575
Email: ccdc@tir.com
Executive Director: Harold Hill
Microloan Contact: Jarasha Washington
Service Area: Genesee county

Northern Economic Initiatives Corp.
228 West Washington St.
Marquette, MI 49855
906-226-1662
800-254-2156
Fax: 906-228-5572
Email: todd_horton@northernminits.com
www.northerninitiatives.com
Microloan Contact: Todd Horton
Service Area: Upper Peninsula of Michigan.

Rural Michigan Intermediary Relending Program, Inc.
121 East Front Street Suite 201
Traverse City, MI 49686
231-941-5858
Fax: 231-941-4616
Email: mhaddad@timbc.com
Executive Director: Michael Haddad
Microloan Contact: Stephen Spencer
Service Area: Emmet, Charlevoix, Antrim, Leelanau, Benzie, Grand, Traverse, Kalkaska, Manistee, Wexford, Missaukee, Cheboygan, Presque Isle, Otsego, Montmorency, Alpena, Crawford, Oscoda, Alcona, Roscommon, Ogemaw, Iosco, Osceola, Mason, Lake counties

Saginaw Economic Development Corporation
301 E. Genesee, 3rd Floor
Saginaw, MI 48607
989-759-1395
Fax: 989-754-1715
Email: SEDCLW@aol.com
www.saginawfuture.com/
Executive Director: Leslie Weaver
Microloan Contact: Leslie Weaver
Service Area: Saginaw county

Minnesota

Northeast Entrepreneur Fund, Inc.
8355 Unity Drive, Suite 100
Virginia, MN 55792

218-749-4191
800-422-0374
Fax: 218-741-4249
Email: info@necfund.org
www.entrepreneurfund.org
Exec. Director: Mary Mathews
Microloan Contact: Alison Beauregard
Service Area: Koochiching, Itasca, St. Louis, Aitkin, Carlton, Cook Cass, Pine and Lake counties

Women Venture
2324 University Ave., Suite 200
St. Paul, MN 55112
651-646-3808
Fax: 651-291-2597
Email: sbaker@womenventure.org
www.womenventure.org
Exec. Director: Tene Heidelberg
Microloan Contact: Jan Jordet
Service Area: Cities of Minneapolis and St. Paul, and Anoka, Carver, Chisago, Dakota, Hennepin, Isanti, Ramsey, Scott, Steele, Washington, and Wright counties

Minneapolis Consortium of Community Developers
2308 Central Ave. NE
Minneapolis, MN 55418
612-789-7337
Fax: 612-789-8448
Email: jroth@cando.org
www.mccdmn.org/
Executive Director: Jim Roth
Microloan Contact: Jim Roth
Service Area: Portions of the City of Minneapolis

Northwest Minnesota Foundation
4225 Technology Drive, NW
Bemidji, MN 56601
218-759-2057
Fax: 218-759-2328
Email: timw@nwmf.org
www.nwmf.org
Executive Director: John Ostem
Microloan Contact: Tim Wang
Service Area: Beltrami, Clearwater, Hubbard, Kittsson, Lake of the Woods, Mahnomen, Marshall, Norman, Pennington, Polk, Red Lake, and Rousseau counties

Southern Minnesota Initiative Foundation
525 Florence Avenue
P.O. Box 695
Owatonna, MN 55060
507-455-3215
Fax: 507-455-2098
Email: patricks@smifoundation.org
www.smifoundation.org/
Executive Director: Patrick T. Stallman
Microloan Contact: Patrick T. Stallman
Service Area: Sibley, Nicollett, LeSueur, Rice, Wabasha, Brown, Watonwan, Blue Earth, Waseca, Dodge, Olmsted, Winona, Martin, Faribault, Freeborn, Mower, Fillmore, and Houston

Southwest Minnesota Foundation
1390 HWY 15 South
P.O. Box 428
Hutchinson, MN 55350
320-587-4848
Fax: 320-587-3838
Email: bernyb@swmnfoundation.com
www.swmnfoundation.org/

Executive Director: Sherry Ristau
Microloan Contact: Bernadette Berger
Service Area: 18 counties of Southwest, MN (Big Stone, Chippewa, Cottonwood, Jackson, Kandiyphi, Lac qui Parle, Lincoln, Lyon, McLeod, Meeker, Murray, Nobles, Pipestone, Renville, Rock, Swift, and Yellow Medicine)

Mississippi
Delta Foundation
819 Main St.
Greenville, MS 38701
662-335-5291
Fax: 662-335-5295
Email: fdn@tecinfo.com
Executive Director: Harry Bowie
Microloan Contact: Lucille Dean
Service Area: Statewide excluding Issaquena, Sharkey, Humphreys, Madison, Leake, Kemper, Copiah, Hinds, Rankin, Newton, Smith, Jasper, Clarke, Jones, Wayne, and Greene counties

Friends of Children of Mississippi, Inc.
939 North President St.
Jackson, MS 39202
601-353-3264
Fax: 601-714-4278
Executive Director: Marvin Hogan
Microloan Contact: Brenetta Walker
Service Area: Statewide

Missouri
Growth Opportunity Connection (Go Connection)
4747 Troost Ave.
Kansas City, MO 64110
816-561-8567
Fax: 816-756-1530
Email: acorbet@kc-cbi.org
www.goconnection.org/
Executive Director: Alan Corbet
Microloan Contact: Alan Corbet
Service Area: Platte, Jackson, Clay and Cass counties.

Justine Petersen Housing & Reinvestment Corporation
5031 Northrup Avenue
St. Louis, MO 63110
314-664-5051 ext. 117
Fax: 314-664-5364
Email: sflanigan@justinepetersen.org
www.justinepetersen.org/
Executive Director: Robert Boyle
Microloan Contact: Sheri Fanigan-Vazquez
Service Area: Counties of Franklin, Jefferson, Lincoln, St. Charles, St. Louis, Warren, and the City of St. Louis

Rural Missouri, Incorporated
1014 Northeast Drive
Jefferson City, MO 65109
573-635-0136
Fax: 573-635-5636
Email: zola@rmiinc.org kluke45@mailexcel.com
www.rminc.org
Executive Director: Ken Lueckenotte
Microloan Contact: Zola Finch
Service Area: Statewide excluding Platte, Jackson, Clay and Cass counties

Montana
Capital Opportunities/District IX HRDC, Inc.
321 E. Main St., Suite 300
Bozeman, MT 59715

406-587-5444
Fax: 406-585-3538
Executive Director: Jeff Rupp
Microloan Contact: Kittie Bowen
Service Area: Gallatin, Park and Meagher counties

Montana Community Development Corp.
110 East Broadway, 2nd Floor
Missoula, MT 59802
406-728-9234
Fax: 406-542-6671
Email: mcdc@mtcdc.org
www.mtcdc.org/
Executive Director: Rosalie Cates
Microloan Contact: Mica Nioleyczik
Service Area: Lake, Mineral, Missoula, Ravalli, and Sanders counties

Nebraska

Rural Enterprise Assistance Project
Center for Rural Affairs
101 S. Tallman St.
P.O. Box 406
Walthill, NE 68067
402-846-5428
Fax: 402-846-5420
Email: gerardr@cfra.org or
Jeffr@alltel.net
www.cfra.org/reap
Executive Director: Chuck Hassebrook
Microloan Contact: Jeff Reynolds/Gerard Ras
Service Area: Adams, Antelope, Banner, Blaine, Boone, Box Butte, Boyd, Brown, Burralo, Burt, Butler, Cass, Cedar, Cherry, Cheyenne, Clay, Colfax, Cuming, Custer, Dakota, Dawes, Deuel, Dixon, Dodge, Fillmore, Franklin, Gage, Garden, Garfield, Greeley, Hall, Hamilton, Harlan, Holt, Howard, Jefferson, Johnson, Kearney, Keya Paha, Kimball, Knox, Lancaster, Loup, Madison, McPherson, Merrick, Morrill, Nance, Nemaha, Nuckolls, Otoe, Pawnee, Phelps, Pierce, Platte, Polk, Richardson, Rock, Saline, Saunders, Seward, Sheridan, Sherman, Sioux, Scottsbluff, Stanton, Thayer, Thurston, Valley, Washington, Wayne, Webster, Wheeler and York counties

West Central Nebraska Development District, Inc.
201 East 2nd Street, Suite C
P.O. Box 599
Ogailala, NE 69153
308-284-6077
Fax: 308-284-6070
Email: mowcndd@lakemac.net
Executive Director: Martin O'Haus
Microloan Contact: Paul Rausch
Service Area: Arthur, Chase, Dawson, Dundy, Frontier, Furnas, Gosper, Grant, Hayes, Hitchcock, Hooker, Keith, Lincoln, Logan, MacPherson, Perkins, Red Willow, and Thomas counties

Nevada

Nevada Microenterprise Initiative
113 West Plumb Lane
Reno, NV 89509
702-734-3555
Fax: 702-734-3530
Email: asiefert@earthlink.net
www.nmimicro.org/
Executive Director: Nancy Erends Bahr
Microloan Contact: Anna Siefert
Service Area: Statewide

New Hampshire

Northern Community Investment Corp.
347 Portland St.
P.O. Box 904
St. Johnsbury, VT 05819
802-748-5101
Fax: 802-748-1884
Email: carol@ncic.org
www.ncic.org
Executive Director:
Microloan Contact: Carol Walker
Service Area: Grafton, Carol and Coos counties

New Jersey

Trenton Business Assistance Corp.
209 E. Front St.
Trenton, NJ 08608
609-396-8271
Fax: 609-396-0559
Email: info@tbacloan.com
www.tbacloan.com
Executive Director: Deborah Osgood
Microloan Contact: Russ Haas
Service Area: Portions of the City of Trenton, Hunterdon, Mercer, Burlington, and Warren counties

Greater Newark Business Development Consortium
774 Broad St., 26th Floor
Newark, NJ 07102-5265
973-242-4134
Fax: 973-242-0485
www.gnbdc.org/
Executive Director: David Means
Microloan Contact: David Means
Service Area: Bergen, Essex, Hudson, Middlesex, Monmouth, Morris, Passaic, Sussex and Ocean counties.

Union County Economic Development Corp.
Liberty Hall Corporate Center
1085 Morris Ave., Suite 531
Union, NJ 07083
908-527-1166
Fax: 908-527-1207
Email: afarrah@ucedc.com
www.ucedc.com
Executive Director: Maureen Tinen
Microloan Contact: Carlos N. Sanchez
Service Area: Union and Somerset counties

Community Lending and Investment Corp. of Jersey City
30 Montgomery Street
Jersey City, NJ 07302
201-333-7797
Fax: 201-946-9367
www.jcedc.org/clic.shtml
Executive Director: Thomas Ahern
Microloan Contact: John Rodgers
Service Area: City of Jersey City

Cooperative Business Assistance Corporation
328 Market St.
2nd Floor, Suite 201
Camden, NJ 08102
856-966-8181
Fax: 856-966-0036
Email: hstonecbac2000@aol.com
www.cbaclenders.com/home.html
Executive Director: R. Michael Diemer
Microloan Contact: R. Michael Diemer

Service Area: Camden, Gloucester, Atlantic, Cape May, Cumberland, and Salem counties

New Mexico
Women's Economic Self Sufficiency Team
414 Silver SW
Albuquerque, NM 87102-3239
505-241-4670
Fax: 505-241-4766
Email: agnes@swcp.com or dbaca@swcp.com
www.wesst.org/
Executive Director: Agnes Noonan
Microloan Contact: Debbie Baca
Service Area: Statewide

New York
Adirondack Economic Development Corporation
60 Main St., Suite 200
P.O. Box 747
Saranac Lake, NY 12983
518-891-5523
Fax: 518-891-9820
Email: beverly@aedconline.com
www.aedconline.com/
Executive Director: Ernest Hohmeyer
Microloan Contact: Beverly Desot
Service Area: Clinton, Essex, Franklin, Fulton, Hamilton, Herkimer, Jefferson, Lewis, Oneida, Oswego, St. Lawrence, Saratoga, Warren and Washington counties

Hudson Development Company
444 Warren St.
Hudson, NY 12534-2415
518-828-4718
Fax: 518-828-0901
Email: jgalvin@mhcable.com
Executive Director: Bernadina C. Torrye
Microloan Contact: John Galvin
Service Area: Columbia and Green counties

Manhattan Borough Development Corp.
55 Johns St., 17th Floor
New York, NY 10038
212-791-3660
Fax: 212-571-0873
Email: ochapman@mbdc.org
www.mbdc.org/
Executive Director: Ollie Chapman
Microloan Contact: Marta Gomez
Service Area: The borough of Manhattan

Rural Opportunities Enterprise Center, Inc.
400 East Avenue
Rochester, NY 14607
585-340-3387
Fax: 585-340-3326
Email: jdallis@ruralinc.org
www.ruralinc.org
Executive Director: Lee Beaulac
Microloan Contact: John Bell
Service Area: Allegheny, Cattaraugua, Cayuga, Chatauqua, Erie, Genessee, Livingston, Niagara, Ontario, Orleans, Seneca, Steuben, Wayne, Wyoming, Ulster, Onandaga, Monroe, Schuyler, Duchess, Chemung, Greene, Orange, Putnam, Sullivan, and Yates counties

Alternatives Federal Credit Union
125 N. Fulton St.
Ithaca, NY 14850
607-273-3582

Fax: 607-277-6391
Email: jhalleron@alternatives.org
www.alternatives.org/
Executive Director: William Myers
Microloan Contact: John Halleron
Service Area: Schuyler, Tompkins, Tioga, Cortland, Chemung, and Broome counties

Buffalo Economic Renaissance Corp. (BERC)
617 Main Street
Buffalo, NY 14203
716-842-6923
Fax: 716-842-6942
Email: mcurrie@berc.org
www.growbfo.org/
Executive Director: Marie F. Curie
Microloan Contact: Marie F. Curie
Service Area: City of Buffalo

Buffalo and Erie County Industrial Land Development Corp.
275 Oak Street
Buffalo, NY 14203
716-856-6525
Fax: 716-856-6754
Email: dkerchof@ecidany.com
www.ecidany.com/
Executive Director: David Kerchoff
Microloan Contact: David Kerchoff
Service Area: Erie County

Community Development Corporation of Long Island
2100 Middle Country Rd
Suite 300
Centereach, NY 11720
631-471-1215
Fax: 631-471-1210
Email: tdavis@cdcli.org
www.cdcli.org
Executive Director: Wilbur Klatsky
Microloan Contact: Trevor Davis
Service Area: Suffolk and Nassau counties

Albany-Colonie Regional Chamber of Commerce
1 Computer Drive South
Albany, NY 12205
518-453-5223
Fax: 518-453-5220
Email: walterb@ac-chamber.org
www.ac-chamber.org/
Executive Director: Madeline Taylor
Microloan Contact: Walter Burke
Service Area: Albany, Rensselaer, Saratoga, Schenectady, Schoharie, Greene, Fulton, and Montgomery counties

NY Assoc. for New Americans, Inc.
17 Battery Place
New York, NY 10004
212-425-5051
Fax: 212-425-7260
Email: mhandelm@nyana.org
www.nyana.org/
Executive Director: Mark Handelman
Microloan Contact: Maya Crawford
Service Area: The borough of Queens, Manhattan, the Bronx, Brooklyn, and Staten Island.

Renaissance Economic Development Corporation
1 Pike Street
New York, NY 10002
212-964-6002

Fax: 212-964-6181
Email: benjamin@renaissance-ny.org
www.renaissance-ny.org/
Executive Director: Benjamin Warnke
Microloan Contact: Susan Yee
Service Area: The boroughs of Brooklyn, Manhattan, and Queens

North Carolina
Self-Help Ventures Fund
301 W. Main St.
P.O. Box 3619
Durham, NC 27701
919-956-4400
Fax: 919-956-4600
Email: bob@self-help.org
www.self-help.com
Executive Director: Martin Eakes
Microloan Contact: Bob Schall/Carolyn Walker
Service Area: Statewide, excluding Watauga, Avery, Mitchell and Yancey counties

W.A.M.Y. Community Action
152 Southgate Dr., Suite 2
Box 2688
Boone, NC 28607
828-264-2421
Fax: 828-264-0952
Email: wamyloan@boone.net
Executive Director: Dr. James Jordan
Microloan Contact: Dave Lindsley
Service Area: Watauga, Avery, Mitchell, and Yancey counties

Neuse River Development Authority, Inc.
233 Middle Street 2rd Floor
New Bern, NC 28563
252-638-6724 Ext. 3032
Fax: 252-638-1819
Email: bbrown@nrda.org
www.nrda.org/
Executive Director: Donald T. Stewart
Microloan Contact: Barbara Brown
Service Area: Carteret, Craven, Duplin, Greene, Jones, Johnston, Lenoir, Onslow, Pamlico and Wayne counties

North Dakota
Lake Agassiz Regional Development Corporation
417 Main Ave.
Fargo, ND 58103
701-235-1197
Fax: 701-235-6706
Email: darin@lakeagassiz.com
Executive Director: Irvin Rustad
Microloan Contact: Darin Bullinger
Service Area: Griggs, Bismarck, Mandan, Jamestown, and Valley City

Dakota Certified Development Corporation
51 Broadway Suite 500
Fargo, ND 58102
701-293-8892
Fax: 701-293-7819
Email: toby@fedc.com or wendy@dakotacdc.com
www.dakotacdc.com/
Executive Director: Toby Sticka
Microloan Contact: Wendy Simek
Service Area: Grand Forks, Devils Lake, Minot, Williston, and Dickinson counties

Ohio
Enterprise Development Corporation
9030 Hocking Hills Dr.
The Plains, OH 45780-1209
740-797-9646
Fax: 740-797-9659
Email: llathan@edcseo.org or
gseeley@edcseo.org
www.edcseo.org/
Executive Director: Gary Seeley
Microloan Contact: Lisa Latham
Service Area: Adams, Ashland, Athens, Belmont, Brown, Carrol, Columbiana, Coshocton, Gallia, Guernsey, Harrison, Highland, Hocking, Holmes, Jackson, Jefferson, Knox, Lawrence, Meigs, Monroe, Morgan, Muskingum, Noble, Perry, Pike, Ross, Scioto, Tuscarawas, Vinton and Washington counties

Community Capital Development Corporation
900 Michigan Ave.
Columbus, OH 43215-1165
614-645-6171
800-756-CCDC
Fax: 614-645-8588
Email: fvincent@columbus.rr.com or bshimp@ccdcorp.org
www.ccdcorp.org/
Executive Director: Brad Shrimp
Microloan Contact: Kendra Krebs-Vincenty
Service Area: Franklin, Delaware, Fairfield, Licking, Union, Pickaway, Fayette, and Madison counties

Hamilton County Development Co., Inc.
1776 Mentor Ave.
Cincinnati, OH 45212
513-631-8292
Fax: 513-631-4887
Email: lawalden@hcdc.com
www.hcdc.com/
Executive Director: David Main
Microloan Contact: Lou Ann Walden
Service Area: City of Cincinnati, Adams, Brown, Butler, Clermont, Clinton, Hamilton, Highland, and Warren counties

Women's Organization for Mentoring, Entrepreneurship, and Networking
526 S. Main St., Suite 235
Akron, OH 44311-1058
330-379-9280
Fax: 330-379-3454
Email: women@ald.net
www.womennet.org/
Executive Director: Janice Robinson
Microloan Contact: Janice Robinson
Service Area:Cuyahoga, Lake, Lorain, Mahoning, Medina, Stark, Summit, and Wayne counties.

County Corp Development
40 W. Fourth St. Ste. 1600
Dayton, OH 45402
937-225-6328
Fax: 937-225-5089
Email: ed@countycorp.com
www.countycorp.com/
Executive Director: Marni Flagle
Microloan Contact: Tracy Shultz
Service Area: Miami, Montgomery, and Greene county

Kent Regional Business Alliance
College of Business #300-A, KSU
Kent, OH 44242

330-672-1275
Fax: 330-672-9338
Email: lyost@bsa3.kent.edu
www.business.kent.edu/dean/krba.htm
Executive Director: Linda Yost
Microloan Contact:
Service Area: Ashtabula, Geauga, Trumbull, Portage, Columbiana, Carroll, Holmes, Coshocton, Tuscarawas, Stark, and Harrison counties

Working for Empowerment through Community Organizing (WECO)
2700 E. 79th Street, 4th Street
Cleveland, OH 44104
216-881-9650
Fax: 216-881-9704
Email: judi@wecofund.com
www.wecofund.com/
Executive Director: Judith W. Miles
Microloan Contact:
Service Area: Cuyahoga county

Oklahoma

Rural Enterprises, Inc.
2912 Enterprise Blvd.
P.O. Box 1335
Durant, OK 74702
580-924-5094
Fax: 580-920-2745
Email: veazie@ruralenterprises.com or debbiep@ruralenterprises.com
www.ruralenterprises.com/
Executive Director: Tom Smith
Microloan Contact: Ray Veazie/Debbie Partin
Service Area: Statewide excluding Adair, Canadian, Cherokee, Cleveland, Craig, Creek, Delaware, Haskell, Hayes, Hughes, Kay, Latimer, Leflore, Lincoln, Logan, McIntosh, Muskogee, Noble, Nowata, Okfuskee, Oklahoma, Okmulgee, Osage, Ottawa, Pawnee, Payne, Pittsburgh, Pottawatomie, Rogers, Seminole, Sequoyah, Wagoner, Washington, and Wayne counties including the city of Tulsa.

Tulsa Economic Development Corporation
907 S. Detroit Ave., Suite 1001
Tulsa, OK 74120
918-585-8332
Fax: 918-585-2473
Email: tmartin@tulsaecondevcorp.com
Executive Director: Rose Washington-Rentie
Microloan Contact: Tara Martin
Service Area: Adair, Canadian, Cherokee, Cleveland, Craig, Creek, Delaware, Haskell, Hayes, Hughes, Kay, Latimer, Leflore, Lincoln, Logan, McIntosh, Muskogee, Noble, Nowata, Okfuskee, Oklahoma, Okmulgee, Osage, Ottawa, Pawnee, Payne, Pittsburg, Pottawatomie, Rogers, Seminole, Sequoyah, Wagoner, Washington, and Wayne counties including the city of Tulsa

Greenwood Community Development
131 N. Greenwood Ave, 2nd Floor
Tulsa, OK 74120
918-585-2084
Fax: 918-585-9268
Email: rgant@tulsacoxmail.com/rking@tulsacoxmail.com
Executive Director: Reuben Gant
Microloan Contact: Reuben Gant
Service Area: Northwest Tulsa county

Little Dixie Community Action
502 West Duke St.
Hugo, OK 74743

580-326-3351
Fax: 580-326-2305
Email: jpool@littledixie.org
www.littledixiecaa.homestead.com/
Executive Director: Jerry Pool
Microloan Contact: Clarke LaForce 580-326-6441
Service Area: Choctaw, McCurtain, and Pushmataha counties

Tulsa Economic Development Corporation
907 S. Detroit Ave., Suite 1001
Tulsa, OK 74120
918-585-8332
Fax: 918-585-2473
Email: tmartin@tulsaecondevcorp.com
Executive Director: Rose Washington-Rentie
Microloan Contact: Tara Martin
Service Area: Adair, Canadian, Cherokee, Cleveland, Craig, Creek, Delaware, Haskell, Hayes, Hughes, Kay, Latimer, Leflore, Lincoln, Logan, McIntosh, Muskogee, Noble, Nowata, Okfuskee, Oklahoma, Okmulgee, Osage, Ottawa, Pawnee, Payne, Pittsburg, Pottawatomie, Rogers, Seminole, Sequoyah, Wagoner, Washington, and Wayne counties including the city of Tulsa

Oregon

Cascades West Financial Services, Inc.
1400 Queen Ave., SE, Suite 205C
P.O. Box 686
Albany, OR 97321
541-924-8480
Fax: 541-967-4651
Email: dsearle@ocwcog.org
www.cascadeswest.com/
Executive Director: Mary Merriman Smith
Microloan Contact: Diane Searle
Service Area: Benton, Clackamas, Hood River, Jefferson, Lane, Lincoln, Linn, Marion, Multnomah, Polk, Tillamook, Wasco, Washington, and Yamhill

Ida-Ore Planning and Development Association, Inc.
10624 W. Executive Dr.
Boise, ID 83713
208-322-7033
Fax: 208-322-3569
Email: pmchoate@ida-ore.com
www.sageidaho.com/
Executive Director: Phillip Choate
Microloan Contact: Bob Richards
Service Area: Harney and Malheur counties

Southern Oregon Women's Access to Credit, Inc.
33 North Central #209
Medford, OR 97501
541-779-3992
Fax: 541-779-5195
Email: dpdavis@sowac.org
www.sowac.org/
Executive Director: Helen Wallace
Microloan Contact: Dennis Davis
Service Area: Jackson, Josephine, Klamath, and Lake counties

Oregon Association of Minority Entrepreneurs Credit Corporation
4134 N. Vancouver Avenue
Portland, OR 97217
503-249-7744
Fax: 503-249-2027
Executive Director: Samuel Brooks
Microloan Contact: Samuel Brooks

Service Area: Multnomah, Washington, Clackamas, Columbia, Tillamook, Clatsop, and Hood Counties

Umpqua Community Development Corporation
738 SE Kane Street
Roseburg, OR 97470
541-673-4909
Fax: 541-673-5023
Email: btamm@mcsi.net/ or rault@mcsi.net
www.umpquacdc.org/
Executive Director: Betty Tamm
Microloan Contact: Bob Ault
Service Area: Coos, Curry and Douglas Counties

Pennsylvania

The Ben Franklin Tech. Center of SE Pennsylvania
11 Penn Center
1835 Market St., Suite 1100
Philadelphia, PA 19103
215-972-6700
Fax: 215-972-5588
Email: bftc@benfranklin.org
www.sep.benfranklin.org/seed/cel.html
Executive Director: Rose Ann Rosenthal
Microloan Contact: Dieter Littles
Service Area: Bucks, Chester, Delaware, Montgomery, and Philadelphia counties

The Washington County Council on Economic Development
40 S. Main Street, Lower Level
Washington, PA 15301
724-228-8223
Fax: 724-250-8202
Email: wcced@cobweb.net
www.washingtoncountypa.org
Exec. Director: Malcolm Morgan
Microloan Contact: Alan A. Hill
Service Area: Southwestern area of Pennsylvania including Greene, Fayette, Washington, and Westmoreland counties

Aliquippa Alliance for Unity and Development
392 Franklin Ave
Aliquippa, PA 15001
724-378-7422
Fax: 724-378-9976
Email: pkribbs@aaud.org
www.aaud.org/
Executive Director: Roseanne Stead
Microloan Contact: Patricia Kribbs
Service Area: Beaver, Butler, and Lawrence counties

Community First Fund
44 N Queen Street P. O. Box 524
Lancaster, PA 17608-0524
866-822-3863
Fax: 717-393-1757
Email: dbetancourt@commfirstfund.org
gmachia@commfirstfund.org
www.commfirstfund.org
Executive Director: Dan Betancourt
Microloan Contact: Glenda Machia
Service Area: Lancaster, York, Berks, Dauphin, Lebanon, Cumberland, Perry, and Adams counties

Community Loan Fund of Southwestern PA, Inc.
1920 Gulf Towers
707 Grant Street
Pittsburgh, PA 15219
412-201-2450
Fax: 412-201-2451

Email: mpeterson@clfund.com mbevan@clfund.com
www.clfund.com
Executive Director: Mark Peterson
Microloan Contact: Laura Swiss
Service Area: Allegheny, Armstong, Beaver, Butler and Indiana counties

Northeastern Pennsylvania Alliance (aka: NEPA)
1151 Oak St.
Pittston, PA 18640-3795
570-655-5581
Fax: 570-654-5137
Email: tompel@nepa-alliance.org
www.nepa-alliance.org/
Executive Director: Cameron Moore
Microloan Contact: Tom Pellegrini
Service Area: Carbon, Lackawanna, Luzerne, Monroe, Pike, Schuylkill, and Wayne counties

MetroAction, Inc.
222 Mulberry Street
P.O. Box 4731
Scranton, PA 18501-0431
570-342-7711
Fax: 570-347-6262
Email: kfrench@scrantonchamber.com
www.scrantonchamber.com
Executive Director: John Kokinchak
Microloan Contact: Kristine French
Service Area: Luzerne, Lackawanna, and Monroe counties

North Central PA Regional Planning & Dev. Commission
651 Montmorenci Avenue
Ridgway, PA 15853
814-773-3162
Fax: 814-772-7045
Email: jfoys@ncentral.com
Executive Director: Ronald W. Kuleck
Microloan Contact: Jill Foys
Service Area: Cameron, Clearfield, Elk, Jefferson, McKean and Potter counties

Northwest Pennsylvania Regional Planning & Dev. Commission
395 Seneca Street
Oil City, PA 16301
814-677-4800
Fax: 814-677-7663
Email: dalem@nwplan.org
www.nwcommission.org/
Executive Director: William Steiner
Microloan Contact: Dale F. Massie
Service Area: Clarion, Crawford, Erie, Forest, Lawrence, Mercer, Warren and Venango counties

Philadelphia Commercial Development Corporation
1315 Walnut Street Suite 600
Philadelphia, PA 19107
215-790-2210
Fax: 215-790-2222
Email: econpcdc@aol.com
www.philadelphiacommercial.com
Executive Director: Curtis Jones, Jr.
Microloan Contact: Rick Dean/Linda House
Service Area: Philadelphia

SEDA-Council of Governments
RR #1, Box 372
Lewisburg, PA 17837
570-524-9190

Fax: 570-524-4491
Email: venditti@seda-cog.org
www.seda-cog.org/
Executive Director: Dennis E. Robinson
Microloan Contact: Thomas J. Venditti
Service Area: Centre, Clinton, Columbia, Juniata, Lycoming, Mifflin, Montour, Northumberland, Perry, Snyder, and Union counties.

Southern Alleghenies Planning & Development Commission
541 58th Street
Altoona, PA 16602
814-949-6545
Fax: 814-949-6505
Email: sapdc@sapdc.org
www.sapdc.org
Executive Director: Edward M. Silvetti
Microloan Contact: Michael Mignogna
Service Area: Bedford, Blair, Cambria, Fulton, Huntingdon, and Somerset counties

Puerto Rico
Economic Development Corporation of San Juan (COFECC)
1103 Avenida Munoz Rivera
P.O. Box 191791
Rio Piedras, PR 00926
787-756-5080
Fax: 787-753-8960
Email: cofecc@worldnet.att.net
www.cofecc.net/
Exec. Director: Giovanna Piovanetti
Microloan Contact: Giovanna Piovanetti
Service Area: Territory wide

Rhode Island
Rhode Island Coalition for Minority Investment
216 Weybosset Street 2nd Floor
Providence, RI 02903
401-351-2999
Fax: 401-351-0990
Email: dbarge.midc@ efortress.com/allawi@prodigy.net
www.midcri.com
Executive Director: Denise Barge
Microloan Contact: Henry Reid
Service Area: Statewide

South Carolina
Charleston Citywide Local Development Corporation
75 Calhoun St., 3rd Floor
Charleston, SC 29403
803-724-3796
Fax: 803-724-7354
Email: brennans@ci.charleston.sc.us
www.ci.charleston.sc.us/ldc.htm
Executive Director: Sharon Brennan
Microloan Contact: Michelle Ingle/Dwayne Jubar
Service Area: City of Charleston

Santee-Lynches Regional Development Corp.
36 West Liberty St.
P.O. Box 1837
Sumter, SC 29150
803-775-7381
Fax: 803-773-6902
Email: slrdc@slcog.org
www.slcog.state.sc.us/
Exec. Director: James Darby, Jr.
Microloan Contact: Walter Dunlap
Service Area: Clarendon, Kershaw, Lee and Sumter counties

Carolina Capital Investment Corporation
P. O. Box 8327
Columbia, SC 29202
803-461-3800
Fax: 803-461-3826
Email: mgaylor@businesscarolina.net
Executive Director: Elliott E. Franks, III
Microloan Contact: Melissa Gaylor
Service Area: Abbeville, Aiken, Allendale, Anderson, Bamberg, Barnwell, Beaufort, Berkeley, Calhoun, Charleston, Cherokee, Chester, Chesterfield, Colleton, Darlington, Dillon, Dorchester, Edgefield, Fairfield, Florence, Georgetown, Greenville, Greenwood, Hampton, Horry, Jasper, Lancaster, Laurens, Lexington, Marion, Marlboro, McCormick, Newberry, Oconee, Orangeburg, Pickens, Richland, Saluda, Spartanburg, Union, and York counties

South Dakota
Lakota Fund
Trade Center
P.O. Box 340
Kyle, SD 57752
605-455-2500
Fax: 605-455-2585
Email: monica@rapidnet.com
www.lakotafund.org/
Exec. Dir.: Elsie Meeks
Microloan Contact: Monica Perkildsen
Service Area: Bennett county, Pine Ridge Indian Reservation, and areas of Shannon and Jackson counties which are surrounded by Indian Lands, and exclusive of Northern Jackson county

Tennessee
Economic Ventures, Inc.
P.O. Box 3550
Knoxville, TN 37927-3550
865-594-8762
Fax: 865-594-8659
Email: kbell@cityofknoxville.org
Executive Director:
Microloan Contact:
Service Area: Anderson, Blount, Campbell, Clairborne, Cocke, Grainger, Hamblen, Jefferson, Knox, Loudon, Monroe, Morgan Roane, Scott, Sevier, Union, Greene, Hancock, Hawkins, Sullivan, Washington, Johnson, Carter, and Unicoi counties

LeMoyne-Owen College Community Development Corporation
802 Walker Avenue, Suite 5
Memphis, TN 38126
901-942-6265
Fax: 901-942-6448
Email: jeffrey_higgs@nile.lemoyne-owen.edu/austin.emeagwai@nile.lemoyne-owen.edu
www.loccdc.org
Executive Director: Jeffrey T. Higgs
Microloan Contact: Austin Emeagwai
Service Area: Memphis and Shelby county

Southeast Community Capital
1020 Commerce Park Drive
Oak Ridge, TN 37830
865-220-2025
Fax: 865-220-2030
Email: hortonw@tech2020.org
www.tech2020.org
Executive Director: Don Welty

Microloan Contact: Louanne Horton-White
Service Area: Statewide

Woodbine Community Organization
222 Oriel Avenue
Nashville, TN 37210
615-833-9580
Fax: 615-833-9727
Email: oliverdent2001@cs.com
Executive Director: Oliver Dent
Microloan Contact: Oliver Dent
Service Area: Cheatham, Davidson, Dickson, Robertson, Rutherford, Sumner, Williamson, and Wilson counties

Texas

Business Resource Center Incubator
401 Franklin
Waco, TX 76701
254-754-8898
Fax: 254-756-0776
Email: john@brc_waco.com
Executive Director: John Dosher
Microloan Contact: John Dosher
Service Area: Bell, Bosque, Coryell, Falls, Hill, and McLennan counties

The Corporation for Economic Development of Harris County, Inc.
118-3 1@ 1 East Tex Freeway
Houston, TX 77027
281-590-5600
Fax: 281-590-5605
Email: jacklyngriffen@cedhc.com
www.cedhc.com/
Executive Director: Jacklyn Griffin
Microloan Contact: Janis Fowler
Service Area: Brazoria, Chambers, Fort Bend, Galveston, Harris, Liberty, Montgomery, and Waller counties

San Antonio Local Development Company
215 S. San Saba, Room 107
San Antonio, TX 78207
210-207-3932
Fax: 210-207-8151
Email: roberta@sanantonio.gov
www.saldc.com/
Executive Director: Ramire Cavazos
Microloan Contact: Robert Ayala
Service Area: Atascosa, Bandera, Bexar, Comal, Frio, Gillespie, Guadalupe, Karnes, Kendall, Kerr, Medina, San Antonio, and Wilson counties

Southern Dallas Development Corporation
351 West Blvd., Suite 800
Dallas, TX 75208
214-428-7332
Fax: 214-948-8104
Email: velmore@sbdc.org
Executive Director: Jim Reid
Microloan Contact: Victor Elmore
Service Area: Portions of the City of Dallas

ACCION Texas, Inc.
2014 S. Hackberry Street
San Antonio, TX 78210
210-226-3664
Fax: 210-226-2940
Email: info@acciontexas.org
www.acciontexas.org/
Executive Director: Janie Barrera

Microloan Contact: Elizabeth Montoya
Service Area: Arkansas, Atascosa, Austin, Bandera, Bastrop, Bee, Bexar, Blanco, Brewster, Brooks, Brownsville, Burnet, Carmeron, Caldwell, Calhoun, Comal, Concho, Corpus Christi, Crockett, Culberson, Dallas,DeWitt, Dimmit, Duval, Edwards, El Paso, Fayette, Fort Worth, Frio, Gillespie, Goliad, Gonzales, Green, Guadalupe, Harris, Hays, Houston, Hidalgo, Hudspeth, Irion, Jackson, Jeff Davis, Jim Hogg, Jim Wells, Karnes, Kendall, Kenedy, Kerr, Kimble, Kinney, Kleberg, Lampasas, Laredo, LaSalle, Lavaca, Lee, Live Oak, Llano, Loving, Mason, Maverick, Medina, McAllen, McCulloch, McMullen, Menard, Midland/Odessa, Nueces, Pecos, Presidio, Real, Reeves, Real, Reeves, Refugio, San Antonio, San Patricio, San Saba, Schleicher, Starr, Sutton, Tarrant, Tom Green, Travis, Uvalde, Val Verde, Victoria , Webb, Willacy, Zapata and Zavala counties

BIG - Businesses Invest In Growth
4100 Ed Bluestein , Suite 207
Austin, TX 78741
512-928-8010
Fax: 512-926-2997
Email: Melissa@big.org
www.bigaustin.org/
Executive Director: Jeannette Peten
Microloan Contact: Jeannette Peten
Service Area: Travis, Williamson, Hays, Bastrop, Blanco, Burnet, Burleson, Milam, Gillespie, Lampasas, Lee, Llano, Mason, Mcculloch, and SanSaba counties

Neighborhood Housing Services of Dimmitt County, Inc.
301 Pena Street
Carrizo Springs, TX 78834
830-876-5295
Fax: 830-876-4136
Email: nhsdc@brushco.net
Executive Director: Manuel Estrada, Jr.
Microloan Contact: Manuel Estrada, Jr.
Service Area: Dimmit, La Salle, Zavala Edwards, Kinney, Real, Uvalde, Val Verde and Maverick counties

Rural Development and Finance Corporation
711 Navarro Street Suite 350
San Antonio, TX 78207
210-212-4552
Fax: 210-212-9159
Email: RDFC@DCCI.COM
www.rdfc.org/
Executive Director: Gloria Guerrero
Microloan Contact: Lucy Brooks
Service Area: Cameron, El Paso, Starr, Hidalgo, Willacy, Maverick, Dimmit, Webb, Zapata, and Zavala counties

Vermont

Economic Development Council of Northern Vermont, Inc.
155 Lake St.
St. Albans, VT 05478
802-524-4546
Fax: 802-527-1081
Email: edcnv@together.net
Executive Director: Connie Stanley-Little
Microloan Contact: William Farr
Service Area: Chittenden, Franklin, Grand Isle, Lamoille, and Washington counties

Northern Community Investments Corporation
347 Portland Street
P.O. Box 904
St. Johnsbury, VT 05819
802-748-5101

Fax: 802-748-1884
Email: carol@ncic.org
www.ncic.org
Executive Director:
Microloan Contact: Carol Walker
Service Area: Caledonia, Essex, and Orleans counties

Vermont Development Credit Union
18 Pearl Street
Burlington, VT 05401
802-865-3404
Fax: 802-862-8971
www.vdcu.org/
Executive Director: Caryl J. Stewart
Microloan Contact: Jeff Smith
Service Area: Addison, Bennington, Orange, Rutland, Windham, and Windsor counties

Virginia
Group Enterprise Development
1038 S. Highland St.
Arlington, VA 22204
703-685-0510
Fax: 703-685-0529
Email: belay.embaye@ecdcinternational.org
www.ecdcinternational.org/
Exec. Director: Tschaye Teferra
Microloan Contact: Haddish Weldaly
Service Area: Prince William, Arlington and Fairfax counties and the cities of Alexandria and Falls Church

Business Development Centre, Inc.
147 Mill Ridge Road
Lynchburg, VA 24502
434-582-6100
Fax: 434-582-6106
Email: rich@lbdc.com
www.lbdc.com
Executive Director: Catherine McFaden
Microloan Contact: Rich Stallings
Service Area: Amherst, Appomattox, Bedford, Campell counties, cities of Lynchburg and Bedford, and the Town of Amherst and Altavista

People Incorporated of Southwest Virginia
1173 W. Main St.
Abingdon, VA 24210
276-619-2239
Fax: 276-628-2931
Email: afortner@naxs.com
www.businessstart.org
Executive Director: Robert G. Goldsmith
Microloan Contact: Amanda Fortner/Phillip Black
Service Area: Buchanan, Carroll, Dickenson, Grayson, Lee, Russell, Scott, Smythe, Tazewell, Wythe, Washington, Wise counties and the cities of Bristol and Norton

Center for Community Development
440 High Street Suite 204
Portsmouth, VA 23704
757-399-0925
Fax: 757-399-2642
Email: profitl@infi.net
www.ccdi-va.net
Executive Director: Bruce Asberry
Microloan Contact: Monique Harrell
Service Area: Chesapeake, Hampton, Newport News, Norfolk, Portsmouth, Suffolk, and Virginia Beach

Lightstone Community Development Corp.
HC 63, Box 73
Moyers, WV 26815
304-249-5200
Fax: 304-249-5310
Email: tony@lightstone.org
www.lightstone.org/
Executive Director: Anthony E. Smith
Microloan Contact: Anthony E. Smith
Service Area: Bath and Highland counties

Richmond Economic Development Corporation
501 E. Franklin St. Suite 358
Richmond, VA 23219
804-780-3013
Fax: 804-788-4310
Email: sjschley@aol.com
www.reacfinance.org
Executive Director: Stephen Schley
Microloan Contact: Brenda Lewis
Service Area: City of Richmond

Total Action Against Poverty
145 Campbell Avenue, S.W. Suite 303
P.O. Box 2868
Roanoke, VA 24011-2868
540-345-6781
Fax: 540-343-9892
Email: chris.scott@taproanoke.org
www.taproanoke.org/
Executive Director: Ted Edlich
Microloan Contact: Chris Scott
Service Area: Alleghany, Bath, Botetourt, Craig, and Roanoke counties including the City of Clifton Forge, Covington, Roanoke, and Salem

Community Development Loan Fund
1624 Hull Street
Richmond, VA 23224
804-233-2014
Fax: 804-233-2158
Email: JFraitesvcdlf@earthlink.net
www.vcdlf.org
Executive Director: Tim Hayes
Microloan Contact: Janice Fraites
Service Area: The counties of Henrico, Chesterfield, Goochland, Hanover, Powatan, and the cities of Petersburg and Hopewell

Washington
Tri-Cities Enterprise Association
124 W. Kennewick Ave.
Kennewick, WA 99336
509-582-9440
Fax: 509-582-9720
Email: kfast@enterprisecenter.net
www.enterprisecenter.net/
Executive Director: Wilfred Henderson
Microloan Contact: Katie Fast
Service Area: Benton, Franklin, Columbia, Garfield, Asotin, Whitman, and Spokane counties

Community Capital Development
1437 South Jackson, Suite 201
Seattle, WA 98144
206-324-4330 ext. 104
Email: artm@seattleccd.com
www.seattleccd.com/
Executive Director: Jim Thomas
Microloan Contact: Art Mickel

Service Area: Adams, Chelan, Douglas, Grant, Kittitas, Klickitat, Okanogan, Yakima, King, Pierce, Skagit, San Juan, Snohomish, Island, Kitsap and Whatcom

Oregon Association of Minority Entrepreneurs Credit Corporation
4134 N. Vancouver Avenue
Portland, OR 97217
503-249-7744
Fax: 503-249-2027
Executive Director: Samuel Brooks
Microloan Contact: Samuel Brooks
Service Area: Clark county

Washington Assn. for Minority Entrepreneurs/
Rural Community Development Resources(RCDR)
24 South 3rd Avenue
Yakima, WA 98902
509-453-5133
Fax: 509-453-5165
Email: delnorte@nwinfo.net
Executive Director: Luz Bazan Gutierrez
Microloan Contact: Luz Bazan Gutierrez
Service Area: Mattawa and Othello in Grant County; Moses Lake and Royal City in Adams County; Walla Walla County; and Pasco in Franklin County; Yakima County

Washington CASH (Community Alliance for Self-Help)
1912 East Madison St.
Seattle, WA 98122
206-352-1945
Fax: 206-352-1899
Email: washcash@nwlink.com
www.washingtoncash.org
Executive Director: Kathy Gilman
Microloan Contact: Kathy Gilman
Service Area: Clark, Cowlitz, Island, King, Kitsap, Lewis, San Juan, Skagit, Snohomish, Thurston, and Whatcom counties

Rural Community Development Resources, Inc.
24 South 3rd Avenue
Yakima, WA 98902
509-453-5133
Fax: 509-453-5165
Email: delnorte@nwinfo.net
President & CEO: Luz Bazan Gutierrez
Service Area: Mattawa and Othello in Grant County; Moses Lake and Royal City in Adams County; Walla Walla County; and Pasco in Franklin County

West Virginia
The Washington County Council on Economic Development
100 West Beau Street, Suite 703
Washington, PA 15301-4432
724-228-6949
Fax: 724-250-6502
Email: waced@cobweb.net
www.washingtoncountypa.org
Executive Director: Malcolm L. Morgan
Microloan Contact: Ray Grudi
Service Area: Monongalia county

Lightstone Community Development Corp.
HC 63, Box 73
Moyers, WV 26815
304-249-5200
Fax: 304-249-5310
Email:tony@lightstone.org
www.lightstone.org/

Executive Director: Anthony E. Smith
Microloan Contact: Anthony E. Smith
Service Area: Statewide

Mountain CAP of West Virginia, Inc.
105 Jerry Burton Drive
Sutton, WV 26601
304-765-7738
Fax: 304-765-7308
Email: mtcapt@rtol.net or kctmountaincap@neumedia.net
www.mountaincap.com/
Executive Director: Mary Chipps
Microloan Contact: Tara Rexroad
Service Area: Barbour, Braxton, Clay, Fayette, Gilmer, Lewis, Nicholas, Randolph, Roane, Upshur Raleigh, Harrison, and Webster Counties

Wisconsin
Advocap, Inc.
19 W. 1st St.
P.O. Box 1108
Fond du Lac, WI 54935
920-922-7760
Fax: 920-922-7214
Email: morta@advocap.org
www.advocap.org/
Executive Director: Michael Bonertz
Microloan Contact: Mort Gazerwitz
Service Area: Fond du Lac, Green Lake, and Winnebago counties

Impact Seven, Inc.
147 Lake Almena Dr.
Almena, WI 54805
715-357-3334
Fax: 715-357-6233
Email: impact7@execpc.com
www.impactseven.org/
Executive Director: William Bay
Microloan Contact: Inger Sanderud
Service Area: Statewide with the exceptions of Fond du Lac, Green Lake, Kenosha, Milwaukee, Oasukee, Racine, Walworth, Waukesha, Washington, and Winnebago counties and inner city Milwaukee

Wisconsin Women's Business Initiative Corporation
2745 N. Dr. Martin Luther King Jr. Dr.
Milwaukee, WI 53212
414-263-5450
Fax: 414-263-5456
Email: info@wwbic.com
www.wwbic.com/
Executive Director: Wendy Werkmeister
Microloan Contact: Carol N. Maria
Service Area: Brown, Dane, Dodge, Jefferson, Kenosha, Milwaukee, Ozaukee, Racine, Walworth, Washington and Waukesha counties

Lincoln Neighborhood Redevelopment Corp.
2266 S. 13th St.
Milwaukee, WI 53215
414-671-5619
Fax: 414-385-3270
Email: LNRC@cbgmail.com
Executive Director: Michael Gapinski
Microloan Contact: Matthew Maigatter
Area Served: Greater Milwaukee SMSA

Northeast Entrepreneur Fund, Inc.
1225 Town Avenue
Superior, WI 54880

800-422-0374
Fax: 715-392-6131
Email: info@neefund.org
www.entrepreneurfund.org/
Executive Director: Mary Mathews
Microloan Contact: Robert Voss
Service Area: Douglas County

Wyoming
Wyoming Women's Business Center
13th and Lewis Streets P.O. Box 3661
Laramie, WY 82071
307-766-3083
Fax: 307-766-3085
Email: wwbc@uwyo.edu
www.wyomingwomen.com/
Executive Director: Rosemary Bratton
Microloan Contact: Rosemary Bratton
Service Area: State Wyoming

Technical Assistance Grant Recipients
Alaska
Juneau Economic Development Council
612 W. Willoughby, Suite A
Juneau, AK 99801-1732
907-463-3662
Fax: 907-463-3929
Email: jedc@ptialaska.net or kflanders@ptialaska.net
www.jedc.org/
Executive Director: Charles Northrip
Microloan Contact: Kirk Flanders
Service Area: Through SBDCs, the Alaska Panhandle

California
Women's Initiative for Self Employment
1390 Market St., Suite 113
San Francisco, CA 94102
415-247-9473
Fax: 415-247-9471
Email: wils@igc.org
www.womensinitiative.org/
Executive Director: Barbara Johnson
Microloan Contact: Corinne Florek
Service Area: defined sectors of San Francisco Bay Area

Connecticut
Woman's Business Development Center
400 W. Main St., Suite 500
Stamford, CT 06902
203-353-1750
Fax: 203-353-1084
Email: sharonwbdc@ferg.lib.ct.us
Executive Director: Fran Pastore
Microloan Contact: Sharon Dubinsky
Service Area: SW corner including Ansonia, Beacon Falls, Bethel, Bridgeport, Bridgewater, Brookfield, Danbury, Darien, Derby, Easton, Fairfield, Greenwich, Milford, Monroe, New Canaan, New Fairfield, New Milford, Newtown, Norwalk, Oxford, Redding, Ridgefield, Seymour, Shelton, Sherman, Stamford, Stratford, Trumbull, Weston, Westport, and Wilton counties

Florida
Lee County Employment and Economic Dev. Corp.
2774 First Street
Fort Myers, FL 33916
239-337-2300
Fax: 239-337-4558
Executive Director: Roy Kennix

Microloan Contact: Roy Kennix
Service Area: Community Redevelopment areas of Lee County including Charleston Park, Dunbar, Harlem Heights, North Fort Myers, and State Road 80

Illinois
Women's Business Development Center
8 South Michigan Ave., Suite 400
Chicago, IL 60603
312-853-3477
Fax: 312-853-0145
Email: wbdc@aol.com
www.wbdc.org/
Executive Director: Hedy Ratner
Microloan Contact: Carol Dougal
Service Area: Boone, Cook, DeKalb, DuPage, Kane, Kankakee, Kendall, Lake, McHenry, Will, and Winnebago counties

Indiana
Community Action of Southern Indiana
1613 E. 8th
P.O. Box 843
Jeffersonville, IN 47130
812-288-6451, ext. 111
Fax: 812-284-8314
www.casijeff.net/
Executive Director: Fred Mitchell
Microloan Contact: Leatha Jackson
Service Area: Clark, Floyd, and Harrison counties

Iowa
Institute for Social and Economic Development
910 23rd Avenue
Coralville, IA 52241
319-338-2331
Fax: 319-338-5824
Email: cpigsley@ised.org
www.ised.org/
Executive Director: Christine Pigsley
Microloan Contact: Christine Pigsley
Service Area: Statewide

Kansas
Great Plains Development, Inc.
100 Military Plaza, Suite 128
P.O. Box 1116
Dodge City, KS 67801
316-227-6406
Fax: 316-225-6051
Exec. Director: Patty Richardson
Microloan Contact: Patty Richardson
Service Area: Statewide

Michigan
Cornerstone Alliance
38 W. Wall St.
P.O. Box 428
Benton Harbor, MI 49023-0428
616-925-6100
Fax: 616-925-4471
Email: gvaughn@ cstonealliance.org
www.cstonealliance.org/
Executive Director: Jeff Noel
Microloan Contact: Gregory Vaughn
Service Area: Berrien County and City of Benton Harbor

Minnesota
Neighborhood Development Center, Inc.
651½ University Ave.

St. Paul, MN 55104
651-291-2480
Fax: 651-291-2597
Email: windndc@mtn.org
www.windndc.org/
Executive Director: Mihailo Temali
Microloan Contact: Mara O'Neil
Service Area: Districts 3, 5, 6, 8, 9, and 16 of the City of St. Paul

Missouri

Community Development Corporation of Kansas City
2420 E. Linwood Blvd., Suite 110
Kansas City, MO 64109
816-924-5800
Fax: 816-921-3350
Exec. Director: William Threatt, Jr.
Microloan Contact: William Dayton
Service Area: Cass, Clay, Platte, Ray and Jackson counties

Montana

Montana Department of Commerce
SBDC Division
1424 9th Ave.
P.O. Box 200505
Helena, MT 59620-0505
406-444-4325
Fax: 406-444-1872
Email: adesch@state.mt.us
http://commerce.state.mt.us/
Executive Director: Ann Desch
Microloan Contact: Robyn Hampton
Service Area: Through SBDCs, Cascade, Chouteau, Fergus, Glacier, Golden Valley, Judity Basin, Musselshell, Petroleum, Pondera, Teton, Toole, and Wheatland counties, and the Blackfeet, Flathead, and Fort Peck Reservations, and the Crow, Fort Belknap, Northern Cheyenne and Rocky Boys Reservations and their Trust Lands

New Mexico

New Mexico Community Development Loan Fund
700 4th Street, SW
P.O. Box 705
Albuquerque, NM 87103-0705
505-243-3196
Fax: 505-243-8803
Email: vgnmcdfl@aol.com
www.nmcdlf.org/
Executive Director: Vangie Gabaldon
Microloan Contact: Rockling Todea
Service Area: Statewide

New York

Brooklyn Economic Development Corporation
175 Remsen Street, Suite 350
Brooklyn, NY 11201
718-522-4600
Fax: 718-797-9286
Email: info@bedc.org or mad@bedc.org
www.bedc.org/
Executive Director: Joan Bartolomeo
Microloan Contact: Hector Rivera
Service Area: The five boroughs of New York City

North Carolina

North Carolina Rural Economic Development Center, Inc.
4021 Carya Dr.
Raleigh, NC 27610
919-250-4314
Fax: 919-250-4325
Email: pblack@mindspring.com
www.ncruralcenter.org/
Executive Director: Billy Ray Hall
Microloan Contact: Phil Black
Service Area: Statewide

Pennsylvania

Women's Opportunities Resource Center
1930 Chestnut Street, Suite 1600
Philadelphia, PA 19103
215-564-5500
Fax: 215-564-0933
Email: worc-pa@erols.com
www.worc-pa.com/
Executive Director: Lynne Cutler
Microloan Contact: Lynne Cutler
Service Area: Bucks, Montgomery, Philadelphia, Chester, and Delaware counties

Texas

Corpus Christi Chamber of Commerce
1201 N. Shoreline
Corpus Christi, TX 78401
361-881-1850
Fax: 361-882-5627
Email: jestell@theccchamber.org
www.corpuschristichamber.org/
Executive Director: Tom Niskala
Microloan Contact: Jerry Estell
Service Area: Nueces and San Patricio counties

Vermont

Champlain Valley Office of Economic Opportunity, Inc.
431 Pine Street, #2
Burlington, VT 05401
802-860-1417
Fax: 802-860-1387
Email: mbdp@together.net
www.cvoro.org/
Executive Director: Jim White
Microloan Contact: Dale Lane
Service Area: Statewide

Virginia

VA SBDC Business Assistance Network
Division of Virginia Department of Business Assistance
P.O. Box 446
Richmond, VA 23218
804-371-6280
Fax: 804-225-3384
Email: seure@dba.state.va.us
www.dba.state.va.us/smdev/
Executive Director: Vicky Humphreys
Microloan Contact:
Service Area: Through SBDCs, statewide

$1.3 Million To Help Your Business

Need money to fix up your parking lot and do some landscaping around your business? What about updating your machinery and equipment? Need help modernizing your facilities? The Certified Development Company (504) Loan Program is a financing tool for economic development within a community. The 504 Program provides growing businesses with long-term, fixed-rate financing for major fixed assets such as land and building. A Certified Development Company is a nonprofit corporation set up to contribute to the economic development of its community, and works with the SBA and lenders to provide financing to small businesses.

Funds can be used for purchasing land and improvements, including existing building, grading, street improvements, utilities, parking lots and landscaping, construction of new facilities or modernizing, renovating or converting existing facilities or purchasing long-term machinery and equipment. Money cannot be used for working capital or inventory, consolidating or repaying debt or refinancing. You can borrow up to $1.3 million with ten to twenty year fixed rate financing close to prime. You must contribute at least 10% of the project cost. There also may be a requirement that a new job be created for every $50,000 borrowed, but there are exemptions to this requirement. It often takes less than two weeks to learn if you qualify for this loan.

Generally, the project assets being financed are used as collateral. To be eligible, the business must be operated for profit and fall within the size standards. A business qualifies as small if it does not have a tangible net worth of more the $7 million and does not have an average net income in excess of $2.5 million after taxes for the preceding two years. Each Certified Development company work is a specific geographic area. Please look at the list below to learn who you need to contact. You can also learn more on the web at the Small Business Administration's website at {www.sba.gov}.

Success Stories

The following examples are excerpted from the Small Business Administration (SBA) web site, and the web sites of the lenders mentioned. Contact the SBA (www.sba.gov) for information on lenders in your region.

Creating Jobs is Child's Play!

In 1989, Sheree Mitchell of Columbus, Georgia, used an SBA 504 loan to construct a child development center. She called it the Growing Room, Inc. – and just like the clients she served, Sheree's business just kept getting bigger. As the company expanded, of course, so did the workforce.

Sheree added 20 employees within her first two years of operation. The children kept coming, and the waiting list grew, so in 1992 Sheree built a $400,000 addition, adding 12 more to her staff. Four years later, a second Growing Room opened in North Columbus in a newly constructed 11,500 square-foot facility, creating 32 additional jobs.

Sheree then took her work to the workplace. She obtained a contract for the Columbus Regional Healthcare Systems' on-site childcare center, adding 15 more employees. Growing Room was also awarded the contract for two on-site childcare centers at the headquarters of Columbus based AFLAC.

Growing Room, Inc., currently employs over 170 people, and will generate almost $4.9 million in revenues this year. Now there are lots of baby steps taken at the Growing Room – all thanks to the big leap Sheree made when she applied to the SBA 504 Loan Program!

One Loan Creates Two Dozen New Jobs!

Several lenders in Hot Springs, Arkansas partnered to provide an SBA 504 Loan Program financing package for a car dealership – and allowed Steve Storey, owner of Resort Ford, to deliver 24 new jobs to the area within two years.

Storey used the 504 loan to expand his dealership's operations and upgrade its facilities. Now, customers visit a sparkling new showroom, housed in a 30,000 square foot facility. Storey also provides maintenance and repair in the modern facility. The upgrades – and the resulting jobs - have helped the small community stay strong.

Almost One Million Dollars to Move Furniture!

Larry O'Toole is over six feet tall, so when he decided to start a moving business, he knew the name to use: "Gentle Giant." The year was 1980. Larry borrowed a friend's truck, placed one ad in a small newspaper (at a cost of $17) and launched what is now a local institution. Nearly everyone in Greater Boston is acquainted with Larry's purple and green "giant" trucks traveling the city streets with the phone # 1-800-GIANT-MEN prominently featured.

In 1997, Larry recognized that the business needed more storage and facilities. After searching for financing to acquire a large building, he decided to work with the Waltham-based Bay Colony Development Corp., an SBA Certified Development Company. In 1998 Bay Colony coordinated a $843,000 SBA 504 loan to complete the $2 million project, and the Gentle Giant found a new home.

"The assistance of the SBA made our dream come true," Larry said. Since Gentle Giant moved to their new building, revenues have grown from $11 million to $16 million, while the number of employees has grown from 135 to 185. Gentle Giant has increased the size of its fleet from 65 trucks to 95. A great improvement, and all with the help of a giant-sized loan!

Money to Bring Contracts In-house

In 1992, Tom Hauke started McDowell Research Corporation (MRC) in Waco, Texas. The company develops power supply products for military and security forces. For the first ten years, Hauke developed and designed the products, and then contracted with assembly operations to build them.

As demand for the MRC's products grew, however, Hauke knew he needed to move the assembly process inside his own facility. He obtained an SBA 504 loan to expand his manufacturing facilities and bring the work in-house. The change allowed Hauke to increase his staff and expand his business.

Now, MRC employs over 100 people. The company has increased in annual sales of $4.1 million in 2000 to 2003 sales of over $19 million. The dramatic increase is an indication of how decision such as bringing contracted business inside can increase company profits. This is exactly why the SBA 504 Loan Program is available – to make your company grow!

The 504 Loan Rescues Jobs from a Fire

Indiana-based Electro-Spec is a well-recognized leader in the specialty plating industry. The company makes components used in the electronics, automotive, aerospace, military, and medical industries, and was renowned for its attention to detail and commitment to service. After a disastrous fire, however, it looked like the firm's strong reputation could not save them. Once they secured a 504 loan, however, they got the equipment up and running and brought 26 employees back to work.

Jean Wojtowicz, president of Indiana Statewide Certified Development Corporation remarked, "When a company is in distress, more than a business is at stake. Families and communities are in peril. The Electro-Spec story is both a practical example and an inspiration. Great things can happen when a bank and two lending programs pull together with a dedicated business owner and other elements in the community."

Arizona
Business Development Finance Corporation
Richard Jeffrey, Vice President
2200 E. Camelback, Suite 215
Phoenix, AZ 85016
602-381-6292
Fax: 602-381-8012
Area of Operation: Counties of Cochise, Graham, Greenlee, Pima, Pinal, and Santa Cruz. Cities of Chandler, Mesa, Tempe in Maricopa County.

Southwestern Business Financing Corporation
Robert D. McGee, President
3200 North Central Avenue, 27th Floor
Phoenix AZ 85012
602-495-6495
Fax: 602-230-0945
Area of Operation: Citywide Phoenix

Alabama Community Development Corporation
117 Southcrest Dr., Suite 100
Homewood, AL 35209
205-942-3360
Fax: 205-942-5984
www.alacom.com
Area of Operation: statewide

Birmingham Citywide Local Development Company
110 12th St., North
Birmingham, AL 35203
205-250-6380
Fax: 205-250-6384
www.bbrconline.com
Area of Operation: statewide

Greater Mobile Development Corporation
1301 Azalea Rd., Suite 201
Mobile, AL 36693

251-650-0826
Fax: 251-650-0827
www.cityofmobile.org
Area of Operation: statewide

Southern Development Council
8132 Old Federal Rd.
Montgomery, AL 36117
334-244-1801
800-499-3034
Fax: 334-244-1421
www.sdcinc.org
Area of Operation: statewide

Alaska

Evergreen Community Development Association
900 Fourth Ave., Suite 2900
Seattle, WA 98201
206-622-3731
800-878-6613
www.ecda.com
Area of Operation: state of Alaska

Arkansas

Arkansas Certified Development Corporation
200 South Commerce
Little Rock, AR 72201
501-374-9247
Area of Operation: Entire state of Arkansas

West Central Arkansas Planning and Development District, Inc.
825 Central Avenue
P.O. Box 1558
Hot Springs, AR 71901
501-624-1036
Area of Operation: Clark, Conway, Garland, Hot Springs, Johnson, Montgomery, Perry Pike, Pope & Yell.

Ark-Tex Regional Development
P.O. Box 5307
Texarkana, TX 75505
903-832-8636
Area of Operation: Miller County

California

California Coastal Rural Development Corporation
Wendy Dodson, SBA 504 Manager
221 Main Street, Suite 301
P.O. Box 479
Salinas, CA 93901
831-424-1099 ext. 222
Fax: 831-424-1094
Email: wendy_dodson@calcoastal.org
Area of Operation: Monterey and Santa Cruz counties

Central Coast Development Corporation
Coast Business Finance
Brian Kearns, Senior Loan Officer
930 S. Broadway, Suite 101
Santa Maria, CA 93454
805-739-1665
Fax: 805-739-9257
Email: ccdc@impulse.net
Area of Operation: Counties of San Luis Obispo, Santa Barbara and Ventura

Fresno Certified Development Corporation
Robert R. Garcia, Executive Director
906 N Street, Suite 100

Fresno, CA 93721
559-485-5735
Fax: 559-485-5302
Email: rgarcia@fresnocdc.com
Area of Operation: Fresno and Kings Counties

Mid State Development Corporation
Keith Brice
4800 Easton Drive, Suite 111
Bakersfield, CA 93309
Mailing address:
  P.O. Box 302
  Bakersfield, CA 93302
661-322-4241
Fax: 661-322-0536
Email: president@midstatedevelopment.com
Area of Operation: Kern County

Stanislaus County Economic Development Corporation
Susan Martin, Vice President, Fin.
1012 I Street, 2nd Floor
Modesto, CA 95354-0808
209-521-9333
Fax: 209-521-9373
Email: suem@scedco.org
Area of Operation: Stanislaus County

Business Finance Center of Tulare County
Lisa Hollingshead, Director of Financial Services
205 E. San Joaquin Street
Tulare, CA 93274
559-688-6666
Fax: 559-688-6899
Email: lisa@edctulare.com
Area of Operation: Tulare County

Business Finance Center
Raymond K. Sakaida, General Manager
6055 E. Washington Blvd., Suite 414
Commerce, CA 90040
213-278-9600
Fax: 213-278-4898
Area of Operation: Los Angeles County

Enterprise Funding Corporation
Jeffery C. Sceranka
101 E. Redlands Blvd.
Suite 219
Redlands, CA 92373
909-792-3803
Fax: 909-792-3813
Area of Operation: San Bernardino County

Long Beach Area Certified Development Corporation
Regina Grant Peterson, Executive Director
11 Golden Shore, Suite 630
Long Beach, CA 90802
310-983-7450
Fax: 310-983-7453
Area of Operation: Cities of Long Beach, Signal Hill and Southern Los Angeles County

Amador Economic Development Corporation
Ron Mittelbrunn, Executive Director
22 North Highway 49
Jackson, CA 95642
Mailing address:
  P.O. Box 1077
  Jackson, CA 95642
209-223-0351

Fax: 209-223-2261
Area of Operation: County of Amador

Economic Development Foundation of Sacramento, Inc.
Frank Dinsmore, Executive Director
7509 Madison Avenue, Suite 111
Citrus Heights, CA 95610
916-962-3669
Fax: 916-962-1822
Area of Operation: Counties of El Dorado, Nevada, Placer,
Sacramento, San Joaquin, Sierra, Sutter, Yolo and Yuba

Greater Sacramento Certified Development Corporation
Raymond Sebastian, Executive Director
5428 Watt Avenue
Sacramento, CA 95660-4945
916-339-1096
Area of Operation: Sacramento, El Dorado, Placer and Yolo
Counties

Tracy/San Joaquian County Certified Development
Corporation
Roger Birdsall
1151 W. Robinhood Drive, Suite B-4
Stockton, CA 95207
209-951-0801
Fax: 209-951-0999
http://www.sjcdc.com
Area of Operation: San Joaquin County

La Habra Local Development Company, Inc.
A. Edwards Evans, Executive Director
441 East Whittier Boulevard, Suite C
La Habra, CA 90631
562-690-6400
Fax: 562-690-6300
Area of Operation: Los Angeles and Orange Counties

Southland Economic Development Corporation
James R. Davis, President
2000 E. Fourth Street, Suite 206
Santa Ana, CA 92705
714-647-1143
Fax: 714-953-0944
Area of Operation: Orange and San Bernardino Counties

CDC Small Business Finance Corporation
Kurt Chilcott, President and CEO
925 Fort Stockton Drive
San Diego, CA 92103
619-291-3594
Fax: 619-291-6954
Mailing address:
   P.O. Box 882228
   San Diego, CA 92108
Area of Operation: Imperial, San Diego, Riverside and
Orange Counties

Arcata Economic Development Corporation
Kathleen E. Moxon, Executive Director
100 Ericson Court, Suite 100
Arcata, CA 95521
707-822-4616
Fax: 707-822-8982
Area of Operation: Humboldt and Del Norte Counties

Bay Area Employment Development Company
James Baird, Executive Director
1801 Oakland Boulevard, Suite 300
Walnut Creek, CA 94596

925-926-1020
Fax: 225-926-1021
Area of Operation: San Francisco, San Mateo, Santa Clara,
Alameda, Contra Costa, Solani, Napa, Sonoma and Marin
Counties

California Statewide Certified Development Corporation
Barbara A. Vohryzek, Executive Director
426 "D" Street
Davis, CA 95616
530-756-9310
800-348-6258
Fax: 530-756-7519
Email: vohryzek@aol.com
Area of Operation: Statewide

Capital Business Group, Inc. dba Capital Access Group
Jacklyn Jordan, President / Kelly McAuliffe, Marketing
Director
300 Beale St., Suite 101
San Francisco, CA 94105
415-284-1460
Fax: 415-284-1590
Area of Operation: California counties of Alemeda, Contra
Costa, Marin, Napa, San Francisco, San Mateo, Santa Clara,
Solano and Sonoma

The Mortgage Capital Development Corporation
Barbara Morrison, President/CEO
611 Front Street
San Francisco, CA 94111
415-989-8855
Fax: 415-989-3382
Area of Operation: California counties of Alameda, Contra,
Costa, Marin, Napa, San Francisco, San Mateo, Santa Clara,
Solano and Sonoma

Economic Development Corporation of Shasta County
Jimce Zanhu, General Manager
410 Hemsted Drive, Suite 220
Redding, CA 96002
530-224-4920
Fax: 530-224-4921
Area of Operation: Shasta, Trinity, Siskiyou and Modoc
counties

Los Medanos Fund, A Local Development Company
Tom LaFleur, Executive V.P.
329 Railroad Avenue
Pittsburgh, CA 94565
Mailing address:
   P.O. Box 1397
   Pittsburgh, CA 94565
510-439-1056
Fax: 510-439-0831
Area of Operation: City of Pittsburg; Alameda, Contra
Costra, Marin, Napa, San Francisco, San Mateo, Santa Clara,
Solano and Sonoma Counties

Colorado
Community Economic Development Company of Colorado
Accredited Lender Program
Small Business Finance Corporation
1111 Osage Street, Suite 110
Denver, CO 80204
303- 893-8989
Fax: 303-892-8398
Email: bill@cedco.org
Area of Operation: Statewide

Denver Urban Economic Development Corporation
1905 Sherman Street, Suite 200
Denver, CO 80203
303-861-4100
Fax: 303-861-9456
Email: stephanieg@duedc.org
Area of Operation: Adams, Arapahoe, Boulder, Denver, Douglas, and Jefferson Counties

Front Range Regional Economic Development Corporation
Preferred Certified Lender
Colorado Lending Source Program
7000 North Broadway, Suite 215
Denver, CO 80221
303-657-0010
Fax: 303-657-0140
Email: mike@coloradolendingsource.org
Area of Operations: Adams, Arapahoe, Boulder, Denver, Douglas, Jefferson, Larimer, Morgan, and Weld Counties

Pikes Peak Regional Development Corporation
228 North Cascade Avenue, Suite 208
Colorado Springs, CO 80903
719-471-2044
Fax: 719-471-2042
Email: doug@pprdc.com
Area of Operations: El Paso County

SCEDD Development Company
1104 North Main
Pueblo, CO 81003
719-545-8680
Fax: 719-545-9908
Email: tomkins.scedd@worldnet.att.net
Area of Operations: Alamosa, Archuleta, Baca, Bent, Chaffee, Conejos, Costilla, Crowley, Custer, Dolores, Fremont, Huerfano, Kiowa, Lake, LaPlata, Las Animas, Mineral, Montezuma, Otero, Prowers, Pueblo, RioGrande, Saguache, San Juan Counties

Associate Development Company (ADC)
Economic Development District of Southwest Colorado
295A Girard Street
Durango, CO 81301
970-247-9621
Fax: 970-247-9513
Email: region9edd@frontier.net
Area of Operation: Archuleta, Dolores, La Plata, Montezuma, and San Juan Counties
Associated with SCEDD Development Company, Pueblo, Colorado

Connecticut

Commercial Loan Partners, INC
20 Tower Lane
Avon, CT 06001
860-667-1004
Fax: 860-667-1047
www.commercialloanpartners.com
Service Area: New Haven, Hartford, Middlesex, New London, Tolland, and Windham Counties

Connecticut Business Development Corporation
999 West Street
Rocky Hill, CT 06067
860-258-7855
Fax: 860-257-7582
Service Area: Statewide

Connecticut Community Investment Corporation, LDC
100 Crown Street
New Haven, CT 06510
203-776-6172, ext. 25
Fax: 203-776-6837
www.ctcic.org
Service Area: Hartford, Middlesex, New Haven, New London, Tolland, and Windham Counties

Housatonic Industrial Development Corporation
57 North Street, Suite 407
Danbury, CT 06810
203-743-0306
Fax: 203-744-0915
Service Area: Fairfield, Hartford (West of Conn. River), Litchfield, Middlesex, (West of Conn River) and New Haven Counties

Delaware

Wilmington Economic Development Corporation (WEDCO)
Constance C. McCarthy, Executive Director
605-A Market Street Mall
Wilmington, DE 19801
302-571-9093
Fax: 302-652-5679
Area of Operation: New Castle County only.

Mid-Atlantic Business Finance Company
Paula Klepper, President
Two Hopkins Plaza, Suite 901
Baltimore MD 21201-2911
410-539-2449
Fax: 410-539-7110
Area of Operation: Kent and Sussex Counties only.

District of Columbia

Community First, Inc.
Tim Walter, President
One Dupont Circle, NW, Suite 700
Washington, DC 20037-7121
202-265-4569
Fax: 202-265-4598
Area Of Operation: Washington, D.C.

Virginia Asset Financing Service Corporation
Sally Robertson, Executive Director
703-352-0504
4165 Chain Bridge Road
Fairfax VA 22030
800-305-0504
Fax: 703-352-9100
Area Of Operation: State of Virginia except for those counties covered by other Virginia CDCs.

Prince George's County Financial Services Corporation
Shelly Gross-Wade, Executive Director
4640 Forbes Blvd., Suite 200
Lanham, MD 20706
301-429-3044
Fax: 301-429-8762
Area Of Operation: Prince George's County

Mid-Atlantic Certified Development Company
Paula Klepper, President
1410 North Crain Highway, Suites 5B
Glen Burnie MD 21061
800-730-0017
Fax: 410-863-7446
Area Of Operation: State of Maryland

Florida

Alabama Community Development Corporation
117 Southcrest Drive, Suite 100
Birmingham, AL 35209
800-239-5909
205-870-3360
Fax: 205 - 942 - 5984
www.alalcom.com
Area of Operation: Bay, Calhoun, Escambia, Franklin,
Gadsden, Gulf, Holmes, Jackson, Leon, Liberty, Okaloosa,
Santa Rosa, Wakulla, Walton and Washington Counties

Business Development Corporation of Northeast FL
9143 Phillips Highway, Suite 350
Jacksonville, FL 32256
904-363-6350
Fax: 904 - 363 - 6356
Area of Operation: Baker, Clay, Flagler, Lake, Nassau, St.
Johns, Seminole, Putnam and Volusia Counties

Business Development Corporation
6801 Lake Worth Road, Suite 209
Lake Worth, FL 33467
561-433-0233
Fax: 561-433-8545
or

780 NW LeJune Rd., Suite 520
Miami, FL 33126
305-567-2646
Fax: 305-567-0735
Area of Operation: Brevard, Broward, Charlotte, Collier,
Dade, Indian River, Lee, Manatee, Martin, Orange, Osceola,
Palm Beach, Polk, St. Lucie and Sarasota Counties

Florida First Capital Finance Corporation, Inc.
P.O. Box 4166
Tallahassee, FL 32315 – 4166
850-681-3601
Fax: 850-681-3699
www.ffcfc.com
Area of Operation: Baker, Bay, Bradford, Brevard, Broward,
Calhoun, Charlotte, Clay, Citrus, Collier, Columbia, DeSoto,
Escambia, Franklin, Gadsden, Glades, Gilchrist, Gulf,
Hamilton, Hardee, Hendry, Hernando, Highland, Holmes,
Indian River, Jackson, Jefferson, Lafayette, Lake, Lee, Leon,
Levy, Liberty, Madison, Manatee, Marion, Martin, Monroe,
Nassau, Okaloosa, Okeechobee, Orange, Osceola, Palm
Beach, Polk, Pasco, St. Lucie, Santa Rosa, Sarasota,
Seminole, Sumter, Suwannee, Taylor, Union, Volusia,
Wakulla, Walton, and Washington Counties

Jacksonville Economic Development Company, Inc.
(JEDCO)
1300 Riverplace Blvd., Suite 105
Jacksonville, FL 32207
904-398-9411
Fax: 904-398-4995
www.jedco.net
Area of Operation: Duval County

North Central Florida Areawide Development Co., Inc.
2009 Northwest 67th Place, Suite A
Gainesville, FL 32653 – 1603
352-955-2199 ext. 107
Fax: 352-955-2209
Area of Operation: Alachua, Bradford, Columbia, Dixie,
Gilchrist, Hamilton, Lafayette, Levy, Madison, Marion,
Suwannee, Taylor and Union Counties

Southern Development Council
8132 Old Federal Road
Montgomery, AL 36116
334-244-1801
Fax: 334-244-1421
Area of Operation: Bay, Calhoun, Escambia, Franklin,
Gadsden, Gulf, Holmes, Jackson, Leon, Liberty, Okaloosa,
Santa Rosa, Wakulla, Walton and Washington Counties

Florida First Capital Finance Corporation, Inc.
1351 North Gadsden Street
Tallahassee, FL 32301
850-681-3601
Fax: 850-681-3699
Area of Operation: Bay, Brevard, Broward, Calhoun,
Charlotte, Citrus, Collier, DeSoto, Escambia, Franklin,
Gadsden, Glades, Gulf, Hardee, Hendry, Hernando,
Highlands, Hillsborough, Holmes, Indian River, Jackson,
Jefferson, Lake, Lee, Leon, Levy, Liberty, Manatee, Marion,
Martin, Monroe, Okaloosa, Okeechobee, Orange, Oceola,
Palm Beach, Pasco, Polk, Santa Rosa, Sarasota, Seminole,
Saint Lucie, Sumter, Wakulla, Walton, Washington and
Volusia Counties

St. Petersburg Certified Development Corporation
dba Gulf Coast CDC
227 Second Avenue North
St. Petersburg, FL 33731
727-895 - 2504
Fax: 727-822 - 2504
Area of Operation: Manatee, Pasco, Pinellas and Sarasota
Counties

Southwest Florida Regional Development Corporation
4980 Bayline Drive, 4th Floor
North Fort Myers, FL 33917
941-656-7726
Fax: 941-656-7724
Area of Operation: Charlotte, Collier, DeSoto, Glades,
Hardee, Hendry, Lee, Polk and Sarasota Counties

Tampa-Bay Economic Development Corporation
2105 North Nebraska Avenue
Tampa, FL 33602
813-274-7971
Fax: 813-274-7551
Area of Operation: Hillsborough County

Georgia

The Business Growth Corporation of Georgia
1450 S. Johnson Ferry Road
Atlanta, GA 30319
404-475-6002
Fax: 404-475-6016

Coastal Area District Development Authority
501 Gloucester Street, Suite 201
Brunswick, GA 31520
912-261-2500
Fax: 912-261-0032
or
#1 Bull Street, Suite 301
Savannah, GA 31401
912-236-9566
Fax: 912-236-9562

CSRA Local Development Corporation
3023 Riverwatch Parkway
Suite A
Augusta, GA 30907-2016

706-210-2010
Fax: 706-210-2006

Economic Devel. Corp. Of Fulton County
141 Pryor St., Suite 5001
Atlanta, GA 30303
404-836-7731 Fulton county only
Fax: 404-836-7712

Uptown Columbus, Inc.
P.O. Box 1237
Columbus, GA 31902
706-596-0111
Fax: 706-596-0012

North Georgia Certified Development Corporation
503 West Waugh St.
Dalton, GA 30720
706-272-2300
Fax: 703-272-2253

Georgia Mountains Regional Economic Development
Corporation
460 Enota Dr.
Gainsville, GA 30503
770-536-7839
Fax: 770-536-9026

Development Corporation of Middle Georgia
175 C Emery Hwy.
Macon, GA 31201
478-751-6160
Fax: 478-751-6517

Small Business Assistance Corp.
111 E. Liberty St., Suite 100
Savannah, GA 31401
912-232-4700
Fax: 912-232-0385

South Georgia Regional Development Corporation
327 West Savannah Ave.
P.O. Box 1223
Valdosta, GA 31601
229-333-5281
Fax: 229-333-5312

Georgia Certified Development Corporation
3353 Peachtree Road, NE, Suite 1155
Atlanta, GA 30326
404-442-2480
Fax: 404-442-2481

Hawaii

HEDCO Local Development Corporation
222 South Vineyard Street
Penthouse – 1
Honolulu HI 96813-2445
808-521-6502
Fax: 808-521-6541
Area of Operation: Statewide and American Samoa

Lokahi Pacific Rural Development, Inc.
Jo-Ann Ridao, Managing Director
1935 Main Street
Wailuku, HI 96793
808-244-2200
Fax: 808-244-2057
Area of Operation: Counties of Maui and Hawaii

Idaho

Capital Matrix, Inc.
1471 Shoreline Drive, Suite 123
Boise ID 83702
208-383-3473
Fax: 208-383-9404
Email: Capmatrx@Capitalmatrix.com
Area of Operation: Idaho Counties of Ada, Adams, Boise,
Canyon, Elmore, Gem, Owyhee, Payette, Valley and
Washington; Oregon Counties of Harney and Malheur

East-Central Idaho Development Company
310 N. 2nd E., Suite 115
Rexburg ID 83440
208-356-4524
Fax: 208-356-4544
Email: david.ogden@ecipda.org
www.ecidc.org
Area of Operation: Bonneville, Butte, Clark, Custer,
Fremont, Jefferson, Lemi, Madison and Tenton Counties

Eastern Idaho Development Corporation
1651 Alvin Ricken Drive
Pocatello ID 83201
208-234-7541
Fax: 208-282-4813
Email: coxpaul@isu.edu
Area of Operation: Bannock, Power, Bear Lake, Bingham,
Caribou, Franklin and Oneida Counties

Region IV Development Corporation, Inc.
315 Falls Avenue
P.O. Box 5079
Twin Falls, ID 83303
208-732-5730
Fax: 208-732-5454
Email: Rparrish@cdi.edu
www.rivdco.org
Area of Operation: Blaine, Camas, Cassia, Gooding, Jerome,
Lincoln, Minidoka and Twin Falls Counties

Panhandle Area Council, Inc.
11100 Airport Drive
Hayden ID 83835
208-772-0584
Fax: 208-772-6196
Area of Operation: 5 Northern Counties of Idaho - Benewah,
Bonner, Boundary, Kootenai and Shoshone

Greater Eastern Oregon Development Corporation
P.O. Box 1041
Pendleton, OR 97801
541-276-6745
Fax: 541-276-6071
Email: gmdavis@OregonVOS.net
Area of Operation: Gilliam, Grant, Morrow, Umatilla,
Wheeler, Union, Baker and Wallowa Counties

Oregon Certified Business Development Corporation
2363 SW Glacier Place
Redmond OR 97756-8120
541-548-8163
Fax: 541-923-3416
Email: mackinnon@coic.org
Area of Operation: Crook, Deschutes, Harney, Jefferson,
Klamath, Lake and Malheur Counties

Illinois

Illinois Business Financial Services
124 Southwest Adams Street, Suite 300

Peoria IL 61602
309-676-0755
Fax: 309-676-7534
Area of Operation: Citywide in Peoria; Counties of Peoria,
Tazewell and Woodford

Illinois Small Business Growth Corporation
2921 Greenbriar Drive, Suite C
Springfield, IL 62704
217-787-7557
Fax: 217-787-2872
Area of Operation: Statewide

Rockford Local Development Corporation
515 North Court Street
Rockford IL 61103
815-987-8127
Fax: 815-987-8122
Area of Operation: City of Rockford

Somercor 504, Inc.
2 East 8th Street, Suite 200
Chicago IL 60605
312-360-3163
Fax: 312-360-9177
Area of Operation: Cook Dupage, Lane Kane, McHenry and
Will Counties

South Central Illinois Regional Planning & Development
Comm.
120 Delmar Avenue, Suite A
Salem IL 62881-2006
618-548-4234
Fax: 618-548-4236
Area of Operation: Counties of Effingham, Fayette and
Marion; also Cities of Centralia and Wamac

CenterPoint 504, Inc.
Governors State University
University Park IL 60466
708-534-4924
Fax: 708-534-8457
Area of Operation: South Suburban Cook and Eastern Will
Counties

Indiana

Business Development Corporation
Kate McCahill/Don Inks
1200 County-City Building
South Bend IN 46601
574-235-9278
Fax: 574-235-9021
Area of Operation: St. Joseph County

Community Development Corporation
Matt Blair
840 City-County Building
Fort Wayne IN 46802
260-427-1127
Fax: 260-427-1375
www.fortwayne-ed.org/business_loans.htm
Area of Operation: Allen County

Indiana Statewide Certified Development Corporation
Jean Wojtowicz, President
4181 East 96th Street, Suite 200
Indianapolis IN 46240
317-844-9810
Fax: 317-844-9815
Area of Operation: Statewide

Premier Capital Corporation
David W. Amick, Executive Director
151 N. Delaware, Suite 750
Indianapolis, IN 46204
317-974-0504
Fax: 317-974-0510
www.premiercapitalcorp.com
Area of Operation: Counties of Boone, Hancock, Hendricks,
Johnson, Marion, Morgan and Shelby

Northwest Indiana Regional Development Corporation
Dennis M. Henson, President
6100 Southport Road
Portage IN 46368
219-763-6303
Fax: 219-763-2653
www.nwirdc.org
Area of Operation: Jasper, Lake LaPorte, Newton, Porter,
Pulaski and Starke Counties

Iowa

Black Hawk Economic Development, Inc.
Stephen A. Brustkern, Executive Director
304 South Street
Waterloo IA 50704
319-235-2960
Fax: 319-235-9171
Area of Operation: Allamakee, Blackhawk, Bremer, Butler,
Buchanan, Chickasaw, Clayton, Grundy, Howard and
Winneshiek Counties

Corporation for Economic Development in Des Moine
Mike Ryan, Development Financing Coordinator
400 East First Street
Des Moines, IA 50309
515-283-4017
Fax: 515-237-1667
Area of Operation: Citywide Des Moines

Iowa Business Growth Company
Dan Robeson, Executive Director
7043 Vista Drive
West Des Moines, IA 50266
515-223-4511
Fax: 515-223-5017

E. Iowa Branch: Jerry Trudo, Branch Manager
805 Wright Brothers Blvd. SW
Cedar Rapids, Iowa 52404-9070
319-632-4242
Fax: 319-632-4241
Area of Operation: Statewide

Siouxland Economic Development Corporation
Ken Beekley, Executive Director
428 Insurance Centre
507 7th Street
Sioux City, IA 51101
712-279-6286
Fax: 712-279-6920
Area of Operation: Woodbury, Plymouth, Cherokee, Ida,
Monona and Sioux Counties in Iowa; Dakota County in
Nebraska; Union and Clay Counties in South Dakota

E.C.I.A. Business Growth, Inc.
Jerry Schroeder, Economic Development Planner
330 Nesler Center, Suite 330
Dubuque IA 52001
563-556-4166
Fax: 563-556-0348

Area of Operation: Cedar, Clinton, Delaware, Dubuque and Jackson Counties as well as the Cities located therein

Kansas
Avenue Area, Inc.
Tom Overby, Executive Director
753 State Avenue, Suite 106
Kansas City, KS 66101
913-371-0065
Fax: 913-321-1019
County served: Wyandotte

Citywide Development Corporation of Kansas City, Kansas
701 North 7th Street, Room 421
Kansas City, KS 66101
913-573-5733
Fax: 913-573-5745
Serves: City of Kansas City

Eastern Kansas Economic Development Group
Wayne Symmonds, Executive Director
702 Commercial, Suite 3A
Emporia, KS 66801
785-776-0417
Fax: 785-776-7204
Counties served: Atchison, Chase, Clay, Coffey, Franklin, Geary, Jackson, Lyon, Marshall, Morris, Nemaha, Osage, Pottawatomie, Riley, Wabaunsee

Four Rivers Development, Inc. (ADC)
Debra J. Peters, Manager
P.O. Box 265
Beloit, KS 67420
785-738-2185
Fax: 785-738-2185
Email: dpeters@nckcn.com
www.ckcn.com/ComEcon/fordi.htm
Counties served: Cloud, Dickinson, Ellsworth, Jewell, Lincoln, Mitchell, Ottawa, Republic, Saline, Washington

Great Plains Development, Inc.
Patty Richardson, Executive Director
100 Military Plaza, Suite 128
P.O. Box 1116
Dodge City, KS 67801-1116
316-227-6406
Fax: 316-225-6051
Counties served: Barber, Barton, Clark, Comanche, Edwards, Finney, Ford, Grant, Gray, Greeley, Hamilton, Haskell, Hodgeman, Kearney, Kiowa, Lane, Meade, Morton, Ness, Pawnee, Pratt, Rush, Scott, Stafford, Seward, Stanton, Stevens, Wichita

Johnson County Certified Development Company
David Long, Executive Director
11111 West 95th Street, Suite 214
Overland Park, KS 66214
913-599-1717
Fax: 913-599-6430
County served: Johnson

McPherson County Small Business Development Association
David A. O'Dell, Executive Director
212 E. Euclid
McPherson KS 67460
620-241-3927
Fax: 620-241-3927
Email: sbda@mpks.net
County served: McPherson

Mid-America, Inc.
Bruce Fairbank, Executive Director
1501 S. Joplin
Pittsburg, KS 66762
316-235-4920
Fax: 316-235-4919
Counties served: Allen, Anderson, Bourbon, Cherokee, Crawford, Labette, Linn, Miami, Montgomery, Neosho, Wilson, Woodson

MoKan Development, Inc.
Director of Economic Development
1302 Faraon
St. Joseph, MO 64501
816-233-3144
Fax: 816-233-8498
Counties served: Atchison, Brown, Doniphan, Jackson, Jefferson, Nemaha

Pioneer Country Development, Inc.
Randy Hrabe, Executive Director
319 North Pomeroy
P.O. Box 248
Hill City, KS 67642-0248
785-625-6116
Fax: 785-628-0533
Counties served: Cheyenne, Decatur, Ellis, Gove, Graham, Logan, Norton, Osborne, Phillips, Rawlins, Rooks, Russell, Sheridan, Sherman, Smith, Thomas, Trego, Wallace

South Central Kansas Economic Development District
Bill Bolin, Executive Director
209 E. William, Suite 300
Wichita, KS 67202
316-262-7035
Fax: 316-262-7062
Counties served: Butler, Chautauqua, Cowley, Elk, Greenwood, Harper, Harvey, Kingman, Marion, McPherson, Rice, Reno, Sedgwick, Sumner

Wakarusa Valley Development, Inc.
Mike O'Donnell, Executive Director
203 Lyon Street
P.O. Box 586
Lawrence, KS 66044-0367
785-865-4425
Fax: 785-865-4400
County served: Douglas

Kentucky
Commonwealth Small Business Development Corporation
111 St. James Court, Suite 504
Frankfort KY 40601
502-696-9444
Fax: 502-696-9493
Area of Operation: Statewide

Capital Access Corporation - Kentucky
120 Webster Street, Suite 330
Louisville, KY 40206
502-584-2175
Fax: 502-584-2173
Email: billfensterer@yahoo.com
Area of Operation: Jefferson, Oldham, Scott, Hardin, Bullitt, Nelson, Daviess, Estill, Henderson, Meade, Pendleton, Pulaski, Shelby, Spencer and Warren Counties

Community Ventures Corporation
1450 N. Broadway
Lexington, KY 40505

859-231-0054
Fax: 859-231-0261
Area of Operation: Bourbon, Boyle, Clark, Fayette, Jessamine, Kenton, Madison, Taylor, & Woodford Counties

Purchase Area Development District
1002 Medical Drive
Mayfield KY 42066
502-247-7171
Fax: 502-247-9000
Area of Operation: Ballard, Calloway, Carlisle, Fulton, Graves, Hickman, Marshall and McCracken Counties
a specific region.

Louisiana
Ark-La-Tex Investment & Development Corporation
5210 Hollywood Avenue
Shreveport LA 71109
MAILING ADDRESS:
  P.O. Box 37005
  Shreveport LA 71109
318-632-2022
Fax: 318-632-2099
Area Of Operation: Parishes of Bienville, Bossier, Caddo, Claiborne, DeSoto, Lincoln, Natchitoches, Red River, Sabine and Webster

JEDCO Development Corporation
3445 North Causeway Boulevard, Suite 300
Metairie LA 70002
504-833-1881
Fax: 504-833-7676
Area Of Operation: Jefferson Parish

Kisatchie-Delta Regional Planning & Development District, Inc.
1611 Arnold Drive, First Floor
Alexandria, LA 71303
318-487-5454
Fax: 318-487-5451
Area Of Operation: Parishes of Avoyelles, Catahoula, Concordia, Grant, La Salle, Rapides, Vernon and Winn

Louisiana Capital Certified Development Company, Inc.
302 La Rue France, Suite 200
Lafayette, LA 70508
MAILING ADDRESS:
  302 La Rue France, Suite 200
  Lafayette, LA 70508
337-234-2977
Fax: 337-234-5535
Area Of Operation: Parishes of Acadia, Calcasieu, Evangeline, Iberia, Lafayette, St. Landry, St. Martin, St. Mary and Vermilion

New Orleans Regional Business Development Loan Corporation
650 Poydras, Suite 1220
New Orleans LA 70130
504-524-6172
Fax: 504-524-0002
Area Of Operation: Parishes of Assumption, Jefferson, Laforuche, Orleans, Plaquemines, St. Benard, St. Charles, St. James, St. John the Baptist, St. Tammany, Tangipahoa, Terrebonne and Washington

Northeast Louisiana Capital, Inc.
1900 North 18th Street, Suite 304
Monroe LA 71201
318-323-0878

Fax: 318-387-8529
Area of Operation: Ouachita, Union, Morehouse, Richland, Caldwell, Jackson, Franklin, Tensas, East Carroll, West Carroll and Madison Parishes

Maine
Androscoggin Valley Council of Governments
Robert J. Thompson
125 Manley Road
Auburn ME 04210
207-783-9186
Fax: 207-783-5211
Area of Operation: Androscoggin, Franklin and Oxford Counties

Coastal Enterprises, Inc.
Ronald L. Phillips, President
Water Street
P.O. Box 268
Wiscasset ME 04578
207-882-7552
Fax: 207-882-7308
Area of Operation: Cumberland, Knox, Lincoln, Sagadahoc and York Counties

Eastern Maine Development Corporation
Victoria Lundgren, Loan Officer
One Cumberland Place, Suite 300
P.O. Box 2579
Bangor ME 04401
207-942-6389
Fax: 207-942-3548
Area of Operation: Hancock, Kennebec, Knox, Penobscot, Piscataquis, Somerset, Waldo and Washington Counties

Maryland
Chesapeake Business Finance Corporation
John Sower, President
4606 Wedgewood Boulevard
Frederick, MD 21603
301-668-1844
Fax: 301-668-1845
Area of Operation: Garrett, Allegany, Charles, Talbot, Dorchester, Cecil, St. Mary's, Washington, Montgomery, Wicomico, Prince George, Carroll, Frederick, Baltimore Counties and the City of Baltimore.

Mid-Atlantic Certified Development Company
Paula Klepper, President
1410 N. Crain Highway, Suite 5B
Glen Burnie, MD 21061
410-863-1600
Fax: 410-863-7446
www.mabfc.com
Area of Operation: Statewide

Prince George's County Financial Services Corporation
1400 McCormick Drive, Suite 240
Largo, MD 20774
301-883-6900
Fax: 301-883-6160
www.pgfsc.com
Area of Operation: Prince George's County

Massachusetts
Bay Colony Development Corporation
David King, Managing Trustee
1601 Trapelo Road, Suite 222
Waltham MA 02451
781-891-3594

Fax: 781-647-4950
Area of Operation: Statewide- except Dukes and Nantucket
Counties

Massachusetts Certified Development Corporation
Elizabeth C.Trifone, Vice President
50 Milk Street
Boston MA 02109
617-350-8877
Fax: 617-350-0052
Area of Operation: Statewide

North Central Massachusetts Certified Development
Corporation
David McKeehan, President
110 Erdman Way
Leominster MA 01453
978-840-4300
Fax: 978-840-4896
Area of Operation: Cities and towns in the Northern
Worcester County and the Western Middlesex County

South Eastern Economic Development Corporation
Maria Gooch, Executive Director
88 Broadway
Taunton MA 02780
508-822-1020
Fax: 508-880-7869
Area of Operation: Counties of Barnstable, Bristol, Dukes,
Nantucket and Plymouth

South Shore Economic Development Corporation
Patricia Faiella
36 Miller Stile Road
Quincy MA 02169
617-479-1111
Fax: 617-479-9274
Area of Operation: Plymouth and Norfolk Counties

Worcester Business Development Corporation
William E. Purcell, Vice President
33 Waldo Street
Worcester MA 01608
508-753-2924
Fax: 508-754-8560
Area of Operation: Worcester County

Michigan

Economic Development Foundation-Certified
1345 Monroe, NW, Suite 132
Grand Rapids, MI 49505
616-458-5416
Area of Operation: Antrim, Barry, Benzie, Charlevoix,
Emmet, Grand Traverse, Kalkaska, Kent, Leelanau,
Manistee, Mason, Missaukee, Muskegon, Oceana, and
Wexford Counties.

Growth Finance Corporation
19498 M-49
PO Box 501
Howard City, MI 49239-0501
231-937-7429
Area of Operation: Allegan, Ionia, Kent, Lake, Mason,
Mecosta, Montcalm, Newaygo, Oceana, Osceola, and
Wexford Counties.

Lakeshore 504
272 East 8th Street
PO Box 1888
Holland, MI 49422-1888

269-392-2389
Area of Operation: Allegan, Berrien, Cass, Kalamazoo,
Muskegon, Oceana, Ottawa, St. Joseph, and Van Buren
Counties.

Metropolitan Growth and Development Corporation
600 Randolph Street, 3rd Floor
Detroit, MI 48226
313-224-0820
Area of Operation: Wayne and Macomb Counties.

Michigan Certified Development Corporation
822 Centennial Way, Suite 180
Lansing, MI 48917
517-886-6612
Area of Operation: State of Michigan.

Oakland County Business Finance Corporation
1200 N. Telegraph
Executive Office Building
Pontiac, MI 48341
248-858-0879
Area of Operation: Oakland County.

SEM Resource Capital
17177 N. Laurel Park Drive, Suite 360
Livonia, MI 48152
734-464-4418
Area of Operation: Genesee, Livingston, Macomb, Monroe,
Washtenaw, and Wayne Counties.

Minnesota

Central Minnesota Development Company
Connie M. Nelson, Executive Director
277 Coon Rapids Boulevard, Suite 212
Coon Rapids, MN 55433
763-784-3337
Fax: 763-784-3338
Area of Operation: Anoka County

Minneapolis Economic Development Company
Michelle Mueller
105 5th Avenue, South, Suite 200
Minneapolis, MN 55401
612-673-5070
Fax: 612-673-5111
www.mcda.org
Area of Operation: Hennepin County

Minnesota Business Finance Corporation
Alexandra Blum, President and CEO
616 Roosevelt Road, Suite 200
St. Cloud MN 56301
320-255-1685
Fax: 320-255-1815
www.mbfc.org
Area of Operation: Statewide

Prairieland Economic Development Corporation
Steve M. Ousek, Director
1 Prairie Drive
507-836-6656
Slayton MN 56172-1142
Fax: 507-836-6309
www.prairielandedc.com
Mailing Address:
  P.O. Box 265
  Slayton MN 56172
Area of Operation: Big Stone, Chippewa, Cottonwood,
Jackson, Lac Qui Parle, Lincoln, Lyon, Murray, Nobles,

Pipestone, Redwood, Rock, Swift and Yellow Medicine
Counties

South Central Business Finance Economic Development
Corp.
Jim Snackenberg, Econ. Dev. Planner
209 South Second St., Suite 311
Mankato MN 56002
507-625-6056
Fax: 507-625-6173
Mailing Address:
   P.O. Box 666
   Mankato MN 56002-0666
Area of Operation: Blue Earth, Brown, Faribault, Le Sueur,
Martin, Nicollet, Sibley, Waseca and Watonwan Counties

Saint Paul/Metro East Development Corporation
Kristin Wood, Executive Director
2459 - 15th Street NW, Suite A
New Brighton MN 55112
651-631-4900
Fax: 651-631-9498
www.spedco.com
Area of Operation: Counties of Dakota, Ramsey and
Washington

Southeastern Minnesota 504 Development, Inc.
Dwayne Lee, Director, Business Development
220 South Broadway, Suite 100
Rochester MN 55904
507-288-6442
Fax: 507-282-8960
Area of Operation: Counties of Dodge, Fillmore, Freeborn,
Goodhue, Hosuton, Mower, Olmsted, Rice, Wabasha,
Winona and City of Blooming Prairie

Twin Cities-Metro Certified Development Company
Robert Heck, President
4105 Lexington Ave North
Suite 170 Arden Woods
Arden Hills MN 55126-6181
651-481-8081
Fax: 651-481-8280
Area of Operation: Counties of Carver, Dakota, Hennepin,
Ramsey, Scott and Washington

Mississippi
Central Mississippi Development Company, Inc.
Thelman L. Anderson, Executive Director
P.O. Box 4935
1170 Lakeland Drive
Jackson, MS 39296-4935
601-981-1625
Fax: 601-981-1515

Three Rivers Local Development Company, Inc.
Vernon R. Kelley, Executive Director
P.O. Drawer B
75 South Main Street
Pontotoc, MS 38863
662-489-2435
Fax: 662-489-6815

Southern Development Council, Inc.
Tamara Y. Lee, Executive Director
Leon Darby, Loan Officer
800-499-3034
8132 Old Federal Road
Montgomery, AL 36117
334-244-1801
Fax: 334-244-1421

ALACOM Finance (Alabama Community Development
Corporation)
Diane Roehrig, President
117 Southcrest Drive, Suite 100
Homewood, AL 35209
205-870-3360
Fax: 205-942-5984

Missouri
Clay/Platte County Development Corporation
Gary R. Moore, Executive Director
8320 North Oak Trafficway, Suite 265
Kansas City, MO 64118
816-468-4989
Fax: 816-468-7778
Area of Operation: Clay and Platte County

EDC Loan Corporation
Kathleen Barney, Loan Manager
10 Petticoat Lane, Suite 250
Kansas City, MO 64106
816-221-0636
Fax: 816-221-0189
Area of Operation: Kansas City

Green Hills Rural Development, Inc.
Michael R. Johns
909 Main Street
Trenton, MO 64683
816-359-5086
Area of Operation: Counties of Caldwell, Daviess, Grundy,
Harrison, Linn, Livingston, Mercer, Putnam, Sullivan,
Chariton and Carroll

Meramec Regional Development Corporation
Mary Elder, Business Development Specialist
#4 Industrial Drive
St. James, MO 65559
573-265-2993
Area of Operation: Phelps, Dent, Crawford, Washington,
Gasconade and Maries Counties

Mo-Kan Development, Inc.
Maurice Owen, Director of Ec. Dev.
1302 Faraon Street
St. Joseph, MO 64501
816-233-3144
Fax: 816-233-8498
Area of Operation: Missouri Counties of Andrew,
Buchanan,Clinton and Dekalb; Kansas Counties of Atchison,
Brown, Doniphan, Jackson, Jefferson, and Nemaha

Business Finance Corporation of St. Louis County
Richard M. Palank, Executive Director
121 South Meramec, Suite 412
Clayton, MO 63105
314-889-7663
Fax: 314-889-7666
Area of Operation: St. Louis County and Jefferson County

Central Ozarks Development, Inc.
James Dickerson, Executive Director
115 West Hwy 54
P.O. Box 786
Camdenton, MO 65020
573-346-5692
Fax: 573-346-2007
Area of Operation: Camden, Laclede, Pulaski, Miller and
Morgan Counties

Economic Development Corporation of Jefferson County,
MO
Patrick Lamping, Executive Director
5217 Highway B
P.O. Box 623
Hillsboro, MO 63050
314-797-5336
Fax: 314-789-4594
Area of Operation: Jefferson County

Enterprise Development Corporation
Michael Crist, Executive Director
910 East Broadway, Suite A
Columbia, MO 65201
573-875-8117
Fax: 573-443-2319
Area of Operation: Audrain, Boone, Callaway, Cole,
Howard, Montgomery and Randolph Counties

Rural Missouri, Inc.
Ken Lueckenotte, Director
1014 Northeast Drive
Jefferson City, MO 65109
573-635-0136
Fax: 573-635-5636
Area of Operation: Statewide

St. Charles County Economic Development Corporation
Gregory Presteman, Executive Director
5988 Mid Rivers Mall Drive
St. Charles, MO 63304
314-441-6880
Fax: 314-441-6881
Area of Operation: Counties of Franklin, Lincoln, St. Charles
and Warren

St. Louis Local Development Company (The)
1015 Locust, Suite 1200
St. Louis, MO 63101
314-622-3400
Fax: 314-622-3413
Area of Operation: St. Louis

Montana
Economic Development Corporation of Yellowstone County
Jeff Leuthold
TW I, #109
404 N. 31st
Billings, MT 59101
406-245-0415
Fax: 208-330-4264
Area of Operation: statewide

Montana Community Finance Corporation
Karen Howard, Executive Director
7 West 6th Avenue
Helena, MT 59624
406-443-3261
Fax: 406-449-5678

Nebraska
Nebraska Economic Development Corporation
Alan Eastman
1033 O Street, Suite 548
Lincoln NE 68508
402-475-2795
Fax: 402-475-2849
Area of Operation: statewide

Nevada
Nevada State Development Corporation
Roberta Bennett, President
6572 South McCarran Blvd.
Reno, NV 89509
775-826-6172
800-726-2494
Fax: 775-826-6398
Area of Operation: Statewide

New Ventures Capital Development Company
Earnest Fountain, Vice President
626 South 9th Street
Las Vegas NV 89101
702-382-9522
Fax: 702-382-0375
Area of Operation: Clark County

Southern Nevada Certified Development Corporation
Thomas J. Gutherie, President/CEO
2770 South Maryland Parkway, Suite 216
Las Vegas NV 89109
702-732-3998
Area of Operation: Mineral, Esmeralda, Nye, Lincoln, Lyon,
Douglas, White Pine and Clark Counties

New Hampshire
Capital Regional Development Council
Niel Cannon, Executive Director
1 South Street
Concord NH 03301
603-228-1872
Fax: 603-226-3588
Mailing Address:
    P.O. Box 664
    Concord NH 03301
Area of Operation: Belknap, Grafton, Merrimack and
Sullivan Counties

Granite State Economic Development Corporation
Alan Abraham, President
1 Cate Street, 5th Floor
Portsmouth NH 03801
603-623-7383
Fax: 603-623-6723
Mailing Address:
    P.O. Box 1491
    Portsmouth, NH 03801
Area of Operation: Statewide

Northern Community Investment Corporation
Paul Denton, President
20 Main Street
St. Johnsbury VT 05819
802-748-1501
Fax: 802-748-1884
Mailing Address:
P.O. Box 396
St. Johnsbury, VT 05819
Area of Operation: Carroll, Coos, and Grafton Counties

New Jersey
New Jersey Business Finance Corp.
Ira Lutsky, President
Bridge Plaza North, Suite 211
P.O. Box 919
Fort Lee, NJ 07024
201-346-0300
Fax: 201-346-1336

Area Of Operation: All New Jersey counties except for
Sussex and Warren.

Corporation for Business Assistance in New Jersey
Barbara Bennett
200 South Warren Street
P.O. Box 990
Trenton NJ 08625
609-292-0184
Fax: 609-292-0368
Area Of Operation: Statewide

New York

The Bronx Initiative Corporation
Madeline Marquez
98 East 161st Street
Bronx, NY 10451
718 590-3948
Fax: 718-590-5814
Area of Operation: The Bronx

Long Island Development Corporation
Roslyn Goldmacher, Executive Director
255 Executive Drive
Plainview, NY 11803
516-349-7800
Fax: 516-349-7881
Area of Operation: Counties of Nassau and Suffolk

Progress Development Corporation
Cynthia C. Clune, Executive Director
19 East Main Street
P.O. Box 3105
Port Jervis, NY 12771
914-858-8358
Fax: 914-858-8002
Area of Operation: Orange County

Albany Local Development Corporation
George Leveille, Vice President
Eagle Street
City Hall, 4th Floor
Albany, NY 12207
518-434-5133
Fax: 518-434-5098
Area of Operation: City of Albany

Empire State Certified Development Corporation
Robert Lazar, President
41 State Street
P.O. Box 738
Albany, NY 12207
518-463-2268
Fax: 518-463-0240
New York City
212-803-3672
Area of Operation: Statewide; except Nassau, Suffolk and
Onondaga Counties

Greater Syracuse Business Development Corporation
Richard Arciero, Executive Director
572 South Salina Street
Syracuse, NY 13202
315-470-1888
Fax: 315-471-8545
Area of Operation: Counties of Onondaga, Cayuga, Cortland
and Madison

Mohawk Valley Certified Development Corporation
Michael Reese, Executive VP & CEO

26 West Main Street
P.O. Box 69
Mohawk, NY 13407
315-866-4671
Fax: 315-866-9862
Area of Operation: Oneida, Herkimer, Fulton, Montgomery
and Schoharie Counties

Monroe County Industrial Development Corporation
Judy Seil, Assistant Secretary
8100 City Place
50 W. Main Street
Rochester, NY 14614
716-428-5060
Fax: 716-428-2147
Area of Operation: Monroe County

Operation Oswego County, Inc.
L. Michael Treadwell, Area Industrial Dir.
44 West Bridge Street
Oswego, NY 13126
315-343-1545
Fax: 315-343-1546
Area of Operation: Oswego County

Rochester Economic Development Corporation
Fashun Ku, President
30 Church Street, Suite 005A
Rochester, NY 14614
716-428-6966
Fax: 716-428-6042
Area of Operation: City of Rochester

Syracuse Economic Development Corporation
Laurenzo James, Deputy Director
223 City Hall
Syracuse, NY 13202
315-488-8107
Fax: 315-448-8036
Area of Operation: Citywide in Syracuse

North Carolina

Asheville-Buncombe Development Corporation
Robert C. Kendrick
347 Barnardsville Hwy.
Weaverville NC 28787-9696
Mail: P.O. Box 7032
Asheville, NC 28802-1010
828-645-0439
Fax: 828-658-2935
Area of Operation: Buncombe County

Centralina Development Corporation, Inc.
Paul K. Herringshaw, Executive Director
1300 Baxter Street
P.O. Box 35008
Charlotte, NC 28235
704-348-2734
Fax: 704-372-1280
Area of Operation: Cabarrus, Gaston, Iredell, Lincoln,
Mecklenburg, Rowan, Stanly & Union Counties

Charlotte Certified Development Corporation
Frcd L. Miller, Executive Director
5970 Fairview Rd. Suite 218
Charlotte, NC 28211
704-442-8145
Fax: 704-442-0429
Area of Operation: Mecklenburg County

Neuse River Development Authority, Inc.
Don Stewart, Senior Loan Officer
233 Middle Street
P.O. Box 1717
New Bern, NC 28563
919-638-6724
Fax: 919-638-3187
Area of Operation: Carteret, Craven, Duplin, Greene,
Johnston Counties

Northwest Piedmont Development Corporation, Inc.
Charles Malone
Director of Economic Development
400 West Fourth Street, Suite 400
Winston-Salem, NC 27101-2805
336-761-2111
Fax: 336-761-2112
Area of Operation: Davie, Forsyth, Stokes, Surry, Yadkin
Counties

Region C Development Corporation, Inc.
Jim Edwards, Executive Director
111 West Court Street
P.O. Box 841
Rutherfordton, NC 28139-0841
828-287-2281
Fax: 828-287-2735
Area of Operation: Cleveland, McDowell, Polk & Rutherford
Counties

Region D Development Corp, Inc.
Executive Arts Building
Furman Road
P.O. Box 1820
Boone, NC 28607
828-265-5434 x125
Fax: 828-265-5439
Area of Operation: Alleghany, Ashe, Avery, Mitchell,
Watauga Counties

Region E Development Corporation
James E. Chandler, Loan Specialist
736 Fourth Street, SW
Hickory, NC 28602
828-322-9191
Fax: 828-322-5991
Area of Operation: Alexander, Burke, Caldwell & Catawba
Counties

Self-Help Ventures Fund
Jim Overton, Commerical Loan Off.
301 W. Main Street
P.O. Box 3619
Durham, NC 27702
919-956-4473
Fax: 919-956-4600
Area of Operation: Statewide

Smokey Mountain Development Corporation
Thomas Fouts, Executive Director
144 Industrial Park Drive
Waynesville, NC 28786
828-452-1967
Fax: 828-452-1352
Area of Operation: Madison, Haywood, Graham, Cherokee,
Clay Counties

Wilmington Industrial Development, Inc.
Susie Parker, Office Manager
1739 Hewlett Drive

P.O. Box 1698
Wilmington, NC 28402
910-763-0013
Fax: 910-763-0106
Area of Operation: New Hanover, Brunswick, Pender
Counties

North Dakota

Dakota Certified Development Company
Toby Sticka, 504 Prog. Director
51 Broadway, Suite 400
Fargo ND 58102
701-293-8892
800-611-8997
Fax: 701-293-7819

Ohio

Cascade Capital Corporation, Inc.
Robert Filipiak, Executive Director
One Cascade Place, 7th Floor
Akron, OH 44308
330-379-3160
Fax: 330-761-0307
Area of Operation: Ashland, Holmes, Portage, Medina,
Summit and Wayne Counties

Certified Development Co. of Butler County
Jenea Norris Allen, Executive Director
130 High Street, 6th Floor
Hamilton, OH 45011
513-887-3404
Fax: 513-785-5723
Area of Operation: Butler County

Certified Development Company of Warren County, Inc.
Steve Jacobs, Loan Manager
320 East Silver St
Lebanon, OH 45036
513-695-1223
Fax: 513-695-2933
Area of Operation: Warren County

Citywide Small Business Development Corp.
Janet White, Director, Economic Development Officer
8 North Main Street
Dayton, OH 45402-1916
937-226-0457
Fax: 937-222-7035
Area of Operation: city limits of Dayton

Clark County Development Corp.
Warren Holden, Loan Manager
300 East Auburn Avenue
Springfield, OH 45505
937-322-8685
Fax: 937-322-7874
Area of Operation: Clark County

Community Capital Development Corporation
Brad Shimp, Executive Director
900 Michigan Avenue
Columbus, OH 43215-1165
614-645-6171
Fax: 614-645-8588
Area Of Operation: Counties of Delaware, Fairfield, Fayette,
Franklin, Licking, Madison, Muskingum, Perry, Pickaway,
Union, Athens, Gallia, Hocking, Lawrence, Meigs, Monroe,
Morgan, Noble, Scioto and Washington Counties.

County Corp Development
Marlene J. Flagel, President
40 West Fourth Street, Suite 1600
Dayton, OH 45402
937-225-6328
Fax: 937-225-5089
Area of Operation: Darke, Miami, Montgomery (outside
Dayton city limits), Shelby, Greene and Preble Counties.

Greene County Development Corp.
Melissa Frost, SBA 504 Coordinator
61 Greene Street
Xenia, OH 45385
937-562-5644
Fax: 937-562-5645
Area of Operation: Greene County

Growth Capital Corporation
Gerald H. Meyer
200 Tower City Center
50 Public Square
Cleveland, OH 44113-2291
216-621-3300
Fax: 216-621-6013
Area of Operation: Cuyahoga, Lake, Geauga, Lorain,
Medina, Portage and Summit Counties

Hamilton County Development Co., Inc.
David K. Main, President
1776 Mentor Avenue
Cincinnati, OH 45212
513-631-8292
Fax: 513-631-4887
Area of Operation: Adams, Brown, Highland, Clermont and
Hamilton Counties

Lake County Small Business Assistance Corporation
Catherine Haworth, Assistant Executive Director
7750 Clocktower Drive
Mentor, OH 44060
440-951-1290
Fax: 440-953-4413
Area Of Operation: Lake County

Lucas County Improvement Corporation
Deborah Campbell
One Maritime Plaza, 7th Floor
Toledo, OH 43604
419-243-8251
Fax: 419-243-1835
Area of Operation: Lucas County

Mahoning Valley Economic Development Corporation
Donald L. French, Executive Director
4319 Belmont Avenue
Youngstown, OH 44505
330-759-3668
Fax: 330-759-3686
Area Of Operation: Mahoning, Columbiana and Trumbull
Counties

Mentor Economic Assistance Corporation
Elaine Kline, Program Administrator
8500 Civic Center Boulevard
Mentor, OH 44060
440-255-1100
Fax: 440-974-5708
Area of Operation: City of Mentor

Ohio Statewide Development Corp.
Dianne Allen, Executive Director
1335 Dublin Road, Suite 200
Columbus, OH 43215
614-481-3214
Fax: 614-481-3215
Area of Operation: 67 counties through out Ohio

Stark Development Board Finance Corporation
Steve Paquette, President
116 Cleveland Avenue, NW, Suite 600
Canton, OH 44702-1730
330-453-5900
Fax: 330-453-1793
Area Of Operation: Stark, Tuscarawas, Harrison, Carroll,
Coshocton and Jefferson Counties

Oklahoma

Metro Area Development Corporation
Dan Fitzpatrick
4200 North Lindsay
Oklahoma City, OK 73105
405-424-5181
Area of Operation: Canadian, Cleveland, Oklahoma Counties

Rural Enterprises, Inc.
Debbie Partin, Dir. of Fin. Service
422 Cessna
P.O. Box 1335
Durant, OK 74702
402-924-5094
Fax: 405-920-2775
Email: debbiep@ruralenterprises.com
Area of Operation: Atoka, Bryan, Carter, Choctaw, Coal,
Creek, Garvin, Haskell, Hughes, Johnston, Latimer, LeFlore,
Lincoln, Logan, Love, Marshall, McCurtain, Murray,
Okfuskee, Payne, Pittsburg, Pontotoc, Pottawatomie,
Pushmataha, Seminole Counties

SWODA Development Corporation
Gary Gorshing, Executive Director
Building 420, Sooner Drive,
Clinton-Sherman Indust. Park
P.O. Box 569
Burns Flat, OK 73624
405-562-4886
Area of Operation: Beckham, Custer, Greer, Harmon,
Jackson, Kiowa, Roger Mills, Washita Counties

Small Business Capital Corporation
Tracie Costello, Assistant Director
Bank of America Center
15 W. Sixth St., Suite 1211
Tulsa, OK 74119-5406
918-584-7888
Area of Operation: Creek, Osage, Tulsa, Washington
Counties

Tulsa Economic Development Corporation
Frank McCrady, Executive Director
907 S. Detroit Avenue
Suite 1001
Tulsa, OK 74120
918-585-8332
Fax: 918-585-2473
Area of Operation: Citywide Tulsa

Verd-Ark-Ca Development Corporation
L.V. Watkins, Executive Director
600 Emporia, Suite A

Muskogee, OK 74403
918-683-4634
Fax: 918-683-7894
Area of Operation: Adair, Cherokee, Craig, Delaware,
Haskell, LeFlore, Mayes, McIntosh, Muskogee, Nowata,
Okmulgee, Ottawa, Rogers, Sequoyah, Tulsa, Washington
Counties

Oregon

Business Development Corporation
Wayne Luzier, Executive Director
744 Southeast Rose Street
Roseburg OR 97470-3941
541-672-6728
Fax: 541-672-7011
Email: wluzier@ccdbusiness.com
www.ccdbusiness.com
Area of Operation: State of Oregon, except Wallowa County

CCDBDC North Bend Office:
2455 Maple Leaf, #13B
North Bend, OR 97459
541-756-4101
888-553-1110
Fax: 541-756-1167
Email: thaga@ccdbusiness.com

CCDBDC Portland Office:
6312 SW Capitol Hwy, Suite 441
Portland, OR 97239
503-245-1175
Email: ccdbusiness@hevanet.com

Cascades West Financial Services, Inc.
Mary Merriman-Smith, Director
P.O. Box 686
Albany, OR 97321-0686
541-924-8430
Fax: 541-967-4651
Email: msmith@cwcog.cog.or.us
www.cascadeswest.com
Area of Operation: Benton, Lane, Lincoln, Linn, Marion,
Polk, Yamhill Counties

Evergreen Community Development Association (ECDA)
Jim Bright, Senior Loan Officer
1618 SW First Avenue, Suite 401
Portland, OR 97201
503-222-7496
503-222-7498
Email: jbright@ecda.com
www.ecda.com
Area of Operation: Clackamas, Clatsop, Columbia, Hood
River, Multnomah, Tillamook, Wasco and Washington
Counties

Greater Eastern Oregon Development Corporation
Melisa Jo Drugge, Executive Director
2016 Airport Road
P.O. Box 1041
Pendleton OR 97801-1041
541-276-6745
Fax: 541-276-6071
Email: mdrugge@OregonVOS.net
Area of Operation: Gilliam, Grant, Morrow, Umatilla,
Wheeler, Union, Baker and Wallowa Counties

Northwest Business Development Association
Louie Robida, Loan Officer
6312 SW Capitol Hwy, Suite 441

Portland, OR 97239
503-245-1175
Email: nwbusiness@hevanet.com
www.nwbusiness.org
Area of Operation: Clark, Cowlitz, Skamania and
Wahkiakum Counties

Northwest Small Business Finance Corporation
Teresa Cowles, President
15455 NW Greenbrier Pkwy., Suite 210
Beaverton OR 97006
503-629-9662
Fax: 877-296-0703
Email: teresa@nsbfc.com
www.nsbfc.com
Area of Operation: Multnomah, Clackamas, Clatsop,
Columbia and Washington Counties

Oregon Certified Business Development Corporation
Jim MacKinnon, Senior Loan Officer
2363 SW Glacier Place
P.O. Box 575
Redmond OR 97756-0575
541-548-8184
Fax: 541-504-3302
Email: mackinon@coic.org
Email: kmears@coic.org
Email: cfolkens@coic.org
www.coic.org
Area of Operation: Crook, Deschutes, Harney, Jefferson,
Klamath, Lake and Malheur Counties

Pennsylvania

Allentown Economic Development Corporation
Janice Gubich, Director of Finance
718 Hamilton Mall
Portland Place - 7th Floor
Allentown, PA 18105
610-435-8890
Fax: 610-435-6166
Area of Operation: Lehigh and Northampton counties

DelVal Business Finance Corporation
Michael Schwartz, President
6100 City Line Avenue
Executive House, Suite P218
Philadelphia, PA 19131
215-871-3770
Fax: 215-871-3776
Area of Operation: Bucks, Chester, Delaware, Lackawanna,
Luzerne, Monroe, Montgomery, Northampton, and
Philadelphia Counties

PIDC Local Development Corporation
Jim Pawlikowski, Client Relations Officer
2600 Centre Square West
1500 Market Street
Philadelphia, PA 19109-2126
215-496-8106
Fax: 215-977-9618
Area of Operation: Philadelphia

SEDA-COG Local Development Corporation
Jerry Bohinski, Chief, Economic Development
R.R. 1 - Box 372, Furnace Road
Lewisburg, PA 17837
570-524-4491
Fax: 570-524-9190
Area of Operation: Adams, Bradford, Centre, Clinton,
Columbia, Cumberland, Dauphin, Franklin, Juniata,

Lancaster, Lebanon, Lycoming, Mifflin, Montour,
Northumberland, Perry, Potter, Sullivan, Synder, Tioga,
Union, and York Counties

South Eastern Economic Development Company of PA
Jay Lowden, Finance Manager
750 Pottstown Pike
Exton, PA 19341
610-363-6110
Fax: 610-363-2160

Certified Development Companies-Pittsburgh
Allegheny-Pittsburgh Business Development Corporation
Dave Thomas, Manager
200 Ross Street
Pittsburgh, PA 15219
412-255-6557
Fax: 412-255-6542
Area Of Operation: Allegheny County

Altoona-Blair County Development Corporation
Martin J. Marasco, Executive Director
4500 Sixth Avenue
Altoona PA 16602
814-944-6113
Fax: 814-946-0157
Area Of Operation: Counties of Blair, Bedford, Cambria,
Clearfield, Franklin, Fulton, Huntingdon, Jefferson and
Somerset Counties

Regional Development Funding Corp.
Executive Director
ST425 Sixth Avenue-Suite 1410
Regional Enterprise Tower
Pittsburgh PA 15219
412-471-1030
Fax: 412-471-3902
Area Of Operation: Counties of Allegheny, Armstrong,
Beaver, Butler, Clarion, Crawford, Erie, Fayette, Forest,
Greene, Indiana, Lawrence, Mercer, Venango, Warren,
Washington and Westmoreland Counties

SEDA-COG Local Development Corporation
Jerry Bohinski, Chief, Economic Development
Box 372 - RD#1
Lewisburg PA 17837
717-524-4491
Fax: 717-524-9190
Mailing Address:
   R.D. #1 Box 372
   Lewisburg PA 17837
Area Of Operation: Adams, Bradford, Centre, Clinton,
Columbia, Cumberland, Dauphin, Franklin, Juniata,
Lancaster, Lebanon, Lycoming, Mifflin, Montour,
Northumberland, Perry, Potter, Snyder, Sullivan, Tioga,
Union And York Counties

Certified Development Companies-Philadelphia
Allentown Economic Development Corporation
Janice Gubich, Director of Finance
718 Hamilton Mall
Portland Place - 7th Floor
Allentown, PA 18101
610-435-8890
Fax: 610-435-6166
Mailing Address:
   P.O. Box 1400
   Allentown, PA 18105
Area of Operation: Lehigh and Northampton Counties

Altoona-Blair County Development Corporation
Martin J. Marasco, President and CEO
4500 Sixth Avenue
Altoona, PA 16602
814-944-6113
Fax: 814-946-0157
www.abcdcorp.org
Area of Operation: Bedford, Blair, Cambria, Clearfield,
Franklin, Jefferson, Huntingdon and Somerset Counties

DelVal Business Finance Corporation
Michael Schwartz, President
6100 City Line Avenue
Executive House, Suite P218
Philadelphia, PA 19131
215-871-3770
Fax: 215-871-3776
www.delval504.com
Area of Operation: Bucks, Chester, Delaware, Lackawanna,
Luzerne, Monroe, Montgomery, Northampton, and
Philadelphia Counties

SEDA-COG Local Development Corporation
Jerry Bohinski, Chief, Economic Development
R.R. 1 - Box 372
Lewisburg, PA 17837
570-524-4491
Fax: 570-524-9190
http://finance.seda-cog.org
Area of Operation: Adams, Bradford, Centre, Clinton,
Columbia, Cumberland, Dauphin, Franklin, Juniata,
Lancaster, Lebanon, Lycoming, Mifflin, Montour,
Northumberland, Perry, Potter, Snyder, Sullivan, Tioga,
Union, and York

South Eastern Economic Development Company of PA
Jay Lowden, Finance Manager
737 Constitution Drive
Exton, PA 19341
610-458-5700
Fax: 610-458-7770
www.ccdcseed.org
Area of Operation: Berks, Bucks, Chester, Delaware,
Lancaster, Lebanon, Montgomery, and Schuykill Counties

Rhode Island
Ocean State Business Development Authority
155 South Main Street, Suite 301
Providence, RI 02903
401-454-4560
Fax: 401-454-4890
Area Of Operation: Providence, Kent, Washington and
Newport Counties

South Carolina
Catawaba Regional Development Corporation
Mr. Harold S. Shapiro
215 Hampton Street
Rock Hill SC 29730
803-327-9041
Fax: 803-327-1912
Mailing Address:
   P.O. Box 450
   Rock Hill SC 29731
Area Of Operation: South Carolina counties of Chester,
Lancaster, Union and York Counties

Certified Development Corporation of South Carolina
Mr. W.C. Grimes
111 Executive Center Drive

Enoree Building, Suite 225
Columbia SC 29210
803-798-4064
Fax: 803-798-1224
Mailing Address:
    P.O. Box 21823
    Columbia SC 29201
Area Of Operation: Statewide

Appalachian Development Corporation
David Mueller, Special Projects/Loan Fund Coordinator
30 Century Circle
Greenville SC 29606
864-242-9733
Fax: 864-242-6957
Mailing Address:
    P.O. Box 6668
    Greenville SC 29606
Area Of Operation: South Carolina Counties of Anderson, Cherokee, Greenville, Oconee, Pickens, and Spartanburg Counties

CSRA Development Companies
Randall E. Griffin - President
3023 Riverwatch Parkway, Suite A
Augusta, GA 30907
706-210-2010
Fax: 706-210-2006
Area Of Operation: South Carolina Counties of Abeville, Aiken, Allendale, Barnwell, Edgefield, McCormick and Saluda Counties

Small Business Assistance Corporation
Tony O'Reilly, Executive Director
111 E. Liberty Street, Suite 100
Savannah GA 31412
912-232-4700
Fax: 912-232-0385
Mailing Address:
    P.O. Box 10750
    Savannah GA 31412
Area Of Operation: South Carolina Counties of Beaufort, Jasper and Hampton Counties

South Dakota

First District Development Company
Roger Clark
124 First Avenue, NW
P.O. Box 1207
Watertown, SD 57201
605-886-7225
Area Of Operation: Counties in Eastern South Dakota with the exception of Clay and Union Counties

Black Hills Community Economic Development, Inc.
Jim Doolittle
P.O. Box 218
Sturgis, SD 57785
605-642-7106
Area Of Operation: Counties in Western South Dakota with exception of Gregory County

South Dakota Development Corporation (The)
Tina Van Camp
711 E. Wells Ave.
Pierre SD 57501
605-773-5032
Fax: 605-773-3256
Area Of Operation: Statewide

Siouxland Economic Development Corporation
Glenda Castleberry
P.O. Box 447
Sioux City, IA 55102
712-279-6286
Area Of Operation: Clay and Union Counties

Tennessee

Alacom Finance
Diane Roehrig
4515 Poplar Avenue, #2, Suite 217
Memphis TN 38119
901-374-0396
Fax: 901-347-0397
Area Of Operation: Lake, Obion, Weakley, Henry, Dyer, Gibson, Carroll, Benton, Lauderdale, Crockett, Tipton, Haywood, Madison, Henderson, Decatur, Shelby, Fayette, Hardeman, McNairy, and Chester Counties

Areawide Development Corporation
Don Woods, Loan Officer
5616 Kingston Pike
P.O. Box 19806
Knoxville TN 37919-2806
865-588-7972
Fax: 865-584-5159
Area Of Operation: Scott, Campbell, Claiborne, Anderson, Union, Morgan, Roane, Loudon, Monroe, Blount, Knox, Grainger, Hamblen, Jefferson, Cocke, Carter, Greene, Hancock, Hawkins, Johnson, Sullivan, Unicoi, Washington and Sevier Counties

Mid-Cumberland Area Development Corporation
Tom McAuley, Small Bus. Loan Off.
501 Union Street
Stalman Building, 6th Floor
Nashville TN 37219-1735
615-862-8855
Fax: 615-862-8840
Area Of Operation: Cheatham, Davidson, Dickson, Houston, Humphreys, Montgomery, Robertson, Rutherford, Stewart, Sumner, Trousdale, Williamson and Wilson Counties

South Central Tennessee Business Development Corp.
Doug Williams, Econ. Dev. Director
815 South Main Street
P.O. Box 1346
Columbia TN 38402
931-381-2041
Fax: 931-381-2053
Area Of Operation: Bedford, Coffee, Franklin, Giles, Hickman, Lawrence, Lewis, Lincoln, Marshall, Maury, Moore, Perry and Wayne Counties

Southeast Local Development Corporation
Joe Guthrie, Executive Director
25 Cherokee Boulevard
P.O. Box 4757
Chattanooga TN 37405
423-266-5781
Fax: 423-267-7705
Area Of Operation: Cannon, Clay, Cumberland, DeKalb, Fentress, Jackson, Macon, Overton, Pickett, Putnam, Smith, Van Buren, Warren, White, Grundy, Sequatchie, Bledsoe, Rhea, Meigs, Marion, Hamilton, Bradley, McMinn and Polk Counties

Tennessee Business Development Corporation
Jim Thigpen
P.O. Box 307

Paris, TN 38242
731-644-7108
Fax: 731-644-5984
Area Of Operation: Benton, Bledsoe, Bradley, Campbell, Cannon, Carroll, Carter, Chester, Claiborne, Clay, Crockett, Cumberland, Decatur, Dekalb, Dyer, Fayette, Fentress, Franklin, Gibson, Giles, Grainer, Greene, Grundy, Hancock, Hardeman, Hardin, Henderson, Henry, Hickman, Houston, Jackson, Johnson, Lake, Lauderdale, McNairy, Macon, Marshall, Meigs, Monroe, Moore, Morgan, Obion, Overton, Perry, Pickett, Polk, Putnam, Rhea, Roane, Scott, Sequatchie, Stewart, Sumner, Tipton, Trousdale, Union, Van Buren and Washington Counties

Texas

Ark-Tex Regional Development Company, Inc.
James C. Fisher, Jr.
122 Plaza West
Texarkana, TX 75501
Mailing Address:
    P. O. Box 5307
    Texarkana, TX 75505-5307
903-832-8636
Fax: 903-832-2672
Area Of Operation: Bowie, Cass, Delta, Franklin, Hopkins, Red River, Lamar, Morris and Titus Counties in Texas; also Miller County in Arkansas

Central Texas Certified Development Company
Bruce Gaines, VP of Operations
1103 Airline Drive
P.O. Box 154118
Waco TX 76715
817-799-0259
Fax: 817-799-0294
Area of Operation: Bell, Bosque, Coryell, Falls, Hamilton, Hill, Freestone, Limestone, McLennan, and Milam Counties

Dallas Business Finance Corporation
Charles English, Executive V.P.
1402 Corinth St., Suite 1150
Dallas TX 75215
214-428-7332
Fax: 214-426-6847
Area of Operation: Dallas County

East Texas Regional Development Company, Inc.
Kent Bryson
3800 Stone Road
Kilgore TX 75662
903-984-8641
Fax: 903-983-1440
Area of Operation: Anderson, Camp, Cherokee, Gregg, Harrison, Henderson, Marion, Panola, Rains, Rusk, Smith, Upshur, Van Zandt and Wood

Fort Worth Economic Development Corporation
Larry McNatt, Executive Director
100 East 15th Street, Suite 500
P.O. Box 136
Fort Worth TX 76102
817-336-6420
Fax: 817-335-4513
Area of Operation: Erath, Denton, Ellis, Hood, Kaufman, Palo, Pinto, Dallas, Tarrant, Wise, Parker and Johnson counties; Excluding the City of Dallas

Greater East Texas Certified Development Company
Judy Loden
P.O. Box 1129

Athens, Texas 75751
903-675-7403
Area of Operation: Anderson, Cherokee, Henderson, Kaufman, Shelby, Smith and Van Zandt Counties

North Texas Certified Development Corporation
Webb Cox, President
1101 East Plano Pkwy., Suite A
Plano TX 75074
214-516-0514
Fax: 214-424-7479
Area of Operation: Grayson, Ranes, Fannin, Hunt, Collin, Cooke and Rockwall Counties

Upper Rio Grande Development Company
Justin R. Ormsby, Executive Director
1100 North Stanton, Suite 610
El Paso TX 79902
915-533-0998
Fax: 915-532-9385
Area of Operation: El Paso, Hudspeth, Culberson, Jeff Davis,Presidio and Brewster Counties

Brownsville Local Development Company, Inc.
1150 East Adams, 1st Floor
P.O. Box 911
Brownsville TX 78520
956-548-6150
Fax: 956-548-6144
Area of Operation: Citywide Brownsville

Lower Rio Grande Valley Certified Development Corporation
Kenneth N. Jones, Jr., Executive Director
311 N. 15th Street
McAllen TX 78501-4705
956-682-3481
Fax: 956-631-4670
Area of Operation: Cameron, Hidalgo and Willacy Counties

Bryan-College Station Certified Development Company
Dennis H. Goehring, Representative
2908 Finfeather Road
Bryan TX 77801
409-775-3699
Fax: 409-775-4393
Area of Operation: Brazo County

Houston-Galveston Area Local Development Corporation
Jeff Sjostrom, Sen. Ec. Dev. Spec.
3555 Timmons Lane, Suite 500
P.O. Box 22777
Houston TX 77227
713-627-3200
Fax: 713-621-8129
Area of Operation: Austin, Brazoria, Chambers, Colorado, Fort Bend, Galveston, Harris, Liberty, Matagorda, Montgomery, Walker, Waller and Wharton Counties

Multi-County Small Business Finance Corporation
Amos M. Brown, Executive Director
3100 Timmons Lane, Suite 222
Houston TX 77027
713-840-8804
Area of Operation: Brazoria, Fort Bend, Galveston, Harris, Liberty, Montgomery and Waller Counties

Southeast Texas Economic Development Foundation
Wilson White, Executive Director
450 Bowie

P.O. Box 3150
Beaumont TX 77704
409-838-6581
Fax: 409-833-6718
Area of Operation: Jefferson and Orange Counties

Council Finance, Incorporated
Rick Womble, Ec. Dev. Specialist
909 North Judge Ely Boulevard
P.O. Box 3195
Abilene TX 79604
915-672-8544
Fax: 915-675-5214
Area of Operation: Brown, Callahan, Coleman, Comanche,
Eastland, Fisher, Haskell, Jones, Kent, Knox, Mitchell,
Nolan, Runnels, Scurry, Shackelford, Stephens, Stonewall,
Taylor and Throckmorton Counties

Caprock Business Finance Corporation, Inc.
Tim Pierce, Director of Ec. Dev.
1323 58th Street
P.O. Box 3730
Lubbock TX 79452-3730
806-762-8721
Fax: 806-765-9544
Area of Operation: Baily, Cochran, Crosby, Dickens, Floyd,
Garza, Hale, Hockley, King, Lamb, Lubbock, Lynn, Motley,
Terry, Gaines, Dawson, Borden, Andrews, Martin, Howard,
Winkler, Ector, Midland, Glasscock, Ward, Crane, Upton and
Yoakum Counties

Texas Panhandle Regional Development Corporation
Doug Nelson
415 West Eighth Avenue
P.O. Box 9257
Amarillo TX 79105-9257
806-372-3381
Fax: 806-373-3268
Area of Operation: Armstrong, Briscoe, Carson, Castro,
Childress,Collingsworth, Deaf Smith, Dallam, Donley, Gray,
Hall, Hansford, Hutchinson, Hartley, Hemphill, Lipscomb,
Moore, Ochiltree, Randall, Oldham, Parmer, Potter, Roberts,
Sherman, Swisher and Wheeler Counties

Capital Certified Development Corporation
Craig Pinkley, Executive Director
Wild Basin One
110 Wild Basin Road, Suite 270
Austin, TX 78746
512-327-9229
800-504-2232
Fax: 512-327-9243
Area Of Operation: Atascosa, Bandera, Bee, Blanco, Burnet,
Caldwell, Calhoun, Comal, Dimmit, Edwards, Fayette, Frio,
Gillespie, Goliad, Hays, Jackson, Karnes, Kendall, Kinney,
La Salle, Lampasas, Lavaca, Lee, Live Oak, Llano,
Maverick, McMullen, Real, Refugio, Travis, Uvalde, Val
Verde, Victoria and most other counties in Texas

Cen-Tex Certified Development Corporation
Rosa Rios Valdez, Executive Director
2212 South Congress Avenue
P.O. Box 220
Mail Stop L-108
Austin TX 78703
512-912-9884
Fax: 512-912-9869
Area of Operation: Austin, Bastrop, Bandera, Blanco, Burnet,
Brown, Burleson, Caldwell, Colorado, Comal, Concho,
Coryell, DeWitt, Edwards, Fayette, Gillespie, Gonzales,

Guadalupe, Hamilton, Hays, Kendall, Kerr, Kimble,
Lampasas, Lavaca, Lee, Llano, Mason, Matagorda,
McCulloch, Medina, Menard, Mills, Real, San Saba, Sutton,
Travis, Uvalde, Waller, Washington, Wharton, Williamson,
Wilson 43 Central Texas Counties

San Antonio Local Development Corporation
Michael Mendoza, Financial Specialist
215 South San Saba
P.O. Box 830505
San Antonio TX 78283-0505
210-207-3930
Fax: 210-207-3939
Area of Operation: Atascosa, Bandera, Bexar, Comal, Frio,
Gillespie, Guadalupe, Karnes, Kendall, Kerr, Medina and
Wilson Counties

Texas Certified Development Company, Inc.
Ernest Perales, President
7801 N. IH-35
P.O. Box 6479
Austin TX 78762
800-486-8620
Fax: 512-433-1821
Area of Operation: Aransas, Atascosa, Bandera, Bastrop,
Bee, Bell, Bexar, Blanco, Brazoria, Brooks, Burleson,
Burnet, Caldwell, Calhoun, Cameron, Comal, Concho,
Crockett, Dallas, Denton, DeWitt, Dimmit, Duval, Edwards,
Ellis, Fayette, Frio, Ft. Bend, Galveston, Gillespie, Goliad,
Gonzales, Grayson, Guadalupe, Hardin, Harris, Hays,
Hidalgo, Irion, Jackson, Jefferson, Jim Hogg, Jim Wells,
Johnson, Karnes, Kendall, Kenedy, Kerr, Kimble, Kinney,
Kleberg, LaSalle, Lampasas, Lavaca, Lee, Liberty, Live Oak,
Llano, Mason, Maverick, McCulloch, McLennan, McMullen,
Medina, Menard, Montgomery, Nueces, Orange, Parker,
Real, Refugio, San Patricio, San Saba, Schleicher, Smith,
Starr, Sutton, Tarrant, Tom Green, Travis, Uvalde, Val
Verde, Victoria, Walker, Waller, Webb, Wichita, Willacy,
Williamson, Wilson, Wise, Zapata, Zavala Counties

Utah
Deseret Certified Development Company
2595 East 3300 South
Salt Lake City, UT 84109
Email: scott@deseretcdc.com
801-474-3232
Fax: 801-493-0111
Area of Operation: Box Elder, Davis, Morgan, and Weber
Counties

Northern Utah Capital, Inc.
2404 Washington Boulevard, Suite 1000
Ogden, UT 84401
801-627-1333
Email: rrichards@nucdc.com
Area of Operation: Statewide Utah
Certified Development Companies are private companies
licensed by the SBA to provide long-term financing to
expanding businesses. The SBA 504 loans provide long-term
fixed-asset financing with a maximum SBA share of $750,000
or 40% of the project cost. At least 10% must be provided by
the borrowers, and the remaining provided by a bank or other
lender.

Vermont
Central Vermont Economic Development Corporation
Richard Angney, Exec. Vice President
1 National Life Drive, 5th Floor
P.O. Box 1439
Montpelier VT 05601

802-223-4654
Fax: 802-223-4655
Area of Operation: Washington and Orange counties

Northern Community Investment Corporation
Paul Denton, President
20 Main Street
P.O. Box 904
Johnsbury VT 05819
802-748-5101
Fax: 802-748-1884
Area of Operation: Caledonia, Essex and Orleans Counties in
Vermont; also Coos, Carroll and Grafton Counties in New
Hampshire

Vermont 503 Corporation
Jo Bradley, Executive Director
58 East State Street
Montpelier VT 05602
802-828-5627
Fax: 802-828-5474
Area of Operation: Statewide

Virginia

Crater Development Company
Post Office Box 1808
1964 Wakefield Street
Petersburg, VA 23805
804-861-1666
Fax: 804-732-8972
Area of Operation: Cities of Colonial Heights, Emporia,
Hopewell and Petersburg. Counties of Chesterfield,
Dinwiddie, Greensville, Prince George, Surry, and Sussex.

James River Dev. Corp.
Capitol Place, Suite 702
1108 East Main Street
Richmond, VA 23219
804-344-0002
Fax: 804-344-0022
Email: fminton@aol.com
Area of Operation: City of Richmond. Counties of Charles
City, Goochland, Hanover, Henrico, James City, New Kent,
Powhatan, Williamsburg, and York.

Rappahannock Econ. Dev. Corp.
3304 Bourbon Street
P.O. Box 863
Fredericksburg, VA 22404
540-373-2890
Fax: 540-899-4808
Area of Operation: City of Fredericksburg. Counties of
Caroline, King George, Stafford, and Spotsylvania.

Tidewater Business Financing Corp.
1226 Suntrust Center
500 E. Main St.
Norfolk, VA 23510
757-623-2691
Fax: 757-623-0660
Area of Operation: Cities of Chesapeake, Hampton, Newport
News, Norfolk, Poquoson, Portsmouth, Suffolk, and Virginia
Beach.

Virginia Economic Dev. Corp.
101 E. High Street
P.O. Box 1402
Charlottesville, VA 22902
434-972-9900
Fax: 972-9900

Email: towens@rlc.net
Area of Operation: City of Charlottesville.Counties of
Albemarle, Fluvanna, Greene, Louisa, and Nelson.

Virginia Asset Financing Corp.
4165 Chain Bridge Road
Fairfax, VA 22030
703-352-0504
Fax: 703-352-9100
Area of Operation: Statewide

Washington

Evergreen Community Development Association
Philip T. Eng, President
900 Fourth Avenue, Suite 2900
Seattle, WA 98164
206-622-3731
Fax: 206-623-6613
Area of Operation: State of Washington; Oregon Counties of
Clackamas, Columbia, Clatsop, Multnomah, Washington,
Hood River, Wasco and Tillamook

Northwest Business Development Association
Gary Whelpley, President
9 South Washington St. #215
Spokane, WA 99201
509-458-8555
Fax: 509-458-8553
State of Washington except Pacific County, Idaho Counties
of Clearwater, Idaho, Latah, Lewis and Nez Perce

West Virginia

Ohio Valley Industrial Business Development Council
Certified Development Corporation
P.O. Box 1029
12th & Chapline Street
Wheeling, WV 26003
304-232-7722
Fax: 304-232-7727
Area of Operation: Brooke, Hancock, Ohio, Marshall and
Wetzel Counties

West Virginia Certified Development Corporation
Patrick A. Tony" Benedetto", President
North Gate Business Park
10 Association Drive
Charleston, WV 25311-1217
304-558-3691
Fax: 304-558-0206
Area of Operation: Statewide

Wisconsin

Great Lakes Asset Corporation
Ms. Cindy Esterling, Loan Officer/Manager
1317 Lombardi Access Rd.
Green Bay, WI 54304
800-281-6444
Fax: 920-499-7331
Email: cdcglac@aol.com
Area of Operation: Brown, Calumet, Kewaunee, Manitowoc,
Marinette, Oconto and Shawano Counties

Milwaukee Economic Development Corporation
Ms. Martha Morrison, Asst. Vice President/Secretary
809 North Broadway
P.O. Box 324
Milwaukee WI 53201-0324
414-286-5853
Fax: 414-286-5778

Email: mmorri@mkedcd.org
Area of Operation: Milwaukee, Ozaukee, Washington and
Waukesha Counties

Racine County Business Development Corporation
Mr. Gordon M. Kacala, Executive Director
4701 Washington Avenue, Suite 215
Racine, WI 53406-3938
414-638-0234
Fax: 414-638-0250

E-mail: rcedc@execpc.com
Area of Operation: Kenosha and Racine Counties

Western Wisconsin Development Corporation
Mr. William Bay, General Manager
126 Soo Street
Almena, WI 54805
715-357-3334
Fax: 715-357-6233
Area of Operation: Barron, Bayfield, Burnett, Chippewa,
Dunn, Polk, Rusk, St. Croix, Sawyer and Washburn Counties

Business Incubators Can Be The Answer

According to the Small Business Administration, small businesses constitute more than 90 percent of all businesses in the U. S., and create more than 80 percent of new jobs. Yet, despite these impressive statistics, as many as 80 percent of all new small businesses fail within their first five years of operation. There are a number of reasons for this failure rate, and business incubators can help address these issues.

A business incubator can come in many different shapes and forms. Typically an incubator provides basic office space and services at a reduced rate or is an exceptional value for the services provided. Generally a variety of sized office spaces are available, with the flexibility for growth. In addition, services such as a receptionist, telephone answering services, janitorial, security, conference and break rooms, and more are provided for the cost of the rent. Basically, this allows new businesses to come in with a desk and phone, and be fully operational. Since incubators are places where companies are encouraged to grow, many offer mentoring, business planning, accounting, and tax services, often at a reduced rate through other vendors. Several also offer their own financing programs, or can direct you to local resources. They want to build a business environment that supports new companies. Businesses usually stay with the incubator for several years, and then graduate, giving space for new start-ups to begin.

In some cases, incubators focus on certain types of businesses. San Jose, California and Manitou Springs, Colorado have incubators whose focus in the arts. New Jersey and New York have incubators that specialize in food service, offering commercial kitchens, food storage, packaging, and more. Many incubators are technology-focused. Often entrepreneurs need access to specialized facilities or equipment, like wet labs and cold storage. Some offer access to universities or outside laboratories, with many offering technical assistance, guidance in developing prototypes, and more. In association with university and government laboratories, many incubators help with technology transfer, converting scientific discoveries and developing them into products for the marketplace.

Whatever your business needs might be, a business incubator can be a great place to start, giving your company time to grow in a nurturing environment amongst a group of others attempting to do the same thing.

For more information on business incubators, contact
National Business Incubation Association
20 E. Circle Dr., #37198
Athens, OH 45701
740-593-4331
Fax: 740-593-1996
www.nbia.org

Alabama

Bessemer Business Center
1020 Ninth Avenue North
Bessemer, AL 35022
205-481-2000
Fax: 205-481-2100
http://www.bessemeral.org/BBIS.ht
ml

Downtown Entrepreneurial Center
401 19th Street North
Bessemer, AL 35020
205-481-4800
Fax: 205-481-4801
http://www.bessemeral.org/BBIS.ht
ml

Entrepreneurial Center
110 12th Street North
Birmingham, AL 35203
205-250-8000
Fax: 205-250-8013
http://www.entrepreneurialctr.com/

Center for Entrepreneurial
Excellence
Business Incubator Center
1301 Azalea Rd.
Mobile, AL 36693
251-660-7002
Fax: 251-660-7004
www.ceebic.org

Business Technology Development
Center
BizTech
102A Wynn Drive
Huntsville, AL 35805
256-704-6000
Fax: 256-704-6002
biztech@biztech.org
http://www.biztech.org/

Montgomery Area Center for
Economic Development - Small
Business Incubator
600 South Court Street
Montgomery, AL 36104
334-832-4790
Fax: 334-240-6869
info@montgomeryincubator.org
www.montgomeryincubator.org/

Northeast Alabama Entrepreneurial
System
Giles McDaniel, Executive Director
1400 Commerce Blvd., Suite 1
Anniston, AL 36207
256-831-5215
Fax: 256-831-8728
http://www.neaes.org/

OADI Technology Center
2800 Milan Court
Birmingham, AL 35211
205-943-6560
Fax: 205-943-6563
http://main.uab.edu/oadi/show.asp?d
urki=29458

Shoals Entrepreneurial Center
3115 Northington Court
Florence, AL 35631
256-760-9014
Fax: 256-740-5530
info@shoalsec.com
www.shoalsec.com

Ozark Technology Center
3269 Hwy. 231 S.
Ozark, AL 36360
334-774-4952
Fax: 334-774-4539
http://www.ozarkalabama.org/

Arizona

Arizona Center for Innovation
University of Arizona Science and
Technology Park
9040 South Rita Road
Suite 2250
Tucson, AZ 85747
520-382-3260
info@azinnovation.com
http://www.azinnovation.org/

Northern Arizona Technology and
Business Incubator
1300 S. Milton Rd. Suite 123
Flagstaff, AZ 86001
928-213-9234
Fax: 928-556-0940
info@natbi.org
www.natbi.org

Arkansas

Spotlight Business Accelerator for
Entrepreneurs
1461 N. Constitution Ave.
Ashdown, AR 71822
870-898-4733
Fax: 870-898-4552
http://www.sbae.org/

Genesis Technology Incubator
700 Research Center Blvd.
Fayetteville, AR 72701
501-575-7227
Fax: 501-575-7446
Genesis@cavern.uark.edu
http://www.uark.edu/~genesis/

Ouachita Valley Business and
Technology Development
Ouachita Partnership for Economic
Development
314 S. Adams Street
Camden, AR 71701
877-248-OPED
fduplantis@ouachitaworks.com
http://www.ouachitaworks.com/

Biomedical Biotechnology Center
4301 West Markham Street, Slot 718
Little Rock, AR 72205
501-686-6696
Fax: 501-686-8501
biotech@uams.edu
http://www.uamsbiotech.com/

California

Central Valley Business Incubator
2555 Clovis Avenue
Clovis, CA 93612
559-292-9033
http://www.cvbi.org/

Charo Community Development
Corporation
4301 E. Valley Blvd.
Los Angeles, CA 90032
323-269-0751
Fax: 323-266-4326
http://www.charocorp.org/

Contra Costa/Tri-Valley
Telecommunication Incubator
2440 Camino Ramon, Suite 225
Bishop Ranch # 6
San Ramon, CA 94583
925-866-4100
Fax: 925-806-0952
gcraft@telcomventures.net
http://www.telcomventures.net/

El Pájaro Community Development
Corporation
23 East Beach Street, #209
Watsonville, CA 95076
831-722-1224
Fax: 831-722-3128
info@elpajarocdc.org
http://www.elpajarocdc.org

Environmental Business Center
2 N. First St.
San Jose, CA 95113
408-938-3920
Fax: 408-271-1904
http://www.environmentalcluster.org
/

FAME Renaissance Center
1968 West Adams Boulevard
Los Angeles, CA 90018
323-730-7700
Fax: 323-737-5717
info@famerenaissance.org
www.famerenaissance.org

International Business Incubator
111 N Market St.
San José, CA 95113
408-351-3300
Fax: 408-351-3332
info@ibi-sv.org
www.ibi-sv.org

Marina Small Business Incubator
3180 Imjin Rd., Suite 149
Marina, CA 93933
831-582-9718
Fax: 831-582-9549
http://www.msbi.org/

NASA Commercialization Center
and Pomona Technology Center
California State Polytechnic Univ.,
Pomona

3801 West Temple Ave., Bldg.
220B-1330
Pomona, CA 91768
909-869-4441
Fax: 909-869-4475
nasaincubatr@csupomona.edu.
www.nasaincubator.csupomona.edu/

Oakland Small Business Growth
Center
675 Hegenberger Road Suite 201
Oakland, CA 94621-1919
510-553-0675
Fax: 510-553-0676
info@osbgc.com
http://www.osbgc.com/

Panasonic Incubator
Cupertino Office:
20300 Stevens Creek Blvd.
Suite #250
Cupertino, CA 95014
408-861-3900
Fax: 408-861-3990
http://www.vcpanasonic.com/

Pasadena Enterprise Center
1015 N. Lake Ave., Suite 100
Pasadena, CA 91104
626-398-9974
http://www.pec-sbi.org/

Renaissance Entrepreneurship Center
275 Fifth Street
San Francisco, CA 94103
415-541-8580
www.rencenter.org/contact.htm

San Jose Arts Incubator
Office of Cultural Affairs
City of San Jose
365 S. Market St.
San Jose, CA 95113
408-277-5144
http://www.sanjoseculture.org/art_in
c/index.html

SDSU Foundation
5250 Campanile Dr.,
San Diego, CA 92182
619-594-0516
Fax: 619-594-0354
http://tto.sdsu.edu/

San Jose Software Business Cluster
2 North First Street, Fourth Floor
San Jose, CA 95113
Fax: 408-535-2711
info@sjsbc.org
http://www.sjsbc.org/cluster/index.ht
ml

The Chamber Business Incubator
445 San Joaquin Street
Stockton, CA 95202
209-954-5089
Fax: 209-954-5605
http://www.stocktonchamber.org/sbc
/sbc.html

Vermont Slauson Economic
Development Center
5918 S. Vermont Avenue
Los Angeles, CA 90044
323-753-2335
Fax: 323-753-6710
HQ@vsedc.org
http://www.vsedc.org/

Women's Technology Cluster
177 Post Street
Suite 900
San Francisco, CA 94108
415-421-5500
INFO@WTC-SF.ORG
http://www.wtc-sf.org/

Daly City Business Center
355 Gellert Blvd., Suite 230
Daly City, CA 94015
650-757-2060
http://www.ci.daly-
city.ca.us/business/dcbizctr.htm

Colorado

The Business of Art Center
513 Manitou Ave.
Manitou Springs, CO 80829
719-685-1861
Fax: 719-685-3080
http://www.thebac.org/

Colorado Springs Technology
Incubator
1420 Austin Bluffs Parkway
Colorado Springs, CO 80918
719-262-3104
Fax: 719-262-3707
www.cstionline.org

Fitzsimons Redevelopment
Authority
12635 E. Montview Blvd., Suite 100
Aurora, CO 80010
720-859-4100
email info@colobio.com
http://www.colobio.com/introduction
.html

Fort Collins Virtual Business
Incubator
Executive Director: Kathy Kregel,
BS, MBA
125 South Howes, #150
Fort Collins, CO 80524
970-221-1301
Fax: 970-498-8924
Info@FortCollinsIncubator.org
http://www.fortcollinsincubator.org/

Pueblo Economic Development
Corporation
301 N. Main Street
P.O. Box 1957
Pueblo, CO 81002
719-544-2000
800-522-1120
Fax: 719-543-1650
info@pedco.org
http://www.pedco.org/

Rose Biomedical
4545 East 9th Ave., Suite 110
Denver, CO 80220
303-320-2998
Fax: 303-333-7511
www.rosebiomed.com

Denver Enterprise Center
3003 Arapahoe St.
Denver, CO 80205
303-296-9400
Fax: 303-296-5542
decinfo@thedec.org
http://www.thedec.org/

Business Incubator Center
2591 B-3/4 Road
Grand Junction, CO 81503
970-243-5242
Fax: 970-241-0771
http://www.gjincubator.org/

Connecticut

Connecticut Enterprise Center
200 Myrtle Street
New Britain, CT 06053
860-229-7700
Fax: 860-229-6847
http://www.cwresources.org/cec.htm

Institute of Technology and Business
Development
185Main St.
New Briton, CT 06051
860-827-7966
www.ccsu.edu/itbd/default.html

Florida

Bay County Small Business
Incubator
2500 Minnesota Ave.
Lynn Haven, FL 32444
850-271-1107
Fax: 850-271-1109
http://www.nfci.org/resource.htm

Business and Emerging Technology
Accelerator
317 Centre St.
Amelia Island, FL 32034
904-261-4334
http://www.beta-1.com/

Center for Technology, Enterprise
and Development
33 Southeast 1st Ave., Suite 102
Delray Beach, FL 33444
561-265-3790
866-353-3790
Fax: 561-265-0806
http://www.tedcenter.org/

Business Development Center
3901 Dr. Martin Luther King Jr.
Blvd.
Fort Myers, FL 33916
239-332-6701
http://www.cityftmyers.com/departm
ents/BDC/bdc.htm

Central Florida Community
Development Corp.
847 Orange Ave.
Daytona Beach, FL 32114
386-258-7520
Fax: 386-238-3428
info@cfcdc.com
http://www.cfcdc.com/

Enterprise Development Corporation
of South Florida
3701 FAU Boulevard, Suite 210
Boca Raton, FL 33431
561-620-8494
Fax: 561-620-8493
edcinfo@edc-tech.org
http://www.edc-tech.org/

Enterprise North Florida Corporation
4905 Belfort Road, Suite 110
Jacksonville, FL 32256
800-659-4744
904-730-4700
Fax: 904-730-4711
http://www.enfc.org/

Technology Research and
Development Authority
5195 South Washington Avenue
Titusville, FL 32780
321-269-6330
Fax: 321-383-5260
admin@trda.org
http://www.trda.org/

Gainesville Technology Enterprise
Center
2153 Hawthorne Road
Suite 101
Gainesville, FL 32641
352-393-6000
Fax: 352-393-6015
http://www.gtecflorida.com/

Seminole Technology Business
Incubation Center
1445 Dolgner Place
Sanford, FL 32771
407-321-3495
Fax: 407-321-4184
hardyw@scc-fl.edu
http://www.seminoleinc.com/

Sid Martin
Biotechnology Development
Incubator
12085 Research Drive
Alachua, FL 32615
386-462-0880
Fax: 386-462-0875
http://www.biotech.ufl.org/

University of Central Florida
Technology Incubator
12565 Research Parkway, Suite 300
Orlando, FL 32826
407-882-0202
Fax: 407-737-2512
www.incubator.ucf.edu/frameset.html

Center for Entrepreneurship
13101 Telecom Dr., Suite 105
Tampa, FL 33637-0914
813-974-7900
Fax: 813-558-1102
ce@coba.usf.edu
http://www.entrepreneurship.usf.edu/

USF Research Foundation
Research Foundation, Inc.
University of South Florida
4202 East Fowler Avenue, FAO126
Tampa, FL 33620-7900
813-974-0994
http://www.research.usf.edu/rf/

Georgia

Advanced Technology Development
Center
Georgia Institute of Technology
75 Fifth Street, N.W., Suite 100
Atlanta, GA 30308 USA
404-894-3575
Fax: 404-894-4545
http://www.atdc.org/

Augusta-Richmond County Small
Business Incubator
3140 Augusta Tech Drive
Augusta, GA 30906-3381
706-792-9044
Fax: 706-792-9905
lgidding@augustatech.org
http://www.arcsbi.com/index.asp

Intelligent Systems Corporation
Incubator Program
Bonnie Herron
Director
4355 Shackleford Road
Norcross, GA 30093
770-564-5504
bherron@intelsys.com
http://www.intelsys.com/

Office of Technology Transfer and
Economic Development
Building CJ (Pavilion III)
Room 3301
Medical College of Georgia
Augusta, GA 30912
706-721-9822
Fax: 706-721-2917
mgabridge@mail.mcg.edu
www.mcg.edu/research/techtransfer/

South Dekalb Business Incubator
1599-A Memorial Drive, S. E.
Atlanta, GA 30317
404-329-4500
Fax: 404-378-0768
http://www.sdbusinc.org/

Southwest Georgia Business
Development Center
1150 Industrial Drive
Vienna, GA 31092
229-268-8944
foster2@sowega.net
http://www.crispdooly.org/

Advanced Technology Development
Center
Georgia Institute of Technology
75 Fifth Street, NW, Suite 100
Atlanta,GA 30308
404-894-3575
Fax: 404-894-4545
www.atdc.org

Augusta-Richmond County Small
Business Incubator
3140 Augusta Tech Drive
Augusta, GA 30906-3381
706-792-9044
Fax: 706-792-9905
www.arcsbi.com

The City of Savannah
The Savannah Entrepreneurial
Center
801 E. Gwinnett Street
Savannah, GA 31401
912-652-3582
Fax: 912-652-3175
www.ci.savannah.ga.us

eCommerce Institute
J. Mack Robinson College of
Business
35 Broad Street, NW, Suite 400
Atlanta, GA 30303
404-651-3887
www.eci.gsu.edu

Fulton County Business Incubator
5534 Old National Highway
Building H, Suite 300
College Park, GA 30349
404-836-7700
Fax: 404-836-7712
www.fcbi.org

Paparelli Ventures
180 Interstate North Pkwy, Suite 260
Atlanta, GA 30339
770-618-8377 ext 288
Fax: 770-618-8365
www.paparelli.com

PhaseNet LLC
4080 McGinnis Ferry Rd., Suite 103
Alpharetta, GA 30005
770-777-9616
www.phasenet.com

South DeKalb Business Incubator
1599-A Memorial Drive, SE
Atlanta, GA 30317
404-329-4500
Fax: 404-378-0768
http://sdbusinc.org

Hawaii

Hawaii Health Care Business
Incubator
Harbor Court
55 Merchant Street
Suite 2500
Honolulu, HI 96813
808-587-4777

Fax: 808-587-4780
info@hhcbi.com
http://www.hhcbi.com/

High Technology Development
Corporation
Manoa Innovation Center, Suite 100
2800 Woodlawn Drive
Honolulu, HI 96822
808-539-3806
htdc@htdc.org,
http://www.htdc.org/

Pacific Gateway Center
720 North King Street
Honolulu, HI 96817
808-845-3918
Fax: 808-842-1962
http://www.pacificgateway.org/

Hawaii Business and Entrepreneur
Acceleration Mentors
Alii Tower. Suite 1800
1099 Alakea Street
Honolulu, HI 96813
808-547-5735
Fax: 808-547-5880
www.hibeam.org

Hawaii Health Care Business
Incubator
55 Merchant Street, Suite 2500
Honolulu, HI 96813
808-587-4777
Fax: 808-587-4780
www.hhcbi.com

High Technology Development
Corporation
Manoa Innovation Center
2800 Woodlawn Drive, Suite 100
Honolulu, HI 96822
808-539-3600
Fax: 808-539-3614
www.htdc.org/mic

Maui Research & Technology Center
590 Lipoa Parkway
Kihei, HI 96753
808-875-2320
www.mrtc.org

Idaho

Bonner Business Center
804 Airport Way
Sandpoint, ID 83864
208-263-4073
Fax: 208-263-4609
http://sandpoint.org/bbc/

Panhandle Area Council
11100 N. Airport Drive
Hayden, ID 83835
208-772-0584
Fax: 208-772-6196
http://www.pacni.org/pachome.htm

University of Idaho Business
Technology Incubator
121 Sweet Avenue

Moscow, ID 83843
208-885-3800
Fax: 208-885-3803
edc@moscow.com
http://www.bti.uro.uidaho.edu/

Illinois

Business Center of Decatur
2121 S. Imboden Ct.
Decatur, IL 62521
217-423-2832
Fax: 217-423-7214
http://www.decaturcenter.com/bcod1
.htm

Des Plaines River Valley Enterprise
Zone
Joliet City Center Partnership
116 N. Chicago St., Suite 101
Joliet, IL 60432
815-723-1800
http://www.jolietdowntown.com/con
tact.asp

EnterpriseWorks
60 Hazelwood Drive
Champaign, IL 61820
217-333-8324
http://www.tech.com/enterprisework
s/

Industrial Council of Nearwest
Chicago
Fulton Carroll Center
2023 W. Carroll Ave., Suite 200
Chicago, IL 60612
312-421-3941
Fax: 312-421-1871
http://www.industrialcouncil.com/

Lincoln Trail eCommerce
Enterprises, Inc.
408 South Cross Street
Robinson, IL 62454
618-544-5374
Fax: 618-544-5453
staff@bizbuilder.org
http://www.bizbuilder.org/default.asp

Office Of Strategic Initiatives
Northwestern University
1801 Maple Avenue
Evanston, Il. 60201-3135
847-491-7600
Fax: 847-491-4486
mary-kelly@northwestern.edu
http://www.northwestern.edu/researc
h/osi/

Quincy Business & Technology
Center
Les McKenzie/Executive Director
301 Oak Street
Quincy, IL 62301
217-228-5500
Fax: 217-228-5501
http://www.quincynet.com/qbtc/

Turner Center For Entrepreneurship
1501 W. Bradley Ave.

141 Jobst Hall
Peoria, IL 61625
309-677-4321
Fax: 309-677-3386
http://www.bradley.edu/turnercenter/

Technology Innovation Center
1840 Oak Ave.
Evanston, IL 60201
800-523-5883
847-864-0800
http://www.theincubator.com/

Area Jobs Development Association
P.O. Box 845
Kankakee, IL 60901-0845
815-933-2537
Fax: 815-933-9919
www.ci.kankakee.il.us/economic.ht
ml

Arts Bridge
At The Athenaeum Theater Building
2936 North Southport, Suite 210
Chicago, IL 60657-4210
773-935-6860
Fax: 773-935-6878
www.artsbridge.org

Business Service Center
7500 S. Pulaski Road, Building 200
Chicago, IL 60652-1299
773-838-0300
Fax: 773-838-0303
http://daley.ccc.edu/courses/business
_training.shtml

Chicago Technology Park Research
Center
2201 W. Campbell Park Drive
Chicago, IL 60612
312-829-7252
Fax: 312-633-3438
www.imdc.org/CTP

Gaebler Ventures Business Incubator
641 West Lake Street, Suite 100
Chicago, IL 60661
312-207-1190, ext 102
Fax: 312-207-1192
www.gaebler.com

Galesburg Business & Technology
Center
3000 Log City Trail
Galesburg, IL 61401
309-343-3002
Fax: 309-345-3526
www.galesburgbtc.org

The Incubator
Evanston Business & Technology
Center
1840 Oak Avenue
Evanston,IL 60201
800-523-5883
847-864-0800
Fax: 847-866-1808
www.theincubator.com

MAIDCO Business and Technology
Center
P.O. Box 6070
Macomb, IL 61455
309-837-4684
Fax: 309-298-2520
www.wiu.edu/users/mimaid/btc/btc.h
tm

Northwestern University/Evanston
Research Park
820 Church Street, Suite 300
Evanston, IL 60201
847-475-7170
Fax: 847-475-7380
http://researchpark.com

Peoria NEXT
1 Illini Drive
Peoria, IL 61605
309-671-8400
Fax: 309-671-8438
www.peorianext.org

Southern Illinois University
Carbondale
Small Business Incubator
150 E. Pleasant Hill Road
Carbondale, IL 62901
618-536-4451
Fax: 618-453-5040
www.siu.edu/~econdev/bip

Sterling Small Business and
Technology Center
1741 Industrial Drive
Sterling, IL 61081
815-625-5255
Fax: 815-625-5094
http://ci.sterling.il.us/main/bus_parks
/

Indiana

Entrepreneur Business Center
55 S. State Ave.
Indianapolis, IN 46201
317-634-7393
http://www.ebc-center.com/

Evansville Small Business Incubator
Small Business Center
1100 West Lloyd Expressway
Evansville, IN 47708
812-426-9991
888-815-9758
Fax: 812-426-6138
jlake@evansvilleincubator.org
http://www.evansvilleincubator.org

Industrial Business Center
5 East Riverside Drive
Evansville, IN 47713
812-426-9991
888-815-9758
Fax: 812-426-6138
jlake@evansvilleincubator.org
http://www.evansvilleincubator.org

Fort Wayne Enterprise Center
1830 Wayne Trace

Fort Wayne, IN 46803
219-422-2304
http://www.fwuea.org/

Lexington Business Center
421 South Second St.
Elkhart, IN 46516
574-522 -0390
Fax: 574 -295-1711
info@thetiedemanngroup.com
http://www.lexingtonbizctr.com/

Uptown Innovation Center
Richmond Wayne County Tech Zone
829 East Main Street
Richmond, IN 47374
765-962-8151
info@rwc-techzone.org
www.rwc-
techzone.org/innovation.html

Purdue Gateways Program
3000 Kent Ave.
West Lafayette, IN 47906
765-494-4600
www.purdue.edu/research/gateways/

Rose-Hulman Ventures
100 South Campus Drive
P.O. Box 3799
Terre Haute, IN 47803-0799
812-244-4000
ideas@rhventures.org
http://www.rhventures.org/

The Star Center
216 W. Allen Street
Bloomington, IN 47403
812-323-STAR
http://www.thestarcenter.com/

Venture Out Business Center
975 Industrial Drive
Madison, IN 47250
812-273-6510 ext. 225
jgarrett@madisonchamber.org
www.madisonchamber.org/page7.ht
ml

Iowa

Iowa State University Research Park
Corporation
2501 North Loop Drive Suite 1600
Ames, IA 50010
515-296-PARK
Fax: 515-296-9924
http://www.isupark.org/

Technology Innovation Center
100 Oakdale Campus
Room 109 TIC
The University of Iowa
Iowa City, IA 52242-5000
319-335-4063
Fax: 319-335-4489
W. Bruce Wheaton, Director
bruce-wheaton@uiowa.edu
http://research.uiowa.edu

Center for Crops Utilization
Research
1041 Food Science Building
Iowa State University
Ames, IA 50011
515-294-0160
Fax: 515-294-6261
www.ccur.iastate.edu

Kansas

Enterprise Center of Johnson County
8527 Bluejacket St.
Lenexa, KS 66214
913-438-2282
Fax: 913-888-6928
http://www.ecjc.com/

Kansas Entrepreneurial Center
1500 Hayes Dr.
Manhattan, KS 66502
786-532-3900
Fax: 785-532-3909
http://www.ksu.edu/tech.transfer/ma
cc/macc.htm

Lawrence Regional Technology
Center
1617 St. Andrews Drive, Suite 210
Lawrence, KS 66047
785-832-2110
Fax: 785-832-8234
info@lrtc.biz
http://www.lrtc.biz/

Wichita Technology Corp.
7829 E. Rockhill Rd., Suite #307
Wichita, KS 67206
316-651-5900
Fax: 316-684-5640
http://www.wichitatechnology.com/

Kentucky

Advanced Science and Technology
Commercialization Center,
Joseph L. Fink III
A256 ASTeCC Building
University of Kentucky
Lexington, KY 40506-0286
859-257-2300, ext. 271
Fax: 859-257-2489
jfink@uky.edu
http://www.rgs.uky.edu/ASTECC/

Community Ventures
1450 North Broadway
Lexington, KY 40505
859-231-0054
800-299-0267
Fax: 859-231-0261
http://www.cvcky.org/

Louisville Enterprise Group
Suite 320
2900 West Broadway
Louisville, KY 40211
502-776-6000
Fax: 502-776-4434
sarahh@morethanabank.com
http://www.morethanabank.com/legp
age/leg.htm

Madison E-Zone
535 Madison Avenue
Covington, KY 41011
859-292-8444
info@madisone-zone.com
http://www.madisone-zone.com/

MetaCyte Business Lab LLC
201 E. Jefferson St.
Louisville, KY 40202-1246
502-569-1020
Fax: 502-569-1021
www.metacyte.biz

Ashland Business Incubator
3000 Louisa Street
Catlettsburg, KY 41129
606 739-5191

bCatalyst
124 North First Street
Louisville, KY 40202
502-583-0400
Fax: 502-583-5606
www.bcatalyst.com

Innovation Group
200 West Vine Street, Suite 420
Lexington, KY 40507
859-233-3502
http://tig.kstc.com

iTRC Incubator
University of Louisiana Shelby
Campus
9001 Shelbyville Road
Louisville, KY 40222
502-582-0900
Fax: 502-852-4701
www.theitrc.com

Kentucky Highlands Incubator
Kentucky Highlands Investment
Corporation
362 Whitley Road
P.O. Box 1738
London, KY 40743
606-864-5175
www.khic.org

University of Kentucky Center for
Manufacturing
220 CRMS Building
College of Engineering
Lexington, KY 40506-0108
859-257-6262
Fax: 859-323-1035
www.mfg.uky.edu

Louisiana

Biomedical Research Foundation of
Northwest Louisiana
P.O. Box 38050
Shreveport, LA 71133
318-675-4100
Fax: 318-675-4120
http://www.biomed.org/staff.html

Dixie Business Center
1810 S. Range Ave.

Denham Springs, LA 70726
225-665-0809
Fax: 225-665-8171
http://www.dixiebusinesscenter.org/

Entergy Arts Business Program
Arts Council of New Orleans
225 Baronne St., Suite 1712
New Orleans, LA 70112
504-523-1465
Fax: 504-529-2430
mail@artscouncilofneworleans.org
http://www.artscouncilofneworleans.
org/

Enterprise Center of Louisiana
3419 N.W. Evangeline Thruway
Carencro, LA 70520
337-896-9115
Fax: 337-896-8736
http://www.ecol.org/

Jefferson Parish Economic
Development Commission (JEDCO)
3445 N. Causeway Blvd.
Suite 300
Metairie, LA 70002
504-833-1881
Fax: 504-833-7676
http://www.jedco.org/Default.asp?P
AGE_ID=1

Louisiana Business and Technology
Center
LBTC Small Business Incubator
South Stadium Drive
LSU
Baton Rouge, LA 70803
225-578-7555
Fax: 225.578.3975
lbtc@lsu.edu
http://www.bus.lsu.edu/lbtc/Incubato
r/

Louisiana Technology Park
7117 Florida Blvd.
Baton Rouge, LA 70806
225-218-1100
Fax: 225-218-0101
info@letachpark.com
http://www.latechpark.com/

Metro/Regional Business Incubator
Diana M. Simek
Vice-President, Business
Development
Ark-La-Tex Export & Technology
Center, Inc.
7100 West Park Road
West Shreveport, LA 71129
318-671-1050
Fax: 318-671-9032
simek@cdconline.org
http://www.cdconline.org/businessin
cubator.htm

NEWCORP
Business Assistance Center
1600 Canal Street, Suite 601
New Orleans, LA 70112

504-539-9340
Fax: 504-539-9343
newcorpinfo@newcorpbac.net
http://www.newcorpbac.net/

The University of New Orleans
Technology Enterprise Center
Lakeshore Drive Room 526
New Orleans, LA 70122
504-280-2000
Fax: 504-280-2222
http://www.uno.edu/~rtp/techcntr.ht
m

Eagle's Nest Business Incubator
6701 I-10 Service Road
New Orleans, LA 70127
504-242-0685
Fax: 504-242-1004

Enterprise Center of Acadia Business
Incubator
11 North Parkerson Avenue
Crowley, LA 70526
337-788-7550 ext 4
Fax: 337-788-4936
www.acadiabusinessincubator.org

Iberia Business & Technology
Incubator, Inc
101 Burk Street
New Iberia, LA 70560
337-367-0834
Fax: 337-367-7421
www.iberiaparishIDF.org

Macon Ridge Business Incubator
903 Louisiana Avenue
Ferriday, LA 71334
318-757-3033
Fax: 318-757-4212
www.maconridge.org

Mahogony's Incubation System
6401 Mosswood Drive
Monroe, LA 71203
318-325-5521
Fax: 318-325-5227

NE Louisiana Business Opportunity
Center
3126 Highway 594, Box 12
Monroe, LA 71203
318-323-0878
Fax: 318-387-8529

New Orleans Business & Industry
District
6600 Plaza Drive, 601
New Orleans, LA 70127
504-242-1300
Fax: 504-242-1344
www.nobid.org

Southeast Louisiana Business Center
1514 Martens Drive
Hammond, LA 70402
985-549-3199
Fax: 985-549-2127
www.selu.edu/businesscenter

Women Entrepreneurs for Economic
Development
1683 N. Claiborne Avenue, Suite
100
New Orleans, LA 70016
504-947-8522
Fax: 504-949-8885

Maine

Maine Aquaculture Innovation
Center
5717 Corbett Hall, Room 438
Orono, ME 04469-5717
207-581-2263/2215
Fax: 207-581-1479
http://www.maineaquaculture.org/

Applied Technology Development
Centers
Department of Economic and
Community Development
59 State House Station
Augusta, ME 04333-0059
207-624-9802
Philip.Helgerson@maine.gov
http://www.atdcmaine.org/

River Valley Technology Center
60 Lowell Street
PO Box 559
Rumford, ME 04276
207-369-9368
info@rivervalleycenter.com
http://www.rivervalleycenter.com/

Target Technology Incubator
20 Godfrey Drive
Orono, ME 04473
207-866-6500
Fax: 207-866-6501
dneuman@maine.edu
http://www.targetincubator.umaine.e
du/

Center for Environmental Enterprise
3 Adams Street
So. Portland, ME 04106
207-767-4302
Fax: 207-767-4306
info@ceemaine.org
http://www.ceemaine.org/aboutus.ht
ml

Thomas M. Teague Biotechnology
Park
Clyde Dyar, Director
Town of Fairfield
P.O. Box 149
Fairfield, ME 04937
207-238-9315
Fax: 207-238-9316
cdyar@biotechme.com
http://www.biotechme.com/html/wel
come.html

Dover-Foxcroft Office
50 North Street
Dover-Foxcroft, ME 04426
207-564-7116
Fax: 207-564-2218

www.penquiscap.org/penquis.nsf/we
bpages/Incubator+Without+Walls

Old Port Technology Center
164 Middle Street
P.O. Box 4615
Portland, ME 04112
207-846-4800
www.optcinfo.com

Penquis Incubator Without Walls
262 Harlow Street
P.O. Box 1162
Bangor, ME 04402-1162
207-973-3500
Fax: 207-973-3699
www.penquiscap.org/penquis.nsf/we
bpages/Incubator+Without+Walls

Maryland

Emerging Technology Centers
2400 Boston St.
The Factory Bldg., 3rd Floor
Baltimore, MD 21224
410-327-9150
http://www.etcbaltimore.com/

Garrett Information Enterprise
Center
685 Mosser Road
McHenry, MD 21541
http://www.giecworks.com/Pages/bu
ilding.html

Rural Development Center
Richard A. Henson Center
Daniel Kuennen, Director
Room 2147, UMES
Princess Anne, MD 21853
410-651-6183
Fax: 410-651-6207
http://skipjack.net/le_shore/rural/

Technical Innovation Center
11400 Robinwood Drive
Hagerstown, MD 21742-6590
301-790-2800
Fax: 301-733-4229
http://www.technicalinnovationcente
r.com/

Technology Advancement Program
(TAP)
1105 TAP Bldg.
387 Technology Drive
University of Maryland
College Park, MD 20742-3371
301-314-7803
Fax: 301-226-5378
http://www.tap.umd.edu/

Rosen Group Staff
3000 Chestnut Avenue, Suite 304
Baltimore, MD 21211
800-642-4314
info@rosengrp.com.
http://www.americancraft.com/artist/
contact.html

UMBC Technology Center
1450 South Rolling Road
Baltimore, MD 21227
410-455-5900
http://www.umbc.edu/techcenter/

Association for Entrepreneurial
Science (AES)
12111 Parklawn Drive
Rockville, MD 20852
301-881-3300 ext 123
Fax: 301-881-7640
www.afbr-bri.com

Calvert County Business Incubator
College of Southern Maryland
65 Duke Street, Suite 103
Prince Frederick, MD 20678
301-934-7585
www.csmd.edu/ProfDevelopment/C
CTI/incubator.html#process

Charles County Business Incubator
College of Southern Maryland
Smallwood Village Shopping Center
#122
Waldorf, MD 20602
301-934-7585
www.csmd.edu/ProfDevelopment/C
CTI/incubator.html#process

Higher Education and Applied
Technology Center (HEAT)
1201 Technology Drive
Aberdeen, MD 21001-1213
410-638-2500
Fax: 410-638-2509
www.heatcentermaryland.com

Maryland Technology Development
Center
9700 Great Seneca Highway
Rockville, MD 20850
240-634-4832
Fax: 240-453-6201
www.mdhitech.org/Entrpreneur

Maryland Technology Development
Corporation (TEDCO)
5575 Sterrett Place, Suite 240
Columbia, MD 21044
410-740-9442
800-305-5556
Fax: 410-470-9422
www.marylandtedco.org/programs/i
ncubator/index.html

Phase 1
312 Laurel Avenue
Laurel, MD 20707
301-206-2224
Fax: 301-598-0769
www.phase1.org

Prince George's County Technical
Assistance Center
4640 Forbes Boulevard
Lanham, MD 20706
301-429-3044

Fax: 301-429-8762
www.pgcedc.com/common/tac.html

Silver Springs Innovation Center
Georgia Avenue & Blair Mill Road
Silver Spring, MD 20910
240-777-2000
Fax: 240-777-2001
www.mc-
mncppc.org/silverspring/public_proj
ects/ssinnovation.shtm

Technology Growth Center at
University Town Center
Prince George's Metro Center
Metro 3 Building
6525 Belcrest Road, Suite 500
Hyattsville, MD 20782
301-779-4800
www.universitytowncenter.net/busin
ess.html

University of Maryland Baltimore
Health Sciences Research Park
800 West Baltimore Street
Baltimore, MD 21201
410-706-8282
www.umaryland.edu/research/resear
chers/ideh.html

Massachusetts

Biosquare Innovation Center
Boston University Medical Center
715 Albany St., X-1
Boston, MA 02118
617-638-5384
http://www.biosquare.org/bdic/BDIC
.html

Commonwealth Corporation
The Schrafft Center
529 Main Street, Suite 110
Boston, MA 02129
617-727-8158
800-439-0183
Fax: 617-242-7660
http://www.commcorp.org/

The Enterprise Center
Salem State College
121 Loring Avenue
Salem, MA 01970
978-542-7528
Fax: 978-542-7061
http://www.enterprisectr.org/

Martin Luther King Jr. Business
Empowerment
Center
237 Chandler Street
Worcester, MA 01609
508-363-0303
Fax: 508-363-2814
jmattier@ix.netcom.com
http://www.mlkj-bec.org/

Massachusetts Biomedical Initiatives
MBIdeas
25 Winthrop Street
West Entrance

Worcester, MA 01604
508-797-4200
Fax: 508-799-4039
http://www.massbiomed.org/

Springfield Enterprise Center
One Federal St.
Building 101
Springfield, MA 01105
413-755-6100
Fax: 413-755-6101
http://sec.stcc.edu/

Cambridge Innovation Center
One Broadway, 14th Floor
Kendall Square
Cambridge, MA 02142
617-758-4200
www.cambridgcincubator.com

Cape Ann Business Center
8 Blackburn Center
Gloucester, MA 01930
978-282-7779
Fax: 978-281-6944
www.businc.org

Massachusetts Innovation Center
One Oak Hill Road
Fitchburg, MA 01420
978-424-2500
www.massinnovation.com

Michigan

The Albion Economic Development
Corporation
309 N. Superior St.
P.O. Box 725
Albion, MI 49224-0725
517-629-3926
877-696-8682
Fax: 517-629-3929
http://www.edc.albion.mi.us/

Central Michigan University
Research Corporation
2625 Denison Drive
Mount Pleasant, MI 48858
989-774-2424
Fax: 989-774-2416
cmurc@cmich.edu
http://www.thecenter.cmich.edu/acce
leration.html

Center for Entrepreneurship
3rd Floor Devos Center
Grand Valley State University
1 Campus Dr.
Allendale, MI 49401-9403
616-331-7200
http://www.gvsu.edu/ssb/index.cfm?
fuseaction=home.home

McAnoy Business Center
71 Edsel Ford Fwy E,
Detroit, MI 48202
313-871-4004
Fax: 313-871-1449
director@mcanoy.com

Southwest Michigan Innovation
Center
4717 Campus Drive
Kalamazoo, MI 49008
269-353-1823
Fax: 269-372-3397
info@southwestmichiganfirst.com
http://www.kazoosmic.com/

Tech Town
Wayne State Research and
Technology Park
One Ford Place, Suite 4AB
Detroit, MI 48202
313-586-9501
info@techtownwsu.org
www.techtownwsu.org

Whetstone Project Business
Accelerator
Muskegon Area First
900 Third Street, Suite 200
Muskegon, MI 49440
231-722-3751
Fax: 231-728-7251
http://www.muskegonareafirst.org/

Idea Works
169 Monroe N.W., Suite 320
Grand Rapids, MI 49503
616-454-4033
Fax: 616-454-4474
www.ideaworksllc.com

MBI International
3900 Collins Road
Lansing, MI 48910-8396
Mailing address:
   P.O. Box 27609
   Lansing, MI 48909-0609
517-337-3181
Fax: 517-337-2122
www.mbi.org

Minnesota

Harlan T. Jacobs, President
Genesis Business Centers, Ltd.
3989 Central Ave. N.E., Suite 630
Columbia Heights, MN 55421
763-782-8576
Fax: 763-782-8578
http://www.genesiscenters.com/

Owatonna Business Incubator
1065 S.W. 24th Ave.
P.O. Box 505
Owatonna, MN 55060
507-451-0517
Fax: 507-455-2788
Obi@owatonnaincubator.com
http://www.owatonnaincubator.com/

University Technology Enterprise
Center
1313 Fifth St., SE
Minneapolis, MN 55414
612-379-3800
www2.pro-ns.net/~utec/

Aitkin Growth Center
316 First Avenue NW
Aitkin, MN 56431
218-927-2172
Fax: 218-927-2173

Breckenridge Industrial Mall
420 Nebraska Avenue
P.O Box 410
Breckenridge, MN 56520-0410
218-643-2733
Fax: 218-643-1173
www.breckenridgemn.net/port.html

Elk River Incubator
13065 Orono Parkway
Elk River, MN 55330
763-635-1041
Fax: 763-635-1090
www.ci.elk-river.mn.us

Itasca Development Corporation
12 NW Third Street
Grand Rapids, MN 55744
218-326-9411
Fax: 218-327-2242
www.itascadv.org

North Shore Business Enterprise
Center
1313 Fairground Road
Two Harbors, MN 55616
218-834-3489
www.nsbec.com

Perham Tech Center
801 Jenny Avenue
Perham, MN 56573
218-347-6300
Fax: 218-347-6309
www.perham.com/techcenter/incubat
or.asp

Soft Center Duluth
11 East Superior Street, Suite 130
Duluth, MN 55802
800-652-5524
218-727-9309
www.softcenterduluth.org

Technology Plus of Mankata, Inc
1961 Premier Drive, Suite 100
Mankato, MN 56001-5901
507-385-3205
Fax: 507-385-3202
www.mankatotechplus.com

Valley Tech Park
2900 University Avenue, Suite 100
Crookston, MN 56716
218-281-8051
http://webhome.crk.umn.edu/%7Epd
owns/vtp/index.htm

Whittier Community Development
Corporation
2845 Harriet Avenue South
Suite 208
Minneapolis, MN 55408
612-879-0109

Fax: 612-871-2923
www.webcenter.org

Mississippi

Coahoma County Industrial
Foundation
1540 DeSoto Avenue
Clarksdale, MS 38614
800-626-3764
662-627-7337
Fax: 662-627-1313
chamberofcommerce@clarksdale-
ms.com
http://www.clarksdale-ms.com/

Golden Triangle Enterprise Center
One Research Boulevard
Suite 201
Starkville, MS 39759
662-320-3990
www.gtec.org

Gulf Coast Business
Technology Center
1636 Popps Ferry Road
Biloxi, MS 39532
228-392-9741
Fax: 228-392-9743
btc@cableone.net
http://www.gcbtc.org/home.asp

Charles E. Beasley, Technology
Incubator Manager
Mississippi Enterprise for
Technology
Building 1103, Suite 140A
John C. Stennis Space Center, MS
39529-6000
228-688-2083
Fax: 228-688-1064
cbeasley@mset.org
http://www.mset.org/incubator.html

Mississippi Technology Alliance
Center
1230 Raymond Rd.
Jackson, MS 39204
601-979-5050
Fax: 601-502-0382
http://www.innovationcenter.ms/

Columbus-Lowndes Business
Development
118 South McCrary Road
Columbus, MS 39702
662-327-7796
Fax: 662-328-9888
www.cldlink.org

Kemper County Industrial Incubator
Center, Inc.
102 Industrial Park Drive
DeKalb, MS 39328
601-743-2754
Fax: 601-743-2760

Vicksburg Business Development
Center
2920 Washington Street
Vicksburg, MS 39180

601-638-2979
Fax: 601-638-5494

Missouri

Center for Emerging Technologies
4041 Forest Park Ave.
St. Louis, MO 63108
314-615-6900
Fax: 314-615-6901
http://www.emergingtech.org/Servic
es.html

Economic Development Center
5988 Mid Rivers Mall Dr.
Suite 100
St. Charles, MO 63304
636-441-6880
Fax: 636-441-6881
info@edcstcharlescounty.com
http://www.edcstcharlescounty.com/i
ncubator/index.php3

Advanced Technology Center
118 N. Second Street
St. Charles, MO 63301
636-410-0300
Fax: 636-940-0408
lrau@edcatc.com
http://www.edcstcharlescounty.com/i
ncubator/index.php3

KCCatalyst
4747 Troost Ave.
Kansas City, MO 64110
816-235-6182
Fax: 816-235-6568
info@kccatalyst.com
http://www.kccatalyst.com/

Rolla Missouri Enterprise Innovation
Center
800 University Drive, Suite 111
Rolla, MO 65401
573-364-8570
Fax: 573-364-6323
http://www.missourienterprise.org/

Dr. Robert J. Calcaterra
President/CEO
Nidus Center for Scientific
Enterprise
893 North Warson Road
St. Louis, MO 63141
314-812-8001
314-812-8000
Fax: 314-812-8080
robert.j.calcaterra@niduscenter.com
http://www.niduscenter.com/

St. Louis County Economic Council
St. Louis Enterprise Centers
Jan DeYoung, director
121 S. Meramec, Suite 900
St. Louis, MO 63105
314-615-7663
314-615-7621
Fax: 314-615-7666
incubators@stlouisco.com
http://www.slcec.com/facilities.htm#
mid St. Louis County Economic
Council

Arts Incubator
115 West 18th Street
Kansas City, MO 64108
816-421-2292
www.incubatingarts.org

Enterprise Center of Johnson County
8527 Bluejacket Street
Lenexa, KS 66214
913-438-2282
Fax: 913-888-6928
www.ecjc.com

Hannibal Small Business Incubator
410 South Maple
Hannibal, MO 63401
573-221-1033

Nidus Center for Scientific
Enterprise
893 North Warson Road
St. Louis, MO 63141
314-812-8001
Fax: 314-812-8080
www.niduscenter.com

Ozark Foothills Business Incubator
3019 Fair Street
Poplar Bluff, MO 63901
573-785-6402
Fax: 573-686-5467
www.ofrpc.com/incubator

Montana

Missoula Area Economic
Development Corporation
1121 E. Broadway, Suite 100
Missoula, MT 59802
406-728-3337
Fax: 406-543-2304
http://www.maedc.org/

Montana Business Incubator
Montana State University - Billings
100 Poly Drive, Suite 150
Billings, MT 59101
406-657-2138
Fax: 406-657-2006
http://www.mtbiz.org/

TechRanch
910 Technology Blvd. Suite A
Bozeman, MT 59718
406-556-0272
Fax: 406-556-0969
info@techranch.org
http://www.techranch.org/cgi-
bin/techranch/index.html

Downtown Great Falls Business
Improvement District
419 Central Avenue
Great Falls, MT 59401
406-727-5430
Fax: 406-727-5431
www.downtowngreatfalls.com

Nebraska

University of Nebraska Technology
Park

4701 Innovation Drive
Lincoln, NE 68521-5330
402-472-4200
Fax: 402-472-4203
info@unebtechpark.com
http://www.unebtechpark.com/

The Food Processing Center
143 Food Industry Complex
Lincoln, NE 68583-0930
402-472-2819
Fax: 402-472-1693
http://fpc.uni.edu/FoodEntrepreneurP
rogram/index.htm

Aurora Technology Center
616 13th Street, Suite 101
Aurora, NE 68818
402-694-3010
Fax: 402-694-6310
www.atbionline.org

Box Butte Development Corporation
Business Assistance Center
204 East Third
P.O. Box 802
Alliance, NE 69301
308-762-1800
Fax: 308-762-4268
www.bbc.net/bbdc/buscenter.htm

Central Community College
Business Incubator
2000 East South Street
Hastings, NE 68901
402-463-9811

Grow Nebraska
Central Plains Business Center
416 Central Avenue
P.O. Box 7
Holbrook, NE 68948
888-GROWNEB
www.growned.com

Nevada

Henderson Business Resource
Center
112 Water Street, Suite 100
Henderson, NV 89015
702-992-7200
Fax: 702-992-7241
info@hendersonbizcenter.com
http://www.hendersonbizcenter.com/

Dandini Research Park
Northern Nevada Science center
2215 Raggio Parkway
Reno, NV 89512
775-673-7316
www.dri.edu/Admin/ResPark/index.
html

Las Vegas Business Center
1951 Stella Lake Street, Suite 24
Las Vegas, NV 89106
702-638-6371
Fax: 702-638-6374
www.ci.las-vegas.nv.us

New Hampshire

Amoskeag Small Business Incubator
670 N. Commercial St.
Manchester, NH 03101
603-629-9511
Fax: 603-629-9510
asbi@grolen.com
http://www.snhu.edu/amoskeagincub
ator/

The Dartmouth Entrepreneurial
Network
14 South Main Street, Suite 2F
Hanover, NH 03755
603-646-0290
dartmouth_entrepreneurial_net@dart
mouth.edu
www.den.dartmouth.edu/contact/

Monadnock Business Ventures, Inc.
375 Jaffrey Rd.
Peterborough, NH 03458
603-924-1600
Fax: 603-924-1631
http://www.mbvinc.com/

New Jersey

High Technology Small Business
Incubator
Burlington County College
900 Briggs Rd.
Mt. Laurel, NJ 08054
Ronald Maxson, Manager
856-222-9311, extension 2801
http://www.bcc.edu/html/SmallBizIn
cubator.html

Food Innovation Research and
Extension Center
87 East Commerce Street
Bridgeton, NJ 08302-2601
856-459-1125
Fax: 856-459-3043
http://www.fire.rutgers.edu/

Enterprise Development Center, Inc.
240 Dr. Martin Luther King Jr. Blvd.
Newark, NJ 07102
973-643--5740
Fax: 973-643-5839
http://www.njit-edc.org/
stash@njit-edc.org

Commercialization Center for
Technology
675 US Highway One
North Brunswick, NJ 08902
732-729-0022
www.njtechcentre.com

Community Options
16 Farber Road
Princeton, NJ 08540
609-951-9900
Fax: 609-951-9112
www.comop.org

First Camden Business Center
520 Market Street
City Hall, 13th Floor

P.O. Box 95120
Camden, NJ 08101-5120
856-968-4788
Fax: 856-968-4787
www.ci.camden.nj.us/economic

Rutgers Camden Technology
Campus
Business Incubator
1000 Atlantic Avenue, Fifth Floor
Camden, NJ 08104
856-225-6400
Fax: 856-225-6399
http://camden-sbc.rutgers.edu/cme

Stevens Technology Ventures
Incubator
Stevens Technologies
Castle Point on Hudson
Hoboken, NJ 07030
201-216-5522
Fax: 201-216-5090
www.stevenstechnologies.com

Trenton Business and Technology
Center
36 Broad Street
Trenton, NJ 08608
609-396-8801
Fax: 609-396-8603
www.mccc.edu/business/sbdc/incuba
tor.html

New Mexico

Los Alamos Commerce &
Development Corporation
P.O. Box 715
Los Alamos, NM 87544
505-662-0001
Fax: 505-662-0099
lacdc@losalamos.org
http://www.losalamos.org/lacdc/

Quality Center for Business
5101 College Blvd.
Farmington, NM 87402
Jasper Welch, Director
505-566-3700
welchj@sanjuancollege.edu
http://www.sjc.cc.nm.us/qcb/

Santa Fe Business Incubator
3900 Paseo del Sol
Santa Fe, NM 87507
505-424-1140
Fax: 505-424-1144
http://www.sfbi.net/

Technology Ventures Corporation
Albuquerque Operations
1155 University Blvd. SE
Albuquerque, NM 87106
505 246-2882
Fax: 505 246-2891
http://www.techventures.org/

Albuquerque Technology Incubator
UNM's Science and Technology
Corporation
1009 Bradbury S. E

Albuquerque, NM 87106
505-272-7500
Fax: 505-842-8018

Arrowhead Research Park
New Mexico University
Box 30001, Department 3RES
Las Cruces, NM 88003
505-646-2481
Fax: 505-646-2480

Cooperative Ownership
Development Corporation
610 N. Silver St.
Silver City, NM 88061
505-388-1604
Fax: 505-538-0480

The Enterprise Center
Quality Center for Business
5101 College Blvd.
Farmington, NM 87402
505-566-3700
Fax: 505-599-0698
www.sjc.cc.nm.us/QCB

Lovelace Respiratory Research
Institute
2425 Ridgecrest S.E.
Albuquerque, NM 87108
505-262-7074
Fax: 505-262-7037

Taos County Small Business
Incubator
Taos Food Center
P. O. Box 1389
Taos, NM 87571-1389
505-758-8731
Fax: 505-758-3201

New York

Action for a Better Community
550 E. Main Street
Rochester, NY 14604
585-325-5116
Fax: 585-325-9108
CAA@ABCinfo.org
www.ABCinfo.org

The Albany Center for Economic
Success, Inc. (ACES)
255 Orange Street
Albany, NY 12210
518-427-7804
Fax: 518-427-6203
contactus@aces-osi.org
http://www.aces-osi.org/

Long Island Forum For Technology
(LIFT)
111 West Main Street
Bay Shore, NY 11706
631-969-3700
Fax: 631-969-4489
info@lift.org
http://www.lift.org/

Mancuso Business Development
Group

56 Harvester Ave.
Batavia, NY 14020
585-343-2800
Fax: 585-343-7096
mancuso@mancusogroup.com
http://www.mancusogroup.com/

Broad Hollow Bioscience Park
One Broad Hollow Bioscience Park
Farmingdale, NY 11735
631-420-2648
http://www.bhbp.org/

Ceramics Corridor Innovation Center
Corning Facility
109 Canada Road
Painted Post, NY 14870
607-962-6387
Fax: 607-962-0645
corridor@ceramicscorridor.org
http://www.ceramicscorridor.org/

Alfred Facility
200 North Main Street
Alfred, NY 14802
607-587-9444
Fax: 607-587-9535
corridor@ceramicscorridor.org
http://www.ceramicscorridor.org/

The County of Orleans Industrial
Development Agency
14016 Route 31 West,
Albion, NY 14411
866-COIDA4U
585-589-3197
Fax: 585-589-2858
http://www.coida.com/

FOODLINK
936 Exchange Street
Rochester, NY 14608
585-328-3380
800-724-9632
Fax: 585-328-9951
http://www.foodlinkny.org/

Glens Falls Economic Development
James Martin, Director
Economic Development Department
City Hall
42 Ridge Street
Glens Falls, NY 12801
518-761-3864
Fax: 518-761-0234
economicdevelopment@cityofglensf
alls.com
http://www.cityofglensfalls.com/eco
n_dev/econ_dev.htm

Lennox Tech Enterprise Center
(TEC)
High Tech Rochester
150 Lucius Gordon Drive, Suite 100
West Henrietta, NY 14586
585-214-2400
Fax: 585-272-0054
http://www.htr.org/

Long Island High Technology
Incubator, Inc.
Box 100, 25 East Loop Road
Stony Brook, NY 11790-3350
631-444-8800
Fax: 631-444-8825
http://www.lihti.org/

Operation Oswego County, Inc.
44 West Bridge Street
Oswego, NY 13126
315-343-1545
Fax: 315-343-1546
ooc@oswegocounty.org
http://www.oswegocounty.org/OOC
_Contact.htm

Simon Balint
Rensselaer Incubator Program
1223 Peoples Ave.
Troy, NY 12180
518-276-6658
Fax: 518-276-6380
balins@rpi.edu
http://www.rpi.edu/dept/incubator/ho
mepage/

Schenectady County Community
Business Center
920 Albany St.
Schenectady, NY 12307
518-382-3069
Fax: 518-688-2028
http://www.sccbc.org/sccbc/

U-Start Business Incubator
4 Nott Terrace
Schenectady, NY 12308
518-631-0473
Fax: 518-631-0475
http://www.incubator.union.edu/

The University at Buffalo
Office of Science, Technology
Transfer, and Economic Outreach
1567 Sweet Home Rd.
Amherst, NY 14228
716-645-5500
Fax: 716-636-5921
www.stor.buffalo.edu

Audubon Business and Technology
Center
3960 Broadway
New York, NY 10032
212-342-7070
Fax: 212-928-4441
www.auduboncenter.org

Binghamton University Incubator
Administration Building, Room 127
P.O. Box 6000
Binghamton, NY 13902
607-777-6136
http://research.binghamton.edu/text/
TECHTRANSFER/INCUBATOR.ht
m

Buffalo Free Trade Complex
85 River Rock Drive

Buffalo, NY 14207
716-842-6923
Fax: 716-842-6942
Email: acaldiero@berc.org

Can-Am Building
100 River Rock Drive
Buffalo, NY 14207
716-842-6923
Fax: 716-842-6942
Email: acaldiero@berc.org

Center for Environmental Sciences
& Technology
University of Albany
High-Technology Business Incubator
251 Fuller Road
Albany, NY 12203
518-437-8600
Fax: 518-437-8610
www.albany.edu/pr/CESTMINCU.ht
ml

Canastota Business Center
11 Madison Boulevard
Canastota, NY 13032
315-697-9817
Fax: 315-697-8169
Email: ida@twcny.rr.com

The CASE Center/ Syracuse
University
2-212 Center for Science &
Technology
Syracuse, NY 13244
315-443-1060
Fax: 315-443-4745
www.case.syr.edu/incubation.asp

Cazenovia Business Center
132 ½ Albany Street
Cazenovia, NY 13035
315-655-8814
Fax: 315-655-4767
www.ravenglass.com/cazenovia/html
/chamber/bizcenter

Ceramics Corridor Innovation
Centers
Corning Facility
109 Canada Road
Painted Post, NY 14870
607-962-6387
Fax: 607-962-0645
Alfred Facility
200 North Main Street
Alfred, NY 14802
607-587-9444
Fax: 607-587-9535
www.ceramicscorridor.org

Chemung Incubator
400 East Church Street
Elmira, NY 14901
607-733-6513
Fax: 607-734-2698
www.steg.com

Conklin Hall Small Business
Incubator

SUNY Farmingdale
Farmingdale, NY 11735
631-847-3540
Email:
jonathan.gibralter@farmingdale.edu

Downstate's Advanced
Biotechnology Incubator
SUNY Brooklyn
450 Clarkson Avenue, Box 129
Brooklyn, NY 11203
718-270-1011
Fax: 718-270-1878
http://incubator.downstate.edu/incub
ator.htm

East Campus at State University of
New York
One University Place
Rensselaer, NY 12244
518-525-2764
Fax: 518-525-2799
Email: eschuler@uamail.albany.edu

Genesee County Economic
Development Center
One Mill Street
Batavia, NY 14020-3118
585-343-4866
Fax: 585-343-0848
www.gcedc.com

Geneva Enterprise Development
Center
47 Castle Street
Geneva, NY 14456
315-789-4393
Fax: 315-789-4294
www.geneva.ny.us

Greenpoint Manufacturing and
Design Center
1155-1205 Manhattan Avenue
Brooklyn, NY 11222
718-383-3935
Fax: 718-383-6339
www.gmdconline.com

Hudson Valley Foodworks
372 Main Street
Poughkeepsie, NY 12601
845-471-9478
Fax: 845-471-9479
Email: h.foodworks3@verizon.net

Imperial Industrial Park
94 Main Mill Street
Plattsburgh, NY 12901
518-563-3898
Fax: 518-563-4246

James Kirkpatrick Economic
Development Center
1010 Wayne Street
Olean, NY 14760
716-373-9260
Fax: 716-372-7912

New Enterprises Incubator
17 West Courtney Street

Dunkirk, NY 14048
716-366-3333
Fax: 716-366-3335

NY Design Business Center
LaGuardia Community College
29-10 Thomson Avenue
Long Island City, NY 11101
718-482-5317
Email: mhoward@lagcc.cuny.edu

James W. Kirkpatrick Economic
Development Center
120 N. Union Street
Olean, NY 14760
716-373-9260
Fax: 716-372-7912
Email: ncurtis@oleanny.com

LISTnet High Tech Incubator at
Briarcliffe College
1055 Stewart Avenue
Bethpage, NY 11714
516-622-8890
Fax: 516-622-8894
www.listnet.org/briarcliffe_incubator
.cfm

MVATC Technology and Incubation
Center
207 Genesee Street
Utica, NY 13501
315-793-8050
Fax: 315-793-8057
Email: paulm@mvatc.com

New York Venture Space
1375 Broadway, 6th Floor
New York, NY 10018
212-764-6850
Fax: 212-764-6013
www.nyventurespace.com

Orange-Ulster BOCES Incubator
92 Seward Avenue
Middletown, NY 10940
845-341-1349
Fax: 845-342-0477
www.ouboces.org/aetopindex/obi/ent
rep.html

RIT High Tech Incubator
125 Tech Park Drive
Rochester, NY 14623
585-239-6000
Fax: 585-475-5583
www.rithti.org

River Rock Industrial Incubator
155-175 Rano Street
Buffalo, NY 14207
716-842-6923
Fax: 716-842-6942
Email: acaldiero@berc.org

Riverside Industrial Center
200 Harrison Street
Jamestown, NY 14701
716-664-3262

Fax: 716-664-4515
Email: taylor@ccida.com

Second Century Innovation & Ideas
PACE University Economic
Development Corporation
One Pace Plaza
New York, NY 10038
212-346-1277
Fax: 212-650-3534
Email: vfg@pace.edu

Soucy USA, Inc.
100 Walnut Street
Champlain, NY 12919
518-298-3099
Fax: 518-298-2744
Email: soucy@primelink1.net

Southern Tier West Center for
Regional Excellence
4039 Route 219
Salamanca, NY 14729
716-945-5301
www.southerntierwest.org

Stony Brook Software Incubator
310 Administration Building
Stony Brook, NY 11794
631-632-6100
Fax: 631-632-6621
Email: carl.hanes@stonybrook.edu

Business Resource Center
Ulster County Community College
1 Development Court
Kingston, NY 12401
845-339-2025
Fax: 845-339-1631
http://ulster.cc.ny.us/programs/incub
ator.asp

Vantage Centre
Niagara County Industrial
Development
6311 Inducon Corporate Drive
Sanborn, NY 14132
716-298-8050
Fax: 716-298-8053
www.ncida.org/industrial_parks/indu
strial_vantage.php

Venture Development Center
P.O. Box 1012, Room 305
Montour Falls, NY 14865
607-535-4341

Watertown Industrial Center LDC
800 Starbuck Avenue
Watertown, NY 13601
315-782-5865
Fax: 315-782-7915

William L. Gaiter Business Center
401 William Gaiter Parkway
Buffalo, NY 14215
716-842-6923
Fax: 716-842-6942
Email: acaldiero@berc.org

North Carolina

BD Technologies
21 Davis Drive
Research Triangle Park, NC 27709
919-597-6357
Fax: 919-549-7572
http://www.bd.com/technologies/

Blue Ridge Business Development
Center
115 Atwood St.
P.O. Box 25
Sparta, NC 28675
336-372-1525
info@blueridgebdc.org
http://www.blueridgebdc.org/

The Ben Craig Center
8701 Mallard Creek Rd.
Charlotte, NC 28262
704-548-9113
Fax: 704-602-2179
info@bencraigcenter.com
http://www.bencraigcenter.com/

Midway Business Center
109 N. Graham St.
Suite 200
Chapel Hill, NC 27516
919-967-8779
Fax: 919-967-0710
info@empowerment-inc.org
http://www.empowerment-inc.org/

Nussbaum Center for
Entrepreneurship
2007 Yanceyville St., Suite 200
Greensboro, NC 27405
336-379-5001
Fax: 336-379-5020
http://www.nussbaumcfe.com/
DIRECTOR@NUSSBAUMCFE.CO
M

Pride of Kinston
327 N. Queen St.
Kinston, NC 28501
252-522-4676
Fax: 252-523-1685
http://www.prideofkinston.org/

Technology Enterprise Center
1800 Greene Street
Greenville, NC 27834
252-328-0063
www.locateincarolina.com/tech.htm

Appalachian Enterprise Center
130 Poplar Grove Connector
Boone, NC 28607
828-264-1613
Email: wcedc@boone.net

Babcock Demon Incubator
3455 University Parkway
Winston-Salem, NC 27106
336-655-4010
Fax: 336-757-1257
www.mba.wfu.edu/incubator/

Biotechnology Incubation and
Training Center
Asheville-Buncombe Technical
Community College
Mailing address:
340 Victoria Road
Asheville, NC 28801
Incubation Center:
1459 Sand Hill Road
Enka, NC
828-254-1921
www.abtech.edu/business/sbc/sbc.ht
m

Centennial Campus Partnership
Office
NCSU Box 7005
Raleigh, NC 27695-7005
919-515-7036
Fax: 919-515-1390
http://centennial.ncsu.edu

Emerging Technologies Center
A.M. Pappas & Associates, LLC
7030 Kit Creek Road
P.O. Box 110287
Research Triangle Park, NC 27709
919-998-3300
Fax: 919-998-3301
www.ampappas.com/about/emerging
-tech_Center.html

EnergyXchange Renewable Energy
Center
66 EnergyXchange Drive
Burnsville, NC 28714
828-674-5541
Fax: 828-675-5542
www.energyxchange.org

Entrepreneurial Development Center
at NC State
920 Main Campus Drive
Centennial Campus
Raleigh, NC 27606
919-424-3750
Fax: 919-424-3752
Email: tdunbar@edcncstate.org

Fayette Small Business Center
2520 Murchison Road
Fayetteville, NC 28301
910-222-8900
Fax: 910-222-8910
www.fayettevillebusinesscenter.com

First Flight Venture Center
2 Davis Drive
Research Triangle Park, NC 27709
919-990-8558
Fax: 919-558-0156
www.nctda.org/bi/rt_incubators.html

Hertford County Regional Small
Business Incubator
109 Community College Road
Ahoskie, NC 29710
252-862-1200
www.roanoke.cc.nc.us/conted/sbc.ht
m

Incumed Incorporated
7429 ACC Boulevard, Suite 107
Raleigh, NC 27617
919-957-8686
www.incu-med.com

Kinston Enterprise Center
Lenoir County Economic
Development Department
301 North Queen Street
P.O. Box 897
Kinston, NC 28502
252-527-1963
Fax: 252-527-1914
www.lenoiredc.com

McDowell Small Business and
Industry Development Center
Route 1, Box 170
Marion, NC 28752
828-652-6021
Fax: 828-659-8038
Email:
dean.kanipe@bbs.mcdowell.cc.nc.us

Midwest Business Center
EmPOWERment, Inc.
109 North Graham Street, Suite 200
Chapel Hill, NC 27516
919-967-8779
Fax: 919-967-0710
www.empowerment-inc.org

NC State Technology Incubator
920 Main Campus Drive, Suite 101
Raleigh, NC 27606
919-424-4409
http://techincubator.ncsu.edu

Pitt County Technology Incubator
111 West Washington Street
P. O. Box 837
Greenville, NC 27835
919-758-1989
Fax: 919-758-0128
www.locateincarolina.com

Raleigh Business & Technology
Center
900 S. Wilmington Street
Raleigh, NC 27601
919-836-8618
Fax: 919-836-8619
Email: W6412@aol.com

Rockingham Community College
Small Business Incubator
302 North Highway Street, Suite #2
Madison, NC 27025
336-548-2322
Fax: 336-548-2365
Email: emerines@rockinghamcc.edu

Roxboro Pearson County Business
Development Center
105 N Main Street
Roxboro, NC 27573
336-599-0032
www.piedmont.cc.nc.us

RTP BioVenture Center
BD Technologies
21 Davis Drive
P.O. Box 12016
Research Triangle Park, NC 27709
919-313-6121
Fax: 919-313-6400
www.bd.com

Smokey Mountain Development
Corporation
100 Industrial Park Drive
Waynesville, NC 28786
828-452-1967
Fax: 828-452-1352
Email: fouts@wcu.edu

Tabor City Small Business
Development Center
Tabor City Industrial Park
Highway 904 West
Tabor City, NC 28463
910-642-7054
Fax: 910-642-3941
www.rcsc.org/bdc.htm

Triangle South Enterprise Center
600 South Magnolia Avenue
Dunn, NC 28334
910-892-2884
Fax: 910-892-8775
www.trianglesouth.com

Whiteville Business Development
Center
163 Brunswick Electric Road
Whiteville, NC 28472
910-652-7054
Fax: 910-642-3941
www.columbusforindustry.com

Wilmington/New Hanover CDC
Incubator
Cape Fear Regional Development
Corporation
509 Cornelius Harnett Drive
Wilmington, NC 28401
910-815-0065
Fax: 910-362-9697
www.cfcdc.org

Winnabow Small Business
Development Center
6361 Ocean Highway East
Winnabow, NC 28479
910-253-3088
Fax: 910-253-3092
www.rcsc.org/bdc.htm

North Dakota

Center for Innovation
Rural Technology Incubator
4300 Dartmouth Drive
Grand Forks, ND 58203
701-777-3132
Fax: 701-777-2339
http://www.innovators.net/

Regional Small Business Center
417 Main Avenue

Fargo, ND 58103
701-235-7885
Fax: 701-235-6706
http://www.lakeagassiz.com/rsbc/

Ohio

ACEnet
94 Columbus Road
Athens, OH 45701
740-592-3854
Fax: 740-593-5451
http://www.acenetworks.org/

Akron Industrial Incubator
526 South Main Street
Akron, OH 44311
330-375-2173
Fax: 330-762-3657
http://www.ci.akron.oh.us/aii/

BIO/START
3130 Highland Avenue, 3rd Floor
Cincinnati, OH 45219-2374
513-475-6610
Fax: 513-221-1980
www.biostart.org
info@biostart.org

Cincinnati Business Incubator
1634 Central Parkway
Cincinnati OH 45202
513-362-2700
513-784 -0812
info@CBIncubator.org
http://www.cbincubator.org/

Pyramid Training Services
6363 Promway Avenue NW
N. Canton, OH 44720
330-305-6786
Fax: 330-305-9292
http://www.pyramid-stark.org/

Enterprise Development, Inc.
11000 Cedar Avenue
Cleveland, OH 44106-3052
216-229-9445
Fax: 216-229-3236
askedi@edinc.org
http://www.enterprise-
development.org/index_fla.html

Edison Technology Incubator
11000 Cedar Ave.
Cleveland, OH 44106
216.229.9445 ext. 168
http://www.enterprise-
development.org/eti.asp

Lewis Incubator for Technology
NASA Site
21000 Brookpark Rd.
MS 501-6
Cleveland, OH 44135
216-433-5300
Fax: 216-977-7108
http://www.liftinc.org/

Greater Hamilton Chamber of
Commerce

201 Dayton Street
Hamilton, OH 45011
513-844-1500
Fax: 513-844-1999
http://www.hamiltonohio.org/chamb
er/

Hamilton County Business Center,
Inc.
1776 Mentor Avenue
Cincinnati, OH 45212
513-631-8292
513-351-0610
http://www.hcdc.com/hcbc/

Office of Technology Transfer and
Economic Development
Kent State University
145 Auditorium Building
P.O. Box 5190
Kent, OH 44242-0001
330-672-2692
Fax: 330-672-2658
http://www.techtrans.kent.edu/econd
ev/econdev.htm

Braintree
201 East Fifth Street
Mansfield, OH 44902
419-525-1614
Fax: 419-525-3492
vdrane@braintreepartners.org
http://www.braintreepartners.org/

National Environmental Technology
(NET) Incubator
Central State University
P.O. Box 1004
Wilberforce, OH 45384
Jerry Mahone
Executive Director
937-376-6234
http://www.centralstate.edu/netincub
ator/about.html

Ohio Agricultural Research And
Development Center
209 Research Services
1680 Madison Ave.
Wooster OH 44691-4096
330-263-3701
Fax: 330-263-3688
oardc@osu.edu
http://www.oardc.ohio-state.edu/

The Innovation Center
340 West State Street, Unit 11
Athens, OH 45701-3751
740-593-1818
Fax: 740-593-0186
http://www.innovationcenter.ohiou.e
du/

Shorebank Enterprise Group
540 East 105th Street
Cleveland, OH 44108
216-268-6100
Fax: 216-268-6107
http://www.shorebankcleveland.com/

The Entrepreneurs Center
714 Monument Avenue
Dayton, OH 45402
937-281-0098
Fax: 937-281-0099
info@techincubator.org
http://www.techincubator.org/

Youngstown Business Incubator
241 Federal Plaza West
Youngstown, OH 44503
330-746-5003
Fax: 330-746-6863
jcossler@ybi.org
http://www.ybi.org

CAMP
4600 Prospect Avenue
Cleveland, OH 44103
800-NOW-CAMP
216-432-4198
www.camp.org

Dayton Miami Valley Entrepreneur
Center
714 Monument Avenue
Dayton, OH 45402
937-281-0098
Fax: 937-281-0099
www.techincubator.org

Oklahoma

Acorn Growth Companies
2701 Liberty Parkway, Ste. 335
Midwest City, OK 73110
405-737-2676
Fax: 405-741-6032
jeff@acorngrowthcompanies.com
http://www.acorngrowthcompanies.c
om/

Fred Jones Business Development
Center
900 West Main
Oklahoma City, OK 73106
405-272-9261
http://www.fjbdc.com/

Meridian Technology Center
1312 South Sangre Road
Stillwater, OK 74074-1899
405-377-3333
info@meridian-technology.com
http://www.meridian-
technology.com/

Emerging Technology
Entrepreneurial Center
eTec,
710 Asp Avenue, Suite 100
Norman, OK 73069
405-573-1900
Fax: 405-573-1999
etec@nedcok.com
www.etecok.com

Northwestern Oklahoma State
University
Dr. Patti Wilber, Director Shockley
Hall

114 709 Oklahoma Blvd.
Alva, OK 73717
580-327-8114
Fax: 580-327-8508
plwilber@nwosu.edu
http://www.nwosu.edu/cbd/binc.html

Oklahoma Technology
Commercialization Center
840 Research Parkway, Suite 250
Oklahoma City, OK 73104
405-235-2305
800-337-OTCC
Fax: 405-235-2252
info@otcc.org
http://www.otcc.org/

Pioneer Technology Center
2101 N. Ash
Ponca City, OK 74601
580-762-8336
webmaster@pioneertech.org
http://www.pioneertech.org/

Pontotoc Technology Center
601 West 33rd St.
Ada, OK 74820
580-310-2200
info@pontotoc.com
http://www.pontotoc.com/

Rural Enterprises of Oklahoma, Inc.
P.O. Box 1335
Durant, OK 74702
800-658-2823
http://www.ruralenterprises.com/incu
bators.htm

Atoka Kiamichi Technology Center
Business Incubator
P.O. Box 240
Atoka, Oklahoma 74525
580-924-5094
www.ruralenterprises.com

Bennington Industrial Center
Highway 70 East
Bennington, OK 74723
580-924-5094
www.ruralenterprises.com

Central Oklahoma Business & Job
Development Corp.
201 North Settle Drive
Drumright, OK 74030
918-352-4517
Fax: 918-352-9545
www.cushingchamber.org/business.h
tm

Dacoma Business Advantage Center
P. O. Box 69
Dacoma, OK 73731
580-871-2204
www.dacoma.ok.us

Greenwood Business Resource
Center
121 North Greenwood Ave.
Tulsa, OK 74120

918-585-2226
www.greenwoodchamber.org

Healdton Business Incubator
624 W. Carter
Healdton, OK 73438
580-924-5094
www.ruralenterprises.com

Hugo Kiamichi Technology Center
Business Incubator
107 South 15th
P.O. Box 699
Hugo, OK 74743
580-924-5094
www.ruralenterprises.com

Major County Economic
Development Incubator
2004 Commerce Street
Fairview, OK 73737
580-227-2512
Fax: 580-227-2513
www.okmajordev.org/mcedc_busine
ss_incubator.htm

McAlester Kiamichi Technology
Center
301 Kiamichi Drive
McAlester, OK 74501
580-924-5094
www.ruralenterprises.com

Northeast Business Resource Center
1500 N. E. 4th Street
Oklahoma City, OK 73117
405-235-0415

Rogers County Business Incubator
P.O. Box 606
Claremore, OK 74018
918-434-8959
http://rcida.com

Stigler Kiamichi Technology Center
Business Incubator
Route 2, Box 1005
Stigler, OK 74462
580-924-5094
www.ruralenterprises.com

Tillman Producers Coop Business
Incubator
218 South 7th
Frederick, OK 73542
580-924-5094
www.ruralenterprises.com

Tri-County Business Assistance
Center
6105 Nowata Road
Bartlesville, OK 74006
918-331-3301
www.tctc.org

The Tulsa Enterprise Center
Atlas Life Building
415 South Boston, Suite 800
Tulsa, OK 74103
918-582-5592

Fax: 918-582-3392
www.otcc.org/incubator

Weatherford Public Works Authority
404 Loomis Road
P.O. Box 569
Weatherford, OK 73096
580-774-4505
Fax: 580-772-7468
www.weatherford-ok.org

Wes Watkins Technology Center
Business Incubator
7892 Hwy 9
Wetumka, OK 74883
405-452-5500
www.wwtech.org/INCUBATOR.htm

Oregon

Business Enterprise Center of Linn
& Benton Counties, Inc.
800 NW Starker Avenue
Corvallis OR 97330-4508
541-758-4009
Fax: 541-758-7319
thebec@thebec.com
http://www.thebec.com/

Incubator Creative Group, Inc.
Villa Ingenieux
Building One
Suite M
P.O. Box 245
Cheshire, OR 97419
541-998-7909
http://www.incubatoronline.com/

Oregon Association Of Minority
Entrepreneurs
4134 N. Vancouver
Portland, OR 97217
503-249-7744
Fax: 503-249-2027
http://www.oame.org/

Oregon Innovation Center
The OiC
P.O. Box 8759
Bend, OR 97708
541-312-5785
Fax: 541-312-5787
info@innovationcenter.org
http://www.oregoninnovation.org/

Business Enterprise Center
2455 Maple Leaf
North Bend, OR 97459
541-756-6778
www.portofcoosbay.com/BEC.HTM

Columbia Learning Center
375 South 18th Street
P.O. Box 1094
St. Helens, OR 97051
503-397-1139
Fax: 503-397-1183
http://clc.colcenter.org

PDX Fashion Incubator
4103 SE Main

Portland, OR 97214
503-241-4004
www.pdxfashionincubator.org

Union County Incubator
1119 Washington Avenue
P.O. Box 1208
La Grande, OR 97850
541-963-0926
Fax: 541-963-0689
www.ucedc.org/incubator.htm

Pennsylvania

Ben Franklin Technology Partners
125 Goodman Drive
Bethlehem, PA 18015-3715
610-758-5200
Fax 610-861-5918
info@nep.benfranklin.org
http://www.nep.benfranklin.org/

Bridgeworks Technology Partners
905 Harrison Street
Allentown, PA 18103
610-770-1015
http://www.thebridgeworks.com/

Carbondale Technology Transfer
Center
10 Enterprise Dr.
Carbondale, PA 18407
570-282-1255
http://www.4cttc.org/

VP of Economic Development
Incubator Program
CBICC Chamber of Business and
Industry of Centre County
200 Innovation Blvd., Suite 201
State College, PA 16803
814-234-1829
Fax: 814-234-5869
http://www.cbicc.org/start.php

The Redevelopment Authority of the
City of Corry
Corry Area Industrial Development
Corporation
1524 Enterprise Road
Corry, PA 16407
814-664-3884
Fax: 814-664-3885
Rnovo@erie.net
http://www.corryidc.org/

Business Accelerator
Center for Research and Economic
Development
East Stroudsburg University
200 Prospect Street
East Stroudsburg, PA 18301-2999
570-422-7920
Fax: 570-422-7951
mpostupack@po-box.esu.edu.
http://www3.esu.edu/CFRED/busacc
elerator.asp

Small Business Incubator
Management Services Group

Eberly College of Business and
Information Technology
10 Robertshaw Center
650 South 13th St.
IUP
Indiana, PA 15705
724-357-2179
Fax: 724-357-4514
www.eberly.iup.edu/incubator

Johnstown Area Regional Industries
JARI
111 Market Street
Johnstown, PA 15901
814-535-8675
Fax: 814-535-8677
www.jari.com

Tri-County Business Start-up
Incubator
453 Lincoln Street
Carlisle PA, 17013
717-249-2356
Fax: 717-249-5444
www.muratabusinesscenter.com/

Greater Erie Industrial Development
Corporation
5240 Knowledge Parkway
Erie, PA 16510-4658
814-899-6022
Fax: 814-899-0250
info@team.org
http://connectforsuccess.org/pages/in
cubators.html

Pottsville-Schuylkill Technology
Incubator
1 South Second St.
Pottsville, PA 17901
570-628-3385
Fax: 570-628-3887
info@incubator-tech.com
http://www.incubator-tech.com/

The Business Center at New
Covenant Campus
7500 Germantown Ave.
Elders Hall, Suite 113
Philadelphia, PA 19119
215-247-2473
Fax: 215-247-2477
http://www.thebizctr.com/index.htm

The Enterprise Center
4548 Market St.
Philadelphia, PA 19139
215-895-4000
Fax: 215-895-4001
info@theenterprisecenter.com
http://www.theenterprisecenter.com/

The Science Center
3701 Market Street, 2nd Floor
Philadelphia, PA 19104
215-966-6000
info@sciencecenter.org
http://www.sciencecenter.org/

Warren County Development
Association
4 Harmar Street
Warren, PA 16365
814-723-3052
http://www.wcda.com/

Business Centers of America
1822 Spring Garden Street
Philadelphia, PA 19130
215-564-6700
Fax: 215-564-6706
www.bca.net

Dublin Technology Enterprise
Center
123 N. Main Street
Dublin, PA 18917
215-249-9401

e-Incubator Laboratory
The Smeal College of Business
Administration
The Pennsylvania State University
401 Business Administration Bldg.
University, PA 16802
814-863-7575
Fax: 814-865-1991
www.smeal.psu.edu/ebrc/lab/index.h
tml

Enterprise Development Center of
Erie County, Inc.
Uniflow Center
2103 East 33rd Street
Erie, PA 16510
814-899-6022
Fax: 814-899-0250
www.team.org/enterie.html

Hatboro Technology Center
2935 Byberry Road
Hatboro, PA 19040
215-672-6510

The Jefferson Center
700 Butler Avenue
Doylestown, PA 18901
215-489-4944

LaunchCyte,LLC
100 Technology Drive, Suite 440
Pittsburgh, PA 15219
412-770-1630
Fax: 412-770-1638
www.launchcyte.com

Model Works Industrial Commons
Incubator
227 Hathaway Street East
Girard, PA 16417
814-774-9339
Fax: 814-774-9235
www.team.org/girard.html

Philadelphia Business Center and
Technology Center
5070 Parkside Avenue
Philadelphia, PA 19131
215-879-8500

Pittsburgh Digital Greenhouse
425 Sixth Avenue, Suite 1850
Pittsburgh, PA 15219
412-201-3423
Fax: 412-201-3444
www.digitalgreenhouse.com

Scranton Enterprise Center Incubator
222 Mulberry Street
Scranton, PA 18503
570-342-7711
Fax: 570-347-6262
www.scrantonenterprisecenter.com/business_incubator.html

Temple Small Business
Development Center
1510 Cecil B Moore Avenue, Suite 300
Philadelphia, PA 19122
215-204-2375
Fax: 215-204-7282

Universal Companies Business
Support Center
1502 Catherine Street
Philadelphia, PA 19146
215-985-9420
www.universalcompanies.org

University of Scranton SBDC
Incubator
University of Scranton
Harper-McGinnis Wing, St. Thomas
Hall
Scranton, PA 18510-4639
570-941-7588
www.sbdc.scranton.edu

University Technology Park
1450 Edgemont Avenue, Suite 210
Chester, PA 19013
610-499-7527
Fax: 610-499-7525
www.universitytechpark.com

Rhode Island
The Center For Design & Business
169 Weybosset Street
Second Floor
Providence, RI 02903
401-454-6108
Fax: 401-454-6559
info@centerdesignbusiness.org
www.centerdesignbusiness.org/

Urban Ventures
150 Colfax Street
Providence, RI 02905
401-780-8833
Fax: 401-780-8844
Contact: Justin Aina
http://www.riedc.com/urban/incubator.htm

South Carolina Biotechnology
Incubation Program (SCBIP)
1 Gregor Mendel Circle, Zone D
Greenwood, SC 29646
864-953-3981

http://www.greenwoodalliance.com/research_development/incubation_program.htm

USC Columbia Technology
Incubator
USC Research Foundation
1334 Sumpter St.
Columbia, SC 29201
803-400-2031
Fax: 803-400-2033
jstevenson@sc.edu
http://incubator.research.sc.edu/

Marine Technology and Aquaculture
Center (MTAC)
Coastal Resources Management
Council
Stedman Government Center, Suite 3
4808 Tower Hill Road
Wakefield, RI 02879-1900
401-783-3370
Fax: 401-783-3767
www.crmc.state.ri.us

South Carolina
Clemson University Student
Business Incubator
401 Sirrine Hall
Clemson, SC 29634
864-656-7235
Fax: 864-656-4468
www.clemson.edu/spiro/outreach/incub.htm

Erskine College
Two Washington Street
Due West, SC 29639
864-379-6515
www.erskine.edu/news/inc.01.29.04.html

South Dakota
Ron Reed Economic Development
Center
2803 6th Street
Brookings, SD 57006
605-697-8103.
Dick Smith, Director
bedc@brookings.net
http://www.incubatorsd.org/

The Enterprise Institute
823 Medary Avenue, Box 525
Brookings, SD 57007-0499
888-747-SDSU (7378)
Marcia_Hendrickson@sdstate.edu
http://sdenterpriseinstitute.org/

Aberdeen Development Technology
Smart Connections Center
416 Production Street
Aberdeen, SD 57401
605-229-5335

Tech Incubator
South Dakota School of Mines and
Technology
501 east Saint Joseph Street
Rapid City, SD 57701

605-394-2400
800-544-8162
Fax: 605-394-6131
www.hpcnet.org/cgi-bin/global/a_bus_card.cgi?SiteID=199937

Tennessee
Chattanooga Area Chamber of
Commerce
Business Assistance Center
811 Broad St.
Chattanooga, TN 37402
423-756-2121
Fax: 423-267-7242
http://www.chattanoogachamber.com/entrepreneurs/home.asp

ETSU Innovation Laboratory
East Tennessee State University
2109 West Market Street
Johnson City, TN 37604
423-439-8500
Fax: 423-439-8520
http://www.etsu.edu/innovationlab/

Emerge Memphis
516 Tennessee St.
Memphis, TN 38103
901-312-7700
Fax: 901-544-7163
http://www.emergememphis.org/

Fairview Technology Center
The Development Corporation
601 W. Summit Hill Drive, Suite 200-A
Knoxville, TN 37902
865-546-5887
http://www.knoxdevelopment.org/fairview.html

Holston Business Development
Center
2005 Venture Park
Kingsport, TN 37660
423-578-6235
Fax: 423-578-6500
www.holstonbusinesscenter.com/

Management Consulting Services
410 Wilson Ave.
Tullahoma, TN 37388
931-455-0155
Fax: 931-455-4375
http://www.theknowisgroup.com/

Nashville Business Incubation
Center
315 Tenth Avenue North, Ste. A
Nashville, TN 37203-3401
615-963-7121
Fax. 615-963-7139
http://www.coh.tnstate.edu/community%20programs/nbic/nbic.htm

Technology 2020
1020 Commerce Park Dr.
Oak Ridge, TN 37830
865-220-2020

Fax: 865-220-2030
http://www.tech2020.org/

Tristar Enterprises
3 North Dunlap Street
Memphis, TN 38163
901-448-7827
Fax: 901-448-2111
mphillips@utmem.edu
www.tristarenterprises.org

Cleveland/Bradley Business
Incubator
3505 Adkisson Drive, Suite 152
Cleveland, TN 37312
423-478-6476
Fax: 423-478-6475
www.cbbi.net

Four Lakes/Hartsville Small
Business Incubation Center
P.O. Box 464
Hartsville, TN 37074-0464
615-374-4607
Fax: 615-374-4608
Email: fourlake@aol.com

IncLabs
1912 Hillsboro Road, Suite 205
Nashville, TN 37212
615-846-1222
www.inclabs.com

Jubilee Business Incubator
123 North Jockey Street
P.O. Box 657
Sneedville, TN 37869
423-733-4195 ext 1626
Fax: 423-733-1624
http://jubileeproject.holston.org

Regional Business Technology
Incubator
P.O. Box 5103
Cookeville, TN 38505-0001
931-372-6333
Fax: 931-372-6249
www.techincubator.com

Texas

Arlington Technology Incubator
202 East Border St.
Arlington, TX 76019
817-272-1463
Fax: 817-272-1254
http://ati.uta.edu/

Austin Technology Incubator
3925 West Braker Lane
Austin, TX 78759
512-305-0000
Fax: 512-305-0009
http://ati.ic2.org/

Bill J. Priest Institute for Economic
Development
1402 Corinth Street
Dallas, TX 75215
214-860-5900
http://www.billpriestinstitute.org/

Entrepreneurial Development Center
Services Cooperative Association
9600 Long Point Rd., Suite 150
Houston, TX 77055
713-932-7495
Fax: 713-932-7498
http://www.servicesca.org/entrepre
urial_business_center.htm

Houston Technology Center
410 Pierce St.
Houston, TX 77002
713-653-1750
Fax: 713-653-1744
http://www.houstontech.org/apply/in
dex.asp

North Texas Enterprise Center for
Medical Technology (NTEC)
Hall Office Park
2611 Internet Blvd., Suite 109
Frisco, TX 75034
214-618-6832
info@ntec-inc.org
http://www.ntec-inc.org/

Tech Fort Worth
1150 S. Freeway Suite 129
Fort Worth, TX 76104
817-339-8968
Fax: 817-332-6465
info@techfortworth.org
http://www.techfortworth.org/

Teksa Innovations Corp.
12000 Network Blvd., Suite B-200
San Antonio, TX 78249
210-877-0111
Fax: 210-877-0200
http://www.teksa.net/

Tyler Area Business Incubator
1530 South-Southwest 323
Tyler, TX 75701
Director: Tony Tadasa
903-510-2982
Fax: 903-510-2978
ttad@tjc.edu

Amarillo Enterprise Center
WTAMU Enterprise Network
2300 N. Western
Amarillo, TX 79214
806-374-9777
www.wtamuenterprisenetwork.com/
amarillo.htm

Borger Economic Development
Corporation
108 East 6th Street
Borger, TX 79008-1157
806-274-5371
Fax: 806-274-2835
www.borger.com/bedc.htm

Brownwood Economic Development
Corporation
P.O. Box 1389
Brownwood, TX 76804
325-646-5775

www.ci.brownwood.tx.us/bedc/ecod
evel.htm

Dumas Economic Development
Corporation
1015 N. Maddox
Dumas, TX 79029
806-934-3332
Fax: 806-934-0180
www.dumasedc.org/

Odessa College Continuing
Education
201 West University
Odessa, TX 79764
432-335-6580
www.odessa.edu/dept/continuing//in
dex.htm

Small Business Incubator Facility
104 East Industrial Drive
Early, TX 76802
915-649-9300
877-643-SBIF
www.earlytx.com/sbif

Utah

The Miller Business Innovation
Center
Salt Lake Community College
Office 9
750 South 300 West Building #5
SLCC Miller Campus
Sandy, UT 84070
801-957-5284
http://www.slcc.edu/pages/1721.asp

Teresa W. McKnight, Manager
USU Innovation Campus
1770 North Research Parkwayt
Suite 120
North Logan, UT 84341
435-797-9606
435-797-9605
mcknight@cc.usu.edu
www.usu.edu/innovationcampus/

CEDO
777 South State Street
Orem, UT 84058
801-226-1521
Fax: 801-226-2678
info@cedo.org
http://www.cedo.org/

Bear River Kitchen Incubator
399 W 9000 S
Paradise, UT 84328
435-245-6003

Emery-Carbon Business Incubator
Airport Road
Cleveland, UT 84518
435-381-5576
Fax: 435-381-5529
www.emerycounty.com

Technology to Market (T2M)
60 E South Temple, Suite 2000
Salk Lake City, UT

801-595-7817
www.t2m.com

Vermont

Bennington County Industrial
Corporation
P.O. Box 357
109 Water Street
N. Bennington, VT 05257
802-442-8975
Fax: 802-447-1101
www.bcic.org

The Intervale
282 Intervale Road
Burlington, VT 05401
802-660-0440
www.intervale.org

Marlboro College
The Graduate Center
28 Vernon Street, Suite 120
Brattleboro, VT 05301
802-258-9200
888-258-5665
Fax: 802-258-9201
www.gradcenter.marlboro.edu/about
/facility.html

Springfield Regional Development
Corporation
PVDC Complex
100 River Street
Springfield, VT 05156
802-885-3061
Fax: 802-885-3027
www.springfielddevelopment.org

Virginia

Advantech
501 E. Franklin St.
Richmond, VA 23219
804-521-4001
www.advantechva.org/home_html

ANGLE Technology LLC
Fairfax County BioAccelerator
7001 Loisdale Road, 2nd Floor
Springfield, VA 22150
703-822-2922
Fax: 703-822-2934
Washington@ANGLETechnology.c
om
http://www.angletechnology.com/

Business Development Centre
147 Mill Ridge Road
Lynchburg, VA 24502
434-582-6100
http://www.lbdc.com/

Incubator Program
Attn.: Tracey White
Greater Reston Chamber of
Commerce
1763 Fountain Dr.
Reston, VA 20191
Twhite@restonchamber.org
www.restonchamber.org/incubator.ht
ml

Hampton Roads Technology
Incubator
Marty Kaszubowski, Director
420 North Center Drive
Bldg. 11, Suite 221
Norfolk, VA 23502
757-233-0875
Fax: 757-233-0876
martinka@hrtc.org
http://www.hr-incubator.org/

Mason Enterprise Center
Keith Segerson, Associate Director
4031 University Drive, Suite 200
Fairfax, VA 22030
703-277-7700
Fax: 703-277-7730
www.masonenterprisecenter.org

Milestone Equity Partners
8619 Westwood Center Drive
Suite 150
Vienna, VA 22182
703-762-1840
Fax: 703-762-1865
mfedeli@milestone-ep.com
http://www.milestone-ep.com/

New River Valley Competitiveness
Center
6580 Valley Center Drive
Radford, VA 24141
540-633-6730
Fax: 540-633-6768
http://www.nrvdc.org/nrvcc.html

NewBizVA
50 Lodge Lane, Suite 114
Verona, VA 24482
540-248-0600
Fax: 540-248-4614
info@newbizva.org
http://www.newbizva.org/

Pioneer Center for Business
Opportunity
Duffield Facility:
P. O. Box 408
Duffield, VA 24244
276-431-7226
info@pcbo.org
http://www.pcbo.org/

Pioneer Center for Business
Opportunity
Norton Facility:
798 Park Avenue NW, Suite 200
Norton, VA 24273
276-679-6500
info@pcbo.org
http://www.pcbo.org/

Richmond International Business
Center
Wytestone Plaza
801 E. Main Street, 14th Floor
Richmond, VA 23219
804-521-4343
http://www.incubator-
usa.com/about.htm

Spinner Technologies
1224 West Main St.
Charlottesville, VA 22903
434-924-2693
Fax: 434-982-1583
http://www.spinnertech.com/

The New Century Venture Center
1354 Eighth Street
Roanoke, VA 24015
540-344-6402
Fax: 540-345-0262
lison@ncvc.com
www.ncvc.com

Virginia BioTechnology Research
Park
800 E. Leigh St.
Richmond, VA 23219
804-828-5390
Fax: 804-828-8566
vbrp@vabiotech.com
www.vabiotech.com

West Piedmont Business
Development Center
22 East Church Street
Martinsville, VA 24112
276-638-2523
Fax: 276-638-2669
wpadm@ci.martinsville.va.us
http://www.wpbdc.org/

Dave Bartles
WIRE Winchester Incubation
Regional Enterprise
2281 Valley Avenue, Suite 220
Winchester, VA 22601
540-450-2200
daveb@winwithwire.com
http://www.winwithwire.com/

City of Franklin Business Incubator
(Opens 2005)
Center for Business Development
600 Mechanic Street
Franklin, VA 23851
757-562-8506
Fax: 757-562-7982
www.franklinva.com/eco_dev/index.
htm

Giles County Incubator
211 Main Street, Suite 101
Narrows, VA 24124
540-726-8201
www.gilescounty.org/incubator.html

Hampton University Business
Incubator
6 W. County Street
Hampton, VΛ 23663
757-722-9283
Fax: 757-722-0785
www.hamptonu.edu/HUBAC/bus_in
c/

Highland Center, Kitchen Incubator
P.O. Box 556
Monterey, VA 24465

540-468-1922
Fax: 540-468-2551
www.highlandcounty.org/Dir-pages/bd-incuk.htm

The Jacksonville Center
P.O. Box 932
Floyd, VA 24091
540-745-2784
www.civic.bev.net/jacksonvillecenter

Jefferson Davis Enterprise Center
8310 Shell Road
Richmond, VA 23237
804-275-5190
Fax: 804-275-5192
www.jdec.net

Orange Business Incubator
2555 Madison Road
Orange, VA 22960
540-672-0666
Fax: 540-672-2036
www.orangebusinessincubator.com

Richlands Business Incubator
Business Development
1928 Front Street
P.O. Box 550
Richlands, VA 24641
276-963-2660
276-963-2670
www.richbizinc.org

Virginia's Center for Innovation
Technology
2214 Rock Hill Road, Suite 600
Herndon, VA 20170-4200
703-689-3000
Fax: 703-689-3041
www.cit.org

Washington

Applied Process Engineering
Laboratory
Chuck R Allen,
350 Hills Street, Suite #101
Richland, WA 99352
509-372-5146
Fax: 509-372-5153
crallen@energy-northwest.com
http://www.apel.org/

Phoenix Development Authority
1000 Prospect
P.O. Box 598
Ellensburg, WA 98926-0598
509-962-7244
Fax: 509-962-7141
ebdainc@kvalley.com
http://www.adsnet.net/ebda/

Tri-Cities Enterprise Center
2000 Logston Blvd.
Richland, WA 99352
509-375-3268
Fax: 509-375-4838
http://www.enterprisecenter.net/

Tri-County Economic Development
District
Ferry County
72 North Clark
P.O. Box 1212
Republic, WA 99166
509-775-3047
Fax: 509-775-3048
ferryeds@rcabletv.com
http://www.teddonline.com/incubator.htm

Stevens County
347 West Second, Suite A
Colville, WA 99114
509-684-4571
800-776-7318
Fax: 509-684-4788
Tedd@plix.com
http://www.teddonline.com/incubator.htm

Pend Oreille County
301 West Spruce, suite E
Newport, WA 99156
509-447-5569
800-813-2032
Fax: 509-447-3706
Edc@povn.com
http://www.teddonline.com/incubator.htm

William M. Factory Small Business
Incubator
1423 E. 29th St.
Tacoma, WA 98404
253-722-5800
Fax: 253-722-5801
http://www.williamfactory.com/

Washington State University
Research and Technology Park
1610 NE Eastgate Boulevard
Pullman, WA 99163-1802
509-335-1216
Fax: 509-335-7237
www.wsu.edu/~rtp/

West Virginia

Charleston Enterprise Center
Business and Industrial Development
Corporation
1116 Smith St.
Charleston, WV 25301
304-340-4253
800-79BIDCO
Fax: 304-340-4275
http://www.charleston-wv.com/organization/economic_development.html

Unlimited Future, Inc.
A Business Development Center
1650 Eighth Avenue
Huntington, WV 25703
304-697-3007
http://www.unlimitedfuture.org/

Wisconsin

Adams County Chamber of
Commerce
115 South Main Street
P.O. Box 576
Adams, WI 53910
608-339-6997
chamber@adamscountywi.com
http://www.adamscountywi.com/resources.shtml

Center for Advanced
Technology & Innovation, Inc.
2320 Renaissance Blvd.
Sturtevant, WI 53177
CATI Director
262-635-2433
Fax: 262-638-0250
mwagner@thecati.com
http://www.thecati.com/

City of Two Rivers Wisconsin
P. O. Box 87
1717 East Park Street
Two Rivers, WI 54241
Dan Pawlitzke
920-793-5565
danpaw@two-rivers.org
http://www.two-rivers.org/departments/area.shtml?area_id=1046888934098976&contact_title=Director

Door County Economic
Development Corporation
185 E. Walnut Street
Sturgeon Bay, WI 54235
920-743-3113
800-450-3113
Fax: 920-743-3811
http://www.doorcountybusiness.com/AboutStaff.htm

Genesis Enterprise Center
Richard Slone
Facility Director
313 W. Beltline Highway
Madison, WI 53713
608-327-8000
info@gecmadison.com
http://www.gecmadison.com/

Advance Business Development
Center
Green Bay Area Chamber of
Commerce
400 S. Washington St.
P.O. Box 1660
Green Bay, WI 54305
920-437-8704

T.E.C. Incubator Center
3591 Anderson Street
Madison, WI 53704
Dr. John Lalor
608-243-4477
jlalor@matcmadison.edu
http://teccenterinc.org/default.htm

Menominee Indian Tribe of
Wisconsin
Business Center
N559 Library Road
PO Box 910
Keshena, WI 54135
715-799-5720
Fax: 715-799-5721
cgrignon@mitw.org
http://www.menominee.nsn.us/Busin
essCenter/BusinessCenter.htm

University Research Park
510 Charmany Drive, Suite 250
Madison WI 53719
608-441-8000
Fax: 608-441-8010
urespark@facstaff.wisc.edu
http://www.universityresearchpark.or
g/

Platteville Business Incubator, Inc.
P.O. Box 415
Platteville, WI 53818
Beth Bickel, Manager
608-348-2758
Fax: 608-348-3426
info@pbii.org
http://www.plattevilleincubator.com/

Wisconsin Women's Business
Initiative Corp.
Business Office
2745 N. Dr. Martin Luther King Jr.
Drive
Milwaukee, WI 53212
414-263- 5450
Fax: 414-263- 5456
info@wwbic.com
http://www.wwbic.com/

Superior Business Center Inc.
1423 North 8th Street
Superior, WI 54880
http://www.superbus.com/

Technology Innovation Center
Guy T. Mascari
Director of Development
Milwaukee County Research Park
10437 Innovation Drive, Ste. 123
Wauwatosa, WI 53226-4815
414-778-1400
Fax: 414-778-1178
gtm@mcrpc.org
http://www.mcrpc.org/#TIC

Madison Enterprise Center
100 South Baldwin St.
Madison, WI 53703
608-256-6565
Sarah Hole, Facilities Director
http://www.cwd.org/mec/indcx.html

Urban Tech Catalyst
222 West Washington Avenue
Madison, WI 53703
608-255-5060
www.network222.com/utc.html

Wausau Business Incubator
1300 Cleveland Avenue,
Wausau, WI 54401
715-848-5880
http://www.wausaudevelopment.com
/incubator.htm

Wisconsin Business Innovation
Corp.
1400 South River St.
Spooner, WI 54801
715-635-2197
Fax: 715-635-7262
www.nwrpc.com

Advance Business Assistance Center
835 Potts Avenue
Green Bay, WI 54304
920-496-9010
Fax: 920-496-6009
www.mybusinesshelp.org/incubator

ADVOCAP Business Center
Business Development Department
19 West First Street
P.O. Box 1108
Fond du Lac, WI 54936-1108
920-922-7760
800-361-7760
Fax: 920-922-7214
www.advocap.org

Ashland Area Enterprise Center
422 Third Street W, Suite 101
Ashland, WI 54806
715-682-8344
Fax: 715-682-8415
www.ashlandareadevelopment.org

CAPsell Center
205 East Main Street
Wautoma, WI 54982
920-787-7461

Chippewa Valley Innovation Center
Eau Claire Area Economic
Development Corporation
3132 Louis Avenue
Eau Claire, WI 54701
715-836-2842
800-836-3945
www.eauclaire-wi.com

Center for Advanced
2320 Renaissance Boulevard
Sturtevant, WI 53177
262-898-7500
Fax: 262-898-7590
www.thecati.com

Community Enterprise of Greater
Milwaukee
3118 North Teutonia Avenue
Milwaukee, WI 53206
414-265-2346
Fax: 414-265-0270

Coulee Region Business Center Inc.
1100 Kane Street
La Crosse, WI 54603

608-782-8022
Fax: 608-784-5505
www.la-
crosse.wi.us/hosting/crbc/CRBC.asp

Faraday Center
2800 S. Fish Hatchery Road
Fitchburg, WI 53711
608-277-2606
Fax: 608-273-6989

Indian Enterprises, Inc.
1426 Indianhead Drive
Menomonie, WI 54751
715-232-6460
Fax: 715-232-6763
www.indianheadenterprises.com

Innovation Center of Hartford
Hartford Area Development
Corporation
935 West State Street
Hartford, WI 53027
262-673-7009
Fax: 262-673-4651
www.hadc.org

Jackson County Incubator
Black River Falls Industrial Park
720 Red Iron Road
Black River Falls, WI 54615
715-284-2020
www.co.jackson.wi.us

Laboratory Associated Businesses
1202 Ann Street
Madison, WI 53713
608-251-3005

Main Street Industries
931 E Main Street
Madison, WI 53703
608-286-MAIN
Fax: 608-286-6248
www.cwd.org/business/msi/msi.aspx

Madison Enterprise Center
Common Wealth Development
100 South Baldwin Street
Madison, WI 53703
608-256-6565
www.cwd.org/business/mec/mec.aspx

Meadowbrook Multi-Tenant
Industrial Center
P.O. Box 431
Ladysmith, WI 54848-0286
715-532-2600
Fax: 715-532-5411
Email: vinbea@mscfs.edu

Micro-Enterprise Center
Cap Services Inc.
5499 Highway 10 East
Stevens Point, WI 54481
715-343-7500
www.capserv.org
Virtual Business Incubator-Incubator
Without Walls
http://virtualincubate.com

Milwaukee County Research Park
10437 Innovation Drive, Suite 123
Wauwatosa, WI 53226-4815
414-778-1400
Fax: 414-778-1178
www.mcrpc.org

Milwaukee Enterprise Center-North
2821 North 4th Street
Milwaukee, WI 53212
414-372-3609
Fax: 414-227-4152

Milwaukee Enterprise Center- South
816 West National Avenue
Milwaukee, WI 53204
414-645-0880
Fax: 414-645-0504

Platteville Business Incubator, Inc.
P.O. Box 415
Platteville, WI 53818
608-348-2758
Fax: 608-348-3426
www.pbii.org

Rapids Business Center
1509 Rapids Drive
Racine, WI 53404
262-632-7711

Watertown Business Incubator
519 East Main Street
Watertown, WI 53094-3873
920-261-6320

Banks Friendly To Small Businesses

Access to credit is vital for small business survival. A key supplier of credit to small companies is the commercial banking system. It is crucial to know how banks are meeting your credit needs and which banks are investing in small businesses.

When you are applying for a loan, you want someone on the other side of the desk who is helpful and understanding. You need someone who has done this before and knows what will make your application a successful one. Certified and Preferred Lenders are banks who have been given this designation because they have a thorough understanding of the Small Business Administration's policies and procedures. These lenders perform a complete analysis of the application, and in turn the SBA strives to make the final loan decision in three working days. A Preferred Lender has been delegated the authority for loan approval, closing, and most servicing and liquidation authority and responsibility. The Small Business Administration does not directly lend money to businesses. What they do is provide loan guarantees to the lender. If you default on your loan, the SBA will guarantee that the lender will not be out the money they are due. Certified and Preferred Lenders know small businesses. These are the banks that people turn to in times of need to help your business grow and expand. Small business lending and borrowing is mostly local in nature: both the borrowers and the lending offices are located in the same community or communities nearby. The Office of Advocacy prepares a directory of lenders who support small business and can be found at the Advocacy website {www.sba.gov/advo/stats/lending}.

We have listed the Certified and Preferred Lenders by state, but remember that all branches of each bank can make loans with a SBA loan guarantee. For more information, you can also check out the Small Business Administration's website at {www.sba.gov}; or you can call the Answer Desk at 800-8-ASK-SBA.

SBA Certified and Preferred Lenders

Alabama
Bancorp South Bank
P. O. Box 789
Tupelo, MS 38801
662 680-2345
Fax: 601 680-2317
http://www.bancorpsouthonline.com/index.html

Bank of the West
3350 Riverwood
Suite 1900
Atlanta, GA
404 237-3140
Fax: 404 237-3141
http://www.bankofthewest.com/

Business Loan Center, Inc.
Mid America Division
121 West Dewey Street
Suite 210
Wichita, KS 67202
316 263-3232
Fax: 316 263-4391

CIT Small Business Lending Corp.
PNB 117731 Montgomery Hwy.
Birmingham, AL 35216
205 824-2810
Fax: 205 824-2811
http://www.smallbizlending.com/res
ources/articles/loaninterview.asp

Columbus Bank & Trust
c/o Synovus SBA Lending
P. O. Box 168
Monroe, GA 30655
770 267-4131
Fax: 770 267-4564
http://www.columbusbankandtrust.c
om/

Comerica Bank
302 Moonlight Drive
Panama City, FL 32407
Ray Lambert
850 236-9226
Fax: 850 236-7633
http://www.comerica.com/cma/cda/st
ateLogin

Compass Bank
P. O. Box 10566
Birmingham, AL 35296
205 297-3346
Fax: 205 297-7672
http://www.compassbank.com/

G.E. Capital Small Business Finance
Corp.
2090 Columbiana Road Suite 200
Birmingham, AL 35216
205 443-0377
Fax: 205 443-0303
http://www.ge.com/capital/smallbiz/

Regions Bank
1457 Mt. Vernon Road
Dunwoody, GA 30338
770 395-9331 x 229
Fax: 770 395-1117
http://www.regions.com/servlet/Regi
onsHome/index.jsp

SouthTrust Bank of Alabama, N.A.
360 Interstate Pkwy. N Suite 500
Atlanta, GA 30339
770 678-3770
Fax: 770 678-3779

Union Planters Bank
9700 Northwest 112th Avenue
Miami, FL 33178
786 777-6772
Fax: 786 845-4488
http://www.unionplanters.com/

Wachovia SBA Lending, Inc.
d/b/a Wachovia Small Business
Capital
1 Perimeter Park South
Suite 100 North
Birmingham, AL 35243
205 982-7900
Fax: 205 982-7904

Washington Mutual Bank, FA
1900 Cooper Landing Drive
Smyrna, GA 30080
770 384-0803
Fax: 770 384-0689
http://www.wamu.com/servlet/wamu
/index.html

Wells Fargo Bank Minnesota N.A.
1455 West Lake Street Suite 306
Minneapolis, MN 55408
612 667-2753
Fax: 612 316-2322

Whitney National Bank
228 St. Charles Avenue
New Orleans, LA 70130
504 586-7107
Fax: 504 599-2144
http://www.whitneybank.com/index.
asp

Alaska

First National Bank of Alaska
PO Box 100720
Anchorage, Alaska 99510-0720
907-777-4362
http://www.fnbalaska.com/

Key Bank of Alaska
Northrim Bank
http://www.northrim.com/

Wells Fargo
http://www.wellsfargo.com/

Denali State Bank
http://www.denalistatebank.com/

First Bank
http://www.firstbankak.com/

CIT Small Business Lending
Corporation
http://www.smallbizlending.com/def
ault.asp

Arizona

AMRESCO Indep. Funding
11811 North Tatum Blvd.,#2530
Phoenix, AZ 85028
602 787-6410

Arizona Business Bank
2700 North Central Ave., #210
Phoenix, AZ 85004
602 240-2704
http://www.azbizbank.com/

Bank of America
201 East Washington St.
Phoenix, AZ 85004
602 523-2651
http://www.bankofamerica.com/

Bank of the West
1702 East Highland Ave.#318
Phoenix, AZ 85016

602 235-9400
http://www.bankofthewest.com/

Bank One Arizona
1515 West 14th St., Bldg. C
Tempe, AZ 85281
888 536-3722

Borrego Springs Bank
One East Camelback #550
Phoenix, AZ 85012
602 636-0977
http://www.borregospringsbank.com/

Business Loan Express
3131 East Camelback Rd. #200
Phoenix, AZ 85016
602 383-3777
http://www.alliedcapitalexpress.com/

California Bank & Trust
3101 North Central #500
Phoenix, AZ 85012
602 212-8826
http://www.calbanktrust.com/

California Center Bank
4110 North Scottsdale Road, #345
Scottsdale, AZ 85251
480 421-0868

CIT Small Business Lending
1540 West Fountainhead
Tempe, AZ 85282
480 784-2300
http://www.smallbizlending.com/def
ault.asp

Community First Nat. Bank
2020 N. Central Avenue
Phoenix, AZ 85004
602 258-5555

Compass Bank
2850 East Camelback Road, #140
Phoenix, AZ 85016
602 522-7533
http://www.compassbank.com/

First National Bank of Arizona
7150 East Camelback Road, #285
Scottsdale, AZ 85251
480 675-5291
http://www.fnbaonline.com/

First Union Small Bus. Capital
3333 East Camelback Road, #112
Phoenix, AZ 85018
602 852-0003

GE Capital Small Bus. Lending
426 South 44th Street, #495
Phoenix, AZ 85008
602 683-3261

M & I Marshall & Ilsley Bank
One East Camelback Road
Phoenix, AZ 85061-1186
602 241-6517
http://www.mibank.com/

National Bank of Arizona
1400 E. Southern Avenue
Tempe, AZ 85282
480 345-8800
http://www.nbarizona.com/

Sonoma National Bank
2398 East Camelback Rd., #615
Phoenix, AZ 85016
602 957-1170
http://www.sonomanationalbank.com/

Stearns Bank
9225 East Shea Blvd.
Scottsdale, AZ 85260
480 314-4200
http://www.stearnsbankaz.com/

Sunrise Bank of Arizona
4350 East Camelback Rd., #100A
Phoenix, AZ 85018
602 522-5706
http://www.sunrisebankofarizona.com/

Union Bank of Arizona
3631 East Baseline Road
Gilbert, AZ 85234
480 926-2265

US Bank
2800 North Central Ave. #1755
Phoenix, AZ 85004
602 241-9806

Valley Bank of Arizona
3550 North Central Avenue #150
Phoenix, AZ 85012
602 274-7500

Wells Fargo Bank
4350 East Camelback Rd. #E-100
Phoenix, AZ 85018
602 977-7414
http://www.wellsfargo.com/

Western Security Bank
16277 Greenway-Hayden Loop
Scottsdale, AZ 85260
480 367-9494

Washington Mutual Bank
2375 E. Camelback Rd., Suite #690
Phoenix, AZ 85016
602 474-3537
http://www.wamu.com/

Arkansas

Amresco Independence Funding, Inc.
214 953-8400

Arkansas Capital Group
800 216-7237

Bank Of America
All Locations
http://www.bankofamerica.com/

Bank Of The West
530 582-3803
http://www.bankofthewest.com/

Bank United
713 543-7063

Business Loan Center, Inc.
800 690-9089

Cit Small Business Lending Corp.
973 355-7524
http://www.smallbizlending.com/resources/articles/loaninterview.asp

Commercial Capital Corporation
212 719-0002
http://www.commercialcapital.ca/

Compass Bank
972 735-3577
http://www.compassbank.com/

Elk Horn Bank And Trust
870 246-5811
http://portal.fxfn.com/3ehbtaa/

First Union Small Business Capital
800 722-3066

First Western Sblc, Inc.
972 349-3209

G E Capital Small Business Fin. Corp.
901 762-4324

Heller First Capital Corp
800 347-6430

Regions Bank
All Locations
http://www.regions.com

Zions First National Bank
801 887-4277
www.zionsbank.com

Arkansas National Bank
706 S. Walton Blvd.
P. O. Box 699
Bentonville, AR 72712
501 271-2800

City National Bank
1222 Rogers Avenue
P. O. Box 47
Fort Smith, AR 72901
501 785-2811
http://www.citynationalbank.com/

Farmers Bank & Trust
200 E. Main St.
P. O. Box 250
Magnolia, AR 71753
870 235-7000
http://www.fbtmagnolia.com/index.html

First Financial Bank
315 W. Main Street

P. O. Box 1754
El Dorado, AR 71730
870 863-7000
http://www.first-financialbank.com/

5106 S. Thompson
Springdale, AR 72764
501 872-1100

First State Bank
915 Salem Road
Conway, AR 72032
501 328-4605
http://www.fsbhome.com/

Firstar Bank
One Riverfront Place
P. O. Box 15008
No. Little Rock, AR 72114
501 688-1000

Mcilroy Bank & Trust
75 N. East Ave.
P. O. Box 1327
Fayetteville, AR 72710
501 575-1000
http://www.qualisteam.com/pages/detailed/3115.html

Metropolitan National Bank
111 Center St.
P. O. Box 8010
Little Rock, AR 72201
501 377-7600
http://www.metbankny.com/

Simmons First National Bank
501 Main Street
P. O. Box 7009
Pine Bluff, AR 71601
870 541-1000
http://www.simmonsfirst.com/

California

Bank of America
2130 Otis
Alameda, CA 94501
510-769-9338

Bank of America CDB
c/o 1456
300 S. Harbor Blvd.
Anaheim, CA 92815
800-263-2055

GE Capital Small Business Finance
Corporation
2400 E. Katella Avenue
Suite 800
Anaheim, CA 92816
714-456-9400

Arcata Economic Development
Corporation
100 Ericson Court
Suite 100
Arcata, CA 95521
707-822-4616
http://www.northcoastprosperity.com
service_providers/prosp_net/aedc/aedc.html

International Bank of California
17100 Pioneer Boulevard
Artesia, CA 90701
562-860-8118
Fax: 562-467-0250
http://www.ibcalifornia.com/

Auburn National Bank
412 Auburn Folsom Road
Auburn, CA 95603
530-887-8182

San Joaquin Bank
4600 California Avenue
Bakersfield, CA 93389
661-281-0325
Fax: 661-281-0333
http://www.sjbank.com/

Bank of America
Community Development Program
10850 White Rock Road
Suite 101
Rancho Cordova, CA 95670
800-263-2055
http://www.bankofamerica.com

U.S. Bank
800-698-8980

Imperial Bank
455 Capital Mall, Suite 300
Sacramento, CA 95814
916-491-1370
http://www.imperialbank.com

California Federal
2290 B Street
Suite 205
Santa Rosa, CA 95401
http://www.citibank.com/domain.cal
fed_converts.htm

Money Store Investment Corporation
800-722-3066
http://www.themoneystore.com

Bank of Walnut Creek
1400 Civic Drive
Walnut Creek, CA 94596-4187
925-932-5353
Fax: 925-932-4861
http://www.bowc.com

Bridge Bank
2120 El Camino Real
Santa Clara, CA 95050
408-556-8334
408-423-8500
Fax: 408-423-8520
http://www.bridgebanksv.com

Business Bank of California
58 South Linden Avenue
South San Fransisco, CA 94080
650-266-6844
http://www.businessbank.com

Business Lenders
15 Lewis Street

Hartford, CT 06103
877-345-6267
http://www.businesslenders.com

Business Loan Center
136 Bufflehead Drive
Mooresville, NC 28117
704-664-3611
Fax: 704-664-3270
http://www.thebusinessloancenter.co
m

California Bank and Trust
2399 Gateway Oaks Drive
Suite 110
Sacramento, CA 95833
916-561-1121
http://ww.californiabankandtrust.co
m

CalFed California Federal Bank
320 North Harbor Boulevard
Suite A
Fullerton, CA 92832
800-500-9810
http://www.calfed.com

Capital One, FSB
877-847-2287
http://www.capitalone.com

Central California Bank
3700 Lone Tree Way
Antioch, CA 94509
925-778-6700
http://www.centralcaliforniabank.co
m

Central Valley Community Bank
600 Pollasky
Clovis, CA 93612
559-323-3384
http://www.clovisbank.com

CIT Small Business Lending
Corporation
980 Ninth Street
16th Floor
Sacramento, CA 95814
530-753-4529
http://www.smallbizlending.com

Citibank
U.S. Service Center
Citi Inquiries
100 Citibank Drive
P.O. Box 769004
San Antonio, TX 78245-9004
Http://www.citibank.com

Comerica Bank of California
333 West Santa Clara Street
San Jose, CA 95113
831-460-1700
http://www.comerica.com

Community National Bank
800-722-2552
http://www.comnb.com

County Bank of San Francisco
550 West Main Street
Merced, CA 95340
209-725-4522
http://www.countybank.com

Cupertino National Bank
408-782-8654
http://www.gbbk.com

Enterprise Capital, Inc.
1485 South County Trail
East Greenwich, RI 02818
401-886-4600
Fax: 401-884-9551
http://www.enterprisecapitalinc.com

Far East National Bank
500 Montgomery Street
San Francisco, CA 94111
415-677-8567
http://www.fareastnationalbank.com

First International Bank (UPS)
35 Glenlake Parkway, NE
Atlanta, GA 30328
213-621-9103
http://www.firstinterbank.com

First Union Small Bus (Wachovia)
P.O. Box 162247
Sacramento, CA 95816
800-998-6888
Fax: 916-787-9568
http://eee.firstunion.com

GE Capital Corporation
6130 Stone Ridge Mall Rd.
Suite 300
Pleasanton, CA 94588
925-730-6466
http://www.gecapital.com

General Bank
4128 Temple City Blvd.
Rosemead, CA 91770
626-582-7221
http://www.generalbank.com

Greater Bay Bank
60 South Market Street, Suite 150
San Jose, CA 95113
408-975-6918
http://www.gbbk.com

Hanmi Bank
3600 Wilshire Blvd.
Penthouse, Suite A
Los Angeles
213-382-2200
Fax: 213-384-8608
http://www.hanmi.com

Heritage Bank of Commerce
Heritage Commerce Corporation
150 Almaden Boulevard
San Jose, CA 95113
408-947-6900
http://www.heritagecommercecorp.c
om

Innovative Bank
360 14th Street
Oakland, CA 94612
510-763-8492
http://www.innovativebank.com

NCB, Federal Savings Bank
National Cooperative Bank NCB,
FSB
SBA Specialists
6 Central Row, 4th Floor
Hartford, CT 06103
860-297-0208
800-252-4030
Fax: 800-361-3265
http://www.ncb.com

Nara National Bank, N.A.
1102 E. El Camino Real
Sunnyvale, CA 94087
408-557-2000
Fax: 408-557-2020
http://www.narabank.com

Pacific Crest Bank
310-413-4431
http://www.paccrest.com
Premier Bank
1630 Stout St.
Denver, CO 80202
303-623-8888
http://www.premierbankusa.com

San Jose National Bank
1 North Market Street
San Jose, CA 95113
408-947-7562
http://www.sjnb.com

Small Business Loan Source, Inc.
9801 Westheimer Road
11th Floor
Houston, TX 77042
800-457-4307 ext. 120
http://www.sbls.com

Sonoma National Bank
815 Fifth Street
Santa Rosa, CA 95404
707-579-0610
http://www.snbank.com

U.S. Bank, N.A.
730 High Street
Auburn, CA 95603
800-303-4722
530-889-6350
http://www.usbank.com

United Commercial Bank
711 Van Ness Avenue
San Fransisco, CA 94102
415-928-0700
http://www.unitedcb.com

Valley Community Bank
1986 Second Street
Livermore, CA 94550
925-243-9600
Fax: 925-243-8853

http://www.valley-community-bank.com

Wells Fargo Bank
800-495-8256
http://www.wellsfargo.com

Century Bank
9145 Wilshire Boulevard
Beverly Hills, CA 90210
310-777-1908
Fax: 310-273-2068

Borrego Springs
547 Palm Canyon Drive
P.O. Box 866
Borrego Springs, CA 92004
760-767-5035
Fax: 760-767-4214
http://www.borregospringsbank.com

Los Angeles National Bank
7025 Orangethorpe Avenue
Buena Park, CA 90621
714-670-2412
http://www.lanatlbank.com/

Western Security Bank
4100 West Alameda Avenue
Burbank, CA 91505
818-557-5626
Fax: 818-567-3246
http://www.wsbank.com/

Capital Bank of North County
2602 El Camino Real
Carlsbad, CA 92008
760-434-4517
http://www.capitalbanknet.com/

Coast Commercial Bank
P.O. Box 2207
Carmel-by-the-Sea, CA 93921-2207
831-458-4560
831-620-0140
http://www.gbbk.com

Community Bank of Central
California
301 Main Street
Salinas, CA 93901
831-422-6642
Fax: 831-422-9143
http://www.community-bnk.com

First National Bank of Central
California
800-698-4722
http://www.1stnational.com

Pacific Commerce Bank
First Counties Bank
15145 Lakeshore Drive
Clearlake, CA 95422
707-995-5236

First Bank of California
2395 Willow Pass Road
Concord, CA 94520
925-246-1066

Borrego Springs Bank
1101 California Street
Suite 100
Corona, CA 91719
909-280-5284
http://www.borregospringsbank.com

Bank of Coronado
106 B. Avenue
Coronado, CA 92119
619-437-8683
Fax: 619-437-8861

California Bank and Trust
3420 Bristol Street
Costa Mesa, CA 92626
714-754-2400
Fax: 714-557-0276
http://www.calbanktrust.com

Goleta National Bank
3151 Airway Drive
Suite B-1
Costa Mesa, CA 92626
http://www.goleta.com

Heller First Capital Corporation
600 Anton Boulevard
Suite 950
Costa Mesa, CA 92626
714-444-9000
800-347-6430
Fax: 714-444-9020

Community Bank
1041 West Badillo Street
Suite 200
Covina, CA 91722
626-732-1325
Fax: 626-732-1301

First Security Bank of California
203 East Badillo Street
Covina, CA 91723
626-915-4424
Fax: 626-851-9969

Cupertino National Bank
20230 Stevens Creek Boulevard
Cupertino, CA 95014
408-996-1144
http://www.cupnb.com/

First National Bank of Northern
California
6600 Mission Street
Daly City, CA 94014
650-992-8800
415-985-2460
http://www.fnbnorcal.com

Mt. Diablo National Bank
156 Diablo Road
Danville, CA 94526
925-743-9200
http://www.diablobank.com

Banco Popular, NA (CA)
11101 La Reina Avenue
Downey, CA 90241

562-662-4710
562-662-4587
Fax: 562-622-6766
http://www.bancopopular.com/

Western State Bank
1801 East Huntington Drive
Duarte, CA 91009
626-357-9611
Fax: 626-357-8750
Fax: 626-358-9613
http://www.westernstatebank.com/

Bay Bank of America
1495 East 14th Street
San Leandro, CA 94577
510-357-2265
http://www.gbbk.com

Valley Independent Bank
1498 Main Street
El Centro, CA 92243
760-337-3243
http://www.vibank.com/

Pacific Business Bank
3920 North Peck Road
El Monte, CA 9132
626-579-5450
Fax: 626-579-1098

First Coastal Bank
275 Main Street
El Segundo, CA 90245
310-322-2222
Fax: 310-322-2411
http://www.firstcoastalbank.com/

Imperial Bank
2000 Powell Street
Suite 2000
Emeryville, CA 94608
510-450-1860

North County Bank
2025 Vineyard Avenue
Escondido, A 92029
760-741-8333
Fax: 760-743-1741

San Diego National Bank
360 W. Grand Avenue
Escondido, CA 92025
760-480-6709
http://www.sdnb.com/

Humbolt Bank
612 G. Street
Eureka, CA 95501
707-269-3120
http://www.humboltbank.com

Six Rivers National Bank
402 F Street
Eureka, CA 95501
707-268-1012
http://www.sixrivers.com/

Bank of the Sierra
1103 W. Visalia Road

Exeter, CA 93221
559-592-4134
Fax: 559-592-2489
http://www.bankofthesierra.com/

Fallbrook National Bank
130 West Fallbrook Street
Fallbrook, CA 92028
760-731-5630
Fax: 760-723-5699
http://www.fallbrooknationalbank.com/

Savings Bank of Mendocino
P.O. Box 1269
Fort Bragg, CA 85437
707-964-4723
http://www.savingsbank.com/

The Bank of Orange County
10101 Slater Avenue
Fountain Valley, CA 92728
714-964-6607
http://www.bankoforangecounty.com/

Fremont Bank
39150 Fremont Boulevard
Fremont, CA 94538
510-791-5748
http://www.fremontbank.com/

General Bank
47000 Warm Springs Boulevard
Fremont, CA 94539
510-440-8855
http://www.generalbank.com/

U.S. Bank of California
39510 Paseo Padre Parkway
Fremont, CA 94538
510-713-8888
http://www.usbank.com/

Bank of Commerce
P.O. Box 26969
San Diego, CA 92196-0969
619-536-4545
Fax: 619-536-2390

California Federal Bank
2540 W. Shaw Lane
Suite 112
Fresno CA 93711
559-447-7423
Fax: 559-447-7435
http://www.citibank.com/

California Bank and Trust
P.O. Box 16279
Fresno, CA 93755
559-438-2650
Fax: 559-438-2687
http://www.calbanktrust.com/

Goleta National Bank
5070 N. Sixth Street
Suite 182
Fresno, CA 93710
559-229-2995

Fax: 559-248-1922
http://www.goleta.com

Heller First Capital
516 W. Shaw Avenue
Suite 200
Fresno, CA 93704-2515
559-221-2615
Fax: 559-221-2677

California Federal Bank
320 North Harbor Boulevard
Fullerton, CA 92832
800-500-9810
Fax: 714-525-9967
http://www.citibank.com

South Valley National Bank
8000 Santa Teresa Boulevard
P.O. Box 1508
Gilroy, CA 95020
408-848-2161
Fax: 408-848-1280
http://www.svnb.com

Goleta National Bank
5827 Hollister Avenue
Goleta, CA 93117
805-683-4944
Fax: 805-683-2082
http://www.goleta.com

Valley Merchants Bank
800 E. Florida Avenue
Hemet, CA 92543
909-766-6666

San Benito Bank (C)
300 Tres Pinos Road
831-637-2265
Fax: 831-637-8091
Http://www.sbbank.com

Eldorado Bank
1 Pacific Plaza
7777 Center Avenue
Huntington Beach, CA 92647
714-891-5730
714-895-2929
Fax: 714-894-5257
http://www.eldoradobank.com

Newcourt Small Business Financial
7755 Center Drive
Suite 1100
Huntington Beach, CA 92647
714-842-2380

Southern California Bank
9042 Garfield Avenue
Suite 203
Huntington Beach, CA 92646
714-963-0775
Fax: 714-963-0646
http://www.scbank.com

Imperial Bank
9920 S. La Cienega Boulevard
Suite 3510
Inglewood, CA 90301

310-417-5600 general
Fax: 310-417-5899
http://www.imperialbank.com

Citibank FSB
8001 Irvine Center Drive
Suite 860
Irvine, CA 92619
949-752-4435
http://www.citibank.com

First Union Small Business Capital
1 Park Plaza, Suite 450
Irvine, CA 92614
949-251-9010
Fax: 949-251-9016

Wells Fargo Bank
2030 Main Street, Suite 900
949-251-4990
http://www.wellsfargo.com

Foothill Independent Bank
5155 Irwindale Avenue, Suite 202
Irwindale, CA 91706
626-814-0231
Fax: 626-814-1222
http://www.foothillindbank.com

Borrego Springs Bank
7777 Alvarado Road
Suite 114
La Mesa, CA 91941
619-668-8147
Fax: 619-668-8150
http://www.borregospringsbank.com

California Bank and Trust
5500 Grossmont Center Drive
Second Floor
La Mesa, CA 91942-3085
619-667-2838
Fax: 619-465-6534
http://www.calbanktrust.com

Antelope Valley Bank
831 West Lancaster Boulevard
Lancaster, CA 93534
661-723-8262
Fax: 661-948-7786
http://www.avbank.com

Bank of Lodi
701 South Ham Lane
Lodi, CA 95242
209-367-2000
209-367-2070
Fax: 209-367-2060
http://www.banklodi.com

Bank of Los Altos
4546 El Camino Real
Los Altos, CA 94022
650-917-5333
http://www.bankoflosaltos.com

Comerica Bank
301 East Ocean Boulevard
18th Floor
Long Beach, CA 90802

562-590-2529
Fax: 562-590-9942
http://www.comerica.com

International City Bank
249 East Ocean Boulevard
Long Beach, CA 90802
652-436-9800
Fax: 562-432-0888
http://www.banklodi.com

California Center bank
4301 West Third Street
Los Angeles, CA 90020
213-637-9622
Fax: 213-427-6080
http://www.calcenterbank.com

California Korea Bank
928 South Western Avenue
Second Floor
Los Angeles, CA 90006
213-386-5168
Fax: 213-380-0679

Cathay Bank
777 North Broadway
Los Angeles, CA 90012
213-625-4709
Fax: 213-625-3915
http://www.cathaybank.com

City National Bank
606 South Olive Street
Suite 2110
213-347-2434
Fax: 213-347-2395
http://www.cnb.com

Far East National Bank
977 North Broadway
Los Angeles, CA 90012
213-687-1381 or 213-687-1300
Fax: 213-626-2431 or 213-680-1535
http://www.fareastnationalbank.com

Founders National Bank
3910 W. Martin Luther King Jr.
Boulevard
Los Angeles, CA 90008
323-290-2487
Fax: 232-290-2637

Hamni Bank
3660 Wilshire Boulevard
Suite 103
Los Angeles, CA 90010
213-427-5761
Fax: 213-382-5345

Nara Bank
2701 Wilshire Boulevard
Suite 302
Los Angeles, CA 90010
213-427-6340
Fax: 213-380-2240
http://www.narabank.com

National Bank of California
145 South FairFax: Avenue

Los Angeles, CA 90036
323-655-6001
Fax: 323-932-1662
http://www.calnationalbank.com

Saehan Bank
3701 Wilshire Boulevard
Suite 130
Los Angeles, CA 90010
213-389-5550
Fax: 213-365-0025
http://www.saehanbank.com

Small Business Loan Source
3435 Wilshire Boulevard
Suite 2270
Los Angeles, CA 90010
213-384-1500
Fax: 213-637-1155

Wells Fargo Bank
10866 Wilshire Boulevard
Suite 1100
Los Angeles, CA 90024
213-253-3566
Fax: 213-628-1867
http://www.wellsfargobank.com

Wilshire State Bank
3200 Wilshire Boulevard
Seventh Floor
Los Angeles, CA 90010
213-427-6595
Fax: 213-427-2474
http://www.wilshirebank.com

World Trade Finance, Inc.
875 N. Virgil Avenue
Los Angeles, CA 90010
323-660-1277
Fax: 213-660-1470
http://www.wtfinc.com

County Bank
550 W. Main Street
Merced, CA 95340
209-725-4520
Fax: 209-725-2220
http://www.countybank.com

Bank of Yorba Linda
27285 Las Ramblas
Suite 180
Mission Viejo, CA 92691
949-348-7434
Fax: 949-367-2939

U.S. Bank of California
2008 McHenry Avenue
Modesto, CA 95354
209-491-5032
Fax: 209-521-3040

Spectrum Bank
2417 West Whittier Boulevard
Montebello, CA 90640
323-726-1410
Fax: 323-726-6125
http://www.spectrumbank.com

Monterey County Bank
601 Munras Avenue
Monterey, CA 93920
831-649-4600
Fax: 831-642-6074
http://www.montereycountybank.com

Napa National Bank
901 Main Street
Napa, CA 94559
707-257-5503

Vintage Bank
1500 Soscol Avenue
Napa, CA 94559
707-258-3964
http://www.thevintagebank.com

Bank of Oakland
360 14th Street
Oakland, CA 94612
510-763-8492

Bank of the West
1300 Clay Street
Suite 600
Oakland, CA 94612
510-464-8050
877-735-1591
http://www.bankofthewest.com

Cathay Bank
710 Webster Street
Oakland, CA 94607
510-208-3608
510-208-3700
Fax: 510-208-3727
http://www.cathaybank.com

Community Bank of the Bay
1750 Broadway
Oakland, CA 94612
510-271-8400
510-433-5400
Fax: 510-433-5431
http://www.communitybankbay.com

Mechanics Bank
One Kaiser Plaza
Suite 750
Oakland, CA 94612
510-419-3916
http://www.mechbank.com

Metropolitan Bank
416 Eighth Street
Oakland, CA 94607
415-986-6999

Transamerica Small Business Capital
1300 Clay Street
Suite 600
Oakland, CA 94612
510-464-8038
http://www.transamerica.com

Citizens Business Bank
701 N. Haven Avenue
Third Floor

Ontario, CA 91764
909-980-4030
http://www.cbbank.com

Bank of Commerce
765 The City Drive
Suite 255
Orange, CA 92668
714-748-7307

Bank U.S.
765 The City Drive
Suite 255
Orange, CA 92668
714-748-7307

North County Bank
171 S. Anita Drive
Suite 104
Orange, CA 92668
714-712-6150
http://www.northcountybank.com

El Dorado Bank
12A Orinda Way
Orinda, CA 94563
925-253-9776

American Commercial Bank
300 Esplanade Drive
Suite 110
Oxnard, CA 93030
805-278-8331
Fax: 805-278-1271

United Commercial Bank
199 S. Los Robles Avenue
Suite 780
Pasadena, CA 91101
626-685-7221
Fax: 626-564-0749
http://www.ibankunited.com

Bank of Petaluma
100 Petaluma Boulevard, South
Petaluma, CA 94952
707-765-2222
http://www.bankofpetaluma.com

Borrego Springs Bank
3748 Buskirk Avenue
Suite 1017
Pleasant Hill, CA 94523
925-746-7172
http://www.borregospringsbank.com

First Union Small Business Capital
5820 Stoneridge Mall Road
100
Pleasanton, CA 94588
925-847-4040

Valley Community Bank
465 Main Street
Pleasanton, CA 94566
925-484-5400
http://www.vcbank.com

First National Bank of Central
California

171547 Vierra Canyon Road
Prunedale, CA 93912
800-698-4722
http://www.1stnational.com

Bank of America Community
Development Bank
10850 White Rock Road
Suite 101
Rancho Cordova, CA 95670
800-489-6563
916-851-6563
Fax: 916-861-9144
http://www.bankofamerica.com/community

Valley Independent Bank
39700 Bob Hope Drive
Suite 100
Rancho Mirage, CA 92270
760-776-4100
http://www.vibank.com

Redlands Centennial Bank
218 E. State Street
Redlands, CA 92373
909-798-3611

Bay Area Bank
900 Veterans Boulevard
Redwood City, CA 94063
415-367-1600
650-216-2438
http://www.bayareabank.com

City National Bank
3484 Central Avenue
Riverside, CA 92506
213-347-2434
800-722-5945
Fax: 213-347-2395
http://www.cnb.com

First Continental Bank
8632 East Valley Boulevard
Suite R
Rosemead, CA 91770
626-307-3293
Fax: 626-307-3296

General Bank
4128 Temple City Boulevard
Rosemead, CA 91770
626-582-7331
Fax: 626-582-7251
http://www.generalbank.com

Bank of Oakland
3017 Douglas Boulevard
Suite 300
Roseville, CA 95661
916-838-4494

First Northern Bank of Dixon
4600 Northgate Building
Suite 115
Sacramento, CA 95834
916-567-6270
http://www.thatsmybank.com

First Union Small Business Capital
(formerly Money Store)
707 3rd Street
2nd Floor
W. Sacramento, CA 95605
800-222-6910
Fax: 916-617-1096

Sacramento Commercial Bank
525 J Street
Sacramento, CA 95814
916-325-4847
916-554-4801
Fax: 916-443-7345
http://www.scbusa.com

Bank of Oakland
3017 Douglas Boulevard
Suite 300
Roseville, CA 95661
916-838-4494

Community Bank of Central
California
301 Main Street
P.O. Box 450
Salinas, CA 93902
831-757-2274
Fax: 831-422-2692
http://www.community-bnk.com

Pacific Century Bank
2740 N. Grand Avenue
Santa Ana, CA 92705
714-771-5050

Redlands Centennial Bank
200 W. Santa Ana Boulevard
Suite 1060
Santa Ana, CA 92701
714-285-9890

Business Bank of California
140 South Arrowhead
San Bernardino, CA 92402
909-888-2265
Fax: 909-884-3172
http://www.businessbank.com

1st Pacific Bank
7728 Regents Road
Suite 503
San Diego, CA 92122
858-677-7866
http://www.1stpacbank.com

Bank of Commerce
9918 Hibert Street
Suite 301
San Diego, CA 92131-1018
619-536-4545
http://www.usbank.com

Bank U.S.
9918 Hibert Street
Suite 301
San Diego, CA 92131-1018
619-5396-4545
http://www.usbank.com

Bank of Coronado
106 B Avenue
Coronado, CA 92118
619-437-8683
http://www.bankofcoronado.com

Bank of Yorba Linda
345 S. Coast Highway 101
Encinitas, CA 92024
760-753-7300

Borrego Springs Bank
7777 Alvarado Road
Suite 501
La Mesa, CA 91941
800-722-5720
619-668-5159 ext. 275
Fax: 619-667-3261
http://www.borregospringsbank.com

Capital Bank of North County
2602 El Camino Real
Carlsbad, CA 92008
760-434-3344
http://www.capitalbanknet.com

Cal Fed
Citibank (West) FSB
P.O. Box 348480
Sacramento, CA 95734-8480
http://www.calfed.com

California Bank and Trust
11622 El Camino Real
Suite 200
San Diego, CA 92130
619-6677-2838
http://www.calbanktrust.com

City National Bank
750 B Street
Suite 1250
San Diego, CA 92101
213-347-2434
800-722-5945
619-238-7460
Fax: 213-347-2395
http://www.cnb.com

Comerica Bank
600 B Street
Suite 100
San Diego, CA 92101
619-230-7325
619-687-5300
http://www.comerica.com

Fallbrook National Bank
900 Canterbury Place
Escondido, CA 92025
760-723-5078
http://www.fallbrooknationalbank.com

First International Bank
318 4th Avenue
Chula Vista, CA 91910
619-476-3255
619-425-5000

First National Bank
401 W A Street
Suite 200
San Diego, CA 92101
619-338-1448

First National Bank of North County
760-736-6059
Goleta National Bank
5369 La Jolla Boulevard
San Rafael, CA 94903
858-488-8849
http://www.goleta.com

Imperial Bank
600 B Street
San Diego, CA 92101
619-687-5300
760-730-7902
http://www.imperialbank.com

International City Bank
4493 Ruffin Road
San Diego, CA 92123
562-436-9800
858-292-9100
http://www.internationalcitybank.com

The Money Store
619-550-1700
North County Bank
760-741-8333

Pacific Crest Bank
1550 N. Hotel Circle
Suite 320
San Diego, CA 92108
619-515-0119

Peninsula Bank of San Diego
619-682-5315

Rancho Bernardo Bank
16495 Bernardo Center Drive
San Diego, CA 92128
858-613-7986
http://www.rbcommbank.com

Rancho Santa Fe National Bank
4365 Executive Drive
Suite 125
San Diego, CA 92121
619-658-0981
Fax: 619-658-0361

San Diego National Bank
1420 Kettner Boulevard
San Diego, CA 92101
619-231-4989
760-480-6709
http://www.sdnb.com

Scripps Bank
619-515-2200
Southwest Community Bank
600 B Street
Suite 2202
San Diego, CA 92101
619-544-0279

760-634-6400
Fax: 619-231-4465
http://www.swcbank.com

Temecula Valley Bank
301 N. Magnolia Drive
Suite 101
El Cajon, CA 92020-3907
619-590-2265
619-749-5570
http://www.temeculavalleybank.com

Union Bank
530 B Street
San Diego, CA 92101
619-230-4423
619-230-3876
http://www.uboc.com

Valle de Oro Bank
8690 Center Drive
La Mesa, CA 91942
619-667-8618
http://www.home.san.rr.com/btgd/vd
ob3.html

CIT Business Lending
4370 La Jolla Village Drive
Suite 400
San Diego, CA 92122
619-261-4613
http://www.wellsfargo.com

Bank of Canton of California
555 Montgomery Street
San Francisco, CA 94111
415-362-4100
http://www.bankcanton.com

Bank of Commerce
185 Berry Street
Suite 4809
San Francisco, CA 94107
415-357-1722

California Bank and Trust
320 California Street
San Francisco, CA 94104
415-445-8078
http://www.calbanktrust.com

Capital Access Group
300 Beale Street
Suite 101
San Francisco, CA 94105
415-284-1460
http://www.capitalaccess.com

Citibank F.S.B. California
1 Sansome Street
Suite 200
San Francisco, CA 94104
415-658-4230
http://www.citibank.com

City National Bank (San Francisco)
150 California Street
13th Floor
San Francisco, CA 94111
415-576-3929

800-722-5945
Fax: 415-576-2794
http://www.cnb.com/

Commercial Bank of San Francisco
333 Pine Street
San Francisco, CA 94104
415-627-0303

Far East National Bank
660 Montgomery Street
San Francisco, CA 94111
415-677-8557
http://www.fareastnationalbank.com

GE Capital Services
210 Mission Street, 27th Floor
San Francisco, CA 94105
415-284-7476
http://www.gecapital.com

Heller First Capital
71 Stevenson Street
20th Floor
San Francisco, CA 94105
415-356-1354
Fax: 415-356-1301

Millenium Bank
180 Sansome Street
San Francisco, CA 94104
415-434-2265

Mission National Bank
3060 16th Street
San Francisco, CA 94103
415-826-3627
http://www.mnbsf.com

Newcourt Small Business Lending
210 Post Street, Suite 908
San Francisco, CA 94108
415-773-2110

TMC Development Corporation
611 Front Street
San Francisco, CA 94111
415-989-8855
Fax: 415-989-3382
http://www.tmcd.com

First Bank of San Luis Obispo
P.O. Box 1249
San Luis Obispo, CA 93406
805-541-6100
Fax: 805-544-2217
http://www.fbslo.com

California Federal Bank
2 West 5th Avenue
San Mateo, CA 94402
650-579-6226
http://www.citibank.com

Pacific Bay Bank
510-215-3359

Goleta National Bank
1050 Northgate Drive
Suite 190

San Rafael, CA 94901
415-444-5150
http://www.goleta.com

Pacific Century Bank
2740 North Grand Avenue
Santa Ana, CA 92705
714-891-1831
Fax: 714-744-1857

Montecito Bank and Trust
1010 State Street
Santa Barbara, CA 93101
805-564-0246
Fax: 805-965-7471
http://www.montecito.com

Bank of Santa Clara
1995 El Camino Real
Santa Clara, CA 95050
408-987-9429
http://www.gbbk.com

Wilshire State Bank
1333 Lawrence Expressway
Suite 205
Santa Clara, CA 95051
408-557-2800
http://www.wilshirestatebank.com

Coast Commercial Bank
720 Front Street
Santa Cruz, CA 95060
831-458-4500
831-458-4560
Fax: 831-423-0604
http://www.gbbk.com

Comerica Bank
55 River Street
Dept. 215
Santa Cruz, CA 95060
408-460-1700
http://www.comerica.com

Santa Cruz Community Credit Union
512 Front Street
Santa Cruz, CA 95060
831-425-7708
http://www.scruzccu.org

Exchange Bank
P.O. Box 403
Santa Rosa, CA 95402
707-524-3168
http://www.exchangebank.com

National Bank of Redwoods
111 Santa Rosa Avenue
Santa Rosa, CA 95404
707-573-4836
http://www.nbronline.com

North Coast Bank
50 Santa Rosa Avenue
Suite 100
Santa Rosa, CA 95404
707-528-6300
http://www.unclewebster.com/lc/bus/
340

Safe-Bidco
1626 Forth Street
Santa Rosa, CA 95404
707-577-8621
http://www.safe-bidco.com

Sonoma National Bank
P.O. Box 14489
Santa Rosa, CA 95402
707-579-2265
707-524-6170
Fax: 707-579-5621
http://www.snbank.com

Community Bank of Central
California
P.O. Box 806
Seaside, CA 93955
831-757-2274 extension 217
http://www.community-bnk.com

First Western Bank
1475 East Los Angeles Avenue
Simi Valley, CA 93065
805-581-2800
Fax: 805-522-4528

First American Bank
625 South Fair Oaks Avenue
Suite 175
South Pasadena, CA 91031
626-287-6100
Fax: 626-285-0225
http://www.firstamerbank.com

Metro Commerce Bank
58 South Linden Avenue
So San Francisco, CA 94080
650-266-6832

First National Bank of Northern
California
975 El Camino Real, 2nd Floor
So San Francisco, CA 94080
650-875-4823
http://www.fnbnorcal.com

Asiana Bank
1082 East El Camino Real
Sunnyvale, CA 94087
408-260-8900
http://www.narabank.com

Temecula Valley Bank
97710 Jefferson Avenue
Suite A-100
Temecula, CA 92593-0690
800-939-3736
Fax: 909-506-1283
http://www.temvalbank.com

Montecito Bank and Trust
P.O. Box 2460
Santa Barbara, CA 93120
805-644-3082
Fax: 644-9782
http://www.montecito.com

Tracy Federal Bank
1003 Centeral Avenue

Tracy, CA 95378
209-839-2150

Bank of the West
10181 Truckee Tahoe Airport Road
Truckee, CA 96160
530-582-3000
http://www.bankofthewest.com

Sunwest Bank
535 E First Street
Tustin, CA 92780
714-730-4427
http://www.sunwestbank.com

Sun Country Bank
123 Ninth Street
Suite 102
Upland, CA 91786
909-982-3813
http://www.suncountrybank.com

Continental Pacific Bank
707-448-1200
Bank of Ventura
5808 East Telephone Road
Ventura, CA 93003
805-650-4405
Fax: 805-650-3056

Montecito Bank and Trust
SBA Lending Department
4476 Market Street
Suite 604
Ventura, CA 93003
805-644-3082
Fax: 805-644-9782
http://www.montecito.com

Desert Community Bank
12530 Hesperia Road
Suite 219
Victorville, CA 92392
760-243-2140
Fax: 760-243-3228
http://www.dcbk.org

Associates Commercial Corp.
500 Ygnacio Valley Road
Suite 290
Walnut Creek, CA 94596
800-831-7963
925-934-1100
Fax: 825-934-1588

Bank of America Community
Development Bank
2033 N. Main Street
Suite 550
Walnut Creek, CA 94563
925-988-4805
http://www.bankofamerica.com

Bank of Walnut Creek
1400 Civic Drive
P.O. Box 8080
Walnut Creek, CA 94596
925-932-5353
http://www.bowc.com

Scott Valley Bank
1333 N. California Boulevard
Walnut Creek, CA 94596
825-934-1601
http://www.scottvalleybank.com

Zion's Small Business Finance
1990 N. California Boulevard
Suite 830
Walnut Creek, CA 94596
925-256-4547

CIT Group
(formerly Newcourt Financial)
1526 Cole Boulevard
Building 3
Suite 200
Golden, CA 80401
800-525-3343 extension 752
Fax: 303-202-3787
http://www.citcredit.com

Commercial Capital Corporation
406 Farmington Avenue
Suite 1018
Farmington, CT 06032
860-676-7811
http://www.comcap.com

Bank of America Community
Development Bank
800 Market Street
St. Louis, MO 63101-2607
314-466-5170
Fax: 314-466-7517
http://www.bankofamerica.com

G.E. Capital Small Business Finance
635 Maryville Centre Drive
Suite 120
St. Louis, MO 63141
314-205-3547
Fax: 314-205-3699
http://www.ge.com/capital/smallbiz

Newcourt Small Business Lending
2 Gatehall Drive
Parsipany, NJ 07054
973-606-3500
Fax: 973-355-7554
http://www.citcredit.com

Zions First National Bank
13545 Barrett Parkway Drive
Suite 335
St. Louis, MO
314-822-0070
Fax: 314-822-0251

First Western SBLC, Inc.
17290 Preston Road
Third Floor
Dallas, TX 75252
972-349-3200
Fax: 972-380-1371

Associates Commercial Corporation
300 East Carpenter Freeway
Suite 1250
Irving, TX 75062

972-652-5304
Fax: 972-652-3340

American Investment Financial
535 East South Temple
Salt Lake City, UT 84102
800-521-1078
http://www.aifusa.com

Zions Bank
2200 S 3270 W
Salt Lake City, UT 84101
801-887-4260
Fax: 801-524-8849
http://www.zionsbank.com

Colorado
Alpine Bank
2000 Grand Avenue
Glenwood Springs, CO 81601
970 945-2424
Fax: 970 945-2296
http://www.bankalpine.com/

AMRESCO Independence Funding
3900 East Mexico Ave., Suite 790
Denver, CO 80210
303 623-1772
Fax: 303 338-2276

Bank One, Colorado, N.A.
1125 17TH St.
Denver, CO 80202
303 241-3271
Fax: 303 296-8176

Bank of Colorado
1199 Main Ave., Drawer N
Durango, CO 81320
970 247-5151
Fax: 970 247-3795
http://www.bankofcolorado.com/

Bank Of Grand Junction
2415 F Rd.
Grand Junction, CO 81501
970 241-9000
Fax: 970 241-4148
http://www.bogj.com/

The Bank of Boulder
3033 Iris Ave.
Boulder, CO 80301
303 443-9090
Fax: 303 443-0181

The Bank Of Durango
125 Sawyer
Durango, CO 81302
970 259-5500
Fax: 970 259-5503
http://www.bankofdurango.com/

The Bank of Cherry Creek
3033 E. First Ave.
Denver, CO 80206
303 394-5100
Fax: 303 329-9629

Borrego Springs Bank
6860 S. Yosemite
Englewood, CO 80112
303 843-0536
Fax: 303 843-0572
http://www.borregospringsbank.com/

Business Loan Express
200 S. Wilcox St., #506
Castle Rock, CO 80104
303 832-1666
Fax: 303 832-2816

CIT Small Business Lending
1576 Cole, Bldg. 3, Suite 200
Golden, CO 80401
303 202-3756
Fax: 303 202-3789

Citizens State Bank of Cortez
77 West Main ST., Drawer T
Cortez, CO 81321
970 565-8421
Fax: 970 565-8791

Citywide Bank, Aurora
10660 E. ColFax: Ave., Box 128
Aurora, CO 80040
303 365-3600
Fax: 303 365-3601

Commerce Bank Of Aurora
15305 E. ColFax: Ave.
Aurora CO 80011
303 344-5202
Fax: 303 364-7636

Commercial Savings Bank
dba Small Business Lending
8480 E. Orchard Rd., Suite 1400
Englewood, CO 80111
303 221-7227
Fax: 303 221-5287
http://www.csbanking.com/csb/about
.html

Colorado Business Bank
101 W. Mineral
Littleton CO 80120
303 292-1555
Fax: 303 730-8430
http://www.cobizbank.com/

First National Bank of Arvada
7530 Grandview Ave.
Arvada CO 80001
303 422-1441
Fax: 303 422-1896
http://www.fnboa.com/

First National Bank Of The Rockies
504 Main Street
Meeker CO 81641
970 878-5073
Fax: 970 878-3484

First State Bank Of Hotchkiss
101 East Bridge Street
Hotchkiss, CO 81419
970 872-3111

Fax: 970 872-4050
http://www.fsb-hotchkiss.com/

First Union Small Business Capital
384 Inverness Dr., South, Suite 204
Englewood, CO 80112
303 792-0363
Fax: 303 792-9245

GE Capital Small Business Finance
8480 E. Orchard Rd., Suite 5000
Englewood, CO 80111
303 488-9000
Fax: 303 694-1848
http://www.ge.com/capital/smallbiz/

Grand Valley National Bank
925 North 7th Street
Grand Junction, CO 81502
970 241-4400
Fax: 970 241-3039
http://www.grandvalleybank.com/

Guaranty Bank/Trust Company
1331 Seventeenth St.
Denver, CO 80217
303 296-9600
Fax: 303 296-0228

The Gunnison Bank & Trust
232 W. Tomishi Ave.
Gunnsion CO 81230
970 641-0320
Fax: 970 641-0054
http://www.visitgunnison.com/busin
esspage.cfm?businessid=471

Key Bank NA
99 S. Broadway
Denver, CO 80209
303 329-5382
Fax: 303 329-5381
http://www.keybank.com/

Matrix Capital Bank
700 17th Street, Suite 100
Denver, CO 80202
720 956-6500
Fax: 720 956-6593
http://www.matrixbank.com/index.as
p

Park National Bank
533 Big Thompson Avenue
Estes Park, CO 80517
303 586-8185
Fax: 303 586-8006
http://www.parknatl.com/

Premier Bank
1630 Stout St.
Denver CO 80202
303 623-8888
Fax: 303 623-8505
SBA EXPRESS LENDER
https://fxfn.com/zpbtfl/

Rocky Mountain Bank & Trust
101 E. Main St.
Florence, CO 81226

719 784-6316
Fax: 719 784-4805
http://www.rmbt.com/

Sierra West
A Division of Bank of the West
1999 Broadway, Suite 1900
Denver, CO 80202
303 672-1877
Fax: 303 672-1876

U.S. Bank
6300 South Syracuse Way, Suite 552
Englewood, CO 80111
303 221-8991 Extension 16
Fax: 303 221-8993
SBA EXPRESS LENDER

Vectra Bank Colorado, NA
8000 E. Bellview Ave.
Greenwood Village, CO 80222
720 947-7700
Fax: 720 947-7760
SBA EXPRESS LENDER
http://www.vectrabank.com/

Wells Fargo
633 Seventeenth Street
Denver, CO 80270
303 721-6378
Fax: 303 574-1396
SBA EXPRESS LENDER
http://www.wellsfargo.com/

California Center Bank
4301 West 3rd Street
Los Angeles, CA 90020
213 637-9622
Fax: 213 427-6080
SBA EXPRESS LENDER

CNL Commercial Lending Corp.
26137 La Paz Rd., Suite 102
Mission Viejo, CA
949 452-0929
Fax: 949 609-3256

Goleta National Bank
5383 Hollister Avenue
Suite 210
Santa Barbara, CA 93111
415 454-9572
Fax: 415 454-9576
SBA EXPRESS LENDER
http://www.goleta.com/

Bank of the West (California)
10181 Truckee Airport Road
Truckee, CA 96161
530 582-3803
Fax: 530 582-2953
SBA EXPRESS LENDER
http://www.bankofthewest.com/

Banco Popular, N.A.
8500 N. Stemmons FW, #6077
Dallas, TX 75247
214 688-0240
Fax: 214 688-0241

Washington Mutual Bank
3200 Southwest Freeway
Houston, TX 77027
713 545-6265
Fax: 713 543-6292
SBA EXPRESS LENDER
http://www.wamu.com/

Comerica Bank (Michigan)
Houston, TX 77210
713 545-6265
Fax: 713 888-2671

Business Loan Center, Inc.
Mid America Division
121 West Dewey St., Suite 210
Wichita, KS 67202
316 263-3232
Fax: 316 263-4391

Community First National Bank
142 East 200 South
Salt Lake City, UT 84111
801 531-3406
Fax: 801 355-4221

Zions First National Bank
One South Main St., 6 Floor
Salt Lake City, UT 84111
801 524-4870
Fax: 801 524-2136
SBA EXPRESS LENDER
http://www.zionsbank.com/

Connecticut

JP Morgan Chase Bank
999 Broad Street
Bridgeport, CT 06604
203 382-6521
Fax: 203 382-6579
http://www.jpmorganchase.com/

People's Bank
850 Main Street
Bridgeport, CT 06604-4913
203 338-7215
Fax: 203 338-6983
http://www.peoples.com

Webster Bank
609 West Johnson Avenue
Cheshire, CT 06410
203 271-7425
Fax: 203 699-2806
http://www.websteronline.com

GE Capital Small Business
44 Old Ridgebury Road
Danbury, CT 06810
203 796-2341
Fax: 203 725-6846

New Mil Bank
301 Main Street
Danbury, CT 06810
203 731-8961
Fax: 203 791-2443
http://www.newmil.com

Union Savings Bank
226 Main Street
Danbury, CT 06810
203 830-4247
Fax: 203 830-4648
http://www.unionsavings.com

Business Loan Express
1165 Main Street
East Hartford, CT 06033
860 290-9299
Fax: 212 290-8281
http://www.alliedcapitalexpress.com/

BankNorth
2461 Main Street
Glastonbury, CT 06033
860 652-6516
Fax: 860 659-1396
http://www.banknorth.com/

CIT Capital Small Business Lending
1110 Boston Post Road
Guilford, CT 06437
203 453-1670
Fax: 203 453-1690

Business Lenders LLC
15 Lewis Street
Hartford, CT 06103
860 244-9202 X118
Fax: 860 241-6018
http://www.businesslenders.com/

First International Bank
280 Trumbull Street
Hartford, CT 06103
860 541-5231
Fax: 860 525-2083

Fleet National Bank
70 Farmington Avenue
Hartford, CT 06105
860 986-1093
Fax: 860 983-3062
www.fleet.com

National Cooperative Bank
6 Central Row
Hartford, CT 06103
860 297-0208
Fax: 860 547-0054

Sovereign Bank
Business Banking
CT 1-PLO-05-03
100 Pearl Street
Hartford, CT 06103
860 757-3433
Fax: 860 757-3441
http://www.sovereignbank.com/Defa
ult.asp?display=truc&javascript=true

Hudson United Bank
30 East Main Street
Meriden, CT 06450
203 639-7893
Fax: 203 237-9224
http://www.hudsonunitedbank.com/

New Haven Savings Bank
195 Church Street
New Haven, CT 06510
203 784-5080
Fax: 203 789-2820
http://www.newhavensavingsbank.co
m/

Wachovia Bank
47 Church Street
New Haven, CT 06510
800 523-0035
Fax: 800 603-1861
http://www.wachovia.com/

Ridgefield Bank
150 Danbury Road
PO Box 2050
Ridgefield, CT 06877
203 431 7455
Fax: 203 438-0831
http://www.ridgefieldbank.com/

The Simsbury Bank
981 Hopmeadow Street
Simsbury, CT 06070
860 658-2265
Fax: 860 651-5942
http://www.simsburybank.com/

Citibank FSB of Connecticut
750 Washington Blvd.
Stamford, CT 06901
203 975-6025
Fax: 203 975-5042

First County Bank
2950 Summer Street
Stamford, CT 06905
203 462-4202
Fax: 203 462-4447
http://www.firstcountybank.com/

Thomaston Savings Bank
203 Main Street
Thomaston, CT 06787
860 283-6150
Fax: 860 283-6274
http://www.thomastonsavingsbank.c
om/

Savings Institute
803 Main Street
Willimantic, CT 06776
860 456-6511
Fax: 860 423-9001

Citizens Bank
100 Sockanosett Crossroads
Cranston, RI 02920
401 734-5617
Fax: 401 734-5621
http://www.citizensbank.com/

Enterprise Capital Inc
1485 South County Trail
E Greenwich, RI 02818
401 886-4600
Fax: 401 884-9551

Commerce Bank
One Royal Road
Flemington, NJ 08822
908 237-4746
Fax: 908 237-4787

Valley National Bank
1334 US Highway 22 East
North Plainfield, NJ 07060
908 561-0271
Fax: 908 753-9817
http://www.valleynationalbank.com/

Home Loan & Investment Bank
One Home Loan Plaza, Ste 3
Warwick, RI 02886
800 223-1700 x253
Fax: 401 453-3865
http://www.homeloanbank.com/

Delaware

Artisans Bank
P. O. Box 8771
Wilmington, DE 19899
302 884-6888
Fax: 302 656-6681
http://www.artisansbank.com/

Atlantic Bank
4604 Coastal Highway
Ocean City, MD 21842
410 524-7333
Fax: 410 524-1843

Baltimore Trust Company
P. O. Box 823
Georgetown, DE 19947
302 855-0459
Fax: 302 855-0460
http://www.baltimoretrustco.com/

Bancorp.com Bank
405 Silverside Rd, Ste 105
Wilmington, DE 19809
302 861-7961
Fax: 302 861-7898

Bank of Delmarva, N.A.
2727 N. Salisbury Blvd
Salisbury, MD 21801
410 548-1325
Fax: 410 742-9588
http://www.bankofdelmar.com/

Broadway National Bank
250 Fifth Avenue
New York, NY 10001
212 689-5292 Ext 219
Fax: 212 685-4136
http://www.broadwaybank.com/

Business Lenders LLC
505 Bay Avenue, Ste 201
Somers Point, NJ 08244
609 601-9890
Fax: 609 927-7666

Capital One Bank
1500 Capitol One Dr

Attn: 12071-0210
Richmond, VA 23248
804 284-1305
Fax: 804 284-1866

Christiana Bank & Trust Company
3801 Kennett Pike, Ste C200
Greenville, DE 19807
302 888-7410
Fax: 302 421-5815
http://www.christianatrust.com/

CitiCapital Small Business Finance,
Inc.
250 E. Carpenter Freeway, FL 115
Irving, TX 75062
972 652-5280
Fax: 972 652-5337

Commercial Capital Corporation
25 W. 43rd Street, Ste 900
New York, NY 10036
212 719-0002 Ext 203
Fax: 212 719-4223
www.comcap.com

County Bank
4299 Highway One, Ste. A1
Rehoboth Beach, DE 19971
302 226-9800
Fax: 302 226-2265

Delaware National Bank
9 S. Dupont Hwy
P. O. Box 250
Georgetown, DE 19947
302 855-2419
302 855-2410
Fax: 302 856-2758
http://www.delawarenational.com/

Felton Bank
120 W. Main St.
P. O. Box 266
Felton, DE 19943
302 284-1629
Fax: 302 284-1606
http://www.feltonbank.com/

First Bank of Delaware
824 N. Market St., Ste 106
Wilmington, DE 19801
302 658-5078
Fax: 302 661-1433

First National Bank of Wyoming
120 W. Camden Wyoming Ave.
Wyoming, DE 19934
302 697-2666
Fax: 302 697-2857
http://www.fnbwyomingde.com/

First Western SBLC, Inc.
18111 Preston Rd., Ste 600
Dallas, TX 75252
972 349-3200 Ext 3209
Fax: 972 349-3265

HSBC Bank USA
1027 Arch Street

Philadelphia, PA 19107
215 592-0700
Fax: 215 592-9492
http://www.hsbc.com/

Hudson United Bank
580 W. Germantown Pike
Plymouth Meeting, PA 19462
610 397-1825
Fax: 610 828-1075
http://www.hudsonunitedbank.com/

Key Bank & Trust
203 W. Main St.
Bel Air, MD 21014
410 893-4213
Fax: 410 893-6979

Maryland Permanent Bank & Trust
9612 Reisterstown Rd
Owings Mills, MD 21117
410 356-4411
Fax: 410 356-4434

Peoples Bank of Oxford
P. O. Box 298
Oxford, PA 19363
610 998-1554
Fax: 610 998-0733
http://www.peoplesoxford.com/

Progress Bank
4 Sentry Parkway, Ste 200
Bluebell, PA 19422
610 941-4809
Fax: 610 825-2046
http://www.progressbank.com/about.
asp

Royal Bank of Pennsylvania
516 E. Lancaster Avenue
Shillington, PA 19607
610 777-3300
Fax: 610 777-5099
http://www.royalbankpa.com/

St. Michaels Bank
8223 Elliott Rd.
Suite 37
Easton, MD 21601
410 820-8600
Fax: 410 820-8354
http://www.stmichaelsmd.org/about/
what2do.html

Sovereign Bank
201 Penn Street
Reading, PA 19601
215 497-8525
Fax: 215 497-8575
http://www.sovereignbank.com/Defa
ult.asp?display=true&javascript=true

Star BIDCO
818 N. Washington Street
Wilmington, DE 19801
302 428-1456
Fax: 302 428-0642
http://www.starbidco.com/

Sun National Bank, Delaware
1300 N. Market Street
Wilmington, DE 19801
302 254-4000 Ext. 8122 or 8136
Fax: 302 425-2339
http://www.sunnb.com/index2.html

United Bank of Philadelphia
300 N 3rd Street
Philadelphia, PA 19106
215 351-4600 Ext. 408
Fax: 215 351-4617
http://www.unitedbankofphiladelphi
a.com/

Vine Street Trust
5901 C Peachtree-Dinwoody Rd
Atlanta, GA 30328
800 758-0038
Fax: 770 551-8781

District of Columbia

AMRESCO Independence Funding,
Inc.
214 953-8908
Fax: 214 758-5260

Adams National Bank
1130 Connecticut Ave., NW
Suite 200
Washington, D.C. 20036
202 466-4090
Fax: 202 835-3871
http://www.adamsbank.com/

Allfirst Bank
410 244-4007
Fax: 410 244-4070

Bank of America, National
Association
916 861-6729
Fax: 916 861-6779

Branch Banking and Trust Company
336 733-3441
Fax: 336 733-3419

Business Lenders LLC
860 244-9202
Fax: 860 527-0884

Business Loan Center, Inc.
800 722-5626
Fax: 316 263-4391

CIT Small Business Lending
Corporation
973 422-6004
Fax: 973 422-6130

California Center Bank
213 637-9622
Fax: 213 427-6080

Citibank, Federal Savings Bank
636 256-5925
Fax: 636 256-5549

Columbia Bank, The
301 474-9293
Fax: 301 474-6258

Community Bank of Northern
Virginia
8150 Leesburg Pike
Vienna, Virginia 22182
703 762-7382
Fax: 703 356-0597
http://www.cbnv.com/

EagleBank
7815 Woodmont Avenue
Bethesda, Maryland 20814
301 986-1800
Fax: 301 986-8529
http://www.eaglebankmd.com/

First International Bank
860 541-5249
Fax: 860 241-2571

The Foster Bank
773 588-3355
Fax: 773 588-7505

G.E. Capital Small Business Finance
Corp
314 205-3602
Fax: 314 205-3691
http://www.gesmallbusiness.com/ho
me.jsp

Key Bank and Trust
410 363-7050
Fax: 410 363-3569
www.keyb-t.com/

Millennium Bank, National
Association
703 464-1975
Fax: 571 203-2107

Money Store Investment
Corporation, The
916 787-9301
Fax: 916 787-9533

Nara Bank, National Association
213 427-6340
Fax: 213 383-0906
http://www.narabankna.com/

PNC Bank, National Association
215 749-6502
Fax: 215 749-8773
www.pncbank.com

Resource Bank
757 431-2425
Fax: 757498-3658
http://www.resourcebankonline.com/

Southern Financial Bank
540 341-8056
Fax: 540 349-8244
www.southernfinancialbank.com

Valley National Bank
908 561-0271
Fax: 908 753-9817
www.valleynationalbank.com/

Wachovia Bank, National
Association (Win
336 735-6193
Fax: 336 735-6181
http://www.wachovia.com/

Wells Fargo Bank Minnesota,
National As
612 667-2753
Fax: 612 316-2322

Florida

AMRESCO Independence Funding
Company, LLC
700 North Pearl St., Ste 2400, LB
359
Dallas, TX 75201 - 7424
214 720-1776
Fax: 214 753-8470

AMRESCO Independence Funding
Company, LLC
7200 Lake Ellenor Drive, Suite 200
Orlando, FL 32809
407 888-1776
Fax: 407 888-1779

Banco Popular North America
7 West 51st Street
New York, NY 10019
212 445-1991
Fax: 212 397-1120
http://www.popularinc.com/bancopo
pular/pages/useng/bppr-useng-
home.jsp

Banco Popular North America
(Florida)
8523 Commodity Circle
Orlando, FL 32819
407 370-7721
Fax: 407 370-7799
http://www.popularinc.com/bancopo
pular/pages/useng/bppr-useng-
home.jsp

BankFIRST
13207 West Colonial Drive
Winter Garden, Florida 34787
Email: None
407 877-0909
Fax: 407 877-0925
http://www.bankfirst.com/

Bank of America
10850 White Rock Road, # 101
Rancho Cordova, CA 95670
916 861-5628
Fax: 916 861-9246
www.bankofamerica.com

Bank of America
50 North Laura Street, Suite 2307
Jacksonville, FL 32202

904 791 -7982
Fax: 904 791-7329
www.bankofamerica.com

Bank of the West
10181 Truckee-Tahoe Airport Rd.
Truckee, CA 96161
530 582-3803
Fax: 530 582-2953
http://www.bankofthewest.com/

Bank of the West
174 W. Comstock Aveune, Suite 201
Winter Park, FL 32789
407 740-5100
Fax: 407 740-5941
http://www.bankofthewest.com/

Business Loan Center, Inc.
121 W. Dewey Street, Suite 210
Wichita, KS 67202
316 263-3232
Fax: 316 263-4391

Business Loan Center, Inc.
415 Breckrich Road, Suite 250
Panama City Beach, FL 32407
850 234-5056
Fax: 850 234-6150

Business Loan Center, Inc.
4190 Belfort Road, Suite 200
Jacksonville, FL 32216
904 279-9124
Fax: 904 279-9126

CIT, SBLC
1 CIT Drive
Livingston, NJ 07039
973 606-5094
Fax: 973 422-6135

CIT, SBLC
4446 Hendricks Avenue, # 369
Jacksonville, FL 32207
904 306 0710
Fax: 904 306-0730
www.smallbizlending.com

CIT, SBLC
522 Hunt Club Boulevard, # 250
Apopka, FL 32703
407 772-4556
Fax: 407 772-4558
www.smallbizlending.com

CNB Bank
9715 Gate Parkway North
Jacksonville, Florida 32246
Email: None
904 265-0283
Fax: 904 265 0294

Califonia Bank & Trust
2399 Gateway Oaks Drive, # 110
Sacramento, CA 95833
916 561-1121
Fax: 916 341-3021

Califonia Bank & Trust
3421 West St. Conrad Street
Tampa, FL 33607
813 874-3226
Fax: 813 874-3327

CenterBank of Jacksonville, N.A.
1325 Hendricks Avenue
Jacksonville, FL 32207
Email: gbossow@centerbankjax.com
904 421-3720
Fax: 904 421-3737
www.centerbankjax.com

CitiCapital Small Business Finance,
Inc.
300 East Carpenter Freeway, Suite
1250
Irving, TX 75062
972 652-4000
Fax: 972 652-3340

Comerica Bank
Post Office Box 4167
Houston, TX 77210-4167
713 888-2670
Fax: 713 888-2671
http://www.comerica.com/

Compass Bank
17218 Preston Road, 2nd Floor
Dallas, TX 75252
972 735-3577
Fax: 972 735-3598
http://www.compassweb.com

First Alliance Bank
311 W. Adams Street
Jacksonville, FL 32202
904 350-7526
Fax: 904 350-7540
http://www.firstalliancebank.com/

First Coast Community Bank
P. O. Box 1739
Fernandina Beach, FL 32034
904 277-4400
Fax: 904 277-8025
http://www.fccbank.com/

First Commercial Bank of Florida
945 S. Orange at Gore
Orlando, FL 32806
407 835-1835
Fax: 407 839-1399
http://www.fcbflorida.com/

First Community Bank of SW
Florida
1565 Red Cedar Drive
Ft. Meyers, FL 33907
941 939-4100
Fax: 941 939-4123

First Guaranty Bank and Trust
Company
P. O. Box 2578
Jacksonville, FL 32203
904 384-7541
Fax: 904 381-7040

First National Bank of Nassau
County
1891 South 14th Street
Fernandina Beach, FL 32035
904 321-0400
Fax: 904 321-1511
http://www.fnb-palm.com/

First National Bank
17005 Emerald Coast Parkway
Destin, FL 32541
Email: fnbsba@fnbfla.com
800 711-7741
Fax: 850 654-5317

First National Bank of NW Florida
101 E. 23rd Street
Panama City, FL 32405
850 769-3207
Fax: 850 785-7096

First National Bank of NW Florida
3725 Dupont Station Court South
Jacksonville, FL 32217
904 731-5086
Fax: 904 731-5246

GE Capital Small Business Fin.
Corp.
635 Maryville Centre Dr.
Suite 120
St. Louis, MO 63141
314 205-3500
Fax: 314 205-3697

Goleta National Bank
445 Pine Street
Goleta, CA 93117
805 692-4350
Fax: 805 692-0635
http://www.goleta.com/

Goleta National Bank
3409 Secret Cove Place
Jacksonville, FL 32255
904 731-9020
Fax: 904 731-0025
http://www.goleta.com/

Liberty National Bank
P. O. Box 522220
Longwood, FL 32752
Email: BHartman@
LibertyNationalBank.com
407 831-1776
Fax: 407 831-1443
http://www.lnbbank.com/

Liberty National Bank
7825 Baymeadows Way, Suite 101A
Jacksonville, FL 32256
Email: libjax@bellsouth.net
904 737-1776
Fax: 904 737-8011
http://www.lnbbank.com/

Monticello Bank
3288 South Third Street
Jacksonville Beach, FL 32250
904 241-6266

Fax: 904 241-7079
http://www.monticellobank.com/

Regions Bank
1457 Mt. Vernon Road
Dunwoody, GA 30338
770 395-9611
Fax: 770 395-9310
http://www.regions.com/

Regions Bank
800 W. Main Street
Inverness, Florida 34451
352 726 - 1559
Fax: 352 726-7616
http://www.regions.com/

South Trust Bank, N. A.
2625 Piedmont Road
Suite 51B
Atlanta, GA 30324
404 841-2184
Fax: 404 841-2187
http://www.southtrust.com

Temecula Valley Bank
27710 Jefferson Avenue, A100
Temecula, CA 92590
909 506-1511
Fax: 909 506-1283
http://www.temvalbank.com/

U. S. Bank
9918 Hibert Street, 3 Floor
San Diego, CA 92131 - 1018
858 536-4545 ext. 304
Fax: 858 536-1502
http://www.usbank.com/

Washington Mutual Bank
3200 SW Freeway, 16th Floor
Houston, TX 77027
713 543-6265
Fax: 713 543-6100
www.wamu.com

Washington Mutual Bank
12819 Swamp Owl Lane
Jacksonville, FL 32258
904 288-9130
Fax: 904 292-3951
www.wamu.com

Wells Fargo, SBA Lending
1455 West Lake Street
Minneapolis, MN 55408
612 667-2753
Fax: 612 316-2322
www.wellsfargo.com

Whitney National Bank
228 St. Charles Avenue
New Orleans, LA 70130
504 586-7107
Fax: 504 599-2144
http://www.whitneybank.com

Advantage Bank
741 US Highway One
North Palm Beach, FL 33408

561 840-3486
Fax: 561 840-6596

AMRESCO Independence Funding
Company
700 N. Pearl Street, Suite 2400
Dallas, TX 75201
214 953-8909
Fax: 214 758-5260

AMRESCO Independence Funding
Company
800 970-2418
561 989-5402
Fax: 561 989-5403

Bank Of America, N.A.
7 West 51st Street
New York, NY 10019
212 445-1991
Fax: 212 397-1120
http://www.bankofamerica.com/

Bank Of America, N.A.
5551 Vanguard Street
Orlando, FL 32819
407 370-7489
Fax: 407 370-7777
http://www.bankofamerica.com/

Bank Of America, N.A.
CA3-701-01-09
10850 White Rock Road, Suite 101
Rancho Cordova, CA 95670-6044
916 861-6729
Fax: 916 861-6779
http://www.bankofamerica.com/

Bank Of America, N.A.
121 Moore-Hopkins Lane
Columbia, SC 29210
803 765-8643
Fax: 803 765-8638
http://www.bankofamerica.com/

Bank Of America, N.A.
CA3-701-01-09
10850 White Rock Road, Suite 101
Rancho Cordova, CA 95670-6044
916 861-6729
Fax: 916 861-6779
http://www.bankofamerica.com/

Bank Of America, N.A.
121 Moore-Hopkins Lane
Columbia, SC 29210
803 765-8643
Fax: 803 765-8638
http://www.bankofamerica.com/

Bank Of America, N.A.
Greater Miami Area
7760 W Flagler St
Miami, FL 33144
305 553-7836
Fax: 305 553-7822
Jacqueline.E.Lungi@bankofamerica.
com
http://www.bankofamerica.com/

Bank of America
Fort Lauderdale/Naples Areas
888 W Cypress Creek Rd, Fort
Lauderdale, FL 33309
954 928-1992
Fax: 954 928-1949
robeert.f.tighe@bankofamerica.com
http://www.bankofamerica.com/

Bank Of America, N.A.
Tampa/Saint Petersburg Area
101 E Kennedy Blvd
Tampa, FL 336025179
813 225-8760
Fax: 813 225-8715
Brad.Owens@bankofamerica.com
http://www.bankofamerica.com/

Bank Of America, N.A.
Orlando Area
407 420-2722
Fax: 407 420-2787
Patrick.J.McEvoy@bankofamerica.c
om
http://www.bankofamerica.com/

Bank Of America, N.A.
Palm Beach Area
625 N Flagler Dr
West Palm Beach, FL 334014025
561 838-2291
Fax: 561 838-5087
Brad.Owens@bankofamerica.com
http://www.bankofamerica.com/

Busey Bank, FSB
201 W. Main
Urbana, IL 61803
217 365-4532
Fax: 217 365-4596
http://www.busey.com/indexhorizont
alf1024.htm
7980 Summerlin Lakes Drive, Suite
204
Fort Myers, FL 3390
941 489-3599
Fax: 941 489-4328
http://www.busey.com/indexhorizont
alf1024.htm

Business Loan Center, Inc.
1301 N. Hamilton Street, Suite 200
Richmond, VA 23230
804 355-4449
Fax: 804 358-9025
415 Beckrich Road, Suite 250
Panama Beach, FL 32407
850 234-5056
Fax: 850 234-6150

Cape Coral National Bank
2724 Del Prado Blvd.
Cape Coral, FL 33904
941 542-5100
Fax: 941 772-8348

Charlotte State Bank
1100 Tamiami Trail
Port Charlotte, FL 33953
941 624-5400

Fax: 941 624-2308
http://www.charlottestatebank.com/

Citibank, FSB
8750 Doral Blvd.
Miami, FL 33102
305 470-7010
Fax: 305 470-5983

Citicapital Small Business Finance,
Inc.
250 E. Carpenter Freeway, 1FL-115
Irving, TX 75062
972 652-4758
Fax: 972 652-5337

Comerica Bank
1900 West Loop South, Suite 220
Houston, TX 77027
713 888-2688
Fax: 713 888-2674
http://www.comerica.com/cma/cda/st
ateLogin

Comerica Bank
1800 Corporate Blvd. NW
Boca Raton, FL 33431
561 241-4801
Fax: 561 241-4828
http://www.comerica.com/cma/cda/st
ateLogin

Comerica Bank
100 NE Third Avenue
Ft. Lauderdale, FL 33301
954 468-0670
Fax: 954 468-0600
http://www.comerica.com/cma/cda/st
ateLogin

Compass Bank
17218 Preston Road
Dallas, TX 75252
http://www.compassweb.com/index.
cfm

Fidelity Federal Bank & Trust
205 Datura Street
West Palm Beach, FL 33401
561 803-9900
Fax: 561 803-9987
561 803-9884
Fax: 561-803-9857
https://www.fidfedonline.com/

First Community Bank Of SW
Florida
1565 Red Cedar Drive
Fort Myers, FL 33907
941 939-4100
Fax: 941 939-4123
https://www.ebankhost.net/swflorida
/ecorp/

First Peoples Bank
1301 SE Port St. Lucie Blvd.
Port St. Lucie, FL 34952
561 398-1388
Fax: 561 398-1399
http://www.1stpeoplesbank.com/

First Union Small Business Capital/
The Money Store
707 3rd Street
West Sacramento, CA 95605
916 617-1038
Fax: 916 617-1090

First Union Small Business Capital/
The Money Store
1800 Pembroke Drive, Suite 300
Orlando, FL 32810
407 667-3530
Fax: 407 667-3533

First Union Small Business Capital/
The Money Store
1200 N. Federal Highway, Suite 200
Boca Raton, FL 33432
561 392-0016
Fax: 561 392-3926

First Western SBLC, Inc.
18111 Preston Road, #600
Dallas, TX 75252

Firstar Bank, N.A.
9918 Hibert Street, 3rd Floor
San Diego, CA 92131
858-536-4545

1200 N. Federal Highway, #200
Boca Raton, FL 33432
561 447-8226
Fax: 561 447-8227
http://www.usbank.com/cgi_w/cfm/a
bout/firstar.cfm

Flagler Bank
1801 W. Forest Hill Blvd.
West Palm Beach, FL 33406
561 432-2122
Fax: 561 432-2123

Fleet National Bank
777 Main Street
Hartford, CT 06115
http://www.flaglerbankusa.com/

GE Capital Small Business Finance
Corp.
635 Maryville Centre Dr., Suite 120
St. Louis, MO 63141
314 205-3602
Fax: 314 205-3691
314 205-3500
Fax: 314 205-3697
http://www.ge.com/capital/smallbiz/

GE Capital Small Business Finance
Corp.
Florida Contacts:
8500 SW 55th Terrace
Miami, FL 33157
305 252-3885
Fax: 305 252-5421
http://www.ge.com/capital/smallbiz/

GE Capital Small Business Finance
Corp.
7650 Courtney Campbell Causeway

Suite 900
Tampa, FL 33607
813 286-4844
Fax: 813 286-4804
http://www.ge.com/capital/smallbiz/

Goleta National Bank
665 Molly Lane, Suite 110
Woodstock, GA 30188
770 516-7744
www.goleta.com/

Liberty National Bank
502 N. Highway 17-92
Longwood, FL 32752
407 831-1776
Fax: 407 831-7686
http://www.lnbbank.com/

Palm Beach National Bank & Trust
Company
3931 RCA Boulevard, Suite 3102
Palm Beach Gardens, FL 33410

Premier Community Bank
160 Pointe Loop Drive
Venice, FL 34293
941 496-9696
Fax: 941 497-6804
http://www.premiercommunity.com/

Premier Community Bank Of Florida
350 East Bay Drive
Largo, FL 33770
727 585-3111
Fax: 727 587-852
http://www.pcb-net.com/

Provident Bank
1549 Ringling Blvd.
Sarasota, FL 34230
941 364-5767
Fax: 941 955-8183
http://www.providentbanking.com/

Riverside National Bank Of Florida
2211 Okeechobee Road
Fort Pierce, FL 34950
561 467-2075 Ext. 2131
Fax: 561 464-3773
http://www.in2m.com/Solutions/FIs/
R/RiversideNation-3299.shtm

Southern Commerce Bank
5650 Breckenridge Park Drive
Suite 110
Tampa, FL 33610
813 621-2080
Fax: 813 626-2834
hcole@sc-bank.com
http://www.blueheronmedia.com/scb
_web/

Southtrust Bank, N.A.
360 Interstate North Parkway
Suite 500
Atlanta, GA 30339
678 627-3770
Fax: 678 627-3779

http://www.southtrust.com/st/default.
htm

Suntrust Bank
302 East Atlantic Avenue
Delray Beach, FL 33483
561 330-1921
Fax: 561 330-1928
http://www.suntrust.com/personal/So
lutions/index.asp

Temecula Valley Bank, N.A.
27710 Jefferson Avenue, Suite A100
Temecula, CA 92593-0690
909 694-9940
625 South Gay Street, Suite 230
Knoxville, TN 37902
865 215-9960
Fax: 865 215-9976
http://www.temvalbank.com/

The Huntington National Bank
7575 Huntington Park Drive
HM3326
Columbus, OH 43235
614 480-1941
Fax: 614 480-1888

The International Bank Of Miami,
N.A.
2121 S.W. Third Avenue
Miami, FL 33129
305 250-7280
Fax: 305 859-9405
305 250-7276
Fax: 305 859-9405
http://www.tibom.com/

TIB Bank Of The Keys
201 8th Street South, Suite 107
Naples, FL 34102
941-430-1911
Fax: 941 430-1916
http://www.tibbank.com/

Tyco Capital Small Business
Lending Corp.
1 Tyco Drive
Livingston, NJ 07039
800 367-9876 Ext. 7550
Fax: 973 606-5198
973 606-5094
Fax: 973 422-6135

Union Planters Bank
9700 NW 112th Avenue
Miami, FL 33178
786 777-6772
Fax: 786 845-4488
http://www.unionplanters.com/

United Bank & Trust Company
5801 49th Street North
Saint Petersburg, FL 33709
727 824-8726
727 521-2234
Fax: 727 521-2233

Wachovia Bank, N.A.
101 N-Cherry Street, 7TH Floor

MC-NC 39071
Winston-Salem, NC 27150
336 735-6193
336 735-6190
Fax: 336 6735-6182

Washington Mutual Bank, FA
6341 E. Campus Circle Drive
Irving, TX 75063
972 714-7430
Fax: 972 714-7470
Regional Contact:
4020 Westchase Blvd., Suite 100
Raleigh, NC 27607
919 839-5511
Fax: 919 839-706
http://www.wamu.com/servlet/wamu
/index.html

Wells Fargo Bank
3660 Hampton Drive, Suite 250
Missouri, TX 77459
281 208-6209
Fax: 281 499-2418
http://www.wellsfargo.com/

West Coast Guaranty Bank
3700 S. Tamiami Trail
Sarasota, FL 34239
http://floridadirectory.biz/html/Bank
s/78.html

California Bank & Trust
Dba Zions Small Business Finance
20801 Biscayne Blvd, Ste. 505
Aventura, FL 33180
305 932-3434
Fax: 305 932-3241
GREATER TAMPA AREA
http://www.calbanktrust.com/

California Bank & Trust
Dba Zions Small Business Finance
3421 W St. Conrad St., Ste. B
Tampa, FL 33607
813 874-3226
Fax: 813 874-3227
http://www.calbanktrust.com/

Bank of America
10 Light Street, 19th Fl.
Baltimore, MD 21202
410 605-4428
800 263-2055
Fax: 410 605-5326
http://www.bankofamerica.com/

Business Loan Center, Inc.
3 S. 12th Street
Richmond, VA 23219
804 344-8160
Fax: 804 344-8301

Business Loan Express
649 N. Lewis Rd, Ste 205
Limerick, PA 19468
610 495-8744 Ext 11
Fax: 610 495-8750
http://www.alliedcapitalexpress.com/

CIT Small Business Lending
634 York Rd, PMB 167
Warminster, PA 18974
215 918-2542
Fax: 215 918-2543

Citizens Bank
919 N. Market St., 2nd Fl.
Wilmington, DE 19801
302 421-2394
Fax: 302 421-2390
http://www.citizensbank.com/

Citizens Bank
13 The Circle, 1st
Georgetown, DE 19947
302 856-4215
Fax: 302 856-4205
www.citizensbank.com

Commerce Bank/Delaware N.A.
P O Box 470
Wilmington, DE 19899
302 683-6810
Fax: 302 683-6889
http://www.commercebank.com/

First International Bank
1 Commerce Square
2005 Market St, 33rd Fl.
Philadelphia, PA 19103
302 587-6487
Fax: 302 587-6497

First Union National Bank
2011 Concord Pike, 2nd Fl.
Wilmington, DE 19803
302 421-7061
Fax: 302 421-7117

GE Capital Small Business Financial
Corp.
104 Temple Terrace
Wilmington, DE 19805
302 654-0800
Fax: 302 654-0900

Money Store Investment Corp.
1620 E. Roseville Pkwy, Ste 100
Roseville, CA 95661
916 787-9301
Fax: 916 787-9533

PNC Bank
300 Delaware Avenue
Wilmington, DE 19801
302 429-2274
Fax: 302 429-2872
http://www.pncbank.com/

Unity Bank
64 Old Highway 32
Clinton, NJ 08809
908 730-7630
Fax: 908 730-9754
http://www.unitybank.com/about.cf
m

Valley National Bank
1334 U.S. Highway 22 E

N Plainfield, NJ 07061
800 722-6772
Fax: 908 753-9817
http://www.valleynationalbank.com/

Washington Mutual Bank, FA
3200 S W Freeway PT 1490
Houston, TX 77027
713 543-7371
Fax: 713 543-6704
http://www.wamu.com/

Wilmington Savings Fund Society
(WSFS)
838 N. Market St.
Wilmington, DE 19801
302 573-3251
Fax: 302 571-6835
http://www.wsfsbank.com/

Wilmington Trust Company
1100 N. Market St WTC/5
Wilmington, DE 19801
302 651-1487
Fax: 302 651-1325
https://www.wilmingtontrust.com

Wells Fargo
1455 West Lake St
Suite 306
Minneapolis, MN 55408
612 667-2753
Fax: 612 316-2322
www.wellsfargo.com

Georgia

Athens First Bank & Trust
c/o Synovus SBA Lending
4159 Mill Street
P.O. Box 2039
Covington, GA 30014
Contact: Kim Hartbarger
770-385-3411
Fax: 770-625-1799
www.athensfirstbank.com/

Atlantic States Bank
2140 Satellite Boulevard
Duluth, GA 30097
Contact: Dana Little
678-473-7632
Fax: 678-473-9919
www.atlanticstatesbank.com/

Bank of America
3350 Riverwood Pkwy, 11th Floor
Atlanta, GA 30339
Contact: Vicki Molinari
770-850-5547
Fax: 770-850-5543
www.bankofamerica.com

Bank of North Georgia
8025 Westside Pkwy
Alpharetta, GA 30004
Contact: Lorraine Poteete
770-751-4765
Fax: 770-754-9959
www.banknorthgeorgia.com

Branch Banking & Trust Company
5901-C Peachtree-Dunwoody Rd.
Suite 420
Atlanta, GA 30328
Contact: Vincent Dailey
770-522-0582
Fax: 770-551-8781
www.bbandt.com

Business Development Corporation
of Georgia, Inc.
1450 S. Johnson Ferry Road
Atlanta, GA 30319
Contact: Tom Dorman
404-475-6011
Fax: 404-475-6013
www.businessgeorgia.com

Business Loan Express
3675 Cloudland Drive, NW
Atlanta, GA 30327
Contact: Rebecca Grant
404-995-7025
Fax: 404-816-2010
www.businessloanexpress.net

California Bank & Trust
Zions Small Business Finance
3330 Cumberland Blvd., Suite 500
Atlanta, GA 30339
Contact: Bruce Bryant
770-690-4218
Fax: 770-690-4217
www.calbanktrust.com

Capitol City Bank & Trust
562 Lee Street
Atlanta, GA 30310
Contact: Willie L. Yancey
404-752-6067
Fax: 404-752-5862

Charter Bank & Trust Company
4159 Mill Street
P.O. Box 2039
Monroe, GA 30655
Contact: Kim Hartbarger
770-385-3411
Fax: 678-625-1799
www.charterbank-trust.com/

Chattahoochee National Bank
3625 Brookside Pkwy, Suite 100
Alpharetta, GA 30022
Contact: Amy Amorose
678-323-7015
Fax: 770-343-9056
www.bankthehooch.com

Citizens Bank & Trust of West
Georgia
Synovus SBA Lending
4159 Mill Street
P.O. Box 2039
Monroe, GA 30655
Contact: Kim Hartbarger
770-385-3411
Fax: 678-625-1799
www.citizensbankandtrust.net

Citizens Trust Bank
75 Piedmont Ave
Atlanta, GA 30303
Contact: Derek Grayson
770-593-6369 ext 121
Fax: 770-593-4980
www.ctbatlanta.com

CIT Small Business Lending
PMB 342
12460 Crabapple Road, Suite 202
Alpharetta, GA 30004-6386
Contact: Claudia Wilson
678-461-0461
Fax: 678-461-0462
www.citgroup.com

The Coastal Bank
27 Bull Street
Savannah, GA 31401
Contact: Tom Butler
912-201-4952
Fax: 912-201-4960

Colonial Bank
4800 Ashford Dunwoody Rd
Dunwoody, GA 30338
Contact: Jennifer Andrews
770-379-8660
Fax: 770-379-8732
www.colonialbank.com

Columbus Bank & Trust
Synovus SBA Lending
4159 Mill Street
P.O. Box 2039
Monroe, GA 30655
Contact: Kim Hartbarger
770-385-3411
Fax: 678-625-1799
www.columbusbankandtrust.com

Comerica Bank
4309 Emperor Blvd. Suite 100
Durham, N.C. 27703
Contact: Michael Schwartz
919-932-8052
Fax: 919-932-8080
www.comerica.com

Commercial Bank & Trust Company
of Troup County
Synovus SBA Lending
4159 Mill Street
P.O. Box 2039
Monroe, GA 30655
Contact: Kim Hartbarger
770-385-3411
Fax: 678-625-1799
www.combanktrust.com

Community Bank & Trust
P.O. Box 1900
Cornelia, GA 30531
Contact: William Galardi
770-287-8650
Fax: 770-287-8683
Contact: Elton Collins
706-335-3151
Fax: 706-335-2564

Compass Bank
P.O. Box 797808
Dallas, TX 75379
Contact: Gregory Clarkson
972-735-3577
Fax: 972-735-3598
www.compassbank.com

Crescent Bank & Trust Company
4475 Towne Lake Parkway
Woodstock, GA 30189
Contact: Jeff K. Roach
678-454-2300
Fax: 678-454-2372
www.crescentbank.com

Decatur First Bank
1120 Commerce Drive
Decatur, GA 30030
Contact: David Senior
404-373-1000
Fax: 404-373-6549
www.decaturfirstbank.com

Fidelity Bank
3490 Piedmont Road, Suite 1450
Atlanta, GA 30305
Contact: Dan Ford
404-240-1526
Fax: 404-240-1560
www.lionbank.com

First National Bank of Trust
Company
120A South Zetterower Avenue
Statesboro, GA 30458
Contact: Bruce Avant
912-764-6600
Fax: 912-764-3755
www.fnb-trust.com

First National Bank of Cherokee
9860 Highway 92
Woodstock, GA 30188
Contact: Sandra Brown
770-591-9000
Fax: 770-928-7298
www.fnbinternet.com

First National Bank of Coffee
County
420 South Madison Avenue
Douglas, GA 31533
Contact: Todd Mullis
912-384-1100
Fax: 912-384-2666
www.fnbcc.com

First National Bank of Nassau
County
1891 South 14th Street
Fernandina Beach, FL 32035
Contact: Durand Childers
904-321-0400
Fax: 904-321-1511
www.fnb-palm.com

FNB South
P.O. Box 2028
Alma, GA 31510

Contact: Jon Lott
912-632-7262
Fax: 912-632-5058
www.fnbalma.com

Foster Bank
5715 Buford Highway, Suite 205
Doraville, GA 30340
Contact: Steve Han
770-451-1220
Fax: 770-451-7725
www.fosterbank.com

G.E. Capital Small Business Finance
1000 Winward Concourse, Suite 400
Alpharetta, GA 30005
Contact: Adam Furth
770-999-6734
Fax: 770-999-6666
www.ge.com/capital/smallbiz/

Georgia Banking Company
6190 Powers Ferry road, Suite 150
Atlanta, GA 30339
Contact: Terri Karr
770-227-8800
Fax: 770-690-9188

Goleta National Bank
665 Molly Lane, Suite 110
Woodstock, GA 30188
Contact: Carolyn Robinson
770-516-7744
Fax: 770-516-5575
www.goleta.com

Gulf Coast Bank & Trust Company
7179 Jonesboro Road, Suite 200
Morrow, GA 30260
Contact: Charlie Stanford
770-960-8818
Fax: 770-960-8143

Gwinnett Banking Company
600 Northwinds Center West
11675 Rainwater Drive, Suite 150
Alpharetta, GA 30004
Contact: Katrina Winberg
770-754-0001 ext.205
Fax: 770-754-1048

Horizon Bank
6340 Sugarloaf Pkwy, Suite 100
Duluth, GA 30097
Contact: Allan Thomes
678-957-5500
Fax: 678-957-5529

Main Street Bank
3430 Hwy 20 SE
Conyers, GA 30013
Contact: J. Daniel Preston
770-761-5339
Fax: 770-761-5543
www.mainstreetbank.com

Nara Bank, National Association
3510 Shallowford Rd, Suite 207
Atlanta, GA 30341
Contact: Karl Y. Chang

770-290-0177
Fax: 770-290-0187

The National Bank of Walton
County
Synovus SBA Lending
4159 Mill Street
P.O. Box 2039
Monroe, GA 30655
Contact: Kim Hartbarger
770-385-3411
Fax: 678-625-1799
www.nbwc.com

Omni National Bank
1100 Abernathy Road
Building 500-Ste. 1100
Atlanta, GA 30328
Contact: Patrick Tracy
678-244-6356
Fax: 770-330-1300

Peoples State Bank
72 E. Parker Street
Baxley, GA 31513
Contact: Steve Rigdon
912-367-3658
Fax: 912-367-4627

Peachtree National Bank
Synovus SBA Lending
4159 Mill Street
P.O. Box 2039
Monroe, GA 30655
Contact: Kim Hartbarger
770-385-3411
Fax: 678-625-1799
www.pchnb.com

Piedmont Bank
3423 Piedmont Road
Atlanta, GA 30305
Contact: Bobby Wimberly
404-926-2426
Fax: 404-926-2434

Quantum National Bank
505 Peachtree Industrial Boulevard
Suwanee, GA 30024
Contact: Bryanne Connelly
770-831-2627
Fax: 770-831-2635
www.quantumbank.com

Regions Bank
6600 Peachtree Dunwoody Rd
400 Embassy Row, Suite 200
Atlanta, GA 30328
Contact: Susan Battle
770-481-4355
Fax: 770-395-1117
www.regions.com

Riverside Bank
1200 Johnson Ferry Road
Marietta, GA 30068
Contact: Robert Garcia
770-509-5910
Fax: 770-973-8753
www.riversidebank.net

Southern National Bank
200 Cherokee Street
Marietta, GA 30060
Contact: Ed Carroll
770-424-2000 ext. 245
Fax: 770-424-1744

SouthTrust Bank, N.A.
360 Interstate North Pkwy.
Suite 500
Atlanta, GA 30339
Contact: Juan Lago
678-627-3771
Fax: 678-627-3779
www.southtrust.com

Summit National Bank
4360 Chamblee-Dunwoody Road
Atlanta, GA 30341
Contact: Andree London
770-454-0441
Fax: 770-457-5531
www.summitbk.com

Sumter Bank & Trust
Synovus SBA Lending
4159 Mill Street
P.O. Box 2039
Monroe, GA 30655
Contact: Kim Hartbarger
770-385-3411
Fax: 678-625-1799
www.sumterbank.com

Sunrise Bank
1545 Peachtree Street, Suite 200
Atlanta, GA 30309
Contact: Charles Green
404-504-9850
Fax: 404-504-9895

SunTrust, Atlanta
25 Park Place, MC 056
Atlanta, GA 30303
Contact: Mike Hudson
404-827-6487
Fax: 404-588-8530
www.suntrust.com

Temecula Valley Bank
6700 Sugarloaf Parkway, Suite 500
Duluth, GA 30097
Contact: Leigh Milton
678-775-6886
Fax: 678-775-6887
www.temeculavalleybank.com

United Community Bank
P.O. Box 398
Blairsville, GA 30514
Contact: Todd Burt
706-745-2151
Fax: 706-781-2511
www.ucbi.com/welcome/welcome.as
p

U.S. Bank National Associations
2839 Paces Ferry Road, Suite 1210
Atlanta, GA 30339
Contact: Shay Corbin Barkley

770-434-6660
Fax: 770-434-0266

Wachovia Bank
1620 East Roseville Pkwy, Suite 100
Roseville, GA 95661
Contact: Tom Collopy
916-787-9394
866-741-3383
www.wachovia.com

Washington Mutual Bank, FA
2375 East Camelback Road
Phoenix, AR 85016
Contact: Hugh O'Donnell
602-474-3540
Fax: 602-957-2935
www.washingtonmutual.com

Hawaii

Bank of Hawaii
P.O. Box 2900
Honolulu, HI 96846
808-537-8568
www.boh.com

Business Loan Express, Inc.
655 N. Central Avenue, 17th Floor
Glendale, CA 91203
818-649-7680
Fax: 818-649-8250
www.businessloanexpress.net

Central Pacific Bank
P.O. Box 3590
Honolulu, HI 96811
808-544-0605
www.centralpacificbank.com

City Bank
P.O. Box 3709
Honolulu, HI 96811
808-535-2460
www.citybankhawaii.com

First Hawaiian Bank
P.O. Box 3200
Honolulu, HI 96847
808-525-7705
www.fhb.com

Hawaii National Bank
P. O. Box 3740
Honolulu, HI 96812
808-528-7823
www.hawaiinational.com

The Money Store Investment
Corporation
Seven Waterfront Plaza
500 Ala Moana Blvd., Suite 400
Honolulu, HI 96813
808-531-0004

Idaho

Bank of America
421 N. Cole Road
Boise, ID 83704
208-323-8700

Bank of Commerce
1455 Northgate Mile
P. O. Box 1887
Idaho Falls, ID 83401
208-523-2020

Bank of the West
9140 W. Emerald
Boise, ID 83704
208-658-9747

Business Loan Express
601 Union Street, Suite 4200
Seattle, WA 98101
206-624-3299
Fax: 206-624-3352
www.businessloanexpress.net

Citizens Community Bank
280 South Arthur
P. O. Box 1689
Pocatello, ID 83204
208-232-5373
http://www.ccb-idaho.com

CIT Small Business Lending
370 N. East Camano Drive, Suite #5
PMB #348
Camano Island, WA 98282
Contact: Doug Wolford
360-387-4752
Fax: 360-387-3790
800-713-4984
www.smallbizlending.com

CIT Small Business Lending
1061 West Riverdale Road, #401
Riverdale, UT 84405
Contact: Mikel Bowman
801-985-2211
800-713-4984
Fax: 801-985-1392
www.smallbizlending.com

Community Bank
609 North Main Street
P.O. Box X
Joseph, OR 97846
541-432-9050

Community First National Bank
142 East 200 South
Salt Lake City, UT 84111
860-693-3667

D. L. Evans Bank
3845 West State Street
Boise, ID 83703
208-342-2226
www.dlevans.com

Farmers & Merchants State Bank
209 N. 12th Street
P. O. Box 9242
Boise, ID 83707
208-343-7848
www.fmsb.com

Farmers National Bank
914 Main

P.O. Box 392
Buhl, ID 83316
208-543-4351

Farm Credit Services
411 Blaine Street
P. O. Box 730
Caldwell, ID 83606-0730
208-455-5500
Fax: 208-455-5505

First Bank of Idaho
111 Main Street
P. O. Box 3239
Ketchum, ID 83340
208-725-0330
Fax: 208-725-0341
https://firstbanksolutions.portalvault.
com/

First Federal Savings
383 Shoshone Street North
P. O. Box 249
Twin Falls, ID 83303
208-733-4222
Fax: 208-736-4437
www.firstfd.com

GE Capital Small Business Finance
Corp.
635 Maryville Center Dr.
Suite 120
St. Louis, MO 63141
Contact: Tammy Christopher
314-205-3500
Fax: 3314-205-3697
www.gesmallbusiness.com

Home Federal Savings
500 12th Avenue South
P.O. box 190
Nampa, ID 83651
208-468-5000
www.homefederalsavings.com

Idaho Banking Company
6010 Fairview Avenue
P. O. Box 44629
Boise, ID 83711
208-472-4700
www.idahobankingco.com

Idaho Independent Bank
8351 West Overland Rd.
Boise, ID 83709
208-323-6000
www.theidahobank.com

Intermountain Community Bank
175 N. 16th Street
P. O. Box 347
Payette, ID 83661
208-642-4773
Fax: 208-642-4884
www.intermountainbank.com

Ireland Bank
33 Bannock
P. O. Box 186
Malad, ID 83252

208-766-2211
www.ireland-bank.com

KeyBank National Association
702 W. Idaho
P. O. Box 2557
Boise, ID 83701
208-364-8500

Magic Valley Bank
222 Shoshone Street East
Twin Falls, ID 83301
208-736-2400
Fax: 208-733-8833
www.magicvalleybank.com

Mountain West Bank
2970 E. St. Lukes Drive
Meridian, ID 83642
208-855-9105
www.mountainwest-bank.com

Pioneer Bank
1990 Washington
P. O. Box 846
Baker City, OR 97814
541-523-5884
www.pioneerbankfsb.com

Silver State Bank
400 N. Green Valley Parkway
Henderson, NV 89014
702-433-8300
Fax: 702-968-8517
www.silverstatebank.com

Sterling Bank
101 Main Street
P. O. Box 221
Cascade, ID 83611
208-382-4233

Syringa Bank
1299 North Orchard Street
P. O. Box 7557
Boise, ID 83707-1557
208-658-0894

The Bank of Idaho
399 North Capital
P. O. Box 1487
Idaho Falls, ID 83403
208-524-5500
Fax: 208-524-6029
www.bankofidaho.com

U. S. National Bank
205 N. 10th Street
P. O. Box 8247
Boise, ID 83702
208-383-7816

Wachovia Small Business Capital
1620 E. Roseville Parkway
Suite 100
Roseville, CA 95661
800-275-3862
www.wachovia.com

Washington Mutual Business
Banking
161 N. Capital Blvd.
Boise, ID 83702
208-373-3151
www.washingtonmutual.com

Washington Trust Bank
7970 Fairview Avenue
Boise, ID 83704
208-378-4040
www.watrust.com

Wells Fargo Bank
877 Main Street
Boise, ID 83702
208-389-4010

Zions Bank
8100 Emerald, Suite 190
Boise, ID 83704
208-658-0606
www.zionsbank.com

Zions Bank
102 West Main
Burley, ID 83318
208-678-2291
www.zionsbank.com

Illinois

Albany Bank & Trust Co.
3400 W. Lawrence Avenue
Chicago, IL 60625
Contact: John Schellinger, Vice
President
773-267-7300
Fax: 773-267-9405
www.albanybank.com

AMCORE Bank
502 Seventh Street
Rockford, IL 61110-0037
Contact: Keith Hinrichs, Credit
Analyst
815- 961-7032
Fax: 815-961-7733
www.amcore.com

Amresco Independence Funding
700 N. Pearl Street, Suite 2400
Dallas, TX 75201-7424
214-720-1776
Fax: 214-953-8383

American Chartered Bank
1199 E. Higgins Road
Schaumburg, IL 60173
Contact: John Mangan, Senior Vice
President
847-540-5210
Fax: 847-540-8609

American National Bank
33 N. LaSalle Street
Chicago, IL 60690
Contact: Paul Collinsworth, Vice
President
614-248-1938

Banco Popular, Illinois, Inc.
4801 W. Fullerton
Chicago, IL 60639
Contact: Eva Aquino, Vice President
773-836-4253
Fax: 773-622-4389
www.bancopopular.com

Bank of America, N.A. (South)
317 Sixth Avenue
P.O. Box 817
Des Moines, IA 50304-0817
Contact: Alan Gross, President
515-235-7280
Fax: 511-243-3435
www.bankofamerica.com

Bank One, NA
One Bank One Plaza
Mail Suite, IL 1-0299
Chicago, IL 60670
Contact: Paul Collinsworth, Vice
President
614-248-1973
www.bankone.com

Bank Illinois
100 W. University
Champaign, IL 61824
Contact: Wes Curtis, Senior Vice
President
217- 351-2759
Fax: 217-351-2771
www.bankillinois.com

Bank of Charleston
621 Lincoln Avenue
Charleston, IL 61920
Contact: Don Mapes, Vice President
217-348-8131
Fax: 217-348-8210

Bank of Springfield
3400 W. Wabash
Springfield, IL 62707
Contact: Lora Pearson, Vice
President
217- 529-5555
Fax: 217-698-4578
www.bankofspringfield.com

Bank One, Illinois, NA
One East Old State Capital Plaza
Springfield, IL 62701
Contact: Mark Vance, Vice President
217- 525-9600
Fax: 217-522-7482
www.bankone.com

Banterra Bank
201 W. Main
Marion, IL 62959
Contact: Myrna Denton, Vice
President
618- 993-2678
Fax: 618-993-8820
www.banterra.com

Busey Bank
201 W. Main

Urbana, IL 61801
Contact: Tom Boaz, Vice President
217-365-4532
Fax: 217-365-4596
www.busey.com

Business Lenders LLC
15 Lewis Street
Hartford, CT 06103
Contact: Kama Giedra
877-345-6267 Ext. 124
www.businesslenders.com

Business Loan Express
1320 Tower Road, Suite 141
Schaumburg, IL 60173
Contact: Steve Lasiewicz
847-885-5632
Fax: 847-885-5634
www.businessloanexpress.net

California Bank & Trust
13545 Barrett Parkway Drive
Suite 335
Ballwin, MO 63021
Contact: Kathy Sweeney
800-722-6226 Ext. 107
Fax: 314-822-0251
www.calbanktrust.com

Central Illinois Bank
525 N. 4th
Springfield, IL 62701
Contact: David Bates, Assistant Vice
President
217-747-0222
Fax: 217-747-0225
www.centralillinoisbank.com

CIT Small Business Lending
Corporation
400 Chesterfield Center
Suite 400
Chesterfield, MO 63017
Contact: Carolyn Gregg
636-458-2330
Fax: 636-458-7666
www.smallbizlending.com

CIT Small Business Lending
Corporation
1601 Colonia Parkway
Inverness, IL 60067
Contact: Richard Trotter
847-934-0559
Fax: 847-934-0594
www.smallbizlending.com

CIT Small Business Lending
Corporation
918 South Austin Blvd., Unit 1-S
Oak Park, IL 60304
Contact: Tim Landry
708-660-1230
Fax: 708-660-1231
www.smallbizlending.com

Citibank FSB
500 W. Madison, 5th Floor
Chicago, IL 60661

Contact: Ginger Siegel, Vice
President
312-627-3184
Fax: 312-627-3577
www.citibank.com

CitiCapital Small Business Finance,
Inc.
300 E. Carpenter Freeway
Irving, TX 75062
Contact: Jeannie Baldwin
972-652-3324
Fax: 972-652-3340

Comerica Bank
1250 S. Grove Avenue, Suite 200
Barrington, IL 60010
Contact: Thomas J. Meyer, Vice
President
847-381-5959
Fax: 847-381-2536
www.comerica.com

Cosmopolitan Bank
801 N. Clark Street
Chicago, IL 60610-3287
Contact: Antonio Gullen, Vice
President
312-335-4553
Fax: 312-335-4512
www.cosmopolitanbank.com

Fifth Third Bank
102 W. Front Street, P.O. Box 589
Traverse City, MI 49685-0589
Contact: Brad Dyskerhouse, SBA
Department Manager
231-922-4124
Fax: 231-922-4034
(Numerous Illinois Locations)
http://53.com

First Bank of Illinois
200 S. Lincoln Avenue
O'Fallon, IL 62269
Contact: Patrick Higgins
314-692-6310
Fax: 314-567-7341

First Mid-Illinois Bank & Trust
1515 Charleston Avenue
Mattoon, IL 61938
Contact: Robert Weber, Vice
President
217-234-7454
Fax: 217-258-0426
www.firstmid.com

First National Bank of Mullberry
Grove
1300 U. S. Highway 40
Greenville, IL 62246
Contact: Preston Smith, President
618-664-0300
Fax: 618-664-0331

First Western SBLC, Inc.
18111 Preston Road, Suite 600
Dallas, TX 75252
Contact: Mary Brownmiller

972-349-3200
Fax: 972-349-3265

Foster Bank
5225 N. Kedzie Avenue
Chicago, IL 60625
Contact: Christine Yoon, Loan
Officer
773-588-3355
Fax: 773-588-2507
www.fosterbank.com

G.E. Capital Small Business Finance
Corp.
635 Maryville Central Park
Suite 120
Saint Louis, MO 63141
Contact: Tammy Christopher
314-205-3500
Fax: 314-205-3697
www.ge.com/capital/smallbiz

Greater Chicago Bank
219 S. Mannheim Road
Bellwood, IL 60104
Contact: George Anderson, Senior
Vice President
708-547-3671
Fax: 708-547-4069
Contact: Robert J. Foy, President
773-465-7555
Fax: 773-465-4598

Great Lakes Bank
11346 S. Cicero
Alsip, IL 60808
Contact: Gary Wesner
708-283-7266
Fax: 708-388-1990
www.great-lakes-bank.com

Harris Trust & Savings Bank
111 W. Monroe Street
Chicago, IL 60690-0755
Contact: Angela Smith, Vice
President
312-461-2330
Fax: 312-765-8348
www.harrisbank.com

Heartland Bank
3400 Court Street
Pekin, IL 61554
Contact: Timothy L. Owen,
Executive Vice President
309-347-6626
Fax: 309-347-7916
www.hbtbank.com

Illinois National Bank
322 E. Capitol
Springfield, IL 62701
Contact: John Maxfield, Vice
President
217-747-5549
Fax: 217-747-5510
www.illinoisnationalbank.com

LaSalle Bank, N.A.
3201 N. Ashland Avenue
Chicago, IL 60657

Contact: Tamina O'Neill, 1st Vice
President & Manager of Government
Lending
773-244-7471
Fax: 773-244-7399
Numerous Illinois Locations
www.lasallebank.com

Marine Bank
3050 W. Wabash Avenue
Springfield, IL 62704
Contact: Don Brookhart, Vice
President
217-726-0600
Fax: 217-726-0619

Nara Bank, N.A.
3701 Wilshire Blvd., Suite 302
Los Angeles, CA 90010
Contact: Jimmy Bang, Vice
President
213-427-6340
Fax: 213-383-0906
www.narabankna.com

National City Bank
236 N. Water
Decatur, IL 62523
Contact: Jerry Furby, Vice President
217-424-2152
Fax: 217-424-2248
www.nationalcity.com

National City Bank
170 N. Ottawa Street
Joliet, IL 60431
Contact: Kim Hopkins, Vice
President
815-740-4774
Fax: 815-740-7236
Contact: Jim Miller, Vice President
217-363-4052
Fax: 217-363-4065
Numerous Illinois Locations
www.nationalcity.com

Old National Bank
509 S. University
Carbondale, IL 62901
Contact: Greg Ingram, Vice
President
618-457-3381
Fax: 618-529-7574
www.oldnational.com

Old National Bank
Two W. Main Street
Danville, IL 61834
Contact: Dean Murphy, Vice
President
217-446-6450
Fax: 217-477-5896
www.oldnational.com

Old Second National Bank of Aurora
37 S. River Street
Aurora, IL 60507
Contact: John Medernach
630-906-5482
Fax: 630-892-2412

Peoples National Bank
413 S. 34th Street
Mount Vernon, IL 62864
Contact: Jo David Cummins, Senior
Vice President
618-244-4777
Fax: 618-244-9561
www.peoplesnationalbank.com

Plaza Bank
7460 W. Irving Park Road
Norridge, IL 60634
Contact: Jack Jones, Commercial
Loan Representative
773-625-4100
Fax: 708-583-3805
www.plazabankillinois.com

South Central Bank & Trust
555 W. Roosevelt Road
Chicago, IL 60607
Contact: Todd Grayson, Vice
President
312-421-7100
Fax: 312-421-1240
www.banksouthcentral.com

South Shore Bank of Chicago
7936 S. Cottage Grove
Chicago, IL 60619
Contact: Joe Crump
773-420-5365
Fax: 773-487-4714

Soy Capital Bank and Trust
Company
455 N. Main Street
Decatur, IL 62523
Contact: Bruce Moore, Vice
President
217-428-7781
Fax: 217-429-8712
www.soybank.com

State Bank of Lincoln
508 Broadway
Lincoln, IL 62656
Contact: Paul Short, Senior Vice
President
217-735-5551
Fax: 217-735-2716
www.sblincoln.com

Union Bank/Sandwich
400 Etna Road
Ottawa, IL 61350
Contact: Tricia Kilburn-Zehr
815-673-4471
Fax: 815-673-4406

Union Federal Savings Bank
45 N. Pennsylvania Street
Indianapolis, IN 46204
Contact: Rob Nance, Assistant Vice
President
317-269-4825
Fax: 317-269-4640

Union National Bank & Trust
Company

1 Fountain Square Plaza
Elgin, IL 60120
Contact: Jay Deihs, Senior Vice
President
847-888-7500
Fax: 847-888-2662

Union Planters
7650 Magna Drive
Belleville, IL 62223
Contact: Ed Broderhausen
800-444-7041
Fax: 618-239-4887
www.unionplanters.com

U S Bank, NA
9918 Hibart Street 3rd Floor
San Diego, CA 92131-1018
Contact: David Bartrum, Senior
Executive Vice President
800-269-4309 Ext. 304
Fax: 858-536-1502
www.usbank.com

Wells Fargo
200 E. Main
Galesburg, IL 61401
Contact: Mr. Charles R. Torman
319-345-4696
Fax: 319-345-4744
www.wellsfargo.com

Wells Fargo
1455 W. Lake Street
Minnesota, MN 55479-2083
Contact: Tom Burke
612-667-2753
Fax: 612-706-0977
www.wellsfargo.com

Indiana

1st Source Bank
100 North Michigan Street
South Bend, IN 46634
574-235-2000
www.1stsource.com

Allied Capital SBLC Corporation
8888 Keystone Crossing, Suite 1300
Indianapolis, IN 46240
317-581-8568

Bank One, Indiana, N.A.
111 Monument Circle
Suite 971
Indianapolis, IN 46277
317-321-3000
www.bankone.com

Bank of the West, N.A.
10181 Truckee Airport Road
Truckee, CA 96161
847-839-7080

Busey Business Bank
10321-B North Pennsylvania Street
Indianapolis, IN 46280
317-574-1540
www.busey.com

Business Loan Center
1301 N. Hamilton Street, Suite 200
Richmond, VA 23230
888-333-6441

CIT Small Business Lending
6732 East State Street, PMB 215
Fort Wayne, IN 46815
Contact: Timothy Berry
260-748-7752
Fax: 260-748-7762
www.smallbizlending.com

CIT Small Business Lending
Corporation
4319 West Clara Lane, #297
Muncie, IN 47304
Contact: Wade Philips
765-254-1940
Fax: 765-254-1952
www.smallbizlending.com

Centier Bank
1500 119th Street
Whiting, IN 46394
219-659-0043
www.centier.com

Comerica Bank
250 East Fifth Street, Suite 1500
Cincinnati, OH 45202
513-762-7660
www.comerica.com

Fifth Third Bank of Central Indiana
251 North Illinois Street, Suite 1000
Indianapolis, IN 46204
317-383-2412
http://53.com

First National Bank and Trust
3901 West 86th Street, Suite 131
P.O. Box 68372
Indianapolis, IN 46268-0372
317-875-9500

G.E. Capital Small Business Finance
Corp.
635 Maryville Centre Drive, Suite
120
St. Louis, MO 63141
800-447-2025 ext. 3568
www.ge.com/capital/smallbiz

Heller Business Finance
500 West Monroe, 19th Floor
Chicago, IL 60661
877-441-0891

Huntington National Bank of Indiana
201 North Illinois, Suite 1701
Indianapolis, IN 46204
317-237-2594
www.huntington.com

KeyBank
10 West Market Street
Indianapolis, IN 46204
317-464-2349
www.keybank.com

National City Bank of Indiana
One National City Center 700E
Indianapolis, IN 46255
317-267-8887
www.nationalcity.com

Old National Bank
101 West Ohio Street
Suite 1400
Indianapolis, IN 46204
317-693-3240
www.oldnational.com

PNC Bank, N.A.
4753 North Broad Street
Philadelphia, PA 19141
215-456-5200
www.pncbank.com

Republic Bank
201 South Capitol, Suite 650
Indianapolis, IN 46225
317-237-5334
www.republicbancorp.com

Sunrise Bank of Arizona
4350 East Camelback Road, Suite
#100A
Phoenix, AZ 85018
602-956-6250
www.sunrisebankofarizona.com

Union Planters Bank, N.A.
One Indiana Square
Indianapolis, IN 46204
317-221-6046
www.unionplanters.com

U.S. Bank
10 West Market Street
Indianapolis, IN 46204
317-822-1800
www.usbank.com

Union Federal Bank
45 North Pennsylvania Street
Indianapolis, IN 46204
317-269-4723
www.unionfedbankonline.com

Unizan Bank, N.A.
8425 Woodfield Crossing Blvd.,
Suite 100
Indianapolis, IN 46240
317-469-7575

Wachovia Small Business Capital
3815 River Crossing Parkway
Suite 100
Indianapolis, IN 46240
317-566-2140
www.wachovia.com/small_biz

Wells Fargo Bank
Indianapolis Office
10401 N Meridian Street
Indianapolis, IN 46290
317-581-6218
www.wellsfargo.com

Wells Fargo Bank Calhoun-Isles
Office
1455 West Lake Street
Minneapolis, MN 55408
612-667-2836
www.wellsfargo.com

Iowa

Bank of America
10850 White Rock Rd., Suite 101
Rancho Cordova, CA 95670
www.bankofamerica.com

Bank of America, N.A.
Locust at Sixth
Des Moines, IA 50309
Contact: Frank Spillers, President
515-235-7180
Fax: 515-243-3435
www.bankofamerica.com

Bank of America, N.A.
705 Grand Ave.
Spencer, IA 51301
Contact: Susan Christensen,
Business Banker
712-262-2200
Fax: 712-262-9338
www.bankofamerica.com

Bankers Trust Company
P.O. Box 897
Des Moines, IA 50309
Contact: Rob Reinard, Asst. Vice
President
515-245-2424
Fax: 515-245-5216

Business Loan Express
121 W. Dewey Street, Suite 210
Wichita, KS 67202
316-263-3232
Fax: 316-263-4391
www.businessloanexpress.net

CIT Capital Small Business Lending
Corporation
1 CIT Drive
Livingston, NJ 07039
800-221-7252
www.citsmallbizlending.com

Commercial Savings Bank
627 N. Adams
P.O. Box 277
Contact: Patrick Moehn, President
Carroll, IA 51401
712-792-4346
Fax: 712-792-1488

Commercial Trust & Savings Bank
600 Lake Ave.
Storm Lake, IA 50588
Contact: Timothy J. Brown,
President
712-732-2190
Fax: 712-732-5049

Community First National Bank
120 W. Water Street

Decorah, IA 52110-0110
563-382-2991

Community Savings Bank
101 E. Union
Edgewood, IA 52042-0077
563-928-6425
www.csbiowa.com

Dubuque Bank & Trust Co.
1398 Central Avenue
Dubuque, IA 52001-0778
563-589-2000
www.dubuquebank.com

Farmers & Merchants Savings Bank
101 E. Main St.
Manchester, IA 52057-0588
563-927-2979

Farmers & Merchants Savings Bank
4020 First Ave. NE
Cedar Rapids, IA 52402
319-366-8681

Farmers State Bank
1310 6th Street
Jesup, IA 50648-0703
319-827-1050

Farmers State Bank
1240 8th Avenue
Marion, IA 52302-0569
319-377-4891

First Central State Bank
914 Sixth Avenue
DeWitt, IA 52742-0119
563-659-3141
www.firstcentralsb.com

First Western SBLC, Inc.
17290 Preston Road
Dallas, TX 75252
212-380-0044

G.E. Capital Small Business Finance
635 Maryville Centre Drive
Suite 120
St. Louis, MO 63141
www.ge.com/capital/smallbiz

Heritage Bank
318 2nd Street
S.W. Willmar, MN 56201-1124
Contact: Thomas E. Kelleher, Vice
President Heritage
612-235-5720

Iowa Bank
300 N 2nd Street
Bellevue, IA 52031-1232
563-872-5515
www.iowabank.net

Iowa State Bank & Trust Co.
102 S. Clinton Street
Iowa City, IA 52244-1700
319-356-5800
www.isbt.com

Maquoketa State Bank
203 N. Main
Maquoketa, IA 52060-1210
563-652-2491
www.maquoketasb.com

Stearns Bank National Association
4191 Second St. S.
Saint Cloud, MN 56302
320-253-6607
800-320-7262
Fax: 320-253-3051
www.stearns-bank.com

Union Planters Bank
4357 Czech Lane NE
Cedar Rapids, IA 52402
319-393-8745
www.unionplanters.com

Union Planters Bank
623 High Street
Des Moines, IA 50309
Contact: Kathy Hioch
515-283-1951
Fax: 515-284-1025
www.unionplanters.com

Union Planters Bank
1510 North First Street
Indianola, IA 50125
Contact: Ralph P. DiCesare III
515-961-9618
Fax: 515-961-9617
www.unionplanters.com

Union Planters Bank
114 N Howard
Indianola, IA 50125
515-961-6241
515-961-9600
www.unionplanters.com

Union Planters Bank
150 E. Court Street
Iowa City, IA 52240
319-351-8262
www.unionplanters.com

Union Planters Bank
368 N Highway 28
Martensdale, IA 50106
641-764-2616
www.unionplanters.com

Union Planters Bank
202 W. 1st Street
Monticello, IA 52310-0231
319-465-3505
www.unionplanters.com

Union Planters Bank
25 N. Frederick
Oelwein, IA 50662-0591
319-283-3361
www.unionplanters.com

Union Planters Bank
2851 86th Street
Urbandale, IA 50322

Contact: Ed Arndorfer
515-237-8630
Fax: 515-270-9730
www.unionplanters.com

Union Planters Bank
100 E. Park Avenue
Waterloo, IA 50703-0090
319-291-5200
www.unionplanters.com

Union Planters Bank
3334 Westown Pkwy
West Des Moines, IA 50266
Contact: Diana Simon
515-235-8340
Fax: 515-223-5469
www.unionplanters.com

U.S. Bank
P.O. Box 828
Ames, IA 50010
Contact: Anthony Hotchkiss,
Business Bank Manager
515-232-8200
Fax: 515-232-5865
www.usbank.com

U.S. Bank NA
201 Jefferson
Burlington, IA 52601-1088
319-752-2761
www.usbank.com

U.S. Bank NA
222 Washington Street
Cedar Falls, IA 50613-0039
319-277-1320
www.usbank.com

U.S. Bank NA
222 Second Avenue SE
Cedar Rapids, IA 52401-1296
319-368-4444
www.usbank.com

U.S. Bank NA
340 5th Avenue S.
Clinton, IA 52732
563-243-1512
www.usbank.com

U.S. Bank NA
201 W. 2nd Street
Davenport, IA 52805-0940
563-328-3100
www.usbank.com

U.S. Bank, N.A.
P.O. Box 906
Des Moines, IA 50309
Contact: Brian Bonds, Asst. Vice
President
515-245-6210
Fax: 515-247-4911
www.usbank.com

U.S. Bank NA
2560 Dodge Street
Dubuque, IA 52003-1030

563-557-9000
www.usbank.com

U.S. Bank NA
301 E. Washington
Mount Pleasant, IA 52641
319-385-3134
www.usbank.com

U.S. Bank
112 W. 2nd Street S.
Newton, IA 50208
Contact: Dennis Porter, Vice
President
515-792-3444
515-792-2206
www.usbank.com

Wells Fargo Bank NA
302 Main Street
Cedar Falls, IA 50613
319-273-8800
www.wellsfargo.com

Wells Fargo Bank
1800 First Avenue NE
Cedar Rapids, IA 52402
319-286-1800
www.wellsfargo.com

Wells Fargo Bank NA
101 Third Ave. SW
Cedar Rapids, IA 52406-1887
319-364-0191
www.wellsfargo.com

Wells Fargo Bank NA
203 W. 3rd Street
Davenport, IA 52801-1977
563-383-3200
www.wellsfargo.com

Wells Fargo Bank, N.A.
P.O. Box 837
Des Moines, IA 50309
Robert L. Stoner, Jr., Vice President
515-245-3131
Fax: 515-245-3128
www.wellsfargo.com

Wells Fargo Bank, N.A.
822 Central Avenue
Fort Dodge, IA 50501
Mike Scacci, Vice President
515-573-6132
Fax: 515-573-6147
www.wellsfargo.com

Wells Fargo Bank NA
191 W. 5th Street
Waterloo, IA 50704-0360
319-235-4800
www.wellsfargo.com

West Des Moines State Bank
1601 22nd Street
West Des Moines, IA 50265
Contact: Michele A. Belden, Vice
President
515-222-2300

Fax: 515-222-2346
www.westbankiowa.com

Kansas

Bank of America National Trust
100 North Broadway
Wichita, KS 67201
Contact: Teresa Wallweber, Vice
President
316-261-2191
Fax: 316-261-2234

Business Loan Express
121 W. Dewey, Suite 210
Wichita, KS 67202
Contact: Deryl Schuster, President
316-263-3232
Fax: 316-263-4391
www.businessloanexpress.com

Business Loan Express
7111 West 151st Street, #221
Overland Park, KS 66223
913-390-6393
Fax: 913-390-6564
www.businessloanexpress.net

Commerce Bank
P.O. Box 637
Wichita, KS 67201
Contact: Ron Heikes, Vice President
316-261-4700
Fax: 316-261-4793
www.commercebank.com

Emprise Bank, N.A.
P.O. Box 400
Hays, KS 67601
Contact: Randy Walker, Vice
President
785-625-6595
Fax: 785-625-9561
www.emprise.com

First Union Small Business Capital
8500 College Blvd. Suite 125
Overland Park, KS 66210
Contact: Reed Nixon, Business
Development Officer
913-338-7144
Fax: 913-338-5093

Farmers Bank & Trust, N.A.
1017 Harrison
Great Bend, KS 67530
Contact: Karesa Harrison, Vice
President
316-792-2411
Fax: 316-793-8526
www.farmersbankna.com

GE Capital Small Business Finance
818 E. Orme
Wichita, KS 67211
Contact: Brent Koehn
316-303-3515
www.ge.com/capital/smallbiz

INTRUST Bank
P.O. Box 1

Wichita, KS 67201
Contact: John J. Luerding, Executive
Vice President
316-383-1266
Fax: 316-383-1665
www.intrustbank.com

Pioneer Bank & Trust
8921 W. 21st Street
Wichita, KS 67205-1812
Contact: L. D. Carney, Jr.
316-721-9660

Transamerica Small Business
Capital, Inc.
9393 W. 110th Street, Suite 534
Overland Park, KS 66210
Contact: Clark A. Churchill, Vice
President
913-451-6776
913-451-6782

Tyco Capital Small Business
Lending Corp.
12120 State Line Rd., Suite 157
Leawood, KS 66209
Contact: Paul Jokerst, Regional
Accounts Manager
816-941-2090
Fax: 816-941-0081

U. S. Bank, N.A.
9918 Hibert St., 3rd Floor
San Diego, CA 92131
Contact: David Bartram, President
www.usbank.com

Kentucky

Amresco Independence Funding Co,
LLC
700 N. Pearl Street, Suite 2400
Dallas, TX 75201-7424
Contact: Mr. Charles Bell
214-953-8908

Bank One, Kentucky, N.A.
P.O. Box 32500
Louisville KY 40232-2500
Contact: Jeff Norton
502-566-4861
www.bankone.com

Branch Banking & Trust Co.
150 S. Stratford Rd., Suite 200
Winston-Salem, NC 27104
Contact: Mr. David Mann
336-733-3441
www.bbandt.com

Business Loan Express
1301 N. Hamilton Street, Suite 200
Richmond, VA 23230
Contact: Mr. Matthew Mcgee
888-333-6441
www.businessloanexpress.nrt

Comerica Bank
P.O. Box 4167
Houston, TX 77210-4167
Contact: Keith Reed

513-762-7660 (Cincinnati Office)
www.comerica.com

Fifth Third Bank
401 S. 4th Avenue
Louisville KY 40202
Contact: Mr. Robert Cline
502-562-5572
http://53.com

Fifth Third Bank Of Northern
Kentucky
8100 Burlington Pike
Florence, KY 41042-1212
606-283-6817
Contact: Mr. Matthew McCoy
(Pendleton & Campbell Co)
606-283-8530
Contact: Mr. D. Scott Robinson
(Kenton & Boone Co)
http://53.com

First Union Small Business Capital
Formerly The Money Store
4555 Lake Forest Drive
650 Westlake Center
Cincinnati, OH 45242
Contact: Mr. Keith Reed
800-890-0092

First Western SBLC Inc
Subsidiary Of PMC Capital Inc
18111 Preston Rd, Suite 600
Dallas, TX 75252
Contact: Ms. Mary J. Brownmiller
972-349-3200

GE Capital Small Business Finance
6100 Fairview Rd., Suite 305
Charlotte, NC 28210
Contact: Mr. Kale B. Gaston
704-643-6360
704-643-6379
www.gesmallbusiness.com

National City Bank
P.O. Box 36000
Louisville, KY 40233-6000
Contact: Mr. Alan Kissel (Louisville
& W. KY)
502-581-6394
Contact: Mr. David Simpson
(Central & E. KY)
606-238-1027
Contact: Randy Goode (Exporting
Loan Officer)
502-581-4086

PNC Bank Kentucky Inc.
Citizens Plaza 5th Floor
Louisville, KY 40296
Contact: Mr. Don Gossman
502-581-2038

Stock Yards Bank & Trust Co.
1040 E. Main St
Louisville, KY 40206
Contact: Mr. Samuel Winkler
502-625-1000

Union Planters Bank Na
7650 Magna Drive
Belleville, IL 62223-3367
Contact: Mr. Ed Broderhausen
618-257-0183
www.unionplanters.com

Unizan Bank
(F/K/A/ Bank First National
66 South Third Street
Columbus, OH 43215
Contact: Mr. James Baemel
614-462-2806

US Bank (Formerly First Star)
4500 Bowling Blvd Suite 100
Louisville, KY 40207
Contact: Mr. Doug Sutton or Mr.
Mark Gibson
502-894-6036
www.usbank.com

The Vine Street Trust Company
360 Vine Street
Lexington KY 40507
Contact: Mr. Brian Faulk
770-0551-8822 (Atlanta Office)

Washington Mutual
4020 Westchase Blvd #100
Raleigh, NC 27607
Contact: Mr. Dave White
919-839-5511
www.wamu.com

Wells Fargo
1455 West Lake St.
Minneapolis, MN 55479
Contact: Mr. Jeff Kirklighter
859-252-9696 (Lexington Office)
www.wellsfargo.com

Louisiana
AT & T Capital Corp.
44 Whippany Road
Morristown NJ 07962
201-397-4077
Fax: 201-397-4086

Bank of W. Baton Rouge
320 N. Alexander Avenue
Port Allen LA 70821
504-387-0011
Fax: 504-383-4420

Central Progressive Bank
400 North Oak Street
Amite, LA 70422-0916
504-748-7157
Fax: 504-748-7426

Dryades Savings Bank
233 Carondelet Street
New Orleans, LA 70130
504-581-5891
Fax: 504-598-7233

First BIDCO
(Source Capital)
455 E. Airport Blvd.

Baton Rouge, LA 70821
504-922-7411
Fax: 504-922-7418

First Western SBLC, Inc.
17290 Preston Rd, 3rd Floor
Dallas TX 75252
214-380-0044
Fax: 214-380-1371

GE Small Business Finance
5068 Woodside Dr.
Baton Rouge, LA 70808
504-201-1180
Fax: 888-997-6560

Gulf Coast Bank
221 South State Street
Abbeville LA 70510
318-893-7733
Fax: 318-893-7319

Gulf Coast Bank & Trust
200 St. Charles Avenue
New Orleans LA 70130
504-581-4561
Fax: 504-581-3583

Hibernia National Bank
313 Carondelet Street
New Orleans LA 70161
504-533-5552
Fax: 504-533-2367

Iberville Trust Savings
23405 Eden Street
Plaquemine LA 70765
504-687-2091
Fax: 504-687-0539

Independence Funding, Inc.
3010 LBJ Freeway, Suite 920
Dallas, TX 75234
800-225-1776
Fax: 972-287-1776

Metro Bank
3235 N. Causeway Blvd.
Metairie LA 70002
504-834-6755
Fax: 504-443-5352

Midsouth Bank
102 Versailles
Lafayette LA 70501
318-237-8343
Fax: 318-237-4434

The Money Store
4050 Innslake Drive, Suite 210
Glen Allen VA 23060
804-273-6859
Fax: 804-273-6871

OMNI Bank
2900 Ridgelake Drive
Metairie LA 70011
504-833-2900
Fax: 504-841-2054

Plaquemine Bank & Trust
24025 Eden Street
Plaquemine LA 70764
504-687-6388
Fax: 504 687-5323

Tri-Parish Bank
301 West Laurel
Eunice LA 70535
318-457-7341
Fax: 318-457-7314

Union Planters Bank
8440 Jefferson Hwy.
Baton Rouge, LA 70809
504-927-1220
Fax: 504-924-9300

Whitney National Bank
228 St. Charles Ave.
New Orleans LA 70161
504-586-7272
Fax: 504-586 3613

Maine
Bangor Savings Bank
3 State Street
Bangor, ME 04401
207-942-5211
Fax: 207-942-2836

Business Lenders, LLC
49 Walnut Park Building
Wellesley, MA 02181
800-223-9949
617-416-9995

Business Loan Express
121 W. Dewey, Suite 210
Wichita, KS 67202
316-263-3232
Fax: 316-263-4391
www.businessloanexpress.net

Citizens Bank of New Hampshire
875 Elm Street
Manchester, NH 03101
603-634-6000
Fax: 603-634-7392

First National Bank of Bar Harbor
102 Main Street
Bar Harbor, ME 04609
207-288-3341
Fax: 207-288-2451

Fleet Bank of Maine
1 City Center
Portland, ME 04104
207-874-5000
Fax: 207-874-5117

Gorham Savings Bank
64 Main Street
Gorham, ME 04038
207-839-3342
Fax: 207-839-4790

Kennebunk Savings Bank
104 Main Street

Kennebunk, ME 04043
207-985-4903
Fax: 207-984-6034

KeyBank National Association
179 John Roberts Road
So Portland, ME 04106
207-842-1051
Fax: 207-842-1050

Merrill Merchants Bank
201 Main Street
Bangor, ME 04402
207-942-4800
Fax: 207-942-9255

Northeast Bank, F.S.B.
232 Center Street
Auburn, ME 04210
207-777-6411
Fax: 207-777-6410

Norway National Bank
132 Main Street, P.O. Box 347
Norway, ME 04268
207-743-7986
Fax: 207-743-5376

Peoples, a Division of Banknorth, N.A.
One Portland Square
Portland, ME 04112
207-761-8500
Fax: 207-761-8536

Pepperell Bank & Trust
163 Main Street
Biddeford, ME 04005
207-284-4591
Fax: 207-282-7908

Sanford Institution For Savings
209 Main Street
Sanford, ME 04073
207-324-2285
Fax: 207-324-1928

Transamerica Small Business
Capital, Inc.
7 N Lawrens Street, Suite 601
Greenville, SC 29601
864-232-6197
Fax: 864-235-8065

Union Trust Company
66 Main Street
Ellsworth, ME 04605
207-667-2504
Fax: 207-667-3601

Maryland

Bank of Annapolis
1000 Bestgate Road, Suite 400
Annapolis, MD 21401
800-582-2651
410-224-4455
www.bankannapolis.com

Bank of America
Small Business Sales

NC1-026-02-02
P.O. Box 25118
Tampa, FL 25118
800-333-6262
www.bankofamerica.com

Branch Banking & Trust
5 Church Circle
Annapolis, MD 21401-1926
410-626-2251
Fax: 410-626-2258
www.bbandt.com

Business Loan Express
645 Madison Avenue
New York, NY 10022
800-SBA-LOAN
Fax: 212-888-3949
www.businessloanexpress.net

CIT Small Business Lending
Corporation
15200 Shady Grove Road, Suite 350
Rockville, MD 20850
301-428-1001
800-713-4984
Fax: 301-428-1881
www.smallbizlending.com

CIT Small Business Lending
Corporation
18222 Flower Hill Way, Suite 142
Gaithersburg, MD 20879
301-947-9634
800-713-4984
Fax: 301-947-9635
www.smallbizlending.com

Carrollton Bank
344 North Charles Street, Suite 300
Baltimore, MD 21201
410-737-7457
www.carrolltonbank.com

Columbia Bank
7168 Columbia Gateway Drive
Columbia, MD 21046
410-296-0490
www.thecolumbiabank.com

Development Credit Fund. Inc.
2530 North Charles Street
Suite 200
Baltimore, MD 21218
410-467-7500
Fax: 410-467-7988
www.developmentcredit.com

Farmers & Merchants Bank and
Trust
59 West Washington Street
Hagerstown, MD 21740
800-228-BANK
www.fmbt.com

Farmers & Merchants Bank
P.O. Box 518
Frederick, MD 21705-0518
301-662-8231
Fax: 301-662-4172

800-388-9500
www.fmbn.com

My First United Bank
Center City Office
Centre & Harrison Streets
Cumberland, MD 21502
888-69-2654
www.mybankfirstunited.com

G.E. Capital Small Business Finance
Corp.
888-335-4372
www.gecommercialfinance.com

The Harbor Bank
3240 Belair Road
Baltimore, MD 21213
410-528-1801
888-833-7920
www.theharborbank.com

K Bank
7F Gwynns Mill court
P.O. Box 429
Owings Mill, MD 21117
410-363-7050
Fax: 410-363-3569
www.kbank.net

M&T Bank
410-512-4771
800-724-6070
www.mandtbank.com
Contact local bank 800 # is for
business banking

Nara Bank
213-427-6340
www.narabank.com

Peninsula Bank
P.O. Box 219
Princess Anne, MD 21853
888-870-0500
410-651-2400
Fax: 410-651-0179
www.peninsulabankmd.com

Provident Bank of Maryland
410-277-2090
800-274-2873
www.provbank.com

Susquehanna Bank
100 West Road
Baltimore, MD 21204
888-400-9866
www.susqbkmd.com

Valley National Bank
1445 Valley Road
Wayne, NJ 07470
800-522-4100
973-305-4034
www.valleynationalbank.com

Westminster Union Bank
P.O. Box 29
Westminster, MD 21158

888-820-5500
410-848-9300
Fax: 410-876-7737
www.westminsterunionbank.com

Massachusetts

Abington Savings Bank
533 Washington Street
Abington, MA 02351
Contact: Mr. James Hanlon, Vice
President
781-982-3667
Fax: 781-878-4149

Bank of Western Massachusetts
29 State Street
Springfield, MA 01103
Contact: Mr. Steven Robinson, Vice
President
413-781-2265
Fax: 413-781-8022

Bay State Savings Bank
28 Franklin Street
Worcester, MA 01608
Contact: Mr. Walter Dwyer, Vice
President
508-890-9051
Fax: 508-751-6459

Business Lenders, LLC
49 Walnut Park Bldg. #5
Wellesley, MA 02481
Contact: Ms. Nancy Reynolds, Vice
President
781-416-9993
Fax: 781-416-9995

Business Loan Express
1 New Hampshire Avenue
Suite 125
Portsmouth, NH 03801
603-882-3379
Fax: 603-766-1907
www.businessloanexpress.net

Cape Cod Bank & Trust Co.
307 Main Street
Hyannis, MA 02601
Contact: Ms. Berta Bruinooge,
Assistant Vice President
508-862-6431
Fax: 508-760-9378

Capital Crossing Bank
101 Summer Street
Boston, MA 02110
Contact: Mr. Kenneth Weidman,
Senior Vice President
617-880-1000
Fax: 617-880-1010

Chittenden Trust Company
P.O. Box 459
Montpelier, VT 05601
Contact: Ms. Alice Durkin, Vice
President
802-223-8550
Fax: 802-223-6165

CIT Small Business Lending
319 Centre Avenue, PMB #164
Rockland, MA 02370
Contact: Ms. Barbara Arena, Sr.
Reg. Acct. Mgr.
781-294-2244
Fax: 781-294-2064
www.smallbizlending.com

Citizens Bank
100 Sockanossett Crossroads
Cranston, RI 02920
Contact: Mr. Gary Heidel,
Director/Government City Programs
401-734-5617
Fax: 401-734-5621

Commerce Bank & Trust
PO Box 15020
Worcester, MA 01615-0020
Contact: Mr. Brian Chandley, Vice
President
508-797-6881
Fax: 508-797-6933

Commercial Capital Corporation
11 Asylum Street
Hartford, CT 06103
Contact: Mr. Edward Burke, Vice
President
860-293-0169
Fax: 860-293-0170

Danvers Savings Bank
1 Conant Street
Danvers, MA 01923
Contact: Mr. Daniel Rich, Senior
Vice President
978-739-0245
Fax: 978-762-6216

Eastern Bank
One Eastern Place
Lynn, MA 01901-1508
Contact: Mr. Pete Kaznoski, Vice
President
781-596-4594
Fax: 781-596-4591

Enterprise Bank & Trust Co.
222 Merrimack Street
Lowell, MA 01852
Contact: Mr. Richard Chavez,
Commercial Loan Officer
978-459-9000
Fax: 978-656-5850

Enterprise Capital, Inc.
1485 South County Trail
East Greenwich, RI 02818
Contact: Mr. Kevin Chamberlain,
Vice President
401-886-4600
Fax: 401-884-9551

First Essex Bank
296 Essex Street
Lawrence, MA 01840
Contact: Ms. Aline Sanz, Assistant
Vice President

978-681-7500
Fax: 978-975-1055

First International Bank
175 Federal Street
Boston, MA 02110
Contact: Mr. Jack Mello, Senior
Vice President
617-357-0511
Fax: 617-357-0502

First Union Small Business Capital
707 3rd St., 2nd Floor
West Sacramento, CA 95605
Contact: Mr. Gary Miller, Vice
President
916-617-1879
Fax: 916-617-1348

Flagship Bank & Trust
120 Front Street
Worcester, MA 01613
Contact: Mr. Blain Marchand, Vice
President
508-890-5173
Fax: 508-797-5163

Fleet Bank
1025 Main Street
Waltham, MA 02451
Contact: Ms. Tracy Murphy, Vice
President
781-788-7406
Fax: 781-788-1027

Florence Savings Bank
85 Main Street
Florence, MA 01062
Contact: Mr. Mark Grumoli,
Assistant Vice President
413-587-1728
Fax: 413-585-9399

GE Capital
635 Maryville Centre Dr., Suite 120
St. Louis, MO 63141
Contact: Mr. William Duffek,
National Risk Manager
314-205-3602
Fax: 314-851-2190
www.gesmallbusiness.com

Home Loan & Investment Bank FSB
One Home Loan Plaza
Warwick, RI 02886
Contact: Mr. James Roche,
Commercial Lending Manager
401-739-8800
Fax: 401-739-9711

Lawrence Savings Bank
30 Massachusetts Avenue
North Andover, MA 01845-3460
Contact: Mr. Steven Ventre, Vice
President
978-725-7614
Fax: 978-725-7607

Massachusetts Business Dev. Corp.
50 Milk Street

Boston, MA 02109
Contact: Ms. Elizabeth M. Trifone,
Vice President
617-350-8877
Fax: 617-350-0052

Middlesex Savings Bank
6 Main Street
Natick, MA 01760
Contact: Mr. Timothy Fahey, Senior
Vice President
508-652-2643
Fax: 508-652-9109

Norwood Cooperative Bank
11 Central Street
Norwood, MA 02062-3570
Contact: Mr. Robert Belanger, Vice
President
781-762-1800
Fax: 781-255-7877

Rockland Trust Co.
288 Union Street
Rockland, MA 02370
Contact: Mr. John E. Berton,
Assistant Vice President
781-982-6442
Fax: 781-982-6531

Sovereign Bank
2 Morrissey Blvd.
Dorchester, MA 02125
Contact: Mr. Michael Savage, Vice
President
617-533-1745
Fax: 617-533-1766

Textron Business Credit, Inc.
40 Westminster Street
Providence, RI 02903
Contact: Ms. Jennifer Walls, Vice
President
401-621-8884
Fax: 401-621-5054

Washington Mutual
4020 Westchase Blvd.
Suite 100
Raleigh, NC 27607
Contact: Mr. Dave White, Senior
Vice President
919-839-5511
Fax: 919-839-0706
www.washingtonmutual.com

Zions First National Bank
2200 South, 3270 West
West Valley City, UT 84119
Contact: Ms. Ruth Defrates, SBA
Manager
801-887-4277
Fax: 801-887-4265

Michigan

Bank One
201 West Schrock Road
Westerville, OH 43081
614-248-1973

Business Lenders, LLC
15 Lewis Street
Hartford, CT 06103
860-244-9202 ext 200
800-646-7689
www.businesslenders.com

Business Loan Express
2250 Butterfield Drive, Suite 210
Troy, MI 48084
248-273-2200
Fax: 248-649-2087
www.businessloanexpress.net

Chemical Bank Midland
333 East Main
P.O. Box 231
Midland, MI 48640
989-839-5214

CIT Small Business Lending Corp.
2843 East Grand River #148
East Lansing, MI 48823
517-699-2331
517-699-2381
www.smallbizlending.com

Citizens Bank
328 S. Saginaw Street
Flint, MI 48502
810-237-4907

Comerica Bank
3551 Hamlin Road
Auburn Hills, MI 48326-7355
248-371-6070

Fifth Third Bank
38 Fountain Square Plaza
Cincinnati, OH 45263
513-744-8188

First International Bank
12900 Hall Road, Suite 270
Sterling Heights, MI 48313
586-323-1253

First Union Small Business Capital
42705 Grand River Avenue, Suite
201
Novi, MI 48375
248-344-9573

Firstar Bank Wisconsin, N.A.
605 North Eighth Street
Sheboygan, WI 53081
920-459-6939

GE Capital Small Business Finance
Corp.
635 Maryville Center Drive
Suite 120
St. Louis, MO 63141
314-205-3639
www.gesmallbusiness.com

Key Bank, N.A.
4910 Tiederman Rd.
Cleveland, OH 44114
216-689-0232

National City
One City Center, Suite 700E
Indianapolis, IN 46255
317-267-8887

Republic Bank
2425 East Grand River
Lansing, MI 48912
517-483-6710

Sky Bank - Mid AM Region
519 Madison Avenue
Toledo, OH 43604
419-249-4984

Standard Federal Bank
124 W. Allegan Street
Lansing, MI 48901
517-377-3333

U.S. Bank, N.A.
2000 Towne Center Drive
Suite 1150
Southfield, MI 48075
248-603-2950

United Bank of Michigan
900 East Paris Avenue, SE
Grand Rapids, Michigan 49546
616-559-4503

Unizan Bank
7 W. Square Lake Road
Bloomfield Hills, MI 48302
248-674-9870

Wells Fargo/Norwest
1455 West Lake Street, Suite 306
Minneapolis, MN 55408
612-667-2753

Minnesota

American Bank
1578 University Avenue
St. Paul, MN 55104
651-628-2661

American Bank of the North
1215 Pokegama Avenue South
Grand Rapids, MN 55744
218-327-1121

Anchor Bank
14665 Galaxie Avenue, Suite 350
Apple Valley, MN 55124
952-808-8075

Associated Bank
1270 Yankee Doodle Road
Eagan, MN 55121-2231
651-306-1657

Border State Bank
1083 - 3rd Street NW
Roseau, MN 56751
218-463-3888

Boundary Waters Community Bank
11800 Aberdeen Street
Suite 120

Blaine, MN 55449
763-862-9962

Bremer Bank NA
8800 Highway 7
St Louis Park, MN 55426
952-932-6592

The Business Bank
11100 Wayzata Blvd, Suite 150
Minnetonka, MN 55305
952-847-1100

CIT Small Business Lending
Corporation
7701 France Ave South
Suite 200
Minneapolis, MN 55435
Contact: Joseph Kammermeier
888-735-1036
Fax: 888-735-1037
www.smallbizlending.com

CIT Small Business Lending
Corporation
7616 Currell Blvd., Suite 200
Woodbury, MN 55125
Contact: Michael Smith
651-264-3033
Fax: 651-264-3034
www.smallbizlending.com

Community First Nat'l Bank
120 N Mill Street
Fergus Falls, MN 56538-0136
218-739-4461

Community Development Bank,
FSB
516 Main Street
Ogema, MN 56569
218-983-3241

Excel Bank
5050 France Avenue So
Edina, MN 55410
952-836-3135

Fidelity Bank
7600 Parklawn Ave
Edina, MN 55435-5125
952-831-6600

First Integrity Bank, NA
111 - 4th Street NE
Staples, MN 56479
218-894-1522

First National Bank of Chaska
301 Chestnut Street
Chaska, MN 55318
952-448-2350

First National Bank
101 Center Ave East
Dilworth, MN 56529
218-233-3136

First Nat'l Bank & Trust
101-2nd Street NW

Pipestone, MN 56164-0190
507-825-3344

First National Bank
301 Main Street
Cold Spring, MN 56320
320-685-8611

First National Bank
729 Main Street
Elk River, MN 55330
763-441-2200

First National Bank
115 North St Paul Street
Fulda, MN 56131
507-425-2575

First National Bank
138 West Broadway
Plainview, MN 55964
507-534-3131

First Union Small Business
7616 Currell Blvd, Suite 200
Woodbury, MN 55125
651-264-3025

Heritage Bank NA
310 SW First Street
Willmar, MN 56201-1124
320-214-5531

Highland Bank
13370 Grove Drive
Maple Grove, MN 55369
763-420-3039

Home State Bank
1601 Highway 12 East
Willmar, MN 56201
320-231-1118

Landmark Community Bank
25 West Main Street
Isanti, MN 55040
763-444-5528

Lake Country Community Bank
111 Division Street
Morristown, MN 55052
507-685-2300

M&I Marshall & Ilsley Bank
180 North Executive Dr, Suite 200
Brookfield, WI 53005
262-814-5701

M&I Marshall Ilsley Bank
6625 Lyndale Avenue South
Richfield, MN 55423-2389
612-798-3898

Merchants Bank
1525 Vermillion Street
Hastings, MN 55033
651-437-3106

Merchants Bank NA
316 Main Street

LaCrescent, MN 55947
507-895-4486

Mainstreet Bank
1650 South Lake Street
Forest Lake, MN 55025
651-464-2880

Midwest Bank
116 East Front Street
Detroit Lakes, MN 56502
218-847-4771

Northern National Bank
2111 Excelsior Road
Baxter, MN 56425-2690
218-855-1320

Northwoods Bank of MN
1202 East 1st Street
Park Rapids, MN 56470
218-732-7221

Pioneer Bank
301 Main Street
Mapleton, MN 56065
507-534-3630

Security State Bank of Pine Island
128 South Main Street
Pine Island, MN 55963
507-356-8328

State Bank of Cokato
101 - 3rd Street SE
Cokato, MN 55321-0220
320-288-2146

State Bank of Faribault
428 Central Avenue
Faribault, MN 55021
507-332-7401

State Bank of Young
800 Faxon Road
Norwood, MN 55368
952-467-2313

Stearns County Nat'l Bank
4191 - 2nd Street So
St Cloud, MN 56301
320-253-6607

Sunrise Community Bank
2265 Como Avenue
St Paul, MN 55108-1700
651-523-7829

United Prairie Bank of Owatonna
110 West Rose Street
Owatonna, MN 55060
507-451-6300

U.S. Bank NA - SBA National
9918 Hilbert Street
San Diego, CA 93131
858-536-4545 ext 307

U.S. Bank NA - SBA Local
33 South 6th St, Suite 4125

Minneapolis MN 55402
612-338-3046

Wachovia Small Business Capital
7616 Currell Blvd, Suite 200
Woodbury, MN 55125
651-264-3025

Wadena State Bank
304 - 1st Street SE
Wadena, MN 56482
218-631-1860

Welcome State Bank
111 Guide Street
Welcome, MN 56181
507-728-8251

Wells Fargo NA SBA Lending
1455 W Lake Street, Suite 306
Minneapolis, MN 55408
612-667-2753

Western Bank
663 University Ave
St Paul, MN 55164-0689
651-224-1371

Woodlands National Bank
424 Main Street East
Onamia, MN 56359
320-532-4142

Mississippi

Allied Capital Corporation
1919 Pennsylvania Ave., NW, 3rd
Floor
Washington, DC 20006
Contact: Tina Del Dona, Executive
Vice President
202-721-1853
Fax: 202-659-2053

AMRESCO Independence Funding
700 N. Pearl Street
Suite 1900
Dallas, TX 75201
Contact: Charles Bell, President
214-720-1776
Fax: 214-969-5478

AmSouth Bank
250 River Chase Parkway
Birmingham, AL 35244
Contact: Cindy Bourne, Sales
Manager
205-560-5114
Fax: 205-560-5152

BancorpSouth Bank
P.O. Drawer 789
Tupelo, MS 38802
Contact: Gary Martin, Vice President
& SBA Loan Coordinator
662-680-2345
Fax: 662-680-2317

Bank Tennessee
1125 W. Poplar Avenue
Collierville, TN 38017

901-854-0854
Fax: 901-316-2266

Business Loan Center, Inc. Mid-
America Division
121 West Dewey Street
Suite 210
Wichita, KS 67202
Contact: Deryl K. Schuster,
President
316-263-3232
800-722-5626
Fax: 316-263-4391
www.businessloanexpress.net

CIT Small Business Lending
735 Montgomery Hwy., #117
Birmingham, AL 35216
Contact: Mike Vance, Regional
Account Manager
205-824-2810
Fax: 205-824-2811
www.smallbizlending.com

CIT Small Business Lending
1812 S Hwy 77, #115
Lynn Haven, FL 32444
Contact: Laurance Hardee
850-271-9914
Fax: 850-271-9915
www.smallbizlending.com

Community Bank - Desoto County
P.O. Box 129
Southaven, MS 38671
Contact: Clay Dunn, Senior Vice-
President
662-280-9700
Fax: 662-349-4700

First Financial Bank
P.O. Box 1754
El Dorado, AR 71731
Contact: Billy Max Stuart, Loan
Officer
870-863-7000
Fax: 870-881-5394

First Louisiana BIDCO (Source
Capital)
455 East Airport Avenue
Baton Rouge, LA 70806
Contact: Walter Anderson, President
504-922-7411
Fax: 504-922-7418

First Security Bank
P.O. Box 690
Batesville, MS 38606
Contact: Jeff Herron, Vice President
662-563-9311
Fax: 662-563-9310

G.E. Capital Small Business Finance
Corporation
635 Maryville Centre Drive
Suite 120
St. Louis, MO 63141
Contact: Michael Pilot, President
314-205-3501

Fax: 314-205-3691
www.gesmallbusiness.com

Hancock Bank
P.O. Box 4019
Gulfport, MS 39501
Contact: Tom Collins, Assistant Vice
President
228-868-4000
Fax: 228-868-4675

InSouth Bank
6141 Walnut Grove Road
Memphis, TN 38120
901-747-5555
Fax: 901-747-5580

Merchants & Farmers Bank
P.O. Box 520
Kosciusko, MS 39090
Contact: Ritchie Berry, Branch
President
601-289-8511
Fax: 601-289-4801

National Bank of Commerce
P.O. Box 1187
Starkville, MS 39759
Contact: Dan Craig, Vice-President
662-323-1341
Fax: 662-324-4790

Pike County National Bank
P.O. Box 1666
McComb, MS 39648
Contact: James Wicker, Senior Vice
President
601-684-7575
Fax: 601-684-7113

Regions Bank
660 Peachtree Dunnwoody Road
400 Embassy Row, Suite 210
Atlanta, GA 30328
770-392-6560
Fax: 770-392-7062

Small Business Loan Source, Inc.
5333 Westheimer, Suite 840
Houston, TX 77056
713-961-5626
Fax: 713-961-9518

South Trust Bank
2625 Piedmont Road
Suite 51B
Atlanta, GA 30324
Contact: John McArthur, Vice
President
404-841-2184
Fax: 404-841-2187

State Bank and Trust Company
P.O. Box 8287
Greenwood, MS 38935
Contact: Joycelyn Mitchell, Vice
President
662-453-6811
Fax: 662-453-4784

535

Trustmark National Bank
106 W. Government Street
Brandon, MS 39042
Contact: Patrician McMahon, Vice-
President
601-825-1854
Fax: 601-825-1837

Union Planters Bank
P.O. Box 23053
Jackson, MS 39225
Contact: Ralph W. Reed, Jr., Vice
President
601-368-2714
Fax: 601-368-2724

Zions First National Bank
13545 Barrett Parkway
St. Louis, MO 63021
314-822-0070
Fax: 314-822-0254

Missouri

Allegiant Bank
4323 North Grand Blvd.
St. Louis, MO 63107
314-534-3000

Amresco Independence Funding,
Inc.
700 North Pearl Street
Suite 2400, LB 359
Dallas, TX 75201-7424
214-720-1776

Bank of America (All location in
Eastern Missouri)
One City Place Drive, Suite 470
St. Louis, MO 63141
314-993-8160

Bank of America
1130 Walnut
Kansas City, MO 64106
816-979-6696

Bank of Sullivan
318 West Main Street
Sullivan, MO 63080
573-468-3191

Bank of Washington
P.O. Box 377
Washington, MO 63090
636-239-7831

Boone County National Bank
720 East Broadway
Columbia, MO 65201
573-874-8100

Business Loan Express
17295 Chesterfield Airport Road
Chesterfield, MO 63005
636-530-3633
Fax: 636-530-3634
www.businessloanexpress.net

California Bank & Trust
Zions Small Business Finance

13545 Barrett Parkway Drive
Suite 335
St. Louis, MO 63021
314-822-0070

Central Trust Bank
238 Madison Street
Jefferson City, MO 65101
573-634-1234

CIT Small Business Lending
Corporation
400 Chesterfield Center Dr., Suite
400
Chesterfield, MO 63017
Contact: Carolyn Gregg
636-458-2330
Fax: 636-458-7666
www.smallbusinesslending.com

CIT Small Business Lending
12120 State Line Road, #157
Leawood, KS 66209
Contact: Paul Jokerst
816-941-2090
Fax: 816-941-0081
www.smallbizlending.com

Commerce Bank (All Commerce
Banks in Eastern Missouri)
8000 Forsyth Boulevard
Clayton, MO 63105
314-726-2255

Commerce Bank & Trust
3035 S. Topeka
Topeka, KS 66611
785-267-0123

Commerce Bank, N.A.
1000 Walnut
Kansas City, MO 64141
816-234-2658

Country Club Bank
414 Nichols Road
Kansas City, MO 64112
816-931-4060

Eagle Bank & Trust Company of
Jefferson County
680 South Mill Street
P.O. Box 129
Festus, MO 63028
636-931-3660

The Exchange National Bank
132 E. High Street
P.O. Box 688
Jefferson City, MO 65102
573-761-6100

Farmers and Merchants Bank of St.
Clair
530 South Main Street
St. Clair, MO 63077
573-629-2225

First Bank
11901 Olive Boulevard

St. Louis, MO 63141
314-567-3600

First Community Bank
P.O. Box 555
1110 S. Mitchell
Warrensburg, MO 64093
816-747-9530

First National Bank of Olathe
444 East Santa Fe
Olathe, KS 66061
913-782-3211

First Union Small Business Capital
111 West Port Plaza, Suite 600
St. Louis, MO 63146
314-275-9165

First Union Small Business Capital
8500 College Blvd., Suite 125
Overland Park, KS 66210
913-338-7144

First Western SBLC, Inc.
17290 Preston Road, 3rd Floor
Dallas, TX 75252
800-486-3223

Firstar
415 Francis Street
P.O. Box 308
St. Joseph, MO 64502
816-233-2000

Guaranty Bank & Trust
1000 Minnesota Ave.
Kansas City, KS 66101
913-371-1200

GE Capital Corporation
7300 College Blvd., Suite 208
Oversland Park, KS 66210
913-696-6200

GE Capital Small Business Finance
635 Maryville Centre Drive, Suite
120
St. Louis, MO 63141-9025
314-205-3500

Gold Bank, N.A.
11301 Nall Avenue
Leawood, KS 66211
913-962-1400

Heller Financial, Inc.
7300 W. 110th St., 7th Floor
Overland Park, KS 66210
877-441-0891

Heller First Capital Corporation
500 West Monroe Street, 19th Floor
Chicago, IL 60661
877-441-0891

Liberty Bank
1414 E. Primrose
Springfield, MO 63804
417-875-5200

Metcalf Bank
7840 Metcalf
Overland Par, KS 66204
913-648-4540

Midwest BankCentre
2191 Lemay Ferry Road
St. Louis, MO 63125-9803
314-631-5500

Peoples Bank and Trust Company of
Lincoln County
Cherry & Wood Streets
P.O. Box G
Troy, MO 63379
573-528-7001

Premier Bank
15301 West 87th St. Parkway
Lenexa, KS 66219
913-541-6176

Transamerica Small Business
Capital, Inc.
7 N. Laurens Street, Suite 601
Greenville, SC 29601
864-232-6197

UMB Bank, N.A.
1010 Grand Boulevard
Kansas City, MO 64106
816-860-7000

UMB Bank of St. Louis
Six South Broadway
St. Louis, MO 63102
314-621-1000

Union Planters Bank, N.A. (All
Union Planters Banks in Eastern
Missouri)
407 N. Kings Highway
Cape Girardeau, MO 63701
573-335-0893

U.S. Bank/SBA Division
7500 College Blvd., Suite 660
Overland Park, KS 66210
913-498-1799

U.S. Bank National Association
16402 Swingley Ridge Road, Suite
340
Chesterfield, MO 63017
636-778-0110
Wells Fargo SBA Lending
100 S. Brentwood Blvd., Suite 300
St. Louis, MO 63105
800-545-0670

Montana
Bank of Bridger
P.O. Box 447
Bridger, MT 59014
406-662-3388

Bitterroot Valley Bank
Drawer 9
Lolo, MT 59847
406-273-2400

CIT Small Business Lending
1526 Cole Blvd., Building 200
Golden, CO 80401
Contact: Rick Ricciardi
303-202-3751
Fax: 303-202-3794
www.smallbizlending.com

Citizens State Bank
P.O. Box 393
Hamilton, MT 59840
406-363-3661

Clark Fork Valley Bank
Frenchtown Shopping Center
Frenchtown, MT 59834
406-626-4500

Community Bank Polson
P.O. Box 1389
Polson, MT 59860
406-883-0600

Empire Bank
P.O. Box 80730
Billings, MT 59108
406-256-1891

Empire Bank
P.O. Box 1048
Bozeman, MT 59771
406-586-2309

Farmers State Bank
P.O. Box 310
Darby, MT 59829
406-821-4646

Farmers State Bank
5501 Old Highway 93
Florence, MT 59833
406-273-0935

Farmers State Bank
1950 1st Street
Hamilton, MT 59840
406-363-0030

Farmers State Bank
P.O. Box 280
Stevensville, MT 59870
406-777-7210

Farmers State Bank
P.O. Box 190
Victor, MT 59875
406-642-3431

First Citizens Bank
P.O. Box 2508
Billings, MT 59103
406-247-4218

First Citizens Bank
P.O. Box 3149
Butte, MT 59702
406-494-4400

First Citizens Bank
P.O. Box 277

Laurel, MT 59044
406-628-4318

First Citizens Bank
4005 Highway 200 East
Missoula, MT 59802
406-721-8400

First Citizens Bank
213 First St West
Polson, MT 59860
406-883-4358

First Interstate Bank
6999 Jackrabbit Lane
Belgrade, MT 59714
406-388-0917

First Interstate Bank
P.O. Box 31317
Billings, MT 59107
406-255-6100

First Interstate Bank
P.O. Box 30918
Billings, MT 59116
406-255-5000

First Interstate Bank
P.O. Box 31438
Billings, MT 59107
406-255-5800

First Interstate Bank
3199 Grand Avenue
Billings, MT 59102
406-255-6090

First Interstate Bank
P.O. Box 578
Bozeman, MT 59715
406-586-4555

First Interstate Bank
P.O. Box 39
Colstrip, MT 59323
406-748-2840

First Interstate Bank
P.O. Box 2000
Cut Bank, MT 59427
406-873-2265

First Interstate Bank
P.O. Box 2002
Eureka, MT 59917
406-296-3116

First Interstate Bank
Highway 89
Gardiner, MT 59030
406-848-7474

First Interstate Bank
P.O. Box 5010
Great Falls, MT 59403
406-454-6250

First Interstate Bank
P.O. Box 2100

Hamilton, MT 59840
406-363-0900

First Interstate Bank
P.O. Box 903
Hardin, MT 59034
406-665-3806

First Interstate Bank
3151 Montana Ave.
Helena, MT 59602
406-457-7170

First Interstate Bank-Evergreen
P.O. Box 5388
Kalispell, MT 59901
406-757-0770

First Interstate Bank
P.O. Box 7130
Kalispell, MT 59904
406-756-5200

First Interstate Bank
P.O. Box 672
Livingston, MT 59047
406-222-2950

First Interstate Bank
P.O. Box 1237
Miles City, MT 59301
406-232-5590

First Interstate Bank
P.O. Box 4667
Missoula, MT 59806
406-523-4234

First Interstate Bank
P.O. Box 1299
Polson, MT 59860
406-883-5363

First Interstate Bank
P.O. Box 100
Whitefish, MT 59937
406-863-8888

First Security Bank
511 W. Main St.
Belgrade, MT 59714
406-388-3725

First Security Bank
670 S. 19th Street
Bozeman, MT 59715
406-585-3954

First Security Bank
P.O. Box 910
Bozeman, MT 59715
406-585-3915

First Security Bank
P.O. Box 4506
Missoula, MT 59801
406-728-3115

First Security Bank
2601 Garfield

Missoula, MT 59801
406-543-1653

First Security Bank
P.O. Box 550
West Yellowstone, MT 59758
406-646-7646

Flathead Bank of Bigfork
P.O. Box 308
Bigfork, MT 59911
406-837-5050

Flathead Bank of Bigfork
P.O. Box 769
Lakeside, MT 59922
406-844-2535

Glacier Bank
307 East Park
Anaconda, MT 59711
406-563-5203

Glacier Bank
Lake Hills Shopping Center
Bigfork, MT 59911
406-837-5980

Glacier Bank
P.O. Box 3048
Butte, MT 59701
406-497-7000

Glacier Bank
P.O. Box 190
Columbia Falls, MT 59912
406-892-7100

Glacier Bank of Eureka
P.O. Box 326
Eureka, MT 59917
406-297-2521

Glacier Bank
P.O. Box 27
Kalispell, MT 59903
406-756-4256

Glacier Bank
P.O. Box 749
Libby, MT 59923
406-293-2412

Glacier Bank
14 2nd Avenue West
Polson, MT 59860
406-883-8300

Glacier Bank
P.O. Box 220
Whitefish, MT 59937
406-863-6300

Heritage Bank
P. O. Box 10006
Bozeman, MT 59719
406-582-9188

Little Horn State Bank
2850 Old Hardin Rd

Billings, MT 59107
406-259-9400

Little Horn State Bank
P.O. Box 530
Hardin, MT 59034
406-665-2332

Mountain West Bank
P.O. Box 10850
Bozeman, MT 59718
406-587-5600

Mountain West Bank
P.O. Box 3607
Great Falls, MT 59403
406-727-2265

Mountain West Bank
P.O. Box 6013
Helena, MT 59604
406-449-2265

Mountain West Bank
P.O. Box 7070
Kalispell, MT 59903
406-758-2265

Mountain West Bank
P.O. Box 5990
Missoula, MT 59801
406-542-6222

Rocky Mountain Bank
P.O. Box 1440
Bigfork, MT 59911
406-837-1400

Rocky Mountain Bank
P.O. Box 80450
Billings, MT 59108
406-656-3140

Rocky Mountain Bank
P.O. Box 347
Broadus, MT 59317
406-436-2611

Rocky Mountain Bank
P.O. Box 788
Plains, MT 59859
406-826-3662

Rocky Mountain Bank
P.O. Box 150
Plentywood, MT 59254
406-765-2265

Rocky Mountain Bank
P.O. Box 199
Stevensville, MT 59870
406-777-5553

Rocky Mountain Bank
P.O. Box 599
Whitehall, MT 59759
406-287-3251

Ronan State Bank
P.O. Box B

Ronan, MT 59864
406-676-4600

Stockman Bank
P.O. Box 80850
Billings, MT 59108
406-655-2700

Stockman Bank-Billings Heights
P.O. Box 50850
Billings, MT 59105
406-896-4800

Stockman Bank-Billings Shiloh
P.O. Box 80350
Billings, MT 59108
406-655-3900

Stockman Bank
P.O. Box 727
Conrad, MT 59425
406-278-5513

Stockman Bank
P.O. Box 1139
Cut Bank, MT 59427
406-873-5517

Stockman Bank
P.O. Box 491
Glendive, MT 59330
406-377-1000

Stockman Bank
2425 Tenth Avenue South
Great Falls, MT 59403
406-453-3700

Stockman Bank
25 5th Street North
Great Falls, MT 59401
406-771-2783

Stockman Bank
900 3rd St. Northwest
Great Falls, MT 59403
406-771-2797

Stockman Bank
P.O. Box 1271
Havre, MT 59501
406-265-5831

Stockman Bank
P.O. Box 312
Hysham, MT 59038
406-342-5214

Stockman Bank
P.O. Box 250
Miles City, MT 59301
406-232-3620

Stockman Bank
P.O. Box 384
Plentywood, MT 59254
406-765-2460

Stockman Bank
P.O. Box 70

Richey, MT 59259
406-773-5521

Stockman Bank
101 S. Central Avenue
Sidney, MT 59270
406-433-8600

Stockman Bank
P.O. Box 6
Terry, MT 59349
406-635-5591

Stockman Bank
P.O. Box 299
Wibaux, MT 59353
406-796-2424

Stockman Bank
P.O. Box 249
Worden, MT 59088
406-967-3612

Three Rivers Bank
P.O. Box 7250
Kalispell, MT 59904
406-755-4271

Two Rivers Bank
P.O. Box 248
Milltown, MT 59851
406-258-2400

United States National Bank
P.O. Box 910
Red Lodge, MT 59068
406-446-1422

Valley Bank
P.O. Box 5269
Helena, MT 59604
406-443-7440

Washington Mutual Bank
P. O. Box 1370
Houston, TX 77251
713-543-6500

Wells Fargo Bank Montana
120 West Park Avenue
Anaconda, MT 59711
406-563-4146

Wells Fargo Bank Montana
P.O. Box 699
Baker, MT 59313
406-778-3348

Wells Fargo Bank Montana
P.O. Box 278
Big Sandy, MT 59520
406-378-2175

Wells Fargo Bank Montana
P.O. Box 30058
Billings, MT 59117
406-657-3400

Wells Fargo Bank Montana
P.O. Box 370

Bozeman, MT 59715
406-586-3381

Wells Fargo Bank Montana
P.O. Box 547
Butte, MT 59703
406-533-7057

Wells Fargo Bank Montana
P.O. Box 580
Chester, MT 59522
406-759-5107

Wells Fargo Bank Montana
P.O. Box 129
Chinook, MT 59523
406-357-2224

Wells Fargo Bank Montana
P.O. Box 0
Circle, MT 59215
406-485-2731

Wells Fargo Bank Montana
P.O. Box 816
Conrad, MT 59425
406-278-3201

Wells Fargo Bank Montana
P.O. Box 1127
Dillon, MT 59725
406-683-4222

Wells Fargo Bank Montana
P.O. Box 1170
Forsyth, MT 59327
406-356-2961

Wells Fargo Bank Montana
P.O. Box 69
Glasgow, MT 59230
406-228-4371

Wells Fargo Bank Montana
2215 10th Avenue South
Great Falls, MT 59405
406-454-5550

Wells Fargo Bank Montana
P.O. Box 5011
Great Falls, MT 59403
406-454-5423

Wells Fargo Bank Montana
P.O. Box 831
Havre, MT 59501
406-265-2264

Wells Fargo Bank Montana
P.O. Box 597
Helena, MT 59624
406-447-2005

Wells Fargo Bank Montana
P.O. Box 88
Kalispell, MT 59904
406-756-4004

Wells Fargo Bank Montana
P.O. Box 1020

Lewistown, MT 59457
406-538-1000

Wells Fargo Bank Montana
P.O. Box 662
Livingston, MT 59047
406-222-3648

Wells Fargo Bank Montana
1800 S. Russell
Missoula, MT 59801
406-327-6281

Wells Fargo Bank Montana
P.O. Box 550
Red Lodge, MT 59068
406-446-1620

Wells Fargo Bank Montana
12 Main Street
Roundup, MT 59072
406-323-2000

Wells Fargo Bank Montana
P.O. Box 248
Rudyard, MT 59540
406-355-4129

Wells Fargo Bank Montana
P.O. Box 912
Shelby, MT 59474
406-434-5528

Wells Fargo Bank Montana
101 2nd Avenue SW
Sidney, MT 59270
406-482-2321

Wells Fargo Bank Montana
Drawer 868
Superior, MT 59872
406-822-4224

Wells Fargo Bank Montana
502 Montana Avenue
Valier, MT 59486
406-279-3225

Western Security Bank
2929 3rd Ave North
Billings, MT 59101
406-238-4940

Valley Bank
321 Fuller
Helena, MT 59601
406-449-3700

Valley Bank
P.O. Box 48
Kalispell, MT 59901
406-752-7123

Yellowstone Bank
P.O. Box 10
Absarokee, MT 59001
406-328-4512

Yellowstone Bank
P.O. Box 81010

Billings, MT 59108
406-652-4100

Yellowstone Bank
P.O. Box 389
Columbus, MT 59019
406-322-5366

Yellowstone Bank
P.O. Box 7
Laurel, MT 59044
406-628-7951

Nebraska

Adams Bank & Trust
315 North Spruce
Ogallala, NE 69153-2517
308-284-4071
Fax: 308-284-3207

American National Bank
8990 West Dodge Road
Omaha, NE 68114
402-399-5000
Fax: 402-399-5057

Bank of Nebraska
7223 So. 84th Street
LaVista, NE 68128-2130
402-331-8550
Fax: 402-331-8570

Business Loan Express
121 West Dewey Street, Suite 210
Wichita, KS 67202
316-263-3232
Fax: 316-263-4391
www.businessloanexpress.net

CIT Small Business Lending
Corporation
1526 Cole Boulevard, Suite 200
Golden, CO 80401
Contact: Annemarie Murphy
719-266-9084
800-525-3343
Fax: 719-264-8009
www.smallbizlending.com

CIT Small Business Lending
1526 Cole Blvd., Building #3, Suite
200
Golden, CO 80401
Contact: Rick Ricciardi
303-202-3751
Fax: 303-202-3794
www.smallbizlending.com

CIT Small Business Lending
5470 W. Hinsdale Avenue
Littleton, CO 80128
Contact: Tom Hollinshead
303-933-4833
Fax: 303-933-4838
www.smallbizlending.com

Community First National Bank
224 Box Butte Ave.
Alliance, NE 69301-3742

308-762-4400
Fax: 308-762-6742

Cornhusker Bank
1101 Cornhusker Hwy.
Lincoln, NE 68521-2350
402-434-2265
Fax: 402-434-3789

First National Bank of North Platte
201 North Dewey Street
North Platte, NE 68101-4036
308-532-1000
Fax: 308-535-6289

First National Bank of Omaha
16th and Dodge Streets
Omaha, NE 68103
402-341-0500
Fax: 402-964-8484

First Westroads Bank, Inc.
10855 West Dodge Road
Omaha, NE 68154-2666
402-330-7200
Fax: 402-330-8272

Five Points Bank
2015 North Broadwell Avenue
Grand Island, NE 68803-2759
308-384-5350
Fax: 308-384-9783

GE Capital Small Business Finance
Corporation
7300 College Blvd., Suite 208
Overland Park, KS 66210
913-696-6206
Fax: 913-696-6219
www.gesmallbusiness.com

Great Western Bank
6015 N.W. Radial Highway
Omaha, NE 68104
402-551-4310
Fax: 402-551-7689

Heritage Bank
1333 No. Webb Road
Grand Island, NE 68803
308-384-5538
Fax: 308-384-6778

Peoples-Webster County Bank
126 West 4th Street
Red Cloud, NE 68970-2433
402-746-2251

Platte Valley State Bank & Trust
Company
2223 2nd Avenue
Kearney, NE 68847-5309
308-234-2424
Fax: 308-237-2413

The Money Store
707 3rd Street
West Sacramento, CA 95605
800-523-0035
Fax: 800-603-1861

Union Bank and Trust Company
3642 South 48th Street
Lincoln, NE 68506
402-488-0941
Fax: 402-488-8188

United Nebraska Bank
700 No. Webb Rd.
Grand Island, NE 68802
308-381-8900
Fax: 308-381-6570

U. S. Bank National Association
1700 Farnam Street
Omaha, NE 68102-2183
402-348-6000
Fax: 402-233-7168

Washington County Bank
1523 Washington St.
Blair, NE 68008-1653
402-426-2111
Fax: 402-426 8177

Wells Fargo Bank
1919 Douglas Street
Omaha NE 68102-1317
402-536-2420
Fax: 402-536-2317

Nevada

Bank of America Federal Savings
6900 Westcliff Drive, 4th Floor
Las Vegas, NV 89145-0197
702-654-6598
Fax: 702-654-6926

Bank of America Federal Savings
901 Main Street, 18th Floor
Dallas, TX 75202
214-209-3015
Fax: 214-209-0506

Bank of Commerce
4343 E. Sunset Road
Henderson, NV 89014
702-307-9800
Fax: 702-876-7490

Bank of Las Vegas
5961 S. Decatur
Las Vegas, NV 89118
702 939-2400
Fax: 702-939-2415

Bank of the West
855 Sparks Blvd.
Sparks, NV 89434
775-685-2244
Fax: 775-685-2250

Bank of the West
701 N. Green Valley Pkwy
Suite 200
Henderson, NV 89014
702-683-9370
Fax: 702-558-9230

Bankwest of Nevada
2700 W. Sahara Avenue

Las Vegas, NV 89102
702-248-4200
Fax: 702-257-1219

Borrego Springs Bank, NA
6655 W. Sahara Avenue, Suite B200
Las Vegas, NV 89146
702-222-4018

Borrego Springs Bank, NA
5370 Kietzke Lane
Reno, NV 89511
775-825-5575
Fax: 775-829-7222

Business Bank of Nevada
6085 W. Twain Avenue
Las Vegas, NV 89103
702-794-0070
Fax: 702-365-8255

Business Lenders LLC
15 Lewis Street
Hartford, CT 06103
800-646-7689
Fax: 860-527-0884
www.businesslenders.com

Business Loan Express
121 W. Dewey Street, Suite 210
Wichita, KS 67202
316-263-3232
Fax: 316-263-4391
www.businessloanexpress.net

California Federal Bank
2625 E. Desert Inn Road
Las Vegas, NV 89121
702-892-8126
Fax: 702-892-9864

California Federal Bank
320 N. Harbour Blvd.
Fullerton, CA 92832
714-525-8967
Fax: 714-525-9967

Celtic Bank
340 E. 400 S.
Salt Lake City, UT 84111
801-363-6500
Fax: 801-363-6562

CIT Small Business Lending
777 Campus Commons Road, Suite
200
Sacramento, CA 95825
Contact: Jennifer Mills
916-457-7360
Fax: 916-457-7381
www.smallbizlending.com

CIT Group
980 Ninth Street, 16th Floor
Sacramento, CA 95814
Contact: Matthew Christie
530-753-4529
Fax: 530-753-4367
www.smallbizlending.com

CIT Small Business Lending
2921 N. Tenaya Way
Suite 106
Las Vegas, NV 89128
Contact: Monica Coburn
702-839-9323
Fax: 702-839-9325
www.smallbizlending.com

Citibank
3900 Paradise Road, Suite 127
Las Vegas, NV 89109
702-796-5961
Fax: 702-796-5966

Citibank
1 Sansome Street, 23rd Floor
San Francisco, CA 94104
415-658-4205
Fax: 415-658-4547

CITI Capital Small Business Finance
Center, Inc.
250 E. Carpentry Freeway, 115
Irvine, TX 75062
800-605-1348
Fax: 972-652-3340

Colonial Bank
P.O. Box 7498
Reno, NV 89510-7498
775-827-7233
Fax: 775-827-7208

Comerica Bank
55 River Street
Santa Cruz, CA 95060
831-560-1700
Fax: 831-423-8302

Comerica Bank
1900 West Loop South, #220
Houston, TX 77027
713-888-2667
Fax: 713-993-0498

Community Bank of Nevada
1400 S. Rainbow Blvd.
Las Vegas, NV 89102
702-878-0700
Fax: 702-878-1060

Compass Bank
P.O. Box 797808
Dallas, TX 75379-7808
972-735-3577
Fax: 972-735-3598

Desert Community Bank
3740 S. Pecos-McLeod
Las Vegas, NV 89121
702-938-0525
Fax: 702-938-0509

Farmers & Merchants Bank
121 W. Pine Street
Lodi, CA 95240-2110
800-752-4722
Fax: 916-686-2527

First Independent Bank of Nevada
6518 S. McCarran Blvd.
Reno, NV 89509
775-824-4350
Fax: 775-828-2071

First National Bank of Arizona
7150 E. Camelback Road, Suite 285
Scottsdale, AZ 85251
480-675-5291
Fax: 480-424-5813

First National Bank of Nevada
770 E. Warm Springs, Suite 340
Las Vegas, NV 89119
702-889-2117
Fax: 702-735-6114

First National Bank of Nevada
2405 Vassar Street
Reno, NV 89502
775-325-3910
Fax: 775-327-4171

First Union Small Business Capital
6991 E. Camelback Road
Suite B101
Scottsdale, AZ 85251
800-722-3066
Fax: 480-426-0006

GE Capital Small Business Finance
5950 Emerald Avenue
Las Vegas, NV 89122
702-598-3885
Fax: 866-699-1025

GE Small Business Capital
2030 E. Flamingo
Las Vegas, NV 89119-5163
702-598-3885
Fax: 702-735-0128

Great Basin Bank
P.O. Box 2808
Elko, NV 89803
775-753-3800
Fax: 775-753-8836

Hawthorne Credit Union
P.O. Box 2288
Hawthorne, NV 89415
775-945-2421
Fax: 775-945-1262

Heritage Bank
P.O. 11920
Reno, NV 89502
775-348-1000
Fax: 775-348-1022

Innovative Bank of Oakland
4154 Tolkien Avenue
Las Vegas, NV 89115
702-643-2240
Fax: 702-243-7644

Innovative Bank of Oakland
360 14th Street
Oakland, CA 94612

510-899-6800
Fax: 510-899-6899

Innovative Bank of Oakland
9101 W. Sahara Avenue
Suite 105-A13
Las Vegas, NV 89117
702-233-2864
Fax: 702-233-2865

Irwin Union Bank
1717 E. College Pkwy.
Carson City, NV 89706
775-886-6926
Fax: 775-886-6910

Kirkwood Bank and Trust Co.
6900 Westcliff Drive, Suite 500
Las Vegas, NV 89145
702-228-0941
Fax: 702-228-1459

Mequite State Bank
11 Pioneer Blvd.
Mesquite, NV 89027
702-346-6600
Fax: 702-346-6615

Nevada Bank and Trust
P.O. Box 658
Ely, NV 89301
775-726-3135
Fax: 775-726-3303

Nevada Commerce Bank
3200 S. Valley View Blvd.
Las Vegas, NV 89102
702-257-7777
Fax: 702-257-7778

Nevada First Bank
2800 W. Sahara
Las Vegas, NV 89102
702-990-6575
Fax: 702-310-4070

Nevada Security Bank
465 S. Meadows Pkwy. #18
Reno, NV 89511
775-853-8600
Fax: 775-853-2058

Nevada State Bank
750 E. Warm Springs, 4th Floor
Las Vegas, NV 89125
702-855-4559
Fax: 702-914-4553

Nevada State Bank
3101 N. Central Avenue, Suite 500
Phoenix, AZ 85012
602-212-8826
Fax: 602-230-1005

Nevada State Development Corp.
1551 Desert Crossing Road
Suite 100
Las Vegas, NV 89144
702-877-9111
Fax: 702-877-2803

Northern Nevada Bank
P.O. Box 20607
Reno, NV 89515
775-689-6560
Fax: 775-689-6554

Placer Community Bank
112 Harding Blvd.
Roseville, CA 95678
916-791-2868
Fax: 916-791-8474

Red Rock Community Bank
10000 W. Charleston
Las Vegas, NV 89135
702-946-7500
Fax: 702-948-3630

Silver State Bank
1325 Air Mobile Way
Suite 175
Reno, NV 89502
775-337-6677
Fax: 775-337-6687

Silver State Bank
691 N. Valle Verde Drive
Henderson, NV 89104
702-433-8300
Fax: 702-968-8517

Sun West Bank
1101 Corporate
Reno, NV 89502
775-856-8300
Fax: 775-856-8310

Sun West Bank
5830 W. Flamingo
Las Vegas, NV 89103
702-949-2214
Fax: 702-949-2288

U.S. Bank
4055 S. Spencer Street, Suite 236
Las Vegas, NV 89121
702-732-7655
Fax: 702-732-0109

U.S. Bank
9918 Hilbert Street, Street 301
San Diego, CA 92131
619-536-4545
Fax: 619-536-2390

U.S. Bank
1575 Dellucchi Lane, Suite 116B
Reno, NV 89502
800-693-2661
Fax: 775-826-6468

Wells Fargo Bank, NA
333 S. Grand Avenue, Suite 820
Los Angeles, CA 90071
213-253-3325
Fax: 213-628-1867

Wells Fargo Bank, NA
4350 Camelback, Suite E-100
Phoenix, AZ 85018

602-977-7415
Fax: 602-977-7490

Wells Fargo Bank, NA
5340 Kietzke Lane, Suite 201
Reno, NV 89511
775-689-6078
Fax: 775-689-6195

Western Bank
376 E. 400 S., Suite 100
Slat Lake City, UT 84111
801-239-1943
Fax: 801-239-1939

World Trade Finance, Inc.
875 N. Virgil Avenue
Los Angeles, CA 90029
323-660-1277
Fax: 323-660-1470

New Hampshire

Bank of New Hampshire N.A.
650 Elm Road
Manchester, NH 03105
Contact: Deborah Morin, Vice
President
603-695-3083
www.banknh.com

The Berlin City Bank
P.O. Box 2130
North Conway, NH 03860
Contact: Richard T. Brunlle, Vice
President
603-356-8010
www.berlincitynbank.com

Business Lenders, LLC
15 Lewis Street
Hartford, NH 06103
Penn Riter, Executive Vice Presidnt
860-244-9202
www.businesslenders.com

Business Loan Express
1 New Hampshire Avenue, Suite 125
Portsmouth, NH 03801
603-882-3379
Fax: 603-766-1901
www.businessloanexpress.net

CIT Small Business Lending
319 Centre Avenue, PMB 164
Rockland, MA 02370
Contact: Barbara Arena
781-294-2244
800-713-4984 ext. 6003
Fax: 781-294-2064
www.smallbizlending.com

Citizens Bank of New Hampshire
875 Elm Street
Manchester, NH 03101
Contact: David Peterson, Vice
President
603-634-7655
www.citizensbank.com

Danvers Savings Bank
1 Conant Street
Danvers, MA 01923
Contact: Daniel Rich
978-739-0245
www.danverssvings.com

Fleet National Bank
188 Main Street
Nashua, NH 03061
Contact: Jonathon Dowst
603-594-1752
www.smallbiz.fleet.com

GE Capital Small Business Finance
1 Middle Street, Suite 206
Portsmouth, NH 03801
Contact: Timothy Dargan
603-433-0261
www.ge.com/capital/smallbiz

Granite Bank
93 Middle Street
Portsmouth, NH 03801
Contact: Stephen H. Witts, Vice
President
603-431-3611
www.granitebank.com

The Howard Bank National
Association
P.O. Box 660
Montpelier, VT 05602
Contact: Rosemarie White,
Commercial Banking Officer
802-223-5203
www.banknorthvt.com

Ocean National Bank
779 South Main Street
Manchester, NH 03102
Contact: John Udaloy, Jr., Vice
President
603-621-5801
www.eoccan.com

New Jersey

Amresco Independence Funding,
Inc.
3010 LBJ Freeway, Suite 920
Dallas, TX 75234
Contact: Mr. Charles Bell, President
972-247-1776
Fax: 972-919-1776

Banco Popular, North America
120 Broadway, 16 th Floor
New York, NY 10271
Contact: Mr. Merv Shorr, SBA
Department
212-417-6782

Bank of New York
1401 Franklin Avenue
Garden City, NY 11530
Contact: Mr. Jon Gamby, Vice
President
516-873-7836
Fax: 516-294-2770

Broadway National Bank
250 Fifth Avenue
New York, NY 10001
Contact: Mr. Ted Morgan, Vice
President
212-689-5292
Fax: 212-685-4136

Business Lenders, LLC
15 Lewis Street
Hartford, CT 06103
Contact: Ms. Judy Hart
860-244-9202, Ext. 117
www.businesslenders.com

Business Loan Center
1301 North Hamilton Street, Suite
200
Richmond, VA 23230
Contact: Mr. Matt McGee, Manager
Director
804-355-4449
Fax: 804-358-9025

Business Loan Express
450 Park Avenue, Suite 1001
New York, NY 10022
Contact: Mr. George Reithoffer,
Regional Associate
212-308-8197
Fax: 212-988-1796

California Bank & Trust
2399 Gateway Oaks Drive #110
Sacramento, CA 95833
Contact: Mr. Paul Herman, Regional
President
916-561-1121
Fax: 916-341-3021

CIT Small Business Lending
1 CIT Drive
Livingston, NJ 07039
Contact: Mr. Chris Lehnes, Vice
President - Business Development
800-713-4984, Ext. 6004
Fax: 800-328-7420
www.smallbizlending.com

Citibank, F.S.B
8750 Doral Blvd.- 6C
Miami, FL 33178
Contact: Ms. Mary Frank, Vice
President Business & Professional
305-599-5876
Fax: 305-470-7063

Citizens Bank
Director, Government Program
Services
100 A Sockanosset Crossroad
Cranston, RI 02920
Contact: Mr. Gary J. Heidel
401-734-5617
Fax: 401-734-5621

CitiCapital Small Business Finance,
Inc.
250 E. Carpenter Freeway, Suite 115
Irving, TX 75062

Contact: Ms. Tari Barber
972-652-4567
Fax: 972-652-5337

City National Bank of NJ
900 Broad Street
Newark, NJ 07102
Contact: Mr. Stanley Weeks, Senior
Vice President
973-624-0865

Columbia Bank
19-01 Route 208, North
Fair Lawn, NJ 07410
Contact: Ms. Barbara Speid, Vice
President
201-599-7077
Fax: 201-599-7063

Comerica Bank, California
910 Louisiana, 50 th Floor
Houston, TX 77002
Contact: Mr. Eric Kern
713-220-5623
Fax: 713-888-3455

Commerce Bank/Central, N.A.
One Royal Road
Flemington, NJ 08822
Contact: Mr. Thomas W. Ort, Vice
President
908-806-6200, ext 4746
Fax: 908-806-7466

Commerce Bank/Shore, N.A.
1701 Route 70 East
Cherry Hill, NJ 08034
Contact: Renae Jordan, Assistance
Vice President SBA Lending
732-505-3000, ext 2515
Fax: 732-505-2907

First Constitution Bank
2650 Route 130
Cranbury, NJ 08512
Contact: Mr. Irving Wischik, Vice
President
609-655-4500
Fax: 609-655-5653

First Washington State Bank
P.O. Box 500
Windsor, NJ 08561-0500
Contact: Betty Solewater, Vice
President
609-426-1000 ext. 239
Fax: 609-443-4819

First Western SBLC, Inc.
18111 Preston Road
Dallas, TX 75252
Contact: Ms. Sharon Nachlinger

Fleet Bank
208 Harris Town Road
Glen Rock, NJ 07452
Contact: Mr. Jay Klatsky
201-251-5749
Fax: 201-251-5987

Flushing Savings Bank
33 Irving Place
New York, NY 10003
Contact: Jim Peterson, Vice
President, Business Lending
212-477-9360

G.E. Capital Small Business Fin.
Corp
100 Walnut Avenue, 6th Floor
Clark, NJ 07066-1247
Contact: Mr. Larry Sherman,
Business Development Executive
732-388-3188
Fax: 732-815-3192

Home Loan and Investment Bank,
F.S.B.
Commercial Lending Services
244 Weybosset Street
Providence RI 02903-3774
Contact: James M. Roche, Vice
President
800-722-5671
Fax: 401-453-3865

Hopewell Valley Community Bank
P.O. Box 999, 4 Route 31
Pennington, NJ 08534
Contact: Mr. Andre J. Caldini,
Assistant Vice President
609-466-2900
Fax: 609-730-9144

HSBC Bank, USA
Buffalo, NY 14203
Contact: Mr. Paul Lewis, AVP One
Marine Midland Center
800-975-4722

Hudson United Bank
530 High Mountain Road
North Haledon, NJ 07508
Contact: Mr. John Kosko, Vice
President
973-636-6052
Fax: 973-636-6045

Independence Community Bank
909 Broad Street
Newark, NJ 07102
Contact: Mr. Paul Orzechowski,
Vice President, SBA Lending
973-639-2990 ext 4202
Fax: 973-643-3273

Independence Funding Co., Ltd.
700 N. Pearl Street
Dallas, TX 75201
Contact: Mr. Charley Bell, President
800-225-1776 ext 217
Fax: 214-758-5260

Interchange State Bank
Park 80 West/Plaza Two
Saddle Brook, NJ 07663
Contact: Ms. Barbara Ruebenacker,
Assistant V.P.
201-703-4477
Fax: 201-845-4640

JPMorgan Chase Bank
Community Development Group
350 Main Street
Huntington, NY 11743
Contact: Mr. Bruce Vaughan
631-673-7425
Fax: 631-421-3428

Lakeland Bank
250 Oak Ridge Road
Oak Ridge, NJ 07439
Contact: Mr. Robert A.
Vandenbergh, Executive Vice
President
973-208-6218
Fax: 973-6975809

The Loan Source, Inc.
353 East 83rd Street
Suite 3H
New York, NY 10028
Contact: Mr. Steven D. Kravitz,
President
212-737-1836
Fax: 212-249-2311

Mellon Bank, N.A.
2 Mellon Bank Center, Room 200
Pittsburgh, PA 15259
Contact: Mr. Robert Schmader, Asst
Vice President
215-553-1693

National Penn Bank
24 N. Reading Ave.
Boyerstown, PA 19512
Contact: Ms. Marcia Amoroso, Vice
President
610-369-6297

Nations Bank, N.A.
1111 E. Main Street
Richmond, VA 23219
Phone 704-386-5000

Newtek Small Business Finance
462 Seventh Avenue, 14th Floor
New York, NY 10018
Contact: Mr. John R. Cox, Chairman
& CEO
212-356-9510 ext. 115
Fax: 212-643-0286

PNC Bank, N.A.
Government Sponsored Lending
1777 Sentry Park West
Gwynedd Hall, Suite 201
Blue Bell, PA 19422-2227
Contact: Ms. Pamela E. Davis,
Manager/Vice President
215-371-4690
Fax: 215-371-4697

Progress Bank
4 Sentry Parkway, Suite 200
Blue Bell, PA 19422
Contact: Mr. James Dana, Vice
President
610-941-4809

Royal Bank of Pennsylvania
516 E. Lancaster Ave.
Shillington, PA 19607
Contact: Mr. A. Mark Rentschler
610-777-3300
Fax: 610-777-5099

Skylands Community Bank
24-26 Crossroads Center, Route 517
Hackettstown, NJ 07840
Contact: Mr.Ed Poolas, Sr. Vice
President
908-850-9010
Fax: 908-850-8525

Small Business Loan Source, Inc.
301 Route 17, North, Suite 800
Rutherford, NJ 07070

Somerset Valley Bank
P.O. Box 931
103 West End Avenue
Somerville, NJ 08876
Contact: Mr. Mike A. Novak, Senior
Vice President
908-704-1188
Fax: 908-685-2180

Sovereign Bank
60-116-CM1
165 Passaic Avenue
Fairfield, NJ 07004
Contact: Mr. Anthony Villanueva,
Assistant Vice President, SBA
Lending Group
973-276-7232
Fax: 973-808-4423

Sun National Bank
100 S. Broad Street
Trenton, NJ 08608
Phone: 609-396-6400
Fax: 609-396-6968

Temecula Valley Bank Natl Assoc
9600 Koger Blvd N
St. Petersburg, FL 33702
Contact: Mr. Gary Allen
727-576-0123, Ext. 223 Fax:

Textron Business Credit, Inc.
40 Westminster Street, 5th Floor
P.O. Box 1555
Providence, RI 02903
Contact: Ms. Katherine Marien,
President
800-211-8884
Fax: 401-621-5054

The Bank
Small Business Lender
303 Egg Harbor Road
Sewell, NJ 08080
Contact: Ms. Jeannie Harrison,
Assistant Vice President
856-582-8883
Fax: 856-582-1391

UnitedTrust Bank
630 George Road

North Brunswick, NJ 08902
Contact: Mr. H. Robert Bechtel, Vice
President & Commercial Loan
Officer/SBA
732-247-3320
Fax: 732-247-1405

Unity Bank
64 Old Highway 22
Clinton, NJ 08809
Contact: Mr. Michael Downs, Sr
Vice Pres & SBA Manager
908-730-7630
Fax: 908-713-4391

Unizan Bank
400 Valley Road, Suite 100
Mt. Arlington, NJ 07856
Contact: Mr. Will Haney
973-288-8012
Fax: 973-288-8112

UPS Capital Business Credit
2025 Lincoln Highway, Suite 130
Edison, NJ 08817
Contact: Mr. Brian D. McGuinness,
Director Business Development
732-287-5881
Fax: 732-287-5888

Valley National Bank
1455 Valley Road
Wayne, NJ 07470
Contact: Mr. Walter Horsting
908-561-7122
Fax: 908-753-9817

Wachovia Small Business Capital
190 River Road
Summit, NJ 07901
Contact: Ms. Lucia DiNapoli
Gibbons, Regional President
908-598-3195
Fax: 908-598-3110

Washington Mutual Bank, FA
17 Lancelot Lane
Basking Ridge, NJ 07920
Contact: Ms. Donna Haibeck, Vice
President
908-696-9611
Fax: 908-696-9612

Woori America Bank, NA
183 Main Street, 2nd Floor
Ft Lee, NJ 07024
Contact: Mr. Steve Seong, SBA
Team Head and Vice President
201-242-8769
Fax: 202-242-9780

Wilmington Savings Fund Society,
FSB
838 Market St
Wilmington, DE 19801
Contact: Ms. Susan Garson
302-571-5266

Zions First National Bank
2399 Gateway Oaks, Suite 110

Sacramento, CA 95833
Contact: Ms. Ruth Defrates, Vice
President
916-561-1160
Fax: 916-561-1170

New Mexico
Bank of America, FSB
201 3rd St NW
Albuquerque, NM 87102
800-263-2055

Bank of the Rio Grande, NA
411 North Downtown Mall
Las Cruces, NM 88001
505-525-8900

Bank of Santa Fe
241 Washington Ave
Santa Fe, NM 87501
505-984-0478

Business Loan Express
10701 Lomas NE, Suite 219
Albuquerque, NM 87112
505-332-8976
Fax: 505-332-8400
www.businessloanexpress.net

Charter Bank for Savings FSB
4400 Osuna Rd NE
Albuquerque, NM 87109
505-341-7300

CIT Small Business Lending
Corporation
4120 Rio Bravo, Suite 301
El Paso, TX 79902
Contact: Elizabeth Pulido
915-845-7605
Fax: 915-845-7621
www.smallbizlending.com

Citizens Bank of Las Cruces
505 South Main St
Las Cruces, NM 88001
505-524-9656

Community First National Bank
201 N Church St
Las Cruces, NM 88004
505-527-6200

Compass Bank
505 Marquette NW
Albuquerque, NM 87102
505-888-9020

First State Bank of Taos
120 West Plaza
Taos, NM 87571
505-758-6652

GE Small Business Financial Corp
635 Maryville Centre Dr., Suite 120
St. Louis, MO 63141
314-205-3500

InterAmerica Bank
2400 Louisiana Blvd NE

Albuquerque, NM 87110
505-880-1700

Lea County State Bank
1017 North Turner
Hobbs, NM 88240
505-397-4511

Ruidoso State Bank
1710 Sudderth Dr
Ruidoso, NM 88345
505-257-4043

Sonoma National Bank
815 Fifth St
Santa Rosa, CA 95404
707-579-0610

State National Bank
555 Telshor
Las Cruces, NM 88011
505-521-0000

Sunrise Bank of Albuquerque
225 Gold SW
Albuquerque, NM 87102
505-244-8000

US Bank National Association
9918 Hibert St., 3rd Floor
San Diego, CA 92131
858-536-4545

Wells Fargo Bank New Mexico, NA
200 Lomas NW
Albuquerque, NM 87002
505-766-6423

Wells Fargo Bank New Mexico
425A S. Telshor Blvd
Las Cruces, NM 88004
505-522-2020

Western Commerce Bank
127 South Canyon St
Carlsbad, NM 88220
505-887-6686

New York

Allied Capital SBLC Corporation
1919 Pennsylvania, NW
Washington, DC 20006
202-331-1112
Fax: 202-659-2053
www.alliedcapital.com

Asia Bank N.A.
135.34 Roosevelt Avenue
Flushing, NY 11354
718-961-9700
Fax: 718-961-6721
www.asiabank-na.com

Astoria Federal Savings
One Astoria Federal Plaza
Lake Success, NY 11042-1085
800-ASTORIA
www.astoriafederal.com

Banco Popular
2852 Broadway 111th Street
New York, NY 10025
800-377-0800
www.bancopopular.com

Bank of Castile
50 North Main Street
Castile, NY 14427
Contact: James W. Fulmer, CEO
716-493-2570 ext. 247
Fax: 716-493-5792

Bank of New York
One Wall Street
New York, NY 10286
212-495-1784
www.bankofny.com

Bank of Smithtown
One East Main Street
Smithtown, NY 11787
631-360-9300
Fax: 631-360-9373
www.bankofsmithtownonline.com

Bridgehampton National Bank
P.O. Box 3005
Bridgehampton, NY 11932
631-537-1000
Fax: 631-537-1835
www.bridgenb.com

Broadway National Bank
2024 Center Avenue
Fort Lee, NJ 07024
201-592-7474
www.bnbbank.com

Business Lenders
15 Lewis Street
Hartford, CT 06103
860-244-9202 ext. 200
www.businesslenders.com

Chase Manhattan Bank
350 Main Street
Buffalo, NY 14202
716-858-1400
www.chase.com

Chase Manhattan Bank
270 Park Avenue
New York, NY 10017
212-270-6000
www.chase.com

CITI Small Business Lending
203 Main Street, PMB 177
Flemington, NJ 08822
609-397-2680
Fax: 609-397-4712
www.smallbizlending.com

Citibank NYS
409 Main Street
Buffalo, NY 14203
Contact: Joseph Wolff, Jr., VP &
CMG Reg. Dir.

716-849-2516
Fax: 716-849-2560

Citibank, N.A.
410 Uniondale Avenue
Uniondale, NY 11553
516-481-4145

Commercial Capital Corporation
25 W. 43rd Street, Suite 90
New York, NY 10036
212-719-0002

Community Capital Bank
111 Livingston Street #LI
Brooklyn, NY 11201
718-802-1212
Fax: 718-243-0312
www.communitycapitalbank.com

Community Mutual Savings Bank
50 Main Street
White Plains, NY 10606
914-686-2600

Fleet Bank
4049 Seneca Street
West Seneca, NY 14224
800-841-4000
www.fleet.com

Fleet National Bank
10 Fountain Plaza
Buffalo, NY 14202
Contact: Joanne M. Campagna, VP
& Reg. Officer
716-849-3645
Fax: 716-847-4409

First National Bank-Hudson Valley
20 Mill Street
Rhinebeck, NY 12572
845-876-7041

Flushing Savings Bank
Irving Place
33 Irving Place
New York, NY 10003
212-477-9360
www.flushingsavings.com

Grow America Fund
National Development Council
5 E. 42nd Street, Suite 300
New York, NY 10017
212-682-1106
Fax: 212-573-6118
www.ndc-online.org

HSBC Bank USA Bank
One HSBC Center
Sterling Kozlowski, Small Business
Strategy Champion
Buffalo, NY 14203
716-841-6738
Fax: 716-841-5391

Home Loan and Investment Bank
One Home Loan Plaza
Warwick, RI 02886

401-739-8800
800-223-1700
Fax: 401-739-9762
www.homeloanbank.com

Hudson Valley Bank
21 Scarsdale Road
Yonkers, NY 10707
914-961-6100

KeyBank
50 Fountain Plaza
Buffalo, NY 14202
Contact: Sharon M. Lochocki, Sr.
Vice President
716-847-7715
Fax: 716-847-7765

Long Island Commercial Bank
1601 Veterans Highway
Islandia, NY 11749
631-348-0888
www.licb.com

M & T Bank
1 Fountain Plaza
Buffalo, NY 14203
716-626-6611

Manufactures and Traders Trust Co.
4925 Main Street
Alfred F. Luhr, Sr. Vice President
Amherst, NY 14226
716-839-8706
Fax: 716-839-8777

New York Business Development
Corporation
50 Beaver Street
Albany, NY 12207
800-923-2504
Fax: 518-463-0240
www.nybdc.com

New York National Bank
1042 Westchester Avenue
Bronx, NY 10459
718-542-0300

North Fork Bank
700 Walt Whitman Road
Melville, NY 11747
631-427-4300

Prestige State Bank
1 Royal Road
Flemington, NJ 08822
908-806-6200
Fax: 908-806-0736

Reliance Bank
1200 Mamaroneck Avenue
White Plains, NY 10605
914-682-7900

Republic National Bank
777 3rd Avenue
New York, NY 10017
212-838-9550
www.rnb.com

State Bank of Long Island
699 Hillside Avenue
New Hyde Park, NY 11040
516-465-2200
www.statebankofli.vom

Staten Island Savings Bank
15 Beach Street
Staten Island, NY
718-447-7900
www.sisb.com

Suffolk County National Bank
4 W 2nd Street
Riverhead, NY 11901
631-208-2200
www.scnb.com

Textron Business Credit
40 Westminster Street
Providence, RI 02940
401-621-4200
www.tfc.textron.com

Valley National Bank
672-6 Somerset Street
North Plainfield, NJ 07060
800-522-4100
www.valleynationalbank.com

Wyoming County Bank
55 North Main Street
Louis J. Burgio, Sr. Vice President
Warsaw, NY 14569
716-786-4347
Fax: 716-786-2024

North Carolina
Bank of Granite
23 N. Main Street
Granite Falls, NC 28630
828-496-2000
Fax: 828-496-2116
www.bankofgranite.com

Branch Banking & Trust Company
200 W. Second Street
Winston Salem, NC 27101
336-733-2000
Fax: 336-733-2279
www.bbandt.com

Business Loan Express
6000 Fairview Road, Suite 1200
Charlotte, NC 28210
704-552-3656
800-SBA-Loan
Fax: 704-552-3657
www.businessloanexpress.net

California Bank & Trust
P.O. Box 25787
Salt Lake City, UT 84125
888-758-5349
www.calbanktrust.com

Capital Bank
4901 Glenwood Avenue
Raleigh, NC 27612
919-878-3100

Fax: 919-645-6401
www.capitalbank-
nc.com/home/home.html

Central Carolina Bank & Trust
Company
202 S. Salem Street
Apex, NC 27502
919-362-8391
www.ccbonline.com

CIT Small Business Lending
Corporation
424 East Six Forks Roads, Suite 109
PMB 331
Raleigh, NC 27609
919-789-0966
Fax: 919-789-0967
www.smallbizlending.com

CIT Small Business Lending
Corporation
10612-D Providence Road, Suite 483
Charlotte, NC 28277
704-814-0409
Fax: 704-814-0410
www.smallbizlending.com

Comerica Corporate Headquarters
Comerica Tower at Detroit Center
500 Woodward Avenue, M/C 3391
Detroit, Michigan 48226
800-292-1300
www.comerica.com

The East Carolina Bank
Highway 264
Engelhard, NC 27824
252-925-9411
Fax: 252-925-6361
www.ecbbancorp.com

The Fidelity Bank
100 S. Main Street
Fuquay-Varina, NC 27526
919-552-2242
Fax: 919-362-1968
www.fidelitybanknc.com

First Gaston Bank of North Carolina
804 S. New Hope Road
Gastonia, NC 28054
704-865-4204
Fax: 704-865-8302
www.firstgaston.com

First Citizens Bank & Trust
239 Fayetteville Street Mall
Raleigh, NC 27602
919-716-7000
Fax: 919-716-2844
www.firstcitizens.com

First Western SBLC, Inc.
18111 Preston Road
Dallas, TX 75252
972-349-3200

FNB Southeast
202 S. Main Street

Reidsville, NC 27320
336-342-3346
Fax: 336-349-8035
www.fnbsoutheast.com

GE Capital Small Business Finance
Corporation
6100 Fairview Road
Suite 350
Charlotte, NC 28210
704-643-6363
www.gesmallbusiness.com

Goleta National Bank
4913 Chastain Avenue, Unit 17
Charlotte, NC 28217
704-527-3555
Fax: 704-527-4449
www.goleta.com

Lighthouse Financial
St. Pauls Office
506 West Armfield Street
St. Pauls, NC 28384
910-865-2562
Fax: 910-865-2563
www.lighthouseus.com

RBC Centura Bank
131 N. church Street
Rocky Mount, NC 27804
252-454-4424
Fax: 252-454-4800
www.centura.com

Self-Help
P.O. Box 3619
Durham, NC 27702
919-956-4400
800-476-7428
www.self-help.org

Small Business Loan Source, Inc
9801 Westheimer Road, 11th Floor
Houston, TX 77042
800-457-4307 ext 120
www.sbls.com

SouthTrust Bank
P.O. Box 11965
Birmingham, AL 35202-1965
800-285-2546
www.southtrust.com

SunTrust Bank
Mail Code HDQ 4109
P.O. Box 85024
Richmond, VA 85024-5024
800-279-4824
www.suntrust.com

Temecula Valley Bank
4374 Dovershire Trace, NW
Norcross, GA 30092
770-662-2470
www.temvalbank.com

Surrey Bank & Trust
145 N. Renfro Street
Mount Airy, NC 27030

336-719-2310
Fax: 336-789-3687

United Community Bank
63 Highway 515
P.O. Box 398
Blairsville, GA 30514
706-781-2265
866-270-7200
Fax: 706-745-8960
www.ucbi.com

Valley National Bank
1445 Valley Road
Wayne, NJ 07470
800-522-4100
www.valleynationalbank.com

Wachovia Bank
Research Triangle Park Branch
4 Park Drive
Research Triangle Park, NC 22709
919-549-8621
www.wochovia.com

North Dakota

Alerus Financial
15 Broadway
Fargo, ND 58102
701-280-5181

Alerus Financial
2401 Demers Avenue
Grand Forks, ND 58206
701-795-3200

American State Bank & Trust
140 First Avenue West
Dickinson, ND 58601
701-225-6811

American State Bank & Trust Co.
223 Main Street
Williston, ND 58801
701-774-4100

Bank Center First
320 North Fourth Street
Bismarck, ND 58501
701-258-2611

BNC National Bank
322 East Main
Bismarck, ND 58502
701-250-3000

Bremer Bank, N.A.
424 Fifth Street
Devils Lake, ND 58301
701-662-4074

Bremer Bank, N.A.
20 First Street SW
Minot, ND 58701
701-852-3361

Community First National Bank
520 Main Avenue

Fargo, ND 58124
701-293-2200

Community First National Bank
142 East 200 South
Salt Lake City, UT 84111
701-531-3404

Community First National Bank
501 Dakota Avenue
Wahpeton, ND 58074
701-642-5567

Community National Bank
1616 South Washington
Grand Forks, ND 58208
701-780-7700

First National Bank & Trust
22 East Fourth Street
Williston, ND 58802
701-572-2113

First Southwest Bank
109 First Street NW
Mandan, ND 58554
701-663-6434

First Western Bank & Trust
900 South Broadway
Minot, ND 58702
701-852-3711

Kirkwood Bank and Trust Co.
Seventh Street & Arbor Avenue
Bismarck, ND 58506
701-258-6550

State Bank of Fargo
3100 13th Avenue South
Fargo, ND 58103
701-298-1500

The National Bank of Harvey
920 Lincoln Avenue
Harvey, ND 58341
701-324-4611

US Bank
4325 17th Avenue SW
Fargo, ND 58107

Wells Fargo Bank North Dakota
406 Main Avenue
Fargo, ND 58126
701-293-4200

Wells Fargo Bank, N.A.
1455 West Lake Street, Suite 306
Minneapolis, MN 55408
612-667-2836

Ohio

American National Bank
5603 Ridge Road
Parma, OH 44129
Contact: Richard Wise
440-843-3171
Fax: 440-884-4022

Bank One
8044 Montgomery Road
Cincinnati, OH 45202
Contact: Larry Bradley
513-985-5087
Fax: 513-985-5060

Bank One OH
1111 Polaris Parkway OH1-1013
Columbus, OH 43240
Contact: Paul Collinsworth
614-248-1973
Fax: 614-244-8794

Bank One OH
Kettering Tower
P.O. Box 1103
Dayton, OH 45401
Contact: Julie Woeste
937-449-6301
Fax: 937-449-7444

Business Loan Center, Inc.
5400 Shawnee Road
Suite 100
Alexandria, VA 22312
Contact: Kyle Stevenson
703-354-5788
Fax: 703-354-5798

Business Loan Center
8888 Keystone Crossing, Suite 1300
Indianapolis, IN 46240
Contact: Bob Hickman
317-581-8568
Fax: 317-581-8569

CIT Small Business Lending
Corporation
4496 Mahoning Avenue
Austintown, OH 44515
Contact: Joe Wojtowicz
330-544-5865
Fax: 330-544-5809
www.smallbizlending.com

CITI Small Business Lending
Corporation
829 Bethel Road, PMB #307
Columbus, OH 43214
Contact: Scott Keasel
614-261-8443
Fax: 614-261-8453
www.smallbizlending.com

Citi Capital Small Business Finance
P.O. Box 6
Cincinnati, OH 45201
Contact: Lorain Horner
877-655-2118
Fax: 513-735-2119

Comerica Bank
3551 Hamlin Road
Auburn Hills, MI 48326
Contact: Troy King
248-371-6070
Fax: 248-371-6213

Commerce National Bank
100 E. Wilson Bridge Rd., Suite 100
Worthington, OH 43085
Contact: Asad Javed or Brian Quiniff
614-848-8700
Fax: 614-848-8830

Cortland Bank
195 W. Main Street
Cortland, OH 44410
Contact: James Gasior
330-637-8040
Fax: 330-638-3018

Fifth Third Bank of Cincinnati
38 Fountain Square Plaza - MD
10905D
Cincinnati, OH 45263
Contact: Michael Shepherd
513-744-8188
Fax: 513-579-5226

Fifth Third Bank of Northwestern
Ohio
606 Madison Avenue
Toledo, OH 43604
Contact: David J. McMacken
419-841-0267
Fax: 419-841-4559

Fifth Third Bank of Western Ohio
123 Market Street
P.O. Box 1117
Piqua, OH 45356-1117
Contact: Dawn Matthews
937-778-5312
Fax: 937-773-5548

First International Bank
Great Northern Corporate Center II
25050 Country Club Blvd., Suite 290
North Olmsted, OH 44070
Contact: Shawn Hapanowicz
440-686-3001
Fax: 440-686-3014

First Merit Bank, NA
106 South Main Street
Akron, OH 44308
Contact: Thomas C. Lundberg
330-384-7399
Fax: 330-996-8003

Firstar Bank
425 Walnut Street
Cincinnati, OH 45202
Contact: Robin Nenninger
513-632-2370
Fax: 513-632-2388

Firstar Bank
175 S. Third Street, 4th Floor
Columbus, OH 43215
Contact: David Entsminger
614-232-8054
Fax: 614-232-8033

Firstar Bank
10 N. Ludlow Street, ML 4821
Dayton, OH 45402

Contact: Ron Cloyd
937-640-7636
Fax: 937-640-7651

First Union Small Business Capital
6450 Rockside Woods Boulevard
South, Suite 100
Independence, OH 44131
Contact: Robert Bruno
216-328-2040
800-722-3066
Fax: 216-328-2039

GE Capital Small Business Finance
635 Maryville Centre Drive
Suite 120
St. Louis, MO 63141
Contact: Katherine K. Miller
314-205-3540
Fax: 314-205-3699

Huntington National Bank
101 West 4th Street
Cincinnati, OH 45202-2712
Contact: Chris J. Shimala
513-762-1860
Fax: 513-762-1873

Huntington National Bank
7575 Huntington Park Drive
Columbus, OH 43235
Contact: Kim Coleman
614-480-1941
Fax: 614-480-6417

Huntington National Bank
Courthouse Plaza, SW, Suite 200
Dayton, OH 45402-1825
Contact: Avery Allen
937-443-5900
Fax: 937-443-5914

Huntington National Bank
18000 Jefferson Park Dr., #102
Middleburg Hts., OH 44130
Contact: Raymond C. Klein
216-515-1851
Fax: 216-515-6813

Key Bank
733 Bethel Road
Columbus, OH 43214
Contact: David Townsend
614-442-6029
Fax: 614-442-6073

Key Bank
34 North Main Street
Dayton, OH 45402-1994
Contact: Phil Steiger
937-586-7168
Fax: 937-586-7029

Key Bank
5181 Natorp Blvd.
Mason, OH 45040
Contact: Phil Steiger
937-586-7168
Fax: 937-586-7029

KeyBank
5915 Landerbrook
Mayfield Heights, OH 44124
Contact: Diane Bradford
440-461-5045
Fax: 440-461-5007

Key Bank
Three Seagate, 2nd Floor
Toledo, OH 43604
Contact: Michael Ash
419-259-5945
Fax: 419-259-8824

Lorain National Bank
457 Broadway
Lorain, OH 44052
Contact: Kenneth P. Wayton
440-244-6000
Fax: 440-244-4133

Metropolitan Bank & Trust
6001 Landerhaven Drive
Mayfield Hts., OH 44124
Contact: Benjamin Greenberg
440-646-1111
Fax: 440-646-0103

National City Bank
23711 Chagrin Boulevard
Beachwood, OH 44122
Contact: Lisa O. Rucker
216-575-3435
Fax: 216-575-3148

National City Bank
155 East Broad Street
Columbus, OH 43251
Contact: Will Bowdish
614-463-7100
Fax: 614-463-7300

National City Bank
6 North Main Street
Dayton, OH 45412
Contact: Dan Davis
937-226-2000
Fax: 937-226-8536

Northside Bank and Trust Co.
4125 Hamilton Ave.
Cincinnati, OH 45223
Contact: Dave Teeters
513-542-7800
Fax: 513-541-6941

Park National Bank
140 East Town Street - Suite 1010
Columbus, OH 43215
Contact: Christine Schneider
614-228-0063
Fax: 614-228-0205

PNC Bank
201 East Fifth Street
P.O. Box 1198
Cincinnati, OH 45201-1198
Contact: James Atteberry or Paul
Taylor

513-651-8000
Fax: 513-651-8794

Republic Savings Bank
29225 Chagrin Boulevard
Pepper Pike, OH 44122
Contact: Craig L. Johnson
216-514-5408
Fax: 216-514-3493

Second National Bank of Warren
108 Main Avenue, SW
Warren, OH 44481-1010
Contact: Norman H. Babcock
330-841-0123
Fax: 330-841-0219

Sky Bank
110 East Main Street
Salineville, OH 43945
Contact: Jayson M. Zatta
330-679-2948
Fax: 330-679-0028

Sky Bank - Mid Am Region
519 Madison Ave.
Toledo, OH 43604
Contact: Donald E. Flick
419-249-4984
Fax: 419-249-4999

State Bank & Trust Company
401 Clinton Street
Defiance, OH 43512
Contact: John M. Matey
440-871-9394
Fax: 440-871-0194

Steel Valley Bank, NA
Main at Liberty Streets
Dillonvale, OH 43917
Contact: George S. Hazlett
614-769-2313
Fax: 614-769-2590

United Midwest Saving Bank
33 N. Third Street, Suite 620
Columbus, OH 43215
Contact: Joseph Arie
614-580-0036
Fax: 614-225-9728

Unizan Bank
5005 Rockside Road, Suite 600
Cleveland, OH 44131
Contact: Roy Holloway
216-573-3720
Fax: 216-573-3724

Unizan Bank
66 S. Third Street
Columbus, OH 43215
Contact: Jennifer Flocken
614-462-2800
Fax: 614-463-6800

US Bank
425 Walnut Street, 2nd Floor
Cincinnati, OH 45201
Contact: Christopher N. Hatcher

513-632-3993
866-261-4127
Fax: 513-632-3969

US Bank - SBA Division
1350 Euclid Avenue, 11th Floor
Cleveland, OH 44115
Contact: Julie Ann Sweet
866-442-8983 (toll free)
216-623-5983
Fax: 216-623-5991

US Bank
175 South Third Street, 12th Floor
Columbus, Ohio 43215
Contact: Darrin Griese
614-232-8139
800-741-2926 Toll Free
Fax: 614-232-2646

Washington Mutual Bank
1500 Chiquita Center
250 East 5th Street
Cincinnati, OH 45202
Contact: George Vredevelt, Jr.
513-762-7677
Fax: 513-762-7689

Washington Mutual Bank
3200 Southwest Freeway, 16th Floor
Houston TX 771027
Contact: Doug Harker
713-543-6265
Fax: 713-543-6100

Wells Fargo Bank, Ohio
114 E. Main Street
Van Wert OH 45891-1725
Contact: Gregory Winkler
419-238-2399
Fax: 419-238-2052

Oklahoma

Albright Title & Trust Company
P.O. Box 51
Newkirk, OK 74647-0051
Contact: John Birch, Senior Vice
President
580-362-2525

Americrest Bank
P.O. Box 25676
Oklahoma City, OK 73125-0676
Contact: Tracy Renfro, Vice
President
405-951-9019

BancFirst
101 N. Broadway, Suite 460
Oklahoma City, OK 73102-8405
Contact: Kent Faison, President
405-270-4736

Bank of America, N.A.
10343 E. 71 St.
Tulsa, OK 74133
Contact: Sam Vaverka, Govt.
Lending Spec.
918-307-8281

Bank of Oklahoma, N.A.
7701 S. Western
Oklahoma City, OK 73139-2400
Contact: Kevin Guarnera, Senior
Vice President
405-616-7501

Bank One, Oklahoma, N.A.
6303 N. Portland, 4th Floor
Oklahoma City, OK 73112
Contact: Danny B. Lawson, CPA,
Vice President
405-440-8535

Business Loan Center, Inc.
121 W. Dewey St., Suite 210
Wichita, KS 67202
Contact: Deryl K. Schuster,
President
316-263-3232
Fax: 316-263-4391
www.businessloanexpress.net

Central National Bank of Poteau
P.O. Box 340
Poteau, OK 74953-0340
Contact: Ron Hall, Vice President
918-647-2233

Chickasha Bank & Trust Company
P.O. Box 1307
Chickasha, OK 73023-1307
Contact: Karen J. Stephens, Senior
Vice President
405-222-0550

CIT Small Business Lending
Corporation
6104 E. 32nd Street, Suite 208
Tulsa, OK 74135
Contact: Terry Jones
918-270-4448
Fax: 918-270-4449
www.smallbizlending.com

Citi Capital Small Business Finance,
Inc.
250 E. Carpenter Freeway
Suite 115
Irving, TX 75062
Contact: Bill Burke, Vice
President/General Mgr.
972-652-8606

Community Bank
P.O. Box 1020
Bristow, OK 74010-1020
Contact: Thomas D. Green, Vice
President
918-367-3343

Community Bank & Trust Company
9004 E. 61
Tulsa, OK 74133
Contact: Sandy Bjornson, President
918-764-1275

First Bethany Bank & Trust, N.A.
P.O. Box 218
Bethany, OK 73008-0218

Contact: Todd Krout, Commercial
Loan Officer
405-789-1110

First Commercial Bank
P.O. Box 32608
Oklahoma City, OK 73123-0808
Contact: Lynn Groves, Senior Vice
President
405-722-8810

First United Bank & Trust Company
P.O. Box 130
Durant, OK 74702-0130
Contact: Greg Massey, President
580-924-2211

First Western SBLC, Inc.
18111 Preston Road
Suite 600
Dallas, TX 75252
Contact: Mary J. Brownmiller,
Senior Vice Pres.
972-349-3209

MidFirst Bank
P.O. Box 268879
Oklahoma City, OK 73126-8879
Contact: Jim D. Gray, Vice President
405-767-7162

Pioneer Bank & Trust
P.O. Box 111
Ponca City, OK 74602
Contact: Jeff Cowan, Senior Vice
President
580-762-5651

RCB Bank
P.O. Box 189
Claremore, OK 74018-0189
Contact: James D. Elliott, Senior
Vice President
918-341-6150

Security First National Bank
P.O. Box 729
Hugo, OK 74743-0729
Contact: Bruce W. Akard, Executive
Vice President
580-326-9641

SpiritBank
9618 S. Memorial
Tulsa, OK 74133
Contact: Pat R. Levering, Vice
President
918-298-7344

The Bank, N.A.
P.O. Box 1067
McAlester, OK 74502-1067
Contact: Greg McNall, Senior Vice
President
918-423-2265, x 114

The First National Bank of Chelsea
P.O. Box 9
Chelsea, OK 74016-0009

Contact: Lavonne Schmidt,
President/CEO
918-789-2581

The Stillwater National Bank &
Trust Co.
P.O. Box 1988
Stillwater, OK 74076
Contact: Jacqueline R. Randle,
Senior Vice Pres.
405-742-1845

Tulsa National Bank
P.O. Box 1051
Tulsa, OK 74101-1051
Contact: Chris Wilson, Vice
President
918-494-4884

Oregon

Albina Community Bank
2002 NE Martin Luther King, Jr.
Blvd
Portland, OR 97212
Contact: Mike Lauinger, SVP
503-331-3782
Fax: 503-287-0197

American Pacific Bank
Business Lending Division
315 SW Fifth Avenue, Suite 201
Portland, OR 97204
503-221-5801
Fax: 503-221-6242
www.apbank.com

Bank of America, NA
10555 NE 8th Street
Bellevue, WA 98006
Contact: Patricia Rogers, SBA Loan
Specialist
206-358-5146
Fax: 206-585-5411

Bank of Astoria
1122 Duane Street
P.O. Box 28
Astoria, OR 97103
Contact: Rhonda Wills, SVP
503-325-8486 ext 32
Fax: 503-325-8487 or 325-6332

Bank of the Cascades
1100 NW Wall Street
Bend, OR 97701
Contact: Cathie Hendrix, AVP &
Bus. Loan Officer
541-617-3616
Fax: 541-617-3617

Bank of Clark County
P.O. Box 61725
Vancouver, WA 98666-1725
Contact: Darryl M. Horowitz, AVP
360-906-9514
Fax: 360-694-7164

Bank of Eastern Oregon
250 NW Gale 54
Heppner, OR 97836

541-676-9125
www.beobank.com

Bank of the West
401 SW 5th Avenue
Portland, OR 97204
Contact: Kellyn Beeck, VP SBA
Division
503-225-1570
Fax: 503-225-1788

Banner Bank
PO Box 1170
Hermiston, OR 97838-3170
Contact: David Richmond, AVP
541-564-4263
Fax: 541-567-9144

Bay Bank
1001 SW Fifth Avenue, Suite 250
Portland, OR 97204
503-222-9164
Fax: 503-222-0501
www.bay-bank.com

Borrego Springs Bank, NA
14674 SE Sunnyside Rd, #111
Clackamas, OR 97015
Contact: Jon D. Pederson, BDO
503-631-7760
Fax: 503-631-7225

CIT Small Business Lending
Corporation
10121 SE Sunnyside Rd, Suite 300
Clackamas, OR 97015
Contact: Brenda Benson or Brad
Benson
503-698-3350
800-713-4984
Fax: 503-698-3353
www.smallbizlending.com

CIT Small Business Lending
Corporation
242 Laurel Drive
Roseburg, OR 97470
Contact: Debbie Caterson
541-677-0599
800-713-4984
Fax: 541-677-0455
www.smallbizlending.com

California Bank & Trust
Zion's Small Business Finance
One World Trade Center
121 SW Salmon St, #1100
Portland, OR 97204
Contact: Jess L. Richardson, VP
Business Development
503-471-1380
Fax: 503-471-1422

Citizens Bank
P.O. Box 30
275 SW Third Street
Corvallis, OR 97339-0030
541-752-5161
Fax: 541-766-2281
www.citizensebank.com

Clackamas County Bank
38975 Proctor Boulevard
P.O. Box 38
Sandy, OR 97055
503-668-5501
www.clackamascountybank.com

CNL Commercial Finance Inc.
26137 La Paz Road, Suite 102
Mission Viejo, CA 92691
Contact: Harvey Torres
949-452-0949
www.cnlonline.com

Columbia Bank
1301 A Street
Tacoma, WA 98402
253-305-1900
Fax: 253-305-0317
www.columbiabank.com

Columbia Bank
314 E. Main Street, Suite A
Hillsboro, OR 97123
503-693-7500
www.columbiacommunitybank.com

Columbia Credit Union
P.O. Box 324
Vancouver, WA 98666
503-285-4521
800-891-4000
www.columbiacu.org

Columbia River Bank
420 E Third Street
Suite 200
P.O. Box 1050
The Dalles, OR 97058
Contact: Britt W. Thomas, VP &
Loan Administrator
541-298-3167
Fax: 541-296-3219

Comerica Bank--California
724 Columbia St. NW, Suite 205
Olympia, WA 98501
Contact: Ray Kulina, BDO
360-357-0077
Fax: 360-357-0067

Community First Bank
6401 W. Clearwater Avenue
Kennewick, WA 99336
509-783-3435
Fax: 509-783-4745
www.community1st.com

Community National Bank
900 Canterbury Place, Suite 300
Escondido, CA 92025
Contact: Gary Youmans, EVP
760-432-1120

Cowlitz Bank
P.O. Box 1518
927 Commerce Avenue
Longview, WA 98632
360-423-9600
800-340-8865

Fax: 360-423-3562
www.cowlitzbank.com

G.E. Capital Small Business
Financial Corp
5335 SW Meadows Rd, Suite 450
Lake Oswego, OR 97035
Contact: Neville Bassett, BD
Executive
503-603-1504
Fax: 503-603-1505

Klamath First Bank
540 Main
Klamath Falls, OR 97601
800-285-0116
www.klamathfirst.com

Key Bank, NA
5075 SW Griffith Dr, Suite 150
Beaverton, OR 97005
Contact: Dan Mogck, District Sales
Leader
503-626-5190
Fax: 503-626-3950

Key Bank
1 Monarch Center
12550 SE 93rd Ave, Suite 350
Clackamas, OR 97015
Contact: Kathy Betteridge, VP/SBA
Specialist
503-353-4203
Fax: 503-355-4210

Kitsap Bank
1700 Mile Hill Dr, Bldg. 700
Port Orchard, WA 98366
Contact: Scott Harvey, VP
360-876-2297
Fax: 360-876-7869

Liberty Bank
P.O. Box 10426
Eugene, OR 97440
541-681-4800
www.elibertybank.com

Matrix Capital Bank
10260 SW Greenburg, Suite 400
Portland, OR 97223
Contact: Dave Painter
503-535-8808
Fax: 503-639-7807

The Merchants Bank
P.O. Box 504
1290 NE Burnside
Gresham, OR 97030
503-661-8688
Fax: 503-665-0424
www.mbankonline.com

Mid-Valley Bank
2540 Newberg Highway
Woodburn, OR 97071
503-981-0100
866-981-0100
Fax: 503-694-6633
www.mvboregon.com

Oregon Pacific Banking Company
705 9th Street
Florence, OR 97439
541-997-7121
www.opbc.com

OSU Federal Credit Union
P.O. Box 306
Corvallis, OR 97339-0306
541-714-4000
800-732-0173
www.osufederal.com

Pinnacle Bank
8880 SW Nimbus Avenue, Suite D
Beaverton, OR 97008
503-644-3000
Fax: 503-643-4459
www.pinnaclebankoregon.com

Pacific Continental Bank
P.O. Box 10727
Eugene, OR 97440
Contact: Damon R. Rose
541-686-8685
Fax: 541-344-2843

Pacific Crest Bank
1550 Hotel Circle North, Suite 320
San Diego, CA 92108
Contact: Tony Parker, VP & SBA
Manager
619-260-6397
Fax: 619-260-4925

Pacific Northwest Bank
P.O. Box 840
Seattle, WA 98111
Contact: David Straus
206-340-4721
Fax: 206-587-2632

Peoples Bank of Commerce
750 Biddle Road
Medford, OR 97504
Contact: Thomas Knox, VP
541-774-7664
Fax: 541-773-5896

Pioneer Trust Bank
109 Commercial Street NE
P.O. Box 2305
Salem, OR 97308
503-363-3136

Premier West Bank
300 E Main Street
Medford, OR 97501
541-245-4650
www.premierwestbank.com

St. Helens Community Federal
Credit Union
1720 St. Helens Street
St. Helens, OR 97051
503-397-2376
www.shcfcu.org

Silver State Bank
Northwest SBA Loan Source

1800 NW 167th Place, #110
Beaverton, OR 97006
Contact: Jerry Casteel, VP/Manager
503-617-6611
Fax: 503-617-1550

ShoreBank Pacific
721 NW 9th Avenue, Suite 230
Portland, OR 97209
503-916-1552
Fax: 503-827-5003
www.eco-bank.com

Silicon Valley Bank
3003 Tasman Drive
Santa Clara, CA 95054
408-654-7400
www.svb.com

Silver Falls Bank
217 East Main Street
P.O. Box 99
Silverton, OR 97381
503-874-8808
Fax: 503-874-8818
www.silverfallsbank.net

Siuslaw Valley Bank
P.O. Box 280
Florence, OR 97489
541-997-3486
www.clicksvb.com

Small Business Loan Source, Inc
9801 Westheimer, Suite 1100
Houston, TX 77042
713-425-3900
Fax: 713-425-3951
www.sbls.com

South Valley State Bank
P.O. Box 5210
803 Main Street
Klamath, OR 97601
880-710-7872
Fax: 541-880-5251
www.sv-bank.com

Sterling Savings Association
111 N. Wall Street
Spokane, WA 99201-0609
800-650-7141
www.sterlingsavingsbank.com

Temecula Valley Bank
500 108th Avenue NE, 9th Floor
Bellevue, WA 98004
Contact: Brett A. Smith
425-638-0200
888-356-2611
Fax: 425-638-0202

Today's Bank
915 MacArthur Boulevard (POB
2669)
Vancouver, WA 98668-2669
Contact: Richard High
360-258-3424
Fax: 360-258-3441

Town Center Bank
10413 SE 82nd Avenue
Portland, OR 97266
503-788-8181
Fax: 503-788-8112
www.towncenterbank.com

Twin City Bank
729 Vandercook Way
Longview, WA 98632
Contact: Don Jones, CEO
Phone: 360-414-4101
Fax: 360-414-5278

Umpqua Bank
1448 NE Weidler
Portland, OR 97232
503-460-0390
www.umpquabank.com

Union Bank of California, NA
407 Southwest Broadway
Portland, OR 97205
503-225-3636
Fax: 503-225-3608
www.uboc.com

U.S. Bank, NA
9918 Hibert Street
San Diego, CA 92131-1018
858-536-4545

Portland Loan Production Office:
US Bank SBA Division
111 SW Fifth Ave
Portland, OR 97204
Contact: Jennifer Grunest or Patrick
Phillips
503-275-4020
Fax: 503-275-3782

Valley Community Bank
465 Main Street
Pleasanton, CA 94566
925-484-5400
Fax: 925-484-9073
www.vcb-ca.com

Venture Bank
721 College Street SE
P.O. Box 3800
Lacey, WA 98509-3800
360-456-0880
www.fcbonline.com

Wachovia Small Business Capital
1620 E Roseville Parkway, #100
Roseville, CA 95661
For New Loan Information Call:
800-523-0035

Washington Mutual Bank dba
Western Bank
SBA Lending Division
12655 SW Center Street, #500
Beaverton, OR 97005
Contact: Becky Griffin
503-672-6644
Fax: 503-520-6854

Wells Fargo Bank, NA
In Portland, NW Oregon & SW
Washington contact:
SBA Lending
9900 SW Greenburg Road, Suite 110
Portland, OR 97223
Contact: Shelly Miller
866-287-8203
In Greater Oregon contact:
Wells Fargo SBA Lending
844 Third Street
Bend, OR 97701
Contact: Kelley Mears
541-408-7851

West Coast Bank
1000 SW Broadway, Suite 1100
Portland, OR 97205
Contact: Kathleen Ayres, VP
503-224-4245
Fax: 503-224-2263

Willamette Valley Bank
101 High Street, NE
Salem, OR 97301
503-458-2222
www.wvbk.com

Pennsylvania

Enterprise Bank
4091 Mt. Royal Boulevard
Allison Park, PA 15101
412-487-6048
Fax: 412-487-4622
www.enterprisebankpgh.com

First Star Bank
418 West Broad Street
Bethlehem, PA 18018
610-691-2233
Fax: 610-691-5658
www.firststarbank.com

Progress Bank
4 Sentry Parkway, Suite 200
Blue Bell, PA 19422
610-825-8800
www.progressbank.com

Commerce Bank/PA, N.A.
Glenview Corp Center, Suite 407
3220 Tillman Drive
Bensalem, PA 19020
215-604-6239
http://bank.commerceonline.com

National Penn Bank
16 West Philadelphia Avenue
Boyertown, PA 19512
610-369-6142
800-822-3321
Fax: 610-369-6429
www.natpennbank.com

Commerce Bank/Harrisburg, N.A.
100 Senate Avenue
Camp Hill, PA 17011
717-972-2875
www.commercepc.com

G.E. Small Business Finance
600 North Bell Avenue
Carnegie, PA 15106
412-279-1980
www.ge.com/capital/smallbiz/sb3.htm

Woori America Bank
7400 Front Street
Cheltenham, PA 19012
215-782-2015
Fax: 215-346-0075
www.wooriamericabank.com

Business Loan Express
100 Springhouse Drive, Suite 105
Collegeville, PA 19426
610-831-9080
Fax: 610-831-1050
www.alliedcapitalexpress.com

Fidelity Deposit & Discount Bank
Drinker & Blakely Streets
Dunmore, PA 18512
570-342-8281 ext. 243
800-388-4380
www.the-fidelity.com

National City Bank of Pennsylvania
801 State Street
Erie, PA 16501
814-871-1225
Fax: 814-871-1384
www.nationalcity.com/personal

Fleet Bank
7111 Valley Green Road
Fort Washington, PA 19034
215-836-3836
www.fleet.com

First National Bank of Pennsylvania
Hermitage Square
3320 East State Street
Hermitage, PA 16148
724-983-3599
Fax: 724-983-4926
www.fnb-online.com

First Commonwealth Bank
t/a Central Bank
P.O. Box 503
Hollidaysburg, PA 16648
Route 220 & N. Juniata Street
814-696-1475
Fax: 814-696-1496
www.fcfbank.com

AmeriServ Financial
216 Franklin Street
P.O. Box 520
Johnstown, PA 15901
814-533-5134
Fax: 814-533-5107
www.ameriservfinancial.com

Sun Bank
349 Main Street
Mill Hall, PA 17751
570-726-3926

Fax: 570-726-3130
www.sunbancorp.com

Sovereign Bank
3 Terry Drive, Suite 102
Newtown, PA 18940
215-497-8525
www.sovereignbank.com

Old Forge Bank
216 South Main Street
Old Forge, PA 18518
570-457-8345
Fax: 570-457-7317
www.oldforgebankpa.com

Asian Bank
1008 Arch Street
Philadelphia, PA 19107
215-592-1188
Fax: 215-592-1130
www.theasianbank.com

Citizens Bank
2001 Market Street
Philadelphia, PA 19103
267-671-1000
www.citizensbank.com/index.asp

Firstrust Bank
1931 Cottmann Avenue, Suite 403
Philadelphia, PA 19111
215-728-8435
Fax: 215-728-8448
800-220-BANK
www.firstrust.com

TRF Reinvestment Fund, Inc.
Cast Iron Bldg
718 Arch Street
Philadelphia, PA 19106
215-925-1130
Fax: 215-923-4764
www.trfund.com

BankPittsburgh
441 Smithfield Street
Pittsburgh, PA 15222
412-281-0780
www.bankpittsburgh.com

Citizens Bank of Pennsylvania
525 William Penn Place
Pittsburgh, PA 15219
412-867-2000
Fax: 412-566-7113
www.citizensbank.com

Dollar Bank
Three Gateway Center, 6 South
Pittsburgh, PA 15222
412-261-7574
Fax: 412-261-0534
www.dollarbank.com

PNC Bank, N.A.
One PNC Plaza
249 Fifth Avenue
Pittsburgh, PA 15265
412-762-2414

Fax: 412-705-0041
www.pncbank.com

Royal Bank of Pennsylvania
516 East Lancaster Avenue
Shillington, PA 19607
610-777-3300
Fax: 610-777-5099
www.royalbankpa.com

Univest National Bank and Trust
10 West Broad Street
Souderton, PA 18964
215-721-2449
www.univest-corp.com

Patriot Bank
300 Old Reading Pike
Building 1, Second Floor
Stowe, PA 19464
610-705-9900 ext. 101
Fax: 610-327-3164
www.patriotbank.com

First Susquehanna Bank & Trust
400 Market Street
Sunbury, PA 17801
570-286-6781
877-843-3477
www.thefirst.com

Grange National Bank
198 East Tioga Street
Tunkhannock, PA 18657
570-836-2100
www.grangebank.com

Eagle National Bank
Upper Darby Branch
8045 West Chester Pike
Upper Darby, PA 19082-1317
610-853-4805
Fax: 610-853-2562
www.eaglenational.com

CIT Small Business Lending
Corporation
634 York Rd
PMB 167
Warminster, PA 18974
215-918-2542
Fax: 215-918-2543
www.smallbizlending.com/default.as
p

PNC Bank
Government Sponsored Lending
126 Easton Road, 2nd Floor
Willow Grove, PA 19090
215-784-1975
www.pncbank.com

Leesport Bank
1240 Broadcasting Rd
P.O. Box 6219
Wyomissing, PA 19610
610-208-0966 ext. 228
Fax: 610- 288-1892
www.leesportfinancialcorp.com

Farmers First Bank
Susquehanna Interim Bank
2951 Whiteford Road
York, PA 17403
800-864-7708 ext. 6105
www.ffb.com

Business Lenders, LLC
15 Lewis Street
Hartford, CT 06103
860-244-9202
www.businesslenders.com

GE Capital Small Business Finance
Corporation
4 North Park Drive, Suite 500
Hunt Valley, MD 21030
410-527-9359
www.ge.com/capital/smallbiz/index.
html

Fleet National Bank
1075 Main Street
Waltham, MA 02451
781-788-7406
Fax: 781-788-1027
www.fleet.com

M&T Bank
4564 Main Street
Amherst, NY 14226
800-724-2440
Fax: 716-634-5609
www.mandtbank.com

Manufacturers and Traders Trust Co.
4925 Main Street
Amherst, NY 14226
716-839-8712
Fax: 716-839-8777
www.mandtbank.com

Unity Bank
64 Old Highway 22
Clinton, NJ 08809
908-730-7630
800-540-4790
Fax: 908-730-9430
www.unitybank.com

UPS Capital Business Credit
2025 Lincoln Highway
Suite 130
Edison, NJ 08817
732-287-5881
www.upscaptial.com

Commerce Bank, N.A. (NJ)
One Royal Road
Flemington, NJ 08822
908-237-4758
http://bank.commerceonline.com

United Trust Bank
630 Georges Rd
North Brunswick, NJ 08902
732-247-3320
www.unitedtrust.com

Hudson United Bank
530 High Mountain Rd
North Haledon, NJ 07508
973-636-6052
www.hudsonunitedbank.com

Valley National Bank
1334 Route 22
P.O. Box 1027
North Plainfield, NJ 07060
908-561-7122
800-522-4100
www.valleynationalbank.com

Puerto Rico
Citibank
500 Tanca Street
P.O. Box 364106
San Juan, PR 00936-4106
787-721-0108
Fax: 787-766-3610

Blanco Belabor Viscera of Puerto
Rico
P.O. Box 364745
San Juan, PR 00936-4745
787-777-2889
Fax: 787-766-6985

Blanco Popular de Puerto Rico
P.O. Box 362708
San Juan, PR 00936-2708
787-765-9800
Fax: 787-756-5055

Blanco Scamander Puerto Rico
P.O. Box 362589
San Juan, PR 00936-2589
787-759-7070
Fax: 787-765-7443

First bank
P.O. Box 9146
San Juan, PR 00908-9146
787-729-8037
Fax: 787-729-8153

Rhode Island
Domestic Bank
815 Reservoir Avenue
Cranston, RI 02910
401-943-1600
800-556-6600
www.domesticbank.com

Independence Bank
Enterprise Capital, Inc.
1485 South County Trail
East Greenwich, RI 02818
401-886-4600
Fax: 401-884-9551
www.enterprisecapitalinc.com

Bank of Newport
528 West Main Road
Middletown, RI 02842
401-845-8726
Fax: 401-849-8665
www.bankofnewport.com

Bank RI
One Turks Head Place
Providence, RI 02903
401456-5015 ext. 1998
www.bankri.com

CIT Small Business Lending
Corporation
10 Dorrance Street, Suite 800B
Providence, RI 02903
401-831-1104
www.smallbizlending.com/default.as
p

Citizens Bank
One Citizens Plaza
Providence, RI 02903
401-456-7324
www.citizensbank.com

Coastway Credit Union
10 Greene Street
Providence, RI 02903
401-455-3200
Fax: 401-455-3299
www.coastway.com

First International Bank, N.A.
55 Dorrance Street
Providence, RI 02903
401-553-2400

Fleet Bank
111 Westminster Street
Providence, RI 02903
401-278-5520
www.fleet.com

Sovereign Bank New England
15 Westminster Street
Providence, RI 02903
401-752-1820
www.sovereignbank.com

Home Loan & Investment Bank
One Home Loan Plaza, Suite 3
Warwick, RI 02886
401-739-8800
800-722-5671 ext. 253
www.homeloanbank.com

Business Loan Express
116 High Street, Suite 214
Westerly, RI 02891
401-596-3200
Fax: 401-596-9103
www.alliedcapitalexpress.com

Business Lenders, LLC
15 Lewis Street
Hartford, CT 06103
860-244-9202
www.businesslenders.com

South Carolina
CIT Small Business Lending Corp.
10612-D Providence Road, Suite 483
Charlotte, NC 28277
704-814-0409

Fax: 704-814-0410
www.smallbizlending.com

Bank of America
901 Main Street
Columbia, SC 29201
803-255-7616
Fax: 803-255-7350
www.bankofamerica.com

Business Development Corporation
of South Carolina
PO Box 21823
Columbia, SC 29221
803-798-4064
Fax: 803-798-1224
www.businessdevelopment.org/inde
x.shtml

Goleta National Bank
6 Office Park Court, Suite 102
Columbia, SC 29223
803-736-1804
Fax: 803-736-6994

South Carolina Bank & Trust
520 Gervais Street
Columbia, SC 2920
803-231-3361
Fax: 803-771-0615
www.scbandt.com

Business Loan Express
220 North Main Street
Suite 604
Greenville, SC 29601
864-232-6197
Fax: 864-235-8065
www.alliedcapitalexpress.com

Lighthouse Community Bank
1204-A East Washington Street
P.O. Box 5697
Greenville, SC 29606
864-232-5080
Fax: 864-232-2444
www.lighthouseus.com

South Trust Bank
2000 Riveredge Parkway
Suite 350-B
Atlanta, GA 30328
770-951-4411
Fax: 770-951-4416
www.southtrust.com

Regions Bank
1457 Mt. Vernon Road
Dunwoody, GA 30338
770-395-9331
Fax: 770-395-1117
www.regions.com

RBC Centura Bank, Inc.
3201 Beachleaf Court, Suite 104
Raleigh, NC 27604
919-788-5961
Fax: 919-788-5446
www.centura.com

Branch Banking & Trust Company
110 South Stratford Road
Suite 200
Winston-Salem, NC 27104
336-733-3441
Fax: 336-733-3499
www.bbandt.com

Wachovia Bank of SC, N.A.
101 North Cherry Street
Winston-Salem, NC 27150
336-735-6193
Fax: 336-735-6180
www.wachovia.com

CitiCapital Small Business Finance,
Inc.
300 East Carpenter Freeway
Suite 1250
Irving, TX
972-652-4666
Fax: 972-652-3340
www.citibank.com

South Dakota
Pioneer Bank & Trust
700 State Street
PO Box 729
Belle Fourche, SD 57717
605-892-2536
Fax: 605-892-2412
www.pioneerbankandtrust.com

First National Bank in Brookings
2220 6th St
PO Drawer 5057
Brookings, SD 57006
800-843-1552
605-696-2200
www.firstnb.com

First Fidelity Bank
Main Street
Burke, SD 57523-0376
605-775-2641
www.ffb-sd.com

Custer
The First Western Bank
648 Mt. Rushmore Road
Custer, SD 57730
605-673-2215
Fax: 605-673-2492
www.firstwesternbank.com

First National Bank
119 North Deadwood
Box 850
Ft. Pierre, SD 57532
605-223-2521
Fax: 605-223-2496
www.firstnationalbanks.com/Branch
es/ft.pierre.htm

First National Bank
103 East Pine Street
PO Box 910
Philip, SD 57567
605-859-2525

American State Bank
700 East Sioux Avenue
PO Box 1178
Pierre, SD 57501-1178
605-224-9233
800-347-6537
Fax: 605-224-1872
www.asbpierre.com

BankWest, Inc.
420 South Pierre Street
PO Box 998
Pierre, SD 57501
605-649-7798
800-253-0362
Fax: 605-224-7393
www.bankwest-sd.com

Great Western Bank
14 Saint Joseph Street
PO Box 2290
Rapid City, SD 57701
605-343-9230
Fax: 605-343-8418
www.greatwesternbanksd.com/index
.shtml

The First National Bank in Sioux
Falls
100 South Phillips Avenue
PO Box 5186
Sioux Falls, SD 57104
605-335-5100
800-339-1160
www.fnbsf.com

First Premier Bank
601 South Minnesota Avenue
PO Box 1348
Sioux Falls, SD 57104
605-357-3000
www.firstpremier.com

Home Federal Savings Bank
225 South Main Avenue
PO Box 5000
Sioux Falls, SD 57117-5000
605-333-9828
800-244-2419
www.homefederal.com/homefederal

Marquette Bank of South Dakota,
N.A.
9th & Main
PO Box 5789
Sioux Falls, SD 57103
605-330-1100

Wells Fargo South Dakota, N.A.
101 North Phillips Avenue
PO Box 5128
Sioux Falls, SD 57104
605-339-7332
www.wellsfargo.com

U.S. Bank National Association
141 North Main Avenue
PO Box 5308
Sioux Falls, SD 57104

605-339-8696
www.usbank.com

The First Western Bank Sturgis
1200 Main Street
PO Box 9
Sturgis, SD 57785
605-347-2562
Fax: 605-347-4829
www.firstwesternbank.com

Community First State Bank
15 East Main Street
PO Box 478
Vermillion, SD 57069
605-624-4431
www.communityfirst.com

First Dakota National Bank
225 Cedar Street
P.O. Box 156
Yankton, SD 57078
605-665-7432
Fax: 605-668-0145
www.firstdakota.com

Tennessee

Citizens National Bank
2 Park Avenue
Athens, TN 37371
888-785-5855
423-745-0261
Fax: 423-745-7718
www.citnatbank.com

Premier Bank of Brentwood
5217 Maryland Way
Brentwood, TN 37027
615-376-0001
Fax: 615-370-2260
www.premierbanker.com

First Volunteer Bank of TN
728 Broad Street
Chattanooga, TN 37402
423-668-4501
Fax: 423-668-4675

First Federal Savings Bank
200 North Second Street
Clarksville, TN 37041
931-552-6176
Fax: 931 552 7763
www.firstfederalsb.com

BankTennessee
1125 West Poplar
Collierville, TN 38017
901-854-0854
Fax: 901-854-6203
www.banktennessee.com

First Farmers & Merchants National
Bank
816 South Garden Street
P.O. Box 1148
Columbia, TN 38402
931-388-3145
Fax: 931-380-8359
www.fandmbank.com

Citizens Bank
300 Broad Street
Elizabethton, TN 37643
423-543-2265
Fax: 423-547-8424
www.citizensbanktricities.com/defau
lt.cfm

Franklin National Bank
230 Public Square
Franklin, TN 37064
615-790-2265
Fax: 615-794-8682
www.franklinnetbranch.com/netbran
ch/default.asp

Union Planters Bank
121 1st. Avenue South
Franklin, TN 37065
615-794-8899
Fax: 615-791-5907
www.unionplanters.com

First Tennessee Bank NA
7640 Poplar Avenue
Germantown, TN 38138
901-759-7828
www.firsttennessee.com

Union Planters Bank
1214. Main Street
Humboldt, TN 38343
731-784-1122
Fax: 731-784-2905
www.unionplanters.com

1st Western Lending
5860 Ridgeway Center, Suite 110
Memphis, TN 38120
901-680-0551
888-332-9650

InSouth Bank
6141 Walnut Grove Road
Memphis, TN 38120
901-747-5555
Fax: 901-747-5540
www.insouth.com

First Bank Lexington
615 Memorial Boulevard
Murfreesboro, TN 37123
615-890-1111
Fax: 615-890-8940
www.bankm.com

Capital Bank & Trust Company
1820 West End Avenue
Nashville, TN 37203
615-327-9000
Fax: 615-321-2126
www.capitalbk.com/default.htm

Tennessee Business and Industrial
Development Corporation (BIDCO)
1301 East Wood Street
P.O. Box 307
Paris, TN 38242
731-644-7108
Fax: 731-644-7019

AmSouth Bank
250 Riverchase Parkway East
Birmingham, AL 35244
214-953-8908
Fax: 217-758-5260

Goleta National Bank
445 Pine Avenue
Goleta, CA 93117
805-681-9943
Fax: 805-683-0635
www.goleta.com

Borrego Springs Bank, NA
7777 Alvarado Road, Suite 501
LaMesa, CA 91941
619-668-5150
Fax: 619-403-5191
www.borregospringsbank.com

CNL Commercial Lending
Corporation (CNL)
26137 La Paz Road, Suite 102
Mission Viejo, CA 92691
949-452-0949
www.cnlonline.com/commercialfina
nce/management.asp

Bank of America, NA
10850 White Rock Rd., Suite 101
Rancho Cordova, CA 95670
916-861-6729
Fax: 916-861-6779
www.bankofamerica.com

US Bank
9918 Hibert Street, 2nd Floor
San Diego, CA 92131-1018
858-536-4545
www.usbank.com

Temecula Valley Bank
27710 Jefferson Avenue, Suite A-
100
Temecula, CA 92590
909-506-1511
800-939-3736
www.temvalbank.com

Bank of the West (CA)
11202 Donner Pass Road
Truckee, CA 96161
530-582-3050
www.bankofthewest.com

Union Planters Bank, NA
9700 NW 112th. Avenue
Medley, FL 33178
786-777-6772
Fax: 786-845-4488
www.unionplanters.com

California Bank & Trust Co.
d/b/a Zions Small Business Finance
3330 Cumberland Boulevard
Suite 500
Atlanta, GA 30339
770-690-4218
Fax: 770-690-4217
www.zsbf.com

SouthTrust Bank
2000 Riveredge Parkway
Suite 350-B
Atlanta, GA 30328
770-951-4411
Fax: 770-951-4416

SunTrust Bank
225 Peachtree Street, NE
Atlanta, GA 30303
404-588-7288
Fax: 404-230-1902
www.suntrust.com/business/Solution
s/index.asp

Regions Bank
1457 Mt. Vernon Road
Dunwoody, GA 30338
770-395-9611
Fax: 770-395-1117
www.regions.com/servlet/RegionsH
ome/index.jsp

Heller Equity Capital Corporation
500 West Monroe Street
Chicago, IL 60661
312-441-7200
Fax: 312-441-7378

Business Loan Express
121 West Dewey Street, Suite 210
Wichita, KS 67202
316-263-3232
800-722-5626
Fax: 316-263-4391
www.businessloanexpress.net

Wells Fargo Bank
1455 West Lake Street, Suite 306
Minneapolis, MN 55408
612-312-8200
www.wellsfargo.com

BancorpSouth Bank
One Mississippi Plaza
P.O. Box 789
Tupelo, MS 38802
662-680-2345
Fax: 662-680-2317
www.bancorpsouthonline.com/index
.html

GE Capital
635 Maryville Center Drive
Suite 120
St. Louis, MO 63141
314-205-3500
www.ge.com/capital/smallbiz/index.
html

Branch Banking and Trust Company
(BB&T)
110 South Stratford Road, Suite 200
Winston-Salem, NC 27104
336-733-3300
www.bbandt.com

CIT Small Business Lending
Corporation
1 CIT Drive

Livingston, NJ 07039
800-713-4984 ext 6004
Fax: 973-422-6130
www.smallbizlending.com

Compass Bank
17218 Preston Road, Suite 3000
Dallas, TX 75252
972-248-7000
www.compassweb.com/index.cfm

PMC Capital, Inc.
18111 Preston Road, Suite 600
Dallas, TX 75252
972-349-3209
800-486-3223
Fax: 972-349-3265
www.pmccapital.com

Texas

Banco Popular North America
1600 East Lamar Boulevard
Arlington, TX 76011
817-274-6315
Fax: 817-274-5903
www.bancopopular.com/bancopopul
ar/welcome.html

American Bank of Commerce
522 Congress Avenue, Suite 110
Austin, TX 78701
512-391-5500
Fax: 512-391-5599
or
2243 West Braker Lane
Austin, TX 78758
512-391-5500
Fax: 512-391-5599
www.theabcbank.com

Bank One, Texas, N.A.
7600 Burnet Road
Austin, TX 78757
512-479-5400
Fax: 512-451-5690
www.bankone.com

Comerica Bank- Texas
804 Congress Avenue, Suite 310
Austin, TX 78701
512-427-7113
Fax: 512-427-7145
www.comerica.com

Compass Bank
5800 North Mopac
Austin, TX 78731
512-419-3401
Fax: 512-419-3467
www.compassweb.com/index.html

Franklin Bank, SSB
3720 Jefferson Street
Austin, TX 78731
512-374-1600
800-552-0784
Fax: 512-374-1199
www.bankfranklin.com/index.html

Frost Bank
3525 Far West Boulevard
Austin, TX 78731
512-473-4343
Fax: 512-473-4915
www.frostbank.com/index.htm

Liberty Bank SSB
900 Congress Avenue
Austin, TX 78701
512-472-5433
Fax: 512-236-2608
www.libertybanktexas.com

Southwest Bank
9430 Research Boulevard, Suite 400
Austin, TX 78759
512-343-3637
Fax: 512-345-2924
www.southwestbank.com

Southwest Bank
P.O. Box 160112
Austin, TX 78701
512-306-7378
Fax: 512-306-7379
www.southwestbank.com

U.S. Bank, SBA Division
9600 Great Hills Trail, Suite 150 W
Austin, TX 78759
512-502-3048
800-986-2120
Fax: 512-502-3024
www.usbank.com

First National Bank of Beeville
1400 East Houston
P.O. Drawer B
Beeville, TX 78104
361-358-1530
Fax: 361-358-7405
www.fnbnet.net

Broadway National Bank
1012 South Main Street
Boerne, TX 78006
830-249-2547
800-531-7650
Fax: 830-249-2678
www.broadwaybank.com

Bank One, Texas
6300 Harry Hines Boulevard
Dallas, TX 75201
214-290-2000
www.bankone.com

Business Loan Express
700 North Pearl Street Suite 1850
Dallas, TX 75201-7424
214-389-6100
Fax: 214-389-6196
www.alliedcapitalexpress.com

Compass Bank
11705 Preston Road
Dallas, TX 75230
214-346-6131
www.compassweb.com/index.html

JPMorgan Chase Bank
2200 Ross Avenue
P.O. Box 660197
Dallas, TX 75266-0197
214-965-4485
Fax: 214-965-4093
www.chase.com

South Texas National Bank
525 South Main
P.O. Box 4120
Del Rio, TX 77840
830-774-6800
Fax: 830-774-7256
www.stnb.com

Security State Bank and Trust
201 West Main Street
P.O. Box 471
Fredericksburg, TX 78624
830-997-7575
Fax: 830-997-7994
www.ssbtexas.com

Southwest Bank
P.O. Box 962020
Fort Worth, TX 76162-2020
800-792-5669
Fax: 817-292-6725
www.southwestbank.com

First Texas Bank
900 South Austin Avenue
Georgetown, TX 78627
512-863-2567
Fax: 512- 869-2387
www.firsttexas-gtwn.com

GE Capital Small Business
Financing
2115 East Vinison #2204
Harlingen, TX 78550
956-412-8600
Fax: 956-412-8602
www.ge.com/capital/smallbiz

Business Loan Express
11011 Richmond Avenue, Suite 940
Houston, TX 77042
713-741-1776
Fax: 713-748-1776
www.alliedcapitalexpress.com

Comerica Bank-Texas
1900 West Loop South
Houston, TX 77027
713-888-2688
800-925-2160
Fax: 713-888-2674
www.comerica.com

JPMorgan Chase Bank
2900 Woodridge, 2nd Floor
Houston, TX 77087
713-640-3384
Fax: 713-640-3355
www.chase.com

U.S. Bank, SBA Division
1800 West Loop South, Suite 1115

Houston, TX 77027
713-629-6868
Fax: 713-629-6966
www.usbak.com

Bank of the Hills
1075 Junction Highway
P.O. Box 2002
Kerrville, TX 78029-2002
830-895-2265
Fax: 830-895-2269
www.bankofthehills.com

Security State Bank and Trust
1130 Junction Highway
Kerrville, TX 78029
830-895-2000
Fax: 830-895-2012
www.ssbtexas.com

Commerce Bank, N. A.
Mann Road & IH 35
Laredo, TX 78042-1511
956-724-2424
Fax: 956-724-9318
www.ibc.com

South Texas National Bank
9801 McPherson Road
Laredo, TX 78045
956-753-1811
Fax: 956-726-3659
www.stnb.com

American Bank of Texas, N.A.
418 Highway 281
Marble Falls, TX 78654
830-693-3676
Fax: 830-693-4150
www.mfnbank.com

First National Bank of Sonora
5710 Sherwood Way
San Angelo, TX 76901
915-949-0099
800-814-0099
http://fxfn.com/x2zfnbss

San Angelo National Bank
3471 Knickerbocker Road
San Angelo, TX 76904
915-659-5822
Fax: 915-659-5709
www.sanb-tx.com

Texas State Bank
2201 Sherwood Way
San Angelo, TX 76902
915-949-3721
Fax: 915-942-7017
www.texasstatebank.com

Bank of America, National
Association
601 Northwest Loop 410, Suite 120
San Antonio, TX 78216
210-525-5440
Fax: 210-525-5088
www.bankofamerica.com

Broadway National Bank
1177 N. E. Loop 410
San Antonio, TX 78209
210-283-6500
800-531-7650
Fax: 210-283-6632
www.broadwaybank.com

JPMorgan Chase Bank
P.O. Box 47531
San Antonio, TX 78265-7531
210-829-6160
Fax: 210-826-6155
www.chase.com

Citizens National Bank
8000 IH-10 West, Suite 600
San Antonio, TX 78230
210-525-7919
Fax: 210-525-7918

Comerica Bank-Texas
115 Wyanoke Drive
San Antonio, TX 78209
210-828-6495
Fax:210-828-2009
www.comerica.com

Compass Bank (Texas)
660 North Main Avenue
San Antonio, TX 78205
210-592-5570
www.compassweb.com/index.cfm

Frost National Bank
100 West Houston Street
San Antonio, TX 78205
210-220-4011
Fax: 210-220-4588
www.frostbank.com/index.htm

Intercontinental National Bank
634 West Sunset
San Antonio, TX 78216
210-283-4821
Fax: 210-824-2026
www.interconbank.com

Plaza Bank, N.A.
400 West Houston Street
San Antonio, TX 78207
210-222-2211
Fax: 210-222-0296
www.plazabank.com

South Texas National Bank
7400 Blanco Road, Suite 127
San Antonio, TX 78216
210-349-1442
Fax: 210-349-8433
www.stnb.com

SouthTrust Bank
4949 Rittman Road
San Antonio, TX 78218
210-731-4579
800-CALL-STB
Fax: 210-650-3847
www.southtrust.com/st/default.htm

SouthTrust Bank
100 St. Cloud
San Antonio, TX 78228
210-731-4517
800-CALL-STB
Fax: 210-736-6904
www.southtrust.com/st/default.htm

CIT Small Business Lending
Corporation
1777 N. E. Loop 410, Suite 600
San Antonio, TX 78217
210-820-2650
Fax: 210-841-5750
www.cit.com

U.S. Bank, SBA Division
100 N.E. Loop 410, Suite 965
San Antonio, TX 78216
210-384-8266
www.usbank.com

Wells Fargo Bank (Texas) N. A.
246 East Commerce Street
San Antonio, TX 78205
210-856-5253
Fax: 210-856-5093
www.wellsfargo.com

Wells Fargo Bank (Texas) N.A.
707 Castroville Road
San Antonio, TX 78237
210-856-6212
www.wellsfargo.com

Frost Bank
231 North Guadalupe
San Marcos, TX 78666
512-393-5600
Fax: 512-393-5641
www.frostbank.com/index.htm

Schertz Bank & Trust
519 Main Street
P.O. Box 800
Schertz, TX 78154
210-945-7400
Fax: 210-945-7424
www.schertzbank.com

First National Bank of Sonora
102 North Main Street
Sonora, TX 76950
915-387-3861
800-725-3861
http://fxfn.com/x2zfnbss

First National Bank of Beeville
142 N. Riedel
P.O. Box 825
Yorktown, TX 78164
361-564-2257
Fax: 361-564-4145
www.fnbnet.net

CIT Small Business Lending
Corporation
1526 Cole Boulevard
Building 3, Suite 200
Golden, CO 80401

303-202-3731
800-525-3343
Fax: 303-202-3789
www.cit.com

CIT Small Business Lending
Corporation
1 CIT Drive
Livingston, NJ 07039
973 740-5000
Fax: 973-422-6062
www.cit.com

Gunnison Valley Bank
10 South Main, Box 220
Gunnison, UT 84634
435-528-7221

Utah

Bank of American Fork
33 East Main
American Fork, UT 84003
801-756-7681
800-815-2265
Fax: 801-763-6666
www.bankaf.com

Barnes Banking Company
100 South 500 West
Bountiful, UT 84010
801-296-1010
Fax: 801-593-0836
http://barnesbank.portalvault.com

First National Bank of Layton
207 S. Main
Bountiful, UT 84010
801-292-3900
www.fnbutah.com

State Bank of Southern Utah
377 North Main Street
Cedar City, UT 84720
435-865-2300
Fax: 435-586-6136
www.sbsu.com

Bank of Ephraim
2 North Main Street
P.O. Box 705
Ephraim, UT 84627
435-283-4621

Lewiston State Bank
17 East Center
Lewiston, UT 84320
435-258-2456
800-233-6510
Fax: 435-258-5346
www.ls-bank.com

Cache Valley Bank
101 North Main Street
Box 3227
Logan, UT 84321
435-753-3020

USU Community Credit Union
695 East 1000th North
Logan, UT 84321

801-753-4450
800-248-6361
www.usuccu.org

First National Bank of Morgan
5015 West Old Hwy Road
Morgan, UT 84050
801-876-3442
www.morgan1st.com

Draper Bank and Trust
5595 South State St
Murray, UT 84107
801-524-8836
Fax: 801-524-4770
www.draperbank.com

Bank of Utah
2605 Washington Blvd, Box 231
Ogden, UT 84401
801-409-5000
www.bankofutah.com

Capital Community Bank
49 West University Parkway
Orem, UT 84058
801-226-6699
Fax: 801-772-0803
www.capitalcombank.com

Frontier Bank
1425 Deer Valley Drive
Park City, UT 84060
435-615-2265
www.frontierbankfsb.com

Western Community
475 East State Road
P.O. Box 340
Pleasant Grove, UT 84062
801-796-3560
www.westerncommunitybank.com

American Bank of Commerce
3670 North University Avenue
Provo, UT 84604
801-377-4222

Bonneville Bank
1675 North 200 West
Provo, UT 84604
801-374-9500

Central Bank & Trust
75 North University Avenue
PO Box 1488
Provo, UT 84603
801-375-1000
www.centralbankutah.com/home.ht
ml

Far West Bank
201 E. Center, Box 448
Provo, UT 84606
801-342-6000
Fax: 801-342-6080
www.farwestbank.com

America First Credit Union
1344 West 4675 South

Riverdale, UT 84405
801-778-8604
www.americafirst.com

Utah Independent Bank
55 South State Street, Box 9
Salina, UT 84654
435-529-7459
www.utahindependentbank.com

American Investment Financial
222 East South Temple
Salt Lake City, UT 84111
801-297-1078
800-358-5125
Fax: 801-297-1176
www.aifusa.com

Bank One
2200 South State Street
Salt Lake City, UT 84115
801-481-5547
www.bankone.com

Brighton Bank
940 West North Temple
Box 21309
Salt Lake City, UT 84116
801-596-2700
Fax: 801-596-0110
www.brightonbank.com

Community First National Bank
142 East 200 South
Salt Lake City, UT 84111
801-531-3400
www.communityfirst.com

First Community Bank
4626 Highland Drive
Salt Lake City, UT 84117
801-272-0150
www.fsbnm.com

Wells Fargo Bank
405 S. Main Street, 11th Floor
Salt Lake City, UT 84111
801-596-2837
www.wellsfargo.com

Holladay Bank & Trust
2020 East 4800 South
Salt Lake City, UT 84117
801-272-4275

Home Credit Bank
1455 East 2100 South
PO Box 526155
Salt Lake City, UT 84105
801-487-0811
Fax: 801-487-0814
www.homecredit.com/index.htm

Liberty Bank
326 South 500 East
Salt Lake City, UT 84102
801-355-7411
Fax: 801-355-7436
www.libertybankofutah.com

U.S. Bank
448 E Winchester Street, Suite 312
Salt Lake City, UT 84107
801-284-5900
www.usbank.com

Wells Fargo
299 South Main Street
Salt Lake City, UT 84111
801-246-1300
800-545-0670
www.wellsfargobank.com

Western Bank
376 East 400 South, Ste 120
Salt Lake City, UT 84111
801-239-1801
www.wamu.com/servlet/wamu/index
.html

First Utah Bank
11015 South State Street
Sandy, UT 84070
801-523-8300
www.firstutahbank.com

Key Bank
10281 South State
Sandy, UT 84040
801-816-3777
www.keybank.com

The Village Bank
94 East Tabernacle
St. George, UT 84770
435-674-5200
888-277-5882
Fax: 435-628-0580
www.thevillagebank.com

Zions First National Bank
5620 West 4100 South
West Valley City, UT 84128
801-594-8475
Fax: 801-549-8477
www.zionsbank.com

Comerica Bank
400 East Van Buren, Suite 900
Phoenix, AZ 85004
602-417-1100
www.comerica.com

Meridian Bank, N.A
2020 North Central Avenue
Phoenix, AZ 85004
602-258-5555
Fax: 602-271-0801
www.combankaz.com/index.html

U.S. Bank
500 North Brand Boulevard, Suite
1285
Glendale, CA 91203
818-246-8325
www.usbank.com

CIT Small Business Lending
1526 Cole Blvd.
Building #3, Room 200

Golden, CO 80401
720-746-1628
www.smallbizlending.com/smallbizlending.html

Commercial Capital Corporation
50 Albany Turnpike Blvd., #4
Canton, CT 06019
860-693-3667

Wells Fargo
1400 Vista Avenue
208-338-5500
Boise, ID 83705
www.wellsfargo.com

Zions Bank
902 Washington
Montpelier, ID 83254
208-847-1531
Fax: 208-847-1536
www.zionsbank.com

Heller Equity Capital Corporation
500 West Monroe Street
Chicago, IL 60661
312-441-7200

GE Capital
635 Maryville Centre Drive
Suite 120
St. Louis, MO 63141
314-205-3500
www.ge.com/capital/smallbiz/index.html

Bank of America, FSB
6900 Westcliff Drive, 3rd Floor
Las Vegas, NV 89145
702-654-6512
www.bankofamerica.com/index.cfm

Small Business Loan Source
9801 Westheimer
Houston, TX 77042
713-961-5626
800-457-4307, ext. 120
www.sbls.com/default.htm

Vermont
Banknorth
111 Main Street
P.O. Box 409
Burlington, VT 05401
802-658-1010
800-462-3666
Fax: 802-860-5542
www.banknorth.com/default_banknorth.aspx

KeyBank, N.A.
149 Bank Street
P.O. Box 949
Burlington, VT 05401
802-660-4160
Fax: 802-864-6908
www.keybank.com

Lyndonville Savings Bank
1033 Broad Street

Lyndonville, VT 05851
802-626-1111
Fax: 802-626-3456
www.lyndonbank.com

Factory Point National Bank
Equinox Square
4928 Main Street
P.O. Box 1566
Manchester Center, VT 05255
802-362-2424
Fax: 802-362-4101
www.factorypoint.com

National Bank of Middlebury
22-32 Main Street
P.O. Box 189
Middlebury, VT 05753
802-388-4982
Fax: 802-388-6077
www.nationalbankmiddlebury.com

Chittenden Bank
112 State Street
P.O. Box 459
Montpelier, VT 05602
802-223-8550
Fax: 802-223-6165
www.chittenden.com

Union Bank
20 Main Street, Route 100
P.O. Box 667
Morrisville, VT 05661
802-888-6600
Fax: 802-888-7697
www.unionbankvt.com/Morrisville.cfm

Northfield Savings Bank
33 Main Street
P.O. Box 347
Northfield, VT 05663
802-485-5871
800-NSB-CASH
Fax: 802-485-7565
www.nsbvt.com

Merchants Bank
275 Kennedy Drive
P.O. Box 1009
South Burlington, VT 05403
802-865-1900
Fax: 802-865-1874
www.merchantsbankvt.com

Passumpsic Savings Bank
124 Railroad Street
P.O. Box 38
St. Johnsbury, VT 05819
802-748-3196
800-370-3196
Fax: 802-751-4275
www.passumpsicbank.com

Virginia
Union Bank & Trust Company
U.S. Route 1 & Ashcake Road
Ashland, VA 23005

804-798-4488
Fax: 804-550-0456
www.unionbankandtrust.com/home.html

National Bank of Blacksburg
100 South Main Street
Blacksburg, VA 24060
540-951-6208
Fax: 540-951-6325
www.nbbank.com

Bank of Northumberland, Inc.
14954 Northumberland Highway
P.O. Box 365
Burgess, VA 22432
804-453-7003
Fax: 804-453-6242
www.bankwithbni.com

Guaranty Bank
1658 State Farm Boulevard
Charlottesville, VA 22906
434-970-1177
Fax: 970-244-6651
www.guarantybankva.com

Monarch Bank
750 Volvo Parkway
Chesapeake, VA 23320
757-222-2100
Fax: 757-222-2101
www.monarchbank.com

National Bank of Fredericksburg
2403 Fall Hill Avenue
Fredericksburg, VA 22401
540-899-3200
Fax: 540-371-5440
www.nationalbankfredericksburg.com

Virginia Heartland Bank
4700 Harrison Road
P.O. Box 7267
Fredericksburg, VA 22408
540-898-1110
Fax: 540-898-0179
www.virginiaheartlandbank.com

Capital One, F.S.B.
11011 West Broad Street
Glen Allen, VA 23060
804-284-1035
Fax: 804-284-1866
www.capitalone.com

Old Point National Bank of Phoebus
1 West Mellen Street
Hampton, VA 23663
757-728-1200
Fax: 757-599-2237
www.oldpoint.com

Rockingham Heritage Bank
110 University Boulevard
Harrisonburg, VA 22801
540-432-9300
Fax: 540-432-1091
www.rhbank.com

Capital One, F.S.B.
11011 West Broad Street
Glen Allen, VA 23060
804-284-1035
Fax: 804-284-1866
www.capitalone.com

Page Valley Bank
17 West Main Street
P.O. Box 609
Luray, VA 22835-1230
540-743-6521
888-331-6521
Fax: 540-743-5536
http://pagevalleybank.com

Southern Financial Bank
10175 Hastings Drive
Manassas, VA 20110
703-365-9628
800-713-6798
Fax: 703-335-9438
www.southernfinancialbank.com

Wachovia Bank
1753 Pinnacle Drive
McLean, VA 22102
703-760-5610
www.wachovia.com

Citizens and Farmers Bank
1400 Alverser Drive
Midlothian, VA 23113
804-378-0332
Fax: 804-378-9129
www.cffc.com

CIT Small Business Lending
Corporation
13146 Midlothian Turnpike, #233
Midlothian, VA 23113-4200
804-594-7233
Fax: 594-7234
www.smallbizlending.com/default.as
p

Harbor Bank
1 Old Oyster Point Road
Newport News, VA 23602
757-249-7800
Fax: 757-249-0840
www.harborbankva.com

Heritage Bank & Trust Company
4815 Colley Avenue
Norfolk, VA 23508
757-423-5074
Fax: 757-423-5127
www.heritagenorfolk.com/news.html

Valley Bank
36 Church Avenue, S.W.
Roanoke, VA 24011
540-342-2265
Fax: 540-342-4514
www.myvalleybank.com

UPS Capital Business Credit
12020 Sunrise Valley Drive, Suite
270

Reston, VA 20191
800-776-0093
703-391-8020
Fax: 703-391-8480
www.upscapital.com

Business Loan Express
3 South 12th Street
Richmond, VA 23219
804-344-8160
888-333-6441
Fax: 804 344-8301
www.alliedcapitalexpress.com

First Market Bank, FSB
111 Virginia Street, Suite 101
Richmond, VA 23219
804 327-5720
Fax: 804-327-7534
www.ncfwebdev.net/firstmarketbank
/business

Branch Banking & Trust Company
(BB&T)
823 East Main Street
Richmond, VA 23219
804-787-1000
www.bbandt.com

Bank of America
1111 East Main Street, 8th Floor
Richmond, VA 23220
804-788-2775
Fax: 804-788-3569
www.bankofamerica.com

Peoples Bank of Virginia
2702 North Parham Road
Richmond, VA 23294
804-270-6800
Fax: 804-270-7230

SunTrust Bank
Mail Code: RVW4323
1001 Semmes Avenue
Richmond, VA 23224
804-319-1542
Fax: 804-319-1496
www.suntrust.com/business/Solution
s/index.asp

UPS Capital Business Credit
8701 Park Central Drive, Suite 240
Richmond, VA 23227
804-261-3373
Fax: 804-261-3532
www.upscapital.com

Wachovia Bank
1021 East Cary Street
Richmond, VA 23219
804-697-7175
www.wachovia.com

Branch Banking & Trust Company
125 North Central Avenue
Staunton, VA 24401
540-885-1561
Fax: 877-739-7979
www.bbandt.com

Resource Bank
3720 Virginia Beach Boulevard
Virginia Beach, VA 23452
757-431-2265
Fax: 757-463-8786
www.resourcebankonline.com

Fauquier Bank
10 Courthouse Square
Warrenton, VA 20186
540-347-2700
Fax: 540-349-0290
www.fauquierbank.com

Marathon Bank
139 North Cameron Street
Winchester, VA 22601
540-542-6130
Fax: 540-542-6615
www.themarathonbank.com

Temecula Valley Bank
27710 Jefferson Avenue
Suite A-100
Temecula, CA 92590
909-506-1511
800-939-3736
www.temvalbank.com

SouthTrust Bank
2000 Riveredge Pkwy
Suite 350-B
Atlanta, GA 30328
770-951-4411
Fax: 770-951-4416

Vine Street Financial
5901-C Peachtree-Dunwoody Road,
Suite 420
Atlanta, GA 30328
770-522-0789
800-758-0038
Fax: 770-551-8781
www.vstfinancial.com/

Business Lenders, LLC
15 Lewis Street
Hartford CT 06103
860-244-9202
Fax: 860-527-0884
www.businesslenders.com

GE Capital Small Business Finance
Corp.
Gaithersburg, MD 20877
301-990-4333
www.ge.com/capital/smallbiz

Valley National Bank
1334 U.S. Highway 22 East
North Plainfield, NJ 07060
908-561-0271
800-522-4100
Fax: 908-753-9817
www.valleynationalbank.com

Washington Mutual Bank, F.A.
4020 Westchase Boulevard
Suite 100
Raleigh, NC 27607

919-839-5511
Fax: 919-839-0706

Washington

Anchor Savings Bank
120 North Broadway
P.O. Box 387
Aberdeen, WA 98520-0094
360-532-6223
www.anchornetbank.com

North County Bank
16419 Smokey Point Boulevard
Arlington, WA 98223
360-657-3105
Fax: 360-659-3305
www.northcountybank.com

Sterling Savings
1261 Auburn Way North
Auburn, WA 98002
253-939-0071
www.sterlingsavingsbank.com

American Marine Bank
249 Winslow Way East
P.O. Box 10788
Bainbridge Island, WA 98110
206-842-5651
800-648-3194
Fax: 206-842-8608
www.americanmarinebank.com

Bank of America
Community Banking Development
10555 NE 8th Street
Bellevue, WA 989004-4333
206-358-5146
www.bankofamerica.com

Charter Bank
10885 NE 4th Street, Suite 100
Bellevue, WA 98004-5531
425-586-5020
www.charterbankwa.com

First Mutual Bank
400 108th Avenue NE
P.O. Box 1647
Bellevue, WA 98009-1647
425-453-5301 ext 953
Fax: 425-455-7330
www.firstmutual.com

Key Bank
601 108th Avenue N.E., Suite 101
Bellevue, WA 98004
425-637-9495
www.keybank.com

Pacifica Bank
10900 NE 4th Street, Suite 200
Bellevue, WA 98004
425-637-1188
Fax: 425-637-0150
www.pacificabank.com

Bank Northwest
100 Grand Street

Bellingham, WA 98225
360-734-0544
Fax: 360-734-9794
www.banknorthwest.com

Peoples Bank
1333 Cornwall Avenue
Bellingham, WA 98225
360-734-9811
www.peoplesbank-wa.com

Horizon Bank
1500 Cornwall Avenue
P.O. Box 580
Bellingham, WA 98227
360-733-3050
www.horizonbank.com

Skagit State Bank
301 East Fairhaven Avenue
P.O. Box 285
Burlington, WA 98233
360-755-0411
www.skagitbank.com

Whidbey Island Bank
1800 South Burlington Boulevard
P.O. Box 302
Burlington, WA 98233
360-757-3416
Fax: 360-757-0175
www.wibank.com

Security State Bank
P.O. Box 1050
Centralia, WA 98531
360-736-0763
www.ssbwa.com

State Bank of Concrete
45872 Main St
P.O. Box 426
Concrete, WA 98237
360-853-8171
www.statebankofconcrete.com

Cascade Bank
2828 Colby Avenue
Everett, WA 98201
425-257-1745
800-326-8787
www.cascadebank.com

Coastal Community Bank
2817 Colby Avenue
P.O. Box 12220
Everett, WA 98201
425-257-9000
Fax: 425-257-0521
www.coastalbank.com

Nara Bank
1010 South 336th Street, Suite #203
Federal Way, WA 98003
213-427-6340
http://narabank.com

Washington State Bank
32303 Pacific Hwy South
Federal Way, WA 98003

253-941-8541
Fax: 253-941-8799
www.wastatebank.com

Islanders Bank
225 Blair Street
P.O. Box 909
Friday Harbor, WA 98250
360-378-2265
800-843-5441
Fax: 360-378-6212
www.islandersbank.com

Venture Bank
7022 Pioneer Way
P.O. Box 2329
Gig Harbor, WA 98335
253-853-5000
www.fcbonline.com

ShoreBank Pacific
203 Howerton Way
P.O. Box 400
Ilwaco, WA 98624
360-642-1166
Fax: 360-642-3780
www.eco-bank.com

Issaquah Bank
1055 NW Maple Street
P O Box 1263
Issaquah, WA 98027
425-392-8000
Fax: 425-392-4707
www.issaquah-bank.com

Banner Bank
202 Kirkland Avenue
Kirkland, WA 98033
425-576-1514
www.banrbank.com

Venture Bank
721 College Street, SE
P.O. Box 3800
Lacey, WA 98509
360-456-0800
www.fcbonline.com

City Bank
14807 Hwy 99
P.O. Box 1036
Lynnwood, WA 98046
425-745-5933
800-569-0006
www.citybank.com

Prime Pacific Bank
4710 196th Street SW
P.O. Box 2518
Lynnwood, WA 98036
425-712-9898

Comerica Bank
724 Columbia Street NW, Suite 205
Olympia, Washington 98501
360-357-0077
Fax: 360-357-0067
www.comerica.com

South Sound Bank
400 Cooper Point Road SW, Suite 10
Olympia, WA 98508
360-705-4200
Fax: 360-705-2244
www.southsoundbank.com

Kitsap Bank
1700 Mile Hill Drive, Suite 700
Port Orchard, WA 98366
360-876-2297
800-656-2297
www.kitsapbank.com/index.htm

Puyallup Valley Bank
1307 East Main Avenue
P.O. Box 578
Puyallup, WA 98372
253-848-2316

Harbor Community Bank
221 Commercial Street
P.O. Box 552
Raymond, WA 98577
360-942-2401
Fax: 360-942-3785
www.harborcommunity.com

Redmond National Bank
15801 NE 85th Street
Redmond, WA 98052
425-881-8111
www.redmondbank.com

Asia Europe America's Bank
1505 Westlake Avenue North
Seattle, WA 98109
206-282-4000
Fax: 206-282-0351
www.aea-bank.com

Business Loan Express
601 Union Street, Suite 4200
Seattle, WA 98101
206-624-3299
Fax: 206-624-3352
www.alliedcapitalexpress.com

Commerce Bank of WA
Two Union Square
601 Union Street, Suite 3600
Seattle, WA 98101
206-292-3900
Fax: 206-625-9457
www.tcbwa.com

Evergreen Bank
301 Eastlake Avenue East
Seattle, WA 98109
206-628-4250
800-331-7922
www.evergreenbank.com

Home Street Bank
1800 Two Union Square
601 Union Street
Seattle, WA 98101-2326
206-389-7781
www.homestreetbank.com

Korea Exchange Bank
900 Fourth Avenue, Suite 1600
Seattle, WA 98164
206-622-7821 Ext.563

Northstar Bank
600 North 34th Street, Suite B
P.O. Box 31816
Seattle, WA 98103
206-632-0200
Fax: 206-632-0465
www.northstarbankwa.com

Northwest Business Bank
1100 Olive Way, Suite 102
Seattle, WA 98101
206-676-8880
Fax: 206-676-8881
www.nwib.com

Pacific Northwest Bank
1111 3rd Avenue
P.O. Box 840
Seattle, WA 98101
206-624-9761
www.pnwbank.com

Seattle Community Capital
Development
P.O. Box 22283
Seattle, WA 98122
206-324-4330
www.seattleccd.com

Union Bank of California
910 Fourth Avenue
Seattle, WA 98164
206-587-6100
Fax: 206-587-3636
www.uboc.com/uboc/home

Viking Community Bank
2237 NW 57th Street
Seattle, WA 98107
206-784-2200
Fax: 206-784-6650
www.vikingbank.com/index.php

Washington Mutual Bank
1201 Third Avenue, Suite 100
Seattle, WA 98101
425-461-4345
www.wamu.com/servlet/wamu/index
.html

Shoreline Bank
18350 Midvale Avenue North
P.O. Box 7129
Shoreline, WA 98133-2129
206-546-8484
877-546-8484
Fax: -206- 546-8430
www.eshorelinebank.com

First Heritage Bank
167 Lincoln Avenue
P.O. Box 550
Snohomish, WA 98291
360-568-0536
www.firstheritage.net

Timberland Bank
2419 224th ST East
P.O. 4940
Spanaway, WA 98387
253-875-4250
www.timberlandbank.com/

Columbia State Bank
1301 A Street
P.O. Box 2156
Tacoma, WA 98401
253-305-1900
800-305-1905
www.columbiabank.com

Heritage Bank
5448 S. Tacoma Way
Tacoma, WA 98409
253-472-3333
http://phx.corporate-
ir.net/phoenix.zhtml?c=71188&p=IR
OL-irhome

Pierce Commercial Bank
1722 South Union Avenue
Tacoma, WA 98411-0488
253-471-1500
https://piercecommercial.portalvault.
com

Wachovia Bank
6991 E. Camelback Road
Scottsdale, AZ 85251
480-425-7983
www.wachovia.com

Borrego Springs Bank
547 Palm Canyon Drive
P.O. Box 866
Borrego Springs, CA 92004
760-767-5035
Fax: 760-767-4214
www.borregospringsbank.com

California Center Bank
4301 West 3rd Street
Los Angeles, CA 980020
213-637-9622
www.calcenterbank.com

Pacific Union Bank
928 South Western Avenue, Suite
260
Los Angeles, CA 90006
213-385-2244
www.pubbank.com

Wilshire State Bank
3200 Wilshire Blvd
Los Angeles, CA 90010
213-427-6595
www.wilshirebank.com

World Trade Finance
875 North Virgil Avenue
Los Angeles, CA 90029
323-660-1277
Fax: 323-660-1470
www.wtfinc.com

California Bank and Trust
20100 Magnolia
Huntington Beach, CA 92646
602-212-8826
www.calbanktrust.com

Goleta National Bank
1050 Northgate Drive Suite 190
San Rafael, CA 94903
415-444-5150

US Bank
9918 Hibert Street, 2nd Floor
San Diego, CA 92131-1018
858-536-4545
www.usbank.com

Pacific Crest Bank
1851 East First Street, Suite 900
Santa Ana, CA 92705
818-865-3241

CIT Small Business Lending
Corporation
1526 Cole Boulevard
Building 3, Suite 200
Golden, CO 80401
303-202-3731
800-525-3343
Fax: 303-202-3789
www.cit.com

Business Loan Express
1919 Pennsylvania Avenue, NW
Washington, DC 20006
202-736-5450
Fax: 202-659-1224
www.alliedcapitalexpress.com

Wells Fargo Bank
1455 West Lake Street, Suite 306
Minneapolis, MN 55408
612-312-8200
www.wellsfargo.com

GE Capital Small Business Finance
Corp.
635 Maryville Centre Drive
Suite 120
St. Louis, MO 63141
314-205-3602
Fax: 314-205-3691
www.ge.com/capital/smallbiz/index.
html

Grow America Fund
51 East 42nd Street, Suite 300
New York, NY 10017
212-682-1106
Fax: 212-573-6118
www.ndc-online.org/gaf.htm

West Coast Bank
1000 SW Broadway, Suite 1100
Portland, OR 97205
503-224-4245
www.westcoastbancorp.com

PMC Capital, Inc.
18111 Preston Rd., Suite 600

Dallas, TX 75252
972-349-3209
800-486-3223
Fax: 972-349-3265
www.pmccapital.com

Small Business Loan Source
9801 Westheimer
Houston, TX 77042
713-961-5626
800-457-4307, ext. 120
www.sbls.com/default.htm

Community First National Bank
142 East 200 South
Salt Lake City, UT 84111
801-531-3400
www.communityfirst.com

West Virginia

1st State Bank
660 Central Avenue
PO Box 295
Barboursville, WV 25504
304-736-5271
www.fsb-wv.com

Bank One West Virginia
500-600 Neville Street
Beckley, WV 25801
304-256-2265
www.bankone.com

Bank One West Virginia
707 Virginia Street East
Charleston, WV 25301
304-348-6948
800-862-2651
www.bankone.com

BB&T
501 Tennessee Avenue
Charleston, WV 25302
304-340-4734
www.bbandt.com

Bank One West Virginia
229 West Main Street
Clarksburg, WV 26301
304-624-3400
www.bankone.com

BB&T
400 West Main Street
P.O. Box 1510
Clarksburg, WV 26301
304-626-1703
www.bbandt.com

WesBanco
140 West Main Street
Clarksburg, WV 26301
304-623-1400
www.wesbanco.com

Bank One West Virginia
1000 Fifth Avenue
PO Box 179
Huntington, WV 25706

304-526-4220
www.bankone.com

BB&T
496 High Street
P.O. Box 698
Morgantown, WV 26505
304-285-2378
www.bbandt.com

WesBanco
2146 Market Street
Wheeling, WV 26003
304-232-0102
800-472-0110
www.wesbanco.com

Allied Capital
1919 Pennsylvania Ave. NW
Washington, DC 20006
202-331-1112
Fax: 202-659-2053
www.alliedcapital.com

Unizan Bank, N.A.
66 S. Third Street
Columbus, OH 43215
614-462-2880
www.unizanbank.com

Steel Valley Bank
81 Main Street
P.O. Box 638
Dillonvale, OH 43917
800-296-9910

BB&T
110 South Stratford Road
Winston-Salem, NC 27104
336-733-3300
Fax: 336-733-0114
www.bbandt.com

National City Bank
801 State Street
Erie, PA 16501
814-871-1225
www.nationalcity.com/smallbusiness
/default.asp

Transamerica Small Business Capital
220 North Main Street, Suite 604
Greenville, SC 29601
864-232-6197

PMC Capital
18111 Preston Road, Suite 600
Dallas, TX 75252
972-349-3209
800-486-3223 ext. 3234
Fax: 972-349-3265
www.pmccapital.com

Business Loan Express
3 South 12th Street
Richmond, VA 25427
304-754-9427
Fax: 304-754-9386
www.businessloanexpress.net

Wisconsin

American National Bank-Fox Cities
2200 North Richmond Street
Appleton, WI 54911
920-739-1040
Fax: 920-739-9216
http://americannationalbank.org

Park Bank
15850 West Bluemound Road
Brookfield, WI 53005
262-827-3655
Fax: 262-827-1077
www.parkbankmilwaukee.com

National Exchange Bank & Trust
Fond du Lac
130 South Main Street
P.O. Box 988
Fond du Lac, WI 54936
920-921-7700
Fax: 920-923-7013
www.nebat.com

Grafton State Bank
101 Falls Road
Grafton, WI 53024-2612
262-377-5511
Fax: 262-377-6328
www.graftonstatebank.com

Associated Bank, N.A.
200 North Adams Street
Green Bay, WI 54301
920-433-3200
Fax: 920-433-3060
www.associatedbank.com

F&M Bank Wisconsin
205 East 4th Street Plaza
Kaukauna, WI 54130
920-766-8160
www.fmbanks.com

Coulee State Bank
1516 Losey Boulevard South
La Crosse, WI 54602
608-784-9550
Fax: 608-784-1069
www.couleestatebank.com

Wells Fargo Bank
305 Fifth Avenue South
La Crosse, WI 54601
608-784-7000
www.wellsfargo.com

First Business Bank
401 Charmany Drive
Madison, WI 53719
608-238-8008
Fax: 608-232-5905
www.fbbmadison.com

First National Bank Manitowoc
402 North 8th Street
P.O. Box 10
Manitowoc, WI 54221
920-684-6611

Fax: 920-683-5699
www.bankfirstnational.com

Investors Community Bank
860 North Rapids Road
P.O. Box 700
Manitowoc, WI 54221-0700
920-686-9998
Fax: 920-686-5688
http://investorscommunitybank.com

Premier Community Bank
230 Mavis Road
Marion, WI 54950
715-754-2535
Fax: 715-754-5905
www.premiercommunity.com

First National Bank Fox Valley
320 Racine Street
Menasha, WI 54952
920-729-6900
Fax: 920-729-6934
www.fnbfoxvalley.com

U.S. Bank
N78 W14545 Appleton Avenue
Menomonee Falls, WI 53051
262-253-7470
877-255-0225
Fax: 262-255-0272
www.usbank.com

M&I Marshall & Ilsley Bank
770 North Water Street
Milwaukee, WI 53202-3593
262-814-5700
Fax: 262-814-5750
www.mibank.com

Park Bank
330 East Kilbourn Avenue
Milwaukee, WI 53202
414-466-8000
Fax: 414-223-3077
www.parkbankmilwaukee.com

Wells Fargo Bank
100 East Wisconsin Avenue
Milwaukee, WI 53202
414-224-4559
Fax: 414-224-3796
www.wellsfargo.com

Monona State Bank
5515 Monona Drive
P.O. Box 6500
Monona, WI 53716
608-223-3000
Fax: 608-223-3007
www.mononabank.com

First State Bank
113 West North Water Street
P.O. Box 268
New London, WI 54961-0268
920-982-3300
Fax: 920-982-4998
www.bankfirststate.com

First Bank Financial
155 West Wisconsin Avenue
P.O. Box 1004
Oconomowoc, WI 53066-6004
262-569-9900
Fax: 262-569-9909
www.fbfcwi.com

Community Bank & Trust
604 North 8th Street
P.O. Box 1409
Sheboygan, WI 53082
920-459-4444
Fax: 920-459-4450
www.communitybankandtrust.com

Wisconsin Business Bank
4706 South Taylor Drive
Shcboygan, WI 53081
920-803-6000
800-793-6001
Fax: 920-803-6010
www.wisbusbank.com/index.cfm

Community First National Bank
118 Elm Street
P.O. Box 308
Spooner, WI 54801
715-635-2161
Fax: 715-635-8905
www.spooner-wi.com/cfb

Hometown Bancorp, LTD
1200 Main Street
St. Cloud, WI 53079
920-999-3563
Fax: 920-999-3501
www.hometownbancorp.com

Stearn's Bank, NA
4191 2nd Street South
St. Cloud, MN 56302
320-253-6607
800-320-7262
Fax: 320-253-3051
www.stearns-bank.com

Baylake Bank
217 North 4th Avenue
P.O. Box 9
Sturgeon Bay, WI 54235
920-743-5551
Fax: 920-743-1598
www.baylake.com

Community State Bank
1500 Main Street
Union Grove, WI 53182
262-878-3763
Fax: 262-878-3637
www.communitystatebank.net

Waukesha Statc Bank
100 Bank Street
Waukesha, WI 53188
262-549-8500
Fax: 262-549-8593
www.waukeshabank.com

Peoples State Bank
1905 Stewart Avenue
Wausau, WI 5440
715-842-2191
Fax: 712-842-3418
www.psbwausau.com

First Citizens State Bank
207 West Main Street
Whitewater, WI 53190
262-473-2112
800-236-8766
Fax: 262-473-3039
www.firstcitizensww.com/default.as
p

CNL Commercial Lending Corp.
26137 La Paz Road, Suite 102
Mission Viejo, CA 92691
949-452-0929
www.cnlonline.com/commercialfina
nce/SBA7a.asp

CIT Small Business Lending
1526 Cole Boulevard
Building 3, Suite 200
Golden, CO 80401
303-202-3751
FAX: 3032-02-3794
www.smallbizlending.com

Bank One
1 Bank One Plaza
Chicago, IL 60670-0736
800-404-4111
312-407-5138
Fax: 312-732-4787
www.bankone.com

CIT Small Business Lending
1601 Colonial Parkway, Suite H
Inverness, IL 60067
847-934-0559
Fax: 847-934-0594
www.smallbizlending.com

Amcore Bank, N.A.
501 Seventh Street
P.O. Box 1537
Rockford, IL 61110-0037
815-961-2721
Fax: 815-961-7733
www.amcore.com

Bank One
111 Monument Circle
Indianapolis, IN 46277
317-321-7020
www.bankone.com

Business Loan Express
121 West Dewey Street, Suite 210
Wichita, KS 67202
316-263-3232
Fax: 316-263-4391
www.businessloanexpress.net
800-722-5626

Wells Fargo Bank
1455 West Lake Street
Minneapolis, MN 55408
612-312-8200
www.wellsfargo.com

Heritage Bancshares Group, Inc.
318 West 2nd Street
P.O. Box 1124
Wilmar, MN 56201
800-344-7048 ext. 108
Fax: 320-235-2234
www.heritagebancshares.com

CIT Small Business Lending
1 CIT Drive
Livingston, NJ 07039
800-713-4984 Ext. 6004
www.smallbizlending.com

Bank One
1111 Polaris Parkway Mall
Columbus, OH 43240
614-213-1678
Fax: 614-244-8794
www.bankone.com

Wyoming

First National Bank of Gillette
319 South Gillette Avenue
Box 3002
Gillette, WY 82717
307-686-3300

The Jackson State Bank
Teton Village Road
P.O. Box 1788
Jackson, WY 83001
307-733-3737
Fax: 307-734-2442
www.jacksonstatebank.com

First National Bank of Laramie
2020 Grand Avenue
P.O. Box 490
Laramie, WY 82070
307-745-7351
Fax: 307-745-4532
www.fnbwyo.com

First National Bank and Trust Co.
245 East First Street
P.O. Box 907
Powell, WY 82435
307-754-2201
800- 377-6909
Fax: 307-754-1414
www.codybank.com

First Interstate Bank
4 South Main
P.O. Box 2007
Sheridan, WY 82801
307-674-7411
www.firstinterstatebank.com

World Trade Finance, Inc.
875 North Virgil Avenue
Los Angeles, CA 90029
323-660-1277
Fax: 323-660-1470
www.wtfinc.com

US Bank, National Association
9918 Hibert Street, Suite 100
San Diego, CA 92131
858-536-4500
www.usbank.com

Business Loan Express
121 West Dewey Street
Suite 210
Wichita, KS 67202
316-263-3232
800-722-5626
Fax: 316-263-4391
www.businessloanexpress.net

Wells Fargo Bank
1455 West Lake Street
Suite 306
Minneapolis, MN 55408
612-312-8200
www.wellsfargo.com

Business Loan Express
700 North Pearl Street
Suite 1850
Dallas, TX 75201
214-389-6100
Fax: 214-389-6196
www.alliedcapitalexpress.com

Community First National Bank
142 East 200 South
Salt Lake City, UT 84111
801-531-3400
www.communityfirst.com

Venture Capital: Finding A Rich Angel

With federal and state money getting harder to come by, and banks experiencing serious problems of their own that restrict their willingness to loan money, anyone interested in starting his own business or expanding an existing one may do well to look into venture capital. Venture capitalists are willing to invest in a new or growing business venture for a percentage of the equity. Below is a listing of some of the associations, government agencies, and businesses that have information available on venture capital.

In addition, there are Venture Capital Clubs throughout the country where entrepreneurs have a chance to present their ideas to potential investors and learn about the process of finding funds for ventures that might be long on innovative ideas for a business, but short on proven track records.

The following examples are excerpted from web sites for the U.S. Small Business Administration, (SBA) The National Association of Small Business Investment Companies (NASBIC), institutional lenders, and venture capital clubs. Please check with the SBA, the NASBIC, and local lenders and venture capital clubs for more information on how they can help you.

Investors Give Cash to a Psychologist

Kelly Upchurch is a psychologist with extensive experience in the field of rehabilitation. He is also a businessman who had a vision: to operate a network of centers that offer supervised daytime care for the elderly throughout rural Kentucky. Nationally, there are more than 6,000 such centers -- usually in metropolitan areas -- but Kelly believed that rural Kentucky had a tremendous unmet need. He quit his job at a local hospital to launch his firm, American Health Management, Inc.

Kelly needed financing to get the business off the ground, and expertise to ensure lasting success. He contacted Kentucky Highlands Investment Corporation (KHIC) in London, KY, and found the combination he needed.

KHIC provided American Health Management with a $75,000 equity investment and $15,000 in working capital for its first center. As part of the deal, KHIC owns a percentage of the company – though Kelly can buy it back over a five-year period.

The KHIC team also provided countless hours of technical assistance, helping Kelly develop his business plan, set up an accounting and cash management system, make financial projections, and plan for the future growth of the business.

After one year, American Health Management was able to finance the opening of a second center in Monticello, Kentucky. Kelly plans to open 16 centers and grow American Health Management into Kentucky's largest adult health care center, creating more than 100 quality jobs -- recreational therapists, nurses' aides, registered nurses -- in a state where good jobs are scarce.

Strut Your Stuff, Attract Investors!

You never know what will win over investors. Here's an example: the Richmond Venture Capital Club invites entrepreneurs to give a five minute presentation about their business plans at club meetings. A taxi driver happened to read the announcement about a club meeting - which had already started - and joined the meeting in progress. He asked to make a presentation at the next meeting, as he was seeking an investor for a bluejean manufacturing business.

When the time came for his presentation at the next meeting, he stood up and announced that he was going to have his "jeans" do his talking for him. A number of models entered the back of the room displaying his blue jeans – and at the next meeting, the driver returned to report that he had raised his capital as a result!

Associations

The National Association of Seed and Venture Funds
301 NW 63rd Street, Suite 500
Oklahoma City, OK 73116
405-843-6550
Fax: 405-842-3299
www.nasvf.org
The National Association of Seed and Venture Funds is an organization of venture capitalists who invest in businesses. The Association helps these organizations network with each other to learn how to better serve their clients. They also offer seminars, conferences, and training programs to better serve their members.

The National Venture Capital Association (NVCA)
1655 N. Fort Meyer Dr., Suite 850
Arlington, VA 22209
703-524-2549
Fax: 703-524-3940
www.nvca.org
The association works to improve the government's knowledge and understanding of the venture capital process. Staff members can answer questions about federal legislation and regulations, and provide statistical information on venture capital. NVCA members include venture capital organizations,

financiers, and individuals interested in investing in new companies.

The association publishes a membership directory that includes a listing of their members with addresses, phone numbers, tax numbers and contacts. There are currently about 289 members. The directory is available for $99.

The Western Association of Venture Capitalists
3000 San Hill Rd.
Bldg. 1, Suite 190
Menlo Park, CA 94025
650-854-1322
www.wavc.net
Publishes a directory of its 140 members. The cost is $100.

National Association of Investment Companies
1300 Pennsylvania Ave., NW, Suite 700
Washington, DC 20004
202-289-4336
Fax: 202-289-4329
www.naicvc.com
It is composed of specialized Small Business Investment Companies (SSBICs). The SSBIC Directory lists about 120 companies across the country

including names, addresses, and telephone numbers. It also describes each company's investment preferences and policies. The 23-page publication costs $25.98.

It also publishes *Perspective*, a monthly newsletter geared toward specialized small business investment companies. This newsletter includes articles about legislation and regulations affecting SSBICs. (Note: This association was formerly called the American Association of Minority Enterprise Small Business Investment Companies (AAMESBIC)).

Technology Capital Network at MIT
222 Third St., Suite 0350
Cambridge, MA 02142
617-253-2337
Fax: 617-258-7395
www.tcnmit.org
This nonprofit corporation tries to match entrepreneurs in need of capital with venture capital sources. Investors and entrepreneurs register with the network for up to 12 months for $300.

Venture Capital Clubs

There are more than 150 Venture Capital Clubs worldwide where inventors can present their ideas to potential investors. At a typical monthly meeting, several entrepreneurs may give short presentations of their ideas. It is a great way for entrepreneurs and potential investors to talk informally.

The International Venture Capital Institute (IVCI)
P.O. Box 1333
Stamford, CT 06904
203-323-3143
The IVCI publishes an annual directory of domestic and international venture groups (venture capital clubs). The cost of the *1995 IVCI Directory of Domestic and International Venture Groups*, which includes contact information for all of the clubs, is $19.95.

Below is a partial listing of clubs in the United States.

Venture Capital Clubs

Alabama
Birmingham Venture Club
Chamber of Commerce
505 20th St., N
Birmingham, AL 35203
205-241-8113
www.birminghamchamber.com

Mobile Venture Club
c/o Mobile Area Chamber of
    Commerce
451 Government St.
Mobile, AL 36652
251-433-6951
Fax: 251-431-8646
www.mobcham.org
Attn: Walter Underwood

Arkansas
Venture Capital Investors
400 W. Capital, Suite 1845
Little Rock, AR 72201
501-372-5900
Fax: 501-372-8181

California
Tech Coast Venture Network
195 S. C St., Suite 250
Tustin, CA 92780
714-505-6493
Fax: 714-669-9341
www.tcvn.org
Attn: Alonzo

Orange Coast Venture Group
P.O. Box 2011
Laguna Hills, CA 92654
949-859-3646
Fax: 949-859-1707
www.ocvg.net

San Diego Venture Group
P.O. Box 9357
San Diego, CA 92169
619-308-9423
Fax: 619-308-9433
www.sdvgroup.org

Colorado
Rockies Venture Club, Inc.
1805 S. Bellaire St., Suite 480
Denver, CO 80222
303-831-4174
Fax: 303-758-3885
www.rockiesventureclub.org

Connecticut
Connecticut Venture Group
1895B Post Rd.
Fairfield, CT 06430
203-256-5955
Fax: 203-256-9949
www.ct-venture.org

District of Columbia
Baltimore-Washington Venture Group
Michael Dingman Center for
    Entrepreneurship
College Park, MD 20742-7215
301-405-2144
Fax: 301-314-9152
www.rhsmith.umd.edu/dingman

Florida
Gold Coast Venture Capital Club
22783 S. State Rd. 7, #56
Boca Raton, FL 33428
561-488-4505
Fax: 561-451-4746
www.beaconmgmt.com/gcvcc

Hawaii
Hawaii Venture Group
University of Hawaii, OTTED
2800 Woodlawn Dr., Suite 280
Honolulu, HI 96822
805-533-1400
Fax: 808-524-2775
www.hawaiiventuregroup.com

Idaho
Rocky Mountain Venture Group
2300 N. Yellowstone, Suite E
Idaho Falls, ID 83402
208-526-9557
Fax: 208-526-0953
Attn: Dennis Cheney

Treasure Valley Venture Capital
    Forum
Idaho Small Business Development
    Center
Boise State University College of
    Business
1910 University Dr.
Boise, ID 83725
208-426-1640
Fax: 208-426-3877
www.idahosbdc.org

Iowa
Iowa City Development
ICAD Group
P.O. Box 2567
Iowa City, IA 52244
319-354-3939
Fax: 319-338-9958
Attn: Marty Kelley

Illinois
Madison Dearborn Partners
3 First National Plaza, Suite 3800

Chicago, IL 60602
312-895-1000
Fax: 312-895-1001
www.mdcp.com

Kentucky
Mountain Ventures Inc.
P.O. Box 1738
London, KY 40743
606-864-5175
Fax: 606-864-5194
www.khic.org

Maryland
Mid Atlantic Venture Association
  (MAVA)
2345 York Rd.
Timonium, MD 21093
410-560-5855
Fax: 410-561-2238
www.mava.org

Massachusetts
Venture Capital Fund of New England
160 Federal St., 23rd Floor
Boston, MA 02110
617-439-4646
Fax: 617-439-4652

Michigan
New Enterprise Forum
Ann Arbor Chamber of Commerce
425 S. Main St.
Ann Arbor, MI 48104
734-214-0104
www.nef.bizserve.com
Attn: Barb Sprague

Minnesota
St. Paul Venture Capital
10400 Viking Drive, Suite 550
Bloomington, MN 55444
952-995-7474
Fax: 952-995-7475
www.st.paulvc.com

Missouri
Missouri Innovation Center
5650 A S. Sinclair Rd.
Columbia, MO 65203
573-884-0492

Nebraska
Grand Island Industrial Foundation
309 W. 2nd St.
P.O. Box 1486
Grand Island, NE 68802-1486
308-382-9210
Fax: 308-382-1154
www.gichamber.com
Attn: Andrew G. Baird, II CED

New Jersey
Venture Association of New Jersey,
  Inc.
177 Madison Ave., CN 1982
Morristown, NJ 07962
973-267-4200

www.vanj.com
Attn: Amy or Jay Trien

New York
Long Island Venture Group
Scott Skodnek Business Development
  Center
Room 243-F, East Wing
145 Hofstra University
Hampstead, NY 11549
516-463-6326
Fax: 516-463-3907
www.livg.com

New York Venture Group
605 Madison Ave., Suite 300
New York, NY 10022-1901
212-832-7300
Fax: 212-832-7338
www.nybusiness.com
Attn: Burt Alimansky

Westchester Venture Capital Network
c/o Chamber of Commerce
235 Mamaroneck Ave.
White Plains, NY 10605
914-948-2110
Fax: 914-948-0122
www.westchesterny.org

Rochester Venture Capital Group
100 Corporate Woods, Suite 300
Rochester, NY 14623
www.rcvg.org

Ohio
Greater Columbus Chamber of
  Commerce
Columbus Investment Interest Group
37 N. High St.
Columbus, OH 43215
614-225-6938
Fax: 614-469-8250
www.columbus.org
Attn: Diane Essex

Ohio Venture Association, Inc.
1120 Chester Ave.
Cleveland, OH 44114
216-566-8884
Fax: 216-696-2582
Attn: Joan McCarthy
www.ohioventure.org

Oregon
Oregon Entrepreneur Forum
222 NW Fifth Ave., #308
Portland, OR 97209
503-222-2270
Fax: 503-241-0827
www.oef.org

Portland Venture Group
P.O. Box 2341
Lake Oswego, OR 97035
503-697-5907
Fax: 503-697-5907
Attn: Glen Smith

Pennsylvania
Enterprise Venture Capital
  Corporation of Pennsylvania
111 Market St.
Johnstown, PA 15901
814-535-7597
Fax: 814-535-8677
www.jari.com

South Dakota
Dakota Ventures Inc.
P.O. Box 8194
Rapid City, SD 57709
605-348-8441
Fax: 605-348-8452
Attn. Don Frankenfeld

Texas
Capital Southwest Venture
  Corporation
12900 Preston Rd., Suite 700
Dallas, TX 75230
972-233-8242
Fax: 972-233-7362
www.capitalsouthwest.com

Utah
Utah Ventures
2755 E. Cottonwood Pkwy., Suite 520
Salt Lake City, UT 84121
801-365-0262
Fax: 801-365-0233
www.utahventures.com

Vermont
Vermont Venture Network
P.O. Box 5839
Burlington, VT 05402
802-658-7830
Fax: 802-658-0978
www.b2law.net/vvn.html

Virginia
Richmond Venture Capital Club
c/o 4900 Augusta Ave., Suite 103
Richmond, VA 23230
804-897-7411
www.ventureclub.com

Washington
Northwest Venture Group
P.O. Box 21693
Seattle, WA 98111-3693
425-746-1973

West Virginia
Enterprise Venture Capital Company
P.O. Box 460
Summerville, WV 26651
304-872-3000
Fax: 304-872-3040
Attn: William Bright

Wisconsin
Wisconsin Innovation Network
P.O. Box 510103
Milwaukee, WI 53203
414-224-7070

Copyright © 2004 Matthew Lesko, Information USA, Inc., 12081 Nebel Street, Rockville, MD 20852 • 1-800-955-7693 • www.lesko.com

Uncle Sam's Venture Capital

What Do Federal Express, Apple Computer, Staples and A Porno Shop on 42nd Street All Have In Common? They All Used Government Venture Money To Get Started

A few years ago I read that the government provided money to a porno shop in New York City through a program call Small Business Investment Companies (SBIC). Since 1960 these organizations have provided venture capital to over 75,000 businesses, so it's easy to see that one of those businesses might be a porno shop. Porno is a legitimate businesses in many areas of the country.

SBICs are licensed by the U.S. Small Business Administration but are privately owned and operate on a for profit basis. Their license allows companies to pool their money with borrowed money from the government in order to provide financing to small businesses in the form of equity securities or long-term debt. These government subsidized investment companies have helped Compaq, Apple, Federal Express and Staples make it to the big time. They have also helped smaller companies achieve success. They've financed Spencer and Vickie Jacobs' hot tub business in Columbus, Ohio, as well as taxi drivers in New York City who needed money to pay for the medallions which allows them to operate their own cabs.

Uncle Sam's Venture Capital Boom

In 1994, new government regulations were imposed that make it easier to become an SBIC. The budget for this program was also greatly expanded. As a result of this change, there will now be over $6 billion worth of financing available to entrepreneurs over the next several years. Now, that's not small change, even to a hotshot entrepreneur. With these new regulations and budget in place, the government expects that there will soon be 200 additional SBICs waiting to serve American entrepreneurs.

Who Gets The Money?

Basically you have to be a small business to apply for this money, and the government's definition includes companies that have less than $18 million in net worth and less than $6 million in profits. Wow, that's some small business! They seem particularly interested in businesses that offer a new product or service that has a strong growth potential. There is special consideration given to minorities and Vietnam Veterans applying for this money.

You do have to be armed with a business plan which should include the following:
1) Identify Your Company
2) Identify Your Product Or Service
3) Describe Your Product Facilities And Property
4) Detail Your Marketing Plan
5) Describe Your Competition
6) Describe Your Management Team
7) Provide A Financial Statement

Where to Apply

You can apply to more than one SBIC at the same time. Each acts as an independent company and they can provide money to both local or out-of-state businesses. At the end of this section is a listing of SBA licensed Small Business Investment Companies. However, this list is growing every day so it would be wise to contact the following office to obtain a current list: Associate Administrator for Investment, U.S. Small Business Administration, Washington, DC 20416; 202-205-6510; {www.sba.gov/inv}.

States Have Venture Money, Too

It's not enough to only look at federal venture capital programs, because some state governments also have venture capital programs. More and more states continue to start new programs every month. Some states, like Maryland, see the value in the new rule changes for becoming an SBIC, and are beginning to apply to become a licensed participant of the Small Business Administration's program. Here is what is available from state governments at the time this book went to press. Be sure to check with your state to see what's new:
1) Arkansas - Seed Capital Investment Program
2) Connecticut - Risk Capital
   - Product Design Financing
   - Seed Venture Fund
3) Illinois - Technology Investment Program
   - Illinois Venture Capital Fund
4) Iowa - Venture Capital Resources Fund
5) Kansas - Venture Capital and Seed Capital
   - Seed Capital Fund
   - Ad Astra Fund
   - Ad Astra Fund II
6) Louisiana - Venture Capital Incentive Program
7) Massachusetts - Venture Capital Program
8) Michigan - Enterprise Development Fund
   - Onset Seed Fund
   - Diamond Venture Associates
   - Semery Seed Capital Fund
   - Michigan Venture Capital Fund

9) Montana - Venture, Equity & Risk Capital
10) New Mexico - Venture Capital Investment Program
11) New York - Corporation for Innovation Development
12) North Carolina - North Carolina First Flight Inc.
13) North Carolina - Seed and Incubator Capital
14) Pennsylvania - Seed Venture Capital
15) South Carolina - Venture Capital Funding Program
16) Tennessee - Venture Capital

Contact your state office of economic development in your state capital for further information on venture capital available in your state (also see the chapter entitled "State Money and Help For Your Business").

Playtime is Big Business

The secret of success is often recognizing a potential product or service in daily life. Here's proof:

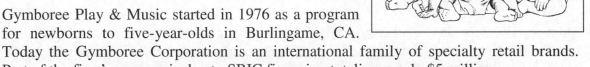

Kids love to run, jump and play hard. Most parents see this as a normal part of childhood. The founders of Gymboree saw it as a business opportunity.

Gymboree Play & Music started in 1976 as a program for newborns to five-year-olds in Burlingame, CA. Today the Gymboree Corporation is an international family of specialty retail brands. Part of the firm's success is due to SBIC financing totaling nearly $5 million.

The company grew rapidly, which allowed officials to take a chance on diversifying. They chose to sell high quality apparel and accessories for children. To make this move, additional funding was needed. Equity financing from four SBICs—Walden Capital Corporation, Norwest Growth Fund, Inc Chemical Venture Capital Associates and Northwest Venture Partners made the growth possible.

Gymboree reported net sales of $530 million and net income of $22 million in 2002. As of August, 2003, the company operated a total of 594 stores in the United States, Canada and Europe, as well as online stores and parent-child developmental play programs.

Next time you want to bottle your child's energy and sell it – maybe you can!

Employees Save Company Jobs with SBIC

Business success is not always a matter of starting from the ground up. Sometimes success is about staying in the race.

The Williams Bros. Lumber Company has been doing business in Atlanta, Georgia, since 1922. In 1985, the Williams family sold their company to another owner, who then decided to sell a portion of the firm. If the deal went, through, 90 people would lose their jobs.

Two senior officers in Williams decided to purchase the part of the company that was up for sale. They wanted to keep the jobs and make the company grow. After talking to about fifteen potential sources of financing, however, they thought their idea was a failure. Then they got in contact with Allied Investment Corporation, an SBIC managed by Allied Capital Advisers in Washington, DC. Within two months of their first meeting, Allied provided support for the purchase.

Over the years, Allied Investment Corporation funneled additional monies for continued growth. Since the company officers bought the business, revenues have increased over 700%—from $22 million to $180 million. And, they not only saved 90 jobs for Atlanta, but added provided 410 more jobs.

Potential Customers Provide Expertise

In 1980, Rebecca Matthias was like millions of other working women: expecting a child, and wearing maternity clothes to the office everyday. She was not satisfied with the maternity fashions she found, however, and was sure other women felt the same way.

Rebecca decided to market executive maternity clothing through a catalog. She called her company Mothers Work, found outfits at wholesale prices on Seventh Avenue in New York City and sent out thousands of catalogs – but sales were slim. She ended up with a net loss of $6,500 and a closet full of maternity clothes.

Then she did what any success-oriented business person would do: she asked the experts what to do. In this case, the experts were other expecting mothers. Rebecca picked up the phone to find out what her customers wanted, calling every person who requested catalogs but did not place an order. She kept notes about what they needed, and was ready to manufacture her own products. Things really took off when she secured SBIC funding. According to Rebecca, this made all the difference.

"I had no experience," she says. "I had no capital. I really had no company. I had an idea. And if it hadn't been for the investment from an SBIC, that's where I'd still be."

The first institutional investor in Mothers Work was Meridian Venture Partners, an SBIC that provided a $250,000 loan with equity features. After a number of expansions and continued investment from the SBIC, the company earns millions of dollars annually.

It is Never Too Late to Be an Entrepreneur!

Think that owning your own company is only for the young? Meet Ely Callaway, who opened his doors when most people are counting the days to their retirement party.

At the age of 63, the former businessman and long time golfer believed he could revolutionize the golf club industry. His started Callaway Golf, which designs, manufactures, and services its products in-house and distributes them in more than 70 countries worldwide.

Ely used his savings to acquire a small company that made golf clubs. He then found two investors: MVenture Corp (now Banc One Capital Partners) and National City Capital Corporation, both of whom were SBICs, and began to manufacture his own designs.

Ely Callaway's designs, supported in its early stages by SBICs, has had a major impact on the world of golf. In 1997, Callaway's Great Big Bertha® Titanium Driver was the #1 driver in use on each of the five major golf tours. The company's success also created thousands of jobs. When the SBICs first invested in Callaway Golf, the company employed just four people – and now employees number in the thousands.

Just goes to show, it is never too late to follow your dream!

Small Business Investment Companies

Alabama

FJC Growth Capital Corporation
William B. Noojin, Manager
165 West Park Loop
P.O. Box 1290
Huntsville, AL 35807
256-922-2918
Fax: 256-922-2909
www.fjcgrowth.com/index.html

Harbinger Mezzanine Partners, L.P.
John Harrison, Contact
One Riverchase Parkway South
Birmingham, AL 35244
615-301-6400
Fax: 615-301-6401
Email: nhartin@harbert.net

Hickory Venture Capital Corp.
J. Thomas Noojin, President
301 Washington St., Suite 100
Huntsville, AL 35801
256-539-1931
Fax: 256-539-5130
www.hvcc.com

TD Javelin Capital Fund II, L.P.
Lyle Hohnke, Manager
2850 Cahaba Road, Suite 240
Birmingham, AL 35223
203-629-8700
Fax: 203-629-9293
www.tullisdickerson.com

Arkansas

Diamond State Ventures, L.P.
Joe T. Hays, Contact
200 South Commerce St, Suite 400
Little Rock, AR 72201-1728

501-374-9247
Fax: 501-374-9425
www.arcapital.com

Small Business Investment Capital, Inc.
Jerry W. Davis, President
12103 Interstate 30
P.O. Box 3627
Little Rock, AR 72203
501-455-6599
Fax: 501-455-6556
Email: jmills@afslr.com

Arizona

Grayhawk Venture Fund I, L.P.
Sherman Chu, Contact
5050 North 40th Street, Suite 310
Phoenix, AZ 85018
602-956-8700
Fax: 602-956-8080
www.gvp.us

Magnet Capital, L.P.
Gregory Mischel/Michael Shields, Contact
3550 North Central Ave.
Suite 1400
Phoenix, AZ 85012
602-222-4801
Fax: 602-222-4807
www.magnetcapital.com

California

AltoTech II, L.P.
Walter Lee, Contact
707 Menlo Avenue, Suite 120
Menlo Park, CA 94025
650-330-0881

Fax: 650-330-0885
www.altotechventures.com

American River Ventures, L.P.
Corley Phillips, Contact
2270 Douglas Blvd., Suite 212
Roseville, CA 95661
916-780-2828
Fax: 916-780-5443
www.arventures.com

Aspen Ventures III, L.P.
Alex Cilento, Thaddeus Whalen, Contacts
1000 Fremont Avenue
Suite 200
Los Altos, CA 94024
650-917-5670
Fax: 650-917-5677
www.AspenVentures.com

AVI Capital, L.P.
P. Wolken, B. Weinman & B. Grossi, Mgrs.
One First Street, Suite 12
Los Altos, CA 94022
650-949-9862
Fax: 650-949-8510
www.avicapital.com

Bank of America Ventures
Hayley Hoad, Manager, Administration
950 Tower Lane, Suite 700
Foster City, CA 94404
650-378-6000
Fax: 650-378-6040
www.bankofamerica.com

Bay Partners L.S. Fund, L.P.
John Freidenrich, Marcella Yano
10600 N. De Anza Blvd., Suite 100
Cupertino, CA 95014
408-725-2444
Fax: 408-446-4502
www.baypartners.com

Bentley Capital (SSBIC)
John Hung, President
592 Vallejo Street, Suite #2
San Francisco, CA 94133
415-362-2868
Fax: 415-398-8209
Email: bc8081@aol.com

Canaan SBIC, L.P.
Eric Young, Manager
2884 Sand Hill Road
Menlo Park, CA 94025
650-854-8092
Fax: 650-854-8127
www.canaan.com

Celerity Partners SBIC, L.P.
Clifford A. Lyon, Contact
11111 Santa Monica Blvd.
Suite 1127
Los Angeles, CA 90025
310-268-1710
Fax: 310-268-1712
www.celeritypartners.com

Charterway Investment Corporation
(SSBIC)
Edmund C. Lau, Chairman
9660 Flair Dr., Suite 328
El Monte, CA 91731
626-279-1189
Fax: 626-279-9062
Email: toysanaba@aol.com

Cardinal Venture Capital, SBIC, L.P.
Christopher J. Hadsell, Contact
1010 El Camino Real, Suite 250
Menlo Park, CA 94025
650-614-4860
Fax: 650-614-4865
www.cardinalvc.com

Draper Associates, a California LP
Timothy C. Draper, President
400 Seaport Court, Suite 250
Redwood City, CA 94063
650-599-9000
Fax: 650-599-9726
www.dfj.com

Draper-Richards L.P.
William Draper III, President
50 California Street, Suite 2925
San Francisco, CA 94111
415-616-4050
Fax: 415-616-4060
www.draperintl.com

East Gate Private Equity Fund III,
L.P.
Ken Choi, Contact
514 High Street, Suite #5

Palo Alto, CA 94301
650-325-5077
Fax: 650-325-5072
www.eg-group.com

Far East Capital Corp.
Eduardo Ho, Manager
350 S. Grand Ave., Suite 4100
Los Angeles, CA 90071
213-687-1200
Fax: 213-687-8511
www.fareastnationalbank.com

Fulcrum Venture Capital
Corporation (SSBIC)
Brian Argrett, President
300 Corporate Pointe, Suite 380
Culver City, CA 90230
310-645-1271
Fax: 310-645-1272
www.fulcrumventures.com

Geraro Klauer Mattison (GKM)
SBIC, L.P.
Jonathan R. Bloch, Contact
11150 Santa Monica Blvd.
Suite 800
Los Angeles, CA 90025
310-268-2600
Fax: 310-268-0870
www.gkm.com

Hall, Morris & Drufva II, L.P.
Ronald J. Hall, Managing Director
26161 La Paz Road, Suite E
Mission Viejo, CA 92691
714-707-5096
Fax: 714-707-5121

Hamilton Apex Technology
Ventures, L.P.
Richard Crosby, Contact
12526 High Bluff Drive, Suite 260
San Diego, CA 92130
858-314-2350
Fax: 858-314-2355
www.hamiltonventures.com

Housatonic Equity Investors SBIC,
L.P.
Barry Reynolds, Will Thorndike
44 Montgomery Street, Suite 4010
San Francisco, CA 94104
415-955-9020
Fax: 415-955-9053
www.housatonicpartners.com

Huntington Capital, L.P.
Morgan Miller and Barry Wilson,
Contacts
11988 El Camino Real, Suite 160
San Diego, CA 92130
858-259-7654
Fax: 858-259-0074
www.huntingtoncapital.com

Inglewood Ventures, L.P.
Dr. M. Blake Ingle, Daniel Wood
12526 High Bluff Drive, Suite 300
San Diego, CA 92130

858-792-3579
Fax: 858-792-3417
www.inglewoodventures.com

J.P. Morgan Partners (SBIC), LLC
101 California Street, 27th Floor
San Francisco, CA 94111
415-393-1283
Fax: 415-393-1205
www.jpmorgan.com

Kline Hawkes California SBIC, L.P.
Frank R. Kline, Manager
11726 San Vicente Blvd., Suite 300
Los Angeles, CA 90049
310-442-4700
Fax: 310-442-4707
www.klinehawkes.com

LaiLai Capital Corp. (SSBIC)
Danny Ku, President
18249-2 Valley Boulevard
City of Industry, CA 91744
626-333-5420
Fax: 626-934-9699
Email: lailaicapital@aol.com

Magna Pacific Investments (SSBIC)
Howard Wong
330 North Brand Blvd., Suite 670
Glendale, CA 91203
818-547-0809
Fax: 818-547-9303
Email: Magnapacific@cs.com

Marwit Capital Company, L.P.
Matthew Witte, President
180 Newport Center Drive, Suite 200
Newport Beach, CA 92660
949-640-6234
Fax: 949-720-8077
www.marwit.com

Milepost Ventures, L.P.
Christine Cordaro, Contact
One Embarcadero Center
Suite 3250
San Francisco, CA 94104
415-391-8950
Fax: 415-391-8937
www.milepostventures.com

Montreux Equity Partners II SBIC,
L.P.
Daniel K. Turner III, Contact
2500 Sand Hill Road, Suite 215
Menlo Park, CA 94025-7073
650-234-1200
Fax: 650-234-1250
www.montreuxequity.com

New Vista Capital Fund, L.P.
Roger Barry & Frank Greene,
Managers
540 Cowper Street, Suite 200
Palo Alto, CA 94301
650-566-2200
Fax: 650-329-6889
www.nvcap.com

Novus Ventures II, L.P.
Daniel D. Tompkins, Managing GP
20111 Stevens Creek Blvd.
Suite 130
Cupertino, CA 95014
408-252-3900
Fax: 408-252-1713
www.novusventures.com

Opportunity Capital Corporation
  (SSBIC)
J. Peter Thompson, President
2201 Walnut Avenue, Suite 210
Fremont, CA 94538
510-795-7000
Fax: 510-494-5439
www.ocpcapital.com

Outlook Ventures III, L.P.
Carl Nichols, Contact
135 Main Street, Suite 1350
San Francisco, CA 94105
415-547-0000
Fax: 415-547-0010
www.iminds.com

Pacific Mezzanine Fund, L.P.
Nathan W. Bell, General Partner
2200 Powell St., Suite 1250
Emeryville, CA 94608
510-595-9800
Fax: 510-595-9801
www.pacmezz.com

Peninsula Equity Partners SBIC, L.P.
Gregory C. Ennis, Contact
3000 Sand Hill Road
Building 3, Suite 125
Menlo Park, CA 94025
650-854-0314
Fax: 650-854-0670
www.peninsulaequity.com

Pinecreek Capital Partners, L.P.
Randall F. Zurbach, President
24 Corporate Plaza, Suite 180
Newport Beach, CA 92660
949-720-4620
Fax: 949-720-4629
www.pinecreekcap.com

Positive Enterprises, Inc. (SSBIC)
Kwok Szeto, President
1489 Webster Street, Suite 228
San Francisco, CA 94115
415-885-6600
Fax: 415-928-6363
www.pei-sba.com

Red Rock Ventures II, L.P.
Robert Todd, Jr., Curtis K. Meyers
180 Lytton Avenue
Palo Alto, CA 94301
650-325-3111
Fax: 650-853-7044
www.redrockventures.com

Rocket Ventures II SBIC, L.P.
David Adams
3000 Sand Hill Road

Building 1, Suite 170
Menlo Park, CA 94025
650-561-9100
Fax: 650-561-9183
www.rocketventures.com

Seacoast Capital Partners, L.P.
Jeff Holland
425 Market Street, Suite 2200
San Francisco, CA 94105
415-956-1400
Fax: 415-956-1459
www.seacoastcapital.com

Selby Venture Partners II, L.P.
Robert Marshall, Contact
3500 Alameda De Las Pulgas
2nd Floor
Menlo Park, CA 94025
650-854-7399
Fax: 650-854-7039
www.selbyventures.com

Shepherd Ventures II, L.P.
George C. Kenney, Contact
12250 El Camino Real, Suite 116
San Diego, CA 92130
858-509-4744
Fax: 858-509-3662
www.shepherdventures.com

Smart Technology Ventures III
  SBIC, L.P.
Joseph Marks, Contact
1801 Century Park West, 5th Floor
Los Angeles, CA 90067
310-203-3800
Fax: 310-203-3801
www.smarttechnologyventures.com

Sorrento Growth Partners I, L.P.
Robert Jaffe, Manager
4370 La Jolla Village Dr., Suite 1040
San Diego, CA 92122
858-452-3100
Fax: 858-452-7607
www.sorrentoventures.com

St. Cloud Capital Partners, L.P.
Terrence Ng, Contact
10866 Wilshire Blvd., Suite 1450
Los Angeles, CA 90024
310-475-2700
Fax: 310-475-0550
www.stcloudcapital.com

Stone Canyon Venture Partners, L.P.
Kenneth R. Kilroy, Contact
2121 Avenue of the Stars
Suite 2800
Los Angeles, CA 90067
310-551-2210
Fax: 310-551-0591
www.stonecanyonvp.com

Tangent Growth Fund, L.P.
Alexander H. Schilling, Manager
180 Geary St., Suite 500
San Francisco, CA 94108
415-392-9228

Fax: 415-392-1928
www.tangentfund.com

TeleSoft Partners IA L.P.
Arjun Gupta, Manager
1450 Fashion Island Boulevard
Suite 610
San Mateo, CA 94404
650-358-2500
Fax: 650-358-2501
www.telesoftvc.com

UnionBanCal Venture Corporation
Robert S. Clarke, President
445 South Figueroa St., Suite 2100
Los Angeles, CA 90071
213-236-6566
Fax: 213-236-7619
www.uboc.com

Utah Ventures II L.P.
Allan Wolfe
720 31st Street
Manhattan Beach, CA 90266
310-546-2777
Fax: 310-546-6757
www.utahventures.com

Walden-SBIC, L.P.
Arthur S. Berliner, Manager
750 Battery Street, 7th Floor
San Francisco, CA 94111
415-391-7225
Fax: 415-391-7262
www.waldenvc.com

Wells Fargo SBIC, Inc.
Steven W. Burge, Managing Director
333 South Grand Avenue, Suite 1150
Los Angeles, CA 90071
213-253-3671
Fax: 213-621-2623
www.wellsfargo.com

Wells Fargo SBIC, Inc.
Richard R. Green, Managing
  Director
One Montgomery Street
West Tower #2530
San Francisco, CA 94104
415-222-1800
Fax: 415-765-1569
www.wellsfargo.com

Western General Capital Corporation
  (SSBIC)
Alan Thian, President
13701 Riverside Drive, Suite 610
Sherman Oaks, CA 91423
818-907-8272
Fax: 818-905-9220

Woodside Fund III SBIC, L.P.
Vincent Occhipinti & Frank
  Mendicino
350 Marine Parkway, Suite 300
Redwood Shores, CA 94065
650-610-8050
Fax: 650-610-8051
www.woodsidefund.com

Colorado

CapEx L.P.
Jeffrey Ross, Manager
518 Seventeenth Street, 17th Floor
Denver, CO 80202
303-869-4700
Fax: 303-869-4602
www.capexsbic.com

Cornerstone Ventures, L.P.
John R. Ord, Contact
11001 West 120th Avenue, Suite 310
Broomfield, CO 80021
303-410-2500
Fax: 303-466-9316
www.cornerstoneventures.com

Hanifen Imhoff Mezzanine Fund,
   L.P.
Edward C. Brown, Manager
1125 17th Street, Suite 2260
Denver, CO 80202
303-297-1701
Fax: 303-297-1702
www.rockycapital.com

NewWest Mezzanine Fund, L.P.
David Henry, Managing General
   Partner
1700 Lincoln Street, Suite 2000
Denver, CO 80203
303-764-9677
Fax: 303-832-6154
www.mezzcap.com

Rocky Mountain Mezzanine Fund II,
   L.P.
Edward Brown & Paul Lyons, Mgrs.
1125 17th Street, Suite 2260
Denver, CO 80202
303-297-1701
Fax: 303-297-1702
www.rockycapital.com

The Roser Partnership III, SBIC,
   L.P.
James Roser and Christopher Roser,
   Mgrs.
1105 Spruce Street
Boulder, CO 80302
303-443-6436
Fax: 303-443-1885
www.roserventures.com

Vista Ventures Advantage, L.P.
Catharine M. Merigold, Contact
103 West Mountain Avenue
Fort Collins, CO 80524
970-482-3037
Fax: 970-482-3840
www.vistavc.com

Wolf Venture Fund III, L.P.
David Wolf, Contacts
1600 Stout Street, Suite 1510
Denver, CO 80202
303-321-4800
Fax: 303-321-4848
www.wolfventures.com

Connecticut

AB SBIC, Inc.
Adam J. Bozzuto, President
275 Schoolhouse Road
Cheshire, CT 06410
203-272-3511
Fax: 203-250-2954
www.bozzutos.com

Bon Secours Community Investment
   Fund, L.P.
Jennifer Plourde, CFO
c/o Smith Whiley & Company
242 Trumbull Street, 8th Floor
Hartford, CT 06103
860-548-2513
Fax: 860-548-2518
www.smithwhiley.com

Brookside Pecks Capital Partners,
   L.P.
80 Field Point Road, Third Floor
Greenwich, CT 06830
203-618-0202
Fax: 203-618-0984

Canaan SBIC, L.P.
Gregory Kopchinsky, Manager
105 Rowayton Avenue
Rowayton, CT 06853
203-855-0400
Fax: 203-854-9117
www.canaan.com

Cygnet Capital Partners L.P. SBIC
Owen S. Crihfield, Contact
281 Tresser Boulevard, 4th Floor
Stamford, CT 06901
203-602-0011
Fax: 203-602-2206
www.hrco.com

FieldPoint Partners SBIC, L.P.
Nestor J.Olivier
80 Field Point Road
Greenwich, CT 06830
203-869-5444
Fax: 203-869-6345
www.dublindpartners.com

First New England Capital 2, L.P.
Richard Klaffky, Manager
100 Pearl Street
Hartford, CT 06103
860-293-3333
Fax: 860-293-3338
www.firstnewenglandcapital.com

GreenLeaf Capital, L.P.
Jon Atkeson, Attorney
177 Broad Street
Stamford, CT 06901
203-973-1400
Fax: 203-973-1422
www.whitney.com

Imprimis SB, LP
Charles Davidson, Joseph Jacobs,
   Mgrs.
411 West Putnam Avenue

Greenwich, CT 06830
203-862-7000
Fax: 203-862-7374
www.wexford.com

Ironbridge Mezzanine Fund, L.P.
Marc Reich, President, Contact
200 Fisher Drive
c/o Ironwood Capital Advisors LLC
Avon, CT 06001
860-409-2100
Fax: 860-409-2120
www.ironwoodcap.com

Marketing 1 to 1 Ventures, L.P.
Bruce Blasnik, Contact
One Landmark Square
Stamford, CT 06901
203-325-4000
Fax: 203-325-8900
www.1to1ventures.com

Main Street Resources MSR I SBIC,
   L.P.
Daniel A. Levinson
8 Wright Street
Westport, CT 06880
203-227-5320
Fax: 203-227-5312
www.mainstreet-resources.com

RFE Capital Partners, L.P.
Robert M. Williams, Managing
   Partner
36 Grove Street
New Canaan, CT 06840
203-966-2800
Fax: 203-966-3109
www.rfeip.com

Saugatuck Capital Company, L.P.
   IV, SBIC
Frank Hawley, Thomas Berardino
One Canterbury Green
Stamford, CT 06901
203-348-6669
Fax: 203-324-6995
www.saugatuckcapital.com

TD Javelin Capital Fund II, L.P.
Two Greenwich Plaza, 4th Floor
Greenwich, CT 06830
203-629-8700

Valentis SB, L.P.
Paul M. Jacobi
411 West Putnam Avenue
Greenwich, CT 06830
203-862-7300
Fax: 203-862-7374
www.wexford.com

Delaware

Blue Rock Capital, L.P.
Virginia Bonker & Paul Collison,
   Mgrs.
5700 Kennett Pike, 2nd floor
Wilmington, DE 19807-1312
302-426-0981

Fax: 302-426-0982
www.bluerockcapital.com

Inflection Point Ventures II, L.P.
Jeffrey A. Davison, Contact
Delaware Technology Park
15 Innovation Way, Suite 280
Newark, DE 19711
302-452-1120
Fax: 302-452-1122
www.inflectpoint.com

District of Columbia
Allied Investment Corporation
Kelly Anderson, Controller
1919 Pennsylvania Avenue, NW
Washington, DC 20006-3434
202-331-1112
Fax: 202-659-2053
www.alliedcapital.com

Broadcast Capital, Inc. (SSBIC)
John E. Oxendine, President
1001 Connecticut Avenue, Suite 705
Washington, DC 20036
202-496-9250
Fax: 202-496-9259
Email: broadcap@aol.com

Core Capital Partners, L.P.
William Dunbar, Jonathan Silver,
  Contact
901 15th Street, Suite 950
Washington, DC 20005
202-589-0090
Fax: 202-589-0091
www.core-capital.com

Florida
Stonehenge Capital BOCF, LLC
Steven F. Lux, Stephen A. Bennett
777 S. Harbour Island Blvd.
Suite 375
Tampa, FL 33602
813-223-9335
Fax: 813-221-6453
www.stonehengecapital.com

Crossbow Venture Partners LP
Stephen J. Warner, Contact
One North Clematis Street, Suite 510
West Palm Beach, FL 33401-5523
561-838-9005
Fax: 561-838-4105
www.cb-ventures.com

Market Capital Corp.
Eugene C. Langford, President
1715 W. Cleveland Street
P.O. Box 3277
Tampa, FL 33606
813-251-5533
Fax: 813-251-1900
www.langfordhill.com

Power Equities, Inc.
Maureen Beavers
50 N. Laura Street, 9th Floor
FL9-001-09-03
Jacksonville, FL 32202

904-791-7601
Fax: 904-791-7516

Georgia
Cordova Enhanced Fund, L.P.
Paul DiBella & Ralph Wright,
  Managers
2500 North Winds Parkway
Suite 475
Alpharetta, GA 30004
678-942-0300
Fax: 678-942-0301
www.cordovaventures.com

EGL/NatWest Equity Partners USA,
  L.P.
Salvatore Massaro, Manager
3495 Piedmont Road
Building Ten, Suite 412
Atlanta, GA 30305
404-949-8303
Fax: 404-949-8311
www.eglholdings.com

First Growth Capital, Inc.
Vijay K. Patel, President
P.O. Box 815
I-75 & GA 42, Best Western Plaza
Forsyth, GA 31029
478-994-9260
Fax: 478-994-1280
Email: vidya.patel@anjgroup.biz

Global Capital Funding Group, L.P.
Brad A. Thompson, Contact
106 Colony Park Drive, Suite 900
Cumming, GA 30040
678-947-0028
Fax: 678-947-6499
Email: bthompson@gcaltd.com

Wachovia Capital Associates, Inc.
Matt Sullivan, Managing Director
1170 Peachtree Street, Suite 1610
Atlanta, GA 30309
404-253-6388
Fax: 404-253-6377
www.peachtreeequity.com

Hawaii
HMS Hawaii
Richard Grey, Contact
Davies Pacific Center
841 Bishop Street, Suite 860
Honolulu, HI 96813
650-906-0488
Fax: 650-856-9864
www.hmsgroup.com

Pacific Century SBIC, Inc.
Darlene Blakeney, Manager
130 Merchant St., 12th Floor
Honolulu, HI 96813
Mailing address:
P.O. Box 2900
Honolulu HI 96846-6000
808-537-8088
Fax: 808-521-7602
www.boh.com

Pacific Venture Capital, Ltd.
Frank Tokioka
222 South Vineyard Street, PH.1
Honolulu, HI 96813
808-521-6502
Fax: 808-521-6541
Email: dperk@lava.net

Illinois
ABN AMRO Capital (USA) Inc.
Paul Widuch, Chairman
135 South LaSalle Street
Chicago, IL 60674
312-904-6445
Fax: 312-904-6376
www.abnamro.com

Alpha Capital III SBIC, L.P.
Andrew H. Kalnow, Contact
122 South Michigan Ave.
Suite 1700
Chicago, IL 60603
312-322-9800
Fax: 312-322-9808
Email: AmyColeman@earthlink.net

Banc One Equity Capital SBIC Fund
  II, L.L.C
Susan Klaus, Contact
55 West Monroe Street, 16th Floor
Chicago, IL 60670
312-732-9825
Fax: 312-732-7495
www.bankone.com

BancAmerica Capital Investors
  SBIC II, L.P.
Dennis McCrary, Robert Perille
231 South LaSalle Street, 7th Floor
Chicago, IL 60697
312-828-1781
Fax: 312-828-6298
www.BankofAmerica.com

BMO Nesbitt Burns Equity
  Investments, Inc.
William C. Morro, President
111 West Monroe Street, 20th Floor
Chicago, IL 60603
312-461-3855
Fax: 312-765-8000
www.bmonb.com

Cardinal Growth, L.P.
Joseph M. McInerney, Contact
311 South Wacker Drive
Suite 5500
Chicago, IL 60606
312-913-1000
Fax: 312-913-1001
www.cardinalgrowth.com

Channel Medical Partners, L.P.
Gregory Shearer, Contact
5750 Old Orchard Road, Suite 310
Skokie, IL 60077
847-779-1550
Fax: 847-779-1535
www.chanmed.com

Chicago Venture Partners, L.P.
John Fife, Manager
303 East Wacker Drive, Suite 311
Chicago, IL 60601
312-297-7000
Fax: 312-819-9701
www.chicagoventure.com

CIVC Partners Fund, LLC
Christopher Perry, Marcus Wedner
231 South LaSalle St., Seventy Floor
Chicago, IL 60697
312-828-6570
Fax: 312-987-0763
Email: christopher.perry@
  bankofamerica.com

Continental Illinois Venture Corp.
Christopher J. Perry, President
209 South LaSalle Street
Mailing address:
231 South LaSalle Street
Chicago, IL 60697
312-828-8023
Fax: 312-987-0887
Email: christopher.perry@
  bankofamerica.com

DNJ Leasing II, L.P.
Jeffery S. Pfeffer, Contact
150 N. Wacker Drive
Suite 3025
Chicago, IL 60606
312-629-2877
Fax: 312-629-2874
www.dnjcapital.com

First Chicago Equity Corporation
David J. Vitale, President
Three First National Plaza
Suite 1330
Chicago, IL 60670
312-895-1000
Fax: 312-895-1001
Email: susan.e.klaus@em.fcnbd.com

High Street Capital III SBIC, L.P.
Joseph R. Katcha, Contact
11 South LaSalle Street, 5th Floor
Chicago, IL 60603
312-423-2650
Fax: 312-423-2655
www.Highsrt.com

Mercantile Capital Partners I, L.P.
Steven Edelson, Contact
1372 Shermer Road
Northbrook, IL 60062
847-509-3711
Fax: 847-509-3715
www.MercantilePartners.com

Midwest Mezzanine Fund II, L.P.
David Gezon & Allan Kayler, Mgrs.
135 South LaSalle Street, 20th Floor
Chicago, IL 60603
312-992-4587
Fax: 312-995-4595
www.midwestmezzanine.com

Open Prairie Ventures I, L.P.
Dennis D. Spice, Contact
115 North Neil Street, Suite 209
Champaign, IL 61820
217-351-7000
Fax: 217-351-7051
www.openprairie.com

Peterson Finance and Investment
  Company (SSBIC)
James S. Rhee, President
3300 West Peterson Avenue, Suite A
Chicago, IL 60659
773-539-0502
Fax: 773-583-6714
Email: jsrhee@aol.com

Prairie Capital II, L.P.
C. Bryan Daniels, Contact
300 South Wacker Drive, Suite 2400
Chicago, IL 60606
312-360-1133
Fax: 312-360-1193
www.prairie-capital.com

Prism Opportunity Fund SBIC, L.P.
Robert A. Finkel, Contact
444 N. Michigan Avenue, Suite 1910
Chicago, IL 60611
312-464-7900
Fax: 312-464-7915
www.prismfund.com

Shorebank Capital Corporation
  (SSBIC)
David Shryock, CEO
7936 S. Cottage Grove Ave.
Chicago, IL 60619
773-371-7030
Fax: 773-371-7035
www.sbk.com

SvoCo, L.P.
John Svoboda, Michelle Collins,
  Contacts
1 North Franklin Street
Suite 1500
Chicago, IL 60606
312-267-8750
Fax: 312-267-6025
www.svoco.com

USHCC Private Equity, L.P.
Victor L. Maruri, Contact
311 South Wacker Drive
Chicago, IL 60606
312-697-4600
Fax: 312-697-0115
www.dufflic.com

Indiana

1st Source Capital Corporation
Eugene L. Cavenaugh, Jr., Vice
  President
100 North Michigan Street
South Bend, IN 46601
574-235-2250
Fax: 574-235-2227
www.1stsource.com

Cambridge Ventures, LP
Ms. Jean Wojtowicz, President
4181 East 96th Street, Suite 200
Indianapolis, IN 46240
317-814-6192
Fax: 317-844-9815
Email: jwojtowicz@
  cambridgecapitalmgmt.com

Centerfield Capital Partners, L.P.
D. Scott Lutzke, Contact
3030 Market Tower
10 West Market Street
Indianapolis, IN 46204
317-237-2323
Fax: 317-237-2325
www.centerfieldcapital.com

Irwin Ventures SBIC LLC
David Meyercord, Contact
500 Washington Street
Columbus, IN 47201
812-373-1434
Fax: 812-376-1709
www.irwinventures.com

White River Venture Partners, LP
Sam Sutphin & Marc DeLong,
  Managers
3603 East Raymond St.
Indianapolis, IN 46203-4762
317-780-7789
Fax: 317-791-2935
Email: madelong@
  driversolutions.com

Iowa

AAVIN Equity Partners I, L.P.
James D. Thorpe, Contact
118 Third Avenue, S.E., Suite 630
Cedar Rapids, IA 52401
319-247-1072
Fax: 319-363-9519
www.aavinvc.com

Berthel SBIC, LLC
Henry Royer & Larry Duncan,
  Contacts
701 Tama Street, Building B
P.O. Box 609
Marion, IA 52302
319-447-5700
Fax: 319-447-4250
www.berthel.com

MorAmerica Capital Corporation
David R. Schroder, President
101 2nd Street, SE, Suite 800
Cedar Rapids, IA 52401
319-363-8249
Fax: 319-363-9683
Email: mbenge@investam.com

Kansas

Kansas Venture Capital, Inc.
John Delton, Manager
6700 Antioch Plaza, Suite 460
Overland Park, KS 66204
913-262-7117

Fax: 913-262-3509
www.kvci.com

MidStates Capital, L.P.
Timothy J. Keeble, Contact
7300 West 110th Street, 7th Floor
Overland Park, KS 66210
913-962-9007
Fax: 913-962-0699
Email: timkeeble@mail.com

Kentucky
Chrysalis Ventures II, L.P.
Lisa K. Aly, Contact
101 South Fifth Street, Suite 1650
Louisville, KY 40202
502-583-7644
Fax: 502 853 7648
www.ChrysalisVentures.com

Equal Opportunity Finance, Inc.
  (SSBIC)
David L. Davis, President
50 E RiverCenter Boulevard
PO Box 391
Covington, KY 41012
859-815-3434
Fax: 859-815-4496
www.ashland.com

Mountain Ventures, Inc.
L. Ray Moncrief, President
P.O. Box 1738
362 Old Whitley Road
London, KY 40743
606-864-5175
Fax: 606-864-5194
www.khic.org

Prosperitas Investment Partners, L.P.
Steven B. Bing, Contact
3600 National City Tower
101 South Fifth Street
Louisville, KY 40202
502-584-4008
Fax: 502-587-1351
www.prosperitasfund.com

Louisiana
Audubon Capital SBIC, L.P.
Robert Cowin, Contact
1100 Poydras Street, Suite 2000
New Orleans, LA 70163
504-585-7730
Fax: 504-585-7731
www.auduboncapital.com

Bank One Equity Investors-BIDCO,
  Inc.
Thomas J. Adamek, President
c/o Stonehenge Capital Corporation
450 Laurel Street, Suite 1450
Baton Rouge, LA 70801
225-408-3000
Fax: 225-408-3090
www.stonehengecapital.com

Hibernia Capital Corp.
Thomas Hoyt, President
313 Carondelet Street

New Orleans, LA 70130
504-533-5988
Fax: 504-533-3873
www.hiberniabank.com

Jefferson Capital Partners I, L.P.
William J. Harper, Contact
3501 N. Causeway Blvd., Suite 420
Metairie, LA 70002
504-828-2088
Fax: 504-828-2014
www.jeffcap.com

Maine
North Atlantic Venture Fund II, L.P.
David M. Coit, Manager
Two City Center, 5th Floor
Portland, ME 04101
207-772-4470
Fax: 207-772-3257
www.northatlanticcapital.com

Maryland
Allegiance Capital, L.P.
Gary Dorsch
2000 West 41st Street
Baltimore, MD 21211
410-338-6314
Fax: 410-662-6816
www.allcapital.com

Anthem Capital II, L.P.
C. Edward Spiva, Contact
16 South Calvert Street, Suite 800
Baltimore, MD 21202
410-625-1510
Fax: 410-625-1735
www.anthemcapital.com

Meridian Management Group
  Ventures, L.P. (SSBIC)
Stanley W. Tucker, Manager
826 E. Baltimore Street
Baltimore, MD 21202
410-333-2548
Fax: 410-333-2552
www.mmggroup.com

Patriot Capital, L.P.
Chris M. Royston, Contact
16 West Madison Street
Baltimore, MD 21201
410 576 2975
Fax: 410-752-2978
www.bengurbryan.com

Security Financial and Investment
  Corp.
Jim Bonfils, Manager
7720 Wisconsin Avenue, Suite 207
Bethesda, MD 20814
301-951-4288
Fax: 301-951-9282
Email: JamesBonfils@aol.com

Spring Capital Partners, L.P.
Jay M. Wilson, General Partner
The Latrobe Building, 5th Floor
2 East Read Street
Baltimore, MD 21202

410-685-8000
Fax: 410-545-0015
www.springcap.com

Toucan Capital Fund II, L.P.
Linda Powers
7600 Wisconsin Avenue, 7th Floor
Bethesda, MD 20814
240-497-4060
Fax: 240-497-4065
www.toucancapital.com

Walker Investment Fund II SBIC,
  L.P.
Gina Dubbe, Contact
3060 Washington Road, Suite 200
Glenwood, MD 21738
301-854-6850
Fax: 301-854-6235
www.walkerventures.com

Massachusetts
Ascent Venture Partners II, L.P.
Frank Polestra, General Partner
255 State Street, 5th Floor
Boston, MA 02109
617-720-9400
Fax: 617-720-9401
www.ascentvp.com

Axxon Capital, L.P.
Paula E. Groves, Contact
28 State Street, 37th Floor
Boston, MA 02109
617-772-0980
Fax: 617-557-6014
www.axxoncapital.com

BancBoston Ventures, Incorporated
Frederick M. Fritz, President
175 Federal Street, 10th Floor
Boston, MA 02110
617-434-2442
Fax: 617-434-1153
www.fleet.com

Chestnut Venture Partners, L.P.
David D. Croll, President
75 State Street, Suite 2500
Boston, MA 02109
617-345-7220
Fax: 617-345-7201
www.mcventurepartners.com

Citizens Ventures, Inc.
Robert Garrow & Gregory Mulligan,
  Mgrs.
28 State Street, 15th Floor
Boston, MA 02109
617-725-5633
Fax: 617-725-5630
www.citizenscapital.com

Crescent Private Capital II, L.P.
Nancy S. Amer, Contact
One Copley Place, Suite 602
Boston, MA 02116
617-638-0050
Fax: 617-638-0090
www.cresentlp.com

Gemini Investors III, L.P.
David F. Millet, Contact
20 William Street
Wellesley, MA 02481
781-237-7001
Fax: 781-237-7233
www.gemini-investors.com

Lancet Capital Health Ventures, L.P.
William Golden, Manager
124 Mount Auburn St., Suite 200N
Cambridge, MA 02138
617-330-9345
Fax: 617-330-9349
www.lancetcapital.com

Longworth Venture Partners II-A,
   L.P.
Paul A. Margolis, Contact
1050 Winter Street, Suite 2600
Waltham, MA 02451
781-663-3600
Fax: 781-663-3619
www.longworth.com

Marathon Investment Partners, L.P.
Paul Bolger, Managing Director
100 Cummings Center, Suite 326-J
Beverly, MA 01915
978-720-3520
Fax: 978-998-6960
www.marathoninvestment.com

New England Partners Capital, L.P.
Robert Hanks, Prin. & Todd
   Fitzpatrick
One Boston Place, Suite 2100
Boston, MA 02108
617-624-8400
Fax: 617-624-8416
www.nepartners.com

North Hill Ventures II, L.P.
Brett Rome, Contact
Ten Post Office Square
Suite 1100
Boston, MA 02109
617-788-2150
Fax: 617-788-2152
Email: brett.rome@capitalone.com

RockPort Capital Partners, L.P.
Bettina Metais, Contact
160 Federal Street, 18th Floor
Boston, MA 02110
617-912-1420
Fax: 617-912-1449
www.rockportcap.com

Seacoast Capital Partners II, L.P.
Walt Leonard, Contact
55 Ferncroft Road
Danvers, MA 01923
978-750-1300
Fax: 978-750-1301
www.seacoastcapital.com

Summer Street Capital Fund I, L.P.
Richard Steele
171 Dwight Rd., Suite 310

Longmeadow, MA 01106
413-567-3366
Fax: 413-567-6556
www.summerstreetcapital.com

UST Capital Corp.
Robert E. Garrow, President &
   Director
28 State Street
Boston, MA 02109
617-725-5635
Fax: 617-725-5630
www.citizenscapital.com

Velocity Equity Partners I SBIC,
   L.P.
David Vogel, Contact
121 High Street, Suite 400
Boston, MA 02110
617-338-2545
Fax: 617-261-3864
www.velocityep.com

Venture Capital Fund of New
   England IV, L.P
Kevin J. Dougherty, Contact
30 Washington Street
Wellesley Hills, MA 02481
781-431-8400
Fax: 781-237-6578
www.vcfne.com

Zero Stage Capital SBIC VII, L.P.
Paul M. Kelly, Contact
101 Main Street, 17th Floor
Cambridge, MA 02142
617-876-5355
Fax: 617-876-1248
www.zerostage.com

Michigan
Comerica Ventures, Inc.
Jay K. Oberg, First Vice President
500 Woodward Avenue
33rd Floor, MC 3379
Detroit, MI 48226
313-222-7833
Fax: 313-222-4013
www.comerica.com

Dearborn Capital Corp. (SSBIC)
William D. Lang, President
c/o Ford Motor Credit Corporation
The American Road
Dearborn, MI 48121
313-337-8577
Fax: 313-390-3783
www.ford.com

EDF Ventures, L.P.
Mary Campbell, Contact
425 North Main Street
Ann Arbor, MI 48104-1147
734-663-3213
Fax: 734-663-7358
www.edfvc.com

InvestCare Partners, L.P.
Malcolm Moss, Manager
32330 W. 12 Mile Road

Farmington Hills, MI 48334
248-489-9000
Fax: 248-489-8819
www.gmacapital.com

Merchants Capital Partners, L.P.
G. Cohen, P. Beach, R. Martin,
   Mgrs.
24 Frank Lloyd Wright Drive
Lobby L, 4th Floor
Ann Arbor, MI 48106
734-994-5505
Fax: 734-994-1376
www.merchantscapitalpartners.com

Motor Enterprises, Inc. (SSBIC)
Lindsey Luttinen, VP and Treasurer
200 Renaissance Center, 10th Floor
PO Box 200
Mail Code: 482-B10-C76
Detroit, MI 48265-2000
316-665-6083
Fax: 313-665-6208
Email: lindsey.luttinen@GM.com

North Coast Technology Investor,
   L.P.
Hugo E. Braun III, Lindsay D.
   Aspegren
206 S. Fifth Avenue Suite 550
Ann Arbor, MI 48104-0648
734-662-7667
Fax: 734-662-6261
www.northcoastvc.com

Pacific Capital, L.P.
Dan Boyle
900 Victor's Way, Suite 280
Ann Arbor, MI 48108
734-747-9401
Fax: 734-747-9704
www.whitepines.com

TD Lighthouse Capital Fund, L.P.
Joan Neuscheler, Contact
303 Detroit Street, Suite 301
Ann Arbor, MI 48104
734-623-6300
Fax: 734-623-2956
www.tullisdickerson.com

White Pines Limited Partnership I
Mr. Ian Bund, President
900 Victor's Way, Suite 280
Ann Arbor, MI 48108
734-47-9401
Fax: 34-47-9704
www.whitepines.com

Minnesota
AAVIN Equity Partners I, L.P.
Daryl Erdman
2500 Rand Tower
Participating Securities and
   Commitments
Minneapolis, MN 55402
612-375-9966
Fax: 319-363-9519
www.aavininc.com

Copyright © 2004 Matthew Lesko, Information USA, Inc., 12081 Nebel Street, Rockville, MD 20852 • 1-800-955-7693 • www.lesko.com

Affinity Ventures III, L.P.
Robin M. Dowdle, Contact
901 Marquette Avenue, Suite 1810
Minneapolis, MN 55402
612-252-9897
Fax: 612-252-9863
www.affinitycapital.net

Agio Capital Partners I, L.P.
Kenneth F. Gudorf, President &
CEO
Interlachen Corporate Center
5050 Lincoln Drive, Suite 420
Edina, MN 55436
952-938-1628
Fax: 952-933-6066
www.agio-capital.com

Bayview Capital Partners, L.P.
Cary Musech, Manager
641 East Lake Street, Suite 230
Wayzata, MN 55391
952-345-2000
Fax: 952-345-2001
www.bayviewcap.com

Convergent Capital Partners I, L.P.
John Mason, Keith Bares
5353 Wayzata Boulevard, Suite 205
Minneapolis, MN 55416
952-595-8102
Fax: 952-595-8113
www.cvcap.com

Dougherty Opportunity Fund II, L.P.
James A. Bernards, Contact
7200 Metro Boulevard
Edina, MN 55439
952-831-6499
Fax: 952-831-1219
www.sbbsl.com

Medallion Capital, Inc.
Tom Hunt, President
3000 W. County Road 42
Suite 301
Burnsville, MN 55337-4827
952-831-2025
Fax: 952-831-2945
Email:
mvannelli@medallioncapital.com

Milestone Growth Fund, Inc.
(SSBIC)
Esperanza Guerrero-Anderson,
President
401 Second Avenue South
Suite 1032
Minneapolis, MN 55401
612-338-0090
Fax: 612-338-1172
www.milestonegrowth.com

Norwest Equity Partners VII-SBIC,
L.P.
John Whaley, Contact
3600 IDS Center
80 S. 8th St.
Minneapolis, MN 55402
612-215-1600

Fax: 612-215-1601
www.nep.com

Piper Jaffray Healthcare Capital L.P.
Lloyd (Buzz) Benson, Manager
800 Nicollet Mall, Suite 800
Minneapolis, MN 55402-7020
612-303-5664
Fax: 612-303-1350
www.piperventures.com

Wells Fargo SBIC, Inc.
John Whaley
3600 IDS Center
80S 8th St.
Minneapolis, MN 55402
612-215-1600
Fax: 612-215-1601
www.nep.com

Mississippi

CapSource 2000 Fund, L.P.
James R. Herndon, Contact
795 Woodlands Parkway, Suite 100
Ridgeland, MS 39157
601-899-8980
Fax: 601-952-1334
www.capsources.com

Sun-Delta Capital Access Center,
Inc. (SSBIC)
Harry Bowie, President
819 Main Street
Greenville, MS 38701
662-335-5291
Fax: 662-335-5295
Email: deltafdn@tecinfo.com

Missouri

American Century Ventures II,
L.L.C.
Diane Mulcahy, Contact
4500 Main Street, 9th Floor
Kansas City, MO 64111
816-340-4054
Fax: 816-340-3278
www.americancentury.com

Bankers Capital Corp.
Raymond E. Glasnapp, President
3100 Gillham Road
Kansas City, MO 64109
816-531-1600
Fax: 816-531-1334
Email: cglasnapp@aol.com

BOME Investors II, L.L.C.
Shelley Whittington, Thomas
Adamek
c/o Gateway Capco II, LLC
8000 Maryland Avenue, Suite 1190
St. Louis, MO 63105
314-721-5707
Fax: 314-721-5135
www.gatewayventures.com

CFB Venture Fund I, Inc.
James F. O'Donnell, Chairman
11 South Meramec, Suite 1430
St. Louis, MO 63105

314-746-7427
Fax: 314-746-8739
www.capitalforbusiness.com

Eagle Fund I, L.P.
Scott Fesler
Bush O'Donnell Capital
101 S. Hanley Road, Suite 1250
St. Louis, MO 63105
314-727-4555
Fax: 314-727-8829
Email: sdf@bushodonnell.com

Kansas City Equity Partners
Ventures II, L.P.
William Reisler, Manager
233 West 47th Street
Kansas City, MO 64112
816-960-1771
Fax: 816-960-1777
www.kcep.com

MorAmerica Capital Corporation
Kevin F. Mullane, Vice President
911 Main Street, Suite 2424
Commerce Tower Building
Kansas City, MO 64105
816-842-0114
Fax: 816-471-7339

Power Equities, Inc.
Craig Fowler
800 Market Street, 13th Floor
MO1-800-15-03
St. Louis, MO 63101
314-466-6634
Fax: 314-466-6238

RiverVest Venture Fund I, L.P.
Thomas C. Melzer, Contact
7733 Forsyth Boulevard, Suite 1650
St. Louis, MO 63105
314-726-6700
Fax: 314-727-6715
www.rivervest.com

UMB Capital Corporation, Inc.
Noel Shull, Manager
1010 Grand Boulevard
Mailing address:
P.O. Box 419226
Kansas City, MO 64141
816-860-7914
Fax: 816-860-7143
www.umb.com

Nevada

Atalanta Investment Company, Inc.
L. Mark Newman, Chairman of the
Board
601 Fairview Blvd.
P.O. Box 7718
Incline Village, NV 89452
775-833-1836
Fax: 775-833-1890
Email: mark@marknewman.net

New Hampshire

MerchantBanc Venture Partners,
L.P.
Jeffrey M. Pollock

Two Wall Street
Manchester, NH 03101
603-623-5500
Fax: 603-623-3972
www.merchantbanc.com

New Jersey

Alliance Mezzanine Investors, L.P.
Robert Eberhardt, Douglas Smith
96 Pompton Road
Verona, NJ 07044
973-239-8900
Fax: 973-239-8909
www.mezcap.com

Blue Rock Capital, L.P.
Virginia G. Bonker
230 Lackawanna Drive
Andover, NJ 07821
973-426-1767
Fax: 973-426-0224
www.bluerockcapital.com

Capital Circulation Corporation
   (SSBIC)
Judy Kao, Manager
2035 Lemoine Avenue
Second Floor
Fort Lee, NJ 07024
201-947-8637
Fax: 201-585-1965
Email: judykao@bellatlantic.net

DFW Capital Partners, L.P.
Donald F. DeMuth, Manager
Glenpointe Center East, 5th Floor
300 Frank W. Burr Blvd.
Teaneck, NJ 07666
201-836-6000
Fax: 201-836-5666
www.DFWCapital.com

Early Stage Enterprises, L.P.
Ronald Hahn and James Millar,
   Managers
995 Route 518
Skillman, NJ 08558
609-921-8896
Fax: 609-921-8703
www.esevc.com

Edison Fund V, L.P.
Ross Martinson, Contact
1009 Lenox Drive, #4
Lawrenceville, NJ 08648
609-896-1900
Fax: 609-896-0066
www.edisonventure.com

Liberty View Equity Partners SBIC,
   L.P.
Scott Flamm, Richard Meckler
   Contacts
Waterfront Corporate Center
111 River Street, 10th Floor
Hoboken, NJ 07030-5776
201-595-2926
Fax: 201-216-8605
Email: dmancilla@cprus.com

MidMark Capital II, L.P.
Matthew W. Finlay, Contact
177 Madison Avenue
Morristown, NJ 07960
973-971-9960
Fax: 973-971-9963
www.midmarkcapital.com

Navigator Growth Partners, L.P.
Bernard Markey
47 Summit Avenue
Summit, NJ 07901
908-273-7733
Fax: 908-273-5566
www.navigatorequity.com

Norwood Venture Corp.
Mark R. Littell, President
65 Norwood Avenue
Montclair, NJ 07043
973-783-1117
www.norven.com

Penny Lane Partners, L.P.
William R. Denslow, Jr., Manager
One Palmer Square
Suite 309
Princeton, NJ 08542
609-497-4646
Fax: 609-497-0611
Email: pennylanepartner@msn.com

Sycamore Venture Capital, L.P.
John Whitman
845 Alexander Road
Princeton, NJ 08540
609-759-8888
Fax: 609-759-8900
www.sycamorevc.com

Tappan Zee Capital Corporation
Jeffrey Birnberg, President
201 Lower Notch Road
Mailing address:
P.O. Box 416
Little Falls, NJ 07424
973-256-8280
Fax: 973-256-2841
Email: tzcc@aol.com

University Ventures, Inc. (SSBIC)
Oscar Figueroa, President
180 University Avenue, 3rd Floor
Newark, NJ 07102
973-0353-5627
Fax: 973-353-1175
Email:
   ofiguero@andromeda.rutgers.edu

Ziegler Healthcare Fund I, L.P.
Douglas Korey, Contact
Executive Center #2, Third Floor
1040 Broad Street
Shrewsbury, NJ 07702
732-578-0533
Fax: 732-578-0501
www.zieglerhealthcare.com

Zon Capital Partners, L.P.
William D. Bridgers, Contact

5 Vaughn Drive, Suite 104
Princeton, NJ 08540
609-452-1653
Fax: 609-452-1693
www.zoncapital.com

New Mexico

Tullis-Dickerson Origen Capital
   Fund, L.P.
Tom Dickerson
150 Washington Avenue, Suite 201
Santa Fe, NM 87501
505-982-7007
Fax: 505-982-7008
www.tullisdickerson.com

New York

399 Venture Partners
William Comfort, Chairman
399 Park Avenue, 14th Floor/Zone 4
New York, NY 10043
212-559-1127
Fax: 212-793-6164
Email: jjarema@cvcltd.com

ACI Capital America Fund, L.P.
Gregory H. Warner, Thomas Israel
900 Third Avenue, 26th Floor
New York, NY 10022-4728
212-634-3333
Fax: 212-634-3330
www.acicapital.com

American Asian Capital Corporation
   (SSBIC)
Howard H. Lin, President
130 Water Street, Suite 6-L
New York, NY 10005
212-422-6880
Fax: 212-422-6880
Email: linwillh@cs.com

Argentum Capital Partners II, L.P.
Daniel Raynor, Chairman
60 Madison Avenue, Suite 701
New York, NY 10110
212-949-6262
Fax: 212-949-8294
www.argentumgroup.com

Avalon Equity Fund, L.P.
Benjamin E. Brandes, Contact
800 3rd Avenue, 31st Floor
New York, NY 10022
212-421-0600
Fax: 212-421-1742
www.avalonequity.com

Bank Austria Creditanstalt SBIC,
   Inc.
Christopher Wrenn, President
245 Park Avenue, 32nd Floor
New York, NY 10167
212-672-5656
Fax: 212-672-5500
Email:
   jvangeldern@hvbamericas.com

BNP Paribas Principal Incorporated
Steven Alexander, President

787 Seventh Avenue, 32nd Floor
New York, NY 10019-8018
212-841-3070
Fax: 212-841-3251
www.bnpparibas.com

Bank of New York Capital Partners,
L.P.
Stratton Heath, Paul Echausse
445 Park Avenue
New York, NY 10022
212-821-1909
Fax: 212-832-6949
www.bankofny.com

BOCNY, LLC
W. Stephen Keller
c/o Stonehenge Capital Corporation
152 West 57th Street, 20th Floor
New York, NY 10019
212-944-2542
Fax: 212-656-1344
www.stonehengecapital.com

Brookside Pecks Capital Partners,
L.P.
Robert Cresci, Contact
One Rockefeller Plaza, Suite 900
New York, NY 10020
212-332-1346
Fax: 212-332-1334
Email: rcresci@pecks.com

Cephas Capital Partners L.P.
Clint Campbell, Jeff Holmes, Mgrs.
16 West Main Street
Rochester, NY 14614
716-231-1528
Fax: 716-231-1530
Email: cephascwc@aol.com

Champlain Capital Partners, L.P.
Dennis M. Leary, Contact
45 Rockefeller Plaza, Suite 2000
New York, NY 10020
212-332-7164
Fax: 212-332-3401
Email: dennis.leary@
  champlaingroup.com

CIBC WG Argosy Merchant Fund 1,
L.P.
Steven A. Flyer, Executive Director
425 Lexington Avenue, 3rd Floor
New York, NY 10017
212-885-4735
Fax: 212-885-4350
Email: steven.a.flyer@us.cibc.com

Citicorp Venture Capital, Ltd.
William Comfort, Chairman of the
  Board
399 Park Avenue, 14th Floor/Zone 4
New York, NY 10043
212-559-1127
Fax: 212-793-6164
Email: jjarema@cvcltd.com

Carl Marks NY Capital II, L.P.
Robert G. Davidoff, General Partner

135 East 57th Street, 26th Floor
New York, NY 10022
212-909-8400
Fax: 212-980-2630
www.carlmarks.com

Coqui Capital Partners, L.P.
Jeffrey S. Davidson, Contact
1775 Broadway, Suite 604
New York, NY 10019
212-247-4590
Fax: 212-247-4801
www.coquicapital.com

Critical Capital Growth Fund, L.P.
Steven Sands Mgr; C. Robinson
90 Park Ave., 39th Floor
New York, NY 10016
212-697-5200
Fax: 212-697-8035
www.sandsbros.com

Deutsche Bank Capital Partners
  SBIC, L.P.
Heide Silverstein, Director
130 Liberty Street, 25th Floor
New York, NY 10006
212-250-8084
Fax: 212-250-7651
www.db.com

Dresdner Kleinwort Capital, LLC
Richard Wolf, Partner
75 Wall Street, 34th Floor
New York, NY 10005
212-429-3131
Fax: 212-429-3099
www.drkw.com

East Coast Venture Capital, Inc.
  (SSBIC)
Zindel Zelmanovitch, President
241 Fifth Avenue, Suite 302
New York, NY 10016
212-686-1515
Fax: 212-686-1131
Email: fstart@aol.com

Easton Hunt Capital Partners, L.P.
John H. Friedman, Contact
641 Lexington Avenue, 21st Floor
New York, NY 10022
212-702 0950
Fax: 212-702-0952
www.eastoncapital.com

Elk Associates Funding Corporation
Gary C. Granoff, President
747 Third Avenue
New York, NY 10017
212-355-2449
Fax: 212-759-3338
www.elkassociates.com

Emigrant Capital Corporation
Lawrence Adolf and John Hart,
  Managers
6 East 43rd Street, 8th Floor
New York, NY 10017
212-850-4460

Fax: 212-850-4839
www.emigrant.com

Empire State Capital Corporation
  (SSBIC)
Dr. Joseph Wu, President
170 Broadway, Suite 1200
New York, NY 10038
212-513-1799
Fax: 212-513-1892
Email: ESC5131799@aol.com

Eos Partners SBIC II, L.P.
Steven Friedman & Brian Young,
  Manager
320 Park Avenue, 22nd Floor
New York, NY 10022
212-832-5800
Fax: 212-832-5815
www.eospartners.com

Esquire Capital Corp. (SSBIC)
Frederick Eliassen, Manager
69 Veterans Memorial Highway
Commack, NY 11725
631-462-6944
Fax: 631-864-8152
Email: esquiremoneta@msn.com

Exeter Capital Partners IV, L.P.
Keith Fox, Kurt Bergquist, Jeff
  Weber
10 East 53rd Street, 32nd Floor
New York, NY 10022
212-872-1172
Fax: 212-872-1198
www.exeterfunds.com

Falcon Private Equity, L.P.
Gregga Baxter, Matthew Snyder,
  Contacts
335 Madison Avenue - 11th Floor
New York, NY 10017
212-922-2333
Fax: 212-922-2351
Email:
  gregga.baxter@saudibank.com

First County Capital Inc. (SSBIC)
Orest Glut, Financial Manager
40-48 Main Street, Suite 301
Flushing, NY 11354
718-461-1778
Fax: 718-461-1835
Email: FirstCounty@AOL.com

Flushing Capital Corporation
  (SSBIC)
Frank J. Mitchell, President
39-06 Union Street, Room 202
Flushing, NY 11354
718-886-5866
Fax: 718-939-7761
Email: flushing.capital@verizon.net

Freshstart Venture Capital
  Corporation
Alvin Murstein, President
437 Madison Avenue
New York, NY 10022

212-328-2110
Fax: 212-328-2125
www.medallionfinancial.com

Fundex Capital Corp.
Larry Linksman, President
387 Park Avenue South, 9th Floor
New York, NY 10016
212-759-2690
Fax: 212-319-1976
www.fundexcapital.com

Gefus SBIC, L.P.
William J. Beckett
375 Park Avenue, Suite 2401
New York, NY 10152
212-308-1111
Fax: 212-308-1182
Email: wbeckett@gefinorusa.com

Hanam Capital Corp.
Robert Schairer, President
38 West 32nd Street, Suite 1512
New York, NY 10001
212-564-5225
Fax: 212-564-5307
Email: hanam@aol.com

Hudson Venture Partners II, L.P.
Dr. Lawrence A. Howard, Contact
660 Madison Avenue, 14th Floor
New York, NY 10021
212-644-9797
Fax: 212-644-7430
www.hudsonptr.com

Ibero American Investors Corp.
   (SSBIC)
Domingo Garcia, President
104 Scio Street
Rochester, NY 14604
716-262-3440
Fax: 716-262-3441
www.iberoinvestors.com

Ibero American Investors Corp.
   (SSBIC)
Christine Ryan, Loan Officer
Statler Towers Bldg.
107 Delaware Avenue, Suite 64
Buffalo, NY 14202
716-842-9908
Fax: 716-842-9925

ING Furman Selz Investments
Brian Friedman, Manager
520 Madison Avenue, 8th Floor
New York, NY 10022
212-284-1708
Fax: 212-284-1717
Email: mluxenberg@ingprivate.com

International Paper Cap. Formation,
   Inc. (SSBIC)
Julius A. Weiss, President
Two Manhattanville Road
Purchase, NY 10577-2196
914-397-1960
Fax: 914-397-1630

J.P. Morgan Partners (23A SBIC),
   LLC
Jeffrey Walker, Managing Gen.
   Partner
1221 Avenue of the Americas
40th Floor
New York, NY 10036
212-899-3500
Fax: 212-622-3799
www.JPMorganPartners.com

KBL Healthcare, L.P.
Marlene Krauss, Michael Kaswan
645 Madison Avenue
New York, NY 10022
212-319-5555
Fax: 212-319-5591
www.kblhealthcare.com

LEG Partners Debenture SBIC, L.P.
Lawrence Golub, Manager
555 Madison Avenue, 30th Floor
New York, NY 10022
212-750-6060
Fax: 212-750-5505
www.golubassoc.com

M & T Capital Corp.
Tom Scanlon, President
One Fountain Plaza, 9th Floor
Buffalo, NY 14203
716-848-3800
Fax: 716-848-3150
www.mandtbank.com

Madison Investment Partners II, L.P.
Susan Goodrich, Contact
52 Vanderbilt Avenue, Suite 1010
New York, NY 10017
212-949-0400
Fax: 212-949-6049
www.madisonpartners.com

Medallion Funding Corporation
Alvin Murstein, President
437 Madison Avenue
New York, NY 10022
212-328-2110
Fax: 212-328-2121
www.medallionfinancial.com

Merchants Capital Partners, L.P.
Jake Wessner
1120 Avenue of the Americas
4th Floor
New York, NY 10036
212-626-6832
Fax: 212-626-6833

Mercury Capital, L.P.
David W. Elenowitz, Manager
153 East 53rd Street, 49th Floor
New York, NY 10022
212-838-0888
Fax: 212-759-3897
Email: hal@dlfi.com

NBT Capital Corporation
Daryl Forsythe & Joe Minor,
   Managers

19 Eaton Avenue
Norwich, NY 13815
607-337-6810
Fax: 607-336-8730
www.nbtbank.com

Needham Capital SBIC II, L.P.
George Needham, John Michaelson,
   Mgrs.
445 Park Avenue
New York, NY 10022
212-371-8300
Fax: 212-751-1450
www.needhamco.com

New York Business Development
   Corp. Capital Corp.
Stephen A. Ross, Vice President
16 West Main Street, Suite 236
Rochester, NY 14614
716-232-6250
www.nybdc.com

New York Business Development
   Corp. Capital Corp.
Robert W. Lazar, President
41 State Street
P.O. Box 738
Albany, NY 12207
518-463-2268
Fax: 518-463-0240
www.nybdc.com

New York Business Development
   Corp. Capital Corp.
Chester A. Sadowski, Sr. V.
   President
633 Third Avenue, 36th Floor
New York, NY 10017
212-803-3672
Fax: 212-803-3675
www.nybdc.com

Penny Lane Partners, L.P.
William R. Denslow, Manager
108 Forest Avenue
P.O. Box 447
Locust Valley, NY 11560
516-609-8065
Fax: 516-759-4653

Pierre Funding Corp.
Elias Debbas, President
805 Third Avenue, 6th Floor
New York, NY 10022
212-888-1515
Fax: 212-688-4252
Email: PierreFunding@AOL.COM

Psilos Group Partners II SBIC, L.P.
Jeffrey M. Krauss, Contact
625 Avenue of the Americas
4th Floor
New York, NY 10011
212-242-8844
Fax: 212-242-8855
www.psilos.com

Pyramid Ventures, Inc.
Brian Talbot, Vice President

130 Liberty Street, 31st Floor
New York, NY 10006
212-250-9571
Fax: 212-250-7651
Email: heide.silverstein@db.com

Quad Venture Partners SBIC, L.P.
Lincoln E. Frank, Contact
650 Fifth Avenue, 31st Floor
New York, NY 10019
212-724-2200
Fax: 212-724-4310
www.quadventures.com

Radius Venture Partners II, L.P.
Daniel C. Lubin, Contact
One Rockefeller Plaza
Suite 920
New York, NY 10020
212-897-7778
Fax: 212-397-2656
www.radiusventures.com

Rand Capital SBIC, L.P.
Allen F. Grum, Jr., Contact
2200 Rand Building
Buffalo, NY 14203
716-853-0802
Fax: 716-854-8480
www.randcapital.com

RBC Equity Investments, Inc.
Sindy Jagger, Manager
One Liberty Plaza
New York, NY 10006
212-858-7157
Fax: 212-858-7468
www.rbcap.com

RBS Capital Corporation
Andrew S. Weinberg, Sr. Vice
  President
101 Park Avenue, 10th Floor
New York, NY 10178
212-401-1330
Fax: 212-401-1390
Email: andrew.weinberg@rbos.com

Regent Capital Partners, L.P.
J. Oliver Maggard, Managing Partner
505 Park Avenue, Suite 1700
New York, NY 10022
212-735-9900
Fax: 212-735-9908
Email: oliverm@cpequity.com

Rock Maple Ventures, L.P.
David W. Freelove, Contact
5 East 57th Street, 15th Floor
New York, NY 10022
212-308-1935
Fax: 212-308-8641
www.rockmapleventures.com

SGC Partners II LLC
Christopher M. Neenan, VP & COO
1221 Avenue of the Americas
8th Floor
New York, NY 10020
212-278-5184

Fax: 212-278-5454
Email:
  frances.madrid@us.socgen.com

Sixty Wall Street SBIC Fund, L.P.
John A. Mayer, Jr., Managing
  Director
1221 Avenue of the Americas
40th Floor
New York, NY 10036
212-648-7778
Fax: 212-648-5032
www.JPMorganPartners.com

Summer Street Capital Fund I, L.P.
Brian D'Amico
70 West Chippewa St., Suite 500
Buffalo, NY 14202
716-566-2900
Fax: 716-566-2910
www.summerstreetcapital.com

T.S. Capital Corporation
James Trainor, Manager
The Rice Building
216 River Street
Troy, NY 12180
518-687-4430
Fax: 518-687-4435
www.troysavingsbank.com

The 1818 SBIC Fund, L.P.
Richard J. Ragoza, Contact
59 Wall Street
New York, NY 10005
212-493-7910
Fax: 212-493-7280
www.bbh.com

Toronto Dominion Capital (U.S.A.),
  Inc.
Mr. Marc H. Michel, President
31 West 52nd Street
New York, NY 10019
212-827-7000
Fax: 212-974-8429
www.tdcapital.com

Triad Capital Corp. of New York
  (SSBIC)
Oscar Figueroa, Manager of Rutgers
  Inv.
305 Seventh Avenue, 20th Floor
New York, NY 10001
212-243-7360
Fax: 212-243-7647
Email: mrobiou@bcf-triad.org

Trusty Capital Inc. (SSBIC)
Yungduk Hahn, President
25 West 37th Street, 5th Floor
New York, NY 10118
212-719-3760
Fax: 212-869-8577
Email: ydhahn@earthlink.net

UBS Capital II LLC
Justin S. Maccarone, President
299 Park Avenue
New York, NY 10171

212-821-6490
Fax: 212-821-6333
www.ubs.com

Walden Capital Partners, L.P.
John Costantino & Allen Greenberg,
  Mgrs.
708 Third Avenue, 21st Floor
New York, NY 10017
212-355-0090
Fax: 212-755-8894
www.waldencapital.com

Wall Street Technology Partners,
  L.P.
Richard H. Wolf, Contact
75 Wall Street, 34th Floor
New York, NY 10005
212-429-2817
Fax: 212-429-2261
Email:
  richard.wolf@dresdnerkc.com

Wasserstein Adelson Ventures, L.P.
Townsend Ziebold, Jr., Manager
1301 Avenue of the Americas
44th Floor
New York, NY 10019
212-702-5600
Fax: 212-702-5635
www.wasserco.com

Westbury Equity Partners SBIC, L.P.
Richard P. Sicoli, Contact
1400 Old Country Road, Suite 313
Westbury, NY 11590
516-333-0218
Fax: 516-333-2724
www.westburypartners.com

Winfield Capital Corp.
R. Scott Perlin, CFO
237 Mamaroneck Avenue
White Plains, NY 10605
914-949-2600
Fax: 914-949-7195
www.winfieldcapital.com

North Carolina

BA Capital Company, L.P.
J. Travis Hain, Managing Member
100 North Tryon Street, 25th Floor
NCI-007-25-02
Charlotte, NC 28255
704-386-8063
Fax: 704-386-6432
www.bankofamerica.com

BB&T Capital Partners, LLC
David Townsend & Martin Gilmore,
  Mgrs.
200 West Second Street, 4th Floor
Winston-Salem, NC 27101
336-733-2420
Fax: 336-733-2419
www.bbandt.com

Blue Ridge Investors II, L.P.
Kevin Jessup, Ronald Stanley,
  Contacts

300 N. Greene Street, Suite 2100
Greensboro, NC 27401
336-275-7002
Fax: 336-275-9155
www.genevamerchantbank.com

Blue Ridge Investors Ltd.
  Partnership
Richard MacLean
922 East Boulevard
Charlotte, NC 28203-5204
704-332-3346
Fax: 704-332-4528

CapitalSouth Partners Fund I, L.P.
Joseph B. Alala, III, Contact
1228 East Morehead St., Suite 102
Charlotte, NC 28204
704-376-5502
Fax: 704-376-5877
www.capitalsouthpartners.com

Centura SBIC, Inc.
Robert R. Anders, Jr., President
200 Providence Road, 3rd Floor
P.O. Box 6261
Charlotte, NC 28207
704-686-1451
Fax: 704-686-1761
www.centura.com

Frontier Fund I, L.P.
Paul W. Stackhouse, Contact
1900 South Boulevard, Suite 300
Charlotte, NC 28203
704-414-2880
Fax: 704-414-2881
www.frontierfunds.com

North Carolina Economic
  Opportunities Fund
H. Dabney Smith, Contact
316 West Edenton Street, Suite 110
Raleigh, NC 27603
919-256-5000
Fax: 919-256-5015
www.dogwoodequity.com

Oberlin Capital, L.P.
Robert Shepley, Manager
702 Oberlin Road, Suite 150
Raleigh, NC 27605
919-743-2544
Fax: 919-743-2501
www.oberlincapital.com

Venture Capital Solutions, L.P.
Philip Martin, Contact
112 Cambridge Plaza Drive
Mailing address:
P.O. Box 24785
Winston-Salem, NC 27114
336-768-9343
Fax: 336-768-6471
www.vcslp.com

Wachovia Capital Partners, Inc.
Tracey M. Chaffin, Chief Financial
  Officer
One First Union Center, 12th Floor

301 South College Street
Charlotte, NC 28288-0732
704-374-4791
Fax: 704-374-6711
www.wachovia.com

North Dakota

North Dakota SBIC, L.P.
John G. Cosgriff, Manager
51 Broadway, Suite 400
Fargo, ND 58102
701-298-0003
Fax: 701-293-7819

Ohio

Banc One Capital Partners, LLC
James Henson
c/o Stonehenge Financial Holdings,
  Inc.
191 W. Nationwide Blvd., Suite 600
Columbus, OH 43215
614-246-2500
Fax: 614-246-2441
www.stonehengefinancial.com

Clarion Capital Corp.
Tom Niehaus, CFO
Ohio Savings Plaza
1801 East 9th Street, Suite 1120
Cleveland, OH 44114
216-687-1096
Fax: 216-694-3545
www.clariongrp.com

Enterprise Ohio Investment
  Company (SSBIC)
Janet White, Manager
8 North Main Street
Dayton, OH 45402
937-226-0457
Fax: 937-222-7035
www.citywidedev.com

Financial Opportunities, Inc.
300 Executive Parkway West
Hudson, OH 44236
330-342-6664
Fax: 330-342-6752
Email: gbudoi@dairymart.com

Key Equity Capital Corporation
David Given, President
127 Public Square, 51st Floor
Cleveland, OH 44114
216-535-4711
Fax: 216-689-3204
www.bluepointcapital.com

Key Mezzanine Capital, LLC
Dennis Wagner
800 Superior Avenue, 10th Floor
Cleveland, OH 44114
216-828-8125
Fax: 216-263-3577
www.mcdinvest.com

National City Equity Partners, Inc.
William H. Schecter, President &
  G.M.
1965 East Sixth Street, Suite 1010

Cleveland, OH 44114
216-575-2491
Fax: 216-575-9965
www.nccapital.com

River Cities Capital Fund II, L.P.
Edwin Robinson, Contact
221 East Fourth Street, Suite 1900
Cincinnati, OH 45202
513-621-9700
Fax: 513-579-8939
www.rccf.com

Walnut Investment Partners, L.P.
Jimmy Gould, Managing Partner
312 Walnut Street, Suite 1151
Cincinnati, OH 45202
513-651-3300
Fax: 513-929-4441
www.TheWalnutGroup.com

Oklahoma

Chisholm SBIC, L.P.
John B. Frick, Contact
One Leadership Square
211 North Robinson St., Suite 1910
Oklahoma City, OK 73102
405-605-1111
Fax: 405-605-1115
www.chisholmvc.com

Council Oak Investment Corporation
T. Kent Faison, Manager
101 North Broadway
Mailing address:
P.O. Box 26788
Oklahoma City, OK 73126
405-270-1000
Fax: 405-270-1089
Email: kfaison@bancfirst.com

First United Venture Capital
  Corporation
John Massey and Greg Massey,
  Managers
1400 West Main Street
Durant, OK 74701
580-924-2256
Fax: 580-924-2430
www.firstunitedbank.com

Oregon

Northern Pacific Capital Corporation
Joseph P. Tennant, President
937 S.W. 14th Street, Suite 200
Mailing address:
P.O. Box 1658
Portland, OR 97207
503-241-1255
Fax: 503-299-6653
Email: Joetpacmar@aol.com

Shaw Venture Partners III, L.P.
Ralph R. Shaw, Manager
400 Southwest Sixth Ave.
Suite 1100
Portland, OR 97204
503-228-4884
Fax: 503-227-2471
Email: judyb@shawventures.com

SmartForest Ventures I, L.P.
Debi Coleman, Contact
209 SW Oak Street, 1st Floor
Portland, OR 97204
503-222-2552
Fax: 503-222-2834
www.smartforest.com

Tamarack Mezzanine Partners, L.P.
John Woolley, Contact
522 SW Fifth Ave., Suite 915
Portland, OR 97204
503-517-8939
Fax: 503-517-8938
www.tamarackcapital.com

Utah Ventures II L.P.
Alan Dishlip
400 Lincoln Center Tower
10260 SW Greenburg Road
Portland, OR 97223
503-293-3588
Fax: 503-293-3527

Pennsylvania

Anthem Capital, L.P.
Gerald A. Schaafsma, General
    Partner
919 Conestoga Road
Building 1, Suite 301
Rosemont, PA 19010
610-526-9982
Fax: 610-526-2234
www.anthemcapital.com

Argosy Investment Partners II, L.P.
Knute C. Albrecht
950 West Valley Road
Suite 2902
Wayne, PA 19087
610-971-9685
Fax: 610-964-9524
www.argosycapital.com

CIP Capital L.P.
Winston Churchill, Jr., Manager
435 Devon Park Drive, Bldg 300
Wayne, PA 19087
610-964-7860
Fax: 610-964-8136
Email: ecarey@safeguard.com

GS Capital, L.P.
Kenneth Sweet, Richard Gessner
435 Devon Park Drive
Suite 612
Wayne, PA 19087
610-293-9151
Fax: 610-293-1979
Email: ahartshorn@safeguard.com

Liberty Ventures I, L.P.
Thomas R. Morse, Manager
One Commerce Square
2005 Market Street, Suite 2040
Philadelphia, PA 19103
215-282-4484
Fax: 215-282-4485
www.libertyvp.com

Mellon Ventures, L.P.
Lawrence Mock & Ronald Coombs,
    Managers
One Mellon Center, Room 151-5210
Pittsburgh, PA 15258
412-236-3594
Fax: 412-236-3593
www.mellonventures.com

Meridian Venture Partners
Robert E. Brown, Jr. General Partner
201 King of Prussia Road, Suite 240
Radnor, PA 19087
610-254-2999
Fax: 610-254-2996
www.meridian-venture.com

NewSpring Ventures, L.P.
Michael DiPiano, Managing G P
500 North Gulph Road, Suite 500
King of Prussia, PA 19406
610-567-2380
Fax: 610-567-2388
www.newspringventures.com

Select Capital Ventures I, L.P.
Michael E. Salerno, Contact
4718 Old Gettysburg Road
Suite 405
Mechanicsburg, PA 17055
717-972-1304
Fax: 717-972-1050
www.selectcapitalcorp.com

Puerto Rico

North America Investment
    Corporation (SSBIC)
Marcelino Pastrana Torres, President
Mercantil Plaza Bldg., Suite 813
Mailing address:
P.O. Box 1831
Hato Rey Sta., PR 00919
787-754-6178
Fax: 787-754-6181
Email: namerica@prtc.net

Puerto Rico Entrepreneurs Fund,
    L.P.
Abdon G. Ruiz, Contact
Union Plaza, Suite 1500
416 Ponce de Leon Avenue
San Juan, PR 00918
787-620-0062
Fax: 787-620-0131
Email: info@miraderocapital@.com

Rhode Island

Domestic Capital Corp.
Nathaniel B. Baker, President
815 Reservoir Avenue
Cranston, RI 02910
401-946-3310
Fax: 401-943-6708
www.Domestic.com

Fleet Equity Partners VI, L.P.
Brian T. Moynihan, Manager
50 Kennedy Plaza, 12th Floor
Mail Stop: RI MO F12C
Providence, RI 02903

401-278-6770
Fax: 401-278-6387

South Carolina

CF Investment Company
William S. Hummers III, Manager
102 South Main Street
Greenville, SC 29601
864-255-4919
Fax: 864-239-6423
Email:
    mary.gentry@thesouthgroup.com

Charleston Capital Corporation
Thomas Ervin, President and
    Secretary
56 Queen Street
P.O. Box 328
Charleston, SC 29402
843-723-6464
Fax: 843-723-1228
Email: yaschik@bellsouth.net

South Dakota

Bluestem Capital Partners II, L.P.
Steve Kirby and Paul Schock,
    Managers
122 South Phillips Ave., Suite 300
Sioux Falls, SD 57104
605-331-0091
Fax: 605-334-1218
www.bluestemcapital.com

Tennessee

Capital Across America, L.P.
Whitney Johns & Chris Brown,
    Managers
501 Union Street, Suite 201
Nashville, TN 37219
615-254-1414
Fax: 615-254-1856
www.capitalacrossamerica.org

Commerce Capital, L.P.
Andrew Higgins, Pres & Rudy
    Ruark, V.P.
5115 Maryland Way, Suite 304
Brentwood, TN 37027
615-244-1432
Fax: 615-242-1407
www.commercecap.com

Delta Venture Partners I, L.P.
Donald L. Mundie, Contact
c/o Delta Capital Management, LLC
8000 Centerview Parkway, Suite 100
Cordova, TN 38018
901-755-0949
Fax: 901-755-0436
www.deltacapital.com

International Paper Cap. Formation,
    Inc. (SSBIC)
Bob J. Higgins, V.P. and Controller
International Place II
6400 Poplar Avenue
Memphis, TN 38197
901-763-6282
Fax: 901-763-6076
Email: Bob.Higgins@ipaper.com

Massey Burch Venture Fund I, L.P.
Don Johnston, President
One Burton Hills Boulevard, Suite
350
Nashville, TN 37215
615-665-3221
Fax: 615-665-3240
www.masseyburch.com

Morgan Keegan Mezzanine Fund,
L.P.
William J. Nutter, Contact
30 Burton Hills Blvd., Suite 500
Nashville, TN 37215
615-665-3636
Fax: 615-665-3670
www.morgankeegan.com

Pacific Capital, L.P.
Jere M. Ervin
Two International Plaza Drive
Suite 200
Nashville, TN 37217
615-367-0770
Fax: 615-367-1771

Petra Mezzanine Fund, L.P.
Michael Blackburn, Joseph O'Brien
172 Second Avenue North, Suite 112
Nashville, TN 37201
615-313-5999
Fax: 615-313-5990
www.petracapital.com

Valley Capital Corp. (SSBIC)
Lamar J. Partridge, President
Suite 212, Krystal Building
100 W. Martin Luther King Blvd.
Chattanooga, TN 37402
423-265-1557
Fax: 423-265-1588
Email: ValleyCapital@aol.com

West Tennessee Venture Capital
Corporation (SSBIC)
Frank Banks, President
5 North Third Street
Memphis, TN 38103
901-522-9237
Fax: 901-527-6091
Email: fjbanks@aol.com

White Pines Limited Partnership I
William D. Orand
Two International Plaza Drive
Suite 200
Nashville, TN 37217
615-367-0770
Fax: 615-367-1771

Texas

Alliance Enterprise Corporation
Donald R. Lawhorne, President
2435 North Central Expressway
Suite 200
Richardson, TX 75080
972-991-1597
Fax: 972-991-4770
www.pacesettercapital.com

AMT Capital, Ltd.
Tom H. Delimitros, CGP
5220 Spring Valley Road, Suite 600
Dallas, TX 75254
214-905-9760
Fax: 214-905-9761
www.amtcapital.com

BA Capital Company, L.P.
Doug Williamson, Sr. Vice President
901 Main Street, 22nd Floor
Dallas, TX 75202
214-508-0900
Fax: 214-508-0985

Capital Southwest Venture Corp.
William R. Thomas, President
12900 Preston Road, Suite 700
Dallas, TX 75230
972-233-8242
Fax: 972-233-7362
www.capitalsouthwest.com

The Catalyst Fund, Ltd.
Richard L. Herrman, Manager
Two Riverway, Suite 1710
Houston, TX 77056
713-623-8133
Fax: 713-623-0473
www.thecatalystgroup.net

Chen's Financial Group, Inc.
(SSBIC)
Samuel S. C. Chen, President
8303 Southwest Freeway, Suite 750
Houston, TX 77074
713-772-8868
Fax: 713-772-2168
Email: chens8868@aol.com

First Capital Group of Texas II, L.P.
Messrs. Blanchard, Greenwood, &
Locy
750 East Mulberry, Suite 305
San Antonio, TX 78212
210-736-4233
Fax: 210-736-5449
www.firstcapitalgroup.com

First Capital Group of Texas II, L.P.
Wm. Ward Greenwood
1601 Rio Grande, Suite 345
Austin, TX 78701
512-494-9754
Fax: 512-494-9756
www.firstcapitalgroup.com

HCT Capital Corp.
Vichy Woodward Young, Jr.,
President
4916 Camp Bowie Blvd., Suite 200
Fort Worth, TX 76107
817-763-8706
Fax: 817-377-8049
Email: VWYoung@email.msn.com

Independent Bankers Capital Fund,
L.P.
Floyd Collins, Barry Conrad,
Contacts

1700 Pacific Avenue, Suite 2740
Dallas, TX 75201
214-765-1350
Fax: 214-765-1360
www.independentbankerscap.com

Jardine Capital Corp.
Lawrence Wong, President
6638 Sharpstown Green Circle
Houston, TX 77036
713-271-7077
Fax: 713-271-7577
www.jardinecapital.com

Main Street Mezzanine Fund, L.P.
Todd A. Reppert, Contact
1300 Post Oak Blvd., Suite 800
Houston, TX 77056
713-350-6029
Fax: 713-350-6042
www.mainstreethouston.com

MESBIC Ventures, Inc.
Donald R. Lawhorne, President
2435 North Central Expressway,
Suite 200
Richardson, TX 75080
972-991-1597
Fax: 972-991-4770
www.pacesettercapital.com

North Texas MESBIC, Inc. (SSBIC)
Allan Lee, President
9500 Forest Lane, Suite 430
Dallas, TX 75243
214-221-3565
Fax: 214-221-3566
Email: NTM168@aol.com

PMC Investment Corporation
(SSBIC)
Andrew S. Rosemore, President
18111 Preston Road, Suite 600
Dallas, TX 75252
972-349-3200
Fax: 972-349-3265
www.pmccapital.com

Power Equities, Inc.
Donald Lawhorne and Thomas
Gerron
2435 North Central Expressway
Suite 200
Richardson, TX 75080
972-991-1597
Fax: 972-991-4770
Email: info@mvhc.com

Red River Ventures I, L.P.
J. Bruce Duty, Contact
15301 Dallas Parkway, Suite 820
Addison, TX 75001
972-687-7770
Fax: 972-687-7760
www.redriverventures.com

Retail & Restaurant Growth Capital,
L.P.
Raymond Hemmig, Joseph Harberg,
Mgrs.

10000 N. Central Expressway
Suite 1060
Dallas, TX 75231
214-750-0065
Fax: 214-750-0060
www.rrgcsbic.com

SBIC Partners II, L.P.
Nicholas Binkley & Gregory Forrest,
   Mgrs
201 Main Street, 27th Floor
Fort Worth, TX 76102
949-222-1987
Fax: 949-222-1988
Email: joe@fbbvc.com

Southwest/Catalyst Capital, Ltd.
Ronald Nixon and Richard Herrman,
   Mgrs.
Two Riverway, Suite 1710
Houston, TX 77056
713-623-8133
Fax: 713-623-0473
www.thecatalystgroup.net

Stratford Capital Partners, L.P.
Michael D. Brown/John Farmer
300 Crescent Court, Suite 500
Dallas, TX 75201
214-740-7377
Fax: 214-740-7393
Email: shenegar@hmtf.com

Stratford Equity Partners, L.P.
Michael Brown, Manager
200 Crescent Court, Suite 1600
Dallas, TX 75201
214-740-7377
Fax: 214-740-7393
Email: shenegar@hmtf.com

Toronto Dominion Capital (U.S.A.),
   Inc.
Martha L. Gariepy,
   VP/Secretary/Treas.
909 Fannin, Suite 1700
Houston, TX 77010
713-653-8225
Fax: 713-652-2647

Trident Growth Fund, L.P.
Larry St. Martin, Contact
700 Gemini, Suite 100
Houston, TX 77058
281-488-8484
Fax: 281-488-5353
www.tridentgrowthfund.com

Victoria Capital Corp.
Steve Selinske, Acting President
c/o Norwest Bank Texas, N.A.
16416 San Pedro
San Antonio, TX 78232
210-856-8804
Fax: 210-856-8848

Western Financial Capital
   Corporation
Andrew S. Rosemore, President
18111 Preston Road, Suite 600

Dallas, TX 75252
972-349-3200
Fax: 972-349-3265
www.pmccapital.com

Utah
First Security Business Investment
   Corp.
Greg Vidrine, Manager
405 S. Main St
Salt Lake City, UT 84111
801-246-1047
Fax: 801-246-1545
Email: gvidrin@fscnet.com

Utah Ventures II L.P.
Alan Dishlip & James Dreyfous,
   Mgrs.
2755 E. Cottonwood Parkway
Suite 520
Salt Lake City, UT 84121
801-365-0262
Fax: 801-365-0233
www.uven.com

UTFC Financing Solutions, LLC
Steve Grizzell, Contact
699 East South Temple, Suite 220
Salt Lake City, UT 84102
801-741-4200
Fax: 801-741-4249
www.utfc.org

vSpring SBIC, L.P.
Greg Warnock, Contact
2795 E. Cottonwood Parkway
Suite 460
Salt Lake City, UT 84121
801-942-8999
Fax: 801-942-1636
www.vspring.com

Wasatch Venture Corporation
Todd J. Stevens, Secretary
1 South Main Street, Suite 1400
Salt Lake City, UT 84133
801-524-8939
Fax: 801-524-8941
www.wasatchvc.com

Virginia
BIA Digital Partners, L.P.
Lloyd R. Sams, Contact
15120 Enterprise Court, Suite 200
Chantilly, VA 20151
703-818-2425
Fax: 703-803-3299
www.bia.com

Continental SBIC
Arthur Walters, President
4141 N. Henderson Road, Suite 8
Arlington, VA 22203
703-527-5200
Fax: 703-527-3700
Email: alwetal@erols.com

Development Capital Ventures, L.P.
Wayne S. Foren, Contact
510 King Street, Suite 311

Alexandria, VA 22314
703-548-3226
Fax: 703-684-8217
www.dccgrowth.com

East West United Investment
   Company (SSBIC)
Dung Bui, President
1568 Spring Hill Road
Suite 100
McLean, VA 22102
703-442-0150
Fax: 703-442-0156
Email: tiffanyd@ewmortgage.com

eCentury Capital Partners, L.P.
Thomas Dann, Contact
8270 Greensboro Drive, Suite 1025
McLean, VA 22102
703-442-4480
Fax: 703-448-1816
www.ecenturycapital.com

GIV Venture Partners, L.P.
Jeff Tonkel, Contact
8150 Leesburg Pike, Suite 1210
Vienna, VA 22182
703-442-3300
Fax: 703-442-3388
www.givinc.com

Virginia Capital SBIC, L.P.
Frederick Russell & Tom Deardorff,
   Mgrs.
1801 Libbie Avenue, Suite 201
Richmond, VA 23226
804-648-4802
Fax: 804-648-4809
www.vacapital.com

Waterside Capital Corporation
Alan Lindauer, President
500 East Main Street, Suite 800
Norfolk, VA 23510
757-626-1111
Fax: 757-626-0114
www.watersidecapital.com

Vermont
Green Mountain Capital, L.P.
Michael Sweatman, General
   Manager
25 Cross Road, Suite 3
Waterbury, VT 05676
802-244-8981
Fax: 802-244-8990
www.gmtcap.com

North Atlantic Venture Fund II, L.P.
Gregory B. Peters, Vice President
76 St. Paul Street, Suite 600
Burlington, VT 05401
802-658-7820
Fax: 802-658-5757

Washington
Bancshares Capital, L.P.
John E. Thoresen, Contact
22020 17th Avenue S.E.
Suite 220

Bothell, WA 98021-8486
425-424-0058
Fax: 425-424-0809
Email: bancshares_lp@msn.com

Integra Ventures III, L.P.
Tim T. Black, Contact
300 E. Pine, 2nd Floor
Seattle, WA 98122
206-832-1990
Fax: 206-832-1991
www.IntegraVentures.net

Northwest Venture Partners II, L.P.
Thomas Simpson & Jean Balek-
   Miner, Mgrs.
221 North Wall Street, Suite 628
Spokane, WA 99201
509-747-0728
Fax: 509-747-0758
www.nwva.com

West Virginia
Mountaineer Capital, L.P.
Patrick A. Bond, Contact
107 Capitol Street
Suite 300

Charleston, WV 25301
304-347-7525
Fax: 304-347-0072
www.mtncap.com

WestVen Limited Partnership
Thomas E. Loehr, President
208 Capitol Street, Suite 300
Charleston, WV 25301
304-344-1794
Fax: 304-344-1998
www.fourthventure.com

Whitney Capital Corporation
Gale Gray, Manager
707 Virginia Street East, Suite 1700
Charleston, WV 25301
304-345-2480
Fax: 304-345-7258
Email: glg.ggm@wvdsl.net

Wisconsin
Banc One Stonehenge Capital Fund
   WI, LLC
Mr. Kent Velde, Manager
3424 N. Shepard Avenue
Milwaukee, WI 53211

414-906-1702
Fax: 414-906-1703
Email: kvelde@att.net

Capital Investments, Inc.
Steve Rippl, Exec. Vice-President
1009 W Glen Oaks Lane, Suite 103
Mequon, WI 53092
262-241-0303
Fax: 262-241-8451
www.capitalinvestmentsinc.com

Facilitator Capital Fund, L.P.
Robert Zobel, Gustavus Taylor
5133 West Terrace Drive, Suite 204
Madison, WI 53718
608-227-2900
Fax: 608-227-2901
www.facilitatorfunds.com

M & I Ventures, L.L.C.
John T. Byrnes, President
770 North Water Street
Milwaukee, WI 53202
414-765-7910
Fax: 414-765-7850
www.masonwells.com

Other Venture Capital Sources

Alabama

Southeastern Technology Fund
207 East Side Square
Huntsville, AL 35801
256-883-8711
Fax: 256-883-8558
www.setfund.com/

California

Foundation Capital
70 Willow Rd., Suite 200
Menlo Park, CA 94025
650-614-0500
Fax: 650-614-0505
www.foundationcap.com

Colorado

5280 Partners I, LP
360 S. Monroe St.
Ste 600
Denver, CO 80209
303-333-1215
Fax: 303-322-3553
Email: info@5280partners.com
www.5280partners.com

Access Venture Partners
8787 Turnpike Drive
Suite 260
Westminster, CO 80030
303-426-8899
Fax: 303-426-8828
Email: frank2@
    accessventurepartners.com
www.accessventurepartners.com

Altira Group
1625 Broadway
Denver, CO 80202
303-825-1600
Fax: 303-623-3525
Email: pedwards@altiragroup.com
www.altiragroup.com

Appian Venture Partners
1700 Lincoln St., Ste 2000
Denver, CO 80203
303-830-2450
Fax: 303-830-2449
www.appianvc.com

Aweida Venture Partners
890 W. Cherry St.
Ste 220
Louisville, CO 80027
303-664-9520
Fax: 303-664-9530
Email: jesse@aweida.com
www.aweida.com

Boulder Ventures
1941 Pearl St.
Ste 300
Boulder, CO 80302

303-444-6950
Fax: 303-449-9699
Email: sara@boulderventures.com
www.boulderventures.com

Cambridge Technology Capital
1209 Pearl St.
Ste #4
Boulder, CO 80302
303-442-9113
Email: walter.knapp@ctp.com
www.ctp.com

Catalyst Partners
730 N. Nevada
Ste 200
Colorado Springs, CO 80903
719-475-0325
Fax: 719-475-0911
Email: ctlystptnr@aol.com
www.catalystpartnersinc.com

Centennial Ventures
1428 Fifteenth St.
Denver, CO 80202
303-405-7500
Fax: 303-405-7575
Email: adamg@centennial.com
www.centennial.com

BV-Cornerstone Ventures
11001 W. 120th Ave.
Ste 310
Broomfield, CO 80021
303-410-2500
Fax: 303-466-9316
Email: info@bvcv.com
www.bvcv.com

CVM Equity Funds
2575 Park Lane
Ste 200
Lafayette, CO 80026
303-440-4055
Fax: 303-440-4636
Email: ewetherbee@cvmequity.com
www.cvmequity.com

Gefinor Ventures
90 S. Cascade Ave., Suite 1130
Colorado Springs, CO 80903
719-447-9700
Fax: 719-447-1940
Email: gcarlisle@
    gefinorventures.com
www.gefinorventures.com

Intel Corp.
666 Newport St.
Denver, CO 80224
206-953-1879
Fax: 206-505-8820
Email: Matt.Gordon@intel.com
www.intel.com

iSherpa Capital
9100 E. Panorama Dr.
Ste 350
Englewood, CO 80112
303-696-9119
Fax: 303-696-1047
Email: lbednarz@isherpa.net
www.isherpa.net

ITU Ventures
9250 Wilshire Blvd., Suite 100
Beverly Hills, CA 90212
310-777-5900
Fax: 310-777-5901
www.itu.com

Meritage Private Equity Funds
1600 Wynkoop St.
Ste 300
Denver, CO 80202
303-352-2040
Fax: 303-352-2050
www.meritagefunds.com

Mobius Venture Capital
100 Superior Plaza Way
Ste 200
Superior, CO 80027
303-642-4000
Fax: 303-642-4001
Email: chris@sbvc.com
www.sbvc.com

Murphee Venture Partners
2005 Tenth St.
Ste D
Boulder, CO 80302
303-413-1264
Fax: 303-413-1266
Email: ebouillion@
    murpheeventures.com
www.murpheeventures.com

Odin Capital Group
1625 Farnam St. Ste 700
Omaha, NE 68102
303-446-5900
Fax: 303-446-5935
Email: dwalsh@odincapital.com
www.odincapital.com

Pearl Street Group Ltd.
1701 Pearl St., Suite 200
Boulder, CO 80302
720-406-1100
Fax: 720-406-1101

Quest Capital Partnership
1700 Lincoln St., Ste 2000
Denver, CO 80203
303-764-9671
Fax: 303-832-6154
Email: sel@quest-intl.com
www.quest-intl.com

RockMountain Venture Funds
830 Bonita Avenue
Ft. Collins, CO 80526
970-377-3900
Fax: 509-562-7556
www.rockventures.com

Roser Ventures
1105 Spruce St.
Boulder, CO 80302
303-443-7935
Fax: 303-443-1885
Email: jroser@roserventures.com
www.roserventures.com

Sage Capital Group
1512 Larimer St. Ste 800
Denver, CO 80202
303-595-7200
Fax: 303-405-8367
www.sage-ventures.com

Sensor Technology Development.
  Fund
5505 Airport Blvd., Ste 101
Boulder, CO 80301
303-546-0452
Fax: 303-546-0478
Email: betty@sensortdf.com
www.sensortdf.com

Sequel Partners
4430 Arapahoe Ave.
Ste 220
Boulder, CO 80303
303-448-2117
Fax: 303-546-9728
Email: tim@sequelvc.com
www.sequel.com

Silvercreek Technology Investors
730 17th St., Ste 690
Denver, CO 80202
303-573-3720
Fax: 303-573-3740
Email:
  bstanfill@silvercreekfund.com
www.silvercreekfund.com

Sovereign Financial Services
1401 17th St.
Ste 1000
Denver, CO 80202
303-292-2294
Email: sovereign@pellrud.com

Stolberg Equity Partners
370 17th St.
Ste 3650
Denver, CO 20202
303-592-4900
Fax: 303-592-4912
www.stolbergep.com

Tango
831 Pearl St.
Denver, CO 80302
303-381-2615
www.tangogroup.com

Telecom Partners
4600 So. Syracuse
Ste 1000
Denver, CO 80237
303-874-1100
Fax: 303-874-1110
Email: info@telecompartners.com
www.telecompartners.com

Thoma Cressey Equity Partners
370 17th St.
Ste 4050
Denver, CO 80202
303-592-4808
Fax: 303-592-4845
Email: tcep@thomacressey.com
www.thomacressey.com

Touchstone Capital Group
1700 Lincoln St.
Ste 1800
Denver, CO 80203
303-764-9677
Fax: 303-832-6154
www.touchstonesoftware.com

Vista Ventures
11001 W. 120th Avenue
Suite 310
Broomfield, CO 80021
303-410-2528
Fax: 303-466-9316
Email: info@vistavc.com
Business Plans:
  www.businessplan@vistavc.com
www.vistavc.com

Wolf Ventures
1600 Stout St.
Suite 1510
Denver, CO 80202
303-321-4800
Fax: 303-321-4848
Email: jconboy@wolfventures.com
www.wolfventures.com

Delaware
Delaware Innovation Fund
Three Mill Rd., Suite 201
Wilmington, DE 19806
302-777-1616
Fax: 302-777-1620
www.delawareinnovationfund.com

Florida
Advantage Capital Partners
100 N. Tampa St., Suite 2410
Tampa, FL 33602
813-221-8700
www.advantagecap.com/

Antaras Capital Corp.
7900 Miami Lakes Dr. West
Miami Lakes, FL 33016
305-894-2888
www.antarescapital.com/

Ballast Point Ventures
880 Carillon Parkway
St. Petersburg, FL 33716

727-567-1500
www.ballastpointventures.com/

Banyan Mezzanine
150 SE Second Ave., Suite 712
Miami, FL 33131
305-205-4681
www.banyanmezzanine.com

C/MAX Capital
515 East Las Olas Blvd.
Suite 1020
Ft. Lauderdale, FL 33301
954-765-3480
www.cmaxcapital.com/

Chartwell Capital Investors, LP
1 Independence Dr., Suite 3120
Jacksonville, FL 32202
904-355-3519

Crossbow Ventures
One North Clematis St., Suite 510
West Palm Beach, FL 33401
561-838-9005
www.cb-ventures.com/

Easton Hunt Capital Partners
240 Crandon Blvd Ste 220
Key Biscayne, FL 33149
305-361-6479
www.eastoncapital.com/

Grace Venture Partners
SunTrust Center, Suite 1850
200 South Orange Avenue
Orlando, FL 32801
407-835-7900
www.graceventure.com

H.I.G. Capital
1001 Brickell Bay Dr., 27th Floor
Miami, FL 33131
305-379-2322
http://site48774.dellhost.com/index.h
  tml

Inflexion Partners
12565 Research Parkway
Orlando, FL 32826
407-381-2675
www.inflexionvc.com/

LM Capital Securities
1200 N. Federal Hwy., Suite 312
Boca Raton, FL 33432
561-351-4114
www.lmcapitalsecurities.com/

Lovett Miller & Co.
100 N. Tampa St., Ste. 2675
Tampa, FL 33602
813-222-1477
www.lovettmiller.com/

New River Capital Partners
1 Financial Plaza, Suite 1100
Ft. Lauderdale, FL 33394
954-713-1160
www.newrivercapital.com/

New South Ventures
5053 Ocean Blvd.
Sarasota, FL 34242
941-358-6000
www.newsouthventures.com/

Quantum Capital Partners
339 South Plant Avenue
Tampa, FL 33606
813-250-1999 x227
www.quantumcapitalpartners.com/

Ridgewood Capital
531 Versailles Drive, Suite 201
Maitland, FL 32751
407-539-2232

River Capital Partners
500 West Cypress Creek Road
Suite 210
Fort Lauderdale, FL 33309
954-776-1115
www.rivercapitalpartners.com/

Riverside Ventures
1925 North Flagler Dr.
West Palm Beach, FL 33401
561-820-9447

Rock Creek Capital Group
1200 Riverplace Blvd., Suite 902
Jacksonville, FL 32207
904-393-9020
www.rockcreekcapital.com/

SI Ventures
12600 Gateway Blvd.
Ft. Myers, FL 33913
941-561-4760
www.siventures.com/

Trivest Inc.
2665 South Bayshore Drive
Suite 800
Miami, FL 33133-5462
305-858-2200
www.trivest.com/

Georgia

Atlanta Technology Angels
430 10th Street, Suite 202-A
Atlanta, GA 30318
404-894-9059
www.angelatlanta.com

Alliance Technology Ventures
8995 Westside Parkway, Suite 200
Alpharetta, GA 30004
678-336-2000
Fax: 678-336-2001
www.atv.com

Cordova Intellimedia Ventures
Three Northwinds Center
2500 Northwinds Parkway
Suite 475
Alpharetta, GA 30004
678-942-0300
Fax: 678-942-0301
www.cordovaventures.com

Encubate Holdings LLC
Prominence in Buckhead
3475 Piedmont Road, Suite 1830
Atlanta, GA 30305
404-442-1300
Fax: 404-442-1301
www.encubateholdings.com/

LiveOak Equity Partners
2500 NorthWinds Parkway
Suite 325
Alpharetta, GA 30004
678-393-9909
Fax: 678-393-9948
www.liveoakequity.com

Mellon Ventures, Inc.
One Buckhead Plaza
3060 Peachtrree Road, Suite 780
Atlanta, GA 30305-2240
404-264-9180
Fax: 404-264-9305
www.mellonventures.com

Monarch Partners
1447 Peachtree Street, Suite 510
Atlanta, GA 30309
404-832-4301
Fax: 404-262-9332
www.monarchpartners.com

Noro-Moseley Partners
9 North Parkway Square
4200 Northside Parkway, NW
Atlanta, GA 30327-3054
404-233-1966
Fax: 404-239-9280
www.noro-moseley.com

UPS Strategic Enterprise Fund
55 Glenlake Parkway, NE
Building 1, 4th Floor
Atlanta, GA 30328
404-828-8814
Fax: 404-828-8088
www.ups.com/sef/sef.html

Hawaii

Davis Bioscience Group
P.O. Box 72356
Davis, CA 95616
530-756-5153
Fax: 530-504-6805
www.davisbioscience.com

Hawaii Energy Alternatives Team
P.O. Box 4664
Honolulu, HI 96812
808-545-1773
www.hawaiiventures.com

Hawaii Strategic Development
  Corporation
No. 1 Capitol District Building
250 South Hotel Street, Suite 503
P.O. Box 2359
Honolulu, HI 96804
808-587-3829
Fax: 808-587-3832
www.htdc.org/hsdc

Hawaii Venture Capital Association
805 Kainui Drive
Kailua, HI 96734
808-262-7329
Fax: 808-262-7329
www.hvca.org

Idaho

Akers Capital, LLC
Eagles Center
223 N 6th Street, Suite 310
Boise, ID 83702
208-345-3456
Fax: 208-345-3427
www.akerscapital.com/index.html

Highway 12 Ventures
802 W. Bannock
11th Floor
Boise, ID 83702
208-345-8383
Fax: 208-345-8484
www.highway12ventures.com

Illinois

ABN AMRO Private Equity
208 South LaSalle Street, 10th Floor
Chicago.IL 60604
312-855-7292
Fax: 312-553-6648
www.abnequity.com

Adams Street Partners
One North Wacker Drive, Suite 2200
Chicago, IL 60606-2807
312-533-7890
Fax: 312-533-7891
www.adamsstreetpartners.com

Allied Capital
401 North Michigan Ave.
Suite 2050
Chicago, IL 60611
312-828-0330
Fax: 312-828-0909
www.alliedcapital.com

Apex Venture Partners
225 West Washington Street
Suite 1500
Chicago, IL 60606
312-857-2800
Fax: 312-857-1800
www.apexvc.com

ARCH Development Partners,
  L.L.C.
350 West Hubbard, Suite 400
Chicago, IL 60610
312-828-9970
www.archdevelopmentpartners.com

ARCH Venture Partners
8725 W. Higgins Road
Suite 290
Chicago, IL 60631
773-380-6600
Fax: 773-380-6606
www.archventure.com

Ark Capital Management
150 North Wacker Drive, Suite 2650
Chicago, IL 60606
312-541-0330
www.arkvc.com

Baird Capital Partners
227 W. Monroe Street, Suite 2100
Chicago, IL 60606
312-609-4700
www.rwbaird.com

Batterson Venture Partners
303 W. Madison Avenue, Suite 1110
Chicago, IL 60601
312-269-0300
www.battersonvp.com

Beecken Petty O'Keefe & Company
Healthcare Equity Partners, L.P.
200 West Madison Street, Suite 1910
Chicago, IL 60606
312-435-0300
Fax: 312-435-0371
www.beeckenpetty.com

BlueStar Ventures LP
208 South LaSalle Street, Suite 1020
Chicago, IL 60604
312-384-5000
Fax: 312-384-5005
www.bluestarventures.com

CID
One North LaSalle Street, Suite 1100
Chicago, IL 60602
312-578-5350
Fax: 312-578-5358
www.cidequity.com

Code Hennessy & Simmons LLC
10 South Wacker Drive, Suite 3175
Chicago, IL 60606
312-876-1840
Fax: 312-876-3854
www.chsonline.com

Devers Group, Inc.
1200 Central Avenue, Suite 306
Wilmette, IL 30091
847-920-1678
www.deversgroup.com

DN Partners
77 West Wacker Drive, Suite 4550
Chicago, IL 60601
312-332-7960
Fax: 312-332-7979
www.dnpartners.com

Duchossois TECnology Partners
845 Larch Avenue
Elmhurst, IL 60126-1196
630-530-6105
Fax: 630-993-8644
www.duchtech.com

The Edgewater Funds
900 N Michigan Avenue, 14th Floor
Chicago, IL 60611

312-649-5666
Fax: 312-664-8649
www.edgewaterfunds.com

Essex Woodlands Health Ventures
1900 South LaSalle St., Suite 2800
Chicago, IL 60603
312-444-6040
Fax: 312-444-6034
www.essexwoodlands.com

First Analysis
Sears Tower
233 South Wacker Drive, Suite 9500
Chicago, IL
312-258-1400
www.firstanalysis.com

Frontenac Company
135 South LaSalle Street, Suite 3800
Chicago, IL 60603
312-368-0044
Fax: 312-368-9520
www.frontenac.com

Gaebler Ventures
641 West Lake Street, Suite 100
Chicago, IL 60661
312-207-1190, ext 102
Fax: 312-207-1192
www.gaebler.com

GTCR Golder Rauner, LLC
6100 Sears Tower
Chicago, IL 60606
312-382-2200
Fax: 312-382-2201
www.gtcr.com

IEG Venture Capital
70 West Madison, 14th Floor
Chicago, IL 60602
312-644-0890
Fax: 312-454-0369
www.iegventure.com

IFC Credit Corporation
8700 Waukegan Road, Suite 100
Morton Grove, IL 60053
888-544-4432
847-633-6700
Fax: 847-663-6702
www.ifccredit.com

Inroads Capital Partners
1603 Orrington Avenue, Suite 2050
Evanston, IL 60201
847-864-2000
Fax: 847-864-9692
www.inroadsvc.com

JK&B Capital
Two Prudential Plaza
180 North Stetson Avenue
Suite 4500
Chicago, IL 60601
312-946-1200
Fax: 312-946-1103
www.jkbcapital.com

KB Partners, LLC
1101 Skokie Boulevard, Suite 260
Northbrook, IL 60062
847-714-0444
Fax: 847-714-0445
www.kbpartners.com

Kettle Partners
350 West Hubbard, Suite 350
Chicago, IL 60610
312-329-9300
www.kettlevc.com

Leo Capital Holdings, LLC
1101 Skokie Boulevard, Suite 255
Northbrook, IL 60062
847-418-3420
Fax: 847-418-3424
www.leocapholdings.com

Marquette Venture Partners
520 Lake Cook Road, Suite 690
Deerfield, IL 60015
847-940-1700
Fax: 847-940-1724
www.marquetteventures.com

MK Capital
233 S. Wacker Drive
The Sears Tower, Suite 9700
Chicago, IL 60606
312-648-1674
www.mkcapital.com

New World Ventures
1603 Orrington Avenue, Suite 1070
Evanston, IL 60201
847-328-0300
Fax: 847-328-8297
www.newworldvc.com

Next Chapter Holdings, L.P.
Port Clinton Square
600 Central Avenue, Suite 205-210
Highland Park, IL 60035
847-432-8700
Fax: 847-432-8709
www.nextchapterholdings.com

North American Funds
135 S. LaSalle Street, Suite 4000
Chicago, IL 60603
312-332-4950
Fax: 312-332-1540
www.northamericanfund.com

Northern Illinois Angels LLC
40 Shuman Boulevard, Suite 220
Naperville, IL 60563
847-909-8817
Fax: 312-577-0507
www.northernillinoisangels.com

OCA Venture Partners, LLC
Chicago Board of Trade Building
141 W. Jackson, 39th Floor
Chicago. IL 60604
312-542-8954
Fax: 312-542-8952
www.ocaventures.com

Origin Ventures LLC
474 N. Lake Shore Drive, Suite 5804
Chicago, IL 60611
312-644-6449
Fax: 312-644-0534
www.originventures.com

Paradigm Group II, LLC
3000 West Dundee Road, Suite 105
Northbrook, IL 60062
800-296-6014
847-562-0700
www.paradigmventure.com

Polestar Venture Capital
180 North Michigan Avenue
Suite 1905
Chicago, IL 60601
312-984-9090
Fax: 312-984-9877
www.polestarvc.com

Portage Venture Partners
One Northfield Plaza, Suite 530
Northfield, IL 60093
847-446-9460
Fax: 847-446-9470
www.portageventures.com

Prairie Angels, LLC
600 West Jackson, Suite 400
Chicago, IL 60661
773-837-8250
www.prairieangels.com

Prospect Partners, LP
200 West Madison Street, Suite 2710
Chicago, IL 60606
312-782-7400
Fax: 312-782-7410
www.prospect-partners.com

Ravenswood Capital
343 W. Erie, Suite 410
Chicago, IL 60610
312-327-2530
www.ravenswoodcapital.com

SB Partners
542 South Dearborn St., Suite 1220
Chicago, IL 60605
312-986-8620
Fax: 312-986-8630
www.sbpartners.com

Sterling Partners
1033 Skokie Boulevard
Suite 600
Northbrook, IL 60062
847-480-4000
Fax: 847-480-0199
www.sterlingcap.com

Svoboda, Collins LLC
One North Franklin St., Suite 1500
Chicago, IL 60606
312-267-8750
Fax: 312-267-6025
www.svoco.com

Technology Crossover Ventures
100 Field Drive, Suite 160
Lake Forest, IL 60045
847-810-4200
Fax: 847-810-4205
www.tcv.com

Thoma Cressey
Sears Tower, 92nd Floor
233 South Wacker Drive
Chicago, IL 60606
312-777-4444
Fax: 312-777-4445
www.thomacressey.com

Trident Capital
272 East Deerpath, Suite 304
Lake Forest, IL 60045
847-283-9890
Fax: 847-283-9901
www.tridentcapital.com

William Blair Capital Partners
227 West Monroe, Suite 3500
Chicago, IL 60606
312-364-8250
Fax 312-236-5728
www.wbcapitalpartners.com

Willis, Stien & Partners
One North Wacker Drive, Suite 4800
Chicago, IL 60606
312-422-2400
Fax: 312-422-2424
www.willisstein.com

Indiana

CID Equity Partners
One American Square, Suite 2850
Indianapolis, IN 46282
317-269-2350
Fax: 317-269-2355
www.cidequity.com

COMMAND Equity Group, LLC
1213 S. High Street
Bloomington, IN 47401
812-339-3690
Fax: 812-339-3794
www.commandequity.com

Gazelle TechVentuers
6325 Digital Way, Suite 460
Indianapolis, IN 46278
317-275-6800
Fax: 317-275-1100
www.gazellevc.com

inception, LLC
7820 Innovation Boulevard
Indianapolis, IN 46278-2721
317-610-2301
www.inceptionllc.com

Rose-Hulman Ventures
100 South Campus Drive
P.O. Box 3799
Terre Haute, IN 47803-0799
812-244-4000
www.rhventures.org

Spring Mill Venture Partners, LLC
Emerging Technology Center
Suite 130
351 W 10th Street
Indianapolis, IN 46202
317-278-9996
www.springmillvp.com

Iowa

AG Ventures Alliance
2023 South Federal
Mason City, IA 50401
641-494-2368
866-260-5775 toll free
Fax: 641-423-2642
www.agadventuresalliance.com

Ames Sccd Capital Fund
1601 Golden Aspen Drive, Suite 10
Ames, IA 50010
515-232-2310
Fax: 515-232-6716
Email: dmaahs@ameschamber.com

Cedar Valley Venture Fund
John Pappajohn Entrepreneurial
   Center
Curris Business Building, Suite 5
University of Northern Iowa
Cedar Falls, IA 50614-0130
319-273-7350
Fax: 319-273-7512
www.jpec.org

Emerging Growth Group
300 SW 5th Street, Suite 2
Des Moines, IA 50309
515-883-3222
Fax: 515-883-2983
www.egrowthgroup.com

Equity Dynamics Inc.
2116 Financial Center, 21st Floor
Des Moines, IA 50309
515-244-2346
Email: kinley@pappajohn.com

Greater Quad City Angel Investor
   Network
2820 East 42nd Court
Davenport, IA 52807
563-355-7613
Fax: 563-355-2530
Email: mark@markandrita.com

Great River Capital, LLC
131 West Second Street, Suite 305
Davenport, IA 52801
563-324-4409 ext 10
www.greatrivercapital.com

Iowa Capital Corporation
2600 Grand Avenuc, Suite 210
Des Moines, IA 50312
515-288-9110
Fax: 515-244-7112
www.cma-inc.net

Iowa First Capital Corporation
c/o Corridor Management Co., LLC

222 Third Avenue SE, Suite 12
P.O. Box 607
Cedar Falls, IA 52406
319-364-4411
Fax: 319-364-4422
Email: achristoffersen@cmanco.com

North Iowa Venture Capital Fund
  LLC
500 College Drive
Mason City, IA 50401
641-422-4111
Fax: 641-422-4129
www.niacc.edu

Silicon Valley Investors, LLC
P.O. Box 1176
Fairfield, IA 52556
641-919-2163

Software and Information
  Technology of Iowa (SITI)
1500 NW 118th Street
Clive, IA 50325
515-327-5579
Fax: 515-327-5577
www.sitiworks.com

Venture Network of Iowa (VNI)
200 East Grand Avenue
Des Moines, IA 50309
515-242-4715
Email: entrepreneurialassistance@
  ided.state.ia.us

Kansas
Kaw Holdings
1617 St. Andrews Drive, Suite 210
Lawrence, KS 66047
785-832-2100
Fax: 785-832-8234
www.lrtc.biz

Manhattan Holdings
1500 Hayes Drive
Manhattan, KS 66502
785-532-3900
Fax: 785-532-3909
www.ksu.edu/tech.transfer/macc/ma
  cc.htm

Milestone Ventures, LLC
Pittsburg, KS 66762
620-235-4927
Fax: 620-235-4030
www.atckansas.com

Prairie Investments for Technology
  Advancement LLC
8527 Bluejacket
Lenexa, KS 66214
913-888-9100
Fax: 913-888-6928
www.ecjc.com

Precede Fund
Kansas University Medical Center-
  Research Institute
3901 Rainbow Boulevard
Kansas City, KS 66160-7702

913-588-1495
Fax: 913-588-5242
www2.kumc.edu/researchinstitute

Quest Ventures
Quest Center
One East Ninth
Hutchinson, KS 67501
620-665-8468
Fax: 620-665-7619
www.hutchquest.com

Wichita Technology Ventures
7829 Rockhill Road, Suite 307
Wichita, KS 67206
316-651-5900
Fax: 316-684-5640
www.wichitatechnology.com

Kentucky
bCatalyst
124 North First Street
Louisville, KY 40202
502-583-0400
Fax: 502-583-5606
www.bcatalyst.com

District Development Fund
917 Perry Park Road
Hazard, KY 41701
606-436-3158
Fax: 606-436-2144

Equal Opportunity Finances, Inc.
420 S. Hurstbourne Parkway
Suite 201
Louisville, KY 40222-8002
502-423-1943
Fax: 502-423-1945

Human Economic Appalachian
  Development Corporation
106 Pasco Street
P.O. Box 504
Berea, KY 40403
606-986-3283
Fax: 606-986-5836

Innovation Group
200 West Vine Street
Suite 420
Lexington, KY 4050
859-233-3502
http://tig.kstc.com

Kentucky Highlands Investment
  Corporation
362 Whitley Road
P.O. Box 1738
London, KY 40743
606-864-5175
www.khic.org

Louisville Community Development
  Bank
2901 West Broadway
Louisville, KY 40211
502-778-7000
www.morethanabank.com

Minerva Ventures
9001 Shelbyville Road
Louisville, KY 40222
502-387-8551
Fax: 52-852-4701
www.minervaventures.louisville.edu

Mountain Association for
  Community Economic
  Development
433 Chestnut Street
Berea, KY 40403
859-986-2373
Fax: 859-986-1299
www.maced.org

Pine Mountain Community
  Development Corporation
Southeast Community College
113 Chrisman Hall
Cumberland, KY 40823
606-589-2145
Fax: 606-589-5423
www.uky.edu/CommunityColleges/S
  ou/pmcdc

Urban County Office of Economic
  Development
200 E. Main Street
Lexington, KY 40507
606-258-3131
www.lfucg.com

Louisiana
Advantage Capital
909 Poydras Street, Suite 2230
New Orleans, LA 70112
504-522-4850
Fax: 504-522-4950
www.advantagecap.com

BizCapital BIDCO
2201 Veterans Memorial Boulevard
Suite 3026
Metairie, LA 70002
504-832-1993
888-870-1562
Fax: 504-832-0589
www.biz-capital.com

Business Resource Capital Specialty
  BIDCO
330 Camp Street
New Orleans, LA 70130
504-524-6172

Chrysalis of Louisiana, LLC
201 St. Charles Avenue, Suite 4400
New Orleans, LA 70170
504-529-3600

ECD Investments BIDCO
PO Box 4754
Monroe, LA 71211-4754
601-944-1100

Enhanced Louisiana
201 St. Charles Avenue
Suite 3700
New Orleans, LA 70170

Copyright © 2004 Matthew Lesko, Information USA, Inc., 12081 Nebel Street, Rockville, MD 20852 • 1-800-955-7693 • www.lesko.com

504-569-7900
www.enhancedcapital.net

FFC Capital Management
601 Poydras Street, Suite 2610
New Orleans, LA 70130
504-566-3958

Gulf Coast Business & Industrial
   Development Corporation
8752 Quarters Lake Road
Baton Rouge, LA 70809
225-922-7717

InterTech Venture Fund
1505 Kings Highway
Shreveport, LA 71103
318-675-4105
www.biomed.org

Lafayette Neighborhood Economic
   Development Corporation
220 East St. Mary Boulevard
Lafayette, LA 70503
337-262-1080

Louisiana Community Development
   Capital Fund
350 Third Street, Suite 100 C&D
Baton Rouge, LA 70801
225-343-1075

North Louisiana BIDCO
130 DeSaird Street, Suite 411
Monroe, LA 71201
318-807-0522

Red River Valley BIDCO
5210 Hollywood Avenue
Shreveport, LA 71109
318-632-2022

SBL Capital Corporation
39433 Highway 929
Prairieville, LA 70769
225-622-0376

Sisung Capital, LLC
Sun Capital, LLC
World Trade Center
Two Canal Street, Suite 2440
New Orleans, LA 70130
504-544-7700
www.sisung.com

Source Capital Corporation
301 Main Street
P.O. Box 3435
Baton Rouge, LA 70821
225-612-2583
www.sourcecap.com

Stonehenge Capital Fund Louisiana,
   LLC
450 Laurel Street, Suite 1450
Baton Rouge, Louisiana 70801
225-408-3000
Fax: 225-408-3090
www.stonehengecapital.com

Wilshire Louisiana Advisers, LLC
650 Poydras Street
New Orleans, LA 70130
504-598-6725
www.newtekcapital.com

Maine

The Borealis Fund, L.P.
10 Allen Street
Hanover, NH 03755
603-643-1500
Fax: 603-643-7600
www.borealisventures.com

Brook Venture Fund II
301 Edgewater Place, 4thFloor
Wakefield, MA 01880
781-295-4000
Fax: 781-295-4007
www.brookventure.com

CEI Community Ventures, LLC
36 Water Street
Wiscasset, ME 04578
207-882-7552
Fax: 207-882-7308
www.ceiventures.com

Coastal Ventures II, LLC
Two Portland Fish Pier, Suite 201
Portland, ME 04101
207-772-5356
Fax: 207-772-5503
www.ceiventures.com

Masthead Venture Partners
3 Canal Plaza, Suite 600
Portland, ME 04101-4080
207-780-0905
Fax: 207-780-0913
www.mvpartners.com

Maryland

ABS Capital Partners
400 East Pratt Street, Suite 910
Baltimore, MD 21202-3116
410-246-5600
Fax: 410-246-5606
www.abscapital.com

Abell Venture Fund
111 South Calvert Street, Suite 2300
Baltimore, MD 21202-6174
410-547-1300
Fax: 410-539-6579
www.abell.org

American Capital
2 Bethesda Metro Center, 14th Floor
Bethesda, MD 20814
301-951-6122
Fax: 301-654-6714
www.americancapital.com

Benchmark Holdings, Inc.
111 South Calvert Street, Suite 2850
Baltimore, MD 21202
410-244-0600
Fax: 410-244-7170
www.benchmarkholdings.com

Boulder Ventures, L.P.
4750 Owings Mills Boulevard
Owings Mills, MD 21117
410-998-3114
Fax: 410-356-5492
www.boulderventuers.com

Calvert Social Ventures Partners,
   L.P.
4550 Montgomery Avenue
Bethesda, MD 20814
800-368-2748
301-961-4786
www.calvert.com/sri.html

China Capital Corporation
6106 Bradley Boulevard
Bethesda, MD 20817
240-432-3270
Fax: 301-365-4580
http://users.erols.com/chinacap

Chesapeake Emerging Opportunities
8808 Centre Park Drive, Suite 204
Columbia, MD 21045
443-367-0101
www.ceopportunities.com

Grotech Capital Group
9690 Deereco Road, Suite 800
Timonium, MD 21093
410-560-2000
Fax: 410-560-1910
www.grotech.com

Inflection Point Ventures
7903 Sleaford Place
Bethesda, MD 20814
301-656-6837
Fax: 301-656-8056
www.inflectpoint.com

Ivy Hill Partners
7 Shipwright Harbor
Annapolis, MD 21401
410-626-1560
Fax: 410-626-1807
www.ivyhill.com

Kinetic Ventures
2 Wisconsin Circle, Suite 620
Chevy Chase, MD 20815
301-652-8066
Fax: 301-652-8310
www.kineticventures.com

New Enterprise Associates
1119 Saint Paul Street
Baltimore, MD 21202
410-244-0115
Fax: 410-752-7721
www.nea.com

Women's Growth Capital Fund
1025 Thomas Jefferson Street, N.W.
Suite 305
Washington, DC 20007
202-342-1431
Fax: 202-342-1203
www.wgcf.com

Woodbrook Capital, Inc.
515 Fairmont Avenue, Suite 900
Towson, MD 21204
410-494-7600

Massachusetts
Advanced Technology Ventures
Bay Colony Corporate Center
1000 Winter Street, Suite 3700
Waltham, MA 02451 .
781-290-0707
Fax: 781-684-0045
www.atvcapital.com

Ampersand Ventures
55 William Street, Suite 240
Wellesley, MA 02481
781-239-0700
Fax: 781-239-0824
www.ampersandventures.com

Atlas Venture Boston
890 Winter Street, Suite 320
Waltham, MA 02451
781-622-1700
Fax: 781-622-1701
www.atlasventure.com

Audax Venture Capital
101 Huntington Avenue
Boston, MA 02199
617-859-1500
Fax: 617-859-1600
www.audaxgroup.com

Battery ventures
20 William Street, Suite 200
Wellesley, MA 02481
781-577-1000
Fax: 781-577-1001
www.battery.com

Bessemer Venture Partners
83 Walnut Street
Wellesley Hills, MA 02481
781-237-6050
Fax: 781-237-7576
www.bessemervp.com

Boston Capital Ventures
114 State Street, 6th Floor
Boston, MA 02109
617-227-6550
Fax: 617-227-3847
www.bcv.com

Cambridge Light Partners
3 Bow Street, 4th Floor
Cambridge, MA 02138-5103
www.cambridgelight.com

Capital Resource Capital
85 Merrimac Street, Suite 200
Boston, MA 02114
617-723-9000
Fax: 617-723-9819
www.crp.com

Charles River Ventures
1000 Winter Street

Waltham, MA 02451
781-768-6000
Fax: 781-768-6100
www.crv.com

Commonwealth Capital Ventures
20 William Street, Suite 225
Wellesley, MA 02481
781-237-7373
Fax: 781-235-8627
www.ccvlp.com

Boston University Community
  Technology Fund
108 Bay State Road
Boston, MA 02215
617-353-4550
Fax: 617-353-6141
www.bu.edu/ctf

Egan-Managed Capital
30 Federal Street
Boston, MA 02110
317-695-2600
Fax: 617-695-2699
www.egancapital.com

Great Hill Partners, LLC
One Liberty Square
Boston, MA 02109
617-790-9400
Fax: 617-790-0401
www.greathillpartners.com

Greylock
880 Winter Street
Waltham, MA 02451
781-622-2200
Fax: 781-622-2300
www.greylock.com

Highland Capital Partners
92 Hayden Avenue
Lexington, MA 02421
871-861-5500
Fax: 781-861-5499
www.hcp.com

High Tech Ventures
18 Hurley Street
Cambridge, MA 02141
617-520-2111
Fax: 617-520-2168
www.htventures.com

HML Venture Partners
222 Berkeley Street
21st Floor
Boston, MA 02116
617-266-0030
Fax: 617-266-3619
www.hlm.net

Inflection Point
30 Washington Street
Wellesley, MA 02481
781-416-5107
Fax: 781-237-6699
www.inflectpoint.com

Ironside Ventures
Bay Colony Corporate Center
950 Winter Street, Suite 1400
Waltham, MA 02451
718-622-5800
Fax: 781-622-5801
www.ironsideventures.com

JMC Venture Partners
2 Oliver Street, 2nd Floor
Boston, MA 02109
617-338-1144
Fax: 617-338-5353
www.jmcventurepartners.com

Kestrel Management
One Boston Place, Suite 1650
Boston, MA 02108
617-451-6722
Fax: 617-451-3322
www.kestrlvm.com

Kodiak Venture Partners
Bay Colony Corporate Center
1000 Winter Street, Suite 3800
Waltham, MA 02451
781-672-2500
Fax: 781-672-2501
www.kodiakvp.com

Levy Trajman Management
  Investment Inc.
67 South Bedford Street, 400 W
Burlington, MA 01803
781-229-5818
Fax: 781-229-1808
www.ltmi.com

Massachusetts Technology
  Development Corporation
40 Broad Street, Suite 818
Boston, MA 02109
617-723-4920
Fax: 617-723-5983
www.mtdc.com

Matrix Partners
1000 Winters Street, Suite 4500
Waltham, MA 02451
781-890-2244
Fax: 781-890-2288
www.matrixpartners.com

Monroe Financial Inc.
945 Concord Street
Framingham, MA 01701
877-847-3300
www.monroecorp.com

Navigator Technology Ventures
Four Cambridge Center, 2nd Floor
Cambridge, MA 02142
617-494-0111
Fax: 617-225-2080
www.ntven.vom

North Bridge Venture Partners
950 Winter Street, Suite 4600
Waltham, MA 02451
781-290-0004

Fax: 781-290-0999
www.nbvp.com

Oxford Bioscience Partners
222 Berkeley Street, Suite 1650
Boston, MA 02116
617-357-7474
Fax: 617-357-7476
www.oxbio.com

Polaris Venture Partners
1000 Winter Street, Suite 3350
Waltham, MA 02451
781-290-0770
Fax: 781-290-0880
www.polarisventures.com

Prism Venture Partners
100 Lowder Brook Drive, Suite 2500
Westwood, MA 02090
781-302-4000
Fax: 781-302-4040
www.prismventure.com

Shawmut Capital Partners
75 Federal Street, 18th floor
Boston, MA 02110
617-368-4900
Fax: 617-368-4910
www.shawmutcapital.com

Spray Venture Partners
2330 Washington Street
Newton, MA 02462
617-332-6060
Fax: 617-332-6070
www.spraypartners.com

Still River Fund
10 Liberty Square, Suite 300
Boston, MA 02109
617-426-3325
Fax: 617-426-6226
www.stillriverfund.com

Strategic Capital
Back Bay Annex
P.O. Box 1010
Boston, MA 02116
617-338-5515
Fax: 617-338-5557
www.strategic-capital.com

Venrock Associates
One Canal Park, Suite 1120
Cambridge, MA 02142
617-679-0300
Fax: 617-679-0301
www.venrock.com

VIMAC Ventures LLC
177 Milk Street
Boston, MA 02109-3410
617-350-9800
Fax: 617-350-9899
www.vimac.com

YAS Broadband Ventures LLC
300 Brickstone Square, Fifth Floor
Andover, MA 01810

978-749-9999
Fax: 978-749-8888
www.yas.com

Michigan

Arbor Partners, LLC
130 South First Street
Ann Arbor, MI 48104
734-668-9000
Fax: 734-669-4195
www.arborpartners.com

Arboretum Ventures
944 N. Main Street
Ann arbor, MI 48104
734-998-3688
Fax: 734-998-3689
www.arboretumvc.com

Beringea Private Equity
32330 W 12 Mile Road
Farmington Hills, MI 48334
248-489-9000
Fax: 248-489-8819
www.gmacapital.com

Blue Water Capital
260 E Brown Street, Suite 310
Birmingham, MI 48009
248-647-2010
Fax: 248-647-1130
www.bluewatercapital.com

Camelot Ventures
20555 Victor Parkway, Suite 100
Livonia, MI 48152
734-805-5133
www.capitalventures.com

Detroit Investment Fund
600 Renaissance Center
Suite 1710
Detroit, MI 48243-1801
313-259-6268
Fax: 313-259-6393
www.detinvfund.com

Great Lakes Angels, Inc
568 Woodway Court, Suite 1
Bloomfield Hills, MI 48302-1572
248-540-3758
www.glangels.org

Huron Capital Partners LLC
One Woodward Avenue, 26th Floor
Detroit, MI 48226
313-496-1050
Fax: 313-496-1060
www.huroncaptial.com

Ralph Wilson Equity Fund, LLC
15400 E. Jefferson Avenue
Grosse Pointe Park, MI 48230-1329
313-821-9122
Fax: 313-821-9101
www.rwequity.com

Sloan Ventures LLC
430 N. Old Woodward Avenue
Birmingham, MI 48009

248-540-9660
www.sloanventures.com

Sterling Capital Funding, LLC
4211 Schaefer Road
Dearborn, MMI 48126
313-212-2378
Fax: 313-581-7574
www.sterlingcapitalfunding.biz

Syneptics
4861 Lone Oak Court
Ann Arbor, MI 48108
734-945-1727
www.syneptics.com

Tullis-Dickerson & Co., Inc.
303 Detroit Street, Suite 301
Ann Arbor, MI 48104
734-623-6300
Fax: 734-623-2956
www.tullisdickerson.com

VentureGrowers
1427 Wedgewood Drive
Saline, MI 48176
734-730-9726
www.venturegrowers.com

Waypoint Ventures
320 N. Main Street, Suite 400
Ann Arbor, MI 48104
734-332-1700
Fax: 734-332-1900
www.wpvc.com

Wind Point Partners
One Towne Square, Suite 780
Southfield, MI 487076
248-945-7200
Fax: 248-945-7220
www.wppartners.com

Wolverine Venture Fund
University of Michigan Business
   School
Institute for Entrepreneurial Studies
701 Tappan Street, 9th Floor
Ann Arbor, MI 48109-1234
734-615-4419
Fax: 734-615-4420
www.zli.bus.umich.edu

Minnesota

Baird Venture Partners
IDS Tower
80 South Eighth Street, Suite 1700
Minneapolis, MN 55402
800-545-9115
612-673-1800
Fax: 612-673-1850
www.rwbaird.com

BlueStream Ventures
225 South Sixth Street, Suite 4350
Minneapolis, MN 55402
612-333-8110
Fax: 612-766-4040
www.bluestreamventures.com

Brightstone Capital
7200 Metro Boulevard
Edina, MN 55349
952-831-6499
Fax: 952-831-1219
www.brightstonevc.com

Cargill Ventures
15407 McGinty Road West
MS 68
Wayzata, MN 55391-2399
952-742-2178
Fax: 952-742-2992
www.cargillventures.com

Carlson Venture Enterprise
Carlson School of Management,
   Room 3-306
321 19th Avenue South
Minneapolis, MN 55455
612-626-8394
www.csom.umn.edu

Cherry Tree Investments
301 Carlson Parkway, Suite 103
Minnetonka, MN 55305
952-893-9012
Fax: 952-893-9036
www.cherrytree.com

Clique Capital LLC
150 South Fifth Street, Suite 1800
Minneapolis, MN 55402
612-672-3602
Fax: 612-672-3777
www.cliquecapital.com

Coral Capital Management
60 South Sixth Street, Suite 3510
Minneapolis, MN 55402
612-335-8698
Fax: 612-335-8668
www.coralcm.com

H.B. Fuller Ventures
1200 Willow Lake Boulevard
St. Paul, MN 55110
651-236-5442
Fax: 651-236-5495
www.hbfuller.com/ventures

Minnesota Investment Network
1600 University Avenue West
Suite 401
St. Paul, MN 55104
651-632-2140
Fax: 651-632-2145
www.mincorp.org

Northeast Ventures
747 Sellwood Building
202 West Superior Street
Duluth, MN 55802
218-722-9915
Fax: 218-722-9871
www.neventures.com

Oak Investment Partners
4550 Wells Fargo Center
90 South Seventh Street

Minneapolis, MN 55402
612-339-9322
Fax: 612-337-8017
www.oakvc.com

Quatris Fund
One Financial Plaza, Suite 2005
120 South Sixth Street
Minneapolis, MN 55402
612-376-7333
Fax: 612-376-7334
www.quatrisfund.com

St. Paul Venture Capital
10400 Viking Drive, Suite 550
Minneapolis, MN 55344
952-995-7474
Fax: 952-995-7475
www.spvc.com

Sherpa Partners
5050 Lincoln Drive, Suite 490
Minneapolis, MN 55436
952-942-1070
Fax: 952-942-1071
www.sherpapartners.com

Space Center Ventures, Inc.
2501 Rosegate
Roseville, MN 55113-2717
651-604-4201
www.scvinc.com

Technology Ventures Partners L.P.
8500 Normandale Lake Boulevard
Suite 2170
Minneapolis, MN 55437
952-646-3000
Fax: 952-646-3010
www.tvp.com

Thomas, McNerney & Partners
60 South 6th Street, Suite 3620
Minneapolis, MN 55402
612-465-8660
Fax: 612-465-8661
www.tm-partners.com

Venturi Group, LLC
2800 Patton Road
St. Paul, MN 55113
651-634-3003
www.venturigroup.com

Missouri
InvestMidwest Venture Capital
   Forum
One Metropolitan Square, Suite 1300
St. Louis, MO 63102
314-444-1151
Fax: 314-206-3277
www.investmidwestforum.com

Missouri Innovation Center, Inc.
Student Health Building
410 South Sixth Street
Columbia, MO 65211-2290
573-884-0496
Fax: 573-884-3600
http://marketmaker.org

Thompson Street Capital Partners
100 S. Bentwood Boulevard
Suite 200
St. Louis, MO 63105
314-727-2112
Fax: 314-727-2118
www.thompsonstreet.net

Nebraska
Invest Nebraska
4701 Innovation Drive
Lincoln, NE 68521
402-472-2063
Fax: 402-472-4203
www.investnebraska.com

Midland Venture Forum
Scott technology Center
6825 Pine Street
Omaha, NE 68106
402-393-0459
Fax: 402-955-1790
www.mvforum.com

Nevada
Nevada Venture
695 Sierra Rose Drive
Reno, NV 89511
775-854-2020
Fax: 775-954-2023
www.nvven.com

Tri Star Investor Network
3960 Howard Hughes Parkway
5th Floor
Las Vegas, NV 89109
866-267-5085
http://network.tsvd.com

New Hampshire
Borealis Ventures
10 Allen Street
Hanover, NH 03755
603-643-1500
Fax: 603-643-7600
www.borealisventures.com

CEI Ventures
2 Portland Fish Pier, Suite 201
Portland, ME 04101
207-772-5356
Fax: 207-772-5503
www.ceicommunityventures.com

Downs Rachlin Martin PLLC
52 Union Street, Suite 3
P.O. Box 560
Littleton, NH 03561-0560
603-444-0216
Fax: 603-444-0768
www.drm.com

Gallagher, Callahan & Gartrell
214 N. Main Street
P.O. Box 1415
Concord, NH 03302-1415
800-528-1181
www.gcglaw.com/services/venture.h
   tml

New Jersey

InnoCal Venture Capital
Park 80 West Plaza One
Saddle Brook, NJ 07663
201-845-4900
Fax: 201-845-3388
www.innocal.com

NJTC Venture Fund
1001 Briggs Road, Suite 280
Mt. Laurel, NJ 08054
856-273-6800
Fax: 856-273-0990
www.njtcvc.com

Technology Crossover Ventures
56 Main Street, Suite 210
Millburn, NJ 07041
973-467-5320
Fax: 973-467-5323
www.tcv.com

New Mexico

ARCH Venture Fund
1155 University Boulevard, SE
Albuquerque, NM 87106
505-843-4293
Fax: 505-843-4294
www.archventure.com

Coronado Ventures Forum
190 Central Park Square
Los Alamos, NM 87544
505-662-0048
Fax: 505-662-0099
www.cvf-nm.org

Flywheel Ventures
1640 Old Pecos Trail, Suite B
Santa Fe, NM 87505
877-810-8104
Fax: 877-810-8104
www.flywheelventures.com

Gathering of Angels
#4 Hawthorne Circle
Santa Fe, NM 87506
505-982-3050
www.gatheringofangels.com

New Mexico Private Investors, Inc.
70 Pinon Hill Place
Albuquerque, NM 87122-1914
505-856-0245
Fax: 505-856-0247
www.nmprivateinvestors.com

Technology Ventures Corporation
1155 University Boulevard, SE
Albuquerque, NM 87106
505-246-2882
Fax: 505-246-2891
www.techventures.org

Vestor Partners, LP
607 Cerrillos Road, Suite D2
Santa Fe, NM 87505
505-988-9100
Fax: 505-988-1958
www.vestor.com

New York

Bressmer Venture Partners
1865 Palmer Avenue, Suite 104
Larchmont, NY 10538
914-833-9100
Fax: 914-833-9200
www.bvp.com

Chapman, Spira & Carson, LLC
110 Wall Street, 15 floor
New York, NY 10005
212-425-6100
Fax: 212-425-6229
www.chapmanspira.com

Lux Capital
245 Park Avenue, 24th Floor
New York, NY 10167
212-792-4188
Fax: 212-372-8798
www.luxcapital.com

Venrock Associates
30 Rockefeller Plaza, Room 5508
New York, NY 10112
212-649-5600
Fax: 212-649-5788
www.venrock.com

Women's Venture Fund, Inc
240 West 35 Street, Suite 501
New York, NY 10001
212-563-0499
Fax: 212-868-9116
www.womensventurefund.org

North Carolina

Academy Funds
11540 North Community House
Road, Suite 150
Charlotte, NC 28277
704-540-9379
Fax: 704-540-9868
www.academyfunds.com

A.M. Pappas & Associates, LLC
7030 Kit Creek Road
P.O. Box 110287
Research Triangle Park, NC 27709
919-998-3300
Fax: 919-998-3301
www.ampappas.com

The Atlantis Group
2530 Meridian Parkway, 2nd floor
Durham, NC 27713
919-806-4340
Fax: 919-806-4739
www.theatlantisgroup.net

The Aurora Funds, Inc.
2525 Meridian Parkway, Suite 220
Durham, NC 27713
919-484-0400
Fax: 919-484-0444
www.aurorafunds.com

Charlotte Angel Partners
www.capnc.com

Eno River Capital
Brightleaf Square
905 West Main Street
Box 44, Suite 25-B
Durham, NC 27701
919-680-4511
Fax: 919-680-3282
www.enorivercapital.com

Intersouth Partners
3211 Shannon Road, Suite 610
Durham, NC 27707
919-493-6640
Fax: 919-493-6649
www.intersouth.com

North Carolina Enterprise
    Corporation
P.O. Box 20429
Raleigh, NC 27619
919-781-2691
Fax: 919-783-9195
www.ncef.com

North Carolina Technology
    Development Authority
First Flight Venture Fund
2 Davis Drive
P.O. Box 13169
Research Triangle Park, NC 27709-
    3169
919-990-8558
Fax: 919-558-0156
www.nctda.org/ic/ffvf.html

Research Triangle Ventures
3110 Edwards Mill Road, Suite 220
Raleigh, NC 27612
919-571-8819
Fax: 919-571-8631
www.rtventures.com

River City Capital Funds
3737 Glenwood Avenue
Suite 100
Raleigh, NC 27612
919-573-6111
Fax: 919-573-6050
www.rccf.com

Southeast Interactive Technology
    Funds
630 Davis Drive, Suite 220
Morrisville, NC 27560
919-558-TECH
Fax: 919-558-2025
www.seinteractive.com

Tri-State Investment Group
405 Tramore Drive
Chapel Hill, NC 27516
www.tignc.com

truePilot, LLC
2530 Meridian Parkway, 3rd Floor
durham, NC 27713
919-806-4930
Fax: 919-806-4845
http://truepilot.com

Wakefield Group
1110 East Morehead Street
Charlotte, NC 28204
704-372-0355
Fax: 704-372-8216
www.wakefieldgroup.com

Ohio

Adena Ventures
20 E. Circle Drive
Box 37235
Athens, OH 45701
740-597-1470
Fax: 740-597-1399
www.adenaventures.com

Alpha Capital
2038 Bedford Road
Columbus, OH 43212
614-487-8780
www.alphacapital.com

Blue Chip Venture Group
1100 Chiquita Center
250 East 5th Street
Cincinnati, OH 45202
513-723-2300
Fax: 513-723-2306
www.bcvc.com

Brantley Partners
Lakepoint
3201 Enterprise Parkway, Suite 350
Beachwood, OH 44122
216-464-8400
Fax: 216-464-8405
www.brantleypartners.com

Capital Works, LLC
1111 Superior Avenue, Suite 970
Cleveland, OH 44114
216-781-3233
Fax: 216-781-6670
www.capitalworks.net

Glengary Ventures LLC
P.O. Box 202526
Cleveland, OH 44120
216-491-4700
Fax: 216-491-4701
www.glengaryventures.com

Isabella Capital LLC
312 Walnut Street, Suite 3540
Cincinnati, OH 45202
513-721-7110
Fax: 513-721-7115
www.fundisabella.com

MCM Capital Partners, L.P.
25101 Chagrin Boulevard
Suite 310
Cleveland, OH 44122
216-514-1840
Fax: 216-514-1850
www.mcmcapital.com

NCIC Capital Fund
3155 Research Boulevard, Suite 203
Dayton, OH 45420

937-253-1777
www.ncicfund.com

Ohio Innovation Fund
1120 Chester Avenue, Suite 418
Cleveland, OH 44114
216-533-2351
Fax: 330-528-3836
www.oifventures.com

Ohio Partners
62 East Broad Street, 3rd Floor
Columbus, OH 43215
614-621-1210
Fax: 614-621-1240
www.ohiopartners.com

Peppertree Partners LLC
3550 Lander Road, Suite 300
Pepper Pike, OH 44124
216-514-4949
Fax: 216-541-4959
www.peppertreefund.com

Primus Venture Partners, Inc
5900 Landerbrook Drive, Suite 200
Cleveland, OH 44124-4020
440-684-7300
Fax: 440-684-7342
www.primusventure.com

River City Capital Funds
221 East Fourth Street, Suite 1900
Cincinnati, OH 45202-4151
513-621-9700
Fax: 513-579-8939
www.rccf.com

Triathlon Medical Ventures
250 East Fifth Street
1100 Chiquita, OH 45202
513-723-2616
Fax: 513-723-2615
www.tmvp.com

Oklahoma

Davis, Tuttle Venture Partners
320 South Boston, Suite 1000
Tulsa, OK 74103-3703
918-584-7272
918-582-3404
www.davistuttle.com

Oklahoma Technology
 Commercialization Center
840 research Parkway, Suite 250
Oklahoma City, OK 73104
405-235-2305
800-337-OTCC
Fax: 405-235-2252
www.otcc.org

Oregon

Empire Venture
1020 SW Taylor Street, Suite 415
Portland, OR 97205
503-222-1556
Fax: 503-222-1607
www.empireventures.com

Madrona Venture Group
101 SW Main Street, Suite 1100
Portland, OR 97204
503-224-5450
Fax: 503-224-5549
www.madrona.com

Northwest Technology Ventures
209 SW Oak Street, First Floor
Portland, OR 97204
503-943-0890
Fax: 503-222-2834
www.nwtechventures.com

OVP Venture Partners
5550 SW Macadam Ave., Suite 300
Portland, OR 97239
503-697-8766
Fax: 503-697-8863
www.ovp.com

Pennsylvania

Adams Capital Management
500 Blackburn Avenue
Sewickley, PA 15143
412-749-9454
Fax: 412-749-9459
www.acm.com

Birchmere Ventures
One North Shore Center, Suite 201
12 Federal Street
Pittsburgh, PA 15212
412-322-3300
Fax: 412-322-3226
www.birchmerevc.com

CEO Venture Fund
One North Shore center, Suite 201
12 Federal Street
Pittsburgh, PA 15212
412-322-2572
Fax: 322-3226
www.ceoventurefund.com

Community Loan Fund of
 Southwestern Pennsylvania, Inc.
1920 Gulf Tower
707 Grant Street
Pittsburgh, PA 15219
412-201-2450
Fax: 412-201-2451
www.clfund.com

Draper Triangle Ventures
2 Gateway Center, Suite 2000
Pittsburgh, PA 15222
412-288-9800
Fax: 412-288-9799
www.drapertriangle.com

Eagle Ventures
400 South Highland Avenue
Pittsburgh, PA 15203
412-683-3400
Fax: 412-683-6388
www.eagleventures.biz

Edison Venture Fund
3 Bala Plaza East, Suite 502

Bala Cynwyd, PA 19004
609-896-1900
Fax: 610-660-4930
www.edisonventure.com

Equity Catalysts
6507 Wilkins Avenue, Suite 200
Pittsburgh, PA 15217-1305
412-361-6760
Fax: 412-361-6762
www.equitycatalysts.com

The Future Fund
215 South Main Street, Suite 1
Zelienople, PA 16063
724-453-6150
www.future-fund.com

G4 Partners LLC
409 Broad Street, Suite 101 B
Sewickley, PA 15143
412-749-4110
Fax: 412-749-4104
www.g4partners.com

Innovation Works
2000 Technology Drive
Suite 250
Pittsburgh, PA 15219-3109
412-681-1520
Fax: 412-681-2625
www.innovationworks.org

Lancet Capital
100 Technology Drive, Suite 200
Pittsburgh, PA 15219
412-471-7101
Fax: 412-471-7102
www.lancetcapital.com

LaunchCyte, LLC
100 Technology Drive, Suite 440
Pittsburgh, PA 15219
412-770-1630
Fax: 412-770-1638
www.launchcyte.com

Lycos Ventures
Two Gateway Center, 20th Floor
Pittsburgh, PA 15222
412-338-8600
Fax: 412-338-8699
http://members.tripod.com/ventures

Mid-Atlantic Venture Funds
Ben Franklin Technology Center
Leigh University
125 Goodman Drive
Bethlehem, PA 18015
610-865-6550
Fax: 610-865-6427
www.mavf.vom

PA Early Stage Venture Funds
1200 Liberty Ridge Drive, Suite 310
Wayne, PA 19087
610-293-4075
Fax: 610-254-4240
www.paearlystage.com

Pi Capital Group, LLC
Pittsburgh, PA 15224
412-681-8652
www.picapitalgroup.com

Redleaf Group
100 First Avenue, Suite 1100
Pittsburgh, PA 15222
412-201-5600
Fax: 412-201-5650
www.redleaf.com

Quaker BioVentures, Inc
1811 Chestnut Street, Suite 700
Philadelphia, PA 19103
215-988-6800
Fax: 215-717-2270
www.quakerbioventures.com

Western Pennsylvania Adventure
  Capital Fund
Scott Towne Center
Suite A-113
2101 Greentree Road
Pittsburgh, PA 15220
412-279-1760
Fax: 412-429-8743
www.wpacf.com

Rhode Island
Zero Stage Capital
40 Westminster Street, Suite 702
Providence, RI 02903
401-351-3036
Fax: 401-351-3056
www.zerostage.com

South Carolina
Charleston Angel Partners
www.charlestonangelpartners.com

Southeast Interactive Technology
  Funds
630 Davis Drive, Suite 220
Morrisville, NC 27560
919-558-TECH
Fax: 919-558-2025
www.seinteractive.com

The Trelys Funds
1901 Assembly Street
Suite 390
Columbia, SC 29201
803-251-7990
Fax: 803-251-7995
www.trelys.com

Tri-State Investment Group
405 Tramore Drive
Chapel Hill, NC 27516
www.tignc.com

Tennessee
The Southern Appalachian Fund
1020 Commerce Park Drive
Oak Ridge, TN 37830
865-220-2020
Fax: 865-220-2030
www.southappfund.com

Texas
ARCH Southwest
6801 N. Capital of Texas Highway
Building 2, Suite 225
Austin, TX 78731
512-795-5830
Fax: 512-795-5849
www.archventure.com

Austin Ventures
300 West 6th Street, Suite 2300
Austin, TX 78701-3902
512-485-1900
Fax: 512-476-3952
www.austinventures.com

Chisholm Private Capital Partners
2435 N. Central Expressway
Suite 600
Richardson, TX 75080
214-236-9509
www.chisholmmvc.com

Murphee Venture Partners
1100 Louisiana, Suite 5005
Houston, TX 77002
713-655-8500
Fax: 713-655-8503
www.murphco.com

Murphee Venture Partners
9600 Great Hills Trail
Suite 300 East
Austin, TX 78759-5681
512-241-8100
Fax: 512-241-8001
www.murphco.com

Sternhill Partners
777 Post Oak Boulevard, Suite 205
Houston, TX 77056
713-622-2727
Fax: 713-622-3529
www.sternhillpartners.com

Utah
Emery County Economic
  Development
P.O. Box 297
Castle Dale, UT 84513
435-381-5576
www.emerycounty.com

435-381-5576
Kendall & Associates
Diamond 'K' Ranch
P.O. Box 430
Huntsville, UT 84317
801-745-1200
Fax: 801-745-0200
www.kendellassociates.com

Virginia
Active Angel Investors
New Vantage Group
402 Maple Avenue West
Vienna, VA 21180
703-255-4930
Fax: 703-255-4931
www.activeangelinvestors.com

Edison Venture Fund
8270 Greensboro Drive, Suite 850
McClean, VA 22102
703-903-8546
Fax: 703-903-9528
www.edisonventure.com

Hampton Roads Private Investor
  Network
Small Business Development Center
  of Hampton Roads
400 Volvo Parkway
Chesapeake, VA 23320
757-825-2957

Mid-Atlantic Venture Funds
11710 Plaza America Drive
Suite 120
Reston, VA 20190
703-904-4120
Fax: 703-904-4124
www.mavf.com

Ridge Capital Partners, LLC
9 North Liberty Street
P.O. Box 2056
Middlebury, VA 20118
540-687-8161
Fax: 540-687-8164
www.ridgecorp.com

Tri-State Investment Group
405 Tramore Drive
Chapel Hill, NC 27516
www.tignc.com

Vermont
Aggregate Capital Partners
2463 Stowe Holoow Road
Stowe, VT 05672
802-253-6843
Fax: 617-812-6040

Freshtracks Capital
5 Park Street
P.O. Box 927
Middlebury, VT 05753
802-388-6283
Fax: 802-388-1606
www.freshtrackscap.com

Vermont Venture Network
30 Main Street
P.O. Box 5839
Burlington, VT 05402
802-658-7830
Fax: 802-658-0978
www.merritt-merritt.com/vvn.html

Washington
Angels With Attitude
Sound Point Venture Fund
206-932-3850
www.soundpointventures.com

Seraph Capital
12345 Lake City Way NE, #398
Seattle, WA 98125
www.seraphcapital.com

Velocity Capital
5400 Carillon Point
5000 Building, 4th Floor
Kirkland, WA 98033
206-264-1415
Fax: 206-264-1931
www.velocitycap.com

West Virginia
Adena Ventures
20 E. Circle Drive
Box 37235
Athens, OH 45701
740-597-1470
Fax: 740-597-1399
www.adenaventures.com

INNOVA Commercialization Group
c/o WVHTC Foundation
1000 Technology Drive, Suite 1000
Fairmont, WV 26554
304-366-2577 ext 226
Fax: 304-366-2699
www.innovawv.org

Natural Capital Investment Fund
Conservation Leadership Network
Route 1, Box 166
Shepherd Grade Road
Shepherdstown, WV 25443
304-876-2815
Fax: 304-876-7751
www.conservationfund.org

The Progress Fund
200 Main Street, 2nd Floor
P.O. Box 400
Dawson, PA 15428-0400
724-529-0384
Fax: 724-529-0386
www.progressfund.org

Walker Ventures
P.O. Box 1027
Flowering Springs Road
Shepherdstown, WV 25443
301-854-6850
Fax: 301-854-6235
www.walkerventures.com

West Virginia Jobs Investment
  Board
1012 Kanawha Boulevard East
Fifth Floor
Charleston, WV 25301
304-345-6200
Fax: 304-345-6262
www.wvjit.org

Wisconsin
Autumnwood Financial Corporation
100 North Main Street
P.O. Box 947
Walworth, WI 53184
262-275-6808
Fax: 262-275-5465
www.autumnwoodfinancial.com

Baird Venture Partners
777 East Wisconsin Avenue
P.O. Box 0672
Milwaukee, WI 53202
800-RWBAIRD
www.rwbaird.com

Early Stage Research, LLC
6502 Grand Teton Plaza
Suite 204
Madison, WI 53719
www.earlystageresearch.com

Mason Wells
770 North Water Street
Milwaukee, WI 53202
414-765-7800
Fax: 414-765-7850
www.masonwells.com

Silicon Pastures
418 E. Silver Spring Drive
Whitefish Bay, WI 53217
www.siliconpastures.com

Venture Adventures LLC
University Research Park
505 S Rosa Road
Suite 100
Madison, WI 53719
608-441-2700
Fax: 608-441-2727
www.ventureinvestors.com

Wisconsin Investment Partners, LLC
6410 Landfill Drive
Madison, WI 53705
608-238-7674
Fax: 608-238-1417
www.wispartners.com

Wyoming
Cheyenne Capital Fund
200 W. 17th Street
Suiet 60
Cheyenne, WY 82001
307-632-0386
www.cheyennefund.com

VentureWest, Inc
1234 Temp Street
Laramie, WY 87070
303-831-4133
www.venturewest.org

$548 Million To Help Improve Communities

Community Development Venture Capital Alliance (CDVCA) is an association of venture capitalists who are looking to invest in companies located in distressed and neglected areas throughout the world to help improve wage and employment opportunities, provide training for workers and businesses, and to help improve society as a whole. The venture capitalists offer assistance when most banks and financial institutions turn down these businesses, or do not offer services in these areas. Often rural and distressed regions are not fully served, and are in need of special types of assistance. The Alliance has over 100 members willing and able to provide the needed help and business assistance to companies willing to take the risk and grow in these communities. As venture capitalists, they do not require immediate loan repayment, but become part owners in the company. They

have a vested interest in the success of your company. To learn more about the programs offered and to see what is available in your area, contact:

Community Development Venture Capital Alliance
330 Seventh Avenue, 19th Floor, New York, NY 10001
212-594-6747
Fax: 212-594-6717
www.cdvca.org/

ACENet Ventures, Inc.
94 Columbus Road
Athens, OH 45701
740-592-3854
Fax: 740-593-5451
http://www.acenetworks.org/
Email: rkrieger@acenetworks.org
ACENet Ventures is a fund whose goal is to improve the lives of low-income people living in Central Appalachia by investing in specialty food and technology businesses. This in turn will provide high-quality jobs, allowing workers to earn living wages and receive good benefits. Investments range between $25,000 to $350,000.
Geographic Area: Central Appalachia, including parts of southern Ohio and western West Virginia.

Adena Ventures, L.P.
143 Technology and Enterprise Building
Athens, OH 45701
740-597-1722
Fax: 740-597-1399
www.adenaventures.com
Email: gellermann@adenaventures.com
Adena Ventures provides capital investment and operational assistance to small businesses and entrepreneurs in Central Appalachia. The goal is to improve economic development in this area, and also to generate a market-rate return for the investors. Areas of interest include information technology, healthcare and e-learning. The fund wants to create new companies to help create new jobs. Investments range from

$200,000 to $2 million. The Fund also provides legal, accounting, recruiting of personnel and business planning assistance.
Geographic Area: Central Appalachia

African-American Venture Capital Fund
310 W. Liberty Street, Suite 507
Louisville, KY 40202
502-561-1204
Fax: 502-584-3918
http://www.aavcf.org
Email: jparham@aavcf.org
The African-American Venture Capital Fund is designed to help African-Americans who want to start a new business, or would like to expand or acquire a business. The goal of the Fund is to improve the livelihood of African-Americans by creating good jobs and businesses. Investments range from $10,000 to $1 million.
Geographic Area: greater Louisville area, and Indianapolis, Indiana and Cincinnati, Ohio.

The Barred Rock Fund
324 Browns Trace
Jericho, VT 05465
802-899-2776
Fax: 802-899-5266
Email: clacy@together.net
The Barred Rock Fund offers investment opportunities to a variety of businesses, with an emphasis on food and other consumer products sold through natural food stores and

grocery store. It also has an interest in goods from developing countries. No technology businesses will receive funding. The goal of the Fund is to help create jobs and good wages for low-income people. Investments range from $50,000-$500,000.
Geographic Area: any state

Baltics Small Equity Fund LLC (BSEF)
Lukiskiu str. 5-319, Vilnius 2600, Lithuania
Pärnu mnt 142, 6th Floor. Tallinn 11317, Estonia
Lacplesa 29-2, Riga, LV 1011, Latvia
http://www.bsef.ee
Email: gdodge@eunet.lt
The Baltics Small Equity Fund invests in businesses in the countries of Estonia, Latvia, and Lithuania. The Fund is interested in growth-oriented companies, offering them financial and technical assistance. The Fund becomes a partner in the business, helping the businesses to run more efficiently and accurately. Interested business types include exporters, tourism, and light industry. Investments range up to $400,000.
Geographic Area: Estonia, Latvia, and Lithuania

Boston Community Venture Fund I and II
56 Warren Street
Boston, MA 02119-3236
617-427-8600
www.bcvfund.com
Email: info@bcvfund.com
The Boston Community Venture Fund provides capital to businesses who will benefit society in some way. Some companies may provide goods and services in distressed areas, or who are owned by a member of a minority group or are women. Improvement in the community is a goal, including the increase in good jobs. Investments range form $250,000 to $1.5 million.
Geographic Area: Northeast

Bridges Community Ventures Ltd
1 Craven Hill
London, W2 3EN
United Kingdom
44 (20) 7262-5566
Fax: 44 (20) 7262-6389
www.bridgesventures.com
Email: info@bridgesventures.com
Bridges Community Ventures invests in businesses in distressed areas of England. The goal is to create jobs and increase the income of these communities. Hopefully successful companies will encourage other investors to supports businesses. In vestments range from 100,000 to 2 million pounds.
Geographic Area: distresses areas of England

CARESBAC Bulgaria
20-22 Zlaten Rog St., Floor 5th,kv.
Lozents, Sofia 1407
Bulgaria
http://www.seaf.bg/caresbac
Email: office@caresbac.com
CARESBAC-Bulgaria is a fund that invests in businesses in Bulgaria. The Fund helps those companies work more efficiently and effectively. Advice and business strategy are provided. The goals are for successful businesses to encourage more investing in the area. Interested company areas include exporters, agribusiness and light industry. Investments range from $100,000 to $500,000.
Geographic Area: Bulgaria

CARESBAC Polska
Ul. Polna 40, 00-635
Warsaw, Poland
http://www.seaf.com/poland
Email: caresbac@it.com.pl
CARESBAC-Polaska is a fund that invests in businesses in Poland. The Fund helps those companies work more efficiently and effectively. Advice and business strategy are provided. The goals are for successful businesses to encourage more investing in the area, to improve the economy and to increase employment opportunities. Interested company areas include exporters, agribusiness and light industry. Investments range from $50,000 to $250,000.
Geographic Area: Poland

Community Development Venture Capital
Alliance (CDVCA) - Central Fund
330 Seventh Avenue, 19th Floor
New York, NY 10001
212-594-6747
Fax: 212-594-6717
Email: dnovick@cdvca.org
http://www.cdvca.org
The Community Development Venture Capital Alliance-Central Fund invests in companies who create jobs and improve the income of people living in distressed communities. The Fund wants to encourage social responsibility and business ownership among the under-represented. Investments range around $250,000.
Geographic Area: North America

CEI Community Ventures, Inc.
2 Portland Fish Pier, Suite 201
Portland, ME 04101
207-772-5356
Fax: 207-772-5503
www.ceicommunityventures.com
Email: mhg@ceicommunityventures.com
The CEI Community Ventures helps to fund businesses that are in under-served markets. The goal is to improve the economy and increase jobs.
Geographic Area: Maine, New Hampshire, and Vermont.

Central & Eastern Europe Growth Fund LLC (Growth Fund)
1050 17th Street NW, Suite 1150
Washington DC 20036
http://www.seaf.com/growth
Email: robbdoub@seaf.com
The Central & Eastern Europe Growth Fund LLC invests in businesses in Central and Eastern Europe. The Fund helps those companies work more efficiently and effectively. Advice and business strategy are provided, in order to assist the companies in becoming more productive and competitive. The goals are for successful businesses to encourage more investing in the area, to improve the economy and to increase employment opportunities. The Fund follows rules regarding child labor, occupational and safety hazards, and environmental concerns. Interested company areas include exporters, agribusiness and light industry. Investments range from $1 million to $3 million.
Geographic Area: Central and Eastern Europe

Inner City Fund Partners, LLC (Chicago Community Ventures)
700 North Sacramento Boulevard, Suite 130
Chicago, IL 60612
773-822-0320
Fax: 773-822 0308
http://www.chiventures.org

Email: info@chiventures.org
The Inner city Fund Partners provides financial and technical assistance to businesses in distresses areas around Chicago. The goal is to increase jobs and the economy in these areas. Investments range from $250,000 to $2,500,000.
Geographic Area: Low income communities in Chicago and Minority and Women Owned businesses throughout the Chicago area.

CL Fund
1920 Gulf Tower, 707 Grant Street
Pittsburgh, PA 15219
412-201-2450
Fax: 412-201-2451
www.clfund.com
Email: info@clfund.com
The CL Fund invests in companies in the Southwestern Pennsylvania area. The Fund typically invests in the technology area, including applied software, information technology, and more. Investments range up to $500,000.
Geographic Area: Southwestern Pennsylvania

CEI Ventures, Inc.
Coastal Ventures I, LP
Coastal Ventures II, LLC
Two Portland Fish Pier, Suite 201
Portland, ME 04101
207-772-5356
Fax: 207-772-5503
www.ceimaine.org/venturecapital
Email: thd@ceimaine.org
CEI Ventures supports companies with potential for profit, as well as companies that increase employment opportunities and encourage business ownership among those under-represented. The Fund offers business and strategy assistance, and often takes a seat on the Board. Investments range from $250,0-00 to $2 million.
Geographic Area: Maine and Northern New England

Community Development Ventures, Inc.
826 E. Baltimore Street
Baltimore, MD 21202
410-333-2548
Fax: 410-333-2552
www.mmgroup.com
Email: contact@mmgroup.com
The Community Development Ventures supports businesses located within distressed areas of Baltimore, with a special emphasis on companies who employ people living within those areas. Not only does the Fund provide financial assistance, but they offer business assistance as well. Increase in employment opportunities and salaries for low-income workers is one of the goals of this program. Investments range from $100,000 to $800,000.
Geographic Area: Baltimore's Empowerment or Enterprise Zones.

Delaware Valley Community Reinvestment Fund Ventures
718 Arch Street, Suite 300 North
Philadelphia, PA 19106-1591
215-925-1130
Fax: 215-923-4764
www.trfund.com
Email: ventures@trfund.com
The Delaware Valley Community Reinvestment Fund invests in existing companies with a potential to grow. The Fund becomes a partner with the company, offering advice and assistance, and then leaves the company after several years. One important goal of this Fund is to create good jobs with good wages, and helps train the employees so they will stay with the company. Interested businesses include those in manufacturing, outsourcing, and health services. Investments range from $250,000 to $1 million.
Geographic Areas: 21 counties surrounding Philadelphia

The EcoEnterprises Fund
4245 North Fairfax Drive
Arlington, VA 22203
703-841-4164
Fax: 703-841-4880
www.ecoenterprisesfund.com
The EcoEnterprises Fund invests in "environmentally and socially responsible businesses." The goal is to increase employment and wages with protecting the fragile ecosystems of this area. Interested businesses include agriculture, forest products (excluding wood), and tourism. Investments range from $50,000 to $800,000.
Geographic Area: Latin America and the Caribbean

ECD Investments, LLC (Enterprise Corporation of the Delta)
308 East Pearl Street, Suite 400
Jackson, MI 39201
601-944-1100
Fax: 601-944-0808
www.ecd.org
Email: ventures@trfund.com
ECD Investments provides fund to companies located within the Delta regions. The goal of the fund is to provide good employment and wage opportunities for low-income people living in this area. Investments range from $50,000 to $1 million.
Geographic Area: the 56 counties and parishes of the Delta regions of Arkansas, Louisiana and Mississippi.

Fondo Capital Activo de Bolivia LLC (FCA Bolivia)
Ed. Eduardo Abaroa, Planta Baja, Sanchez
Lima, esq. Belisario Salinas, La Paz, Bolivia
http://www.seaf.com/bolivia
Email: johnbays@aol.com
Total Committed Capital: US $8.6 million
Amount Invested: US $4.2 million (49%)
The Fondo Capital Activo de Bolivia provides funding to businesses located within Bolivia. The Fund not only provides financial assistance, but marketing strategy and business management assistance as well. The goal is to help these businesses grow, increasing employment and salaries for workers in this area. By helping these companies succeed, there is an increased likelihood of investments from others. Interesting companies include those in the light industry, exporters, business services and those that help the environment or society. Investments range from $100,000 to $1,000,000.
Geographic Area: La Paz, Cochabamba, Santa Cruz and Bolivia.

Foursome Investments Limited
8-13 New Inn Street
London, EC2A 3PY
United Kingdom
44 0(20) 7739-0001
Fax: 44 0(20) 7739-9218
www.foursome.net
Email: mail@foursome.net
Foursome Investments provides funding to businesses in the United Kingdom, with the goal of helping the both the business and society. Investments range from $200,000 to $500,000.
Geographic Area: United Kingdom

Impact Seven, Inc.
147 Lake Almena Drive
Almena WI 54805
715-357-3334
Fax: 715-357-6233
www.impactseven.org
Email: impact@impactseven.org
Impact Seven invests in companies located throughout
Wisconsin. The goal is to help improve the economy of the
state by investing in companies with high potential. Any type
of business is eligible. Investments range from $50,000 to $3
million.
Geographic Focus: Wisconsin

*Inner City Fund Partners, LLC (Chicago Community
Ventures)*
700 North Sacramento Boulevard, Suite 130
Chicago, IL 60612
773-822-0320
Fax: 773-822 0308
http://www.chiventures.org
Email: info@chiventures.org
Inner City Fund partners invests in companies in distressed
areas throughout the Chicago region. Not only do they
provide financial assistance, but they also offer business
assistance to help the company grow. The goal of this fund is
to improve the employment and wage opportunities in the
community. Investments range from $250,000 to $2,500,000.
Geographic Focus: Distressed communities in Chicago and
Minority and Women Owned businesses in the Chicago area.

Kentucky Highlands Investment Corporation
P.O. Box 1738
London, KY 40743-1738
606-864-5175
Fax: 606-877-6486
www.khic.org
Email: khicnet@khic.org
Kentucky Highlands Investments offers financial assistance
to companies located in Southeastern Kentucky. Not only do
they provide needed capital, but they also offer business
assistance to get companies up and running. The goal of the
Fund is to increase wage and employment opportunities for
residents of the region. Investments range from $500 to $5
million.
Geographic Area: Southeastern Kentucky.

*Mountain Association for Community Economic
Development (MACED)*
433 Chestnut Street
Berea, KY 40403
859-986-2373
Fax: 859-986-1299
web: www.maced.org
Email: info@maced.org
The Mountain Association for community Economic
Development invests in companies located in Eastern
Kentucky and Central Appalachia. They assistance new
businesses reaching their full potential. One of the goals of
the Fund is to help create new employment and wage
possibilities for those who live in the region. An emphasis is
placed on using the natural resources of the area as an asset.
Geographic Area: Eastern Kentucky and Central Appalachia

MetaFund Corporation
2225 N. May Ave.
Oklahoma City, OK 73107
405-949-0001
Fax: 405-949-9005
www.metafund.org

Email: info@metafund.org
MetaFund invests in companies located in Oklahoma. The
goal is to assist companies who will help create jobs and
improve wages in distressed or neglected areas of the state.
No particular industry is preferred. Investments range from
$250,000 to $1 million.
Geographic Area: Oklahoma

Milestone Growth Fund, Inc.
401 2nd Ave. South, Suite 1032
Minneapolis, MN 55401
612-338-0090
Fax: 612-338-1172
www.milestonegrowth.com
Email: inquirymgf@milestonegrowth.com
The Milestone Growth Fund invests in minority-owned
companies in Minnesota. In addition to financing, business
assistance is also provided to help these companies grow and
succeed. Investments range from $300,000 to $500,000.
Geographic Area: Minnesota

Minnesota Investment Network Corporation
1600 University Avenue West, Suite 401
St. Paul, MN 55104
651-632-2140
Fax: 651-632-2145
www.mincorp.org
Email:info@mincorp.org
The Minnesota Investment network invests in businesses
located in rural Minnesota. The goal is to improve the
employment opportunities in the area. Investments range
from $50,000 to $1.3 million.
Geographic Area: Minnesota

Murex Investments, Inc.
4700 Wissahickon, Suite 126
Philadelphia, PA 19144
215-951-0300
Fax: 215-849-7360
www.murexinvests.com
Email: jacob@murexinvests.com
Murex Investments provides financial assistance to
companies located in distressed areas. The goal is increase
employment and wage opportunities for people who live in
these areas. Manufacturing businesses are preferred.
Investments range from $50,000 to $500,000.
Geographic Area: Philadelphia, and surrounding area and
states.

Natural Capital Investment Fund, Inc.
P.O. Box 1889
Shepherdstown, WV 25443
304-876-2815
Fax: 304-870-2208
www.freshwaterinstitute.org
Email: ncif@freshwaterinstitute.org
The Natural Capital Investment Fund provides funding to
companies in West Virginia who are doing "natural resource-
based activities." This Fund wants to help improve the
employment and wage opportunities of the region, while at
the same time taking advantage of and preserving the natural
resources of the area. Investments range from $50,000 to
$250,000.
Geographic Area: West Virginia

The New York City Investment Fund
One Battery Park Plaza
New York, NY 10004-1479
212-493-7548
Fax: 212-809-9815

www.nycif.org
Email: mgotsch@nycp.org
The New York City Investment Fund provides funding to businesses located in new York City. The goal is to improve in employment and wages for those who live in the area. Not only is financing available, but business assistance is provided as well. This Fund also supports new or exciting ideas. Investments range from $250,000 to $3 million.
Geographic Area: New York City

New York Community Investment Company
110 William Street, 32nd Floor
New York, NY 10038
212-693-0870 ext. 16
Fax: 212-693-0949
www.nycic.com
Email: info@nycic.com
New York Community Investment Company provides funding to businesses located throughout New York State and surrounding areas. The emphasis is on businesses who have significant growth potential. Minority, women-owned or companies located in distressed areas are emphasized. Not only is financing available, but business assistance is also offered. Investments range from $350,000 to $1,000,000.
Geographic Area: New York State, central and northern New Jersey and Southern Connecticut.

Fundusz Polnocny Spolka Akcyjna (The North Fund)
Linki 5/5, Olsztyn 10-534, Poland
http://www.seaf.com/northfund
Email: northfund@fp.org.pl
The North Fund invests in companies in Northern Poland. Financial, business, and technical assistance are provided to companies located in this distressed and neglected area. The goal of the Fund is to increase the available of good jobs with good wages, and to improve the economy of the area. The Fund wants these companies to grow and succeed, and will do whatever is necessary to make that happen. Interested companies include those who export, and those with most potential for success. Investments range from $25,000 to $400,000.
Geographic Area: Northern Poland

Northeast Ventures
202 West Superior Street, Suite 747
Duluth, MN 55802
218-722-9915
Fax: 218-722-9871
www.neventures.com
Email: ventures@neventures.com
Northeast Ventures provides financing to companies located in Northeastern Minnesota to help improve the economy of the area. In addition to financing, the Fund also offers business assistance to help the companies grow. Investments range from $250,000 to $500,000.
Geographic Area: Minnesota

Pacific Community Ventures
(PCV Investment Partners I and II)
539 Bryant Street, Suite 302
San Francisco, CA 94107
415-442-4300
Fax: 415-442-4313
www.pacificcommunityventures.org
Email: info@pcvmail.org
Pacific Community Ventures provides funding to companies located in distressed areas throughout California. The goal of the Fund is to increase the job, benefits, and wage opportunities in the area, and provide needed job training assistance to employees. Investments range from $250,000 to $1 million.
Geographic Area: California

Penn Ventures Partners
132 State Street - Suite 200
Harrisburg, PA 17101
717-236-2300
Fax: 717-236-2350
www.pennventures.com
Email: gpeck@pennventures.com
Penn Ventures Partners invests in companies located in Central and Northern Pennsylvania. The Fund seeks to improve wage and employment opportunities for people living in rural or distressed areas. An emphasis is placed on manufacturing or technology businesses. Investments range from $250,000 to $2 million.
Geographic Area: Central and Northern Pennsylvania

Renaissance Ventures
51 Broadway, Suite 500
Fargo, ND 58102
701-293-8892
Fax: 701-293-7819
www.innovators.net/rz.html
Email: art@ndventures.com
Renaissance Ventures offers financing to businesses located within North Dakota's Renaissance Zones. The goal of the Fund is to improve wage and employment opportunities for those who live in the area. Investments range between $100,000 to $350,000.
Geographic Area: North Dakota's Renaissance Zones

Republic Redevelopment Fund
2101 6th Ave. N., Suite 120
Birmingham, AL 35203
205-986-4450
Fax: 205-986-4440
www.republicfund.com
Email: info@republicfund.com
Republic Redevelopment Fund invests in companies located in distressed or near-distressed areas in Southeastern United States. Business with potential for growth are targeted. The goal is to help increase wage and employment opportunities in the area. Investments range from $250,00 to $1.5 million.
Geographic Area: Southeastern United States

Cascadia Revolving Fund's
Rural Development Investment Fund
1901 NW Market Street
Seattle, WA 98107
206-447-9226 ext. 101
Fax: 206-682-4804
www.cascadiafund.org
Email: info@cascadiafund.org
The Rural Development Investment Fund provides financial assistance to businesses in rural Washington and Oregon. In addition to financing, business assistance is available as well. The goal of the fund is to improve wage and employment opportunities for those who live in the area. Interested businesses are those who take advantage of the area.
Geographic Area: Pacific Northwest

Rural West Fund
Mountain Maryland Entrepreneurial Development Center, Inc.
101 Decatur Street, P.O. Box 1835
Cumberland, MD 21501-1835
301-777-9301
Fax: 301-777-9397

www.mmedc.org
Email: grow@mmedc.org
The Rural West Fund provides financial and business assistance to companies with the potential for growth in Western Maryland. Investments range around $150,000.
Geographic Area: Western Maryland

SEAF Croatia LLC
Head Office: Britanski trg 5/11
10 000 Zagreb, Croatia
http://www.seaf.hr/english
Email: info@seaf.hr
SEAF Croatia offers financial and technical assistance to businesses located within Croatia. The Fund provides a wealth of technical assistance to help companies run more efficiently and effectively to increase their growth potential. The goal is to help improve the economy and society. With successful businesses, the hope is this will increase the likelihood of further investments by others. Interested companies include exporters, agriculture and technology. Investments range from $100,000 to $1,000,000.
Geographic Area: Croatia

SEAF-Macedonia LLC
Metropolit Teodosij Gologanov 28
1000 Skopje, Macedonia
http://www.seaf.com.mk
Email: office@seaf.com.mk
SEAF Macedonia offers financial and technical assistance to businesses located within Macedonia. The Fund provides a wealth of technical assistance to help companies run more efficiently and effectively to increase their growth potential. The goal is to help improve the economy and society. With successful businesses, the hope is this will increase the likelihood of further investments by others. Interested companies include exporters, agriculture and technology. Investments range from $150,000 to $2,000,000.
Geographic Area: Macedonia

ShoreGrowth Fund
540 E. 105th St.
Cleveland, OH 44108
216-268-6100
Fax: 216-268-6107
www.shorebankenterprisegroup.com
The ShoreGrowth Fund provides financial assistance to small businesses in the Cleveland area.
Geographic Area: Cleveland

Sichuan SME Investment Fund LLC (SSIF)
West China Investment Consultants
88 Babau Street, Guoxin Plaza, Office 16A Chengdu
Peoples Republic of China 610031
http://www.seaf.com/sichuanfund.htm
Email: wcicjon@guoxun.net
The Sichuan SME Investment Fund provides financial assistance to businesses located in the Sichuan and neighboring Provinces. In addition to this investment, the fund provides needed business and marketing assistance to help the companies grow and succeed. One of the goals of the fund is to help improve the economy, providing jobs and good wages for workers. Interested companies include exporters, technology and software based companies, and those providing local goods for sale. Investments range from $100,000 to $1,000,000.
Geographic Area: Sichuan Province or neighboring provinces in China.

Small Enterprise Growth Fund
P.O. Box 619

Augusta, ME 04332-0619
207-623-3263, 800-228-3734
Fax: (207) 623-0095
www.segfmaine.com
Email: info@segfmaine.com
The Small Enterprise Growth Fund provides funding for businesses located in Maine. An emphasis is placed on companies who show strong growth potential. The goal is to help the economy of the region. Investments range from $150,000 to $350,000.
Geographic Area: Maine

Southeast Community Capital Corporation
1020 Commerce Park Dr.
Oak Ridge, TN 37830
865-220-2025
Fax: 865-220-2030
www.sccapital.org
Southeast community Capital corporation provides financial assistance to businesses in distressed areas in the state of Tennessee. In addition to financing this Fund also provides a wealth of business assistance to help the companies grow and prosper.
Geographic Area: Tennessee

SJF Ventures
(formerly Sustainable Jobs Fund)
400 West Main Street, Suite 604
Durham, NC 27701
919-530-1177
Fax: 919-530-1178
or
255 S. 17th Street, Suite 1301
Philadelphia, PA 19103
215-545-1750
Fax: 215-545-1751
www.sjfund.com
Email: dkirkpatrick@sjfund.com
SJF Ventures offers investment opportunities to companies with high growth potential. One goal is to focus on those that "provide unique products and services." The hope is that these companies will increase the employment opportunities for the areas in which they are located. A wide variety of businesses are eligible. Investments range from $250,000 to $1 million.
Geographic Area: Eastern United States

Trans-Balkan SME Equity Fund LLC (TBF)
Sophia, Bulgaria
Zagreb, Croatia
Bucharest, Romania
http://www.seaf.com/transbalkan
The Trans-Balkan SME Equity Fund provides financing to companies located in the Balkans. In addition to this investment, the fund provides needed business and marketing assistance to help the companies grow and succeed. One of the goals of the fund is to help improve the economy, providing jobs and good wages for workers. Interested companies include exporters, and those with a potential for growth, and those providing local goods for sale. Investments range from $100,000 to $500,000.
Geographic Area: Romania, Bulgaria, Croatia, Bosnia/Herzegovina, and Albania

Trans-Balkan Bulgaria Fund LLC (TBBF)
20-22 Zlaten Rog St., Floor 5th,kv.
Lozents, Sofia 1407
Bulgaria
http://www.seaf.bg
Email: office@seaf.bg

The Trans-Balkan Bulgaria Fund provides financing to companies located in Bulgaria. In addition to this investment, the fund provides needed business and marketing assistance to help the companies grow and succeed. One of the goals of the fund is to help improve the economy, providing jobs and good wages for workers. Interested companies include exporters, and those with a potential for growth, and those providing local goods for sale. Investments range from $100,000 to $500,000.
Geographic Area: Bulgaria

SEAF Trans-Balkan Romania Fund LLC
Bd Uni. Unirii, nr. 62, bl. K5, sc. 1. et. 6-7, ap. 22. Sector 3
Bucharest, Romania
http://www.seaf.com/romania.htm
Email: info@tbrf.ro
The Trans-Balkan Romania Fund provides financing to companies located in Romania. In addition to this investment, the fund provides needed business and marketing assistance to help the companies grow and succeed. One of the goals of the fund is to help improve the economy, providing jobs and good wages for workers. Interested companies include exporters, and those with a potential for growth, and those providing local goods for sale. Investments range from $100,000 to $500,000.
Geographic Area: Romania

TRF Urban Growth Partners
Cast Iron Building, 718 Arch Street, Suite 300 North
Philadelphia, PA 19106-1591
215-574-5802
Fax: 214-574-5902
www.urbangrowthpartners.com
Email: ann.barratt@trfund.com
The TRF Urban Growth Partners invests in companies in the Mid-Atlantic region. The goal is to help companies with growth potential and to increase the wage and employment opportunities for those who live in the region. Businesses run by minorities or women are emphasized. Investments range from $2 million to $5 million.
Geographic Area: Pennsylvania, New Jersey, Delaware, Maryland, and Washington, D.C.

New Hampshire Community Loan Fund (NHCLF)
Vested for Growth - Capital for Business Development (VfG)
7 Wall Street
Concord, NH 03301
603-224-6669 ext. 239
http://vestedforgrowth.com
Email: jhamilton@nhclf.org

Vested For Growth offers financing to businesses in New Hampshire with a potential for growth and a willing to include employees in the running and profits of the company. Not only do they provide financing, but they also provide business assistance to help the company succeed. There is a strong commitment to working with employees, keeping them learning and developing. Investments range from $200,000 to $500,000.
Geographic Area: New Hampshire

Virgin Islands Capital Resources, Inc.
325 Chestnut Street, Ste 1110
Philadelphia, PA 19106
267-671-0900
Fax: 267-671-0909
www.seslia.com
Email: sesmarcia@erols.com
Virgin Islands Capital Resources provides funding to businesses located in the U.S. Virgin Islands. The goal is to help the community, including helping to increase employment and wage opportunities. The Fund has an emphasis on improving the community. Investments range from $50,000 to $250,000.
Geographic Area: US Virgin Islands

West Virginia Jobs Investment Trust
West Virginia Jobs Investment Trust Board
Fifth Floor, 1012 Kanawha Boulevard, East
Charleston, WV 25301
304-345-6200
Fax: 304-345-6262
www.wvjit.org
Email: board@wvjit.org
The West Virginia Jobs Investment Trust provides financial support to companies located in West Virginia who create jobs in the State. The goal of the Trust is to improve the economy of the region.
Geographic Area: West Virginia

Wisconsin Rural Enterprise Fund
1400 South River Street
Spooner, WI 54801
715-635-2197
Fax: 715-635-7262
www.nwrpc.com
Email: mueller@wbic-newventures.com
Wisconsin Rural Enterprise Fund provides investment opportunities to those businesses located in rural Northwest Wisconsin. The goal is to improve the wage and employment opportunities for residents of the region. Investments range from $25,000 to $300,000.
Geographic Area: Northwest Wisconsin

Getting Money Back in Taxes to Start a Business

Federal Tax Credits For Businesses

Don't you want the government to give you thousands of dollars for your business? Of course you do! Taking the time to learn about and to take advantage of tax credits the federal government provides to businesses is well worth the time and effort. You can save big. For example, you can receive:

- $150,000 in tax credits by providing childcare facilities and services
- $500 in tax credits to start a pension plan
- $8,500 in tax credits for hiring a long-term welfare recipient
- $5,000 to make your business handicap accessible
- 20% tax credit for fixing historical buildings
- $2,400 for hiring a resident of an empowerment zone

In addition there are tax credits for energy efficiency, donations, locating your business in an empowerment zone, and more. Added together, these credits can make your first business years more profitable. Don't just stop at the federal government though. States, cities and counties can also offer these benefits. To learn more about the federal government credits, you can contact the Internal Revenue Service at 800-829-1040 or check them out online at {www.irs.ustreas.gov}. Don't forget to check out State Tax Credits beginning on page 624.

$150,000 in Tax Credits for Employer Provided Childcare Facilities and Services

Internal Revenue Service
1111 Constitution Avenue, NW
Washington, DC 20224
202-622-5000
800-829-1040 (Business Tax Questions)
www.irs.ustreas.gov/formspubs/index.html
(Credit for Employer Provided Childcare Facilities and Services)

Businesses that provide childcare facilities and services for their employees can claim a tax credit for qualified expenditures. The credit is 25% of qualified childcare facility expenditures, and 10% of qualified childcare resource and referral expenditures, with a limit of $150,000 per tax year. Qualified childcare facility expenditures include costs to purchase, construct, rehabilitate or expand property that is to be used as part of a childcare facility of the taxpayer. Qualified childcare resource and referral expenditures include costs incurred under a contract to provide childcare resource and referral services to employees of the taxpayer. Use IRS Form 8882, Credit for Employer Provided Childcare Facilities and Services, to apply for the credit. Copies of this form are available from your local IRS office or the IRS website listed above. To order forms by phone, call 800-829-3676; to order by Fax, call 703-368-9694.

$500 in Tax Credits for Small Businesses that Start a Pension Plan

Internal Revenue Service
1111 Constitution Avenue, NW
Washington, DC 20224
202-622-5000
800-829-1040 (Business Tax Questions)
www.irs.ustreas.gov/formspubs/index.html
(Credit for Small Employer Pension Plan Start-up Costs)

Eligible small employers can claim a credit for start up costs incurred in establishing an eligible employee pension plan. The credit is limited to $500 per year for the first credit year and the two following tax years. Use IRS Tax Form 8881, Credit for Small Employer Pension Plan Start-up Costs, to apply for the credit. Copies of this form are available from your local IRS office or the IRS website listed above. To order forms by phone, call 800-829-3676; to order by Fax, call 703-368-9694.

Tax Credits for Businesses that Increase Research and Development Programs

Internal Revenue Service
1111 Constitution Avenue, NW
Washington, DC 20224
202-622-5000
800-829-1040 (Business Tax Questions)
www.irs.ustreas.gov/formspubs/index.html
(Credit for Increasing Research Activities)
Businesses can receive a tax credit of up to 20% of their increase in research and development expenditures for qualified research. This research must be performed for the purpose of discovering technical information which must be used to develop a new product or improve an existing product. Use IRS Form 6765, Credit for Increasing Research Activities, and Instructions for Form 6765 to apply for the credit. Copies of these forms are available from your local IRS office or the IRS website listed above. To order forms by phone, call 800-829-3676; to order by Fax, call 703-368-9694.

Tax Credit for Investing in a Community Development Entity

Internal Revenue Service
1111 Constitution Avenue, NW
Washington, DC 20224
202-622-5000
800-829-1040 (Business Tax Questions)
www.irs.ustreas.gov/formspubs/index.html
(New Market Credit)
Businesses can receive a tax credit for qualified equity investments in community development entities. The credit is allowed for seven years from the date of the initial investment, and is 5% of the investment for years 1-3, and 6% for years 4-7. To claim this credit, use IRS Form 8874, New Market Credit. Copies of this form are available from your local IRS office or the IRS website listed above. To order forms by phone, call 800-829-3676; to order by Fax, call 703-368-9694.

Tax Credits to Sellers of Electricity

Internal Revenue Service
1111 Constitution Avenue, NW
Washington, DC 20224
202-622-5000
800-829-1040 (Business Tax Questions)
www.irs.ustreas.gov/formspubs/index.html
(Renewable Electricity Production Credit)
This credit is available to sellers of electricity produced in the U.S. from qualified energy sources such as wind, cogeneration, closed-loop biomass, and poultry waste. Qualified facilities may apply for the credit for 10 years after the date the facility was originally placed in service. The credit for 2003 is 1.8 cents per kilowatt-hour of electricity sold. Use IRS Form 8835, Renewable Electricity Production Credit, to apply for the credit. Copies of this form are available from your local IRS office or the IRS website listed above. To order forms by phone, call 800-829-3676; to order by Fax, call 703-368-9694.

Tax Credits for Alcohol Fuel Producers

Internal Revenue Service
1111 Constitution Avenue, NW

Washington, DC 20224
202-622-5000
800-829-1040 (Business Tax Questions)
www.irs.ustreas.gov/formspubs/index.html
(Credit for Alcohol Used as Fuel)
Producers of alcohol fuels for mixtures such as gasohol or ethanol can receive a tax credit for the sale or use of such fuels. The amount of credit varies with the type of fuel, and ranges from 10 cents per gallon for qualified ethanol fuel production to 60 cents per gallon for alcohol fuel mixtures other than ethanol. Use IRS Form 6478, Credit for Alcohol Used as Fuel, to apply for the credit. Copies of this form are available from your local IRS office or the IRS website listed above. To order forms by phone, call 800-829-3676; to order by Fax, call 703-368-9694.

Tax Credits for Taxes Paid to Foreign Governments

Internal Revenue Service
1111 Constitution Avenue, NW
Washington, DC 20224
202-622-5000
800-829-1040 (Business Tax Questions)
www.irs.ustreas.gov/formspubs/index.html
(Foreign Tax Credit)
Corporations can claim a foreign tax credit for income taxes, war profits taxes, and excess profits taxes paid or accrued, during the tax year, to any foreign country or U.S. possession. This includes foreign taxes on profits from overseas operations or investments. To apply for the credit, use IRS Form 1118, Foreign Tax Credit. Copies of this form are available from your local IRS office or the IRS website listed above. To order forms by phone, call 800-829-3676; to order by Fax, call 703-368-9694.

Extra $35,000 Depreciation Deduction for Empowerment Zone Companies

Internal Revenue Service
1111 Constitution Avenue, NW
Washington, DC 20224
202-622-5000
800-829-1040 (Business Tax Questions)
www.irs.ustreas.gov/formspubs/index.html
(Increased Section 179 Tax Deduction)
Section 179 of the Internal Revenue Code allows a business to deduct all or part of the cost of certain qualifying property in the year it is put to use instead of taking depreciation over several years. The maximum credit allowed under Section 179 is $100,000. Increased Section 179 deductions apply to qualified empowerment zone businesses that are acquired and placed in service after 2001 and before 2010. The increased deduction can be up to an additional $35,000. Use IRS Form 4562, Depreciation and Amortization, to apply for the deduction. Copies of Form 4562, Publication 954, Tax Incentives for Empowerment Zones and Other Distressed Communities, and Publication 946, How to Depreciate Property, are available from your local IRS office or the IRS website listed above. To order forms and publications by phone, call 800-829-3676; to order by Fax, call 703-368-9694. For more information on Empowerment Zone tax incentives for businesses call 800-998-9999, or go to www.hud.gov/offices/cpd/economicdevelopment/programs/rc/index.cfm.

Refunds of Federal Gas Tax

Internal Revenue Service
1111 Constitution Avenue, NW
Washington, DC 20224

202-622-5000
800-829-1040 (Business Tax Questions)
www.irs.ustreas.gov/formspubs/index.html
(Gasoline Tax Credit)
Consumers of gasoline and other fuels can receive a tax credit or refund for the federal excise tax paid on fuel when the fuel is used for certain purposes such as on a farm, off highway use, export, commercial fishing, school, intercity or local bus, or nonprofit education organization. The amount of credit varies by type of fuel. For example the credit for gasoline is .184 cents per gallon, gasohol is .15436 cents per gallon, and diesel fuel is .244 cents per gallon. Use IRS Form 4136, Credit for Federal Tax Paid on Fuels, to apply for the credit. Copies of this form are available from your local IRS office or the IRS website listed above. To order forms by phone, call 800-829-3676; to order by Fax, call 703-368-9694.

Tax Credits for Oil Companies

Internal Revenue Service
1111 Constitution Avenue, NW
Washington, DC 20224
202-622-5000
800-829-1040 (Business Tax Questions)
www.irs.ustreas.gov/formspubs/index.html
(Enhanced Oil Recovery Credit)
Businesses that significantly expand a domestic oil recovery project that uses certain tertiary recovery methods can take a credit for 15% of their oil recovery costs for the tax year. Such recovery methods may include the injection of liquids, gasses or other matter to increase crude oil production. Use IRS Form 8830, Enhanced Oil Recovery Credit, to apply for the credit. Copies of this form are available from your local IRS office or the IRS website listed above. To order forms by phone, call 800-829-3676; to order by Fax, call 703-368-9694.

Tax Credits on FICA Taxes Paid on Restaurant Employee Tips

Internal Revenue Service
1111 Constitution Avenue, NW
Washington, DC 20224
202-622-5000
800-829-1040 (Business Tax Questions)
www.irs.ustreas.gov/formspubs/index.html
(Credit for Employer Social Security and Medicare Taxes Paid on Certain Employee Tips)
Restaurant waiters and other food service employees must report their tips to their employer. The employer must then pay Social Security and Medicare tax on this money, regardless of whether the employee reports the tip income to the IRS. The amount of this credit is the employer's FICA tax rate, currently 7.65%, times any employee reported tip income which was not used to support tip credit for minimum wage purposes. To claim this credit, use IRS Form 8846, Credit for Employer Social Security and Medicare Taxes Paid on Certain Employee Tips. Copies of this form are available from your local IRS office or the IRS website listed above. To order forms by phone, call 800-829-3676; to order by Fax, call 703-368-9694.

$10,000 in Tax Credits for Timber Businesses

Internal Revenue Service
1111 Constitution Avenue, NW
Washington, DC 20224
202-622-5000
800-829-1040 (Business Tax Questions)
www.irs.ustreas.gov/formspubs/index.html
(Reforestation Credit)
Timber production businesses can claim a 10% reforestation credit up to $10,000 by amortizing reforestation costs for qualifying timber property over a period of 84 months. Qualified timber property must be located in the United States, used for the commercial production of timber products, and consist of at least one acre planted with tree seedlings in the manner normally used in forestation or reforestation. Qualifying costs include site preparation, seeds or seedlings, labor, tools, and depreciation on equipment used in planting and seeding. Use IRS Form 4368, Investment Credit, and Instructions for Form 4368, to apply for the credit. Copies of these forms are available from your local IRS office or the IRS website listed above. To order forms by phone, call 800-829-3676; to order by Fax, call 703-368-9694.

$5,000 for Small Businesses to Become Handicap Accessible

Internal Revenue Service
1111 Constitution Avenue, NW
Washington, DC 20224
202-622-5000
800-829-1040 (Business Tax Questions)
www.irs.ustreas.gov/formspubs/index.html
(Disable Access Credit)
Small businesses that have less than $1,000,000 in annual revenue or 30 or fewer full time employees can apply for a tax credit for expenditures incurred by complying with the Americans with Disabilities Act. Eligible expenditures include the costs associated with removing architectural barriers, providing interpreters or other methods of making audio materials available to the hearing impaired, to provide readers or other methods of making visual materials available to the visually impaired, or to acquire or modify equipment or devices for individuals with disabilities. The maximum credit is$5,000, or 50% of the eligible yearly access expenditures up to $10,000. There is no credit for the first $250 of expenditures. Use IRS Form 8826, Disabled Access Credit, to apply for the credit. Copies of this form are available from your local IRS office or the IRS website listed above. To order forms by phone, call 800-829-3676; to order by Fax, call 703-368-9694.

$8,500 for Hiring a Long-Term Welfare Recipient

Internal Revenue Service
1111 Constitution Avenue, NW
Washington, DC 20224
202-622-6080 (Karin Loverud)
800-829-1040 (Business Tax Questions)
www.irs.ustreas.gov/formspubs/index.html
(Welfare to Work Tax Credit-Long Term Welfare Recipients)
The Welfare-to-Work Tax Credit for newly hired employees that have worked 400 or more hours or 180 days is 35% of wages the first year and 50% of wages for the second year. Qualified wages are capped at $10,000 per year. Wages include tax-exempt amounts received under accident or health plans, as well as educational assistance and dependent assistance programs. To apply for certification, employers must: 1) Complete IRS Form 8850, Pre-screening Notice and Certification Request for the Work Opportunity and Welfare-to-Work Tax Credits, by the date the job offer is made; 2) Complete either the ETA Form 9062, Conditional

Certification From, if it is provided by the job seeker, or ETA Form 9061, Individual Characteristics Form, if the job seeker has not received a Conditional Certification; and 3) mail the signed and dated IRS and ETA forms to their State Employment Security Agency/ State Workforce Agency/WOTC/WTW Coordinator. The IRS 8850 Form must be mailed within 21 days after the new hire's employment start date. Copies of IRS forms are available from your local IRS office or the IRS website listed above. To order forms by phone, call 800-829-3676; to order by Fax, call 703-368-9694. ETA Forms and a listing of coordinators are available through Fax-on-Demand at 877-828-2050 or from the Department of Labor website at www.uses.doleta.gov/wtw.asp.

$4,000 Tax Credit for Every Native American Employee or Spouse

Internal Revenue Service
1111 Constitution Avenue, NW
Washington, DC 20224
202-622-5000
800-829-1040 (Business Tax Questions)
www.irs.ustreas.gov/formspubs/index.html
(Indian Employment Credit)
Businesses that employ an enrolled member of an Indian tribe, or the spouse of an enrolled member, are entitled to claim a federal tax credit for 20% of the first $20,000 of wages and health insurance costs for each qualified employee. Use IRS Form 8845, Indian Employment Credit, to apply for the credit. Copies of this form are available from your local IRS office or the IRS website listed above. To order forms by phone, call 800-829-3676; to order by Fax, call 703-368-9694.

$4,000 in Tax Credits for Purchasing an Electric Vehicle

Internal Revenue Service
1111 Constitution Avenue, NW
Washington, DC 20224
202-622-5000
800-829-1040 (Business Tax Questions)
www.irs.ustreas.gov/formspubs/index.html
(Qualified Electric Vehicle Credit)
For each qualified vehicle placed in Service before 2004, the credit is 10% of the vehicle's cost (less any section 179 deductions), up to a maximum credit of $4,000. For qualified electric vehicles placed in service in 2004, the credit is 7.5% of the vehicle's cost (minus any section179 deductions) up to $3,000. To apply for this credit use IRS Form 8834, Qualified Electric Vehicle Credit. Copies of this form are available from your local IRS office or the IRS website listed above. To order forms by phone, call 800-829-3676; to order by Fax, call 703-368-9694.

$3,000 per Employee Tax Credit for Empowerment Zone Businesses

Internal Revenue Service
1111 Constitution Avenue, NW
Washington, DC 20224
202-622-5000
800-829-1040 (Business Tax Questions)
www.irs.ustreas.gov/formspubs/index.html
(Empowerment Zone Employment Credit)
Businesses located in designated empowerment zones can receive a tax credit of up to $3,000 per year for every employee they hire from the zone. The credit is up to 20% of

the first $15,000 of wages. To apply for the credit, use IRS Form 8844, Empowerment Zone Employment Credit. Copies of Form 8844 and Publication 954, Tax Incentives for Empowerment Zones and Other Distressed Communities are available from your local IRS office or the IRS website listed above. To order forms by phone, call 800-829-3676; to order by Fax, call 703-368-9694. For more information or to identify empowerment zone locations see {www.hud.gov/offices/cpd/economicdevelopment/programs/rc/index.cfm}.

70% Tax Credit for Building, Buying or Rehabilitating Low Income Housing

Internal Revenue Service
1111 Constitution Avenue, NW
Washington, DC 20224
202-622-5000
800-829-1040 (Business Tax Questions)
www.irs.ustreas.gov/formspubs/index.html
(Low Income Housing Credit)
A tax credit is available for low-income housing that was constructed, rehabilitated, or acquired after 1986. The credit is for up to 70% of the qualified basis of non-federally subsidized units, or 30% of the qualified basis of units financed with tax-exempt bonds or other federal subsidies. The credit must be claimed over a period of ten years. Use IRS Form 8586, Low Income Housing Credit, to apply for the credit. Copies of this form are available from your local IRS office or the IRS website listed above. To order forms by phone, call 800-829-3676; to order by Fax, call 703-368-9694.

$100,000 Tax Credit for Donations and Loans to Nonprofits

Internal Revenue Service
1111 Constitution Avenue, NW
Washington, DC 20224
202-622-5000
800-829-1040 (Business Tax Questions)
www.irs.ustreas.gov/formspubs/index.html
(Credit for Contributions to Selected Community Development Corporations)
Gifts or long-term loans to certain community development corporations that provide employment and business opportunities to low income individuals are eligible for a tax credit. The credit, figured over a 10 year period starting with the tax year in which the contribution was made, is for 5% of the amount of the contribution. The maximum credit allowed is $100,000. Qualified Community Development Corporations are selected by the Secretary of HUD. To apply

for this credit use IRS Form 8847, Credit for Contributions to Selected Community Development Corporations. Copies of this form are available from your local IRS office or the IRS website listed above. To order forms by phone, call 800-829-3676; to order by Fax, call 703-368-9694.

50% Tax Credit for Testing Drugs for Rare Diseases

Internal Revenue Service
1111 Constitution Avenue, NW
Washington, DC 20224
202-622-5000
800-829-1040 (Business Tax Questions)
www.irs.ustreas.gov/formspubs/index.html
(Orphan Drug Credit)
Drug companies can take a tax credit equal to 50% of the qualified clinical testing expenses for drugs that treat rare diseases and conditions. To apply for the credit, use IRS Form 8820, Orphan Drug Credit. Copies of this form are available from your local IRS office or the IRS website listed above. To order forms by phone, call 800-829-3676; to order by Fax, call 703-368-9694.

10% Tax Credit for Investments in Solar or Geothermal Energy

Internal Revenue Service
1111 Constitution Avenue, NW
Washington, DC 20224
202-622-5000
800-829-1040 (Business Tax Questions)
www.irs.ustreas.gov/formspubs/index.html
(Business Energy Tax Credit)
Businesses that invest in or purchase qualified solar or geothermal energy property can take a credit of up to 10% of the investment or purchase and installation amount. The credit is limited to $25,000 per year plus 25% of the total tax remaining after the credit is taken. To apply for the credit, use IRS Form 3468, Investment Credit, and Instructions for Form 3468. Copies of these forms are available from your local IRS office or the IRS website listed above. To order forms by phone, call 800-829-3676; to order by Fax, call 703-368-9694.

20% Tax Credit for Fixing up Historic Buildings

Internal Revenue Service
1111 Constitution Avenue, NW
Washington, DC 20224
202-622-5000
800-829-1040 (Business Tax Questions)
www.irs.ustreas.gov/formspubs/index.html
(Rehabilitation Credit-Historic Buildings)
This credit is for qualified rehabilitation expenditures made on any certified historic building. The credit is for 20% of the rehabilitation costs. To qualify for the credit the building must be a certified historic building, be substantially rehabilitated (costs exceeding $5,000), and be placed in service before the start of rehabilitation. To apply for this credit, use IRS Form 3468, Investment Credit and Instructions for Form 3468. Copies of these forms are available from your local IRS office or the IRS website listed above. To order forms by phone, call 800-829-3676; to order by Fax, call 703-368-9694.

10% Tax Credit for Fixing up Buildings Built Before 1936

Internal Revenue Service
1111 Constitution Avenue, NW
Washington, DC 20224
202-622-5000
800-829-1040 (Business Tax Questions)
www.irs.ustreas.gov/formspubs/index.html
(Rehabilitation Credit-Non-Historic Buildings)
This credit is for qualified rehabilitation expenditures made on non-historic buildings built before 1936. The credit is for 10% of the rehabilitation costs. To qualify for the credit, the building must be substantially rehabilitated (costs exceeding $5,000), be placed in service before the start of rehabilitation, and 75% of the external and internal walls must be retained. To apply for this credit, use IRS Form 3468, Investment Credit, and Instructions for Form 3468. Copies of these forms are available from your local IRS office or the IRS website listed above. To order forms by phone, call 800-829-3676; to order by Fax, call 703-368-9694.

$2,400 for Hiring a Supplemental Security Income Recipient

Internal Revenue Service
1111 Constitution Avenue, NW
Washington, DC 20224
202-622-6080 (Karin Loverud)
800-829-1040 (Business Tax Questions)
www.irs.ustreas.gov/formspubs/index.html
(Work Opportunity Tax Credit-SSI Recipient)
For each Supplemental Security Income recipient hired by the employer, a tax credit of up to $2,400 (40% of first year wages) is available under the Work Opportunity Tax Credit. All new adult employees must work a minimum of 120 or 400 hours. The tax credit is $750 for 120 hours, $1,200 for 400 hours. To apply for certification, employers must: 1) Complete IRS Form 8850, Pre-screening Notice and Certification Request for the Work Opportunity and Welfare-to-Work Tax Credits, by the date the job offer is made; 2) Complete either the ETA Form 9062, Conditional Certification Form, if it is provided by the job seeker, or ETA Form 9061, Individual Characteristics Form, if the job seeker has not received a Conditional Certification; and 3) mail the signed and dated IRS and ETA forms to their State Employment Security Agency/ State Workforce Agency/WOTC/WTW Coordinator. The IRS 8850 Form must be mailed within 21 days after the new hire's employment start date. Copies of IRS forms are available from your local IRS office or the IRS website listed above. To order forms by phone, call 800-829-3676; to order by Fax, call 703-368-9694. ETA Forms and a listing of coordinators are available through Fax-on-Demand at 877-828-2050 or from the Department of Labor website at www.uses.doleta.gov/wotcdata.cfm.

** At the time of printing, the legislative authority for the WOTC and WTW tax credit programs had expired as of December 31, 2003. Congress has introduced bills to re-authorize these tax credits, but in the meantime they are considered on hiatus. To be eligible for these tax credits during a hiatus, employers are required to file for requests for certification in a timely manner. State Workforce agencies will continue to accept requests for certification but will not issue any certifications until/unless the tax credits are reauthorized. In the past, Congress has retroactively covered authorization lapses, but there is no guarantee that this will happen again.

$2,400 for Hiring a Welfare Recipient

Internal Revenue Service
1111 Constitution Avenue, NW
Washington, DC 20224
202-622-6080 (Karin Loverud)
800-829-1040 (Business Tax Questions)
www.irs.ustreas.gov/formspubs/index.html
(Work Opportunity Tax Credit-Welfare Recipient)

For each Welfare Recipient hired by the employer, a tax credit of up to $2,400 (40% of first year wages) is available under the Work Opportunity Tax Credit. All new adult employees must work a minimum of 120 or 400 hours. The tax credit is $750 for 120 hours, $1,200 for 400 hours. Welfare recipients must be a member of a family that received Temporary Assistance for Needy Families or Aid to Families with Dependent Children for at least 9 of the 18 months before the date of hire. To apply for certification, employers must: 1) Complete IRS Form 8850, Pre-screening Notice and Certification Request for the Work Opportunity and Welfare-to-Work Tax Credits, by the date the job offer is made; 2) Complete either the ETA Form 9062, Conditional Certification Form, if it is provided by the job seeker, or ETA Form 9061, Individual Characteristics Form, if the job seeker has not received a Conditional Certification; and 3) mail the signed and dated IRS and ETA forms to their State Employment Security Agency/ State Workforce Agency/WOTC/WTW Coordinator. The IRS 8850 Form must be mailed within 21 days after the new hire's employment start date. Copies of IRS forms are available from your local IRS office or the IRS website listed above. To order forms by phone, call 800-829-3676; to order by Fax, call 703-368-9694. ETA Forms and a listing of coordinators are available through Fax-on-Demand at 877-828-2050 or from the Department of Labor website at www.uses.doleta.gov/wotcdata.cfm.

** At the time of printing, the legislative authority for the WOTC and WTW tax credit programs had expired as of December 31, 2003. Congress has introduced bills to re-authorize these tax credits, but in the meantime they are considered on hiatus. To be eligible for these tax credits during a hiatus, employers are required to file for requests for certification in a timely manner. State Workforce agencies will continue to accept requests for certification but will not issue any certifications until/unless the tax credits are reauthorized. In the past, Congress has retroactively covered authorization lapses, but there is no guarantee that this will happen again.

$2,400 for Hiring an Ex-Felon

Internal Revenue Service
1111 Constitution Avenue, NW
Washington, DC 20224
202-622-6080 (Karin Loverud)
800-829-1040 (Business Tax Questions)
www.irs.ustreas.gov/formspubs/index.html
(Work Opportunity Tax Credit-Ex-Felon)

For each Ex-Felon hired by the employer who is a member of a low-income family, a tax credit of up to $2,400 (40% of first year wages) is available under the Work Opportunity Tax Credit. All new adult employees must work a minimum of 120 or 400 hours. The tax credit is $750 for 120 hours, $1,200 for 400 hours. To apply for certification, employers must: 1) Complete IRS Form 8850, Pre-screening Notice and Certification Request for the Work Opportunity and Welfare-to-Work Tax Credits, by the date the job offer is made; 2) Complete either the ETA Form 9062, Conditional Certification Form, if it is provided by the job seeker, or ETA Form 9061, Individual Characteristics Form, if the job seeker

has not received a Conditional Certification; and 3) mail the signed and dated IRS and ETA forms to their State Employment Security Agency/ State Workforce Agency/WOTC/WTW Coordinator. The IRS 8850 Form must be mailed within 21 days after the new hire's employment start date. Copies of IRS forms are available from your local IRS office or the IRS website listed above. To order forms by phone, call 800-829-3676; to order by Fax, call 703-368-9694. ETA Forms and a listing of coordinators are available through Fax-on-Demand at 877-828-2050 or from the Department of Labor website at www.uses.doleta.gov/wotcdata.cfm.

** At the time of printing, the legislative authority for the WOTC and WTW tax credit programs had expired as of December 31, 2003. Congress has introduced bills to re-authorize these tax credits, but in the meantime they are considered on hiatus. To be eligible for these tax credits during a hiatus, employers are required to file for requests for certification in a timely manner. State Workforce agencies will continue to accept requests for certification but will not issue any certifications until/unless the tax credits are reauthorized. In the past, Congress has retroactively covered authorization lapses, but there is no guarantee that this will happen again.

$2,400 for Hiring a Veteran Whose Family is on Food Stamps

Internal Revenue Service
1111 Constitution Avenue, NW
Washington, DC 20224
202-622-6080 (Karin Loverud)
800-829-1040 (Business Tax Questions)
www.irs.ustreas.gov/formspubs/index.html
(Work Opportunity Tax Credit-Veterans and Family)

For each veteran hired by the employer a tax credit of up to $2,400 (40% of first year wages) is available under the Work Opportunity Tax Credit. The veteran or a member of his/her family must have received food stamps for at least 3 months during the 15 month period ending before the date of hire. All new adult employees must work a minimum of 120 or 400 hours. The tax credit is $750 for 120 hours, $1,200 for 400 hours. To apply for certification, employers must: 1) Complete IRS Form 8850, Pre-screening Notice and Certification Request for the Work Opportunity and Welfare-to-Work Tax Credits, by the date the job offer is made; 2) Complete either the ETA Form 9062, Conditional Certification Form, if it is provided by the job seeker, or ETA Form 9061, Individual Characteristics Form, if the job seeker has not received a Conditional Certification; and 3) mail the signed and dated IRS and ETA forms to their State Employment Security Agency/ State Workforce Agency/WOTC/WTW Coordinator. The IRS 8850 Form must be mailed within 21 days after the new hire's employment start date. Copies of IRS forms are available from your local IRS office or the IRS website listed above. To order forms by phone, call 800-829-3676; to order by Fax, call 703-368-9694. ETA Forms and a listing of coordinators are available through Fax-on-Demand at 877-828-2050 or from the Department of Labor website at www.uses.doleta.gov/wotcdata.cfm.

** At the time of printing, the legislative authority for the WOTC and WTW tax credit programs had expired as of December 31, again.2003. Congress has introduced bills to re-authorize these tax credits, but in the meantime they are considered on hiatus. To be eligible for these tax credits during a hiatus, employers are required to file for requests for certification in a timely manner. State Workforce agencies will continue to accept requests for certification but will not issue any certifications until/unless the tax credits are reauthorized. In the past, Congress has retroactively covered authorization lapses, but there is no guarantee that this will happen again.

$2,400 for Hiring a Vocational Rehabilitation Referral

Internal Revenue Service
1111 Constitution Avenue, NW
Washington, DC 20224
202-622-6080 (Karin Loverud)
800-829-1040 (Business Tax Questions)
www.irs.ustreas.gov/formspubs/index.html
(Work Opportunity Tax Credit-Vocational Rehabilitation Referral)

For each vocational rehabilitation referral hired by the employer a tax credit of up to $2,400 (40% of first year wages) is available under the Work Opportunity Tax Credit. A vocational Rehabilitation referral is a disable person who completed or is completing rehabilitative services. All new adult employees must work a minimum of 120 or 400 hours. The tax credit is $750 for 120 hours, $1,200 for 400 hours. To apply for certification, employers must: 1) Complete IRS Form 8850, Pre-screening Notice and Certification Request for the Work Opportunity and Welfare-to-Work Tax Credits, by the date the job offer is made; 2) Complete either the ETA Form 9062, Conditional Certification Form, if it is provided by the job seeker, or ETA Form 9061, Individual Characteristics Form, if the job seeker has not received a Conditional Certification; and 3) mail the signed and dated IRS and ETA forms to their State Employment Security Agency/ State Workforce Agency/WOTC/WTW Coordinator. The IRS 8850 Form must be mailed within 21 days after the new hire's employment start date. Copies of IRS forms are available from your local IRS office or the IRS website listed above. To order forms by phone, call 800-829-3676; to order by Fax, call 703-368-9694. ETA Forms and a listing of coordinators are available through Fax-on-Demand at 877-828-2050 or from the Department of Labor website at www.uses.doleta.gov/wotcdata.cfm.

** At the time of printing, the legislative authority for the WOTC and WTW tax credit programs had expired as of December 31, again.2003. Congress has introduced bills to re-authorize these tax credits, but in the meantime they are considered on hiatus. To be eligible for these tax credits during a hiatus, employers are required to file for requests for certification in a timely manner. State Workforce agencies will continue to accept requests for certification but will not issue any certifications until/unless the tax credits are reauthorized. In the past, Congress has retroactively covered authorization lapses, but there is no guarantee that this will happen again.

$2,400 for Hiring a 18-24 Year Old Member of a Family Receiving Food Stamps

Internal Revenue Service
1111 Constitution Avenue, NW
Washington, DC 20224
202-622-6080 (Karin Loverud)
800-829-1040 (Business Tax Questions)
www.irs.ustreas.gov/formspubs/index.html
(Work Opportunity Tax Credit-18-24 year old Food Stamp Recipient)

For each 18-24 year old member of a family receiving Food Stamps hired by the employer a tax credit of up to $2,400

(40% of first year wages) is available under the Work Opportunity Tax Credit. The family must have received food stamps for at least 3 months in the 15 month period ending before the date of hire. All new adult employees must work a minimum of 120 or 400 hours. The tax credit is $750 for 120 hours, $1,200 for 400 hours. To apply for certification, employers must: 1) Complete IRS Form 8850, Pre-screening Notice and Certification Request for the Work Opportunity and Welfare-to-Work Tax Credits, by the date the job offer is made; 2) Complete either the ETA Form 9062, Conditional Certification Form, if it is provided by the job seeker, or ETA Form 9061, Individual Characteristics Form, if the job seeker has not received a Conditional Certification; and 3) mail the signed and dated IRS and ETA forms to their State Employment Security Agency/ State Workforce Agency/WOTC/WTW Coordinator. The IRS 8850 Form must be mailed within 21 days after the new hire's employment start date. Copies of IRS forms are available from your local IRS office or the IRS website listed above. To order forms by phone, call 800-829-3676; to order by Fax, call 703-368-9694. ETA Forms and a listing of coordinators are available through Fax-on-Demand at 877-828-2050 or from the Department of Labor website at www.uses.doleta.gov/wotcdata.cfm.

** At the time of printing, the legislative authority for the WOTC and WTW tax credit programs had expired as of December 31, again.2003. Congress has introduced bills to re-authorize these tax credits, but in the meantime they are considered on hiatus. To be eligible for these tax credits during a hiatus, employers are required to file for requests for certification in a timely manner. State Workforce agencies will continue to accept requests for certification but will not issue any certifications until/unless the tax credits are reauthorized. In the past, Congress has retroactively covered authorization lapses, but there is no guarantee that this will happen again.

$2,400 for Hiring a 18-24 Year Old Resident of an Empowerment Zone

Internal Revenue Service
1111 Constitution Avenue, NW
Washington, DC 20224
202-622-6080 (Karin Loverud)
800-829-1040 (Business Tax Questions)
www.irs.ustreas.gov/formspubs/index.html
(Work Opportunity Tax Credit-18-24 year old Empowerment Zone resident)

For each 18-24 year old Empowerment Zone resident hired by the employer a tax credit of up to $2,400 (40% of first year wages) is available under the Work Opportunity Tax Credit. An Empowerment Zone resident is a person that lives in one of the 145 federally designated Empowerment Zones or Enterprise Communities. For more information about the location of these areas go to {www.hud.gov/cpd/ezec/ezeclist.html} , or call 800-998-9999. All new adult employees must work a minimum of 120 or 400 hours. The tax credit is $750 for 120 hours, $1,200 for 400 hours. To apply for certification, employers must: 1) Complete IRS Form 8850, Pre-screening Notice and Certification Request for the Work Opportunity and Welfare-to-Work Tax Credits, by the date the job offer is made; 2) Complete either the ETA Form 9062, Conditional Certification Form, if it is provided by the job seeker, or ETA Form 9061, Individual Characteristics Form, if the job seeker has not received a Conditional Certification; and 3) mail the signed and dated IRS and ETA forms to their State Employment Security Agency/ State Workforce Agency/WOTC/WTW Coordinator. The IRS 8850 Form must be mailed within 21 days after the new hire's employment start date. Copies of IRS forms are available from your local IRS office or the IRS website listed above. To order forms by phone, call 800-829-3676; to order by Fax, call 703-368-9694. ETA Forms and a listing of coordinators are available through Fax-on-Demand at 877-828-2050 or from the Department of Labor website at www.uses.doleta.gov/wotcdata.cfm.

** At the time of printing, the legislative authority for the WOTC and WTW tax credit programs had expired as of December 31, again.2003. Congress has introduced bills to re-authorize these tax credits, but in the meantime they are considered on hiatus. To be eligible for these tax credits during a hiatus, employers are required to file for requests for certification in a timely manner. State Workforce agencies will continue to accept requests for certification but will not issue any certifications until/unless the tax credits are reauthorized. In the past, Congress has retroactively covered authorization lapses, but there is no guarantee that this will happen again.

$2,400 for Hiring a 16-17 Year Old Resident of an Empowerment Zone

Internal Revenue Service
1111 Constitution Avenue, NW
Washington, DC 20224
202-622-6080 (Karin Loverud)
800-829-1040 (Business Tax Questions)
www.irs.ustreas.gov/formspubs/index.html
(Work Opportunity Tax Credit-16-17 year old EZ/EC resident)
For each 16-17 year old EZ/EC resident hired by the employer a tax credit of up to $2,400 (40% of first year wages) is available under the Work Opportunity Tax Credit. An Empowerment Zone resident is a person that lives in one of the 145 federally designated Empowerment Zones or

Enterprise Communities. For more information about the location of these areas go to {www.hud.gov/cpd/ezec/ezeclist.html} , or call 800-998-9999. Summer youth employees must work a minimum of 120 hours between May 1 and September 15. To apply for certification, employers must: 1) Complete IRS Form 8850, Pre-screening Notice and Certification Request for the Work Opportunity and Welfare-to-Work Tax Credits, by the date the job offer is made; 2) Complete either the ETA Form 9062, Conditional Certification Form, if it is provided by the job seeker, or ETA Form 9061, Individual Characteristics Form, if the job seeker has not received a Conditional Certification; and 3) mail the signed and dated IRS and ETA forms to their State Employment Security Agency/ State Workforce Agency/WOTC/WTW Coordinator. The IRS 8850 Form must be mailed within 21 days after the new hire's employment start date. Copies of IRS forms are available from your local IRS office or the IRS website listed above. To order forms by phone, call 800-829-3676; to order by Fax, call 703-368-9694. ETA Forms and a listing of coordinators are available through Fax-on-Demand at 877-828-2050 or from the Department of Labor website at www.uses.doleta.gov/wotcdata.cfm.

** At the time of printing, the legislative authority for the WOTC and WTW tax credit programs had expired as of December 31, again.2003. Congress has introduced bills to re-authorize these tax credits, but in the meantime they are considered on hiatus. To be eligible for these tax credits during a hiatus, employers are required to file for requests for certification in a timely manner. State Workforce agencies will continue to accept requests for certification but will not issue any certifications until/unless the tax credits are reauthorized. In the past, Congress has retroactively covered authorization lapses, but there is no guarantee that this will happen again.

State Tax Credits

Similar to the federal tax credits, states offer a variety of credits to help businesses succeed. This could be worth hundreds of thousands of dollars to help your business grow or expand. Your state Department of Revenue and your state Department of Economic Development can be of assistance in finding and understanding these tax credits. This is well worth your time and effort as the money saved could be put to better use.

By moving or locating your business in an enterprise zone, you can receive thousands of dollars in tax credits. In addition for each employee you hire in the zone or each new job created, you will receive tax credits. All the money saved can be put to use buying more equipment, setting up the business, or getting ready for your next big sale. Other tax credits include:

- Get a portion of student's wages paid back as a credit for approved work-based learning programs in Maryland.
- Get 25% credit for new equipment and materials to make wine in Missouri.
- Get up to $1,000 in tax credits for the purchase of art for your business in Rhode Island.
- In Alabama, you can get 20% back as a credit of the cost of educating your employees to get their GED. This will make your workers more capable and grateful for the helping hand.
- In Arkansas and many other states you can get up to $5,000 of your workers' salaries paid back as credit if you hire needy people.
- Clean up the environment and save 10% in Arizona.
- Provide child care for your workers (making them happy) and receive a great tax credit in Arkansas, California, Kansas, Maine, Mississippi, New Mexico, South Carolina, Rhode Island, Tennessee, and more. Even gibber tax credits are available in Georgia where 75% of employers direct cost for providing child care and 100% tax credit for the purchase of child care facilities are available.
- Receive 100% sales tax credit for purchasing an electric car for your company in Connecticut.
- Receive $6,000 tax credit for each job created for businesses in rural Florida.
- Get a tax credit for hiring a teacher in the summer in Indiana.
- Provide drug and alcohol abuse treatment for workers in Indiana and get $6,250 in credits.
- Many states offer a credit to help make your building handicapped accessible.
- Several states offer tax abatements for the restoration of building in certain areas of the state.

These are only the tip of the iceberg. Contact your state Department of Revenue or your state Department of Economic Development to learn more. In addition many cities and counties offer tax credits as well. To learn about these contact your city or county government or the chamber of commerce for help in getting the most for your dollar.

Alabama

Alabama Department of Revenue
50 North Ripley
Montgomery, AL 36132
334-242-1490
Fax: 334-242-8916
www.ador.state.al.us

Economic Development Office
Alabama Development Office
401 Adams Avenue, Suite 670
Montgomery, AL 36130-4106
800-248-0033
334-242-0400
Fax: 334-242-0415
www.ado.state.al.us

Alabama is the only state to allow the deduction of all federal income taxes paid.
No inventory tax for businesses.
Corporate income tax limited to 6.5 percent.

Income Tax Capital Credit: If a business entity invests in a qualifying project that meets certain requirements and is approved by the Alabama Department of Revenue, the company may receive an annual credit against its income tax liability generated from the qualifying project. The capital credit is equivalent to 5% of the capital costs of the qualifying project, and can be utilized for a period of 20 years beginning during the year the project is placed in service.

Net Operating Loss Carryforward: Corporate income tax law provides for a 15-year carryforward of net operating losses. In computing net income, a corporation is allowed a deduction for the sum of the net operating losses which are carried forward. Each net operating loss may be carried forward and deducted only during the 15 consecutive year period immediately following the year in which it arose.

Pollution Control Equipment Deduction: All amounts invested in pollution control equipment/materials acquired or constructed in Alabama primarily for the control, reduction, or elimination of air or water pollution are deducted directly from the income apportioned to Alabama.

Enterprise Zone Credit: The corporate income tax enterprise zone credit is offered to help encourage economic growth to areas in Alabama that are considered economically depressed. To qualify for this credit, a business must meet detailed requirements concerning site location and employee qualifications.

Educational Tax Credit: An employer could qualify to receive a credit of 20% of the actual cost of an employer sponsored educational program that enhances basic skills of employees up to and including the twelfth grade functional level.

Assessed Value fixed by Alabama Constitution: Amendment 373 of the Constitution provides that business property will be assessed at 20% of its fair market value. That is, for property with a fair market value of $1,000,000, the assessed value would be $200,000 ($1,000,000 x 20%). The combined state and local millage rate would then be applied to the assessed value.

Low Millage Rates: Section 214 of the Constitution limits the state millage rate on both real and personal property to 6.5 mills. This rate is equivalent to a tax of $6.50 for every $1000 of assessed value. However, both cities and counties may levy millage rates in addition to the state's 6.5 mills. These local rates vary but the average rate for any one locality is 43 mills, including the state's 6.5 mills. For business property with a fair market value of $1,000,000 the average property tax would be only $8,600 ($1,000,000 x 20% x .043).

Tax Incentive Reform Act: Allows qualified industries to receive abatements of non-educational ad valorem taxes for new businesses locating to Alabama, and for expansions of existing facilities in Alabama.

Raw Materials, Finished Goods, and Inventory Exemptions: All raw materials, finished goods, and stocks of goods, wares, and merchandise held for resale are statutorily exempt from property taxes.

Class 6 Cities – Exemptions from City Property Taxes: Alabama cities are classified by population. According to the 1970 Census, the following are currently Class 6 Cities: Alexander City, Athens, Auburn, Cullman, Enterprise, Fairfield, Homewood, Mountain Brook, Opelika, Ozark, Prattville, Sheffield, Sylacauga, and Talladega. These cities can grant two kinds of exemptions, separately from, and in addition to the tax abatements mentioned above. First, partial or complete exemption from "city property taxes" (which does not include city educational property taxes) for "any parcel of land or personal property located within the city for a period of not more than 15 years." Second, with respect to any parcel of commercial property located within the municipality, for a period of not more than 15 years, a partial or complete exemption from the portion of the municipal and county ad valorem taxes allocated for municipal educational purposes which exceeds 20 mills" subject to the provision that the property taxes from the parcel of property, for municipal educational purposes, for the year preceding the first year of exemption, do not decrease under the exemption.

Film Productions: Exemptions are allowed from sales tax, use tax, and lodgings tax for film projects approved by the Alabama Film Office.

Utility Gross Receipts Tax Exclusion: Electricity or natural gas used in an electrolytic or electrothermal manufacturing or compounding process may be excluded from the utility gross receipts tax and the utility service use tax.

Alaska

Alaska Department of Revenue
333 Willoughby Avenue, 11th Floor
Juneau, AK 99811
907-465-2320

Fax: 907-465-2375
www.revenue.state.ak.us

Economic Development Office
Alaska Department of Commerce, Community and Business
Development, and Economic Development
P.O. Box 110800
Juneau, AK 98111
907-465-2017
800-478-LOAN
Fax: 907-465-3767
www.dced.state.ak.us/cbd/

For information on these programs, contact Alaska
Employment Service, WOTC Coordinator, P.O. Box 25509,
Juneau, AK 99802; 907-465-5953.

- *Work Opportunity Tax Credit (WOTC):* Offers
  employers tax credits as an incentive to hire people
  from seven target groups including Alaska Temporary
  Assistance Program (ATAP) and Temporary Assistance
  for Needy Families (TANF) recipients, food stamp
  recipients, veterans, vocational rehabilitation recipients,
  ex-felons, and SSI recipients. The credit amount is two-
  tiered credit based on the first $6,000 of wages. There is
  a 25% credit for workers that worked at least 120 hours,
  but less than 400 hours. The next level has a 40% credit
  for those who worked 400 hours with a maximum
  credit of $2,400.

- *Welfare-to-Work Tax Credit (W2W):* The W2W tax
  credit is available for hiring long-term ATAP and
  TANF clients. The W2W tax credit is 35% of the first
  $10,000 in wages paid the first year, and 50% of the
  first $10,000 paid for the second year. The maximum
  tax credit is $3,500 the first year and $5,000 the second
  year for a total of $8,500.

Exploration Incentive: Up to $30 million in qualifying costs
can be credited against future state corporate income tax,
mining license tax and production royalties. Geophysical and
geochemical surveys, trenching, bulk sampling, drilling,
metallurgical testing and underground exploration are
included as qualifying costs. Unused credit can be retained
for 15 years and may be assigned to successors in interest.
For more information, contact Department of Natural
Resources, Division of Oil and Gas, 550 West 7th Ave., Suite
800, Anchorage, AK 99501; 907-269-8900;
{www.dog.dnr.state.ak.us/oil/programs/incentives/incentives.
htm}.

Arizona

Arizona Department of Revenue
1600 West Monroe
Phoenix, AZ 85007-4772
602-255-2060
Fax: 602-542-4772
www.revenue.state.az.us

Economic Development Office
Department of Commerce
3800 N. Central, Suite 1500
Phoenix, AZ 85012
602-280-1300
800-542-5684
Fax: 620-280-1339
www.commerce.state.az.us/

Corporate income tax is levied for all firms at 6.968 percent.
The minimum filing amount is $50. In general, Arizona:

- Has no corporate franchise tax
- Business inventories are exempt from property tax
- Levies no state income tax on dividends from
  controlled subsidiaries in other states (parent
  companies).
- Has a five-year accelerated depreciation schedule
  for assessing valuation of class three and class
  four personal property.
- No worldwide unitary tax
- Virtually all services are exempt from sales tax
- 100% of NOL may be carried forward for five
  years

Military Reuse Zone: The Arizona Legislature designated the
former Williams Air Force Base, now known as Williams
Gateway Airport, as a Military Reuse one. Companies
locating within this zone will have their personal property
classified as class 6, representing an 40-60 percent property
tax saving, for five years. In addition, there is a transaction
privilege tax exemption for many types of construction that is
performed for an eligible company located in a military reuse
zone. There are also income tax credits for each new job
created. {www.azcommerce.com/Business/MRZ%20Home%
20Page.html}

Research and Development Income Tax Credit: This is a
state income tax credit for qualified research and
development done in Arizona. This includes research
conducted at a state university and funded by the company.
The maximum credit is $100,000 in year one, $250,000 in
year two, $400,000 in year three, and $500,000 in year four
and subsequent years. The program allows a 15-year carry-
forward. {www.azcommerce.com/Business/Rdincometax
credit.html}

Pollution Control Tax Credit: Provides a 10 percent income
tax credit on real or personal property used to control or
prevent pollution. {www.azcommerce.com/Business/polluti
on%20control.htm}

Accelerated Depreciation: Provides an aggressive
depreciation schedule to encourage new capital investment
and reduce personal property tax liability. {www.az
commerce.com/Business/Accelerated%20Depreciation.html}

The Enterprise Zones Program: Arizona's Enterprise Zone
Program offers a state income tax credit up to $3,000 over a
three-year period. It also offers property tax reclassification
for eligible companies meeting employment and industry
requirements. Benefits are based on net new job creation,
employment of economically disadvantaged or dislocated
workers and location in an enterprise zone. {www.az
commerce.com/Business/ez%20Home%20page.html}

Information Technology Tax Credit: A tax credit for
businesses for the training of up to 20 employees in IT skills
during a calendar year. The maximum per employee tax
credit is $1,500. {www.azcommerce.com/workforce/IT%20
Training%20Tax%20Credit.html}

Government Property Lease Excise Tax Program:
Businesses that lease parcels from the City instead of owning
them outright, can enjoy a tax benefit. All real property tax is
waived and replaced with an excise tax which is an
established rate per square foot and based on the type of use.
The rate is then reduced every ten years by 20% until the 51st
year when the tax becomes zero. In the Downtown
Commerce Park, the excise tax has been abated for the first 8
years after the certificate of occupancy.

Arkansas

Arkansas Department of Finance and Administration
1900 West 7th Street
Little Rock, AR 72201
501-682-7089
Fax: 501-682-7094
www.ark.org/dfa

Economic Development Office
Arkansas Economic Development Commission
1 State Capitol Mall
Little Rock, AR 72201
501-682-1121
Fax: 501-682-7394
www.aedc.state.ar.us

Arkansas Economic Development Act (AEDA): To utilize the AEDA program, companies must sign a financial agreement prior to construction outlining the terms of the incentives and stipulations. There are two basic incentives provided: A state corporate income tax credit up to 100% of the total amount of annual debt service paid to the lender financing a project; Refund of sales and use taxes on buildings and equipment associated with a project during the period specified by the financial agreement. {www.1-800-arkansas.com/incentives/aeda.htm}

Advantage Arkansas Program: A job tax credit program for qualifying new and expanding companies which provides corporate income tax credits and sales and use tax refunds to companies locating or expanding in Arkansas. The state income tax credit is equal to 100 times the average hourly wage of each new employee, with a $3,000 cap per employee. That multiplier increases to 400 with a $6,000 cap per employee to businesses located in a high unemployment county. {www.1-800-arkansas.com/incentives/advantage _arkansas.com}

Income Tax Credit: Advantage Arkansas provides a credit on income tax equal to the average hourly wage of each new worker times 100, with a $3,000 cap per employee. The multiplier increases from 100 to 400 when a business locates in a county that had an unemployment rate equal to or in excess of 150 percent of the state's average unemployment rate for the previous calendar year; there is a $6,000 cap per employee in these counties. Employees must be Arkansas taxpayers to qualify for the credit. The income tax credit begins in the year in which the new employees are hired. Any unused portion of the credit may be applied against income tax for the succeeding nine years. {www.1-800-arkansas.com/incentives/advantage_arkansas.com}

InvestArk Tax Credit: Available to industries established in Arkansas for 2 years or longer investing $5 million or more in plant or equipment. A credit against the manufacturer's state sales and use tax liability of 7% of the total project cost, not to exceed 50% of the total sales and use tax liability in a single year, is allowed. {www.1-800-arkansas.com/incentives/investark.htm}

Free Port Law: No tax on goods in transit or raw materials and finished goods destined for out-of-state sales. {www.1-800-arkansas.com}

Child Care Facility Incentive Program: Companies can receive a sales and use tax refund on the initial cost of construction materials and furnishings purchased to build and equip an approved child care facility. Additionally, a corporate income tax credit of 3.9% of the total annual payroll of the workers employed exclusively to provide childcare service, or a $5,000 income tax credit for the first year the business provides its employees with a day care facility is also available. {www.1-800-arkansas.com/incentives/child_care.htm}

Tourism Development: Provides state sales tax and corporate income tax credits up to 10% of approved project costs for the creation or expansion of eligible tourist attractions exceeding $500,000. The sales tax credit ranges between 10% and 25%. The corporate income tax credit is equal to 100 times the average hourly wage of each new worker, with a $3,000 cap per employee. The multiplier increases to 400 for locations in high unemployment counties. Those credits have a cap of $6,000 per employee. {www.1-800-arkansas.com/incentives/tourism_development.htm}

Recycling Equipment Tax Credit: Allows taxpayers to receive a tax credit for the purchase of equipment used exclusively for reduction, reuse, or recycling of solid waste material for commercial purposes, whether or not for profit, and the cost of installation of such equipment by outside contractors. The amount of the credit shall equal 30% of the cost of eligible equipment and installation costs. {www.1-800-arkansas.com/incentives/recycling_equipment.htm}

Motion Picture Incentive Act: Qualifying motion picture production companies spending in excess of $500,000 within six months, or $1 million within 12 months may receive a refund of state sales and use taxes paid on qualified expenditures incurred in conjunction with a film, telefilm, music video, documentary, episodic television show, or commercial advertisement. {www.1-800-arkansas.com/Incentives/motion_picture.htm}

Biotechnology Development and Training Act: Offers three different income tax credits to taxpayers furthering biotechnical business development. The first credit is a 5% income tax credit applied to costs to build and equip eligible biotechnical facilities. The second credit allows a 30% income tax credit both for eligible employee training costs and for contract with state-supported institutions for higher education to conduct qualified cooperative research projects. The third credit allows an income tax credit for qualified research in biotechnology, including but not limited to the cost of purchasing, licensing, developing, or protecting intellectual property. This credit is equal to 20% of the amount the cost of qualified research exceeds the cost of such resource in the base year. {www.1-800-arkansas.com/incentives/biotechnology.htm}

Emerging Technology Development: Manufactures of high-growth energy technologies on the verge of full entry into the world market are eligible for a state income tax credit. The credit is equal to 50% of the cost of purchasing or constructing a facility that designs, develops, or produces photvoltaics (solar cells), electric vehicle components, fuel cells, micro-turbines, Stirling engines, and nanotechnology. There is a carry-forward of 14 years. {www.1-800-arkansas.com/Incentives/Emerging_Technology.htm}

Tuition Reimbursement Tax Credit: Eligible businesses that reimburse employees for educational expenses can receive a 30% income tax credit for approved expenses. The education must be from an accredited Arkansas post-secondary institution. {www.1-800-arkansas.com/Incentives/index.htm}

Tax Back: Advantage Arkansas participants are eligible for a refund of sales and use taxes for building materials and taxable equipment connected with the eligible project. Applicants for this program must obtain an endorsement resolution from the local governing authority, must meet the same qualification criteria as Advantage Arkansas and must be approved by the Arkansas Department of Economic Development.

Chemical, Catalysts and Reagents Exemption on Sales Tax: Arkansas exempts from sales and use tax catalysts, chemicals, reagents, and solutions that are consumed or used in manufacturing processes. Chemicals, catalysts and reagents used in manufacturing to reduce or prevent air, water, and other contamination are also exempt from sales and use taxes.

Public Roads Improvement Credit: The Arkansas Public Roads Improvement Credit Act of 1999 provides an income tax credit to any individual or corporation that contributes to the Public Road Incentive Fund. The contribution may be made to a specific project or a general fund. The credit cannot exceed 33 percent of the taxpayer's contribution. In any one tax year, the credit cannot exceed 50 percent of the taxpayer's net Arkansas state income tax liability after all other credits and reductions have been calculated. Any amount over 50 percent can be carried forward up to three years.

ArkPlus Program: This program allows a state credit of 10% of the total cost of an approved new investment project in the state. It must involve an investment of $2 million to $5 million in plant construction or expansion project. The credit may not exceed 50% of the annual Arkansas income tax liability resulting from the project. There are also employment conditions attached.

Research and Development Credit: There is a 33% income tax credit for individuals that pay for research performed at Arkansas universities. There is now an additional credit of 10% for eligible businesses that perform in-house research, capped at $10,000 per year. Targeted businesses may also earn transferable income tax credits equal to 33% of approved expenditures for in-house research.

Targeted Business Credits: Incentives are available for start-up companies in the form of a transferable income tax credit that is equal to 10% of payroll for up to five years, a transferable income tax credit for 33% of eligible research and development costs, and sales and use tax refunds on building materials and necessary equipment. The business must be in an emerging sector that is less than five years old, have an annual payroll between $200,000 and $1 million, and pay at least 150 percent to 180 percent of the county's current average hourly wage, depending upon the tier of the county in which the business locates.

Create Rebate: Businesses hiring specified new, full-time, permanent employees within 24 months after completion of an approved expansion and/or new location project may be eligible for the Create Rebate Program. The company may receive a financial rebate from 3.9% to 5% of the annual payroll of the new, full-time, permanent employees. The rebate is dependent on the county in which the business is located. A minimum payroll of $2 million annually is required. Incentives are available approximately 12 months after the business has fulfilled the minimum payroll requirements.

California

California Franchise Tax Board
P.O. Box 1468
Sacramento, CA 95812-1468

916-845-6600
Fax: 916-845-6614
www.ftb.ca.gov

Economic Development Office
California Trade and Commerce Agency
1102 Q Street, Suite 6000
Sacramento, CA 95814
916-324-3788
http://commerce.ca/gov/state.Hca/ Hca_homepage.jsp

Manufacturers Investment Credit: Manufacturers operating in California are eligible for a 6% manufacturers' investment credit (MIC). This credit is generally unlimited.

Partial Sales & Use Tax: Provides "new" or start up companies the option of a 5% partial sales or use tax exemption on all qualifying manufacturing property purchased or leased generally during the company's first three years of operation.

Research and Development Credit: Research and development tax credits allow companies to receive a credit of 11% for qualifying research expenses (research done in-house) and 24% for basic research payments (payments to an outside company), making it the highest in the nation.

Net Operating Loss Carryover: Allows businesses that experience a loss for the year to carry this loss forward to the next year in order to offset income in the following year.

Enterprise Zone Program: Encourages business development in 39 designated areas through numerous special zone incentives.

Local Agency Military Base Recovery Area: Designations which are similar to enterprise zones allowing communities to extend the aforementioned California tax credits to companies locating in a LAMBRA zone.

Child Care Tax Credit: For employers who pay or incur costs for the start up of a child care program or construction of an on-site child care facility are eligible for a credit against state income taxes equal to 30% of its costs, up to a maximum of $50,000 in one year. Excess credits may be carried over to succeeding years.

Joint Strike Fighter Income Tax Credits: California recently created two entirely new income tax credits for businesses involved in the Joint Strike Fighter Program. They are 1) a hiring wage credit and 2) a property credit. These credits apply to taxpayers under initial contract or subcontract to manufacture property for ultimate use in a Joint Strike Fighter. The credits are available for taxable years beginning on or after January 1, 2001, and before January 1, 2006.

Rural Investment Tax Exemption (RITE) Program: RITE provides a partial sales and use tax exemption to qualifying businesses that are located in one of twelve designated high unemployment counties. Qualifying investments and job creation levels must be maintained for at least 24 months.

In-Lieu Sales or Use Tax Refund: A business may prefer to claim an in-lieu sales or use tax refund equal to the MIC available for the current year. The company can elect to file a claim for refund equal to the amount of MIC the company could have used to offset current year franchise or income tax liability and can be claimed no sooner than the MIC could have been claimed.

Manufacturing Enhancement Area (MEA): The purpose of this program is to stimulate job creation in areas experiencing triple the State's unemployment in a Border Environment Cooperation Commission Region. Special state and local incentives encourage business investment and promote the creation of new jobs. Program benefits for companies located in MEAs include: streamlined local regulatory controls; reduced local permitting fees; and $26,894 or more in state tax credits for each qualified employee hired.

The Tulare Targeted Tax Area (TTA): this program is very similar to Enterprise Zones. TTA incentives are only available to companies located in the TTA and engaged in a trade or business within specified Standard Industrial Codes. State incentives include: tax credits for sales and use taxes paid on certain machinery, machinery parts, and equipment; tax credits for hiring qualified employees; fifteen year net operating loss carry-forward; and accelerated expensing deduction.

For information on the above programs, contact the website at {commerce.ca.gov/state/ttca/ttca_investment_display.jsp}

Colorado

Colorado Department of Revenue
1375 Sherman Street
Denver, CO 80261
303-866-3091
www.revenue.state.co.us

Economic Development Office
Office of Economic Development and International Trade
1625 Broadway, Suite 1710
Denver, CO 80202
303-892-3840
Fax: 303-892-3848
TDD: 800-659-2656
www.state.co.us/gov_dir/oed.html

For all tax incentive programs, contact the website at {www.state.co.us/oed/bus_fin/contents.html}

Investment Tax Credits: The Colorado Tax Equity Act, signed into law during the 1987 legislative session, reinstates the Colorado Investment Tax Credit, up to $1,000 per year, for tax years beginning on or after January 1, 1998, based on 10% of what the Federal Investment Tax Credit would have been had such credit not been restricted by the Tax Reform Act of 1986. Excess credits may be carried forward up to three years.

Enterprise Zone Tax Credits: Enterprise Zones are geographic areas designated to promote economic development. Sixteen such zones have been designated in Colorado. They cover most rural areas of the state with the exception of the ski area/resort counties. There are also urban zones designated to attract investment and jobs to selected areas. Enterprise Zones offer the following advantages to businesses locating or expanding within their boundaries:

- A $500 credit for each new full-time employee working within the Zone.
- Double job tax credit for agricultural processing or manufacturing.
- $200 job tax credit for employer health insurance.
- Local government incentives.
- 3% investment tax credit for businesses making investments in equipment used exclusively in an Enterprise Zone.

- Exemption from state sales and use taxes for manufacturing equipment.
- Income tax credit of up to 3% for expenditures on research and development activities (as defined in federal tax laws) in an Enterprise Zone.
- A credit of 25% of qualified expenditures up to $50,000 to rehabilitate buildings which are at least 20 years old which have been vacant at least two years.
- A 25% tax credit for private contributions to local zone administrators for qualifying projects or programs within zones.
- A 10% tax credit for employer expenditures for qualified job training programs.
- A $2,000 tax credit for each new employee hired in economically depressed rural areas. (An additional $500 per employee hired in value-added agricultural processing business begins as of January 1, 2003.)

Sales Tax Exemptions: For purchases over $500 on machinery and machine tools purchased for use in manufacturing; Purchases of electricity, coal, gas, or fuel oil for use in processing, manufacturing, and all industrial uses; Sale of tangible personal property used in BioTech Research and Development; Interstate long distance telephone charges; component parts; packaging materials; aircraft parts used in general maintenance; ink and newsprint; and farm equipment and machinery.

Local Governments: May provide incentive payments or property tax credits based on the amount of increased property taxes for qualifying new business activity in their jurisdictions.

Connecticut

Connecticut Department of Revenue Services
25 Sigourney Street
Hartford, CT 06106
800-382-9463 (in-state)
860-297-5962
Fax: 860-297-5698
www.drs.state.ct.us/index.html

Economic Development Office
Economic Resource Center
Department of Economic and Community Development
805 Brooks St., Bldg. 4
Rocky Hill, CT 06067-3405
860-571-7136
800-392-2122
Fax: 860-571-7150
www.cerc.com

Corporate Tax Credits:
- 50% for financial institutions constructing new facilities and adding new employees
- 5% annual credit for fixed capital investment in tangible personal property
- 5% annual credit for investments in human capital, employee training, childcare, and donations to higher education for technology training
- 10% credit for increased investment in machinery and equipment for companies with 250 or fewer full-time permanent employees
- 5% credit for companies with 251 to 800 full time permanent employees in the state
- Research and development credits from 1% to 6% research and development expenditures

Getting Money Back In Taxes

- 100% credit for property taxes paid on data processing hardware, peripheral equipment and software
- 25% credit for an increase in grant to institutions of higher learning for R&D related to technology advancement
- 100% credit for investment over 10 years in an investment fund creating insurance related facilities and jobs
- 100% credit for SBA loan guarantee fees paid by companies with less than $5 million in gross receipts
- Other credits for low-income housing, contributions to neighborhood assistance programs, and alternative employee transportation

Corporate Business Tax Exemptions:
- All insurance companies (Connecticut incorporated and non-Connecticut incorporated)
- Corporate income, insurance premiums and sales and use taxes for certain banks, insurers and investment companies located in the Hartford Financial Services Export Zone that conduct all business with non-US persons
- Capital gains from the sale of protected open space or class I or II water company land to the state or certain entities
- Non-US corporations whose sole activities in Connecticut are trading stocks, securities or commodities for their own account

Corporate Sales Tax Exemptions:
- 100% on machinery used in the manufacture of finished products or in the biotechnology industry and materials, tools, and fuel used in the manufacture or fabrication of finished products or in the biotechnology industry. 50% on machinery, tools, fuels and equipment that may not meet the requirements for the 100% exemption
- 100% on computer and data processing services beginning July 1, 2002. Declining 1% annually from current 3%
- 100% on repair, replacement and component parts for manufacturing machinery
- 100% calibration services, registration and compliance services related to ISO 9000 and personnel training services offered by colleges or universities
- 100% on vehicles powered by alternative fuels, vehicle conversion equipment and alternative fuel filling station equipment
- 100% on fuel and electric power used in manufacturing or to heat a manufacturing facility, provided that a 75% usage test is met
- 100% of the cost of services related to creating and maintaining a website
- 100% of the cost of aircraft, repairs, parts and services on aircraft exceeding 6,000 pounds maximum takeoff weight
- 100% on safety apparel worn by employees
- 100% on goods purchased inside or outside Connecticut for use outside Connecticut provided all conditions are met

Real and Personal Property Tax Exemptions
- 100% for 5 years on newly acquired and installed machinery and equipment eligible for 5-7 year depreciation
- 100% for inventories
- 30% to 100% from the increased assessment for personal property for manufacturers and 20% to 50% for eligible real property improvements can

be offered by towns for 2 to 7 years, depending on the investment amount
- 100% for unbundled software and machinery and equipment that will be exempt once installed and used
- 100% for 5 years on new commercial motor vehicles weighing over 26,000 pounds that are used to transport freight for hire and on all new commercial vehicles weighing over 55,000 pounds

Other Tax Incentives
- Connecticut's corporation business tax rate is 7.5%. There is no tax on Subchapter S companies.
- Passive investment companies that hold loans secured by real property are not subject to corporation business tax
- Financial service companies are allowed a single factor apportionment method based on customer location
- Net operating loses can be carried forward 20 years for losses incurred on or after January 1, 2000

Delaware
Delaware Department of Finance
Division of Revenue
820 North French Street
Wilmington, DE 19801
800-292-7826 (in-state)
302-577-8205
Fax: 302-577-8202
www.state.de.us/revenue

Economic Development Office
Delaware Economic Development Office
John D. Wilk
99 Kings Highway
P.O. Box 1401
Dover, DE 19901
302-739-4271
Fax: 302-739-2028
www.state.de.us/dedo/ index.htm

Bank Franchise Tax Credits: For taxable years beginning after December 31, 1996, credits against bank franchise taxes are available to qualifying firms. Credits are $400 per year for each new qualifying employee in excess of 50 new employees and are for a period of ten years.

Export Trading Company Exemption: Delaware exporters who qualify as an Export Trading Company can receive exemption from Delaware income and gross receipts taxes.

Targeted Area Tax Incentives: Firms which qualify for targeted industry credits and are located in one of the targeted areas, qualify for corporate income tax credits of $650 for each new employee and $650 for each new $100,000 investment.

Retention and Expansion Tax Credits: Corporate income tax credits and gross receipts tax reductions are available to qualifying manufacturers and wholesalers planning new facilities or large expansions. The maximum annual credit cannot exceed $500,000. Gross receipts tax reductions are limited to a maximum total credit of $500,000 over the ten-year life.

Green Industries Tax Credits: Manufacturers that reduce their chemical waste, as reported under the Toxics Release Inventory, by 10% or use 25% of recycled materials, are granted a $400 corporate income tax credit.

Public Utility Tax Rebates for Industrial Users: Industrial firms meeting the criteria for targeted industries tax credits are eligible for a rebate of 50% of the Public Utilities Tax imposed on new or increased consumption of gas and electricity for five years.

Property Tax Incentives: The cities of Wilmington, Newark, Dover and the counties of New Castle and Kent offer a variety of property tax incentives for new construction, renovation, and property improvements. Amounts vary.

District of Columbia

Office of the Chief Financial Officer
1350 Pennsylvania Avenue, NW, Suite 203
Washington, DC 20004
202-727-2476
Fax: 202-727-1643
http://cfo.dc.gov/main.asp

Economic Development Office
Office of Economic Development
1350 Pennsylvania Ave., NW, Suite 317
Washington, DC 20004
202-727-6365
www.dcbiz.dc.gov

Enterprise Zones: Consists of 65 census tracts with 20% and higher poverty rate. Benefits include:
- *Tax-Exempt Bond Financing*: Up to 15 million.
- *Federal Capital Gains Exemption*: Requires 80% of the business' total gross income be derived from a business or trade conducted within the enterprise zone.
- *Employment Tax Credit*: Up to $3,000 for each employee at the EZ facility who is also a D.C. resident.
- *Special Expensing Allowance*: $38,500 - $44,000 available for business equipment and depreciable property purchase by EZ businesses.

Public Schools Tax Credit: Available for contributions to school rehabilitation and repair, the provision of school equipment, materials and teacher training and the advancement of innovative K-12 programs.

Work Opportunity Tax Credits: $2,400 annual work opportunity tax credit for each worker in the first year of employment.

Welfare-To-Work Tax Credit: $8,500 welfare to work one-time tax credit for employees certified by D.C. DOES.

Supermarket Exemption Act: exempts the owner of a qualified supermarket in a priority development area from sales taxes on the purchase of building materials and equipment for construction or substantial rehabilitation of a qualified supermarkets.

NET 2000 Incentives (available only to qualified high technology companies):
- *NET 2000 Affordable Facilities*: District agrees to defray facility costs of qualified high tech companies by creating a program to provide funding assistance for security deposits, and more.

- *NET 2000 Capital Gains Tax Exemption*: Exclusion from taxation of certain capital gains from the sale, exchange or rollover of stock, partnership interests and other assets of qualified high tech companies.
- *NET 2000 Employment Training Credits*: Credit for each employee of up to $20,000 for costs of approved training during the first 18 months of employment.
- *NET 2000 Franchise Tax Reduction*: Zero franchise tax on unincorporated business.
- *NET 2000 Personal Property Tax Abatement*: Ten-year exemption of personal property taxes.
- *NET 2000 Real Property Tax Abatement*: Five-year abatement of increases in property tax rates attributable to renovations to accommodate technology companies.
- *NET 2000 Relocation Expense Reimbursement*: $5000 reimbursement of certain moving expenses. Up to $7,500 reimbursement of payments for lease or purchase of employee's primary residence in District.
- *NET 2000 Sales and Use Tax Exemption*: Qualified high tech companies are exempt from certain sales taxes.
- *NET 2000 Wage Tax Credit:* Credit of 1% of wages paid for the first 24 months of employment up to $5000 per employee.

Florida

Florida Department of Revenue
1379 Blountstown Highway
Tallahassee, FL 32304-2716
800-352-3671 (in-state)
850-488-6800
Fax: 850-922-3676
www.myflorida.com/dor

Economic Development Office
Florida Economic Development Council
P.O. Box 3186
Tallahassee, FL 32315
850-201-FEDC
Fax: 850-201-3330
www.fedc.net

Enterprise Florida
390 N. Orange Ave., Suite 1300
Orlando, FL 32801
407-316-4600
Fax 407-316-4599
www.floridabusiness.com

No corporate income tax on limited partnerships, individuals, estates, and private trusts and subchapter S corporations.
No state personal income tax.
No inventory or goods in transit tax.
No collected or assessed property tax at the state level.
No sales tax on "Boiler Fuels" used at a fixed Florida location in an industrial manufacturing, processing, production or compounding process.
No sales and use tax on goods manufactured or produced in the state for resale for export outside the state.
No corporate franchise tax on capital stock.
No sales tax on purchase of raw materials incorporated in a final product for resale
No sales tax on co-generation of electricity.

The Qualified Target Industry Tax Refund Program: This program provides an inducement for target industry to locate new facilities in Florida or to expand existing facilities in

Florida. The program provides tax refunds of $3,000 per new job created. The incentive is increased to $6,000 per job if the company locates in a rural county or an Enterprise Zone. Higher awards are available to companies paying very high wages. To quality for the "QTI" program, a company must create at least 10 new jobs (or a 10% increase for expanding Florida companies), pay an average of at least 115% of area wages, have a significant positive impact on the community and have local support.

Enterprise Zone Program: Offers financial incentives to businesses to encourage private investment as well as employment opportunities for residents of 30 designated Enterprise Zones. Tax incentives are available to all types of businesses located within a designated zone which employ zone residents, rehabilitate real property or purchase business equipment to be used in the zone. Tax credits, sales tax exemptions and refunds are also available. {www.eflorida.com/infocenter/incentives/incentives.htm}

Sales and Use Tax Exemptions:

- Semiconductor, defense and space technology-based industry transactions involving manufacturing or research equipment.
- Purchases of machinery and equipment used by a new or expanding Florida business to manufacture, produce, or process tangible personal property for sale.
- Labor, parts and materials used in repair of and incorporated into machinery and equipment that qualify for sales tax exemption upon purchase (phased in over four years, 75% exempt on July 1, 2000).
- Aircraft parts, modification, maintenance and repair, sale or lease of qualified aircraft.
- Commercial space activity-launch vehicles, payloads and fuel, machinery and equipment for production of items used exclusively at Spaceport Florida.
- Labor component of research and development expenditures.
- Electricity used in the manufacturing process

Georgia

Georgia Department of Revenue
1800 Century Center Boulevard, NE
Atlanta, GA 30345-3205
404-417-4900
Fax: 404-417-4901
www2.state.ga.us/Departments/DOR

Economic Development Office
Office of Economic Development
60 Executive Park South, NE
Suite 250
Atlanta, GA 30329-2231
404-679-4940
Fax: 800-736-1155
www.dca.state.ga.us

Research and Development Tax Credit: Companies are eligible for a tax credit on research expenses for research conducted within Georgia for any business or headquarters of any such business engaged in manufacturing, warehousing and distribution, processing, telecommunications, tourism, and research and development industries. The credit is 10% of the additional research expense over the base amount and may be carried forward ten years, but may not exceed 50% of the business' net tax liability in any one year. {www.dca.state.ga.us/economic/summary.html}

Small Business Growth Companies Tax Credit: Tax credit is granted for any business or headquarters of any such business engaged in manufacturing, warehousing and distribution, processing, telecommunications, tourism, and research and development industries having a state net taxable income which is 20% or more above that of the preceding year if its net taxable income in each of the two preceding years was also 20% or more. The credit applies to companies whose total tax liability does not exceed $1.5 million. {www.dca.state.ga.us/economic/summary.html}

Georgia Employment Tax Credit Program: A tax credit on Georgia income taxes for eligible businesses that create new jobs in counties or "less-developed" census tract areas. {www.dca.state.ga.us/economic/taxcredit.html}

Job Tax Credit: Companies engaged in manufacturing, warehousing and distribution, processing, telecommunications, tourism or research and development that create 5 – 25 jobs, depending on which tier county they are located in, may receive between a $750 and $3,500-per-job tax credit. Companies that locate in industrial enterprise zones are required to create 10 new jobs to be eligible for this tax credit. {www.dca.state.ga.us/economic/taxcredit.html}

Investment Tax Credit: Taxpayers operating an existing manufacturing or telecommunications facility or telecommunications support facility in Georgia for three years may obtain a tax credit. The credit is based on a tier system. There are four tier counties. The county in which your business is located determines what percentage of credit you can receive. There is a 1% to 5% range for a credit with a $50,000 investment. That credit increases by 3% for recycling, pollution control and defense conversion activities. {www.dca.state.ga.us/economic/summary.html}

Optional Investment Tax Credit: Taxpayers qualifying for the investment tax credit may choose an optional investment tax credit with the following threshold criteria: Designated Minimum % Tax Area Investment Credit: Tier 1: $5 million 10%; Tier 2, $10 million 8%; Tier 3 or Tier 4, $20 million 6%. The credit may be claimed for 10 years, provided the qualifying property remains in service throughout that period. A taxpayer must choose either the regular or optional investment tax credit. Once this election is made, it is irrevocable. {www.dca.state.ga.us/economic/summary.html}

Industrial Enterprise Zones: The City of Atlanta, as authorized under a special provision of Georgia law, has designated two industrial parks as industrial enterprise zones. Companies in both the Atlanta and Southside industrial parks receive 100% freeport on all three classes of inventory and may receive real property tax reduction for up to 25 years. All buildings constructed in these enterprise zones are exempted from local property taxes at levels that begin at 100%. These exemptions decrease in increments of 20% every five years. New businesses in both parks are eligible for a $2,500-per job tax credit for a payroll of ten or more persons.

The Atlanta Empowerment Zone: Businesses which locate in the federally designated City of Atlanta Empowerment Zone and employ residents from this zone are eligible for various federal and state tax incentives, job training benefits and other assistance. A local executive board decides and manages the allocation of federal funds that are channeled through the State of Georgia.

Commercial Enterprise Zone: City of Atlanta offers a commercial enterprise zone designation for office employers applying in portions of the city including the central business district. Substantial property tax relief is possible.

Child Care Credits: Employers who provide or sponsor child care for employees are eligible for a tax credit of up to 75% of the employers' direct costs. The credit cannot be more than 50% of the taxpayer's total state income tax liability for that taxable year. Any credit claimed but not used in any taxable year may be carried forward for five years from the close of the taxable year in which the cost of the operation was incurred. In addition, employers who purchase qualified child care property will receive a credit totaling 100% of the cost of such property. These two child care credits can be combined.

Retraining Tax Credit: This credit allows some employers to claim certain costs of retraining employees to use new equipment, new technology, or new operating systems. The credit can be worth 50% of the direct costs of retraining full-time employees up to $500 per employee per approved retraining program per year. The credit cannot be more than 50% of the taxpayer's total state income tax liability for a tax year. Credits claimed but not used may be carried forward for 10 years. {www.dca.state.ga.us/economic/summary.html}

Ports Activity Job Tax & Investment Credits: Businesses or the headquarters of any such businesses engaged in manufacturing, warehousing and distribution, processing, telecommunications, tourism, or research and development that increase their port traffic tonnage through Georgia ports by more than 10% over their 1997 base year port traffic, or by more than 10% over 75 net tons, five containers or 10 20-foot equivalent units (TEU's) during the previous 12-month period are qualified for increased job tax credits or investment tax credits. {www.dca.state.ga.us/economic/summary.html}

Headquarters Tax Credit: Companies establishing their headquarters or relocating their headquarters to Georgia may be entitled to a tax credit if certain criteria are met. The credit may be taken against Georgia income tax liability and a company's withholding taxes. Credits may be carried forward for 10 years. {www.dca.state.ga.useconomic/summary.html}

The Georgia Tax Credit for Adult Basic Skills Education: Designed to encourage businesses to provide or sponsor basic skills education programs for their employees. Business enterprises may benefit by providing or sponsoring for their employees basic education skills that enhance reading, writing, or mathematical skills up to and including the 12th grade level. {www.dtae.org/adultlit/workplaceliteracy.html}

Job Tax Credit For Joint Development Authorities: Provides for an additional $500 job tax credit per job for a business locating within the jurisdiction of a joint authority of two or more contiguous counties.

State Tax Exemptions:

- *Manufacturing Machinery and Computer Sales Tax Exemption*: Provides for an exemption from the sales and use tax for 1) machinery used directly in the manufacture of tangible personal property when the machinery is bought to replace or upgrade machinery in a manufacturing plant presently existing in the state and machinery components which are purchased to upgrade machinery used directly in the manufacture of tangible personal property in a manufacturing plant; 2) machinery used directly in the manufacture of tangible personal property when the machinery is incorporated as additional machinery for the first time into a manufacturing plant presently existing in this state; 3) machinery which is used directly in the manufacture of tangible personal property when the machinery is incorporated for the first time into a new manufacturing plant located in this state; 4) machinery used directly in the remanufacture of aircraft engines, parts, and components on a factory basis; 5) on the first $150,000 on each part and phased in in 20% increments from January 1, 2001 to January 1, 2005, the sale or use of repair or replacement parts, machinery clothing or replacement machinery clothing, molds or replacement molds, dies or replacement dies, and tooling or replacement tooling for machinery used directly in the manufacture of tangible personal property in a manufacturing plant presently existing in this state; 6) overhead material consumed in the performance of certain contracts between the Department of Defense or NASA and a contractor employing 500 or more full time employees engaged in manufacturing; 7) the sale or lease of computer equipment to be used at a facility or facilities in this state to any high-tech company classified under certain NAICS Codes where such sale of computer equipment for any calendar year exceeds $15 million, or, in the event of lease of such computer equipment, the fair market value of such leased computer equipment for any calendar year exceeds $15 million; and 8) the sale of machinery, equipment and materials incorporated into and used in the construction or operation of a clean room of Class 100 or less in Georgia, provided that such clean room is sued directly in the manufacture of tangible personal property. {www.dca.state.ga.us/economic/summary.html}

- *Primary Materials Handling Sales Tax Exemption*: Purchases of primary material handling equipment and racking systems which are used directly for the storage, handling, and moving of tangible personal property in a new or expanding warehouse or distribution facility when such new facility or expansion is valued at $5 million or more and does not have greater than 15% retail sales are exempt from sales and use taxes. {www.dca.state.ga.us/economic/summary.html}

- *Electricity Exemption*: Electricity purchased that interacts directly with a product being manufactured is exempt from sales taxes when the total cost of the electricity exceeds 50% of the cost of all materials used, including electricity, in making the product.

For further information on sales tax exemptions, contact Georgia Department of Revenue, Room 310, 270 Washington Street, Atlanta, GA 30334; 404-656-4060; {www.dca.state.ga.us/economic/summary.html}.

Hawaii

Hawaii Department of Taxation
P.O. Box 259
Honolulu, HI 96809-0259
800-222-3229
808-587-4242
Fax: 808-587-1488
www.state.hi.us/tax/tax.html

Economic Development Office
Department of Business and Economic Development and Tourism
P.O. Box 2359
Honolulu, HI 96804
No. 1 Capitol District Bldg.
250 S. Hotel Street
Honolulu, HI 96813

808-586-2423
Fax: 808-587-2790
www.hawaii.gov/dbedt/

Hawaii has only two levels of government taxation: state and local.

No personal property tax.

No tax on inventories, furniture, equipment or machinery.

Credit against taxes paid on the purchase of capital goods, machinery, and equipment.

No state tax on goods manufactured for export.

No stock transfer tax: All security exchange transactions are exempt from general excise tax, as an incentive to financial institutions.

No unincorporated business tax.

Banks and financial institutions pay only one business tax.

Manufactured products or those produced for export are exempt from the general excise tax, including custom computer software.

Manufacturers, wholesalers, processors, millers, refiners, packer and canners are taxed on 0.5% of gross proceeds.

Insurance solicitors and agents are taxed at .15 percent.

Contractors are taxed 4% of gross proceeds. All sales of retails goods and services are taxed at 4% of gross income.

Purchase of depreciable and tangible property is allowed with a refundable tax credit against excise and use taxes.

Vessels engaged in intrastate transportation are exempt from use tax.

The corporate tax rate is 4.4% of income up to $25,000; 5.4% of taxable income up to $100,000; and 6.4% of income exceeding $100,000. The capital gains tax rate is 4% for corporations.

General excise tax exemptions are in effect for air pollution control facilities, certain scientific contracts with the United State, ships used in international trade and commerce, sugar and pineapple manufacturers, and sales of tangible personal property to the federal government.

A use tax is imposed upon tangible personal property, imported or purchased from unlicensed out-of-state sellers for use or for further resale in Hawaii. This use tax is levied at the rate of .05 percent, if the property is intended for resale at retail; 4 percent if property is intended for use by importer or purchaser, No tax is imposed if the property is intended for resale at wholesale.

Enterprise Zones Program: The Hawaii Enterprise Zones (EZ) Program was created to stimulate certain types of business activity and job creation in areas with above-average unemployment and/or below-average income levels. 19 zones now exist statewide. Eligible businesses that satisfy EZ hiring requirements are exempt from the Hawaii General Excise Tax (GET), and can claim two partial state personal or corporate income tax credits for up to seven consecutive years. Licensed construction and construction trade contractors are also exempt from GET on work done for EZ-enrolled businesses. The counties also offer a variety of incentives, usually involving incremental property tax relief, priority permit processing, and/or fee waivers.

Hawaii's Foreign Trade Zone: Hawaii's Foreign Trade Zone (FTZ) lies outside U.S. Customs territory for tax, duty, and quota purposes, helping companies engaged in international trade significantly reduce their operating costs. The zone and subzone sites are used to store, exhibit, manufacture, assemble, re-label, import and export products. Currently, about 330 companies employ over 2,100 workers at the FTZ.

Three additional zone sites are being considered for Hawaii County and one for Maui. 808-586-2509

Idaho

Idaho State Tax Commission
800 Park Blvd., Plaza IV
Boise, ID 83712
800-972-7660
208-334-7660
www2.state.id.us/tax/index.html

Economic Development Office
Idaho Department of Commerce
700 West State Street
P.O. Box 83720
Boise, ID 83720-0093
208-334-2470
Fax: 208-334-2631
www.idoc.state.id.us/

Idaho's Investment Tax Credit: Equal to 3% of qualified investment (not to exceed more than 50% of a given year's tax liability) and may be carried forward for 14 years.

Property Tax Exemptions: Include inventories, livestock, property in transit, pollution control facilities, vessels, aircraft, the first $50,000 of the value of a primary residence, and properly licensed motor vehicles. Statewide, tax rates vary generally from 0.8 to 2.8 percent, with an average of 1.5 percent.

Net Operating Loss: A net operating loss of up to $100,000 may be carried back two years or carried forward 20 years until it is completely absorbed. Both accelerated depreciation and the accelerated cost recovery system can be used to depreciate assets. {www.idoc.state.id.us/business/idaho works/D.BizFinance.htm}

New Jobs Tax Credit: Eligible businesses are allowed a $500 income tax credit for each new employee hired. This credit cannot exceed 3.25% of the business' net income. Eligible businesses are those that produce, assemble, fabricate, manufacture, or process natural resource products.

Research and Development Tax Credit: Businesses that conduct research and development activities may receive a tax credit. The credit is a combination of 5% of the excess of qualified research payments over the base amount and 5% of the basic research payments according to IRS code. {www.idoc.state.id.us/business/idahoworks/D2.bizincent.htm}

Excluded from a 5% sales tax: The Production Exemptions exempts equipment that I used in manufacturing, processing, mining, farming, fabricating operations, and clean rooms from the 5% sales and use tax. {www.idoc.state.id.us/busi ness/idahoworks/D2.bizincent.htm}

Investment Tax Credit: Businesses that are involved in mining, manufacturing, and retailing are eligible for a tax credit when they make qualified investments.

5% Research and Development Credit: available for basic research and costs of qualified research that is performed in Idaho.

3% Broadband Telecom Credit: up to $750,000 on Idaho State income tax for qualified broadband equipment.

100% Industrial Fuels and Raw Materials Exemption: no Idaho sales tax.

Up to $2,000 New Employee Training Reimbursement: available for each qualifying new job through Idaho's Workforce Development Training Fund program.

Illinois

Illinois Department of Revenue
101 West Jefferson Street
Springfield, IL 62702
217-524-4772
Fax: 217-785-3400
www.revenue.state.il.us

Economic Development Office
Dept. of Commerce and Community Affairs
620 E. Adams
Springfield, IL, 62701
100 West Randolph St., Suite 3-400
Chicago, IL 60601
217-782-7500
Fax: 217-524-3701
www.commerce.state.il.us

No local personal income taxes.
Retirement income is not taxed.

Enterprise Zones: Incentives for businesses within a designated Enterprise Zone include:
- Sales tax exemption on building materials to be used in an Enterprise Zone.
- Sales tax exemption on purchases of tangible personal property to be used in the manufacturing or
- Assembly process or in the operation of a pollution control facility within an Enterprise Zone.
- Tax exemption on gas, electricity and the Illinois Commerce Commission's administrative charge is available to business located in Enterprise Zones.
- Tax credit of 0.5% is allowed a taxpayer who invest in qualified property in a Zone.
- Dividend Income Deduction for individual, corporations, trust, and estates are not taxed on dividend income from corporation doing substantially all their business in a Zone.
- Jobs tax credit allows a business a $500 credit on Illinois income tax for each job created in the Zone for which a certified eligible worker is hired.
- Financial institutions are not taxed on the interest received on loans for development within a Zone.
- Businesses may deduct double the value of a cash or in-kind contribution to an approved project of a designated Zone organization form taxable income.

Corporate Income Tax: Corporate income is taxed at 7.3% which includes a 4.8% state income tax and a 2.5% personal property replacement tax.
Incentives include:
- The 2.5% replacement tax may be deducted from the 4.8% state income tax.
- After 2000, apportionment will be based on in-state sales alone.
Tax Credits include:
- 0.5% credit for investment in mining, manufacturing or retailing, plus an additional 0.5% if employment increases over 1%; a 1/6% training expense tax credit; and a 6.5% Research and Development credit.
- There are no local corporate income taxes in Illinois.

Sales Tax Exemptions: Purchases of manufacturing machinery as well as replacement parts and computers used to control manufacturing machinery; purchases of farm machinery; pollution controls, building materials to be used in an Enterprise Zone; and materials consumed in the manufacturing process in Enterprise Zones. Purchases or manufacturing machinery receive a credit equal to 50% of what the taxes would have been if the manufacturing machinery was taxable, making it possible for the manufacturers to use this credit to offset any other sales tax liability they incur. Food and drugs are taxed at the reduced rate of 1%.

Property Tax Exemptions: All property other than real estate is exempt from the property tax. Taxing bodies within Enterprise Zones may abate property taxes without a dollar limit for the life of the zone.

Utility Tax:
- Illinois does not tax water and sewer utilities.
- Electricity and natural gas tax exemptions are available in Illinois Enterprise Zones.
- Natural gas bought from producers outside the state is not subject to the natural gas tax.

Unemployment Compensation Taxes: The maximum rate for Unemployment Compensation Tax for an employer with less than $50,000 in total wages in a given quarter is 5.4%.

Indiana

Indiana Department of Revenue
100 North Senate Avenue
317-233-4018
Fax: 317-233-2329
www.ai.org/dor

Economic Development Office
Indiana Department of Commerce
One North Capitol, Suite 700
Indianapolis, IN 46204
317-232-8800
800-463-8081
Fax: 317-232-4146
www.state.in.us/doc/index.html

Information on all of the following incentives can be found at {www.in.gov/doc/compare/TaxIncentives.html}.

Indiana Corporate Income Tax: Taxpayers eligible for state corporate income tax credits apply the value first against gross tax liability, then against corporate adjusted gross tax liability and finally against supplemental net liability. Some credits may be applied against future tax liabilities if the amount of current credit exceeds taxes due.

College and University Contribution Credit: A credit for contributions to Indiana colleges and universities. Limited to the lesser of: (a) $1,000; (b) 50% of the contribution; or (c) 10% of the adjusted gross income tax.

Neighborhood Assistance Credit: Credit to corporate or individual taxpayers contributing to neighborhood organizations or who engage in activities to upgrade disadvantaged areas. Up to 50% of the amount invested, not to exceed $25,000 in any taxable year.

Drug and Alcohol Abuse Credit: Maximum credit is $6,250 for corporations with more than 1,000 employees, and $3,750 for corporations with fewer than 1,000 employees.

Research Expense Credit: Credit to any corporate taxpayer entitled to the Federal Research Expense Credit who incurs qualified Indiana research expenses.

Teacher Summer Employment Credit: Credit to persons who hire a public school teacher during the summer in a position that is relevant to a teaching-shortage area in which the teacher is certified. Limited to the lesser of: (a) $2,500; or (b) 50% of the compensation paid.

Industrial Recovery Tax Credit: Credit for qualifying investments to rehabilitate vacant industrial facilities ("dinosaurs") that are at least 20 years old and at least 300,000 square feet in size.

Personal Computer Tax Credit: Credit for donations of computer units to the "Buddy-Up with Education Program." A credit of $125 per computer unit is allowed.

Twenty-First Century Scholars Program Support Fund Credit: Credit for contributions to the fund. A maximum credit of the lesser of (a) $1,000; (b) 50% of the contribution made; or (c) 10% of the adjusted gross income tax is available.

Maternity Home Credit: Credit for maternity-home owners who provide a temporary residence for a pregnant woman (women).

Prison Credit: Credit for investments in Indiana prisons to create jobs for prisoners. The amount is limited to 50% of the inventory in a qualified project plus 25% of the wages paid to the inmates. The maximum credit a taxpayer may claim is $100,000 per year.

Property Tax Abatement: Property tax abatement in Indiana is authorized under Indiana Code 6-1.1-12.1 in the form of deductions from assessed valuation. Any property owner in a locally designated Economic Revitalization Area (ERA) who makes improvements to the real property or installs new manufacturing equipment is eligible for property tax abatement. Land does not qualify for abatement. Used manufacturing equipment can also qualify as long as such equipment is new to the state of Indiana. Equipment not used in direct production, such as office equipment, does not qualify for abatement. 317-232-8888

Real-Property Abatement Calculation: Real-property abatement is a declining percentage of the increase in assessed value of the improvement based on one of the three following time periods and percentages as determined by the local governing body.

Enterprise Zones: {www.in.gov/doc/communities/enterprise_index.html}The purpose of the enterprise zone program in the state of Indiana is to stimulate local community and business redevelopment in distressed areas. An enterprise zone may consist of up to three contiguous square miles. There are 23 enterprise zones in Indiana. In order to stimulate reinvestment and create jobs within the zones, businesses located within an enterprise zone are eligible for certain tax benefits. These tax benefits include:

- A credit equal to 100% of property-tax liability on inventory.
- Exemption from Indiana Gross Income Tax on the increase in receipts from the base year.
- State Investment Cost Credit (up to 30% of purchase price) for individuals purchasing an ownership interest in an enterprise zone business.
- State Loan Interest Credit on lender interest income (5%) from qualified loans made in an enterprise zone.
- State Employment Expense Credit based on wages paid to qualified zone-resident employees. The credit is the lesser of 10% of the increase in wages paid over the base year, or $1,500 per qualified employee.
- Tax deduction to qualified zone-resident employees equal to the lesser of 50% of their adjusted gross income or $7,500.

Interstate Inventory Tax Exemption: Indiana has a modest inventory tax with a number of deductions available, including the Interstate Inventory Tax Exemption. Finished goods awaiting shipment to out-of-state destinations are usually exempt from the inventory tax. In most instances, a taxpayer may determine the exemption by applying the percentage of that location's total shipments, which went out of state during the previous year.

Industrial Recovery Site (Dinosaur Building): Much like the dinosaurs, many large buildings that were once used for mills, foundries and large manufacturers are obsolete for today's new production methods and technologies. Because of this, these buildings now stand vacant. This program offers special tax benefits to offset the cost of adaptive reuse. Tax benefits are available for 10 years from date of project approval and include the following:

Local Option Inventory Tax Credit: A municipality or county has the option of awarding an Inventory Tax Credit to tenants of "dinosaur" buildings.

Maritime Opportunity District: A geographical territory designated at Indiana ports by the Indiana Port Commission. Companies located in a designated district are eligible for tax benefits through the authority of the commission.

Tax Increment Financing (TIF): provides for the temporary allocation to redevelopment or economic districts of increased tax proceeds in an allocation area generated by increases in assessed value. Thus, TIF permits cities, towns or counties to use increased tax revenues stimulated by redevelopment or economic development to pay for the capital improvements needed to induce the redevelopment or economic development. Bond amounts are determined by the size of the project and the amount of the increment available. 317-232-3777

Economic Development for a Growing Economy (EDGE): Provides tax credits based on payroll. Individual income tax withholdings for the company's employees can be credited against the company's corporate income tax. Excess withholdings shall be refunded to the company.

Enterprise Zone Employment Expense Credit: A taxpayer who conducts a business in an enterprise zone is entitled to a maximum credit of $1,500 for each employee who is an enterprise zone resident and who is employed primarily by the taxpayer.

Enterprise Zone Loan Interest Credit: A credit equal to 5% of the lender interest income from qualified loans that benefit businesses or residents of an enterprise zone.

Hoosier Business Investment Tax Credit: The Hoosier Business Investment Tax Credit equals 30% of the amount of the qualified investment.

Iowa

Iowa Department of Revenue
1305 East Walnut
Des Moines, IA 50319
515-281-6695
Fax: 515-242-6487
www.state.ia.us/tax/index.html

Economic Development Office
Department of Economic Development
200 East Grand Ave.
Des Moines, IA 50309-1827
515-242-4700
Fax: 515-242-4809
TTY: 800-735-2942
www.state.ia.us/ided

New Jobs and Income Program (NJIP): Provides a package of tax credits and exemptions to businesses making a capital investment of at least $10.38 million and creating 50 or more jobs meeting wage and benefit targets. Contact {www.iowa smart.com/services/new_business/njip.html}. Qualifying businesses participating in NJIP receive substantial benefits, including:

- Local property tax exemptions for up to 20 years on the value added to the property.
- Additional funding for training new employees. If applicable, these funds would be in addition to those authorized under the Iowa New Jobs Training Program.
- Refunds of sales, services, or use taxes paid to contractors or subcontractors during construction.
- An investment tax credit of up to 10% of the capital investment in machinery and equipment, land, buildings, and improvements to existing buildings. This Iowa tax credit may be carried forward for up to seven years until depleted.
- An additional research and development tax credit of up to 6.5%, which may be refundable. This Iowa tax credit is based on increasing research activities within the state and is available while the business is participating in the program for up to 10 years.

Enterprise Zones: Manufacturers and other businesses expanding or locating in new or existing facilities and creating new jobs in economically distressed areas of Iowa have a new incentive to do so. Contact: {www.iowasmart. com/services/new_business/enterprise_zones.html}.
Businesses expanding or locating in an Enterprise Zone can receive the following benefits:

- A local property tax exemption on the value added to the property.
- Additional funding for training new employees. If applicable, these funds would be in addition to those authorized under the Iowa New Jobs Training Program.
- A refund of state sales, service, or use taxes paid to contractors or subcontractors during construction.
- An investment tax credit of up to a maximum of 10% of the new investment in machinery and equipment, land, buildings, and improvements to existing buildings. This Iowa tax credit may be carried forward for up to seven years or until depleted.
- An additional research and development tax credit of up to 6.5%, which may be refundable. This Iowa tax credit is based on increasing research activities within the state and is available while the business is participating in the program for up to 10 years.

New Jobs Tax Credit: Businesses entering into an agreement under the state's training program, and which increase workforce by at least 10 percent, may qualify for this credit to their Iowa corporate income tax. This credit is equal to 6% of the state unemployment insurance taxable wage base. The tax credit can be carried forward up to 10 years. {www.iowasmart.com/services/new_business/enterprise_zon es.html}.

Exempt Sales and Services: 911 surcharge, advertising, aircraft sales, rental and services, agriculture, containers, coupon books and gift certificates, educational, religious or charitable activities, finance charges, food, freight charges, fuel, government entities, green houses, hospitals, industrial machinery and equipment design and installation, industrial machinery, equipment computers, replace parts, insulin, interstate commerce, lease and rental, medical, mobile homes, newspapers, nonprofit organizations, prescription drugs, printers and publishers, prizes, processing, railroads, repair, resale, resales of property connected with a service, transportation, vehicles, vehicle manufacturing. {www.state.ia.us/tax/educate/78539.html}.

Iowa Corporate Income Tax: The non-unitary tax is based only on the percentage of total sales income within the state-no corporate income tax is paid on products sold outside of Iowa. The State allows 50% deductibility of federal taxes from Iowa corporate income tax and Iowa corporate income tax may be reduced or eliminated by the New Jobs Tax Credit.

No Sales or Use Tax on Manufacturing Machinery and Equipment: the purchase of industrial machinery and equipment and computers assessed as real property is exempt from Iowa sales or use tax. No sales tax is due on electricity and natural gas purchase used directly in the manufacturing process.

No Property Tax on New Industrial Machinery and Equipment: Manufacturing machinery and equipment computers used to process data by insurance companies and financial institutions are exempt from property tax.

No Personal Property (Inventory) Tax: Personal property includes corporate inventories of saleable goods, raw materials and goods in process.

Local Tax Abatement: Cities and counties are allowed to abate local property taxes for value added to industrial real estate.

Pollution Control or Recycling Property Tax Exemption: Improvements to real property where the main use is to control pollution of air or water, or primarily used for recycling, may qualify for a property tax exemption; {iowa smart.com/services/entrepreneurial/tax_advantage.html}.

Research and Development Tax Credit: A company that meets the requirements of the federal research activities credit may be eligible for a state tax credit when the company increases research activities equal to 6.5% of their allotted share of qualifying research expenditures; {iowasmart.com/ services/entrepreneurial/tax_advantage.html}.

Assertive Device Tax Credit: Small businesses in the State can reduce their taxes by renting or buying products or equipment, or by making physical changes to the workplace to assist disabled employees in maintaining or getting a job. They must employ 14 or fewer full-time employees or have $3 million dollars or less in gross annual receipts. The credit is equal to one-half of the first $5,000 in qualifying expenses per tax year. Excess credits can be refunded or carried over to the next year. Contact: 515-242-4819; 800-532-1215; {www. iowasmart.com/services/entrepreneurial/tax_credit.html}.

Kansas

Kansas Department of Revenue
Docking State Office Building, Room 150
915 SW Harrison Street
Topeka, KS 66612
877-526-7738 (outside Topeka)
785-368-8222 (in Topeka)
Fax: 785-291-3614
www.ksrevenue.org/index.htm

Business Development Division
Department of Commerce and Housing
1000 SW Jackson St., Suite 100
Topeka, KS 66612-1357
785-296-5298
Fax 785-296-3490
TTY 785-296-3487
http://kdoch.state.ks.us

Enterprise Zone Act: Establishes a non-metropolitan regional business incentive program and provides for business expansion and development incentives on a statewide basis. Businesses throughout the state may be eligible for 1) a one-time job creation tax credit of $1,500 per new job; 2) an investment tax credit of $1,000 per $100,000 qualified business facility investment; 3) sales tax exemptions on the purchase of personal property or services purchased for construction, reconstruction, enlargement, remodel, or equipment of a qualified business facility. Businesses in a qualified non-metropolitan region may receive an enhanced job creation tax credit of $2,500. Contact 785-296-1868 for more information. Tax credits may be used to offset up to 100% of the business' annual Kansas income tax liability. Unused credits may be carried forward indefinitely.

High Performance Incentive Program (HPIP): Provides incentives to qualified companies which make significant investment in employee training and pay higher than average wages. Incentives include 1) a Sales Tax Exemption; 2) a potentially substantial Training Tax Credit; 3) a generous Investment Tax Credit; 4) priority consideration for other business assistance programs; and 5) grants to be used to cover half of consulting costs to help increase the growth of the business up to $12,500. Contact 785-296-7174 for information. Tax credits may be used to offset 100% of the business' annual Kansas income tax liability. Unused credits may be carried forward and must be used within a 10-year time frame.

Sales Tax Exemption On Manufacturing Machinery & Equipment: Manufacturing machinery and equipment used directly and primarily for the purposes of manufacturing, assembling, processing, finishing, storing, warehousing, or distributing articles of tangible personal property intended for resale are exempt from sales tax.

Research & Development Tax Credits: May be claimed at 6.5% of the amount which exceeds the business' average R&D expenditures during the preceding three years. A maximum of 25% of the total credits may be used in any given year and unused credits may be carried forward indefinitely.

Child Day Care Tax Credits: Available to businesses that pay for, or provide, child day care services to their employees. The credit is 30% of the annual cost of providing the service, not to exceed $30,000 total credit. A credit of up to 50%, not to exceed $45,000, may be earned during the first year on the costs of establishing a child day care facility. Multiple taxpayers may work together to establish such a facility.

Local Seed Capital Pool Tax: Designed to encourage cash investments in certified local seed capital pools. Credit is equal to 25% of the taxpayer's cash investment.

Job Expansion And Investment Tax Credit Act Of 1976: Allows an income tax credit for a period of 10 years, up to 50% of a business' Kansas income tax liability. The Job Expansion Tax Credit is $100 for each qualified business facility employee. The Investment Tax Credit is $100 for each $100,000 in qualified investment.

Business Machinery and Equipment Credit: This credit is equal to 15% of the personal property tax paid on commercial and industrial machinery and equipment.

Disabled Access Credit: A tax credit is available for a project that makes an existing building or facility accessible to persons with a disability. The credit is equal to 50% of the costs of the project, or $10,000, whichever is less.

Community Service Tax Credit: Businesses that make contributions to eligible community service organizations or government entities that are involved in activities that meet a demonstrated community need can receive a tax credit. The credit cannot exceed 50% of the amount donated to a community service organization, or 70% of the amount given to a rural community service organization.

Alternative-Fuel Tax Credit: Credit to owners of qualified alternative-fueled motor vehicle licensed in Kansas. 50% credit for vehicles placed in service between January 1, 1996 and January 1, 2005 up to $3,000. 40% credit for vehicles placed in service after January 1, 2005 up to $2,400. 50% credit for qualified alternative-fuel fueling stations placed in service between January 1, 1996 and January 1, 2005 up to $200,000. 40% credit for qualified alternative-fuel fueling station placed in service after January 1, 2005 up to $160,000.

Employer Health Insurance Contribution Credit: An income tax credit for employers for amounts paid on behalf of an eligible employee to provide health insurance or care. The credit is $35 per month per eligible employee or 50% of the total amount paid by the employer during the taxable year, whichever is less, for the first two years of participation. In the third year, the credit is equal to 75% of the lesser of $35 per month per employee or 50% of the total amount paid by the employer during the taxable year. In the fourth year, the credit is equal to 50% of the lesser of $35 per month per employee or 50% of the total amount paid by the employer during the taxable year. In the fifth year, the credit is equal to 25% of the lesser of $35 per month per employee or 50% of the total amount paid by the employer during the taxable year. For the sixth and subsequent years, no credit shall be allowed.

Venture Capital Credit: Designed to encourage investments in certified Kansas venture capital companies. The credit is 25% of the total amount of cash investment in the stock. Any unused credit may be carried forward until the amount is used.

Sales Tax Exemption For A Specific Project: An exemption from sales tax is granted on all tangible personal property or services purchased for the purpose of and in conjunction with the construction, reconstruction, expansion or remodeling of a business or a retail business. Machinery and equipment purchased and installed at the business or retail business is also exempt from sales tax.

Utility Sales Tax Exemption: Electricity, gas or water may be exempt from sales tax depending on the use of the utility. Utilities used in the following industries and ways are exempt from sales tax: agriculture, irrigation of crops, noncommercial residential, ingredient or component part, consumed in production, providing taxable service, movement in interstate commerce, and severing of oil.

Kentucky

Kentucky Revenue Cabinet
200 Fair Oaks Lane
Frankfort, KY 40620
502-564-4581
Fax: 502-564-3875
http://revenue.ky.gov/revhome.htm

Economic Development Office
Kentucky Cabinet for Economic Development
2300 Capital Plaza Tower
500 Mero Street
Frankfort, KY 40601
502-564-7670
www.edc.state.ky.us/

Kentucky Industrial Development Act (KIDA): Investments in new and expanding manufacturing projects may qualify for tax credits. Companies that create at least 15 new full-time jobs and invest at least $100,000 in projects approved under KIDA may receive state income tax credits for up to 100% of annual debt service costs (principal and interest) for up to 10 years on land, buildings, site development, utility extensions, architectural and engineering services, building fixtures and equipment used in a project, or the company may collect a job assessment fee of 3% of the gross wages of each employee whose job is created by the approved project and who is subject to Kentucky income taxes.

Kentucky Rural Economic Development Act (KREDA): Larger tax credits are available for new and expanding manufacturing projects that create at least 15 new full time jobs in counties with unemployment rates higher than the state average in each of the five preceding calendar years and invest at least $100,000. {www.edc.state.ky.us/kyedc/kybizince.asp}

Kentucky Jobs Development Act (KJDA): Service and technology related companies that invest in new and expanded non-manufacturing, non-retail projects that provide at least 75% of their services to users located outside of Kentucky, and that create new jobs for at least 15 full-time Kentucky residents may qualify for tax credits.

Kentucky Industrial Revitalization Act (KIRA): Investments in the rehabilitation of manufacturing operations that are in imminent danger of permanently closing or that have closed temporarily may qualify for tax credits. Companies that save or create 25 jobs in projects approved under KIRA may receive state income tax credits and job assessment fees for up to 10 years limited to 50% of the costs of the rehabilitation or construction of buildings and the reoutfitting

or purchasing of machinery and equipment. Contact: 502-564-4554, ext. 4428.

Other Income Tax Credit:
- A credit of $100 is allowed for each unemployed person hired for at least 180 consecutive days.
- Credits are allowed for up to 50% of the installed costs of equipment used exclusively to recycle or compost business or consumer wastes (excluding secondary and demolition wastes) and machinery used exclusively to manufacture products substantially from recycled waste materials.
- A credit is allowed for up to 4.5% of the value of Kentucky coal (excluding transportation costs) used for industrial heating or processing.

Kentucky Enterprise Zone Program: State and local tax incentives are offered to businesses located or locating in zones, and some regulations are eased to make development in the area more attractive. A zone remains in effect for 20 years after the date of designation.

Tourism Development Sales Tax Credit: Approved new or expanding tourism attractions will be eligible for a sales tax credit against sales tax generated by visitors to the attraction.

Property Tax Exemptions: Manufacturing machinery, pollution control facilities, raw materials and work in process, tangible personal property in foreign trade zones.

Sales Tax Exemptions: Machinery for new and expanded industry, raw materials, industrial tools, energy and energy-producing fuels to the extent they exceed 3% of the cost of production, pollution control equipment, containers, packaging and wrapping materials, motor fuels for highway use, items purchased for resale, industrial supplies, industrial machinery sold and delivered out-of-state to manufacturers or processors use out-of-state.

Bluegrass State Skills Corporation - The Skills Training Investment Credit: Bluegrass State Skills Corporation has an income tax credit to businesses for 50% of their approved occupational and skills upgrade training costs. The credit is for $500 per Kentucky resident employed with a maximum of $100,000 per company per biennium. For more information, contact 502-564-2021; {www.thinkkentucky.com/bssc}.

Kentucky Investment Fund Act (KIFA): Certain personal and corporate investors in approved investment funds can receive a 40% tax credit. The minimum fund size is $500,000 and must have no less than 4 unaffiliated investors. The investment must be in a qualified business where 50% of the assets, operations, and employees are located in Kentucky; have a net worth less than $5 million; and have no more than 100 employees.

Economic Opportunity Zone: New or expanding manufacturing or service/technology companies may be permitted an income tax credit up to 100% of the Kentucky income tax liability on income generated of a Zone project and a job development assessment fee of up to 5% of gross wages.

Enterprise Zones: Encourages new or renewed development to targeted areas of the state by offering special tax incentives and eased regulations to businesses locating in a zone.

Louisiana

Louisiana Department of Revenue
617 North Third Street
Baton Rouge, LA 70802
225-219-7318
www.rev.state.la.us

Economic Development Office
Dept. of Economic Development
P.O. Box 94185
Baton Rouge, LA 70804-9185
225-342-3000
www.lded.state.la.us

Industrial tax exemption: Exempts any manufacturing establishment entering Louisiana or any manufacturing establishment expanding its existing Louisiana facility from state, parish, and local property taxes for a period of up to ten years. Contact 225-342-5254.

Enterprise zone: Provides a tax credit of $2,500 for each net new job created in specially designated areas. Also provides for a rebate of state sales/use taxes on building materials and operating equipment. Local sales/use taxes may also be rebated. Credits can be used to satisfy state corporate income and franchise tax obligations. Contact 225-342-9228.

Restoration tax abatement: Encourages restoration of buildings in special districts by abating Ad Valorem taxes on improvements to the structure for up to ten years. Contact 225-342-5402.

Inventory tax credit: Provides tax credits against state corporate income and franchise tax obligations for the full amount of inventory taxes paid. When credits are in excess of tax obligations, a cash refund is made. Contact 225-342-5360.

Quality Jobs Program: Louisiana's Quality Jobs Program grants qualifying industry and manufacturing businesses cash rebated up to 6% of its annual gross payroll.

Video and Production Tax Credit: Allows tax credits on percentage of production costs associated with motion picture production companies producing nationally distributed movies, videos, commercials, television series, etc. The credit is 10% for spending of $300,000 to $1,000,000, and 15% for spending over $1 million.

Automotive and Aerospace Industry Tax Credit: The program provides a $5,000 one-time tax credit per new job for companies in the automotive and aerospace industries that participate in the state's Enterprise Zone program.

Maine

Maine Revenue Services
24 State House Station
Augusta, ME 04333-0024
207-287-2076
Fax: 207-624-9694
www.state.me.us/revenue

Economic Development Office
Office of Business Development
Department of Economic and Community Development
59 State House Station
Augusta, ME 04333
207-624-9804

Fax: 207-287-5701
www.econdevmaine.com

Business Equipment Property Tax Reimbursement Program: Program reimbursed, for up to 12 years, all local property taxes paid on eligible business property. Contact 207-626-8475; {www.state.me.us/revenue}.

Employee-Assisted Day Care Credit: Provides an income tax credit of up to $5,000. The credit is limited to the lesser of $5,000, 20% of the cost incurred or $100 for each child of an employee enrolled on a full-time basis or for each full-time equivalent throughout the tax year.

Employer Provided Long-term Care Benefits Credit: Provides an income tax credit equal to the lesser of $5,000, 20% of the cost incurred or $100 per employee covered by a long-term care policy as part of a benefits package.

Employment Tax Increment Financing (ETIF): This program returns between 30%, 50%, or 75% of new employees' income withholding tax to companies who add new workers. To qualify, employees must be paid a wage equal to or above the per capita wage in their labor market area, and be provided group health insurance and access to an ERISA qualified retirement program. The company must also demonstrate that ETIF funding is an essential component of the expansion project's financing. Contact 207-624-9800.

High-Technology Investment Tax Credit: Offers businesses engaged in high-tech activities that purchase and use eligible equipment a credit amount equal to the adjusted basis of equipment place in service less any lease payments received during the taxable year.

Jobs and Investment Tax Credit: This program helps businesses with an income tax credit on equipment and facilities that generate new jobs. The program provides a 10% credit against Maine income taxes for investment in most types of personal property that generates at least 100 new jobs within two years, as long as the investment is at least $5 million for the taxable year. The credit amount is tied to the federal investment tax credit and is limited to $500,000 per year with carry-forwards available for six years.

Custom Computer Programming Sales Tax Exemption: Exempts from sales tax the purchase of custom computer programming.

Biotechnology Sales Tax Exemption: Exempts sales tax of purchase of machinery, equipment, instruments and supplies used by any biotechnology company directly and primarily in a biotechnology application.

Manufacturing Sales Tax Exemptions: Sales of machinery and equipment used by any manufacturing company directly and primarily in the production of tangible personal property and also the repair and replacement of parts is eligible for a sales tax exemption.

Research Machinery and Equipment Sales Tax Exemption: Sales of machinery and equipment used by the purchaser directly and exclusively in research and development by any business is eligible for a sales tax exemption.

Fuel and Electricity Sales Tax Exemption: Program exempts any business from sales tax 95% of the sales price of all fuel and electricity purchased for use at the manufacturing facility.

Maine Seed Capital Tax Credit Program: FAME authorizes state income tax credits to investors in an amount equal to 60% of the cash equity they provide to eligible Maine businesses. {www.famemaine.com}

Research Expense Credit: A 5% income tax credit is provided to companies that sustain qualifying research expenses that exceed their average research expenses. A 7.5% credit is also provided to companies that incur basic research payments to qualified organizations, educational institutions and other research organizations.

Super Credit for Substantially Increased Research and Development: Businesses that qualify for the Research Expense Credit and whose qualified research expenses for the taxable year exceed 150% of their average research expenses for the 3 taxable years prior to September 1997, are eligible for a tax credit. The credit is equal to the amount of research expenses that exceed the 150% average, and may not exceed 50% of the net tax due after the allowance of any other credits.

Pine Tree Development Zones: Maine offers businesses significant tax advantages for locating in one of Maine's designated Pine Tree Zones.

Maryland

Comptroller of Maryland
Revenue Administration Center
Annapolis, MD 21411-0001
800-MD-TAXES
410-260-7980
www.marylandtaxes.com

Economic Development Office
Department of Business and Economic Development
217 East Redwood St.
Baltimore, MD 21202
800-541-8549
Fax: 410-333-8628
TDD/TTY: 410-333-6926
www.dbed.state.md.us/

No unitary tax on profits.
No income tax on foreign dividends.
No gross receipts tax on manufacturers.
No corporate franchise tax.
No separate school taxes.

Job Creation Tax Credits: Income tax credits granted to businesses for the creation of jobs. Credit granted will be the lesser of $1,000 or 2 1/2% of a year's wages for each qualifying permanent job.

MD Disability Employment Tax Credit: Includes tax credits for wages paid and for child care or transportation expenses for qualifying individuals with disabilities.

Employment Opportunity Tax Credit: Includes credits for wages and child care or transportation expenses for qualifying employees who were recipients of state benefits from the "Aid to Families with Dependent Children" program immediately prior to employment.

Neighborhood Partnership Program Tax Credit: Provides tax credits for business contributions to approved projects run by nonprofit organizations. The maximum credit is for up to $125,000 per year.

Property Tax Exemptions and Credits: Maryland does not impose a personal property tax on business. For those jurisdictions that do tax personal property, exemptions and credits available include the following: machinery, equipment, materials and supplies use in manufacturing or research; manufacturing inventory; commercial inventory for warehousing and distribution; custom computer software.

Enterprise Zones Tax Credits:
1. Property Tax Credits: Ten-year credit against local property taxes on a portion of real property improvements. Credit is 80% the first five years, and decreases 10% annually thereafter to 30% in the tenth and last year.
2. Income Tax Credits: One to three year credits for wages paid to new employees in the zone. The general credit is a one-time $1000 credit per new workers. For economically disadvantaged employees, the credit increases to a total of $6,000 per worker distributed over three years.
3. Priority access to Maryland's financing programs.
4. Focus Area Tax Credits: Businesses that are located in a focus area within Baltimore City, Prince George's County or St. Mary's County/Lexington Park enterprise zones may be eligible for the following credits:
5. Real property tax credits: Ten-year 80% credit against local real property taxes on a portion of real property improvements.
6. Personal property tax credits: Ten-year 80% credit against local personal property on new investments in personal property in a focus area.
7. Income tax credits: One- or three-year credit for wages paid to new employees. This is generally a one-time $1,500 credit for each new employee. For economically disadvantaged employees, the credit increases to a total of $9,000 for each new employee and is distributed over 3 years.

There are 29 enterprise zones in Maryland. For information on these programs, call 410-767-6438

Empowerment Zone Incentives: Firms locating in the federally designated Empowerment Zone in Baltimore, one of six in the nation, may be eligible for state enterprise zone incentives including: income tax credits for job creation; property tax credits for real property improvements. Businesses in the Zone may also qualify for potential federal incentives such as: wage tax credits; increased depreciation on equipment; tax exempt bond financing; employment development incentives. Contact: 410-783-4222.

Brownfields Tax Incentives: The counties, Baltimore City or incorporated municipalities may elect to grant a five-year credit equal to between 50% and 70% of real property taxes attributable to the increase in the assessment resulting from cleanup and improvement of a qualified Brownfields site. The Brownfields real property credit may be expanded as follows: localities may grant an additional credit of up to 20%; localities may extend the credit by an additional five years if the site is in a state-designated enterprise zone; a credit will also apply against state real property taxes for the same percentage and duration.

Sales Tax Exemptions: The following are major business-oriented exemptions from the Maryland Sales and Use tax. Local jurisdictions do not impose a sales tax:
1. Sales of capital and noncapitalized manufacturing machinery and equipment, including equipment used for testing finished products; assembling, processing or refining; in the generation of electricity; or used to produce or repair production equipment.

2. Sales of safety and quality control equipment use on a production activity site; and equipment used to move a finished product on the production site.

3. Sales of tangible personal property consumed directly in manufacturing, testing of finished products.

4. Sales of fuels used in manufacturing, except those used to cool, heat and light the manufacturing facility.

5. Sales for resale and tangible personal property to be incorporated in other tangible personal property manufactured for resale. In addition, there is an exemption for sales of computer programs reproduced for sale or incorporated in whole or in part into another computer program intended for sale.

6. Sales of customized computer software.

7. Sales of equipment and materials used or consumed in research and development, to include testing of finished products.

8. Sales of aircraft, vessels, railroad rolling stock, and motor vehicles used principally in the movement of passengers or freight in interstate and foreign commerce.

9. Sales of certain end-item testing equipment used to perform a contract for the U.S. Department of Defense and transferred to the federal government.

10. Sale of items and services purchased or rented for film and video productions, made in Maryland for commercial distribution; includes short-term rental of vehicles used in film production activities.

One Maryland Tax Credit Program: Up to $5.5 million in tax credits is available for qualifying businesses. Those companies that invest in an economic development project in a qualified distressed county, may be eligible for project tax credits of up to $5 million and start-up tax credits of up to $500,000. Contact 410-767-6438 for information.

Research and Development Tax Credit: Business that incur qualified research and development expenses and that are certified by the Department, are eligible for a tax credit. The Basic Research and Development Credit is 3% of eligible research and development expenses that do not exceed the firms average research and development expenses over the past four years. The Growth Research and Development Credit is 10% of eligible research and development expenses that exceed the firms average research and development expenses over the past four years. For information, call 410-767-6438.

Water Quality Improvement Credit: A business may be eligible for a tax credit for the additional commercial fertilizer costs necessary to convert agricultural production to a certified nutrient management plan.

Work-Based Learning Program Credit: Companies that hire students, as part of an approved work-based learning program may be eligible for a tax credit for a portion of the wages paid.

Businesses that Create New Jobs Credit: Those companies that create new jobs and establish or expand business facilities in Maryland are eligible for a tax credit. However, the business must first have been given a property tax credit by a local government for creating new jobs.

Clean Energy Incentive Tax Credit: Income credits are available for the purchase and installation of solar water heating property and photovoltaic property or the use of waste material to produce electricity that is sold to an unrelated person.

Commuter Tax Credit: Businesses that provide commuter benefits for employees are eligible for a tax credit for a part of the amounts paid in one year.

Green Building Tax Credit: A business is eligible for a credit for the construction or rehabilitation of a building that conforms to specific standards intended to save energy and to mitigate environmental impact.

Long-term Employment of Ex-Felons Tax Credit: Businesses that hire and retain one or more ex-felons between July 1, 2002 and December 31, 2004, may qualify for a tax credit.

Maryland-Mined Coal Tax Credit: A co-generator, a public service company, or an electricity supplier that buys Maryland mined coal may qualify for a credit against their taxes.

Massachusetts

Massachusetts Department of Revenue
51 Sleeper Street
Boston, MA 02205
617-626-3550
www.dor.state.ma.us/dorpg.htm

Economic Development Office
Massachusetts Office of Business Development
10 Park Plaza, 3rd Floor
Boston, MA 02116
617-973-8600
800-5-CAPITAL
Fax: 617-727-8797
www.state.ma.us/mobd

Investment Tax Credit: Massachusetts gives businesses a 3% Investment Tax Credit against the corporate excise tax for the construction of manufacturing facilities. The credit also applies to the purchase or lease of equipment. It is available to companies involved in manufacturing, research and development, agriculture or commercial fishing.

R&D Tax Credit: Massachusetts has permanent 10% and 15% R&D tax credits with a fifteen-year or indefinite carry-forward provision for companies investing in research and development. Companies are allowed to compute defense and non-defense R&D separately. This constitutes one of the highest R&D tax credits in the nation.

Economic Opportunity Areas: Qualified businesses operating within one of 36 Economic Target Areas are eligible for tax and financing incentives: A 5% Investment Tax Credit for all businesses, not just manufacturing; A 10% Abandoned Building Tax Deduction (at least 75% vacant for at least 24 months); Local Property Tax Benefits (Special Tax Assessment or Tax Increment Financing); Priority status for state capital funding.

Economic Target Areas (ETA) are designated throughout Massachusetts. Within ETAs, Economic Opportunity Areas of particular economic need and priority are further defined. Businesses that undertake certified projects within Economic Opportunity Areas can qualify for additional investment incentives: 5% Investment Tax Credit for Certified Projects, 10% Abandoned Building Tax Deduction within designated areas, Municipal Tax Benefits (Tax Increment Financing or Special Assessments on Property Values), Priority for state capital funding.

Tax Increment Financing: Businesses may also benefit from the substantial property tax savings offered through Tax Increment Financing (TIF). TIF enables municipalities to enter into agreements with private companies to determine a baseline property value level at which taxes will be levied for a specified number of years.

New Market Tax Credit Program: The New Market Tax Credit Program is designed to increase investments in new private capital into low-income urban and rural communities. Individuals and corporations who make equity investments in an eligible "Community Development Entity" receive a tax credit worth 39% of their investment over a seven-year period. The Community Development Entities then make equity investments or loans to businesses serving low-income communities.

Michigan
Michigan Department of Treasury
Lansing, MI 48922
517-636-4660
Fax: 517-636-4520
www.michigan.gov/treasury

Economic Development Corporation
Michigan Jobs Commission
300 North Washington Square
Lansing MI 48913
517-373-9808
http://medc.michigan.org

Enterprise Zones: The program allows a designated community to provide a business and property tax abatement reducing property taxes approximately 50% on all new investment.

Tax-Free Renaissance Zones: 33 regions of the state designated as virtually tax free for any business or resident presently in or moving to a zone. The zones are designed to spur new jobs and investment. Each Renaissance Zone can be comprised of up to six smaller zones (sub zones) which are located throughout the community to give businesses more options on where to locate.

MEGA Jobs Tax Credit: Companies engaged in manufacturing, research and development, wholesale and trade, or office operations that are financially sound and that have financially sound proposed plans, are eligible to receive a tax credit against the Michigan Single Business Tax for a new location or expansion project and/or the amount of personal income tax attributable to new jobs being created.

Industrial Property Tax Abatements: Can be granted by the state and by local units of government. They reduce property tax on buildings, machinery and equipment by 50% for new facilities, 100% for existing.

Air Pollution Control Systems Tax Exemptions for Installation: Relieves a company of sales tax, property tax, and use taxes for air pollution control equipment. {www.deq.state.mi.us}

Economic Growth Authority: Awards credits against the Single Business Tax to eligible companies for up to 20 years to promote high quality economic growth and job creation that otherwise would not occur without this program. {www.growthalliance.com/incmega.html}

Registered Apprenticeship Tax Credit: Makes available a tax credit of up to $2,000 annually per apprentice to employers who, through registered apprenticeships, train young people while they are still in high school. {www.michigan.gov/emi}

Work Opportunity Tax Credit: The tax credit is 35% of the first $6,000 in wages paid during the first year of employment for each eligible employee.

Property Tax Exemptions:
- Special tool, dies, jigs, and patterns in manufacturing
- Electricity and natural gas used in production
- Air and water pollution control abatement equipment

Minnesota
Minnesota Department of Revenue
600 North Robert Street
St. Paul, MN 55146
651-282-5225
Fax: 651-297-2265
www.taxes.state.mn.us

Economic Development Office
Department of Trade and Economic Development
500 Metro Square Bldg.
121 7th Place East
St. Paul, MN 55101-2146
651-297-1291
800-657-3858
www.dted.state.mn.us

Enterprise Zones: Qualifying businesses that are located or relocate to one of the Enterprise Zone areas, are eligible for business tax credits. The categories of credits are property tax credits, debt financing credit on new construction, sales tax credit on construction equipment and materials, and new or existing employee credits.

Mississippi
Mississippi Treasury Department
P.O. Box 138
Jackson, MS 39205-0138
601-359-3600
www.treasury.state.ms.us

Economic Development Office
Mississippi Development Authority
P.O. Box 849
Jackson, MS 39205-0849
601-359-3155
Fax: 601-359-2832
www.decd.state.ms.us

Jobs Tax Credit: Provides a five-year tax credit to the company's state income tax bill for each new job created by a new or expanding business. Amounts: $2,000 per new job for less developed counties, $1,000 per new job for moderately developed counties, and $500 per new job for developed counties.

R&D Jobs Tax Credit: Provides a five-year credit of $1,000 per year for each net new R&D job created by new or expanding businesses.

Headquarter Jobs Tax Credit: Provides a five-year tax credit of $500 per year for each net new job created by the transfer of a national or regional headquarters to Mississippi.

Child/Dependent Care Income Tax Credit: An income tax credit of 50% of qualified expenses is offered to any employer providing child/dependent care for employees during working hours.

Basic Skills Training Tax Credit: Provides a tax credit to new or existing businesses that pay for certain basic skills training or retaining for their employees. Credit is equal to 25% of qualified expenses of the training.

Rural Economic Development Credits: Companies financing projects through the Small Enterprise Development or Industrial Revenue Bond Program may be eligible to receive credits on corporate income taxes.

Mississippi State Port Income Tax Credit: Provides an income tax credit to taxpayers who utilize the port facilities at state, county, and municipal ports in Mississippi. The taxpayer receives a credit in an amount equal to certain charges paid by the taxpayer of export cargo.

County Property Tax Exemptions: For new or expanding manufacturers, certain properties may be exempted from county property taxes, except school taxes, for up to ten years at the local option. Local authorities may grant a fee in lieu of taxes, including school taxes, on projects over $100 million.

Free Port Warehouse Law: Exempts finished goods from property taxes, including school taxes.
No state property tax except school taxes.

Sales Tax Exemptions: No sales tax on purchases of raw materials, processing chemicals, or packaging materials. No sales tax on direct purchases of construction materials, machinery, and equipment for businesses that are financed through certain bonds or located in less developed counties.

Partial Sales Tax: 50% sales tax exemptions for purchases of construction materials, machinery and equipment in moderately developed and developed counties. A 1 1/2% sales tax on machinery and parts used directly in manufacturing and on industrial electricity, natural gas, and fuels.

Corporate Franchise Tax: A tax incentive of $2.50 per $1,000 of the value of capital used, invested or employed in the state.

Bond Finance Program: A full sales and use tax exemption is available to qualified businesses which finance component building materials and machinery and equipment with bond proceeds.

Temporary Assistance for Needy Families (TANF) Program: This program provides an income tax credit available to employers who hire individuals who receive Temporary Assistance for Needy Families benefits at the hire date. The credit is based on a sliding scale depending on the wage paid to the employee.

Missouri

Missouri Department of Revenue
Harry S. Truman State Office Building
301 West High Street, Room 330
Jefferson City, MO 65101
800-877-6881
573-751-5860

Fax: 573-751-4800
www.dor.mo.gov

Economic Development Office
Department of Economic Development
301 W. High St., Room 680
P.O. Box 1157
Jefferson City, MO 65102
573-751-4962
Email: ecodev@mail.state.mo.us
www.ecodev.state.mo.us

Business Facility Tax Credit Program: State income tax credits are provided to the business based on the number of new jobs and amount of new investment created at the qualifying facility. The credits are provided each tax year for up to ten years after the project commences operations. The tax credits are earned each tax period for up to 10 years. The formula to earn the tax credits is based on:
- $100 (or $75 for a new MO company) for each new job created at the project.
- $100 (or $75 for a new MO company) per $100,000 of the new capital investment at the project.

Community Development Corporation Tax Credit: The purpose of this program is to induce investment into Community Development Corporation, which then invest in new or growing small businesses or real estate development, resulting in an expansion of the tax base, elimination of blight, reduction of reliance on public assistance and the creation of jobs. A contributor may obtain state tax credits based on 50% of investments or contributions in a Community Development Corporation. The Community Development Corporation then makes equity investments or loans to a business, redevelopment project, or investment in real estate development within a target area. No more than $100,000 can be invested or loaned by the Community Development Corporation for any one business (including any affiliated or subsidiary of the business) or real estate development.

Enterprise Zone Tax Benefits: State income tax credits are provided to the business based on the number of new jobs and amount of new investment created at the qualifying facility. The business may earn credits based on the facility's new jobs and investment, the number of zone residents and "special" employees hired and trained for the facility.

Historic Tax Credit: The program provides state tax credits for 25% of eligible costs and expenses of the rehabilitation of an approved historic structure.

Missouri Development Finance Board (MDFB): Provides state tax credits to a contributor based on 50% of the contribution. The contributed funds are granted to a public entity to finance infrastructure needed to facilitate an approved project. Eligible contributors receive a tax credit of 50% of the contribution against Chapter 143 (excluding certain withholding taxes), 147, and 148 taxes. Contributions may be eligible for federal tax deductions also.

Research Tax Credit Program: Purpose of the Research Tax Credit Program is to induce existing businesses to increase their research efforts in Missouri by offering a tax credit. The amount of qualified research expenses for which tax credits shall apply, may not exceed 200% of the taxpayer's average qualified research expenses incurred during the three-year period immediately prior to the tax period the credits are being claimed. The aggregate of all tax credits authorized shall not exceed $9.7 million in any taxable year.

Small Business Incubator: The purpose of the Small Business Incubator Tax Credit Program is to generate private funds to be used to establish a "protective business environment" (incubator) in which a number of small businesses can collectively operate to foster growth and development during their start-up period. The minimum tax credit is $1,500 per contributor. The maximum tax credit is $50,000 per contributor if made to a single incubator and $100,000 per contributor if made to multiple incubators. The overall maximum amount of tax credits that can be issued under this program in any one calendar year is $500,000.

Tax Increment Financing Program: A method to invent redevelopment of a project that otherwise would not occur. TIF redirects an approved portion of certain local taxes caused by the project to reduce project costs. The amount and length of the increment is negotiated by the TIF Commission based on the least amount to cause the project to occur. The "increment" may be up to 100% of the increased amount of real property taxes and 50% of local sales, utility and (in St. Louis and Kansas City) earnings taxed for a period of up to 23 years, as approved by the municipality.

Transportation Development Tax Credit Program: A company (or individual) may be provided a state income tax credit for up to 50% of a contribution to a public entity for eligible activities. The project is needed to facilitate a business project or is a community development/public infrastructure improvement.

Wine and Grape Production: To assist vineyards and wine producers with the purchase of needed equipment and materials by granting tax credits. A grape grower or wine producer is allowed a 25% state income tax credit on the amount of the purchase price of all new equipment and materials used directly in the growing of grapes or the production of wine in the state.

Rebuilding Communities Tax Credit: This program provides tax credits to businesses in order to stimulate activity in Missouri's "Rebuilding Areas".
- New or Relocating Businesses: eligible businesses can choose one of the 40% Tax Credits in addition to the 1.5% Employee Tax Credit.
- 40% Income Credit: 40% credit on state income tax for 3 years
- 40% Specialized Equipment Credit: 40% credit based on the amount of funds used for computer equipment and its maintenance, medical laboratories and equipment, research laboratory equipment, manufacturing equipment, fiber optic equipment, high speed telecommunication, wiring or software development expense.
- 1.5% Individual Credit: a credit equal to 1.5% of each employees gross salary. This credit can be earned for each of the 3 years that the business receives one of the 40% credits.
- Existing Business: Eligible businesses located in a distressed area can get a 25% tax credit against state income taxes for funds spent on specialized equipment that exceeds their average from the prior two years for that equipment.
- "Enhanced" Existing Business: An existing business that doubles the number of existing employees from the date the Pre-application was submitted, may apply for one of the 40% tax credits and the 1.5% Employee tax credit as a "New or Relocating Business".

Neighborhood Preservation Act: Homeowners or developers that construct a new home that is, or will be, owner-occupied in designated areas of the state, will receive a state income tax credit.

Skills Development Tax Credit: Businesses that are located in distressed areas of the state will receive a tax credit to upgrade the occupational skills of its employees through educational programs and training. The credit is for 50% of actual training costs with a maximum amount of $1,500 each year. The credit can be claimed for 2 years.

Dry Fire Hydrant Tax Credit Program: Any person, firm, or corporation that installs a dry fire hydrant that meets standards, will receive a state income tax credit. The credit can be carried forward for up to 7 years.

Neighborhood Assistance Tax Credit Program: Businesses that donate money to an approved Neighborhood Assistance (NAP) project, are eligible for a 50-70% income tax credit.

Youth Opportunities Program: Eligible organizations, which include Missouri businesses, that administer approved positive youth development or crime prevention projects, are eligible for tax credits. The credits are 50% for monetary contributions raised in the community and wages paid to youth in an apprenticeship, intern or employment project; and 30% for property or equipment contributions used specifically for the project.

Montana
Montana Department of Revenue
125 North Roberts, 3rd Floor
Helena, MT 59604
406-444-0629
Fax: 406-444-2980
www.state.mt.us/revenue/css/default.asp

Economic Development Office
Department of Commerce
Economic Development Division
1429 Ninth Ave.
PO Box 200505
Helena, MT 59620-0505
406-444-3814
Fax: 406-444-1872
http://commerce.state.mt.us/ EconDev/index.html

New and Expanding Industry Tax Credit: Credit is equal to 1% of new wages paid by any corporation that is either brand new or has expanded its number of jobs by 30% or more.

Recycling Tax Credit: Income tax deduction for purchase of recycled material.

Research and Development Exemption: Exemption from the corporation income of license tax on the net income of a newly organized research and development firm during its first 5 years of operation.

Dependent Care Assistance Credit: A company can claim a credit for the amount paid or incurred during the taxable year for dependent care assistance actually provided to or on behalf of an employee.

Infrastructure Fees Credit: A nonrefundable tax credit is available against the corporation license tax or income tax for the portion of the fees that are charged to a specified new business for the use of the infrastructure that is built with loans.

Inventory Tax Exemption: Business inventories are exempt from property tax.

Property Tax Incentives for Selected Businesses: Reduction in property tax rates are available to: real and personal property used in the production of gasohol, machinery and equipment used in electrolytic reduction facilities (production of aluminum), market value on machinery and equipment used in a maltiny barley facility, market value on machinery and equipment used in a canola seed oil processing facility.

Property Tax Incentives for Specific Industries: Reduction in property tax rates are available to: industries that manufacture, mill, mine, produce, process, or fabricate materials; that convert materials unserviceable in their natural state into commercial products or materials, engage in the mechanical or chemical transformation of materials of substance into new products, engage in the transportation, warehousing or distribution of commercial products or materials, or if 50% or more of their annual gross income comes from out of state sales. Additional property tax reductions are available to: research and development firms, agricultural or forestry product processing plants, and property used in the production of motion pictures or television commercials.

Local Option Property Tax Incentives: Property tax reduction is available to: new and expanding industries, businesses making improvements, machinery and equipment, business incubators, industrial parks, buildings or land sold or donated to a local economic development organization, and air and water pollution-control equipment.

Montana Agricultural Loan Authority (Beginning Farmer Loan Program): An existing farmer/ranch landowner may be eligible for a reduction in taxable income of $50,000 for selling to a beginning farmer.

Alternative Fuel Motor Vehicle Conversion Credit: Businesses can get a credit against taxes for equipment and labor costs in order to convert a motor vehicle to operate on alternative fuel. The credit is for 50% of equipment and labor up to $500 for a vehicle under 10,000 pounds or $1,000 for a vehicle weighing over 10,000 pounds.

Capital Gains and Dividends from Small Business Investment Company Tax Exemption: A business is eligible for a tax exemption for any capital gains of dividends income from an investment in a SBIC.

Qualified Endowment Credit: Businesses may receive a credit for a planned gift to a qualified charitable endowment. The amount of the credit is dependent on the type of gift and the date it is given.

Contractors Gross Receipts Tax Credit: Contractors and some sub-contractors are eligible for a credit when they perform public construction work under a government contract.

Credit for Increasing Research Activities: Businesses that have increases in qualified research expense and basic research payments for research done in Montana are eligible for a 5% credit equal to those expenses. The credit can be carried back 2 years and forward 15 years.

Credit for Contributions to Housing Trust Fund: Contributions to "affordable housing revolving loan account" can bring a credit equal to 10% of the donation amount up to $10,000. However, the credit may not be claimed if it was taken as a deduction for tax purposes.

Energy Conservation Investment: A taxpayer may deduct up to $1,800 from gross corporate income for a capital investment in a building for energy conservation purposes that are not financed by government or private grant funds for energy conservation. Alternatively, $3,600 can be deducted for commercial building investment.

Investment Tax Credit: Small businesses are eligible for a credit for the purchase of certain qualified, depreciable property. The credit has a maximum of $500.

Montana Capital Company Credit: Certain businesses can qualify for a credit when they invest in a qualified Montana capital company. The credit is for 50% of the investment up to $150,000. Excess credit can be carried back 3 years and forward for 15 years.

Montana College Contribution Credit: Qualified businesses are eligible for a credit of 10% of the amount of a charitable contribution to the Montana University System foundations or to the fund of a private college. The maximum claim per year is $500.

Montana Disability Insurance for Uninsured Montanans Credit: Montana businesses that have been operational for at least 12 month, employ 20 or fewer employees that work at least 20 hours per week, and pay for at least half of each employee's disability insurance premium, are eligible for a credit. The credit is equal to $25 a month per employee if the employer pays 100% of the premium and for a proportionate amount of $25 for an employer that pays less than 100%.

Alternative Energy Production Credit: Businesses that invest $5,500 or more in certain depreciable property which generates energy through an alternative renewable energy source, are eligible for a 35% credit of those expenditures.

Nebraska

Nebraska Department of Revenue
301 Centennial Mall South
Lincoln, NE 68509-4818
800-742-7474
402-471-5729
www.revenue.state.ne.us/index.html

Economic Development Office
Department of Economic Development
P.O. Box 94666
301 Centennial Mall South
Lincoln, NE 68509-4666
402-471-3111
800-426-6505 (in NE)
Fax: 402-471-3778
TDD: 800-833-7352
www.neded.org

Employment and Investment Growth Act: With a $3 million investment in qualified property and addition of 30 full-time employees, a business qualifies for: direct refund of all sales and use taxes paid on purchases of qualified property; 5% tax credit on the amount of the total compensation paid to employees; 10% tax credit on total investment in qualified property, 10% tax credits applied to income tax liability or used to obtain refund of sales and use taxes paid on other purchases.

With a $10 million investment in qualified property and addition of 100 full-time employees, a business qualifies for: all of the above plus up to a 15 year personal property tax exemption on newly acquired: turbine-powered aircraft, mainframe computers and peripheral components, equipment used directly in processing agricultural products. Investment in qualified property resulting in a net gain of $20 million with no increased employment qualifies a business for direct refund of all sales and use taxes paid on purchases of qualified property.

Employment Expansions and Investment Incentive Act: Provides tax credits for any business which increase investment by at least $75,000 and increase net employment by an average of two full-time positions during a taxable year. Credits of $1,500 per net new employee and $1,000 per $75,000 net new investment may be used to reduce a portion of the taxpayer's income tax liability or to obtain a refund of sales and use taxes paid.

Enterprise Zones: Within these areas, tax credits are given for qualifying businesses which increase employment and make investments in the area.

For more information, contact Nebraska Department of Revenue, 301 Centennial Mall South, P.O. Box 94818, Lincoln, NE 58609-4818; 402-471-5729; 800-742-7474.

Invest Nebraska Act: A business is eligible for a tax credit when they make a qualified investment and create new full-time jobs. There are three options with this program: 1) Invest $10 million and create 25 new full-time jobs with pay that is equal to the state average; 2) Invest $50 million and create 500 new full-time jobs; or 3) Invest $100 million and create 25 full-time jobs with pay equal to 110% of the state average.

Rural Economic Opportunity Act: The creation of full-time employment plus a qualified investment in specified counties will bring the investing business tax credits. The credit is a 10% investment credit and a 5% credit on the taxable wages of the new employees.

Nevada

Nevada Department of Taxation
1550 East College Parkway, Suite 115
Carson City, NV 89706
775-687-4820
Fax: 775-687-5981
http://tax.state.nv.us

Economic Development Office
State of Nevada Commission on Economic Development
108 E. Proctor St.
Carson City, NV 89701
775-687-4325
800-336-1600
Fax: 775-687-4450
www.expand2nevada.com/index2.html
555 E. Washington Avenue, Suite 5400
Las Vegas, NV 89101
702-486-2700
Fax: 702-486-2701

No Personal Income Tax
No Corporate Income Tax
No Franchise Tax on Income
No Unitary Tax
No Inheritance, Estate, or Gift Tax
No Admissions Tax

Freeport: Protects shipments in transit from taxation and cuts the cost of doing business both domestically and internationally.

Sales and Use Tax Abatement: Partial sales/use tax exemption on machinery and equipment purchases.

Sales and Use Tax Deferral: Tax deferral on machinery and equipment purchases in excess of $100,000.

Business Tax Abatement: A tax exemption determined on a case by case basis.

Property Tax Abatement: 50% tax exemption on real and personal property for qualified recycling businesses.

Personal Property Tax Abatement: An abatement of personal property tax for businesses that meet job creation, employee health plan minimum capital investment, and wage requirements.

Property Tax Exemptions: The following are exempt from property tax:
- All personal property stored, assembled or processed for interstate transit;
- All raw materials and supplies utilized in the manufacturing process;
- Inventories held for sale within Nevada;
- All real and personal property that qualified and is used for the purpose of air and/or water pollution control.

Renewable Energy Abatements: Companies involved in the production of renewable energy resources have a package of abatements available including sales/use tax and property tax.

New Hampshire

New Hampshire Department of Revenue Administration
45 Chenell Drive
Concord, NH 03302-0457
603-271-2191
Fax: 603-271-6121
TDD: 800-735-2964
http://webster.state.nh.us/revenue

Economic Development Office
State of New Hampshire
Department of Resources and Economic Development
172 Pembroke Road
Concord, NH 03302-1856
603-271-2341
Fax: 603-271-6784
www.nheconomy.com
Email: info@nheconomy.com

No general sales tax
No tax on inventories
No property tax on machinery or equipment
No software tax
No Internet tax
No broad base income tax.
No capital gains tax.
No tax on tangible business property.

New Jersey

New Jersey Division of Taxation
50 Barrack Street
Trenton, NJ 08625

609-292-6400
Fax: 609-826-4500
TDD: 800-286-6613
www.state.nj.us/treasury/taxation/index.html

Economic Development Office
New Jersey Economic Development Authority
P.O. Box 990
Trenton, NJ 08625-0990
609-292-1800
www.njeda.com
Email: njeda@njeda.com

Urban Enterprise Zones: Provide significant incentives and benefits to qualified businesses located within their borders. Such benefits include sales tax to customers (3% instead of 6%), corporation tax credits for the hiring of certain employees, and subsidized unemployment insurance costs. 609-777-0885

No net worth tax, no business personal property tax, no commercial rent or occupancy tax and no retail gross receipts tax.

Property Tax Abatements and Exemptions: Available for commercial and industrial properties in areas in need or redevelopment.

New Jobs Investment Tax Credit: Companies that make certain investments in new or expanded business facilities that are directly related to the creation of new jobs may be eligible for credits.

Manufacturing Equipment and Employment Investment Tax Credit: Certain investments made by companies for manufacturing equipment with a recovery life of four years or more are eligible for a credit.

Recognition of Subchapter S Status for Corporations: S corporations are provided a reduced corporation tax rate.

Research and Development Tax Credit for Corporation Business Tax: Businesses may be eligible for a credit for certain increased research expenditures in the state.

Neighborhood and Business Child Care Incentive Program Tax Credit: Members of a small to medium sized child-care consortium are eligible for a tax credit for the expenditures of the child-care facility.

Redevelopment Authority Project Tax Credit: Corporations that actively conduct business at a location within a project that is being financed or carried out under an agreement with the Redevelopment Authority can get a tax credit. The credit may be carried forward one year.

Research and Development Tax Credit Carry Forward Extension: Qualified R&D tax credits incurred between 7-1-98 and 6-30-01 may be carried forward for 15 years.

Smart Moves for Business Program Tax Credit: Businesses that participate in the employee commute option program may receive a tax credit.

New Mexico

New Mexico Taxation and Revenue Department
1100 South St. Francis Drive
Santa Fe, NM 87504
505-827-0800

Fax: 505-827-9873
www.state.nm.us/tax

Economic Development Office
Economic Development Department
Joseph M. Montoya Bldg.
1100 S. St. Francis Drive
Santa Fe, NM 87503
505-827-0300
800-374-3061
Fax: 505-827-0407
www.edd.state.nm.us

Aerospace Research and Development Deduction: The Aerospace Research and Development tax deduction was implemented to facilitate the location of a spaceport in New Mexico.

Agriculture-Related Tax Deductions/Exemptions: Feed and fertilizer, warehousing, threshing, harvesting, growing, cultivating and processing agricultural products, agricultural products, fish raised for human consumption, poultry or animals raised for hides or pelts; selling seeds, roots, bulbs, plants, soil conditioners, fertilizers, insecticides, germicides, water for irrigation, ranching; certain agricultural products; and livestock feeding.

Gross Receipts and Compensating Tax Abatement: "Compensating tax" is an excise tax imposed for the privilege of using property in New Mexico. In New Mexico it is called gross receipts tax for purchases made within the state. For purchases made outside New Mexico and imported into the state, it is called compensating tax. Abatement of the state's portion of any sales, gross receipts, compensating or similar tax on machinery and equipment, and other movable personal property for an eligible facility. In New Mexico construction or rehabilitation of non-speculative office buildings, warehouses, manufacturing facilities, and service oriented facilities not primarily engaged in the sale of goods or commodities at retail are eligible.

Enterprise Zones: The Enterprise Zone Act is designed to stimulate the creation of new jobs and to revitalize economically distressed areas. $50,000 tax credit to property owners for the rehabilitation of qualified business facilities, technical assistance, training reimbursement, and other benefits. 505-827-0089

Filmmakers Gross Receipts Tax Incentive: Implemented to facilitate the filming of movies, television shows and commercials in New Mexico. A qualified production company may execute nontaxable transaction certificates with its suppliers for tangible personal property or services. The suppliers may then deduct their receipts from the gross receipts tax.

Indian Employment Credit: Provides for a tax credit to employers of Indians on Indian lands to encourage economic development. The maximum credit per employee is $4,000.

Cultural Property Preservation Tax Credit: Property owners are eligible to receive a personal or corporate tax credit for restoring, rehabilitating or otherwise preserving cultural properties. Specifically, a tax credit is available where historic structures are certified as having received rehabilitation to preserve and enhance their historic character. Offers a maximum tax credit of 50% of the cost of restoration, rehabilitation or preservation up to $25,000.

Gross Receipts Tax Deduction: Equipment that goes into a plant financed with industrial revenue bonds is exempt for the gross receipts or compensating tax of 5%.

Telemarketing Gross Receipts Tax Exemption: This program exempts receipts from the provision of wide area telephone services (WATS) and private communications services from the interstate telecommunications gross receipts tax. Wide-area telephone service means a telephone service that entitles a subscriber to either make or receive large volumes of communications to or from persons in specified geographical areas.

Investment Tax Credit Program: Provides a general incentive for manufacturers to locate in New Mexico and to hire New Mexicans. Imported equipment is eligible if essential, used directly and exclusively in a manufacturing facility, and depreciated for federal income tax purposes. The creation of new, full time jobs is required to qualify for the credit. The credit allows the manufacturer to offset the amount of compensating tax paid on eligible equipment. The credit equals the amount of compensating tax actually paid, and may be applied against compensating tax, gross receipts tax or withholding tax due.

Preferential Tax Rate for Small Wineries and Breweries: Wine produced by a small winery carries a tax of 10 cents per liter on the first 80,000 liters; 20 cents on production over that level. The basic tax rate for wine is 45 cents per liter. Beer produced by a microbrewery is taxed at 8 cents per gallon. The basic tax rate for beer is 41 cents per gallon.

Tax Increment Financing: At the beginning of a project, the valuation of the project properties is summed. As the project proceeds, these properties are developed or otherwise improved, increasing their valuations. The tax proceeds flowing from the increase in valuation may be diverted to finance the project. Tax increment financing in New Mexico is available only in a designated enterprise zone.

Property Tax Abatement: Land, buildings and equipment associated with an eligible project are exempt from ad valorem tax, generally to promote economic development.

Aircraft Refurbishing or remodeling Tax Deduction: Refurbishing, remodeling or otherwise modifying transport category aircraft over 65,000 pound gross landing weight may be deducted from gross receipts.

Child Care Corporate Income Tax Credit: Corporations that provide or pay for licensed child care services for employee's children under age 12 can get a 30% deduction of eligible expenses. A company that operates a value-added day care center for its employees can use the credit to reduce the cost to provide that service.

Inventory Tax Exemption: There is no tax on business inventories until they are sold.

Laboratory Partnership with Small Business Tax Credit: A national laboratory is eligible for a tax credit when it incurs expenses from giving certain types of assistance to small businesses in New Mexico. This credit means that those businesses can use Sandia National Laboratory for up to $10,000 worth of assistance at no cost.

Rural Job Tax Credit: Eligible employers that create new jobs in rural New Mexico are entitled to a tax credit. The credit must be taken over a period of time. Its amount depends on the area of employment, but is for either 25% or 12.5% of the first $16,000 in wages, with a maximum annual credit of $1,000 per job. This can be carried forward for up to 3 years.

Welfare-to-Work Tax Credit: This is a state credit that is equal to 50% of the federal welfare-to-work credit. The maximum credit amount for the first year is $1,750 and $2,500 for the second year for each qualifying employee. There is a 3-year carry forward.

Business Facility Rehabilitation Tax Credit: The restoration, rehabilitation, or renovation project of a qualified business facility in an enterprise zone, is eligible for a tax credit. The facility must have been vacant for at least 24 months prior to the project and must be put into use immediately after by a person in the manufacturing, distribution, or service industries. The credit is equal to 50% of project costs with a maximum of $50,000.

Renewable Energy Production Credit: A credit is given to a business that uses a qualified energy source for 10 consecutive years beginning with the first year of production. Contact: Energy, Minerals and Natural Resources Department, Energy Conservation and Management Division, P.O. Box 6429, Santa Fe, NM 87505; 505-476-3319; Fax: 505-476-3220.

Film Production Tax Credit: Filmmakers may apply for a 15% tax credit on the total direct production costs incurred in New Mexico. Most direct costs are eligible. Contact: New Mexico Film Office, 1100 St. Francis Drive, Santa Fe, NM 87505; 505-827-9810; 800-545-9871; Fax: 505-827-9799; {www.nmfilm.com}.

Aircraft Manufacturing Tax Deduction: This program provides a gross receipt deduction for sale of aircraft by an aircraft manufacturer.

Double Weight Sales Factor: Through the year 2010, manufacturers that use the 3-factor formula to figure income, may use a modified formula. The new formula gives the sales factor a 50% weight, reducing payroll and property to 25% apiece. The formula must be used for at least 3 consecutive years. Construction, farming, power generation and processing of natural resources are excluded.

Texas/Mexico Border Residents' Tax Exemption: Texas residents that work a specifically located manufacturing facility in New Mexico, do not have to pay state income tax on their wages. The business must be located within 20 miles of the Mexican border, have at least 5 employees who are New Mexico residents and does not receive in-plant training funds.

Space Gross Receipts Tax Deduction: The following are the three separate deductions connected with the operation of a spaceport in New Mexico:
1) Receipts from launching, operating or recovering space vehicles or payload.
2) Receipts from preparing a payload in New Mexico.
3) Receipts from operating a spaceport in New Mexico.

Research & Development Gross Receipts Tax: Research and Development services that are exported from the state are not charged gross receipts tax.

Rural Software Gross Receipts Tax Deduction: To stimulate new business development in rural areas of New Mexico, a gross tax receipts deduction is allowed for certain software development services where the business is located in a qualified area.

Technology Jobs Tax Credit: This is a two-part credit; a basic credit and an additional credit where each is equal to 4% of the qualified expenditures on qualified research at a qualified facility. The credit amount doubles for expenditures for facilities located in New Mexico.

Web Hosting Gross Receipts Tax Deduction: Receipts from hosting world-wide web sites may be deducted from gross receipts.

Call Center Capital Equipment Tax Credit Act: A tax credit for the purchase of capital equipment was created to encourage in-bound call centers to expand or relocate in New Mexico.

Tribal Land Business Tax Credit: A Corporation that is involved in growing, processing or manufacturing on Indian land is eligible for a credit of 50% of the total taxes from business activities by an Indian nation, tribe or pueblo located entirely, or in part, in New Mexico.

New York

New York State Department of Taxation and Finance
W.A. Harriman Campus
Albany, NY 12227
800-972-1233
www.tax.state.ny.us

Economic Development Office
Empire State Development
30 S. Pearl St.
Albany, NY 12245
and
633 Third Ave.
New York, NY 10017-6706
518-474-7756
800-STATE-NY (782-8369)
Email: esd@empire.state.ny.us
www.empire.state.ny.us

Investment Tax Credit: Businesses that make new investments in production property and equipment and create new jobs may qualify for tax credits of up to 10% of their eligible investment.

Research and Development Tax Credit: Investments in research and development facilities are eligible for a 9% tax credit against corporate tax.

Sales Tax Exemptions: Purchases of production machinery and equipment, research and development property, and fuels/utilities used in manufacturing and R&D.

Real Property Tax Abatement

No Personal Property Tax

Economic Development Zones/Empire Zone Tax Credits: New York State has currently designated 52 economically distressed areas - certified as Economic Development Zones. They want to encourage the creation of jobs in these areas. In a zone they offer an investment tax credit of up to 19 percent. They can provide a tax break of up to 25% for new investors in these areas. They offer a host of benefits to make doing business easier, ranging from discounts on electric power to wage tax credits for new employees. They also have set aside Zone Equivalent Areas for special tax credits.

Empowerment Zone Program: Wage tax credits for businesses in severely distressed areas.

Pollution Control Facilities: Facilities are exempt from local real property taxes and ad valorem levies.

North Carolina

North Carolina Department of Revenue
501 North Wilmington Street
Raleigh, NC 27604
877-252-3052
www.dor.state.nc.us

Economic Development Office
Department of Commerce
Commerce Finance Center
301 N. Wilmington St.
Raleigh, NC 27601
MAILING ADDRESS:
  4301 Mail Service Center
  Raleigh, NC 27699-4301
919-733-4151
Fax: 919-715-9265
www.commerce.state.nc.us/

Inventory Tax Exemption: There is no local or state property tax on inventory held by manufacturers, wholesale and retail merchants or contractors.

Computer Software Tax Exemptions: There are no local or state sales taxes on custom computer programs. Additionally, there is no property tax on computer software.

Recycling Equipment: Equipment or facilities installed for the purpose of recycling solid waste or resource recovery from solid waste receives the same treatment under the tax laws as that given to pollution abatement equipment described below.

Pollution Abatement Equipment: Property used to reduce air or water pollution receives special treatment under the tax law if the Board of Environmental Management certifies that the property complies with the requirements of the Board.

OSHA Equipment: The cost of equipment and facilities mandated by the Occupational Safety and Health Act may be amortized over 60 months for income tax purposes.

Equipment to Reduce Hazardous Waste: Equipment and facilities acquired for the purpose of reducing the volume of hazardous waste generated may be amortized over a period of 60 months for income tax purposes.

Jobs Creation Tax Credit: Provides a tax credit for creating jobs based on the number of jobs created and the location of the business.

Machinery and Equipment Investment Tax Credit: Available to eligible companies that invest in machinery and equipment and based on the amount of machinery purchased.

Worker Training Tax Credit: Up to a 50% credit against eligible training expenses if the firm provides training for 5 or more employees. Maximum credit is $1,000 per employee.

Research and Development Tax Credit: A credit of 50% of the increase in research and development expenses apportioned to North Carolina taken by an eligible company.

Business Property Tax Credit: Equals 4.5% of tangible personal business property capitalized under the tax code, up to a maximum single-year credit of $4,500.

Central Administrative Office Tax Credit: Available to companies who have purchased or leased real property in North Carolina to be used as a central administrative office for the company. Maximum credit is $500,000.

Ports Authority Tax Credits at Morehead City & Wilmington: Both importers and exporters who use the North Carolina ports can apply and qualify for a tax credit. The credit is earned on incremental increases in imports and exports over a 3-year period, or new business to the Ports.

Credit for Construction of Cogenerating Power Plants: Any corporation that constructs a cogenerating power plant in North Carolina is allowed a credit equal to 10% of the costs required to purchase and install the electrical or mechanical power generation equipment of that plant.

Sales Tax Exemptions and Discounts: Available for industrial machinery and equipment; coal, coke and fuel oil used in manufacturing; electricity or piped natural gas used in connection with manufacturing; raw materials used for production, packaging, and shipping, as well as things bought for resale; motor vehicles; aircraft, boats, railway cars, and mobile offices; purchases of ingredients or component parts of manufactured products; packaging material that becomes a part of a manufactured product. Contact: NC Department of Revenue, Box 25000, Raleigh, NC 27640; 919-733-3991; {www.dor.state.nc.us/}.

Credit for Investing in Renewable Energy Property: A tax credit for 35% of the cost of renewable energy property is available for a business that has constructed, leased, or purchased the property and placed it in service.

Credit for Dwelling Units for Handicapped Persons: Corporations that own multi-family rental units can get an income tax credit for each dwelling unit constructed for physically handicapped persons. The credit is for $550 per unit completed in one year.

Credit for Construction of Renewable Energy Equipment Facility: A corporation is allowed a 25% credit for the cost of installation and construction equipment for the construction of a facility for the manufacture of renewable energy.

Credit for Real Property Donated for Conservation Purposes: A corporation that makes a qualified donation of an interest in real property is allowed a credit equal to 25% of the fair market value of the property. The maximum credit amount is $500,000.

Credit for Conservation Tillage Equipment: A corporation can receive a 25% credit for the cost of conservation tillage equipment that is used in a farming business, including tree farming.

Credit for Gleaned Crop: A corporation that grows and allows the gleaning of the crop will be allowed a tax credit of 10% of the market price of the crop.

Income Tax Credit for Poultry Composing Facility: Corporations that construct a poultry composting facility are allowed a 25% credit equal to the installation, materials, and equipment costs.

North Dakota

North Dakota Office of the State Tax Commissioner
600 East Boulevard Avenue
Bismarck, ND 58505-0599
701-328-2770
Fax: 701-328-3700
www.state.nd.us/taxdpt/index.html

Economic Development Office
Department of Economic Development and Finance
400 E. Broadway, Suite 50
Bismarck, ND 58502-2057
701-328-5300
Fax: 701-328-5320
TTY: 800-366-6888
www.growingnd.com

No personal property tax including equipment, inventory, materials in process or accounts receivable.
Allows the entire amount of federal income tax liability to be deducted before calculating state corporate tax.

County Property Tax Exemptions: Any new or expanding business may be granted an exemption for up to five years. Other possible exemptions include: rehabilitation of buildings more than 25 years old; Geothermal, solar or wind energy systems.

Corporate Tax Credits: A primary sector business such as manufacturing, agricultural processing and back office operations such as telemarketing may qualify for a five-year income tax exemption. Other items that may qualify for corporate tax credits include: research expenditures within the state; seed capital investments; wages and salaries for new businesses, investments in a Renaissance Zone corporation, investment in the preservation or renovation of historic property in a Renaissance Zone, part of the wages paid to chronically mentally ill or develop mentally disabled employees, installation of alternative fuel equipment on a licensed motor vehicle, installation of geothermal, solar or wind energy devices, contributions to nonprofit high schools and private colleges in the state.

Sales and Use Tax: New or expanding businesses qualify for an exemption on computer and telecommunications equipment, agricultural processing plant construction materials, tangible personal property used to construct wind-powered electrical generating facilities, machinery, building materials and equipment used for manufacturing, processing or recycling. There is no sales tax on electricity, water or money when used for manufacturing purposes.

Property Tax Reduction: A centrally assessed wind turbine electric generation unit with a nameplate generation capacity of at least 100 kilowatts has a taxable value calculated at 3% instead of the usual 10%.

Jobs Training Assistance: This program will assist your new or expanding business with training new employees. The cost of the training under this program is paid for in whole or in part with the income tax withheld from the new employees.

Ohio

Ohio Department of Taxation
30 east Broad Street
Columbus, OH 43215
888-405-4039
Fax: 614-466-6401
http://tax.ohio.gov/

Economic Development Office
Ohio Department of Development
77 S. High St.
P.O. Box 1001
Columbus, OH 43216-1001
614-466-2317
800-848-1300
Fax: 614-463-1789
www.odod.state.oh.us

Community Reinvestment Areas: Local tax incentives for businesses that expand or locate in designated areas of Ohio. Up to 100% exemption of the improved real estate property tax valuation for up to 15 years. In some instances, local school board approval may be required. Business must undertake new real estate investment. {www.odod. state.oh.us/edd/cra}

Enterprise Zones: Local and state tax incentives for businesses that expand or locate in designated areas of Ohio. Up to 75% exemption in incorporated areas and up to 60% in unincorporated areas of the improved real estate or new tangible personal property tax valuation for up to 10 years. {www.odod.state.oh.us/EDD/ez}

Ohio Manufacturing Machinery & Equipment Investment Tax Credit: A non-refundable corporate franchise or state income tax credit for a manufacturer that purchases new machinery and equipment that is located in Ohio and is used in the production or assembly of a manufactured good. The manufacturer shall receive a 7.5% tax credit on the increase of the investment that is in excess of the three-year annual average investment on machinery and equipment.

Ohio Job Creation Tax Credit: State and municipal tax incentives are available for businesses that expand or locate in Ohio. State guidelines regulate the type of business and project eligible for the incentive. A business can receive a tax credit or refund against its corporate franchise tax based on the state income withheld on new, full-time employees. The amount of the tax credit can be up to 75% for up to ten years. The tax credit can exceed 75% upon recommendation of the Director of ODOD when there is an extraordinary circumstance. Municipalities can provide a similar arrangement with their local employee income taxes. {www.odod.state.oh.us/EDD/jctc}

Technology Investment Tax Credit: Taxpayers who invest in small, research and development and technology-oriented firms may reduce their state taxes by up to 25% of the amount they invest.

Ohio Job Retention Job Credit: Businesses that employ an average 1,000 full-time employees at a project site and retain those 1,000 employees for the term of agreement with the Tax Credit Authority, are eligible for a credit. The credit is against the corporate franchise tax based on state income withheld on the employees with a maximum credit of 75% for 10 years. 614-466-2317

Training Tax Credit: Eligible businesses that train existing employees that are at risk of losing their jobs due to skill deficiencies can get up to $100,000 per year in tax credits.

Research & Development Sales Tax Exemption: Businesses can be completely exempted from State and County sales tax for the purchases of machinery used primarily for research and development.

Manufacturing Machinery and Equipment Sales Tax Exemption: Businesses can be completely exempted from State and County sales tax for the purchases of machinery used primarily for manufacturing.

Warehouse Machinery and Equipment Sales Tax Exemption: Businesses can be completely exempted from State and County sales tax for the purchases of eligible machinery and equipment.

Warehouse Inventory Tax Exemption: Inventory brought into Ohio from out of state and then held for storage only and then sent out of state again, will be subject to a reduced personal tangible property assessment rate.

Oklahoma

Oklahoma Tax Commission
2501 North Lincoln Boulevard
Oklahoma, OK 73194
405-521-3160
Fax: 405-522-0465
www.oktax.state.ok.us

Economic Development Office
Department of Commerce
900 North Stiles
P.O. Box 26980
Oklahoma City, OK 73126-0980
405-815-6552
800-879-6552.
Fax: 405-815-5199
www.locateok.com
www.odoc.state.ok.us/index.html

Ad Valorem Tax Exemptions: New and expanding qualifying manufacturers, research and development companies, certain computer services and data processing companies with significant out-of-state sales, aircraft repair and aircraft distribution may be eligible for ad valorem exemptions.

Exempt Inventory: Oklahoma's Freeport Law exempts goods, wares, and merchandise from taxation that come into Oklahoma from outside the state and leave the state within nine months.

Sales Tax Exemptions: Exemptions are available in the following areas: machinery and equipment used in manufacturing; tangible personal property used in manufacturing including fuel and electric power; tangible personal property which becomes part of the finished product; tangible personal property used in design and warehousing and located on the manufacturing site.

Aircraft Maintenance Facilities: Sales tax exemption on aircraft and parts.

Telecommunications: Exemptions apply to various services as part of an inducement to contract for wireless telecommunications services.

Sales and Use Tax Refunds: Refunds of sales/use tax are available for purchase of data processing equipment, related peripherals and telephone or telecommunications services or equipment and for construction materials.

Technology Transfer Income Tax Exemption: The taxable income of any corporation is decreased for transfers of technology to qualified small businesses located in Oklahoma not to exceed 10% of the amount of gross proceeds received by such corporation as a result of the technology transfer.

New Products Development Income Tax Exemption: Royalties earned by an inventor on products developed and manufactured in Oklahoma are exempt from state income tax.

Agricultural Commodity Processing Facility Income Tax Exclusion: Owners of agricultural commodity processing facilities may exclude a portion from taxable income based on investment.

Income Tax Credit for Investment in Oklahoma Producer-Owned Agriculture Processing: An income tax credit of 30% of investment is available to agricultural producer investors in Oklahoma producer-owned agricultural processing ventures, cooperative, or marketing associations.

Income Tax Credit for Computer/Data Processing/ Research & Development Jobs: Credit is available for a net increase in the number of full-time employees engaged in computer services, date processing or R & D. The credit allowed is $500 per employee, up to 50 employees.

Insurance Premium Tax Credit: Insurance companies which locate or expand regional home offices in Oklahoma are eligible for special tax credits against the tax imposed in the Insurance Code ranging from 15% to 50% based on number of full-time employees.

Small Business Capital Formation Tax Credit: Authorizes an income tax credit of 20% of equity investment for investors in qualified businesses.

Rural Small Business Capital Formation Tax Credit: Authorizes an income tax credit of 30% of equity investment for investing in a small business in a rural area.

Recycling, Reuse and Source Reduction Incentive Act: Manufacturing and service industries may receive an income tax credit of up to 20% of investment cost for equipment and installation or processes used to recycle, reuse, or reduce the source of hazardous waste. Credits are limited $50,000.

Income Tax Exemption for Interest Paid on Bonds: Interest payment received as a result of bonds issued by nonprofit corporations on behalf of towns, cities, or counties for housing purposes are not subject to state income tax.

Tax Incentives on Former Indian Reservation Lands:
1. Employee Credit: Businesses located on qualified areas of former Indian reservations are eligible for a tax credit based on the increase in qualifying annual wages paid to enrolled Indian tribal members or their spouses. The credit equal 20% of the increased wages.
2. Depreciation Incentive: Provides a shorter recovery period of approximately 40% for most non-residential depreciable property being used in an active trade or business.

Work Opportunity Tax Credit Program: A tax credit is available up to $2,400 for each new hire from a target group of individuals.

Welfare-to-Work Tax Credit: Available to employers who hire individuals certified and long-term assistance recipients. The credit is as much as $8,500 per new hire.

Investment/New Jobs Income Tax Credit: Allows a five-year tax credit on the greater of (1%) per year of investment in qualified new depreciable property or a credit of $500 per year per new job, doubled in an Enterprise Zone.

Sales/Income Tax Credit for Tourism Attraction Projects: Projects of approved companies that bring more tourists to Oklahoma can get a credit against the company's income tax or sales tax liability.

Alternative Energy Source Tax Credit: Producers of electricity and small wind turbine manufacturers that use alternative energy are eligible for tax credits.

Gas Usage Tax Credit for Manufacturing: Manufacturing operators are allowed a credit against the tax proportioned to the amount of gas used or consumed in Oklahoma manufacturing operations.

Small Business Administration (SBA) Guarantee Fee Tax Credit: Every small business operating in the state may claim a credit equal to the amount of the fee paid to obtain financing from the SBA.

Commercial Space Industry Credit: Investors in qualifying projects which encourage the development of commercial space industries may take a credit equal to 5% of their investment.

Historic Rehabilitation Tax Credit: Tax credits for investment in any certified historic hotel or newspaper plant building in an increment district are freely transferable. This state credit equals the federal credit.

Empowerment Zone Incentives: There are tax credits of up to $3,000 yearly for each new or existing employee that lives and works in the Zone for businesses that are located in the Zone. The Welfare-to-Work and work opportunity credits are also enhanced in the Zone.

Oregon
Oregon Department of Revenue
955 Center Street, NE
Salem, OR 97301-2555
800-356-4222 (in-state)
503-378-4988
www.dor.state.or.us

Economic Development Office
Economic and Community Development Department
775 Summer St., Suite 200
Salem, OR 97301-1280
503-986-0123
800-233-3306 (in OR)
www.econ.state.or.us/

Corporate Income Tax Credits: Oregon businesses may be eligible for a number of tax credits allowed under Oregon law. Some of these business-related tax credits include:
- pollution control tax credit,
- business energy tax credit,

- research tax credit,
- reclaimed plastics product tax credit,
- dependent child care tax credit, and
- donation of computers and scientific equipment in Oregon.

Enterprise Zone Program: Created as a business incentive to create new jobs by encouraging business investment in economically lagging areas of the state. Construction of new facilities in an enterprise zone entitles a business to a 100% property tax abatement for three to five years on a new plant and most of the equipment installed.

Construction in Progress Exemption: Under Oregon law, new facilities are exempt from property taxes for up to two years while they are under construction and not in use on July 1 of the taxing year. The Construction in Progress Exemption also applies to any machinery or equipment installed in the unoccupied facility on July 1. The exemption does not apply to land. For more information, contact the county assessor or Oregon Department of Revenue, Property Tax Division, Room 256, Revenue Building, Salem, OR 97310; 503-945-8290.

Strategic Investment Program: Provides property tax exemptions for significant projects that will benefit Oregon's key industries. Properties developed under this program are exempted from local property taxes for up to 15 years on assessed value in excess of $100 million. With local government approval, participating companies pay property taxes on the first $100 million in assessed value for the approved project. This base amount ($100 million) is increased by 3% per year. Participating companies also make a direct community service payment to the local government equal to 25% of the abated amount, not to exceed $2 million per year. After local government approval, the Oregon Economic Development Commission is authorized to determine that the project is eligible for the program and determine the maximum eligible cost of real and personal property for the project.

Small-City Taxable Income Exemption for Business Development: Certified businesses can deduct 100% of their income/profit generated from its overall taxable income when the business facility is located in a specified area.

The following are some costs that businesses in Oregon do not face:
- No Sales tax.
- No inventory tax.
- No worldwide unitary tax.
- No motor vehicle excise tax.
- No business and occupations tax.
- No direct levies on intangible properties, such as stocks, bonds and securities.

Pennsylvania
Pennsylvania Department of Revenue
Revenue Place
Harrisburg, PA 17128
717-787-1064
888-PA-TAXES
www.revenue.state.pa.us/revenue/site/default.asp

Economic Development Office
Department of Community and Economic Development
4th Floor, Commonwealth Keystone Bldg.
Harrisburg, PA 17120-0225

800-379-7448
Email: fa-DCEDCS@state.pa.us
www.inventpa.com

Governor's Action Team
100 Pine Street, Suite 100
Harrisburg, PA 17101
717-787-8199
888-4TEAMPA
Fax: 717-772-5419
www.teampa.com

Job Creation Tax Credits: A $1,000-per-job tax credit to approved businesses that agree to create jobs in the Commonwealth within three years.

Local Economic Revitalization Tax Assistance Act: Local municipalities, school districts and counties can offer up to 100% abatements on property taxes for up to 10 years.

Neighborhood Assistance Tax Credit: Up to either 50% or 70% of the amount invested, depending on the type of assistance, of the amount invested in programs that help families or communities in impoverished areas.

Enterprise Zone Credit Program: Allows corporations a tax credit of up to 20% on investments to rehabilitate or improve buildings or land in an Enterprise Zone.

Research and Development Tax Credits: Employers that qualify for the federal Research and Development tax credit will receive a 10% tax credit for increased research activities in Pennsylvania over a base period.

Educational Improvement Tax Credit: Eligible businesses that contribute to a scholarship organization or educational improvement organization are eligible for a tax credit equal to 75% of the contribution up to $100,000 per taxable year.

Keystone Opportunity Zones (KOZ): Provides state and local tax abatements to businesses, property owners and residents locating in one of 12 designated zones.

Rhode Island
Rhode Island Division of Taxation
One Capital Hill
Providence, RI 02908
401-222-1120
Fax: 401-274-3676
www.tax.state.ri.us

Economic Development Office
Economic Development Corporation
One West Exchange St.
Providence, RI 02903
401-222-2601
Fax: 401-222-2102
Email: riedc@riedc.com
www.riedc.com

No Income Tax for Insurance Carriers.

Passive Investment Tax Exemption: A corporation's investment income may be exempt from the Rhode Island income tax if it confines its activity to the maintenance and management of its passive intangible assets, maintains an office in Rhode Island, and employs at least five persons in Rhode Island.

Telecommunication Sales Tax Exemption: Regulated investment companies with at least 500 full-time equivalent employees are exempt from the sales and use tax imposed on toll-free terminating telecommunication service.

Insurance and Mutual Holding Companies: Rhode Island allows a mutual insurance company to create a mutual holding company, owned by the policy holders exactly as they now own the mutual company. This holding company, however, would then own the actual insurance company as a stockholder, while the insurance company itself could issue stock to raise capital. The process could be controlled by the mutual holding company, which means that policyholders would be protected from any dilution of control over the majority stockholder of the company. Policyholders ownership of the insurance subsidiary would be shared with other stockholders only to the extent that they choose to issue stock to raise capital for expansion.

Captive Insurance Companies: Rhode Island allows captive insurance companies to capitalize with a letter of credit or cash as in other states.

Insurance Company Retaliatory Tax Exemption: Foreign insurance companies are exempt from gross premiums retaliatory taxes in Rhode Island when their home jurisdiction does not impose a like tax.

Income Allocation Modification for Manufacturers of Medical Instruments and Supplies (SIC Code 384) and Drugs (SIC Code 283): A Rhode Island manufacturer of Medical Instruments and Supplies or Drugs registered and certified by the United States Food and Drug Administration with a place of business outside the state may modify the numerator in the allocation formula for the current tax year.

4% Credit for Equipment and Facilities Used in Manufacturing: Manufacturers may take a 4% tax credit for new tangible personal and other tangible property that is located in Rhode Island and is principally used by the taxpayer in the production of goods by manufacturing, processing, or assembling.

Research and Development Expense Credit: A special Rhode Island credit is allowed against the business corporation taxes and Rhode Island personal income tax for qualified research expenses. The credit is computed at 22.5% of the expense as defined in Section 41 of the Internal Revenue Code for companies increasing research and development expenditures, making Rhode Island the highest in the nation. The credit drops to 16.9% for R&D expenditures above the first $25,000 of credit. Unused credit may be carried forward for up to seven years.

Rhode Island Job Training Tax Credit: A special Rhode Island credit allows companies to receive a credit of $5,000 per employee against the business corporation taxes in any three year period against the cost of offering training and/or retraining to employees. This tax credit is critically important to existing Rhode Island employers, which formerly were not provided any tax incentives for the retraining of existing employees. With this tax credit, Rhode Island businesses will be able to reduce costs, be more efficient, and add to their competitiveness.

Rhode Island Employer's Apprenticeship Tax Credit: The annual credit allowed is 50% of the actual wages paid to the qualifying apprentice or $4,800, whichever is less. The credit applies to the following trades in the metal and plastic industries: machinist, toolmaker, modelmaker, gage maker,

patternmaker, plastic process technician, tool & machine setter, diesinker, moldmaker, tool & die maker, machine tool repair.

Educational Assistance and Development Credit: A credit is 8% of the contribution in excess of $10,000 made to a Rhode Island institution of higher education and the contribution is to be for the establishment or maintenance of programs of scientific research or education. "Contributions" include the cost or other basis (for federal income tax purposes) in excess of $10,000 of tangible personal property excluding sale discounts and sale-gift arrangements concerning the purchase of equipment. Amounts of unused credit may be carried over for 5 years and documentation of the credit requires a written statement from the institution.

Work Opportunity Tax Credit: Long-term welfare recipients can now earn their employers a Welfare to Work tax credit of up to $2400.

Adult Education Tax Credit: The Rhode Island Adult Education Tax Credit allows for both a worksite and nonworksite tax credit for vocational training or basic education of 50% of the costs incurred up to a maximum of $300 per employee and $5,000 per employer per calendar year.

Child and Adult Daycare Tax Credit: Credits are available against the business corporation tax, the bank excise tax, the insurance companies gross premiums tax and the personal income tax. These credits are computed at 30% of the amount of Rhode Island licensed daycare purchased and 30% of the cost to establish and/or operate a Rhode Island licensed daycare facility whether established and/or operated by the taxpayer alone or in conjunction with others. The maximum annual credit for purchased daycare is $30,000 per year and the amounts of unused credit may not be carried forward. For daycare facilities and rents/lease foregone, the maximum total credit is $30,000 per year and amounts of unused may be carried forward for 5 years.

Tax Incentives for Employers to Hire Unemployed Rhode Island Residents: The incentive of 40% of an eligible employee's first year wages up to a maximum of $2,400 may be used to reduce the gross Rhode Island income of businesses and individuals that employ and retain previously unemployed Rhode Island residents.

SBA Credit for Loan Grantee Fee: A small business may take a tax credit equal to any guaranty fee they pay to the United States Small Business Administration pursuant to obtaining SBA financing.

Rhode Island Enterprise Zone Program Tax Benefits: Rhode Island offers an Enterprise Zone Program developed to revitalize distressed urban areas in Rhode Island. The program provides an aggressive and comprehensive incentive package to businesses willing to relocate or expand into the designated Enterprise Zones.

Resident Business Owner Tax Modification: Business owners who operate a qualified business and who live in the same Enterprise Zone are eligible for a three year modification of $50,000 from their federal adjusted gross income when computing their state income tax liability and a $25,000 modification for years four and five.

Interest Income Tax Credit: Corporations or taxpayers that make new loans to qualified Enterprise Zone businesses are eligible to receive a 10% tax credit on interest earned from the loan. The maximum credit per taxpayer is $10,000 per year.

Donation Tax Credit: A taxpayer is eligible for a credit of 20% for any cash donation against the state tax imposed for donations to public supported improvement projects in the zone.

Tax Credit Available to Certified Mill Building Owner(s): A specialized investment tax credit equal to 10% of the cost of the substantial rehab. The rehab must occur within two years following certification.

Tax Credits Available to Lenders: A credit equal to 10% of the interest earned on loans to eligible businesses. Maximum of $10,000 per taxable year. A credit equal to 100% of the interest on loans made solely and exclusively for the purpose of substantial rehab of a Certified Building. Maximum of $20,000 per taxable year.

Credit for Artwork Exhibition: A credit is available against the personal income tax for 10% of each $1000 of the purchasing price of qualifying artwork, up to a maximum purchase price of $10,000.

Computer Software Developer Tax Credit: Developer is allowed 10% tax credit against the Rhode Island business corporation tax and the personal income tax on purchased or leased equipment.

Disabled Access Credit for Small Business: The expenses must be made to enable the small business to comply with federal or state laws protecting the rights of persons with disabilities. The credit is equal to 10% of the total amount expended during the tax year in Rhode Island, up to a maximum of $1,000, for removing architectural, communication, physical, or transportation barriers; providing qualified interpreters or other effective methods of delivering aurally delivered materials to persons with hearing impairments; providing readers, tapes, or other effective means of making visually delivered materials available to persons with visual impairments; providing job coaches or other effective means of supporting workers with severe impairments in competitive employment; providing specialized transportation services to employees or customers with mobility impairments; buying or modifying equipment for persons with disabilities; and providing similar services, modifications, material or equipment for persons with disabilities.

Sales and Use Tax Exemptions: Manufacturers' machinery and equipment is exempt; Manufacturers' machinery, equipment, replacement parts and computer software used in the manufacturing process are exempt.

Professional Services: Services such as those provided by physicians, attorneys, accountants, engineers, and others are exempt. However, the tax applies to any tangible personal property that may be sold at retail by such professionals (i.e.--opera glasses, field glasses, etc.).

Occupational Services: Services such as provided by barbers, beauty parlors, bootblacks, cleaning and pressing shops, laundries, and similar service establishments are exempt. However, if delivery to the purchaser or his agent is consummated within, the tax applies to any tangible personal property that may be sold at retail by such establishments.

Sales in interstate commerce: A shipment by common carrier, United States mail, or delivery facilities not operated by the seller to a purchaser outside Rhode Island is not subject to the tax. If the purchaser takes delivery within the state, the tax applies.

Intangibles: Sales or transfers of intangible personal property such as stocks, bonds, accounts receivable, money, or insurance policies are exempt.

Pollution Control Equipment: Sales of air and water pollution control equipment for incorporation into or used and consumed directly in the operation of a facility or installation approved by the Rhode Island Director of Environmental Management are exempt.

Scientific Equipment: Sales of scientific equipment, computers, software and related items to a qualifying firm to be used predominantly by that firm for research and development purposes. The qualifying firm must furnish the vendor with a Rhode Island Research and Development Exemption Certificate.

Boat Sales: The sale of boats has been exempted from the state sales tax. Boats are also exempt from local property taxes.

Local Property Taxes: Intangible property is not taxed.

Inventory & Equipment Tax Exemption For Manufacturer: Manufacturers' machinery and equipment used in the production process and inventories of manufacturers in Rhode Island are exempt from property taxes.

Real Estate Property Tax Exemption/Stabilization: Any city or town in Rhode Island may exempt or stabilize the tax on real and personal property used for manufacturing, or commercial purposes, for a period not exceeding ten years. The incentive may not be used to encourage a firm to move from one municipality to another in Rhode Island.

Property Tax Exemption/Stabilization For Wholesaler's Inventory: Any city or town in Rhode Island may exempt or stabilize the tax on a wholesaler's inventory for a period of up to twenty five years. The incentive may not be used to encourage a firm to move from one municipality to another in Rhode Island.

Property Tax Exemption/Stabilization Office Equipment: Any city or town in Rhode Island may exempt or stabilize the tax on computers, telephone equipment and other office personal property for a period of up to twenty five years. The incentive may not be used to encourage a firm to move from one municipality to another in Rhode Island.

Energy Related Property Tax Exemptions: For local tax purposes, solar, wind, or cogeneration equipment shall not be assessed at more than the value of the conventional heating, cooling, or energy production capacity that would otherwise be necessary to install in the building.

Rhode Island has no *Gift Tax*.

South Carolina
South Carolina Department of Revenue
301 Gervais Street
Columbia, SC 29214
803-898-5000
Fax: 803-898-5822
www.sctax.org/default.htm

Economic Development Office
Department of Commerce
P.O. Box 927
Columbia, SC 29202
803-737-0400
800-868-7232
Fax: 803-737-0418
www.callsouthcarolina.com

Jobs Tax Credit: Provides income tax credits for companies locating in or expanding current business in any county in South Carolina ranging from $1,500 to $9,000.

Child Care Credit: Payments made to licensed and/or registered child care facilities for the benefit of an employee are eligible for a credit against state corporate income tax not to exceed a maximum of $3,000 per employee.

Corporate Headquarters Credit: Firms establishing headquarters or expanding existing headquarters in South Carolina are eligible for credits to state corporate income taxes or corporate license fees.

Sales and Use Tax Exemptions: The following items are exempt for manufacturers from sales and use tax: production machinery and equipment; repair parts; materials which will become an integral part of the finished product; industrial electricity and fuels used in the manufacturing process; packaging materials.

Property Tax Exemptions: The following items are exempt from property tax: manufacturing inventory; intangible property; facilities or equipment of industrial plants designed for elimination, mitigation, prevention, treatment, abatement, or control of water, air, or noise pollution.

Environmental Impact Zone Investment Tax Credit: Credit against company's corporate income tax of up to 5%.

Research and Development Tax Credit: Credit equal to 5% of qualified expenditures.

Other Corporate Income Tax Incentives:
- No state property tax
- No unitary taxes on worldwide profits
- No wholesale sales taxes
- No local income tax
- No inventory tax
- No sales tax on manufacturing machinery, industrial power or materials for finished products

Enterprise Program: Offers tax advantages for new jobs to businesses located anywhere in the state.

South Dakota
South Dakota Department of Revenue and Regulation
445 East Capitol Avenue
Pierre, SD 57501-3185
605-773-3311
800-TAX-9188
www.state.sd.us/drr2/revenue.html

Economic Development Office
Governor's Office of Economic Development
711 East Wells Ave.
Pierre, SD 57501-3369
605-773-5032
800-872-6190

Fax: 605-773-3256
Email: goedinfo@state.sd.us
www.sdgreatprofits.com

South Dakota is one of only two states with no corporate income tax, no personal income tax, no personal property tax, no inheritance tax and no business inventory tax.

Tennessee
Tennessee Department of Revenue
500 Deaderick Street
Andrew Jackson Building, Room 1200
Nashville, TN 37242-1099
615-253-0600
800-342-1003
www.state.tn.us/revenue

Economic Development Office
Department of Economic and Community Development
Rachel Jackson Bldg., 8th Floor
320 Sixth Avenue North
Nashville, TN 37243-0405
615-741-3282
800-342-8470 (in TN)
800-251-8594
Fax: 615-741-7306
www.state.tn.us/ecd

Personal Income: Earned income is not taxed in Tennessee; however, certain dividend and interest income received by a Tennessee resident is taxable.

Energy Fuel and Water: Reduced sales tax on manufacturers' use of energy fuel and water at manufacturing site; tax-exempt if they have direct contact with product during manufacturing process.

Pollution Control Equipment: Exempt from sales tax.

Raw Materials: Exempt from sales tax.

Industrial Machinery: Exempt from sales tax.

Work-In-Progress: Exempt from property tax.

Finished Product Inventory: Exempt from property tax.

Investment Tax Credit: Manufacturers are allowed a tax credit of 1% of the cost of industrial machinery.

Franchise Tax Jobs Credit: Allows a $2,000 or $3,000 tax credit against franchise tax liability for each new full-time employee of qualified business that increases employment by 25 or more and meets required capital investment.

Child Care: Credit against franchise and excise taxes for businesses that establish a day care center for employee's children.

Texas
Texas Comptroller of Public Accounts
Lyndon B. Johnson State Office Building
111 East 17th Street
Austin, TX 78774
800-531-5441
512-463-3620
Fax: 512-475-1610
www.cpa.state.tx.us/m23taxes.html

Economic Development Office
Department of Economic Development
P.O. Box 12728
Austin, TX 78711
512-936-0260
800-888-0511
www.tded.state.tx.us

Enterprise Zone Program: Designed to induce capital investment and create new permanent jobs into areas of economic distress. Qualified businesses located in an enterprise zone may qualify for a variety of local and state incentives including a refund of state sales and use taxes, franchise tax reductions, and state administered program priority.

Research and Development Franchise Tax Credit: Credit for certain incremental qualified research expenses incurred and basic research payments made for research conducted in Texas.

Job Creation Franchise Tax Credit: Credit of 5% of wages paid for new qualifying jobs created in strategic investment areas.

Capital Investment Franchise Tax Credit: A credit against franchise taxes due equal to 7.5% of qualified investment made in a Strategic Investment Area.

Texas does not have statewide business tax incentives. These are handled at the city and/or county level in the city/county in which a business enterprise is based.

Utah

Utah State Tax Commission
210 North 1950 West
Salt Lake City, UT 84116
800-662-4335
801-297-2200
Fax: 801-297-7699
TDD: 801-297-2020
http://tax.utah.gov

Economic Development Office
Business and Economic Development Division
324 South State St., Suite 500
Salt Lake City, UT 84111
801-538-8800
Fax: 801-538-8889
www.utah.org/dbed/welcome.htm

No inventory or worldwide unitary taxes.

New Equipment: An exemption of sales and use taxes are available for the purchase or lease of new equipment or machinery for manufacturing facilities.

Economic Development Area/Tax Increment Financing: Tax increment financing (TIF) is utilized in areas that have been targeted for economic development. Redevelopment areas are determined by local municipalities. Portions of the new property tax generated by new development projects are returned to project developers in the form of infrastructure development, land cost write down or other appropriate means. Details of TIF are site specific. Development of a proposal is relatively simple, yet the benefits can be great.

Enterprise Zones: The act passed by the Utah State Legislature provides tax credits for manufacturing companies

locating in rural areas that qualify for assistance. A $750 tax credit is given for all new job created plus a credit of $1,250 for jobs paying at least 125% of the average wage for the industry. In addition, investment tax credits are available for all investment in new plant and equipment as follows: 10% for first $100,000; 5% of next $250,000. Tax credits can be carried forward for 3 years. Enterprise Zones benefits are only available in certain non-metro counties.

Research and Development Tax Credit for Machinery and Equipment: A 6% credit on the purchase price of machinery and equipment purchased and primarily used in qualified research.

Research Tax Credit: A 6% credit for qualifying expenses incurred in conducting eligible research.

Special programs such as Affirmative Action, Targeted Job Tax Credits and veterans programs are also available.

Vermont

Vermont Department of Taxes
109 State Street
Montpelier, VT 05609-1401
802-828-25-5
Fax: 802-828-2701
www.state.vt.us/tax

Economic Development Office
Department of Economic Development
National Life Building
Drawer 20
Montpelier, VT 05620-0501
802-828-3221
800-341-2211
Fax: 802-828-3258
www.thinkvermont.com

Payroll Tax Credit: A firm may receive a credit against income tax liability equal to a percentage of its increased payroll costs.

Research and Development Tax Credit: A firm may receive a credit against income tax liability in the amount of 10% of qualified research and development expenditures.

Workforce Development Tax Credit: A firm may receive a credit against income tax liability in the amount of 10% of its qualified training, education and workforce development expenditures. A 20% credit may be taken for qualified training, education and workforce development expenditures for the benefit of welfare to work participants.

Small Business Investment Tax Credit: A firm may receive a credit against income tax liability in the amount equal to 5% to 10% of its investments within the state in excess of $150,000 in plants, facilities, and machinery and equipment.

Sales and Use Tax Exemptions:
1. Sales of electricity, oil, gas and other fuels used on site directly in the production of projects or services.
2. Sales of building materials within any three consecutive years in excess of $1 million in purchase value used in the construction, renovation or expansion of facilities that are used exclusively for the manufacture of tangible personal property for sales. The threshold for sales of building materials can be reduced to $250,000 for businesses that receive approval from VEDC or are located in a designated downtown development district.

3. Machinery and equipment, including system-based software used directly in the production of products or services.

Construction In Progress Property Tax Exemption: A tax exemption for a period not to exceed two years is available for real property, excluding land, consisting of unoccupied new facilities, or unoccupied facilities under renovation or expansion that are less than 75% complete.

Brownfields Property Tax Exemption: Exempt from the statewide education property tax are real property consisting of the value of remediation expenditures incurred by a business for the construction of new, expanded or renovated facilities on contaminated property.

Rehabilitation Investment Tax Credit: A federal income tax credit is available for 20% of the costs of rehabilitating income-producing historic buildings.

Sprinkler System Rebate: A building owner who installs a complete automatic fire sprinkler system in an older or historic building that has been certified for one of the state building rehabilitation tax credits is eligible for a rebate for the cost of a sprinkler system, not to exceed $2,000.

Employee Training Tax Credit: An employer can claim up to $400 in tax credits per year for training qualified employees if the employer does business in a designated downtown district with the intent of providing permanent employment.

Credit For Income From Commercial Film Production: A credit shall be available against the tax imposed for that taxable year upon the taxable income received from a dramatic performance in a commercial film production during that taxable year. The credit shall be in the amount by which the Vermont tax on such income, without regard to this credit, exceeds the highest personal income tax rate in the taxpayer's state of residence, multiplied by the Vermont commercial film production income.

Export Tax Credit: A business that makes sales outside Vermont may be authorized for a credit on income tax.

High-Tech Growth Incentives: A certified high-tech business may apply for credits including: machinery and equipment, technology infrastructure, workforce development, and sales and use tax for personal computers and software.

Virginia

Virginia Department of Taxation
3610 West Broad
Richmond, VA 23230
804-367-8037
Fax: 804-367-1820
www.tax.state.va.us

Economic Development Office
Economic Development Partnership
P.O. Box 798
Richmond, VA 23206
804-371-8100
Fax: 804-371-8112
www.yesvirginia.org/

Major Business Facility Job Tax Credit: Qualified companies locating or expanding in Virginia receive a $1,000 corporate income tax credit for each new full-time job created over a threshold number of jobs

Recycling Equipment Tax Credit: An income tax credit is available to manufacturers for the purchase of certified machinery and equipment for processing recyclable materials. The credit is equal to 10% of the original total capitalized cost of the equipment.

Day Care Facility Investment Tax Credit: Corporations may claim a tax credit equal to 25% of all expenditures incurred in the construction, renovation, planning or acquisition of facilities for the purpose of providing day care for children of company employees. The maximum credit is $25,000.

Neighborhood Assistance Tax Credit: An income tax credit is provided for companies that make donations to neighborhood organizations conducting approved community assistance programs for impoverished people. The credit equals 45% of the total donation.

Clean Fuel Vehicle Job Creation Tax Credit: Businesses manufacturing or converting vehicles to operate on clean fuel and manufacturers of components for use in clean fuel vehicles are eligible to receive an income tax credit for each new full-time job created over and above the previous year's employment level. The credit is equal to $700 in the year the job is created, and in each of two succeeding years if the job is continued, for a maximum of $2,100 per job.

Clean Fuel Vehicle Tax Credit: An income tax credit is available to companies which purchase clean fuel vehicles or invest in related refueling facilities. The credit is equal to 10% of the IRS allowed deduction or credit for these purchases.

Worker Retraining Tax Credit: Employers are eligible to receive an income tax credit equal to 30% of all expenditures made by the employer for eligible worker retraining.

Property Tax Incentives: No property tax at the state level; real estate and tangible personal property are taxed at the local level. Virginia differs from most states in that its counties and cities are separate taxing entities. A company pays either county or city taxes, depending on its location. No tax on intangible property; manufacturers' inventory, manufacturers' furniture, fixtures, or corporate aircraft. Exemptions include: certified pollution control facilities and equipment; certified recycling equipment, rehabilitated commercial/industrial real estate; manufacturers' generating equipment; certified solar energy devices.

Sales and Use Tax Exemptions: Manufacturers' purchases used directly in production; items purchased for re-sale by distributors; certified pollution control equipment and facilities; custom computer software; purchases used in research and development; most film, video and audio production related purchases.

Enterprise Zones: Designed to stimulate business development in distressed urban and rural areas. Incentives include:
1. General Tax Credit: A 10 year tax credit is available against state income tax liability (80% first year and 60% in years two through ten) that results from business activity within an enterprise zone.
2. Refundable Real Property Improvement Tax Credit: A tax credit equal to 30% of qualified zone real property improvements is available to businesses that rehabilitate property or undertake new construction in an enterprise

zone. The maximum credit within a five-year period is $125,000.

3. Investment Tax Credit For Large Qualified Zone Projects: Projects with an investment of at least $100 million and creating at least 200 jobs are eligible for a negotiated credit of up to 5% of total investment in real property, machinery and equipment.

Washington

Washington Department of Revenue
P.O. Box 47476
Olympia, WA 98504
800-647-7706
360-902-7175
http://dor.wa.gov

Economic Development Office
Office of Trade and Economic Development
128 10th Ave., SW
P.O. Box 42525
Olympia, WA 98504
360-725-4000
800-237-1233
www.oted.wa.gov

Sales/Use Tax Exemption On Machinery And Equipment: Manufacturers and processors for hire are not required to pay the sales or use tax on machinery and equipment used directly in manufacturing operations. In addition, charges made for labor and services for installing the machinery and equipment are not subject to the sales tax.

Distressed Area Sales/ Use Tax Deferral/Exemptions: Grants a waiver of sales/use tax for manufacturing, research and development, or computer-related businesses (excluding light and power businesses) locating in specific geographical areas. In certain other locations, the sales/use taxes on qualified construction and equipment costs are waived when all qualifications are met for a specified period of time.

Distressed Area Business And Occupation Tax Credit: A program for increasing employment provides credits from $2000 to $4000 against the B&O tax for each new employment position created and filled by certain businesses located in distressed areas. A distressed county is one with unemployment rates at 20% or above.

High Technology Sales/Use Tax Deferral/Exemption: Businesses in the following research and development technology categories may be eligible for a sales/use tax deferral/exemption, if they start new research and development or pilot scale manufacturing operations, or expand or diversify a current operation by expanding, renovating or equipping an existing facility anywhere in Washington.

High Technology Business And Occupation Tax Credit: An annual credit of up to $2 million is allowed for businesses that perform research and development in Washington in specified high technology categories and meet the minimum expense requirements. The credit cannot exceed the amount of the business and occupation tax due for that calendar year. The rate for the credit is: Nonprofit corporation or association: 515% (.00515) of the expenses. For profit businesses: 2.5% (.025) of the expenses.

Aerospace Industry Manufacturer Tax Incentives: This program provides a tax incentive for persons engaged in manufacturing commercial airplanes and manufacturers of component parts of commercial airplanes.

Warehouse Tax Incentive: The Warehouse Tax Incentive allows businesses to exempt 100 percent of the construction costs from the state's retail sales and use tax. The incentive also allows 50 percent exemption from the state retail sales and use tax for qualifying equipment acquisition costs.

West Virginia

West Virginia Department of Tax and Revenue
1206 Quarrier Street
Charleston, WV 25301
800-982-8297
304-558-3333
Fax: 304-558-3269
www.state.wv.us/taxrev/

Economic Development Office
West Virginia Development Office
1900 Kanawha Blvd., East
Charleston, WV 25305-0311
304-558-2234
800-982-3386
Fax: 304-558-0449
www.wvdo.org

Business Investment and Jobs Expansion Tax Credit (Super Tax Credit Program): Provides substantial tax credits for companies that create jobs in industries such as manufacturing, information processing, distribution, and destination tourism projects. A business that creates 50 jobs or more can offset up to 80% of its basic business tax liability over ten years with this credit. This innovative program is based on a formula calculated by using a job creation and a qualified investment factor. In addition, small businesses in industries previously mentioned may qualify for the credit by creating at least 10 jobs over three years.

Corporate Headquarters Relocation Credit: Available to corporations in particular industries that relocate their headquarters to West Virginia. If at least 15 jobs are created, the allowable credit is 10% of qualified investment. If the corporate headquarters relocation results in 50 or more new jobs, then the allowable credit is 50% of qualified investment. Qualified investment includes the reasonable and necessary expenses incurred by the corporation to move its headquarters to this state.

West Virginia Capital Company Credit: Established to encourage the formation of venture capital in West Virginia. Investors in qualified capital companies are entitled to a state tax credit equal to 50% of their investment. Capital companies must have a capital base of at least $1 million but not greater than $4 million.

Warehouse Freeport Amendment: Allows goods in transit to an out-of-state destination to be exempt from local ad valorem property tax when "warehoused" in West Virginia. This exemption is specifically applicable to finished goods inventories.

Research and Development Project Credits: Manufacturers, producers of natural resources, generators of electric power and persons providing manufacturing services may qualify for the credit for research activities conducted within the state. The credit generally equals 10% of the qualified investment in depreciable personal property, wages and other expenses incurred for conducting a qualified research or development project.

Wood Processing Tax Credit: This credit is available for new wood processing operations. The tax credit is $250 per year per full time employee for 10 years to new or expanding companies involved in the manufacture of value-added wood products. The finished product must be consumer ready.

Sales Tax Exemption: For materials and equipment used directly in manufacturing process.

Industrial Expansion or Revitalization Tax Credit: Available for manufacturers as a credit against the business franchise tax.

Economic Opportunity Credit: Offsets 80% of taxes for up to 13 years. Minimum job requirement: 20

"Five-for-Ten" Program: provides a tax incentive to businesses that make qualified capital improvements of at least $50 million to an existing base of $100 million or more. It assesses the new capital addition at a salvage value of 5% for the first ten years.

Manufacturing Investment Credit: allows a 50% corporate net income tax and franchise tax based on investment with no new job creation required.

Consumer Sales and Service Tax and Use Tax Exemption-Purchases Directly Used in Research & Development: Tax exemption for purchases of services and tangible personal property directly used in qualified research and development activities in West Virginia.

Business Franchise Tax Exemption for Venture Capital Companies: Exemption from business franchise tax for qualifying venture capital companies in West Virginia

Coal-Base Synthetic Fuels Credit: Credit allowed to taxpayers who place qualified investment of at least $10 million into service over a period of one year in a new industrial facility for producing coal-based liquids used to produce synthetic motor oil.

Aerospace Industrial Facility Credit: Eligible taxpayers are allowed a credit against business franchise tax and corporate net income tax for qualified investment in an aerospace industrial facility.

West Virginia Military Incentive Credit: Employers that hire economically disadvantaged veterans of the Korean or Vietnam conflict are allowed a credit equal to 30% of the first $5,000 in wages.

Historic Rehabilitation Buildings Investment Credit: The qualified rehabilitation buildings investment credit applies against personal or corporate net income tax equal to 10 percent of qualified rehabilitation expenditures. Credit is available for both commercial residential and nonresidential buildings located in West Virginia.

Convenience Food Store Security Tax Credit: The convenience food store security credit is available to owners of convenience food stores that operate between the hours of 12:00 a.m. and 5:00 a.m., who install and maintain a security camera in proper working order with gross annual sales of less than $1 million.

Wisconsin

Wisconsin Department of Revenue
2135 Rimrock Road
Madison, WI 53713
608-266-2772
Fax: 608-267-0834
www.dor.state.wi.us

Economic Development Office
Department of Commerce
201 W. Washington Avenue
Madison, WI 53707
Business Helpline:
    1-800-HELP-BUSiness
Fax Request Hotline:
    608-264-6154
Export Helpline:
    1-800-XPORT-WIsconsin
www.commerce.state.wi.us

Development Zone Program: A tax benefit initiative designed to encourage private investment and to improve both the quality and quantity of employment opportunities. The program has $21 million in tax benefits available to assist businesses that meet certain requirements and are located or willing to locate in one of Wisconsin's 20 development zones.

Enterprise Development Zone Program: This program promotes a business start-up or expansion on a particular site in any area of the state that suffers from high unemployment, declining incomes and property values, and other indicators of economic distress. The program pays on performance. Tax credits can be taken only on income generated by business activity in the zone. The maximum amount of tax credits per zone is $3 million. Up to 79 sites can be designated around the state for projects that are not likely to occur or continue unless a zone is created. Types of Credits: A business in an enterprise development zone is eligible to earn the following tax credits:
1. The jobs credit: Equal to 40% of the first $8,000 in qualified wages for the first and second years of employment of a member of a "target group."
2. The non-target group jobs credit: A non-refundable jobs credit of up to $6,000 for new full-time jobs being created and filled by Wisconsin residents who are not members of target groups.
3. The environmental remediation credit: Equal to 50% of cost of the remediation of contaminated land.

Research Expenditures Credit: A nonrefundable research expenditure credit for noncapital expenditures related to research activities conducted in Wisconsin is available to businesses.

Research Facilities Credit: This credit applies to capital investments to construct and equip new research facilities or expand existing facilities in Wisconsin. The credit is equal to 5% of the amount of qualified investments in intangible, depreciable property that is not replacement property.

Sales Tax Credit for Fuel and Electricity Used in the Manufacturing Process: This is an income and franchise tax credit available for sales tax paid on fuel and electricity used directly in the manufacturing process.

Supplement to Federal Historic Rehabilitation Credit: A nonrefundable credit designed to encourage the rehabilitation of historic buildings in Wisconsin.

Wyoming

Wyoming Department of Revenue
122 West 25th Street
Herschler Building, 2nd Floor West
Cheyenne, WY 82002-0110
307-777-7961
http://revenue.state.wy.us

Economic Development Office
Wyoming Business Council
214 W. 15th St.
Cheyenne, WY 82002
307-777-2800

800-262-3425
Fax: 307-777-2838
www.wyomingbusiness.org

No personal income tax.
No corporate income tax.
No tax on intangible assets such as bank accounts, stocks, or bonds.
No tax on retirement income earned and received from another state.
No inventory tax.
No tax on goods-in-transit or made from out-of-state.

Money and Help for Women, Minorities, Disabled and Veteran Entrepreneurs

Special programs exist to help these groups start or expand businesses. The government wants these populations to succeed and has developed services and assistance to help these entrepreneurs develop business plans, find funding, and more. Read on.

Women Entrepreneurs

Did you know that the recent surge in economic growth is actually being driven by small businesses that are in large part owned by women? That's right — women are starting businesses at **twice** the rate of men, and it's probably because women are finding that their dual careers as businesswomen and mothers are not being accommodated by big business very well at all. An increasing number of women are finding that rigid corporate structures fail to make allowances for their roles as executives, wives, and mothers. Because of this inflexibility, more and more women are striking out on their own or with a partner that shares a similar philosophy, and these women are finding success on their own terms. Corporate America has held women as a group back long enough, and for that reason, women are launching their own businesses in unprecedented numbers.

When someone mentions the word "entrepreneur", most people conjure up an image of someone like Donald Trump smiling on the cover of some glossy business trade magazine. But these days, chances are that smiling face will be decidedly more feminine looking than Donald's — it might be Donna's face, as in Donna Karan, who grew her apparel business into a million dollar money maker in just a few short years. As with men, hard work and commitment to make a business work are the ingredients women are using to create their own success, and not waiting for others to hand it to them. Just look at some of these incredible statistics that the U.S. Small Business Administration has gathered on women business owners:

- Over the last 15 years, the number of women-owned businesses has almost **doubled**.
- In that same amount of time, the percentage of women-owned businesses increased by 10%, while those owned by men decreased by as much.
- Over one-third of all businesses are now owned by women.
- Women-owned businesses were awarded over $2 billion in federal prime contracts last year, compared to only $180 million ten years ago, an increase of over ten fold.

- 75% of new businesses started by women succeed, compared to only 25% of those started by men.

Since most people in the U.S. actually work for small businesses, the government has been forced to take notice of this ever-increasing trend toward women-owned businesses. Chances are your new boss or CEO is going to be a woman, not someone like Lee Iacocca. Why else would the Small Business Administration (SBA) put a women's business ownership specialist at over 100 SBA offices across the country? You don't see the Small Business Administration bending over to help men out with special programs — anyone who reads the statistics can see who's going to be the most powerful group of emerging business owners over the next couple of decades.

As you'll see in this chapter, both the Federal and state governments have created special programs to help women business owners compete and succeed like never before. Make sure to check out "Other Resources for Assistance for Women, Minorities, Veterans, and the Disabled" at the end of this chapter for more places to turn for help and information.

Small Business Administration Pilot Program

The Women's Pre-Qualified Loan Program is being tested in Charlotte, North Carolina, and other cities nationwide. This program will give the Small Business Administration greater influence on the number of loans extended to women.

This program began on June 1, 1994. Through the program, women business owners can go directly to the Small Business Administration (SBA) for a loan guarantee review, instead of being required to go to a bank first. If the woman business owner qualifies, the SBA will issue a commitment letter that she can present as part of her loan application to a bank. If the bank approves the loan, the application is returned to the SBA for final review. The SBA's decision will be based on the ability of the woman business owner to pay back the loan.

Businesses must be 51% owned and operated by women to qualify for the lending program. Only Mecklenburg County businesses qualify for Charlotte's pilot program. The pilot women's program backs loans up to $250,000. The women's program backs loans up to $250,000, and will guarantee 90% of loans up to $155,000. Bigger loans will be backed 85%. There is no cap on the number of loans that will be processed through the pilot program.

Following the guidelines for the pilot program, women applicants will go to a "facilitator", who will screen applications for the SBA for a small fee. These fees have not been established as of this printing. Pilot sites for the Women's Pre-qualification Pilot Loan Program are: Buffalo, New York; Chicago, Illinois; Columbus, Ohio; Louisville, Kentucky; New Orleans, Louisiana; Philadelphia, Pennsylvania; Portland, Oregon; St. Louis, Missouri; and San Francisco, California. The program is offered statewide in the following states: Colorado, Maine, Massachusetts, Montana, New Mexico and Utah. While there is no way to monitor the number of women applicants who are rejected at the bank level under the existing system, the pilot program will work to improve that situation.

For more information, contact the Charlotte SBA office during business hours at 6302 Fairview Road, Suite 300, Charlotte, NC 28210; 704-344-6563; Fax: 704-344-6769. You can also check the Small Business Administration website at {www.sba.gov}.

Fight Suppliers Who Won't Give You Credit

Federal Trade Commission (FTC)
600 Pennsylvania Ave., NW   877-FTC-HELP
Washington, DC 20580   202-326-2222
www.ftc.gov/bcp/conline/pubs/credit/ecoa.htm
Often women who have been divorced have trouble establishing credit. And you need credit if you're going to run a business. The Federal Trade Commission (FTC) enforces the laws that prohibit creditors and credit bureaus from discriminating against women because of their sex or marital status, and they can send you the free publication, *Equal Credit Opportunity*. This pamphlet explains your credit rights under the law, how to get help in establishing your own credit, and what to do if you feel your credit application has been unfairly denied.

Grants, Loans and Loan Guarantees for Women-Owned Businesses

Contact your state office of Economic Development located in your state capital.
All federal money programs aimed at small business do not discriminate between women and non-women-owned businesses. However, at the state level there are a number of specific money programs that are set aside only for women-owned businesses. The programs vary from state to state and are changing all the time so it is best to check with your State Office of Economic Development in your state capital to insure you have the latest available information. Here is a listing of what a few states offer specifically for women entrepreneurs:

- Illinois has low interest loans up to $50,000
- Iowa has grants up to $25,000 and loan guarantees up to $40,000
- Louisiana has loans and loan guarantee programs up to $250,000
- Minnesota offers low interest loans for up to 50% of your project

- New York offers low interest loans from $20,000 to $500,000
- Wisconsin offers low interest loans for women-owned businesses under $500,000 in sales

Federal Government Set-Asides For Women Entrepreneurs

Contact your state office of Economic Development
located in your state capital
or
Superintendent of Documents
Government Printing Office   866-512-1800
Washington, DC 20402   Fax: 202-512-2168
www.onlinewbc.gov/DOCS/procure/sellgov.doc
Many Federal government contracting offices are trying to insure that a certain percentage of their contracts go to women entrepreneurs. Most even have special offices that will help women entrepreneurs sell to their agencies. For help in selling your product or service to the government, contact your State Economic Development Office in your state capital and obtain a copy of *Equal Credit Opportunity*. It is available from the Government Printing Office or free online.

15% Set-Aside for Women Entrepreneurs

Contact your state office of Economic Development
located in your state capital.
Not only is the Federal government active in insuring that women get a fair share of government contracts, but many state governments are becoming involved. Some states, like California for example, have passed laws that force their state agencies to give at least 15% of their contracts to women and minority-owned firms. Other states like Illinois, Iowa, Maine, Minnesota, Montana, New Jersey, Oregon, and Washington are among those who are active in insuring that women obtain a fair share of state government contracts. Contact your State Office of Economic Development to see how your business can take advantage of set-asides in your state.

28 States Offer Free Consulting To Women Only

Contact your state office of Economic Development
located in your state capital.
Although every state offers free help to any person wishing to start or expand a business in their state, there are 28 states that have set up special offices just for women entrepreneurs. As an example, Colorado established a women's clearinghouse which provides hands-on assistance with business planning, marketing, financing, and government contracts. They also hold seminars at 16 locations throughout the state. Ohio offers a wide range of free services including loan packaging and marketing research. Contact your State Office of Economic Development to see what your state has to offer. If they don't have a "Women Only" office, don't let that stop you. It just means you'll have to share the help available with the men in your state.

What To Do If You Suspect Your Bank Denied You Credit Because You Are a Woman or Divorced

Credit Practices Division
Federal Trade Commission
600 Pennsylvania Ave., NW   877-FTC-HELP
Washington, DC 20580   202-326-2222
www.ftc.gov/bcp/bcpcp.htm
Women looking for money to start up and run their businesses might run into lenders that discriminate against them simply because they are women or divorced. The Federal Trade Commission (FTC) enforces the Equal Credit Opportunity Act, which prohibits any creditor from denying credit to a consumer on the basis of sex or marital status. If you think you've been discriminated against by a lender, contact the Federal Trade Commission. While the Federal Trade Commission won't act on individual complaints, a number of complaints against the same lender may force them to investigate. If necessary, the Federal Trade Commission can take violators to court to get them to stop their illegal practices. If you want your complaint investigated and action taken immediately, contact one of the following agencies, depending on the type of lending institution involved:

National Banks
Comptroller of the Currency, Compliance Management, Mail Stop 7-5, U.S. Department of the Treasury, Washington, DC 20219, 202-874-5000.

Savings & Loans
Office of Thrift Supervision, U.S. Department of Treasury, 1700 G St., NW, Washington, DC 20552, 202-906-6000.

FDIC State-Chartered Bank (not member of Federal Reserve System)
Federal Deposit Insurance Corporation, Consumer Affairs Division, Washington, DC 20429

Federally-Chartered Credit Union
National Credit Union Administration, Consumer Affairs Division, Washington, DC 20456

Small Loan/Finance Company, Public Utility, Credit Card or Government Lending Program
Consumer Response Center, Federal Trade Commission, Washington, DC 20580

For all other complaints against creditors, contact: Department of Justice, Civil Rights Division, Washington, DC 20530

How To Juggle The Stress of Your Business and Your Family

National Institute for Occupational Safety and Health
200 Independence Ave., SW, Room 715H   800-356-4674
Washington, DC 20201   202-401-6997
Trying to run a business can put a lot of added stress on you, your family, and your marriage, especially when business isn't going very well. The National Institute for Occupational Safety and Health offers a variety of information in the subject including: Stress…At Work booklet, Working with Stress video and a listing of other work stress resources. All of this information about stress and more is available at {www.cdc.gov/niosh/stresshp.html}.

Free Publications For Women Business Owners

Women's Bureau
Office of the Secretary
U.S. Department of Labor
200 Constitution Ave., NW, Room S-3311   800-827-5355
Washington, DC 20210   202-693-6731
Are you interested in how many other women business owners there are in the U.S? How about what your chances are for climbing up through various management levels? If you're interested in finding out more about women in the workforce, including trends and future projections, you might find the following free publications informative:

Characteristics of Self-Employed Women
Developments in Women's Labor Force Participation
Employed Women About as Likely as Men to be Looking for Jobs
Marriage, Children and Women's Employment: What Do We Know
Married Women, Work and Values
Much Variation in Women's Employment Across Metropolitan Areas
'Second-Chance' Strategies for Women Who Drop Out of School
Twenty Facts on Women Workers
Women Business Owners
Women in High-Tech Jobs
Women in Jobs Recessions
Women in Jobs Recoveries
Women at the Millennium
Women's Share of Labor Force to Edge Higher by 2008
Differences in Women's and Men's Earnings by Age
Income and Spending Patterns for Working Women
Women in Managerial, Professional Occupations Earn More Than Others
Women's Earning's: An Overview
Job Absent Rate Higher for Women Than for Men
Women in the Construction Workplace: Providing Equitable Safety and Health Protection
Work Injuries and Illnesses Occurring to Women

These titles can also be accessed online at {www.dol.gov/dol/audience/aud-women.htm}.

How To Get Start-Up Capital From Being Pregnant, Sexually Harassed, or From A Bad Shopping Experience

U.S. Customs Service
Fraud Division
1300 Pennsylvania Avenue, NW
Washington, DC 20229   800-BE-ALERT
www.customs.ustreas.gov
or
Equal Employment Opportunity Commission (EEOC)
1801 L St., NW   800-669-4000
Washington, DC 20570   202-663-4900
www.eeoc.gov   800-669-3362 (publications)

More people would quit what they're doing and start their own business if they had a small windfall of money to get them started. Here are two government programs that may turn a bad experience into the capital needed to begin a business.

As a business owner, there are times you may come across unscrupulous wholesalers who try to sell you some counterfeit products at cut-rate prices. Instead of risking your business by buying and reselling the bogus products, report the fraud to the U.S. Customs Service. If your complaint, which will be kept completely anonymous, leads to the seizure of counterfeit goods, you could receive a reward of up to $250,000, depending on the size of the case. What small business couldn't use some extra operating capital like that to keep it going?

So you want to start your own business because you've just been fired because you were pregnant, or wouldn't sleep with your boss to get a promotion? Before you go taking out any business loan, contact the Equal Employment Opportunity Commission (EEOC) and report how you think your former boss discriminated against you. The EEOC will investigate your complaint, and if they think there are grounds for prosecuting your former boss, they'll proceed with the case. If

they prove the case, you could end up with enough money in back pay and other remedies to finance your own company.

Health Insurance for Divorcees Who Start Their Own Business

Women Work
1625 K St. NW, #300   202-467-6346
Washington, DC 20006   Fax: 202-467-5366
www.womenwork.org

Under the new law, divorced and separated women and their children can continue to receive the same health insurance coverage they had before they were divorced or separated from their husbands at the group rate. The only difference is that they must pay the premium. This law applies to all private businesses that employ more than 20 people and to federal, state, and local government plans. Depending on the reason for displacement, you may be eligible to continue coverage for up to 36 months. You must contact the health plan within 60 days of the divorce or separation to indicate that you're electing to continue coverage. If the plan refuses to honor the law, contact your state's Insurance Commissioner, and they will investigate your complaint and get you the coverage to which you're entitled. For more information on this law, contact the Women Work at the above address.

Meet Women Entrepreneurs In Your Neighborhood For Lunch

Office of Women's Business Ownership
U.S. Small Business Administration
409 3rd St., SW   800-8-ASK-SBA
Washington, DC 20416   202-205-6673
www.sba.gov/womeninbusiness/wnet.html

One of the biggest problems women entrepreneurs face is breaking into the "old boys" network of successful business-men, and important opportunities can be lost without access to these kinds of connections. To help women interested in networking with other successful business people, the U.S. Small Business Administration has a new program that pairs up a woman who is just starting out with an experienced female Chief Executive Officer running the same kind of company. This business mentor can help the novice business-woman make connections that might otherwise take her years to make on her own. Those interested in networking should also think about joining relevant professional associations, such as the National Association of Women Business Owners at 800-55-NAWBO or the National Association for Female Executives at 212-351-6451 or 800-927-6233, or by contacting their local Chamber of Commerce.

Seminars On How Women Can Sell to the Government

Office of Women's Business
U.S. Small Business Administration
409 3rd St., SW   800-8-ASK-SBA
Washington, DC 20416   202-205-6673
www.sba.gov/womeninbusiness/wnet.html

If you're not sure how to start doing business with the government, you might consider taking a seminar sponsored by the U.S. Small Business Administration on the procurement process. These seminars will give you a complete overview on what you'll need to know and do to get involved in bidding on and landing government business contracts. For information on when these seminars are scheduled in your area, contact the office above, or the Women's Business Ownership Representative nearest you listed elsewhere in this chapter.

Creative Financing for Women Entrepreneurs

Office of Women's Business Ownership
U.S. Small Business Administration
409 3rd St., SW   800-8-ASK-SBA
Washington, DC 20416   202-205-6673
www.sba.gov/womeninbusiness/wnet.html

One of the toughest parts of running a business is finding the capital resources to do it: MONEY. The Women's Business Ownership Office runs seminars on how women can use creative ways to locate financing if they've been turned down for loans by regular banks. For more information about these seminars, contact the office above or the Women's Business Ownership Representative nearest you listed elsewhere in this chapter.

Free Mentors for New Women Entrepreneurs

Office of Women's Business Ownership
U.S. Small Business Administration
409 3rd St., SW   800-8-ASK-SBA
Washington, DC 20416   202-205-6673
www.sba.gov/womeninbusiness/wnet.html

How valuable would it be to your business to find a successful role model who's already gone through what's facing you as a female entrepreneur and who's willing to share her expertise with you at no charge? Through the Small Business Administration's Women's Network for Entrepreneurial Training (WNET) you can be paired up with a successful mentor who will meet with you at least once a week for an entire year, allowing you to learn from her experience and begin networking with other successful business people. If you've had your business going for at least a year and have gross receipts of at least $50,000, you can qualify for the WNET program. For more information, contact the office above or the Women's Business Ownership Representative nearest you listed elsewhere in this chapter.

Changing Laws to Help Women Business Owners

Congressional Caucus for Women's Issues
409 12th Street, SW, Suite 310   202-554-2323
Washington, DC 20024   Fax: 202-554-2346
www.womenspolicy.org/caucus

If you think that the climate for women business owners could be improved by passing a new law, you might think of sending your ideas to the Congressional Caucus for Women's Issues. This group keeps track of the issues most important to women across the country and introduces new legislation that can help meet those needs, including those of the community of women entrepreneurs. Recently, a new law was passed that allowed federal funding for U.S. Small Business Administration Demonstration Centers that specialize in offering counseling to women interested in starting and expanding businesses. Contact this office if you have any new ideas or would simply like them to send you information about the most recent legislation currently before Congress that concerns women business owners.

Women's Business Ownership Representatives

Women entrepreneurs have special needs, and the U.S. Small Business Administration recognizes those needs. That's why they've added staff members who specialize in promoting women-owned businesses in the U.S. These Women's Business Ownership (WBO) reps can help solve your unique business problems, such as how to network with other women business owners, where to find financial assistance on the state level, or how to get in on the lucrative government procurement programs, especially the ones that offer preferences to women-owned businesses. The WBO rep serving your area is your best ally in helping you cut through the red tape and direct you to free counseling and other valuable information sources. Remember, these offices do not have grants to start a business, but they do have access to very low interest loans for women entrepreneurs, as well as hundreds of other resources to help you successfully start your business!

Alabama
Susan Baxter
U.S. Small Business Administration
801 Tom Martin Dr., Suite 201
Birmingham, AL 35211
205-290-7707
www.sbaonline.sba.gov/al/index.html

Alaska
Diana Storo
U.S. Small Business Administration
510 L Street, Suite 310
Anchorage, AK 99501
907-271-4537
www.sbaonline.sba.gov/ak/index.html

Arizona
Arlene Binkowski
U.S. Small Business Administration
2828 North Central, Suite 800
Phoenix, AZ 85004-1093
602-745-7233
www.sbaonline.sba.gov/az/index.html

Arkansas
Johnna Bach
U.S. Small Business Administration
2120 Riverfront, Suite 100
Little Rock, AR 72202
501-324-5871, ext. 297
www.sbaonline.sba.gov/ar/index.html

California
Lola Robinson
U.S. Small Business Administration
455 Market St., 6th Floor
San Francisco, CA 94105
415-744-8485
www.sbaonline.sba.gov/ca/sf/index.html

Gilda Perez
U.S. Small Business Administration
650 Capitol Mall, Suite 7-500
Sacramento, CA 95814-2413
916-930-3707
www.sbaonline.sba.gov/ca/sacr/index.html

Cynthia Harris
U.S. Small Business Administration
550 W. C St., Suite 550
San Diego, CA 92101
619-557-7250, ext. 1149
www.sbaonline.sba.gov/ca/sandiego/index.html

Vicki Reynolds
U.S. Small Business Administration
200 W. Santa Ana Blvd., Suite 700
Santa Ana, CA 92701-4134
714-550-7420, ext. 3711
www.sbaonline.sba.gov/ca/santa/index.html

Marchelle Bailey
U.S. Small Business Administration
330 N. Brand Blvd., Suite 1200
Glendale, CA 91203-2304
818-552-3334
www.sbaonline.sba.gov/ca/la/index.html

Bonnie Chadwick
U.S. Small Business Administration
2719 N. Air Fresno Dr., Suite 200
Fresno, CA 93727-1547
559-487-5785, ext. 135
www.sbaonline.sba.gov/ca/fresno/index.html

Colorado
Jeanette DeHerrera
U.S. Small Business Administration
721 19th St., Suite 426
Denver, CO 80202-2599
303-844-2607, ext. 226
www.sbaonline.sba.gov/co/index.html

Connecticut
Kathleen Duncan
U.S. Small Business Administration
330 Main St., 2nd Floor
Hartford, CT 06106
860-240-4700, ext. 236
www.sbaonline.sba.gov/ct/index.html

Delaware
Carlotta Catullo
U.S. Small Business Administration
824 Market St., Suite 610
Wilmington, DE 19801
302-573-6380
www.sbaonline.sba.gov/de/index.html

District of Columbia
Ms. Cynthia Pope
U.S. Small Business Administration
1110 Vermont Ave. NW, 9th Floor
Washington, DC 20005
(P.O. Box 34500
Washington, DC 20043-4500)
202-606-4000, ext. 345
www.sbaonline.sba.gov/dc/index.html

Florida
Donna Padgug
U.S. Small Business Administration
7825 Bay Meadows Way, Suite 100B
Jacksonville, FL 32256-7504
904-443-1971
www.sbaonline.sba.gov/fl/north/index.html

Althea Harris
U.S. Small Business Administration
100 S. Biscayne Blvd., 7th Floor
Miami, FL 33131
305-536-5521 ext. 152
www.sbaonline.sba.gov/fl/south/inde
x.html

Georgia
Charlotte Johnson
U.S. Small Business Administration
233 Peachtree Street, NE, Suite 1900
Atlanta, GA 30303
404-331-0100 ext. 405
www.sbaonline.sba.gov/ga/index.ht
ml

Hawaii
Doreen Ezuka
U.S. Small Business Administration
300 Ala Moana, Room 2-235
Honolulu, HI 96850-4981
808-541-2971
www.sbaonline.sba.gov/hi/index.html

Idaho
Sherrie Sudgen
U.S. Small Business Administration
1020 Main St., Suite 290
Boise, ID 83702-5745
208-334-1696, ext. 234
www.sbaonline.sba.gov/id/index.html

Illinois
Carole Harris
U.S. Small Business Administration
500 W. Madison St., Suite 1240
Chicago, IL 60661-2511
312-353-4003
www.sbaonline.sba.gov/il/index.html

Valerie Ross
U.S. Small Business Administration
511 W. Capitol St., Suite 302
Springfield, IL 62704
217-492-4416, ext. 108

Indiana
Joyce Able
U.S. Small Business Administration
429 N. Pennsylvania St., Suite 100
Indianapolis, IN 46204
317-226-7272, ext. 243
www.sbaonline.sba.gov/in/index.html

Iowa
Carolyn Tonn
U.S. Small Business Administration
215 4th Ave. SE, Suite 200
Cedar Rapids, IA 52401
319-362-6405, ext. 207
www.sbaonline.sba.gov/ia/cedar/ind
ex.html

Jackie Blanchard
U.S. Small Business Administration
210 Walnut St., Room 749
Des Moines, IA 50309
515-284-4560

www.sbaonline.sba.gov/ia/desmo/in
dex.html

Kansas
Iris Newton
U.S. Small Business Administration
271 W. 3rd St., North, Suite 2500
Wichita, KS 67202
316-269-6631, ext. 213
www.sbaonline.sba.gov/ks/index.ht
ml

Kentucky
Carol Halfield
U.S. Small Business Administration
600 Dr. Martin Luther King, Jr. Pl.
Room 188
Louisville, KY 40202
502-582-5971, ext. 238
www.sbaonline.sba.gov/ky/index.ht
ml

Louisiana
Loretta Poree
U.S. Small Business Administration
365 Canal St., Suite 2820
New Orleans, LA 70130
504-589-2853
www.sbaonline.sba.gov/la/index.html

Maine
Helen Brimigion
U.S. Small Business Administration
68 Sewall Street, Room 512
Augusta, ME 04330
207-622-8394
www.sbaonline.sba.gov/me/index.ht
ml

Maryland
Martha Brown
U.S. Small Business Administration
10 S. Howard St., Suite 6220
Baltimore, MD 21201
410-962-6195, ext. 339
www.sbaonline.sba.gov/md/index.ht
ml

Massachusetts
Lisa Gonzalez
U.S. Small Business Administration
10 Causeway St., Room 265
Boston, MA 02222-1093
617-565-5588
www.sbaonline.sba.gov/ma/index.ht
ml

Harry Webb
U.S. Small Business Administration
1441 Main St., Room 410
Springfield, MA 01103
413-785-0484

Michigan
Catherine Gase
U.S. Small Business Administration
477 Michigan Ave., Room 515
Detroit, MI 48226
313-226-6075, ext. 223

www.sbaonline.sba.gov/mi/index.ht
ml

Minnesota
Cynthia Collett
U.S. Small Business Administration
100 N. 6th St., Suite 610C
Minneapolis, MN 55403-1563
612-370-2312
www.sbaonline.sba.gov/mn/index.ht
ml

Missouri
Janice Bowman
U.S. Small Business Administration
830 East Primrose, #101
Springfield, MO 65807-5254
417-890-8501 ext. 203

Cassandra Parks
U.S. Small Business Administration
323 W 8th, Suite 307
Kansas City, MO 64105
816-374-6380
www.sbaonline.sba.gov/mo/kansas/i
ndex.html

Laverne Johnson
U.S. Small Business Administration
815 Olive St., Suite 242
St. Louis, MO 63101
314-539-6600, ext. 232
www.sbaonline.sba.gov/mo/stlouis/i
ndex.html

Mississippi
Judith Adcock
U.S. Small Business Administration
One Hancock Plaza
Suite 1001
Gulfport, MS 39501
601-863-4449

Valencia Jamila
U.S. Small Business Administration
Am South Polaza
uite 900
210 East Capitol
Jackson, MS 39201
601-965-4378, ext. 234
www.sbaonline.sba.gov/ms/index.ht
ml

Montana
U.S. Small Business Administration
301 South Park Ave., Room 334
Helena, MT 59626
406-441-1081
www.sbaonline.sba.gov/mt/index.ht
ml

Nebraska
Barbara Foster
U.S. Small Business Administration
11145 Mill Valley Rd.
Omaha, NE 68154
402-221-7212
www.sbaonline.sba.gov/ne/index.ht
ml

Nevada
Donna Hopkins
U.S. Small Business Administration
400 S. Fourth St., Suite 250
Las Vegas, NV 89101
702-388-6684
www.sbaonline.sba.gov/nv/index.ht
ml

New Hampshire
Alice Zachs
U.S. Small Business Administration
143 N. Main St.
Concord, NH 03301
603-225-1400, ext. 122
www.sbaonline.sba.gov/nh/index.ht
ml

New Jersey
Karen D'Antico
U.S. Small Business Administration
2 Gateway Center, 15th Floor
Newark, NJ 07102
973-645-3683
www.sbaonline.sba.gov/nj/index.html

New Mexico
Susan Chavez
U.S. Small Business Administration
625 Silver SW, Room 320
Albuquerque, NM 87102
505-346-6759
www.sbaonline.sba.gov/nm/index.ht
ml

New York
Martha Soffer
U.S. Small Business Administration
26 Federal Plaza, Room 3100
New York, NY 10278
212-264-1472
www.sbaonline.sba.gov/ny/ny/index.
html

U.S. Small Business Administration
100 S. Clinton St., Room 1073
P.O. Box 7317
Syracuse, NY 13261
315-448-0428

Patricia Estelle
U.S. Small Business Administration
333 E. Water St., 4th Floor
Elmira, NY 14901
607-734-8130, ext. 24

Donald Butzek
U.S. Small Business Administration
111 W. Huron St., Room 1311
Buffalo, NY 14202
716-551-5670
www.sbaonline.sba.gov/ny/buffalo/i
ndex.html

U.S. Small Business Administration
35 Pinelawn Rd., Room 207W
Melville, NY 11747
631-454-0766

Cathy Pokines
U.S. Small Business Administration
401 South Salina Street, 5th Floor
Syracuse, NY 13202
315-471-9393 ext. 241
www.sbaonline.sba.gov/ny/syracuse/
index.html

Marcia Ketchum
U.S. Small Business Administration
100 State St., Room 410
Rochester, NY 14614
716-263-6700, ext. 103

North Carolina
April Gonzalez
U.S. Small Business Administration
6302 Fairview Road, Suite 300
Charlotte, NC 28210
704-344-6811
www.sbaonline.sba.gov/nc/index.ht
ml

North Dakota
Fay Behm
U.S. Small Business Administration
657 Second North Ave., Room 219
Fargo, ND 58102
701-239-5131
www.sbaonline.sba.gov/nd/index.ht
ml

Ohio
Rosemary Darling
U.S. Small Business Administration
1111 Superior Ave., Suite 630
Cleveland, OH 44144
216-522-4180 ext. 228
www.sbaonline.sba.gov/oh/cleveland
/index.html

Carole Bailey
U.S. Small Business Administration
2 Nationwide Plaza, Suite 1400
Columbus, OH 43215-2542
614-469-6860, ext. 232
www.sbaonline.sba.gov/oh/columbu
s/index.html

Bonnie Schenck
U.S. Small Business Administration
JWP Federal Building
550 Main St., Room 2522
Cincinnati, OH 45202
513-684-2814, ext. 207

Oklahoma
Cindy Anderson
U.S. Small Business Administration
Federal Building
301 NW 6th Street
Oklahoma City, OK 73102
905-609-8000
www.sbaonline.sba.gov/ok/index.ht
ml

Oregon
Sue Richardson
U.S. Small Business Administration

1515 SW 5th Ave., Suite 1050
Portland, OR 97201
503-326-7251
www.sbaonline.sba.gov/or/index.html

Pennsylvania
Ana Gallardo
U.S. Small Business Administration
Robert N.C. Nix Federal Building
900 Market St.
Philadelphia, PA 19107
215-580-2707
www.sbaonline.sba.gov/pa/phil/inde
x.html

Linda Carey
U.S. Small Business Administration
1000 Liberty Ave.
Federal Bldg., #1128
Pittsburgh, PA 15222
412-395-6560, ext. 118
www.sbaonline.sba.gov/pa/pitt/index
.html

Rhode Island
Patricia O'Rourke
U.S. Small Business Administration
380 Westminister St., 5th Floor
Providence, RI 02903
401-528-4592
www.sbaonline.sba.gov/ri/index.html

South Carolina
Teresa Singleton
U.S. Small Business Administration
1835 Assembly St., Room 358
Columbia, SC 29201
803-253-3121
www.sbaonline.sba.gov/sc/index.html

South Dakota
Darla Newborg
U.S. Small Business Administration
110 S. Phillips Ave., Suite 200
Sioux Falls, SD 57104-6727
605-330-4243, ext. 38
www.sbaonline.sba.gov/sd/index.ht
ml

Tennessee
Lisa Denson
U.S. Small Business Administration
50 Vantage Way, Suite 201
Nashville, TN 37228-1550
615-736-5881, ext. 247
www.sbaonline.sba.gov/tn/index.html

Texas
Suze Aguirre
U.S. Small Business Administration
10737 Gateway West
Suite 320
El Paso, TX 79925
915-633-7003
www.sbaonline.sba.gov/tx/elpaso/in
dex.html

Wila Lewis
U.S. Small Business Administration

8701 S. Gessner Drive, Suite 1200
Houston, TX 77074
713-773-6500, ext. 222
www.sbaonline.sba.gov/tx/hous/inde
x.html

Graciela Guillen
U.S. Small Business Administration
222 E. Van Buren St.
Suite 500
Harlingen, TX 78550
956-427-8533, ext. 225
www.sbaonline.sba.gov/tx/harlingto
n/index.html

Joanna White
U.S. Small Business Administration
1205 Texas Ave., Suite 408
Lubbock, TX 79401
806-472-7462, ext. 245
www.sbaonline.sba.gov/tx/lubbock/i
ndex.html

U.S. Small Business Administration
17319 San Pedro, Suite 200
San Antonio, TX 78232-1411
210-403-5900
www.sbaonline.sba.gov/tx/sanantoni
o/index.html

Adrienne Hudson
U.S. Small Business Administration
4300 Amon Carter Blvd.
Suite 114
Ft. Worth, TX 76155
817-684-5500
www.sbaonline.sba.gov/tx/dallas/ind
ex.html

Debbie Fernandez
U.S. Small Business Administration
606 N. Caranchua

Corpus Christi, TX 78476
361-879-0017, ext. 30

Utah
Melinda Workman
U.S. Small Business Administration
125 S. State St., Room 2229
Salt Lake City, UT 84138-1195
801-524-3213
www.sbaonline.sba.gov/ut/index.html

Vermont
Brenda Fortier
U.S. Small Business Administration
87 State St., Room 205
Montpelier, VT 05602
802-828-4422, ext. 206
www.sbaonline.sba.gov/vt/index.html

Virginia
Emma Wilson
U.S. Small Business Administration
400 North 8th Street, Suite 1150
Richmond, VA 23240-0126
804-771-2400 x154
www.sbaonline.sba.gov/va/index.ht
ml

Washington
Carol McIntosh
U.S. Small Business Administration
1200 Sixth Ave., Suite 1700
Seattle, WA 98101
206-553-7315
www.sbaonline.sba.gov/wa/seattle/in
dex.html

Coralie Myers
U.S. Small Business Administration
801 W. Riverside Ave., Suite 240
Spokane, WA 99201

509-353-2800
509-353-2630
www.sbaonline.sba.gov/wa/spokane/
index.html

West Virginia
Sharon Weaver
U.S. Small Business Administration
Federal Center, Suite 330
320 West Pike
Clarksburg, WV 26301
304-623-5631, ext. 239
www.sbaonline.sba.gov/wv/index.ht
ml

Wisconsin
Becky Freund
U.S. Small Business Administration
740 Regent Street, Suite 100
Madison, WI 53715
608-441-5519
www.sbaonline.sba.gov/wi/index.ht
ml

Mary Trimmier
U.S. Small Business Administration
310 W. Wisconsin Ave., Suite 400
Milwaukee, WI 53203
414-297-1093
www.sbaonline.sba.gov/wi/index.ht
ml

Wyoming
Debra Farris
U.S. Small Business Administration
100 E. B St., Room 4001
Casper, WY 82602-2839
307-261-6509
www.sbaonline.sba.gov/wy/index.ht
ml

Local Woman-To-Woman Entrepreneur Help Centers

The U.S. Small Business Administration (SBA) has co-funded 60 Demonstration Centers across the country to assist women interested in starting up and expanding small businesses. What is unique about these programs is that most offer woman-to-woman, one-on-one counseling in all aspects of business, from employee relations, budgeting, and dealing with lenders, to legal, marketing, and accounting assistance. Unlike the help you might receive at an SBA office, these centers offer help by women exclusively for women. These nonprofit centers are public/private-funded ventures, which means they will charge nominal fees for their services, although much less than you'd expect to pay for your own private business advisor.

Alabama
Women's Business Center of Southern Alabama
Kathryn Cariglino, Director
1301 Azalea Road
Suite 201A
Mobile, AL 36693
251-660-2725
800-378-7461
Fax: 251-660-8854
Email: womenbiz@aol.com
http://ceebic.org/~wbac

Central Alabama Women's Business Center
Trudy M. Phillips, President
110 12th Street North
Birmingham, AL 35203
866-252-5787
205-453-0249
Fax: 205-453-0253
Email: info@cawbc.org
www.cawbc.org

Alaska
WOMEN$ Finance
Jennifer Abbott, Program Director
245 West Fifth Avenue
P.O. Box 102059
Anchorage, AK 99510-2059
907-274-1524
Fax: 907-272-3146
Email: jabbott@wcaak.org
www.alaskabizbuilders.org/women$fund

Arizona
Self-Employment Loan Fund, Inc. (SELF)
1601 N. 7th Street, Suite 340
Phoenix, AZ 85340
602-340-8834
Fax: 602-340-8953

Email: milnerachel@hotmail.com
www.selfloanfund.org

Microbusiness Advancement Center of Southern Arizona
P. O. Box 42100
10 East Broadway Road
Suite 210
Tucson, AZ 85733-2108
520-620-1241
Fax: 520-622-2235
Email: admin@mac-sa.org
www.mac-sa.org

Arkansas
Arkansas Women's Business Development Center
Miriam Karanja, Program Director
2304 W. 29th Avenue
Pine Bluff, AR 71603
870-535-6233 ext. 14
888-323-6233
Fax: 870-535-0741
Email: mkaranja@ehlot.org
Email: info@goodfaithfund.org
www.goodfaithfund.org

California
Renaissance Entrepreneurship Center
Janet Lees, Program Director
275 Fifth Street
San Francisco, CA 94103-4120
415-541-8580, ext. 237
Fax: 415-541-8589
Email: janet@rencenter.org
www.rencenter.org

Women's Initiative for Self Employment (WI)
Laura Hoover, Microfinance and Business Development Manager
1390 Market Street, Suite 113

San Francisco, CA 94102
415-247-9473
Fax: 415-247-9471
Email: lhoover@womensinitiative.org
www.womensinitiative.org

WEST Company - Ukiah Office
367 North State Street
Suite 201
Ukiah, CA 95482
707-468-3553
Fax: 707-468-3555
Email: info@westcompany.org
www.westcompany.org

WEST Company - Fort Bragg Office
306 East Redwood Avenue
Suite 2
Fort Bragg, CA 95437
707-964-7571
Fax: 707-964-7576
Email: joy@westcompany.org
www.westcompany.org

Colorado
Mi Casa Resource Center for Women, Inc.
360 Acoma Street
Denver, CO 80223
303-573-1302
Fax: 303-595-0422
Email: info@micasadenver.org
www.micasadenver.org

Mi Casa Resource Center for Women, Inc.
505 West Abriendo Avenue
Pueblo, CO 81004
719-542-0091
Fax: 719-542-1006
Email: info@micasadenver.org
www.micasadenver.org

Connecticut

Women Business Development Center (WBDC)
Fran Pastore, Director of Training and Programs
400 Main Street, Suite 500
Stamford, CT 06901
203-353-1750
Fax: 203-353-1084
Email: fpastore@ctwbdc.org
www.ctwbdc.org

SBA and OWBO-CT at The Entrepreneurial Center of Hartford's College for Women
Jean Blake-Jackson, Director
50 Elizabeth Street
Hartford, CT 06105-2280
860-768-5681
Fax: 860-768-5622
Email: entrectr@hartford.edu
http://uhaweb.hartford.edu/entrectr

District of Columbia

Women's Business Center of the Capital Area
Susan Kuhn, Director of Program Services
1001 Connecticut Ave. NW
Suite 312
Washington, DC 20036
202-785-4922
Fax: 202-785-4110
Email: info@womensbusinesscenter.org
www.womensbusinesscenter.org

Florida

Women's Business Center of Northwest Florida
Rosemary Fraser, Director
6235 North David Hwy.
Suite 111 B
Pensacola, FL 32504
850-484-2765
Fax: 850-484-3697
Email: womenbiz@womenbiz.biz

Georgia

Greater Atlanta Women's Business Project
241 Peachtree Street NW, Suite 200
Atlanta, GA 30303
404-965-3983, ext.108
404-659-5955
Fax: 404-880-9561
www.graspnet.org

Hawaii

Hawaii Women's Business Center
Beverly Cabrera, Executive Director
1041 Nuuanu Ave.
Suite A
Honolulu, HI 96817
808-522-8136 ext. 227
Fax: 808-522-8135
Email: info@hwbc.org
www.Hawaiiwbc.org

Idaho

Entrepreneurial Resources, Inc.
Amy Davis, Executive Director
119 North 9th Street
P.O. Box 6700
Boise, ID 83707-0700
208-336-5464
Fax: 208-375-9333
Email: frontdesk@wcidaho.org
www.wbcidaho.org/index.asp

Illinois

Women's Business Development Center (WBDC)
8 South Michigan Avenue, Suite 400
Chicago, IL 60603-3306
312-853-3477, ext. 517
Fax: 312-853-0145
Email: wdbc@wbdc.org
www.wbdc.org

Indiana

Women's Enterprise, A Program of the Fort Wayne's Women's Business Bureau
Leslie Alford, Director
3521 Lake Ave., Suite 1
Fort Wayne, IN 46805-5533
260-424-7977
Fax: 260-426-7576
Email: info@womensenterprise.org
www.womensenterprise.org

Iowa

The Iowa Women's Enterprise Center
910 23rd Avenue
Coralville, IA 52241
888-849-9589
319-338-2331
Fax: 319-338-5824
Email: info@ised.org
www.ised.org/EconomicDevelopment/WomenEntCenter.asp

Kansas

Kansas Women's Business Center
Sandy Licata, Executive Director
8527 Bluejacket Street
Lenexa, KS 66214
913-492-5922
Fax: 913-888-6928
Email: slicata@kansaswbc.com
www.kansaswbc.com

Kentucky

Women's Enterprise Institute
Nicole Bryan, Interim Director
512 East Stephens Street
Midway College
Midway, KY 40347-1120
859-846-5800
Fax: 859-546-5872
Email: wei@midway.edu
www.weimidway.org

Louisiana

Urban League of Greater New Orleans Women's Business Resource Center

2322 Canal Street, Suite 100
New Orleans, LA 70119
504-620-9650
Fax: 504-620-9659
www.urbanleagueneworleans.org/womensbusinessresource.htm

Maine

Coastal Enterprises Inc. (CEI)
Women's Business Development Program (WBDP)
Ellen Golden, Senior Project Manager
P.O. Box 268
36 Water Street
Wiscasset, ME 04578
207-882-7552
Fax: 207-882-7308
Email: cci@ccimaine.org
www.ceimaine.org

Maryland

Women Entrepreneurs of Baltimore, Inc. (WEB)
Amanda Crook Zinn, Chief Executive Officer
1118 Light Street, Suite 202
Baltimore, MD 21230
410-727-4921
Fax: 410-727-4989
Email: services@webinc.org
www.webinc.org

Women's Business Institute, Inc.
Beatrice Checket, Chief Executive Officer
10 S. Howard St., 6th Floor
Baltimore, MD 21201
410-266-8746
Email: checket@juno.com

Massachusetts

Center for Women & Enterprise
Cheri Boegemann, Program Coordinator
150 Elm Street, 2nd Floor
Worcester, MA 01609
508-363-2300
Fax: 508-363-2323
Email: cboegemann@cweonline.org
www.cweboston.org

Center for Women & Enterprise
Alison Corwin, Program Manager
Renaissance Park
1135 Tremont Street, Suite 480
Boston, MA 02120
617-536-0700 ext. 223
Fax: 617-536-7373
Email: acorwin@cwconline.org
www.cweboston.org

Michigan

Women's Initiative for Self-Employment (WISE)
Center for Empowerment and Economic Development (CEED)
Michelle Richards, Executive Director

2002 Hogback Road, Suite 12
Ann Arbor, MI 48105
734-677-1400
Fax: 734-677-1465
Email: mrichards@miceed.org
www.miceed.org

Grand Rapids Opportunities for Women (GROW)
Rita VenderVen, Executive Director
25 Sheldon SE, Suite 210
Grand Rapids, MI 49503
616-458-3404
Fax: 616-458-6557
Email: grow@voyager.net
www.growbusiness.org

Detroit Entrepreneurship Institute, Inc.
Cathy McClelland, President
455 W. Fort Street, 4th Floor
Detroit, MI 48226
313-961-8426
Fax: 313-961-8831
Email: cmcclelland@deibus.org
www.deibus.org

Minnesota
The People Connection
Michelle Landsverk, Operations Director
226 East 1st Street
Fosston, MN 56542
218-435-2134
Fax: 218-435-1347
Email: michelle@thepeopleconnection.org
www.thepeopleconnection.org

Women Venture
Tene Wells, President
2324 University Avenue West
Suite 200
St. Paul, MN 55114
651-646-3808
Fax: 651-641-7223
Email: twells@womenventure.org
www.womenventure.org

Mississippi
MACE Women's Business Center
Ruby Buck, President
119 South Theobald Street
Greenville, MS 38701
662-335-3523
Fax: 601-334-2939
Email: mace@tecinco.com
www.deltamace.org

Missouri
Women's Business Center at Growth Opportunity Connection, Inc.
Alan Corbet, Executive Director
4747 Troost Avenue
Kansas City, MO 64110
816-235-6146
Fax: 816-235-6177
Email: acorbet@goconnection.org
www.goconnection.org

Grace Hill Neighborhood Services
Lynette Watson, Director
2600 Hadley Street
St. Louis, MO 63106
314-539-7500
Fax: 314-241-8938
Email: LynneS@gracehill.org
www.gracehill.org

Montana
Business Resource Center
Travis Brazill, Director
347 North Last Chance Gulch
Helena, MT 59601
800-254-6607
406-443-0800
Fax: 406-442-2745
Email: tbrazill@ctibrc.org
www.ctibrc.org

Nebraska
Rural Enterprise Assistance Project
P.O. Box 136
145 Main Street
Lyons, NE 68038
402-687-2100
Fax: 402-687-2200
Email: REAPinfo@cfra.org
www.cfra.org/reap/default.htm

New Hampshire
Women's Business Center, Inc.
Ellen Fineberg, Executive Director
150 Greenleaf Avenue, #8
Portsmouth, NH 03801
603-430-2892
Fax: 603-430-3706
Email: info@womenbiz.org
www.womenbiz.org

New Jersey
New Jersey Association of Women Business Owners, Women's Business Center
Penni Nafus, Director
White Horse Commercial Park
127 US Highway 206 South
Suite 28
Hamilton, NJ 08610
609-581-2220
Fax: 609-581-6749
Email: wbcnj@njawbo.org
www.njawbo.org

New Mexico
Women's Economic Self-Sufficiency Team (WESST Corp.)
414 Silver Southwest
Albuquerque, NM 87102
800-GO-WESST
505-241-4753
Fax: 505-241-4766
www.wesst.org

Women's Economic Self-Sufficiency Team Corp.
4601 East Main Street, Suite 580
Farmington, NM 87401
800-GO-WESST

505-325-0678
Fax: 505-325-0695
www.wesst.org

New York
Women's Venture
240 West 35 Street, Suite 501
New York, NY 10001
212-563-0499
Fax: 212-868-9116
Email: info@wvf-ny.org
www.womensventurefund.org

The Women's Business Resource Center (Hunts Point)
Josephine Infante, Executive Director
866B Hunts Point Avenue
Bronx, NY 10474
718-842-8888
Fax: 718-842-6592
Email: Jinfante@huntspointedc.org
www.hpwbrc.org

Queens Women's Business Center
Madeleine Gordillo, Program Officer
120-55 Queens Boulevard, Suite 309
Kew Gardens
Queens, NY 11424
718-263-0546
Fax: 718-263-0594
Email: services@queensny.org
www.queensny.org

The Local Development Corporation of East New York
80 Jamaica Avenue
Brooklyn, NY 11207
718-385-6700
Fax: 718-385-7505
Email: ldceny@hotmail.org
www.ldceny.org

North Carolina
The Women's Center of Fayetteville
Sylvia Ray, Executive Director
230 Hay Street
Fayetteville, NC 28301
910-323-3377
Fax: 910-323-8828
Email: jsuperak@wcof.org
www.wcof.org

North Carolina Institute of Minority Economic Development
Verona P. Edmond, Director
114 West Parrish Street, 4th Floor
P.O. Box 1331
Durham, NC 27701
919-956-8889
Fax: 919-688-4358
Email: info@ncimed.com
www.ncimed.com/wbc/index.cfm

North Dakota
The Center for Technology and Business
Tara Holt, Project Director
1022 East Divide Avenue
P.O. Box 2535

Bismarck, ND 58502
866-294-2136
701-223-0707
Fax: 701-223-2507
Email: holt@techwomen.org
www.techwomen.org

Ohio
*Ohio's Women's Business
Development Council, Inc.*
Linda Steward, Program Director
3360 E. Livingston Ave., Suite 213
Columbus, OH 43227
614-621-0881
Fax: 614-238-0168

Oklahoma
*Oklahomans for Indian Opportunity
(OIO) Women's Business Center*
Betty Olivas, Program Director
3001 South Berry Road, Suite B
Norman, OK 73072
800-375-3737
405-329-3737
Fax: 405-329-8488
Email: bolivas@oiooio.com
www.oiooio.com

*Rural Enterprise of Oklahoma, Inc.
(REO) Rural Women's Business
Center*
Barbara Rackley, Program Director
P.O. Box 1335
2912 Enterprise Drive
Durant, OK 74702
800-658-2523
580-924-5094
Fax: 580-920-2745
Email:
barbara@ruralenterprise.com
www.ruralenterprises.com/wbc.htm

*Center for Entrepreneurial
Excellence*
Anne Coleman, Executive Director
2709 West I-44 Service Road
Oklahoma City, OK 73112
405-601-1930
Fax: 405-601-1935
Email: info@helpyourbiz.org
www.helpyourbiz.org

Oregon
*Southern Oregon Women's Access to
Credit (SOWAC)*
Helen Wallace, Director
33 North Central, Suite 209
Medford, OR 97501
866-608-6094
541-779-3992
Fax: 541-779-5195
Email: hwallace@sowac.org
www.sowac.org

Pennsylvania
*Women's Business Development
Center (WBDC)*
1315 Walnut Street
Suite 1116

Philadelphia, PA 19107-4711
215-790-9232
Fax: 215-790-9231
Email: info@womensbdc.org
www.womensbdc.org

Puerto Rico
Women's Business Institute (WBI)
Universidad Del Sagrado Corazon
(The University of the Sacred Heart)
Teresa Sotero, Director
Center for Women's Entrepreneurial
Development
P.O. Box 12383
San Juan, PR 00914-0383
787-726-7045
Fax: 787-726-6550
Email: empresaria@sagrado.edu
www.wbipr.org

Rhode Island
*Center for Women & Enterprise, Inc.
(CWE)*
Carol Malysz, Director
55 Claverick Street, Suite 102
Providence, RI 02903
401-277-0800
Fax: 401-277-1122
Email: cmalysz@cweonline.org
www.cweboston.org

South Carolina
*South Carolina Manufacturing
Extension Partnership/WBC*
Haidee Stith, Client Impact
817 Calhoun Street
Columbia, SC 29201
800-MEP-4MFG
803-252-6976, ext. 225
Email: hstith@scmep.org
www.scmep.org

South Dakota
Center for Women Business Institute
Tricia Cole, Interim Executive
Director
1101 W. 22nd Street
Sioux Falls, SD 57105
866-556-6744
605-331-6697
Fax: 605-331-6615
Email: tricia.cole@usiouxfalls.edu
www.usiouxfalls.edu/als/bus_institut
e.htm

Tennessee
*The National Assn. for Women
Business Owners - Nashville Chapter
(NAWBO)*
Janice S. Thomas, Executive
Director
P.O. Box 292283
1112 8th Avenue South
Nashville, TN 37229-2283
615-746-5930
Fax: 615-256-2706
Email: info@nawbo.com
www.nashvillenawbo.com

Southeast Women's Business Center
Sandi Brock, Program Director
P.O. Box 4757
535 Chestnut Street
Chattanooga, TN 37405
423-266-5781
Fax: 423-267-7705
Email: sbrock@sedev.org
www.sewbc.com

Texas
*Women's Empowerment Business
Center*
1201 University Drive
Edinburg, TX 78539-2999
956-292-7535
Fax: 956-292-7561
Email: webc@panam.edu
www.coserve.org/webc/

*Texas Center for Women's Business
Enterprise (CWBE)*
Dianne Olson, Project Director
4100 Ed Bluestein Boulevard,
Building 5
Austin, TX 78721
888-352-2525
512-472-8522
Fax: 512-472-8513
Email: dianne@txcwbe.org
www.txcwbe.org

Women's Business Border Center
Terri Adams-Reed, Project Director
201 E. Main Street, Suite 100
El Paso, TX 79901
915-566-4066
Fax: 915-566-9714
Email: treed@ephcc.org
www.womenbordercenter.com

*Fort Worth Women's Business
Center*
M. Tipper, Program Director
1150 South Freeway
Fort Worth, TX 76104
817-871-6001
Fax: 817-871-6031
Email: mtipper@fwbac.com
www.fwbac.com

Utah
*Womens Business Center at the
Chamber*
Salt Lake Area Chamber of
Commerce
Nancy Mitchell, Director
175 East 400 South, Suite 600
Salt Lake City, UT 84111
801-364-3631
Fax: 801-328-5098
Email:
nmitchell@saltlakechamber.org
www.saltlakechamber.org

Vermont
*Vermont Women's Business Center
(CVCAC)*
Linda Ingold, Project Director
660 Elm Street

Montpelier, VT 05602
800-266-4062
802-229-2181
Fax: 802-229-2141
Email: lmase@cvcac.org
www.vwbc.org

Virgin Islands

St. Croix Foundation for Community Development, Inc.
Virgin Islands Women's Business Center
Bernadette Richards, Program Director
72 Flag Drive, Gallows Bay
St. Croix, USVI 00820
340-773-4995
Fax: 340-773-8503
Email: staff@wbcvi.org
www.wbcvi.org

Virginia

Women's Business Center of Northern Virginia
Barbara Wrigley, Director
7001 Loisdale Road, Suite C
Springfield, VA 22150
703-778-9922
Fax: 703-768-0547
Email: bwrigley@wbcnova.org
www.wbcnova.org

Washington

Northwest Women's Business Center
728 134th Street, SW
Everett, WA 98204
425-787-9856
Fax: 425-745-5563
Email: info.nwwbc@seattleccd.com
www.seattleccd.com/wbc-nw/index.htm

Women's Business Center
P.O. Box 22283
1437 South Jackson Street
Seattle, WA 98144
206-324-4330
Fax: 206-324-4322
Email: info@seattleccd.com
www.seattleccd.com/wbc/index.htm

West Virginia

Women's Business Institute, Inc. (WBI)
Kathryn Johnston,
1000 Technology Drive
Allan B. Mollahan Technical Center
Fairmont, WV 26554
304-366-1400
Email: wbifairmontkj@hotmail.com
www.wbi-wv.org

Women's Business Institute
Beatrice Checket
Grand Central Business Ctr., #3050
One Grand Central Park
Keyser, WV 26726
301-786-4646
Fax: 304-788-1687
Email: keyserwbi@juno.com
www.wbi-wv.org

Wisconsin

Wisconsin Women's Business Initiative Corporation (WWBIC)
Wendy K. Baumer, President
2745 North Dr. Martin Luther King Jr. Drive
Milwaukee, WI 53212
414-263-5450
Fax: 414-263-5456
Email: info@wwbic.com
www.wwbic.com

Wisconsin Women's Business Initiative Corporation (WWBIC)
Jill French, Project Director
2300 South Park Street, Suite 4
Madison, WI 53713
608-257-5450
Fax: 608-257-5454
Email: info@wwbic.com
www.wwbic.com

Western Dairyland Women's Business Center (WDWBDC)
Renee Walz, Business Development Director
P.O. Box 125
23122 Whitehall Road
Independence, WI 54747
715-985-2391, ext 210
800-782-1063, ext 210
Fax: 715-985-3239
Email: info@westerndairyland.org
www.westerndairyland.org

Wyoming

Wyoming Women's Business Center
Andrea Lewis, Program Coordinator
University of Wyoming
Education Annex/Business Technology Center
Rooms 155 & 158
13th and Lewis Streets
P.O. Box 764
Laramie, WY 82071
307-766-3084
888-524-1947
Fax: 307-766-3085
Email: wwbc@uwyo.edu
www.wyomingwomen.org

Millions Set Aside For Welfare Moms
To Start Their Own Businesses

If you are on public assistance, you're in luck. Uncle Sam wants to give you the start-up capital necessary to get your business off the ground and keep it flying. The Job Opportunities for Low Income Individuals (JOLI) program can turn any good idea into a money making powerhouse, and it won't cost you a cent. Of all the business startup programs the government offers, this has got to be one of the best.

Under the JOLI program, grants are awarded each year to nonprofit organizations that, in turn, work to create permanent jobs for people who are interested in running their own successful small businesses. As a collaborative partnership, the JOLI projects bring together community support services to lend a hand to those who want to climb that tough ladder of success.

Depending on your state, you can receive:
- loan guarantees
- help getting restrictive asset rules waived
- free child care and transportation
- business skills training
- help with business plans and loan applications
- personal and family development assistance
- ongoing technical advice and feedback

For federal information on grants in your area, contact the federal JOLI office at the Department of Health and Human Services, Office of Community Services, 370 L'Enfant Promenade, SW, Fifth Floor, Washington, DC 20447; 202-401-9346, Fax: 202-401-4687; {www.acf.hhs.gov/programs/ joli/welcome.htm}. They have a complete list.

What follows is a listing of the community development organizations that have received federal grant money over the last three years to run JOLI self-employment programs for low-income people. Call the one nearest you for more information on what services are available.

Alaska
Fairbanks Native Association
201 First Avenue, Suite 200
Fairbanks, AK 99701-4892
907-452-1648
Fax: 907-456-4148
www.fairbanksnative.org

Arkansas
Arkansas Enterprise Group
Mr. William Brandon, President

605 Main Street, Suite 202
Arkadelphia, AR 71923
870-246-9736
Fax: 870-246-2182

California
Jobs for Homeless Consortium, Inc.
436 14th Street, Suite 716
Oakland, CA 94612
510-587-7394

Silicon Valley Economic
Development
Ms. Consuelo Santos-Killins,
President
1155 N. First Street, Suite 107
San Jose, CA 95112
408-298-8455
www.sved.org

Stitches Technology Sewn Products
Training Centers, Inc.

Ms. Clotee McAfee
Executive Director
5609 McKinley Avenue
Los Angeles, CA 90011
323-846-5110
www.dreams.20m.com/about.html

Valley Economic Development
Center, Inc.
5121 Van Nuys Boulevard, 3rd Floor
Van Nuys, CA 91403
818-907-9977
Fax: 818-907-9720
Email: info@vedc.org
www.vedc.org

District of Columbia
United Planning Organization
301 Rhode Island Avenue, NW
Washington, DC 20001-1826
202-238-4600
Email: info@upo.org
www.upo.org

Georgia
GRASP Enterprises, Inc.
241 Peachtree St., NE, Suite 200
Atlanta, GA 30303
404-659-5955
Fax: 404-880-9561
www.graspnet.org

Hawaii
Parents and Children Together
1505 Dillingham Boulevard
Suite 208
Honolulu, HI 96819
808-841-2245
Fax: 808-842-9604
http://pacthawaii.org

Illinois
Bethel New Life, Inc.
4950 W. Thomas
Chicago, IL 60651
773-473-7870
Fax: 773-473-7871
www.bethelnewlife.org

Community & Economic
Development
Association of Cook County, Inc.
208 S. LaSalle
Suite 1900
Chicago, IL 60604
312-795-8983
Fax: 312-795-0240

Gateway East Metropolitan Ministry
Mr. Frank Childress
Executive Director
575 N. 14th Street
East St. Louis, IL 62205
618-482-5733

Women's Self-Employment Project
11 South LaSalle - Suite 1850
Chicago, IL 60603
312-606-8255

Fax: 312-606-9215
www.wsep.net

Iowa
Institute for Social and Economic
Development
910 23 rd Avenue
Coralville, IA 52241
319-338-2331
Fax: 319-338-5824
www.ised.org

Kentucky
Kentucky River Foothills
Development Council, Inc.
1623 Foxhaven Drive
P.O. Box 743
Richmond, KY 40476
606-624-2046
www.kyriverfoothills.org

Massachusetts
Jewish Vocational Service
105 Chauncy Street
Boston, MA 02111
617-451-8147
Fax: 617-451-9973
www.jvs-boston.org

Minnesota
St. Paul Urban League
Ms. Willie Mae Wilson, President
401 Selby Avenue
St. Paul, MN 55102
651-224-5771

Missouri
George Washington Carver House
3035 Bell Avenue
St. Louis, MO 63106
314-652-8485

Nebraska
Lincoln Action Program, Inc.
210 O Street
Lincoln, NE 68502
402-471-4515
www.lincoln-action.org/

Omaha Opportunities
Industrialization Center, Inc.
2724 North 24th Street
Omaha, NE 68110
302-457-4222
Fax: 402-457-6635
www.oicofamerica.org

New York
Centros Sor Isolina Ferre, Inc.
P.O. Box 34360
Ponce, PR 00734-4360
787-844-7743/7720 or 7745
Fax: 787-843-2347

Massachusetts Avenue Project
382 Massachusetts Avenue
Buffalo, NY 14213
716-882-9239

Northern Manhattan Improvement
Corporation
Ms. Barbara Lowry
Executive Director
76 Wadsworth Avenue
New York, NY 10033
212-822-8300 Ext. 336
www.nmic.org

North Dakota
Turtle Mountain Community College
P. O. Box 340
Belcourt, ND 58316
701-477-5605
www.turtle-mountain.cc.nd.us/

Ohio
The Neighborhood House, Inc.
1000 Atcheson Street
Columbus, OH 43203
614-252-4941 ext. 41

WSOS Community Action
Commission, Inc.
109 S. Front Street
P. O. Box 590
Fremont, OH 43420
419-334-8911
www.wsos.org/viewpage/

Oklahoma
Housing Partners of Tulsa, Inc.
P. O. Box 6369
415 E. Independence
Tulsa, OK 74148-0369
918-581-5777
www.tulsahousing.org/

Pennsylvania
Northside Leadership Conference
415 East Ohio Street
Suite 300
Pittsburgh, PA 15212
412-231-4714
Fax: 415-231-5306
www.pittsburghnorthside.com

South Carolina
Innovative Alternative for Education,
Inc.
Ms. Jennifer A. Sgro, Chairperson
MSC Box 1002
701 East Bay Street - Suite 3A-100
Charleston, SC 29403
843-577-2103

Tennessee
UMCA of Greater Memphis
766 S. Highland
Memphis, TN 38111
901-323-323-2211
Fax: 901-458-3784

Texas
Business Invest In Growth, Inc.
1009 East 11th Street, Suite 216
Austin, TX 78702
512-494-8044

George Gervin Youth Center, Inc.
6903 Sunbelt Drive South
San Antonio, TX 78218
210-804-1786
Fax: 210-804-1469

Vermont
Central Vermont Community Action
Council, Inc.
195 US Route 302 -- Berlin
Barre, VT 05641
802-479-1053
www.cvcac.org/default.aspx

Virginia
Arlington Community Action
Program, Inc.
P. O. Box 6250
Arlington, VA 22206
703-241-2040 ext. 25
www.arlingtoncap.org/

Washington
Metropolitan Development Council
J. Lindsey Hinand, President
622 Tacoma Avenue South

Tacoma, WA 98402
253-597-6703

Wisconsin
Western Dairyland Economic
Opportunity Council, Inc.
Mr. James W. Schwartz, Exec. Dir.
23122 Whitehall Road
P.O. Box 45
Independence, WI 54747
715-985-2391
www.westerndairyland.org/

Money to Start a Business if You Are a Minority

Minorities now own nearly 15% of American businesses, and over 90% of them are small businesses. The ownership of businesses by minorities has more than doubled in the last two decades. Some of this growth can be credited to all levels of government who have been encouraging the development and expansion of minority owned businesses. Lack of financial capital is one impediment to the success of small businesses, and in particular minority owned firms. There are many different resources and places you can turn for information, assistance, and loans. The Small Business Administration has helpful loans and loan guarantee programs, and services to help minority businesses. To learn more contact the SBA at 800-8-ASK-SBA or online at {www.sba.gov}. The following are national organizations to help you start or expand your business, as well as government agencies to assist you in making your dreams come true. Make sure to check out "Other Resources for Assistance for Women, Minorities, Veterans, and the Disabled" at the end of this chapter for more places to turn for help and information.

National Minority Organizations

The National Association of Minority Contractors

666 11th Street, NW, Suite 520   866-688-6262
Washington, DC 20001   202-347-8259
www.namcline.org   Fax: 202-628-1876
The National Association of Minority Contractors can provide your business with information and support on issues that concern minority contractors. Education and training is available through the state chapters throughout the country.

The National Association of Minority Contractors State Chapters

Arizona Association of Minority Contractors
2455 South 7th Street, Suite 155   602-495-9800
Phoenix, AZ 85034   Fax: 602-495-9801

Arkansas Association of Minority Contractors
P.O. Box 2882   501-375-2152
Little Rock, AR 72203-2882   Fax: 501-372-2261

Northern California Association of Minority Contractors
900 Murmansk Street, Suite 2   510-385-9713
Oakland, CA 94607   Fax: 510-482-4571

Southern California Association of Minority Contractors
3947 W. Slauson Avenue   323-296 8005
Los Angeles CA 90043   Fax: 323-296 8381

District of Columbia Association of Minority Contractors
313 Parkland Place, SE   202-373-5590
Washington, DC 20032   Fax: 202-562-4142

Miami Florida Association of Minority Contractors
1730 Biscayne Boulevard, Suite 201-A   305-577-3738
Miami, FL 33132   Fax: 305-577-0198

Northeast Florida Association of Minority Contractors
5903 Norwood Avenue   904-766-9868
Jacksonville, FL 32208   Fax: 904-766-1687
www.namcnfc.com

Greater Atlanta Georgia Association of Minority Contractors
75 Piedmont Avenue
Suite 906   404-688-6996
Atlanta, GA 30303-2505   Fax: 404-688-6122

Northern Louisiana Association of Minority Contractors
1808 North Market   318-222-4759
Shreveport, LA 71107   Fax: 318 227-9886

Maryland Association of Minority Contractors
1605 Saint Paul Street   410-783-9091
Baltimore, MD 21202   Fax: 410-783-9092
www.mwmca.org

Minnesota Association of Minority Contractors
4248 Park Glen Drive   952-928-4667
Minneapolis, MN 55416   Fax: 952-929-1318
www.namc-um.org

Southern Nevada Association of Minority Contractors
726 Casino Center Boulevard
Suite 204   702-366-0054
Las Vegas, NV 89101   Fax: 702-366-0564
www.namc-lv.org

New Jersey Association of Minority Contractors
67 Sanford Street, Suite 2
East Orange, NJ. 07018   973-667-1600 ext. 105

New York Association of Minority Contractors
c/o Brooklyn Navy Yard,
Building 280, 4th Floor   718-246-8380
Brooklyn, NY 11205   Fax: 718-246-8376

New England/Massachusetts Association of Minority
  Contractors
348 D Street   617-954-2458
South Boston, MA 02127   Fax: 617-269-4035

Central Ohio Association of Minority Contractors
2188 Oriole Place   614-258-5673
Columbus, OH 43219-2038   Fax: 614-372-0333

Dayton Ohio Association of Minority Contractors
P.O. Box 279   937-854-0281
Dayton, OH. 45417-0279   Fax: 937-837-4890

Philadelphia Association of Minority Contractors
544 E Haines Street   215-843-7210
Philadelphia, PA 19144   Fax: 215-843-2692

Pittsburgh Association of Minority Contractors
Coady Bolden Building
7249 Frankstown Avenue   412-247-4822
Pittsburgh, PA 15208   Fax: 412-247-4471

Memphis-Tri-State Tennessee Association of Minority
  Contractors
3360 Fontaine Road   901-332-5670
Memphis, TN 38116   Fax: 901-332-5680

Houston Texas Association of Minority Contractors
500 Lovett Street, Suite 225   713-524-6766
Houston, TX 77006   Fax: 713-524-4322
namchou@aol.com

Wisconsin Association of Minority Contractors
3100 W. Concordia Street   414-449-0837
Milwaukee, WI 53216   Fax: 414 964-9216
www.namc-wi.org

United States Hispanic Chamber of Commerce

2175 K Street, NW, Suite 100   800-USHCC86
Washington, DC 20037   202-842-1212
www.ushcc.com   Fax: 202-842-3221

The United States Hispanic Chamber of Commerce was established nearly 25 years ago to provide a business network that promotes Hispanic-owned businesses. Through the National organization and over 150 local Hispanic Chamber of Commerce offices, a variety of programs are available.

Alianza! The Gateway to Capital: The USHCC and Bank One have formed Alianza to help Hispanic-owned businesses. Affinity Rewards is one of the programs that provide dollars to develop educational programs to the Hispanic chamber members.

America's On-Line Directory of Hispanic Businesses: A national online bilingual directory of Hispanic businesses.

Anna Maria Arias Memorial Business Fund: The Fund provides cash awards from $1,000 to $5,000 to outstanding Latino business owners throughout the country.

Capital!: The Capital! Loan program provides small business loans to businesses in high-growth Hispanic markets throughout the country.

Federal Procurement Council: This Council works to assist Hispanic businesses with federal procurement opportunities.
Franchising Initiative: This seminar initiative helps increase the knowledge of franchising opportunities for Hispanic business owners.

International Trade: The International Trade mission builds relationships between U.S. Hispanic based businesses and their counterparts in Latin America.

Procurement Networking Seminars: The Networking Seminars are designed to generate real sales opportunities for certified Hispanic businesses through exclusive procurement opportunities for Hispanic suppliers to meet corporate buyers.

US Pan Asian American Chamber of Commerce

1329 18th Street, NW   202-296-5221
Washington, DC 20036   Fax: 202-296-5225
www.uspaacc.com

The US Pan Asian American Chamber of Commerce (USPAACC) represents all Asian Americans and Asian American related businesses. Contact the regional office in your area for additional information.

Asian American Supplier Council: This one-stop shop for Asian American businesses is designed to nurture and develop mutually benefit business relationships with corporate America, government agencies and with one another

US Pan Asian American Chamber of Commerce East Coast
  Region
525 7th Avenue, 2nd Floor   212-764-8989
New York, NY 10018   Fax: 212-768-2113

US Pan Asian American Chamber of Commerce Midwest
  Region
5410 W. Roosevelt Road, Suite 231   773-626-3100
Chicago, IL 60644   Fax: 773-626-5541

US Pan Asian American Chamber of Commerce Southwest
  Region
505 East Border Street   817-543-4299
Arlington, TX 76010   Fax: 817-261-7389

US Pan Asian American Chamber of Commerce West Coast
  Region
8907 Warner Avenue, Suite 108   714-842-8036
Huntington Beach, CA 92647   Fax: 714-842-7332

The Minority Business Enterprise Legal Defense and Education Fund, Inc.

419 New Jersey Avenue, SE   202-289-1700
Washington, DC 20003   Fax: 202-289-1701
www.mbeldef.org

The Minority Business Enterprise Legal Defense and Education Fund is a national nonprofit law firm that creates programs for the benefit of racial/ethnic minorities.

The National Minority Business Council, Inc.

25 West 45th Street
Suite 301
New York, NY 10036

212-997-4753
Fax: 212-997-5102

www.nmbc.org
The National Minority Business Council provides business assistance, educational opportunities, seminars, purchasing listings and many services to minority-owned businesses members.

Financial Assistance: The NMBC Micro-Loan Fund provides short-term loans at competitive rates for working capital from $1,500 to $25,000 to qualified NMBC members.

Initial Public Offering (IPO) Service: The service provides support to members who are interested in capital markets through either an IPO or a Limited Public Offering (LPO).

Education and Training: Seminars and workshops on a variety of topics.

Consultation and Needs Assessment: Consultants are available to assist members assess their business needs and to make recommendations.

Minority Business Network

www.mbnet.com
This free online service provides online methods for marketing, supporting and growing your minority-owned business.

Minority Business News

TexCorp Communications, Inc.
11333 North Central Expressway
Suite 201
Dallas, TX 75243

214-369-3200

www.minoritybusinessnews.com
The Minority Business News provides information on minority business enterprise and diversity. You can view current and previous issues online with a free membership.

National Minority Supplier Development Council, Inc.

1040 Avenue of the Americas
Second Floor
New York, NY 10018

212-944-2430
Fax: 212-719-9611

www.nmsdcus.org
The National Minority Supplier Development Council is a member based organization committed to providing increased procurement and business opportunities for minority owned businesses.

Advanced Management Education Program: This custom executive program is designed to provide certified, established, expansion-oriented MBE's with tools and skills needed to achieve and sustain accelerated growth.

The Business Consortium Fund (BCF): The BCF provides contract financing to NMSDC certified minority business throughout the country.

Certification: The National Minority Supplier Development Council provides consistent certification of minority-owned businesses through their regional offices.

National Minority Supplier Development Council Regional Offices

Alabama
South Regions Minority Business Council
4715 Alton Court
Birmingham, AL 35210

205-957-1883

www.srmbc.org

Arizona
Grand Canyon Minority Supplier Development Council
802 N. 5th Avenue
Phoenix, AZ 85003

602-495-9950
Fax: 602-495-9943

www.gcmsdc.org

Arkansas
Arkansas Regional Minority Supplier Development Council
300 Spring Building, Suite 415
Little Rock, AR 72201

501-374-7026
Fax: 501-371-0409

www.armsdc.org

California
Northern California Supplier Development Council
1999 Harrison Street, Suite 655
Oakland, CA 94612

510-587-0636
Fax: 510-587-0649

www.ncsdc.org

Southern California Minority Business Development Council
515 S. Flower Street, Suite 1301
Los Angeles, CA 90071

213-689-6960
Fax: 213-689-1707

www.scmbdc.org

Greater San Diego Business Development Council
2870 Fourth Avenue, Suite 205
San Diego, CA 92103

619-293-0760

www.gsdbdc.org

Colorado
Rocky Mountain Minority Supplier Development Council
1445 Market Street, Suite 310
Denver, CO 80202

303-623-3037
Fax: 303-595-0027

www.rmmsdc.org

Connecticut
Connecticut Minority Supplier Development
4133 Whitney Avenue
Hamden, CT 06518

203-288-9744
Fax: 203-288-9310

www.cmsdc.org

Florida
Florida Regional Minority Business Council
600 NW 79th Avenue, #136
Miami, FL 33126-4018

305-260-9901
Fax: 305-260-9902

www.frmbc.org

Florida Minority Supplier Development Council
6880 Lake Ellenor Drive, Suite 104A
Orlando, FL 32809

407-245-6062
Fax: 407-857-8647

www.nmsdcfl.org

Georgia
Georgia Minority Supplier Development Council
100 Edgewood Avenue, Suite 1610
Atlanta, GA 30303

404-589-4929
Fax: 404-589-4925

www.gmsdc.org

Illinois
Chicago Minority Business Development Council
One East Wacker Drive, Suite 1200

312-755-8880

Chicago, IL 60601   Fax: 312-755-8890
www.cmbdc.org

Indiana
Indiana Regional Minority Supplier Development Council
2126 North Meridian Street   317-923-2110
Indianapolis, IN 46202   Fax: 317-923-2204
www.irmsdc.org

Kentucky
Kentuckiana Minority Business Council
614 W. Main Street, Suite 5500   502-625-0135
Louisville, KY 40202   Fax: 502-625-0082
www.kmbc.biz

Louisiana
Louisiana Minority Business Council
935 Gravier Street, 20th Floor   504-523-7110
New Orleans, LA 70112   Fax: 504-592-6645
www.lambc.org

Maryland/District of Columbia
Maryland/District of Columbia Minority Supplier
  Development Council
10770 Columbia Pike
First Floor, Suite 300   301-592-6700
Silver Springs, MD 20901   Fax: 301-592-6704
www.mddccouncil.org

Massachusetts
New England Minority Supplier Development Council
100 Huntington Avenue
Boston, MA 02116   617-578-8900
www.nemsdc.org

Michigan
Michigan Minority Supplier Development Council
3011 W. Grand Boulevard, Suite 230   313-873-3200
Detroit, MI 48202   Fax: 313-873-4783
www.mmbdc.com

Minnesota
Minnesota Minority Supplier Development Council
250 2nd Avenue South, Suite 106A   612-465-8881
Minneapolis, MN 55401   Fax: 612-465-8887
www.mmsdc.org

Missouri
Missouri Minority Supplier Council
9300 Metcalf, Suite 350   913-534-2704
Overland Park, KS 66212   Fax: 91-534-2047
www.m-s-c.org

St. Louis Minority Business Council
308 North 21st Street, 7th Floor   314-241-1143
St. Louis, MO 63103   Fax: 314-241-1073
www.slmbc.org

Nebraska
Great Plains Minority Supplier Development Council
9140 W. Dodge Road, Suite 225   402-614-9355
Omaha, NE 68114   Fax: 402-614-8824
www.gpmsdc.org

Nevada
Nevada Minority Business Council
1785 East Sahara Avenue, Suite 360
Las Vegas, NV 89104   702-894-4477
www.nvmpc.com

New York
The Minority Supplier Development Council of New York
  and New Jersey
330 Seventh Avenue, 8th Floor   212-502-5663
New York, NY 10001   Fax: 212-502-5807
www.msdcnynj.org

Upstate New York Regional Minority Purchasing Council,
  Inc.
85 River Rock Drive, Suite 113
Mail Slot 14   716-871-4120
Buffalo, NY 14207   Fax: 716-871-3725
www.unyrmpci.org

North Carolina
Carolinas Minority Supplier Development Council
Lincoln Center
10400 Mallard Creek Road, Suite 340   704-549-1000
Charlotte, NC 28262   Fax: 704-549-1616
www.carolinasmsdc.org

Ohio
Northern Ohio Minority Business Council
Tower City Center
50 Public Square, Suite 200   216-621-3300
Cleveland, OH 44113-2291   Fax: 2116-621-5461
www.nombconline.org

South Central Ohio Minority Business Council
37 North High Street   614-225-6959
Columbus, OH 43215   Fax: 614-221-1669
www.scombc.com

Oklahoma
Oklahoma Minority Supplier Development Council
The Pavilion Building
6701 N. Broadway, Suite 216   405-767-9900
Oklahoma City, OK 73116   Fax: 405-767-9901
www.omsdc.org

Pennsylvania
The Minority Supplier Development Council of PA-NJ-DE
42 South 15th Street, Suite 1060   215-569-1005
Philadelphia, PA 19102   Fax: 215-569-2667
www.msdc-panjde.org

Pittsburgh Regional Minority Purchasing Council
Regional Enterprise Towers   412-391-4423
425 Sixth Avenue, Suite 2690   Pittsburgh, PA 15219
Fax: 412-391-3132
www.prmpc.org

Puerto Rico
Puerto Rico Supplier Development Council
P.O. Box 192410
San Juan, PR 00919-2410   787-759-9445 ext 219
www.sdcpr.org

Tennessee
Tennessee Minority Supplier Development Council
Metro Center, Plaza I Building
220 Athens Way, Suite 105   615-259-4699
Nashville, TN 37228   Fax: 615-259-9480
www.tmsdc.net

Texas
Central and South Texas Minority Business Council
912 Bastrop Highway, Suite 101
Austin, TX 78741   512-386-8766
www.cstmbc.org

Dallas/Fort Worth Minority Business Development Council
1000 Stemmons Tower South
2720 Stemmons Freeway   214-630-0747
Dallas, TX 75207-2212   Fax: 214-637-2241
www.dfwmbdc.com

Houston Minority Business Council
6671 Southwest Freeway, Suite 110   713-271-7805
Houston, TX 77074   Fax: 713-271-9770
www.hmbc.org

Virginia
Virginia Minority Supplier Development Council
Bank of America Center
1111 East Main Street
Third Floor Pavilion   804-780-2322
Richmond, VA 23219   Fax: 804-780-3171
www.vmsdc.org

Washington
Northwest Minority Business Council
320 Andover Park East, Suite 205   206-575-7748
Tukwila, WA 98188-7635   Fax: 206-575-7783
www.nmbc.biz

Wisconsin
Wisconsin Supplier Development Council
P.O. Box 8577   608-241-5858
Madison, WI 53708-8577   Fax: 608-241-9100
www.suppliercouncil.org

Airport Minority Advisory Council
Shirlington Gateway
2800 Shirlington Road   703-379-5701
Shirlington, VA 22206   Fax: 703-379-5703
www.amac-org.com

The Airport Minority Advisory Council (AMAC) is dedicated to promoting minority-owned businesses in airport contracts. AMAC co-sponsors an annual Airport Business Diversity Conference as a forum for education, advocacy and networking.

Business Consortium Fund, Inc.
605 Seventh Street, 20th Floor   212-243-7360
New York, NY 10001   Fax: 212-243-7647
www.bcfcapital.com

The Business Consortium Fund provides access to capital to selected Minority Business Enterprises. Contact their office to see if your business qualifies for funds.

Minority Business Development Centers

If you want to start or expand a business and you belong to a minority group, the Department of Commerce has something special just for you. The Minority Business Development Agency funds Business Development Centers (MBDC), Native American Business Development Centers (NABDC), Business Resource Centers (BRC) and Minority Business opportunity Committees (MBOC) nationwide to assist with the start-up, expansion, and

acquisition of competitive minority owned firms offering quality goods and services. These centers provide business assistance for bonding, bidding, estimating, financing, procurement, international trade, franchising, acquisitions, mergers, and joint ventures to increase opportunities in domestic and international markets for minority entrepreneurs. Individuals that are eligible for the centers' business assistance are those that are socially or economically disadvantaged individuals who own or wish to start a business. Such persons include: Spanish Speaking Americans, Asian Pacific Americans, Asian Indians, Native and African-Americans, Aleuts, Eskimos, Puerto Ricans, and Hasidic Jews.

These centers are operated by private firms, nonprofit organizations, state and local government agencies, Native American tribes, and educational institutions. The centers provide one-on-one counseling for accounting, administration, business planning, construction, and marketing information. They also identify minority owned firms for contract and subcontract opportunities with federal, state, and local government agencies, and the private sector. The centers identify both private and public sector sources of financing for minority owned firms and assist with the preparation of financial documents and plans for submission to lenders.

The Minority Business Development Agency is also a co-sponsor with the Small Business Administration on activities for Minority Enterprise Development Week (MED Week), which is a national yearly celebration that honors American minority entrepreneurs and the individuals and organizations that support their business development. Regional MED Week activities are held in the weeks prior to the observed MED Week, which is the first full week of October.

The following lists contain the local Business Development Centers to contact. If you need more information, you may contact the national headquarters at Minority Business Development Agency, 14th and Constitution, Washington, DC 20230; 202-482-3917; 888-324-1551; {www.mbda.gov}, Email: help@mbda.gov.

Minority Business Development Centers

Alaska

Alaska Statewide MBDC
122 1st Avenue, Suite 60
Fairbanks, AK 99701
907-452-8251
Fax: 907-459-3851
www.tananachiefs.org/mbdc/default.
htm
Email: lallen@tananachiefs.org

Arizona

Arizona Statewide MBDC
255 East Osborn Road, Suite 201
Phoenix, AZ 85012
602-248-0007
Fax: 602-279-8900
Email: izzyg@azhcc.com

California

MBDA National Enterprise Center
221 Main Street, Room 1280
San Francisco, CA 94105
415-744-3001
Fax: 415-744-3061
Email: sfro-info@mbda.gov

East Los Angeles County MBDC
5271 East Beverly Blvd.
Los Angeles, CA 90022
323-726-7734
Fax: 323-721-9794
www.elambdc.org
Email: info@elambdc.org

South Los Angeles County MBDC
110 South La Brea Avenue, Suite
200
Inglewood, CA 90301
310-419-8745
Fax: 310-419-8755
www.laul.org/rbbc/ron_brown_busin
ess_center_inglew..htm
Email: wshine@laul.org

West Los Angeles County MBDC
3550 Wilshire Blvd., Suite 905
Los Angeles, CA 90010
213-368-1450
Fax: 213-368-1454
www.westlambdc.org
Email: info@westlambdc.org

Los Angeles Regional Enterprise
Center
Pasadena Office Tower
150 South Los Robles Avenue
Suite 460
Pasadena, CA 91101
626-768-1015
Fax: 626-768-1020
www.mbda.gov

Northern California Regional
Headquarters
300 Frank Ogawa Building
Suite 210
Oakland, Ca 94612

510-832-1110
Fax: 510-832-1105
www.ncmbdc.com
Email: rjmedrano@earthlink.net

Central Valley Satellite
5528 N. Palm Avenue, Suite 114
Fresno, CA 93701
559-449-0875
Fax: 559-447-1374
www.cvmbdc.com

Bakersfield Office
2100 Chester Avenue
Bakersfield, CA 93301
661-717-3125
Fax: 661-395-4134
www.cvmbdc.com

Small Business Growth Institute
11075 Santa Monica Blvd., #175
Los Angeles, CA 90025
310-575-1100
Fax: 310-575-1121
Email:
sevans@bizresourcegroup.com

Inland Empire
4053 Chestnut Street
Riverside, CA 92501-3536
909-320-7020
Fax: 909-320-7023
www.inlandempire-mbdc.com
Email: lrios@inlandempire-
mbdc.com

CHARO Community Development
Corporation
4301 E. Valley Boulevard
Los Angeles, CA 90032
323-269-0751
Fax: 323-266-4326
www.charocorp.com
Email: camador@charocorp.com

Colorado

Denver MBDC
3840 York Street, Suite 230B
Denver, CO 80205
303-455-3099
Fax: 303-455-3076
www.dmbdg.com
Email: info@denvermbdc.com

District of Columbia

Washington Metro MBDC
64 New York Avenue, NE
Washington, DC 20005
202-671-1552
Fax: 202-671-3073
Email: rtaylor@ncrc.org

Florida

Miami District Office
51 SW First Avenue
Room 1314, Box 25
Miami, FL 33130

305-536-5054
Fax: 305-530-7068
www.mbda.gov
Email: rsuarez@mbda.gov

Miami/Ft.Lauderdale MBDC
3050 Biscayne Blvd., Suite 201
Miami, FL 33137
786-316-0888
800-730-5581
Fax: 786-316-0090
www.mbdcsouthflorida.org
Email: info@mbdcsouthflorida.org

Miami/Ft. Lauderdale MBDC
Satellite Office
3800 West Broward Blvd., Suite 101
Bank of America Building
Ft. Lauderdale, FL 33313
954-660-7601
800-730-5581
Fax: 954-587-3703
www.mbdcsouthflorida.org
Email:
rmartinez@mbdcsouthflorida.org

Georgia

MBDA Regional Office
401 West Peachtree Street, NW
Suite 1715
Atlanta, GA 30308
404-730-3300
Fax: 404-730-3313
www.mbda.gov
Email: aro-info@mbda.gov

Atlanta MBDC
1559A Memorial Dr. SE, Suite 134
Atlanta, GA 30317
404-577-7734
Fax: 404-577-7737
www.atlmbdc.com
Email: richard@sdbusinc.org

Georgia Statewide Minority
Business Development Center
760 Spring Street NW
Atlanta, GA 30332
404-894-2096
Fax: 404-894-1192
www.georgiambdc.org
Email: donna.ennis@edi.gatech.edu

Hawaii

Honolulu MBDC
1088 Bishop St., Suite 2506
Honolulu, HI 96813
808-521-6221
Fax: 808-524-3313
www.mbdc-honolulu.com
Email: info@mbdc-honolulu.com

Illinois

MBDA National Enterprise Center
55 East Monroe Street, Suite 1406
Chicago, IL 60603
312-353-0182

Fax: 312-353-0191
www.mbda.gov
Email: cro-info@mbda.gov

Chicago MBDC
3512 West Fullerton Avenue
Chicago, IL 60647
773-252-5211
Fax: 773-252-7065
www.lacc1.com
Email:
hbonner@latinamericanchamberofco
mmerce.com
Email2: cpaclacc@ix.netcom.com

Massachusetts
Boston Regional Enterprise Center
10 Causeway Street, Suite 418
Boston, MA 02222
617-565-6850
Fax: 617-565-8897
www.mbda.gov

New Jersey
New Jersey Statewide MBDC
744 Broad Street, Suite 2001
Newark, NJ 07102
973-297-1142
Fax: 973-297-1439
Email: mgreene@newjersey-
mbdc.com

New Mexico
New Mexico Statewide MBDC
718 Central SW
Albuquerque, NM 87102
505-843-7114
Fax: 505-242-2030
www.nedainc.net
Email: info@nedainc.net

New York
MBDA National Enterprise Center
26 Federal Plaza, Room 3720
New York, NY 10278
212-264-3262
Fax: 212-264-0725
Email: nyro-info@mbda.gov

Manhattan/Bronx MBDC
350 5th Avenue, Suite 2202
New York, NY 10118
212-947-5351
Fax: 212-947-1506
www.manhattan-bronx-mbdc.org
Email: mbmbdc@manhattan-bronx-
mbdc.org

Queens/Brooklyn MBDC
90-33 160th Street
Jamaica, NY 11432
718-206-2255
Fax: 718-206-3693
www.jbrc.org
Email: jbrc@jbrc.org

Williamsburg (Brooklyn) MBDC
12 Heyward Street
Brooklyn, NY 11211
718-522-5620
Fax: 718-522-5931
www.odabdc.org
Email: charnas@odabdc.org

North Carolina
North Carolina Statewide Minority
Business Development Center
114 West Parrish Street, 5th floor
Durham, NC 27702
919-956-8889
www.ncimed.com
Email: alif@ncimed.com

Ohio
Ohio Statewide MBDC
7162 Reading Road, Suite 630
Cincinnati, OH 45237-4757
513-631-7666
Fax: 513-631-7613
www.ohiostatewidembdc.org
Email:
omartin@ohiostatewidembdc.org

Oklahoma
Oklahoma City MBDC
4205 Lincoln Blvd., Room 109
Oklahoma City, OI 73105
405-962-1623
Fax: 405-962-1639
Email: nalexander@lunet.edu

Oregon
Portland MBDC
8959 SW Barbur Blvd., Suite 102
Portland, OR 97219
503-245-9253

Pennsylvania
Philadelphia Regional Enterprise
Center
600 Arch Street, Suite 10128
Philadelphia, PA 19106
215-861-3597
Fax: 215-861-3595
www.mbda.gov

Pennsylvania Statewide MBDC
4548 Market Street
Philadelphia, PA 19139
215-895-4005
Fax: 215-895-4001
www.mbdc.gov
Email: vmallet@pambdc.com

Puerto Rico
Puerto Rico Islandwide MBDC
406 Capitan Espada Street
Hato Rey, PR 00918
787-753-8484
Fax: 787-753-0855

www.mbdcpr.com
Email: teresaberrios@mbdcpr.com

South Carolina
South Carolina Statewide MBDC
1515 Richland Street
Columbia, SC 29201
803-779-5905, ext. 28
Fax: 803-779-5915
www.scmbdc.com
Email: busdev@scmbdc.com

Texas
MBDA National Enterprise Center
1100 Commerce Street, Room 7B19
Dallas, TX 75242
214-767-8001
Fax: 214-767-0613
Email: dro-info@mbda.gov

Corpus Christi MBDC
400 South Padre Island Drive
Suite 100
Corpus Christi, TX 78405
361-883-1809
Fax: 361-289-1106
Email: ugues@davlin.net
Email2: smartinez@davlin.net

Dallas/Ft. Worth/Arlington MBDC
545 East John Carpenter Freeway
Suite 100
Irving, TX 75062
214-688-1612
Fax: 214-688-1753
www.dallasfwmbdc.com
Email: mmora@dmbdc.com

Houston MBDC
2900 Woodridge, Suite 310
Houston, TX 77087
713-644-0821
Fax: 713-644-3523
www.houstonmbdc.com
Email:
mthibodeaux@gacompanies.com

San Antonio MBDC
501 West Duranog Blvd.
San Antonio, TX 78207-4415
210-458-2488
Fax: 210-458-2491
www.iedtexas.org/mbdc
Email: fparks@utsa.edu

Washington
Washington Statewide MBDC
1437 South Jackson Street, Suite 320
Seattle, WA 98144
206-267-3131
Fax: 206-267-3132
www.seattleccd.com
Email: jjimt@seattleccd.com

Native American Business Development Centers (NABDCs)

Arizona
Arizona Statewide NABDC
953 East Juanita Avenue
Mesa, AZ 85204
480-545-1412
Fax: 480-545-4208
www.aznabdc.com
Email: mncaiedbeem@aol.com

California
California Statewide NABDC
11138 Valley Mall, Suite 200
El Monte, CA 91731
626-442-3701
Fax: 626-442-7115
www.ncaied.org/offices/proff.html
Email: nschamders@ncaied.org

Minnesota
Minnesota NABDC
P.O. Box 217
15542 State Highway 317 NW
Cass Lake, MN 56633
218-335-8928

Fax: 218-335-7712
www.paulbunyan.net/users/mcteda
Email: mcteda@paulbunyan.net

North Carolina
North Carolia Cherokee NABDC
801 Acquoni Road
P.O. Box 1200
Cherokee, NC 28719
828-497-1666
Fax: 828-497-1665
www.nc-cherokee.com
Email: cnabdc@nc-cherokee.com

North Carolina Cherokee Satellite
Office
70 Woodfin Place, Suite 305
Asheville, NC 28801
828-252-2516
Fax: 828-252-6047
Email: ashevillebdc@yahoo.com

North/South Dakota
North/South Dakota NABDC

3315 University Drive
Bismarck, ND 58504-7596
701-530-0608
Fax: 701-530-0607
Email: bmaxon@uttc.edu

Oklahoma
Oklahoma Statewide NABDC
3540 East 31st Street, Suite 5
Tulsa, OK 74135
918-592-1113
Fax: 918-592-1217
www.indiansbusiness.org
Email: mvega@indiansbusiness.org

Washington
Northwest NABDC
3327 NE 125th Street, Suite 101
Seattle, WA 91825
206-365-7735
Fax: 206-365-7764
www.ncaied.org/offices/nwroff.html
Email: ncaiedmg@aol.com

Minority Business Opportunity Committees

Alabama
Birmingham MBOC
710 20th Street, North
Birmingham, AL 35203
205-254-2799
Fax: 205-254-7741
www.birminghammboc.com
Email: ajmayo@ci.birmingham.al.us

California
Los Angeles MBOC
200 North Spring Street
Mezzanine Level (8th Floor)
Los Angeles, CA 90012
213-978-0671
Fax: 213-978-0690
Email: mboc@mayor.lacity.org

Florida
Orlando MBOC
6880 Eleanor Drive, Suite 104A
Orlando, FL 32809
407-245-6062
Fax: 407-857-8647

www.mbocflorida.org
Email: mboc@fmsdc.org

Illinois
Chicago MBOC
11 South LaSalle Street, Suite 850
Chicago, IL 60603
312-755-8888
Fax: 312-755-8891
www.chicagomboc.org
Email: info@chicagomboc.org

Indiana
Northwest Indiana MBOC
504 Broadway Street, Suite 337
Gary, IN 46402
219-886-9572
Fax: 219-881-4999
www.nimboc.com
Email: dwilliams@nimboc.com

Maryland
National Capital MBOC
4640 Forbes Blvd., Suite 200

Lanham, MD 20706
301-429-2168
Fax: 310-429-8762
www.ncmboc.com
Email: nshaw@ncmboc.com

Puerto Rico
Puerto Rico MBOC
530 Ponce de Leon Avenue
Atrium Office Center, Suite 320
San Juan, PR 00901
787-289-7880
Fax: 787-289-8750
www.puertoricomboc.com
Email: juan@woodroffe.com

Texas
South Texas MBOC
1201 West University Drive
Edinburg, TX 78539
956-316-2610
Fax: 956-316-2612
Email: jrcisneros@panam.edu

Business Resource Centers

Puerto Rico
Puerto Rico BRC
Rosales Street, Stop 261/2
SBARAT Building, Suite BS103
San Turce, PR 00908
787-726-8040
Fax: 787-726-8135

www.prsbabrc.net
Email: joseramos@sba.gov

Wisconsin
Wisconsin BRC
111 West Pleasant Street
Milwaukee, WI 53212

414-289-6767
Fax: 414-289-8562
www.wi-brc.org
Email: info@wi-brc.org

Free Help and Money for the Disabled

Over 43 million Americans have disabilities of one kind or another. Many of them dream of supporting themselves with good paying jobs but can't make this dream come true because of their disabilities or because their lack of job skills stand in the way of leading independent lives. It's the kind of discouragement felt by many, regardless of their age, ambition, or economic status.

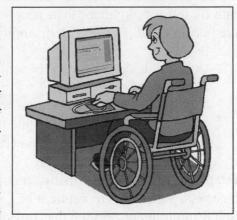

The Federal Government has stepped in and funded programs across the country to help the disabled and handicapped reach their goals by providing them with all kinds of services to get them on their way. The help available ranges from free information services, self help groups (for specific disabilities and disabilities in general), free legal aid, and independent living programs, to free money for education, job training, living expenses, transportation, equipment, and mobility aids. You can even get money to have your home retrofitted to make it more accessible to you, given your specific handicap. And if you're denied any of these programs or services, there are several free sources of legal help that can get you what you're legally entitled to.

Typical of the free services available in your state:

- medical examinations and treatment
- vocational evaluation, training, and placement
- disability counseling
- assistive devices
- transportation
- occupational equipment
- rehabilitation engineering
- postemployment services
- independent living training
- student services
- financial assistance
- supported employment
- deaf services

Your state Vocational Rehabilitation office will evaluate your skills, needs, and goals, and work with you to keep you a productive member of society. As their client, they will assist you in getting the equipment you need to do your job, and sometimes even help you with transportation to work. College is also an option. We know of a massage therapist who developed carpal tunnel syndrome and got a four-year college degree paid for so she could be trained for a new profession.

Want to start a business? The Office of Disability Employment Policy {www.dol.gov/odep} knows that people with disabilities have a strong interest in working for themselves. In fact statistics show that people with disabilities have a higher rate of self-employment than people without disabilities (12.2% versus 7.8%). But there are barriers that people with disabilities must face:

- possible loss of cash benefits for Social Security or Supplemental Security disability programs
- possible loss of health care benefits associated with cash programs
- possible loss of housing and other subsidies
- inability to access capital needed to start a business.

Despite these barriers, many enterprising people with disabilities do run successful business. The U.S. Department of Labor has developed a new office call Small Business Self-Employment Service that links to other entrepreneurship sites, provides information on a variety of technical assistance resources, as well as resources for writing business plans, financing, and other issues. These services are provided at no cost. Contact:

Small Business and Self-Employment Service
Job Accommodation Network
P.O. Box 6080
Morgantown, WV 26506
800-526-6234
Fax: 304-293-5407
www.jan.wvu.edu/SBSES

You can also learn about programs and activities in your state for people with disabilities who want to work by checking out {www.ssa.gov/work}. Also don't forget to check out the federal government's website {www.disability.gov} that lists all the government programs relating to disabilities.

You can be like Jim Bell:

Jim Bell was classified as disabled the same year he was downsized out of his job. He always dreamed of starting a home-based business, and began looking through Matthew's Free Money To Change Your Life book. He found the VESID (Vocational Educational Services for Individuals with Disabilities) program, which is part of the New York State Education Department. This is a special program to help disabled individuals start a business. After working with someone from VESID for a couple of months, Jim was awarded an $11,000 grant to help buy inventory, a computer, fax machine, and office supplies. He now sells golf equipment online at www.bellmerchandise.com and www.golferscaddy.com. This past year Jim was awarded the honor of being "Disabled Entrepreneur of the Year."

Terri Handshoe was the youngest member of her family, and was the only one who was deaf. In 1977, she dropped out of high school with no plans for the future. Sitting at home soon grew old, so she decided to work on getting her GED. She studied and passed, and a friend suggested that she contact the vocational rehabilitation office to see about furthering her education or vocational training. After working with her counselor, Terri attended a local college for a quarter. Her counselor was able to persuade Terri to transfer to Gallaudet University in Washington, DC, the world renowned school for students who are deaf. During school, vocational rehabilitation provided a much needed interpreter and books. "It was great! I had to study hard, but I didn't have to worry about those things," said Terri, referring to the assistance that she was provided that made getting her education so much easier. Terri went on to complete a graduate degree and is now a program coordinator for the deaf.

Sandy Smith lost her sight in high school because of an operation to treat a brain tumor. She worked with vocational rehabilitation upon her return to school. She liked office work and was very motivated to find a job that would put her new skills to good use. Sandy was hired as a switchboard operator for a major hotel. Because she couldn't see the blinking lights on the multi-line telephone keypad, Sandy couldn't determine which line was ringing. Vocational rehabilitation was able to custom design a plastic overlay which allows pins to pop out wherever a line is ringing. The device cost $3,000 which vocational rehabilitation paid for. They were also able to supply Sandy with a computer so she could put through calls on her own. Sandy is very satisfied with her job, and says, "If you don't try, you'll never know if you can do it."

The three best places where you should begin your search for information about services and money programs for the disabled and handicapped are:

- The Social Security Administration
- your State Office of Vocational Rehabilitation
- Client Assistance Programs

In this section, you'll find descriptions and listings of contacts for these three programs, along with several additional best places for self help and aid for handicapped or disabled individuals. Make sure to check out "Other Resources for Assistance for Women, Minorities, Veterans, and the Disabled" at the end of this chapter for more places to turn for help and information.

General Information Sources

Clearinghouse on Disability Information

Office of Special Education and Rehabilitation Services
U.S. Department of Education
Room 3132 Switzer Building
Washington, DC 20202-2524   202-205-8241
http://www.ed.gov/about/offices/list/osers/index.html
The clearinghouse responds to inquiries, provides referrals, and gives out information about services for individuals with disabilities at the national, state, and local levels. Free publications include:

- *Pocket Guide to Federal Help for Individuals with Disabilities*
- Brochure: *America needs us all, people with disabilities learning and earning.*
- *Clearinghouse on Disability Information* fact sheet

National Association of Rehabilitation Agencies

National Association of Rehabilitation Agencies
11250 Roger Baron Dr., Suite 8   703-437-4377
Reston, VA 20190-5202   Fax: 703-435-4390
http://www.naranet.org/
A private membership organization of rehabilitation agencies and professionals. Refer inquiries to members.

National Dissemination Center for Children with Disabilities

P.O. Box 1492   800-695-0285
Washington, DC 20013-1492 202-884-8200 (Voice/TDD)
http://www.nichcy.org/
The Clearinghouse is an information and referral center that provides information on disabilities and disability related issues, as well as referrals to a wide network of specialists from agencies and organizations across the nation. They focus on children and youth ages birth to 22. There is a great state resources section to help you find the right office.

National Rehabilitation Association

633 South Washington St.   703-836-0849 (TDD)
Alexandria, VA 22314   703-836-0850
http://www.nationalrehab.org
A private membership organization of professionals, vendors and suppliers of rehabilitation services, consumers and family members, students and professors. Refer inquiries to members.

ABLEDATA

ABLEDATA
8630 Fenton St., Suite 930   800-227-0216
Silver Spring, MD 20910   TTY: 301-608-8912
www.abledata.com
National database containing information on assistive technology and rehabilitation equipment for persons with disabilities. Contains more than 25,000 products from over 2,700 manufacturers and distributors. Publications include the *Assistive Technology Directory*; *ABLEDATA thesaurus*; *ADA Source book*; Fact sheets and computer guides.

Rehabilitation Information Hotline

National Rehabilitation Information
Center (NARIC)   800-346-2742
4200 Forbes Blvd.   301-459-5900
Suite 202   TTY: 301-495-5626
Lanham MD 20706   Fax: 301-562-2401
http://www.naric.com
The National Rehabilitation Information Center, a library and information center on disability and rehabilitation, collects and disseminates the results of federally funded research projects. NARIC also maintains a vertical file of pamphlets and fact sheets published by other organizations. NARIC has documents on all aspects of disability and rehabilitation including, physical disabilities, mental retardation, psychiatric disabilities, independent living, employment, law and public policy and assistive technology.

Their user services include the ABLEDATA database which describes thousands of assistive devices from eating utensils to wheelchairs. A printed listing of fewer than 50 products is $5; NARIC charges $10 for 51 to 100 products, and $5 for each additional hundred products. ABLEDATA also provides an information specialist to answer simple information requests and provide referrals immediately at no cost. 800-227-0216.

Free Money for Education and Job Training

If your disability stops you from being able to keep a full time job or from being able to competitively look for a job, your state's Office of Vocational Rehabilitation (OVR) can help. OVR can give you up to $6,000 each year for job training or education. You can use this grant money, which you do not have to repay, to cover any expenses related to your training or education, including tuition and fees, travel expenses, books, supplies, equipment (computers, motorized wheelchairs, etc.), food allowances, tutoring fees, photocopies, and so on. For more information, contact your state's Office of Vocational Rehabilitation listed at the end of this section.

Technical Assistance Project

Rehabilitation Engineering and Assertive Technology
Society of North America (RESNA)
1700 North Moore Street, #1540   703-524-6686
Arlington, VA 22209   TTY: 703-524-6639
www.resna.org   Fax: 703-524-6630
This project, funded by the U.S. Department of Education, has established an office in each state that provides information about how the latest technology can improve the lives of disabled persons. They also have an equipment loan program, which allows people to borrow new technology devices before purchasing them. They provide information on sources of funding for equipment and special loans. For more information contact your state office listed at the end of this section.

Training and FREE Computers for Disabled Entrepreneurs

The CURE Network, Inc.
P.O. Box 11092
Arlington, VA 22210   Phone/fax: 703-522-1921
www.cure.org
Disabled individuals completing the computer training program administered by the Council United for Recovery and Education (CURE) are given free computers upon graduation. The program is open to individuals with mental or physical disabilities or who are home-bound. CURE

operates a state-of-the-art computer training facility in Alexandria, VA; classes are offered in Windows98, Office97, the internet, desktop publishing, and other business-related software programs. In-home instruction is available for those unable to get to the computer center. Program graduates receive free 486 computers and continued support from CURE. The network is affiliated with the Virginia Computer Recycling Consortium, an organization that rebuilds donated used computers and redistributes them to individuals with disabilities who would otherwise be unable to afford to purchase new systems.

What To Do When OVR Benefits Are Denied

The first place to start when your state Office of Vocational Rehabilitation denies you handicap or disability benefits is your nearest state Client Assistance Program (CAP) office. CAP is a free information, referral, and legal service that helps disabled or handicapped individuals appeal a denial by OVR (or another agency). For a variety of reasons, it is not uncommon for a disabled individual to be turned down for services by OVR even when he/she is in fact eligible to receive them. It is often helpful to get a photocopy of section 103 of Chapter 34 of the *Code of Federal Regulations of the U.S. Department of Education* from your local or county library. These are the federal guidelines that each state OVR must follow when determining eligibility. This part of the code is only a few pages in length and can help you explain to the Client Assistance Program officer why you believe you are eligible even though you've been denied. CAP can take your appeal process from the first stages all the way to the U.S. Supreme Court if necessary ☐ and it won't cost you a penny.

It is also sometimes helpful to contact the state Office of Vocational Rehabilitation (OVR) itself and make the executive director aware of your circumstances. When it appears that progress via CAP is stalled or has been dragging on for months, it can also be very helpful to contact the regional commissioner of the Rehabilitation Services Administration (RSA), a branch of the Office of Special Education Programs of the U.S. Department of Education. RSA is responsible for overseeing and funding the state OVR agencies and is generally receptive to a short explanatory phone call and letter from those who believe they can clearly show that they have been wrongly denied OVR services. If they think you've got a case, they'll contact the OVR in question and make sure that they review your application more favorably.

To get in touch with a Rehabilitation Services Administration official, contact the U.S. Department of Education, Office of Special Education and Rehabilitative Services, RSA, Washington, DC 20202: 202-205-5465, and ask for the address and phone number of the regional commissioner for the ED-OSERS-RSA office serving your area, or check the website {http://www.ed.gov/about/offices/list/osers/index.html}.

Three Important Tips When Appealing an OVR Denial Of Services

1. If your state Office of Vocational Rehabilitation (OVR) denies you services based on other similar cases in which they have denied other prospective clients, it is important and effective to argue that such reasons for denial are not allowable under federal regulations. The 34 Code of Federal Regulations Chapter III section 361.31(b)(1) states clearly that the barriers faced by a disabled individual are unique to each individual and to each individual set of circumstances.

2. If you have previously been accepted by your state Office of Vocational Rehabilitation (OVR) as a client and you have gained employment but your disability has not improved and you lose employment due to no fault of your own, then OVR can again provide you with their services to help you regain employment. For more specifics, consult again the 34 Code of Federal Regulations, Chapter III and check under the *Post-Employment Services* sections and *Supported Employment* sections.

3. If you're currently receiving Social Security Disability (SSD), make sure that your state Office of Vocational Rehabilitation (OVR) and Client Assistance Program (CAP) are aware of this fact. Because of the more restrictive SSD definition of what it means to be disabled (compared to OVR), being on SSD almost always automatically qualifies an SSD recipient for OVR services. It is very difficult for OVR to argue otherwise.

More Free Legal Help for the Disabled

A national nonprofit law and policy center, the Disability Rights Education and Defense Fund (DREDF) can provide you with direct legal representation and act as co-counsel in cases of disability based discrimination. They also seek to educate legislators and policy makers on issues affecting the rights of people with disabilities. Contact: Disability Rights Education and Defense Fund (DREDF), 2212 Sixth St., Berkeley, CA 94710; 510-644-2555 (Voice/TDD); http://www.dredf.org.

Plan for Achieving Self- Support (PASS)

Many people with disabilities want to work, and you're probably one of them. But maybe you need to go back to school before you can get a job. Or, maybe you'd like to start your own business, but you don't have the money. Whatever your work goal may be, a PASS can help you reach it. A PASS lets you set aside money and/or other things you own to help you reach your goal. For example, you could set aside money to start a business or to go to school or to get training for a job.

Your goal must be a job that will produce sufficient earnings to reduce your dependency on Supplemental Security Income (SSI) payments. A PASS is meant to help you acquire those items, services or skills you need so that you can compete with able-bodied persons for an entry level job in a professional, business or trade environment. If you have graduated from college or a trade/technical school, we usually consider you capable of obtaining such a position without the assistance of a PASS. You can contact your local Social Security office to find out whether a PASS is appropriate for you.

How Will A Plan Affect My SSI Benefit?

Under regular SSI rules, your SSI benefit is reduced by the other income you have. But the income you set aside for a PASS doesn't reduce your SSI benefit. This means you can get a higher SSI benefit when you have a PASS. But you can't get more than the maximum SSI benefit for the state where you live.

Money you save or things you own, such as property or equipment, that you set aside for a PASS won't count against the resource limit of $2,000 (or $3,000 for a couple). Under regular SSI rules, you wouldn't be eligible for SSI if your resources are above $2,000. But with a plan, you may set aside some resources so you would be eligible.

Who Can Have A PASS?

You can, if:
- you want to work;
- you get SSI (or can qualify for SSI) because of blindness or a disability; or
- you have or expect to receive income (other than SSI) and/or resources to set aside toward a work goal.

What Kinds Of Expenses Can A Plan Help Pay For?

A plan may be used to pay for a variety of expenses that are necessary to help you reach your work goal.

For example, your plan may help you save for:
- supplies to start a business;
- tuition, fees, books and supplies that are needed for school or training;
- employment services, such as payments for a job coach;
- attendant care or child care expenses;
- equipment and tools to do the job;
- transportation to and from work; or
- uniforms, special clothing and safety equipment.

These are only examples. Not all of these will apply to every plan. You might have other expenses depending on your goal.

How Will A Plan Affect Other Benefits I Get?

You should check with the agency that is responsible for those benefits to find out if the plan (and the extra SSI) might affect those benefits.

In many cases, income and resources set aside under a plan will not be counted for food stamps and housing assistance provided through the U.S. Department of Housing and Urban Development. But, it's important that you contact the particular agency to find out how your benefits will be affected.

For more information, ask Social Security for the booklet, *Working While Disabled-How We Can Help* (Publication No. 05--10095); {www.ssa.gov}.

Ticket To Work

Maximus Inc.
866-968-7842 (toll-free 866-YOUR-TICKET)
866-833-2967 (TTY)
www.ssa.gov/work

Ticket to Work is part of the new Work Incentives Improvement Act which increases your choice in obtaining rehabilitation and vocational services. It removes the barriers that require people with disabilities to choose between health care coverage and work. Most Social Security and Supplemental Security Income (SSI) disability beneficiaries will receive a "ticket" they may use to obtain vocational rehabilitation, employment or other support services from an approved provider of their choice to help them go to work and achieve their employment goals. This is voluntary program. Medicare coverage is extended for a period of time and states have the option of extending Medicaid coverage. Maximus Inc. is managing the program for Social Security.

State Vocational Rehabilitation Offices

Alabama
Steven Shivers, Commissioner,· Alabama Department of Rehabilitation Services, 2129 East South Boulevard, P.O. Box 11586, Montgomery, AL 36111-0586; 334-281-8780, 800-441-7607, TDD: 334-613-2249, Fax: 334-281-1973; {www. rehab.state.al.us}. Assistance offered:

- medical examinations and treatment
- psychological evaluation
- vocational evaluation, training and placement
- disability counseling
- assistive devices
- transportation
- occupational equipment
- rehabilitation engineering
- postemployment services
- independent living training
- student services
- Hemophilia Program
- OASIS Project (Older Alabamians System of Information and Services)
- in home care
- financial assistance
- Business Enterprise Program (BEP)
- supported employment
- deaf services

Alaska
Duane French, Director, Division of Vocational Rehabilitation, 801 West 10th St., Suite A, Juneau, AK 99801-1894; 907-465-2814, 800-478-2815; Email: {stevie.raleigh@educ.state.ak.us}, {http://www.labor.state.ak.us/dvr/home.htm}. Assistance offered:

- medical and psychiatric examinations
- vocational evaluation, training, and placement
- medical treatment
- adaptive equipment
- transportation
- postemployment counseling

American Samoa
Peter P. Galea'i, Director, Division of Vocational Rehabilitation, Dept. Of Human Resources, American Samoa Government, Pago Pago, AS 96799, 011684-699-1371, {www.ipacific.com/samoa/samoa.html}

Arizona
Fred "Skip" Bingham, Administrator, Arizona Rehabilitation Services Administration, 1789 West Jefferson 2, NW, Phoenix, AZ 85007; 602-542-3651, 800-563-1221, TDD: 602-542-6049, Fax: 602-542-3778, Email: {mepps@mail.de.state.az.us}, {http://www.de.state.az.us/rsa}. Assistance offered:

- vocational evaluation, training, and evaluation
- independent living counseling
- Business Enterprise Program (BEP)
- deaf and Blind services
- communication devices
- adaptive equipment

Arkansas
John Wyvill, Director, Division of Vocational Rehabilitation, 1616 Brookwood Drive, Little Rock, AR 72203;, 501-296-1661, 800-285-7192, TDD: 501-296-1669, Fax: 501-296-1655, Email: {jcwyvill@ars.state.ar.us}, {http://www.arsinfo.org}. Assistance offered:

- individual and family counseling
- adaptive equipment
- in home care services
- vocational evaluation, training, and placement
- rehabilitation facilities

James C. Hudson, Director, Division of Services for the Blind, Dept. of Human Services, 522 Main Street, Little Rock, AR 72203; 501-682-0198, 800-960-9270, TTY: 501-682-0093, Fax: 501-682-0366; http://www.state.ar.us/dhs/dsb/index.html. Assistance offered:

- vocational training and placement
- medical diagnosis and treatment
- counseling on independent living
- personal adjustment counseling for family and children
- Vending Facility Program
- library materials
- radio reading service
- information referrals

California
Catherine Campisi, Director, Department of Rehabilitation, P.O. Box 944222, Sacramento, CA 95815; 916-263-8981, TTY: 916-263-7477, {http://www.doc.ca.gov/}. Assistance offered:

- medical and vocational evaluation
- medical treatment
- job training and placement
- transportation
- occupational licenses and equipment
- family services
- reader and interpreter services
- communication devices
- rehabilitation engineering
- adaptive equipment
- supported employment
- small business incentives
- postemployment services

Colorado
Diana Huerta, Director, Division of Vocational Rehabilitation, Dept. Of Social Services, 2211 West Evans, Bldg. B, Denver, Co 80223; 720-884-1234 (V/TDD), Fax: 720-884-1213, Email: {debbiepowell@state.co.us}, {http://www.cdhs.state.co.us/ods/dvr}. Assistance offered:

- vocational evaluation, training, and placement
- employer services
- rehabilitation engineering
- personal adjustment counseling
- Client Assistance Program (CAP)

Connecticut

Bureau of Rehabilitation Services, Department of Social Services, 25 Sigourney St., Hartford, CT 06106-5033, 800-842-4848, 860-424-4848; TDD: 860-424-4839, Fax: 860-424-4850, Email: {john.halliday@po.state.ct.us}, {http://www.brs.state.ct.us/}. Assistance offered:

- vocational counseling, training, and placement
- physical therapy
- adaptive technology
- psychotherapy
- academic training
- occupational tools and licenses
- architectural modifications to home and workplace
- rehabilitation employment
- supported employment
- transportation

Donna Balaski, Director, Board of Education and Services for the Blind, Vocational Rehabilitation Division, 184 Windsor Avenue, Windsor, CT 06095; 800-842-4510 (in CT), 860-602-4000, TTY: 860-602-4002, Fax: 860-602-4020, Email: {besb@po.state.ct.us}, {http://www.besb.state ct.us}. Assistance offered:

- Radio Information Service
- individual and family counseling
- mobility instruction
- vocational training and placement
- industries opportunities
- financial counseling
- legal benefits
- recreation
- follow up services
- low vision exams and treatment
- home management training
- communication devices
- information and referral

Delaware

Andrea Guest, Director, Division of Vocational Rehabilitation, P.O. Box 9969, 4425 N. Market Street, Wilmington, DE 19809-0969; 302-761-8275, TDD: 302-761-8336, Fax: 302-761-6611, Email: {director@dvr.state.de.us}, {http://www.delawareworks.com/dvr/welcome.htm}. Assistance offered:

- vocational training and placement
- independent living counseling
- adaptive equipment
- family counseling
- home management training
- transportation
- financial assistance
- physical therapy
- occupational tools and licenses

Harry B. Hill, Director, Division for the Visually Impaired, Biggs Building, Health & Social Services Campus, 1901 N. Dupont Highway, New Castle, DE 19720; 302-255-9800, Fax: 302-255-4441, {http://www.state.de.us/dhss/dvi/dvihome.htm}. Assistance offered:

- low vision services
- counseling
- education
- mobility instruction
- job training and placement
- deaf/blind services
- independent living training

- personal adjustment counseling
- optical aids
- preventive examinations
- information and referral
- communication devices

District of Columbia

D.C. Rehabilitation Services Administration, Dept. of Human Services, 801 East Building, 2700 Martin Luther King Ave., SE, Washington, DC 20032; 202-279-6002, 202-729-6014, http://dhs.dc.gov. Assistance offered:

- vocational evaluation, training, and placement
- adaptive equipment
- personal adjustment counseling
- physical therapy
- transportation
- postemployment services
- occupational tools and licenses
- small business assistance

Florida

Tamira Bibb Allen, Director, Division of Vocational Rehabilitation, Dept. Of Labor and Employment, Security, Building A, 2002 Old St. Augustine Road, Tallahassee, FL 32399-0696; 850-245-3399, Information & Referral line: 800-451-4327, {http://www.rehabworks.org/}. Assistance offered:

- vocational and medical evaluation
- financial assistance
- job training and placement
- work adjustment training
- in home care
- postemployment counseling
- supported employment
- determination of benefit eligibility

Craig Kiser, Director, Division of Blind Services, Department of Education, 2551 Executive Center Circle, Tallahassee, FL 32399; 800-342-1330, 800-342-1828 (in FL), 850-488-1330, Fax: 850-487-1804, {http://www.state.fl.us/dbs/}. Assistance offered:

- medical, psychological, and vocational evaluation
- counseling
- medical services
- mobility instruction
- job training and placement
- rehabilitation facilities
- communication skills and equipment
- family and children services
- in home instruction
- Bureau of Business Enterprises
- library services

Georgia

Peggy Rosser, Director, Division of Rehabilitation Services, Georgia Department of Human Resources, Suite 510 Sussex Place, 148 Andrew Young International Blvd., NE, Atlanta, GA 30303; 404-232-3910; Email: {Gradye@gomail.doas.state.ga.us}, {http://www.vocrehabga.org/}. Assistance offered:

- vocational rehabilitation programs for competitive employment and sheltered employment
- independent living counseling

- evaluate clients to determine eligibility for health care and disability benefits
- refer clients to appropriate nearby facilities for rehabilitation services

Guam

Nobert Ungacto, Director, Dept. Of Vocational Rehabilitation, Government of Guam, 122 Harmon Plaza, Room B201, Harmon Industrial Park, Guam 96911; 011-671-475-4646, {www.gov.gu/}.

Hawaii

Neil Shim, Administrator, Division of Vocational Rehabilitation & Services for the Blind, Dept. Of Human Services, Bishop Trust Bldg., 1000 Bishop St., Room 615, Honolulu, HI 96813; 808-586-5366, Fax: 808-586-5377, {http://www.state.hi.us/dhs/}. Assistance offered:

- optical aids
- personal adjustment counseling
- independent living training
- communication devices
- low vision services
- preventive eye care
- vocational evaluation, training and placement
- job site modification

Idaho

Barry J. Thompson, Administrator, Division of Vocational Rehabilitation, P.O. Box 83720, 650 West State Street, Room 150, Boise, ID 83720-0096; 208-334-3390, TDD: 208-327-7040, Fax: 208-334-5305, Email: {pyoung@idvr.state.id.us}, {http://www2.state.id.us/idvr/idvrhome.htm}. Assistance offered:

- vocational evaluation, training, and placement
- medical treatment
- assistive devices
- occupational tools and licenses
- Business and Industry Program
- specialized rehabilitation
- personal adjustment counseling
- independent living training
- kidney program
- transportation
- recreation programs
- attendant care
- communication aids
- family services
- information and referral
- housing
- health maintenance

Michael Graham, Director, Idaho Commission for the Blind, Division of Vocational Rehabilitation, P.O. Box 83720, 341 West Washington, Boise, ID 83720, 208-334-3220, 800-542-8688 (in ID), Fax: 208-334-2963, Email: {mstarkov@icbvi.state.id.us}, {http://www.icbvi.state.id.us}. Assistance offered:

- Business Enterprise Program
- radio reading and taping
- independent living counseling
- information and referral
- job training and placement
- financial assistance
- orientation and adjustment center

- adaptive equipment
- prevention programs
- academic training
- home instruction

Illinois

Robert E. Davis, State Director, Illinois Office Rehabilitation Services, 100 South Grand Ave., E, 3r^d Floor, Springfield, IL 62762, 217-785-0234, 800-843-6154, Fax: 217-558-4270, Email: {ors@dhs.state.il.us}, {http://www.state.il.us/agency/dhs}. Assistance offered:

- job training and placement
- educational assistance
- transportation
- independent living training
- in home care
- Illinois Children's School and Rehabilitation Center
- supported employment
- information and referral
- interpreter services
- personal adjustment counseling
- vending Facility Program
- Disability Determination Services

Indiana

Deputy Director, Department of Human Services, Vocational Rehabilitation Services, Room W453, 402 West Washington St., P.O. Box 7083, Indianapolis, IN 46207-7083; 800-545-7763 (IN only), 317-232-1319, TDD: 317-232-1427, {http://www.in.gov/fssa/}. Assistance offered:

- vocational evaluation, training and placement
- assistive devices
- rehabilitation engineering
- physical therapy
- information referral
- financial assistance
- transportation
- communication devices
- personal adjustment counseling
- independent living training

Linda Quarles, Deputy Director, Division of the Blind and Visually Impaired, Room W453, 402 W. Washington St., P.O. Box 7083, Indianapolis, IN 46207-7083; 317-232-1438; 877-241-8144; {www.state.in.us/fssa/servicedisabl/blind/index.html}.

Iowa

R. Creig Slayton, Director, Department for the Blind, 524 4th Street, Des Moines, IA 50309-2364; 515-281-1333, 800-362-2587 (IA only), TTY: 515-281-1355, {www.blind.state.ia.us}. Assistance offered:

- library services
- vocational evaluation, training and placement
- orientation and adjustment center
- independent living counseling
- Business Enterprises Program (BEP)
- adaptive equipment
- occupational tools
- registry of the blind
- information and referral
- communication training and equipment

Iowa Division of Vocational Rehabilitation Services, 510 East 12th Street, Des Moines, IA 50319, 515-281-4211 (V/TTY), 800-532-1486 (V/TTY); Email: {webmaster@ dvrs.state.ia.us}, {http://www.dvrs.state.ia.us}.

Kansas

Vocational Rehabilitation, Department of Social and Rehabilitation Services, 915 Harrison Street, 6th Floor, Docking State Office Building, Topeka, Kansas 66612; 785-296-5301, Fax: 785-296-2173, {http://www.srskansas.org}.

Kentucky

Mr. Sam Serraglio, Commissioner, Kentucky Department of Vocational Rehabilitation, 209 St. Clair St., Frankfort, KY 40601; 800-372-7172 (KY), 502-564-4440, Fax: 502-564-6742, {http://kydvr.state.ky.us}. Assistance offered:

- Assessment for determining eligibility and vocational rehabilitation needs
- Counseling and guidance
- Information and referral to other agencies
- Physical and mental restoration services
- Vocational and other training services
- Supported employment
- Transportation and other services necessary to participate fully in your rehabilitation program
- Personal assistance services
- Interpreter and note taking services
- Telecommunications, sensory, and other technological aids and devices
- Rehabilitation technology
- Job Placement and Job Retention Services
- Employment follow-up and postemployment services

Department for the Blind, P.O. Box 757, 209 St. Clair Street, Frankfort, KY 40602; 502-564-4754, 800-321-6668, TDD: 502-564-2929, Fax: 502-564-2951, {http://www.kyblind. state.ky.us}. Assistance offered:

- diagnosis and evaluation
- counseling
- medical treatment
- vocational training and placement
- room and board
- transportation
- reader services
- orientation and mobility training
- optical aids
- communication technology
- occupational licenses, tools and equipment
- postemployment services
- Business Enterprises Program (BEP)
- Industries for the Blind

Louisiana

Mary Nelson, Director, Rehabilitation Services, Department of Social Services, 8225 Florida Blvd., Baton Rouge, LA 70806; 225-925-4131, 800-737-2958, Fax: 225-925-4481, {www.dss.state.la.us/}. Assistance offered:

- vocational evaluation, training and placement
- assistive devices
- personal adjustment counseling
- independent living training
- in home care services
- deaf and blind services
- communication training
- transportation
- financial assistance
- occupational licenses and tools

Maine

Maine Bureau of Rehabilitation Services, 150 State House Station, Augusta, ME 04333, 207-624-5950, 800-698-4440, TTY: 888-755-0023, 207-624-5980, {www.state.me.us/ rehab}.

Maryland

Division of Vocational Rehabilitation, State Department of Education, 2301 Argonne Drive, Baltimore, MD 21218-1696; 410/554-9385, 888/554-0334, TTY: 410/554-9411, Fax: 410/554-9412, Email: {dors@msde.state.lib. md.us}, {www.dors.state.md.us/voc_rehab.html}. Assistance offered:

- physical therapy
- vocational evaluation, training, and rehabilitation
- personal adjustment counseling
- transportation
- financial assistance
- occupational licenses and equipment
- assistive devices
- psychological evaluations
- independent living training

Massachusetts

Rehabilitation Commission, Fort Point Place, 27-43 Wormwood Street, Boston, MA 02210-1616; 800-245-6543, 617-204-3600, Fax: 617-727-1354, {http://www.mass.gov/ mrc}. Assistance offered:

- head injury program
- home based employment
- adaptive housing
- injured workers program
- supported employment
- deaf services
- bilingual specialty services
- independent living center
- transportation
- home care assistance program
- personal care assistance
- disability determination
- library services
- job training and placement
- job site modification
- information and referral

Commission for the Blind, 88 Kingston St., Boston, MA 02111-2227; 617-727-5550, 800-392-6450 (in MA), TDD: 617-727-9063, {http://www.mass.gov.gov/mcb}. Assistance offered:

- talking book and radio reading services
- administer Medicaid
- low vision and hearing aids
- information referral
- individual and family counseling
- homemaker services
- mobility instruction
- home management training
- protective services, including arranging guardianship
- interpreter services
- elder blind services
- recreation, housing assistance, and advocacy
- services for multi-handicapped individuals

- vocational training and placement
- Ferguson Industries program

Michigan

Patrick Cannon, Director, Commission for the Blind, 201 N. Washington Square, P.O. Box 30652, Lansing, MI 48909; 517-373-3390, TDD: 517-373-4025, Fax: 517-355-5140, {http://www.michigan.gov/mdcd}. Assistance offered:

- vocational evaluation
- financial aid
- academic instruction
- postemployment services
- medical treatment
- transportation
- reader services
- occupational licenses and equipment
- interpreter services
- daily living costs assistance
- disability determination

Michigan Rehabilitation Services, Michigan Department of Career Development, P.O. Box 30010, Lansing, MI 48909, 517-241-0377, 800-605-6722, Fax: 513-373-0565, {http://www.michigan.gov/mdcd}.

Minnesota

Paul Bridges, Ed.D., Department of Employment and Economic Development, Rehabilitation Services Branch, 390 North Robert Street, St. Paul, MN 55101; 651-296-9981, 800-328-9095, 888-GET-JOBS, TTY: 651-296-3900, {http://www.dccd.state.mn.us}. Assistance offered:

- vocational evaluation, training, and placement
- personal adjustment counseling
- independent living training
- assistive devices
- transportation
- information referral
- postemployment services
- physical therapy

Richard C. Davis, Minnesota Department of Economic Security, State Services for the Blind, 2200 University Ave. W. #240, St. Paul, MN 55114-1840; 651-642-0500, TTY: 651-642-0506, 800-652-9000, Email: {Richard.Davis@state.mn.us}, {http://www.mnssb.org}. Assistance offered:

- personal adjustment counseling
- training in independent living
- job training, placement and retention
- assistive technologies
- rehabilitation engineering
- low vision services
- blind vendor program
- child development
- parent support
- communication equipment and aids, including transcription to tape or braille

Mississippi

Mississippi Department of Rehabilitation Services, 1281 Highway 51 North, Madison, MS 39110, P.O. Box 1698, Jackson, MS 39215, 601-853-5100, 800-443-1000, {www.mdrs.state.ms.us}.

Missouri

Ronald Vessell, Director, Missouri Division of Vocational Rehabilitation, 3024 Dupont Circle, Jefferson City, MO 65109; 573-751-3251, 573-751-0881, TTY: 877-222-8963, {http://vr.dese.mo.gov}. Assistance offered:

- medical examinations
- vocational evaluation, training, and placement
- health care
- assistive devices
- living expenses and transportation assistance
- occupational tools and licenses
- counseling in independent living
- Personal Care Assistance Program

Missouri Rehabilitation Services for the Blind, P.O. Box 88, Jefferson City, MO 65103-0088; 573-751-4249, 800-592-6004, Fax: 573-751-4984, Email: {mgiboney@mail.state.mo.us}, {http://www.dss.mo.gov/dfs/rehab/index.htm}. Assistance offered:

- diagnosis and evaluation
- physical restoration
- instruction in daily living
- vocational training, including college
- job placement
- adaptive technology
- rehabilitation facilities
- Business Enterprise Program (BEP)
- counseling for children, adults, and families
- vision screening
- resource referrals

Montana

Joe Matthews, Administrator, Dept. Of Social and Rehabilitation Services, Rehabilitation/Visual Services, 111 North Sanders, Helena, MT 59620; P.O. Box 4210, Helena, MT 59604-4210; 406-444-2590, 877-296-1197, TDD: 406-444-2590, Fax: 406-444-3632, {http://www.dphhs.state.mt.us/dsd/index.htm}. Assistance offered:

- vocational evaluation, training and placement
- work adjustment training
- supported and sheltered employment
- counseling and training in independent living
- resource referrals
- adaptive equipment
- housing assistance
- Native American Vocational Rehabilitation Projects
- low vision treatment
- financial assistance

Nebraska

Director, Frank C. Lloyd, Vocational Rehabilitation Services, 301 Centennial Mall South, P.O. Box 94987, Lincoln, NE 68509; 402-471-3644, 877-637-3422, Fax: 402-471-0788, {http://www.vocrehab.state.ne.us}. Assistance offered:

- vocational evaluation, training, and placement
- transportation
- medical treatment
- personal adjustment counseling
- financial assistance
- postemployment services

Cheryl Puff, Director, Services for Visually Impaired, Dept. Of Public Institutions, 4600 Valley Road, Suite 420, Lincoln,

NE 68510-4844; 402-471-2891, 877-809-2419; {www.ncbvi. state.ne.us/}. Assistance offered:

- training for independent living
- educational assistance
- vocational evaluation, training and placement
- occupational equipment
- small business enterprises program
- medical services
- advocacy services
- individual and family counseling
- consultation services for employers
- computer training
- peer support groups

Nevada

Maynard Yasmer, Administrator, Department of Employment, Training and Rehabilitation, Rehabilitation Division, Bureau of Vocational Rehabilitation, 505 E. King St., #501, Carson City, NV 89701-3704; 775-684-4040, Fax: 775-684-4186, {http://detr.state.nv.us/rehab/reh_index.htm}. Assistance offered:

- adaptive equipment
- physical and occupational therapy
- vocational training and placement
- occupational tools and licenses
- communication services and technology
- education for employers
- transportation
- counseling in independent living
- rehabilitation engineering
- resource referrals

New Hampshire

Paul K. Leather, Director, Division of Vocational Rehabilitation, 78 Regional Drive, Concord, NH 03301-9686; 603-271-3471, 800-299-1647, Email: {cfairneny@ ed.state.nh.us}, {www.ed.state.nh.us/}, Assistance offered:

- vocational evaluation, training, and placement
- independent living counseling
- physical and mental restoration
- assistive devices
- supported employment
- financial assistance
- postemployment services
- information and referral

New Jersey

Thomas G. Jennings, Director, 135 East State Street, P.O. Box 398, Trenton, NJ 08625-0398; 609-292-5987, TTY: 609-292-2919, Fax: 609-292-8347, Email: {dvradmin@ dol.state.nj.us}, {http://www.state.nj.us/labor/}. Assistance offered:

- medical and psychological evaluation
- vocational counseling, training, and placement
- adaptive equipment
- financial assistance with equipment and transportation

Jamie Casabianca-Hilton, Director, Commission for the Blind and Visually Impaired, Dept. of Human Services, 153 Halsey Street, 6th Floor, P.O. Box 47017, Newark, NJ 07102; 973-648-2324, Email: {ddaniels@dhs. state. nj.us}, {http://www.state.nj.us/humanservices/cbvi/index.html}. Assistance offered:

- childcare
- individual and family counseling
- tutoring
- vocational evaluation, training, and placement
- high school and college counseling
- business enterprise programs
- instruction in independent living, including housing assistance
- eye health screenings and education
- community benefits for the disabled

New Mexico

Terry Brigance, Director, Division of Vocational Rehabilitation, 435 St. Michael's Drive, Building D, Santa Fe, NM 87505; 505-954-8500, 800-224-7005, Fax: 505-954-8562, Email: {SKelley@state.nm.us}, {http://www.dvrgets jobs.com}. Assistance offered:

- vocational evaluation, training, and placement
- academic training
- work adjustment training
- adaptive equipment
- job site modification
- counseling
- postemployment services
- physical and psychological examination
- independent living counseling
- medical services
- occupational supplies
- meal allowance and transportation
- job coach assistance
- supported employment
- job seeking skills training
- postemployment counseling

New York

New York State Education Department, Vocational and Educational Services for Individuals with Disabilities, One Commerce Plaza, Room 1624, Albany, NY 12234; 800-222-JOBS; {www.vesid.nysed.gov}.

John A. Johnson, Commissioner, Dept. Of Social Services, Commission for the Blind and Visually Handicapped, 40 North Pearl Street, Albany, NY 11243--0001; 518-473-1675, TDD: 518-473-1698, Fax: 518-473-9255, Email: {CBVH@ dfa.state.ny.us}, {http://www.ocfs.state.ny.us/main/cbvh}. Assistance offered:

- children services
- independent living training
- communications training and equipment
- mobility instruction
- vocational evaluation, training, and placement
- low vision aids
- medical exams
- counseling
- vending facility program
- academic instruction
- information and referral

North Carolina

George McCoy, Director, Division of Vocational Rehabilitation Services, 2801 Mail Service Center, Raleigh, NC 27699; 919-855-3500, Fax: 919-733-7968, {http://dvr. dhhs.state.nc.us}. Assistance offered:

- vocational evaluation, training, and placement
- assistive devices
- personal adjustment counseling
- independent living training
- financial assistance
- transportation

John DeLuca, Director, Division of Services for the Blind, 309 Ashe Ave., Raleigh, NC 27606; 919-733-9822, Fax: 919-733-9769, Email: {johndeluca@ ncmail.net}, {http://www.dhhs.state.nc/dsb}. Assistance offered:

- vision screening
- eye health education
- low vision services
- job evaluation, training, and placement
- small business assistance
- individual and family adjustment counseling
- housing and home improvement services
- home management training
- consultation and training for preschool visually impaired children and their families
- communication resources
- financial assistance

North Dakota
Gene Hysjulien, Director, N.D. Disability Services Division, Vocational Rehabilitation, 600 South 2nd Street, Suite 1B, Bismarck, ND 58504; 701-328-8950, 800-472-2622, TDD: 701-328-8968, Fax: 701-328-8969, Email: {dhsds@ state.nd.us}, {http://www.state.nd.us/humanservicesservices/disabilities/vr/}. Assistance offered:

- diagnosis and evaluation
- vocational training and placement, including resume writing and interviewing workshops
- physical and mental retardation
- trade school/college training
- transportation
- rehabilitation engineering services
- postemployment services
- adaptive equipment

Ohio
John M. Connelly, Administrator, Ohio Rehabilitation Services Commission, 400 E. Campus View Blvd., Columbus, OH 43235-4604; 800-282-4536 (OH only), 614-438-1200, Fax: 614-438-1257, {http://www.state.oh.us/rsc/}. Assistance offered:

- determination of benefit eligibility
- vocational evaluation, training, and placement
- rehabilitation engineering
- medical and psychological evaluation
- personal care assistance
- independent living counseling
- community centers for the deaf
- peer counseling
- supported employment
- business enterprise programs
- head injury program
- communication technology and resources

Oklahoma
Linda Parker, Director, Dept. of Rehabilitation Services, 3535 NW 58th St., Suite 500, Oklahoma City, OK 73112-4815; 405-951-3400, 800-845-8476, Fax: 405-951-3529,

Email: {drspiowm@onenet.net}, {http://www.okrehab. org}. Assistance offered:

- medical examinations and treatment
- assistive devices
- job training and placement
- interpreter services
- maintenance and transportation
- occupational licenses and equipment
- initial inventory for small businesses
- rehabilitation engineering
- library services
- communication equipment
- independent living training
- supported employment
- work-study program
- school for the deaf
- school for the blind

Oregon
Gary K. Weeks, Director, Vocational Rehabilitation Division, Administration Office, 500 Summer Street NE, Salem, OR 97310-1012; 503-945-5880, TTY: 503-945-5894, Fax: 503-945-8991, Email: {dhr.info@state.or.us}, {http://www.dhs.state.ir.us/vr}. Assistance offered:

- vocational evaluation, training (including on-the-job), and placement
- education
- books, supplies, or tools
- transportation
- medical treatment
- adaptive equipment
- postemployment services
- independent living counseling
- Disability Determination Services (DDS)

Charles Young, Administrator, Commission for the Blind, 535 SE 12th Avenue, Portland, OR 97214; 503-731-3221, 888-202-5463, Email: {ocbmail@state.or.us}, {www.cfb. state.or.us}. Assistance offered:

- mobility instruction
- alternative communication skills and technology
- counseling on independent living
- optical and environmental aids
- individual, group, and family counseling
- employment counseling, training, and placement

Pennsylvania
Susan L. Aldrete, Executive Director, Office of Vocational Rehabilitation, Labor & Industry Building, 1521 N. 6th St., Harrisburg, PA 17102; 717-787-5244, 800-257-4232, TTY: 800-233-3008, Email: {ovr@dli.state.pa.us}, {www.dli. state.pa.us/}. Assistance offered:

- medical, psychological, and audiological exams
- vocational evaluation, training, and placement
- academic instruction
- counseling
- adaptive equipment
- occupational and physical therapy
- independent living training
- transportation
- occupational licenses and tools
- home and auto modifications
- attendant care
- communication devices

Rose Putric, Acting Director, Bureau of Blindness & Visual Services, Dept. of Labor and Industry, 1521 N. 6th St., Harrisburg, PA 17102; 717-787-6176, {http://www. dli.state.pa.us/}. Assistance offered:

- optical aids
- low vision services
- communication devices and training
- transportation
- personal adjustment counseling
- vocational evaluation, training and placement

Rhode Island

Raymond A. Carroll, Administrator, Office of Vocational Rehabilitation Services, Department of Human Services, 40 Fountain St., Providence, RI 02908; 800-752-8088, ext. 2300, 401-421-7005, TDD: 401-421-7016, Fax: 401-421-9259, Email: {rcarroll@ors.state.ri.us}, {www.ors.ri.gov}. Assistance offered:

- optical aids
- low vision services
- transportation
- personal adjustment counseling
- communication training
- vocational and medical evaluation
- job training and placement
- information referral

South Carolina

South Carolina Vocational Rehabilitation Department, 1410 Boston Ave., P.O. Box 15, West Columbia, SC 29171-0015, 803-896-6500, TDD: 803-896-6635, Fax: 803-896-6529, Email: {scvrd@rehabnet.work.org}, {http://www.scvrd.net}.

South Dakota

Grady Kickul, Director, Division of Rehabilitation Services, East Highway 34, Hillsview Plaza, c/o 500 East Capitol Avenue, Pierre, SD 57501; 605-773-3195, Fax: 605-773-5483, Email: {infors@dhs.state.sd.us}, {http://www.state.sd.us/dhs/drs/}. Assistance offered:

- vocational and medical diagnosis
- family and individual personal adjustment counseling
- physical restoration through treatment and/or hospitalization
- orthotic and prosthetic devices
- job training and placement
- occupational licenses, tools, and equipment
- postemployment services
- transportation and financial assistance

Gaye Mattke, Director, Division of Service to the Blind and Visually Impaired, Hillsview Plaza, E. Hwy 34, c/o 500 East Capitol, Pierre, SD 57501-5070; 605-773-4644, Fax: 605-773-5483, Email: {infosbvi@dhs. state.sd.us}, {http://www. state.sd.us/dhs/sbvi}. Assistance offered:

- orientation and mobility counseling
- home management training and equipment
- communication skills training
- specialized library and radio reading services
- optical aids
- training for health care professionals and employers

Tennessee

Tennessee Division of Rehabilitation Services, 400 Deadrick St., Nashville, TN 78248, 615-313-4700, TTY: 800-270-1349, Fax: 615-741-4165, {http://www.state.tn.us/humanserv/}

Texas

Vernon M. Arrell, Commissioner, Texas Rehabilitation Commission, 4900 North Lamar Blvd, Austin, TX 78751; 800-628-5115, 512-424-4410, TDD: 512-424-4417, {www.rehab.state.tx.us/}. Assistance offered:

- vocational evaluation, training, and placement
- personal adjustment counseling
- independent living training
- physical therapy
- information referral

Terry Murphy, Executive Director, Texas Commission for the Blind, 4800 North Lamar, Austin, TX 78756-3175; 512-459-2500, Voice/TDD: 800-252-5204, Fax: 512-459-2685, {www.tcb.state.tx.us/}. Assistance offered:

- orientation and mobility instruction
- home management training
- communication skills and equipment
- occupational therapy
- low vision services
- college prep
- therapeutic recreation
- independent living counseling
- medical/health management
- optical aids
- vocational evaluation, training, and placement
- Business Enterprises Program (BEP)
- bilingual services

Utah

Blaine Petersen, Executive Director, Vocational Rehabilitation Services, 250 East 500 South, Salt Lake City, UT 84111; 801-538-7530, 800-473-7530, Fax: 801-538-7522, {http://www.usor.utah.gov}. Assistance offered:

- vocational evaluation, training, and placement
- personal adjustment counseling
- medical treatment
- psychotherapy
- physical and occupational therapy
- assistive devices
- academic instruction
- transportation
- occupational tools and licenses
- interpreter services
- postemployment services
  - information and referral

Vermont

Diane P. Dalmasse, Director, Division of Vocational Rehabilitation, 103 South Main Street, Waterbury, VT 05671-2303; 802-241-2186, 866-879-6757; {http://www.vocrehabvermont.org}. Assistance offered:

- vocational evaluation and placement
- transportation
- interpreter services
- adaptive equipment

- books, supplies, and tools
- financial support
- occupational and personal adjustment services
- supported employment

Division for the Blind and Visually Impaired, 103 S. Main St., Waterbury, VT 05671-2304; 802-241-2210, Fax: 802-241-3359, Email: {fred@dad.state.vt.us}, {www.dad.state.vt.us/dbvi}. Assistance offered:

- physical restoration
- adaptive aids
- vocational aassessment and training
- optical aids
- education
- personal adjustment through counseling
- job placement
- researching available financial benefits

Virgin Islands

Caterine Mall, Administrator, Division of Disabilities & Rehabilitation Services, Dept. Of Human Services, 1303 Hospital Road, St. Thomas, VI 00802; 340-774-0930, Email: {humanservices@usvi.org}, {http://www.usvi.org/humanservices}.

Virginia

Joseph Ashley, Director, Virginia Department of Rehabilitation Services, 8004 Franklin Farms Drive, P.O. Box K-300, Richmond, VA 23288; 800-552-5019, 804-662-7000, TTY: 800-464-9950, Fax: 804-662-9533, Email: {DRS@drs.state.va.us}, {http://www.vadrs.org/}. Assistance offered:

- physical, psychological, and vocational evaluation
- counseling
- restoration services
- job training and placement
- transportation
- interpreter services
- telecommunication aids
- occupational licenses and equipment
- supported employment
- postemployment services
- Long-Term Mentally Ill Program
- school-to-work transition programs
- personal assistance
- assistive devices
- independent living services
- Transitional Living Center

W. Roy Grizzard, Jr., Commissioner, Dept. For the Visually Handicapped, Commonwealth of Virginia, 397 Azalea Avenue, Richmond, VA 23227; 804-371-3140, 800-622-2155, {http://www.vdbvi.org}. Assistance offered:

- deaf-blind services
- independent living counseling
- information and referral
- low vision examinations and training
- determine eligibility for financial assistance
- youth programs
- instructional material center
- transportation
- medical, psychological, and vocational evaluation
- job training and placement
- medical treatment
- library services

- rehabilitation center
- small business assistance

Washington

Jeanne Munro, Director, Division of Vocational Rehabilitation, Dept. Of Social & Health Services, P.O. Box 45340, Olympia WA 98504; 612 Woodland Sq. Loop SE, Lacey, WA 98503-1044;, 800-637-5627, 360-438-8000, Fax: 360-438-8007, {http://www1.dshs.wa.gov/dvr}. Assistance offered:

- school-to-work transition program
- on-the-job training
- job placement
- supported employment
- independent living counseling
- attendant care
- assistive technology
- family counseling
- transportation
- medical treatment
- occupational supplies
- postemployment services

Bill Palmer, Acting Director, Dept. Of Services for the Blind, 402 Legion Way, SE, Suite 100, P.O. Box 40933, Olympia, WA 98504-0933; 360-586-1224, 800-552-7103, TDD: 360-586-6437, Fax: 360-586-7627, {www.dsb.wa.gov}.

- vocational evaluation, training and placement
- Business Enterprise Program (BEP)
- training center for independent living
- coordination of community and educational resources for adults and children
- in home training for the elderly
- recreation program

West Virginia

Janice Holland, Director, West Virginia Department of Education and the Arts, Division of Rehabilitation Services, State Capitol, P. O. Box 50890, Charleston, WV 25305-0890; 800-642-8207, 304-766-4600, Fax: 304-766-4690, Email: {penneyh@mail.drs.state.wv.us}, {http://www.wvdrs.org}. Assistance offered:

- vocational evaluation, training, and placement
- personal adjustment counseling
- communication devices
- physical, occupational, speech, and hearing therapy
- rehabilitation hospital
- low vision services
- medical treatment
- remedial education
- driver education
- counseling
- information and referral
- crisis intervention
- student financial aid

Wisconsin

Tom Dixon, Administrator, Division of Vocational Rehabilitation, 2917 International Lane, Suite 300, P.O. Box 7852, Madison, WI 53707-7852; 800-442-3477, 608-243-5600, TTY: 608-243-5601, Fax: 608-243-5680 or 608-243-5681, {http://www.dwd.state.wi.us/dvr}. Assistance offered:

- medical, psychological and vocational evaluation
- counseling
- job placement
- job training
- transportation
- job seeking skills
- job site modification
- technological aids and devices
- small business opportunities
- home based business development and marketing assistance
- occupational licenses and equipment
- independent living services
- training and education in approved schools
- cost of living benefits

Wyoming

Gary W. Child, Administrator, Division of Vocational Rehabilitation, Department of Employment, 1100 Herschler Building, Cheyenne, WY 82002; 307-777-7389, {http://wyomingworkforce.org}. Assistance offered:

- evaluation of rehabilitation potential
- individual and family personal adjustment counseling
- information referrals
- physical and mental restoration
- job training and placement
- financial assistance
- communication aids and training
- transportation
- occupational licenses, tools, and equipment
- Business Enterprise Program (BEP)
- attendant services
- postemployment services

State Client Assistance Program (CAP)

The first place to start when your state Office of Vocational Rehabilitation denies your handicap or disability benefits is your nearest state Client Assistance Program (CAP) office. CAP is a free information, referral, and legal service that helps disabled or handicapped individuals appeal a denial by OVR (or other agency). CAP can take your appeal process from the first stages all the way to the U.S. Supreme Court if necessary — and it won't cost you a penny.

A CAP Specialist can help in many ways by:
- Providing assistance and advocacy services to help you resolve any problems you may have in applying for or receiving rehabilitation services;
- Explaining your rights and your responsibilities throughout the rehabilitation process;
- Helping you to communicate your concerns to DORS staff;
- Giving you accurate information on rehabilitation programs and services;
- Explaining DORS policies and procedures to you;
- Helping you when a service has been denied or when you are not satisfied with a service provided;
- Providing legal services when necessary to represent you in a formal hearing; and
- Providing information about your employment rights under the Americans With Disabilities Act.

Alabama
Jerry Norsworthy, Director
Client Assistance Program
2125 East South Boulevard
Montgomery, AL 361116-2454
334-281-2276
In-State Toll Free: 800-228-3231
Email: sacap@hotmail.com
http://www.clik.to/SACAP

Alaska
Pam Stratton, Director
Client Assistance Program
2900 Boniface Parkway, #100
Anchorage, AK 99504-3195
907-333-2211
800-478-0047
Fax: 907-333-1186
Email: akcap@alaska.com
http://home.gci.net/~alaskacap/

American Samoa
Hellene F. Stanley, Director
Client Assistance Program
P. O. Box 3937
Pago Pago, American Samoa 96799
011-684-633-2441
Fax: 011-684-633-7286
Email: opad@samoatelco.com

Arizona
Arizona Center for Disability Law
100 N. Stone Ave., Suite 305
Tucson, AZ 85701
520-327-9547 (V/TTY)
800-922-1447 (V/TTY)
Fax: 520-884-0992
Emaiol: center@acdl.com
http://www.acdl.com

Arkansas
Eddie Miller, Director
Client Assistance Program
Disability Rights Center, Inc.
Evergreen Place, Suite 201
1100 North University
Little Rock, AR 72207
501-296-1775
800-482-1174
Fax: 501-296-1779
Email: panda@advocacyservices.org
www.arkdisabilityrights.org

California
Sheila Conlen-Mentkowski, Director
Client Assistance Program
2000 Evergreen Street, 2nd Floor
Sacramento, CA 95815
916-263-8981
TTY: 916-263-7477

800-952-5544
Fax: 916-263-7464
Email:
smentkow@rehab.cahwnet.gov
www.dor.ca.gov

Colorado
Jeff Peterson, Director
Client Assistance Program
The Legal Center
455 Sherman Street
Suite 130
Denver, CO 80203
303-722-0300
800-288-1376
Fax: 303-722-0720
Email: tlcmail@thelegalcenter.org
http://www.thelegalcenter.org

Connecticut
Susan Werboff, Director
Client Assistance Program
Office of P&A for Persons with
Disabilities
60B Weston Street
Hartford, CT 06120-1551
860-297-4300
860-566-2102 (TDD)
800-842-7303 (statewide)
Fax: 860-566-8714

Email: hn2571@handsnet.org
www.state.ct.us/opapd

Delaware
Theresa Gallagher, Director
Client Assistance Program
United Cerebral Palsy, Inc.
254 East Camden-Wyoming Avenue
Camden, DE 19934
302-698-9336
800-640-9336
Fax: 302-698-9338
Email: capucp@magpage.com

District of Columbia
Joseph Cooney, Director
Client Assistance Program
University Legal Services
220 I Street, NE, Suite 130
Washington, DC 20002
202-547-0198
Fax: 202-547-2662
Email: jcooney@uls-dc.com
www.depanda.org

Florida
Ann Robinson, CAP Program
Advocacy Center for Persons with
Disabilities
2671 Executive Center, Circle West
Webster Building, Suite 100
Tallahassee, FL 32301-5092
Phone: 850-488-9071
800-342-0823
800-346-4127 (TDD)
Fax: 850-488-8640
www.advocacycenter.org

Georgia
Charles Martin, Director
Client Assistance Program
123 N. McDonough
Decartur, GA 30030
404-373-2040
800-822-9727
Fax: 404-373-4110
Email: GaCAPDirector@
theOmbudsman.com
www.theOmbudsman.com/CAP/

Guam
Fidela Limtiacho
President of the Board
Client Assistance Program
Parent Agencies Network
P.O. Box 23474
GMF, Guam 96921
671-649-1948
Fax: 671-472-2568

Hawaii
Executive Director
Client Assistance Program
Protection & Advocacy Agency
900 Fort St. Mall, Suite 1040
Honolulu, HI 96814
808-949-2922
800-882-1057
Fax: 808-949-2928

Email: pahi@pixi.com
www.hawaiidisabilityrights.org

Idaho
Shawn DeLoyola, Director
Client Assistance Program
Co-Ad, Inc.
4477 Emerald, Suite B-100
Boise, ID 83706
208-336-5353
866-262-3462
Fax: 208-336-5396
Email: coadinc@mcleodusa.net
http://users.moscow.com/co-ad

Illinois
Cynthia Grothaus, Director
Client Assistance Program
100 N. First Street, 1st Floor
Springfield, IL 62702
217-782-5374
800-641-3929
Fax: 217-524-1790
www.dhs.state.il.us/ors/cap/

Indiana
Amy Ames
Client Assistance Program
Indiana Protection and Advocacy
Services
4701 N. Keystone Ave., Suite 222
Indianapolis, IN 46204
317-722-5555
800-622-4845
Fax: 317-722-5564
Email: tgallagher@ipas.state.in.us
http://www.in.gov/ipas/

Iowa
Harlietta Helland, Director
Client Assistance Program
Division on Persons with Disabilities
Lucas State Office Building
Des Moines, IA 50319
515-281-3957
800-652-4298
Fax: 515-242-6119
Email:
dhr.disabilities@dhr.state.ia.us
http://www.state.ia.us/government/d
hr/pd/pdfs/DisabilityRightsGuide.pdf

Kansas
Mary Reyer, Director
Client Assistance Program
3640 SW Topeka Blvd., Suite 150
Topeka, KS 66611
785-266-8193
800-432-2326
Fax: 785-266-8574
Email: mreyer5175@aol.com
http://www.srskansas.org/rehab/text/
CAP.htm

Kentucky
Gerry Gordon-Brown, Consumer
Advocate
Client Assistance Program
209 St. Clair, 5th Floor

Frankfort, KY 40601
Phone: 502-564-8035
800-633-6283
Fax: 502-564-2951
Email:
dianehigh@uky.campus.mci.net
http://kydvr.state.ky.us/index.htm

Louisiana
Susan Howard, CAP Director
Client Assistance Program
Advocacy Center for the Elderly and
Disabled
225 Baronne, Suite 2112
New Orleans, LA 70112-1724
Phone: 504-522-2337
800-960-7705
Fax: 504-522-5507
Email: simplo@advocacyLA.org
http://www.advocacyla.org

Maine
Steve Beam, Director
Client Assistance Program
CARES, Inc.
4-C Winter Street
August, ME 04330
Phone: 207-622-7055
800-773-7055
Fax: 207-621-1869
Email: capsite@aol.com
http://www.caresinc.org

Maryland
Peggy Dew, Director
Client Assistance Program
Maryland Rehabilitation Center
Division of Rehabilitation Services
2301 Argonne Drive
Baltimore, MD 21208
410-554-9361
800-638-6243
Fax: 410-554-9362
Email: cap@dors.state.md.us
http://www.dors.state.md.us/services
/ client_assist.htm

Massachusetts
Barbara Lybarger
Client Assistance Program
Massachusetts Office on Disability
One Ashburton Place, Room 1305
Boston, MA 02108
617-727-7440
800-322-2020
Fax: 617-727-0965
Email: blybarger@modi.state.ma.us
www.mass.gov/mof

Michigan
Amy Maes, Director
Client Assistance Program
Michigan P&A Service
106 West Allegan
Suite 300
Lansing, MI 48933
517-487-1755
CAP only: 800-288-5923
Fax: 517-487-0827

Email: ebauer@mpas.org
www.mpas.org

Minnesota

Pamela Hoopes, Director
Client Assistance Program
Minnesota Disability Law Center
430 First Avenue North, Suite 300
Minneapolis, MN 55401-1780
612-332-1441
800-292-4150
Fax: 612-334-5755
Email hn0518@handsnet.org
http://www.mnlegalservices.org/

Mississippi

Presley Posey, Director
Client Assistance Program
3226 N. State Street
P.O. Box 4958
Jackson, MS 39296
601-362-2585
Email: pposey8803@aol.com

Missouri

Cecilia Callahan, Director of
Advocacy
Client Assistance Project
Missouri P&A Services
925 S. Country Club Drive, Unit B-1
Jefferson City, MO 65109
573-893-3333
800-392-8667
Fax: 573-893-4231
Email: mopasjc@socket.net
www.moadvocacy.org

Montana

Lynn Wislow, Director
Client Assistance Project
Montana Advocacy Program
316 N. Park, Room 211
P.O. Box 1680
Helena, MT 59624
406-449-2344
800-245-4743
800-245-4743
Fax: 406-444-0261
Email: advocate@mt.net
http://www.mtadv.org

Nebraska

Victoria L. Rasmussen, Director
Client Assistance Program
Division of Rehabilitation Services
Nebraska Department of Education
301 Centennial Mall South
Lincoln, NE 68509
402-471-3656
800-742-7594
Fax: 402-471-0117
Email: Vicki_r@nde4.nde.state.ne.us
http://www.cap.state.ne.us/

Nevada

William E. Bauer, Director
Client Assistance Program
505 East King St.
Carson City, NV 89701-3705

775-688-1440
800-633-9879
Fax: 775-688-1627
Email: detrcap@nvdetr.org
http://www.detr.state.nv.us/rehab/reh
_cap.htm

New Hampshire

Michael D. Jenkins
Executive Director
Client Assistance Program
Governor's Commission on
Disability
57 Regional Drive
Concord, NH 03301-9686
603-271-4175
800-852-3405
Fax: 603-271-2837
Email: bhagy@gov.state.nh.us
www.state.nh.us/disability/caphome
page.html

New Jersey

Ellen Lence, Director
Client Assistance Program
New Jersey P&A, Inc.
210 S. Broad Street, 3rd Floor
Trenton, NJ 08608
609-292-9742
800-922-7233
Fax: 609-777-0187
Email: advoca@njpanda.org
www.njpanda.org

New Mexico

Barna Dean, CAP Coordinator
Protection & Advocacy, Inc
1720 Louisiana Blvd., NE, Suite 204
Albuquerque, NM 87106
505-256-3100
800-432-4682
Fax: 505-256-3184
Email: nmpanda@nmprotection-
advocacy.com
www.nmpanda.org

New York

Gary O'Brien, Director
Client Assistance Program
NY Commission on Quality of Care
for the Mentally Disabled
401 State Street
Schenectody, NY 12305-2397
518-381-7098
800-624-4143 (TDD)
Fax: 518-381-7095
www.cqc.state.ny.us
michealp@cqc.state.ny.us

North Carolina

Kathy Brack, Director
Client Assistance Program
North Carolina Division of
Vocational Rehabilitation Services
2801 Mail Service Center
Raleigh, NC 27699-2801
919-855-3600
800-215-7227
Fax: 919-715-2456

Email: kbrack@dhr.state.nc.us
http://dvr.dhhs.state.nc.us/DVR/CAP
/ caphome.htm

North Dakota

Teresa Larsen, Director
Client Assistance Program
600 South 2nd Street, Suite 1B
Bismarck, ND 58504-5729
701-328-8964
800-207-6122
Fax: 701-328-8969
Email: panda@state.nd.us
http://www.state.nd.us/cap/

N. Marianas Islands

Client Assistance Program
Northern Marianas
Protection and Advocacy System,
Inc.
P.O. Box 3529 C.K.
Saipan, MP 96950
011-670-235-7274/3
Fax: 011-670-235-7275
Email: lbarcinasp&a@saipan.com
http://www.saipan.com/gov/branches
/ovr/ service.htm

Ohio

Caroline Knight, Director
Client Assistance Program
Ohio Legal Rights Service
8 East Long Street, 5th Floor
Columbus, OH 43215
614-466-7264
800-282-9181
Fax: 614-644-1888
Email: cknight@mail.olrs.ohio.gov
http://drs.ohio.gov

Oklahoma

Helen Kutz, Director
Client Assistance Program
Oklahoma Office of Handicapped
Concerns
2712 Villa Prom
Oklahoma City, OK 73107
405-521-3756
800-522-8224
Fax: 405-943-7550
Email: cap@ohc.state.ok.us
www.ohc.state.ok.us/cap

Oregon

Barbara Fields, Director
Client Assistance Program
Oregon Advocacy Center
620 W. Fifth Ave., 5th Floor
Portland, OR 97204-1428
503-243-2081
TTY: 503-323-9161
800-452-1694
TTY: 800-556-5351
Email: welcome@oradvocacy.org
http://www.oradvocacy.org

Pennsylvania

Stephen Pennington
Executive Director

Client Assistance Program
Center for Disability Law & Policy
1617 J.F.K. Blvd.
Suite 800
Philadelphia, PA 19103
215-557-7112
888-745-2357
Fax: 215-557-7602
Email: capcdkt@trfn.clpgh.org
http://www.equalemployment.org/cap.html

Puerto Rico
Enrique Rodriguez Otero, Director
Client Assistance Program
Office of the Governor
Ombudsman for the Disabled
P. O. Box 41309
San Juan, PR 00902-4234
787-725-2333
TTY: 787-725-4014
800-981-4125
Fax: 787-721-2455
Email: erodriguez@oppi.gobierno.pr
http://www.oppi.prstar.net

Republic of Palau
Client Assistance Program
Bureau of Public Health
Ministry of Health
P.O. Box 6027
Koror, Republic of Palau 96940
011-680-488-2813
Fax: 011-680-488-1211
Email phpa@palaunet.com

Rhode Island
Raymond Bandusky, Director
Client Assistance Program
Rhode Island Disability Law Center
Inc.
151 Broadway
Providence, RI 02903
401-831-3150
401-831-5335 (TDD)
800-733-5332
Fax: 401-274-5568
Email: hn7384@handsnet.org
http://ridlc.org/RIDLC/ridlc.html

South Carolina
Larry Barker, Director
Client Assistance Program
Office of the Governor
Division of Ombudsman and Citizen
Services
1205 Pendleton St.
Columbia, SC 29205
803-734-0285
800-868-0040
TDD: 803-734-1147
Fax: 803-734-0546
Email: mbutler@govoepp.state.sc.us
http://www.govoepp.state.sc.us/cap

South Dakota
Nancy Schade, Director
Client Assistance Program

South Dakota Advocacy Services
221 South Central Avenue
Pierre, SD 57501
605-224-8294
800-658-4782
Fax: 605-224-5125
Email:sdas@sdadvocacy.com
www.sdadvocacy.com

Tennessee
Dann Suggs, Director
Client Assistance Program
Tennessee P&A, Inc.
P. O. Box 121257
Nashville, TN 37212
615-298-1080
TTY: 615-298-2471
800-342-1660
Fax: 615-298-2046
Email: shirleys@tpainc.org
www.tpainc.org

Texas
Judy Sokolow, Coordinator
Client Assistance Program
Advocacy, Inc.
7800 Shoal Creek Blvd.
Suite 171-E
Austin, TX 78757
512-454-4816
800-252-9108
Fax: 512-323-0902
Email: hn2414@handsnet.org
www.advocacyinc.org

Utah
Nancy Friel, Director
Client Assistance Program
Disability Law Center
455 East 400 South
Suite 410
Salt Lake City, UT 84111
801-363-1347
800-662-9080
Fax: 801-363-1437
Email: info@disabilitylawcenter.org
www.disabilitylawcenter.org

Vermont
Laura Phillips, Director
Client Assistance Program
57 North Main St., Suite 2
Rutland, VT 05401
802-775-0021
800-769-7459
Email: nbrieden@vtlegalaid.org
http://www.vtlegalaid.org

Virginia
Client Assistance Program
Virginia Office for Protection and
Advocacy
1910 Byrd St., Suite 5
Richmond, VA 23230
804-225-2042
800-552-3962
Fax: 804-662-7057
www.vopa.state.va.us

Virgin Islands
Amelia Headley LeMont
Client Assistance Program
Virgin Islands Advocacy Agency
63 Estate Cane Carlton
Frederiksted
St. Croix, USVI 00840
340-772-1200
340-776-4303
340-772-4641 (TDD)
Fax: 340-772-0609
Email: info@viadvocacy.org
http://www.viadvocacy.org

Washington
Jerry Johnsen, Director
Client Assistance Program
2531 Ranier Ave. South
Seattle, WA 98144
206-721-5999
800-544-2121
Fax: 206-721-4537
Email: capseattle@att.net
http://www.wata.org/resource/legal/agencies/cap.htm

West Virginia
Susan Edwards, Director
Client Assistance Program
West Virginia Advocates, Inc.
Litton Bldg, 4th Floor
1207 Quarrier Street
Charleston, WV 25301
304-346-0847
800-950-5250
Fax: 304-346-0867
Email: wvadvocates@newwave.net
www.wvadvocates.org

Wisconsin
Linda Vegoe
Department of Health and
Family Services
Client Assistance Program
2811 Agriculture Dr.
P.O. Box 8911
Madison, WI 53708-8911
608-224-5070
800-362-1290
Fax: 608-224-5069
Email:
linda.vegoe@datcp.state.wi.us
http://www.dwd.state.wi.us/dvr/cap.htm

Wyoming
Jeanne Thobro, Director
Client Assistance Program
Wyoming P&A System
320 West 25th St., 2nd Floor
Cheyenne, WY 82001
307-632-3496
800-821-3091 (Voice/TDD)
800-624-7648
Fax: 307-638-0815
Email: wypanda@vcn.com
http://wypanda.vcn.com

Money and Help for Veterans

If you are a Veteran and thinking about starting your own small business take the time to check out all of the assistance that is available to you. There are many organizations that help veteran entrepreneurs get started, find financing, and provide other business related assistance. The SBA's Office of Veterans Business Development is dedicated to serving the veteran entrepreneur by formulating, executing and promoting policies and programs that provide assistance to veterans seeking to start and develop small businesses. Listed below are some programs available to qualified veterans through the SBA and other organizations. Make sure to check out "Other Resources for Assistance for Women, Minorities, Veterans, and the Disabled" at the end of this chapter for more places to turn for help and information.

Vocational and Educational Counseling For All Vets

Contact your nearest Department of Veterans Affairs Regional Office or Vets Center listed at the end of this chapter.

Servicemembers, veterans, and dependents of deceased or totally disabled veterans may receive a full range of educational and vocational counseling and testing. This program aids in selecting an educational or vocational goal, and providing facilities that may help satisfy that goal. To locate your nearest counseling center, contact your nearest Department of Veterans Affairs Regional Office or Vets Center listed below.

Vocational Rehabilitation For Vets With Disabilities

Contact your nearest Department of Veterans Affairs Regional Office or Vets Center listed at the end of this chapter.

Veterans and servicemembers who served in the Armed Forces on or after September 16, 1940, were discharged under honorable conditions, and have a disability rating of at least 20%, may be eligible for up to four years of rehabilitation services. Most veterans participate on a full time basis, but less than full time is possible. Veterans may: 1) enroll in a trade, business, or technical school or in college level institutions; 2) train on the job or in an apprenticeship program; 3) take on-farm training; 4) enter programs which combine school and on-the-job training; 5) train in special rehabilitation facilities or at home when this is necessary because of serious disability; or, self employment. The government pays for all the costs for tuition, fees, books, supplies and equipment — and may also pay for special services like tutorial assistance to gain additional work skills. The eligibility period for this benefit is 48 months to be used with 12 years from the award date, with certain exceptions.

Vocational Training For Retired Veterans

Contact your nearest Department of Veterans Affairs Regional Office or Vets Center listed at the end of this chapter.

Veterans who were awarded a pension prior to December 31, 1995 may be eligible for up to 24 months — or more under certain circumstances — of vocational training. This includes trade school, college, apprenticeships, and even self-employment assistance. Program participants may also receive up to 18 months of employment-counseling, job search assistance and work adjustment services.

Free Workshop For Vets Leaving The Military

Veterans' Employment and Training Service
U.S. Department of Labor
200 Constitution Ave., NW (S-1316)   202-693-4700
Washington, DC 20210   Fax: 202-693-4754
www.dol.gov/dol/vets/public/aboutvets/contacts/main.htm

The Transition Assistance Program (TAP) established a partnership with the Department of Defense, Veterans Employment and Training Service, Department of Veterans Affairs and the Labor Department to meet the needs of separating service members by offering job search assistance and related services within 180 days of separation or retirement.

TAP consists of comprehensive three-day workshops at selected military installations throughout the nation. Workshop attendees learn how to conduct successful job searches, decisions in careers, current occupational and labor market conditions, resume and cover letter preparation, and a realistic evaluation of their employability.

Service members leaving the military with a service connected disability are offered the Disabled Transition Assistance Program (DTAP) which includes the three day TAP workshop and four hours of instruction to help determine job readiness and address the special needs of disabled veterans.

For additional information, contact the main office listed above or your nearest Veterans Affairs Center listed on page 723.

VETGazette

Small Business Administration
Office of Small Business Development
409 Third Street S.W.
Washington, DC 20416
202-205-6773
Fax: 202-205-7292
www.sba.gov/vets/news.html

VETSGazette is a SBA veteran newsletter that highlights current news and opportunities to veteran business owners.

Veterans Business Outreach Program

The Veterans Business Outreach Program (VBOP) is designed to provide entrepreneurial development services such as business training, counseling and mentoring and referrals for eligible veterans who own or are considering staring their own business.

Sacramento Veterans Resource Center
Veteran's Business Outreach Center
7270 E. Southgate Drive
Sacramento, CA 95823
916-393-8387
Fax: 916-393-8389
www.vietvets.org
Serving California

2500 Minnesota Avenue
Lynn Haven, FL 32444
800-542-7232
850-271-1108
Fax: 850-271-1109
www.vboc.org
Serving Alabama, Florida, Georgia, Kentucky, Mississippi, North Carolina, South Carolina and Tennessee.

Veterans Business Outreach Program
41 State Street
Albany, NY 12246
877-875-VETS (8387)
www.nyssbdc.org/SpecialtyMain/Veterans/veterans.html
Serving New York State

The University of Texas-Pan American
1201 W. University Drive
Edinburg, TX 78539-2999
956-292-7535
Fax: 956-292-7561
www.coserve.org/vboc/
Serving Arkansas, Louisiana, New Mexico, Oklahoma, and Texas.

Veteran Exposition, Inc

P.O. Box 05623
Sarasota, FL 34232
941-951-2561
www.vetsexpo.org

Veteran Exposition is a veteran owned and operated organization dedicated to improving opportunities for U.S. Military Veteran business owners. The site aims to create awareness and business for U.S. military veteran owned businesses so that the public and government can locate veteran businesses. The site contains a directory of veteran-owned businesses and information about possible discounts to veterans.

Office of Small and Disadvantaged Business Utilization

U.S. Department of Veteran Affairs
810 Vermont Avenue, N.W.
Washington, DC 20420
202-565-8124
800-949-8387
Fax: 202-565-8156
www.va.gov/osdbu/

The Office of Small and Disadvantaged Business Utilization serves as the Department of Veteran Affairs advocate to assist and support interests of veteran-owned small businesses.

The Center for Veterans Enterprise

U.S. Department of Veteran Affairs
810 Vermont Avenue, N.W.
Washington, DC 20420
202-303-3260
866-584-2344 Toll free
Fax: 202-254-0238
www.vetbiz.gov

VETBiz is the federal web site for veterans in business. They offer information on everything a veteran needs to start a small business including a register of veteran owned businesses.

VetFran Business Program

International Franchise Association
1350 New York Avenue, NW Suite 900
Washington, DC 20005-4709
202-628-8000
Fax: 202-628-0812
www.franchise.org

VetFran helps to make owning a franchise operation more affordable for U.S. veterans. Veterans can get started in a franchise with initial investment assistance.

The Veterans Corporation

1800 Diagonal Road, Suite 230
Alexandria, VA 22314
866-283-8267
www.veteranscorp.org

The Veterans Corporation is a business e-portal for current and prospective Veteran business owners and for those interested in working with Veteran-owned businesses.
Veterans Entrepreneurial Training Program: Veterans Corporation offers "FastTrac New Venture" for veterans wanting to become entrepreneurs and "FastTrac Planning" for veteran business owners that want to expand their existing business.

Financing: Veterans Corporation help veterans meet their capital needs by offering assistance to qualified veteran business owners. They have loans ranging from microloans to $2 million or more.

Small Business Administration

Loans To Veterans To Start A Business

Director
Loan Policy and Procedures Branch
Small Business Administration
409 Third St., SW   202-205-6570
Washington, DC 20416   800-827-5722
www.sba.gov

The United States Congress has authorized the Small Business Administration to make loans for business purposes. However, before SBA can consider a loan application, the applicant must show that funding is not otherwise available on reasonable terms.

A letter of declination from the bank is required. These are loans, not grants, and the applicant must demonstrate that the loan can be repaid from the earnings of the business. There are no grants available for starting and maintaining a small business. Veterans who meet SBA loan criteria are placed ahead of non-veterans who apply on the same day (see Special Consideration below). There is a pre-qualification program available in most states to veterans, that pre-approves a loan between $15,000 to $200,000 before you even go to the bank.

All veterans must meet the same SBA standard loan criteria as any other applicant. If you are a veteran who is a farmer or from a rural community, contact the United States Department of Agriculture Rural Business - Cooperative Service. For those eligible, SBA offers a broad range of loan programs. Many of these loans are made by financial institutions and are guaranteed by SBA. Regular business loans are available to veterans on a special consideration basis. Loans range from $500 to $750,000, with approximately $16 million worth of loans made per year. Contact the Veterans Affairs Officer at your local U.S. Small Business Administration Field office listed below or you can call the national toll free number, 800-827-5722 (800-U-ASK-SBA), or online at {www.sba.gov}.

"Special Consideration" To Start A Business

Office of Veterans Affairs
U.S. Small Business Administration
409 Third St., SW, Suite 6500   800-U-ASK-SBA
Washington, DC 20416   TDD: 202-205-7333

The Small Business Administration (SBA) wants veterans to receive the benefits of all programs the agency provides. To ensure that this happens, a policy was adopted giving veterans "special consideration" in agency programs. Special Consideration involves designing unique management training programs specifically for veterans, processing veterans loan applications before non-veteran applications submitted the same day, monitoring loan and procurement activities to measure veteran participation, coordinating training and counseling activities for veterans with other agency departments and allocating a portion of direct loan funds for veterans. To get additional information on SBA services, contact the main office listed above or the VAO (Veterans Affairs Officer) in your nearest SBA office listed below.

Veteran's Guide To Entrepreneurship

Small Business Administration
409 Third St., SW, Suite 6500
Washington, DC 20416   800-U-ASK-SBA

A Veteran's Guide to Entrepreneurship is a publication that was developed by the Office of Veterans Affairs and will assist those servicemembers who choose to start a business. Many servicemembers choose self-employment for various reasons.

This publication will help provide the needed information on starting a business. The information is very comprehensive and will assist with all aspects of having your own business. In addition, there is a *Veteran's Handbook* which also may be very helpful. To get both publications, contact the main office listed above or the VAO in your nearest SBA office listed below.

In each local Small Business Administration office, there is a person who is designated as the Veterans Business Development Officer (VBDO). This person should be your initial contact and resource person for SBA programs. You can contact the VBDO by calling the applicable number listed below.

Small Business Administration
Field Offices and Phone Numbers

Region I
John Gardner
Veterans Affairs Officer
68 Sewall St., Room 512
Augusta, ME 04330
207-622-8555
Fax: 207-622-8277

Donna Harper
Veterans Affairs Officer

Stewart Nelson Plaza
143 North Main Street, Suite 202
Concord, NH 03301
603-225-1400

Thomas Schroeder
Veterans Affairs Officer
87 State St. Room 205
Montpelier, VT 05602
802-828-4422, ext. 204
Fax: 802-828-4485

Horace Cammack
Veterans Affairs Officer
10 Causeway Street, Room 265
Boston, MA 02222-1093
617-565-5597
Fax: 617-565-5597

Paul Bouchard
Veterans Affairs Officer
380 Westminister St.
Room 511

Providence, RI 02903
401-528-4691

Harvey Morrison
Veterans Affairs Officer
330 Main St. 2nd Floor
Hartford, CT 06106-1800
860-240-4700, ext. 232

Region II
Ana Maria Vera
Veterans Affairs Officer
252 Ponce De Leon Ave.
Suite 201
San Juan, PR 00918
787-766-5309

Frank Dito
Veterans Affairs Officer
26 Federal Plaza, Room 3100
New York, NY 10278
212-264-7752
Fax: 212-264-4963

David Laveck
Veterans Affairs Officer
401 South Salina, 5th Floor
Syracuse, NY 13260-2413
315-471-9393, ext. 247

Richard Keffer
Veterans Affairs Officer
111 West Huron St. Room 1311
Buffalo, NY 14202
716-551-5664

Howard Garrity
Veterans Affairs Officer
333 East Water Street, 4th Floor
Elmira, NY 14901
607-734-8130, ext. 30

Dan O'Connel
Veterans Affairs Office
1 Computer Drive South
Albany, NY 12205
518-446-1118, ext. 231

Martin McHenry
Veterans Affairs Officer
Two Gateway Center, 15th Floor
Newark, NJ 07102
973-645-2427

Region III
Stanley Karwacki
Veterans Affairs Officer
10 S. Howard Street, Suite 6220
Baltimore, MD 21202
410-962-6195, ext. 340

Joyce Howard
Veterans Affairs Officer
1110 Vermont Avenue, 9th Floor
Washington, DC 20005
202-606-4000, ext. 204

Jane Armstrong
Veterans Affairs Officer
1824 Market Street, Suite 610

Wilmington, DE 19801
302-573-6294

William Durham
Veterans Affairs Officer
405 Capital Street, Room 412
Charleston, WV 25301
304-347-5350

Leroy Harris
Veterans Affairs Officer
400 North 8th Street
Suite 1150
Richmond, VA 23240
804-771-2400, ext. 132

Donald Nemchick
Veterans Affairs Officer
700 River Ave., Suite 510
Pittsburgh, PA 15212
412-322-6441
Fax: 412-322-3513

William Dougherty
Veterans Affairs Officer
Stegmaier Bldg., Suite 407
Wilkes-Barre, PA 18702
570-826-6497

Joe McDevitt
Veterans Affairs Officer
Robert N.C. Nix Federal Building
900 Market St., 5th Floor
Philadelphia, PA 19107
215-580-2706

Region IV
Charles Atwood
Veterans Affairs Officer
7825 Baymeadows Way
Suite 100-B
Jacksonville, FL 32256-7504
904-443-1951

Robert Chavarria
Veterans Affairs Officer
1045 16th St. South
St. Petersburg, FL 33705
727-893-9683
Fax: 727-893-9688

Tommie Causey
Veterans Affairs Officer
188 Federal Office Bldg.
600 Martin Luther King Place
Louisville, KY 40211
502-571-1144, ext. 245

Don Winters
Veterans Affairs Officer
50 Vantage Way, Suite 201
Nashville, TN 37228-1500
615-736-5881, ext. 248

Edgar Fleetwood
Veterans Affairs Officer
6302 Fairview Rd., Suite 300
Charlotte, NC 28210-2227
704-344-6587, ext. 1134

Susan Chavis
Veterans Affairs Officer
1835 Assembly St., Room 358
Columbia, SC 29201
803-765-5378

Charlotte Johnson
Veterans Affairs Officer
233 Peachtree St., Suite 1900
Atlanta, GA 30309
404-331-0100, ext. 405
Fax: 404-331-0244

Raymond Hembree
Veterans Affairs Officer
801 Tom Martin Dr., Suite 201
Birmingham, AL 35211
205-290-7340, ext. 226
Fax: 205-290-7404

Tommy Traxler
Veterans Affairs Officer
210 E. Capitol St., Suite 900
Jackson, MS 39201
601-965-4378, ext. 241

Gary Reed
Veterans Affairs Officer
2909 13th Street, Suite 203
Gulfport, MS 39501-1949
228-863-4449, ext. 14
Fax: 228-864-0179

Region V
George Saumweber
Veterans Affairs Officer
100 North 6th St., Suite 210-C
Minneapolis, MN 55403-1525
612-370-2322

Jon Lonsdale
Veterans Affairs Officer
Henry Russ Federal Plaza
310 West Wisconsin Avenue
Suite 400
Milwaukee, WI 53203
414-297-1231
Fax: 414-297-1377

Charles T. Davis
Veterans Affairs Officer
477 Michigan Avenue, Room 515
Detroit, MI 48226
313-226-6075, ext. 245

Steve Konkle
Veterans Affairs Officer
500 W. Madison St., Room 1250
Chicago, IL 60661
312-886-4208

Jim Ryan
Veterans Affairs Officer
511 West Capitol Street, Suite 302
Illinois Financial Center
Springfield, IL 62704
217-492-4416, ext. 109

Paul Wyatt
Veterans Affairs Officer

429 N. Pennsylvania Street
Suite 100
Indianapolis, IN 46204-1873
317-226-7272, ext. 240

Russell Miller
Veterans Affairs Officer
1111 Superior St., Room 630
Cleveland, OH 44114
216-522-4996

Douglas Sweazy
Veterans Affairs Officer
2 Nationwide Plaza, Suite 1400
Columbus, OH 43215-2542
614-469-6860, ext. 276

Ronald Carlson
Veterans Affairs Officer
550 Main St., Room 2-522
Cincinnati, OH 45202
513-684-2814, ext. 205

Region VI

Willie Williams
Veterans Affairs Officer
365 Canal Street., Suite 2820
New Orleans, LA 70130
504-589-2706

Andy Lamonica
Veterans Affairs Officer
2120 River Front Drive #100
Little Rock, AR 72202
501-324-5871, ext. 239

Sandra Ransome
Veterans Affairs Officer
210 Park Avenue, Suite 130
Oklahoma City, OK 73102
405-231-5521, ext. 247
Fax: 405-231-4876

Alonzo Garcia
Veterans Affairs Officer
2412 S. Closner
Edinburg, TX 78539
956-316-2610, ext. 226
Fax: 956-316-2612

Stephen Curry
Veterans Affairs Officer
8701 South Gessner Dr.
Houston, TX 77054
713-773-6500, ext. 242
Fax: 713-773-6550

Armando Garcia
Veterans Affairs Officer
1205 Texas Ave., Room 408
Lubbock, TX 79401-2693
806-472-7462, ext. 244
Fax: 806-472-7487

Henry Cardenas
Veterans Affairs Officer
727 E. Durango Blvd., Room A-527
San Antonio, TX 78206-1204
210-472-5928
Fax: 210-472-5942

Daniel Chacon
Veterans Affairs Officer
10737 Gateway West., Suite 320
El Paso, TX 79935
915-633-7031
Fax: 915-633-7005

Bill Medina
Veterans Affairs Officer
4300 Amon Carter Blvd.
Suite 114
Ft. Worth, TX 76155
817-684-5517
Fax: 817-684-5516

John Tillotson
Veterans Affairs Officer
625 Silver SW, Suite 320
Albuquerque, NM 87102
505-346-6736
Fax: 505-346-6711

Region VII

Dennis Larkin
Veterans Affairs Officer
11145 Mill Valley Road
Omaha, NE 68154-3949
402-221-7208
Fax: 402-221-3680

Tom Harbison
Veterans Affairs Officer
210 Walnut St., Room 749
Des Moines, IA 50309
515-284-4653
Fax: 515-284-4572

Roger Hoffman
Veterans Affairs Officer
Small Business Administration
215 4th Avenue, SE, Suite 200
Cedar Rapids, IA 52401-1806
319-362-6405, ext. 218
Fax: 319-362-7861

Patrick Carney
Veterans Affairs Officer
217 W. 3rd St., N, Suite 2500
Wichita, KS 67202-1212
316-269-6273, ext. 225
Fax: 316-269-6618

F. Steven Parker
Veterans Affairs Officer
323 W. 8th Street, Suite 501
Kansas City, MO 64105
816-374-6708, ext. 226
Fax: 816-374-6759

Garry Ayers
Veterans Affairs Officer
7062 N. Jefferson Ave.
St. Louis, MO 63103
314-436-2202, ext. 324
Fax: 314-436-2627

Brent Jones
Veterans Affairs Officer
830 E. Primrose St.
Springfield, MO 65807-5254

417-890-8501, ext. 209
Fax: 417-889-0074

Region VIII

Donald Dahlseide
Veterans Affairs Officer
10 West 15th St., Suite 1100

Helena, MT 59626
406-441-1081, ext. 134
Fax: 406-441-1090

Dave Denke
Veterans Affairs Officer
100 East B. St., Suite 400
P.O. Box 2839
Casper, WY 82602
307-261-6523
Fax: 307-261-6535

Eric Giltner
Veterans Affairs Officer
202 N. 3rd St., Suite 300
Grand Forks, ND 58203
701-746-5160
Fax: 701-746-5748

E. Chuck Schroder
Veterans Affairs Officer
110 S. Phillips Ave., Suite 200
Sioux Falls, SD 57104
605-330-4243, ext. 15
Fax: 605-330-4215

Loy Rasmuson
Veterans Affairs Officer
125 South State St., Room 2231
Salt Lake City, UT 84138
801-524-3207
Fax: 801-524-4410

Jeannette Deherrera
Veterans Affairs Officer
721 19th Street, Suite 426
Denver, CO 80202
303-844-2607, ext. 266
Fax: 303-844-6539

Region IX

Chuck Stewart
Veterans Affairs Officer
455 Market Street, 6th Floor
San Francisco, CA 94105
415-744-6791
Fax: 415-744-9062

Alan Converse
Veterans Affairs Officer
550 West "C" Street, Suite 550
San Diego, CA 92101
619-557-7250 ext. 1116
Fax: 619-557-5894

Reynold Johnson
Veterans Affairs Officer
2719 North Air Fresno Drive
Suite 200
Fresno, CA 93727-1547
559-487-5785, ext. 114
Fax: 559-487-5636

David Casteneda
Veterans Affairs Officer
650 Capitol Mall
Suite 7-500
Sacramento, CA 65814
916-930-3709
Fax: 916-930-3737

Sami Marcos
Veterans Affairs Officer
200 West Santa Ana Blvd.
Suite 700
Santa Ana, CA 92701
714-550-7420, ext. 3702
Fax: 714-550-7409

Gabriel Cartwright
Veterans Affairs Officer
330 N. Brand Blvd.
Suite 1200
Glendale, CA 91203
818-552-3314
Fax: 818-552-3620

Pete Peterson
Veterans Affairs Officer
300 Las Vegas Blvd. South

Suite 1100
Las Vegas, NV 89101
702-388-6800
Fax: 702-388-6469

Jerry Dukauskas
Veterans Affairs Officer
2828 North Central Avenue
Suite 800
Phoenix, AZ 85004-1093
602-745-7221
Fax: 602-745-7210

Albert Sampson
Veterans Affairs Officer
First Hawaiian Bank Bldg
Suite 302
Mongnong, GU 96927
671-472-7277
Fax: 671-472-7365

Kimberly Hite
Veterans Affairs Officer
300 Ala Moana, Room 2-235
Honolulu, HI 96850-4981
808-541-3024
Fax: 808-541-2976

Region X
Tom Ewbank
Veterans Affairs Officer
Small Business Administration
1200 6th Ave., Suite 1700
Seattle, WA 98101-1128
206-553-0961
Fax: 206-553-6259

Dennis Lloyd
Veterans Affairs Officer
1515 SW Fifth Ave., Suite 1050
Portland, OR 97201-5494
503-326-5205
Fax: 503-326-2808

Rod Grzadzieleski
Veterans Affairs Officer
1020 Main Street, Suite 290
Boise, ID 83702-5745
208-334-1696, ext. 233

Terrence Moore
Veterans Affairs Officer
510 L Street, Suite 310
Anchorage, AK 99501
907-271-4854
Fax: 907-271-4545

Veterans' Employment and Training Service and Regional Administrators

The Veterans' Employment and Training Service has 10 regional offices as well as at least one office in every state. The regional offices are administered by Regional Administrators (RAVET), and the state offices are administered by a Director for Veterans' Employment and Training. These offices can give you information about veterans employment and training programs, and reemployment rights for veterans reservists and members of the National Guard.

Veterans Employment and Training Services Offices

Region I
(Connecticut, Maine, Massachusetts, New Hampshire, Rhode Island, Vermont)
David Houle, Regional Administrator
Barbara Thompson, Management Services Assistant
Christine Beech, Secretary
Veterans' Employment and Training Service
U.S. Department of Labor
J.F. Kennedy Federal Building
Room E-315, Government Center
Boston, MA 02203
617-565-2080
Fax: 617-565-2082
Email: houle-david@dol.gov
Email: thompson-barbara@dol.gov
Email: beech-christine@dol.gov

Region II
(New Jersey, New York, Puerto Rico, Virgin Islands)
Vacant, Regional Administrator
Tim Hays, Veterans' Program Specialist
Sonia J. Sanchez, Management Services Assistant
Veterans' Employment and Training Service
U.S. Department of Labor
201 Varick Street, Room 766
New York, NY 10014
212-337-2211
Fax: 212-337-2634
Email: sanchez-sonia@dol.gov
Email: hays-timothy@dol.gov

Region III
(Delaware, District of Columbia, Maryland, Pennsylvania, Virginia, West Virginia)
Joseph W. Hortiz. Jr., Regional Administrator
Raymond Minor, Veterans Program Specialist
Rosie Baker, Veterans Program Specialist
Cheryl Grigsby Thomas, Management Services Assistant
Veterans' Employment and Training Service
U.S. Department of Labor
The Curtis Center
VETS/770 West
170 S. Independence Mall
Philadelphia, PA 19106-3310
215-861-5390
Fax: 215-861-5389
Email: hortiz-joseph@dol.gov

Region IV
(Alabama, Florida, Georgia, Kentucky, Mississippi, North Carolina, South Carolina, Tennessee)

William J. Bolls, Jr., Regional Administrator
Harry Bean, Jr., Assistant Regional Administrator
Janice W. Lane, Senior Investigator, VPS
Joseph J. Miles, Senior Investigator, VPS
Vivian D. Blair, Secretary
Veterans' Employment and Training Service
U.S. Department of Labor
Atlanta Federal Center
61 Forsyth Street, SW, Room 6-T85
Atlanta, GA 30303
404-562-2305
Fax: 404-562-2313
Email: bolls-william@dol.gov
Email: lane-janice@dol.gov
Email: miles-jospeh@dol.gov
Email: blair-vivian@dol.gov
Email: beam-henry@dol.gov

Region V
(Illinois, Indiana, Michigan, Minnesota, Ohio, Wisconsin)
Ronald G. Bachman, Regional Administrator
Cheryl Santilli, Senior Investigator
Kristine Alvarez, Veterans' Program Specialist
Shirley Skoien, Veterans' Program Specialist
Caroline Neal, Administrative Officer
Calvin Lane, Secretary
Veterans' Employment and Training Service
U.S. Department of Labor
230 South Dearborn, Room 1064
Chicago, IL 60604
312-353-4942
312-353-0970 (ans. machine)
Fax: 312-886-1184
Email: bachman-ronald@dol.gov
Email: santilli-cheryl@dol.gov
Email: alvarez-kristine@dol.gov

Region VI
(Arkansas, Louisiana, New Mexico, Oklahoma, Texas)
Lester L. Williams, Jr., Regional Administrator
Bernadette Clay, Administrative Office
Ramona C. Lopez, Secretary
Veterans' Employment and Training Service
U.S. Department of Labor
525 Griffin Street, Room 858
Dallas, TX 75202
214-767-4987
Fax: 214-767-2734
Email: williams-lester@dol.gov
Email: clay-bernadette@dol.gov
Email: lopez-ramona@dol.gov

Region VII
(Iowa, Kansas, Missouri, Nebraska)
Lester L. Williams, Jr, Regional Administrator
Sharon Harrison, Assistant Regional Administrator
Ricardo L. Martinez, Veterans' Program Specialist
Veterans Employment and Training Service
U.S. Department of Labor
City Center Square Building
1100 Main Street, Suite 850
Kansas City, MO 64105-2112
816-426-7151
Fax: 816-426-7259
Email: williams-lester@dol.gov
Email: harrison-sharon@dol.gov
Email: martinez-ricardo@dol.gov

Region VIII
(Colorado, Montana, North Dakota, South Dakota, Utah, Wyoming)
Ronald G. Bachman, Regional Administrator
Veterans' Employment and Training Service
U.S. Department of Labor
1999 Broadway, Suite 1730
Denver, CO 80202
303-844-1175
303-844-1176
303-844-1178
Fax: 303-844-1179
Email: bachman-ronald@dol.gov

Region IX
(Arizona, California, Hawaii, Nevada)
Vacant, Regional Administrator
Vincent Rios, Assistant Regional Administrator
Joleen Sherrill-Irish, Veterans' Program Specialist
Nelia Bedia Nacor, Management Services Assistant
Veterans' Employment and Training Service
U.S. Department of Labor
71 Stevenson Street, Suite 705
San Francisco, CA 94105
415-975-4700 (ans. machine)
415-975-4701
415-975-4702
415-975-4754
415-975-4703
Fax: 415-975-4704
Email: Rios-Vincent@dol.gov
Email: irish-joleen@dol.gov
Email: nacor-canosa-nelia@dol.gov

Region X
(Alaska, Idaho, Oregon, Washington)
Regional Administrator Vacant
Senior Investigator Karen Marin
Veterans' Employment and Training Service
U.S. Department of Labor
1111 Third Avenue, Suite 800
Seattle, WA 98101-3212
206-553-4831
Fax: 206-553-6853
Email: marin-karen@dol.gov

Veterans' Employment And Reemployment Rights Assistance And Information

Alabama
Thomas M. Karrh, Director
Robert D. Franks, Assistant Director
Gay Coughlin, Veterans' Program Assistant
Veterans' Employment and Training Service
U.S. Department of Labor
649 Monroe Street, Room 2218
Montgomery, AL 36131-6300
334-223-7677
334-242-8115
Fax: 334-242-8927
Email: franks-robert@dol.gov
Email: karrh-Thomas@dol.gov
Email: coughlin-gay@dol.gov

Alaska
Dan Travis, Director
Arnold Lauri, Veterans' Program Assistant
Veterans' Employment and Training Service
U.S. Department of Labor
P.O. Box 25509
1111 West 8th Street
Juneau, AK 99802-5509
907-465-2723
Fax: 907-465-5528
Email: travis-dan@dol.gov
Email: lauri-arnold@dol.gov

Arizona
Michael Espinosa, Director
Alfredo Mendoza, Assistant Director
Veterans' Employment and Training Service
U.S. Department of Labor
P.O. Box 6123-SC760E
1400 West Washington
Phoenix, AZ 85005
602-379-4961
Fax: 602-542-4103
Email: espinosa-michael@dol.gov
Email: mendoza-alfredo@dol.gov

Arkansas
Billy R. Threlkeld, Director
Olga "Gene" Richards, Veterans' Program Assistant
Veterans' Employment and Training Service
U.S. Department of Labor
Employment Security Building #2
State Capitol Mall, Room G-12
Little Rock, AK 72201
P.O. Box 128
Little Rock, AK 72203
501-324-5502
501-682-3786
Fax: 501-682-3752
Email: threlkeld-billy@dol.gov
Email: richards-olga@dol.gov

California
Rosendo A. "Alex" Cuevas, Director
Leonard Dobish, Assistant Director
John E. Giannelli, Jr., Assistant Director
Tracy V. Tooley, Veterans' Program Assistant
Veterans' Employment and Training Service
U.S. Department of Labor
800 Capitol Mall, Room W1142
P.O. Box 826880
Sacramento, CA 94280-0001
916-654-8178
Fax: 916-654-9469
Email: cuevas-rosendo@dol.gov
Email: dobish-leonard@dol.gov
Email: giannelli-john@dol.gov
Email: tooley-tracy@dol.gov

Steven L. Bragman, Assistant Director
Veterans' Employment and Training Service
U.S. Department of Labor
2550 Mariposa Mall, Room 1080
Fresno, CA 93721-2296
559-445-5193
Fax: 559-445-5023
Email: bragman-steven@dol.gov

Christopher Still, Assistant Director
Veterans' Employment and Training
Service
U.S. Department of Labor
363 Civic Drive
Pleasant Hills, CA 94523-1987
925-602-1541
Fax: 925-602-5023
Email: still-christopher@dol.gov

Kevin D. Nagel, Veterans' Program
Specialist
EDD, Redlands Field Office
814 W. Colton Avenue
Redlands, CA 92374-2930
909-335-6763
Fax: 909-335-8303
Email: nagel-kevin@dol.gov

Linda Jacobe, Assistant Director
Veterans' Employment and Training
Service
U.S. Department of Labor
320 Campus Lane
Suisun, CA 94583
707-863-3583
Fax: 707-864-3216
Email: jacobe-linda@dol.gov

Carolyn C. McMillan, Assistant
Director
Veterans' Employment and Training
Service
U.S. Department of Labor
1501 East Arrow Hwy.
Pomona, CA 91767-2198
909-392-2675
Fax: 909-593-8913
Email: mcmillan-carolyn@dol.gov

Michael S. Beadle, Assistant
Director
Veterans' Employment and Training
Service
U.S. Department of Labor
932 Broadway
Santa Monica, CA 90401-2383
310-576-6444
Fax: 310-395-4819
Email: beadle-michael@dol.gov

Nancy Ise, Assistant Director
Veterans' Employment and Training
Service
U.S. Department of Labor
2450 E. Lincoln Avenue
Anaheim, CA 92806-4175
714-687-4845
Fax: 714-518-2391
Email: ise-nancy@dol.gov

Edward J. Scheer, Assistant Director
Veterans' Employment and Training
Service
U.S. Department of Labor
8977 Activity Road
San Diego, CA 92126-4427
619-689-6008
Fax: 619-689-6012
Email: scheer-edward@dol.gov

Colorado
Mark A. McGinty, Director
Milton Gonzales, Assistant Director
Thresa Kitzmiller, Veterans'
Program Assistant
Veterans' Employment and Training
Service
U.S. Department of Labor
Tower #2, Suite 400
1515 Arapahoe Street
P.O. Box 46550
Denver, CO 80202-2117
303-844-2151
303-844-2152
Fax: 303-620-4257
Email: mcginty-mark@dol.gov
Email: gonzales-milton@dol.gov
Email: kitzmiller-thresa@dol.gov

Donald Rincon, Assistant Director
Veterans' Employment and Training
Service
U.S. Department of Labor
2555 Airport Road
Colorado Springs, CO 80910-3176
719-475-3750
Fax: 719-636-1682
Email: rincon-donald@dol.gov

Connecticut
William Mason, Jr., Director
Lisa Jones, Assistant Director
Karen King, Veterans' Program
Assistant
Veterans' Employment and Training
Service
U.S. Department of Labor
Connecticut Department of Labor
Building
200 Folly Brook Boulevard
Wethersfield, CT 06109
860-263-6490
Fax: 860-263-6498
Email: mason-william@dol.gov
Email: jones-lisa@dol.gov
Email: king-karen@dol.gov

Delaware
David White, Director
Virginia M. Youst, Veterans'
Program Assistant
U.S. Department of Labor
Veterans' Employment and Training
Service
4425 North Market Street, Room 420
Wilmington, DE 19809-0828
302-761-8138/9
Fax: 302-761-6621 (temp)
Email: white-david@dol.gov
Email: youst-virginia@dol.gov

District of Columbia
Stanley K. Williams, Director
Veterans' Employment and Training
Service
U.S. Department of Labor
1500 Franklin St., NE
Washington, DC 20018
202-576-3082

Fax: 202-576-3113
Email: williams-stanley@dol.gov

Florida
Derek W. Taylor, Director
Ursula Lemme, Assistant Director
Bernadette Walsh, Veterans Program
Assistant
Veterans' Employment and Training
Service
U.S. Department of Labor
P.O. Box 1527
Tallahassee, FL 32301-5006
Marathon Building, Suite 205
2574 Seagate Drive
Tallahassee, FL 32399-0676
904-942-8800
904-877-4164
904-488-2967
Fax: 904-922-2690
Email: lemme-ursula@dol.gov
Email: taylor-derek@dol.gov
Email: walsh-bernadette@dol.gov

Richard Bate, Assistant Director
Veterans' Employment and Training
Service
U.S. Department of Labor
P.O. Box 17747
Jacksonville, FL 32245-7747
904-359-6080, ext. 2191
Fax: 904-359-6154
Email: bate-richard@dol.gov

Ronnie L. Carter, Assistant Director
Veterans' Employment and Training
Service
U.S. Department of Labor
P.O. Box 149084
1001 Executive Drive
2nd Floor, Room 26
Orlando, FL 32803-2999
954-677-5818
Fax: 954-677-5820 (call ahead)
Email: carter-ronnie@dol.gov

Craig Spry, Assistant Director
Veterans' Employment and Training
Service
U.S. Department of Labor
P.O. Box 12528
St. Petersburg, FL 33731-0084
3160 - 5th Avenue North, Suite 200
St. Petersburg, FL 33713
727-893-2415
Fax: 727-893-2378 (call ahead)
Email: spry-craig@dol.gov

Oscar G. Fuentes, Assistant Director
Veterans' Employment and Training
Service
U.S. Department of Labor
c/o Ft. Lauderdale Jobs & Benefits
Office
2660 West Oakland Park Boulevard
Ft. Lauderdale, FL 33311-1347
P.O. Box 5124
Ft. Lauderdale, FL .32814-9084
954-677-5400

Fax: 954-457-2889
Email: fuentes-oscar@dol.gov

Georgia

Ed Gresham, Director
June Scott, Assistant Director
Stephen Dewer, Assistant Director
Tina Frett, Veterans' Program
Assistant
Veterans' Employment and Training
Service
U.S. Department of Labor
Georgia State Employment Service
Sussex Place, Suite 504
148 International Boulevard, NE
Atlanta, GA 30303-1751
404-656-3127
404-656-3138
404-331-3893
Fax: 404-657-7403
Email: gresham-ed@dol.gov
Email: scott-june@dol.gov
Email: dewey-stephen@dol.gov
Email: frett-tinorah@dol.gov

Hawaii

Gilbert N. Hough, Director
Sharon N. Muraki, Veterans'
Program Assistant
Veterans' Employment and Training
Service
U.S. Department of Labor
P.O. Box 3680
Honolulu, HI 96811
830 Punchbowl Street, Room 315
Honolulu, HI 96813
808-522-8216 (ans. service)
Fax: 808-586-9258
Email: hough-gilbert@dol.gov
Email: muraki-sharon@dol.gov

Idaho

Director (vacant)
Pam Langley, Assistant Director
Karla Draper, Veterans' Program
Assistant
Veterans' Employment and Training
Service
U.S. Department of Labor
P.O. Box 2697
Boise, ID 83701
317 Main Street, Room 303
Boise, ID 83735
208-334-6163
Fax: 208-334-6389
208-334-6430
Email: langley-pamela@dol.gov
Email: draper-karla@dol.gov

Illinois

Samuel Parks, Director
Dottress Reeres, Assistant Director
Carol Motley, Assistant Director
Randall Hori, Assistant Director
Bianca Elmore, Veterans' Program
Assistant
Veterans' Employment and Training
Service
U.S. Department of Labor

401 South State Street, Room 744
North
Chicago, IL 60605
312-793-3433
Fax: 312-793-4795
Email: parks-samuel@dol.gov
Email: curry-dottress@dol.gov
Email: Motley-Carol@dol.gov
Email: elmore-bianca@dol.gov
Email: hori-randall@dol.gov

David Lyles, Assistant Director
Veterans' Employment and Training
Service
U.S. Department of Labor
555 S. Pasfield
Springfield, IL 62704
217-524-7769
Fax: 217-785-9715
Email: lyles-david@dol.gov

James R. Harris, Assistant Director
Veterans' Employment and Training
Service
U.S. Department of Labor
221 N. Genesee Street
Waukegan, IL
847-543-7400, ext. 273
Fax: 847-543-7465
Email: harris-james@dol.gov

Indiana

Bruce Redman, Director
George Patrick, Assistant Director
Harry "Jack" Hale, Assistant
Director
Velma Brock, Veterans' Program
Assistant
Veterans' Employment and Training
Service
U.S. Department of Labor
10 North Senate Ave., Room SE 103
Indianapolis, IN 46204
317-232-6804
COM 317-232-6805
Fax: 317-233-4262
Email: redman-david@dol.gov
Email: patrick-george@dol.gov
Email: hale-harry@dol.gov
Email: brock-velma@dol.gov

Iowa

Anthony J. Smithhart, Director
Vacant, Assistant Director
Aurea Neal, Veterans' Program
Assistant
Veterans' Employment and Training
Service
U.S. Department of Labor
150 Des Moines Street
Des Moines, IA 50309-5563
515-281-9061
Fax: 515-281-9063
Email: smithhart-anthony@dol.gov
Email: neal-aurea@dol.gov

Kansas

Gayle A. Gibson, Director
Juan A. Talavera, Jr., Assistant
Director

Shawn Johnson, Veterans' Program
Assistant
Veterans' Employment and Training
Service
U.S. Department of Labor
401 Topeka Boulevard
Topeka, KS 66603-3182
785-296-5032
Fax: 785-296-0264
Email: gibson-gayle@dol.gov
Email: talavera-juan@dol.gov
Email: johnson-shawn@dol.gov

Kentucky

Charles R. "Rick" Netherton,
Director
Bonnie J. Kunkle, Veterans' Program
Asst.
Veterans' Employment and Training
Service
U.S. Department of Labor
c/o Department for Employment
Services
275 East Main Street
(CHR Building), 2nd Floor West.
2WD
Frankfort, KY 40621-2339
502-564-7062
Fax: 502-564-1476
Email: kunkle-bonnie@dol.gov
Email: netherton-charles@dol.gov

Robert Kuenzli, Veterans' Program
Specialist
Veterans' Employment and Training
service
U.S. Department of Labor
320 Garrard Street
Covington, KY 41011
859-292-6666, ext. 253
Fax: 859-292-6708
Email: kuenzle-robert@dol.gov

Louisiana

Lester L. Parmenter, Director
Woody S. Lambert, Senior
Investigator
Ramona M. Hand, Assistant Director
Dorothy Vaughan, Veterans'
Program Assistant
Veterans' Employment and Training
Service
U.S. Department of Labor
Louisiana Department of Labor
Administration Building, Room 184
1001 North 23rd Street
Baton Rouge, LA 70802
P.O. Box 94094, Room 184
Baton Rouge, LA 70804-9094
225-389-0440
Fax: 225-342-3066
Email: parmenter-lester@dol.gov
Email: lambert-woody@dol.gov
Email: hand-ramona@dol.gov
Email: vaughan-dorothy@dol.gov

Maine

Jon Guay, Director
Edwina Bagley, Veterans' Program
Assistant

Veterans' Employment and Training
Service
U.S. Department of Labor
5 Mollison Way
P.O. Box 3106
Lewiston, ME 04243
207-753-9090
Fax: 207-783-5304
Email: guay-jon@dol.gov
Email: bagley-edwina@dol.gov

Maryland

Gary Lobdell, Director
Janet L. Boyd, Veterans' Program
Assistant
U.S. Department of Labor
Veterans' Employment and Training
Service
1100 North Eutaw Street, Room 210
Baltimore, MD 21201
410-767-2110
410-767-2111
Fax: 410-333-5136
Email: labdell-gary@dol.gov
Email: boyd-janet@dol.gov

Larry Mettert, Assistant Director
U.S. Department of Labor
Veterans' Employment and Training
Service
201 Baptist Street
Salisbury, MD 21801
410-334-6897
Email: mettert-larry@dol.gov

James Theriault, Assistant Director
Charles "Nick" Dawson, Senior
Investigator
U.S. Department of Labor
Veterans' Employment and Training
Service
P.O. Box 1317
Wheaton, MD 20915
301-929-4379
Fax: 301-929-4383
Email: theriault-james@dol.gov

Massachusetts

Paul Desmond, Director
George Kincannon, Assistant
Director
Patricia Newsom, Veterans' Program
Assistant
Veterans' Employment and Training
Service
U.S. Department of Labor
C.F. Hurley Building, 2nd Floor
19 Staniford Street
Boston, MA 02114-2502
617-626-6690
Fax: 617-727-2330
Email: kincannon-george@dol.gov
Email: desmond-paul@dol.gov
Email: newsom-patricia@dol.gov

Reginald E. Dupuis, Assistant
Director
Veterans' Employment and Training
Service
U.S. Department of Labor

Division of Employment Security
72 School Street
Taunton, MA 02780
508-977-4414
Fax: 617-727-2112
Email: dupuis-reginald@dol.gov

Michigan

Kim Fulton, Director
Robert Castillo, Assistant Director
Dennis Opoka, Veterans' Program
Specialist
Mary Bivens, Veterans' Program
Assistant
Veterans' Employment and Training
Service
U.S. Department of Labor
3032 W. Grand Blvd., Suite 48202
Detroit, MI 48202
313-456-3180
Fax: 313-456-3181
Email: fulton-kim@dol.gov
Email: bivens-mary@dol.gov

Edgar J. Hekman, Assistant Director
Veterans' Employment and Training
Service
U.S. Department of Labor
Employment Security Commission
3391 Plainfield, NE
Grand Rapids, MI 49505
616-361-3254
Email: hekman-edgar@dol.gov

Minnesota

Michael Graham, Director
Dennis Dahlien, Assistant Director
Vacant, Veterans' Program Assistant
Veterans' Employment and Training
Service
U.S. Department of Labor
390 Robert St. North, 1st Floor
St. Paul, MN 55101-1812
651-296-3665
Fax: 651-282-2711
Email: graham-michael@dol.gov
Email: dahlien-dennis@dol.gov

Vacant, Assistant Director
Veterans' Employment and Training
Service
U.S. Department of Labor
Job Service
320 West 2nd Street, Room 205
Duluth, MN 55802
218-723-4766

Mississippi

Angelo Terrell, Director
Melanie Jackson, Veterans Program
Assistant
Veterans' Employment and Training
Service
U.S. Department of Labor
P.O. Box 1699
1520 West Capitol Street
Jackson, MS 39215-1699
601-965-4204
601-961-7588
Fax: 601-961-7717

Email: terrell-angelo@dol.gov
Email: jackson-melanie@dol.gov

Missouri

Mick Jones, Director
Dennis R. McElroy, Assistant
Director
Patricia A. Baughman, Veterans'
Program Assistant
Veterans' Employment and Training
Service
U.S. Department of Labor
421 East Dunklin Street
Jefferson City, MO 65104-3138
P.O. Box 1087
Jefferson City, MO 65104-1087
573-751-3921
Fax: 573-751-6710
Email: jones-mickey@dol.gov
Email: mcelroy-dennis@dol.gov
Email: baughman-patricia@dol.gov

Montana

H. Polly LaTray-Holmes, Director
Alvy Chapman, Veterans' Program
Assistant
Veterans' Employment and Training
Service
U.S. Department of Labor
1215 8th Avenue
Helena, MT 59601
406-449-5431
406-442-2541
Fax: 406-444-3365
Email: latray-holmes-hazel@dol.gov
Email: chapman-alvy@dol.gov

Nebraska

Richard "Rick" Nelson, Director
Greg Wiltshire, Veterans' Program
Assistant
Veterans' Employment and Training
Service
U.S. Department of Labor
550 South 16th Street
Lincoln, NE 68508
P.O. Box 94600
Lincoln, NE 68509-4600
402-471-9833
Fax: 402-471-2092
Email: nelson-richard@dol.gov
Email: henson-brenda@dol.gov

Nevada

Judy A. Carlisle, Director
Veterans' Program Assistant
(Vacant)
Veterans' Employment and Training
Service
U.S. Department of Labor
1923 North Carson Street, Room 205
Carson City, NV 89702
702-687-4632
Fax: 702-687-3976
Email: carlisle-judy@dol.gov

New Hampshire

John Gagne, Director
Eileen Woods, Veterans' Program
Assistant

Veterans' Employment and Training
Service
U.S. Department of Labor
143 North Main Street, Room 208
Concord, NH 03301
603-225-1424
Fax: 603-225-1545
Email: gagne-john@dol.gov
Email: woods-eileen@dol.gov

New Jersey
Alan E. Grohs, Director
Robert F. Ranger, Assistant Director
Coleen Warren, Veterans' Program
Assistant
U.S. Department of Labor
Veterans' Employment and Training
Service
Labor Building
11th Floor, CN-058
Trenton, NJ 08625
609-292-2930
609-989-2305
609-989-2396
Fax: 609-292-9070
Email: grohs-alan@dol.gov
Email: ranger-robert@dol.gov
Email: warren-coleen@dol.gov

James J. Curcio, Assistant Director
U.S. Department of Labor
Veterans' Employment and Training
Service
2600 Mr. Ephraim Ave.
Camden, NJ 08104
856-614-3163
Fax: 856-614-3156
Email: curcio-james@dol.gov

New Mexico
Sharon Mitchell, Acting Director
Dolores M. "Monica" Martinez,
Veterans' Program Assistant
Veterans' Employment and Training
Service
U.S. Department of Labor
501 Mountain Road, NE
Albuquerque, NM 87102
P.O. Box 25085
Albuquerque, NM 87125-5085
505-346-7502
Fax: 505-346-7503
Email: mitchell-sharon@dol.gov
Email: martinez-dolores@dol.gov

New York
James H. Hartman, Director
J. Frank Merges, Assistant Director
Joan M. Cramer, Veterans' Program
Assistant
U.S. Department of Labor
Veterans' Employment and Training
Service
Harriman State Campus Bldg. 12,
Room 518
Albany, NY 12240-0099
518-457-7465
518-435-0831
Fax: 518-435-0833
Email: hartman-james@dol.gov

Email: merges-frank@dol.gov
Email: cramer-joan@dol.gov

Alice F. Jones, Assistant Director
Daniel A. Friedman, Assistant
Director
Veterans' Employment and Training
Service
U.S. Department of Labor
345 Hudson Street, Room 8209
P.O. Box 668, Mail Stop 8C
New York, NY 10014-0668
212-227-5213
212-352-6184
Fax: 212-352-6185
Email: jones-alice@dol.gov
Email: friedman-daniel@dol.gov

Vacant, Assistant Director
U.S. Department of Labor
Veterans' Employment and Training
Service
State Office Building, Room 702
207 Genesee Street
Utica, NY 13501
315-793-2323
Fax: 315-793-2303

James C. Donahue, Assistant
Director
U.S. Department of Labor
Veterans' Employment and Training
Service
290 Main Street, Room 231
Buffalo, NY 14202-4076
716-851-2748
Fax: 716-851-2792
Email: donahue-james@dol.gov

Frank J. Policastri, Assistant Director
U.S. Department of Labor
Veterans' Employment and Training
Service
450 South Salina St.
2nd Floor, Room 200
Syracuse, NY 13202-2402
315-479-3381
Fax: 315-479-3421
Email: policastri-frank@dol.gov

North Carolina
Steven W. Guess, Director
Angel H. Alvarez, Assistant Director
Evon Digregorio, Assistant Director
Lela Norman, Veterans' Program
Assistant
Veterans' Employment and Training
Service
U.S. Department of Labor
P.O. Box 27625
Raleigh, NC 27611-7625
700 Wade Avenue
Building M
Raleigh, NC 27605-1154
828-466-5535
919-856-4792
919-733-7402
Fax: 919-733-1508
Email: norman-lela@dol.gov
Email: alvarez-angel@dol.gov

Email: guess-steven@dol.gov
Email: digregorio-evon@dol.gov

Thomas West, Assistant Director
Veterans' Employment and Training
Service
U.S. Department of Labor c/o
NCESC
3301 Highway US 70 SE
Newton, NC 28658
828-466-5535
Fax: 828-466-5545
Email: west-tom@dol.gov

North Dakota
Gerald Meske, Director
Noreen Bartlett, Veterans' Program
Assistant
Veterans' Employment and Training
Service
U.S. Department of Labor
P.O. Box 1632
1000 E. Divide Avenue
Bismarck, ND 58502-1632
701-250-4337
701-328-2865
Fax: 701-328-2890
Email: meske-gerald@dol.gov
Email: bartlett-noreen@dol.gov

Ohio
Carl Price, Director
Cloudy Williams, Assistant Director
Roy Davis, Veterans' Program
Specialist
Dorinda Johnston, Veterans'
Program Assistant
Veterans' Employment and Training
Service
U.S. Department of Labor
P.O. Box 1618
Columbus, OH 43216
145 South Front Street
Room 523
Columbus, OH 43215
Com 614-466-2768/2769
Fax: 614-752-5007
Email: price-carl@dol.gov
Email: williams-cloudy@dol.gov
Email: davis-roy@dol.gov
Email: johnston-dorinda@dol.gov

Kevin Patterson, Assistant Director n
Veterans' Employment and Training
Service
U.S. Department of Labor
684 N. Park Avenue
P.O. Box 1188
Warren, OH 44482-1188
330-399-8114
Fax: 330-399-1957
Email: patterson-kevin@dol.gov

William Forester, Assistant Director
Veterans' Employment and Training
Service
U.S. Department of Labor
1841 Prospect Ave.
Cleveland, OH 44115
216-787-5660

Fax: 216-787-5213
Email: forester-william@dol.gov

Oklahoma
Darrell H. Hill, Director
Joseph "Joe" Dyer, Assistant
Director
Carolyn S. Clark, Veterans' Program
Assistant
Veterans' Employment and Training
Service
U.S. Department of Labor
2401 N. Lincoln Blvd., Room 304-2
Oklahoma City, OK 73105
P. O. Box 52003
Oklahoma City, OK 73152-2003
405-231-5088
405-557-7189
Fax: 405-557-7123
Email: hill-darrell@dol.gov
Email: dyer-joseph@dol.gov
Email: clark-carolyn@dol.gov

Oregon
Ron Cannon, Director
Vacant, Veterans' Program Assistant
Veterans' Employment and Training
Service
U.S. Department of Labor
Employment Division Building,
Room 108
875 Union Street, NE
Salem, OR 97311-0100
503-947-1490
Fax: 503-947-1492
Email: cannon-ron@dol.gov

Ronja Pardo, Assistant Director
Veterans' Employment and Training
Service
U.S. Department of Labor
1433 Southwest 6th Avenue
Portland, OR 97201
503-731-3478
Fax: 503-229-5829
Email: pardo-tonja@dol.gov

Pennsylvania
Larry Babitts, Director
Phillip Potter, Veterans' Program
Assistant
U.S. Department of Labor
Veterans' Employment and Training
Service
Labor and Industry Bldg., Room
1108
Seventh and Forster Streets
Harrisburg, PA 17121
717-787-5834
717-787-5835
Fax: 717-783-2631
Email: babitts-larry@dol.gov
Email: potter-phillip@dol.gov

Darrell R. Fritzinger, Assistant
Director
U.S. Department of Labor
Veterans' Employment and Training
Service
10th Floor, 640 Hamilton Street

Allentown, PA 18103
610-821-6571
Email: fritzinger-darrell@dol.gov

Denise M. Adair, Veterans' Program
Specialist
U.S. Department of Labor
Veterans' Employment and Training
Service
State Office Building
300 Liberty Avenue, Room 1307
Pittsburgh, PA 15222
412-565-2469
Fax: 412-565-2518
Email: adair-denise@dol.gov

Wayne E. Faith, Assistant Director
U.S. Department of Labor
Veterans' Employment and Training
Service
Job Service Office
135 Franklin Avenue
Scranton, PA 18503
717-963-4735
Email: faith-wayne@dol.gov

Richard P. Schaffer, Assistant
Director
Veterans' Employment and Training
Service
U.S. Department of Labor
71 South Union Avenue
Lansdowne, PA 19050
610-284-7588
Email: schaffer-richard@dol.gov

Puerto Rico
Angel Mojica, Director
Miguel Gonzales, Veterans' Program
Assistant
U.S. Department of Labor
Veterans' Employment and Training
Service
Puerto Rico Department of Labor
and Human Resources
#198 Calle Guayama
Hato Rey, PR 00917
787-754-5391
787-751-0731
Fax: 787-754-2983
Email: gonzales-miguel@dol.gov
Email: mojica-angel@dol.gov

Rhode Island
John F. Dunn, Director
Agnes Entwistle, Veterans' Program
Assistant
U.S. Department of Labor
Veterans' Employment and Training
Service
4808 Tower Hill Road
Wakefield, Ri 02879
401-528-5134
Fax: 401-528-5106
Email: dunn-john@dol.gov
Email: entwistle-agnes@dol.gov

South Carolina
William C. Plowden, Jr., Director
Willie J. Perry, Assistant Director

Rebecca L. Baston, Veterans'
Program Assistant
Veterans' Employment and Training
Service
U.S. Department of Labor
P.O. Box 1755
Columbia, SC 29202-1755
Lem Harper Building
631 Hampton Street, Suite 141
Columbia, SC 29201
803-765-5195
803-253-7649
Fax: 803-253-4153
Email: plowden-william@dol.gov
Email: perry-willie@dol.gov
Email: baston-rebecca@dol.gov

South Dakota
Earl R. Schultz, Director
Shirley H. Moffenbier, Veterans'
Program Assistant
Veterans' Employment and Training
Service
U.S. Department of Labor
P.O. Box 4730
420 South Roosevelt Street
Aberdeen, SD 57402-4730
605-626-2325
Fax: 605-626-2322
Email: schultz-earl@dol.gov
Email: moffenbier-shirley@dol.gov

Tennessee
Richard E. Ritchie, Director
Deann Schloesser, Veterans'
Program Assistant
Cynthia (Cindy) M. Morrison,
Assistant Director
Veterans' Employment and Training
Service
U.S. Department of Labor
P.O. Box 280656
Nashville, TN 37228-0656
615-736-7680
615-741-2135
Fax: 615-741-4241
615-736-5037
Email: ritchie-richard@dol.gov
Email: morrison-cynthia@dol.gov
Email: schloesser-deann@dol.gov

Jim George Pearson, Assistant
Director
Veterans' Employment and Training
Service
U.S. Department of Labor
1309 Poplar Avenue
Memphis, TN 38104-2006
901-543-7853
Fax: 901-543-7882
Email: pearson-jim@dol.gov

Texas
John D. McKinny, Director
Donald L. Watson, Assistant
Director
Denise D. Mayfield, Veterans'
Program Assistant
Veterans' Employment and Training
Service

U.S. Department of Labor
TWC Building, Room 516-T
1117 Trinity Street
Austin, TX 78701
P.O. Box 1468
Austin, TX 78767
512-463-2207
512-463-2815
512-463-2814
Fax: 512-475-2999
Email: mckinny-john@dol.gov
Email: watson-donald@dol.gov
Email: mayfield-denise@dol.gov

Ronny J. Hays, Assistant Director
Veterans' Employment and Training
Service
U.S. Department of Labor
1602 16th Street
Lubbock, TX 79401
P.O. Box 2858
Lubbock, TX 79408-2858
806-763-6416
Fax: 806-747-8629
Email: hays-ronny@dol.gov

Randy Walker, Assistant Director
Veterans' Employment and Training
Service
U.S. Department of Labor
8323 Culebra Road, Suite #103
San Antonio, TX 78251
Mailing Address:
P.O. Box 830277
San Antonio, TX 78283-0277
210-684-1051, ext. 241
Fax: 210-684-1822
Email: walker-randolph@dol.gov

Alberto Navarro, Assistant Director
Veterans' Employment and Training
Service
U.S. Department of Labor
5425 Polk St., G-20
Houston, TX 77023
713-767-2022
Fax: 713-767-2489

Albert L. Arredondo, Assistant
Director
Veterans' Employment and Training
Service
U.S. Department of Labor
412 South High Street
Longview, TX 75606
P.O. Box 2152
Longview, TX 75606-2152
903-758-1783 Ext 211
Fax: 903-757-7835
Email: arredondo-albert@dol.gov

Vacant, Assistant Director
Veterans' Employment and Training
Service
U.S. Department of Labor
3649 Leopard Street, Suite 600
Corpus Christi, TX 78408
512-882-3994
Fax: 512-882-1621

Robert A. Marterella, Assistant
Director

Veterans' Employment and Training
Service
U.S. Department of Labor
301 W. 13th Street, Room 407
FT. Worth, TX 76102-4699
P.O. Box 591
Ft. Worth, TX 76101-0591
817-335-5111, ext 404
Fax: 817-336-8723
Email: marterella-robert@dol.gov

Utah

Dale Brockbank, Director
Nancy Bailey, Veterans' Program
Asst.
Veterans' Employment and Training
Service
U.S. Department of Labor
Suite 209, 140 East 300 South
Salt Lake City, UT 84111-2333
801-524-5703
Fax: 801-524-3099
Email: brockbank-howard@dol.gov
Email: bailey-nancy@dol.gov

Vermont

Richard Gray, Director
Geri Orton, Veterans' Program
Assistant
Veterans' Employment and Training
Service
U.S. Department of Labor
P.O. Box 603
Post Office Building
87 State Street, Room 303
Montpelier, VT 05601
802-828-4441
Fax: 802-828-4445
Email: gray-richard@dol.gov
Email: orton-geraldine@dol.gov

Virginia

Roberto L. Pineda, Director
Heather Higgins, Assistant Director
Veterans' Employment Commission
13370 Minnieville Road
Woodbridge, VA 22192
703-897-0433
Fax: 703-897-0440
Email: pineda-roberto@dol.gov
Email: higgins-heather@dol.gov

Patricia Sykes, Veterans' Program
Assistant
U.S. Department of Labor
Veterans' Employment and Training
Service
703 East Main Street, Room 118
Richmond, VA 23219
804-786-7270
804-786-7269
804-786-6599
Fax: 804-786-4548
Email: sykes-patricia@dol.gov

Michael T. Skidmore, Assistant
Director
U.S. Department of Labor
Veterans' Employment and Training
Service

Virginia Employment Commission
P.O. Box 40008
Roanoke, VA 24022
5060 Valleyview Boulevard, N.W.
Roanoke, VA 24012
540-561-7494
Fax: 540-561-7510
Email: skidmore-michael@dol.gov

Virgin Islands

Vacant, RAVET
Tim Hays, Veterans Program
Specialist
Sonia Sanchez, MSA
Veterans' Employment and Training
Service
U.S. Department of Labor
201 Varick Street, Room 766
New York, NY 10014
Email: hays-timothy@dol.gov
Email: sanchez-sonia@dol.gov

Washington

Tom Pearson, Director
James Arrington, Assistant Director
Gregory Mercer, Assistant Director
Kathy Smith, Veterans Program
Assistant
Veterans' Employment and Training
Service
U.S. Department of Labor
P.O. Box 165
Olympia, WA 98507-0165
605 Woodview Square Loop, SE,
3rd Floor
Lacey, WA 98503-1040
360-438-4600
Fax: 360-438-3160
Email: pearson-thomas@dol.gov
Email: arrington-james@dol.gov
Email: mercer-gregory@dol.gov
Email: smith-kathy@dol.gov

West Virginia

Charles Stores, Jr., Director
Cynthia Collins, Veterans' Program
Assistant
U.S. Department of Labor
Veterans' Employment and Training
Service
Capitol Complex, Room 204
112 California Avenue
Charleston, WV 25305-0112
304-558-4001
Fax: 304-344-4591
Email: stores-charles@dol.gov
Email: collins-cynthia@dol.gov

Wisconsin

James Gutowski, Director
Daniel Schmitz, Assistant Director
Thomas R. Stehlik, Veterans'
Program Assistant
Veterans' Employment and Training
Service
U.S. Department of Labor
P.O. Box 8310
Madison, WI 53708-8310

201 East Washington Ave., Room
G201A
Madison, WI 53703
FTS 8-608-264-5371
COM 608-266-3110
Fax: 608-261-6710
Email: gutowski-james@dol.gov
Email: schmitz-daniel@dol.gov
Email: stehlik-thomas@dol.gov

Wyoming
David McNulty, Director
Teri Muller, Veterans' Program
Assistant
Veterans' Employment and Training
Service
U.S. Department of Labor
P.O. Box 2760
100 West Midwest Avenue

Casper, WY 82602-2760
307--261-5454
307-235-3281
307-235-3282
Fax: 307-473-2642
Email: mcnulty-david@dol.gov
Email: muller-teri@dol.gov

U.S. Department of Veterans Affairs
Regional Offices and Vet Centers

Department of Veterans Affairs Headquarters
810 Vermont Ave. NW
Washington, D.C. 20420
202-273-5400
www.va.gov

Alabama
Regional Office:
Montgomery Regional Office
345 Perry Hill Rd.
Montgomery, AL 36109
800-827-1000
334-213-3400
Fax: 334-213-3407

Vet Centers:
Birmingham Vet Center
1500 5th Avenue South
Birmingham, AL 35205
205-731-0550
Fax: 205-731-0564

Mobile Vet Center
Festival Center
3725 Airport Blvd. Suite 143
Mobile, AL 36608
205-304-0108

Alaska
Regional Office:
Anchorage Regional Office
2925 DeBarr Road
Anchorage, AK 99508-2989
800-827-1000

Vet Centers:
Anchorage Vet Center
4201 Tudor Center Drive Suite 115
Anchorage, AK 99508
907-563-6966
Fax: 907-561-7183

Fairbanks Vet Center
540 4th Avenue, Suite 100
Fairbanks, AK 99701
907-456-4238
Fax: 907-456-0475

Kenai Vet Center
43335 K-Beach Rd.
Building F, Suite 4

Soldotna, AK 99669
907-260-7640
Fax: 907-260-7642

Wasila Vet Center
851 E. Westpoint Ave.
Suite 111
Wasila, AK 99654
907-376-4318
Fax: 907-373-1883

Arizona
Regional Office:
Phoenix Regional Office
3225 N. Central Ave.
Phoenix, AZ 85012
800-827-1000

Vet Centers:
Phoenix Vet Center
77 E. Weldon, Suite 100
Phoenix, AZ 85012
602-640-2981
Fax: 602-640-2967

Prescott Vet Center
161 S. Granite St.
Suite B
Prescott, AZ 86303
520-778-3469
Fax: 520-776-6042

Tucson Vet Center
3055 North 1st Avenue
Tucson, AZ 85719
520-882-0333
Fax: 520-670-5862

Arkansas
Regional Office:
North Little Rock Regional Office
Building 65, Fort Roots
P.O. Box 1280
Little Rock, AR 72115
800-827-1000

Vet Centers:
North Little Rock Vet Center
201 W. Broadway, Suite A
Little Rock, AR 72114
501-324-6395

California
Regional Offices:
Los Angeles Regional Office
Federal Building
11000 Wilshire Boulevard
Los Angeles, CA 90024
800-827-1000

Oakland Regional Office
1301 Clay Street
Room 1300 North
Oakland, CA 94612
800-827-1000

San Diego Regional Office
8810 Rio San Diego Drive
San Diego, CA 92108
800-827-1000

Vet Centers:
Anaheim Vet Center
859 S. Harbor Blvd.
Anaheim, CA 92805
714-776-0161

Santa Cruz County Vet Center
1350 41st Ave., Suite 102
Capitola, CA 95010-3906
831-464-4575

Chico Vet Center
25 Main St., Suite 100
Chico, CA 95928
530-899-8549

Commerce Vet Center
VA East L A. Clinic
5400 E. Olympic Blvd., # 140
Commerce, CA 90022
213-728-9966

Concord Vet Center
1899 Clayton Rd.
Suite 140
Concord, CA 94520
925-680-4526

Culver City Vet Center
5730 Uplander Way
Suite 100
Culver City, CA 90230
310-641-0326

Eureka Vet Center
2839 G St., Suite A
Eureka, CA 95501
707-444-8271

Fresno Vet Center
3636 N. 1st. St. Suite 112
Fresno, CA 93726
559-487-5660

Los Angeles Vet Center
S. Central LA
251 W. 85th Pl.
Los Angeles, CA 90003
310-215-2380

Peninsula Vet Center
2946 Broadway St.
Redwood City, CA 94062-1594
650-299-0672

Oakland Vet Center
1540 Franklin St., Suite 200
Oakland, CA 94612
510-763-3904

Riverside Vet Center
4954 Arlington Ave., Suite A
Riverside, CA 92571
909-359-6342

Rohnert Park Vet Center
6225 State Farm Dr., Suite 101
Rohnert Park, CA 94928
707-586-3295

Sacramento Vet Center
1111 Howe Ave., Suite 390
Sacramento, CA 95825
916-566-7430

San Diego Vet Center
2900 6th Ave.
San Diego, CA 92103
858-294-2040

San Francisco Vet Center
505 Polk St.
San Francisco, CA 94102
415-441-5051

San Jose Vet Center
278 N. 2nd St.
San Jose, CA 95112-4017
408-993-0729

Colorado
Regional Office
Denver Regional Office
155 Van Gordon St.
Lakewood, CO 80228
800-827-1000

Vet Centers:
Boulder Vet Center
2336 Canyon Blvd.
Suite 130
Boulder, CO 80302
303-440-7306

Colorado Springs Vet Center
416 E. Colorado Avenue
Colorado Springs, CO 80903
719-471-9992

Denver Vet Center
7465 E. First Avenue, Suite B
Denver, CO 80220
303-326-0645
303-433-7123

Connecticut
Regional Office:
Hartford Regional Office
450 Main Street
Hartford, CT 06103
800-827-1000

Vet Centers:
Hartford Vet Center
30 Jordan Lane
Wethersfield, CT 06109
860-240-3543

New Haven Vet Center
141 Captain Thomas Blvd.
New Haven, CT 06516
203-932-9899

Norwich Vet Center
100 Main Street
Norwich, CT 06360
203-887-1755

Delaware
Regional Office:
Wilmington Regional Office
1601 Kirkwood Hwy.
Wilmington, DE 19805
800-827-1000

Vet Centers:
Wilmington Vet Center
VAMROC Bldg. 2
1601 Kirkwood Hwy.
Wilmington, DE 19805
302-994-1660

District of Columbia
Regional Office:
Washington DC Regional Office
1120 Vermont Avenue N.W.
Washington DC, DC 20421
800-827-1000

Vet Center:
Washington DC Vet Center
911 Second St., NE
Washington, DC 20002
202-543-8821
Fax: 202-745-8648

Florida
Regional Office:
St. Petersburg Regional Office
9500 Bay Pines Blvd.
Bay Pines, FL 33708
800-827-1000

Vet Centers:
Ft. Lauderdale Vet Center
713 NE 3rd Ave.
Ft. Lauderdale, FL 33304
954-356-7926
Fax: 954-356-7609

Jacksonville Vet Center
1833 Boulevard St.
Jacksonville, FL 32206
904-232-3621

Miami Vet Center
2700 SW 3rd Ave., Suite 1A
Miami, FL 33129
305-859-8387
Fax: 305-530-7870

Orlando Vet Center
5001 Orange Ave., Suite A
Orlando, FL 32809
407-857-2800

Palm Beach Vet Center
2311 10th Ave., North #13
Palm Beach, FL 33461
561-585-0441

Pensacola Vet Center
4501 Twin Oaks Dr., Suite 104
Pensacola, FL 32506
850-456-9403

Sarasota Vet Center
4801 Swift Road
Sarasota, FL 34231
941-927-8285

St. Petersburg Vet Center
2880 1st Ave., N.
St. Petersburg, FL 33713
727-893-3791

Tallahassee Vet Center
249 E. 6th Ave.
Tallahassee, FL 32303
850-942-8810

Tampa Vet Center
1507 W. Sligh Ave.
Tampa, FL 33604
813-228-2621

Georgia
Regional Office:
1700 Clairmont Rd.
Decatur, GA 30033
800-827-1000

Vet Centers:
Atlanta Vet Center
77 Peachtree Pl., NW
Atlanta, GA 30309
404-347-7264

Savannah Vet Center
8110 White Bluff Road
Savannah, GA 31406
912-652-4097

Guam

Vet Centers:
Guam Vet Center
222 Chalan Santo Papast
Reflection Center, Suite 102
Agana, GU 96910
705-472-7161

Hawaii

Regional Office:
Honolulu Regional Office
459 Patterson Rd., E-Wing
Honolulu, HI 96819-1522
800-827-1000
Fax: 808-433-0390
Toll Free From:
Neighboring Islands: 800-827-1000
Guam: 475-8387
American Samoa: 800-844-7928

Vet Centers:
Hilo Vet Center
120 Keawe St. Suite 201
Hilo, HI 96720
808-969-3833

Honolulu Vet Center
1680 Kapiolani Blvd, Suite F
Honolulu, HI 96814
808-566-1764

Kallua-Kona Vet Center
Pottery Terrace, Fern Bldg.
75-5995 Kuakini Hwy. #415
Kallua-Kona, HI 96740
808-329-0574

Kauai Vet Center
3367 Kuhio Hwy., Suite 101
Lihue, HI 96766-1061
808-246-1163

Maui Vet Center
35 Lunaliho St., Suite 101
Wailuku, HI 96793-2523
808-242-8557

Idaho

Regional Office:
Boise Regional Office
805 W. Franklin Street
Boise, ID 83702
800-827-1000

Vet Centers:
Boise Vet Center
5440 Franklin Rd., Suite 100
Boise, ID 83705
208-342-3612
Fax: 208-342-0327

Pocatello Vet Center
1800 Garrett Way
Pocatello, ID 86303
208-232-0316

Illinois

Regional Office:
Chicago Regional Office
436 S. Clark St.
Chicago, IL 60605-1523
800-827-1000
Fax: 312-353-2907

Vet Centers:
Chicago Vet Center
1514 E. 63rd Street
Chicago, IL 60637
774-684-5500

Chicago Heights Vet Center
1600 Halsted Street
Chicago Heights, IL 60411
708-754-0340
Fax: 708-754-0373

Evanston Vet Center
565 Howard Street
Evanston, IL 60202
847-332-1019
Fax: 847-332-1024

Oak Park Vet Center
155 S. Oak Park Avenue
Oak Park, IL 60302
708-383-3325
Fax: 708-383-3247

Peoria Vet Center
3310 N. Prospect Street
Peoria, IL 61603
309-671-7300

Springfield Vet Center
624 S. 4th Street
Springfield, IL 62701
217-492-4955

East St. Louis Vet Center
1269 N. 89th Street, Suite 1
St. Louis, IL 62203
618-397-6602

Indiana

Regional Office:
Indianapolis Regional Office
575 N. Pennsylvania St.
Indianapolis, IN 46202
800-827-1000

Vet Centers:
Fort Wayne Vet Center
528 West Berry St.
Fort Wayne, IN 46802
219-460-1456

Indianapolis Vet Center
3833 Meridian
Indianapolis, IN 46208
317-927-6440

Merillville Vet Center
6505 Broadway
Merillville, IN 46410-3009
219-736-5633
Fax: 219-736-5936

Iowa

Regional Office:
Des Moines VA Regional Office
210 Walnut Street
Des Moines, IA 50309
800-827-1000
Fax: 515-284-4149
Cedar Rapids 319-378-0016

Kansas

Regional Office:
Wichita Regional Office
5500 E. Kellogg
Wichita, KS 67211
800-827-1000

Vet Centers:
Wichita Vet Center
413 S. Pattie
Wichita, KS 67211
800-478-3381
316-265-3260

Kentucky

Regional Office:
Louisville Regional Office
545 S 3rd St.
Louisville, KY 40202
800-827-1000

Vet Centers:
Lexington Vet Center
301 East Vine St., Suite C
Lexington, KY 40503
606-253-0717

Louisville Vet Center
1347 South 3rd St.
Louisville, KY 40208
502-634-1916

Louisiana

Regional Office:
New Orleans Regional Office
701 Loyola Avenue
New Orleans, LA 70113
800-827-1000

Vet Centers:
New Orleans Vet Center
1529 N. Claiborne Avenue
New Orleans, LA 70116
504-943-8386

Shreveport Vet Center
2800 Youree Drive
LA Suite l-105
Shreveport, LA 71104
318-861-1776

Maine

Medical and Regional Office:
Togus VA Medical/Regional Office
Center
1 VA Center
Togus, ME 04330
207-623-8411

Maryland
Regional Office:
Baltimore Regional Office
31 Hopkins Plaza federal Building
Baltimore, MD 21201
800-827-1000

Vet Centers:
Baltimore Vet Center
6666 Security Blvd., Suite 2
Baltimore, MD 21207
410-277-3600
Fax: 410-277-3601

Cambridge Vet Center
5510 West Shore Drive
Cambridge, MD 21613
410-228-6305, ext. 4123

Elkton Vet Center
103 Chesapeake Blvd., Suite A
South Bridge Street
Elkton, MD 21921
410-392-4485
Fax: 410-392-6381

Silver Spring Vet Center
1015 Spring Street, Suite 101
Silver Spring, MD 20910
301-589-1073
Fax: 301-588-4882

Massachusetts
Regional Office:
Boston VA Regional Office
JFK Federal Building
Government Center
Boston, MA 02114
800-827-1000

Vet Centers:
Boston Vet Center
665 Beacon Street
Suite 100
Boston, MA 02215
617-424-0665

Brockton Vet Center
1041-L Pearl Street
Brockton, MA 02401
508-580-2730

Lowell Vet Center
Community Care Center
81 Bridge Street
Lowell, MA 01852
508-934-9124

Springfield Vet Center
1985 Main Street
Springfield, MA 01103
508-737-5167

Winchendon Vet Center
Town Hall
Winchendon, MA1475
508-297-3028

Worcester Vet Center
605 Lincoln Street

Worcester, MA 01605
508-856-7046

Michigan
Regional Office:
Detroit Regional Office
Patrick V. McNamara Federal Bldg.
477 Michigan Ave.
Detroit, MI 48226
800-827-1000

Vet Centers:
Detroit Vet Center
4161 Cass Ave.
Detroit, MI 48201
313-831-6509

Grand Rapids Vet Center
1940 Eastern Ave. SE
Grand Rapids, MI 49507
616-243-0385

Lincoln Park Vet Center
1766 Fort St.
Lincoln Park, MI 48146
313-381-1370

Minnesota
Regional Office:
St. Paul Regional Office
1 Federal Drive, Fort Snelling
St. Paul, MN 55111-4050
800-827-1000

Vet Centers:
Duluth Vet Center
405 East Superior St.
Duluth, MN 55802
218-722-8654

St. Paul Vet Center
2480 University Ave.
St. Paul, MN 55114
612-644-4022

Mississippi
Regional Office:
Jackson Regional Office
1600 E. Woodrow Wilson Avenue
Jackson, MS 39216
800-827-1000
601-364-7000
Fax: 601-364-7007

Vet Centers:
Biloxi Vet Center
313 Abbey Court
Biloxi, MS 39531
228-388-9938

Jackson Vet Center
4436 N. State St., Suite A3
Jackson, MS 39206
601-965-5727

Missouri
Regional Office:
St. Louis Regional Office
Federal Building

400 South, 18th Street
St. Louis, MO 63103
800 827 1000

Vet Centers:
Kansas City Vet Center
3931 Main Street
Kansas, MO 64111
816-753-1866
FTS: 816-753-2328

St. Louis Vet Center
2345 Pine Street
St. Louis, MO 63103
314-231-1260
Fax: 314-289-6539

Montana
Regional Office:
Fort Harrison Medical and Regional
Office
William Street off Highway
Fort Harrison, MT 59636
800-827-1000

Vet Centers:
Billings Vet Center
1234 Ave. C
Billings, MT 59102
406-657-6071

Missoula Vet Center
500 N. Higgins Avenue
Missoula, MT 59802
406-721-4918

Nebraska
Regional Office:
Lincoln Regional Office
5631 South 48th Street
Lincoln, NE 68516
800-827-1000

Vet Centers:
Lincoln Vet Center
920 L. St.
Lincoln, NE 68508
402-476-9736

Omaha Vet Center
2428 Cuming St.
Omaha, NE 68131-1600
402-346-6735

Nevada
Regional Office:
Reno Regional Office
1201 Terminal Way
Reno, NV 89520
800-827-1000

Vet Centers:
Las Vegas Vet Center
704 S 6th St.
Las Vegas, NV 89101
702-388-6368

Reno Vet Center
1155 W. 4th St.
Suite 101

Reno, NV 89503
702-323-1294

New Hampshire
Regional Office:
Manchester Regional Office
Norris Cotton Federal Bldg.
275 Chestnut St.
Manchester, NH 03101
800-827-1000

Vet Centers:
Manchester Vet Center
103 Liberty St.
Manchester, NH 03104
603-668-7060

New Jersey
Regional Office:
Newark Regional Office
20 Washington Place
Newark, NJ 07102
800-827-1000

Vet Centers:
Jersey City Vet Center
115 Christopher Columbus Dr.
Room 200
Jersey, NJ 07302
201-645-2038

Newark Vet Center
157 Washington St.
Newark, NJ 07102
201-645-5954
Fax: 201-645-5932

Trenton Vet Center
171 Jersey St., Bldg. 36
Trenton, NJ 08611
609-989-2260

Ventnor Vet Center
6601 Ventnor Ave., Suite 401
Ventnor, NJ 08406
609-927-8387

New Mexico
Regional Office:
Albuquerque Regional Office
Danis Chavez Federal Building
500 Gold Avenue, SW
Albuquerque, NM 87102
800-827-1000

Vet Centers:
Albuquerque Vet Center
1600 Mountain Road NW
Albuquerque, NM 87104
505-346-6562
Fax: 505-346-6572

Farmington Vet Center
4251 E. Main, Suite B
Farmington, NM 87402
505-327-9684
Fax: 505-327-9519

Santa Fe Vet Center
2209 Brothers Rd., Suite 110

Santa Fe, NM 87505
505-988-6562
Fax: 505-988-6564

New York
Regional Offices:
Buffalo Regional Office
Federal Building
111 W Huron St.
Buffalo, NY 14202
800-827-1000
(Serves Counties not served by the New York, NY Regional Office).

New York Regional Office
245 W Houston St.
New York, NY 10014
800-827-1000
Fax: 212-807-4024
(Serves the Counties of Albany, Bronx, Clinton, Columbia, Delaware, Dutchess, Essex, Franklin, Fulton, Greene, Hamilton, Kings, Montgomery, Nassau, New York, Orange, Otsego Putnam, Queens, Rensselaer, Richmond, Rockland, Saratoga, Schenectady, Schoharie, Suffolk, Sullivan, Ulster, Warren, Washington, and Westchester).

Vet Centers:
Albany Vet Center
875 Central Ave.
Albany, NY 12206
518-438-2505

Babylon Vet Center
116 West Main Street
Babylon, NY 11702
516-661-3930

Bronx Vet Center
226 East Fordham Road
Room 220
Bronx, NY 10458
718-367-3500

Brooklyn Vet Center
25 Chapel St., Suite 604
Brooklyn, NY 11201
718-330-2825

Buffalo Vet Center
564 Franklin Street
Buffalo, NY 14202
716-882-0505
Fax: 716-882-0525

Harlem Vet Center
55 West 125th Street, 7th Floor
New York, NY 10027
212-870-8126

Manhattan Vet Center
201 Varick St., Room 707
New York, NY 10014
212-620-3306

Rochester Vet Center
134 South Fitzhugh St.

Rochester, NY 14614
716-263-5710

Staten Island Vet Center
150 Richmond Terrace
Staten Island, NY 10301
718-816-4499

Syracuse Vet Center
716 East Washington St.
Syracuse, NY 13203
315-478-7127

White Plains Vet Center
300 Hamilton Avenue
White Plains, NY 10601
914-682-6250

Queens Vet Center
75-108 91st Avenue
Woodhaven, NY 11421
718-296-2871

North Carolina
Regional Office:
Winston-Salem Regional Office
Federal Building
251 N. Main Street
Winston-Salem, NC 27155
800 827 1000

Vet Centers:
Charlotte Vet Center
223 S. Brevard St., Suite 103
Charlotte, NC 28202
704-333-6107

Fayetteville Vet Center
4140 Ramsey Street, Suite 110
Fayetteville, NC 28311
910-488-6252

Greensboro Vet Center
2009 Elm-Eugene St.
Greensboro, NC 27406
910-333-5366

Greenville Vet Center
150 Arlington Blvd., Suite B
Greenville, NC 27858
919-355-7920

North Dakota
Medical and Regional Office:
Fargo VA Medical/Regional Office Center
2101 Elm Street
Fargo, ND 58102
800-827-1000
701-232-3241
Fax: 701-239-3705

Vet Centers:
Fargo Vet Center
3310 Feichtner Dr.
Suite 100
Fargo, ND 58102
701-237-0942
Fax: 701-237-5734

Minot Vet Center
3041 3rd St., NW
Minot, ND 58703
701-852-0177
Fax: 701-862-5225

Ohio
Regional Office:
Cleveland Regional Office
A.J. Celebrezze Federal Building
1240 East 9th Street
Cleveland, OH 44199
800-827-1000

Vet Centers:
Cincinnati Vet Center #204
801 B. West 8th Street
Suite 126
Cincinnati, OH 45203
513-763-3500
Fax: 513-763-3505

Cleveland Vet Center #206
11511 Lorain Ave.
Cleveland, OH 44111
440-845-5023
Fax: 440-845-5024

Cleveland Heights Vet Center #205
2134 Lee Rd.
Cleveland Heights, OH 44118
216-932-8476

Columbus Vet Center #221
30 Spruce St.
Columbus, OH 43215
614-257-5550
Fax: 614-257-5551

Dayton Vet Center #225
111 W. 1st Street
Dayton, OH 45402
937-461-9150
937-461-9151

Oklahoma
Regional Office:
Muskogee Regional Office
125 South Main Street
Muskogee, OK 74401
800-827-1000
Oklahoma City: 405-270-5184
Tulsa: 918-748-5105

Oregon
Regional Office:
Portland Regional Office
1220 SW 3rd Avenue
Portland, OR 97204
800-827-1000

Vet Centers:
Eugene Vet Center
1255 Pearl St., Suite 200
Eugene, OR 97401
541-465-6918
Fax: 541-465-6656

Grants Pass Vet Center
211 SE 10th Street

Grants Pass, OR 97526
541-479-6912
Fax: 541-474-4589

Portland Vet Center
8383 N.E. Sandy Blvd.
Suite 110
Portland, OR 97220
503-273-5370
Fax: 503-273-5377

Salem Vet Center
617 Chemeketa St., NE
Salem, OR 97301
503-362-9911
Fax: 503-364-2534

Pennsylvania
Regional Offices:
Philadelphia Regional Office and
Insurance Center
5000 Wissahickon Avenue
Philadelphia, PA 19101
800-827-1000

Pittsburgh Regional Office
1000 Liberty Avenue
Pittsburgh, PA 15222
800-827-1000

Vet Centers:
Erie Vet Center
1000 State Street
Suite 1-2
Erie, PA 16501
814-453-7955

Harrisburg Vet Center
1007 N. Front Street
Harrisburg, PA 17102
717-782-3954

McKeesport Vet Center
2001 Lincoln Way
McKeesport, PA 15131
412-678-7704

Philadelphia Vet Center
801 Arch Street
Philadelphia, PA 19107
215-627-0238

Philadelphia Vet Center
101 E. Olney Ave. , Box C-7
Philadelphia, PA 19120
215-924-4670

Pittsburgh Vet Center
954 Penn Ave.
Pittsburgh, PA 15222
412-765-1193

Scranton Vet Center
959 Wyoming Ave.
Scranton, PA 18509
570-344-2676

Philippines
Regional Office:
Manila Regional Office

1131 Roxas Blvd., Ermita
Manila, PI 96440
800-827-1000
011-632-528-2500
FTS: 011-632-528-2500

Puerto Rico
Regional Office:
San Juan Regional Office
150 Carlos Chardon Avenue
Hato Rey, PR 00918
800-827-1000
Fax: 787-772-7458

Vet Centers:
Arecibo Vet Center
52 Gonzalo Marin St.
Arecibo, PR 00612
809-879-4510
FTS: 809-879-4581

Ponce Vet Center
35 Mayor Street
Ponce, PR 00731
809-841-3260

San Juan / Rio Piedros Vet Center
Condomino Medical Center Plaza,
Suite LCBA, LC9, La Riviera
San Juan, PR 00921
787-783-8794

Rhode Island
Regional Office:
Providence Regional Office
380 Westminister Mall
Providence, RI 02903
800-827-1000

Vet Centers:
Cranston Vet Center
789 Park Avenue
Cranston, RI 02910
401-528-5271

Providence Vet Center
909 N. Main St.
Providence, RI 02904
401-528-5271

South Carolina
Regional Office:
Columbia Regional Office
1801 Assembly Street
Columbia, SC 29201
800-827-1000

Vet Centers:
Columbia Vet Center
1513 Pickens St.
Columbia, SC 29201
803-765-9944

Greenville Vet Center
14 Lavinia St.
Greenville, SC 29601
803-271-2711

North Charleston Vet Center
5603A Rivers Ave.

North Charleston, SC 29418
803-747-8387

South Dakota
Regional Office:
Sioux Falls Regional Office
P.O. Box 5046, 2501 W 22nd St.
Sioux Falls, SD 57117
800-827-1000

Vet Centers:
Rapid City Vet Center
610 Kansas City St.
Rapid City, SD 57701
605-348-0077

Sioux Falls Vet Center
601 South Cliff Ave. Suite C
Sioux Falls, SD 57102
605-332-0856

Tennessee
Regional Office:
Nashville Regional Office
110 9th Avenue South
Nashville, TN 37203
800-827-1000

Vet Centers:
Chattanooga Vet Center
425 Cumberland St.
Suite 140
Chattanooga, TN 37404
423-855-6570

Johnson City Vet Center
1615A Market St.
Johnson City, TN 37604
615-928-8387

Knoxville Vet Center
2817 E. Magnolia Ave.
Knoxville, TN 37914
423-545-4680

Memphis Vet Center
1835 Union, Suite 100
Memphis, TN 38104
901-722-2510

Texas
Regional Offices:
Houston Regional Office
6900 Almeda Road
Houston, TX 77030
800 827 1000

Waco Regional Office
1 Veterans Plaza
701 Clay Ave.
Waco, TX 76799
800-827-1000

Vet Centers:
Amarillo Vet Center
3414 E. Olsen Blvd.
Suite E.
Amarillo, TX 79109
806-354-9779
Fax: 806-351-1104

Austin Vet Center
1110 W. William Canon Dr.
Suite 301
Austin, TX 78723
512-416-1314

Corpus Christi Vet Center
3166 Reid Dr., Suite 1
Corpus Christi, TX 78404
512-854-9961

Dallas Vet Center
5232 Forest Lane, Suite 111
Dallas, TX 75244
214-361-5896

El Paso Vet Center
Sky Park II
6500 Boeing
Suite L-112
El Paso, TX 79925
915-772-0013
Fax: 915-772-3983

Fort Worth Vet Center
1305 W. Magnolia, Suite B
Fort Worth, TX 76104
817-921-9095

Houston Vet Center
503 Westheimer
Houston, TX 77006
713-523-0884

Houston Vet Center
701 N. Post Oak Road
Houston, TX 77024
713-682-2288

Laredo Vet Center
6020 Mcpherson Road
Laredo, TX 78041
956-723-4680

Lubbock Vet Center
3208 34 St.
Lubbock, TX 79410
806-792-9782
Fax: 806-792-9785

McAllen Vet Center
1317 E. Hackberry Street
McAllen, TX 78501
956-631-2147

Midland Vet Center
3404 W. Illinois, Suite 1
Midland, TX 79703
915-697-8222
Fax: 915-697-0561

San Antonio Vet Center
231 W. Cypress Street
San Antonio, TX 78212
210-229-4025

Utah
Regional Office:
Salt Lake City Regional Office
125 South State Street

Salt Lake City, UT 84147
800-827-1000

Vet Centers:
Provo Vet Center
750 North 200 West, Suite 105
Provo, UT 84601
801-377-1117

Salt Lake City Vet Center
1354 East 3300, South
Salt Lake City, UT 84106
801-584-1294

Vermont
Regional Office:
White River Junction Regional
Office
N. Hartland Road
White River Junction, VT 05009
800 827 1000

Vet Centers:
South Burlington Vet Center
359 Dorset St.
Burlington, VT 05403
802-862-1806

White River Junction Vet Center
2 Holiday Dr.
Gilman Office Building # 2
White River Junction, VT 05001
802-295-2908

Virginia
Regional Office:
Roanoke Regional Office
210 Franklin Rd. SW
Roanoke, VA 24011
800-827-1000

Vet Centers:
Alexandria Vet Center
8796 D Sacramento Dr.
Alexandria, VA 22309
703-360-8633
Fax: 703-360-6143

Norfolk Vet Center
2200 Colonial Ave. Suite 3
Norfolk, VA 23517
804-623-7584

Richmond Vet Center
3022 West Clay St.
Richmond, VA 23230
804-353-8958

Roanoke Vet Center
320 Mountain Ave SW
Roanoke, VA 24016
703-342-9726

Virgin Islands
Vet Centers:
St. Croix Vet Center
Box 12, R.R. 02
Village Mall, #113
St. Croix, VI 00850
809-778-5553

St. Thomas Vet Center
Buccaneer Mall
St. Thomas, VI 00801
809-774-6674

Washington
Regional Office:
Seattle Regional Office
Federal Building
915 2nd Avenue
Seattle, WA 98174
800-827-1000

Vet Centers:
Bellingham Vet Center
3800 Byron, Suite 124
Bellingham, WA 98226
360-733-9226
Fax: 360-733-9117

Seattle Vet Center
2030 9th Ave., Suite 210
Seattle, WA 98121
206-553-2706
Fax: 206-553-0380

Spokane Vet Center
100 N. Mullan Rd., Suite 102
Spokane, WA 99206
509-444-8387
Fax: 509-444-8388

Tacoma Vet Center
4916 Center St., Suite E
Tacoma, WA 98409
206-565-7038
Fax: 253-589-4026

West Virginia
Regional Office:
Huntington Regional Office
640 Fourth Ave.

Huntington, WV 25701
800-827-1000
Fax: 304-529-5776

Vet Centers:
Beckley Vet Center
101 Ellison Ave.
Beckley, WV 25801
304-252-8220

Charleston Vet Center
512 Washington St. West.
Charleston, WV 25302
304-343-3825

Huntington Vet Center
1005 6th Ave.
Huntington, WV 25701
304-523-8387

Martinsburg Vet Center
900 Winchester Ave.
Martinsburg, WV 25401
304-263-6776
Fax: 304-262-7448

Morgantown Vet Center
1083 Greenbag Road
Morgantown, WV 26508
304-285-4303

Mt. Gay Vet Center
Mt. Gay, WV 25637
304-752-4453

Princeton Vet Center
905 Mercer St.
Princeton, WV 24740
304-425-5653

Wheeling Vet Center
1070 Market St.

Wheeling, WV 26003
304-232-0587

Wisconsin
Regional Office:
Milwaukee Regional Office
5000 West National Avenue
Milwaukee, WI 53295
800 827 1000

Vet Centers:
Madison Vet Center
147 S. Butler Street
Madison, WI 53703
608-264-5342

Milwaukee Vet Center
3400 Wisconsin
Milwaukee, WI 53208
414-344-5504

Wyoming
Medical and Regional Office:
Cheyenne VA Medical/Regional
Office Center
2360 E. Pershing Blvd.
Cheyenne, WY 82001
800-827-1000

Vet Centers:
Casper Vet Center
111 S. Jefferson, Suite 100
Casper, WY 82601
307-261-5355

Cheyenne Vet Center
2424 Pioneer Ave., Suite 103
Cheyenne, WY 82001
307-778-7370
Fax: 307-638-8923

Other Resources for Assistance for Women, Minorities, Veterans, and the Disabled

State Departments of Economic Development offer a wealth of services to anyone interested in starting or expanding a business. In addition, many states also have specific offices set up to help minorities, women, disabled people, veterans, and others who may need help locating programs specific to their needs. The federal government and states also offer certification programs to allow disadvantaged businesses access to procurement opportunities. The following list is just a start. Explore what your area may have to offer. You may also contact the Small Business Administration to see what other resources are available to you at 800-8-ASK-SBA or {www.sba.gov}.

National

Small Disadvantaged Business (SDB)
Office of Small Disadvantaged Business Certification & Eligibility
409 Third Street, SW-8th Floor
Washington, DC 20416
202-619-1850
www.sba.gov/sbd/indexaboutsdb.html
Email: SDB@sba.gov

Certification in the SBD program allows Small Disadvantaged Businesses to be eligible for special bidding benefits in federal procurement, which will help the business become more successful. It also allows Evaluation credits for prime contractors who achieve SBD subcontracting targets, which will boost subcontracting opportunities for SDBs. The program offers instruction on how to compete in the federal contracting arena and how to take advantage of greater subcontracting opportunities. Certified businesses are included in the on-line registry of SBD-certified firms, where they will remain for a 3-year period. Contracting officers and large business prime contractors may search the list for potential suppliers. SBDs are eligible for price evaluation adjustments of up to 10% when bidding on federal contracts in certain industries. The credits are allowed in those categories where SDBs are underrepresented. The categories are: Agriculture, Fishing, Forestry, Construction, Mining, Manufacturing, Transportation, Communication, Electric, Gas, Sanitary Service, Wholesale trade, Retail trade, Finance, Insurance, and Real Estate services. To be eligible, a small business must be at least 51% owned and controlled by a socially and economically disadvantaged individual(s). African Americans, Hispanic American, Asian Pacific Americans, Subcontinent Asian American, and Native American are presumed to qualify. Individuals that can prove that it is more likely than not that they have suffered prejudicial treatment, may also qualify. All individuals must have a net worth of less than $750,000, excluding the equity of the business and primary residence. Applicants must also meet size standards for small businesses in their industry. To apply for certification, contact the office above or take the online training course on SBA certifications at {www.sba.gov/training/certprograms.html}.

Alabama

Office of Minority Business Enterprise
Alabama Department of Economic and Community Affairs
401 Adams Ave.
Montgomery, AL 36130
334-242-5370
800-447-4191
www.adeca.alabama.gov

Assists minorities in achieving effective and equitable participation in the American free enterprise system and in overcoming social and economic disadvantages that have limited their participation in the past. Management and technical assistance is provided to minority firms on request.

Alabama Department of Transportation
Human Resources Bureau
1409 Coliseum Boulevard
P.O. Box 303050
Montgomery, AL 36130-3050
334-242-6358
www.dot.state.al.us/bureau/hr/dbe/how.asp

This office develops outreach programs to recruit and inform disadvantaged business enterprises about contracting opportunities with the Department of Transportation. It also has a business support component which assesses business needs for training and technical assistance.

Alaska

Alaska Department of Transportation
Civil Rights Office
2200 East 42nd Avenue
PO Box 196900
Anchorage AK 99519-6900
907-269-0851
1-800-770-6236 (AK)
Fax: 907-269-0847
www.dot.state.ak.us/cvlrts/index.html

This office develops outreach programs to recruit and inform disadvantaged business enterprises about contracting opportunities with the Department of Transportation. It also has a business support component which assesses business needs for training and technical assistance.

Arizona

Office of Minority/Women-Owned Business Enterprises
Minority & Women Owned Businesses
Arizona Department of Commerce
Executive Tower, Suite 600
1700 W. Washington
Phoenix, AZ 85007
602-771-1100
800-526-8421
http://www.commerce.state.az.us/SmallBus
Acts as a resource and advocate for women and minority small businesses. Services include: a statewide directory of women/minority-owned businesses, Professional Women's conference sponsorship, newsletter containing calendar of events and relevant articles, marketing to state agencies and businesses, and certification seminars. They certify small, women and minority businesses to participate in state purchasing programs.

Arizona Department of Transportation
Civil Rights Office
1739 West Jackson
Room 127, Mail Drop 154A
Phoenix, AZ 85007
602-712-7761
Fax: 602-712-8429
www.dot.state.az.us/ABOUT/CRO/DBEP.htm
Email: lwormington@dot.state.az.us
This office develops outreach programs to recruit and inform disadvantaged business enterprises about contracting opportunities with the Department of Transportation. It also has a business support component which assesses business needs for training and technical assistance.

Arkansas

Arkansas Economic Development Commission
One Capitol Mall
Little Rock, AR 72201
501-682-6105
800-ARKANSAS
www.1-800-arkansas.com/Small_Business
The Minority and Small Business Development Division provides business loan packaging, contract procurement assistance, bonding information, general business counseling, seminars, workshops, and referrals to other agencies.

Arkansas State Highway and Transportation Department
Programs and Contracts Division
10324 Interstate 30
Little Rock, AR 72211
501-569-2261
www.ahtd.state.ar.us/Contract/contract.htm
Email: pcd@ahtd.state.ar.us
This office develops outreach programs to recruit and inform disadvantaged business enterprises about contracting opportunities with the Department of Transportation. It also has a business support component which assesses business needs for training and technical assistance.

California

California Small Business & DVBE
Department of General Services
707 Third Street
West Sacramento, CA 95605
916-375-4940
800-559-5529
www.pd.dgs.ca.gov/smbus
This office helps minority businesses interested in participating in the state's purchasing/contracting system along with counseling and outreach programs.

California Department of Transportation
Civil Rights Program - MS #79
1823 14th Street
Sacramento, CA 95814
916-324-1700
866-810-6346
Fax: 916-324-1949
www.dot.ca.gov/hq/bep/contactus.htm
richard_novoa@dot.ca.gov
This office develops outreach programs to recruit and inform disadvantaged business enterprises about contracting opportunities with the Department of Transportation. It also has a business support component which assesses business needs for training and technical assistance.

Colorado

Office of Economic Development and International Trade
1625 Broadway, Suite 1710
Denver, CO 80202
303-892-3840
Women's Business Office: Strives to keep the women entrepreneurs of Colorado informed about pertinent issues through all modes of communication. {www.state.co.us /oed/wbo}

Minority Business Office: Acts as a clearinghouse to disseminate information to the minority business community. Promotes economic development for minority businesses in cooperation with the state economic development activities. Establishes networks between majority and minority business sectors. Promotes minority participation in state procurement. Assists Colorado in achieving its Minority Procurement Goals of 17%. Works with the Minority Business Advisory Council and the minority community in promoting minority business development. {www.state.co.us/oed/mbo}

Colorado Department of Transportation
Business Programs Office
1325 South Colorado Boulevard
Building B, Suite 404
Mailing Address:
  4201 East Arkansas Avenue
  Denver, CO 80222
303-757-9599
800-925-3427
Email: greg.diehl@dot.state.co.us
www.dot.state.co.us/EEO/DBEProgramPage.htm
This office develops outreach programs to recruit and inform disadvantaged business enterprises about contracting opportunities with the Department of Transportation. It also has a business support component which assesses business needs for training and technical assistance.

Connecticut

Department of Administrative Services
Business Connections/Set-Aside Unit
165 Capitol Ave., Room 110
Hartford, CT 06106
860-718-5228
www.das.ct.us/busopp.asp
Procurement Program: Set-Aside Program requires state agencies and political subdivisions to set aside 25% of their budget for construction, housing rehabilitation and the purchasing of supplies. These services are awarded to certified small business contractors, minority businesses, enterprises, nonprofit corporations and individuals with a disability. 25% of this amount is to be awarded to certified minority owned firms.

Community Economic Development Fund
430 New Park Avenue, 2nd Floor
West Hartford, CT 06110-1142
860-249-3800
800-656-4613
www.cedf.com
A loan guarantee program designed to help women and minority-owned businesses obtain financing. The funds are available for start-up as well as for the growth of an existing company.

Connecticut Department of Transportation
Bureau of Finance & Administration
2800 Berlin Turnpike
Newington CT 06131-7546
860-594-2171
Fax: 860-594-3016
Email: Shari.Pratt@po.state.ct.us
www.ct.gov/dot/cwp/view.asp?A=1394&Q=259534
This office develops outreach programs to recruit and inform disadvantaged business enterprises about contracting opportunities with the Department of Transportation. It also has a business support component which assesses business needs for training and technical assistance.

Delaware
Minority Enterprise Office
800 N. French St., 6th Floor
Wilmington, DE 19801
302-576-2121
www.ci.wilmington.de.us/mbeo.htm
The agency assists minority businesses in the city of Wilmington by providing technical assistance, certificate of minority businesses, and workshops. They sponsor a Minority Business Trade Fair (the largest in the Northeast) once a year. The agency works with the Wilmington Economic Development Corporation to provide financing.

Department of Administrative Services
Office of Minority and Women Business Enterprise
Margaret O'Neill Building
410 Federal Street
Dover, DE 19901
302-739-7830
www2.state.de.us/omwdbe/
The office promotes women and minority businesses in state procurement process. Advocates for programs and activities that support these businesses. They assist in the certification of minority and women owned businesses.

Delaware Department of Transportation
DBE Office
P.O. Box 778
Dover, DE 19903
302-760-2035
www.deldot.net/static/business/dbe/prog_plan.html
lsmith@mail.dot.state.de.us
This office develops outreach programs to recruit and inform disadvantaged business enterprises about contracting opportunities with the Department of Transportation. It also has a business support component which assesses business needs for training and technical assistance.

District of Columbia
Office of Local Business Development
DBE, 441 4th Street, NW, Suite 970
Washington, DC 20001
202-727-3900
http://olbd.dc.gov

Office of Local Business Development Disadvantaged Business Enterprise: Promotes equal opportunity in all aspects of District life and fosters minority business development through:
- *Certified Contractors List*.
- *Local, Small and Disadvantaged Business Certification Program*
- *Technical Assistance Program*: Aids minority business enterprises through workshops, contracting conferences, referrals to bid and compete on District Government contracts.

Florida
Office of Supplier Diversity
Florida Department of Management Services
4050 Esplanade Way, Suite 360
Tallahassee, FL 32399-0950
850-487-0915
http://dms.myflorida.com
Office of Supplier Diversity (OSD): Responsible for certifying minority business enterprises to do business with state agencies. Develops statewide initiative to help minority and women-owned businesses prosper in Florida and the global marketplace. Advocates for minority economic development and provides assistance to minority businesses and organizations in many ways, including identifying agencies who would buy their product or service. They also offer a Florida Minority Business Loan Mobilization Program. This provides working capital loans to businesses that are vendors on state agency contracts.

Florida Black Business Investment Board
1711 S. Gadsen St.
Tallahassee, Fl 32301
850-487-4850
www.fbbib.com
Black Business Investment Board: Oversees the state's investment in black business investment corporations, which provide technical assistance and loans, loan guarantees, and venture capitol to black-owned businesses.

Enterprise Florida
Suite 1300, 390 N. Orange Ave.
Orlando, FL 32801
407-316-4600
www.eflorida.com/smallbusiness/assistance.asp
Florida Small Disadvantaged Manufacturers Corporation (FSDMC): Services are provided for minority and women owned manufacturing businesses in order to increase their viability, competitiveness and capabilities. As members, those businesses will get on-site business assessment, workshops and seminars, technical assistance and counseling, and more.

Florida Minority Business Opportunity Committee
6880 Lake Ellenor Drive, Suite 104G
Orlando, FL 32809
407-245-6493
www.mbocflorida.org/
The Florida MBOC provides opportunities for minority-owned companies to access capital, develop strategies for success through mentoring and to bring businesses and organizations together.

Florida Department of Transportation
Equal Opportunity Office
605 Suwannee Street, MS 65
Tallahassee, FL 32399-0450
850-414-4747
866-374-FDOT (3368)

www.dot.state.fl.us/equalopportunityoffice
Email: arthur.wright@dot.state.fl.us
This office develops outreach programs to recruit and inform disadvantaged business enterprises about contracting opportunities with the Department of Transportation. It also has a business support component which assesses business needs for training and technical assistance.

Georgia
GRASP
241 Peachtree St., NE, Suite 200
Atlanta, GA 30303
404-659-5955
www.graspnet.org
The Atlanta Women's Business Center: A major new resource for women who want to start a business or for those who already operate a business. The center offers assistance with various aspects of business operations including cash flow and profit margin projections. The center has a well organized information section stocked with computers, manuals, books and audio and videotapes on various business topics. Counselors from GRASP are available to women entrepreneurs. Workshops and seminars are offered throughout the year and cover such topics as the basics of starting a business, developing a business plan, marketing, sources of business capital, and technology as a business tool.

Governor's Small Business Center
200 Piedmont Ave.
Suite 1102, West Tower
Atlanta, GA 30334
404-656-6315
800-495-0053
www.doas.state.ga.us
Georgia Minority Subcontractors Tax Credit: Provides for an income tax adjustment on the State Tax Return, to any company which subcontracts with a minority-owned firm to furnish goods, property or services to the State of Georgia. The law allows a corporation, partnership, or individual, in computing Georgia taxable income, to subtract from federal taxable income or federal adjusted gross income, up to $100,000 of the amount of qualified payments to minority subcontractors. Businesses can also be certified as minority-owned for government contract purposes.

Minority Small Business Resource Organizations: These organizations provide a variety of technical counseling and financial assistance to minority small businesses:
1. *Atlanta Business League*, PO Box 92363, Atlanta, GA 30314; 404-584-8126; {www.theabl.org}.
2. *Atlanta Public Schools*, Contract Compliance Office, 1631 LaFrance Street, NE, Atlanta, GA 30307;404-371-7130; {www.atlanta.k12.ga.us/inside_aps/finance/contractw/default.htm}.
3. *Business Development Center – NAACP*, 2034 Metropolitan Parkway, SW, Atlanta, GA 30315; 404-761-1266; {www.atlantanaacp.org}.
4. *Department of Commerce*, Minority Business Development Agency (MBDA), Summit Building, Room 1715, 401 West Peachtree Street, NW, Atlanta, GA 30308; 404-730-3300; {www.mbda/gov}.
5. *Small Business Administration*, Minority Enterprise Development, 233 Peachtree St., NE, Suite 1900, Atlanta, GA 30303; 404-331-0100; {www.sba.gov/ga}.

Georgia Department of Transportation
Equal Opportunity Division
No. 2 Capitol Square, SW, Room 142
Atlanta, GA 30303

404-656-5323
www.dot.state.ga.us/dot/eeo-div/dbeapp.shtml
Email: charles_French@dot.ga.us
This office develops outreach programs to recruit and inform disadvantaged business enterprises about contracting opportunities with the Department of Transportation. It also has a business support component which assesses business needs for training and technical assistance.

Hawaii
Aliiaimoku Building
869 Punchbowl Street
Honolulu, HI 96813
DBE Program Manager
Email: melanie.martin@hawaii.gov
808-587-2023
Fax: 808-587-2025
www.hawaii.gov/dot/administration/dbe/index.htm
This office develops outreach programs to recruit and inform disadvantaged business enterprises about contracting opportunities with the Department of Transportation. It also has a business support component which assesses business needs for training and technical assistance.

Idaho
DBE Supportive Services
Idaho Transportation Department
P.O. Box 7129
Boise, ID 83707-1129
208-334-8567
800-634-7790
www.itd.idaho.gov/civil/external.htm
Email: civilrights3@itd.state.id.us
This office develops outreach programs to recruit and inform disadvantaged business enterprises about contracting opportunities with the Department of Transportation. It also has a business support component which assesses business needs for training and technical assistance.

Illinois
Business Enterprise Program for Minorities, Females, and Persons with Disabilities
100 W. Randolph St., Suite 4-400
Chicago, IL 60601
312-814-4190
800-356-9206
www.state.il.us/cms/purchase/bep/about.htm
Business Enterprise Program for Minorities, Females, and Persons with Disabilities (BEP): Promotes the economic development of businesses owned by minorities, females, and persons with disabilities. The Business Enterprise for Minorities, Females, and Persons with Disabilities Act is designed to encourage state agencies to purchase needed goods and services from businesses owned and controlled by members of minority groups, women, and/or persons with disabilities.

Illinois Department of Commerce and Economic Opportunity
620 E. Adams St.
Springfield, IL 62701
217-524-0165
www.commerce.state.il.us/ilfactsheets/busfinance.html
Surety Bond Guaranty Program: Designed to provide Illinois' small, minority and women contractors technical assistance, help them receive experience in the industry and assist in obtaining bid, performance and payment bonds for government, public utility and private contracts.

Illinois Department of Commerce
Business Finance Division

100 W. Randolph, Suite 3-400
Chicago, IL 60601
312-841-9303
www.commerce.state.il.us/bus/plp.html
Minority, Women and Disabled Participation Loan Program: The Minority, Women and Disabled Participation Loan Program offers financing, but may not exceed 50% of the project, subject to a maximum of $50,000.

Illinois Women's Business Ownership Council
Illinois Department of Commerce and Community Affairs
State of Illinois Center
100 W. Randolph St.
Suite 3-400
Chicago, IL 60601
312-814-7179
www.illinoisbiz.biz/bus/IWBOChome.html
The Small Business Advocate specializes in helping women, minorities, startups, and home-based business owners cut through the bureaucratic red tape and get the answers they need by offering information and expertise in dealing with various state, federal, and local agencies.

Minority Business Council
Illinois Department of Commerce and Economic Opportunity
Minority Business Council
100 W. Randolph, Suite 3-400
Chicago, IL 60601
312-814-8841
www.commerce.state.il.us
Minority Business councils advocate and provide resources to minorities wishing to start or expand their businesses.

Office of Minority and Women's Business Development
Illinois Department of Commerce and Economic Opportunity
100 W. Randolph St., Suite 3-400
Chicago, IL 60601
312-814-8841
www.commerce.state.il.us
Businesses owned by minorities, women, veterans and persons with disabilities can turn to this office for advice on technical, management and financial assistance issues.

Illinois Department of Transportation
Office of Business and Workforce Diversity
Bureau of Small Business Enterprises
2300 South Dirksen Parkway
Springfield, IL 62764
217-782-9103
http://dot.state.il.us/sbe/dbeprogram.html
This office develops outreach programs to recruit and inform disadvantaged business enterprises about contracting opportunities with the Department of Transportation. It also has a business support component which assesses business needs for training and technical assistance.

Indiana

Indiana Small Business Development Corporation (ISBD Corp.)
One N. Capital Ave., Suite 900
Indianapolis, IN 46204
317-234-2082
888-ISDB-244
www.isbdc.org
Women and Minorities in Business Group (WMBG): Eligibility: Indiana businesses owned by women and/or minorities. Services/Uses: Counsels emerging and mature businesses. Client needs are determined, evaluated and advised at no cost. Services include: workshops and seminars, direct counseling, information clearinghouse and

referral source, general information, including statistics regarding women- and minority-owned businesses.

Department of Administration
402 West Washington Street, Room W474
Indianapolis, IN 46204
317-232-3061
www.in.gov/idoa/minority/index.html
Minority Business Development: The Department of Administration administers the state of Indiana's Minority Business Enterprise Program. Some of the services provided are the offering of state purchasing opportunities; workshops on state procurement; monitoring and providing networking assistance; and matching majority owned businesses with minority owned businesses.

Indiana Department of Administration
Deputy Commissioner for Minority and Women's Business Enterprises
402 West Washington Street W474
Indianapolis, IN 46204
317-232-3061
www.ai.org/idoa/minority/index.html
This office develops outreach programs to recruit and inform disadvantaged business enterprises about contracting opportunities with the Department of Transportation. It also has a business support component which assesses business needs for training and technical assistance.

Iowa

Iowa Department of Economic Development
200 E Grand Ave.
Des Moines, IA 50309
515-242-4819
800-532-1215
www.iowasmart.com/services/small_business/tsbfap.html
Targeted Small Business Financial Assistance Program (TSBFAP): Designed to assist in the creation and expansion of Iowa small businesses that have an annual gross sales of $3 million and are at least 51% owned, operated and managed by women, minorities or persons with a disability. The business must be certified as a "Targeted Small Business" by the Iowa Department of Inspections and Appeals before applying for or receiving TSB funds. Awards may be obtained in one of the following forms of assistance:

- Low-interest loans - Loans of up to $25,000 may be provided at interest rates of 0-5 percent, to be repaid in monthly installments over a five- to seven-year period. The first installment can be deferred for three months for a start-up business and one month for an existing business.
- Loan guarantees are available up to $40,000. Loan guarantees can cover up to 75% of a loan obtained from a bank or other conventional lender. The interest rate is at the discretion of the lender.
- In limited cases, equity grants - to be used to leverage other financing (SBA or conventional) - are available in amounts of up to $25,000.
- TSB funds may be used to purchase equipment, acquire inventory, provide operating capital or to leverage additional funding.

Iowa Department of Economic Development
200 E Grand Ave.
Des Moines, IA 50309
515-242-4819
800-532-1215
www.iowasmart.com/services/small_business/selp.html
Self-Employment Loan Program (SELP): This program is designed to assist in the creation and expansion of businesses

owned, operated and managed by women, minorities, or persons with a disability. To qualify for a SELP loan, applicants must have an annualized family income that does not exceed current income guidelines for the program. An applicant is automatically eligible for SELP if he or she is receiving Family Investment Plan (FIP) assistance or other general assistance such as disability benefits. The applicant can also qualify for SELP funds if determined eligible under the Job Training Partnership Act, or is certified as having a disability under standards established by the Iowa Department of Education, Division of Vocational Rehabilitation Services. SELP loans of up to $10,000 are available. The interest rate is 5 percent, and the loan is to be repaid in monthly installments over a five-year period. The first installment can be deferred for three months for a start-up business and one month for an existing business.

Iowa Department of Economic Development
200 E Grand Ave.
Des Moines, IA 50309
515-242-4819
www.iowasmart.com/services/entrepreneurial/ewd.html
Entrepreneurs With Disabilities (EWD): Helps qualified individuals with disabilities establish, acquire, maintain or expand a small business by providing technical and financial assistance. To be eligible for the program, applicants must be active clients of the Iowa Department of Education Division of Vocational Rehabilitation Services or the Iowa Department for the Blind. Technical Assistance grants of up to $10,000 may be used to pay for any specific business-related consulting service such as developing a feasibility study or business plan, or accounting and legal services. Financial Assistance grants of up to $10,000 may be used to purchase equipment, supplies, rent or other start-up, expansion or acquisition costs identified in an approved business plan. Total financial assistance provided to an individual may not exceed 50% (maximum of $10,000) of the financial package. EWD financial assistance must be fully matched by funding from other sources.

Institute of Social and Economic Development
901 23rd Avenue
Coralville, IA 52241
319-338-2331
Fax: 319-338-5824
www.ised.org
Institute of Social and Economic Development: Focuses on minorities, women, persons with disabilities and low-income individuals. Encourages self-sufficiency through the growth of small business and self-employment opportunities, and provides services for any person who wants to start or expand a business employing up to five employees, including the owner(s).

Iowa Department of Transportation
Office of Contracts
EEO Section
800 Lincoln Way
Ames, IA 50010
515-239-1422
www.dot.state.ia.us/contracts/contracts_eeoaa.htm
This office develops outreach programs to recruit and inform disadvantaged business enterprises about contracting opportunities with the Department of Transportation. It also has a business support component which assesses business needs for training and technical assistance.

Kansas

Kansas Department of Commerce
1000 SW Jackson St., Suite 100
Topeka, KS 66612

785-296-5298
www.kansascommerce.com
Office of Minority & Women Business Development: Promotes and assists in the development of minority-owned and women-owned businesses in Kansas. The program provides assistance in procurement and contracting, financing resources, business planning, and identification of business opportunities. A directory of minority-owned and women-owned businesses in Kansas is published annually. Responsible for certifying minority-and-women-owned businesses as small disadvantaged businesses for non-highway related firms.

Kansas Department of Transportation
Office of Engineering Support
Docking State Office Building
Topeka, KS 66612-1568
785-296-7940
Fax: 785-296-0723
800-854-3613
www.ksdot.org/offengsupp/dbe.htm
This office develops outreach programs to recruit and inform disadvantaged business enterprises about contracting opportunities with the Department of Transportation. It also has a business support component which assesses business needs for training and technical assistance.

Kentucky

Small and Minority Business
Kentucky Cabinet for Economic Development
500 Mero Street
Capital Plaza Tower
Frankfort, KY 40601
502-564-2064
877-355-3822
www.thinkkentucky.com/SMBD/
The Small and Minority Business Division is a resource center for small and minority business owners/managers. It identifies construction contracts, procurement opportunities, and offers training programs that address the business needs of these enterprises. It focuses on new job creation and job retention by serving existing small and minority businesses in the roles of ombudsman and expediter for business growth and retention. It assists small, women and minority-owned businesses in getting certified.

Kentucky Transportation Cabinet
Division of Contract Procurement
200 Mero Street, 3rd Floor West
Frankfort, KY 40622
502-564-3500
Fax: 502-564-8961
www.kytc.state.ky.us/Contract/DBE
This office develops outreach programs to recruit and inform disadvantaged business enterprises about contracting opportunities with the Department of Transportation. It also has a business support component which assesses business needs for training and technical assistance.

Louisiana

Louisiana Economic Development
Capital Annex
1051 N. 3rd Street
P.O. Box 94185
Baton Rouge, LA 70804-9185
225-342-3000
www.lded.state.la.us/businessresources/rules_matching.asp
The Louisiana Minority Venture Capital Matching Grant Program allows qualifying minority-owned businesses to invest $1 in their business and receive $2 of private capital.

Louisiana Department of Transportation & Development
Compliance programs Section
P.O. Box 94245
Baton Rouge, LA 70804-9245
225-379-1382
Fax: 225-379-1382
www.dotd.state.la.us/programs_grants/dbe/ladotddbe.shtml
This office develops outreach programs to recruit and inform
disadvantaged business enterprises about contracting
opportunities with the Department of Transportation. It also
has a business support component which assesses business
needs for training and technical assistance.

Maine

Maine Department of Transportation
Office of Human Resources
#16 State House Station
Augusta, ME 04333-0016
207-624-3066
Fax: 207-624-3051
TDD: 207-287-3392
www.maine.gov/mdot/disadvantaged-business-
enterprises/dbe-home.php
This office develops outreach programs to recruit and inform
disadvantaged business enterprises about contracting
opportunities with the Department of Transportation. It also
has a business support component which assesses business
needs for training and technical assistance.

Maryland

Maryland Department of Business and Economic
Development
Governor's Office of Minority Affairs
217 East Redwood Street
Baltimore, MD 21202
410-767-8232
http://mdminoritybusiness.com
Assists minority firms in Maryland seeking contract and
procurement opportunities with the State. OMA provides
referral assistance and consultation to minority business
owners on both public and private sector opportunities and
resources, co-sponsors conferences and seminars that provide
information to minority entrepreneurs regarding business
opportunities and more.

Maryland Department of Transportation
7201 Corporate Center
Hanover, MD 21076
410-865-1241
www.mdot.state.md.us/MBE_Program/DBE.html
Email: mbe@mdot.state.md.us
This office develops outreach programs to recruit and inform
disadvantaged business enterprises about contracting
opportunities with the Department of Transportation. It also
has a business support component which assesses business
needs for training and technical assistance.

Helping Minorities Build Better Businesses
Association for Minority Economic Expansion
55 Baileys Court
Silver Spring, MD 20906
866-301-0245
Fax: 301-924-9009
www.amee-metro.org/
Helping Minorities Build Better Businesses
The Association for Minority Economic Expansion (AMEE)
is focused on providing African Americans with loans and
assistance services for starting a business. AMEE offers
microloans to individuals in economically depressed areas
who have sound business ideas and the desire translate them

into a commercial enterprise. Microloans are up to $25,000
and there is no application fee. Accompanying counseling on
the fundamentals of business start-up, technical assistance
programs and extensive information and referral services are
available to all clients. AMEE links entrepreneurs to other
cost-saving services, such as discount business phone service
plans, internet hosting options, insurance plans, and low-cost
legal service providers. AMEE Business Services will also
print business cards, stationary, and custom pieces for start-
up businesses at cut-rate prices.

Money To Open Sports Stores
Development Credit Fund, Inc.
2530 North Charles Street, Suite 200
Baltimore, MD 21218
410-467-7500
Fax: 410-467-7988
www.developmentcredit.com/
The Development Credit Fund has partnered with Nike (yes,
the powerhouse marked by a swoosh) and the Maryland
Department of Business and Economic Development to
provide start-up business loans to minorities for the
establishment of retail athletic specialty stores. The launch
site for the Minority Retail Entrepreneurial Fund is
Baltimore, with an initial loan fund of $1 million to promote
minority entrepreneurship. Loans of one to ten year terms are
available for working capital, leaseholds, inventory,
equipment and machinery. Minorities looking to open
sporting stores in Maryland, DC, Virginia and Delaware are
invited to apply. Applications are available on-line and must
be accompanied by a business plan, detailed description of
the applicant's experience in athletics/retail, and financial
projections. Nike must approve the chosen location for the
retail store.

Massachusetts

Department of Commerce
10 Park Plaza, Suite 3740
Boston, MA 02116
617-973-8692
www.somwba.state.ma.us
*State Office of Minority and Women Business Assistance
(SOMWBA)*: Certifies companies as minority or women-
owned or controlled, and publishes a directory listing of
verified firms. SOMWBA provides management and
technical assistance seminars and workshops for minority and
women entrepreneurs on a wide variety of business topics.

Massachusetts Office of Business Development
10 Park Plaza, Suite 4510
Boston, MA 02116
617-973-8600
800-5-CAPITAL
www.mass.gov
Minority Business Financing: A MOBD Business Finance
Specialist can guide a company to several targeted financing
programs including the Community Development Finance
Corporation's Urban Initiative Fund, the Economic
Development Fund and others.

Community Development Finance Corporation
100 City Hall Plaza, Suite 300
Boston, MA 02108
617-523-6262
www.mcdfc.com
*Massachusetts Community Development Finance
Corporation (CDFC):* One of the goals of CDFC is to invest
in small business, which will result in job growth. They do
this through the following programs:

- CDFC's Minority & Women Contractor Bond Program- Technical and financial assistance is available to help contractors to qualify for surety bonds while establishing a relationship with a surety company.
- Urban Initiative Fund (UIF)- Minority-owned businesses with less than $500,000 in annual sales can get technical assistance and loans to strengthen their business from this fund. It also provides loans and grants for a variety of innovative economic development and human service projects.

State Office of Minority and Women Business Assistance
SOMWBA
10 Park Plaza, Suite 3740
Boston, MA 02116
617-973-8692
Fax: 617-973-8637
www.somwba.state.ma.us
Email: wsomwba@state.ma.us
This office develops outreach programs to recruit and inform disadvantaged business enterprises about contracting opportunities with the Department of Transportation. It also has a business support component which assesses business needs for training and technical assistance.

Michigan
Minority And Women's Prequalification Loan and the Women's Pre-Qualification Loan Program: Use intermediaries to assist prospective minority and women borrowers in developing viable loan application packages and securing loans. The women's program uses only nonprofit organizations as intermediaries; the minority program uses for-profit intermediaries as well.

Michigan Economic Development Corporation
300 N Washington Square
Lansing, MI 48913
517-373-9808
http://medc.michigan.org
The Michigan Economic Development Corporation provides a number of general business start-up and expansion services, which include a Directory of minority and women-owned businesses.

Michigan Department of Transportation
Bureau of Highways
P.O. Box 30049
Lansing, MI 48909
517-322-6181
Fax: 517-322-5664
www.michigan.gov/mdot/0,1607,7-151-9625_21539_23108---,00.html
This office develops outreach programs to recruit and inform disadvantaged business enterprises about contracting opportunities with the Department of Transportation. It also has a business support component which assesses business needs for training and technical assistance.

Minnesota
Minnesota Department of Employment and Economic Development
500 Mero Square Bldg.
121 E. 7th Place
St. Paul, MN 55121
651-297-1170
800-657-3858
www.dted.state.mn.us
Urban Initiative Loan Program: Exists to assist minority owned and operated businesses and others that will create jobs in low-income areas of the Twin Cities. Urban Initiative

Board enters into partnerships with local nonprofit organizations, which provide loans and technical assistance to start-up and expanding businesses. Project must demonstrate potential to create jobs for low-income people, must be unable to obtain sufficient capital from traditional private lenders, and must be able to demonstrate the potential to succeed. Eligible projects: Start-up and expansion costs, including normal business expenses such as machinery and equipment, inventory and receivables, working capital, new construction, renovation, and site acquisition. Financing of existing debt is not permitted. Micro enterprises, including retail businesses, may apply for up to $10,000 in state funds. Maximum available: The maximum total loan available through the Urban Initiative Program is $300,000. The state may contribute 50% of the loan up to $150,000.

Department of Administration
Materials Management Division
Administrative Building, Room 112
St. Paul, MN 55155
651-296-2600
http://www.mmd.admin.state.mn.us
This office certifies women-owned businesses to participate in the Small Business Program for procurement opportunities with the state. Once certified, a business earns a 6% preference on government contract bids.

Minnesota Department of Transportation
Office of EEO
395 John Ireland BLVD M.S. 170
St. Paul, MN 55155
651-297-3589
Email: EqualOpportunity@dot.state.mn.us
www.dot.state.mn.us/eeocm/dbe.html
This office develops outreach programs to recruit and inform disadvantaged business enterprises about contracting opportunities with the Department of Transportation. It also has a business support component which assesses business needs for training and technical assistance.

Mississippi
Mississippi Development Authority
P.O. Box 849
Jackson, MS 39205
601-359-3552
Fax: 601-357-3619
www.mississippi.org
Minority Business Enterprise Division (MBED): Provides assistance to businesses in those categories. The division acts as principal advocate on behalf of minority- and women-owned business enterprises and promotes legislation that will help them operate more effectively. Developing funding sources, including state funding, bonding resources, federal and local funds, and others is among the major aims of MBED. But identifying funding sources represents only one aspect of MBED's service to Mississippi's women- and minority-owned firms. The division also attempts to put those businesses in touch with potential customers; MBED maintains an outreach program designed to include them in contracting of goods and services and procurement of contracts. A regional and statewide network of workshops, seminars, and trade shows continually provide training to stimulate the role of entrepreneurship in Mississippi's economic development.

Minority Surety Bond Guaranty Program: Program enables minority contractors, not meeting the surety industry's standard underwriting criteria, to obtain bid and performance bonds on contracts with state agencies and political subdivisions. Maximum bond guarantee is 90% of contract bond amount, or $175,000, whichever is less.

Minority Business Enterprise Loan Program: Designed to provide loans to socially and economically disadvantaged minority-or women-owned small businesses. Loan proceeds may be used for all project costs associated with the establishment or expansion of a minority business, including the purchase of fixed assets or inventory or to provide working capital. The minimum loan is $2,000 and the maximum loan is $250,000. MDA may fund up to 100% of a total project.

Micro Loan Program: Minority businesses can apply for gap financing to fund small projects. Funding ranges from $2,000 to $35,000 and owners' equity injection is only 5%. The money may be used for the purchase of fixed assets, working capital, or inventory purchase.

Mississippi Department of Transportation
Office of Civil Rights
ATT: DBE Coordinator
P.O. Box 1850
Jackson, MS 39215-1850
601-359-7466
www.gomdot.com/business/dbe/dbe.htm
Email: cmurphy@mdot.state.ms.us
This office develops outreach programs to recruit and inform disadvantaged business enterprises about contracting opportunities with the Department of Transportation. It also has a business support component which assesses business needs for training and technical assistance.

Missouri

Trish Rogers
Central Ozarks Private Industry Council
1202 Forum Drive
Rolla, MO 65401
800-638-1401 ext. 153
Fax: 573-634-1865
Workforce Readiness for Women: This particular program provides skills for employment in manufacturing industries for women living in Camden, Laclede, and Pulaski Counties. Training includes classroom instruction, one-on-one instruction and tutoring, computer training and work experience assignments with private employers who agree to provide the necessary supervision and work experience to assist participants with skills development and transition into employment in the manufacturing industry.

Capital for Entrepreneurs
4747 Troost Ave.
Kansas City, MO 64110
816-561-4646
Fax: 816-756-1530
Capital for Entrepreneurs, Kansas City: Seed capital fund divided into three separate funds of $1 million each: Fund for Women, Fund for Hispanics, and Fund for African-Americans.

Missouri Department of Economic Development
Office of Minority Business
301 W. High St.
P.O. Box 118, Room 720
Jefferson City, MO 65102
573-751-3237
888-791-3237
www.ded.mo.gov/business/officeofminoritybusiness
Office of Minority Business (OMB): Charged with the responsibility of identifying and developing support systems that assist the minority business community in gaining a foothold in the mainstream of Missouri's economy. This responsibility entails counseling minority small businesses on business start-up, retention, expansion, financing, and procurement; also including but not limited to providing ready access to information regarding current legislation and regulations that affects minority business. The staff of the Office of Minority Business can provide assistance with; administering technical and financial assistance programs; providing new and small businesses with management expertise; business development information; tying minority firms to national and global markets; connecting minority firms to the labor market; accessing research and technology; and other customized assistance.

Missouri Women's Council
P.O. Box 1684
421 East Dunklin Street
Jefferson City, MO 65102
573-751-0810
877-426-9284
www.womenscouncil.org
The Council helps women small business owners through various programs, seminars, and conferences. The Missouri Council on Women's Economic Development and Training assists women in small business enterprises. The Council conducts programs, studies, seminars, and conferences. It promotes increased economic and employment opportunities through education, training, and greater participation in the labor force.

Missouri Department of Transportation
External Civil Rights Office
P.O. Box 270
Jefferson City MO 65102-0270
573-751-2859
Fax: 573-526-0558
www.modot.state.mo.us/business/contractor_resources/exter
nalcivilrights.htm
Email: dbe@mail.modot.state.mo.us
This office develops outreach programs to recruit and inform disadvantaged business enterprises about contracting opportunities with the Department of Transportation. It also has a business support component which assesses business needs for training and technical assistance.

Montana

Montana Department of Transportation
Civil Rights Bureau
PO Box 201001
2701 Prospect Avenue
Helena, MT 59620-1001
406-444-6337
www.mdt.state.mt.us/civilrights
Email: lwootan@state.mt.us
This office develops outreach programs to recruit and inform disadvantaged business enterprises about contracting opportunities with the Department of Transportation. It also has a business support component which assesses business needs for training and technical assistance.

Nebraska

Office of Women's Business Ownership
Small Business Administration
11145 Mill Valley Rd.
Omaha, NE 68154
402-221-4691
www.sba.gov/ne

The office directs Small Business Administration (SBA) programs to women business owners through special women's groups, seminars, networks, and other activities for women in the private sector.

Nebraska Department of Roads
DBE Office
P.O. Box 94759
Lincoln, Nebraska 68509-4759
1500 Highway 2, Lincoln
402-479-4531
Fax: 402-479-4854
www.dor.state.ne.us/letting/dbeinfo.htm
Email: jkisicke@dor.state.ne.us
This office develops outreach programs to recruit and inform disadvantaged business enterprises about contracting opportunities with the Department of Transportation. It also has a business support component which assesses business needs for training and technical assistance.

Nevada
State of Nevada Department of Transportation
Contract Compliance Division
Nevada Unified Certification Program
1263 South Stewart Street
Carson City, NV 89712-0002
775-888-7497
800-267-1971
Fax: 775-888-7235
www.nevadadbe.com
Email: info@nevadadbe.com
This office develops outreach programs to recruit and inform disadvantaged business enterprises about contracting opportunities with the Department of Transportation. It also has a business support component which assesses business needs for training and technical assistance.

New Hampshire
Office of Business and Industrial Development
Division of Economic Development
172 Pembroke Rd.
P.O. Box 856
Concord, NH 03302-0856
603-271-2411
www.nheconomy.com
This office serves as a clearinghouse and referral center of programs for women and minority-owned businesses.

New Hampshire Department of Transportation (NHDOT)
DBE Coordinator
P.O. Box 483
1 Hazen Drive
Concord, NH 03302-0483
603-271-6612
http://www.nh.gov/dot/humanresources/dbe/index.htm
This office develops outreach programs to recruit and inform disadvantaged business enterprises about contracting opportunities with the Department of Transportation. It also has a business support component which assesses business needs for training and technical assistance.

New Jersey
New Jersey Department of Commerce and Economic Development
Office of Small, Women, and Minority-owned Businesses
CN 835
Trenton, NJ 08625
609-777-0885
www.state.nj.us/commerce/smallbiz/html

Services For Businesses Owned By Women And Minorities: Businesses owned by women and minorities play an important role in the New Jersey economy. New Jersey offers a number of services to help these businesses compete and overcome the special challenges they face. These services include financial assistance, advice and instructional materials, training and education, and certification necessary to receive certain contracts.

Set Aside Contracts: State law requires that 25% of the contracts awarded by the State be given to businesses owned by minorities, small business, and women. Women and minorities interested in establishing franchise businesses may receive investments from the Small Business Investment Company, which works in conjunction with the New Jersey Economic Development Authority's Commercial Lending Division.

New Jersey Economic Development Authority
P.O. Box 990
Trenton, NJ 08625
609-292-1800
www.njeda.com
Contractors Assistance Program: Small contracting businesses owned by women or minorities may receive training courses and consultations with experienced executives of large construction companies designed to make it easier to get performance bonds and successfully bid on major construction projects. This service is provided by the New Jersey Economic Development Authority's Community Development and Small Business Lending Division.

New Jersey Development Authority For Small Businesses, Minorities' And Women's Enterprises: This office offers women and minority-owned small businesses financial, marketing, procurement, technical and managerial assistance. Loans of up to $1 million can be made for real estate, fixed asset acquisition, and working capital. Guarantees to banks are also available for fixed asset acquisition and for working capital. To be eligible, a business must be certified as a small, minority-owned or women-owned enterprise. Most of the funds are targeted to enterprises located in Atlantic City or providing goods or services to customers in Atlantic City, including but not limited to the casinos. Limited monies are available for businesses located in other parts of the state.

New Jersey Department of Transportation
Division of Procurement
P.O. Box 600
Trenton, NJ 08625-0600
609-530-6355
Fax: 609-530-6586
www.state.nj.us/transportation/business/procurement
This office develops outreach programs to recruit and inform disadvantaged business enterprises about contracting opportunities with the Department of Transportation. It also has a business support component which assesses business needs for training and technical assistance.

New Mexico
First Nations Development Institute
2300 Fall Hill Avenue, Suite 412
Fredericksburg, VA 22401
540-371-5615
Fax: 540-371-3505
www.firstnations.org
Eagle Staff Fund: Seeks to support Native grassroots and tribal organizations that are working to create Native-controlled reservation economies. Promotes economic

development through technical assistance and financial resources.

WESST Corp.
414 Silver SW
Albuquerque, NM 87102
505-848-4753
Fax: 505-241-4766
Women's Economic Self-Sufficiency Team: Provides consulting, training and support programs as well as financial assistance (loans).

Economic Development Department
State Purchasing Division
P.O. Drawer 26110
Santa Fe, NM 87502
505-827-0425
www.state.nm.us/clients/spd/spd.html
The Procurement Assistant Program educates business owners in all phases of government contracting, and provides comprehensive technical procurement counseling for obtaining defense, federal, state, and local government contracts. It offers training seminars (hands-on workshops), and offers small, minority, and women-owned businesses the opportunity to be entered into the annual New Mexico MSBPAP Business Directory.

New Mexico Department of Transportation
Equal Opportunity Programs
1596 Pacheo Aspen Plaza
Santa Fe, NM 87501
505-827-1774
800-544-0936
http://nmshtd.state.nm.us/bus_oeop/default.asp
This office develops outreach programs to recruit and inform disadvantaged business enterprises about contracting opportunities with the Department of Transportation. It also has a business support component which assesses business needs for training and technical assistance.

New York
Division of Minority and Women's Business
Empire State Development
30 South Pearl Street
Albany, NY 12245
800-STATE-NY
or
633 Third Ave.
New York, NY 10017
212-803-2410
www.nylovesbiz.com/Small_and_Growing_Businesses/mwbe.asp
Division of Minority and Women-owned Business Development: Administers, coordinates, and implements a statewide program to assist the development of M/WBE's and facilitate their access to state contracting opportunities. Through the process of certification, the agency is responsible for verifying minority and women-ownership and control of firms participating in the program.

Division of Minority and Women's Business Development Lending Program: Loans up to $7,000 from the Microenterprise Loan Fund and up to $50,000 from the Minority and Women Revolving Loan Trust Fund.

Minority Revolving Loan Fund: Certified minority-and women-owned businesses have access to loans for working capital or for the acquisition of real property, machinery or equipment. Loans range from $20,000 to $500,000.

Transportation Capital Assistance Program: Government contract loans are provided to enterprises that have transportation-related government contracts under the New York State Department of Transportation. The loans range from $20,000 to $500,000

New York Department of Transportation
Office of Equal Opportunity Development & Compliance
1220 Washington Avenue
Building 4, Room G16
Albany, NY 12232-0444
518-457-1129 /1134
Fax: 518-457-9678
www.dot.state.ny.us/oeodc/support.html
This office develops outreach programs to recruit and inform disadvantaged business enterprises about contracting opportunities with the Department of Transportation. It also has a business support component which assesses business needs for training and technical assistance.

North Carolina
Small Business and Technology Development Center
333 Fayetteville Street Mall, Suite 1150
Raleigh, NC 27601
919-715-7272
800-258-0862 (in NC)
www.sbtdc.org
The SBTDC offers specialized market development assistance in the areas of government procurement, international business development, and new product and technology development. The SBTDC provides the strongest counseling resource for minority clients in the state. 25% of the 5,200 clients counseled each year are minority businesses. In addition to extensive business counseling, special focus training programs on topics such as "Equal Access to Credit" & "Minority, Women and Disadvantaged Business Enterprise Certification" are presented periodically across the state.

North Carolina Department of Transportation
Civil Rights & Business Development Section
P.O. Box 25201
Raleigh, NC 27611-5201
919-733-2300
800-522-0453
Fax: 919-733-8649
www.ncdot.org/administration/civilrights/certreqinfo/disadbus.htm
This office develops outreach programs to recruit and inform disadvantaged business enterprises about contracting opportunities with the Department of Transportation. It also has a business support component which assesses business needs for training and technical assistance.

North Dakota
North Dakota Department of Commerce
1600 E. Century Ave., Suite 2
Bismarck, ND 58503
701-328-5885
www.techwomen.org/index.htm
Women & Technology Partnership: A partnership funded by the Economic Development and Finance Division and the U.S. Small Business Administration brought about this program, which is designed to serve women in business or about to start a business. It also provides technical assistance and training to help women so they may join the technology revolution.

North Dakota Department of Transportation
Civil Rights Office

608 East Boulevard Avenue
Bismarck, ND 58505-0700
701-328-2576
www.state.nd.us/dot/dbebidinfo.html
Email: digoe@state.nd.us
This office develops outreach programs to recruit and inform disadvantaged business enterprises about contracting opportunities with the Department of Transportation. It also has a business support component which assesses business needs for training and technical assistance.

Ohio

Division of Minority Business Affairs
Ohio Department of Development
77 S. High Street
P.O. Box 1001
Columbus, OH 43216
614-466-5700
800-848-1300
www.odod.state.oh.us
Management and Technical Services: Provides assistance in management analysis, technical assistance, educational services and financial consulting. Supports overall growth and development of minority firms throughout the State. Counseling is provided at no charge.

Minority Contractor and Business Assistance Program: Provides management, technical, financial, and contract procurement assistance; loan, grant, bond packaging services. Networks with all levels of government, private businesses. Aids in economic growth and development of the minority community; increases awareness of local, state, and federal business assistance programs. Counseling is provided at no charge. Fees may be charged for some programs using federal funding.

Minority Business Bonding Program: Surety bonding assistance for state-certified minority businesses. Maximum bond pre-qualification of up to $1,000,000 per Minority Business. The bond premium for each bond issued will not exceed 2% of the face value of the bond.

Minority Direct Loan: Purchase or improvement of fixed assets for state-certified minority-owned businesses. Up to 40% of total project cost at 4.5% fixed for up to 15 years (maximum).

Ohio Mini-Loan Program: Fixed assets and equipment for small businesses. Start-up or existing business expansion. Projects of $100,000 or less. Up to 45% guarantee of an eligible bank loan. Interest rate of the State guarantee of the loan is currently 5.5%, and may be fixed for 10 years. Eligibility: Small business entrepreneurs with fewer than 25 employees, targeted 50% allocation to businesses owned by minorities and women.

Office of Small Business
Ohio Department of Development
P.O. Box 1001
Columbus, OH 43266-0101
614-466-2711
800-848-1300
www.odod.state.oh.us/edd/osb/sbdc/women.htm
Under the Women's Business Resource Program, women can get help for start-up, expansion and management of their businesses. The program seeks to provide women with equal access to assistance and lending programs, and helps businesswomen locate government procurement opportunities. This office also acts as a statewide center of workshops, conferences, and Women's Business Owners

statistics. All of the program's services are free. This office also publishes *Ohio Women Business Leaders*, a directory of women-owned businesses in Ohio, along with other free publications.

Ohio Department of Transportation
Office of Transit
1980 West Broad Street, Second Floor
Columbus, OH 43223
614-644-8436
800-459-3778
Fax: 614-466-0822
www.dot.state.oh.us/ptrans/Other_PT_Programs/dbe.htm
This office develops outreach programs to recruit and inform disadvantaged business enterprises about contracting opportunities with the Department of Transportation. It also has a business support component which assesses business needs for training and technical assistance.

Oklahoma

Oklahoma Department of Commerce
Small Business Division
P.O. Box 26980
Oklahoma City, OK 73126-0980
405-815-6552
http://www.odoc.state.ok.us
Under the Women Owned Business Assistance Program, businesswomen can get a variety of technical assistance, from business planning and marketing assistance, to financial information and government procurement practices.

The Minority Business Development Program provides support and assistance in the establishment, growth, and expansion of viable business enterprises. Counseling in the preparation of business plans and marketing strategies is available. The program also provides assistance for loan packaging, bid preparation, feasibility studies, and certification requirements.

Oklahoma Department of Transportation
Regulatory Services Division
200 NE 21st Street, Room 1-C-5
Oklahoma City, OK 73105
405-521-6046
Fax: 405-522-2136
www.okladot.state.ok.us/regserv/dbeinfo/index.htm
dbeinfo@odot.org
This office develops outreach programs to recruit and inform disadvantaged business enterprises about contracting opportunities with the Department of Transportation. It also has a business support component which assesses business needs for training and technical assistance.

Oregon

SOWAC
33 N. Central Avenue, Suite #209
Medford, OR 97501
541-779-3992
Fax: 541-779-5195
www.sowac.org
Southern Oregon Women's Access to Credit: Offers a business development program for new and existing business owners in Jackson, Josephine and Klamath counties. Focuses on training, mentoring and financing.

Oregon Association of Minority Entrepreneurs
4134 N. Vancouver
Portland, OR 97217
503-249-7744
Fax: 503-249-2027

www.oame.org

Association of Minority Entrepreneurs: A nonprofit, tax exempt organization formed to promote and develop entrepreneurship and economic development for ethnic minorities in the State of Oregon. OAME works as a partnership between ethnic minorities, entrepreneurs, education, government and established corporate business. OAME provides a core of services to start-up and/or existing minority businesses. These services include:
- Technical Assistance
- Access To Capital/Loan Fund
- Capability And Opportunity Matching (OAME's Marketing/Clearinghouse)
- Administrative Services
- Incubator With & Without Walls Development

ONABEN
11825 SW Greenburg Road B3
Tigard, OR 97223
503-968-1500
Fax: 503-968-1545
www.onaben.org

Native American Business Entrepreneurs Network: Created by Northwest Indian Tribes to increase the success of private businesses owned by Native Americans. ONABEN's approach consists of technical training, access to capital, (conditional on an on-going consulting relationship), access to markets and mentors. The program is organized to integrate community resources. It assists and encourages tribes to share business development resources amongst themselves and with non-Indian neighbors. The program works where no predecessor has succeeded because it approaches business ownership as an expression of Native Americans' common values; inter-generation and community awareness, mutual respect, non-destructive harvest.

Governor's Office
Governor's Advocate for Minority and Women Businesses
155 Cottage Street, NE
Salem, OR 97301
503-373-1224, ext. 25
www.hr.das.state.or.us/minority

The Governor's Advocate for Minority and Women Businesses: This office has the responsibility to identify and remove barriers that prevent minority and women owned businesses from entering the mainstream of commercial activity.

Office of Minority, Women & Emerging Small Businesses
P.O. Box 14480
Salem, OR 97309-0405
503-947-7922
http://www.cbs.state.or.us

This office certifies women-owned, disadvantaged, and emerging small businesses, allowing them to participate in the state's targeted purchasing programs.

Oregon Department of Transportation
Office of Civil Rights
800 Airport Road SE
Salem, OR 97301-4798
503-986-4350
Fax: 503-986-6382
www.odot.state.or.us/civilrightspub/disadvantaged.html

This office develops outreach programs to recruit and inform disadvantaged business enterprises about contracting opportunities with the Department of Transportation. It also has a business support component which assesses business needs for training and technical assistance.

Pennsylvania

Pennsylvania Minority Business Development Authority
404 Forum Bldg.
Harrisburg, PA 17120
717-787-1127
www.inventpa.com

PA Minority Business Development Authority: Low-interest loan financing to businesses which are owned and operated by minorities. Amounts: Manufacturing, industrial, high-tech, international trade or franchise companies with loans up to $500,000 (within Enterprise Zones, $750,000) or 75% of total eligible project costs, whichever is less, retail or commercial firms loans of up to $250,000 ($350,000 in Enterprise Zones).

Department of Community and Economic Development
400 North Street, 4th Floor
Harrisburg, PA 17120
800-280-3801
717-783-5700
www.inventpa.com

Minority Business Advocate: Encourages the development of minority-owned businesses as part of the overall economic development strategy of the Commonwealth. Serves as an advocate for minority owned business owners in resolving issues with state agencies and interacting with other government agencies.

Women's Business Advocate: Works to assist women businesses in the development of their business, specifically assisting in resolving issues with state agencies, exploring marketing options and identifying financing strategies.

Bureau of Minority & Women Business Opportunities
North Office Building, Room 502
Harrisburg, PA 17125
717-787-6708
www.dgs.state.pa.us/bcabd

The Bureau of Minority and Women Business Opportunities provides resources for minority and women business owners to compete for and participate in the state contracting process. Minority and women owned business can be certified and instructed on the statewide compliance program.

Pennsylvania Department of Transportation
Bureau of Equal Opportunity
Project Management & Business Assistance Division
P.O. Box 3251
Harrisburg, PA 17105-3251
717-787-5891
800-468-4201
Fax: 717-772-4026
www.dot.state.pa.us/penndot/bureaus/BEO.nsf/infoPMBAD?readform

This office develops outreach programs to recruit and inform disadvantaged business enterprises about contracting opportunities with the Department of Transportation. It also has a business support component which assesses business needs for training and technical assistance.

Rhode Island

Office of Minority Business Assistance
Department of Economic Development
One West Exchange St.
Providence, RI 02903
401-222-6670
www.rimbe.org

This office certifies women and minority-owned businesses under federal and state set-aside and goal programs and provides counseling assistance to these companies.

Minority Business Enterprise Compliance Office
One Capitol Hill, 2nd Floor
Providence, RI 02908
401-222-6670
Fax: 401-222-5799
www.purchasing.ri.gov/mbeinfo.asp
Email: lfrancis@mail.state.ri.us
This office develops outreach programs to recruit and inform disadvantaged business enterprises about contracting opportunities with the Department of Transportation. It also has a business support component which assesses business needs for training and technical assistance.

South Carolina

Governor's Office of Small and Minority Business Assistance
1205 Pendleton Street, Suite 329
Columbia, SC 29201
803-734-0657
www.govoepp.state.sc.us/osmba/
The goals of Office of Small and Minority Business Assistance are to promote the growth and development of small and minority owned businesses in South Carolina and to advocate that an equitable portion of State procurement contracts be awarded to small and minority owned businesses

South Carolina Department of Transportation
Office of DBE Program and Development
955 Park Street, Room 403
Columbia, SC 29201
803-737-1372
Fax: 803-737-2021
www.dot.state.sc.us/doing/dbe.html
This office develops outreach programs to recruit and inform disadvantaged business enterprises about contracting opportunities with the Department of Transportation. It also has a business support component which assesses business needs for training and technical assistance.

South Dakota

Women's Business Center
University of Sioux Falls, Center for Women
Sioux Falls, SD 57104
605-331-6721
866-556-1778
www.thecoo.edu/als/cfw.html
The center provides advice, planning and support for women starting their own business.

South Dakota Department of Transportation
Compliance Division
700 E. Broadway Avenue
Becker-Hansen Building
Pierre, SD 57501
605-773-4906
www.sddot.com/operations/compliance/dbe.asp
This office develops outreach programs to recruit and inform disadvantaged business enterprises about contracting opportunities with the Department of Transportation. It also has a business support component which assesses business needs for training and technical assistance.

Tennessee

Tennessee Minority Purchasing Council
Metro Center, Plaza 1 Building
220 Athens Way, Suite 105
Nashville, TN 37225
615-259-4699

Purchasing Councils: Encourages mutually beneficial economic links between ethnic minority suppliers and major purchasers in the public and private sectors..

Office of Minority Business Enterprise
Department of Economic & Community Development
312 8th Avenue North
Nashville, TN 37243
800-342-8470 (in TN)
615-741-1888
http://www.state.tn.us/ecd/minority.htm
This office offers information, advocacy, referral, procurement, and other services to minority businesses in the state. They publish a directory of minority businesses, offer conferences and seminars on topics useful to business owners, and serve as a clearinghouse of important information to women and minorities. They also match vendors with potential clients and help women and minorities identify and obtain procurement opportunities.

Tennessee Department of Transportation
Civil Rights Division
James K. Polk Building
505 Deaderick Street, Suite 700
Nashville, TN 37243-0349
615-741-3681
www.tdot.state.tn.us/civil-rights/Smallbusiness.htm
This office develops outreach programs to recruit and inform disadvantaged business enterprises about contracting opportunities with the Department of Transportation. It also has a business support component which assesses business needs for training and technical assistance.

Texas

Texas Department of Transportation
Construction Division
125 East 11th Street
Austin, TX 78701-2483
512-416-2500
Fax: 512-416-2539
www.dot.state.tx.us/business/dbeinfo.htm
This office develops outreach programs to recruit and inform disadvantaged business enterprises about contracting opportunities with the Department of Transportation. It also has a business support component which assesses business needs for training and technical assistance.

Utah

Offices of Ethnic Affairs
Department of Community and Economic Development
324 S. State St.
Salt Lake City, UT 84114
877-4UT-DCED
http://dced.utah.gov
Offices of Ethnic Affairs: Recognizing that state government should be responsive to all citizens, and wishing to promote cooperation and understanding between government agencies and its ethnic citizens, these offices were created:
- Office Of Asian Affairs
- Office Of Black Affairs
- Office Of Hispanic Affairs
- Office Of Polynesian Affairs
- Division of Indian Affairs

Utah Procurement Technical Assistance Center
324 S. State St., Suite 500
Salt Lake City, UT 84111
801-538-8625
http://dced.utah.gov/procure

Minority and Women Owned Business Source Directory:
Offered by the Utah PTAC (Procurement Technical
Assistance Center). The directory includes approximately
850 companies, and is the most complete such listing
available. However, listings are voluntary, having been
obtained through surveys, and this is not to be construed as a
comprehensive catalog. There are some 4,400 minority-
owned employers in the state, and 46,000 that are women-
owned.

Utah Department of Transportation
Civil Rights Division
4501 South 2700 West
Mail Stop 141200
Salt Lake City, UT 84114-1200
801-965-4100
Fax: 801-965-4101
www.dot.utah.gov/index.php?m=c&tid=198
Email: bcrawford@utah.gov
This office develops outreach programs to recruit and inform
disadvantaged business enterprises about contracting
opportunities with the Department of Transportation. It also
has a business support component which assesses business
needs for training and technical assistance.

Vermont
Women's Small Business Program
Trinity College
208 Colchester Avenue
Burlington, VT 05401
802-846-7160
The Women's Small Business Program offers many services
to women seeking to identify, start, stabilize, and expand a
small business. Services include: Getting Serious, a
workshop to determine a business idea and whether business
meets personal goals; Start-Up, a 15-week intensive course to
develop a business plan and business management skills; and
Working Solutions, a topic specific workshops for microbusiness owners. Courses are offered statewide. Grants and
scholarships for training are available to income eligible
women.

Vermont Agency of Transportation
Office of Civil Rights & Labor Compliance
National Life Building, Drawer 33
Montpelier VT 05633-5001
802-828-2715
Fax: 802-828-1047
www.aot.state.vt.us/CivilRights/Dbe.htm
Email: nancy.bruce@state.vt.us
This office develops outreach programs to recruit and inform
disadvantaged business enterprises about contracting
opportunities with the Department of Transportation. It also
has a business support component which assesses business
needs for training and technical assistance.

Virginia
Women's Enterprise Program
P.O. Box 446
Richmond, VA 23218
804-371-8200
800-980-8923
www.dba.state.va.us/mwbusinesses/wob.asp
VWBE Certification Program: Helps Virginia's women-
owned and operated companies certify themselves as WBE's
to better compete in government and corporate procurement
markets. In addition to being listed in the directory, certified
companies will be registered in the WBE website, as well as
in the Virginia Procurement Pipeline website. Certified
WBE's also have the privilege of using the WBE seal on

marketing materials and letterhead. They also receive
information on other resources available to women-owned
businesses regarding government contracting, management
issues, and women's ownership.

Women's Business Center of Northern Virginia
Department of Business Assistance
7001 Loisdale Rd., Suite 6
Springfield, VA 22150
703-778-9922
www.cbponline.org
The Center provides women with the training, assistance and
support need to start or expand a successful business.

Virginia Department of Transportation
Construction Division, Prequalification Section
1401 East Broad Street
Richmond, VA 23219
804-786-2941
virginiadot.org/business/const/prequal.asp
Email: vdotinfo@virginiadot.org
This office develops outreach programs to recruit and inform
disadvantaged business enterprises about contracting
opportunities with the Department of Transportation. It also
has a business support component which assesses business
needs for training and technical assistance.

FREE Grant Money and Programs for Women Business
Owners in Virginia
The Virginia Federation of Business and Professional
Women's Clubs, Inc.
P.O. Box 4842
McLean, VA 22103-4842
703-549-1417
202-293-1100
www.bpwva.advocate.net/
Women who are starting up a business can receive grant
money from the Virginia Federation of Business and
Professional Women (BPW/VA) and it's associated
Foundation. The organization's Eunice V. Davis Grant Fund
awards female entrepreneurs sums ranging from $1,000 to
$3,000 to cover expenses associated with starting a small
business, such as the purchase of capital equipment and
supplies and fees associated with obtaining professional and
business licenses. Applicants must be women 21 years of age
or older who reside in Virginia, must be U.S. citizens and
must be a member of BPW/VA. Applications are available
online and must be accompanied by a business plan and a
description of financial need. Membership costs $20;
additional benefits include professional development
programs, networking opportunities, information and
referrals for business owners and other services geared
toward the professional and personal success of women.

Low Cost Training And Services For Virginia Women
WBCNoVa
7001 Loisdale Road
Springfield, VA 22150
703-778-9922
Fax: 703-768-0547
www.wbcnova.org/
The Women's Business Center of Northern Virginia provides
low-cost – and sometimes free – services and programs
designed to help women start up and run successful small
businesses. A start-up series of programs covers business
planning, licensing and tax issues, and financial backing.
Classes on strategic planning, investment opportunities,
marketing, management, procurement, and Internet business
solutions are offered for more established ventures. Training
fees are low and tuition assistance is available. Free one-on-

one business counseling and access to computers and the Internet is available on an appointment basis. Center staff can provide computer training on word processing and other business software packages and can assist in the design and production of business cards, stationary and collateral materials. The center offers a variety of other services geared toward the female self-starter, including referrals to investors and lenders, marketing assistance, networking opportunities, and networking opportunities. Additionally, for $100, four one-hour sessions with a personal life coach can assist women in formulating and implementing action plans to achieve success in both their new business and their personal lives.

Washington

Office of Trade and Economic Development
Small Business Resources
Minority and Women's Business Development
2001 6th Avenue, Suite 2600
Seattle, WA 98121
www.ctcd.wa.gov
Linked Deposit Loan Program: Allows minority or women-owned businesses with 50 or fewer employees to apply at participating banks for reduced rate loans.

Office of Minority and Women's Business Enterprises
P.O. Box 41160
Olympia, WA 98504-1160
360-753-9693
www.omwbe.wa.gov
This office helps women and minority-owned businesses interested in participating in state contracting opportunities by moving them through the certification process. Once certified, businesses are eligible to receive a 5% preference when bidding competitively on goods and services purchased by the state. Upon request, businesses can be placed on bid lists maintained by individual agencies, education institutions, or contractors by contacting them directly.

Washington State Department of Transportation
Office of Equal Opportunity
PO Box 47314
310 Maple Park
Olympia WA 98504-7314
360-705-7095
Fax: 360-705-6801
www.wsdot.wa.gov/oeo/dmwbe.htm
Email: MatsuiJ@wsdot.wa.gov
This office develops outreach programs to recruit and inform disadvantaged business enterprises about contracting opportunities with the Department of Transportation. It also has a business support component which assesses business needs for training and technical assistance.

West Virginia

Center for Economic Options
214 Capitol Street, Suite 200
Charleston, WV 25302
304-345-1298
Fax: 304-342-0641
www.centerforeconomicoptions.org
Center for Economic Options: A nonprofit statewide, community-based organization which promotes opportunities that develop the economic capacity of West Virginia's rural citizens and communities. Working with members of society who traditionally have been excluded from economic decision-making, the Center advocates equity in the workplace, coordinates alternative approaches for economic development, and works to impact the direction of public

policy. The Center coordinates three strategies to accomplish these goals:

1. *Community Resources*: Coordinates a pool of facilitators and training specialists who provide technical assistance to individuals, organizations, and community groups in many areas including strategic planning, business plan development, board development, and community assessments. The program also provides workshops and resource materials on community-based development.

2. *Enterprise Development*: Promotes rural job creation through self-employment and links small-scale, sector-specific entrepreneurs in statewide production and marketing networks. The Center facilitates the development of these flexible networks and connects the business owners with information, resources, training opportunities, and markets.

3. *Public Policy*: Researches and recommends policy in several areas including worker equity, enterprise development, sustainable development, work force training, and economic equity. Through the program, consultants on establishing equity in the workplace and meeting state and federal sex equity regulations are provided.

West Virginia Women's Commission
Building 6, Room 850
1900 Kanawha Boulevard, East
Charleston, WV 25305
304-558-0070
Fax: 304-558-5167
www.wvdhhr.org/women/index.asp
West Virginia Women's Commission: Offers women opportunities to learn to be advocates for themselves and to work with others to address systemic change. Projects include leadership and legislative conference like the Women's Town Meeting and Women's Day at the Legislature among others.

West Virginia Small Business Development Center
Women and Minority-Owned Business DataBase
Capitol Complex
1900 Kanawha Blvd., East
Building 6, Room 652
Charleston, WV 25305-0311
304-558-2960
www.sbdcwv.org/women-minority.php#pagetitle
The West Virginia Minority and Women-Owned Business Database provides companies with exposure to purchasing agents from all levels of government as well as the private sector.

West Virginia Department of Transportation
Equal Employment Opportunity Division
Building 5, Room 925
1900 Kanawha Boulevard, East
Charleston, WV 25305-0430
304-558-3931
Fax: 304-558-4236
www.wvdot.com/3_roadways/3D9_EEO.HTM
Email: pwhite@dot.state.wv.us
This office develops outreach programs to recruit and inform disadvantaged business enterprises about contracting opportunities with the Department of Transportation. It also has a business support component which assesses business needs for training and technical assistance.

Wisconsin

Bureau of Minority Business Development
Department of Commerce
201 W. Washington Ave.
P.O. Box 7970
Madison, WI 53707
608-267-9550
Fax: 608-267-2829
www.commerce.state.wi.us
Certifies companies to be eligible to participate in state's minority business bid preference. Company must be at least 51% owned, controlled, and managed by minority (being a woman is not considered a minority).
Certification to participate in the state's minority business purchasing and contracting program is available to minority vendors. Interested firms may apply through the department. They are then listed in the *Annual Directory of Minority-Owned Firms*.

Marketing Assistance of various kinds is offered to minority-owned firms. Certified minority vendors are listed in the department's database for access by the purchasing community. Minority-owned firms can receive help developing marketing plans. Each year, the department sponsors the Marketplace Trade Fair to encourage business contacts between minority vendors and state and corporate buyers.

American Indian Liaison: Provides advice, training, technical assistance, and economic development information to the Wisconsin tribes, tribal communities, and American Indian entrepreneurs, and serves as state economic development liaison. 608-261-7712

Minority Business Development Revolving Loan Fund (RLF) Program: Designed to help capitalize RLFs administered by American Indian tribal governing bodies or local development corporations that target their loans to minority-owned businesses. The corporation must be at least 51-percent controlled and actively managed by minority-group members, and demonstrate the expertise and commitment to promote minority business development in a specific geographic area.

Minority Business Development Loan Program: Offers low-interest loans for start-up, expansion or acquisition projects. To qualify for the fund, a business must be 51-percent controlled, owned, and actively managed by minority-group members, and the project must retain or increase employment.

Financial Consulting and Technical Assistance: The bureau counsels individuals who want to start, buy or expand a business. Economic consultants provide information regarding structuring financial plans, preparing loan applications, strategic planning and guidance for writing business plans.

Minority Business Early Planning Grant: The EPG program allows applicants to hire an independent third party to assist in the preparation of a comprehensive business plan. Grants provide for up to 75% of project costs up to $3,000. Eligible businesses include manufacturing, paper/forest products, printing, biotechnology, tourism, automation, agriculture/food products, medical devices, information technology and childcare (not in-home).

Minority Business Entrepreneurial Training Grant: Grants to pay for up to 75% of the tuition for the SBDC's Entrepreneurial Training Course. Entrepreneurs completing the course will have a comprehensive business plan that fully evaluates the feasibility of the proposed start-up or expansion.

WWBIC
2745 N. Dr. Martin Luther King Drive
Milwaukee, WI 53212
414-263-5450
Fax: 414-263-5456
www.wwbic.com
Wisconsin Women's Business Initiative Corporation (WWBIC): Offers micro loans to businesses owned by women, minorities, and low-income individuals. WWBIC also offers training and technical assistance

Department of Commerce
P.O. Box 7970
Madison, WI 53707
608-266-1018
800-435-7287 (in WI)
http://commerce.wi.gov
The Women's Business Services offers assistance in gaining information about the state's loan programs available to women business owners. The office keeps track of the top 50 fastest growing and top 10 women-owned businesses in Wisconsin. They also maintain a database of women-owned businesses in the state.

Wisconsin Housing and Economic Development Authority
One South Pinckney St., #500
P.O. Box 1728
Madison, WI 53701-1728
800-334-6873
608-266-7884
http://www.wheda.com
Under the Linked Deposit Loan Program, women or minority-owned businesses with gross annual sales of less than $500,000 can qualify for low rate loans. Loans are available under the prime lending rate for purchase or improvement of buildings, equipment, or land, but not for working capital. Business must be in manufacturing, retail trade, tourism, or agriculture packaging or processing.

Wisconsin Department of Transportation
Office of DBE Program, Room 451
4802 Sheboygan Avenue
P.O. Box 7965
Madison, WI 53707-7965
608-266-6961
Fax: 608-267-3641 or 266-7818
www.dot.wisconsin.gov/business/engrserv/dbe-main.htm
This office develops outreach programs to recruit and inform disadvantaged business enterprises about contracting opportunities with the Department of Transportation. It also has a business support component which assesses business needs for training and technical assistance.

Wyoming

Wyoming Business Council
214 West 15th Street
Cheyenne, WY 82002
307-777-2800
800-262-3425
www.wyomingbusiness.org
The Wyoming Women's Council provides business development and training opportunities along with other women's issues.

Wyoming Department of Transportation
Business Enterprise

State Construction Engineers Office
5300 Bishop Boulevard
Cheyenne, WY 82009-3340
307-777-4457
http://dot.state.wy.us/web/business/dbe.html

This office develops outreach programs to recruit and inform disadvantaged business enterprises about contracting opportunities with the Department of Transportation. It also has a business support component which assesses business needs for training and technical assistance.

Start a Business With Zero Money

More and more people are realizing that there are many benefits to freelancing. In fact, every day more data show that the demand for freelancing is growing. Permanence in the workforce is an illusion. Dan Pink, publisher of Free Agent Nation, estimates that there are one in four workers or more than 30 million" free agents" in the workforce, which include free lancers, independent contractors, and operators of very small businesses[1]. In the last five years, the number of temporary agencies that supply these kinds of workers increased from 3,500 to 7,000[2]. Manpower, one of these temporary agencies, now employs more than General Motors or IBM. In a small business study done by the Small Business Administration in 2004, it was found that 53% of small businesses are based in the home[3].

We've heard the terms in recent years: downsizing, rightsizing, restructuring, streamlining, reinventing, and now outsourcing. All this boils down to more and more companies becoming less and less interested in providing for the long term wellbeing of its employees. It's a trend that's likely to continue at an even greater pace.

Companies want to be lean and mean. They want to be flexible and don't want to take on the responsibility and financial burden of full time employees. This may be bad for employees, but it's great for the world of freelancing. And don't think of freelancing as losing benefits: think of it as an exchange of benefits. Your personal freedom and control over your life are worth more than your health and retirement benefits and the security of your job, all of which are disappearing fast anyway. The new status symbol of the new millenium won't be doing your own thing, it will be controlling your own time.[4]

Here are some advantages to being a freelancer:

♦ You can still be looking for a full time job while you are pretending to look for freelancing or consulting work.

♦ You can give yourself a title while you are out of work, such as an independent consultant, freelance wordprocessor, etc.

♦ You can take more tax deductions around the home and at play, such as the part of your house and car you use for business. Even some of your meals and entertainment expenses may fall into this category.

♦ You can have more control over your hours, take vacations when you want, or only work certain days.

♦ It's ideal for a household member that is only interested in a part time job while staying at home with the kids. A freelance artist can easily work 20 hours a week at home and still be with the children.

And here are some advantages from the employer's eyes. You may even want to include some of these points in your sales letter:

♦ They don't have to commit to you forever, and then worry about firing you when they want to downsize.

♦ They don't have to pay you benefits, overhead, supplies, etc.

♦ They can show their bosses that they are getting more work done with less people because freelancers are not counted as employees, and are often paid from a different budget than that of full time employees.

♦ They can get a project done and not worry about keeping those people busy once the project is completed.

♦ They can get more value for their money by hiring more qualified people for a shorter period of time.

♦ They have less liability from the potential harmful effects of employee protection laws like Equal Employment Opportunity Laws.

What Do You Need To Be A Freelancer?

The only thing you really need is a customer. And this is basically true for any business. If you have a customer or a client, you're in business. The tools that will make getting a customer easier are a phone, a desk, and business cards. And the next level of tools you will find helpful are a resume, a brochure, or samples of your work.

If you think you need a lot of expensive equipment you may want to rethink being a freelancer. The beauty of freelancing is that you can start a business without any money. All your money should be invested in getting business, not in equipment. Even if you think you need to buy a lot of equipment to do the work you want to do, for heaven's sake don't go out and buy it. Nothing can put you out of business faster than having equipment around that is not being used because you don't have a lot of business. Rent the equipment only when you need it, or use someone else's equipment at night.

Believe me, all your resources should be spent in getting customers. Once you have a steady flow of customers, then you should look into buying your own equipment. Sure it would be nice to have all the fancy equipment you need, right in your house, but in the beginning that can be a ticket to failure. The most important part of being a successful freelancer is staying in business long enough to reap the rewards of all the seeding that you are planting in your "garden of opportunity." What you plant today will come back to you next year, and what you plant next year will come back to you the year after.

The trick is to be around a few years from now so that you can enjoy the benefits of what you planted today. Buying all the equipment you need will just you to run out of money faster, so that you will have less of a chance of being around and in business next year. It's a game of beat the clock. You have to figure out how to get all the customers you need before you run out of money.

How To Get Free Legal, Marketing, and Tax Advice

What stops many people from starting their own freelancing career is misinformation. Here's the kind of thinking that can go through your head when you think about freelancing. "Gee. I'm going to start a business at home. If something goes wrong, somebody will sue me and I'll lose my house. I wonder if incorporating as a business will protect me?" Now that the "what ifs" got you, you're smart enough to know that this sounds like a legal question and you'd better talk to an attorney. So you call a friend of a friend who is an attorney and they tell you it will cost you $500 to $1000 to help you solve this problem. You don't have an extra $500 to $1000, so you figure you will put off starting your new career until you get the extra money. **You don't have to do that.** You can get free legal advice on this or any other subject if you just contact one of the local Small Business Development Centers that are located in almost every city in the country. *(See page 188 for a state-by-state listing for Small Business Development Centers.)*

These centers will sit down with you for free and help you figure out any kind of legal, management, financial, or even tax problem you are having in trying to start and develop a business. They will even help you get the business you need. They can help you identify potential clients and will work with you to devise a plan for getting development money. You just can't beat that.

The Government Will Buy Your Freelancing Services

The government buys more freelancing services than anyone else in the world. They buy typing services, legal services, accounting services, and landscaping services, to name just a few. One year the government even spent $30,000 for the services of a freelance priest. And you don't have to be living in Washington, DC to get the work. Only about 20% of all government business is done in Washington, DC. The rest is done all over the country and all over the world.

Freelancing can be your first step to a multimillion dollar business. The time is right and you can do it without any money of your own.

Sources:

[1] Dan Pink, Free Agent Nation, www.freeagentnation.com, 2004.

[2] The Network Society, Peter Drucker, The Wall Street Journal, Page A12, March 29, 1995.

[3] Home-Based Business and Government Regulation, Henry Beale, Small Business Administration, February 2004.

[4] Job Shock, Harry S. Dent, Jr., St. Martin's Press, New York, NY.

Government Contracts:
How to Sell Your Goods and Services
To The World's Largest Buyer

If you produce a product or service, you've probably always wondered how you could offer what you produce to the biggest client in the world — the Federal government. Have you thought of the government as being a "closed shop" and too difficult to penetrate? Well, I'm happy to say that you're entirely wrong on that score. The Federal government spends over $200 billion each year on products ranging from toilet paper to paper clips and writes millions of dollars in contracts for services like advertising, consulting, and printing. Most Americans believe that a majority of those federal purchasing contracts have been eliminated over the last few years, but that's simply not true — they've just been replaced with new contracts that are looking for the same kinds of goods and services. Last year the government took action (either initiating or modifying) on over 500,000 different contracts. They buy these goods and services from someone, so why shouldn't that someone be you? To be successful doing business with the government, you need to learn to speak "governmenteze" to get your company into the purchasing loop, and I can show you how to accomplish that in just a few easy steps.

When To Apply

Keep in mind that because new contracts are awarded at the beginning of the government's fiscal year in October, you should make sure that an agency you're interested in working for has seen your portfolio by late spring or early summer-this will give them enough time to consider you and the services that you offer for the current fiscal year. Otherwise you may have to wait an entire year before you get any work, especially the larger contracts.

Know The Rules

If you are going to do business with the government, you must know how play the game. The federal government's procurement system has many laws, rules and regulations. Each agency must follow these rules to procure any goods or services. You will be ahead of the game if you know how this system works. You can view the regulations online at {www.arnet.gov/far}.

Identify Your Product or Service

The government uses the North American Industry Classification System to identify many products and services. Many government product and service listings and future procurements are identified by these codes. You can search web sites for the codes that correspond to the products and services you have to offer and then go after those contracts. You can view the codes at {www.census.gov/epcd/www/naics.html} or at {www.fpdc.gov}.

Get Registered

The Federal Acquisition Regulation requires contract registration with the Central Contract Registration (CCR). The CCR is the government database for many contracting opportunities. The CCR is the primary vendor database for the Department of Defense, NASA, Department of Transportation and Department of Treasury. They offer a Dynamic Small Business Database to showcase those businesses interested in doing business with the federal government. You can register your business at {www.ccr.gov}. In order to register with the CCR, you must first have a DUNS Number. You can obtain one online at {www.dnb.com}.

Get Certified As a Small Business

If you are a freelancer, you are a small business. You can find assistance with a number of organizations, starting with the Small Business Administration. If you qualify with the SBA as a specially identified business, you may be eligible for opportunities not available for larger businesses. Their web site "Government Contracting" {www.sba.gov/GC} lists programs to help businesses which include: *Small Disadvantaged Business, Very Small Business Program, Assistance for Women Business Owners (CAWBO), 8(a) Business, Veterans* and others.

BiZMatch Tool is an automated online database of minority businesses operated by the Department of Commerce's Minority Business Development Agency (MBDA). This database is used by Federal, state and local governments to locate minority enterprises to meet their procurement needs. You must register with the MBDA to be included in this database. {http://www.mbda.gov/index.php?section_id=4}

Procurement Levels

Now that you know something about the Federal government procurement procedures you must look for procurement opportunities. There are many "vehicles" or ways to win government contracts. The way a Federal agency will contract partially depends on the dollar amount threshold for each contract. Each agency conducts their procurement procedure slightly differently, so you should contact that agency directly.

- *Micro-Purchases*: Purchases under $2,500, which can be made at the sole discretion of the Contracting Officer or purchasing official to either large or small businesses with no competition.

- *Simplified Acquisition Procedure*: All purchases between $2,500 and $100,000 are reserved exclusively for small businesses providing that the Contracting Officer expects to obtain offers from at least two small businesses.
- *Formal Contracting Procedures*: Over $100,000

Get Assistance

All you need to do is ask. There are many organizations that are prepared to help you get a contract with the Federal government.

- The Small Business Administration can answer many of your questions.{www.sba.gov}
- Federal Procurement Technical Assistance Offices (listed in this book)
- Office of Small and Disadvantaged Business Utilization (listed in this book)
- State Procurement Offices (listed in this book)
- Each Federal agency's Procurement Office (listed in this book)

Check Out The Past And Look Into The Future

You can check out past winning contracts to get an understanding of what is purchased and what makes a successful bid contract. Through the Freedom of Information Act Request from the agency in question, you can get copies of winning bids from previous years. Remember, the competition is very high but most freelancers don't know about this information to give them an edge in the procurement process.

You can also look into the future of each agency. By law, each agency must publish their procurement forecast for the coming year. This information can help you prepare for what each agency will need in the future. You can contact the agency directly or check AcqNet at {www.acqnet.gov} to see the current forecasts.

Step 1

Each department within the Federal government has a procurement office that buys whatever the department requires. Most of these offices have put together their own *Doing Business With the Department of* _____ publication, which usually explains procurement policies, procedures, and programs. This booklet also contains a list of procurement offices, contact people, subcontracting opportunities, and a solicitation mailing list. Within each department there is also an Office of Small and Disadvantaged Business Utilization, whose sole purpose is to push the interests of the small business, and to make sure these companies get their fair share of government contracts. Another good resource is the listing in this book for Federal Procurement Technical Assistance Offices in your state.

Step 2

Once you have familiarized yourself with the process, you need to find out who is buying what from whom and for how much. There are three ways to get this important information.

A. Federal Business Opportunities (FedBizOpps)

FedBizOpps lists products and services (costing more than $25,000) needed by Government buyers directly on the Internet. Businesses wanting to sell to the Federal Government can search, monitor and retrieve opportunities solicited by the entire Federal contracting community. It is sorted by Department, then office within that agency, and then each specific office location lists opportunities. For instance, the General Services Administration has recently posted 4,125 solicitations for each of their offices throughout the states. Within that, the Public Building Services has posted 167 business possibilities. Synopses and solicitations are listed by posted date, class code, award and set aside. They can also be searched by the same criteria as well as zip code, agency, and office.

Sellers can sign up for the Vendor Notification Service. This sends emails containing announcements, presolicitations and their modification, notices of solicitation and amendment releases, and general procurement announcements. Notices can be received based on solicitation number, specific organizations, and product service classification, or all procurement notices. Other items of interest to sellers are the FBO Datafeed, which lists daily postings in html format daily, and Interested Vendors Module that promotes teaming opportunities for businesses wanting to sell to the government.

The General Services Administration Federal Supply Service publishes the FBO Vendors Guide that explains the system in detail. To begin viewing the vast amounts of potential opportunities, go to {www.fedbizopps.gov}. For information, call 877-472-3779; {fbo.support@gsa.gov}.

B. Federal Procurement Data System (FPDC)

This Center distributes consolidated information about federal purchases, including research and development. FPDC can tell you how much the Federal government spent last quarter on products and services, which agencies made those purchases, and what contractors did business with the government. FPDC summarizes this information through two types of reports: The FPDC standard report and the FPDC special report. The standard report compilation containing statistical procurement information in "snapshot" form for over 60 federal agencies, as well as several charts, graphs, and tables which compare procurement activities by state, major product and service codes, method of procurement, and contractors can be printed out, in whole or in part, at the website below. The report also includes quarterly and year-to-year breakdowns of amounts and percentages spent on small, women owned, and minority businesses. Special reports are prepared upon request for a fee, based on computer and labor costs. They are tailored to the specific categories, which can be cross-tabulated in numerous ways. A special report can help you analyze government procurement and data trends, identify competitors, and locate federal markets for individual products or services. Your Congressman may have access to the Federal Procurement Database from his/her office in Washington, which you may be able to use for free. For more information, contact: General Services Administration, Government Wide Information Systems Division, Federal Procurement Data System, 7th and D St., SW, Room 5652, Washington, DC 20407; 202-401-1529; {www.fpdc.gov/}.

C. Other Contracts

For contracts under $25,000, you must be placed on a department's list for solicitation bids on those contracts. The mailing list forms are available through the Procurement Office, the Office of Small and Disadvantaged Business Utilization, or your local Small Business Association office. Last year 18.7 billion dollars was spent on these "small" purchases, so these contracts should not be overlooked. Smaller contracts, completed over the course of a fiscal year, can mean lots of revenue for your business bottom line.

Step 3: Subcontracting Opportunities

All of the federal procurement offices or Offices of Small and Disadvantaged Business Utilization (SDBU) can provide you with information regarding subcontracting. Many of the departments' prime contracts require that the prime contractor maximize small business subcontracting opportunities. Many prime contractors produce special publications which can be helpful to those interested in subcontracting. The SDBU Office can provide you with more information on the subcontracting process, along with a directory of prime contractors. Another good source for subcontract assistance is your local Small Business Administration (SBA) office, 1-800-827-5722. SBA develops subcontracting opportunities for small businesses by maintaining close contact with large business prime contractors and by referring qualified small firms to them. The SBA has developed agreements and close working relationships with hundreds of prime contractors who cooperate by offering small firms the opportunity to compete for their subcontracts. In addition, to complete SBA's compliance responsibilities, commercial market representatives monitor prime contractors in order to assess their compliance with laws governing subcontracting opportunities for small businesses. Check the website at {www.sba.gov}. For a list of major federal OSDBU offices, check the listing in this book entitled "Offices of Small and Disadvantaged Business Utilization."

Step 4: Small Business Administration's 8(a) Program

Are you a socially or economically disadvantaged person who has a business? This group includes, but is not limited to, Black Americans, Hispanic Americans, Native Americans, Asian Pacific Americans, and Subcontinent Asian Americans. Socially and economically disadvantaged individuals represent a significant percentage of U.S. citizens, yet account for a disproportionately small percentage of total U.S. business revenues. The 8(a) program assists firms in participating in the business sector and to become independently competitive in the marketplace. SBA may provide participating firms with procurement, marketing, financial, management, or other technical assistance. A Business Opportunity Specialist will be assigned to each firm that participates, and is responsible for providing the firm with access to assistance that can help the firm fulfill its business goals. SBA undertakes an extensive effort to provide government contracting opportunities to participating businesses. To apply for the 8(a) program, you must attend an interview session with an official in the SBA field office in your area. For more information, contact your local Small Business Administration Office, or call 1-800-827-5722 or {www.sba.gov/8abd} for the SBA office nearest you.

Step 5: Bond

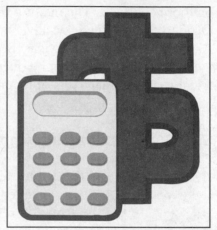

A Surety bond is often a prerequisite for government and private sector contracts. This is particularly true when the contract involves construction. In order for the company to qualify for an SBA Guarantee Bond, they must make the bonding company aware of their capabilities based on past contract performance and meeting of financial obligations. SBA can assist firms in obtaining surety bonding for contracts that do not exceed $6,000,000. SBA is authorized, when appropriate circumstances occur, to guarantee as much as 90 percent of losses suffered by a surety resulting from a breach of terms of a bond. Check their website at {www.sba.gov/osg}.

Step 6: Publications

The Government Printing Office has several publications for sale which explain the world of government contracts. For ordering information, contact: Superintendent of Documents, Government Printing Office, Washington, DC 20402; 202-512-1800; {www.gpo.gov}.

- *Guidebook for Performance-Based Services Acquisition in the Department of Defense*. This publication highlights the key elements of performance-based services acquisition and encourages innovative business practices within the Department of Defense acquisition process. S/N 008-020-01501-6 $7.00
- *Code of Federal Regulations, Title 41, Public Contracts and Property Management*. Chapter 1-100. S/N 869-044-00162-4 $22.00
- *Best Practices: How to Avoid Surprises in the World's Most Complicated Technical Process, The Transition From Development to Production*. This is a guide for defense contractors that shows common mistakes that were made at all stages of the procurement process, form proposal submission to research, test and development. S/N 008-050-00234-4 $33.50

- *Federal Acquisition Regulation (FAR Subscription)* Access to all critical information you need to profitably contract with the Federal Government. Subscribe to the FAR and get all the information you need to fully understand the solicitation bids that interest you. S/N 922-006-00000-8 $220.00 On CD-ROM S/N 721-034-00000-3 $70.00

- *Defense Acquisition Deskbook CD-ROM* This easy-to-use reference system is an encyclopedia of information invaluable to anyone who wants to do business with Department of Defense (DoD) or other Government agencies. Provided on CD-ROM, it contains a comprehensive library of all the policies and regulations. S/N 708-097-00000-4 $37.00

Step 7: What is GSA?

General Services Administration (GSA) is the Government's business agent. On an annual budget of 16 billion dollars, it directs and coordinates nearly $8 billion a year worth of purchases, sales, and services. Its source of supply is private enterprise, and its clients include all branches of the Federal government. GSA plans and manages leasing, purchase, or construction of office buildings, laboratories, and warehouses; buys and delivers nearly $10 billion worth of goods and services; negotiates the prices and terms for an additional $2.3 billion worth of direct business between federal groups and private industry; sets and interprets the rules for federal travel and negotiates reduced fares and lodging rates for federal travelers; and manages a 185,000 vehicle fleet with a cumulative yearly mileage of over 1 billion. For a copy of *Doing Business With GSA* go to {www.gsa.gov/smallbusiness} and click on "Publications" or call Office of Small Business Utilization headquarters at 202-501-1021 or your regional Small Business Utilization Center. For information on GSA's architect and engineer services, such as who is eligible for GSA professional services contracts, how to find out about potential GSA projects, what types of contracts are available, and where and how to apply, contact: Public Buildings Service, GSA, 1800 F Street, NW, Washington, DC 20405; 202-501-1100.

Step 8: Bid and Contract Protests

The General Accounting Office (GAO) resolves disputes between agencies and bidders of government contracts, including grantee award actions. The free publication, *Bid Protests at GAO; A Descriptive Guide*, contains information on GAO's procedures for determining legal questions arising from the awarding of government contracts. Contact General Accounting Office, 441 G  Street, NW, Room LM, Washington, DC 20548; 202-512-6000. For Contract Appeals, the GSA Board of Contract Appeals works to resolve disputes arising out of contracts with GSA, the Departments of Treasury, Education, Commerce, and other independent government agencies. The Board also hears and decides bid protests arising out of government-wide automated data processing (ADP) procurements. A contractor may elect to use either the GSA Board or the General Accounting Office for resolution of an ADP bid protest. Contractors may elect to have their appeals processed under the Board's accelerated procedures if the claim is $50,000 or less, or under the small claims procedure if the claim is $10,000 or less. Contractors may also request that a hearing be held at a location convenient to them. With the exception of small claims decisions, contractors can appeal adverse Board decisions to the U.S. Court of Appeals for the Federal Circuit. For more information, contact: Board of Contract Appeals, General Services Administration, 1800 F Street, NW, Washington, DC 20405; 202-501-0116; {www.gsbca.gsa.gov}. There are other Contract Appeals Boards for other departments. One of the last paragraphs in your government contract should specify which Board you are to go to if a problem with your particular contract should arise.

Market, Market, Market

After you have identified your customers, researched their requirements and familiarized yourself with procurement regulations and strategies, it is time to market your product or service. Here are some things to remember:

- You must network to be successful.
- Remember to be competitive, persistent and patient.
- Attend conferences and workshops.
- Attend Trade Shows.
- Check out the SBA calendar of events {www.sba.gov/calendar}.
- Maintain a one-to-one contact with the Contract Officer or Contracting Specialist.

Federal Department Procurement Offices

Agriculture Department
1400 Independence Avenue, SW
Mail Stop 9303
Washington, DC 20250
202-720-7527
Fax: 202-720-8972
www.usda.gov/procurement
The United States Department of Agriculture procurement office has prepared a kit, *Doing Business With USDA*. This kit is available online to assist businesses that are interested in selling their products or services to the USDA.

Commerce Department
Office of Acquisition Management
14th and Constitution Avenue, NW
Washington, DC 20230
202-482-4248
http://oamweb.osec.doc.gov
The Department of Commerce has a great web site to provide information about the Acquisition Management Office and what it can do for you. Listed below are the divisions of the Department of Commerce and their procurement offices.

National Institute of Standards and Technology (NIST)
Acquisition Office
100 Bureau Drive, Stop 3460
Gaithersburg, ND 20899-3460
301-975-NIST
www.nist.gov/admin/od/contract/contract.htm
The National Institute of Standards and Technology relies on contractors and vendors to supply many goods and services necessary to fulfill their mission. Every year NIST buys

millions of dollars worth of supplies and services. Check out their web site to see if some of the millions could be for your work.

National Oceanic and Atmospheric Administration
Acquisition Management Division
1305 East West Highway, 7th Floor
Silver Springs, MD 20910
301-713-0325
www.ofa.noaa.gov/%7Eago/index.html

Patent and Trademark Office
USPTO Contact Center
Crystal Plaza 3, Room 2C02
P.O. Box 1450
Alexandria, VA 22313-1450
800-786-9199
703-308-4357
www.uspto.gov/web/offices/ac/comp/proc/

U.S. Census Bureau
Acquisition Management Office
4700 Silver Hill Road
Washington, DC 20233-0001
301-763-3342
www.census.gov/procur/www/
Even the Census Department buys goods and services from freelancers. Check their web site for information on how to get a contract with the Census Bureau.

Education Department

400 Maryland Avenue, SW   202-401-2000
Washington, DC 20202   Fax: 202-401-0689
www.ed.gov/fund/contract/about/booklet1.html
The Department of Education publishes Doing Business With the Department of Education. You can view a copy online at the above web address.

Energy Department

Office of Procurement and Assistance Management
1000 Independence Ave., SW   800-dial-DOE
Washington, DC 20585   202-586-5575
www.pr.doe.gov   Fax: 202-586-4403
The Department of Energy's e-center site is a one-stop information center for all of your contracting needs. You can browse opportunities online 24 hours a day. They provide information on the procurement process, competing for awards, sealed bid purchases, small business programs and other issues. The Department of Energy even provides a DVD titled "Doing Business with the Department of Energy" that you can download onto your computer. {http://ipvideo. lbl.gov:554/ramgen/DoingBusinessWithDoe.rm}

US Environmental Protection Agency

Ariel Rios Building
Office of Acquisition Management
1200 Pennsylvania Avenue, N.W.
Mail Code 3801R
Washington, D.C. 20460   202-564-4310
www.epa.gov/oam/

Federal Communications Commission

Office of Procurement
445 12th Street SW   202-418-1952
Washington, DC 20554   Fax: 202-418-0237
www.fcc.gov/omd/contracts/
This office is responsible for the nationwide procurement needs for the Federal Communications Commission.

Federal Emergency Management Administration

Financial & Acquisitions Management
500 C Street, SW
Washington, DC 20472   202-646-4006
www.fema.gov/ofm/toc.shtm
The Federal Emergency Management Administration publishes a guide Doing Business with FEMA to assist firms develop marketing strategies and help answer questions to those new to government contracting. The publication is a wealth of information. You may also call FEMA for information concerning small business matters, solicitations or disaster contracting. When an award exceeds $25,000 it will be published in the Commerce Business Daily.

Food and Drug Administration

Office of Facilities, Acquisitions and Central Services
Room 2074, HFA 230
5600 Fishers Lane   301-827-7211
Rockville, MD 20857   Fax: 301-827-7228
www.fda.gov/oc/ofacs/contracts/
The Food and Drug Administration (FDA) post its solicitations on the FedBizOpps web site at {www.fed bizopps.gov}. In addition, the FDA web site lists the FDA programs and the contract coordinator to contact if you want to do business with the FDA. The FDA publishes a magazine called the FDA Consumer that has very limited writing freelance opportunities for writers with a record of successful translation of scientific and medical material into easy-to-read articles. Explore the web site at {www.fda.gov/fdac} to

determine if you may qualify. If you think you can contribute you will need to send a resume and samples of your work to the FDA.

Forest Service

USDA Forest Service Acquisition Management
1621 North Kent Street
Suite 707 RP-E   703-605-4744
Arlington, VA 22209-2131   Fax: 703-605-5100
www.fs.fed.us/business
The Forest Service Acquisition Management office can help you if you are interested in freelancing for the Forest Service. This is the office you should contact if you are interested in a radio contract.

General Services Administration Headquarters

1800 F Street NW   202-501-0445
Washington, DC 20405-0001   Fax: 202-208-5938
www.gsa.gov
Serving the United States
To become a GSA Schedule contractor, you must first submit an offer in response to the applicable GSA Schedule solicitation. GSA awards contracts to that offer commercial items falling within the generic descriptions in the GSA Schedule solicitations. They offer a publication Doing Business with General Services that can be viewed on their web site. GSA offers many free workshops on how to obtain GSA Schedules contracts.

Sheron Snyder
General Services Administration Regional Office
400 15th SW
Auburn, WA 98001-6599
253-931-7956
Fax: 253-804-4887
Sheron.snyder@gsa.gov
Serving: Alaska, Idaho, Oregon, and Washington

Lori Falkenstrom
General Service Administration Regional Office
450 Golden Gate Avenue
Room 5-6535
San Francisco, CA 94102-3434
415-522-2700
Fax: 415-522-2705
Lori.falkenstrom@gsa.gov
Serving: Arizona, California, Hawaii, and Nevada

Willie Heath
General Services Administration Regional Office
819 Taylor Street
Fort Worth, TX 76102
817-978-0800
Fax: 817-978-0440
Willie.heath@gsa.gov
Serving: Arkansas, Louisiana, New Mexico, Oklahoma, and Texas

Shirley Hopkins
General Services Administration Regional Office
Federal Center #41, Room 240
P.O. Box 25006
Denver, CO 80225
303-236-7408
Fax: 303-236-7403
Shiley.Hopkins@gsa.gov
Serving: Colorado, Montana, North Dakota, South Dakota, Utah and Wyoming

France Lopez
General Services Administration Regional Office
Thomas P. O'Neill Jr. Federal Building
10 Causeway Street
Boston, MA 02222-1047
617-565-8100
Fax: 617-565-8101
France.lopez@gsa.gov
Serving: Connecticut, Massachusetts, Maine, New Hampshire, Rhode Island, and Vermont

Angela Ditommaso
General Services Administration Regional Office
20 North Eighth Street, 9th Floor
Philadelphia, PA 19107-3191
215-446-4918
Fax: 215-446-5133
Angela.ditommaso@gsa.gov
Serving: Delaware, Maryland, Pennsylvania, Virginia, and West Virginia

Colleen Pappas
General Services Administration Regional Office
18-130
26 Federal Plaza
New York-Manhattan, NY 10278-0000
212-264-1236
Fax: 212-264-2760
Colleen.pappas@gsa.gov
Serving: New York and New Jersey

Rebecca Vanover
General Services Administration Regional Office
77 Forsyth Street, Room 600
Atlanta, GA 30303-0000
404-331-3374
Fax: 404-331-1721
Rebecca.vanover@gsa.gov
Serving: Alabama, Florida, Georgia, Kentucky, Mississippi, North Carolina, South Carolina, and Tennessee

Beverly Coley
General Services Administration Regional Office
230 S Dearborn Street, Room 3718
Chicago, IL 60604
312-353-1100
Fax: 312-886-9893
Beverly.coley@gsa.gov
Serving: Indiana, Illinois, Michigan, Minnesota, Ohio, and Wisconsin

Ruby Rice
General Services Administration Regional Office
1500 E. Bannister Road
Kansas City, MO 64131-3009
816-926-7203
Fax: 816-823-1167
Ruby.rice@gsa.gov
Serving: Iowa, Kansas, Missouri, and Nebraska

Public Buildings Service
Design Excellence Program
1800 F Street NW
Washington, DC 20405-0001
202-501-2635
www.gsa.gov
This program is part of General Service Administration. They seek the finest architects and artists to commission their work for public buildings throughout the United States.

Health and Human Services Department
Office of Acquisition Management
Room 517-D, Hubert H. Humphrey Building
200 Independence Avenue, SW   202-401-6103
Washington, DC 20201   Fax: 202-690-6902
www.hhs.gov/ogam/oam
The Office of Acquisition Management (OAM) provides information and training to help understand the acquisition process. The web site lists contracting opportunities in a variety of areas. To view the Health and Human Services Contracting Opportunities Forecasts go to {www.hhs.gov/sdbu/publications/forecast.html }.

Homeland Security Department
1800 G Street NW, 10th Floor
Washington, DC 20528   202-786-0036
www.dhs.gov/dhspublic/display?theme=37
Listed below are the divisions of the US Department of Homeland Security (DHS) and their procurement offices. Their web site contains business and contracting forms to help you do business with the DHS. They also publish a handbook How to do Business with the Department of Homeland Security that is a valuable resource.

US Customs Service
1300 Pennsylvania Avenue, NW
Suite 1310
Washington, DC 20229
202-927-1229
Fax: 202-927-1190
www.customs.gov/xp/cgov/toolbox/contracting/

US Coast Guard
2100 2nd Street, SW, Room 2606
Washington, DC 20593
202-267-1146
Fax: 202-267-4011
www.uscg.mil/ccs/cfp/cpm/index.html

Housing and Urban Development Department
451 7th Street S.W.
Washington, DC 20410   202-708-1112
www.hud.gov/offices/cpo/contract.cfm
The Department of Housing and Urban Development offers their procurement forecast, Guide to Contracting With HUD, and a list of current competitive procurements to help your business win bids with HUD.

Interior Department
1849 C Street, NW
Washington, DC 20240   202-208-3100
www.doi.gov/pam/dave.html
The Department of Interior's acquisition office provides information on how to get contracts with their department. Listed below are the divisions of the Department of Interior and their procurement offices.

Bureau of Land Management
National Business Center Acquisition Division
P.O. Box 25047, MS BC660
Denver, CO 80225-0047
303-236-0226
Fax: 303-236-9470
www.blm.gov/natacq/
The Bureau of Land Management hires arts/graphics designers, film/video production services as well as, general photographic services. Check out their web site for information on how to get work with the BLM.

Bureau of Reclamation
Acquisition and Assistance Management Division
P.O. Box 25007
Denver, CO 80225-0007
303-445-2783
www.usbr.gov/pmts/acquisitions/
The Bureau of Reclamation publishes an Acquisition Handbook to guide prospective freelancers through the contracting process.

US Fish and Wildlife Service
Division of Contracting and Facilities Management
4401 N. Fairfax Drive, Suite 212
Arlington, VA 22203
703-358-2225
Fax: 703-358-2264
http://contracts.fws.gov
The Division of Contracting and Facilities Management supports the acquisitions of the Fish and Wildlife Service. The Washington Office supports nationwide and headquarter acquisitions with Regional Contracting Offices supporting regional and local requirements. They offer assistance to vendors and contractors interested in doing business with the Fish and Wildlife Service. All vendors interested in doing business must be registered in the Central Contractor Registration (CCR) prior to being awarded a contract.

U.S. Geological Survey Headquarters
Business Utilization and Development Specialist
12201 Sunrise Valley Drive
Mail Stop 205P
Reston, Virginia 20192
703-648-7346
www.usgs.gov/contracts

U.S. Geological Survey-Central Region
Business Utilization and Development Specialist
Box 25046 Denver Fed. Center
Denver, Colorado 80225
303-236-9331
Serving: Arkansas, Colorado, Iowa, Kansas, Louisiana, Montana, Minnesota, Missouri, Nebraska, New Mexico, North Dakota, Oklahoma, South Dakota, Texas and Wyoming.

U.S. Geological Survey-Western Region
Business Utilization and Development Specialist
345 Middlefield Road
Mail Stop 285
Menlo Park, California 94025
650-329-4162
Serving: Washington, Idaho, Oregon, California, Nevada, Arizona, Utah, Alaska, and Hawaii.

U.S. Geological Survey-Eastern Region
Business Utilization and Development Specialist
12201 Sunrise Valley Drive
Mail Stop 152
Reston, Virginia 20192
703-648-7375
Serving Connecticut, Illinois, Indiana, Kentucky, Maine, Maryland, Delaware, Massachusetts, Michigan, New Hampshire, New Jersey, New York, Ohio, Pennsylvania, Vermont, Virginia, West Virginia, Wisconsin. Southeast states: Alabama, Florida, Georgia, Mississippi, North Carolina, Caribbean, South Carolina, South Carolina, and Tennessee.

All of these U.S. Geological Survey offices can assist you in contracting opportunities. The web site has the departments acquisition forecast so you can see if they will need your services in the future.

Office of Surface Mining
1951 Constitution Avenue, NW
Washington, DC 20240
202-208-2719
www.osmre.gov/business.htm

Minerals Management Service
381 Elden Street
Herndon, VA 20170
703-787-1358
Fax: 703-787-1009
www.mms.gov/adm/procure.htm

National Park Service
Business and Economic Development Office
P.O. Box 37127 Mail Stop 3130
Washington, DC 20013-7127
http://www.nps.gov/legacy/business.html
The National Park service offers a limited number of freelance opportunities. They do contract for architectural services, audio-visual arts and other arts related work. Contact the National Park Service or go directly to the office you want consideration.

Artist-in-Residence Program
National Park Service
1849 C Street NW
Washington, DC 20240
202-208-6843
www.nps.gov/volunteer/air.htm
The National Park Service offers opportunities for two-dimensional visual artists, photographers, sculptors, performers, writers, composers and craft artists to live and work in the parks. Currently, there are 27 parks participating in the Artist-in-Residence program. Check the web site for current programs.

Justice Department

950 Pennsylvania Avenue, NW   202-307-0608
Washington, DC 20530-0001   Fax: 202-307-0086
www.usdoj.gov/07business
The Department of Justice's web site Doing Business with DOJ provides information to people seeking business opportunities with the Department of Justice. Listed below are the divisions of the Department of Justice and their procurement offices.

Bureau of Alcohol, Tobacco, Firearms and Explosives
Acquisitions and Business Opportunities
650 Massachusetts Avenue, NW, Room 8290
Washington, DC 20226
202-927-8332
Fax: 202-927-7311
www.atf.gov/acquisition/

Bureau of Prisons
320 First Street, N.W.
Washington, DC 20534
202-307-3067
Fax: 202-514-4418
www.bop.gov/contract.html
The Bureau of Prisons publishes an online publication How To Do Business With the Bureau of Prisons to help freelancers. If you are interested in work for the Bureau of Prisons monitor their web site for the most up-to-date acquisition information.

Drug Enforcement Administration
Office of Acquisition Management
2401 Jefferson Davis Highway
Alexandria, VA 22301
202-353-9505 Acquisition Management
202-307-4921 Small Business Specialist
http://128.121.209.186

The Drug Enforcement Administration (DEA) buys the products and services it needs to through the Office of Acquisition Management. The DEA conducts the majority of its procurements as full and open competitive or small and small disadvantaged business set-aside, including 8(a)'s. This office supports acquisitions at the simplified acquisition threshold of $2500-$100,000.

Federal Bureau of Investigation
Procurement and Management Section
J. Edgar Hoover Building, Room 6823
935 Pennsylvania Avenue, NW
Washington, DC 20535
202-324-2143
Fax: 202-324-1172
www.fbi.gov/business/business.htm

The Federal Bureau of Investigation encourages the participation of small, Women-owned, Disadvantaged Business owners in their contracting activities. Their web site lists products and services purchased by the FBI as well as procurement procedures.

Justice Management Division
1331 Pennsylvania Avenue, NW
Suite 1000
NPB 1000
Washington, DC 20530
202-307-2000
Fax: 202-307-1933
www.usdoj.gov/jmd/pss/

The Procurement Services Staff (PSS) provides acquisition support to litigation components. In 2002, contracts totaled approximately $1 billion. Of this amount, about 23% was awarded to small businesses and 2.5% to small and disadvantaged businesses.

United States Marshals Service
National Procurement & Acquisition Office
CS-3, Room 1124
600 Army-Navy Drive
Arlington, VA 22202
202-307-8640
Fax: 202-307-9695
www.usdoj.gov/marshals/doing.html

If you've always wanted to work with a Marshal, this may be the department for you. The United States Marshal Service buys services from video production to graphic design.

Labor Department

U.S. Department of Labor
Frances Perkins Building
200 Constitution Avenue, NW   202-219-4631
Washington, DC 20210   Fax: 202-219-6853
www.dol.gov/dol/business.htm

The Department of Labor's web site Doing Business With the Department of Labor, is a wealth of information for all kinds of contracting options. The Office of the Assistant Secretary for Administration and Management through the Department's Procurement Executive is responsible for the Department's procurement programs.

National Aeronautics and Space Administration

Headquarters Information Center   202-358-0000
Washington, DC 20546-0001   Fax: 202-358-3251
http://www.hq.nasa.gov/office/procurement/

There are many business opportunities at NASA. Their web site offers information on NASA acquisition forecasts, financial and contractual status of active procurements, marketing to NASA and how to prepare and submit unsolicited proposals. NASA's Acquisition Internet Service Business Opportunities (NAIS) gives entrepreneurs on-line access to contract opportunities at NASA, a procurement reference library and other procurement information. You can search freelance contract opportunities in its database and also be notified by e-mail when procurement announcements are made. Procurement opportunities are available throughout the country at individual NASA centers so don't forget to check them out too when looking for freelance work.

NASA Procurement Sites

NASA, Ames Research Center
Mail Stop 241-1/T.Kolis
Moffett Field, CA 94035-1000
650-604-4690
Fax: 650-604-4646
http://server-mpo.arc.nasa.gov/Services/Proc/home.tml
www.arc.nasa.gov

Dryden Flight Research Center
P.O. Box 273
Edwards, CA 93523-0273
661-258-3311
www.dfrc.nasa.gov/Business/Procurement/index.html

Glenn Research Center
Mail Stop 500-313
21000 Brookpark Road
Cleveland, OH 44135-3191
216-433-4000
www.grc.nasa.gov/WWW/Procure/home.htm

Goddard Space Flight Center
Code 200
Greenbelt, MD 20771-0001
301-286-3596
Fax: 301-286-0237
http://genesis.gsfc.nasa.gov/procure.htm

Jet Propulsion Laboratory Acquisition Division
4800 Oak Grove Drive
Pasadena, CA 91109
818-354-6190
http://acquisition.jpl.nasa.gov/

The Jet Propulsion Laboratory (JPL) is a government-owned, Federally Funded Research and Development Center. JPL procurements are California Institute of Technology contracts, not government-direct contracts. Contractors should contact Caltech/JPL to become familiar with how JPL contracts are awarded.

NASA-Johnson Space Center
Mailcode BA
Houston, TX 77058
281-244-2100
http://jsc-web-pub.jsc.nasa.gov/bd01/

Kennedy Space Center
Code OP
Kennedy Space Center, FL 32899

321-867-5000
www.ksc.nasa.gov/procurement

NASA Langley Research Center
100 NASA Road
Mail Stop 134
Hampton, VA 23681-2199
757-864-1000
http://procurement.larc.nasa.gov/

Marshall Space Flight Center
Code PS01
Marshall Space Flight Center, AL 35812
256-544-2121
http://ec.msfc.nasa.gov/msfc/home.shtml

Stennis Space Center
Code DA00
Stennis Space Center, MS 39529-6000
228-688-3341
www.ssc.nasa.gov/~procure/scripts/welcome.cgi

The National Science Foundation
4201 Wilson Boulevard   703-292-5111
Arlington, VA 22230   800-877-8339
www.nsf.gov/home/about/contracting/
The National Science Service offers composition and printing contracts, which are listed on their web site. If you are interested in working for the NSF contact them at the office listed above.

Office of Personnel Management
1900 E Street NW
Washington, DC 20415-1000   202-606-1800
www.opm.gov/procure/index.asp
The Office of Personnel Management publishes a guide titled Contracting Opportunities. Check their web site for your next freelance contract.

US Government Printing Office
Printing Procurement Department
Room C-899
North Capitol & H Streets, N.W.   202-512-0327
Washington, D.C. 20401   Fax: 202-512-1745
www.access.gpo.gov/procurement/index.html

US Postal Service
Services Purchasing
475 L'Enfant Plaza West, SW
Washington, DC 20260-6237   202-268-2826
www.usps.com/purchasing
Although the Postal Service is a government agency, it is also an independent program under the executive branch of the United States. They are therefore exempt from laws that usually apply to US government agencies. To view their regulations you can view their publication, Purchasing Manual, online.

Social Security Administration
Office of Acquisition and Grants
1710 Gwynn Oak Avenue
Baltimore, MD 21207-5279
www.ssa.gov/oag/
The Social Security Administration can assist you in the acquisition process.

State Department
2201 C Street NW

Washington, DC 20520   202-647-4000
www.statebuy.gov/home.htm
The State Department provides community training and counseling about doing business with the Department of State.

Transportation Department
Acquisition and Grants
400 7th Street, S.W., Room 9414   800-532-1169
Washington, DC 20590   202-366-1930
www.dot.gov/ost/m60/index.html   Fax: 202-366-7538
The Department of Transportation (DOT) offers a publication on the web site, Contracting with the DOT, to help anyone interested in doing business with the DOT. The publication offers a wealth of information, DOT contacts and links to many useful services. You can also get a procurement forecast at {http://osdbuweb.dot.gov/business/procurement/forecast.html} to see if the DOT is planning on using a service you would be able to provide.

Treasury Department
1500 Pennsylvania Avenue, NW
Washington, DC 20220   202-622-2000
www.ustreas.gov/offices/management/dcfo/procurement/
Listed below are the bureaus of the Department of Treasury and their procurement offices.

Bureau of Engraving and Printing
Contract Administration Division
14th and C Streets, S.W., Room 705A
Washington, DC 20228
202-874-2065
www.moneyfactory.com/procurement/index.cfm/113
The Bureau of Engraving and Printing provides a yearly forecast document that can be viewed on the web site. The Bureau of Engraving Contract Division administers all contracts awarded in the Office of Procurement.

Financial Management Service
Acquisition Management
401 14th Street, SW
Room 110, Liberty Center
Washington, DC 20227
202-874-6910
http://fms.treas.gov/aboutfms/business.html

Department of Internal Revenue
Office of Procurement Operations
Room 700, Constellation Centre
6009 Oxon Hill Road
Oxen Hill, MD 20745
202-283-1610
Fax: 202-283-1514
www.procurement.irs.treas.gov/

Bureau of Public Debt
Bureau of the Public Debt
Division of Procurement
200 Third Street, UNB 4th Floor
Parkersburg, WV 26101-5312
304-480-7137
www.publicdebt.treas.gov/oa/oaprocr.htm

Veterans Affairs Department
Office of Acquisition and Materiél Management
810 Vermont Avenue, NW   202-273-6029
Washington, DC 20420   Fax: 202-273-6163
www.appc1.va.gov/oamm/index.htm

Free Local Help: The Best Place To Start To Sell To The Government

Within each state there are offices that can help you get started in the federal procurement process. As stated previously, your local Small Business Administration (SBA) office is a good resource. In addition to their other services, the SBA can provide you with a list of Federal Procurement Offices based in your state, so you can visit them in person to gather valuable information. Another place to turn is your local Small Business Development Center (look under Economic Development in your phone book). These offices are funded jointly by federal and state governments, and are usually associated with the state university system in your area. They are aware of the federal procurement process, and can help you draw up a sensible business plan that will be successful.

Some states have established programs to assist businesses in the federal procurement process for all departments in the government. These programs are designed to help businesses learn about the bidding process, the resources available, and provide information on how the procurement system operates. They can match the product or service you are selling with the appropriate agency, and then help you market your product. Several programs have online bid matching services, whereby if a solicitation appears on FedBizOpps that matches what your company markets, then the program will automatically contact you to start the bid process. The program office can then request the appropriate documents, and assist you in achieving your goal. These Procurement Technical Assistance Centers (PTAC) are partially funded by the Department of Defense to assist businesses with Defense Procurement. For a current listing of PTACs contact:

Defense Logistics Agency
Office of Small and Disadvantaged Utilization
Bldg. 4, Cameron Station, Room 4B110
    Alexandria, VA 22304-6100   703-767-1661
  {www.dla.mil/db}, then go to the small business site
(See page 779 for a complete listing.)

Let Your Congressman Help You

Are you trying to market a new product to a department of the Federal government? Need to know where to try to sell your wares? Is there some problem with your bid? Your Congressman can be of assistance. Because they want business in their state to boom, most Congressmen will make an effort to assist companies in obtaining federal contracts. Frequently they will write a letter to accompany your bid, or if you are trying to market a new product, they will write a letter to the procurement office requesting that they review your product. Your Congressman can also be your personal troubleshooter. If there is some problem with your bid, your Congressman can assist you in determining and resolving the problem, and can provide you with information on the status of your bid. Look in the blue pages of your phone book for your Senators' or Representatives' phone numbers, or call them in Washington at 202-224-3121.

Small Business Set-Asides

The Small Business Administration (SBA) encourages government purchasing agencies to set aside suitable government purchases for exclusive small business competition. A purchase which is restricted to small business bidders is identified by a set aside clause in the invitation for bids or request for proposals. There is no overall listing of procurements which are, or have been, set aside for small business. A small business learns which purchases are reserved for small business by getting listed on bidders' lists. It also can help keep itself informed of set aside opportunities by referring to the FedBizOpps. Your local SBA office can provide you with more information on set asides, and so can the Procurement Assistance Offices listed at the end of this section. To locate your nearest SBA office, call 1-800-827-5722 or {www.sba.gov}.

Veterans Assistance

Each Small Business Administration District Office has a Veterans Affairs Officer which can assist veteran-owned businesses in obtaining government contracts. Although there is no such thing as veterans set aside contracts, the Veterans Administration does make an effort to fill its contracts using veteran-owned businesses whenever possible. Contact your local SBA office for more information, or check the following websites: {www.sba.gov/VETS}; {www.va.gov}.

Woman-Owned Business Assistance

There are over 3.7 million women-owned businesses in the United States, and the number is growing each year. Current government policy requires federal contracting officers to increase their purchases from women-owned businesses. Although the women-owned firms will receive more opportunities to bid, they still must be the lowest responsive and responsible bidder to win the contract. To assist these businesses, each SBA district office has a Women's Business Ownership Representative, who can provide you with information regarding government programs. Most of the offices hold a *Selling to the Federal Government* seminar, which is designed to educate the business owner on the ins and outs of government procurement. There is also a helpful publication, *Women Business Owners: Selling to the Federal Government*, which provides information on procurement opportunities available. Contact your local SBA office or your Procurement Technical

Assistance Center (listed below) for more information; or check the website at {http://onlinewbc.gov}.

Minority and Labor Surplus Area Assistance

Some areas of the country have been determined to be labor surplus areas, which means there is a high rate of unemployment. Your local SBA office can tell you if you live in such an area, as some contracts are set asides for labor surplus areas. For more information, contact your local Small Business Administration office (call 1-800-827-5722 for the SBA office nearest you; or online at {www.sba.gov}), or call the Procurement Technical Assistance Center in your state (listed below).

Federal Procurement Technical Assistance Centers

Alabama
Charles Hopson
Alabama Small Business
  Development Consortium
2800 Milan Ct., Suite 124
Birmingham, AL 35211
205-934-6750
Fax: 205-934-7645
Email: charlesh@uab.edu
www.asbdc.org/procurement

Alaska
Mike Taylor
University of Alaska Anchorage
Small Business Development Center
430 W. 7th Ave.
Suite 110
Anchorage, AK 99501-3550
907-274-7232
800-478-7232
Fax: 907-274-9524
Email: angmtl@uaa.alaska.edu
www.ptacalaska.org

Procurement Technical Assistance
  Center of Alaska
613 Cushman Street, Suite 209
Fairbanks, AK 99701
907-456-7232
800-478-1701
Fax: 907-456-7233
www.ptacalaska.org

Arizona
Elaine Young
The National Center for AIED
National Center Headquarters
953 E. Juanita Ave.
Mesa, AZ 85204
480-545-1298, ext. 223
Fax: 480-545-4208
Email: Ncaiedely@aol.com
www.ncaied.org/mpsp

APTAN, Inc
459 North Gilbert Road. Suite A215
Gilbert, AZ 85234

480-632-1800
Fax: 480-632-1931
Email: aptan@primenet.com
www.aptan.com

Cyndi Bosworth
Maricopa County PTAC
201 N. Central Avenue, 27th Floor
Phoenix, AZ 85073
602-495-6467
Fax: 602-495-8913
Email:
  cbosworth@phoenixchamber.com

Arkansas
Sue Coates
University of Arkansas
Cooperative Extension Service
103 East Page St.
Malvern, AR 72104
501-337-5355
Fax: 501-337-5045
Email: apac@uaex.edu
www.arcommunities.org/APAC/defa
  ult.asp

California
Bob Truex
Riverside Community College
  District
Procurement Assistance Center
13745 Riverside Drive
Riverside, CA 92518
909-571-6442
Fax: 909-653-1051
Email: Bob.Truex@rcc.edu
www.rcchelpsbusiness.com

Jane E. McGinnis
Action Business Center
California Central Valley PTAC
2000 "M" St.
Merced, CA 95340
209-385-7686
Fax: 209-383-4959
Email: ptac1@pacbell.net
www.abc.merced.ca.us/ptac.html

Ken Hollis
Imperial County Community and
  Economic Development
836 Main Street
El Centro, CA 92243
760-337-7814
800-317-8432
Fax: 760-337-8907
www.icced.com

J. Gunnar Schalin
Southwestern Community College
Contracting Opportunities Center
3443 Camino Del Rio South
Suite 116
San Diego, CA 92108-3913
619-285-7020, ext. 3005
Fax: 619-285-7030
Email: sdcoc@pacbell.net
www.ptac-sandiego.org

Debbie Johnson
Los Angeles County Office of Small
  Business and Procurement
  Technical Assistance
4800 Cesar E. Chavez Avenue
Los Angeles, CA 90022
323-260-2311
800-555-3815
Fax: 323-881-1871
Email: dcabrier@lacdc.org
www.laosb.org

Jack Tooney
Federal Technology Center PTAC
4700 Roseville Road, Suite 105
Sacramento, CA 95660
916-334-9388
866-FTC-PTAC
Fax: 916-334-9078
Email: jack@TheFTC.org
www.theftc.org/ptac

Colorado
Denver Small Business Development
  Procurement Center
1445 Market Street
Denver, CO 80202

303-620-8076
Fax: 303-534-3200
Email: Denver.sbdc@den-chamber.org
www.denverchamber.org/chamber/programs/sbdc/index.htm

Connecticut
Arlene M. Vogel
Southeastern Connecticut Enterprise
    Region (seCTer)
190 Governor Winthrop Blvd
Suite 300
New London, CT 06320
860-437-4659, ext. 208
1-888-6-SECTER
Fax: 860-437-4662
Email: ptap@secter.org
www.secter.org/

Delaware
Juanita Beauford
Delaware Government Marketing
    Assistance Program
Small Business Development Center
1318 North Market Street
Wilmington, DE 19801
302-571-1555
Fax: 302-571-5222
www.delawarecontracts.com

District of Columbia
No PTAC awarded

Florida
Laura Subel
University of West Florida
Florida PTA Program
401 East Chase St.
Suite 100
Pensacola, FL 32502
850-473-7806
Fax: 850-473-7813
Email: lsubel@uwf.edu
www.fptac.com
Serving: Pensacola, Panama City and
Tallahassee areas.

Regina Bell
University of West Florida
    Purchasing Department
Minority Enterprise Procurement
    Program
11000 University Parkway
Pensacola, FL 32514
850-474-2632
Email: rbell@uwf.edu
www.fptac.org

Paul Briere
University of West Florida
34 Miracle Strip Pkwy, S.E. (US 98)
Ft. Walton Beach, FL 32548
850-243-3514
Email: pbriere@uwf.edu
www.fptac.org
Serving Ft. Walton Beach and
Crestview areas

Bob Raiser
Chamber of Commerce Small
    Business Center
5000-3 Norwood Avenue
Jacksonville, FL 32208
904-924-1100 ext 231
Email: bob.riser@myjaxhamber.com
www.fptac.org
Serving the Jacksonville area

Glenda Rife
University of North Florida
110 E. Silver Springs Boulevard
Ocala, FL 34470-6613
352-622-8763 (Mondays and
    Fridays)
352-334-7230 (Tuesdays)
Email: ger-sbdc@atlantic.net
www.fptac.org
Serving Ocala and Gainesville areas

Charlene Bostic
University of South Florida
1101 Channelside Drive, Suite 210
Tampa, FL 33602
813-905-8526
800-733-7232
Email: cbostic@coba.usf.edu
www.fptac.org
Serving Tampa, Bartow, Orlando,
Ocala and Melbourne areas

Carol Bowers
University of South Florida
The Pinellas Park Technical Services
    Building
6051 78th Avenue
Pinellas Park, FL 33780
727-541-0805 ext 2108
Email: cbowers@coba.usf.edu
www.fptac.org
Serving St. Petersburg, Sarasota and
Pasco counties

Carole Hart
Florida Atlantic University
777 Glades Road T-9
Boca Raton, FL 333431
561-291-1145
Email: chart@fau.edu
www.fptac.org
Serving the Boca Raton area

Jackie Rule
Florida Atlantic University
8500 SW 8th Street, Suite 224
Miami, FL 33144-4002
561-297-1145
Email: jrule1@fau.edu
www.fptac.org
Serving the Miami area

Dan Telep
Florida Gulf Coast University
12751 Westlinks Drive
Building 3, Unit 7
Ft. Myers, FL 33913-8615
239-225-4218
Email: dtelep@fgcu.edu
www.fptac.org

Serving Lee, Collier, Charlotte,
Glades and Hendry counties

Georgia
Georgia Institute of Technology
Georgia Tech Procurement
    Assistance Center
760 Spring Street, Suite 330
Atlanta, GA 30332-0640
478-953-3155
888-272-2104
Fax: 478-953-3169
Email: gtpac@edi.gatech.edu
www.edi.gatech.edu

Alan Barfoot
Georgia Institute of Technology
Georgia Tech Procurement
    Assistance Center
Dublin Regional Office
1200-A Hillcrest Parkway
Dublin, GA 31201
478-275-6543
Fax: 478-275-6544
Email: centralregion@edi.gatech.edu
www.edi.gatech.edu

Jill Winkelman
Georgia Institute of Technology
Georgia Tech Procurement
    Assistance Center
Savannah Regional Office
210 Technology Circle
Savannah, GA 31407
912-963-2509
Fax: 912-963-2522
Email: coastalregion@edi.gatech.edu
www.edi.gatech.edu

Todd Hurd
Georgia Institute of Technology
Georgia Tech Procurement
    Assistance Center
Augusta Regional Office
1054 Claussen Road, Suite 301
Augusta, GA 30907
706-737-1414
Fax: 706-737-1420
Email: eastregion@edi.gatech.edu
www.edi.gatech.edu

Karen Fite
Georgia Institute of Technology
Georgia Tech Procurement
    Assistance Center
Athens Regional Office
1180 E. Broad Street
Chicopee Complex
Athens, GA 30602-5413
706-542-8900
Fax: 706-542-8899
Email:
    northeastregion@edi.gatech.edu
www.edi.gatech.edu

Jerry Zolkowski
Georgia Institute of Technology
Georgia Tech Procurement
    Assistance Center
Dalton Regional Office

213 N. College Drive
Dalton, GA 30720
706-272-2702
Fax: 706-272-2701
Email: northwestregion@
 di.gatech.edu
www.edi.gatech.edu

Art Ford
Georgia Institute of Technology
Georgia Tech Procurement
 Assistance Center
Albany Regional Office
125 Pine Avenue, Suite 220
P.O. Box 587
Albany, GA 31702-0587
229-430-4188
Fax: 229-430-4200
Email: southregion@edi.gatech.edu
www.edi.gatech.edu

Jennifer Trapp
Georgia Institute of Technology
Georgia Tech Procurement
 Assistance Center
Newman Regional Office
31-B Postal Parkway
Newman. GA 30263
770-254-7381
Fax: 770-254-7449
Email: westregion@edi.gatech.edu
www.edi.gatech.edu

Tyler McGhee
United Indian Development
 Association Consulting Group,
 Inc.
86 South Cobb Drive, MZ 0510
Marietta, GA 30063-0510
770-494-0431
Fax: 770-494-1236
Email: uida@uida.org
www.uida.org/ptac.html

Hawaii
No PTAC awarded

Idaho
Larry Demirelli
Idaho Department of Commerce
State of Idaho
700 West State St.
Boise, ID 83720-0093
208-334-2470
Fax: 208-334-2631
Email: ibn@idoc.state.id.us
www.idahoworks.com

Illinois
Pedro Pereira
Latin American Chamber of
 Commerce
The Chicago Pac
3512 W. Fullerton
Chicago, IL 60647
773-252-5211
Fax: 773-252-7065
Email: cmontoya@lacc1.com
www.lacc1.com

Lois Van Meter
State of Illinois
Department of Commerce and
 Community Affairs
620 E. Adams St., Third Floor
Springfield, IL 62701
217-557-1823
Fax: 217-785-6328
Email: ivanmete@
 ommerce.state.il.us
www.commerce.state.il.us

Al Meroz
Moraine Valley Community College
10900 S. 88th Avenue
Palos Hills, IL 60465-0937
708-974-5452
Fax: 708-974-0078
Email: meroz@morainevalley.edu
www.morainevalley.edu/ptac/default
 .htm

Rita Hatcher
College of DuPage PTAC
425 Fawell Boulevard
Glen Ellyn, IL 60137-6599
630-942-2184
Fax: 630-942-3789
Email: hatcher@cdnet.cod.edu
www.cod.edu/BPI/ptac.htm

Susan Gorman
Illinois Central College PTAC
124 S.W. Adams Street
Suite 300
Peoria, IL 61602-1388
309-495-5970
Fax: 309-676-7534
Email: sgorman@icc.edu
www.icc.edu/ptac

Marc N. Violante
College of Lake County PTAC
19351 West Washington Street
Grayslake, IL 60030-1198
847-543-2025
Fax: 847-223-9371
Email: clcptac@clc.cc.il.us
www.clcillinois.edu/ddd/dept/pta.asp

Teresa Ebeler
East St. Louis PTAC
Southern Illinois University
601 J.R. Thompson Dr. Room 2090
East St. Louis, IL 62001
618-482-8330
Email: tmeehan@siue.edu
www.siue.edu/ESL/small_business/s
 mall_business.htm

Rich Fyke
John A. Logan College PTAC
700 Logan College Road
Carterville, IL 62918
618-985-2828
800-851-4720
Fax: 618-985-2867
Email: rich.fyke@jal.cc.il.us
www.jal.cc.il.us/bus_ind/ptac.html

William Hett-Dobricky
NORBIC PTAC Center
5353 West Armstrong Avenue
Chicago, IL 60646
773-594-9562
Fax: 773-594-9416
Email: whdobricky@norbic.org
www.norbic.org/procurement_assista
 nce.htm

John DiGiacoma
Rock Valley College PTAC
3301 North Mulford Rd, Room 262
Rockford, IL 61114-5640
Phone: 815-921-2086
Fax: 815-921-3059
Email: jdigiacomo@rvc.cc.il.us
www.rvc.cc.il.us/business/procure

David Talbot
South Suburban College
15800 South State Street
South Holland, IL 60473-1270
708-596-2000 Ext. 2431
Fax: 708-225-5834
Email: dtalbot@southsuburban
 ollege.edu
www.ssc.cc.il.us/bci/ptac.html

Kristin Johnson
Women's Business Development
 Center PTAC
8 South Michigan Avenue, Suite 400
Chicago, IL 60603-3302
312-853-3477 Ext. 18
Fax: 312-853-0145
Email: kjohnson@wbdc.org
www.wbdc.org

Carol Cusumano, Freida Schreck
Central Illinois Regional PTAC
P.O. Box 203
Riverton, IL 62561
217-789-1017
Fax: 217-522-3512
Email: PRAXIS535@aol.com

Indiana
Kathy DeGuilio-Fox
Partners in Contracting Corporation
PTA Center
6100 Southport Rd.
Portage, IN 46368
219-762-8644
Fax: 219-763-1513
Email: picc@piccorp.org
www.piccorp.org

Iowa
Bruce Coney
Iowa State University
Iowa Procurement Center
2272 Howe Hall
Ames, IA 50011-2270
515-294-4473
800-458-4465
Fax: 515-294-4483
Email:
 bruce.coney@ciras.iastate.edu
www.ciras.iastate.edu/ipoc

Kansas

Terri Bennett
Heartland Procurement Technical
    Assistance Center
Missouri Southern State College
3950 E. Newman Rd.
Joplin, MO 64801-1595
417-625-9538
Fax: 417-625-9782
Email: heartlandptac@mail.mssc.edu
www.mssc.edu/heartlandptac

Jesse James III
Heartland Procurement Technical
    Assistance Centers
Entrepreneurial Growth Resource
    Center
Bloch School of Business University
    of Missouri - Kansas City
4747 Troost Building, 203
Kansas City, MO 64110
816-235-2891
Fax: 816-235-2947
Email: jamesje@umkc.edu

Kentucky

Tim Back
Kentucky Cabinet For Economic
    Development
Dept. of Community Development
500 Mero St.
2200 Capital Plaza Tower
Frankfort, KY 40601
800-838-3266
502-564-4252
Fax: 502-564-5932
Email: tback@mail.state.ky.us
www.thinkkentucky.com/kyedc/proa
    ssist.asp

Louisiana

Sherrie Mullins
Louisiana Productivity Center
University of Southwest Louisiana
P.O. Box 44172
241 E. Lewis St.
Lafayette, LA 70504-4172
337-482-6767
Fax: 337-482-5837
Email: sbm3321@louisiana.edu
www.louisiana.edu

Kelly Ford
Northwest Louisiana Government
    Procurement Center
Shreveport COC
400 Edwards St.
P.O. Box 20074
Shreveport, LA 71120-0074
318-677-2500
Fax: 318-677-2541
Email: kellyford@
    shreveportchamber.org
www.lagpc.org

Maine

Rick Alexander
Eastern Maine Development Corp.
Market Development Center

One Cumberland Pl., Suite 300
P.O. Box 2579
Bangor, ME 04402-2579
207-942-6389
800-339-6389
Fax: 207-942-3548
Email: ralexander@emdc.org
www.mdcme.org

Rick Alexander
Market Development Center
95 Park Street, Suite 411
Lewistown, ME 04240
207-777-5067
Email: ralexander@emdc.org
www.mdcme.org

Rick Alexander
Market Development Center
P.O. Box 1517
Portland, ME 04101
207-780-8894
Email: egray@clinic.net
www.mdcme.org

Maryland

Greg Prouty
Maryland PTAC
Small Business Development Center
7100 Baltimore Avenue, Suite 303
College Park, MD 20740
301-403-2739
866-228-0432
Fax: 301-403-8303
Email: gprouty@mdptap.edu
www.mdptap.umd.edu

Massachusetts

Peter J. Cokotis
University of Massachusetts at
    Amherst
Office of Grants and Contracts
121 Presidents Drive
Room 227 S.O.M.
Amherst, MA 01033-9310
413-737-6712
Email: pcokotis@som.umass.edu
http://msbdc.som.umass.edu/ptac

Michigan

Sandy Gelman
Schoolcraft College Business
    Development Center
18600 Haggerty Rd.
Livonia, MI 48152-2696
734-462-4438
Fax: 734-462-4439
Email: sgelman@
    schoolcraft.cc.mi.us
www.schoolcraft.cc.mi.us/bdc/defaul
    t.htm

Mike Black
Southwest Michigan Technical
    Assistance Center
Western Michigan University
4717 Campus Drive, Box 100
Kalamazoo, MI 49008
269-372-3941
Fax: 269-353-5569

Email: Michael.black@wmich.edu
www.michigantac.org

Paula Boase
Downriver Community Conference
Economic Development
15100 Northline Road
Southgate, MI 48195
734-362-3477
Fax: 734-281-6661
Email: paulab@dccwf.org
www.dccwf.org

James Millhench
Warren, Center Line
Sterling Heights Chamber of
    Commerce
30500 Van Dyke Ave.
Suite 118
Warren, MI 48093
586-751-3939
Fax: 586-751-3995
Email:
    jmillhench@wcschamber.com
www.michigantac.org

Pamela Vanderlaan
West Central Michigan Works!
PTA Center
110 Elm St.
Big Rapids, MI 49307
231-796-4891, ext. 16
Fax: 231-796-8316
Email: ptac@michworkswc.org
www.michworks.swc.org

James F. Haslinger
Northwestern Michigan Council of
    Governments
PTA Center
1209 South Garfield Ave.
Traverse City, MI 49685-0506
231-929-5036
Fax: 231-929-5042
Email: jhasling@nwm.cog.mi.us
www.nwm.org/business/procure/

Pennie Southwell
Technical Assistance Center of
    South Central Michigan
The Enterprise Group of Jackson,
    Inc.
One Jackson Square
Jackson, MI 49201
517-788-4680
Fax: 517-782-0061
Email: pennie@enterprisegroup.org
www.enterprisegroup.org

Pemale Vanderlaan
Michigan Works! West Central
900 Third Street
Suite 113
Muskegon, MI 49440
231-722-7700
800-528-8776
Fax: 231-722-6182
Email: psvander@wmis.net
www.michworks.swc.org

Dustin Frigy
Flint-Genesee Economic Growth
  Alliance
519 South Saginaw Street, Suite 210
Flint, MI 48502
810-238-8845
Fax: 810-238-7866
Email: dfrigy@flint.org
www.michigantac.org

Sally Beck
Economic Development Alliance of
  St. Clair County
735 Erie Street, Suite 250
Port Huron, MI 48060
810-982-9511
Fax: 810-982-9531
Email:
  sbeck@edaofstclaircounty.com
www.edaofstclaircounty.com

Delena Spates-Allen
Saginaw Future, Inc.
301 East Genesee, Suite 300
Saginaw, MI 48607
989-754-8222
Fax: 989-754-1715
Email: dsallen@saginawfuture.com

Jody Wilson
Michigan Works!
3270 Wilson St.
Marlette, MI 48453
989-635-3561
Fax: 989-635-2230
Email: wilsonjo@thumbworks.org

Denise Hoffmeyer
NE Michigan Consortium
P.O. Box 711
Onaway, MI 49765
989-733-8548
Fax: 989-733-8069
Email: denise@miworks-
  nemc.gen.mi.us

John Chichester
Wayne State University
Room 240 Rands
Detroit, MI 48202
313-577-2241
Fax: 313-577-4354
Email: ac1538@wayne.edu

Denise Hoffmeyer
Northeast Michigan Consortium
20709 State Street
P.O. Box 711
Onaway, MI 49765
517-733-8548
800-371-2533
Fax: 517-733-8069
Email: General@miworks-
  nemc.gen.mi.us
www.miworks-
  nemc.gen.mi.us/index.html

Minnesota

George Johnson
Minnesota Project Innovation, Inc.

Procurement Technical Assistance
  Center
100 Mill Place
111 Third Ave. South
Minneapolis, MN 55401-2551
612-338-3280
Fax: 612-349-2603
Email: gjohnson@mpi.org
www.mpi.org/ptac/index.htm

Tom Allen
Minnesota Project Innovation, Inc.
2720 River Woods Lane
Burnsville, MN 55337
952-707-6301
Email: tcallen@mpi.org
www.mpi.org

Rodney McGee
Minnesota Project Innovation, Inc.
1821 University Avenue
Suite S-340
St. Paul, MN 55104
651-644-3786
Fax: 651-603-6764
Email: rmcgee@mpi.org
www.mpi.org

Sherri Komrosky
Minnesota Project Innovation, Inc.
Moorhead State University
Box 303 MSU 615 - 11th Street
Moorhead, MN 56563-0001
218-299-5801
Fax: 218-236-2280
Email: skom@linkup.net
www.mpi.org

Christina Nebel
Minnesota Project Innovation, Inc.
616 Roosevelt Rd
St. Cloud, MN 56301
320-202-6496
Fax: 320-654-5412
Email: cnebel@mpi.org
www.mpi.org

Charles Wallschlaeger
Minnesota Project Innovation, Inc.
560 Dunnell Dr
Merrill Building
Suite 214
Owatonna, MN 55060
507-446-2310
Fax: 507-446-2311
Email: cwallsch@mpi.org
www.mpi.org

Mississippi

Richard L. Speights
Mississippi Contract Procurement
  Center, Inc.
1636 Poppsferry Rd.
Suite 229
Biloxi, MS 39532
228-396-1288
Fax: 228-396-2520
Email: mprogoff@aol.com
www.mscpc.com

Bill Estes
Central Mississippi Contract
  Procurement Center
Jackson Enterprise Center
931 Highway 80, West #32
Jackson, MS 39204
601-352-0804
Fax: 601-948-3250
Email: cmpc@mscpc.com
www.mscpc.com
Serving Adams, Claiborne, Copiah,
Franklin, Hinds, Jefferson, Jefferson
Davis, Lawrence, Lincoln, Madison,
Rankin, Simpson, Warren counties

Beth Woodyard
Delta Mississippi Contract
  Procurement Center
P.O. Box 1179
Greenville, MS 38702
662-334-2656
Fax: 662-334-2709
Email: dcpc@mscpc.com
www.mscpc.com
Serving Bolivar, Carroll, Coahoma,
DeSoto, Grenada, Holmes,
Humphreys, Issequena, LeFlore,
Panola, Quitman, Sharkey,
Sunflower, Tallahatchie, Tate,
Tunica, Washington, Yalobusha,
Yazoo counties

Bill Burge
Northeast Mississippi Contract
  Procurement Center
P.O. Box 1328
Columbus, MS 39703-1328
662-329-1077
Fax: 662-327-6600
Email: nmcpc@mscpc.com
www.mscpc.com
Serving Alcorn, Attala, Benton,
Calhoun, Chickasaw, Choctaw, Clay,
Itawamba, Lafayette, Lee, Lowndes,
Marshall, Monroe, Montgomery,
Noxubee, Oktibbeha, Pontotoc,
Prentiss, Tippah, Tishomingo,
Union, Webster, Winston counties

Bill Mabry
East Central Mississippi Contract
  Procurement Center
Meridian Community College
910 Highway 19 N
Meridaian, MS 39307
601-482-7658
Fax: 601-482-5803
Email: eccpc@mscpc.com
www.mscpc.com
Serving Clarke, Covington, Jasper,
Jones, Kemper, Lauderdale, Leake,
Neshoba, Newton, Scott, Smith,
Wayne counties

Richard L. Speights
South Mississippi Contract
  Procurement
1636 Popps Ferry Road, Suite 229
Biloxi, MS 39532
228-396-1288

Fax: 228-396-2520
Email: smcpc@mscpc.com
www.mscpc.com
Serving Amite, Forrest, George,
Greene, Hancock, Harrison, Jackson,
Lamar, Marion, Pearl River, Perry,
Pike, Stone, Walthall, Wilkinson
counties

Missouri
Mark Hudson
Missouri Procurement Technical
    Assistance Center
University of Missouri-Columbia
300 University Place
Columbia, MO 65211
573-882-3597
Fax: 573-884-4297
Email: hudsonm@missouri.edu
www.smallbusinesslearning.net/ptac/
    index.asp

Lauren Tucker
Missouri Procurement Technical
    Assistance Center-St. Louis
100 North Tucker, Suite 530
St. Louis, MO 63101
314-621-7280
Fax: 314-621-9871
Email: tuckerlh@missouri.edu
www.smallbusinesslearning.net/ptac/
    index.asp

Donna Leonard
Missouri Procurement Technical
    Assistance Center
University of Missouri-Kansas City
4747 Troost Building, Room 227
Kansas City, MO 64110
816-235-2891
Fax: 816-235-2947
Email: leonardd@umkc.edu
www.bloch.umkc.edu/egrc/Missouri
    PTAC/

Terri Bennett
Missouri Southern State College
3950 E. Newman Rd.
Joplin, MO 64801-1595
417-625-9538
Fax: 417-625-9782
Email: heartlandptac@mail.mssc.edu
www.mssc.edu/heartlandptac

Montana
Maureen Jewell
Big Sky Economic Development
    Authority
222 North 32nd Street
Billings, MT 59101-1931
406-256-6871
Fax: 406-256-6877
Email: jewell@bigskyeda.org
www.bigskyeda.org/PTAC

Karl J. Dehn
Montana PTAC
710 First Avenue North
P.O. Box 2568
Greta Falls, MT 59403-2568

406-454-1934
Fax: 406-454-2995
Email: karl@gfdevelopment.org
www.gfdevelopment.org/govtcont.htm

Nebraska
Michael Hall
Economic Business Development
    Center
PTA Omaha Business Technology
    Center
2505 North 24th Street, Suite 103
Omaha, NE 68182-0072
402-595-3511
Fax: 402-595-3832
Email: mikehallneptac@netscape.net

Joe Breault
Nebraska Business Development
    Center
Lincoln Chamber Building
1135 M Street, Suite 200
City Campus Mailboc 0224
Lincoln, NE 68588-0224
402-472-1177
Fax: 402-472-3363
Email:
    JBreaultNEPTAC@netscape.net
http://nbdc.unomaha.edu/consulting/
    growth/ptac.cfm

Mike Hall
Nebraska Business Development
    Center
Peter Kiewit Conference Center
1313 Farnum, Suite 230
Omaha, NE 68182
402-595-3511
Fax: 402-595-2385
Email:
    MikeHallNEPTAC@netscape.net
http://nbdc.unomaha.edu/consulting/
    growth/ptac.cfm

Nevada
Rick Horn
555 East Washington, Suite 5400
Las Vegas, NV 89101
702-486-2716
800-336-1600
Fax: 702-486-2701
Email: lvpop8@bizopp.state.nv.us
www.nvoutreachcenter.com

Kathy Dow
Procurement Outreach Program
108 E. Proctor
Carson City, NV 89701
775-687-1913
Fax: 775-687-4450
Email: kdow@bizopp.state.nv.us
www.nvoutreachcenter.com

New Hampshire
Joseph Flynn
State of New Hampshire
Office of Business and Industrial
    Development
P.O. Box 1856
172 Pembroke Rd.

Concord, NH 03302-1856
603-271-2591
Fax: 603-271-6784
Email: j-flynn@dred.state.nh.us
www.nheconomy.com/nheconomy/pt
    ac/main/index.php

New Jersey
Shashee Joshi
Union County Economic
    Development Corporation
PTA Program
1085 Morris Ave., Suite 531
Lib Hall Center
Union, NJ 07083
908-527-1166
Fax: 908-527-1207
Email: sjoshi@ucedc.com
www.ucedc.com/services/contracts.s
    html

Dolcey Chaplin
Foundation at New Jersey Institute
    of Technology (NJIT)
240 Martin Luther King Blvd.
Newark, NJ 07102
973-596-3105
Fax: 973-596-5806
Email: chaplin@admin.njit.edu
www.nyit.edu/old/DPTAC

Madeline Britman
New Jersey Small Business
    Development Centers
Procurement Program
43 Bleeker Street
Newark, NJ 07102
973-353-5960
Fax: 973-353-1930
Email: britman@njsbdc.com
www.njsbdc.com/procurment

Jan D. Mirijanian
New Jersey Institute of Technology
Atlantic Community College
1535 Bacharach Blvd., Room 211
Atlantic City, NJ 08401
609-343-4845
Fax: 609-343-4823
www.njit.edu/old/DPTAC/

New Jersey Institute of Technology
Camden Office
One Federal Street
Camden, NJ 08103
856-614-5486
Fax: 856-614-5498
www.njit.edu/old/DPTAC/

New Jersey Institute of Technology
Trenton Office
Mary G. Roebling Building
20 W. State Street
Trenton, NJ 08650
609-292-3861
www.njit.edu/old/DPTAC/

New Jersey Institute of Technology
Mt. Holly Office
60 High Street

Mt. Holly, NJ 08060
609-267-5618
www.njit.edu/old/DPTAC/

New Mexico
Michael Vinyard
State of New Mexico General
    Services Department
Procurement Assistance Program
P.O. Drawer 26110
Santa Fe, NM 87502
505-827-0425
Fax: 505-827-0499
Email: mvinyard@state.nm.us
www.state.nm.us/spd/pap/index.html

New York
Dina Terry
South Bronx Overall Economic
    Development Corp.
55 Bergen Avenue
Bronx, NY 10455
718-292-3113
Fax: 718-292-3115
Email: dterry@sobro.org
www.sobro.org

Joseph J. Williams
Cattaraugus County
Department of Economic
    Development
Plan and Tour
303 Court St.
Little Valley, NY 14755
716-938-9111, ext. 2331
Fax: 716-938-9431
Email: josewi@lv.co.
    cattaraugus.ny.us
www.co.cattaraugus.ny.us/economic
-development/gma/index.asp?did=6

Solomon Soskin
Long Island Development
    Corporation
PTA Program
45 Seamon Ave.
Bethage, NY 11714
516-433-5000
Fax: 516-433-5406
Email: gov-contracts@lidc.org
www.lidc.org/assist.htm

Gordon Richards
New York City Dept. of Business
    Services
Procurement Outreach Program
110 William St., 2nd Floor
New York, NY 10038
212-513-6472
Fax: 212-618-8899
Email: grichard@sbs.nyc.gov
www.nyc.gov/html/sbs/html/pop.htm
l

Rockland Economic Development
    Corporation
Procurement
One Blue Hill Plaza, Suite 1110
Pearl River, NY 10965-1575
845-735-7040

Fax: 845-735-5736
Email: ptac@redc.org
www.redc.org/business/sell_to_gov/i
    ndex_sell_to_gov.html

Benjamin Hunt
Laguardia Community College
Urban Center for Economic
    Development
31-10 Thomson Ave., Room E-405
Long Island City, NY 11101
718-482-5315
Fax: 718-482-5176
Email: bhunt@lagcc.cuny.edu
www.lagcc.cuny.edu/ace/luced

Paulette Birch
Rochester Business Alliance
150 State Street
Rochester, NY 14614
585-327-5907
Email: pauletteb@RBAlliance.com
www.RochesterPTAC.com

North Carolina
Tom Elam
Small Business and Technology
    Development Center
5 West Hargett Street, Suite 600
Raleigh, NC 27601-1348
919-715-7272
800-258-0862 (NC only)
Email: info@sbtdc.org
www.sbtdc.org/services/gov_procure
    ment.asp

North Dakota
No PTAC awarded

Ohio
Bob Fenn
NE Ohio PTAC
Lake Erie College
391-W. Washington St.
Painesville, OH 44077
440-357-2294
Fax: 440-357-2296
Email: neoptac@lcedc.org
www.lcedc.org/neoptac.htm

Kelly Lawhorn
Lawrence Economic Development
    Corporation
Procure Outreach Center
216 Collins Ave.
P.O. Box 488
South Point, OH 45680-0488
740-377-4550
800-408-1334
Fax: 740-377-2091
Email: klawhorn@zoominternet.net
www.lawrencecountyohio.org/5.htm

Eric Van Otteren
Ohio Department of Development
Procurement Technical Assistance
    Centers of Ohio
77 South High Street, 28th Floor
P.O. Box 1001
Columbus, OH 43216-1001

614-466-5700
800-848-1300
Fax: 614-466-4172
Email: evanotteren@odod.state.oh.us
www.odod.state.oh.us/dmba/ptac.ht
m

Stephen J. Danyi
Mahoning Valley Economic
    Development Corporation
4319 Belmont Ave.
Youngstown, OH 44505-1005
330-759-3668
Fax: 330-759-3686
Email: steve@mvedc.com
www.mvedc.com/development.htm

Keith Tarbett
Kent PTAC Satellite
Kent Regional Business Alliance
Kent State University
College of Business Room 300B
Kent, OH 44242
330-672-9448
Fax: 330-672-9338
Email: ktarbett@bsa3.kent.edu
http://business.kent.edu/KRBA/PTA
    C.asp

Sharon Williams
Appalachian PTAC
20 Circle Drive
The Ridge Ohio University
143 Technology and Enterprise Bldg
Athens, OH 45701
740-597-1868
Fax: 740-597-1399
Email:
    sharonw@voinovichcenter.edu
www.ohiou.edu/ptac/

Richard Archer
Bowling Green/Toledo PTAC
Bowling Green State University
140B Jerome Library
Bowling Green, OH 43403
419-372-9257
Fax: 419-372-7996
Email: rarcher@bgnet.bgsu.edu
www.bgsu.edu/colleges/library/ptac

Jeanatta Brown
Cincinnati PTAC TechSolve
1111 Edison Drive
Cincinnati, OH 45216
513-948-2083
Fax: 513-948-2083
Email: brown@techsolve.org
www.techsolve.org

Deborah Wallace-Flagg
Dayton PTAC
3155 Research Boulevard, Suite 106
Dayton, OH 45420
937-259-1321
Fax: 937-259-1303
Email: dwallace@emtec.org
dwallaceflagg@who.rr.com
www.dayptac.org

Oklahoma

Scott Dean
Oklahoma Department of Vocational
 and Technical Education
Oklahoma Bid Assistance Network
1500 W. Seventh Ave.
Stillwater, OK 74074-4364
405-743-5592
Fax: 405-743-6821
Email: sdean@careertec.org
www.okcareertech.org/business/oban
 /oban.htm

Roy Robert Gann, Jr.
Tribal Government Institute
421 E. Comanche, Suite B
Norman, OK 73071
405-329-5542
Fax: 405-329-5543
Email: tgi40019@worldnet.att.net

Terry Henneke
Autry Technology Center
1201 West Willow
Enid, OK 73703-2598
580-242-2750
Fax: 580-233-8262
Email: thenneke@autrytech.com
www.autrytech.com

David Hoffmeier
Gordon Cooper Technology Center
One John C. Bruton Blvd
Shawnee, OK 74804
405-273-7493 Ext 314
Fax: 405-273-6354
Email: davidh@gctech.org
www.gctech.org

Clayton Evans
High Plains Technology Center
3921 34th Street
Woodward, OK 73801-7000
580-571-6155
Fax: 580-571-6186
Email: cevans@hptc.net
www.hptc.net

John Hasler
Indian Capital Technology Centers
2403 N. 41st Street East
Muskogee, OK 74403-1799
918-687-6383 Ext. 253
Fax: 918-687-6624
Email: john@azalea.net
www.icavts.tec.ok.us/

Wendell Marley
Kiamichi Technology Centers
301 Kiamichi Dr
McAlester, OK 74501
918-426-1560
Fax: 918-426-1626
Email: wmarley@kavts.tec.ok.us
www.kiamichi-mcalester.tec.ok.us/
 new_page_8.htm

Mitchell Slemp
Mid-America Technology Centers
POB H

Wayne, OK 73095-0210
405-449-3391
Fax: 405-449-3421
Email: mslemp@matech.org
www.matech.org/adult.htm

Bill Crain
Mid-Del Technology Centers
1621 Maple Drive
Midwest City, OK 73110-4825
405-739-1712
Fax: 405-739-1751
Email: wacrain@hotmail.com
www.mid-del.tec.ok.us/

Teresa Smith
Pioneer Technology Center
2101 N. Ash
Ponca City, OK 74601-1110
580-718-4261
Fax: 580-765-5101
Email: teresas@pioneertech.org
www.pioneertech.org

Dana Harwell
Red River Technology Centers
P.O. Box 1807
Duncan, OK 73534-1807
580-255-2903 Ext. 270
Fax: 580-255-0491
Email: dharwell@redriver.tec.ok.us
www.redriver.tec.ok.us

Dale Latham
Southwest Technology Center
711 W. Tamarack
Altus, OK 73522-8086
580-477-2250
Fax: 580-477-0138
Email: dlatham@swtc.org
www.swtc.org/BID.HTM

Judy Robbins
Francis Tuttle Technology Center
3500 NW 150th Street
Oklahoma City, OK 73134
405-717-4750
Fax: 405-752-0307
Email: bis@francistuttle.com
www.francistuttle.com/bis/training/g
 c/default.asp

Pat Young
Tri County Technology Center
6101 SE Nowata Road
Bartlesville, OK 74006-6010
918-331-3311
Fax: 918-335-2197
Email: pyoung@tctc.org
www.tctc.org

Lynda Speller
MetroTech Economic Development
 Center
1700 Springlake Drive
Oklahoma City, OK 73111
405-605-4792
Email: lynda.speller@metrotech.org
www.metrotech.org

Oregon

Jan Hurt
The Organization for Economic
 Initiatives
Government Contract Assistance
 Program
1144 Gateway Loop, Suite 203
Springfield, OR 97477
541-736-1088
800-497-7551
Fax: 541-736-1090
Email: info@gcap.org
www.gcap.org

Pennsylvania

Daniel Shade
Southern Alleghenies Planning and
 Development Commission
541 58th Street
Altoona, PA 16602
814-949-6528
Fax: 814-949-6505
Email: shade@sapdc.org
www.sapdc.org

Ron Moreau
Indiana University of Pennsylvania
650 South 13th Street
Robert Shaw Building, Room 10
Indiana, PA 15705-1087
724-357-7824
Fax: 724-357-3082
Email: rfmoreai@iup.edu
www.eberly.iup.edu/gcap

Deborah S. Wojcik
Mon-Valley Renaissance
CA University of Pennsylvania
250 University Ave.
California, PA 15419
724-938-5881
Fax: 724-938-4575
Email: wojcik@cup.edu
www.cup.edu

Dianne McCartney
NW Pennsylvania Regional Planning
 and Development Commission
395 Seneca Street
Oil City, PA 16301
814-677-4800
Fax: 814-677-7663
Email: diannem@
 newcommission.org
www.nwcommission.org

Pete Chirillo
Johnstown Area Regional Industries
Defense PAC
111 Market St.
Johnstown, PA 15901
814-535-8675
Fax: 814-535-8677
www.jari.com

Chris Wilusz
Seda Council of Governments
201 Furnace Road
Lewisburg, PA 17837
570-524-4491

Fax: 570-524-9190
Email: cwilusz@seda-cog.org
www.seda-
cog.org/seda_cog/site/default.asp

Clyde Stoltzfus
University of Pennsylvania-Wharton
SE-PA PTAP
3733 Spruce St.
Vance Hall, 4th Floor
Philadelphia, PA 19104-6374
215-898-1282
Fax: 215-573-2135
Email: clycles@wharton.upenn.edu
www.pasbdc.org/consulting

David Kern
Economic Development Council of
Northeast Pennsylvania
Local Development District
1151 Oak St.
Pittston, PA 18640
570-655-5581
Fax: 570-654-5137
Email: dkk@nepa-alliance.org
www.nepa-alliance.org/ptac.htm

Puerto Rico
Carmen Y. Rosario
Commonwealth of Puerto Rico
Economic Development
Administration
P.O. Box 362350
San Juan, PR 00936-2350
787-753-6861
Fax: 787-751-6239
Email: prptac@hotmail.com

Rhode Island
Dorothy Reynolds
Rhode Island Development
Corporation
Business Expansion Division
One W. Exchange St.
Providence, RI 02903
401-222-2601
Fax: 401-222-2102
Email: dreynolds@riedc.com
www.riedc.com/growth/procure/proc
urementframe.html

South Carolina
University of South Carolina
Frank L. Roddey SBDC of South
Carolina
1200 Woodruff Rd.
Suite C-38
Greenville, SC 29607
864-297-1016
Fax: 864-329-0453
http://business.clemson.edu/sbdc/pag
e7.htm

South Dakota
Kareen H. Dougherty
The University of South Dakota
414 Clark Street
Vermillion, SD 57069-2390
605-677-5287

Fax: 605-677-5238
Email: kdougher@usd.edu

Tennessee
Jim Slizewski
Center for Industrial Services
University of Tennessee
193C Polk Avenue
Nashville, TN 37210
615-532-8657
888-763-7439
Fax: 615-532-4937
Email: cjs@tennessee.edu
www.cis.utk.edu/PTAC

Texas
Edmond Esparza
Panhandle Regional Planning
Commission
Economic Development Unit
P.O. Box 9257
Amarillo, TX 79105-9257
806-372-3381
Fax: 806-373-3268
Email: eesparza@prpc.cog.tx.us
www.prpc.cog.tx.us/programs/econ/e
con_contract.htm

Jim Hicks
University of Texas at Arlington
Automation and Robotics Research
Institute
Cross Timbers Procurement Center
Box 19125
Arlington, TX 76019
817-272-5978
Fax: 817-272-5952
Email: jhicks@arri.uta.edu
http://arri.uta.edu/crosstimbers

Rosalie Manzano
University of Texas at
Brownsville/ITSC
Center for Business and Economic
Development
1600 E. Elizabeth St.
Brownsville, TX 78520
956-548-8713
Fax: 956-548-8717
Email: vptac@utb1.utb.edu
www.utb.edu

Carey Joan White
University of Houston, TIPS
2302 Fannin, Suite 200
Houston, TX 77002
713-752-8444
Fax: 713-756-1515
Email: cwhite@uh.edu
http://SmBizSolutions.uh.edu

Otilo Castellano
Texas Technical University
VP for Research and Tech Transfer
2579 S. Loop 289, Suite 210
Lubbock, TX 79423
806-745-3973
Fax: 806-745-6207
Email: o.castellano@nwtsbdc.org
www.nwtsbdc.org/pac/pac.htm

Thomas E. Brewer, Jr.
Angelina College
Procurement Assistance Center
P.O. Box 1768
Lufkin, TX 75902-1768
936-639-1301
888-326-5223
Fax: 936-639-4299
Email: acpac@texucom.net
www.angelina.cc.tx.us/comserv/cs%
20procur.htm

Albert Vela
San Antonio Procurement Outreach
Program
Economic Development Department
P.O. Box 839966
215 S. San Saba
San Antonio, TX 78283
210-207-3900
Fax: 210-207-3909
Email: albertv@sanantonio.gov
www.sanantonio.gov/edd/small_bus/
contracting/ptac.asp

Don Bostic
El Paso Community College
Office of Workforce Development
and Lifelong Learning
P.O. Box 20500
El Paso, TX 79998
915-831-7722
Fax: 915-831-4420
Email: donb@epcc.edu
www.epcc.edu/admin/wfd/contract_op
portunity_ctr.htm

Sean Smith
Del Mar College
Division of Business
101 Bladwin and Ayers
Corpus Christi, TX 78401
361-698-1023
Fax: 361-698-1024
Email: spsmith@delmar.edu
www.delmar.edu/sbdc/ptac.html

Utah
Ron Spindler
Utah Department of Community and
Economic Development
Utah Procurement Technical
Assistance Center (UPTAC)
324 South State St., Suite 500
Salt Lake City, UT 84111
801-538-8680
Fax: 801-538-8611
Email: uptac@utah.gov
http://dced.utah.gov/procure

Vermont
Greg Lawson
State of Vermont
Dept. of Economic Development
109 State St.
Montpelier, VT 05609
802-828-5237
Fax: 802-828-3258
Email: greg@thinkvermont.com
www.vermontbidsystem.com/

Virginia

James Regan
George Mason University
Mason Enterprise Center
4031 University Dr., Suite 200
Fairfax, VA 22030
703-277-7757
Fax: 703-352-8195
Email: ptap@gmu.edu
www.gmu.edu/gmu/PTAP

John Fedkenheuer
Crater Planning District Commission
Crater Procurement Assistance
  Center
1964 Wakefield St.
P.O. Box 1808
Petersburg, VA 23805
804-861-1666
Fax: 804-732-8972
Email: jfedkenheuer@cpd.state.va.us
www.craterpdc.state.va.us/PAC/pac
  main.htm

Glenda D. Calver
Southwestern Virginia Community
  College
Economic Development Division
P.O. Box SVCC
Richlands, VA 24641
276-964-7334
Fax: 276-964-7575
Email: glenda.calver@sw.vccs.edu
www.sw.vccs.edu/ptac2

Linda Hutson Green
Virginia Center for Innovative
  Technology
530 Main Street, Suite 204
Danville, VA 24541
434-791-5376
Fax: 434-791-5378
Email: lgreen@cit.org
www.cit.org/ptac-04.asp

Washington

John Tamble
Economic Development Council of
Snohomish County
728 134th St., SW
Bldg. A, Suite 219
Everett, WA 98204
425-743-4567
Fax: 425-745-5563
Email: ptac@snoedc.org
www.snoedc.org/securing_governme
nt_contracts.jsp

Diane McLeod
Economic Development Association
  of Skagit County
204 W. Montgomery
P.O. Box 40
Mount Vernon, WA 98273
360-336-6114
Fax: 360-336-6116
Email: diane@skagit.org
www.skagit.org/subcategorypages/pr
  ocurement.htm

Angela Brooks
Bellingham Whatcom Economic
  Development Council
105 E. Holly Street
P.O. Box 2803
Bellingham, WA 98227
360-676-4255
Fax: 360-647-9413
Email: angela@bwedc.org
www.bwedc.org/ptac.html

Deb Wallace
Columbia River Economic
  Development Council
1101 Broadway, Suite 120
Vancouver, WA 98660
360-567-1061
Fax: 360-694-9927
Email: dwallace@credc.org
www.credc.org/ptac.htm

Teresa Lemmons Tom Westerlund
Metropolitan Development Council
Economic Development Services
15 N Broadway, #B
Tacoma, WA 98403
253-591-7026
Fax: 253-572-5583
Email: ceo@mdc-tacoma.org
www.snoedc.org/securing_governme
  nt_contracts.jsp

Johann Curtiss
WSU Tri-City Business LINKS
2710 University Drive
Richland, WA 99352
509-372-7142
Fax: 509-372-7512
Email: buslinks@tricity.wsu.edu
www2.tricity.wsu.edu/links/ptac.htm

West Virginia

Bridgette Venanzi
Regional Contracting Assistance
  Center, Inc.
1116 Smith St., Suite 202

Charleston, WV 25301
304-344-2546
Fax: 304-344-2574
Email: bvenanzi@rcacwv.com
www.rcacwv.com

Belinda Sheridan
Mid-Ohio Valley Regional Council
PTA Center
P.O. Box 5528
Parkersburg, WV 26105
304-428-6889
Fax: 304-428-6891
Email: ptac@access.mountain.net
www.wvptac.org

West Virginia Procurement
  Technical Center
#2 Rosemar Circle, Suite B
Parkersburg, WV 26101
304-428-6889
Fax: 304-428-6891
Email: Belinda@cssiwv.con
www.wvptac.org

Wisconsin

Denise Kornetzke
Madison Area Technical College
Business PAC
3591 Andersen St., Suite 100
Madison, WI 53704
608-243-4490
Fax: 608-243-4486
Email: bpac@matcmadison.edu
http://matcmadison.edu/bpac/home.h
  tm

Ania Vilumsons
Wisconsin Procurement Institute,
  Inc.
756 N. Milwaukee St.
Milwaukee, WI 53202
414-270-3600
Fax: 414-270-3610
Email: info@wispro.com
www.wispro.com

Wyoming

Rudy Nesvik
University of Wyoming
Government Resources and
  Opportunities for Business (GRO-
  BIZ)
1400 E. College Dr.
Cheyenne, WY 82007
307-637-5029
Fax: 307-632-6061
Email: nesvik@wyoming.com
www.gro-biz.com

How To Become a Consultant With The Government

If you are between jobs or just thinking about quitting the one you have and want something to tide you over until you get your next one, you should seriously think about freelancing for the Federal government.

The Interior Department hires ecologists and geologists. The Justice Department hires business consultants. The Department of Energy hires conservation consultants. Here's a sample listing of the kinds of projects freelance consultants do for the Federal government:

Types of Government Freelancing

Landscaping
Carpentry Work
Painting and Paper Hanging
Security Guards
Computer Services
Data Processing
Detective Services
Electrical Work
Plumbing
Accounting Services
Chaplain Services (Priest)
Management Consulting
Engineering Services
Information Retrieval
  Services
Real Estate Agents
Secretarial Services
Court Reporting
Legal Services
Business Consulting
Photography
Insurance Agents
Computer Programming
Research
Drafting
Interior Decorating
Library Services
Word Processing

Translation Services
Courier and Messenger Services
Cleaning Services
Food Service
Auditing Services
Advertising Services
Nursing Services
Housekeeping Services
Administrative Support
  Services
Education and Training
Medical Services
Social Services
Special Study and Analysis
Wildlife Management
Salvage Services
Travel Agent
Personnel Testing Services
Photography
Animal Care
Mathematics and Computer
  Science
Environmental Research
Historians
Recreation Research
Economic Studies
More, More, More...

Practically every major government agency hires freelance consultants to work on both small and large projects — which might be exactly what you need until you land a full time job down the road.

The feds hire all kinds of professionals to perform consulting work, from accountants and business specialists, to computer experts, social scientists, and security and surveillance consultants. The offices listed below, called Offices of Small and Disadvantaged Business Utilization, specialize in helping individuals and small businesses get involved in contracting with their agency.

Subcontracting

Not only do the feds themselves hire consultants, so do the large prime contractors who sell their products and services to the government. By law, any large company that receives contracts worth $500,000 or more from the Federal government must make an effort to subcontract some of that work to small businesses. So, for example, if a company gets a large computer consulting contract with the Defense Department, they have to make an effort to hire some freelance computer consultants to work on that contract. And that could be you.

How to Find Subcontracting Work

All of the federal procurement offices or Offices of Small and Disadvantaged Business Utilization (SADBU) (see list below) can provide you with information regarding subcontracting. Many of the departments' prime contracts require that the prime contractor maximize small business subcontracting opportunities. The SADBU offices can show you the way to get this work.

Each of the large federal agencies listed below, except the Department of Education, maintain directories of large contractors who are looking to do work with the feds in your area of expertise. And since the companies listed in these directories, for the most part, have just landed big government contracts, they might very well be looking to take on more full-time employees to help fulfill those contracts. A great lead on new job openings that probably won't be listed in the Sunday newspaper!

Offices of Small and Disadvantaged Business Utilization

Note: Offices designated as Offices of Small and Disadvantaged Business Utilization (OSDBUs) provide procurement assistance to small, minority, 8(a) and women-owned businesses. Their primary function is to ensure that small and disadvantaged businesses receive their fair share of U.S. Government contracts. "OSDBUs" are the contacts for their respective agencies and are excellent sources of information.

Agency for International Development
Ronald Reagan Building
1300 Pennsylvania Ave., NW
Washington, DC 20523-7800
202-712-1500
Fax: 202-216-3056
www.usaid.gov/procurement_bus_op
p/osdbu/

Air Force Department
The Pentagon
SASSB 1060 Air Force
Washington, DC 20330-1060
703-696-1103
Fax: 703-696-1170
www.selltoairforce.org/sell2airforce/
toc.htm

Army Corps of Engineers
441 G Street, NW
Washington, DC 20314-1000
202-761-0725
Fax: 202-761-4609
www.usace.army.mil/business.html

Army Department
106 Army Pentagon
Washington, DC 20310-0106
703-697-2868
Fax: 703-693-3898
www.sellingtoarmy.info

Corporation for National and Community Service
1201 New York Ave., NW
Washington, DC 20525
202-606-5000
Fax: 202-565-2777
www.nationalservice.org

Defense Contract Management Agency
6350 Walker Lane
Alexandria, VA 22310
703-428-0786
Fax: 703-428-3578
www.dcma.mil/DCMAHQ/dcma_sb/index.htm

Defense Information Systems Agency
701 S. Courthouse Road
D04 Room 1108B
Arlington, VA 22204-2199
703-607-6436
Fax: 703-607-4173
www.disa.mil/main/sadbu.html

Defense Logistics Agency
8725 John J. Kingman Road
DB Room 1127
Ft. Belvoir, VA 22060-6221
703-767-1662
Fax: 703-767-1670
www.dla.mil.db

Department of Agriculture
14th and Independence, SW
Room 1566, South Bldg.
Washington, DC 20250-9400
202-720-7117
Fax: 202-720-3001
www.usda.gov/osdbu

Department of Commerce
14th and Constitution Ave, NW
Room 6411
Washington, DC 20230
202-482-1472
Fax: 202-482-0501
www.osec.doc.gov/osdbu

Department of Defense
1177 North Kent Street, Suite 9100
Washington, DC 22209
703-588-8620
Fax: 703-588-7561
www.acq.osd.mil/sadbu

Department of Education
400 Maryland Ave., SW
Room 3120-ROB-3
Washington, DC 20202

202-708-9820
Fax: 202-401-6477
www.ed.gov/fund/contracts/about/booklet1.html

Department of Energy
1000 Independence Ave., SW
Room 5B148
Washington, DC 20585
202-586-7377
Fax: 202-586-5488
http://smallbusiness.doe.gov

Department of Health and Human Services
200 Independence Ave., SW
Room 517D
Washington, DC 20201
202-690-7300
Fax: 202-260-4872
www.hhs.gov/osdbu

Department of Homeland Security
Attn: OSDBU Room 3514
Washington, DC 20528
202-205-0050
www.dhs.gov

Department of Housing and Urban Development
451 7th St., SW, Room 3130
Washington, DC 20410
202-708-1428
Fax: 202-708-7642
www.hud.gov/offices/osdbu/index.cfm

Department of the Interior
1331 Pennsylvania Ave., NW
National Place Building
Room 1010
Washington, DC 20240
202-208-3493
Fax: 202-219-2131
www.doi.gov/osdbu

Department of Justice
Director, OSDBU
U.S. Department of Justice
Washington, DC 20530
202-616-0521
800-345-3712
Fax: 202-616-1717
www.usdoj.gov/jmd/osdbu/index.html

Department of Labor
200 Constitution Ave., NW
Room C-2318
Washington, DC 20210
202-693-6460
Fax: 202-693-6485
www.dol.gov/osbp/programs/osdbu.htm

Department of State
SA-6, Room L500
Washington, DC 20522-0602

703-875-6822
Fax: 703-875-6825
www.state.gov/m/a/sdbu

Department of Transportation
400 7th St., SW, Room 9414
Washington, DC 20590
202-366-1930
800-532-1169
Fax: 202-366-7538
http://osdbuweb.dot.gov

Department of the Treasury
1500 Pennsylvania Ave., NW
Room 1310 G, 400 West
Washington, DC 20220
202-622-0530
Fax: 202-622-4963
www.ustreas.gov/sba

Department of Veterans Affairs
810 Vermont Ave., NW
Washington, DC 20420
202-565-8124
800-949-8387
Fax: 202-565-8156
www.va.gov/osdbu

Environmental Protection Agency
1200 Pennsylvania Ave., NW
Mail Code 1230-A
Washington, DC 20460
202-564-4142
Fax: 202-401-1080
www.epa.gov/osdbu

Export-Import Bank of the U.S.
811 Vermont Ave., NW
Room 1023
Washington, DC 20571
202-565-3338
Fax: 202-565-3528
www.exim.gov/

Federal Communications Commission
Office of Communications Business Opportunities
445 12th Street SW
Washington, DC 20554
202-418-0990
Fax: 202-418-0235
www.fcc.gov/ocbo

Federal Emergency Management Agency
Financial and Acquisition Management
500 C St., SW
Washington, DC 20472
202-646-3743
Fax: 202-646-3846
www.fema.gov/ofm

Federal Trade Commission
600 Pennsylvania Ave., NW
Room 600
Washington, DC 20580
202-326-2258
Fax: 202-326-3529
www.ftc.gov/ftc/oed/fmo/procure/pr
ocure.htm

**General Services
Administration**
Office of Enterprise Development
1800 F Street, NW
Washington, DC 20405
202-501-1021
Fax: 202-208-5938
www.gsa.gov/

**National Aeronautics and
Space Administration**
Headquarters, Code K
300 E St., SW
Washington, DC 20546
202-358-2088
Fax: 202-358-3261
www.hq.nasa.gov/office/codek

National Institute of Health
6100 Executive Blvd., Room 6D05
Bethesda, MD 20892-7540
301-496-9639
Fax: 301-480-2506
http://sbo.od.nih.gov/sbomain.htm

**National Science
Foundation**
4201 Wilson Blvd., Room 5505
Arlington, VA 22230
703-292-7082
Fax: 703-292-9057
www.nsf.gov/bfa/dacs/contracts/start
.htm

Navy Department
720 Kennon Street SE, Room 207
Washington Navy Yard, DC 20374-
5015
202-685-6485
Fax: 202-685-6865
www.hq.navy.mil/sadbu

**Nuclear Regulatory
Commission**
Small Business Program
Washington, DC 20555
301-415-7380
Fax: 301-415-5953
www.nrc.gov/who-we-are/small-
business.html

**Executive Office of the
President**
725 17th St., NW, Room 5001
Washington, DC 20503
202-395-7669
Fax: 202-395-3982

**Office of Personnel
Management**
Contracting Division
1900 E St., NW
Washington, DC 20415
202-606-2180
Fax: 202-606-1464
www.opm.gov/procure/index.htm

**Small Business
Administration**
Office of Government Contracting
409 Third St., SW, 8th Floor
Washington, DC 20416
202-619-1850
Fax: 202-693-7004
www.sba.gov/sdb

Smithsonian Institution
Small and Disadvantaged Business
Utilization Program
905 L'Enfant Plaza, SW
Washington, DC 20560-0921
202-287-3588
Fax: 202-287-3492
www.si.edu/oeema

**Social Security
Administration**
Office of Acquisition and Grants
1710 Gwynn Oak Avenue
Baltimore, MD 21207-5279
410-965-9498 Office of Contracts
and Grants
Fax: 410-965-9560
410-965-9478 Office of Information
Technology Acquisition
Fax: 410-966-9310
www.socialsecurity.gov/oag/acq/oag
acq_smallbusiness.htm

Tennessee Valley Authority
P.O. Box 292409
Nashville, TN 37229-2409
615-232-6169
www.tva.gov

**Transportation Security
Administration**
7th and D Streets, SW
Room 3124-A

Washington, DC 20590
202-385-1842
www.tsa.dot.gov/public/display?the
me=3

U.S. Postal Service
475 L'Enfant Plaza, SW, Room 3821
Washington, DC 20260-5616
202-268-6578
Fax: 202-268-6573
www.usps.gov/purchasing

**U.S. Agency for
International Development**
Ronald Reagan Building
1300 Pennsylvania Avenue, NW
Room 7.8 E
Washington, DC 20523-7800
202-712-1500
Fax: 202-216-3056
www.usaid.gov/procurement_bus_op
p/osdbu

Veteran Affairs
OSDBU Office
810 Vermont Avenue, NW
202-565-8124
800-949-8387
Fax: 202-565-8156
www.va.gov/OSDBU

**Office of Federal
Procurement Policy**
725 17th St., NW, Room 9013
Washington, DC 20503
202-395-6811
Fax: 202-395-5105
www.whitehouse.gov/omb/procurem
ent/index.html

Railroad Retirement Board
844 N. Rush St.
Chicago, IL 60611
312-751-4987
Fax: 312-751-4923
www.rrb.gov

**Minority Business
Development Agency**
Department of Commerce
Herbert C. Hoover Bldg.
14th & Constitution Ave., NW
Room 5093
Washington, DC 20230
202-482-1712
Fax: 202-482-5117
www.mbda.gov

State Procurement Assistance

Have you ever wondered where the government buys all of the products that it works with each day? You might be surprised to learn that they buy from small businesses just like yours that produce products such as:

- work clothing
- office supplies
- cleaning equipment
- miscellaneous vehicles
- medical supplies and equipment

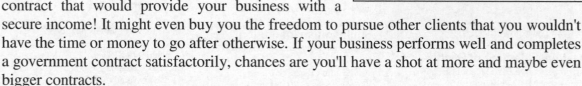

Imagine what your bottom line could look like each year if you won just ONE lucrative government contract that would provide your business with a secure income! It might even buy you the freedom to pursue other clients that you wouldn't have the time or money to go after otherwise. If your business performs well and completes a government contract satisfactorily, chances are you'll have a shot at more and maybe even bigger contracts.

The offices listed below are starting places for finding out who in the state government will purchase your products or services.

State Procurement Offices

Alabama
Finance Department
Purchasing Division
100 N. Union, Suite 192
Montgomery, AL 36104
334-242-7250
Fax: 334-242-4419
www.purchasing.state.al.us

Alaska
State of Alaska
Department of Administration
Division of General Services
P.O. Box 110210
Juneau, AK 99811-0210
907-465-2250
Fax: 907-465-2189
www.state.ak.us/local/akpages/ADM
   IN/dgs/purchasing/home.htm

Arizona
State Procurement Office
100 North 15th Ave., Suite 104
Phoenix, AZ 85007
602-542-5511
Fax: 602-542-5508
http://sporas.ad.state.az.us

Arkansas
Office of State Procurement

P.O. Box 2940
Little Rock, AR 72203
501-324-9316
Fax: 501-324-9311
www.accessarkansas.org/dfa/purchas
   ing/index.html

California
Procurement Division
Department of General Services
707 Third Street, 2nd Floor
West Sacramento, CA 95605
916-375-4400
800-559-5529
Fax: 916-375-4613
www.pd.dgs.ca.gov/default.htm

Colorado
State Purchasing Office
225 E. 16th Ave., Suite 802
Denver, CO 80203
303 866-6100
Fax: 303-894-7445
www.gssa.state.co.us

Connecticut
State of Connecticut
Department of Administrative
   Services
Bureau of Procurement/Purchasing

165 Capitol Ave., Room G-8a
Hartford, CT 06106
860-713-5086
Fax: 860-622-2915
www.das.state.ct.us/busopp.asp

Delaware
Division of Support Services
820 Silver Lake Blvd., Suite 100
Delaware City, DE 19904
302-739-5371
Fax: 302-739-3779
www.state.de.us/purchase

District of Columbia
Office of Contracts and Procurement
441 4th St. NW, Suite 700 South
Washington, DC 20001
202-727-0252
Fax: 202-724-5673
http://ocp.dc.gov/main.shtm

Florida
Department of Management Services
State Purchasing Office
4050 Esplanade Way
Tallahassee, FL 32301
850-488-8440
www.myflorida.com/myflorida/busin
   ess/purchasing.html

Georgia
Administrative Services Department
State Purchasing Office
200 Piedmont Ave
Room 1308 West Tower
Atlanta, GA 30334-9010
404-656-3240
Fax: 404-657-8444
www.doas.state.ga.us

Hawaii
State Procurement Office
Department of Accounting and
General Services
1151 Punch Bowl St.
Honolulu, HI 96813
808-586-0554
Fax: 808-586-0570
www.spo.hawaii.gov

Idaho
Division of Purchasing and Bids
Administration Department
5569 Kendall St.
Boise, ID 83720
208-327-7465
Fax: 208-327-7320
www2.state.id.us/adm/purchasing

Illinois
Department of Central Management
Services
Procurement Services Division
401 South Spring
801 Stratton Bldg.
Springfield, IL 62706
217-782-2301
Fax: 217-782-5187
www.state.il.us/cms/purchase/default
.htm

Indiana
Department of Administration
Procurement Division
402 W. Washington St.
Room W-468
Indianapolis, IN 46204
317-232-3053
Fax: 317-232-7312
www.state.in.us/idoa/proc

Iowa
State of Iowa
Department of General Services
Operations/Purchasing Division
Hoover State Office Building
Des Moines, IA 50319
515-281-6355
Fax: 515-242-5974
www.state.ia.us/government/dgs/purc
hase/business.htm

Kansas
Division of Purchasing
900 Jackson, Room 102N
Landon State Office Bldg.
Topeka, KS 66612
785-296-2376

Fax: 785-296-7240
http://da.state.ks.us/purch

Kentucky
Purchases, Department of Finance
Room 367, Capital Annex Building
Frankfort, KY 40601
502-564-4510
877-973-HELP
Fax: 502-564-7209
www.thinkkentucky.com/kyedc/proa
ssist.asp

Louisiana
State Purchasing Office
Division of Administration
1201 N. 3rd Street, Suite 2-160
P.O. Box 94095
Baton Rouge, LA 70804-9095
225-342-8010
Fax: 225-342-8688
www.doa.state.la.us/osp/osp.htm

Maine
Division of Purchases
Burton Cross Building, 4th Floor
9 State House Station
Augusta, ME 04333
207-624-7340
Fax: 207-287-6578
www.state.me.us/purchase

Maryland
Office of Procurement and
Contracting
301 W. Preston St.
Mezzanine, Room M3
Baltimore, MD 21201
410-767-4628
Fax: 410-333-5482
www.dgs.state.md.us

Massachusetts
Purchasing Agent Division
One Ashburton Place
Room 1017
Boston, MA 02108
617-720-3197
Fax: 617-727-4527
www.comm-pass.com

Michigan
Office of Purchasing
Mason Bldg., 2nd Floor
P.O. Box 30026
Lansing, MI 48909
or 530 W. Ellegan, 48933
517-335-0230
Fax: 517-335-0046
www.michigan.gov/doingbusiness

Minnesota
State of Minnesota
Materials Management Division
112 Administration Bldg.
50 Sherburne Ave.
St. Paul, MN 55155
651-296-2600

Fax: 651-297-3996
www.mmd.admin.state.mn.us

Mississippi
Office of Purchasing and Travel
1401 Woolfolk Building, Suite A
501 North West St.
Jackson, MS 39201
601-359-3409
Fax: 601-359-3910
www.mmrs.state.ms.ujs/Purchasing/
ms_pur.htm

Missouri
State of Missouri
Division of Purchasing and Materials
Management
P.O. Box 809
301 W. High St., Room 630
Jefferson City, MO 65102
573-751-2387
Fax: 573-751-2387
www.oa.state.mo.us/purch/purch.ht
m

Montana
Department of Administration
State Procurement Bureau
165 Mitchell Bldg.
125 North Roberts St.
Helena, MT 59620-0135
406-444-2575
Fax: 406-444-2529
www.discoveringmontana.com/doa/g
sd/css/default.asp

Nebraska
State Purchasing Bureau
DAS Material Division
301 Centennial Mall S., Mall Level
P.O. Box 94847
Lincoln, NE 68509
402-471-2401
Fax: 402-471-2089
www.das.state.ne.us/material/purcha
sing/purchasing.html

Nevada
Nevada State Purchasing Division
755 N. Roop Street
Metcalf Building, Room 211
Carson City, NV 89701
775-684-0170
Fax: 775-684-0188
http://purchasing.state.nv.us/

New Hampshire
State Purchasing Department
25 Capitol St.
State House Annex, Room 102
Concord, NH 03301
603-271-2201
Fax: 603-271-2700
http://admin.state.nh.us/purchasing/i
ndex.html

New Jersey
Division of Purchase and Property
P.O. Box 230

Trenton, NJ 08625
609-292-4700
Fax: 609-292-0490
www.state.nj.us/treasury/purchase

New Mexico
State Purchasing Division
1100 St. Frances Dr.
Joseph Montoya Bldg., Room 2016
Santa Fe, NM 87505
505-827-0472
Fax: 505-827-2484
www.state.nm.us/spd

New York
Procurement Services Group
Corning Tower, Room 3711
Empire State Plaza
Albany, NY 12242
518-474-6717
Fax: 518-474-2437
www.ogs.state.ny.us/purchase/defaul
t.asp

North Carolina
Department of Administration
Division of Purchase and Contract
116 W. Jones St.
Raleigh, NC 27603-8002
919-733-3581
Fax: 919-733-4782
www.doa.state.nc.us/PandC

North Dakota
Central Services Division
State Procurement Office
14th Floor, Capital Tower
600 E Blvd., Dept. 012
Bismarck, ND 58505-0310
701-328-2683
Fax: 701-328-1615
www.state.nd.us/csd.spo

Ohio
State Procurement
Rhodes Tower
30 Broad St., 40th Floor
Columbus, OH 43215-3414
614-466-8218
Fax: 614-466-7525
http://procure.ohio.gov/proc/index.asp

Oklahoma
Office of Public Affairs
Central Purchasing Division
Suite 116, Rogers Bldg.
2401 N. Lincoln
P.O. Box 528803
Oklahoma City, OK 73152
405-522-0955
Fax: 405-521-4475
www.dcs.state.ok.us/okdcs.nsf/html
media/central_purchasing.html

Oregon
General Services
State Procurement Office

1225 Ferry St., SE
Salem, OR 97310
503-378-4642
Fax: 503-373-1626
http://das.state.or.us/purchasing

Pennsylvania
Bureau of Purchases
414 N. Office Bldg.
Harrisburg, PA 17125
717-787-5733
Fax: 717-783-6241
www.dgs.state.pa.us

Rhode Island
Department of Administration
Purchases Office
One Capital Hill
Providence, RI 02908-5855
401-222-2317
Fax: 401-222-6387
www.purchasing.ri.gov

South Carolina
Materials Management Office
General Service Budget and Control
Board
1201 Main St., Suite 600
Columbia, SC 29201
803-737-0600
Fax: 803-737-0639
www.state.sc.us/mmo/

South Dakota
Offices of Purchasing and Printing
523 E. Capitol Ave.
Pierre, SD 57501
605-773-3405
Fax: 605-773-4840
www.state.sd.us/boa/opm

Tennessee
Department of General Services
Division of Purchasing
Third Floor, Tennessee Towers
312 8th Ave. North
Nashville, TN 37243-0557
615-741-1035
Fax: 615-741-0684
www.state.tn.us/generalserv/purchasi
ng

Texas
Texas Building and Procurement
Commission
P.O. Box 13047
Austin, TX 78711
512-463-3420
Fax: 512-463-8872
www.tbpc.state.tx.us/stpurch

Utah
Division of Purchasing and General
Services
Department of Administrative
Services
3150 State Office Bldg.

Capitol Hill
Salt Lake City, UT 84114
801-538-3026
Fax: 801-538-3882
www.purchasing.state.ut.us

Vermont
Purchasing and Contract
Administration
1078 US Route 2-Middlesex
Drawer 33
Montpelier, VT 05633-7601
802-828-2211
Fax: 802-828-2222
www.bgs.state.vt.us/pca

Virginia
Department of General Services
Division of Purchasing and Supply
P.O. Box 1199
805 E. Broad St.
Richmond, VA 23218
804-786-3842
Fax: 804-371-8936
http://dps.dgs.virginia.gov/dps

Washington
Office of State Procurement
Department of General
Administration
210 11th Ave. SW, Room 201
P.O. Box 41017
Olympia, WA 98501
360-902-7400
Fax: 360-586-2426
www.ga.wa.gov/purchase

West Virginia
Department of Administration
Purchasing Division
2019 Washington St. East
P.O. Box 50130
Charleston, WV 25305-0130
304-558-2538, ext. 213
Fax: 304-558-6026
www.state.wv.us/admin/purchase

Wisconsin
Division of State Agency Services
Bureau of Procurement
101 E. Wilson, 6th Floor
P.O. Box 7867
Madison, WI 53707-7867
608-266-7897
Fax: 608-267-0600
http://vendornet.state.wi.us/vendorne
t/default.asp

Wyoming
Department of Administration
General Services Division
801 West 20th Street
Cheyenne, WY 82002
307-777-7253
Fax: 307-777-5852
http://ai.state.wy.us/generalservices/
procurement.asp

How Artists, Designers, Writers, Videotographers and Photographers Can Get Freelance Government Contracts

The Federal government spends millions of dollars each year for the services of artists, graphic designers, illustrators, painters, calligraphers, photographers, computer graphics specialists, and other art-related specialists. Because the government is involved, many artists might shy away from finding out how they can get in on these worthwhile opportunities. The following listing is put together to help you get in contact — often in just one phone call — with the people who hire artists like yourself. Don't forget to check the general section on freelancing, as well as checking out state contracts.

It's difficult to get a clear estimate of the amount of government contracts that go to artists. If you count prime contracts as well as subcontracts, the figure could be as high as $20 to $30 million dollars. Here are what some of the major agencies spend each year:

Spending By Major Agencies On Artists

Department of Agriculture	$186,000	Food and Drug Administration	$200,000
National Science Foundation	$187,500	Federal Emergency Management Agency	$ 25,000
Labor	$400,000	U. S. Customs Service	$ 40,000
Postal Service	$378,000	National Park Service	
U. S. Geological Survey	$100,000	$1,900,000	

Here are some examples of artists who have landed art contracts with the government:

Artists Who Received Government Contracts

Jacob Lawrence received **$95,000** to create a ceramic tile wall mosaic to be placed in the Joseph P. Addabbo Federal Building in Queens, NY. GSA, 1989.

Linda Sherman Design, Inc., of Gaithersburg, MD, received **$432,000** to provide graphic art and editorial support services to NASA in 1990.

Manuel Neri received **$100,000** to create a marble sculpture entitled "Ventana al Pacifico" that was placed outside the Gus J. Solomon Courthouse in Portland, Oregon. GSA, 1989.

Gerald Farrar and Associates, Inc., of Tulsa, OK, received **$3,540** to provide graphic art services to the Department of Energy in 1991.

Lehman-Scaffa Photo and Art of Silver Spring, MD, received **$12,000** to provide graphic arts services to the National Science Foundation, including viewgraphs, slides, charts, maps, mechanical and conceptual drawings, page layouts, publication covers, signs, typesetting, posters, prints, negatives, and exhibit materials.

Hugh Moore and Associates of Alexandria, VA, received **$35,000** from the National Science Foundation to provide graphic art support services, including designing educational pieces for a national science program.

Inkwell, Inc., of Washington, D.C., received **$10,000** from the USDA to provide graphic art support services.

Douglass Harding Group of Washington, D.C., received **$32,000** from the USDA to provide graphic art support services in 1990.

Thomas Baldwin, Inc., of Alexandria, VA, received **$138,000** from the Forest Service to design the interior of the Service's National Visitors Center.

Standsbury Ronsaville Wood Inc., of Annapolis, MD, landed a contract from the National Park Service worth **$16,000** to provide graphic design services, including illustrations, layout, exhibit production, publication design, and more in 1991.

Nelson/Hendrickson of Purcellville, VA, landed a contract from the National Park Service worth **$72,948** to provide production-ready wayside exhibit plan packages.

Maria Alquilar received **$19,000** to create a high fired clay sculpture for the General Services Administration that was placed in the Main Border Station in San Luis, AZ.

Caleb Bach received **$18,000** to produce two paintings entitled "The Effects of Good and Bad Government" that were placed in the Seattle Courthouse.

Robert Brooks received **$4,000** to create a photographic mural that was placed in the U.S. Border Station in Fort Kent, ME. GSA, 1984.

Houston Conwill received **$49,000** to create a bronze sculpture on a granite platform that was placed in the Joseph P. Addabbo Federal Building in Queens, NY.

The painter, **Blue Sky**, received **$12,600** to create an oil painting entitled "Moonlight on the Great Pee Dee" which was placed in the J.M. McMillan Federal Building in Florence, SC. GSA, 1978.

Frank Smith received **$20,000** to create a ceramic tile wall mural for the Joseph P. Addabbo Federal Building in Queens, NY. GSA, 1989.

Another Color, Inc., received **$422,000** to provide graphic art and editorial support services to NASA in 1990.

Creative Service, Inc., received **$200,000** to provide graphic art and editorial support services to NASA in 1990.

Artists Who Received Money from the National Park Service in a Recent Year:

Lloyd Townsend	$ 6,663	Chris White Design	$ 50,974
Hugh Brown	$ 14,721	Dorothy Novick	$ 4,056
Robert Hynes	$ 4,020	G.S. Images	$236,294
Louis Glanzman	$ 9,362	General Graphics	$268,363
Glenn Moy	$ 9,511	G.S. Images	$ 86,643
Charles Hazard	$ 3,528	Specialty Graphics	$103,932
Steven Patricia	$ 7,020	General Graphics	$ 17,246
Robert Hynes	$ 8,786	Scribing Graphics	$100,167

Freelance opportunities are everywhere throughout the federal government. Plan on taking some time to get to know the system and to market yourself, your product and services. Your time will be well worth the effort when you receive a government contract.

When To Apply

Keep in mind that because new contracts are awarded at the beginning of the government's fiscal year in October, you should make sure that an agency you're interested in working for has seen your portfolio by late spring or early summer-this will give them enough time to consider you and the services that you offer for the current fiscal year. Otherwise you may have to wait an entire year before you get any work, especially the larger contracts.

Know The Rules

If you are going to do business with the government, you must know how play the game. The federal government's procurement system has many laws, rules and regulations. Each agency must follow these rules to procure any goods or services. You will be ahead of the game if you know how this system works. You can view the regulations online at {www.arnet.gov/far}.

Identify Your Product or Service

The government uses the North American Industry Classification System to identify many products and services. Many government product and service listings and future procurements are identified by these codes. You can search web sites for the codes that correspond to the products and services you have to offer and then go after those contracts. You can view the codes at {www.census.gov/epcd/www/naics.html} or at {www.fpdc.gov}.

Get Registered

The Federal Acquisition Regulation requires contract registration with the Central Contract Registration (CCR). The CCR is the government database for many contracting opportunities. The CCR is the primary vendor database for the Department of Defense, NASA, Department of Transportation and Department of Treasury. They offer a Dynamic Small Business Database to showcase those businesses interested in doing business with the federal government. You can register your business at {www.ccr.gov}. In order to register with the CCR, you must first have a DUNS Number. You can obtain one online at {www.dnb.com}.

US General Service Administration

The US General Service Administration provides a procurement vehicle for vendors interested in selling to the federal government. This "contract vehicle" is a procurement vehicle where federal agencies can place orders. GSA Schedule contracts are an important vehicle for businesses in the federal procurement process. Because of the GSA Schedules ease of use, many federal agencies choose a GSA Schedule Contractor to fill a product or service need within their agency. In addition, GSA offers classes on "How to Contract with the Federal Government" throughout the country. You can find them at {www.gsa.gov}.

Get Certified As a Small Business

If you are a freelancer, you are a small business. You can find assistance with a number of organizations, starting with the Small Business Administration. If you qualify with the SBA as a specially identified business, you may be eligible for opportunities not available for larger businesses. Their web site "Government Contracting" {www.sba.gov/GC} lists programs to help businesses which include: *Small Disadvantaged Business, Very Small Business Program, Assistance for Women Business Owners (CAWBO), 8(a) Business, Veterans* and others.

BiZMatch Tool is an automated online database of minority businesses operated by the Department of Commerce's Minority Business Development Agency (MBDA). This database is used by Federal, state and local governments to locate minority enterprises to meet their procurement needs. You must register with the MBDA to be included in this database. {http://www.mbda.gov/index.php?section_id=4}

Procurement Levels

Now that you know something about the Federal government procurement procedures you must look for procurement opportunities. There are many "vehicles" or ways to win government contracts. The way a Federal agency will contract partially depends on the dollar amount threshold for each contract. Each agency conducts their procurement procedure slightly differently, so you should contact that agency directly.

- *Micro-Purchases*: Purchases under $2,500, which can be made at the sole discretion of the Contracting Officer or purchasing official to either large or small businesses with no competition.
- *Simplified Acquisition Procedure*: All purchases between $2,500 and $100,000 are reserved exclusively for small businesses providing that the Contracting Officer expects to obtain offers from at least two small businesses.
- *Formal Contracting Procedures*: Over $100,000

Get Assistance

All you need to do is ask. There are many organizations that are prepared to help you get a contract with the Federal government.

- The Small Business Administration can answer many of your questions.{www.sba.gov}
- Federal Procurement Technical Assistance Offices (listed in this book)
- Office of Small and Disadvantaged Business Utilization (listed in this book)
- State Procurement Offices (listed in this book)
- Each Federal agency's Procurement Office (listed in this book)

Find Current Procurement Opportunities

The federal government has developed a single point-of-entry for procurement opportunities over $25,000. Government buyers publicize their business opportunities by posting them on {www.FedBizOpps.gov}. You can monitor and retrieve opportunities by the entire Federal contracting community.

Check Out The Past And Look Into The Future

You can check out past winning contracts to get an understanding of what is purchased and what makes a successful bid contract. Through the Freedom of Information Act Request from the agency in question, you can get copies of winning bids from previous years. Remember, the competition is very high but most freelancers don't know about this information to give them an edge in the procurement process.

You can also look into the future of each agency. By law, each agency must publish their procurement forecast for the coming year. This information can help you prepare for what each agency will need in the future. You can contact the agency directly or check AcqNet at {www.acqnet.gov} to see the current forecasts.

Subcontracting

Federal prime contractors are required by law to subcontract with small businesses whenever possible. So you can get a contract with a company that has done all of the work to get a Federal contract. A small business can contact the prime contractor or a Federal agency directly. You can get a listing of prime contractors at {www.acq.osd.mil/sadbu/publications/subdir/index.html}. The Small Business Administration also maintains a site devoted to subcontracting at {http://web.sba.gov/subnet/}.

The Words "Poor and Starving" Don't Have To Apply To Artists Any Longer!

National Endowment for the Arts Grants to Organizations

The National Endowment for the Arts (NEA) is an independent agency of the Federal government that was created to encourage and support American art and artists who are actively creating art in various mediums. The Endowment does this by awarding grants to nonprofit arts organizations in all fields, as well as through its own leadership activities. The agency does not direct the creative activities of individual artists or arts organizations but acts as a catalyst and as a partner with others who support the arts. The NEA helps to enhance the quality of life for Americans through a breathtaking array of cultural activity: from the best in theaters and touring dance companies to folk festivals and music concerts; from museums and orchestras to arts programs in our nation's schools that reach millions of students each year who might otherwise lack exposure to the arts.

The Endowment awards grants to nonprofit organizations in three areas: Grants for Arts Projects, Leadership Initiatives and Partnership Agreements. In addition, individual fellowships in literature and honorary fellowships in jazz and the folk and traditional arts are awarded. Forty percent of Endowment funds are awarded to state and regional arts organizations. For more information, contact National Endowment for the Arts, 1100 Pennsylvania Avenue, NW, Washington, DC 20506; 202-682-5482; Fax: 202-682-5626; {www.nea.gov}.

Grants for Arts Projects

Grants for Arts Projects support exemplary projects in dance, design, folk and traditional arts, literature, media arts, museums, music, musical theater, opera, theater, visual arts and multidisciplinary forms. Grants are awarded on the basis of artistic excellence and merit, including such factors as the project's potential influences and the applicant's ability to carry out the project. Grants are awarded to organizations in the following areas:

Artistic Creativity and Preservation
- **Creativity:** To support the creation and preservation of artistically excellent and significant work.
- **Heritage and Preservation**: To preserve those forms of artistic expression and practice that reflects our nation's many cultural traditions.

- **Services to Arts Organizations and Artists**: To help arts organizations and artists become more effective in realizing their artistic and public service goals.

Challenge America: Access to the Arts: To provide communities throughout the country greater access to the arts.

Learning in the Arts for Children and Youth: To increase the availability of arts education.

Leadership Initiatives

The Endowment takes an active role in developing and carrying out hallmark projects of national significance in the arts. Such projects reach communities in all 50 states, promote international exchanges or link the arts in new ways with non-arts fields. In addition, the

Endowment currently maintains over 25 collaborative partnerships with other federal agencies including the Department of Education and the Department of Justice.

Partnership Agreements

Each year 40 percent of the Endowments monies are directed to state, jurisdictional and regional arts organizations. These organizations then make grants and offer services to their communities. The Partnership Agreement for the state arts agencies includes an arts education, arts in underserved communities and Challenge America components.

Fellowships & Awards

The Endowment recognizes individual achievements through the *American Jazz Masters Fellowship, National Heritage Fellowship* and the *National Medal of Arts*. Published creative writers and translators in poetry and prose are recognized by the Endowment through their *Literature Fellowships*.

Attention Artists!
Over $180,000,000 Available From State Governments

How do most struggling artists perfect their craft? By working alongside masters in their specific craft, and believe it or not, there are money programs administered on the state level to help you do just that. If you are working with an arts group, there are state grants to assist you in organizing special productions, grants that will allow you the resources to travel around the state to represent your art organization, or grants that would allow you to hire people with special capabilities to enhance your productions.

Here's just a sampling of what some states can provide:

- $2,000 to study music, dance, or storytelling (Alaska)
- $2,500 for choreographers (California)
- Money for architects to help school children (Georgia)
- $5,000 to work with a master artist in their studio (Idaho)
- $10,000 for creative writers (Idaho)
- $10,000 for photographers (Illinois)
- $1,000 for poets (Iowa)
- $2,000 for art teachers to attend a workshop (Maine)
- $150 a day for artists who can spend two days a week at a local school (Massachusetts)
- $10,000 to put on a program of poetry readings (Nebraska)
- $8,000 for dancers (North Carolina)
- $500 for writers to attend a workshop (North Carolina)
- $10,000 for art critics (North Dakota)
- $2,000 to put on an arts festival (Oklahoma)
- $5,000 for printmakers (Texas)
- $500 to writers on a first-come first-served basis (Virginia)

Eligibility Requirements

Almost every state requires that you be a state resident to receive money through these programs. The exceptions to this rule are often found in those programs where the state will pay an artist from another state to come to work with school children within their state. Eligibility requirements for all programs vary greatly. Some states, like Pennsylvania, require that you have lived in the state for two years and have three years of professional experience. States like Rhode Island require that you be at least 18 years of age and have resided in the state for at least one year. With residency requirements being as minimal as one year, it may be worth looking for a state that has some specific programs that interest you, and to establish residency there.

What Are Your Chances?

Remember, you have to play to win, and your chances of winning and receiving these funds will be slightly different for each of the programs listed. For instance, Virginia has a program that gives out money on a first-come first-served basis. So, if your application is the first received, your chances of success are 100 percent. Vermont, on the other hand, has one of the more competitive programs that awards funds to only approximately 5% of their applicants. Whatever your chances, remember that each year the money has to be awarded to someone, and your chances will be just plain zero if you don't apply!

How To Work With Arts Organizations

A lot of the state money programs are awarded to art organizations. Therefore, if you have trouble getting money as an individual it may be worth your time to find an art organization to collaborate with or perhaps become your own art organization. Your state arts council can help you locate organizations that may be willing (and even eager) to work with you in order to be awarded this grant money. Talk to your local community college, community group, or even your church about joining together to win funding. You might make an arrangement where you share the proceeds of the program if you win, and both you and the community group lose nothing if your efforts are unsuccessful.

Some of the money given to organizations requires matching grants in order to receive the funding. A matching grant requires that the recipient raise funds in some proportion to the amount awarded. This may not be as difficult as it sounds because oftentimes, in-kind goods and services may be used as matching grants. An in-kind contribution of goods is an offering of any tangible, useable item that the organization would have otherwise had to purchase. An in-kind contribution of a service includes intangible contributions such as donations of volunteer time, or the use of facilities or equipment.

Alabama

Alabama State Council on the Arts
201 Monroe St., Suite 110   334-242-4076
Montgomery, AL 36104   334-240-3269
www.arts.state.al.us

Eligibility requirements: For individual artist programs state residency is required, unless otherwise specified. Grants to organizations must be matched by at least an equal amount from other sources located by the applicant.

Programs Available:

$5,000 To Art Administrators (Fellowship in Arts Administration)
$10,000 For Artists, Craftsmen, Photographers (Artists Fellowships)
$1,000 To Develop Administrative Skills (Technical Assistance)
Money To Be An Artist In Residence (Artist Residences)
$5,000 For Master Folk Artists (Folk Art Apprenticeships)
Money For Schools To Hire Artists (Arts in Education Projects)
$500 For Folk Artists (Folklife Program)
$1,000 For Community Arts Projects (Project Assistance Programs)
Awards To Master Folk Artists (Folk Heritage Awards)
Money For Artists To Perform At Rural Schools (Rural Touring School Program)

Alaska

Alaska State Council on the Arts
411 W. 4th Ave., Suite 1E   907-269-6610
Anchorage, AK 99501-2343   Fax: 907-269-6601
www.eed.state.ak.us/aksca

Eligibility requirements: State residency is required for individual grants to artists. The Council awards funds only to Alaskan nonprofit organizations, schools, or government agencies.

Programs Available:

$2,500 For Artists To Develop New Works (Individual Artist Fellowships)
$2,000 To Study With a Master Craftsperson, Musician, Dancer, or Storyteller (Master Arts and Apprentice Grants in Traditional Native Arts)
Money For Local Art Agencies (Grants to Local Arts Agencies)
Money To Support a Local Art Project (Project Grants)
Money To Pay Artists To Speak At Workshops (Workshop Grants)
Money For Schools To Have An Artist Program (Artist In Schools)
Money To Support Short-term Projects Of Professional Artists In Visual, Literary, Media, Performing or Folk And Traditional Arts (Career Opportunity Grants)

$2,000 To Non-profit Art Groups And Organizations
(Community Art Development Grants)
Money To Cover The Production Costs Of Activities Of Art
Organizations (Operating Support Grants)
$1,000 For Artists To Train And Speak At Workshops (AIE
Incentive Grants)

Arizona

Arizona Commission on the Arts
417 W. Roosevelt St.   602-255-5882
Phoenix, AZ 85003   Fax: 602-256-0282
www.arizonaarts.org
Eligibility requirements: Individual Artist Fellowships require
state residency. Priority for organizational funding is given to
projects in rural areas of the state and projects coordinated by
ethnic-run organizations or those that primarily serve ethnic
communities.

Programs Available:
$5,000 For Artists To Use For Research And Travel (Artist
Projects)
Money For Schools To Have Artists In Residence Programs
(Artists in Residence)
Money For Schools With New Ideas In Art (Education
Initiatives)
$5,000 For Artists And Writers (Fellowships)
Over $50,000 In Grants To Support Administrative Expenses
Of Art Organizations (General Operating Grants)
Grants To Artists And Organizations To Support Special Art
Projects (Project And Development Grants)
Money For Local Art Agencies (Grants To Local Agencies)

Arkansas

Arkansas Arts Council
1500 Tower Bldg.
323 Center St.   501-324-9766
Little Rock, AR 72201   Fax: 501-324-9207
www.arkansasarts.com
Eligibility requirements: State residency is required for
individual artist programs. Individuals must be at least 25-
years old. Funds awarded to nonprofit organizations and
educational institutions must be at least equally matched by
the applicant organization with cash from sources other than
the Council or National Endowment for the Arts (NEA).

Programs Available:
$5,000 To Craftspersons and Artists (Individual Artist
Fellowship Program)
$50,000 To Arts Organizations (General Operating Support
Grants)
Grants To Put On Art Shows For The Public (Program
Support Grants)
Money For Schools Or Communities To Have An Artist In
Residence (Arts-in-Education)
More Money For Schools Or Communities To Have An Artist
In Residence (Artists In Residence)
Grants To Support New And Emerging Organizations (Major
Arts Partners)
$1,000 For Emergency Arts Funding (Assistance Mini-grants)
Money To Support Community Arts Activities (Arts On Tour
Program)

California

California Arts Council
13001 I Street, Suite 930   916-332-6555
Sacramento, CA 95814   Fax: 916-332-6575
www.cac.ca.gov
Eligibility requirements: State residency is required for
individual artists programs.

Programs Available:
Based on reduction to the agency's budget, all grant
programs have been suspended. Contact the California Arts
Council for updated information on grants programs.

Colorado

Colorado Council on the Arts (CCAH)
1380 Lawrence St., Suite 1200   303-866-2723
Denver, CO 80204-2059   Fax: 303-866-4266
www.coloarts.state.co.us
Eligibility requirements: For individual artist programs, state
residency is required, unless otherwise specified. Money
available: $220,000.
Programs Available:
Colorado currently has only one grants program available.
The *Grants to Artists and Organizations* is a broad based
program that funds: collaborations between schools and
artists, increased cultural participation, community building
through the arts, folk or traditional arts, technical assistance
services and professional development. Matching grants
amounts range from $2,000 to a maximum of 3.5% of the
total grants funding pool.

Connecticut

Connecticut Commission on the Arts
1 Financial Program
775 Main Street   860-566-4770
Hartford, CT 06103   Fax: 860-566-6462
www.ctarts.org
Eligibility requirements: Individual Artist Programs: State
residency is required, unless otherwise specified.
Programs Available:
$2,500 For Visual Artists (Artist Fellowship)
Money For Organizations To Hire An Artist In Residence
(Artists Residencies)
Money For Organizations To Conduct Public Art Programs
(Organizational Support Program)
$1,000 For Organizations To Engage In Professional
Development Activities (Arts Management Technical
Assistance Program)
Matching Grants For Organizations And Local Art Agencies
To Culturally Improve The Community (Arts
Partnerships For Stronger Communities)
$1,000 To Performing Artists (Arts Presentation Grants)
Grants To Assist In The Long-term Stabilization Of The
State's Arts Industry (Connecticut Arts Endowment Fund)
$2,500 to Arts Administrator (Elizabeth L. Mahaffey Arts
Administration Fellowship)

Delaware

Delaware Division of the Arts
Carvell State Office Building
820 North French St.   302-577-8278
Wilmington, DE 19801   Fax: 302-577-6561
www.artsdel.org
Eligibility requirements: Individual artist programs require
state residency, unless otherwise specified.
Programs Available:
Money For New Or Established Artists (Individual Artist
Fellowships)
Money For Operating Expenses (General Operating Support
Grants)
Money For Schools To Have An Artist In Residence (Arts in
Education Residencies)
Money For The Professional Development Of Organizations
(Technical Assistance Grants)
More Money To Support Art Organizations (Delaware Arts
Stabilization Fund)
$750 For Art Organizations (Opportunity Grants)

Money To Support Art Programs In Schools (Education Partnership Planning Grants)

District of Columbia

District of Columbia Commission on Arts and
    Humanities
410 Eight St., NW, 5th Floor
Stables Art Center   202-724-5613
Washington, DC 20004   Fax: 202-727-4135
http://dcarts.dc.gov

Eligibility requirements: Individual artist programs require residency in the District of Columbia for at least one year prior to application deadline and the applicant must maintain residency during the grant period. Individuals and arts organizations may apply in one of the following disciplines: crafts, dance, interdisciplinary/performance art (individuals only), literature, media, multi-disciplinary, music, theater, and the visual arts.

Programs Available:

$1,000 To Individual Artists And Organizations (Small Projects Program)

$2,500 To Professional Artists (Individual Artist Fellowship Program)

Money For Artists To Promote Art In Local Communities (City Arts Project)

To Provide Funds For Art Projects, Workshops, Performance And Residencies In Schools (Arts Education Program)

$2,500 to Young Artists For Innovative Projects (Young Artist Program)

Florida

Florida Arts Council
Division of Cultural Affairs
1001 DeSoto Park Drive   850-245-6470
Tallahassee, FL 32301   Fax: 850-245-6492
www.florida-arts.org

Eligibility requirements: Individual Artist Programs: State residency is required, unless otherwise specified.

Programs Available:

$5,000 To Professional Artists (Individual Artist Fellowship Program)

Grants To Schools And Organizations Involved In Lifelong Art Education Projects (Arts In Education)

Money For Special Projects (Challenge Grant Program)

Money For Local Arts Agencies (Local Arts Agency/State Service Organization Program)

$1,500 For Professional Development In Art Organizations (Quarterly Grant Assistance Program)

Technical Assistance For Art Organizations In Rural Communities (Underserved Arts Communities Assistance Program)

Grants To Sponsoring Organizations To Cover Project Costs (State Touring Program)

Money To Support Programming That Fosters Diversity In Art (Cultural Support Grants)

Money For Organizations Involved In International Exchange Projects (International Cultural Exchange)

Georgia

Georgia Council for Arts
260 14th St., NW, Suite 40   404-685-2787
Atlanta, GA 30318   Fax: 404-685-6788
www.web_dept.com/gca

Eligibility requirements: In general, grant categories include: architecture/environmental arts, dance, arts-related education, film-making, folk arts/heritage arts and crafts, arts-related historic preservation, literary arts, multi-media, museums, music, photography, public radio and television, theater and visual arts. No individual funding is available. Money available: $2,300,000.

Programs Available:

Grants For Art Groups To Tour (Georgia Touring Grants)

$1000 To Hire An Arts Consultant (Technical Assistance Grants)

Money To Support Art Organizations (General Operating Support)

$20,000 For Art Related Activities (Specific Project Support)

Up To $100,000 For Organizations (Challenge Grant Program)

Money For Schools To Have An Artist In Residence (Artists Residencies)

$30,000 For Curriculum-Based Arts Education Programs (The Georgia Challenge)

$5,000 To Support Traditional Arts (Folklife Grant Program)

Grants For Students To Learn From Master Folk Artists (Traditional Arts Apprenticeship Program)

Hawaii

Hawaii State Foundation on Culture and Arts (SFCA)
250 South Hotel St., 2nd Floor   808-586-0300
Honolulu, HI 96813   Fax: 808-586-0308
www.state.hi.us/sfca

Eligibility requirements: State residency is required for individual artist programs. Money available: $1,432,000.

Programs Available:

$5,000 To Talented Visual And Performing Artists (Individual Artists Fellowship Program)

Money For Schools To Promote Art Education (Arts In Education Program)

Grants To Individuals And Organizations To Preserve Folk Arts In Hawaii (Folk Arts Program)

$3,000 For Artists To Study As An Apprentice (Folk Arts Apprenticeship Awards)

Money For Arts In Public Places Program

Idaho

Idaho Commission on Arts
P.O. Box 83720   800-334-2488
2410 North Old Penitentiary Road 208-334-2119
Boise, ID 83720-0008   Fax: 208-334-2488
www2.state.id.us/arts

Eligibility requirements: Individual artist programs require state residency, unless otherwise specified.

Programs Available:

Money For An Arts Group (General Operating Support)

Money To Build A Cultural Facility (Cultural Facilities Grants)

Money For Schools Or Nursing Homes To Have An Artist In Residence (Artists in Residence)

$3,500 For Artists, Dancers, Designers, and Craftspersons (Fellowship Awards)

$8,000 To Be A Writer In Residence (Writer In Residence Award)

Money To Fund Art Activities (Quick Art$ Program)

$2,000 To Study With A Master Craftsperson (Traditional Arts Apprenticeship Program)

Illinois

Illinois Arts Council
State Of Illinois Center
100 West Randolph
Suite 10-500   312-814-6750
Chicago, IL 60601   Fax: 312-814-1471
www.state.il.us/agency/iac

Eligibility requirements: Individual artist programs require state residency, unless otherwise specified. In addition to the programs detailed, grants are funded for choral music and opera, dance, ethnic and folk arts, symphonies and ensemble, theater, and visual arts programs.

   Copyright © 2004 Matthew Lesko, Information USA, Inc., 12081 Nebel Street, Rockville, MD 20852 • 1-800-955-7693 • www.lesko.com

Programs Available:

$7,000 for Artists, Photographers, Writers, and Poets (Fellowships)

Grants To Artists To Study As Apprentices (Apprenticeship Program)

Money For Writers And Nonprofit Magazines (Literary Awards)

Money To Provide Art To Communities Normally Deprived Of Art (Access Program)

Money For Touring Art Groups (ArtsTour)

Special Money For Arts Programs and Projects (Special Assistance Grants)

Money For Schools Or Other Organizations To Have An Artist In Residence (Artists in Residence)

Grants For Schools To Develop Special Art Classes (Arts Resource)

Grants For Art Organizations To Solve Technical Or Administrative Problems (Technical Assistance Program)

Indiana

Indiana Arts Commission
150 West Market St., #618
Indianapolis, IN 46204
www.state.in.us/iac
317-232-1268
Fax: 317-252-5595

Eligibility requirements: Individual Artist Programs: State residency is required, unless otherwise specified. Grants are awarded in 16 categories: dance, design arts, education, expansion arts, folk arts, literature, local arts agencies, media arts, multi-arts, museums, music, presenters, statewide arts service organizations, theater, and visual arts.

Programs Available:

Grants To Arts Organizations (General Operating Support)

Grants To Local Arts Organizations (State and Local Partnership)

Grants To Run Special Art Projects (Arts Projects and Series)

Money For Artists In Residence Programs (Arts in Education Grants)

Money For Art Administrators To Attend Workshops (Technical Assistance)

Iowa

Iowa Arts Council
Capitol Complex
600 Locust
Des Moines, IA 50319-0290
www.iowaartscouncil.org
515-281-6412
Fax: 515-242-6498

Eligibility requirements: Individual artist programs require state residency, unless otherwise specified.

Programs Available:

Cash Matching Grants For Non-Profit Organizations To Develop Art Projects (Organization Projects)

Grants To Individual Artists (Artists Projects)

Money For Schools To Have An Artist In Residence (Arts In Education/Residencies)

Annual Monetary Awards For Art Organizations (Operational Support Grant Program)

$1,000 To High School Seniors Who Are Involved In The Arts (Iowa Scholarship For The Arts)

$3,000 For Elementary Schools To Plan For Art (Art Partners for Achievement)

$200 For Schools To Be Trained In Character Counts! (Character Counts Through the Arts!)

Money To Participate In Significant Arts-Related Programs (Conference, Workshop & Forum Grants and Mini-Grants)

Matching Grants For Folk and Traditional Arts Projects (Folk & Traditional Arts Projects Grants and Mini-Grants)

Kansas

Kansas Arts Commission
Jayhawk Tower
700 Jackson, Suite 1004
Topeka, KS 66603-3761
http://arts.state.ks.us
785-296-3335
Fax: 785-296-4989

Eligibility requirements: Individual Art programs require state residency. The Commission provides direct or indirect funding to artists, schools, government units, and cultural, social and educational organizations as well as nonprofit organizations. Major grants are awarded each May for the following fiscal year. Money available: $1,432,123.

Programs Available:

$5,000 For Artists And Writers (Fellowships in the Performing Arts)

$500 For Artists Creating Original Work (Artist Mini-Fellowship)

Grants To Produce Art Publications, Workshops, Exhibits, and Performances (Project Support)

Money For Schools and Organizations To Have An Artist In Residence (Artist in Residency and Visiting Artist Grants)

Matching Grants For Programming and Administrative Costs (Operational Support for Arts & Cultural Organizations)

$7,500 To Help Pay For Performance Fees (Kansas Touring Program)

$1,200 To Develop New Public Exhibitions of Kansas Artists (Kansas Visual Arts Program)

$2,000 4:1 Matching Grant For Rural, Multicultural, Culturally Specific and Emerging Organizations (Grassroots Grants)

$2,000 2:1 Matching Grant For Rural, Multicultural, Culturally Specific Emerging Organizations and Arts & Cultural Organizations (Technical Assistance)

Kentucky

Kentucky Arts Council
300 West Broad
Frankfort, KY 40601
www.kyarts.org
502-564-3757
Fax: 502-564-2839

Eligibility requirements: Matching grants from the Council are available to Kentucky nonprofit organizations committed to providing arts programs and services to the public. Grant amounts vary from year to year and depend upon the availability of funds. Non-matching fellowships are available to Kentucky artists. Interim Grants are available in all program areas to provide one-time funding for emergencies or for unexpected and outstanding opportunities in the arts.

Programs Available:

Grants To Arts Organizations (Challenge Grants)

Money To Help Pay Artists And Art Administrators (Arts Development Grants)

Money For Schools To Have An Artist In Residence (Artists in Residence Grants)

Grants For Teachers To Put Art In Their Classrooms (Teacher Incentive Project Grants)

$7,500 For The Professional Development Of Individual Kentucky Artists (Artist Fellowships)

$500 To Fund Activities That Help Artists Develop Their Careers (Individual Artist Professional Development Program)

$7,500 To Fund Public Performing Arts Events (Kentucky Arts On Tour)

$3,000 For Master Artists To Teach Students (Folk And Traditional Arts Apprenticeship)

$3,000 To Spend On Art Projects (Folk Arts Project And Tour)

$3,000 For Organizations To Enhance Art Programs (Project Grant Program)

Up To $5,000 To Establish Art Organizations (Community Arts Development Grants)

Money For Operating Expenses For Arts and Cultural Organizations (General Operating Support Grants I and II)

$5,000 To encourage Partnerships That Contribute To The Cultural, Social and Economic Growth Of The Community (Arts Build Community Grants)

$1,050 To Bring Professional Artists Into Early Childhood/Preschool Facilities (ArtStart! Grants Program)

Louisiana

Louisiana State
Division of the Arts
P.O. Box 44247   225-342-8180
Baton Rouge, LA 70804   Fax: 225-342-8173
www.crt.state.la.us/arts

Eligibility requirements: Individual artist programs require state residency.

Programs Available:

$5,000 For Artists To Work With A Master (Folklife Apprenticeships)

$20,000 For Art Organizations (Project Assistance Program)

$20,000 To Support Arts In Education (Arts In Education Program)

Up To $250,000 For Art Groups (General Operating Support Program)

Up To $250,000 For Local Art Agencies (Local Arts Agency Program)

Grants For Specific Art Activities (Individual Artist Mini-Grant Program)

Money For Artists, Craftspersons, Designers And Musicians (Artist Fellowships)

Maine

Maine Arts Commission
State House Station 25   207-287-2724
Augusta, ME 04333   Fax: 207-287-2335
www.mainearts.com

Eligibility requirements: Individual artist programs require state residency. Maine offers an Institutional Support Program which provides two-year funding for established professional, nonprofit cultural organizations, schools, and other organizations for specific local arts projects and programs.

Programs Available:

$3,000 To Artists (Fellowships)

Up To $20,000 For Special Art Programs (Project Support)

$4,000 For School Teachers To Go To Art Seminars (Professional Development for Teachers)

$5,000 To Support Art Projects (Public Art Grants)

Money For Students To Learn From Master Artists (Traditional Arts Apprenticeships)

$1,000 For Artist Ideas And Improvement (Good Idea Grant)

$7,500 To Assist Art Organizations Collaborate With The Community (Artist In Maine Communities Program)

Maryland

Maryland State Arts Council
175 West Ostend St., Suite E   410-767-6555
Baltimore, MD 21230   Fax: 410-333-1062
www.msac.org

Eligibility requirements: The Council provides direct grants to individual artists, offers professional advice, and initiates projects that provide services and opportunities for Maryland artists. State residency is required for participation. The Council's Community Arts Development program supports county arts council organizations in each of the 23 counties of Maryland and Baltimore City. Funds are used in each county to regrant to local arts organizations, support various arts programs, assist local arts groups with fund raising, publicity, promotion and planning, and to support the operating expenses of the county arts council.

Programs Available:

$6,000 For Creative Artists (Individual Artist Awards)

Money For Large Arts Organizations (Grants to Major Institutions)

Help For Those Interested In Maryland Folklife (Maryland Folklife Program)

Money For Poets, Artists, and Performers To Be At Schools (Artists in Education Program)

Grants For Organizations To Support One-Time Public Activities (Arts Project Grants)

$1,000 For Individuals To Develop Their Artwork (Individual Artist Mini-Grant Program)

Money For Technical Assistance (Grant For Organizations)

Money To Help Underserved Audiences (Arts in Communities)

Help For Local Arts Councils (Community Arts Development Grants)

Assist Schools Obtain Quality Performers (Visiting Performers Program)

Massachusetts

Massachusetts Cultural Council
10 St. James Avenue, 3rd Floor   617-727-3668
Boston, MA 02116   Fax: 617-727-0044
www.massculturalcouncil.org

Eligibility requirements: Individual artist programs require state residency, unless otherwise specified. Programs are open to individuals, organizations and schools.

Programs Available:

Money For Arts Organizations (Organizational Support Grant)

Funds To Provide Art To Children (Creative Schools Program)

$5,000 Awarded To Individual Artists (Artist Fellowship Grants)

Money For Artists To Work In Schools (Local Cultural Council Program)

$6,000 To Support The Teaching Of Traditional Arts (Traditional Arts Apprenticeship)

Funds To Subsidize The Cost Of Field Trips (PASS Program)

Money To Help Youth In Need By Providing Arts Related Activities (YouthReach Initiative)

Michigan

Michigan Council for the Arts
702 West Kalamazoo Street
P.O. Box 30705   517-241-4011
Lansing, MI 48909   Fax: 517-241-3979
www.michigan.gov/hal

Any nonprofit organization or institution, artist, local government, school or community group in Michigan is eligible to apply for MCA grant funds. All funded activities must take place within the state and comply with Equal Opportunity Standards. Contact the Council for specific program guidelines.

Programs Available:

Money For Artists To Teach In Schools (Arts And Learning Program)

Grants For Schools To Have An Artist In Residence (Artists In Schools Program (AIS))

Grants To Organizations For Art Projects And Programs (Anchor Organization Program)

Grants To Small Organizations (Arts Organization Development Program (AOD))

Money For Regional Cultural Projects (Cultural Projects Program)

Grants To Community Based Organizations (Art Agencies Services Program)

$4,000-$10,000 To Support the Arts, Culture, Heritage, and History of 39 Identified Counties (Rural Arts and Cultural Program)

$4,000 Matching Grants for locally Developed Art and Cultural Programs (Mini-Grant Regional Regranting Program)

$100,000 Matching Grant to Improve Facilities (Capital Improvements Program)

Grant Money To Improve Curriculum (The Big Culture Lesson)

$30,000 2:1 Match For Non-Profit Organizations Fund Arts Projects (Arts Project Program)

Minnesota

Minnesota State Arts Board
400 Sibley St., Suite 200   651-215-1600
St. Paul, MN 55101   Fax: 651-215-1602
www.arts.state.mn.us

Eligibility requirements: Individual artist programs require state residency, unless otherwise specified.

Programs Available:

Money For Schools To Have An Artist In Residence (School Support Grants)

$6,000 For Community-Based Projects By Artists Or Organizations (Cultural Collaborations)

Grants To Art Organizations (Institutional Support)

Money To Display Art In Public Places (Percent For Art In Public Places Program)

$2,000-$6,000 Awarded To Artists At Various Stages Of Their Careers (Artist Initiative Grants)

Mississippi

Mississippi Arts Commission
239 North Lamar St., Suite 207   601-359-6030
Jackson, MS 39201   Fax: 601-359-6008
www.arts.state.mo.us

Eligibility requirements: Individual artist programs require state residency.

Programs Available:

$5,000 For Writers, Composers, Video Producers (Artist Fellowships)

$25,000 For Arts And Cultural Organizations (General Operating Support)

$7,500 For Local Schools To Improve Their Art Programs (Arts In Education)

$7,500 For New Artists (Project Grants)

$2,000 To Fund Community Based Traditional Art Forms (Folk Art Apprenticeship Program)

$500 Mini-Grants (Mini-Grants For Artists)

Missouri

Missouri Arts Council
Wainwright Office Complex
111 N. 7th St., Suite 105   314-340-6845
St. Louis, MO 63101-2188   Fax: 314-340-7215
www.missouriartscouncil.org

Eligibility requirements: The Council offers financial assistance through seven art areas: dance, literature, media, multi-discipline, music, theater, and visual arts. A program administrator supervises applications in each area.

Programs Available:

Money For Smaller Arts Organizations (Community Arts Program (CAP))

Money For Arts Groups Serving The Entire State (Statewide Arts Service Organizations)

Money For Art Organizations To Perform Outside Their Home Areas (Missouri Touring Program)

Money To Incorporate Arts Education Programs Into School Curricula (Missouri Alliance For Arts Education)

$2,500 To Help Nonprofit Develop Skills (Organizational Development Program)

$30,000 To Fund A Variety Of Arts Activities (Discipline Program Assistance)

Money For Folklife Festivals (Folk Arts Program)

Funds For A Three-Year Period (Mid-Sized Arts Organizations Operating and Program Support)

Money For Non-Traditional Arts Venues (Minority Arts Program)

Montana

Montana Arts Council
316 N. Park Ave., Suite 252
P.O. Box 202201   406-444-6430
Helena, MT 59620-2201   Fax: 406-444-6548
www.art.state.mt.us

Eligibility requirements: Individual artist programs require state residency.

Programs Available:

Grants For Arts Preservation, Media Arts, Archaeology, and Folklore (Cultural and Aesthetic Project Grants)

Biennial Grants To Art Organizations (Organizational Excellence Grants)

Grants To Community Based And Traditional Artists (Folk Arts Program)

$1,000 To Artists And Organizations For Opportunities Or Emergencies (Opportunity Grants)

Money To Help Non Profit Organizations Hire Artists (Artists in Schools & Communities)

Funds Targeted For Use With Rural or Underserved Communities For Arts Programs (Building Arts Participation)

$500 Matching Fee Support For Touring Companies (Fee Support for Touring Companies)

Nebraska

Nebraska Arts Council
Jocelyn Castle Carriage House
3838 Davenport St.   402-595-2122
Omaha, NE 68131-2329   Fax: 402-595-2334
www.nebraskaartscouncil.org

Eligibility requirements: Individual artist programs require state residency.

Programs Available:

Money For Writers, Artists, and Performers (Individual Artist Fellowships)

Grants To Arts Organizations (Basic Support Grant)

Over $2,500 To Pay For Artists' Residencies In Schools (Artists In Residency)

Grants To Support Art Projects In Schools (Impact: Arts Education Program)

Money To Support Organizations That Sponsor Collaborative Arts Projects (Impact: Collaborative Arts)

Money To Pay For Programs Of Cultural Organizations (Multi-Cultural Assistance Program)

Grants For People Of Color In Existing Or New Arts Programming (Multi-Cultural Organization)

Money For Touring Exhibits And Programs (Nebraska Touring And Exhibits Sponsor Grant)

Grants To Organizations For Professional Development, Emergencies And New Ventures (Special Opportunity Support)

Nevada

Nevada Arts Council
716 North Carson St., Suite A   775-687-6680
Carson City, NV 89701   Fax: 775-687-6688
http://dmla.clan.lib.nv.us/docs/arts

Eligibility requirements: Individual artist programs require state residency. Money available: $600,000.

Programs Available:
$5,000 For Artists To Create New Works (Artists Fellowships)
$2,500 For Master Folk Artists To Teach Apprentices (Folk Arts Apprenticeships)
Money For Schools To Have An Artist In Residence (Artist in Residence Program)
Money to Stimulate Local Cultural Activity (Nevada Touring Initiative)
$3,000 For Commissioned Artwork (Governor's Arts Awards)
Money For Art Education For Youths At Risk (YouthReach Nevada)
Grants For Arts Education Workshops For Educators (Professional Development Grants)
$2,500 For Innovative Arts Education Programs (Special Project Grants For Schools and Organizations)

New Hampshire
New Hampshire Division of Arts
Council of the Arts
2 1/2 Beacon Street, 2nd Floor   603-271-2789
Concord, NH 03301-4974   Fax: 603-271-3584
www.state.nh.us/nharts
Eligibility requirements: Individual artist programs require state residency, unless otherwise specified.
Programs Available:
$5,000 For Individual Artists (Individual Artist Fellowships)
$5,000 For Special Projects And Developing Artists (Exploration/New Works Grant)
$3,000 To Learn From An Experienced Artist (Traditional Arts Apprenticeships)
$10,000 To Support Cultural Organizations (Operating Grant)
$3,500 For Schools To Bring In Artists (Artists In Residence)
$2,500 For Arts Education In Schools (Arts Link Initiative)
$3,500 To Support Art Projects In Communities (Community Arts Project Grant)
$1,000 More For Arts In Communities (Mini-Grants Program)
$500 Matching Grants For Consultations (Peer Mentorship Program)
$5,000 Matching Grants For Artists To Serve As Resources For Teachers (AIE Leadership Grant)

New Jersey
New Jersey State Council on the Arts
225 West State St.
P.O. Box 306   609-292-6130
Trenton, NJ 08625   Fax: 609-989-1440
www.njartscouncil.org
Eligibility requirements: Individual artist programs require state residency, unless otherwise specified.
Programs Available:
Grants For Artists, Mimes, Sculptors, Poets, and Opera Singers (Fellowships)
Money For Regional and State-Wide Organizations (General Operating Support)
Grants To Support Special Art Projects (Special Project Support)
Money For Art Programs In Local Schools (Projects Serving Artist Grants)
Funding For Arts Organizations (Support Grants)
Money For Public Or Parochial School Art Programs (Educational Funding: Arts in Education Programs (AIE))
Money For Jazz, Folk, And Theater Artists In Residence (Artists in Education Programs)
Grants For A Consortium of Community Organizations (Community Arts Collaboration Grants)
Money For Grants and Regrants in 21 Counties (Local Arts Program)
Support For County Arts Agencies To Increase Permanent Arts Staff (Local Arts Staffing Initiative)

Funds To Support The Passing On Of Folk Arts (Folk Arts Apprenticeship)

New Mexico
New Mexico Arts
P.O. Box 1450   505-827-6490
Santa Fe, NM 87504-1450   Fax: 505-827-6043
www.nmarts.org
Eligibility requirements: The New Mexico Art Division is unable to fund fellowships to individuals. It strongly encourages applicant organizations to involve resident New Mexico artists. However, the Division does support local sponsorship of out-of-state artists or organizations to enrich a resident group or when the services fill a need that is not being met locally. Organizational Funding: New Mexico administers awards to nonprofit organizations. Generally, award applicants must provide at least a one-to-one cash match.
Programs Available:
Grants For Community Based Organizations (Organizations For The Arts Program)
Grants To Organizations That Produce Performing Arts Exhibits And Outreach (Arts Organizations Touring And Outreach)
Money For Folk Artists In Communities (Rural Arts Economic Development Initiative)
Money For Students To Learn From Master Artists (Folk Arts Program)
Grants For Preserving Folk Arts (Folk Arts Program)
Grants For Schools To Have Artists In Residence (Artists Residencies)
Money For Art Projects In Schools (Arts In Education Program)

New York
New York State Council on the Arts
175 Varick Street   212-627-4455
New York, NY 10014   Fax: 212-387-7164
www.nysca.org
Eligibility requirements: Individual artist programs require state residency. Nonprofit organizations can obtain support in 17 areas including: architecture, planning and design, arts in education, capital funding initiative, dance, electronic media and film, folk arts, individual artists, literature, museum, music, musical instrument revolving loan fund, presenting operations, special arts services, state local partnership, theater, and the visual arts.
Programs Available:
Money For Artists (Individual Artist Programs)
Grants For Arts Organizations (General Operating Support)
Money For School Art Programs In Music, Theater, and Media (Arts in Education)
$5,000 For Local Art Groups (State And Local Partnership Program)
Grants To Support Professional And Ethnic Art Activities (Special Arts Services)
Grants To Support Traditional Art In Communities (Folk Arts Program)
Support Excellence In Design And Planning in the Public Realm (Architecture Planning & Design)

North Carolina
North Carolina Arts Council
Department of Cultural Resources   919-733-2111
Raleigh, NC 27699-4632   Fax: 919-733-4834
www.ncarts.org
Eligibility requirements: Individual artist programs require state residency. Money for arts organizations is in eight categories: community development, dance, folklife, literature, music, theater, touring/presenting, and the visual

arts. Support includes funding for program support, interdisciplinary/ special projects, and organizational development grants.

Programs Available:

$8,000 For Artists, Dancers, Musicians, and Writers (Fellowships)

Grants To Schools For Art Projects (Arts in Education)

Grants To Visual Artists And Writers For Residencies (Residency Center Opportunities)

Money For Artists And Organizations That Document Folk Art (Folklife Documentary Program)

Money For Public Folk Art Awareness Projects (Folklife Projects)

Grants To Support Art Organizations (General Support Grant)

Money For Local Arts Program (Grassroots Arts Program)

Money For Organizations To Learn About Management (Technical Assistance)

Money For Individual Art Projects (Regional Artist Project Grants)

$15,000 Support Over Three Years To Improve Arts Education (Arts In Education Rural Development)

$20,000 For Artists Residencies (Arts In Education Artist Residencies)

$5,000 Grants For Communities To Develop Public Art Design (Creating Place: Community Public Art and Design Development)

$5,000 Matching Grants For Communities To Carry Out Their Public Art Design (Creating Place: Community Public Art and Design Implementation)

$10,000 Matching Grants to Commission New Work (Literary, Performing and Visual Arts Program Support)

Money To Develop and Sustain Organizations That Serve Multicultural and People With Disabilities (Outreach)

$35,000 Matching Grants For Organizations That Provide Arts Services On A State Or Regional Basis (Statewide Service Organizations)

$10,000 Matching Grants For Artist Fees, Travel, Marketing and Project Related Costs (Touring/Presenting)

North Dakota

North Dakota Council On Arts
1600 East Century Avenue, Suite 6   701-328-7590
Bismarck, ND 58503   Fax: 701-328-7595
www.state.nd.us/arts

Eligibility requirements: Individual artist programs require state residency, unless otherwise specified.

Programs Available:

Money For Artists, Dancers, Opera Singers, Photographers, and Writers (Artists Fellowships Program)

Money For Schools To Have An Artist In Residence (Artists in Residence)

$2,000 For Students To Learn From Master Artists (Traditional Arts Apprenticeship Program)

$500 For Artists To Improve Their Skills (Professional Development)

$1,000 For Performances, Exhibitions And Special Events (Institutional Support Program)

$2,000 For Organizations To Serve Rural Communities (Access Programs)

$600 For New Projects And Touring Events (Special Project Grants)

$300 To Teachers To Explore New and Creative Ways To Incorporate the Arts into Non-Arts Curriculum (Teacher Initiative)

$3,000 To Communities For Performances, Exhibitions, Murals and Special Events (Lewis and Clark Community Grant)

Ohio

Ohio Council on Arts
727 East Main St.   614-466-2613
Columbus, OH 43205   Fax: 614-466-4494
www.oac.state.oh.us

Eligibility requirements: State residency is required, unless otherwise specified.

Programs Available:

$10,000 For Artists And Art Critics (Individual Artist Fellowships)

$1,000 For Artists To Attend Workshops (Professional Development Assistance)

$2,000 For An Artist To Work With A Master (Traditional and Ethnic Arts Apprenticeship Program)

Grants To Arts Organizations (Major Institution Support)

Money To Support Special Projects (Project Support)

Money For Administrative Expenses (Operating Support)

$2,000 For Special Art Opportunities (Sudden Opportunity Grants)

Grants For Specific Projects (Artists Projects Program)

Grants For Activities That Promote Art In Education (Arts In Education Program)

Grants To Organizations For Community Art Projects (Arts Education Partnership)

Grants To Have Professional Artists in Residency (Artists in Residence Program)

Money To Support Out-of-School Arts Opportunities For At Risk Youth (YouthReach Ohio)

$2,000 To Assist Artists, Art Organizations and Citizens In 29 Appalachian Counties (Appalachian Arts Program)

Oklahoma

State Arts Council of Oklahoma
2101 N. Lincoln Blvd.
P.O. Box 52001-2001   405-521-2931
Oklahoma City, OK 73152-2001   Fax: 405-521-6418
www.oklaosf.state.ok.us/~arts/

Eligibility requirements: The Council is unable to fund individuals. Applications are accepted from non-religious, nonprofit, tax exempt organizations. Colleges, schools, and universities which receive funding through the State Regents for Higher Education or substantial private sources, are a lower funding priority, except in areas where the university or college is the sole source of arts events in a community. Money available: $1,600,000. All funding for the Advanced Request, Over $4,000 and Under $4,000 Project Assistance categories must be matched dollar for dollar by the applicant. Fifty percent of the matching funds must be cash. The Council will fund personnel or administrative costs associated with a project. The Council does not fund general administrative expenses or general organizational support.

Programs Available:

Grants For Community Arts Celebrations (Fairs and Festival Funding)

Money For An Artist In Residence In Schools Or Community Groups (Artists in Residences Program)

Money For Artists To Tour (Oklahoma Touring Program)

Grants For Students To Learn From Professional Folk Artists (Master Apprenticeship Program)

Grants To Schools For Arts Activities (ArtsPower Education Grant)

Money For Arts Projects (Project Assistance)

Funds For Community Arts Projects and Events (MiniGrant)

Grants For DHS Childcare Centers For Quality Arts Based Projects (Youth Arts Program)

Oregon

Oregon Arts Commission
775 Summer St., NE   503-986-0082
Salem, OR 97301   Fax: 503-986-0260

www.oregonartscommission.org
Eligibility requirements: Individual artist programs require
state residency, unless otherwise specified.
Programs Available:
Money To Be An Artist In Residence (Artist Residencies)
Money For Arts Programs In Oregon Communities (Arts
Build Communities Grants)
More Money For Arts Programs In Schools (Regional Arts
Education Partnerships)
Grants To Small Arts Groups And Artists (Regional Arts
Partnerships)
Grants To Folk Artists And Organizations (Oregon Folklife
Program)
Grants For Oregon Schools (Oregon Arts Education Network
Grants)
Matching Funds To Support Projects Advancing the
Commission's Arts Education Goals (Arts Education
Leadership Grants)
Money To Support Projects That Demonstrate the Connection
Between the Arts, Landscape, Outdoor Recreation and
Trail Corridors (Arts and Trails)

Pennsylvania
Pennsylvania Council on the Arts
Room 216, Finance Bldg.   717-787-6883
Harrisburg, PA 17120   Fax: 717-783-2538
www.pacouncilonthearts.org
Eligibility requirements: For individual artist programs,
applicants must have lived in Pennsylvania for two years prior
to applying for funding and should have had a minimum of
three years professional experience in their field.
Organizational funding programs require that organizations
must be nonprofit, tax exempt corporations that provide arts
programming and/or services to Pennsylvania. Categories
include: broadcast of the arts, crafts, interdisciplinary arts,
dance, literature, local arts services, local government, media
arts, museums, music, presenting organizations, theater, and
visual arts. Nonprofit organizations may apply on behalf of an
unincorporated arts group. In this capacity, the organization
becomes a "conduit" for grant funds and is financially,
administratively, and programmatically responsible for a
grant.
Programs Available:
Grants To Artists Who Work In Schools (Arts In Residence)
Grants To Teach Literary, Performing Or Visual Arts (Arts In
Education Projects)
Grants To Arts Organizations And Artists (Local Government
Grants)
Grants To Underserved Artists (Pennsylvania Partners In The
Arts)
Grants To Cultural Arts Groups (Preserving Diverse Cultures)
Money To Hire A Consultant For Your Art Group
(Professional Development And Consulting)
$10,000 To Dancers, Jazz Composers, Writers And Artists
(Fellowships)
Money For New Arts Organizations And Projects (Entry
Track)
Money For Regular Arts Organizations And Programs (AOAP
Track)

Rhode Island
RI State Council on The Arts
83 Park Street, 6th Floor   401-222-3880
Providence, RI 02903   Fax: 401-222-3018
www.arts.ri.gov
Eligibility requirements: Applicants for the individual artist
programs must be eighteen years of age or older and have
lived in the state for at least one year prior to application.
Minimum grants awarded to organizations is $100 and funds
must be expended during the fiscal year of the award. Program

grants, with the exception of general operating support, are
divided into two categories. Level I grants range from $100 to
$2,000. Level II grants range from $2,001 to $5,000. A dollar
for dollar cash match is required.
Programs Available:
$3,000 For Artists, Choreographers, Designers, and
Printmakers (Fellowships)
$2,000 For Folk Art Apprenticeships (Folk Arts
Apprenticeships)
Grants To Art Organizations (Expansion Grants)
Money For Operating Expenses (General Operating Support)

South Carolina
South Carolina Arts Commission
1800 Gervais St.   803-734-8696
Columbia, SC 29201   Fax: 803-734-8526
www.state.sc.us/arts
Eligibility requirements: Individual artist programs require
state residency.
Programs Available:
$5,000 For Artists, Performers, Writers, And Craftsmen
(Fellowships)
$1,000 To Be Used For Professional Development (Quarterly
Grants)
Up To $500,000 To Arts Groups (General Support Grants)
Money To Bring Art Programs To Schools (Arts in the Basic
Curriculum)
Money For Schools To Have An Artist In Residence (Arts in
Education)
Grants To Non-Profit Organizations To Present Performances
Of South Carolina Artists (Community Tour)
Money For Organizations To Utilize Artistic and Cultural
Resources (Cultural Visions For Underserved
Communities Grant)
$7,500 To Support Programs That Promote Traditional Art
Forms (Folklife and Traditional Arts Program)
$2,000 For Qualified Master Artists To Instruct an Apprentice
(Folklife and Traditional Arts Apprenticeship Initiative)
Up To $3,000 To Support the Creation of a Five-Year Arts
Education Program (AIE Comprehensive Planning Grant)
Up To $20,000 To Help School Districts Create Arts
Curriculum Coordinator Positions (AIE District Arts
Coordinator Initiative Grant)

South Dakota
South Dakota Arts Council
800 Governors Dr.   605-773-3131
Pierre, SD 57501   Fax: 605-773-6962
www.state.sd.us/deca/sdarts
Eligibility requirements: Individual artist programs require
state residency. Applicant organizations and individuals are
funded up to 50% of projected costs. Funding is available in
the following arts disciplines: dance, music, opera/music
theater, theater, visual arts, design arts, crafts, photography,
media arts, literature, and folk arts.
Programs Available:
$500 For Arts Groups To Hire Consultants   (Technical
Assistance)
$500 For Art Group Managers To Improve Their Skills
(Professional Development)
Money For Touring Art Groups (Touring Arts)
Money For Schools To Have An Artist In Residence (Artists
in Schools)
Grants To Arts Institutions (Arts Challenge Grants)
Money To Present Music Programs In Native American
Communities (Music Residency Program)
$3,000 For Artists To Work On Specific Projects (Artist
Project Grants)
Money To Bring In Musicians Into Communities (Importation
of Musicians)

Matching Funds To Transport Students To Programs In
Another Town (Excursion Program)

Grants To Encourage Multi-State Collaboration (Artist
Collaboration Grants)

Funds Provide Master Artists the Opportunity to Teach
Qualified Apprenticeships (Traditional Arts
Apprenticeship Grants)

Tennessee

Tennessee Art Commission
401 Charlotte Ave.   615-741-1701
Nashville, TN 37243-0780   Fax: 615-741-8559
www.arts.state.tn.us

Eligibility requirements: Individual artist programs require
state residency.

Programs Available:

$2,500 For Artists, Musicians, Writers, And Dancers
(Individual Artists Fellowships)

Grants For Arts Organizations (Arts Build Communities)

$6,000 For Special Art Projects (Arts Projects)

Grants To Operate An Arts Organizations (General Operating
Support)

$2,500 To Hire Out-Of-Town Consultants
(Technical Assistance Program)

$10,000 For A Nonprofit Agency To Have An Artist In
Residence (Artists Residencies)

Grants To Art Organizations Of Color (Advancement And
Expansion)

Grants For Established Large Arts Organizations (Major
Cultural Institutions)

Grants For Activities In Rural Areas (Rural Arts Projects
Support)

Texas

Texas Commission on the Arts
920 Colorado, Suite 501
P.O. Box 13406
Capitol Station   512-463-5535
Austin, TX 78711-3406   Fax: 512-475-2699
www.arts.state.tx.us

Eligibility requirements: Texas does not offer direct funding
to individuals. Individual artists are funded indirectly through
the Arts in Education and the Touring Programs. In addition,
individual artists may apply to the Commission under the
umbrella of a nonprofit organization or government entity.

Programs Available:

$25,000 To Support Projects Demonstration Artistic Merit and
"Best Practices" in Arts Education (Arts Education)

$2,000 Funding For Strategic Development in Arts Education
(Arts Education Team Building)

$35,000 Support For Organizations To Present, Promote and
Produce Artistic Programs (Core Support Organizations
and Local Arts Agencies)

$3,000 To Encourage Non-Profit Organizations, Governments
and Schools in Rural Areas To Expand the Arts (County
Arts Expansion Program)

$2,000 Mini-Grants To Enhance the Growth of the Arts
Industry (Cultural Connections)

$15,000 To Ethnically-Specific/Minority Organizations That
Serve Ethnically-Specific/Minority Communities
(Development Assistance To Minority Organizations)

$7,500 To Prepare Art Exhibits (Exhibit Preparation To Tour)

$15,000 For Project Assistance (Project Support)

$35,000 For Administrative Support (Statewide Services)

$2,500 For 8th to 12th Graders to Attend Arts Programs
(Young Masters Program)

Utah

Utah Arts Council
617 E. South Temple   801-236-7555
Salt Lake City, UT 84102   Fax: 801-236-7556
http://arts.utah.gov

Eligibility requirements: Individual artist programs require
state residency, unless otherwise specified.

Programs Available:

$5,000 For Artists, Printmakers, Photographers, and Video
Artists (Visual Artist Fellowships)

$5,000 For Creative Writers (Creative Writing Award)

$2,000 For An Artist To Learn From A Master (Folk Arts
Apprenticeship Program)

Money For Schools To Have An Artist In Residence (Artist In
Residence)

$2,000 For Teachers In The Arts (Professional Development)

$12,000 For Arts Organizations And Museums
(Community Arts Program)

Grants For Arts Organizations (General Operating Support)

$12,000 For Artists Who Work In Underserved Communities
(AIE Underserved Communities)

Vermont

Vermont Council on Arts
136 State St., Dr 33   802-828-3291
Montpelier, VT 05633-6001   Fax: 802-828-3363
www.vermontartscouncil.org

Eligibility requirements: Individual artist programs require
state residency. Money available: $600,000.

Programs Available:

$15,000 For Arts Groups (Operating Grants)

Grants To Develop Art-Related Courses (Development
Grants)

$500 For Artists To Attend Classes And Workshops
(Development Grants)

$5,000 For Art Projects (Standard Project And Program)

$750 For New Art Projects (Incentive Project And Program)

$750 For Arts In Communities (Technical Assistance)

$7,000 To Arts Organizations (Opportunity Grants)

Money For Arts In Schools (Arts In Education Initiative)

Virginia

Virginia Commission for the Arts
Lewis House
223 Governor St.   804-225-3132
Richmond, VA 23219-2010   Fax: 804-225-4327
www.arts.state.va.us

Eligibility requirements: Individual artist programs require
state residency.

Programs Available:

$5,000 For Professional Artists To Advance Their Careers
(Project Grants)

$15,000 To Run An Arts Organization (General Operating
Support)

$750 To Hire Management Consultants (Technical Assistance
Grants)

$5,000 To Help Local Governments Support The Arts (Local
Government Challenge Grants)

Money For Artists To Tour The State (Touring Assistance
Programs)

Money For Schools To Have An Artist In Residence (Artist in
Education Residencies)

Grants For Community Colleges To Have An Artist In
Residence (Community College Artist Residencies)

Funding For Workshops and Consultants In Arts Education
(Arts in Education Development Grants)

$300 For Teachers To Develop Innovative Art Programs
(Teacher Incentive Grant Program)

Money To Hire Consultants Or Attend Conferences In Arts
Education (Arts In Education Technical Assistance)

Washington

Washington State Arts Commission
234 E. 8th Ave.
P.O. Box 42675　　　　　　　　360-753-3860
Olympia, WA 98504-2675　　　Fax: 360-586-5351
www.arts.wa.gov

Eligibility requirements: Individual artist programs require state residency.

Programs Available:

$5,000 To Professional Literary, Performing, and Two-Dimensional Artists (Artist Fellowship Awards)

Grants To Ethnic Heritage Artists (Governor's Ethnic Heritage Awards)

$2,000 For Short-Term Art Projects (Project Support)

$10,000 For Arts Organizations (Organizational Support)

Money To Support Arts Organizations (Institutional Support Program)

Money For Schools To Have An Artist In Residence (Artists in Residence Program (AIR))

Money For Communities To Build Strong Arts Programs (Arts Education Community Consortium Grant)

$500 To Attend Workshops (Professional Development Assistance Program)

Funds For Master Artists To Instruct Students (Apprenticeship Program)

West Virginia

Arts and Humanities Division
Division of Culture and History
Cultural Center
1900 Kanawha Blvd. East　　　　304-558-0240
Charleston, WV 25305-0300　　Fax: 304-558-2779
www.wvculture.org/arts

Money available: $2,431,110.

Programs Available:

Money For Individual Artists (Individual Artist Programs)

Money For The Professional Development Of Artists (Support for Artists Program)

$15,000 For An Art Exhibition (Presenting West Virginia Artists Program)

$125,000 For Art Organizations (Major Institutions Support Grant)

$25,000 For Theaters, Galleries, and Museums (Support for Arts Institutions/Arts Organizations)

Money To Fund Art Programs (Touring Program)

Money To Support New Works Of Composers, Playwrights, Writers, and Choreographers (Performing Arts)

Money to Develop Special Art Programs For Schools (Arts in Education)

Funds For Music, Theater and Dance Groups To Support Unique Production Costs With New Works (Support For New Productions)

Funds For Traditional Arts, Ethnic, Folk or Culturally Diverse Arts Festivals (Support The Festivals)

Grants For the Presentation of Arts Events Which Involve People With Disabilities (Access)

$1,000 To Present West Virginia Artists in Performances, Workshops and Other Projects (Mini-Grant Program)

Money For Special Educational Projects (Arts In Education: Special Projects)

Funding For Art Organizations To Expand Their "Arts Services" (Cultural Facilities and Capital Resources Grant)

Wisconsin

Wisconsin Arts Board
101 E. Wilson St., Suite 301　　　608-266-0190
Madison, WI 53702　　　　　　Fax: 608-267-0380
www.arts.state.wi.us

Eligibility requirements: Individual artist programs require state residency. For most programs, recipients must match state awards with cash or donated services.

Programs Available:

$8,000 For Artists, Writers, and Folk Artists (Fellowships)

$3,000 For Small Groups And Individual Artists (Small Organization Support)

Grants To Community Art Programs (Community Arts Program)

Support For The Performing Arts Network (Performing Arts Network (PAN)-Wisconsin)

Money For Organizations To Bring In Professional Touring Artists (Wisconsin Touring Program)

$5,000 For Folk Artists (Folk Arts Opportunity Grants)

Grants For Culturally Diverse Art Projects (Cultural Diversity Initiative)

Money For Schools To Have An Artist In Residence (Artists in Education Residency)

Money For Schools To Bring Artists Into The Classroom (Educational Opportunity Grants)

$3,000 To Encourage Collaborative Projects Between Artists and Their Communities (Artist and Community Collaboration)

Money To Provide Artistic, Program and Operational Support To Nonprofit Arts Institutes (Artistic Program Support)

Assistance To Arts Organizations To Leverage Income From Private Sources (Arts Challenge Initiative)

Wyoming

Wyoming Arts Council
2320 Capitol Ave.　　　　　　　307-777-7742
Cheyenne, WY 82002　　　　　Fax: 307-777-5499
http://wyoarts.state.wy.us

Eligibility requirements: Individual fellowships require state residency. For educational funding, grants require a one-to-one cash match.

Programs Available:

Grants For Arts Organizations (Organizational Funding)

Grants To Strengthen An Arts Organization (Technical Assistance)

Grants To Schools And Organizations To Plan Arts Programs (Art is Essential Grant)

Grants For Schools To Have An Artist In Residence (Artist In Residence Grants)

Money To Develop Art Courses In Schools (Project Grants)

$3,000 For Writers (Literary Awards)

$1,000 For Arts Projects (Community Services Program)

$500 For Arts Programs And Events (Open Door Grants)

$300 For Artists To Work In Communities (Arts Across Wyoming)

Money For Arts Organizations And Artists (Art Access)

$2,500 For Performers (Fellowship)

How To Start Or Become A Nonprofit Organization

Don't be Afraid...Read on!

Sound impossible? No way! Yes it can be bureaucratic and there's some red tape you'll have to wade through, but if you are a qualifying type of organization, getting nonprofit status is definitely the way to go, especially if you want to get grants from funding groups. Attaining nonprofit status for yourself as a group or organization may be critical in order to receive those grants that you are hoping will fund you, and it will only cost you a couple hundred dollars! Many grants are only available to nonprofits. So don't wince at the mention of what may sound like an overwhelming and daunting task. Dive in! It may be easier than you think.

First and foremost in establishing or creating a nonprofit is filing for Federal and state nonprofit tax status. Nonprofit status is not available to individuals, only to organizations, so your group must be incorporated or exist as an association or trust. To help you determine if your organization may qualify for tax-exempt status, or to find out what you will need to do in order to qualify, request Publication 557 from the local office of the Internal Revenue Service. This publication takes you step-by-step through the filing process, and contains instructions and checklists to help you provide all of the necessary information required to process your application the first time around. The fee to become exempt can be as low at $150! The IRS has even established a hotline at 877-829-5500 staffed with experts on completing the forms and can help you with any questions you may have. They can't make it any easier for you! You can also check out any questions you may have at {http://www.irs.ustreas.gov/charities/index.html}.

Most organizations seeking tax-exempt status from the Federal government must use either; Form 1023, Application for Recognition of Exemption Under Section 501(c) (3) of the Internal Revenue Code; Form 1024, Application for Recognition of Exemption Under Section 501(a) or for Determination Under Section 120. The forms will ask you to provide the following information:

➡ A description of the purposes and activities of your organization
➡ Financial information, and if you have not yet begun operation, a proposed budget, along with a statement of assets and liabilities (if you have any)
➡ Information on how you intend to finance your activities, through fundraisers, grants, etc.

Another great feature available directly from the IRS is the Tax-Exempt Organization Tax Kit. Basically it's a packet that contains all the necessary forms for filing for exemption status, all informational publications and even forms for filing your tax return, the various versions of Form 990, Return of Organization Exempt from Income Tax. These publications are downloadable, grouped together at the IRS website, within the Tax-Exempt section. They are also available by calling 800-TAX-FORM, toll-free.

Critical when filing for tax-exempt status, obviously, is to have an organization that has a darned good reason for asking for exemption. The IRS has separated the classifications of acceptable organizations into ten groups within which your potential organization may fall, thus possibly qualifying for exemption.

* Charitable Organizations
    - Charitable
    - Religious
    - Educational
    - Scientific
    - Literary
    - Testing for public safety
    - Fostering national or international amateur sports competition
    - Prevention of cruelty to children or animals

* Social Welfare Organizations
    - Civic Leagues
    - Community Organizations

* Labor and Agricultural Organizations
    - Labor Unions, Councils or Committees
    - Farm Bureaus
    - Agricultural and Horticultural Organizations

* Social Clubs
    - Hobby Clubs
    - Country Clubs

* Business Leagues
    - Trade Associations
    - Chambers of Commerce
    - Real Estate Boards
    - Professional Associations

* Fraternal Societies
    - Lodges and Similar Orders and Associations

* Veteran's Organizations
  - Posts or organizations of past or present members of the Armed forces of the United States

* Employees' Associations
  - Voluntary employees' benefit associations
  - Local associations of employees

* Political Organizations
  - Campaign committees
  - Political parties
  - Political action committees

* Other Tax-Exempt Organizations
  - Miscellaneous qualifying organizations

The organization must also have an Employer Identification Number (EIN), be in the process of applying, or apply directly while applying for exemption status. Form SS-4, Application for Employer Identification Number, gives detailed instructions on obtaining an EIN over the phone, online, by fax, or by mail. The form is downloadable from the IRS web site. Once you have your EIN enter it into your application for exemption form. Please note the correct IRS contact information for exempt organizations seeking an EIN.

If you have no legal residence, principal place of business, or principal office or agency in any state, contact:

> Internal Revenue Service
> Attn: EIN Operation
> Philadelphia, PA 19255
> 215-516-6999
> Fax-Tin: 215-516-3990
> www.irs.gov/pub/irs-pdf/fss4.pdf

If your principal business, office, agency, or, in the case of an individual, legal residence is located in Connecticut, Delaware, Washington District of Columbia, Florida, Georgia, Maine, Maryland, Massachusetts, New Hampshire, New Jersey, New York, North Carolina, Ohio, Pennsylvania, Rhode Island, South Carolina, Vermont, Virginia, or West Virginia contact:

> Internal Revenue Service
> Attn: EIN Operation
> P.O. Box 9003
> Holtsville, NY 11742-9003

800-829-4933
Fax: TIN 631-447-8960

If your principal business, office, agency, or, in the case of an individual, legal residence is located in Illinois, Indiana, Kentucky, or Michigan contact:

Internal Revenue Service
Attn: EIN Operation
Cincinnati, OH 45999
800-829-4933
Fax: TIN 859-669-5760

If your principal business, office, agency, or, in the case of an individual, legal residence is located in Alabama, Alaska, Arizona, Arkansas, California, Colorado, Hawaii, Idaho, Iowa, Kansas, Louisiana, Minnesota, Mississippi, Missouri, Montana, Nebraska, Nevada, New Mexico, North Dakota, Oklahoma, Oregon, Puerto Rico, South Dakota, Tennessee, Texas, Utah, Washington, Wisconsin, or Wyoming contact:

Internal Revenue Service
Attn: EIN Operation
Philadelphia, PA 19255
800-829-4933
Fax: TIN 215-516-3990

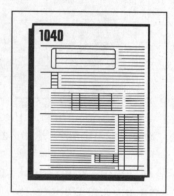

Call the business and specialty tax line for assistance applying for an EIN: 800-829-4933

The applications require detailed financial status. If it is a new organization, current financial statements must be provided along with projected budgets for the coming two years. Organizations in existence three years or more also must provide current information as well as detailed info from the last two years. Once you have submitted the necessary forms and fees, and all goes well, a ruling or determination letter should be on its way to you in no time.

To receive help and information directly from the IRS, contact your local office listed in the government pages of your telephone book or contact:

Exempt Organizations Technical Division
Internal Revenue Service
U.S. Department of Treasury
1111 Constitution Ave., NW, Room 6411   202-283-2300
Washington, DC 20224   {www.irs.gov}

Once you are granted tax-exempt status, you must move on to the task of filing new forms to account for your tax year. And careful, detailed accounting is a must. Filing your organization's Form 990, the IRS nonprofit tax return, requires some rigorous financial reporting. As a nonprofit organization, you must report carefully the following:

1. An object revenue & income statement, with particular categories specified (rental revenue),

2. A balance sheet, with particular categories specified like cash, accounts receivable, accounts payable (salaries, postage etc.),

3. A statement of functional expenses, in which all expenses are allocated to program services, fundraising, or operations,

4. A report of expenses segregated by individual program service (educational mailings, a seminar program),

5. A support schedule that details the organization's sources of revenue, with particular categories specified (charitable donations, membership fees, investment income).

Never fear! While it may sound confusing and tedious, there is hope! Luckily there is accounting software available to help you with your reporting. Sort of like Turbo Tax for nonprofits, these available software systems, if set up appropriately, can make your IRS reporting pretty easy. Thank goodness!

Although we do not recommend any particular accounting software, a simple Internet search turned up a wealth of software systems. Here is a sampling of what we found:

- NfpAcounting Technologies, 4540 Kearny Villa Road, Suite 221, San Diego, CA 92123; 800-273-1514; Fax: 858-499-8958; {www.nfpaccounting.com}.

- CYMA Systems, 2330 W. University Dr., Suite 7, Tempe, AZ 85281; 800-292-2962; 480-303-2962; Fax: 480-303-2969; {www.cyma.com}.

- Araize, 130 Iowa Lane, Suite 102, Cary, NC 27511; 800-745-4037; 919-319-1770; Fax: 919-460-5983; {www.araize.com}.

- ACI Associates, Inc., P.O. Box 1144, Frederick, MD 21702-0144; 800-966-6725; {www.automationc.com}.

- SunGard Bi-Tech, 890 Fortress St., Chico, CA 95973; 530-891-5281; Fax: 530-891-5011; {www.bitech.com}.

- Fund EZ Department Corp., 106 Corporate Park, White Plains, NY 10604; 877-696-0900; Fax: 914-696-0948; {www.fundez.com}.

- Intuit Foundation, 6430 Fiddlers Green Circle, Suite 500, Greenwood Village, CO 80111; 800-551-4458; Fax: 303-756-3514; {http://publicsector.intuit.com}.

- MIP, 313 East Anderson Lane, Suite 120, Austin, TX 78752; 800-647-3863; 512-454-1246; {www.mip.com}.

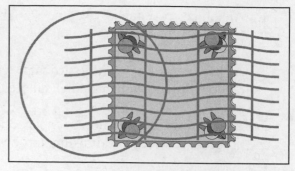

There are many advantages to becoming a nonprofit organization. An obvious one is getting reduced rates on things like postage. But the United States Postal Service may not consider your group a nonprofit just because you have tax-exempt status. There are many rules, regulations and restrictions. For example, nonprofits must fall into categories somewhat like the IRS categories listed above, and then they must file Form 3624 in order to have their request processed. The acceptable categories are: religious, agricultural, educational, labor, scientific, veterans, philanthropic and fraternal. For more information, forms for application and all the Post Office rules, visit the USPS website, {www.usps.gov} and search the Postal Explorer, for "nonprofit."

Another thing that some nonprofits are able to do is set up lobbying groups. Again, there can be substantial red tape involved. You must file forms with the IRS and be of a particular nature to qualify. Basically, nonprofits may lobby if they are publicly funded in some way, educational or hospital medical research organizations, or organizations supporting government schools. Any group lobbying in any inappropriate way will not be permitted to do so. If it goes beyond the limits and lobbying is substantial, (this usually determined by proportion of moneys spent), the organization is likely to lose its Federal tax-exempt status.

State Registration

As with any filing of a tax application or return, when you send in something to the Federal government, you need to notify your state government as well. Although it is the IRS that gives you the authority to raise money as a tax-exempt organization, your state government will want to know about the proposed activities of your organization. Relevant information that your state will be interested in includes:

- ➡ The name and address of registrant
- ➡ The purpose of the nonprofit
- ➡ Any articles of incorporation
- ➡ The names and addresses of any board of directors

In existence is something known as the Unified Registration Statement, (URS) which serves as a kind of standard form that most of the states in the country accept as the ample documentation to register within said state as a nonprofit organization. The state will also want to know how much of a tax-exempt contribution you expect to attain over the course of a year. Some states have maximum amounts before you must register, while others have no minimum. Some states' fees are based upon the amount of contributions, and some are flat fees. The usual fee for filing this information with most states is minimal, usually from $30.00 to $50.00, with some states requiring no fee, and others going much higher. Contact the appropriate state corporation office, listed on page 824 to obtain the necessary forms, and see the state listings below for more specific state-by-state information. The state will also require an annual financial report, and most will accept a completed Federal IRS report.

Don't forget that state and Federal laws are not the only ones to which nonprofit organizations are subject. Governments of smaller jurisdictions, such as counties, cities, municipalities, small towns, and really any form of governmental authority, can and do implement laws that may be stricter or at least different than their superior governments. Such an authority may require organizations to register specifically within their jurisdiction, in addition to all other state and Federal registrations. Any soliciting organizations, no matter where they are based, that make charitable solicitations to residents of these jurisdictions, and don't adhere to the local law and its associated regulations, may be subject to legal action by that jurisdiction's governmental authority.

State Registration Requirements

Alabama
Office of the Attorney General
Consumer Affairs Section
11 South Union St.
Montgomery, AL 36130
334-242-7335

800-392-5658
www.ago.state.al.us

Registration Requirements
State form or URS
IRS Determination Letter

Articles of Incorporation or charitable organizational charter
$25 Registration fee

Organizations exempt from registration:
Educational institutions and their authorized and related
foundations;
Religious organizations;
Political organizations;
Fraternal, patriotic, benevolent, social, educational, alumni,
heath care foundation, historical and civil rights
organizations, including fraternities and sororities;
Civic leagues and civic organizations, which solicit solely
from their own membership;
Any charitable organization which does not intend to solicit
and receive and does not actually receive contributions
in excess of $25,000 during the fiscal year, provided all
of its fundraising functions are carried on by persons
who are unpaid for their services;
Persons requesting any contributions collected for the relief
of a specific named individual if all contributions do
not exceed $10,000 and are turned over to the named
beneficiary;
Any post, camp, chapter of a bona fide veteran's
organization, or organization of volunteer firefighters,
ambulance companies, or rescue squads and affiliates of
those organizations, whose fundraising is done by
unpaid volunteers

Annual Reporting Requirements
Due within 90 days of fiscal year end
Annual written report in required format
Annual $25 filing fee
IRS 990 or financial report
Registration renewal required annually on or before
September 30th

Alaska
Attorney General
Alaska Department of Law
P.O. Box 110300
Juneau, AK 99811-0300
907-465-2133
Fax: 907-465-2075
www.law.state.ak.us

Registration Requirements
State form -(URS not accepted)
IRS Form 990
Audit
Due September 1st
$25 fee for registration

Organizations exempt from registration:
Religious organizations;
Charitable organizations that do not intend to or do not raise
or receive contributions, excluding government grants,
in excess of $5,000 during a fiscal year;
Organizations that do not receive contributions from more
than ten (10) persons during a fiscal year if either, 1) all
functions, including solicitation, are carried on by
volunteers and/or, 2) an officer or member of the
organization is not paid or does not otherwise receive
all or part of the assets or income of the charitable
organization

Annual Reporting Requirements
There are no annual reporting requirements once an
organization is registered.

Arizona
Secretary of State
Charitable Organizations
1700 West Washington, 7th Floor
Phoenix, AZ 85007-2888
602-542-6670, or toll-free 800-458-5842
www.sos.state.az.us

Registration Requirements
State Form A.R.S 44-6552 - (URS not accepted)
IRS Form 990

Organizations exempt from registration:
A charitable organization that is established and operated
within Arizona exclusively for a charitable purpose and
that has a board of directors that serves without
remuneration, if the solicitations are conducted under
any of the following conditions 1) by volunteers who
receive no remuneration or 2) by bona fide paid
employees or 3) at meetings or assemblies of the
membership or with individual members;
Nonprofit hospitals and their foundations;
Nonprofit blood banks and their foundations;
Schools, colleges and universities, their associations and
foundations;
Licensed public radio and TV stations that are raising monies
for their own operations;
Solicitations solely from private foundations;
Political parties, candidates and campaign committees
required to file financial information with election
commissions or agencies;
Organizations soliciting contributions not exceeding $25,000;

Annual Reporting Requirements
State financial report form

Arkansas
Office of Attorney General
Consumer Protection Division
Fund Raiser Registration
323 Center St., #200
Little Rock, AR 72201-2610
501-682-6150, or toll-free 800-482-8982
www.ag.state.ar.us

Registration Requirements
State Registration Form or URS
IRS Form 990, or
IRS Form 990-Ez and AR Attachment to IRS Form 990, or
Annual Report of Charitable Organization
IRS Determination letter
Copy of Irrevocable Consent for Service
No registration fee required

Organizations exempt from registration:
Nonprofits raising less than $25,000 per year with no paid
staff or fundraisers;
Religious organizations;
Accredited educational institutions and parent-teacher
associations associated with accredited institutions;
Governmental organizations -departments, branches or
instrumentality of federal, state and local governments;
Nonprofit hospitals licensed in AR or any other state;
Political candidates and organization - any candidate for
national, state, or local office or a political party or
other committee required to file information with the
Federal Election Commission or any other state election
commission

Annual Reporting Requirements

Due Date on or before May 15th or within 6 months after close of fiscal year

No annual filing fee

IRS 990 -EZ or annual report

Audit required for organizations with gross revenue in excess of $500,000

California

State of California
Office of Attorney General
Registry of Charitable Trusts
P.O. Box 903447
Sacramento, CA 94203-4470
916-445-2021
http://caag.state.ca.us/charities

Registration Requirements

State Form CT-1 or URS
Certificate/Articles of Incorporation
Bylaws
IRS Form 990
IRS Determination Letter

Organizations exempt from registration:

Religious corporations;
Religious organizations;
Government agencies;
Political committees;
Schools and hospitals

Annual Reporting Requirements

Due January 15th
Form RRF-1
$25 for organizations with assets or revenue exceeding $100,000 during fiscal year
IRS 990
Financial Report

Colorado

Colorado Secretary of State
Business Division
1560 Broadway, Suite 200
Denver, CO 80202-5169
303-894-2200
Fax: 303-869-4864
www.sos.state.co.us

Registration Requirements

State Form 300
IRS Form 990
Filing fee $50

Organizations Exempt from Registration

Churches
Political parties
Charitable organizations that raise less than $25,000 in a fiscal year
Charitable organizations that receive contributions from less than 10 persons during a fiscal year

Annual Reporting Requirements

Fee is $25 for filing on paper
Fee is $10 to file online
The report is due to the Secretary of State within two months following the month in which it is due to a reporting entity

Connecticut

Office of Attorney General
Public Charities Unit
55 Elm St.
Hartford, CT 06106-1746
860-808-5030
www.cslib.org/attygenl/

Registration Requirements

State Form CPC-63 or URS
One-time filing fee of $20.00

Organizations exempt from registration:

Nonprofits normally receiving less than $25,000 annually provided organization does not compensate any person primarily to conduct solicitations;
Religious corporations, institutions, and societies;
Parent-teacher associations or accredited educational institution;
Nonprofit hospitals licensed under laws of CT or another state;
Government units or instrumentalities of any state or the United States;

Organizations seeking an exemption must file Form CPC-54, "Claim of Exemption From Registration" (no fee required)

Annual Reporting Requirements

Due Date: Within 5 months of the fiscal year end
Form CPC-60, Annual Report Sheet
IRS Form 990
$25.00 filing fee
Audit if gross receipts (excluding government grants and fees) exceeds $100,000

Delaware

There is no registration requirement in Delaware at this time.

District of Columbia

Department of Consumer & Regulatory Affairs
941 N Capital St. NE, Room 7211
Washington, DC 20002-4259
202-442-4400
TDD: 202-442-9480
http://dcra.dc.gov/

Registration Requirements

District form or URS
Certificate/Articles of Incorporation
Bylaws
IRS Form 990
IRS Determination Letter

Organizations exempt from registration:

Organizations receiving less than $1,500 in gross total receipts in a calendar year, provided individuals who are unpaid carry out all functions, including fundraising;
Educational organizations raising money for educational purposes;
Church or religious corporations or organizations under the control of a church or religious corporation;
The American Red Cross;
Organizations where solicitations are made exclusively among the membership of the soliciting agency

Please note that exempt organizations are required to file a claim to that exemption.

Annual Reporting Requirements
Due April 15th
$25 filing fee
Financial report

Florida
Florida Dept. of Agriculture & Consumer Services
The Capitol
407 S. Calhoun
Tallahassee, FL 32399-0800
850-488-3022
www.doacs.state.fl.us

Registration Requirements
State form - (URS not accepted)
IRS Form 990 or financial report on state form
IRS Determination letter
Fees range from $10-$400

Organizations exempt from registration:
Anyone soliciting for a named individual, provided all contributions collected without any deductions are turned over to the beneficiary;
Charitable organizations, which limit solicitation of contributions to the membership of the organization

Annual Reporting Requirements
There is no reporting requirement after registration, which must be renewed annually.

Georgia
Secretary of State
Securities and Business Regulation
Suite 802, West Tower
2 Martin Luther King Jr. Dr.
Atlanta, GA 30334
404-656-3920
Fax: 404-657-8410
www.sos.state.ga.us

Registration Requirements
State Form C100 or URS
IRS Form 990
IRS Determination Letter
$25 Registration fee
Audit if gross revenue over $1,000,000
Financial report reviewed by a CPA for organizations with revenue between $500,000 and $1,000,000

Organization exempt from registration:
Nonprofit educational institutions;
Professional, business and trade associations that do not solicit members or funds from the general public;
Fraternal, civic, benevolent, patriotic and social organizations if solicitations are carried on by persons for their services and are confined to their memberships;
Any solicitations for a named person where all contributions are turned over to named person;
Charitable organizations whose total gross revenue is less than $25,000
Any local or state organization of hunters, fishermen and target shooters having tax-exempt status
Political parties, action committees and candidates for federal or state office who are required to file financial information to election commissions;
Publishers of commercial publications that solicit advertisement and provide a percentage of revenue for a charitable purpose

Please note that proof of exemption is required.

Annual Reporting Requirements
Due within one year of filing
$25 renewal/filing fee
IRS 990
Financial report required if proceeds are $500,000 or more (CPA); independent CPA review required for proceeds of $100,000 to $500,000
Audit required if revenue is over $1,000,000

Hawaii
There is no registration required in Hawaii at this time.

Idaho
There is no registration required in Idaho at this time.

Illinois
Office of the Illinois Attorney General
Charitable Trust and Solicitations Bureau
100 West Randolph Street, 11th Floor
Chicago, IL 60601-3175
312-814-2595
TTY: 312-814-3374
www.ag.state.il.us/

Registration Requirements
State Form CO-1 or URS
Certificate/Articles of Incorporation
Bylaws
IRS Form 990
IRS Determination Letter
Audit if over $150,000 in gross revenue
$15 Registration fee
Financial report on state Form CO-2

Organizations exempt from registration:
Government agencies or subdivisions;
Educational institutions;
Religious organizations

Annual Reporting Requirements
Due within 6 months of close of fiscal year
$15 filing fee ($100 late fee if registration expires)
IRS 990
Financial report on state Form AG990-IL
Audit if revenue over is $150,000 or professional fundraiser used

Indiana
There is no registration required in Indiana at this time.

Iowa
There is no registration required in Iowa at this time.

Kansas
Secretary of State
First Floor, Memorial Hall
120 SW 10th Avenue
Topeka, KS 66612-1594
785-296-4564
www.kssos.org

Registration Requirements
State Form SC or URS
Certificate/Articles of Incorporation

IRS Form 990
IRS Determination Letter
Audit if contributions exceed $100,000.

Organizations exempt from registration:
Any religious corporation, trust or organization;
Accredited educational institutions or any of their foundations;
Any other educational institution confining its solicitation to the student body, alumni, faculty and trustees;
Fraternal, social, alumni organizations and historical societies when solicitation is confined to their membership;
Any organization, which does not receive contributions in excess of $10,000 per year

Annual Reporting Requirements
Due within 6 months of fiscal year end
$20 filing fee
IRS 990 (or financial report)
Audit if contributions exceed $100,000

Kentucky
Office of Attorney General
The Capitol, Suite 118
700 Capitol Avenue
Frankfort, KY 40601-3449
502-696-5300
Fax: 502-864-2894
http://ag.ky.gov/

Registration Requirements
State form or URS
IRS Form 990

Organizations exempt from registration:
Organization soliciting contributions solely of its members and their families;
Religious organizations soliciting funds for religious purposes;
Accredited educational institutions soliciting contributions from alumni, faculty, students and families

Annual Reporting Requirements
Must be filed between January 1 and June 30 in the year following the year in which the corporation was incorporated
$50 filing fee
IRS 990, unless no 990 yet filed with the IRS

Louisiana
Dept. of Justice
Public Protection Division
Livingston Building
1885 N. Third Street
Baton Rouge, LA 70802
225-326-6400
Fax: 225-326-6497
www.ag.state.la.us

Registration Requirements
URS
IRS Determination letter
Certificate/Articles of Incorporation
Bylaws
Financial statement
Copies of Contracts with professional solicitors
List of all states where organization is registered
$25 Registration fee

Organizations exempt from registration:
Any charitable organization not utilizing the services of professional fundraisers;
Religious organizations, including exempt from federal income tax under IRS 501(c)(3), if not primarily supported by funds solicited outside its own membership or congregation; Educational institutions recognized or approved by the Louisiana Dept. of Education; Voluntary health organizations organized under Louisiana or federal law.

Annual Reporting Requirements
Due on the anniversary of annual registration
$25 renewal fee
IRS 990

Maine
Department of Prof. & Financial Regulation
Charitable Solicitation Registration
35 State House Station
Augusta, ME 04333-0007
207-624-8500
Fax: 207-624-8690
TTY: 207-624-8563
www.state.me.us/pfr/pfrhome.htm

Registration Requirements
State of Maine Charitable Organization Registration Form or URS
IRS Form 990
IRS Determination Letter
$20 Articles of Incorporation

Organizations exempt from registration:
Organizations that solicit primarily within their membership and where members conduct solicitation activities;
Organizations that do not receive contributions from the public in excess of $10,000 or do not receive contributions from more than 10 people during the calendar year, if fundraising is carried on by volunteers;
Educational institutions registered or approved by Dept. of Education;
Hospitals that are nonprofit and charitable;
Persons soliciting contributions for the relief of any individual specified by name at the time of the solicitation where all contributions go directly to said person for individual's use.

Organizations claiming exemptions must submit a copy of form letter from IRS, any other appropriate financial statements and a $10 fee.

Annual Reporting Requirements
Due by November 30th
Annual Report $20 fee
IRS 990
Financial Report may be submitted instead of IRS 990
Audit required if gross revenue is more than $30,000

Maryland
Office of the Secretary of State
Charitable Organizations Division
State House
Annapolis, MD 21401
800-825-4510
410-974-5534
www.sos.state.md.us

Registration Requirements
State Form COR-92 or URS
Certificate/Articles of Incorporation
Bylaws
IRS Form 990
IRS Determination Letter
Financial review (if revenue is between $100,000 and 200,000)
Audit (if gross income from charitable contributions equals or exceeds $200,000)
Fee ranging from $50-$200

Organizations exempt from registration:
Religious organizations;
Organizations soliciting funds from their own memberships
Organizations that raise less than $25,000

Please note that organizations claiming exemption must provide evidence of its exemption.

Annual Reporting Requirements
Due within 6 months of fiscal year end
$300 report fee
IRS 990
Financial review (conducted by independent CPA if gross income from charitable contributions is greater than $100,000 but less than $200,000)
Audit (by an independent CPA if gross income from charitable contributions is greater than $200,000)

Massachusetts
The Commonwealth of Massachusetts
Office of Attorney General
Division of Public Charities
One Ashburton Place, Room 1413
Boston, MA 02108-1698
617-727-2200
TTY: 617-727-4765
www.ago.state.ma.us
For fax numbers in the Boston area office, please call and explain your request to the switchboard, who will direct you to the proper division for assistance, where you can be given the specific fax number.

Registration Requirements
State form Short Form- Schedule A-2 or URS
Certificate/Articles of Incorporation
Bylaws
$50 Registration fee

Organizations exempt from registration:
Religious;
The Red Cross and certain veteran's organizations

Annual Reporting Requirements
Due within 4 1/2 months of fiscal year end
Annual filing fees range from $35-250
IRS 990
Financial report - must use MA Form PC
Audit if revenue exceeds $100,000

Michigan
Department of Attorney General
Charitable Trust Section
P.O. Box 30214
Lansing, MI 48909-7714
517-373-1152
www.michigan.gov/ag

Registration Requirements
State forms or URS
Certificate/Articles of Incorporation
Bylaws
IRS Form 990
IRS Determination Letter

Organization exempt from registration:
Religious organizations with tax-exempt status;
Educational institutions certified by the state board of education;
Veterans groups organized under federal law;
Licensed nonprofit hospitals and their foundations and auxiliaries;
Organizations that receive less than $8,000 per year and pay no individuals;
Solicitations that are exclusively for the benefit of a named individual;
Private foundations that receive only from members, directors, incorporators, or their family members.
Governmental entities;
Service Clubs;
Organizations licensed by the state to serve children and families;
Organizations whose sole source of funding is another licensed charity

Please note that organizations seeking exemption must file a questionnaire before determination of exemption.

Annual Reporting Requirements
Due 30 days prior to registration expiration.
IRS 990
Financial Report.
Audit if revenue is over $250,000, financial review required if revenue is between $100,000 and $250,000

Minnesota
Office of Attorney General
Charities Unit, Suite 1200, NCL Tower
445 Minnesota St.
St. Paul, MN 55101-2130
651-296-8019
TTY: 651-296-1410
www.ag.state.mn.us

Registration Requirements
State registration form or URS
Certificate/Articles of Incorporation
IRS Form 990
IRS Determination Letter
$25 Registration fee

Organizations exempt from registration:
Organizations that do not employ paid staff of professional fundraisers and that do not receive or plan to receive more than $25,000 in one year;
Religious organizations exempt from filing IRS Form 990;
Certain educational institutions;
Organizations limiting solicitations to persons who have a right to vote as a member;

Annual Reporting Requirements
Due by July 15 or the 15th day of the 7th month of the charity's fiscal year
Financial statement (Atty. Gen. Annual Report form)
IRS 990, 990-EZ, or 990-PF
Audit if revenue exceeds $350,000
$25 renewal fee

Mississippi

Mississippi Secretary of State
Charities Registration
P.O. Box 136
Jackson, MS 39205-0136
601-359-1633 or (toll free) 888-236-6167
www.sos.state.ms.us

Registration Requirements
State forms additional to URS- "Supplement to URS"
    including Annual Financial Reporting form
IRS Form 990
IRS Determination Letter
Certificate/Articles of Incorporation
Bylaws
$50.00 registration fee
Audit required if gross revenues over $100,000 (or over
    $25,000, if a professional fundraiser is used), or request
    for audits may occur on a case-by-case basis for
    registrants between $25,000 and $100,000.

Organizations exempt from registration:
Accredited educational institutions;
Educational institutions that solicit solely from students,
    alumni, faculty, trustees and families;
Fraternal, patriotic, social, educational alumni organizations
    and historical societies when solicitation of
    contributions is made solely by their membership;
Any charitable organization that does not intend to solicit and
    receive and does not actually receive contributions in
    excess of $4,000 provided persons who are unpaid for
    such services carry on all fundraising functions

Organizations seeking exemption must file Form CE.

Annual Reporting Requirements
Reporting must be done on the URS and by doing so, renew
    registration and submit financial report simultaneously
Due at anniversary of original registration
$50.00 filing fee
IRS 990
Financial Report
Audit if gross revenues exceed $100,000 (or over $25,000, if
    a professional fundraiser is used). Audits may be
    requested on a case-by-case basis for registrants
    between $25,000-$100,000

Missouri

Missouri Attorney General
P.O. Box 899
207 West High Street
Jefferson City, MO 65102-0899
573-751-3321
Fax: 573-751-0774
www.moago.org

Registration Requirements
State registration Form 1-A or URS
Articles of Incorporation
IRS Form 990
IRS Determination Letter
$15 initial Registration fee, $50 thereafter

Organizations exempt from registration:
Religious organizations;
Educational institutions and their authorized and related
    foundations;
Fraternal organizations provided solicitations are limited to
    membership of such organizations;

Hospitals, provided fundraising not done by professional
    fundraiser;
All 501(c) 3, 501(c) 7 and 501(c)(8) organizations that have
    obtained and can document such status from the federal
    government

Annual Reporting Requirements
Due within 2 1/2 months of fiscal year end
$50 annual fee, after initial $15
IRS 990
Financial Report

Montana

There is no registration required in Montana at this time.

Nebraska

There is no registration required in Nebraska at this time.

Nevada

There is no registration required in Nevada at this time.

New Hampshire

Department of Justice
Charitable Trust Division
33 Capitol St.
Concord, NH 03301-6397
603-271-3591
http://webster.state.nh.us/nhdoj/

Registration Requirements
State forms or URS
Conflict-of-interest policy
Certificate/Articles of Incorporation
Bylaws
IRS Form 990.
IRS Determination Letter
$25 Registration fee

Organizations exempt from registration:
Religious organizations

Annual Reporting Requirements
Due within 4 1/2 months of fiscal year end
Financial report on state Form NHCT-2A or
IRS 990 or
IRS 990-EZ or
IRS 990-PF

New Jersey

N.J. Division of Consumer Affairs
Charities Registration Section
124 Halsey Street, 7th Floor
P.O. Box 45021
Newark, NJ 07101
973-504-6215
www.state.nj.us/lps/ca/home.htm

Registration Requirements
State Form CRI-200, CRI-150I, CRI-300R or URS
Certificate/Articles of Incorporation
Bylaws
IRS Form 990
IRS Determination Letter

Organizations exempt from registration:
Religious organizations;
Educational institutions filing their curricula with the Dept. of Education

Annual Reporting Requirements
Due within 6 months of fiscal year end
Filing fees range from $0-$200
IRS 990
Financial report certified by authorized officer of organization if revenue under $100,000
Audit for revenue $100,000 and over

New Mexico
Office of Attorney General
Charitable Organization Registry
111 Lomas Blvd., NW, Suite 300
Albuquerque, NM 87102
505-222-9000
509-222-9090
www.ago.state.nm.us

Registration Requirements
State form or URS
Certificate/Articles of Incorporation
IRS Form 990
IRS Determination Letter
Audit if total revenue is in excess of $500,000

Organizations exempt from registration:
Any church or group organized for the purpose of worship, religious teaching, or other religious activity;
A school, college or other institution with a defined curriculum, student body and (faculty, conducting classes on a regular basis;
Charitable organizations that receive less than $2,500 per year in contributions;
Local affiliates of statewide or national organizations for which all local fundraising expenses are paid by a registered parent organization

Annual Reporting Requirements
Due within 6 months of fiscal year
IRS 990
Financial Report may be submitted instead of 990
Audit if total revenue is in excess of $500,000

New York
Department of Law, Charities Bureau
120 Broadway 3rd Floor
New York, NY 10271
212-416-8000
www.oag.state.ny.us/

Registration Requirements:
State form CHAR410 or URS
Certificate/Articles of Incorporation
Bylaws
IRS Form 990
IRS Determination Letter
Audit if over $250,000 in revenues (CPA review if between $150,000-$250,000).
$25.00 Registration fee

Organizations exempt from registration
Religious agencies and organizations and charities operated, supervised, or controlled in connection with a charity organized under the Religious Corporations Law;

Educational institutions confining solicitations to student body, alumni, faculty and trustees and their families;
Fraternal, patriotic, social and alumni organizations and historical societies chartered by Board of Regents when soliciting memberships;
Organization receiving $25,000 or less and not paying professional fundraisers;
Local post, camp, chapter or county unit of a veteran's organization;
Educational institutions or libraries that file annual financial reports with Regents of University of State of New York or with an agency having similar jurisdiction in another state
Estates or trusts
Cemetery corporations
Parent teacher associations

Please note that even exempt organizations must submit Form CHAR006, which must be filed annually.

Annual Reporting Requirements
Due date 41/2 months after fiscal year end
Fees $10 or $25 depending on revenue generated
IRS 990
Financial Report - must be reviewed by CPA if revenue $100,001-$250,000.
Audit if revenue $250,000 and over

North Carolina
Department of Secretary of State
Division of Facility Services/
Solicitations Licensing Section
2 S. Salisbury St.
P.O. Box 29622
Raleigh, NC 27626-0622
919-907-2214
800-830-4989
www.secstate.state.nc.us

Registration Requirements
State form- (URS not accepted)
Certificate/Articles of Incorporation
Bylaws
IRS Form 990
IRS Determination Letter
Fees range from $0-$200

Organizations exempt from registration:
Any person that solicits for a religious organization;
Solicitations of charitable contributions by the federal, State or local governments or their agencies;
Any person who receives less than 25,000 in contributions in a calendar year and does not provide compensation to any officer, trustee, organizer, incorporator, fund-raiser or solicitor;
Any educational institution, the curriculum of which, in whole or in part, is registered, approved, or accredited by the Southern Assoc. of Colleges and Schools or an equivalent regional accrediting body, and any foundation or department having an established identity with any of these educational institutions;
Any licensed hospital and any foundation or department having established identity with that hospital if the governing board of the hospital, authorizes the solicitation and receives an accounting of the funds collected and expended;
Any noncommercial radio or television station;
A qualified community trust;

A bona fide volunteer fire department, rescue squad, or
emergency medical service;

A YMCA or YWCA;

A nonprofit continuing-care facility;

An attorney, investment counselor, or banker who advises a
person to make a charitable contribution

Annual Reporting Requirements

Due within 4 1/2 months of end of fiscal year
Fees range from $50-$200
IRS 990 or financial report

North Dakota

Secretary of State
State of North Dakota
600 E. Boulevard Ave., Dept. 108
Bismarck, ND 58505-0500
701-328-3665
800-352-0867 ext.83665
Fax: 701-328-1620
www.state.nd.us/sec

Registration Requirements

State Form SFN 11300, ($25 fee) and SFN 7974 ($10 fee) in
addition to URS

State Articles of Incorporation for Nonprofit Form SFN
13003 ($30 fee)

IRS Form 990

Organizations exempt from registration:

A duly constituted religious organization, or any group
affiliated with and forming an integral part of that
organization that has tax-exempt status from the
government of the United States;

Organizations soliciting funds for institutions of higher
learning;

Private or public elementary or secondary school;

Charitable organizations using only volunteer unpaid
fundraisers and soliciting funds for a political sub-
division or other government entity or for a civic or
community project with no contributions benefiting any
individual;

Candidates for national, state and local elective office or
political party or other committee required to file
information with the federal or state election
commission or similar agency

Annual Reporting Requirements

Due February 1st
$10 filing/renewal fee
Annual report /renewal application on required Form SFN
11302A

Ohio

Office of the Attorney General
Charitable Law Section
150 East Gay Street, 23rd Floor
Columbus, OH 43215-3130
614-466-3180
www.ag.state.oh.us

Registration Requirements

State forms or URS
Certificate/Articles of Incorporation
Bylaws
IRS Form 990
IRS Determination Letter
Registration fees range from $0-$200

Organizations exempt from registration:

Any religious agencies and organizations, and charities,
agencies, and organizations operated, supervised, or
controlled by a religious organization;

Any educational institution, when solicitation of
contributions is confined to alumni, faculty, trustees, or
students and their families;

Any organization that does not receive gross revenue,
excluding grants or awards from the government or a
501(c)(3) organization, in excess of $25,000 and does
not compensate any person primarily to solicit;

Every person other than an individual, when solicitation of
contributions for a charitable purpose or on behalf of a
charitable organization is confined to its members,
present and former employees, or present and former
trustees

Annual Reporting Requirements

Due within 4 1/2 months of fiscal year end
Fee: $50 -$200
IRS 990 or financial report (Attorney General's Form)

Oklahoma

Office of the Secretary of State
2300 N. Lincoln, Room 101
Oklahoma City, OK 73105-4897
405-521-3911
www.sos.state.ok.us

Registration Requirements

State form or URS
IRS Form 990
IRS Determination letter
Financial statement (SOS Form 0102)
$15 Registration fee

Organizations exempt from registration:

Organizations formed for religious purposes and other
organizations directly operated, supervised, or
controlled by a religious organization;

Educational institutions which have a faculty and regularly
enrolled students, and offer courses of study leading to
the granting of recognized degrees when solicitations of
contributions are limited to students and their families,
alumni, faculty, and trustees;

Fraternal organizations, when soliciting from their own
members, and patriotic and civic organizations, when
solicitations of contributions are confined to
membership of said organization and managed by
membership without paid solicitors;

Persons soliciting contributions for the relief of a named
person where all contributions are turned over to named
beneficiary;

Any organization, which collects from charitable solicitations
less than $10,000/year

Annual Reporting Requirements

Due by March 31st or with annual registration renewal
Fee: $15
IRS 990
Financial report (state form required)

Oregon

Oregon Dept. of Justice
Charitable Activities
1515 SW 5th Ave. #410
Portland, OR 97201
503-229-5725
Fax: 503-229-5120

TDD: 503-378-5938
www.doj.state.or.us
Email: charitable.activities@doj.state.or.us

Registration Requirements
State registration Form RF-C or URS
IRS Determination letter
Certificate/Articles of Incorporation
Bylaws
No registration fees required

Organizations exempt from registration:
Cemetery corporations
Child-caring agencies regulated by the Department of Human Services
Foreign corporations or foundations making only grants or donations in the state of OR
Government agencies or sub-divisions
Post-secondary educational institutions holding no property in OR with individual solicitations confined to alumni
Religious organizations holding property solely for religious purposes
Corporations organized in Oregon as mutual benefit, nonprofit corporation
Organizations which are not incorporated and are not a trust

Annual Reporting Requirements
Due within 4 1/2 months of fiscal year end
Form CT-12, CT-12F, or CT-12S
Filing fees from $10.00-$200.00
IRS 990
Financial Report

Pennsylvania
Department of State
Bureau of Charitable Orgs.
207 N. Office Building
P.O. Box 8723
Harrisburg, PA 17120
800-732-0999
717-783-1720
Fax: 717-783-6014
www.dos.state.pa.us

Registration Requirements
State forms or URS
IRS Form 990
IRS Determination Letter
Audit required in certain cases
Certificate/Articles of Incorporation
Bylaws
Annual Registration Fees: ($15-$250)

Organizations exempt from registration:
Organizations of law enforcement personnel, firefighters, or other persons who protect public safety, not benefiting any person outside active membership of organization;
Religious institutions and separate groups or corporations that form an integral part that are tax exempt and primarily supported by fees charged for services rendered, government grants or contracts, or solicitations from their own memberships, congregations, or previous donors;
Accredited educational institutions and any associations, foundations and support groups that are directly responsible to educational institutions;
Hospitals subject to regulation by the Dept. of Health or Dept. of Public Welfare and any foundation, which is an integral part;

Nonprofit libraries that file an annual fiscal report with the state library system;
Senior citizen centers and nursing homes that are nonprofit, charitable and tax exempt, and have all fundraising activities carried out by volunteers;
Organizations raising $25,000 or less annually that do not compensate anyone;
Local post, camp, or chapter of any veterans' organization chartered under federal law and any service foundations recognized in their by-laws.

Annual Reporting Requirements
Due 135 days after end of fiscal year
Fee: $15-$250
IRS 990
Financial Report reviewed by CPA if contributions $25,000-$100,000
Audit if contributions $125,000 or more

Rhode Island
Department of Business Regulation
Securities Division,
233 Richmond St #232
Providence, RI 02903-4232
401-222-3048
401-222-8246
Fax: 401-222-6098
www.dbr.state.ri.us

Registration Requirements
State form or URS
IRS Form 990
Audit if annual gross budget exceeds $500,000
$75 Registration fee
IRS Determination Letter

Organizations exempt from registration:
Religious organizations;
Institutions indirectly affiliated with any religious organization that maintain and operate homes for the aged, orphans or unwed mothers;
Accredited educational institutions;
Organizations raising $25,000 or less in a calendar year, whose fundraising activities are carried on by volunteers;
Nonprofit hospitals;
Organizations soliciting contributions solely from their membership;
Public libraries;
Veteran's organizations and their auxiliaries;
Public art museums

Please note that organizations must file annually for exemptions.

Annual Reporting Requirements
Due on anniversary of registration
$75 filing/renewal fee
IRS 990
Financial Report
Audit if proceeds exceed $100,000

South Carolina
Office of the Secretary of State
Public Charities Section
P.O. Box 11350
Columbia, SC 29211
803-734-1728
www.scsos.com

Registration Requirement
State form or URS
IRS Determination letter
$50 Registration fee

Organizations exempt from registration:
Organizations expecting less than $20,000 in contributions, that have no paid staff, and have tax-exempt status;
Veteran's organizations chartered by Congress;
Membership organizations for which there are specific qualification for joining Other than paying dues)
Educational institutions
Political subdivisions of the state
Organizations established by persons requesting relief of an individual specified by name
Organizations which raise less than $5,000 in a calendar year

Annual Reporting Requirements
Due within 5 1/2 months of fiscal year
$50 filing/renewal fee
IRS 990
Financial Report (may be submitted instead of 990)

South Dakota

There is no registration required in South Dakota at this time.

Tennessee

Secretary of State
Charitable Solicitations
312 Eighth Avenue North
8th Floor, William R. Snodgrass Tower
Nashville, TN 37243-0308
615-741-2555
www.state.tn.us/sos/

Registration Requirements
State forms SS-6001 or URS, and SS-6002
Certificate/Articles of Incorporation
Bylaws
IRS Form 990
IRS Determination Letter
Audit if gross revenue over $300,000
$50 filing fee

Organizations exempt from registration:
Churches;
Educational institutions, their booster clubs, parent organizations and affiliated groups;
Volunteer fire departments, rescue squads and local civil defense organizations;
Organizations raising less than $30,000 in gross contributions during their fiscal year

Annual Reporting Requirements
Due within 6 months of fiscal year end
Fees range from $100 -$300
IRS 990
Financial Report required when revenue is more than $100,000
Audit unless proceeds do not exceed $300,000

Texas

There is no registration required in Texas at this time.

Utah

Department of Commerce
Division of Consumer Protection
160 East 300 South
P.O. Box 146704
Salt Lake City, UT 84114-6704
801-530-6601
800-721-SAFE
Fax: 801-530-6001
www.commerce.utah.gov/dcp/

Registration Requirements
State form- URS accepted if you include the Supplement to Unified Registration Statement
$100 registration
Certificate/Articles of Incorporation
Bylaws
IRS Form 990
IRS Determination Letter
Audit
Renewal required annually on the 1st of January, April, July, or October following the completion of 12 months after initial registration

Organizations exempt from registration:
A solicitation that an organization conducts among its own bona fide membership exclusively through the voluntary efforts of other members or officers of the organization;
A bona fide religious, ecclesiastical, or denominational organization if 1) the solicitation is for a church, missionary, religious or humanitarian purpose and 2) the organization is a physical place of worship where nonprofit religious services and activities are regularly conducted and carried on OR a bona fide religious group that does not maintain a specific place of worship, that is not subject to federal income tax and not required to file an IRS Form 990 under any circumstance OR a separate group or corporation that is an integral part of an institution that is income tax exempt and is not primarily supported by funs solicited outside its own membership or congregation;
A broadcast media owned or operated by an educational institution or governmental entity;
Any school or institution of higher learning accredited by the state or club, parent, teacher, student organization within and authorized by the school in support of the operation and activities of the school;
A volunteer fire department, rescue squad or local civil defense organization whose financial oversight is under the control of a local governmental entity.

Annual Reporting Requirements
Due quarterly during year one 30 days after end of quarter
Due 30 days after end of fiscal year thereafter
Financial report or IRS 990

Vermont

There is no registration required in Vermont at this time.

Virginia

Commonwealth of Virginia
Dept. of Agriculture and Consumer Services
Division of Consumer Affairs
1100 Bank Street
P.O. Box 526

Richmond, VA 23218
804-786-2042
www.vdacs.state.va.us

Registration Requirements
State Form 102 or URS
Certificate/Articles of Incorporation
Bylaws
IRS Form 990 or audit
IRS Determination Letter
$100 Registration fee

Organizations exempt from registration:
Any accredited educational institutions or related foundations, and any other educational institution confining its solicitation of contributions to its student body, alumni, faculty and trustees, and their families;

Persons requesting contributions for the relief of any individual specified by name at the time of solicitation when all contributions are turned over directly to named beneficiary;

Charitable organizations that do not intend, in a calendar year or the three preceding years, to receive contributions from the public in excess of $5,000, and all of whose functions are carried out by volunteers;

Organizations that solicit only within the membership of the organization;

Organizations that have no office within the Commonwealth and solicit within the state, solely by means of telephone, telegraph, direct mail or advertising in national media and have a registered chapter, branch or affiliate within the Commonwealth;

Tax-exempt health care institutions licensed by their state Dept. of Health or Mental Health and any supporting organizations;

Civic organizations such as a local service club, veterans' post, fraternal society or association, volunteer fire or rescue group, or local civic league or association operated exclusively for educational or charitable purposes for the benefit of the community Organizations seeking exemption must file "Forms 100A-100H" as applicable.

Labor unions, associations and organizations with tax-exempt status;

Agencies designated by the Virginia Department for the Aging as area agencies on aging;

Nonprofit debt counseling agencies

Please note that exempt organizations must file appropriate forms and a $10 filing fee.

Annual Reporting Requirements
State Form 102
Due within 4 1/2 months of fiscal year end
Registration renewal fee: $30 - $325
IRS 990,990-PF, 990-EZ or certified annual audit or certified treasurer's report where proceeds are less than $25,000
Current list of officers, directors, trustees, and principal salaried staff members
Current copies of contracts with paid fund-raising organizations
Certificate/Articles of Incorporation or amendments to those documents not previously filed;
Bylaws or amendments to that document not previously filed;
IRS Determination letter

Washington
Office of Secretary of State
Charities Program

P.O. Box 40234
801 Capitol Way South
Olympia, WA 98504-0234
800-332-4483
800-332-GIVE
360-753-0863
Email: charities@secstate.wa.gov
www.secstate.wa.gov

Registration Requirements
State form or URS
IRS Form 990
IRS Determination letter
$20 Registration fee

Organizations seeking exemption must file an exemption form.

Annual Reporting Requirements
Due within 4 1/2 months of fiscal year end
$10 filing/renewal fee
IRS 990
Financial Report

West Virginia
Secretary of State
Building 1, Room 157-K
1900 Kanawha Blvd. East
Charleston, WV 25305-0770
304-558-6000
Fax: 304-558-0900
www.wvsos.com

Registration Requirements
State form - (URS not accepted)
IRS Form 990
IRS Determination letter
Fees range from $15-50
Audit if contributions exceed $100,000

Organizations exempt from registration:
Educational institutions, the curriculums of which in whole or in part are registered or approved by the state board of education, either directly or by acceptance of accreditation by an accrediting body and any auxiliary associations, foundations and support groups which are directly responsible to any such educational institutions;

Persons requesting contributions for the relief of any individual specified at the time of solicitation when all of the contributions collected without any deduction are turned over to the named beneficiary;

Hospitals, which are nonprofit;

Organizations which solicit only within the membership of the organization by members thereof: provided that the term "membership" shall not include those persons who are granted membership upon making a contribution as the result of solicitation;

Churches, synagogues, associations or conventions of churches, religious orders or religious organizations that are an integral part of a church, which qualifies as tax exempt under 501(c)(3);

Organizations sponsoring single fund-raising events for a named charitable organization;

Organizations such as local youth athletic organizations, community service clubs, fraternal organizations, volunteer fireman or auxiliaries are exempt if they do not employ a professional solicitor or fund-raiser or do not intend to solicit or receive contributions in excess of $10,000 during the calendar year.

Annual Reporting Requirements
There is no annual reporting requirement other than registration renewal.

Wisconsin

Department of Regulation & Licensing
Charitable Organizations
1400 E. Washington Ave.
P.O. Box 8935
Madison, WI 53708-8935
608-266-5511, ext. 441
Fax: 608-267-386
Email: dorl@drl.state.wi.us
www.drl.wi.gov/

Registration Requirements
State forms or URS
Certificate/Articles of Incorporation
Bylaws
IRS Form 990
IRS Determination Letter
Audit if contributions exceed $100,000
$15 Registration fee

Organizations exempt from registration:
Candidate for national, state or local office or a political party or other committee or group required to file financial information with the federal elections commission;
Organizations that do not raise or receive contributions in excess of $5,000;
Fraternal, benevolent, patriotic or social organizations that solicit contributions solely from their membership;
Veteran's organizations;
Nonprofit postsecondary educational institutions;
Organizations soliciting contributions for relief of a named individual if all contributions are given to the named individual
Religious organizations

Annual Reporting Requirements
Due July 31st
$15 filing/renewal fee
IRS 990
Financial Report if contributions from exceed $5,000 organizations must file either
Audit if charitable contributions exceed $100,000

Wyoming

There is no registration required in Wyoming at this time.

State Corporation Divisions

Alabama

Division of Corporation, Secretary of State, 11 S. Union St., Suite 207, Montgomery, AL 36104 or P.O. Box 5616, Montgomery, AL 36103-5616, 334-242-5324, Fax: 334-240-3138; {www.sos.state.al.us}. Selected Publications: Guide to Incorporation. Phone Information: 334-242-5324. Office is completely computerized and can do word search or partial name search by officer, incorporator, or serving agent. Copies of documents on File: Available online or by written request for $1 per page plus $5 for certified copies. Can provide information over the phone at no cost. Mailing Labels: No. Magnetic Tape: No. Microfiche: No. New Corporate Listings: No. Custom Searches: Can do word or partial name search. Printout of search results by mail is free. Online Access: Yes. Number of active corporations on File: 250,000

Alaska

State of Alaska, Division of Banking, Securities and Corporation, Corporation Section, 150 Third Street, Suite 119, P.O. Box 110808, Juneau, AK 99811-0808, 907-465-2530, Fax: 907-465-3257; {www.dced.state.ak.us/bsc/home.htm}. Selected Publications: None. Phone information: 907-465-2530. Copies of Documents on File: Complete corporate record (Articles of Incorporation, annual report, amendments, etc.) Cost $30, certified copies add $5, list of officers and directors cost $1, Certificate of Status cost $10. Mailing Labels: No. Magnetic tape: no, only diskettes. Copy of complete master file excluding officers and directors is priced at $100. Monthly supplements are an additional $10. Microfiche: No, only disk and email. New corporate listings: yes. Custom Searches: yes. Online Access: Yes. Number of active corporations on file: 25,172.

Arizona

Arizona Corporations Division, Records Division, Secretary of State, 1300 W. Washington, Phoenix, AZ 85007 or P.O. Box 6019, Phoenix, AZ 85005, 602-542-3026, Fax: 602-542-3414; {www.cc.state.az.us}. Selected Publications: Sample packet with forms and statutes mailed for $8. Guideline booklets will be available soon. Phone Information : 602-542-3026. Copies of Documents on File: Cost $5 plus 50 cents per page, $10 for certified copies. Mailing Labels: No. Magnetic Tape: Master File $400, issued monthly. Requester must supply blank tape. Microfiche: All corporations statewide $75. New Corporate Listing: Monthly Listing of New Domestic Companies for $200 plus $200 for new foreign listings. Custom searches: Yes, request in writing or in person. Can search by company name, agent name or officer name. Online Access. There is a charge for filing online. Contact business connection for forms 602-542-3135. Available through Information America, Dunn and Bradstreet and other commercial services. Number of corporations on file: 100,000

Arkansas

Secretary of State, Business and Commercial Services Division, Victory Building, Suite 250, 1401 West Capitol Avenue, Little Rock, AR 72201, 501-682-3409, Fax: 501-682-3437; {http:\\sos.state.ar.us}. Selected Publications: None. Phone Information: 501-682-3409. Copies of Documents on file: Call 501-371-3431 for copies at 50 cents per page plus $5 for certified copies. Domestic companies $50, Foreign companies $300. Mailing labels: No. Magnetic Tape: Master file 2 cents per name. Microfiche: No. New

corporate Listing: Statistics only. Custom Searches. Categories include foreign, domestic, profit, and nonprofit corporations. Cost: 10 cents per name, $10 minimum search fee. Online Access: Yes. Number of active corporations on file: 1,000,000

California

Corporations, Information Retrieval and Certification, Secretary of State, 1500 11th Street, CA 95814-5701, 916-653-6814, {www.ss.ca.gov}. Selected Publications: Corporations Checklist Booklet. Request must be in writing and cost is $5. Phone Information: 916-653-6814. Copies of Documents on File: Articles of Incorporation: cost is $1 for first page, 50 cents for each additional page plus $5 for certified copies, Certificate of status $5, Statement of officers $5 and $10 for certified copies (written requests only). You must pay in advance or send blank check not to exceed $20. Send requests to secretary of state, Attention IRC unit. Mailing Labels: No. Magnetic Tape: Yes, Master copy $17,600 annually. Call 916-657-5448 for information. Hard copy $14,000.13. Microfiche: No. Custom Searches: Computer generated listing of Active Stock ($17,030), Active Non-Stock ($422). Active Non-Stock by Classification $150 per list. All orders must be submitted in writing. Basic cost of magnetic tape copy is $1.02 per 1,000 names. Basic cost of same run, for custom search, printed on paper, is $4.13 per 1,000 names. $150 minimum is applied to both. Online Access: Yes. Number of Corporations on File: 2,000,000.

Colorado

Business Center, Secretary of State, 1560 Broadway, Suite 200, Denver, CO 80202, 303-894-2200, Fax: 303-869-4864; Forms Fax Back: 303-860-6975; {www.sos.state.co.us}. Selected Publications: Corporate Guide. Copies of Documents on File: Cost is 50 cents per page, plus $10 for certification. Mailing Labels: No. Magnetic Tape: Available for $500 for complete set of five. Tapes must be purchased individually. Categories: Foreign and Domestic. Microfiche: available at $1 a sheet (includes Summary of Master Computer File, must be purchased in its entirety). New Corporate Listings: Reporting Service costs $200 a year. Weekly list of New Corporations. Written requests only. Custom searches: Yes. Categories: Foreign and Domestic available on a cost recovery basis. The minimum fee is $50. Online Access: Available. Fee is $300 for 3 months or $1,000 per year. Number of Corporations on File: 235,000.

Connecticut

Office of Secretary of State, Commercial Recording Division, 30 Trinity Street, Hartford, CT 06106; Fax: 860-509-6068; {www.sots.state.ct.us}. Selected Publications: None, but to get a copy of Connecticut General Statutes, call 860-509-6190. Phone Information: 860-509-6001. Copies of Documents on File: Fees are $20 regardless of number of pages, $25 for certified. Written requests only. Mailing Labels: No. Magnetic Tape: Copy of master database of corporations $300. Requester must provide tapes. Microfiche: No. New Corporate Listing: No. Custom Searches: No. Online Access: Yes. Number of Corporations on File: over 200,000

Delaware

Delaware Department of State, Division of Corporations, Secretary of State, P.O. Box 898, Dover, DE 19903, 302-739-3073, Fax: 302-739-3812; {www.state.de.us\corp}.

Selected Publications: Incorporating in Delaware. Phone Information: 302-739-3073. Copies of Documents on File: (for domestic only) Available at $1 per page $30 for certification. Short forms $20 and $100 for long forms of good standing. Certificate of incorporation $114 minimum, amendment certificate $129 minimum, change of registered agents $104. Requests may be faxed to 302-739-3812, but written requests are preferred. Requests must be paid for in advance, add county fee and send a check. Call for number of pages. Documents filed prior to 1983 are not on computer and must be requested in writing. They offer same day or 24-hour expedited services to file or retrieve certified documents. Same day request completed and released by 5pm, when requested by 2pm. Additional fee is $100 for same day and $50 for 24-hour service. Mailing Labels: No. Magnetic Tape: No. Microfiche: No. New Corporate Listings: No. Custom Searches: Yes, domestic corporations only. Number of Active Corporation on File 397,829

District of Columbia

Corporations Division, Consumer and Regulatory Affairs, 941 N. Capitol NE, 1st Floor, Washington, DC 20002, 202-442-4430, Fax: 202-442-4523; {http://dcra.dc.gov/main.shtm}. Selected Publications: Guideline and Instruction Sheet for Profit, Nonprofit, Foreign, or Domestic. Phone Information: 202-442-9453. Copies of Documents on File: Available for $25 each (all copies certified). Mailing Labels: Will be available in near future. Profit and nonprofit lists updated quarterly. Magnetic Tape: No. Microfiche: No. New Corporate Listings No. Custom Searches: Computer searches on registered agents are available. Online Access: Yes. Number of Active Corporations on File: 50,000.

Florida

Division of Corporations, Secretary of State, 409 E. Gaines Street, PO Box 6327, Tallahassee, FL 32314, 850-487-6000, Fax: 850-487-6012; {www.sunbiz.org}. Selected Publications: Copy of the Law Chapter 607 (corporate law). Forms included. (Publications on laws of nonprofit corporations and limited partnerships also available.) Phone Information: 800-755-5111. Limit of up to 3 inquiries per call. $10 charge to receive hard copy of microfiche on the corporations, no charge for faxing copies. Copy of Documents on File: Available at $1 per page if you do it yourself. Written requests must be paid for in advance: $1 for non-certified annual report; $10 for plain copy of complete file; $8.75 per 8 pages and $1 each additional, for any certified document including complete file. Microfiche: No. Magnetic Tape: No. New Corporate Listings: No. Custom Searches: No. Online Access: Yes. Corporate data is available on CD-ROM, 5 disc set for $594.98. Contact Jenny Gowdy at 850-488-1486. Number of active Corporations on File: 745-797.

Georgia

Corporations Division, Secretary of State, Suite 315, West Tower #2, Martin Luther King Drive, SE, Atlanta, GA 30334, 404-656-2817, Fax: 404-657-2248; {www.sos.state.ga.us}. Selected Publications: None, but information package on how to file sent upon request. Phone Information: 404-656-2817. Copies of Documents on File: Available for a minimum of $10 for less than 50 pages. For more than 50 pages, $20 plus 25 cents per page. All copies certified. Mailing Labels: No. Magnetic Tape: No. Microfiche: No. New Corporate Listings: Yes. Custom Searches: No. Online Access: Yes Number of Active Corporations on File: 350,000

Hawaii

Business Registration Division, Department of Commerce and Consumer Affairs, 335 Merchant Street, 2nd Floor, PO Box 40, Honolulu, HI 96810, 808-586-2744, Fax: 808-586-2733; {www.state.hi.us/dcca/breg-seu/}. Selected Publications: None. Phone Information: 808-586-2727. Copies of Documents on File: Available at 25 cents per page, plus $20 per page for certified copies. Expedited service available for $10 fee plus 25 cents per sheet, plus $1 per page. Mailing Labels: No. Magnetic Tape: No. Microfiche: No. New Corporate Listing: Weekly printout available but only for walk-ins. Custom Searches: No. Online Access: Yes. Downloading information from database available through eHawaiiGov Subscriber Services at 808-587-4220. Number of Active Corporations on File: 45,000.

Idaho

Commercial Division, Secretary of State, 700 West Jefferson Street, Statehouse, Boise, ID 83720, 208-334-2301, Fax: 208-334-2847; {www.idsos.state.id.us}. Selected Publications: Idaho Corporation Law. Phone Information: 208-334-2300. Copies of Documents on File: Available at 25 cents per page, $10 for certified copies. Mailing Labels: Very flexible and may be combined with custom search. Fee is $10 for computer base, 25 cents for first 100 pages, 10 cents for next 500 pages and 5 cents per page thereafter. Magnetic Tape: available for $20 per tape if you supply the tape. They will supply diskette for additional $10. Microfiche: Available for $10, 50 cents for each additional copy of same. Custom Searches: Yes. You supply the tapes or they will supply them at cost. New Corporate Listing: No, but published weekly in The Idaho Business Review. Online Access: Yes. Number of Active Corporations on File 21,839.

Illinois

Corporations Division, Michael J. Howlett Building, Room 328, 501 S. 2nd Street, Springfield, IL 62756, 217-782-6961, Fax: 217-782-4528; {www.sos.state.il.us}. Selected Publications: Guide for Organizing (Domestic, Nonprofit, or Foreign). Phone Information: 217-782-7880. Copies of Documents on File: available at $5 per page up to first 10 pages; 50 cents for each page thereafter. Mailing Labels: No. Magnetic Tape: yes. Categories: Domestic and Foreign cost $1,500; Not-for-Profit cost $1,500. You must supply tape. Microfiche: Available for $171. New Corporate Listings: Daily list of newly formed corporations costs $185 per year; Monthly List priced at $105 per year. Contact Sharon, 217-782-4104 for more information. Custom Searches: No. Other: Certified List of Domestic and Foreign Corporations (Address of Resident Agent included) costs $38 for two volume set. Online Access: Yes.

Indiana

Business Services Division, Secretary of State, E018, 302 West Washington Street, Indianapolis, IN 46204, 317-232-6581, Fax: 317-232-6393; {www.in.gov/sos}. Selected Publications: Guide Book. Request by calling 800-726-8000. Phone Information: 317-232-6576. Copies of Documents on File: Available at $1 per page and $15 to certify. May pay in advance or be billed. Mailing Labels: No. Magnetic Tape: No. Microfiche: No. New Corporate Listings: Daily Listing is published monthly for $30 a month. One time bulk download or CD is $3000. Custom Searches: No. Online Access: Available: Yes. Number of Active Corporations on file: 200,000.

Iowa

Business Services, Secretary of State, First Floor, Lucas Building, Des Moines, IA 50319, 515-281-5204, Fax: 515-242-6566; {www.sos.state.ia.us}. Selected Publications: Iowa Profit Corporations. Phone Information 515-281-5204. Copies of Documents on File: available at $1 per page;

certified copies cost $5. Mailing Labels: No. Magnetic Tape: No. Master file is available on CD-Rom for $200. Microfiche: No. New Corporate Listings: No. Custom Searches: Yes. Searches by name of corporation or partial name. Online Access: Yes. Number of Active Corporations on File: 200,000.

Kansas

Corporate Division, Secretary of State, Capitol Building, Second Floor, 300 SW 10th Avenue, Topeka, KS 66612-1594, 785-296-4564, Fax: 785-296-4570; {www.kssos.org}. Selected Publications: None. Will send out forms with instruction sheets. Phone Information: 785-296-4564. Copies of Documents on File: Available at 50 cents per page plus $7.50. Certificate of Good Standing $15, Letter of Good Standing $10, Written Record Search $10. Magnetic Tape: Yes. Master file is available. Microfiche: No. Other: New Corporate Listings: No. Custom Searches: Yes. Online Access:Yes. Number of Active Corporations on File: 66,000.

Kentucky

Corporate Division, Secretary of State, Room 154, Capitol Building, 700 Capitol Avenue, PO Box 718, Frankfort, KY 40601, 502-564-2848, Fax: 502-564-4075; {www.sos.state. ky.us}. Selected Publications: None. Phone Information: 502-564-2848. Copies of Documents on File: Call 502-564-7330 to obtain number of copies in advance. Cost is 50 cents per page; $5 for certified copies. Computer screen print out is $1. Mailing label: No. Magnetic Tape: No. CD Rom available for free and they can send it to you for free. Microfiche: No. New Corporate Listings: available for $50 a month. Custom Searches: Yes, partial name search. Online Access: Yes. Number of Active Corporations on File: 400,000.

Louisiana

Corporate Division, Secretary of State, 8549 United Plaza Boulevard, Baton Rouge, LA 70809, 225-925-4704, Fax: 225-925-4726; {www.sec.state.la.us}. Selected Publications: Corporate Law Book ($10). Phone Information: 225-925-4704. Copies of Documents on File: Available starting at $15 for certified articles only. Cost for complete file, including amendments is $20. Mailing Label: No. Magnetic Tape: No. Microfiche: No. New Corporate Listing: Weekly Newsletter at no charge. Requester must supply self addressed stamped envelope. Custom Searches: Yes, can search by agents and individual names. Online Access: Yes. Number of Active Corporations on File: 120,000.

Maine

Information and Report Section, Bureau of Corporations, Secretary of State, 101 State House Station, Augusta, ME 04333-0101, 207-624-7752, Fax: 207-287-5874; {www.state. me.us/sos/cec/}. Selected Publications: None at this time. Phone Information: 207-624-7752. Copies of Documents on File: Available for $2 per page, plus $5 for certified copies. Mailing Labels: No. Magnetic tape: No. Microfiche: No. New Corporate Listings: Monthly Corporations Listing costs $10. Custom Searches: Yes, by corporation name. Online Access: Yes. Number of Active Corporations on File 58,000.

Maryland

Corporate Charter Division, Department of Assessments and Taxation, 301 W. Preston Street, Baltimore, Maryland 21201, 410-767-1340, Fax: 410-333-7097; {www.dat.state.md.us}. Selected Publications: Information Guides for Filing and other issues are available. Phone Information: 410-225-1330. Copies of Documents on File: Available for $1 per page, plus $20 for certified copies. There is a $20 expediting fee.

Certificate of good standing $20, Articles of Incorporation $20. Mailing Labels: No. Magnetic Tape: available on 6 tapes for $75 each. Contact Joe Jenkins of Specprint in Timonium, 410-561-9600. Microfiche: No. New Corporate Listings: Monthly corporate Computer Printout costs $50 a month. Custom Searches. Yes. They can search for names, agents, principal offices, and documents filed by the corporation. Online Access: Yes. Number of Active Corporations on File: 300,000.

Massachusetts

Corporate Division, Secretary of State, 1 Ashburton Place, Boston, MA 02108, 617-727-9640; {www.state.ma.us/sec/cor}. Selected Publications: Compendium of Corporate Law ($15). Phone Information: 617-727-9640. Copies of Documents on File: available for 30 cents per page, $12 for certified copies. Mailing Labels: No. Magnetic Tape: Cost is $300 for copy of master file and record layout. Requester must supply tapes. Microfiche: Yes. New Corporate Listings: Semi-monthly Filings cost $15; Quarterly Filings cost $50; bi-weekly printout cost $15. Custom Searches: available on a cost recovery basis. Online Access: Yes. Number of Corporations on File: 400,000.

Michigan

Corporation Division, Department of Labor and Economic Growth, PO Box 30054, 611 W. Ottawa, Lansing, MI 48909, 517-334-6302, Fax: 517-334-8048; {www.michigan.gov/cis}. Selected Publications: None. Phone Information: 517-241-6470; Fax: 517-241-0538. Copies of Documents on File: available at a minimum of $6 for 6 pages or less, $1 for each page thereafter. Certified copies cost $10. (Request a price list.) Mailing Labels: No. Magnetic Tape: No. Microfiche: Available for $145. New Corporate Listings: Monthly Listing ranges at about $80 per month (each month is priced differently). Custom Searches: No. Online Access: Yes. Number of Corporations on File: 251,000.

Minnesota

Business Services, Secretary of State, 180 State Office Building, 100 Reverend Dr. Martin Luther King Jr. Blvd., St. Paul, MN 55155, 651-297-7067; {www.sos.state.mn.us}. Selected Publications: Guide to Starting a Business in Minnesota. Phone Information: 651-297-7067. Copies of Documents on File: Available for $3 per copy, $8 for certified copies. Request copies by sending a letter, indicating your address or fax number. Mailing Labels: No. Magnetic Tape: Yes, on 9 tapes for $12,000 annually and $500 per month. Microfiche: No. New Corporate Listings: Daily Log costs 25 cents per page. Custom Searches: Available on a cost recovery basis. Categories same as for mailing labels. Online Access: Yes. Number of Corporations on File: 194,500

Mississippi

Business Services, Secretary of State, PO Box 136, Jackson, MS 39201, 601-359-1350, Fax: 601-359-1499; or street address: 700 North Street,, Jackson, MS 39201; {www. sos.state.ms.us}. Selected Publications: None. Phone Information: 601-359-1607. Copies of Documents on File: $1 per page plus $10 for certified copies. Mailing Labels: No. Magnetic tape: No. Microfiche: No. New Corporate Listings: Yes, $25 for new monthly listings. Custom Searches: Available to limited extent. Printout costs $2 per page. Online Access: Yes. Number of Active Corporations on File: 80,000.

Missouri

Corporate Division, Secretary of State, 600 W. Main and 208 State Capitol, PO Box 778, Jefferson City, MO 65102, 573-

751-4153, 866-223-6535; Fax: 573-751-5841; {www.sos.mo. gov}. Selected Publications: Corporation Handbook (free). Phone Information: 573-751-4153. Copies of Documents on File: available at 50 cents per page plus $10 for certified copies. Mailing Labels: No. Magnetic Tape: No. Microfiche: No. New Corporate Listings: not usually, but can be set up on special request. Custom Searches: Yes, on website. Online Access: Yes. Number of active Corporations on File: 192,000.

Montana

Corporate Division, Secretary of State, Capitol Station, Helena, MT 59620, 406-444-3665, Fax: 406-444-3976; {http://sos.state.mt.us/css}. Selected Publications: None. Phone Information: 406-444-3665. Copies of Documents on File: available for 50 cents per page; $10 for certification. Prepaid accounts are available for obtaining certificates and other information. Mailing Labels: No. Magnetic Tape: No. Microfiche: No. New Corporate Listings: No. Custom Searches: No but can search by name of corporation only. Online access: Yes. Number of Active Corporations on File: 33,000

Nebraska

Corporate Division, Secretary of State, Room 1301, State Capitol, P.O. Box 94608, Lincoln, NE 68509, 402-471-4079, Fax: 402-471-3666; {www.sos.state.ne.us}. Selected Publications: None. Phone Information: 402-471-4079. Copies of Documents on File: Available for $1 per page, $10 for certified copies. Fax your requests and they will bill you, or request over the phone. Mailing Labels: No, but database is available on floppy or CD-Rom. Magnetic Tape: Contact Nebraska Online at 800-747-8177; 402-471-7810. Microfiche: No. New Corporate Listings: also available through Nebraska Online. Custom Searches: No: Online Access: Yes. Number of Active Corporations on File: 50,000.

Nevada

Office of Corporations, Secretary of State, Capitol Complex, 202 N. Carson Street, Carson City, NV 89710, 775-684-5708, Fax: 702-684-5724; {www.sos.state.nv.us}. Selected Publications: Guidelines. Phone Information: Corporate Status call 900-535-3355, $3.50 per call. Copies of Documents on File: available for $2 per page, $30 for certified copies. Prepayment required (they will not send a bill). Mailing Labels: No. Magnetic Tape: Copy of master file available, 702-684-5715. Corporations takes 2 tapes which requester supplies. Cost per tape is $25. Microfiche: No. New Corporate Listings: Monthly Listing of New Corporations costs $20 a month. Custom Searches: yes. Cost determined at time of request. Online access: Yes. Number of Active Corporations on File: 60,000.

New Hampshire

Corporate Division, Secretary of State, State House Annex, Room 341, 25 Capitol Street, Concord, NH 03301, 603-271-3244; {http://webster.state.nh.us/sos/corporate/}. Selected Publications: None. Phone Information: 603-271-3246. Copies of Documents on File: Available for $1 per page, plus $5 for certified copies, and $25 expedited services. Annual report can be faxed to you for $10. Mailing Labels: No. Magnetic Tape: No. Microfiche: Complete listing of all registrations. No breakdown by type of entity (updated monthly). Annual Subscription costs $500. New Corporate Listings: Monthly Subscriber List costs $50 plus postage. Custom Searches: No. Online Access: Yes. Number of Active Corporations on File: 33,000.

New Jersey

Division of Revenue, Records Unit, Secretary of State, 225 W. State St., P.O. Box 450, Trenton, NJ 08625, 609-292-9292; {www.state.nj.us/treasury/revenue/}. Selected Publications: Corporate Filing Packet. Phone Information: General Information call 609-292-5977; Forms call 609-292-9292; Expedite Service call 609-984-7107. There is a charge for standard information, $15 look-up fee for each verbal or fax request plus $10 expedited service fee. User may pay with Visa, Master Card or Discover. Requests may be sent by Fax at 609-984-6855. Copies of Documents on File: available for $1 per page plus $25 for certified copies (except for LLCs and Nonprofit corporations, which cost $15 to certify). Mailing Labels: No. Magnetic Tape: No. Microfiche: No. New Corporate Listings: No. Custom Searches: Yes. Each request is reviewed on individual basis. Requester is billed for computer time. Online Access: Yes. Number of Active Corporations on File: 436,314.

New Mexico

Public Regulation Commission, Corporations Bureau, 1120 Pasco De Peratta, PO Drawer 1269, Santa Fe, NM 87504-1269, 800-947-4722, 505-827-4500, Fax: 505-476-0324; {www.nmprc.state.nm.us}. Selected Publications: None. Phone Information: 505-827-4500. Copies of documents on File: Available for $1 per page, minimum $5, plus additional $10 for certified copies. Mailing Labels: No. Magnetic Tape: No. Microfiche: No. New Corporate Listings. Yes. Monthly listings available. Requester must send manila self-addressed envelope, with postage worth $1.70 each, for as many listings as you would like. Online Access: Yes. Custom Searches: Yes, call their information line, 505-827-4509. They provide free printouts of certificates of good standing, officers and agent names. Number of Active Corporations on File: Over 100,000.

New York

New York State, Department of State, Division of Corporations, 41 State Street, Albany, NY 12231, 518-473-2492; Fax: 518-474-4478; {http:\\www.dos.state.ny.us\corp\corpwww.html}. Copies of Documents on File: Available for $5 per document, $10 for certified copies. Call 900-835-2677 to obtain information on a filed corporation or status of a corporation. To receive copies of documents on file, send in a letter of request. Mailing Labels: No. Magnetic Tape: No. Microfiche: No. New Corporate Listing: Report of Corporations is printed daily and mailed out every other day. It is available in the Daily Report through subscription only, for $125 per year, $75 for 6 months or $40 for 3 months. Online Access: Yes. Number of Corporations on File: 1,200,000.

North Carolina

Division of Corporation, Secretary of State, 300 N. Salisbury Street, Raleigh, NC 27603-5909, 919-807-2225, Fax: 919-807-2039; {www.secstate.state.nc.us}. Selected publications: North Carolina Business Corporation Guidelines, North Carolina's Nonprofit Corporation Handbook. Phone Information 919-807-2225. Copies of Documents on File: available for $1 per page, $15 for certified copies. Mailing Labels: No. Magnetic Tape: No. Microfiche: No. New Corporate Listings: Available for $20 per month and issued in hard copy only. Custom Searches: Yes. Categories: Type of Corporation, Professional Corporations, Insurance Corporations, Banks, and Savings and Loans. Online Access: Available. Number of Active Corporations on File: 400,000.

North Dakota

Corporation Division, Secretary of State, Capitol Building, 600 E. Boulevard Ave., Bismarck, ND 58505, 701-328-4284, Fax: 701-328-2992; {www.state.nd.us/sec}. Selected Publications: Phone Information: 701-328-4284. Copies of Documents on File: $1 per page. Certified copies $7 for first page, $1 for each additional page. Written or phone requests accepted. Fax on demand service will send you the forms you need, 701-328-0120. Mailing Labels: No. Magnetic Tape: No. Microfiche No. New Corporate Listings: Monthly Corporation list costs $35-$37 per month. Custom Searches: No. Online Access: Yes. Number of Active Corporations on File: 22,500.

Ohio

Business Services, Secretary of State, 30 East Broad Street, 14th Floor, Columbus, OH 43215, 877-767-3453, 614-466-3910, Fax: 614-466-3899; {www.sos.state.oh.us/sos}. Selected Publications: Corporate Checklist. Phone Information: Corporate Status call 614-466-3910; Name Availability call 614-466-0590. Copies of Documents on File: contact 614-466-3910. Available for $1 per page, $5 for certified copies. Mailing Labels: No. Magnetic Tape: available for $125 for 6,250 corporation names, thereafter the cost is 2 cents per corporate name with a maximum of 25,000 names. Microfiche: No. New Corporate Listing: List is updated monthly. $27.50. Custom Searches: Yes. Categories: location (county), Foreign, Domestic, Profit, Nonprofit. Online Access: Yes. Number of Active Corporations on File: 400,000.

Oklahoma

Corporations, Secretary of State, Business Records Department, 2300 N. Lincoln Blvd., Room 101, Oklahoma City, OK 73105, 405-522-4582, Fax: 405-521-3771; {www.sos.state.ok.us}. Selected Publications: Forms and Procedures to Incorporate. Phone Information: 900-733-2424 for record search. Three (3) searches per call. Charge is $5 per call. Copies of Documents on File: available for $1 per page, $10 for certified copies. Mailing Labels: No Magnetic Tape: No. Microfiche: No. New Corporate Listings: New Master Download $500. Weekly filing update, $150. Custom Searches: Yes, date of incorporation and registered agent information is provided. Online Access: Yes. Number of Corporations on File: 224,159.

Oregon

Corporation Division, Secretary of State, 255 Capitol St., NE, Suite 151, Salem, OR 97310-1327, 503-986-2200, Fax: 503-986-2308; {www.filinginoregon.com}. Selected Publications: None. Phone Information: 503-986-2200. Copies of Documents on File: Available for $5 for all documents in a corporation's file except annual report. Annual reports are an additional $5. Certification fee is $15. Business Registry on diskette, CD-ROM or email is $15 per month or $150 per year. Mailing Labels: No. Magnetic Tape: No Complete master file costs $200 on CD-ROM. Microfiche: No. New Corporate Listings: Statistical Report of New Corporations is available for $15 per monthly issue. Custom Searches: Yes, minimum charge is $50. Online Access: Yes. Number of Active Corporations on File: 73,000.

Pennsylvania

Corporation Bureau, 206 N. Office Building, Harrisburg, PA 17120, 717-787-1057, Fax: 717-783-2244; {www.dos.state.pa.us}. Selected Publications: Corporate Guide. Phone Information: 717-787-1057. Copies of Documents on File: Available for $15 plus $3 per page. Certified copies are $55 plus $3 per page. Business lists are $12 plus 25 cents per

name. Mailing Labels: No. Magnetic Tape: Copy of master file available for $3500 startup fee. Monthly, you will be charged $48.12 for each tape received. This is the only way to receive the master file. It is not currently on disk or CD-Rom. Microfiche: No. New Corporate Listings: County or area listing available for cents per name. Custom Searches: Yes. Categories: Nonprofit, Domestic, Foreign county location, Limited partnerships, Fictitious name, Trademarks, Foreign Nonprofits, Cooperatives, Professional Corporations $15 per name. Online Access: Yes. Number of Corporations on File: 1,500,000.

Rhode Island

Corporations Division, Secretary of State, 100 North Main Street, First Floor, Providence, RI 02903, 401-222-3040, Fax: 401-222-1309; {www.state.ri.us}. Selected Publications: Instruction sheet, The Rhode Island Law Manual (Free). Phone Information: 401-222-3040. Staff will look up two corporations per call. Copies of Documents on File: Available for 15 cents per page, $5 for certified sheet. Mailing Labels: No. Magnetic Tape: Yes, master file is available. Microfiche: No. New Corporate Listings: Not usually provided. New corporate listings are published weekly in The Providence Journal, Sunday Business Section. Send a letter requesting weekly printouts. Custom Searches: No. Online Access: Yes. Number of Active Corporations on File: 90,000.

South Carolina

Division of Corporation, Secretary of State, Edgar Brown Bldg., 1205 Pendleton St., Suite 525, PO Box 11350, Columbia, SC 29211, 803-734-2158, Fax: 803-734-2164; {www.scsos.com}. Selected Publication: None. Phone Information: 803-734-2158. Copies of Documents on File: available for $2 for first page, $1 thereafter. $2 for certified copies. Mailing Labels: No. Magnetic Tape: No. Microfiche: No. New corporate Listing: Yes. Custom Searches: No. Online Access: Yes. Number of Active Corporations on File: 250,000.

South Dakota

Corporate Division, Secretary of State, 500 East Capitol, Pierre, SD 57501, 605-773-4845; Fax: 605-773-4550; {www.state.sd.us/sos/sos.htm}. Selected Publications: None. Phone Information: 605-773-4845. Copies of Documents on File: Available for $1 per page plus $10 for certification. Fax fee is $5. Mailing Labels: No. Magnetic Tape: No. Microfiche: No. New Corporate Listings: No. Custom Searches: No. Online Access: No. Number of Active Corporations on File: 30,000.

Tennessee

Office of Secretary of State, Business Services Division, 312 Eighth Avenue North, 6th Floor, William R. Snodgrass Tower, Nashville, TN 37243-0306, 615-741-2286, Fax: 615-741-7310; {www.state.tn.us/sos/}. Selected Publications: None. Phone Information: 615-741-2286. Copies of Documents on File: All available information on a corporation is available for $20. Certified copies of documents on file are $20. Mailing Labels No. Magnetic Tape: Yes. Categories: All Corporations on file, Foreign, Domestic Profit, Nonprofit, Banks, Credit Unions, Cooperative Associations. Charge of an additional $2 for each tape supplied. Cost, done on a cost recovery basis, is determined at time of request. Contact Mr. Thompson at 615-741-0584. Microfiche: No. New Corporate Listings: Monthly New Corporation Listing on a cost recovery basis of 25 cents per page, 8 names per page. Call 615-741-1111. Custom

Searches: Yes. Online Access: Yes. Number of Active Corporations on File: 140,000.

Texas

Corporation Section, Statute Filing Division, Secretary of State, PO Box 13697, Austin, TX 78711, 512-463-5578, Fax: 512-463-5643; {www.sos.state.tx.us}. Selected Publications: Filing Guide to Corporations. Phone Information: 512-463-5578. Copies of Documents on File: Available for $35; for names and all filings of corporations. Certification is $10 plus $1 for each additional page. $10 for express services. Business entity information, excluding individual names is $3 per call, 10 cents for each page up to 50 pages, 15 cents per page for more than 50 pages. Fax transmissions are $2 per page. Mailing Labels: No. Magnetic Tape: No. Microfiche: Names of officers and directors available. Cost determined at time of request. New Corporate Listings: Weekly Charter Update costs $27.50 per week. Custom Searches: No. Online Access: Available through SOS Direct. Contact Lori Castro at 512-475-2755. Number of Active Corporations on File: Not Available.

Utah

Corporations and UCC, Division of Business Regulations, P.O. Box 45801, 160 East 300 South Street, Second Floor, Salt Lake City, UT 84145-0801, 801-530-4849, 877-526-3994 (within Utah), Fax: 801-530-6111 or 801-530-6438; {www.commerce.utah.gov}. Selected Publications: Doing Business in Utah; A Guide to Business Information (available online). Phone Information: 801-530-4849. Copies of Documents on File: Available for 30 cents a page plus $12 for certified copies. Mailing Labels: No. Magnetic Tape: No. Microfiche: No. New Corporate Listing: Updated every ten days. You can obtain by calling their information line. Custom Searches: Yes. Cost includes printing charge of 30 cents per page. Online Access: Yes. Number of Active Corporations on File: 40,000.

Vermont

Corporate Division, Secretary of State, 81 River Street, Drawer 09, Montpelier, VT 05609-1104, 802-828-2386, Fax: 802-828-2853; {www.sec.state.vt.us}. Selected Publications: None. Phone Information: 802-828-2386. Copies of Documents on File: Available for $1 per page, $5 for certified copies. Send the $5 certification fee in advance. They will bill you for the copies. Mailing Labels: No. Magnetic Tape: No. Microfiche: No. Corporate Listings: Yes. Monthly New Corporations an Trade names on diskette cost $6 plus 1 cent per name. Total cost is never more than $15. Out-of-State Corporations, $50 for complete list. Custom Searches: Yes. Categories: Foreign, Domestic, Nonprofits, by date of registration. Cost is 1 cent per name plus $6 to run list. Online Access: Yes. Number of Active Corporation on File: 24,000.

Virginia

Clerk of Commission, State Corporation Commission, Secretary of State, 1300 East Main Street 23219, 804-371-9733, Fax: 804-371-9654; {www.state.va.us/scc}. Selected Publications: Business Registration Guide. Phone Information: 804-371-9733. Copies of Documents on File. Available for $1 per page, $3 for certified copies. Mailing Labels: No. Magnetic Tape: Yes. They provide you tapes for $1,000 a month and you do not have to provide blank tapes.

Microfiche: No. New Corporate Listings: No. Custom Searches: Yes. Online Access: Available through Direct Access. You will dial into their database for free to obtain the information you need. Call 804-371-9733 to ask for a password. Number of Active Corporations on File: 160,000.

Washington

Corporate Division, Secretary of State, 801 Capitol Way South, P.O. Box 40234, Olympia, WA 98504, 360-753-7115, Fax: 360-586-5629; {www.secstate.wa.gov}. Selected Publications: None. Phone Information: 360-753-7115. Copies of Documents on File: Fees are $1 plus 20 cents per page. Certified copies are $5 plus 20 cents per page. Certificates are $10. Mailing Labels: No Magnetic Tape: No. Microfiche: Cost is $10 a month. New Corporate Listings: No. Custom Searches: No. Online Access: Yes. Number of Active Corporations on File: 145,000.

West Virginia

Corporate Division, Secretary of State, Room 139 West, State Capitol, Charleston, WV 25305, 304-558-8000, Fax: 304-558-0900; {www.wvsos.com}. Selected Publications: None. Phone Information: 304-558-8000. Copies of Documents on File: Available for 50 cents per page, $10 for certified copies. Mailing Labels: No. Magnetic Tape: No. Microfiche: No. New Corporate Listing: Monthly Report costs $5 a month or $50 per year. Custom Searches: yes. Cost is $5 for each hour or fraction thereof. Online Access: No. Number of Active Corporations on File: 39,000.

Wisconsin

Corporate Division, Secretary of State, PO Box 7846, Madison, WI 53707; Street address: 345 West Washington Avenue, 3rd Floor, Madison, WI 53703, 608-261-7577, Fax: 608-267-6813; {www.wdfi.org}. Selected Publications: Chapter 180 Statutes Book ($4). Phone Information: 608-266-3590. Copies of Documents on File: For simple copy request must be in writing. Fee is $2. Requests for certified copies may be phoned in. Fee is $10, $25 for expedited search. Mailing Labels: No. Magnetic Tape: No. Microfiche: Yes. Monthly new Corporations costs $12 per month. New Corporate Listing: Yes (see Microfiche entry). Minimum cost is $10 per week. Custom Searches: Yes. Online Access: yes. Number of Active Corporations on File: 130,708.

Wyoming

Corporate Division, Secretary of State, State of Wyoming, Capitol Building, Room 110, Cheyenne, WY 82002, 307-777-7311; Fax: 307-777-5339; {http:\\soswy.state.wy.us}. Selected Publications: Wyoming Business Corporation Act (available free on website). Phone Information: 307-777-7311. Copies of Documents on File: available for 50 cents for first 10 pages then 15 cents per page, $3 for certified copies. Mailing Labels: No. Magnetic Tape: No. Microfiche: No. New corporate Listings: yes: $300/yr for monthly listing of both foreign and domestic corporations, or $150 each. Custom Searches: Yes: Categories: Foreign, Domestic, Statutory trust, Nonprofit and Profit, Limited Partnership, Limited Liability, Trade names and Trademarks. Listing of all active profit corporations can be purchased for $25 on diskette. They can email it to you at no cost. Contact Jeanie Sawyer, 307-777-5334. Online Access: Yes. Number of Active Corporations on File: 33,000.

More Help In Finding A Grant

No one source can be a complete guide to finding a grant, including ours, so we wanted to include other resources you can use in your search. There are publications, experts, and even classes you can take to assist you in making your dreams come true.

As we stated earlier, The Foundation Center is a nonprofit organization which gathers and disseminates factual information on foundations. The Center's libraries in New York City, Atlanta, San Francisco, Cleveland, and Washington, DC, contain copies of foundations' tax returns, extensive collections of books, documents, and reports about the foundation field, and current files on the activities and programs of about 50,000 U.S. foundations, plus knowledgeable staff to assist users in locating appropriate information.

The Foundation Center also publishes funding directories specific to certain fields, such as: aging; arts and culture; children, youth, and families; health; higher education; international programs; libraries and information services; religion; women and girls; and elementary and secondary education.

In addition, the Center has established cooperating reference collections in each state, where Center publications and information on foundations in the immediate state or region can be consulted. A list of cooperating libraries housing these regional collections appears below. The Center also offers classes and seminars on a variety of topics, including proposal writing, basics of seeking a grant, and "how to" classes on the use of the resources and website. For further information, contact the Foundation Center, 79 Fifth Avenue, New York, NY 10003; 800-424-9836; 212-620-4230; Fax: 212-691-1828; {http://fdncenter.org}.

Foundation Center Reference Collections

The Foundation Center
2nd Floor, 79 Fifth Ave.
New York, NY 10003
212-620-4230
Fax: 212-691-1828
http://fdncenter.org/newyork/index.h
   tml

The Foundation Center
312 Sutter St., #606
San Francisco, CA 94108-4323
415-397-0902
Fax: 415-397-7670
http://fdncenter.org/sanfrancisco/ind
   ex.html

The Foundation Center
1627 K Street, NW, 3rd Floor
Washington, DC 20006-1708
202-331-1400
Fax: 202-331-1739
http://fdncenter.org/washington/inde
   x.html

The Foundation Center
Kent H. Smith Library
1422 Euclid, Suite 1600
Cleveland, OH 44115-2001
216-861-1934
Fax: 216-861-1936
http://fdncenter.org/cleveland/index.
   html

The Foundation Center
Suite 150, Grand Lobby
Hurt Building
50 Hurt Plaza
Atlanta, GA 30303
404-880-0094
Fax: 404-880-0087
http://fdncenter.org/atlanta/index.html

Cooperating Collections

Alabama
Birmingham Public Library
Government Documents
2100 Park Place

Birmingham, AL 35203
205-226-3620

Huntsville Public Library
915 Monroe St.
Huntsville, AL 35801
256-532-5940

Mobile Public Library
West Regional Library
5555 Grelot Road
Mobile, AL 36609-3643
251-340-8555

Auburn University at Montgomery
Library
74-40 East Drive
Montgomery, AL 36117-3596
334-244-3200

Alaska
Consortium Library
3211 Providence Dr.
Anchorage, AK 99508
907-786-1848

Juneau Public Library
Reference
2929 Marine Way
Juneau, AK 99801
907-586-5267

Arizona
Flagstaff City-Coconino County
Public Library
300 West Aspen Avenue
Flagstaff, AZ 86081
928-779-7670

Phoenix Public Library
Information Services Department
1221 N. Central
Phoenix, AZ 85004
602-262-4636

Tucson Pima Library
101 N. Stone Ave.
Tucson, AZ 87501
520-791-4393

Arkansas
University of Arkansas-Fort Smith
Boreham Library
5210 Grand Ave.
Ft. Smith, AR 72913
479-788-7204

Central Arkansas Library System
100 Rock St.
Little Rock, AR 72201
501-918-3000

California
Humboldt Area Foundation
Rooney Resource Center
373 Indianola
P.O. Box 99
Bayside, CA 95524
707-442-2993

Ventura County Community
Foundation
Resource Center for Nonprofit
Organizations
1317 Del Norte Rd.
Suite 150
Camarillo, CA 93010
805-988-0196

Fresno Regional Foundation
Nonprofit Advancement Center
3425 N. First St., Suite 101
Fresno, CA 93726
559-226-0216

Center for Nonprofit Management in
Southern California
Nonprofit Resource Library
606 South Olive Street, Suite 2450
Los Angeles, CA 90014
213-623-7080

Flintridge Foundation
Philanthropy Resource Library
1040 Lincoln Ave., Suite 100
Pasadena, CA 91103
626-449-0839

Kern County Library
Beale Memorial Library
701 Truxton Avenue
Bakersfield, CA 93301
661-868-0750

Los Angeles Public Library
Mid-Valley Regional Branch Library
16244 Nordhoff Street.
North Hills, CA 91343
818-895-3654

East Bay Resource Center for
Nonprofit Support
359 Frank H. Ogawa Plaza
Oakland, CA 94612
510-834-1010

Shasta Regional Community
Foundation Center for Nonprofit
Resources
Building C, Suite A
2280 Benton Dr.
Redding, CA 96003
530-244-1219

Richmond Public Library
325 Civic Center Plaza
Richmond, CA 94804
510-620-6561

Riverside Public Library
3581 Mission Inn Ave.
Riverside, CA 92501
909-782-5201

Nonprofit Resource Center
Sacramento Public Library
828 I St., 2nd Floor
Sacramento, CA 95814
916-264-2772

San Diego Foundation
Funding Information Center
1420 Kettner Blvd.
Suite 500
San Diego, CA 92101
619-239-2300

Compasspoint Nonprofit Services
Nonprofit Development Center
Library
1922 The Alameda
Suite 212
San Jose, CA 95126
408-248-9505

Peninsula Community Foundation
Peninsula Nonprofit Center
1700 S. El Camino Real, R201
San Mateo, CA 94402-3049
650-358-9392

Foundation Center Office and
Library
312 Sutter Street, Suite 606
San Francisco, CA 94108
415-397-0902

Los Angeles Public Library
San Pedro Regional Branch
9131 S. Gaffey St.
San Pedro, CA 90731
310-548-7779

Volunteer Center of Greater Orange
County
Nonprofit Management Assistance
Center
1901 E. 4th St., Suite 100
Santa Ana, CA 92705
714-953-5757

Santa Barbara Public Library
40 E. Anapamu St.
Santa Barbara, CA 93101-1019
805-962-7653

Santa Monica Public Library
1343 Sixth St.
Santa Monica, CA 90401
310-458-8600

Seaside Branch Library
550 Harcourt St.
Seaside, CA 93955
408-899-8131

Sierra Nonprofit Support Center
39 North Washington St., Suite F
Sonora, CA 95370
209-533-1093

Sonoma County Library
3rd and E Streets
Santa Rosa, CA 95404
707-545-0831

Colorado
El Pomar Nonprofit Resource
Library
Penrose Library

20 N. Cascade
Colorado Springs, CO 80903
719-531-6333

Denver Public Library
General Reference
10 West 14th Parkway
Denver, CO 80204
720-865-1111

Connecticut
Danbury Public Library
170 Main St.
Danbury, CT 06810
203-797-4527

Greenwich Library
101 West Putnam Ave.
Greenwich, CT 06830
203-622-7900

Hartford Public Library
500 Main St.
Hartford, CT 06103
860-695-6292

New Haven Free Public Library
Reference Department
133 Elm St.
New Haven, CT 06510-2057
203-946-7431

Delaware
University of Delaware
Hugh Morris Library
181 South College Avenue
Newark, DE 19717-5267
302-831-2432

Florida
Volusia County Library
City Island
105 E. Magnolia Ave.
Daytona Beach, FL 32114-4484
386-257-6036

Nova Southeastern University
Research and Information
   Technology Library
3301 College Ave.
Fort Lauderdale, FL 33314
954-262-4613

Indian River Community College
Learning Resources Center
3209 Virginia Ave.
Fort Pierce, FL 34981-5596
561-462-4757

Jacksonville Public Libraries
Grants Resource Center
122 N. Ocean St.
Jacksonville, FL 32202
904-630-2665

Miami-Dade Public Library
Humanities/Social Science
101 W. Flagler St.
Miami, FL 33130
305-375-5575

Orange County Library System
Social Sciences Department
101 E. Central Blvd.
Orlando, FL 32801
407-425-4694

Selby Public Library
Reference
1331 First St.
Sarasota, FL 34236
941-316-1100

Hillsborough County Public Library
   Cooperative
John F. Germay Public Library
900 N. Ashley Dr.
Tampa, FL 33602
813-273-3652

Community Foundation of Palm
   Beach and Martin Counties
700 South Dixie Highway
Suite 200
West Palm Beach, FL 33401
561-659-6800

State Library of Florida
R.A. Gray Building
Tallahassee, FL 32399-0250
850-245-6600

Georgia
Atlanta-Field Office and Library
Suite 220, Grant Lobby
Hurt Building
50 Hurt Plaza
Atlanta, GA 30303-2914
404-880-0094

Washington Memorial Library
1180 Washington Ave.
Macon, GA 31201
478-744-0828

Hall County Library System
127 Main Street, NW
Gainesville, GA 30501
770-532-3311

Thomas County Public Library
201 N. Madison St.
Thomasville, GA 31792
229-225-5252

Hawaii
University of Hawaii
Hamilton Library
General/Humanities/Social Science
   Reference Department
2550 The Mall
Honolulu, HI 96822
808-956-7214

Idaho
Funding Information Center
Boise Public Library
715 S. Capitol Blvd.
Boise, ID 83702
208-384-4024

Caldwell Public Library
1010 Dearborn St.
Caldwell, ID 83605
208-459-3242

Illinois
Donors Forum of Chicago
208 South LaSalle, Suite 735
Chicago, IL 60604
312-578-0175

Evanston Public Library
1703 Orrington Ave.
Evanston, IL 60201
847-866-0300

Rock Island Public Library
401 19th St.
Rock Island, IL 61201-8143
309-732-7323

Nonprofit Resource Center
University of Illinois at Springfield
Brookens Library
One University Plaza
MSLib 140
Springfield, IL 62703-5407
217-206-6633

Indiana
Evansville-Vanderburgh County
   Public Library
22 Southeast Fifth St.
Evansville, IN 47708
812-428-8200

Allen County Public Library
200 East Berry St.
Ft. Wayne, IN 46802
219-421-1238

Indianapolis-Marion County Public
   Library
202 N. Alabama
Indianapolis, IN 46206
317-269-1700

Vigo County Public Library
1 Library Square
Terre Haute, IN 47807
812-232-1113

Iowa
Cedar Rapids Public Library
Foundation Center Collection
500 First St., SE
Cedar Rapids, IA 52401
319-398-5123

Southwestern Community College
Learning Resource Center
1501 W. Townline Rd.
Creston, IA 50801
515-782-7081

Des Moines Public Library
100 Locust
Des Moines, IA 50309-1791
515-283-4152

Sioux City Public Library
529 Pierce St.
Sioux City, IA 51101-1202
712-255-2933

Kansas
Dodge City Public Library
1001 2nd Ave.
Dodge City, KS 67801
316-225-0248

Topeka and Shawnee County Public
Library
1515 SW 10th Ave.
Topeka, KS 66604
785-580-4400

Wichita Public Library
223 S. Main St.
Wichita, KS 67202
316-261-8500

Pioneer Memorial Library
375 West 4th Street
Colby, KS 67701
785-462-4770

Kearny County Library
101 East Prairie
Lakia, KS 67860
620-355-6674

Salina Public Library
301 West Elm
Salina, KS 67401
785-825-4624

Kentucky
Western Kentucky University
Helm-Cravens Library
110 Helm Library
Bowling Green, KY 42101-3576
270-745-6163

Lexington Public Library
140 E. Main St.
Lexington, KY 40507-1376
859-231-5520

Louisville Free Public Library
301 York Street
Louisville, KY 40203
502-574-1617

Louisiana
East Baton Rouge Parish Library
Centroplex Branch Grants Collection
120 St. Louis
Baton Rouge, LA 70802
225-389-4967

Beauregard Parish Library
205 S. Washington Ave.
De Ridder, LA 70634
318-463-6217

Ouachita Parish Public Library
1800 Stubbs Ave.
Monroe, LA 71201
318-327-1490

New Orleans Public Library
Business and Sciences Division
219 Loyola Ave.
New Orleans, LA 70112
504-596-2580

Shreve Memorial Library
424 Texas St.
Shreveport, LA 71120-1523
318-226-5894

Maine
The Maine Philanthropy Center
University of Southern Maine
Library
314 Forrest Ave.
Portland, ME 04104-9301
207-780-5029

Maryland
Enoch Pratt Free Library
Social Science and History
400 Cathedral St.
Baltimore, MD 21201
410-396-5320

Massachusetts
Associated Grantmakers of
Massachusetts (AGM)
55 Court St., Room 520
Boston, MA 02108
617-426-2606

Boston Public Library
Social Science Reference
700 Boylston St.
Boston, MA 02116
617-536-5400

Western Massachusetts Funding
Resource Center
65 Elliot St.
Springfield, MA 01101-1730
413-452-0697

Worcester Public Library
Grants Resource Center
3 Salem Square
Worcester, MA 01608
508-799-1654

Michigan
Alpena County Library
211 N. First St.
Alpena, MI 49707
989-356-6188

University of Michigan- Ann Arbor
Graduate Library
Reference and Research Services
Department
Ann Arbor, MI 48109-1205
734-763-1539

Willard Public Library
Nonprofit and Funding Resource
Collections
7 W. Van Buren St.
Battle Creek, MI 49017
616-968-8166

Henry Ford Centennial Library
Adult Services
16301 Michigan Ave.
Dearborn, MI 48126
313-943-2330

Wayne State University
134 Purdy/Kresge Library
5265 Cass Ave.
Detroit, MI 48202
313-577-6424

Michigan State University Libraries
100 Library
Main Library Funding Center
East Lansing, MI 48824-1049
517-432-6123

Farmington Community Library
32737 West 12 Mile Rd.
Farmington Hills, MI 48334
248-553-0300

Francis Willson Thompson Library
University of Michigan- Flint
Library
Flint, MI 48502-1950
810-762-3413

Grand Rapids Public Library
Reference Department
111 Library St. NE
Grand Rapids, MI 49503-3268
616-988-5400

Michigan Technological University
Harold Meese Center
Corporate Services
1400 Townsend Dr.
Houghton, MI 49931-1295
906-487-2228

West Shore Community College
Library
3000 North Stiles Road
Scottville, MI 49454-0277
231-845-6211

Traverse Area District Library
610 Woodmere Avenue
Traverse City, MI 49686
231-932-8500

Minnesota
Duluth Public Library
520 W. Superior St.
Duluth, MN 55802
218-732-3802

Southwest State University
University Library
North Highway 23
Marshall, MN 56253
507-537-6108

Minneapolis Public Library
Sociology Department
250 Marquette Ave.
Minneapolis, MN 55401
612-630-6000

Rochester Public Library
101 2nd St., SE
Rochester, MN 55904-3777
507-285-8002

St. Paul Public Library
90 W. Fourth St.
St. Paul, MN 55102
651-266-7000

Brainerd Public Library
416 South Fifth Street
Brainerd, MN 56401
218-829-5574

Mississippi
Jackson/Hinds Library System
300 N. State St.
Jackson, MS 39201
601-968-5803

Library of Hattiesburg, Petal and
Forrest County
329 Hardy Street
Hattiesburg, MS 39401-3824
601-582-4461

Missouri
Council on Philanthropy
University of Missouri-Kansas City
4747 Troost, #207
Kansas City, MO 64171-0813
816-235-1176

Kansas City Public Library
14 West 10th Street
Kansas City, MO 64105-1702
816-701-3541

St. Louis Public Library
1301 Olive Street
St. Louis, MO 63103
314-241-2288

Springfield-Greene County Library
4653 S. Campbell
Springfield, MO 65810
417-874-8110

Montana
Montana State University- Billings
Library- Special Collections
1500 North 30th St.
Billings, MT 59101-0245
406-657-1687

Bozeman Public Library
220 E. Lamme
Bozeman, MT 59715
406-582-2402

Montana State Library
Library Services
1515 E. 6th Ave.
Helena, MT 59620-1800
406-444-3115

University of Montana
Maureen and Mike Mansfield
Library
32 Campus Drive, #9936

Missoula, MT 59812
406-243-6800

Lincoln County Public Libraries
Libby Public Library
220 West 6th Street
Libby, MT 59923
406-293-2778

Nebraska
University of Nebraska- Lincoln
225 Love Library
14th and R Sts.
Lincoln, NE 68588-2848
402-472-2848

Omaha Public Library
Social Sciences Department
215 S. 15th St.
Omaha, NE 68102
402-444-4826

Nevada
Clark County Library
1401 E. Flamingo
Las Vegas, NV 89119
702-507-3400

Washoe County Library
301 S. Center St.
Reno, NV 89501
775-327-8300

Great Basin College Library
1500 College Parkway
Elko, NV 89801
775-753-2222

New Hampshire
Concord Public Library
45 Green St.
Concord, NH 03301
603-225-8670

Herbert H. Lamson Library
Plymouth State College
Plymouth, NY 03264
603-535-2258

New Jersey
Cumberland County Library
800 E. Commerce St.
Bridgeton, NJ 08302
609-453-2210

Free Public Library of Elizabeth
11 S. Broad St.
Elizabeth, NJ 07202
908-354-6060

County College of Morris
Learning Resource Center
214 Center Grove Rd.
Randolph, NJ 07869
973-328-5296

New Jersey State Library
Governmental Reference Services
185 W. State St.

Trenton, NJ 08625-0520
609-292-6220

Newark Enterprise Community
Resource Development Center
303-309 Washington St., 5th Floor
Newark, NJ 07102
973-624-8300

New Mexico
Albuquerque Bernalillo County
Library System
501 Copper Avenue, NW
Albuquerque, NM 87102
505-768-5141

New Mexico State Library
Information Services
1209 Camino Carlos Rey
Santa Fe, NM 87507
505-476-9702

New York
New York State Library
Humanities Reference
Cultural Education Center, 6th Floor
Empire State Plaza
Albany, NY 12230
518-474-5355

Southeast Steuben County Library
300 Nasser Civic Center Plaza
Corning, NY 14830
607-936-0713

Brooklyn Public Library
Social Sciences/Philosophy Division
Grand Army Plaza
Brooklyn, NY 11238
718-230-2122

Buffalo and Erie County Public
Library
Business, Science and Technology
Department
1 Lafayette Square
Buffalo, NY 14203-1887
716-858-7097

Huntington Public Library
338 Main St.
Huntington, NY 11743
516-427-5165

Queens Borough Public Library
Social Sciences Division
89-11 Merrick Blvd.
Jamaica, NY 11432
718-990-0700

Levittown Public Library
1 Bluegrass Lane
Levittown, NY 11756
516-731-5728

The Riverhead Free Library
330 Court Street
Riverhead, NY 11901
631-727-3228

Adriance Memorial Library
Special Services Department
93 Market St.
Poughkeepsie, NY 12601
914-485-3445

Rochester Public Library
Social Sciences
115 South Ave.
Rochester, NY 14604
716-428-8120

Onondago County Public Library
447 S. Salina St.
Syracuse, NY 13202-2494
315-435-1900

Utica Public Library
303 Genessee St.
Utica, NY 13501
315-735-2279

White Plains Public Library
100 Martine Ave.
White Plains, NY 10601
914-422-1480

Yonkers Public Library
Riverfront Library
One Larkin Center
Yonkers, NY 10701
914-337-1500

North Carolina
Community Foundation of Western
   North Carolina
Pack Memorial Library
67 Haywood Street
Asheville, NC 28801
828-254-4960

The Duke Endowment
100 N. Tryon St
Suite 3500
Charlotte, NC 28202-4012
704-376-0291

Durham County Public Library
301 North Roxboro
Durham, NC 27702
919-560-0100

Forsyth County Public Library
660 W. 5th St.
Winston Salem, NC 27408
336-727-2264

North Dakota
Bismarck Public Library
515 N. Fifth St.
Bismarck, ND 58501-4801
701-222-6410

Fargo Public Library
102 N. 3rd St.
Fargo, ND 58102
701-241-1491

Minot Public Library
516 Second Avenue, SW

Minot, ND 58701-3792
701-852-1045

Ohio
Stark County District Library
Humanities
715 Market Ave. N
Canton, OH 44702
330-452-0665

Public Library of Cincinnati and
   Hamilton County
Grants Resource Center
800 Vine St.
Library Square
Cincinnati, OH 45202-3071
513-369-6000

Foundation Center Office and
   Library
1422 Euclid Avenue, Suite 1600
Cleveland, OH 44115
216-861-1934

Columbus Metropolitan Library
Business and Technology
96 S. Grant Ave.
Columbus, OH 43215
614-645-2590

Dayton Metro Library
Grants Resource Center
215 E. Third St.
Dayton, OH 45402
937-227-9500 ext. 322

Mansfield/Richland County Public
   Library
42 W. 3rd St.
Mansfield, OH 44902
419-521-5100

Toledo-Lucas County Public Library
Social Sciences Department
325 Michigan St.
Toledo, OH 43612
419-259-5209

Public Library of Youngstown and
   Mahoning County
305 Wick Ave.
Youngstown, OH 44503
330-744-8636

Portsmouth Public Library
1220 Gallia Street
Portsmouth, OH 45662
740-354-5688

Oklahoma
Oklahoma City University
Dulaney Browne Library
2501 N. Blackwelder
Oklahoma City, OK 73106
405-521-5822

Tulsa City-County Library
400 Civic Center
Tulsa, OK 74103
918-596-7977

Oregon
Oregon Institute of Technology
Library
3201 Campus Dr.
Klamath Falls, OR 97601-8801
541-885-1770

Pacific Non-Profit Network
Southern Oregon University
1600 N. Riverside, Suite 1001
Medford, OR 97501
541-779-6044

Multnomah County Library
Government Documents
801 SW Tenth Ave.
Portland, OR 97205
503-988-5123

Oregon State Library
State Library Building
250 Winter Street, NE
Salem, OR 97310
503-378-4277

Pennsylvania
Northampton Community College
The Paul and Harriett Mack Library
3835 Green Pond Rd.
Bethlehem, PA 18017
610-861-5360

Erie County Library System
160 East Front St.
Erie, PA 16507
814-451-6927

Hazleton Area Public Library
55 North Church Street
Hazleton, PA 18201
570-454-2961

Dauphin County Library System
East Shore Area Library
4501 Ethel Street
Harrisburg, PA 17109
717-652-9380

Lancaster County Public Library
125 N. Duke St.
Lancaster, PA 17602
717-394-2651

Free Library of Philadelphia
Regional Foundation Center
1901 Vine Street, 2nd Floor
Philadelphia, PA 19103-1189
215-686-5423

Carnegie Library of Pittsburgh
Foundation Center
Library Center
414 Wood Street
Pittsburgh, PA 15222
412-281-7143

Pocono Northeast Development
   Fund
James Pettinger Memorial Library
1151 Oak St.

Pittston, PA 18640
570-655-5581

Reading Public Library
100 South Fifth St.
Reading, PA 19602
610-655-6355

Martin Library
159 Market St.
York, PA 17401
717-846-5300

James V. Brown Library
19 East Fourth Street
Williamsport, PA 17701
570-326-0536

Puerto Rico
Universidad Del Sagrado Cosazon
M.M.T. Guevara Library
Santurce, PR 00914
787-728-1515, ext. 4354

Rhode Island
Providence Public Library
225 Washington St.
Providence, RI 02906
401-455-8088

South Carolina
Anderson County Library
300 McDuffie Street
Anderson, SC 29622
864-260-4500

Charleston County Library
68 Calhoun St.
Charleston, SC 29401
843-805-6930

South Carolina State Library
1500 Senate St.
Columbia, SC 29211
803-734-8666

Community Foundation of Greater
Greenville
27 Cleveland St., Suite 101
Greenville, SC 29601
864-233-5925

South Dakota
South Dakota State Library
800 Governors Dr.
Pierre, SD 57501-2294
605-773-3131
800-423-6665 (SD only)

Dakota State University
Nonprofit Management Institute
Nonprofit Grants Assistance
820 N. Washington
Madison, SD 57042
605-782-3089

Black Hills State University
E.Y. Berry Library-Learning Center
1200 University St., Unit 9676

Spearfish, SD 67799-9676
605-642-6833

Tennessee
Knox County Public Library
500 W. Church Ave.
Knoxville, TN 37902
865-215-8751

Memphis and Shelby County Public
Library
3030 Poplar Oak Ave.
Memphis, TN 38111
901-415-2734

Nashville Public Library
615 Church Street
Nashville, TN 37219
615-862-5800

United Way of Greater Chattanooga
Center for Nonprofits
630 Market Street
Chattanooga, TN 37402
423-265-0514

Texas
Amarillo Area Foundation
Grants Center
801 S. Fillmore
Amarillo, TX 79101
806-376-4521

Hogg Foundation for Mental Health
3001 Lake Austin Blvd.
Austin, TX 78703
512-471-5041
888-404-4336

Beaumont Public Library
801 Pearl St.
Beaumont, TX 77704-3827
409-838-6606

Corpus Christi Public Library
Funding Information Center
805 Comanche St.
Corpus Christi, TX 78401
361-880-7000

Dallas Public Library
Urban Information
1515 Young St.
Dallas, TX 75201
213-670-1487

University of Texas at El Paso
Community Nonprofit Grant Library
500 W. University
Benedict Hall, Room 103
El Paso, TX 79968-0547
915-747-7969

Southwest Border Nonprofit
Resource Center
1201 W. University Dr.
Edinburgh, TX 78539-3299
956-384-5920

Funding Information Center of Fort
Worth
329 S. Henderson
Ft. Worth, TX 76104
817-334-0228

Houston Public Library
Bibliographic Information Center
500 McKinney
Houston, TX 77002
823-393-1313

Laredo Public Library
Nonprofit Management and
Volunteer Center
1120 East Carlton Rd.
Laredo, TX 78041
956-795-2400

Longview Public Library
222 W. Cotton St.
Longview, TX 75601
903-237-1350

Lubbock Area Foundation, Inc.
1655 Main St., Suite 209
Lubbock, TX 79401
806-762-8061

Nonprofit Resource Center of Texas
7404 Highway 90 West
San Antonio, TX 78212-8270
210-227-4333

Waco-Mclennan County Library
1717 Austin Ave.
Waco, TX 76701
254-750-5941

Nonprofit Management Center of
Wichita Falls
2301 Mell Blvd., Suite 218
Wichita Falls, TX 76308
940-322-4961

Utah
Salt Lake City Public Library
210 East 400 South
Salt Lake City, UT 84111
801-524-8200

Grand County Public Library
25 South 10 East
Moab, UT 84532
435-259-5421

Vermont
Vermont Department of Libraries
Reference and Law Information
Services
109 State St.
Montpelier, VT 05609
802-828-3261

Ilsley Public Library
75 Main Street
Middleburg, VT 85753
802-388-4095

Virginia

Hampton Public Library
4207 Victoria Blvd.
Hampton, VA 23669
757-727-1314

Washington County Public Library
205 Oak Hill
Abingdon, VA 24210
276-676-6222

Richmond Public Library
Business, Science and Technology
101 East Franklin St.
Richmond, VA 23219
804-646-7223

Roanoke City Public Library System
Main Library
706 S. Jefferson
Roanoke, VA 24016
540-853-2471

Washington

Mid-Columbia Library
Reference Department
1620 South Union Street
Kennewick, WA 99336
509-783-7878

Seattle Public Library
Fundraising Resource Center
800 Pike Street
Seattle, WA 98101-3922
206-386-4645

King County Library System
Redmond Regional Library
Nonprofit and Philanthropy
  Resource Center

15990 NE 85th
Redmond, WA 98052
425-885-1861

Spokane Public Library
Funding Information Center
906 W. Main Ave.
Spokane, WA 99201
509-444-5300

Tacoma Library
University of Washington
1900 Commerce Street
Tacoma, WA 98403-3100
253-692-4440

Wenatchee Valley College
John A. Brown Library
Funding Information Center
1300 Fifth Street
Wenatchee, WA 98807
509-664-2520

West Virginia

Kanawha County Public Library
123 Capitol St.
Charleston, WV 25301
304-343-4646

Shepherd College
Ruth A. Scarborough Library
King Street
Shepherdstown, WV 25443-3210
304-876-5424

Wisconsin

University of Wisconsin- Madison
Memorial Library
Grants Information Center
728 State St.

Madison, WI 53706
608-262-3242

Marquette University Memorial
  Library
Funding Information Center
1355 W. Wisconsin Ave.
Milwaukee, WI 53201-3141
414-288-1515

University of Wisconsin- Stevens
  Point
Library- Foundation Collection
900 Reserve St.
Stevens Point, WI 54481-3897
715-346-2540

Wyoming

Laramie County Community College
Instructional Resource Center
1400 E. College Dr.
Cheyenne, WY 82007-3299
307-778-1206

Campbell County Public Library
2101 4-J Rd.
Gillette, WY 82718
307-687-0115

Teton County Library
125 Virginia Lane
Jackson, WY 83001
307-733-2164

Sheridan County Fulmer Public
  Library
335 West Alger Street
Sheridan, WY 82801
307-674-8585

(Library list courtesy of The Foundation Center)

Foundation Center Publications

(Remember that many of these publications are located in your library or in the state foundation libraries listed above. For further information, contact the Foundation Center, 79 Fifth Avenue, New York, NY 10003; 800-424-9836; 212-620-4230; Fax: 212-691-1828; {http://fdncenter.org}.)

* *Foundation Directory* ($215): Provides a description of over 10,000 large American foundations having at least $3 million in assets or $200,000 in annual giving. Each entry includes factual and financial data, statement of purpose and activities, and grant application procedures; indexed by fields of interest, names of donors, trustees, and administrators, and by state and city.

* *The Foundation Directory, Part 2* ($185): provides information on 8,700 private and community foundations making grants of $50,000-$200,000 annually and holding assets of less than $3,000,000. This is a guide to smaller but significant grantmakers whose giving often supports local organizations. Over 83% of the entries include geographic limitation statements showing preferences for giving within specific cities or states. The directory provides lists of sample grants whenever available, to provide concrete indications of the foundation's fields of interest, geographic preferences, and range of giving.

* *Foundation Grants Index* on CD-ROM ($165): Describes over 125,000 grants awarded by approximately 1,000 foundations within the previous year or two. This is a selective listing, useful for identifying potential funding sources based on previously awarded foundation grants. The main listing of grants is arranged by major subject fields with the grants listed alphabetically by state. A typical grant record includes the name and location of the recipient, the amount awarded, the date authorized and a description of the grant. Grant descriptions are succinct but descriptive, for example: "To promote community involvement in ground water protection in Ohio." Includes a detailed subject index.

* *The Foundation Directory Supplement* ($125): Provides revised entries for hundreds of foundations in *The Foundation Directory* and *The Foundation Directory Part 2*. The Supplement reflects any changes in giving interests, updates on staff, financial data, contact information, and more.

* *Foundation Grants to Individuals* ($65): While the majority of foundations in the United States limit their grants to nonprofit organizations, this publication gives information on funds available to individuals from approximately 5,500 foundations. Emphasis is placed on educational and scholarship awards. Six indexes help users target prospective grants by subject area, types of support, geographic area, sponsoring company (for employee restricted awards), educational institutions, and foundation name. Bibliography included.

* *Guide to U.S. Foundations, Their Trustees, Officers, and Donors* ($325): Lists over 50,000 private, corporate, operating, and community foundations, including thousands of smaller ones not described in other sources. These smaller foundations are especially important as local sources of funding. Overall arrangement is by state, with foundations listed from largest to smallest in terms of grants awarded. For each foundation, the Guide gives the foundation's address, telephone number (when available), financial summary, list of officers, trustees and donors, geographic limitation, and (when available) contact person.

* *The Foundation 1000* ($295): Provides data on the 1,000 largest U.S. foundations, including names of officers and staff to contact, current program interests, and names of nonprofit organizations which have already received grants for similar projects. Indexed by subject field, foundation name, type of support, and geographic location.

* *National Directory of Corporate Giving* ($195): Comprehensive descriptions of over 3,600 corporate foundations plus 1,300 direct giving programs. Alphabetically arranged by company name with a general description of the company and its activities and a description of the company's direct giving program and/or foundation for each entry. Indexed by corporation, officers, donors, trustees, geographic areas, types of support, subject, and types of business.

Other Interesting Publications:

Annual Register of Grant Support 2001: A Directory of Funding Sources. New Providence, NJ, R. R. Bowker. Annual. ($239): Descriptions of over 3,000 government and private programs, arranged by broad fields of interest, which give purpose, types of awards, eligibility requirements, financial data, application, and deadline information. Access is provided by subject, organization, geographic, and personnel indexes.

Directory of Research Grants 2004. Greenwood Publishing Group. Annual. ($159.50): Concise descriptions of nearly 6,000 research programs that offer nonrepayable funding for projects in medicine, the physical and social sciences, education, the arts, and humanities. Grant programs are listed in alphabetical order, followed by three indexes: subject, sponsoring organization, and program type.

Internet Resources

The dynamic nature of the Internet means that information resources appear and disappear without warning. The sources listed below were chosen because the organizations which provide the home pages are stable, committed to the sharing of grant information on the Internet.

It is possible to find additional Internet resources by using different World Wide Web search engines, such as AltaVista (www.altavista.com), InfoSeek (www.infoseek.com), Yahoo (www.yahoo.com), Lycos (www.lycos.com), Hotbot (www.hotbot.com), Excite (www.excite.com), Metacrawler (www.metacrawler.com), and others. When searching for grants or funding resources, combine a subject of interest (e.g., education or small business) with terms such as:

- grants
- financial aid or financial assistance
- charities or charity
- foundations
- fund raising or fundraising

Current and updated information on Internet grants sources can also be found in newspapers and such periodicals as Internet World, Internet User, Yahoo Internet Life, and The Net, which may be available at a local public, university, or research library.

National Technical Information Service (NTIS) {www.ntis.gov}: An official resource for U.S. scientific, technical, engineering, and business-related information. Whether you are a research scientist, corporate librarian, or government engineer, NTIS can help you through its mission as the central source for U.S. government scientific, technical, and business information. You can conduct detailed subject searches through the NTIS Government Research Center's online databases or lookup any of the 600,000 documents in their collection.

GRANTSNet: {www.os.dhhs.gov/grants}: GrantsNet is a tool for finding and exchanging information about the U.S. Department of Health and Human Services (HHS) and selected other Federal grant programs. It is part of the much-publicized national movement toward providing government resources to the general public in a more accessible and meaningful manner. HHS has approximately 300 grant programs, most of which are administered in a decentralized manner by several agencies, and they do not have a single publication that describes all the grant programs. This site provides links to grant resources and other assistance for grantseekers.

FEDIX (Federal Information Exchange): {www.sciencewise.com/}: FEDIX is a free outreach tool that provides grant information to educational and research organizations, as well as others, from participating federal agencies. You can select one of the agencies and search for funding opportunities. You can also search for foundation and corporate grants from this site.

Council on Foundations: {www.cof.org}: The Council on Foundations is a nonprofit association of grantmaking foundations and corporations. For those interested in starting a foundation, the COF is a great resource. It explains what a foundation is, the different types of foundations, as well as the steps you need to take in establishing one. There are also helpful links, resources, workshops, and conferences.

The Internet Nonprofit Center: {www.firstgov.org/business/nonprofit.shtml}: The Internet Nonprofit Center provides a wealth of information about nonprofits. An extensive topic list is posted in their Library section, and they have links and other resources as well.

NonProfit Gateway: {www.nonprofit.gov}: This incredible website is the federal government's attempt to help nonprofits access programs. There are links to departments and agencies that have programs of interest to nonprofits. You can learn about services and resources for nonprofits, general governmental information, and much more. Past grant recipients are often listed in the links. You can search the *Catalog of Federal Domestic Assistance*, and learn more about the various rules and regulations.

Help For Inventors

Patents, Trademarks, and Copyrights

Most inventors realize that it's vitally important to protect their idea by copyrighting it and obtaining the necessary patents and copyrights, but did you know that it's also important to look around for loans and other grants to support your business while working on your invention? If you want an idea to become an actual product, you have to invest an awful lot of your time into its research, and not just on a part time basis. Loans and grants programs for inventors  help you do just that. For example, Hawaii offers low cost loans to inventors, as do other states around the country. First, let's talk about getting the necessary information concerning trademark and patent procedures.

Patent and Trademark Office

United States patent and trademark laws are administered by the Patent and Trademark Office (PTO). States also have trade secret statutes, which generally state that if you guard your trade secret with a reasonable amount of care, you will protect your rights associated with that secret. The PTO examines patent and trademark applications, grants protection for qualified inventions, and registers trademarks. It also collects, assembles, and disseminates the technological information patent grants. The PTO maintains a collection of almost 6 million United States patents issued to date, several million foreign patents, and more than 2.2 million trademarks, together with supporting documentation. Here's how to find out what you need to do to patent your idea.

What a Great Idea!

To help you get started with patenting your invention, the Patent and Trademark Offices will send you a free booklet upon request called *General Information Concerning Patents*. There are three legal elements involved in the process of invention: the conception of the idea, diligence in working it out, and reducing it to practice - i.e., getting a finished product that actually works. If you have a great idea you think might work, but you need time to develop it further before it is ready to be patented, what should you do? For answers to general questions on patent examining policies and procedures, contact the Patent Assistance Center at 800-PTO-9199 or 703-308-HELP; TTY: 703-305-7785; Email: {usptoinfo@uspto.gov}. They will not answer legal questions or opinions. Applications, forms, and part or all of pamphlets are at their website; {www.uspto.gov}. You can order them online from {http://bookstore.gpo.gov}. To order them through the mail write to:

Superintendent of Documents
U.S. Government Printing Office
P.O. Box 371954 202-512-1800
Pittsburgh, PA 15250-7954   Fax: 202-512-2250
www.access.gpo.gov/su_docs

What is a Patent?

A patent is a grant of a property right to the inventor for an invention. It lasts for 20 years from the date that the application is filed. United States patent grants are effective within the US, its territories and its possessions. By the language of the grant it is "the right to exclude others from making, using, offering for sale, or selling" the invention in the US or "importing" the invention into the US. It is not the right of the inventor to do so himself that is granted. It is personal property and can be sold or mortgaged, bequeathed or transferred and that person then has the same rights as the original grantee.

What Can Be Patented?

A patent can be received for an invention or discovery of any new and useful process, machine, manufacture, or composition of matter, or any new and useful improvement to

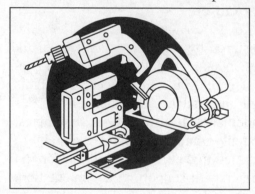

the original. A design patent is the invention of any new and non-obvious ornamental design for an article of manufacture. Its appearance is protected, not its structural or functional features. A plant patent is the invention or discovery and asexually reproduction of any distinct and new variety of plant. This includes cultivated sports, mutants, hybrids, and newly found seedlings, other than a tuber-propagated plant or a plant found in an uncultivated state. Physical phenomena, abstract ideas, and laws of nature can not be patented. There must be a complete description and not just an idea or suggestion of a subject. It must also do what it claims to do; it must work.

If an invention has been described in a publication anywhere in the world, or has been used publicly, or put up for sale, a patent must be applied for before one year passes, or the right to a patent is lost.

Who May Apply?

There are only a few situations where a person other than the inventor may apply for a patent application.
- a representative if the inventor has died
- a guardian if the inventor is insane
- a joint inventor or a person that has ownership interest if the inventor refuses to apply or can not be found

If two or more persons are the inventors, they may file jointly. However, someone who contributed only financially, is not a joint inventor and cannot be included on the application.

Non-Provisional Application

The application must include:
1) a written document consisting of the specifications of the invention, and an oath or declaration
2) a drawing where it is necessary
3) the filing fee.

It must be in English, legible and written on only one side of white paper with a typewriter or its equivalent. The applicant will be notified if all the requirements are not met. The date that the completed application is filed will then become the filing date. Specifications must include a written description of the invention and the method and process of how it was made and is to be used. It must be in clear, concise, and exact terms to allow any skilled person related to the area of the invention to make and use the same discovery. The oath or declaration is a statement made by the inventor that he/she is the original and first inventor of the subject matter, as well as various other statements, made in front of a notary. The filing fee, excluding design and  plant inventions, is a basic fee and additional fees. The basic fee covers 20 claims, including not more than 3 in independent form. There is an additional fee for each claim over 20, whether independent or dependent. The filing fees are cut in half for applicants that file a verified statement claiming small entity status; independent inventor, small business or nonprofit. The drawing must show every feature of the invention specified in the claim. Generally, photographs are not accepted. Applications have legal requirements and must be followed precisely.

Provisional Application

These applications create an early effective filing date and the term "Patent Pending" can be applied to the invention. There must be a written description of the invention, any necessary drawings and the name of the inventor(s). Claims and oath or declarations are not required. Also needed, is a cover sheet that states it is a provisional application and a filing fee. The filing date is the date that the PTO receives the application. This type of application can not be filed for design inventions. A non-provisional application must be filed within 12 months or else it will be discarded.

Protect Your Idea for $10

You can file a Disclosure Document with the Patent and Trademark Office, and they will keep it in confidence as evidence of the date of conception of the invention or idea.

> Disclosure Document
> Commissioner for Patents
> Box DD
> Washington, DC 20231
> Disclosure Office 800-786-9199
> www.uspto.gov/web/offices/pac/disdo.html   703-308-HELP

Send an 8 1/2 x 11" drawing, a copy, signed disclosure, SASE, and a check or money order for $10 to file. Upon request, the above office will also send you a free brochure on Disclosure Documents.

This is the best way to keep the idea you are working on completely secret and yet document the date you conceived the idea. You can file the Disclosure Document at any time after the idea is conceived, but the value of it will depend on how much information you put into it - so put as much detail into this statement as you can.

The Purpose of Documenting The Date of Conception

If someone else should try to patent your idea, filing a Disclosure Document shows that you thought of it first, although filing this statement does not legally protect your invention. Documentation of the conception date gives you time to patent your invention, and is invaluable if you need to prove when you thought of your idea if a dispute should arise. (Note that filing a Disclosure Document gives you limited defensive legal protection only if you follow it up with a patent in two years. Unlike a patent, it cannot be used offensively, to stop someone else from patenting the same idea.) When you go to file for a patent, if you and a competitor get into a dispute as to who was the first to invent it, the Patent and Trademark Office (PTO) will hold an Interference Proceeding. If you thought of the idea first, your Disclosure Document will go a long way towards establishing that you were the first inventor and should therefore receive the patent for it.

Examining the Application

They look to see that the application follows the legal requirements and also that the invention is new, useful and non-obvious and meets all requirements. It is not unusual for some, or all, of the claims to be rejected on the first examination few are accepted as filed The applicant will be notified in writing of any errors found. Then the inventor must request reconsideration, specifically pointing out and addressing any errors found and any amend any claims that to be revised. The second examination will generally be made final. Patents are granted in about every 2 out of 3 applications that are filed.

Patent Electronic Business Center

This is the center where you can do business electronically with the USPTO. In order to check the status of your patent application and also find general patent information, you can access the Patent Application Information Retrieval (PAIR). You will also be able to search for specific patents or applications by their number. The Electronic Filing System (EFS) accepts electronically filed applications, but you must have a digital certification and meet other requirements first. This program is only open to select number of people at this time because it is in the beginning stages of operation. Contact the office to see if you may participate!

Research Resources That Can Help You Turn Your Idea Into Reality

While diligently working out the details of your invention you can use the extensive resources of over 190,000 scientific and technical journals, articles, and books at the Scientific and Technical Information Center in Arlington, VA.

Facilitating public access to the more than 25 million cross-referenced United States patents is the job of PTO's Technology Assessment and Forecast Program (TAF); 703-306-2600. It has a master database which covers all United States patents, and searches are available free. A TAF search will not result in an in-depth patent search. (More on that, and how to find classifications in the *Conducting Your Own Patent Search* section below.) TAF extracts information from its database and makes it available in a variety of formats, including publications, custom patent reports, and statistical reports. The purpose of most of the reports generated by a TAF search is to reveal statistical information.

Copies of the specifications and drawings of all patents are available from PTO. Design patents and trademark copies are $3 each. Plant patents in color are $15 each. To make a request, you must have the patent number. For copies, contact:

Office of Public Records (OPR) 800-972-6382
Crystal Gateway 4, Suite 300 703-308-9726
Arlington, VA 22202 Fax: 703-305-8759
Email: {dsd@uspto.gov}

Assistant Secretary and Commissioner
P.O. Box 9
ATTN: PTCS
Washington, DC 20231
Public Information Line   703-305-8716

Conducting Your Own Patent Search

Before investing too much time and money on patenting your idea, you will want to see if anyone has already patented it. You may conduct the search yourself on the PTO website at {http://www.uspto.gov} or hire someone to do it for you. If you wish to hire a professional to do your patent search, consult the local yellow pages or again, search the PTO website for a roster of patent attorneys. Even if your search is not as in-depth as that of a patent attorney or a patent agent, you may still find the information that you need. You may also conduct your patent search at the Patent and Trademark Office Search Room.

> Patent and Trademark Office (PTO)
> Patent and Trademark Search Room
> Crystal Plaza 3, 1A01
> 2021 Jefferson Davis Highway
> Arlington, VA 22202 703-305-4463

For information about the Patent and Trademark Depository Library, contact the office listed below.

> Patent and Trademark Depository Library (PTDL)
> U.S. Patent and Trademark Office
> Crystal Park 3, Suite 481 703-308-5558
> Washington, DC 20231   Fax: 703-306-2654

You may also conduct your patent search at any of the 83 Patent Depository Libraries (PDLs) throughout the country as listed below.

Patent and Trademark Depository Libraries
Alabama
Ralph Brown Draughon Library, Auburn University, 231 Mell Street, Auburn, AL 36849-5606; 334-844-1737; {www.lib.auburn.edu/scitech/resguide/patents/ptd/html}.

Birmingham Public Library, 2100 Park Place, Birmingham, AL 35203; 205-226-3620; {www.bplonline.org/GovDocs/patents.html}.

Alaska
Z.J. Loussac Municipal Library, 3600 Denali Street, Anchorage, AK 99503-6093; 907-343-2975; {www.muni.org/library1/index.cfm }.

Arkansas
Arkansas State Library, One Capitol Mall, Little Rock, AR 72201; 501-682-2053; Fax: 501-682-1529; {www.asl.lib.ar.us/patents/index.html}.

California
Los Angeles Public Library, 630 West Fifth Street, Los Angeles, CA 90071; 213-228-7220; Fax: 213-228-7209; {www.lapl.org/central/science.html}.

California State Library, Library & Courts Building I, 914 Capitol Mall, Sacramento, CA 95814; 916-654-0069; {www.library.ca.gov/index.html}.

San Diego Public Library, 820 E Street, San Diego, CA 92101-6478; 619-236-5813; {www.sandiego.gov/public-library/index.shtml}.

San Francisco Public Library, 100 Larking Street, San Francisco, CA 94102; 415-557-4500; {http://sfpl.lib.ca.us}.

Sunnyvale Center for Innovation, Invention & Ideas, 665 West Olive Avenue, Sunnyvale, CA 94086; 408-730-7300; Fax: 408-735-8762; {www.sci3.com}.

Colorado
Denver Public Library, 10 West 14th Avenue Parkway, Denver, CO 80204; 720-865-1111; {www.denver.lib.co.us/index.html}

Connecticut
Hartford Public Library, 500 Main Street, Hartford, CT 06103; 860-695-6300; {www.hartfordpl.lib.ct.us}.

Delaware
University of Delaware Library, 181 South College Avenue, Newark, DE 19717-5267; 302-831-2965; {www.lib.udel.edu}.

District of Columbia
Founders Library, Howard University, 500 Howard Place, NW, Washington, DC 20059; 202-806-7234; {www.founders.howard.edu}.

Florida
Broward County Main Library, 100 South Andrews Avenue, Fort Lauderdale, FL 33301; 954-357-7444; {www.co.broward.fl.us/lil12515. htm}.

Dade Public Library, 101 West Flagler Street, Miami, FL 33130; 305 375 2665; {www.mdpls.org}.

University of Central Florida Libraries, 4000 Central Florida Blvd., Orlando, FL 32816; 407-823-2562; {http://library.ucf.edu/GovDocs/PAT_TRAD. htm}.

Tampa Campus Library, 4202 East Fowler Avenue, Tampa, FL 33620-5400; 813-974-2729; {www.lib.usf. edu/ virtual/govdocs}.

Georgia
Library and Information Center, Georgia Institute of Technology, 2nd Floor-East Building, Atlanta, GA 30332; 404-894-4508; {http://gtel.gatech.edu/ patents}.

Hawaii
Hawaii State Library, 478 South King Street, 2nd Floor, Honolulu, HI 96813-2994; 808-586-3477; {www.state.hi.us/libraries/feddocs}

Idaho
University of Idaho Library, Rayburn St., Moscow, ID 83844-2350; 208-885-6235; {www.lib.uidaho.edu/ internet/links/intellectual_property}

Illinois
Chicago Public Library, 400 South State St., 4th Floor, Chicago, IL 60605; 312-747-4450; {www.chipublib. org/008subject/009scitech/patents.html}

Illinois State Library, 300 South 2nd Street, Springfield, IL 62701-1796; 217-782-5659; {www. cyberdriveillinois.com/library/isl/isl.html}

Indiana
Indianapolis-Marion County Public Library, 40 E. St. Clair St., Indianapolis, IN 46204; 317-269-1741; {www.imcpl.lib.in.us/bst_patents.htm}.

Siegesmund Engineering Library, Purdue University, 1530 Stewart Center, Potter Room 160, W. Lafayette, IN 47907; 765-494-2869; {www.lib.purdue. edu/engr/patent.html}.

Iowa
State Library of Iowa, 1112 East Grand Avenue, Des Moines, IA 50319; 515-281-6541; {www.silo.lib.ia. us}.

Kansas
Ablah Library, Wichita State University, 1845 Fairmont, Wichita, KS 67260-0068; 316-978-3622; 800-572-8368; {http://library.wichita.edu/govdoc/ patents.html}.

Kentucky
Louisville Free Public Library, 301 York Street, Louisville, KY 40203; 502-574-1611; {http://lfpl. org/govdoc.htm}.

Louisiana
Troy H. Middleton Library, Louisiana State University, Baton Rouge, LA 70803; 225-388-5652; {www.lib.lsu.edu/index.html}.

Maine
University of Maine, 5729 Raymond H. Fogler Library, Orono, ME 04469-5729; 207-581-1678; {http://library.umaine.edu/patents/default.htm}.

Maryland
Engineering and Physical Sciences Library, University of Maryland, College Park, MD 20742-7011; 301-405-9152; {www.lib.umd.edu/ENGIN/working/pa tents.html}.

Massachusetts
Physical Sciences and Engineering Library, Lederle Graduate Research Center, Room 273, University of Massachusetts, Amherst, Amherst, MA 01003-4630; 413-545-1370; {www.library.umass.edu/subject/ science/scieng8.htm}.

Boston Public Library, 700 Boylston St., Copley Sq., Boston, MA 02116; 617-536-5400, ext. 2226; {www.bpl.org/research/govdocs/patent_ trademark.htm}.

Michigan
Media Union Library, University of Michigan, 2281 Bonisteel Boulevard, Ann Arbor, MI 48109-2094; 734-647-5735; {www.lib.umich.edu/ummu/pattm. html}.

Abigail S. Timme Library, Ferris State University, Big Rapids, MI 49307-2747; 231-591-3500; {www.ferris. edu/library/patent/homepage.html}.

Great Lakes Patent and Trademark Center, Detroit Public Library, 5201 Woodward Avenue, Detroit, MI 48202; 313-833-3379, 800-547-0619; {www. detroit.lib.mi.us/glptc}.

Minnesota
Minneapolis Public Library, 250 Marquette Ave., Minneapolis, MN 55401-1992; 612-630-6000; {www.mplib.org}.

Mississippi

Mississippi Library Commission, 1221 Ellis Ave., Jackson, MS 39289-0700; 601-961-4120, 877-KWIK-REF; {www.mlc.lib.ms.us/reference_and_informa tion_services/patent_&_trademark/index.htm}.

Missouri

Linda Hall Library, Science, Engineering, & Technology, 5109 Cherry Street, Kansas City, MO 64110-2498; 816-363-4600, 800-662-1545; {www.lindahall.org}.

St. Louis Public Library, 1301 Olive Street, St. Louis, MO 63103; 314-241-2288, ext. 390; {www.slpl.lib. mo.us/library.htm}.

Montana

Montana Tech Library, 1300 West Park Street, Butte, MT 59701; 406-496-4281; {www.mtech.edu/library/ patents.htm}.

Nebraska

Engineering Library, Nebraska Hall, 2nd Floor West, City Campus 0516, Lincoln, NE 68588-0410; 402-472-3411; {www.unl.edu/libr/libs/engr/ engr.html}.

Nevada

Clark County Library, 1401 East Flamingo Road, Las Vegas, NV 89119; 702-507-3400; {www.lvccld.org/ special_collections/patents/index.htm}.

Getchell Library, University of Nevada, 2nd Floor, Reno, NV 89557; 775-784-6500 ext. 309; {www. library.unr.edu/depts/bgic}.

New Hampshire

New Hampshire State Library, 20 Park Street, Concord, NH 03301; 603-271-2143; {www.state.nh. us/nhsl/patents/index.html}.

New Jersey

Newark Public Library, 3rd Floor, Main Library, 5 Washington St., Newark, NJ 07101; 973-733-7779; {www.npl.org/Pages/Collections/bst.html}.

Library of Science and Medicine, Rutgers University, 165 Bevier Road, Busch Campus, Piscataway, NJ 08854-8009; 732-445-3854; {www.libraries.rutgers. edu/rul/libs/lsm_lib/lsm_lib.shtml}.

New Mexico

Centennial Science and Engineering Library, The University of New Mexico, Albuquerque, NM 87131; 505-277-5327; {http://zoobert@unm. edu/newcse/}

New York

New York State Library, Cultural Education Center, Empire State Plaza, Albany, NY 12230; 518-474-5355; {www.nysl.nysed.gov/patents.htm}.

Buffalo and Erie County Library, 1 Lafayette Square, Buffalo, NY 14203-1887; 716-858-8900; {www. buffalolib.org/home}.

Science Industry and Business Library, New York Public Library, 188 Madison Avenue, New York, NY 10016; 212-592-7000; {www.nypl.org/research/ sibl/pattrade/pattrade.htm}.

Central Library of Rochester & Monroe County, 115 South Ave., Rochester, NY 14604-1896; 585-428-8110; {www.rochester.lib.ny.us/central}.

Science & Engineering Library, SUNY at Stony Brook, Stony Brook, NY 11794; 631-632-7148; {www.sunysb.edu/sciencelibs/patents.htm}.

North Carolina

D.H. Hill Library, North Carolina State University, 2205 Hillsborough Street, Raleigh, NC 27695-7111; 919-515-2935; {www.lib.ncsu.edu/risd/ govdocs}.

North Dakota

Chester Fritz Library, University of North Dakota, University Station, Grand Forks, ND 58202; 701-777-4888; {www.und.nodak.edu/dept/library/resources/ patents/ptdlp.new.jsp}.

Ohio

Akron-Summit County Public Library, 55 South Main Street, Akron, OH 44326; 330-643-9000; {http://ascpl.lib.oh.us/pat-tm.html}.

Public Library of Cincinnati and Hamilton County, 800 Vine Street, 2nd Floor, North Building, Cincinnati, OH 45202-2071; 513-369-6971; {www.cincinnatilibrary.org/info/main/pd}.

Cleveland Public Library, 325 Superior Avenue, NE, Cleveland, OH 44114-1271; 216-623-2800; {www.cpl.org/}.

Paul Laurence Dunbar Library, Wright State University, Dayton, OH 45435; 937-775-2925; {www.libraries.wright.edu/libnet/subj/gov/ptdl/}

Science and Engineering Library, Ohio State University, 175 West 18th Avenue, Columbus, OH 43210-1150; 614-292-3022; {www.lib.ohiostate. edu/OSU_profile/phyweb}.

Toledo-Lucas County Public Library, 325 N. Michigan Street, Toledo, OH 43624; 419-259-5209; {www.toledolibrary.org/discover/maintwo.htm}.

Oklahoma

Oklahoma State University, 206 CITD, Stillwater, OK 74078-8085; 405-744-7086; {www.library.okstate. edu/patents/index.htm}.

Oregon

Paul L. Boley Law Library, Northwestern School of Law Lewis and Clark College, 10015 SW Terwilliger Boulevard, Portland, OR 97219; 503-768-6786; {www.lclark.edu/~lawlib/ptointro.html}.

Pennsylvania

The Free Library of Philadelphia, 1901 Vine Street, Philadelphia, PA 19103; 215-686-5331; {www.library.phila.gov/}.

Carnegie Library of Pittsburgh, Science and Technology Department, 4400 Forbes Avenue, 3rd Floor, Pittsburgh, PA 15213; 412-622-3138; {www.clpgh.org/clp/Scitech/PTDL/}.

Schreyer Business Library, 301 Paterno Library, 3rd Floor, University Park, PA 16802; 814-865-6369; {www.libraries.psu.edu/crsweb/business/ patents}.

Puerto Rico

General Library, University of Puerto Rico at Mayaguez, Mayaguez, PR 00681; 787-832-4040, ext. 2022; {www.uprm.edu/library/patents}.

General Library, Bayamon Campus, #170 Road 174 Minillas Industrial Park, Bayamon, PR 00959; 787-786-5225; {www.uprb.upr.edu}.

Rhode Island

Providence Public Library, 225 Washington Street, Providence, RI 02903-3283; 401-455-8027; {www.provlib.org}.

South Carolina

R.M. Cooper Library, Clemson University, Clemson, SC 29634-3001; 864-656-3024; {www.lib.clemson.edu/govdocs/patents/newpat.htm}.

South Dakota

Devereaux Library, 501 East Saint Joseph Street, 2nd Floor, Rapid City, SD 57701; 605-394-1275; {www.sdsmt.edu/services/library/library.html}.

Tennessee

Stevenson Science & Engineering Library, 3200 Stevenson Center, Nashville, TN 37240; 615-322-2717; {www.library.vanderbilt.edu/science/patents.html}.

Texas

McKinney Engineering Library, University of Texas at Austin, ECJ 1.300, Austin, TX 78713; 512-495-4500; {www.lib.utexas.edu/engin/patent/ uspat.html}.

Evans Library, Texas A&M University, College Station, TX 77843; 409-845-5745; {http://library.tamu.edu/govdocs/intprop.html}.

Dallas Public Library, 1515 Young Street, 6th Floor, Dallas, TX 75201; 214-670-1468; {http://dallaslibrary.org/central.htm}.

Fondren Library, MS225 Rice University, Houston, TX 77251-1892; 713-348-5483; {www.rice.edu/Fondren/PTDL}.

Texas Tech University Libraries, 18th and Boston, Lubbock, TX 79409-0002; 806-742-2282; {www.lib.ttu.edu/govdocs/index.htm}

San Antonio Public Library, 600 Soledad, 2nd Floor, San Antonio, TX 78205; 210-207-2500; {www.sanantonio.gov/library/central/govdocs.asp}.

Utah

Marriott Library, University of Utah, 295 South 1500 E, Salt Lake City, UT 84112; 801-581-8394; {www.lib.utah.edu/govdocs}.

Vermont

Bailey/Howe Library, University of Vermont, Burlington, VT 05405; 802-656-2542; {http://library.uvm.edu/reference/government/patent.html}.

Virginia

James Branch Cabell Library, Virginia Commonwealth University, 901 Park Avenue, 1st Floor, Richmond, VA 23284-2033; 804-828-1104; {www.library.vcu.edu/jbc/govdocs/govhome.html}.

Washington

Engineering Library, University of Washington, Box 352170, Seattle, WA 98195; 206-543-0740; {www.lib.washington.edu/Engineering/ptdl}.

West Virginia

Evansdale Library, West Virginia University, P.O. Box 6105, Morganstown, WV 26506; 304-293-4696; {www.libraries.wvu.edu/patents/index.htm}.

Wisconsin

Wendt Library, University of Wisconsin, 215 North Randall Ave., Madison, WI 53706; 608-262-6845; {www.wisc.edu/wendt/patent/patent.html}.

Milwaukee Public Library, 814 West Wisconsin Avenue, Milwaukee, WI 53233; 414-286-3051; {www.mpl.org/}.

Wyoming

Wyoming State Library, 2301 Capitol Ave., Cheyenne, WY 82002; 307-777-7281; {www-wsl.state.wy.us/sis/ptdl/index.html}.

The Patent and Trademark Library Program distributes the information to the 83 PDLs. The information is kept on CD-Rom discs, which are constantly updated, and you can use them to do a patent search. CD-Rom discs have been combined to incorporate CASSIS (Classification and Search Support Information System). CD-Rom discs do not give you online access to the PTO database. Online access is available through APS (Automated Patent Systems), and is presently available to public users of the PTO Search Room and to the 83 Patent Libraries. Each PDL with the online APS has its own rules regarding its use. To use the online APS at the PTO Search Room, it is recommended that you take a class at the Search Room. West, East, and X-Search classes are offered once per month for a cost of $25. Off Schedule 3-hour personal training sessions are available for a fee of $120. Online access costs $40 per connect hour, and the charge for paper used for printouts is an additional $.25 per sheet. Public user Ids are required to access all Public Search Facilities. They are available at the Search Room Reception Desk with a valid government issued photo ID.

If you do not live near a PDL, several CD-Rom discs are available through subscription. You may purchase the Classification disc, which dates back to 1790, for $300; the Bibliography disc, which dates back to 1969, for $300; and the ASIST disc, which contains a roster of patent attorneys, assignees, and other information for $200. You can also conduct your patent search and get a copy of it through commercial database services such as:

MeadData Central, Nexis, Lexis: 1-800-422-1337; Fax: 1-800-421-5585; {www.lexisnexis.com/patentservices}. Printouts are billed per page plus shipping. Copies are available via email, mail, fax, or on a CD-Rom. If you intend on doing many searches over time, Nexis Lexis will customize a package for you as a subscriber for approximately $250 per month.

Derwent, 1725 Duke St., Suite 250, Alexandria, VA 22314; 1-800-337-9368, Fax: 1-800-457-0850; {www.derwent.com}. Patent searches are free, but the printouts range from $3.95 to $29.50 per page plus shipping.

If you are going to do your own patent search at your local Patent Depository Library, begin with the Manual and Index to U.S. Patent Classifications to identify the subject area where the patent is placed. Then use the CD-Rom discs to locate the patent. CD-Rom discs enable you to do a complete search of all registered patents but do not enable you to view the full patent, with all its specific details. Lastly, view the patent, which will be kept on microfilm, cartridge, or paper. What information there is to view varies by library, depending on what they have been able to purchase. If the library you are using does not have the patent you want, you may be able to obtain it through inter-library loan.

Copies of patents can be ordered from the PTO at 703-308-9726; 800-972-6382; Fax: 703-305-8759, for $3 per copy.

To obtain a certified copy of a patent, call 703-308-9726 (Patent Search Library at the PTO). The fee is $25 and you must have the patent number. For a certified copy of an abstract of titles, the fee is $25. For a certified copy of patent assignments, with a record of ownership from the beginning until present, call 703-308-9726. The cost is $25, and to request specific assignments you must have the reel and frame number.

Now You Have Got Your Patent

Once a Notice of Allowance stating that your application for patents approved, you have 3 months to pay another filing fee. If not, the application will be deemed abandoned. There are also maintenance fees due at 31/2, 71/2, and 111/2 years after the original grant. After it has expired, anyone may make, use, offer for sale, or sell or import the invention without the patentee's approval. A patent is personal property.

Tips

- Most importantly, do not reveal the details of your invention to anyone! If you need to do so, establish a confidential relationship with them by law or regulation, or a written agreement. Your plans and information you have gathered can be trade secrets and you must protect them.

- Record your discovery in detail as soon as possible and keep a record as you go. Have it witnessed by two reliable persons with a confidentiality agreement.

- Developing a new product is time consuming and expensive. Determine how much of your time, money, and effort you can invest. Know your personal limitations and when to get professional help.

- Twenty percent of patents issued each year are to private inventors. They must be effective business people to also research business concepts.

- Read articles by successful inventors for tips on what it took for them to market their product. Talk to potential customers to see what they would look for in the type of product that you are discovering.

- Remember, if a product similar to yours exists, you can still patent an improvement that is significant.

- Lastly, many times it is not the first try at inventing a product that is successful, it gets better as you go.

What Are Trademarks and Servicemarks?

A trademark is a word, name, symbol or device used in trade with goods to indicate the source of the goods and to set them apart from the goods of others. A servicemark is used to distinguish the source of a service instead of a product. Trademark or mark is generally the term used to refer to both trademarks and servicemarks. They are to keep others from using a confusingly similar mark, but not to keep others from making or selling the same goods or services under a clearly different mark. The Trademark Assistance Center will provide general information about the registration process and will respond to questions concerning the status of a specific trademark application and registration. They are available Monday through Friday from 8:30am to 5pm at 703-308-9000; {www.uspto.gov/main/ trademarks.htm}.

Trademarks

Registering a trademark for your product or service is the way to protect the recognition quality of the name you are building. The PTO keeps records on more than 2.2 million trademarks and records. Over 500,000 active trademarks are kept on the floor of the library, while "dead" trademarks are kept on microfilm. Books contain every registered trademark ever issued, starting in 1870. You can visit the Patent  and Trademark Office to research a trademark using the US Trademark Search Database at www.uspto.gov/tmdb/index.html. However, it will be replaced by the US Trademark Electronic Search System (TESS) soon. For now, both systems will be running. You can access TESS at http://tess.uspto.gov. You can then conduct your search manually for no charge or use their Trademark Search System (T-Search) for $40 per hour, plus $.25 cents per page.

> Assistant Commissioner of Trademarks
> Trademark Search Library
> 2900 Crystal Dr.
> Second Floor, Room 2B30
> Arlington, VA 22202 703-308-9800/9805

If you can't do it yourself, you can hire someone to do the search for you. For an agent to do this, consult the local yellow pages under "Trademark Agents/Consultants" or "Trademark Attorneys". You can also locate an agent by calling your local bar association for a referral.

To conduct your own search at a Patent Depository Library, use the CD-Rom disc on trademarks. It is available for purchase. The CD-Rom discs deliver patent and trademark information including full-text facsimile images and searchable text records. Images can be found in the *Official Gazette*, which contains most current and pending trademarks. The price for an annual subscription to the *Official Gazette* for trademarks is $980. It is issued every Tuesday and can be ordered from the U.S. Government Printing Office. You can also purchase an image file which contains pending and registered trademarks and corresponding serial or registration numbers through Thomson and Thomson by calling 1-800-692-8833. The information contained in it dates back to April 1, 1987 and is updated by approximately 500 images weekly. However, the PDL you use is likely to have an image of the trademark on microfilm or cartridge, and also have copies of the *Official Gazette*. If not, and you have the registration number, you may obtain a copy of the trademark you want for $3 from the PTO. Contact:

Assistant Commissioner of Trademarks
2900 Crystal Dr.
Second Floor, Room 2B30
Arlington, VA 22202   703-308-9800

There are also several commercial services you can use to conduct trademark searches.

Trademark Scan produced by Thomson and Thomson. It can be purchased by calling 1-800-692-8833 (ask for online services), or accessed directly via Saegis. Trademark Scan is updated three times per week, and includes state and federal trademarks, foreign and domestic. To access Trademark Scan you must already have Dialog or Saegis. Many online options are free. The Internet address is {www.thomson-thomson.com}.

Derwent, 1-800-337-9368, is a commercial service that will conduct patent searches only. The cost ranges from $100 and up with a turnaround time of 2-5 days. The Internet address is {www.derwent.com}.

Online services and database discs for both patents and trademarks are constantly being expanded. For information on an extensive range of existing and projected products, call the PTO Office of Electronic Information at 703-306-2600 and ask for the U.S. Department of Commerce, PTO Office of Information Systems' *Electronic Products Brochure*. For example, there is a Weekly Text File, containing text data of pending and registered trademarks. Information can be called up by using almost any term. It can be purchased from AvantIQ and Thomson & Thomson. You can reach AvantIQ at 1-800-320-6366, 973-594-0076, or online at {http://www.avantiq.lu/}. You can reach Thomson & Thomson at 1-800-692-8833 or online at {www.thomson-thomson.com}.

How to Register a Trademark

The right of a trademark comes from either the actual use of the mark, or by filing the correct application. There are two types of rights in a mark, the right to register it and the right to use the mark. The right to register is given to the first party that uses a mark in commerce, or who files an application at the PTO. The right to use a mark can be a complicated matter. For example, in the case where two people who do not know each other, start to use the same or similar marks without a registration. A court will have to decide who has the right to use the mark. Trademark rights last indefinitely if the owner continues its use. The registration lasts 10 years with 10-year renewal periods. You can order a free copy of Basic Facts about Trademarks from the U.S. Government Printing Office, or by calling the Trademark Search Library at 703-308-9000.

Types of Applications

The "use" application is for an applicant that already has been using their mark in commerce. The "intent-to-use" application is for those who have a bona fide intention of using the mark in commerce. These offer protection only in the US and its territories. Applications must be filed in the name of the owner of the mark.

For automated information about the status of a trademark application and registration, call 703-305-8747.

The Trademark Electronic Center

The Trademark Electronic Application System (TEAS) has step-by-step instructions for filling out forms and also contains information about the USPTO's procedures and practices. It also allows you to fill out the trademark forms, check them to be sure they are complete, and using e-TEAS, submit it on-line. You must be able to attach either a black-and-white GIF or JPG file to apply for a stylized or design mark. If a sample of actual use in commerce is needed, a scanned image or digital photo in GIF or JPG format must be attached. The final requirement is payment with a credit card or from an account already set up with the PTO. One mark can be filed with each application for a fee of $325, except for Class 9 and Class 25, where there is a $650 fee. E-TEAS will not accept applications from 11pm Saturday to 6am Sunday. Also, if you prefer to send the forms by mail, you can use PrinTEAS to print out your completed forms. You can send check, money order, or make arrangements for payment through a USPTO account. This system can be accessed 24 hours a day, 7 days a week.

You can check the status of marks using TARR-Trademark Applications and Registrations Retrieval at {http://tarr.uspto.gov}.

Symbols

Anyone who claims rights in a mark can use the symbols, TM (trademark) or SM (servicemark) to show that right. However, the registration symbol, an r in a circle ®, can not be used until the mark is registered.

The Right Way to Get a Copyright

Copyrights are filed on intellectual property. A copyright protects your right to control the sale, use of distribution, and royalties from a creation in thought, music, films, art, or books. It is an automatic form of protection for authors of published and unpublished "original works of authorship." The concrete form of expression as opposed to the subject matter is what is protected. Since a copyright is automatic when a work is created, registration is not required for protection. However, there are advantages to registration. If it is registered within 5 years of publication of the work, it establishes prima facie evidence of its validity and can be helpful in case of a court action. Generally the work is protected for the author's life plus 70 years after death.

For more information, contact:

> Library of Congress
> Copyright Office
> 101 Independence Avenue SE
> Washington, DC 20559-6000 TTY: 202-707-6737
> Public Information Office 202-707-3000
> Email: copyinfo@loc.gov
> www.loc.gov
> www.loc.gov/copyright
> www.copyright.gov

If you know which copyright application you require, you can call the Forms Hotline, open 7 days per week, 24 hours per day at 202-707-9100. The fee is $30 for each registration. Information on all of the different types of copyrights and their applications can be found at their web site.

The Library of Congress provides information on copyright registration procedures and copyright card catalogs that cover several million works that have been registered since 1870. The Copyright Office will research federal copyrights only for varying fees. Requests must be made in writing and you must specify exactly what information you require. If a work does not show any elements of copyright notice, you can search the Copyright Office's catalogs and records. The records from January 1, 1978, to the present can be searched on the Internet through the Library of Congress Information System (LOCIS). That web site address is {www.loc.gov/ copyright/rb.html}.

Contact the Copyright Office, Reference and Bibliography, Library of Congress, 101 Independence Ave., SE, Washington, DC 20559; 202-707-6850, Public Information 202-707-3000.

What is Not Protected by Copyright

Works that have not been notated, recorded, or written can not be protected by copyright. Here are some others:

- titles, short phrases, and slogans; familiar symbols or designs; variations of ornamentation, lettering or coloring, listings of ingredients or contents
- concepts, methods, systems, principles, or devices, as opposed to description, explanation, and illustration
- works that are entirely made of information that is common property and do not contain any original authorship

Invention Scams: How They Work

Fake product development companies prey on amateur inventors who may not be as savvy about protecting their idea or invention as experienced inventors might be. Most of the bogus/fake companies use escalating fees.

The following is a description of how most of them operate:

- The inventor is invited to call or write for free information.

- The inventor is then offered a free evaluation of his idea.

- Next comes the sales call. The inventor is told he has a very good potential idea and that the company is willing to share the cost of marketing, etc. Actual fact, there is no sharing with these companies. Most times the inventor has to come up with the money (usually several hundred dollars or more) for a patent search and a market analysis. Neither of these are worth anything.

- Then the inventor receives a professional/ impressive looking portfolio which contains no real information at all. All the paper crammed into this portfolio looks topnotch, but it's all computer generated garbage.

- Upon receiving this portfolio, the inventor is lured into signing a contract that commits him to giving the company thousands of dollars to promote/license the product. The company sends some promotional letters to fulfill their obligation, but large manufacturers simply toss them into the trash.

After all this, the inventor has spent thousands of dollars, wasted a lot of time, and gotten nowhere with his product.

How To Avoid Losing a Fortune

According to the experts, the inventor should:

- Beware of the come-ons offered by these unethical companies. Avoid using the invention brokers who advertise on TV late in the evening; in public magazines; those who offer 800 numbers; and those on public transit display signs.

- When upfront money is required, look out. There are very few legitimate consultants who insist on a retainer or hourly fee.

- Don't allow the enthusiasm of your idea to take over your inherent common sense. Talk to your patent attorney and see if he knows anything about this company. Plus, check with inventors associations in the state, and see what they have to say about this particular company.

- Demand to know what percentage of ideas the company accepts. Legitimate brokers might accept 2 ideas out of every 100. The fake companies tend to accept about 99 out of 100.

- Find out their actual success rate. Any corporation/ company that will not give you their success rate (not licensing agreements) is a company to stay away from.

- Get an objective evaluation of your invention from reputable professionals. This will save you plenty of money on a bad idea.

A number of highly recommended programs are listed in the next section.

Free Help for Inventors

If you have a great idea and want to turn it into reality, don't rush out and spend what could be thousands of dollars for a private invention company and a patent attorney. You can get a lot of this help for free or at a fraction of the cost. There is a lot of help out there; university-sponsored programs, not-for-profit groups, state affiliated programs, profit-making companies, etc. Depending on the assistance and the organization, some services are free, others have reasonable fees.

Many of the inventors' organizations hold regular meetings where speakers share their expertise on topics such as licensing, financing and marketing. These groups are a good place for inventors to meet other inventors, patent attorneys, manufacturers, and others with whom they can talk and from whom they can get help.

If the listings in the state-by-state section of this chapter do not prove to be useful, you can contact one of the following organizations for help.

1. Small Business Development Center
    Washington State University
    Parkplace Building
    1200 6th Ave., Suite 1700 206-553-7328
    Seattle, WA 98101   Fax: 206-553-7044
    www.wsbdc.org

This service will evaluate your idea for a fee. They also provide counseling services and can assist you with your patent search.

2. Wisconsin Innovation Service Center/Technology
    Small Business Development Center
    Melissa Rick, Director
    University of Wisconsin - Whitewater
    402 McCutchan Hall   262-472-1365
    Whitewater, WI 53190Fax: 262-472-1600
    www.sbdc.uww.edu

The only service that is guaranteed is the evaluation. However, efforts are made to match inventors with exceptional high evaluation scores with manufacturers seeking new product ideas. (Do not offer direct invention development or marketing services). WISC charges a $495 flat fee for an evaluation. The goal is to keep research as affordable as possible to the average independent inventor. Most evaluations are completed within 30 - 45 days. Those inventions from specialized fields may require more time. WISC also provides preliminary patent searches via on-line databases to client.

3. Drake University
    Small Business Development Center
    Ms. Sherry Shafer, Director
    Drake Business Center   515-271-2655
    2507 University   1-800-532-1216
    Des Moines, IA 50311-4505Fax: 515-271-1899
    www.iabusnet.org

INVENTURE is a program of the Drake University Business Development and Research Institute designed to encourage the development of valid ideas through the various steps to becoming marketable items. INVENTURE has no paid staff. The entire panel is made up of volunteers. The administration of the program is handled by existing staff from the Small Business Development Center and the College of Business and Public Administration. They will review items from **any person** regardless of their place of residence. They will review a product idea and check it for market feasibility. INVENTURE may link individuals with business and/or financial partners.

INVENTURE screens every product submitted, but will not consider toy/game or food items. Products are evaluated on 33 different criteria, (factors related to legality, safety, business risk, and demand analysis, to market acceptance/ competition). It normally takes up to 6 weeks to receive results of the evaluation. Evaluators are experienced in manufacturing, marketing, accounting, production, finance and investments.

INVENTURE acts in a responsible manner to maintain confidence of an idea, but cannot guarantee confidentiality.

For assistance with business plans, financial projections, and marketing help, you're encouraged to contact your Small Business Development Center (SBDC).

4. U.S. Department of Energy
    Mail Stop EE-24
    1000 Independence Ave., SW202-586-1478
    Washington, DC 20585-0121Fax: 202-586-7114
    www.oit.doe.gov/inventions/

Financial assistance is available at 2 levels: up to $40,000 and up to $200,000 by the Inventions and Innovations program as stated by the Office of Industrial Technologies (OIT) Department of Energy (DOE) for ideas that significantly impact energy savings and future commercial market potential. Successful applicants will find technical guidance and commercialization support in addition to financial assistance.

DOE has given financial support to more than 500 inventions with nearly 25% of these reaching the marketplace bringing in nearly $710 million in cumulative sales.

5. **U.S. Environmental Protection Agency**
   Center for Environmental Research Information
   Cincinnati, OH 45268   513-569-7578
   www.epa.gov

Directory Description: Environmental Protection Agency, Office of Research and Development, 1200 Pennsylvania Ave., NW, Mail Code 8101R, Washington, DC 20460; 202-564-6620, Fax: 202-565-2910.

The Office of Research and Development conducts an Agency wide integrated program of research and development relevant to pollution sources and control, transport and fate processes, health/ecological effects, measurement/monitoring, and risk assessment. The office provides technical reviews, expert consultations, technical assistance, and advice to environmental decision-makers in federal, state, local, and foreign governments.

Center for Environmental Research Information

26 W. ML King Drive, Cincinnati, OH 45268; 513-569-7578; Fax: 513-569-7585.
A focal point for the exchange of scientific/ technical information both within the federal government and to the public.

Office of Research and Development

Is responsible for working with laboratories, program offices, regions to produce information products that summarize research, technical, regulatory enforcement information that will assist non-technical audiences in under-standing environmental issues. Contact Office of Research and Development, U.S. Environmental Protection Agency, 1200 Pennsylvania Ave., NW, Washington, DC 20460; 202-564-6620; Fax: 202-565-2910.

Office of Exploratory Research

1200 Pennsylvania Ave., NW, Washington, DC 20460; 202-564-6825.

The Office of Exploratory Research (OER) plans, administers, manages, and evaluates the Environmental Protection Agency's (EPA) extramural grant research. It supports research in developing a better understanding of the environment and its problems. Main goals are: to support the academic community in environmental research; maintain scientific/technical personnel in environmental science/ technology; to support research for the identification/solution of emerging environmental problems.

Goals are accomplished through four core programs:

1. **The Research Grants Program:**
   Supports research initiated by individual investigators in areas of interest to the agency.

2. **The Environmental Research Centers Program:**
Has two components: The Academic Research Center Program (ARC) and the Hazardous Substance Research Centers Program (HSRC).

3. **The Small Business Innovation Research (SBIR) Program:**
Program supports small businesses for the development of ideas relevant to EPA's mission. Focuses on projects in pollution control development. Also receives 1.5% of the Agency's resources devoted to extramural Superfund research.

4. **The Visiting Scientists Program:**
Components are an Environmental Science and Engineering Fellows Program and a Resident Research Associateship Program. The Fellows Program supports ten mid-career post-doctoral scientists and engineers at EPA headquarters & regional offices. The Research Associateship Program attracts national and international scientists and engineers at EPA research laboratories for up to 3 years to collaborate with Agency researchers on important environmental issues.

Other programs available are:
A Minority Fellowship Program
A Minority Summer Intern Program
The Agency's Senior Environmental Employment Program (SEE)
The Federal Workforce Training Program
An Experimental Program to Stimulate Competitive Research (EPSCoR).

To learn more, contact Grants Administration, U.S. Environmental Protection Agency, 1200 Pennsylvania Ave., NW, Washington, DC 20460; 202-260-2090. The best way, though, is to search for the word "grant" at the EPA's website, {www.epa.gov}.

State Sources for Inventors

Below is a listing of a variety of inventors groups, listed state by state. Some organizations listed under the state where they are located are regional or national in scope. In states where there is no specific program for inventors, the Small Business Development Centers (under the U.S. Small Business Administration) can often be of help. They are usually found at the colleges and universities. The Small Business Development Center office is located at 409 Third St., SW, Suite 4600, Washington, DC 20416; 202-205-6766; 800-UASK-SBA; {www.sba.gov}.

Alabama

Office for the Advancement of Developing Industries
University of Alabama - Birmingham
2800 Milan Ct.   205-934-6560
Birmingham, AL 35211   205-934-6563
http://main.uab.edu/oadi/show.asp?durkj=29458
Inventors can receive help on the commercialization and patent processes and critical reviews of inventions in this office. Assessments can be made on an invention's potential marketability and assistance is available for patent searches. There is a charge for services.

Small Business Development Center
University of Alabama at Birmingham
901 S. 15th St.   205-934-6760
Birmingham, AL 35294   Fax: 205-934-0538
www.business.uab.edu/SBDC/Index.htm
The center offers counseling for a wide range of business issues and problems.

U.S. Small Business Administration
Business Development
801 Tom Martin Drive   205-290-7101
Birmingham, AL 35211   Fax: 205-290-7443
www.sba.gov
This office offers counseling for a wide range of business issues and problems.

Invent Alabama
Bruce Koppenhoefer
137 Mission Circle   205-663-9982
Montevallo, AL 35115   Fax: 205-250-8013
Email: brucek@quixnet.net

Alaska

UA Small Business Development Center of Alaska
430 W. 7th Ave., Suite 110   907-274-7232
Anchorage, AK 99501   Fax: 907-274-9524
www.aksbdc.org
The SBDC provides general assistance, including free counseling to inventors on commercialization and patent processes, and arranging meetings between inventors, investors, manufacturers, and others who can be of help.

Alaska Inventors and Entrepreneurs Association
P.O. Box 241801
Anchorage, AK 99524   907-563-4337 (phone and fax)
www.artic.net/~inventor
Email: inventors@artic.net
They provide access to the tools and resources needed in order to empower inventors to bring their product to market. The InventorNet Resource Directory lists professional service providers, agents, designers, and much more. There are also monthly meetings, magazine subscription discounts, free access to the Internet and other benefits. There is a membership fee.

Inventors Institute of Alaska
Al Jorgensen
PO Box 876154
Wasilla, AK 99687   907-376-5114

Arizona

Arizona SBDC Network
2411 West 14th Street   480-731-8720
Tempe, AZ 85281   Fax: 480-731-8729
www.dist.maricopa.edu/sbdc
The center offers counseling for a wide range of business issues and problems.

Inventors Association of Arizona   520-721-9966
3104 E. Camelback #344   888-299-6787
Phoenix, AZ 85016   Fax: 602-912-9455
www.azinventors.org/
Email: linda@kangaring.com
Their goal is to guide the creativity of the members through experience, support and confidentiality so that they will be able to market their new invention or idea. Some of the areas they offer assistance in are, patent, trademark, and copyrights, manufacture, finance, and obtaining a product license. Benefits include discounts for legal services, Trade Magazine subscriptions, and consulting, as well as comprehensive information concerning the steps from concept to market. There is a membership fee.

Arkansas

Small Business Development Center
University of Arkansas at Little Rock800-862-2040 (AR only)
100 S. Main, Suite 401   501-324-9043
Little Rock, AR 72201   Fax: 501-324-9049
http://asbdc.ualr.edu
The center offers counseling for a wide range of business issues and problems.

Inventors Congress Inc.
Garland Bull
Rt 2, Box 1630
Dandanell, AR 72834   501-229-4515

California

Small Business Development Center
1410 Ethan Way   916-563-3210
Sacramento, CA 95825   Fax: 916-563-2366
www.sbdc.net

Email: info@sbdc.net

The center offers counseling for a wide range of business issues and problems.

Inventors' Alliance
P.O. Box 390219   650-964-1576
Mountain View, CA 94039-390219   Fax: 650-964-1576
www.inventorsalliance.org
Email: president@inventorsalliance.org

They have monthly meeting with guest speakers on topics such as marketing and product development. These meetings are designed to increase the inventors knowledge and create contacts for a successful production of a product.

Inventors Forum
80 Huntington St. #9   714-540-2491
Huntington Beach, CA 92648   Fax: 714-668-0583
www.inventorsforum.org
Email: infor@inventorsforum.org

This nonprofit group teaches inventors about the invention process. Some of the products and services they provide are, the Invention Showcase, a listing of service providers for a number of different services, and an inventors message base with a range of topics.

Redwood Empire Small Business
Development Center   888-346-SBDC
606 Healdsburg Avenue   707-524-1770
Santa Rosa, CA 95401   Fax: 707-524-1772
www.santarosa.edu/sbdc/
Email: sbdc@santarosa.edu

They have a Patent Information Network where inventor clients perform initial patent searches to help in forming an assessment of an idea or design. They also offer one-on-one professional business consulting. There is no charge for these services.

Central Valley Inventor's Assn.
John Christensen
P.O. Box 1551
Manteca, CA 95336   209-239-8090
Email: cdesigns@softcom.net

Inventors Forum of San Diego
Greg Lauren
11292 Poblado Road   858-451-1028
San Diego, CA 92127   Fax: 858-451-6154
Email: Enovex@aol.com

Bruce Sawyer Center
Steve Schneider
4261 Brookshire Circle
Santa Rosa, CA 95405   707-524-1773
Email: sbdc1@ap.net

American Inventor Network
Jeff McGrew
1320 High School Rd.   707-823-3865
Sebastopol, CA 95472   Fax: 707-823-0913

Inventors Alliance of Northern California
Jim DeLang
6514 Elmira Drive
Redding, CA 96001   530-241-5222
Email: sagn@charter.net
www.inventorsnorcal.org

Established in 1999, the IANC assists inventors in the patent process, and the development and marketing of ideas and products.

Idea to Market Network
Sidnee Cox
P.O. Box 12248
Santa Rosa, CA 95406   1-800-ITM-3210
www.ideatomarket.org
Email: sidnee@ap.net

Idea to Market is a network of inventors who guide fellow members through the inventive process.

Colorado

Affiliated Inventors Foundation, Inc.
1405 Porter St., #107   719-380-1234
Colorado Springs, CO 80909   Fax: 800-380-3862
To order free Info Kit   800-525-5885
www.affiliatedinventors.com
Email: info@affiliatedinventors.com

This foundation counsels inventors on commercialization and patent processes, and provides detailed information on the steps needed to reach commercialization. Preliminary appraisals, evaluations and other services are available for a fee.

Small Business Development Center
Office of Economic Development
1625 Broadway, Suite 1710   303-892-3864
Denver, CO 80202   Fax: 303-892-3848
www.state.co.us/oed/sbdc

The center offers counseling for a wide range of business issues and problems.

Rocky Mountain Inventors & Entrepreneurs
Congress (RMIC)
P.O. Box 36233   303-670-3760
Denver, CO 80236-0233   Fax: 720-962-5026
www.RMinventor.org
Email: info@RMinventor.org

Their mission is to help people with new ideas to fulfill their greatest potential. Their members include new and established inventors, prototypers, manufactures, marketers, patent attorneys and others connected to the invention process. Besides dinner and round table meetings, they have networking sessions, monthly educational meetings and an annual conference. They offer information on the invention process, the tools needed and advice on what to do with the invention. Three is a dinner meeting fee.

Connecticut

Small Business Development Center
University of Connecticut
2100 Hillside Road, Unit 1094   860-486-4135
Storrs, CT 06269-1094   Fax: 860-486-1576
www.sbdc.uconn.edu
Email: CSBDCinformation@sba.uconn.edu

The center offers counseling for a wide range of business issues and problems.

Inventors Association of Connecticut
9-B Greenhouse Road   203-866-0720
Bridgeport, CT 06606-2130   Fax: 781-846-6448
www.inventus.org
Email: IACTWinventus.org

This is a nonprofit group who has members that include inventors, designers, engineers, attorneys, and business people. They look to nurture, stimulate creativity and advance the image of independent inventors by education, promotion and sharing of member resources. They have monthly meeting with pre-meeting session, and a newsletter to accomplish this goal. There is a monthly fee.

Inventors Assn. of Connecticut
Pal Asija
7 Woonsocket Ave.
Shelton, CT 06484 203-924-9538
Email: pal@ourpal.com

Delaware

Small Business Development Center
University of Delaware
One Innovation Way, Suite 301 302-831-1555
Newark, DE 19711 Fax: 302-831-1423
www.delawaresbdc.org
The office offers management counseling and seminars on
various topics, and can counsel inventors on areas such as the
commercialization and patenting processes. Services are by
appointment only.

Delaware Economic Development
99 Kings Highway 302-739-4271
Dover, DE 19901 Fax: 302-739-2028
www.state.de.us/dedo/departments/finance/sbir.htm
Assistance is available to any applicant located in Delaware
or relocating to Delaware, who has been granted a phase I
SBIR award and has submitted a Phase II SBIR application.

Early Stage East
3 Mill Road, Suite 201A
Wilmington, DE 19806 302-777-2460
Email: info@earlystageeast.org

District of Columbia

U.S. Department of Commerce
U.S. Patent and Trademark Office
Crystal Plaza 3, Room 2C02 800-PTO-9199
Washington, DC 20231 703-308-4357
www.uspto.gov
Email: usptoinfo@uspto.gov

District of Columbia Small Business Development
Center
Howard University
2600 6th St., NW, Suite 128 202-806-1550
Washington, DC 20059 Fax: 202-806-1777
www.bschool.howard.edu/sbdc/index.htm
Email: husbdc@cldc.howard.edu
The center offers counseling for a wide range of business
issues and problems.

U.S. Small Business Administration
1110 Vermont Ave., NW, 9th Floor 202-606-4000
Washington, DC 20005 Fax: 202-606-4225
www.sba.gov
This office provides general assistance and information on
funding.

Inventors Network of the Capital Area
Ray Gilbert
6501 Inwood Drive 703-971-7443
Springfield, VA 22150 Fax: 703-971-9216
Email: Raybik@aol.com
http://inca.hispeed.com
This is a nonprofit educational organization offering monthly
meetings, guest speakers, and networking with fellow
inventors.

Florida

Small Business Development Center
University of North Florida 904-620-2476
12000 Alumni Drive 800-450-4624 (in FL)
Jacksonville, FL 32224 Fax: 904-620-2567

www.sbdc.unf.edu
Email: smallbiz@unf.edu
The center offers counseling for a wide range of business
issues and problems.

Small Business Development Center
University of West Florida
1170 Martin L. King, Jr. Blvd. 850-863-6543
Fort Walton Beach, FL 32547 Fax: 850-863-6543
www.sbdc.uwf.edu
The center offers counseling for a wide range of business
issues and problems.

Florida SBDC Network
19 W. Garden St., Suite 302 850-595-5480
Pensacola, FL 32501 Fax: 850-595-5487
www.floridasbdc.com
The network provides general assistance; conducts market/
technical assessments; offers legal advice on patents and
licensing; provides funding information; and assists in
building a prototype. Inventors get to showcase their
inventions and meet with other inventors and investors.

University of Central Florida
Small Business Development Center
12565 Research Parkway, Suite 300 407-823-5554
Orlando, FL 32826-2909 Fax: 407-384-2868
www.bus.ucf.edu/sbdc
The center provides general assistance, funding information
and conducts market assessments. Inventors meet other
inventors.

Edison Inventors Association
P.O. Box 07398 941-275-4332
Ft. Meyers, FL 33919 Fax: 941-267-9746
www.edisoninventors.org
Email: drghn@aol.com
They are a nonprofit group whose goal is to aid creativity and
assistance inventors and entrepreneurs to be successful. They
have monthly meetings.

Inventors Society of South Florida
P.O. Box 4306
Boynton Beach, FL 33424 954-486-2426
Email: abbysideas@aol.com
They consider themselves a nonprofit educational society.
The guest speakers include patent agents, attorneys,
government sources, engineers, technicians and more. You
will be able to ask questions of the guest and also network
with other inventors at monthly meetings.

Tampa Bay Inventors' Council
5901 Third Street South
St. Petersburg, FL 33705 727-866-0669 (phone/fax)
http://patent-faq.com/tbichome.htm
Email: KIEWIT@patent-faq.com
This nonprofit organization educates its members and others
about invention product development and marketing. The
meetings are a public forum for people who have information
for inventors and for inventors that have questions. Members
also get a monthly newsletter, a current member directory
and reference materials. There is a membership fee.

Space Coast Inventors Guild
1221 Pine Tree Drive
Indian Harbour Beach, FL 32937 321-773-4031 (phone/fax)
They accept the challenge to help people in the development
of an idea so they can present for a patent. The monthly
meetings are open to the public and there is no charge to
attend.

Inventors Council of Central Florida
David Flinchbaugh
4855 Big Oaks Ln.
Orlando, FL 32806-7826 407-859-4855

Georgia
Small Business Development Center
University of Georgia
Chicopee Complex
1180 East Broad Street 706-542-7436
Athens, GA 30602 Fax: 706-542-6803
www.sbdc.uga.edu
The center offers counseling for a wide range of business issues and problems.

Inventor Associates of Georgia
P.O. Box 888163
Dunwoody, GA 30356 478-474-6948
www.geocities.com/iaggroup/ Fax: 478-474-2602
Email: miquelon80@aol.com
A group of experts and novices that assist independent inventors with the process of developing their ideas so that they can be marketed. Partly, this is accomplished by Q&A with members and impartial evaluations of inventions. There are monthly meetings with roundtable discussions afterwards. There is a membership fee.

Inventor Assoc. of Georgia, Inc.
Scott Parker
PO Box 888163
Dunwoody, GA 30356 770-908-7386 (phone/fax)
Email: tropez99@yahoo.com
www.geocities.com/iaggroup
IAG, Inc. assists independent inventors in getting their product to market.

Hawaii
Small Business Development Center
University of Hawaii at Hilo
308 Kamehameha Avenue, Suite 201 808-974-7515
Hilo, HI 96720 Fax: 808-974-7683
http://hawaii-sbdc.org
The center offers counseling for a wide range of business issues and problems.

Idaho
Idaho Research Foundation, Inc.
University of Idaho
Morrill Hall 103
P.O. Box 443003 208-885-4550
Moscow, ID 83844 Fax: 208-885-0105
www.irf.uro.uidaho.edu
Email: irf@uidaho.edu
This foundation counsels inventors on commercialization and patent processes, and provides critical reviews on inventions. Computerized data searching and marketing service is available. It takes a percentage of intellectual property royalties.

Small Business Development Center
Boise State University 800-225-3815 (in ID)
1910 University Drive 208-426-1640
Boise, ID 83725 Fax: 208-426-3877
www.idahosbdc.org
Email: info@idahosbdc.org
The center offers counseling for a wide range of business issues and problems.

Idaho Small Business Development Center
College of Southern Idaho

P.O. Box 1238
315 Falls Ave. 208-733-9554
Twin Falls, ID 83303-1238 Fax: 208-733-9316
www.csi.edu/support/isbdc/sbdc.html
Email: srust@csi.edu
The center conducts market assessments and provides funding information.

Idaho Small Business Development Center
Lewis-Clark State College
500 8th Ave. 208-792-2465
Lewiston, ID 83501 Fax: 208-792-2878
www.lcsc.edu/isbdc
Email: SLWagner@lcsc.edu
The center provides general assistance and funding information. They also conduct market assessments.

Idaho State University
Small Business Development Center
2300 N. Yellowstone 208-523-1087
Idaho Falls, ID 83401 Fax: 208-528-7127
Email: woodrhon@isu.edu
The center provides general assistance and funding information, and conducts technical assessments. Inventors meet with other inventors and investors.

Illinois
Small Business Development Center
Department of Commerce and Community Affairs
620 East Adams St., 3rd Floor 217-782-7500
Springfield, IL 62701 Fax: 217-785-6328
www.commerce.state.il.us
The center offers counseling for a wide range of business issues and problems, including commercialization and patent processes.

Small Business Development Center
Evanston Business Investment Corp.
1840 Oak Avenue 847-866-1817
Evanston, IL 60201-3670 Fax: 847-866-1808
The center provides general assistance and funding information.

Western Illinois University
Technical Center and Small Business Development Center
Seal Hall 214 309-298-2211
Macomb, IL 61455-1390 Fax: 309-298-2520
The center provides general assistance; conducts market/technical assessments; provides investment and funding information; and aids in building a prototype. Inventors meet with other inventors and investors, and get the chance to showcase their inventions.

Illinois Innovators and Inventor's Club
P.O. Box 623
Edwardsville, IL 62025 618-656-7445
Email: invent@charter-IL.com
They are a nonprofit group created to exchange useful information and ideas. Membership fees cover monthly meetings, newsletters, and events.

Inventors' Council
431 South Dearborn, Suite 705 312-939-3329
Chicago, IL 60605 Fax: 312-922-7706
www.donmoyer.com
Email: patent@donmoyer.com
There is a multitude of information and links to information at this web site. Patent searching tools, how to get a free patent application if you are eligible, technology information,

science facts, where to look for money, and so much more is available. Mostly, their workshops are in virtual reality on the web, but they still hold some of them in person, and they are free! They list tips from them, such as The Fool Rule, The secrets Rule and other basics. Mr. Moyer cannot answer questions over the phone, but he will do so through Email.

Indiana

Small Business Development CenterToll-free: 888-ISBD-244
One North Capitol, Suite 900   317-234-2082
Indianapolis, IN 46204   Fax: 317-232-8872
www.isbdcorp.org
The center offers counseling for a wide range of business issues and problems.

Indiana Inventors Association
5514 South Adams   765-674-2845
Marion, IN 46953   Fax: 765-733-0579
Email: arhumbert@bpsinet.com
This is an informal nonprofit group. Their members include inventors, engineers, educators and more. They are concerned with the innovation process and look to answer questions and solve problems at the monthly meetings. There is no fee.

Iowa

Small Business Development Center
Iowa State University
2501 N. Loop Drive   800-373-7232
Bldg. 1, Suite 1615   515-296-7828
Ames, IA 50010-8283   Fax: 515-296-6714
www.iabusnet.org
The center offers counseling for a wide range of business issues and problems.

Drake Small Business Development Center and
Inventure Program
2507 University Avenue   515-271-2655
Des Moines, IA 50311   Fax: 515-271-1899
The Inventure Program is a program within the Small Business Development Center. In the program, they will evaluate a product so that the inventor can decide if it is feasible to go to market. There is a fee of $125 and it is open to all people in the nation. The Small Business Development Center offers counseling on commercialization and other business aspects. There is no charge for this and it is only open to residents of Iowa.

Kansas

Small Business Development Center
Wichita State University
Campus Box 148
1845 Fairmont   316-978-3193
Wichita, KS 67260-0148   Fax: 316-978-3647
http://webs.wichita.edu/depttools/user_home/?view=ksb
dc
Email: wsusbdc@wichita.edu
The center offers counseling for a wide range of business issues and problems.

Inventors' Association of South Central Kansas
2302 Amarado
Wichita, KS 67205   316-721-1866
www.networksplus.net/aledarich
Email: aledarich@networksplus.net
They have monthly meetings with a guest speaker who takes questions after finishing the speech. Reports of important information concerning the group, discussions and workshops are included. Guests and members must sign a non-disclosure agreement to protect the ideas that are discussed. There is a membership fee.

Kansas Association of Inventors
Clayton Williamson
272 W. 6th St.
Hoisington, KS 67544   316-653-2165
Email: clayton@hoisington.com

Kentucky

Small Business Development Center
University of Louisville
Burhans Hall, Room 122
Shelby Campus   502-852-7854
Louisville, KY 40292   Fax: 502-852-8573
www.ksbdc.org
This center counsels inventors on commercialization and patent processes and provides critical reviews of inventions. It provides assistance in technically refining inventions. There are no fees.

Small Business Development Center
Kentucky Small Business Development Center
Center for Business Development
College of Business and Economics Building
225 Business and Economics Building
University of Kentucky   859-257-7668
Lexington, KY 40506-0034   Fax: 859-323-1907
www.ksbdc.org
The center offers counseling for a wide range of business issues and problems.

Kentucky Transportation Center
176 Oliver H. Raymond Bldg.   859-257-4513
Lexington, KY 40506-0281   Fax: 859-257-1815
www.engr.uky.edu/ktc
The center works closely with various federal, state and local agencies, as well as the private sector to conduct research supported by a wide variety of sources.

Central Kentucky Inventors & Entrepreneurs
117 Carolyn Drive   606-885-9593
Nicholosville, KY 40356   Fax: 606-887-9850
Email: nashky@IBM.net
This is a nonprofit group that helps each other with patents, analysis, and a business plan so that their products can be marketed. Membership fees cover monthly meetings and a newsletter.

Central Kentucky Inventors Council, Inc.
Donald L. West, President
3060 Pine Ridge Road
Winchester, KY 40391   859-842-4110
Email: dlwest3@yahoo.com

Louisiana

Small Business Development Center
Northeast Louisiana University
College of Business Administration
700 University Avenue, Room 2-57   318-342-1224
Monroe, LA 71209   Fax: 318-342-1209
The center offers counseling for a wide range of business issues and problems.

Louisiana Department of Economic Development
P.O. Box 94185
101 France St.
Baton Rouge, LA 70804-9185   225-342-3000
www.lded.state.la.us
The department provides general assistance.

Maine

Department of Industrial Cooperation
5717 Corbet Hall, Room 480   207-581-2200
Orono, ME 04469-5711   Fax: 207-581-1479
www.umaine.edu/dic

On March 15, 1984, the Inventors Forum of Maine, Inc. (IFM), was formed and became a nonprofit corporation in the state of Maine. It was organized to stimulate inventiveness and entrepreneurship, and to help innovators and entrepreneurs develop and promote their ideas. It allows inventors and entrepreneurs to join together, share ideas and hopefully improve the chance for success. It gives encouragement, professional expertise, evaluation assistance, confidentiality and moral support of the University of Maine's Network and the University of Southern Maine's Small Business Development Center.

The Inventors Forum of Maine generally meets on the first Tuesday evening of each month at the University of Southern Maine, Campus Center, Room A, B & C on Bedford Street in Portland. Membership is open to all. For information regarding the Inventors Forum of Maine, contact Jake Ward, 207-581-1488.

Portland Inventors' Forum
5717 Corbett Hall, Room 480
University of Maine   207-581-1488
Orono, ME 04469-5717   Fax: 207-581-1479
www.umaine.edu/DIC/Invent/IFM.htm
Email: jsward@maine.edu

This group of inventors and business people offer encouragement, professional expertise, confidentiality and evaluation assistance to its members. At the monthly meeting they have Show & Tell, speakers and open discussions. There is no membership fee.

Maryland

Inventions and Innovations
Department of Energy
Forrestal Building
1000 Independence Ave., SW
Washington, DC 20585-0121   202-586-2079
www.oit.doe.gov/inventions

The office evaluates all promising non-nuclear energy-related inventions, particularly those submitted by independent inventors and small companies for the purpose of obtaining direct grants for their development from the U.S. Department of Energy.

Small Business Development Center
MMG, Inc.
826 E. Baltimore Street   410-333-2548
Baltimore, MD 21202   Fax: 410-333-2552
www.mmggroup.com

The center offers counseling for a wide range of business issues and problems.

Massachusetts

Massachusetts Small Business Development Center
Salem State College
121 Loring Avenue, Suite 310
Salem, MA 01970   978-542-6343
www.salemsbdc.org

The center offers counseling for a wide range of business issues and problems.

Small Business Development Center
227 Isenberg School of Management
121 Presidents Drive
University of Massachusetts   413-545-6301

Amherst, MA 01003-9310   Fax: 413-545-1273
http://msbdc.som.umass.edu

The center provides general assistance and funding information.

Smaller Business Association of New England
204 2nd Ave.   781-890-9070
Waltham, MA 02451   Fax: 781-890-4567
www.sbane.org

The association provides general assistance and funding information.

Inventors Association of New England (IANE)
P.O. Box 335   978-433-2397
Lexington, MA 02420-0004   Fax: 978-433-3516
www.inventne.org
Email: crholt@aol.com

At the monthly meetings, they discuss things such as patent protection, licensing, manufacturing and avoiding scams. They also have guest speakers and free workshops. Their inventor shows and exhibits showcase member's inventions. Membership dues cover meetings, a monthly newsletter, and discounts to trade shows, and some publications.

Inventors Resource Network
P.O. Box 137
Shutesbury, MA 01072-0137   413-259-2006
http://pages.prodigy.net/pwassoc/irn.html
Email: info@irnetwork.org

The center of this group of inventors and business people have either created successful businesses with their invention, or they have been licensed. They focus on getting the product to market. Monthly meeting alternate between public and private. They involve networking, announcements, assistance and a guest speaker.

Worcester Area Innovators
132 Sterling Street   508-835-6435
West Boylston, MA 01583   Fax: 805-799-2796
Email: lore1930@aol.com

This group has monthly meetings with informal networking and guest speakers. There are no summer meetings. They put out a monthly newsletter and there is a minimal membership fee.

Cape Cod Inventors Association
Ernest Bauer
Briar Main
P.O. Box 143
Wellfleet, MA 02667   508-349-1628

Greater Boston Inventors Association
Inventors Association of New England
Chris Holt
P.O. Box 577   978-433-2397
Pepperal, MA 01463   Fax: 978-433-3516
Email: crholt@aol.com
www.inventne.org

Expert speakers and members join together to provide guidance to inventors in the areas of patents, marketing, and product development.

Michigan

Small Business Development Center
Grand Valley State University
Seidman School of Business
510 W. Fulton Street   616-336-7480
Grand Rapids, MI 49504   Fax: 616-336-7485
www.mi-sbdc.org

The center offers counseling for a wide range of business issues and problems.

Inventors Club of America
524 Curtis Road
East Lansing, MI 48823   517-332-3561
They meet monthly where a roll call is kept. They have an open quorum and look to help each other with past experiences.

Inventor's Council of Mid-Michigan (ICMM)
519 South Saginaw Street, Suite 200   810-232-7909
Flint, MI 48502   Fax: 810-233-7437
www.flintchamber.org
Email: bross@flint.org
The goal is to help members with patents, trademarks, and copyrights and to get their inventions to market without a large cost. The monthly dues cover meetings and a 2 year subscription to Inventors Digest.

Inventors Association of Metropolitan Detroit
Frank Wales
749 Clairepointe Circle
St. Clair, MI 48081
Email: unclefj@yahoo.com

Minnesota

Minnesota Project Innovation, Inc.
100 Mill Place
111 Third Ave. S.   612-338-3280
Minneapolis, MN 55401   Fax: 612-349-2603
www.mpi.org
This project is affiliated with the Minnesota Dept. of Energy and Economic Development, U.S. Small Business Administration, and private companies. It provides referrals to inventors for sources of technical assistance in refining inventions.

Minnesota Inventors Congress (MIC)
P.O. Box 71   507-637-2344
Redwood Falls, MN 56283   Fax: 507-637-8399
www.invent1.org   800-INVENT1
Email: mic@invent1.org
The Minnesota Inventors Congress (MIC) is a nonprofit organization established in 1958 to promote creativity, innovation, entrepreneurship by assisting the inventor and entrepreneur with education, promotion and referral. It's a professional organization composed of private individuals and corporations, who are creating and developing useful technologies. MIC is for inventors at every development stage - the novice and experienced; male or female; young and old; and supporters of invention and innovation. Workshops are also available. These are for individuals with ideas or inventions not yet successfully on the market; for companies, entrepreneurs looking for such inventions or new products.

"World's Oldest Annual Invention Convention," promotes the spirit of invention and innovation. Each year a 3-day convention presents more than 200 inventions and attracts some 10,000 visitors from around the world. The MIC provides a meeting place for:

1. Inventors to showcase their new products, connecting with manufacturers/investors, product test market, educational seminars, publicity, inventors network, and $1,500 in cash awards.

2. Manufacturers, marketers, investors and licenses seeking new products.

3. Inventors, viewers and exhibitors, seeking free counsel and literature on the invention development process.

4. Public to view the latest inventions, by adults and students, purchase MarketPlace products and meet global inventors.

University of Minnesota, Duluth
Center for Economic Development
Duluth Technology Village   Toll free: 888-387-4594
11 East Superior Street, Suite 210.   218-726-7298
Duluth, MN 55802   Fax: 218-726-6338
www.umdced.com
The center offers counseling for a wide range of business issues and problems.

Society of Minnesota Inventors
10355 Riverdale Drive, Suite 500-236   763-753-2766
Cedar Rapids, MN 55448   Fax: 763-753-6817
www.inventorsnetwork.org
Email: paulparis@uswest.net
With two meetings a month, this group aims to educate inventors. They have inventor question and answer, discussion sessions, and conduct general business. There is a small monthly fee.

Inventors' Network (Mpls./St.Paul)
Bill Baker
23 Empire Dr., Suite 105
St. Paul, MN 55103

Mississippi

Mississippi State University
Small Business Development Center
P.O. Box 5288   662-325-8684
Mississippi State, MS 39762   Fax: 662-325-4016
www.cbi.msstate.edu/cobi/sbdc/sbdc.html
The center provides general assistance; conducts market assessments; and provides funding information.

Small Business Development Center
Meridian Community College   800-MCC-THE1
910 Highway 19 North   601-482-7445
Meridian, MS 39307   Fax: 601-482-5803
www.mcc.cc.ms.us/webbcenter/sbdchome.htm
The center provides general assistance and funding information; conducts market/technical assessments; and offers legal advice on patents and licensing. Inventors meet with other inventors and investors.

Society of Mississippi Inventors
B19 Jeanette Phillips Dr.
P.O. Box 1848   800-725-7232 (MS)
University of Mississippi   601-232-5001
University, MS 38677-1848   Fax: 601-232-5650
www.olemiss.edu/depts/msbdc/invent.html
Email: msbdc@olemiss.edu
This Small Business Development Center specializes in assisting inventors. They help inventors to get started with an idea, give them sources for evaluation, patents, trademarks, finance, and specialized assistance. There are also seminars and workshops.

Mississippi SBDC Inventor Assistance
Bob Lantrip   662-915-5001
B 19 Jeanette Phillips Dr.   800-725-7232 (in MS only)
Fax: 662-915-5650
Email: blantrip@olemiss.edu
http://www.olemiss.edu/depts/mssbdc/invent.html
This organization provides a wide range of services to assist Mississippi residents through the invention process.

Missouri

Missouri Innovation Center
5650 S. Sinclair Rd.   573-446-3100
Columbia, MO 65203   Fax: 573-443-3748
www.marketmaker.org/aboutus.htm
Email: info@marketmaker.org
This group provides communications among inventors, manufacturers, patent attorneys and venture capitalists, and provides general consultations. It is sponsored by the state, city of Columbia, and the University of Missouri. There are fees for some services.

Inventors Association of St. Louis
P.O. Box 410111
St. Louis, MO 63141   314-432-1291
www.uspto.gov/web/offices/com/comm06feb2002.html
Email: dayjobiasl@webtunet
The group holds monthly meetings, provides communications among inventors, manufacturers, patent attorneys, and venture capitalists. It publishes a newsletter. There are annual dues.

Small Business Development Center
University of Missouri - Columbia
1205 University Ave.
Suite 1800 University Pl.   573-882-7096
Columbia, MO 65211   Fax: 573-882-9931
Email: sbdc-c@ext.missouri.edu
www.mo-sbdc.org
The center offers counseling for a wide range of business issues and problems.

Women's Inventor Project
Betty Rozier
7400 Foxmount
Hazlewood, MO 63042

Mid-America Inventors Association
Carl Minzes
8911 East 29th St.   816-254-9542
Kansas City, MO 64129-1502 Fax: 816-221-3995

Montana

Small Business Development Center
Montana Department of Commerce
301 South Park
P.O. Box 200505   406-841-2746
Helena, MT 59620   Fax: 406-841-2728
www.commerce.state.mt.us
Email: adesch@state.mt.us
The center offers counseling for a wide range of business issues and problems.

Montana Inventors Association
5350 Love Lane   406-586-1541
Bozeman, MT 59715   Fax: 406-585-9028
They have a yearly 2-day meeting for inventors. The guest speaker is a known inventor or a patent officer. They will answer questions and have discussions and some of the inventors talk about the process they used to market their product. They also have a member directory.

Blue Sky Inventors
Warren George
1200 Blair Lane, Apt. #1
Billings, MT 59102   406-259-9110

Nebraska

University of Nebraska – Lincoln
Engineering Extension

W 191 Nebraska Hall   402-472-5600
Lincoln, NE 68588-0525 Fax: 402-472-0015
www.engext.unl.edu/engext.html
Upon request, the University will send a packet of information so that the individual may go to the location and conduct their own Patent and Trademark search.

Nebraska Business Development Center
University of Nebraska at Omaha
Roskens Hall
CBA, Room 415   402-554-2521
Omaha, NE 68182-02458 Fax: 402-554-3473
The center offers counseling for a wide range of business issues and problems.

Lincoln Inventors Association
Roger Reyda
92 Ideal Way
Brainard, NE 68626   402-545-2179 (phone/fax)

Nevada

Nevada Small Business Center
University of Nevada - Reno
College of Business Administration, Room 411
Reno, NV 89557-0100   775-784-1717
www.nsbdc.org   Fax: 775-784-4337
Email: nsbdc@unr.nevada.edu
The center provides general assistance and funding information. Inventors meet with other inventors and get to showcase their inventions.

Nevada Small Business Center
3720 Howard Hughes Pkwy., Suite 130 702-734-7575
Las Vegas, NV 89109   Fax: 702-734-7633
www.nsbdc.org
Email: nsbdc@univ.edu
The center provides general assistance and funding information. Inventors meet with other inventors.

Inventors Society of Southern Nevada
3627 Huerta Drive
Las Vegas, NV 89121   702-435-7741
Email: InventSSN@aol.com
Here inventors will learn the process from A to Z. The group will answer questions and send its members in the correct direction to accomplish their goals. They host different speakers from the field at monthly meetings which are open to the public. All ideas are kept confidential. There are yearly dues that cover all of this plus a newsletter.

Nevada Inventors Association
P.O. Box 11008   702-677-0123
Reno, NV 89510-1108   Fax: 702-677-1322
www.nevadainventors.org
Email: inventors@nevadainventors.org
They offer education, assistance, and networking to their members. Anywhere from one to nine guests will show up at the monthly meetings. They also put together a monthly newsletter.

New Hampshire

Small Business Development Center
University of New Hampshire
108 McConnell Hall   603-862-2200
Durham, NH 03824   Fax: 603-862-4876
www.nhsbdc.org
Email: mary.collins@unh.edu
The center offers counseling for a wide range of business issues and problems.

Small Business Development Center
670 N. Commercial Street
Fourth Floor, Suite 1   603-624-2000
Manchester, NH 03101   Fax: 603-647-4410
www.nhsbdc.org
Email: rte@cisunix.unh.edu
The Small Business Development Center provides general assistance and funding information, and offers legal advice on patents and licensing. Inventors meet with other inventors.

New Hampshire Inventors Association
P.O. Box 2772
Concord, NH 03302   603-526-6939
www.patentcafe.com/inventor_orgs/nhia.html
Email: dunmark@tdk.net
It is their mission to encourage and assist inventors in evaluating, patenting and commercializing their products. They teach them about the patent process and supply them with information and resources. There are speakers at the monthly meetings, workshops, and seminars. Inventors will be able to learn from others through networking. The membership fee covers all of this and a newsletter.

New Jersey

Small Business Development Center
Rutgers University
43 Bleeker St.   973-353-5950
Newark, NJ 07102-1897   Fax: 973-353-1030
http://njsbdc.com/home
The Small Business Development Center offers counseling for a wide range of business issues and problems.

Jersey Shore Inventors Club
416 Park Place Avenue   732-776-8467
Bradley Beach, NJ 07720   Fax: 732-776-5418
Email: 2edeilmcclain@msn.com
They have monthly meetings where inventors can learn from each other.

National Society of Inventors
94 North Rockledge Dr.   973-994-9282
Livingston, NJ 07039-1121   Fax: 973-535-0777
This group is "Inventor Friendly". They are inventors helping each other in the New Jersey area. They offer meetings that either have speakers or round table discussions that are open to the public. There is a minimal membership fee.

Kean Univ. SBDC
Mira Kostak
215 North Ave., Room 242   908-527-2946
Union NJ 07083   Fax: 908-527-2960
Email: mkostak@cougar.kean.edu

New Jersey Entrepreneurs Forum
Jeff Millinetti
325 Kimball Ave   908-789-3424
Westfield, NJ 07090   Fax: 908-789-9761

New Mexico

New Mexico Invention Club
P.O. Box 30062
Albuquerque, NM 87190   505-266-3541 (phone/fax)
The contact is Dr. Albert Goodman, president of the club. The club meets on a monthly basis for speakers and presentations by different inventors. Members include patent attorneys, investors, and manufacturers.

Small Business Development Center
Santa Fe Community College
6401 Richards Ave.   800-281-7232
                                     505-428-1362

Santa Fe, NM 87505   Fax: 505-428-1469
www.nmsbdc.org
Email: info@nmsbdc.org
The center offers counseling for a wide range of business issues and problems.

New York

Small Business Development Center
University of Albany
One Pinnacle Place, Suite 218   518-443-9567
Albany, NY 12203-3439   Fax: 518-443-9572
www.nyssbdc.org
Email: albsbdc@nycap.rr.com
The center offers counseling for a wide range of business issues and problems.

New York State Energy Research and Development Authority
17 Columbia Circle   Toll free: 866-NYSERDA
Albany, NY 12203-6399   518-862-1090
www.nyserda.org   Fax: 518-862-1091
The office provides general assistance and investment and funding information. It assists in building a prototype.

SUNY Institute of Technology
Small Business Development Center
P.O. Box 3050   315-792-7547
Utica, NY 13504   Fax: 315-792-7554
www.sbdc.sunyit.edu
Email: sbdc@sunyit.edu
The center provides general assistance and funding information; conducts market/technical assessments; offers legal advice on patents and licensing, and assists in building a prototype. Inventors meet with other inventors.

Small Business Technology Investment Fund
New York State Science and Technology Foundation
30 South Pearl St.   800-782-8369
Albany, NY 12245   518-473-9741
www.empire.state.ny.us/
Email: sbtif@empire.state.ny.us
The program provides financing assistance for technology-based start-up companies with initial investment as much as $300,000.

Inventors Alliance of America-Rochester Chapter
97 Pinebrook Drive   716-225-3750
Rochester, NY 14616   Fax: 716-225-2712
Email: InventNY@aol.com
This nonprofit group helps inventors by educating them to develop their business and offer support and recognition. The members and guest speakers offer useful information and contacts at the monthly meetings.

New York Society of Professional Inventors
Box 216   516-798-1490
Farmingdale, NY 11735-9996   Fax: 516-799-1362
Email: dan.weiss.pe@juno.com
They are a networking group that meets once a month. Speakers that are experts on different areas of inventing attend. There is a membership fee.

Long Island Forum for Technology, Inc.
Phil Orlando
Farmingdale, NY 11735   631-755-3321
Email: porlando@lift.org   Fax: 631-755-9264

Inventors Society of Western New York
Bob Murray
52 Manor Hill Drive

Fairport, NY 14450   585-223-1225
Email: inventnewyork@aol.com

Innovators Resource Network of Central NY
Mark Pierson
65 Hospital Hill Road
Binghamton, NY 13901   607-648-4626
Email: mvpierson@aol.com

North Carolina

Small Business Development Center
University of North Carolina
333 Fayetteville Street Mall, #1150   919-715-7272
Raleigh, NC 27601   Fax: 919-715-7777
The center offers counseling for a wide range of business issues and problems.

North Dakota

Center for Innovation
University of North Dakota
4300 Dartmouth Drive
P.O. Box 8372   701-777-3132
Grand Forks, ND 58202-8372   Fax: 701-777-2339
www.innovators.net
This center conducts occasional seminars and workshops with speakers; counsels on the commercialization and patenting process; provides communications among inventors, manufacturers, and patent attorneys. There are fees for services, but the first consultation is free.

Small Business Development Center
118 Gamble Hall
University of North Dakota
Box 7308   701-777-3700
Grand Forks, ND 58202-7308   Fax: 701-777-3225
www.und.nodak.edu/dept/
The center offers counseling for a wide range of business issues and problems.

North Dakota Inventors Congress
Michael S. Neustel
2534 South University Drive
Suite 4   800-281-7009
Fargo, ND 58103   Fax: 701-237-0544
Email: neustel@patent-ideas.com
www.ndinventors.com
The NDIC provides inventors and entrepreneurs with all the information needed to see an idea through to fruition.

Ohio

Inventors Council of Dayton
Mr. George Pierce, President
P.O. Box 611   937-224-8513
Dayton, OH 45409   Fax: 413-691-1630
www.xec.com/invent/index.html
Email: geopierce@earthlink.net
This association meets on a regular basis and provides communication among inventors, manufacturers, patent attorneys, etc., and often publishes newsletters.

Docie Marketing
73 Maplewood Drive   740-594-5200
Athens, OH 45701   Fax: 740-594-4004
http://docie.com
Email: idea@docie.com
Docie Marketing provides assistance to inventors worldwide, including free educational material, free referrals to legitimate invention service providers, commission-based brokerage, and fee-based services for inventors.

Small Business Development Center
Department of Development
77 S. High Street   800-848-1300
P.O. Box 1001   614-466-2480
Columbus, OH 43216-1001   Fax: 614-466-5167
www.connectohio.com
Email: connect@odod.state.oh.us
The center offers counseling for a wide range of business issues and problems.

Inventors Connection of Greater Cleveland, Inc.
P.O. Box 360804   216-226-9681
Strongsville, OH 44136   Fax: 440-543-0354
http://members.aol.com/icgc/index.htm
Email: icgc@usa.com
This is a nonprofit organization of inventors helping inventors that help to make ideas into marketable products. They provide information on patent developments, educate them on things pertaining to the inventing process, and identify needs for those inventions that have a possible market. Monthly meetings cover many topics, but stress the introduction of ideas into the marketplace.

Inventors Council of Canton
303 55th Street, NW
North Canton, OH 44720   330-499-1262
Email: fleisherb@aol.com
The Council provides an opportunity for inventors to meet and share ideas. They hold monthly meetings to further this goal.

Inventors Network
1275 Kinnear Road
Columbus, OH 43212   614-470-0144
Email: 13832667@msn.com
This is a nonprofit group with members in varying occupations. Entrepreneurs and inventors are educated on the invention process and production. They meet monthly to network and question various guest speakers. They cover topics like manufacturing, prototyping, and marketing. They also have a yearly seminar.

Inventor's Council of Cincinnati
Andrea Brady, President
121 Bradford Drive   513-831-0664
Milford, OH 45150   Fax: 513-831-6328
Email: InventorsCouncil@fuse.net

Youngstown-Warren Inv. Assn.
Robert J. Herberger
500 City Center One
PO Box 500
Youngstown, OH 44501-0500   330-744-4481
Email: rjh@mm-lawyers.com

Oklahoma

Small Business Development Center
Southeastern Oklahoma State University
517 University
P.O. Box 2584   405-924-0277
Durant, OK 74701   Fax: 405-924-7071
The center offers counseling for a wide range of business issues and problems.

Inventors Assistance Program   877-577-7632 (in OK)
395 Cordell South   405-744-8727
Stillwater, OK 74078-8015   Fax: 405-744-8516
http://techweb.ceat.okstate.edu/ias

This is a service to help inventors navigate the process from idea to marketplace using information, education and referrals. The service itself is free.

Oklahoma Inventors Congress
3212 NW 35th Street
Oklahoma City, OK 73112
405-947-5782
Fax: 405-947-6950
Email: wbaker@tanet.net

They are a self-help group that shares knowledge and experience with each other in order to help in the invention process. They hold monthly meetings.

Oregon

Eastern Oregon University
Small Business Development Center
One University Blvd.
541-962-3391
La Grande, OR 97850
Fax: 541-962-3668
Email: lagrande@bizcenter.org

Oregon Institute of Technology
Small Business Development Center
3201 Campus Dr.
Boivin Hall, Room 119
541-885-1760
Klamath Falls, OR 97601-8801
Fax: 541-885-1761
www.oit.edu/sbdc/5
Email: sbdc@oit.edu

Southern Oregon University
Small Business Development Center
332 W. 6th St.
541-772-3478
Medford, OR 97501
Fax: 541-734-4813
www.sou.edu/business/sbdc.htm

Small Business Development Centers (SBDCs) at three state colleges and the community colleges can counsel inventors and direct them where to go for patent process, etc.

Oregon Small Business Development Center
44 W. Broadway, Suite 501
541-726-2250
Eugene, OR 97401-3021
Fax: 541-345-6006
www.bizcenter.org

The center provides general assistance and funding information.

Small Business Development Center
2025 Lloyd Center mall
503-978-5080
Portland, OR 97232
Fax: 503-288-1366
www.sbdc.citysearch.com
Email: yjohnson@pcc.edu

The center provides general assistance and funding information.

Oregon State Library
State Library Building
250 Winter St., NE
503-378-4277
Salem, OR 97310-3950
Fax: 503-588-7119
www.osl.state.or.us

Organization's name and address may be given to individual inventors for referrals.

Southern Oregon Inventors Council
332 West 6th Street
541-772-3478
Medford, OR 97501
Fax: 541-734-4813
Email: sbdc@s.oregonstate

This is a group that supports each other through the sharing of ideas. They learn the process of going about developing an invention and answer each others' questions at monthly meetings. They also have guest speakers who cover topics such as, marketing, on-line marketing, and manufacturing. The meetings are open to the public. There is a small membership fee.

South Coast Inventors Group
Lori Capps
c/o Southwestern Business Development Center
2110 Newmark
541-888-7100
Coos Bay, OR 97420
Fax: 541-888-7113
lcapps@southwestern.cc.or.us

Pennsylvania

Small Business Development Center
Bucknell University
Toll free: 866-375-6010
125 Dana Engineering Bldg.
570-524-1249
Lewisburg, PA 17837
Fax: 570-524-1768
www.departments.bucknell.edu/sbdc/
Email: sbdc@bucknell.edu

The center offers counseling for a wide range of business issues and problems.

Pennsylvania Small Business Development Center
Vance Hall
3733 Spruce Street
215-898-4861
Philadelphia, PA 19104
Fax: 215-898-1063
www.pasbdc.org

The center provides general assistance and funding information. It also conducts market and technical assessments. It also oversees all centers in Pennsylvania.

American Society of Inventors
(ATTN: Henry H. Skillman)
P.O. Box 58426
Philadelphia, PA 19102-5426
215-546-6601
www.asoi.org
Email: hskillman@ddhs.com

This group offers members legal, technical, and business information. Some of the services that they have are, the Information Index, the Inventors Notebook, and the Invention Conception, all provided to help the member become creative and successful. They have bi-monthly meetings and newsletters. At the Board Meeting, 2 members will be allowed to have their inventions evaluated.

Pennsylvania Inventors Association
2317 East 43rd
Erie, PA 16510
814-825-5820
www.pa-invent.org
Email: dhbutler@velocity.net

"What we are able to conceive, we are meant to create", is the motto of this group. They bring together people with ideas, link inventors to industry, and get support for inventors. Meetings are open to local inventors and others interested in promoting creativity.

Central Pennsylvania Inventors Assn.
Scott Pickford
9 First Avenue
Wormleysburg, (Harrisburg) PA 17043
717-763-5742
Email: S1Pickford@aol.com

Puerto Rico

Puerto Rico Inventors Association
Bill Diaz
PO Box 1081
Saint Just, PR 00978
787-760-5074
Email: acuhost@novacomm-inc.com

Rhode Island

Service Corps of Retired Executives (SCORE)
c/o U.S. Small Business Administration
380 Westinghouse, Room #511
Providence, RI 02903
401-528-4571
www.swns.net/score/main1.html

Volunteers in the SCORE office are experts in many areas of business management and can offer advice to inventors in areas including marketing and the commercialization process.

Small Business Development Center
30 Exchange Terrace
Providence, RI 02903   401-831-1330
The center offers counseling for a wide range of business issues and problems.

Small Business Development Center
Bryant College
1150 Douglas Pike   401-232-6111
Smithfield, RI 02917-1284   Fax: 401-232-6933
www.risbdc.org
The center provides general assistance and conducts market and technical assessments.

The Center for Design & Business
Cheryl A. Daria, Director
20 Washington Place   401-454-6108
Providence, RI 02903   Fax: 401-454-6559
Email: cfaria@risd.edu

South Carolina

Small Business Development Center
South Carolina State University
School of Business
300 College Ave.
Campus Box 7176   803-536-8445
Orangeburg, SC 29117   Fax: 803-536-8066
The center offers counseling for a wide range of business issues and problems.

South Carolina Small Business Development Center
University of South Carolina
1710 College Street
College of Business Administration   803-777-4907
Columbia, SC 29208   Fax: 803-777-4403
The center provides general assistance and funding information.

Inventors & Entrepreneurs Association of South Carolina
Charles Sprouce
P.O. Box 4123
Greenville, SC 29608   864-244-1045

Carolina Inventors Council
Johnny Sheppard
2960 Dacusville Highway
Easley, SC 29640   864-859-0066
Email: john17@home.com

South Dakota

Small Business Development Center
University of South Dakota
School of Business
414 East Clark St.   605-677-5287
Vermillion, SD 57069-2390   Fax: 605-677-5427
www.usd.edu/brbinfo
Email: brbinfo@usd.edu
The center offers counseling for a wide range of business issues and problems.

South Dakota Inventors Congress
Kent Rufer
P.O. Box 2220
SDSU-EERC   605-688-4184
Brookings, SD 57007   Fax: 605-688-5880
Email: kent_rufer@sdstate.edu

Tennessee

Jackson State Community College
Small Business Development Center
2046 North Parkway Street   901-424-5389
Jackson, TN 38301   Fax: 901-425-2641
The center offers counseling for a wide range of business issues and problems.

Tennessee Inventors Association
P.O. Box 11225
Knoxville, TN 37939-1225   865-981-2927
www.uscni.com/tia
Email: bealaj@aol.com
Their main goal is the advancement of technology through Tennessee by providing guidance, information, and encouragement. They have a TIA Inventor's Guide that has topics such as the Inventors Log, how to market your product yourself, prototypes, and licensing. Their members include inventors, small business developers, research scientist and more to network with. There is a lot more information available with this group.

Inventors' Association of Middle Tennessee and South Kentucky
Marshal Frazer
3908 Trimble Rd.
Nashville, TN 37215   615-269-4346

Texas

North Texas-Dallas Small Business Development Center
Dallas Community College District
1402 Corinth Street   214-860-5900
Dallas, TX 75215   Fax: 214-565-5815
www.billpriestinstitute.org/dallas_sbdc.htm
The center offers counseling for a wide range of business issues and problems.

Texas Tech University
Small Business Development Center
2579 S. Loop 289, St. 114   806-745-1637
Lubbock, TX 79423   Fax: 806-745-6717
www.lubbock-sbdc.org
The center provides general assistance and funding information.

Amarillo Inventors Association
7000 West 45th Street, Suite 2   806-352-6085
Amarillo, TX 79109   Fax: 806-352-6264
Email: kiefer7000@aol.com
They have monthly meetings in order to inform inventors of steps that they can take to enhance their invention.

Houston Inventors Association
2916 West T.C. Jester Blvd., Suite 105   713-686-7676
Houston, TX 77018   Fax: 281-326-1795
www.inventors.org
Email: kenroddy@nol.net
Speakers at monthly meeting discuss their success stories, technical areas, and share tips on making money from inventions. There are also monthly workshops on patent fundamentals, injection moldings and more. They will put together members having a problem with members who can help them.

Technology Advocates of San Antonio
Inventors & Entrepreneurs SIG
9406 Hays Point
San Antonio, Texas 78250
Richard Rodriguez - Co-Chair   210-680-5754
Email: richard@kenrod.biz   Fax: 210-680-5755
Edward Hopkins - Co-Chair

Email: hopkinsedward@msn.com 210-452-7405
www.tasa.org

Texas Inventors Association
Barbara Pitts
P.O. Box 251248
Plano, TX 75025 972-312-0090
Email: barb@asktheinventors.com
www.asktheinventors.com
Successful inventors providing experienced advice for new inventors.

Utah

Utah Small Business Development Center
1623 S. State St. 801-957-3840
Salt Lake City, UT 84115 Fax: 801-957-3489
www.slcc.edu/schools/cce/atc/cad/sbac.html
Email: finnermi@slcc.edu
The center provides general assistance and funding information, and conducts market research and strategy.

Vermont

Economic and Development Office
State of Vermont
National Library Bldg.
6th Floor North 802-828-3211
Montpelier, VT 05620-0501 Fax: 802-828-3258
www.state.vt.us/dca
Inventors will be given references to businesses that can assist with the commercialization and marketing process.

Small Business Development Center
P.O. Box 188 Toll free: 800-464-7232 (in VT)
Randolph Center, VT 05061 802-728-9101
www.vtsbdc.org Fax: 802-728-3026
The center offers counseling for a wide range of business issues and problems.

Inventors Network of Vermont
Dave Dionne
4 Park Street
Springfield, VT 05156 802-885-5100
Email: comtu@turbont.net 802-885-8178

Invent Vermont
Norman Elkind
PO Box 82
Woodbury, VT 05681 802-472-8741
Email: Netkind@att.net

Virginia

Virginia Small Business Development Center
707 E. Main St., Suite 300
P.O. Box 446 804-371-8111
Richmond, VA 23218-0446 804-371-8200
www.dba.state.va.us
The center offers counseling for a wide range of business issues and problems.

Small Business Development Center
2000 Holiday Drive, Suite 200 434-295-8198
Charlottesville, VA 22901 Fax: 434-817-0664
http://monticello.avenue.org/Market/SBDC
Email: sbdc@cstone.net
The center provides general assistance, conducts market studies, and refers inventors to companies that conduct market and technical assessments.

Blue Ridge Inventor's Club
P.O. Box 6701 804-973-3708
Charlottesville, VA 22906-6701 Fax: 804-973-2648

www.inventorclub.org
Email: mac@luckycat.com
The purpose of this club is to help people protect their innovations, provide information on patents, trademarks, and copyrights, and inform them how the US Patent and Trademark Office operates.

Inventors Network of the Capital Area
Ray Gilbert
6501 Inwood Drive 703-971-7443
Springfield, VA 22150 Fax: 703-971-9216
Email: Raybik@aol.com
http://inca.hispeed.com
This is a nonprofit educational organization offering monthly meetings, guest speakers, and networking with fellow inventors.

Washington

Innovation Assessment Center
180 Nickerson St., Suite 207 206-464-5450
Seattle, WA 98109 Fax: 206-464-6357
www.wsbdc.org/services/innovation_assessment.htm
Part of the Small Business Development Center, this center performs commercial evaluations of inventions, counseling and provides assistance with patentability searches. There are fees for services.

Small Business Development Center
Washington State University
Spokane, WA 99201 509-358-7765
www.wsbdc.org
Email: sbdc@wsu.edu
The center offers counseling for a wide range of business issues and problems.

Small Business Development Center
Western Washington University
Bellingham Towers
119 N. Commercial St., Suite 195 360-733-4014
Bellingham, WA 98225 Fax: 360-733-5092
www.cbe.wwu.edu/sbdc
The center provides general assistance, and investment and funding information.

Inventors Network
P.O. Box 5575
Vancouver, WA 98668 503-239-8299
This is a nonprofit inventor's self-help club whose goal it is to make an invention a reality. They will not do it for you, but rather help you to do it yourself. There is an annual membership fee.

Whidbey Island Inventor Network
Matthew Swett
P.O. Box 1026
Langley, WA 98260 360-678-0269
Email: wiin@whidbey.com
http://www2.whidbey.net/wiin
WIIN is designed as a forum for independent inventors to network with one another.

West Virginia

Small Business Development Center
West Virginia University
912 Main St. 304-465-1434
Oak Hill, WV 25901 Fax: 304-465-8680
The center offers counseling for a wide range of business issues and problems.

West Virginia Small Business Development Office
2000 7th Ave. 304-696-6246

Huntington, WV 25703-1527 Fax: 304-696-4835
www.marshall.edu/ibd/sbdc.htmlx
The center provides information on investment and funding.

West Virginia Inventors Council, Inc.
Katherine Morgan
The Discovery Lab
Eng. Research Building
West Virginia University
P.O. Box 6070
Morgantown, WV 26506 304-293-3612, ext. 3730

Wisconsin

Wisconsin Innovation Service Center
402 McCutchan Hall
UW-Whitewater 262-472-1365
Whitewater, WI 53190 Fax: 262-472-1600
http://academics.uww.edu/BUSINESS/innovate/innovate
.htm
Email: innovate@uwwvax.uww.edu
Provides early stage market research for inventors. There is a
flat fee of $495 for services.

Small Business Development Center
University of Wisconsin
975 University Ave., Room 3260 608-263-7680
Madison, WI 53706 Fax: 608-263-0818
www.wisconsinsbdc.org
Email: sbdc@uwex.edu
The center offers counseling for a wide range of business
issues and problems.

Wisconsin Department of Commerce
201 W. Washington Ave.
P.O. Box 7970 608-266-1018
Madison, WI 53707 Fax: 608-267-8969
www.commerce.state.wi.us
The office provides information on investment and funding.

Central Wisconsin Inventors Association
P.O. Box 915
Manawa, WI 54949 920-596-3092
Email: dr.heat@mailexcite.com

Inventors Network of Wisconsin
1066 St. Paul Street
Green Bay, WI 54304 920-429-0331
http://inventor.tsnnet.com
Email: inventorgb@msn.com
This group holds monthly meetings to advance the
knowledge of its members. They do this through speakers,
networking, and other resources.

Wyoming

Small Business Development Center 800-348-5207
300 South Wolcott, Suite 300 307-234-6683
Casper, WY 82601 Fax: 307-577-7014
http://uwadmnweb.uwyo.edu/sbdc
Dr. Leonard Holler, who works in the office, is able to help
inventors on a wide range of issues including patenting,
commercialization and intellectual property rights. There are
fees for services.

National Organizations

United Inventors Association of the USA
Carol Oldenburg
P.O. Box 23447 585-359-9310
Rochester, NY 14692 Fax: 585-359-1132
Email: UIAUSA@aol.com
http://www.uiausa.com
The MISSION of the UIA is to provide leadership, support
and services to inventor support groups and independent
inventors.

National Congress of Inventor Organizations
Stephen Gnass
P.O. Box 93669 213-878-6952
Los Angeles, CA 90093-6690 Fax: 213-962-8588
Email: ncio@inventionconvention.com
http://inventionconvention.com/ncio/index.html

International Organizations

International Federation of Inventors' Associations
(IFIA)
http://www.invention-ifia.ch
A nongovernmental organization created by inventor
associations in 1968. Its membership represents some 100
countries.

Canada

Canadian Innovative Centre 800-265-4559
490 Dutton Drive, Unit 1A 519-885-5870
Waterloo, Ontario Canada N2L 6H7 Fax: 519-5885-5729
www.innovationcentre.ca
Email: info@innovationcentre.ca
Provides inventors with market research, idea testing, and
helps guide inventors up to the patent stage.

Inventors Alliance of Canada
Mark Ellwood
350 Sunnyside Ave.
Toronto, Ontario M6R 2R6 416-410-7792
Email: ellwood@netcom.ca
http://www.inventorsalliance.com
The Inventor's Alliance is a nonprofit group designed to help
inventors develop their business through education,
recognition, friendship, and support.

British Columbia Inventors' Society
Richard Parson
P.O. Box 78055
Vancouver, BC Canada V5N 5W1
Joann Robertson 604-707 0250
Email: admin@bcinventor.com
www.bcinventor.com

Durham East Independent Inventors Group
George Cheung
1945 Denmar Rd., Ste.#56
Pickering, Ontario
Canada L1V 3E2 905-686-7172
Email: gc7591@hotmail.com

Inter Atlantic Inventors Club
Tomas Romero
28021 Tacoma PO 902-435-5218
Dartmouth NS Canada B2W 6E2 Fax: 902-434-4221

Saskatchewan Research Council
Marie Savostianik
15 Innovation Blvd.
Saskatoon - Saskatc Canada S7N 2X8 306-933-5400

Waterloo - Wellington Inventors Club
Harry VanDyke
65 Woodland Drive
Cambridge, ONT Canada N1R 2X7 519-653-8848
Email: svandyk@bserv.com

Women's Inventor's Project - Toronto Canada
107 Holm Crescent 905-731-0328
Thornhill, Ontario L3T 5J4 Fax: 905-731-9691
Canada
http://www.interlog.com/~womenip

Government Buys Bright Ideas From Inventors: Small Business Innovative Research Programs (SBIR)

The Small Business Innovative Research Program (SBIR) stimulates technological innovation, encourages small science and technology based firms to participate in government funded research, and provides incentives for converting research results into commercial applications. The program is designed to stimulate technological innovation in this country by providing qualified U.S. small business concerns with competitive opportunities to propose innovative concepts to meet the research and development needs of the Federal government. Eleven federal agencies with research and development budgets greater than $100 million are required by law to participate: The Departments of  Defense, Health and Human Services, Energy, Agriculture, Commerce, Transportation, and Education; the National Aeronautics and Space Administration; the National Science Foundation; the Nuclear Regulatory Commission; and the Environmental Protection Agency.

Businesses of 500 or fewer employees that are organized for profit are eligible to compete for SBIR funding. Nonprofit organizations and foreign owned firms are not eligible to receive awards, and the research must be carried out in the U.S. All areas of research and development solicit for proposals, and the 2001 budget for SBIR is $1.158 billion. There are three phases of the program: Phase I determines whether the research idea, often on high risk advanced concepts, is technically feasible; whether the firm can do high quality research; and whether sufficient progress has been made to justify a larger Phase II effort. This phase is usually funded for 6 months with awards up to $100,000. Phase II is the principal research effort, and is usually limited to a maximum of $750,000 for up to two years. The third phase, which is to pursue potential commercial applications of the research funded under the first two phases, is supported solely by nonfederal funding, usually from third party, venture capital, or large industrial firms. SBIR is one of the most competitive research and development programs in the government today. About one proposal out of ten received is funded in Phase I. Generally, about half of these receive support in Phase II. Solicitations for proposals are released once a year (in a few cases twice a year). To assist the small business community in its SBIR efforts, the U.S. Small Business Administration publishes the Pre-Solicitation Announcement (PSA) in December, March, June, and September of each year. Every issue of the PSA contains pertinent information on the SBIR Program along with details on SBIR solicitations that are about to be released. This publication eliminates the need for small business concerns to track the activities of all of the federal agencies participating in the SBIR Program. In recognition of the difficulties encountered by many small firms in their efforts to locate sources of funding essential to finalization of their innovative products, SBA has developed the Commercialization Matching System. This system contains information on all SBIR awardees, as well as financing sources that have indicated an interest in investing in SBIR innovations. Firms interested in obtaining more information on the SBIR Program or receiving the PSA, should contact the Office of Technology, Small Business Administration, 409 3rd St., SW, MC/6470, Washington, DC 20416, 202-205-6450.

SBIR representatives listed below can answer questions and send you materials about their agency's SBIR plans and funding:

Department of Agriculture
Dr. Charles Cleland, Directory SBIR Program, U.S. Department of Agriculture, Stop 2243, Waterfront Centre, Suite 2312, 1400 Independence Avenue, SW, Washington, DC 20250-2243; 202-401-6852, Fax: 202-401-6070; Email: Ccleland@reeusda.gov

Department of Commerce
Dr. Joseph Bishop, Department of Commerce, 1335 East-West Highway, Room 106, Silver Springs, MD 20910, 301-713-3565, Fax: 301-713-4100, Email: Joseph.Bishop@NOAA.GOV

Department of Defense
Ivory Fisher, SBIR/STTR Program Manager, Office Under Secretary of Defense, U.S. Department of Defense, 1777, North Kent Street, Rosslyn Plaza North, Suite 9100, Arlington, VA 22209, 800-382-4634, 703-588-8616, Fax: 703-588-7561, Email: fisherij@acq.osd.mil

Department of Education
Lee Eiden, SBIR Program Coordinator, Department of Education, Room 508 D-Capitol Place, 555 New Jersey Avenue, NW Washington DC 20208, 202-219-2004, Fax: 202-219-1407, Email: Lee_Eiden@ed.gov

Department of Energy
Dr. Robert E. Berger, SBIR/STTR Program Manager, US Department of Energy, SC-32 19901 Germantown Road, Germantown, MD 20874-1290, 301-903-2900, Fax: 301-903-5488, Email: Robert.Berger@science.doe.gov

Department of Health and Human Services
Debbie Ridgely, Director OSDBU, Office of the Secretary, U.S. Department of Health and Human Services, 200 Independence Ave., Washington, DC 20201; 202-690-7235, Fax: 202-260-4872; Email: debbie.ridgely@hhs.gov.

Department of Transportation
Joseph D. Henebury, SBIR Program Director, DTS-22, US Department of Transportation, Volpe Center, 55 Broadway, Kendall Square, Cambridge, MA 02142-1093, 617-494-2712, Fax: 617-494-2370, Email: Henebury@volpe.dot.gov

Environmental Protection Agency

James Gallup, Office of Research and Development, US Environmental Protection Agency, ORD/NCER (8722R), 1200 Pennsylvania Ave., NW, Washington DC 20460, 202-564-6823, Fax: 202-565-2447, Email: Gallup.James@epa.gov

National Aeronautics and Space Administration

Dr. Robert L. Norwood, SBIR Program, National Aeronautics Space Administration-HQ, 300 E. St, SW, Code XC, Washington, DC 20546-0001; 202-358-2320, Fax: 202-358-3878

Small Business Administration

Maurice Swinton, US Small Business Administration, 409 3rd Street, SW, Mail Code:6540, Washington, DC 20416, 202-205-6450, Fax: 202-205-6390, Email: maurice.swinton@sba.gov

Money and Help to Sell Your Goods And Services Overseas

If you've found that the domestic market for your product or service is dwindling, it's time to consider broadening your sales base by selling overseas. Hey, it's not as complicated as you might think. There is a lot of information available to us in this country about other countries that isn't even available in that particular country. In other words, we have access to things like marketing trend reports on countries like Turkey that business people in Turkey can't even get! Important expertise and assistance for new and more experienced exporters continue to increase at both the federal and state level.

That widget that you invented in your garage so many years ago is now found in every hardware store in this country — why shouldn't it be in every French hardware store? Or the line of stationery that sold so well for you in this country could definitely be a hit in British stores that specialize in selling fine writing papers. So how do you go about finding what countries are open to certain imports and what their specific requirements are? If you're smart, you go to the best source around — the government — and make it work for you.

Polypropylene In Countries That Don't Even Count People

A few years ago a Fortune 500 company asked us to identify the consumption of polypropylene resin for 15 lesser-developed countries. It was a project they had been working on without success for close to a year. After telexing all over the world and contacting every domestic expert imaginable, we too came up empty handed. The basic problem was that we were dealing with countries that didn't even count people, let alone polypropylene resin.

Our savior was a woman at the U.S. Commerce Department named Maureen Ruffin, who was in charge of the World Trade Reference Room. Ms. Ruffin and her colleagues collect the official import/export statistical documents for every country in the world as soon as they are released by the originating countries. Although the data are much more current and more detailed than those published by such international organizations as the United Nations, the publications available at this federal reference room are printed in the language of origin. Because none of the 15 subject countries manufacture polypropylene resin, Ms. Ruffin showed us how to get the figures by identifying those countries which produce polypropylene and counting up how much each of them exported to the countries in question. To help us even further, she also provided us with free in-house translators to help us understand the foreign documents.

Exporter's Hotline

The Trade Promotion Coordinating Committee has established this comprehensive "one-stop shop" for information on U.S. Government programs and activities that support exporting efforts. This hotline is staffed by trade specialists who can provide information on seminars and conferences, overseas buyers and representatives, overseas events, export financing, technical assistance, and export counseling. They also have access to the National Trade Data Bank.

Trade Information Center
800-USA-TRADE
www.ita.doc.gov

U.S. Department of Commerce
Washington, DC 20230
202-482-0543
Fax: 202-482-4473
TDD: 800-833-8723
www.commerce.gov

Country Experts

If you are looking for information on a market, company or most any other aspect of commercial life in a particular country, your best point of departure is to contact the appropriate country desk officer at the U.S. Department of Commerce. These experts often have the information you need right at their fingertips or they can refer you to other country specialists that can help you. Experienced trade specialists provide individual counseling over the phone and by email, and will continue to offer advice and guidance once you have entered the international marketplace. Call the USA TRADE hotline and ask for the expert for your country of interest — anywhere from Afghanistan to Zimbabwe. These experts have information that you won't find anywhere else.

U.S. and Foreign Commercial Services (FCS)
International Trade Administration
U.S. Department of Commerce, Room 2810
Washington, DC 20230
202-482-5777
800-USA-TRADE
Fax: 202-482-5013
www.export.gov

All the Department of Commerce/US & FCS field offices around the country are listed later in this chapter. (You will also find a separate roster of international trade offices maintained by the states.)

State Department Country Experts

If you need information that is primarily political, economic or cultural in nature, direct your questions first to the State Department Country Desk Officers. An operator at the number listed below can direct you to the appropriate desk officer.

U.S. Department of State
2201 C Street, NW
Washington, DC 20520
202-647-4000
www.state.gov

Foreign Specialists at Other Government Agencies

The following is a listing by subject area of other departments within the federal government which maintain country experts who are available to help the public:

1) **Foreign Agriculture:**
   Foreign Agriculture Service, Outreach and Exporter Assistance, U.S. Department of Agriculture, Room 3121S, 1400 Independence Ave., SW, Washington, DC 20250, 202-720-9509; {www.fas.usda.gov}.

   Food Safety and Inspection Service, International Programs, U.S. Dept. of Agriculture, Room 341-E, 14th and Independence Ave., SW, Washington, DC 20250-3700, 202-720-3473; {www.fsis.usda.gov}.

   Animal and Plant Health Inspection Service, Import-Export, U.S. Department of Agriculture, 4700 River Road, Riverdale, MD 20737, 301-734-8093; {www.aphis.usda.gov}.

2) **Energy Resources:**
   Office of Export Assistance, U.S. Department of Energy, 1000 Independence Ave., SW, Washington, DC 20585, 202-586-6797; {www.energy.gov}.

   Office of Fossil Energy, U.S. Dept. of Energy, 1000 Independence Ave., SW, Washington, DC 20585, 202-586-6503; Fax: 202-586-5146; {www.fe.doe.gov}.

3) **Economic Assistance to Foreign Countries:**
   Business Office, U.S. Agency for International Development, 320 21st St. NW, Washington, DC 20523, 202-712-4810; {www.usaid.gov}.

4) **Information Programs and Cultural Exchange:**
   Office of Citizen Exchanges (ECA/PE/C), Bureau of Educational and Cultural Affairs, U.S. Department of State, SA-44, 501 Fourth Street, SW, Washington, DC 20547; 202-619-5348; {http://exchanges.state.gov}.

5) **Metric:**
   Office of Metric Programs, National Institute of Standards and Technology, 100 Bureau Drive, Building 411, Room A146, Gaithersburg, MD 20899, 301-975-3690; {ts.nist.gov/ts}.

6) **Telecommunications Information:**
   Bureau of International Communications and Information Policy, U.S. Department of State, Washington, DC 20520, 202-647-5212.

7) **Fisheries:**
   Office of Trade and Industry Services, Fisheries Promotion and Trade Matters, National Marine Fisheries Service, 1315 East-West Highway, Silver Spring, MD 20910, 301-713-2379; {www.nmfs.noaa.gov}.

Money for Selling Overseas

1) **State Government Money Programs:**
Some state government economic development programs offer special help for those who need financial assistance in selling overseas. See the section presented later in this chapter entitled *State Government Assistance To Exporters*.

2) **Export-Import Bank Financing (Eximbank):**
The Export-Import Bank facilitates and aids in the financing of exports of United States goods and services. Its programs include short-term, medium-term, and long-term credits, small business support, financial guarantees, and insurance. In addition, it sponsors conferences on small business exporting, maintains credit information on thousands of foreign firms, supports feasibility studies of overseas programs, and offers export and small business finance counseling. To receive *Marketing News* Fact Sheets, or the *Eximbank Export Credit Insurance* booklet, or the Eximbank's *Program Selection Guide,* contact: Export-Import Bank, 811 Vermont Ave. NW, Washington, DC 20571, 202-565-3946, 1-800-565-3946; Fax: 202-565-3380; {www.exim.gov}.

3) **Small Business Administration (SBA) Export Loans:**
This agency makes loans and loan guarantees to small business concerns as well as to small business investment companies, including those that sell overseas. It also offers technical assistance, counseling, training, management assistance, and information resources, including some excellent publications to small and minority businesses in export operations. Contact your local or regional SBA office listed in the blue pages of your telephone book under Small Business Administration, or Small Business Administration, Office of International Trade, 409 3rd St., SW, Washington, DC 20416, 202-205-6720; {www.sbaonline.sba.gov/oit/ finance}.

4) **Overseas Private Investment Corporation (OPIC):**
This agency provides marketing, insurance, and financial assistance to American companies investing in 140 countries and 16 geographic regions. Its programs include direct loans, loan guarantees, and political risk insurance. OPIC also sponsors U.S. and international seminars for investment executives as well as conducts investment missions to developing countries. The Investor Services Division offers a computer service to assist investors in identifying investment opportunities worldwide. A modest fee is charged for this service and it is also available through the Lexis/Nexis computer network. OPIC has supported investments worth nearly $112 billion, generated $56 billion in U.S. exports, and helped to create 230,000 American jobs. Specific Info-Kits are available identifying basic economic, business, and political information for each of the countries covered. In addition, it operates:

> *Program Information Hotline*
> Overseas Private Investment Corporation
> 1100 New York Ave., NW
> Washington, DC 20527
> 202-336-8799 (Hotline)
> 202-336-8400 (General Information)
> 202-336-8636 (Public Affairs)
> 202-336-8680 (Press Information)
> 202-408-9859 (Fax)
> Email: {info@opic.gov}
> www.opic.gov

5) **Agency for International Development (AID):**
The Agency for International Development was created in 1961 by John F. Kennedy. AID offers a variety of loan and financing guarantee programs for projects in developing countries that have a substantial developmental impact or for the exportation of manufactured goods to AID-assisted developing countries. Some investment opportunities are region specific, which include the Association of Southeast Asian National, the Philippines, and Africa. For more information, contact the Office of Investment, Agency for International Development, 515 22nd St. NW, Room 301, Washington, DC 20523-0231; 202-712-4810; {www.info.usaid.gov}.

6) **Grants to Train Local Personnel**
The Trade and Development Agency has the authority to offer grants in support of short-listed companies on a transaction specific basis. These are usually in the form of grants to cover the cost of training local personnel by the company on the installation, operation, and maintenance of equipment specific to bid the proposal. The average grant awarded is $320,000. Contact: Trade and Development Agency, 1000 Wilson Blvd., Suite 1600, Arlington, VA 22209; 703-875-4357; Fax: 703-875-4009; {www.tda.gov}.

7) **Consortia of American Businesses in Eastern Europe (CABEE):**
CABEE provides grant funds to trade organizations to defray the costs of opening, staffing, and operating U.S. consortia offices in Eastern Europe. The CABEE grant program initially began operations in Poland, the Czech Republic, Slovikia, and Hungary, targeting five industry sectors: agribusiness/agriculture, construction/ housing, energy, environment, and telecommunications. Contact: CABEE, Department of Commerce, 14th and Constitution Avenue, Room 1104, Washington, DC 20230, 202-482-5004; Fax: 202-482-1790; {www.ita.doc.govoetca}.

8) **Consortia of American Businesses in the Newly Independent States (CABNIS):**
This program was modeled after CABEE and stimulates U.S. business in the Newly Independent States (NIS) and assists the region in its move toward privatization. CABNIS is providing grant funds to nonprofit organizations to defray the costs of opening, staffing, and operating U.S. consortia offices in the NIS. Contact: CABNIS, Department of Commerce, 14th and Constitution Ave., Washington, DC 20230, 202-482-4655; {www.bisnis.doc.gov/nis}.

Marketing Data, Custom Studies, and Company Information

Further information on any of the following services and products can be obtained by contacting a U.S. Department of Commerce/ US & FCS field office listed later in this chapter, or by contacting the US & FCS at: United States and Foreign Commercial Services, U.S. Department of Commerce, Room 3810, HCH Building, 14th and Constitution Ave., NW, Washington, DC 20230, 202-482-4767 or call 1-800-USA-TRADE.

1) **International Industry Experts:**
A separate Office of Trade Development at the Commerce Department handles special marketing and company problems for specific industries. Experts are available in the following international market sectors:

Technology and Aerospace Industries:	202-482-1228
	www.ita.doc.gov/aerospace
Office of Automotive Affairs:	202-482-0554
	www.ita.doc.gov/auto
Consumer Goods	202-482-7880
	www.ita.doc.gov/td/ocg
Environmental Technologies Exports	201-482-3888
	http://environment.ita.doc.gov
Machinery	202-482-4436
	www.ita.doc.gov/td/machinery
Medical Equipment	202-482-2470
	www.ita.doc.gov/td/medical
Telecommunications:	202-482-0261
	www.ita.doc.gov/td/sif
Service, Industries and Finance:	202-482-5261
Textiles, Apparel and Consumer Goods:	202-482-3737
	otexa.ita.doc.gov

You can also talk to industry desk officers at the Department of Commerce. They can provide information on the competitive strengths of U.S. industries in foreign markets from abrasives to yogurt. You can call the Department of Commerce at 202-482-2000 (main office) or 1-800-872-8723 (trade information) to locate specific industry analysts. You can also contact them online at {www.trade.gov/td/tic}.

2) **Trade Lists:**
Directories of overseas customers for U.S. exports in selected industries and countries: They contain the names and product lines of foreign distributors, agents, manufacturers, wholesalers, retailers, and other purchasers. They also provide the name and title of key officials as well as telex and cable numbers, and company size data. Prices range up to $40 for a list of a category.

3) **Country Statistics:**
There are multiple ways to get up to date statistics for most countries worldwide. The Census Bureau maintains a listing of country statistics on its website: {www.census.gov/}.

InfoNation is another easy to use database for quick statistical information for every country that is a member of the United Nations. Maintained by the U.N., InfoNation is a very helpful site for being able to easily compare statistics using its two-step database. Contact InfoNation at {www.un.org/Pubs/CyberSchoolBus/ infonation/e_infonation. htm}.

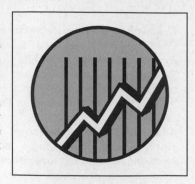

4) **Demographic and Social Information:**
The Center for International Research compiles and maintains up to date global demographic and social information for all countries in its International Data Base (IDB). Last year, the IDB represented 227 countries and areas worldwide. The IDB has all vital information available for easy download from its website. The only requirements are that your machine must be a PC compatible, 386 computer (or higher). Contact: Systems Analysis and Programming Staff, 301-457-1403; Fax: 301-457-1539; Email: {idb@census.gov}; {www.census.gov/pub/ipc/www/}.

5) **Customized Export Mailing Lists:**
Selected lists of foreign companies in particular industries, countries, and types of business can be requested by a client. Gummed labels are also available. Prices start at $35.

6) **World Traders Data Reports:**
Background reports are available on individual firms containing information about each firm's business activities, its standing in the local business community, its creditworthiness, and overall reliability and suitability as a trade contact for exporters. The price is $100 per report.

7) **Agent Distributor Service (ADS):**
This is a customized search for interested and qualified foreign representatives on behalf of an American client. U.S. commercial officers overseas conduct the search and prepare a report identifying up to six foreign prospects which have personally examined the U.S. firm's product literature and have expressed interest in representing the firm. A fee of $250 per country is charged. Contact them online at {www.export.gov}.

8) **New Product Information Service:**
This service is designed to help American companies publicize the availability of new U.S. products in foreign markets and simultaneously test market interest in these products. Product information which meets the criteria is distributed worldwide through *Commercial News USA* and Voice of America broadcasts. A fee is charged for participation.

9) **Customized Market Analysis (CMA):**
At a cost of $800 to $13,500 per country per product, these studies are called "Comparison Shopping Service." They are conducted by the U.S. Embassy foreign commercial attaches and can target information on quite specific marketing questions such as:

➡ Does the product have sales potential in the country?
➡ Who is the supplier for a comparable product locally?
➡ What is the going price for a comparable product in this country?
➡ What is the usual sales channel for getting this type of product into the market?
➡ What are the competitive factors that most influence purchases of these products in the market (i.e., price, credit, quality, delivery, service, promotion, brand)?
➡ What is the best way to get sales exposure in the market for this type of product?
➡ Are there any significant impediments to selling this type of product?
➡ Who might be interested and qualified to represent or purchase this company's products?
➡ If a licensing or joint venture strategy seems desirable for this market, who might be an interested and qualified partner for the U.S. company?

10) **New Markets in Eastern European Countries (EEBIC):**

The Eastern Europe Business Information Center is stocked with a wide range of publications on doing business in Eastern Europe. These include lists of potential partners, investment regulations, priority industry sectors, and notices of upcoming seminars, conferences, and trade promotion events. The center also serves as a referral point for programs of voluntary assistance to the region.

Eastern Europe Business Information Center
U.S. Department of Commerce
Room 7412
Washington, DC 20230
202-482-2645
Fax: 202-482-4473
www.mac.doc.gov/ceebic

11) **Exporting to Japan: Japan Export Information Center (JEIC)**

The Japan Export Information Center (JEIC) provides business counseling services and accurate information on exporting to Japan. The JEIC is the point of contact for information on business in Japan, market entry alternatives, market information and research, product standards and testing, tariffs, and non-tariff barriers. The center maintains a commercial library and participates in seminars on various aspects of Japanese business. Contact: Japan Export Information Center, U.S. Department of Commerce, Room 2320, Washington, DC 20230; 202-482-2427; Fax: 202-482-0469; (www.ita.doc.gov/}.

12) **Office of Export Trading Company Affairs**

The Office of Export Trading Company offers various information as well as promoting the use of export trading companies and export management companies; offers information and counseling to businesses and trading associations regarding the export industry; and administers the Export Trade Certificate of Review program which provides exporters with an antitrust "insurance policy" intended to foster joint export activities where economies of scale and risk diversification are achieved. Contact: Office of Export Trading Company Affairs, U.S. Department of Commerce, 14th and Constitution Ave., NW, Room 1104, Washington, DC 20230; 202-482-5131; Fax: 202-482-1790; {www.ita.doc.gov/td/oetca}.

13) **U.S.-Asia Environmental Partnership**

US-AEP is a comprehensive service to help U.S. environmental exporters enter markets in the Asia/Pacific region. It is a coalition of public, private and non-governmental organizations which promotes environmental protection and sustainable development in 34 nations in the Asia/Pacific area. Contact: U.S.-Asia Environmental Partnership, 1819 H Street, NW, 7th Floor, Washington, DC 20006; 202-835-0333; Fax: 202-835-0366; Email: {usasia@usaep.org}; {www.usaep.org}.

14) **Technical Assistance with Transportation Concerns**

The Department of Transportation provides technical assistance to developing countries on a wide range of problems in the areas of transportation policy, highways, aviation, rail and ports. It also supports AID in the foreign aid development program. Contact: International Transportation and Trade: 202-366-4368; {http://ostpxweb.dot.gov/aviation}; Federal Aviation Administration: 202-267-3173; Fax: 202-267-5306; {www.faa.gov}; Federal Highway Administration: 202-366-0111; Fax: 202-366-9626; {www.fhwa.dot.gov}; Federal Railroad Administration: 202-493-6395; {www.fra.dot.gov}; Maritime Administration: 202-366-5773; Fax: 202-366-3746; {www.marad.dot.gov}.

15) **"First Business"**

The "First Business" television program is a half-hour long monthly televised business program sent by satellite to more than 100 countries highlighting innovation and excellence in U.S. business. The program consists of segments on new products, services, and processes of interest to overseas buyers and promising research. "First Business" is produced by Worldnet Television, a division of the International Broadcasting Bureau. Contact: Worldnet Television, 202-619-1783; Fax: 202-205-2967; Email: {worldnet@ibb.gov}; {www.ibb.gov/worldnet}.

16) **Environmental Technology Network for Asia (ETNA):**

ETNA matches environmental trade leads sent from U.S.-Asia Environmental Partnership (USAEP) Technology Representatives located in 11 Asian countries with appropriate U.S. environmental firms and trade associations that are registered with ETNA's environmental trade opportunities database. U.S. environmental firms receive the trade leads by Broadcast Fax system within 48 hours of leads being identified and entered electronically from Asia.

Companies may register online to join ETNA's 2400 firms and associations. Contact: Environmental Technology Network for Asia, US-AEP, 1819 H Street, NW, 7th Floor, Washington, DC 20006; 202-835-0333; Fax: 202-835-0446; {www.usaep.org/ouractiv/etna.htm}.

17) **Automated Trade Locator Assistance System:**
The SBAtlas is a market research tool that provides free of charge two types of reports: product- specific and country-specific. The product report ranks the top 35 import and export market for a particular good or service. The country report identifies the top 20 products most frequently traded in a target market. This service is free of charge. SBAtlas is available through SBA district offices, Service Corps of Retired Executives (SCORE) office, and Small Business Development Centers, to get the address and phone number to the nearest office call 1-800-U-ASK-SBA.

18) **Export Contact List Service (ECLS):**
This database retrieval service provides U.S. exporters with names, addresses, products, sizes and other relevant information on foreign firms interested in importing U.S. goods and services. Similar information is also available on U.S. exporters to foreign firms seeking suppliers from the U.S. Names are collected and maintained by Commerce district offices and commercial officers at foreign posts. Contact your nearest district Commerce office located in this book or call 1-800-USA-TRADE.

Trade Fairs and Missions

Trade fairs, exhibitions, trade missions, overseas trade seminars, and other promotional events and services are sponsored by the Export Promotion Services Group, U.S. and Foreign Commercial Services, U.S. Department of Commerce, 14th and E Streets, NW, Room 2810, Washington, DC 20230; 202-482-6220. This office or one of its field offices, which are listed later in this chapter, can provide additional details on these activities.

1) **Industry-Organized, Government-Approved Trade Missions:**
Such missions are organized by trade associations, local Chambers of Commerce, state trade development agencies, and similar trade-oriented groups that enjoy U.S. Department of Commerce support.

2) **Catalog Exhibitions:**
Such exhibitions feature displays of U.S. product catalogs, sales brochures, and other graphic sales materials at American embassies and consulates or in conjunction with trade shows. A Department of Commerce specialist assists in the exhibition. Call 202-482-3973; Fax: 202-482-2716.

3) **Video Catalog:**
This catalog is designed to showcase American products via videotape presentation. This permits actual product demonstrations giving the foreign buyer an opportunity to view applications of American products. Federal specialists participate in these sessions. Call 202-482-3973; Fax: 202-482-2716.

4) **U.S. Specialized Trade Missions:**
These missions are distinct from those mentioned above since the U.S. Department of Commerce plans the visits and accompanies the delegation. They are designed to sell American goods and services as well as establish agents or representation abroad. The Department of Commerce provides marketing information, advanced planning, publicity, and trip organization. Call 1-800-USA-TRADE.

5) **U.S. Seminar Missions:**
The objective here is to promote exports and help foreign representation for American exporters. However, unlike trade missions, these are designed to facilitate the sales of state-of-the-art products and technology. This type of mission is a one to two day "seminar" during which team members discuss technology subjects followed by private, sales-oriented appointments. Call 1-800-USA-TRADE.

6) **Matchmaker Trade Delegations:**
These Department of Commerce-recruited and planned missions are designed to introduce new-to-export or new-to-market businesses to prospective agents and distributors overseas. Trade Specialists from Commerce evaluate the

potential firm's products, find and screen contacts, and handle logistics. This is followed by an intensive trip filled with meetings and prospective clients and in-depth briefings on the economic and business climate of the countries visited. Contact: 202-482-0481; Fax: 202-482-0115.

7) **Investment Missions:**
These events are held in developing countries offering excellent investment opportunities for U.S. firms. Missions introduce U.S. business executives to key business leaders, potential joint venture partners, and senior foreign government officials in the host country. Call Investment Missions, 202-336-8799; Fax: 202-408-5155.

8) **Foreign Buyer Program:**
This program supports major domestic trade shows featuring products and services of U.S. industries with high export potential. Government officials recruit on a worldwide basis qualified buyers to attend the shows. Call Export Promotion Services, 202-482-0481; Fax: 202-482-0115.

9) **Trade Fairs, Solo Exhibitions, and Trade Center Shows:**
The Department of Commerce organizes a wide variety of special exhibitions. These events range from solo exhibitions representing U.S. firms exclusively at trade centers overseas to U.S. pavilions in the largest international exhibitions. Call 1-800-USA-TRADE.

10) **Agent/Distributor Service (ADS):**
Looking for overseas representatives to expand your business and boost your export sales? Commerce will locate, screen, and assess agents, distributors, representatives, and other foreign partners for your business. Contact: 1-800-USA-TRADE.

11) **Trade Opportunities Program (TOP):**
The Trade Opportunities Program (TOP) provides companies with current sales leads from international firms seeking to buy or represent their products or services. TOP leads are printed daily in leading commercial newspapers and are also distributed electronically via the U.S. Department of Commerce Economic Bulletin Board. Call 1-800-STAT-USA, 202-482-1986; Fax: 202-482-2164.

Special Programs for Agricultural Products

The following programs are specifically aimed at those who wish to sell agricultural products overseas. Agricultural exporters should also be sure not to limit themselves only to programs under this heading. Programs listed under other headings can also be used for agricultural products.

1) **Office Space for Agricultural Exporters:**
The Foreign Agriculture Service (FAS) maintains overseas agricultural trade offices to help exporters of U.S. farm and forest products in key overseas markets. The facilities vary depending on local conditions, but may include a trade library, conference rooms, office space, and kitchens for preparing product samples. Contact: Foreign Agriculture Service, U.S. Department of Agriculture, 14th and Independence Ave. SW, Washington, DC 20250, 202-720-7420; Fax: 202-205-9728; {www.fas.usda.gov}.

2) **Foreign Market Information:**
A special office serves as a single contact point within the Foreign Agriculture Service for agricultural exporters seeking foreign market information. The office also counsels firms that believe they have been injured by unfair trade practices. Contact: Trade Assistance and Promotion Office, U.S. Department of Agriculture, 14th and Independence Avenue, SW, Washington, DC 20250, 202-720-7420; Fax: 202-720-9728.

3) **Export Connections:**
The AgExport Action Kit provides information which can help put U.S. exporters in touch quickly and directly with foreign importers of food and agricultural products. The services include trade leads, a *Buyer Alert* newsletter, foreign buyer lists, and U.S. supplier lists. This bi-weekly newsletter, distributed by USDA's overseas offices, can introduce your food and agricultural products to foreign buyers around the world. *Buyer Alert* reaches more than 15,000 importers in 75 countries. Last year, *Buyer Alert* helped generate confirmed export sales of $100 million. Contact:

AgExport Connection, Ag Box 1052, U.S. Department of Agriculture, FAS/AGX, Washington, DC 20250, 202-690-3421; Fax: 202-690-4374. Export Kit: {www.fas.usda.gov/agexport/exporter.html}. Buyer Alert: {www.fas.usda.gov/agexport/bainfo.html}

Export Regulations, Licensing, and Product Standards

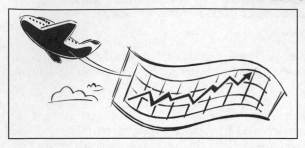

Talk to ELVIS — Bureau of Export Administration (BXA)
BXA is responsible for controlling exports for reasons of national security, foreign policy, and short supply. Licenses on controlled exports are issued, and seminars on U.S. export regulations are held domestically and overseas. Contact: Bureau of Industry and Security, U.S. Department of Commerce, 14th St. and Pennsylvania Ave., Room 2705 (for mail), Room 1099 (for visitors), Washington, DC 20230; 202-482-4811; Fax: 202-482-3617; {www.bxa.doc.gov}; or BXA Western Regional Office, 3300 Irvine Ave., Suite 345, Newport Beach, CA 92660; 949-660-0144; 949-660-9347.

Export license applications may be submitted and issued through computer via the *Export License Application and Information Network (ELAIN)*. The *System for Tracking Export License Application (STELA)* provides instant status updates on license applications by the use of a touch-tone phone.

The *Export Licensing Voice Information (ELVIS)* is an automated attendant that offers a range of licensing information and emergency handling procedures. Callers may order forms and publications or subscribe to the *Office of Export Licensing (OEL) Insider Newsletter*, which provides regulatory updates. While using ELVIS, a caller has the option of speaking to a consultant.

Office of Export Licensing	202-482-0436
	Fax: 202-482-3322
ELAIN	202-482-4811
STELA	202-482-2752
ELVIS	202-482-4811
Export Seminars	202-482-6031

The National Institute of Standards and Technology provides a free service that will identify standards for selling any product to any country in the world. This federal agency will tell you what the standard is for a given product or suggest where you can obtain an official copy of the standard.

National Center for Standards and Certification
National Institute of Standards and Technology
Building 820, Room 164
Gaithersburg, MD 20899

301-975-4040
Fax: 301-926-1559
www.nist.gov

Cheap Office and Conference Space Overseas

If you are traveling overseas on a business trip, you may want to look into renting office space and other services through the American Embassy. Depending on the country and the space available, the embassy can provide temporary office space for as low as $25 per day, along with translation services, printing, and other services. Meeting rooms, seminar or convention space along with promotion services, mailings, freight handling, and even catering may be available in many

countries. Contact the Department of Commerce/US & FCS field office, which is listed later in this chapter, or the appropriate country desk officer at the U.S. Department of Commerce in Washington, DC.

Other Services, Resources, and Databases

The following is a description of some of the additional services and information sources that can be useful to anyone investigating overseas markets:

1) **Foreign Demographic Profiles:**
   The Government Printing Office has a publication called the CIA *World Factbook*. Produced annually, this publication provides country-by-country data on demographics, economy, communications, and defense. The cost is $29 (GPO: 041-015-00173-6). Order by contacting Superintendent of Documents, Government Printing Office, Washington, DC 20402; 202-512-1800; {www.gpo.gov}.

2) **International Prices:**
   Export price indexes for both detailed and aggregate product groups are available on a monthly basis. Price trends comparisons of U.S. exports with those of Japan and Germany are also available. Contact: International Prices Division, Bureau of Labor Statistics, U.S. Department of Labor, 2nd Massachusetts Ave., NE, Room 3955, Washington, DC 20212, 202-691-7179; {www.bls.gov}.

3) **U.S. and Foreign Commercial Service:**
   This service provides information on government programs to American businesses, and uncovers trade opportunities for U.S. exporters. They also locate representatives and agents for American firms, assist U.S. executives in all phases of their exporting, and help enforce export controls and regulations. They operate through 47 district offices located in major U.S. cities and in 124 posts in 69 foreign countries. In addition, a valued asset of the U.S. and Foreign Commercial Services is a group of about 525 foreign nationals, usually natives of the foreign country, who are employed in the U.S. embassy or consulate and bring with them a wealth of personal understanding of local market conditions and business practices. U.S. exporters usually tap into these services by contacting the Department of Commerce/US & FCS field office in their state (listed later in this chapter), or Office of U.S. and Foreign Commercial Service, U.S. Department of Commerce, Washington, DC 20230; 1-800-USA-TRADE; {www.export.gov}.

Or contact regional directors at:

Africa, Near East	202-482-4925
Asia and Pacific	202-482-5251
Europe	202-482-5638
Japan	202-482-2427

4) **Latest News on Foreign Opportunities:**
In addition to technical reports on foreign research and development, National Technical Information Service sells foreign market airgrams and foreign press and radio translations. A free video is available explaining NTIS services. Contact: National Technical Information Service, U.S. Department of Commerce, 5285 Port Royal Rd., Springfield, VA 22161, 703-605-6000; Fax: 703-605-6900; {www.ntis.gov}.

5) **Planning Services for U.S. Exporters:**
In its effort to promote economic development in Third World countries, the Trade and Development Program finances planning services for development projects leading to the export of U.S. goods and services. A free pamphlet is available that describes the planning services offered by the Trade and Development Program. To obtain a copy, contact: U.S. Trade and Development Program, Department of State, Room 309 SA-16, Washington, DC 20523-1602, 202-647-5991.

6) **Terrorism Abroad:**
Assistance is available to companies doing business abroad to assess current security conditions and risk in certain cities and countries that may pose a threat. Over 1600 U.S. companies are already affiliated with the OSAC. The OSAC has numerous publications on security guidelines available from its website at {www.ds.osac.org}. Contact: Overseas Security Advisory Council (OSAC), U.S. Department of State, Washington, DC 20522-1003, 202-663-0533; Fax: 202-663-0868; Email: {osca@dsmail.state.gov}.

7) **Trade Remedy Assistance Office (TRAO):**
The Center provides information on remedies available under the Trade Remedy Law. It also offers technical assistance to eligible small businesses to enable them to bring cases to the International Trade Commission. Contact: ITC Trade Remedy Assistance Center, U.S. International Trade Commission, 500 E St. SW, Washington, DC 20436, 202-205-2200; Fax: 202-205-2139; {www.usitc.gov}.

8) **International Expertise:**
Staff in the following offices will prove helpful as information sources regarding the international scope of their respective subject areas:

Economics:
International Investment, Bureau of Economic Analysis, U.S. Department of Commerce, 1441 L St., NW, Washington, DC 20230, 202-606-9800; {www.bea.doc.gov}.

Productivity and Technology Statistics:
Bureau of Labor Statistics, U.S. Department of Labor, 2 Massachusetts Ave., NE, #2150, Washington, DC 20212, 202-691-5600; Fax: 202-691-5664; {www.bls.gov}.

Investments and Other Monetary Matters:
Office of Assistant Secretary for International Affairs, U.S. Department of the Treasury, 1500 Pennsylvania Ave., Washington, DC 20220, 202-622-2000; Fax: 202-622-6415; {www.ustreas.gov}.

Population:
International Program Center, Bureau of Census, U.S. Department of Commerce, Room 205, Washington Plaza, Washington, DC 20233, 301-457-1403; {www.census.gov}.

Population Reference Bureau, Inc., 1875 Connecticut Ave., NW, Suite 520, Washington, DC 20009, 202-483-1100; 800-877-9881; Fax: 202-328-3937; Email: {popref@prb.org}; {www.prb.org}.

Country Development:
Inter-American Development Bank, 1300 NY Ave., NW, Washington, DC 20577, 202-623-1000; Email: {pic@iadb.org}; {www.iadb.org}.

International Monetary Fund, 700 19th St. NW, Washington, DC 20431, 202-623-7000; Fax: 202-623-6278; Email: {publicaffairs@ifm.org}; {www.imf.org}.

World Bank, 1818 H St. NW, Washington, DC 20433, 202-473-1000; Fax: 202-477-6391; {worldbank.org}.

9) **National Trade Data Bank (NTDB):**

This is a "one-stop" source for export promotion and international trade data collected by 17 U.S. government agencies. Updated each month and released on CD-ROM, the Data Bank enables a user with an IBM-compatible personal computer equipped with a CD-ROM reader to access over 100,00 trade documents. It contains the latest Census data on U.S. imports and exports by commodity and country; the complete Central Intelligence Agency (CIA) *World Factbook*; current market research reports compiled by the U.S. and Foreign and Commercial Service; the complete Foreign Traders Index which has over 60,000 names and addresses of individuals and firms abroad interested in importing U.S. products; and many other data services.

It is available for free at over 900 Federal Depository Libraries and can be purchased for $35 per disc or $360 for a 12-month subscription. Contact: Economics and Statistics Administration, U.S. Department of Commerce, Washington, DC 20230; 202-482-1986; Fax: 202-482-2164; {www.stat-usa.gov}.

10) **Free Legal Assistance:**

The Export Legal Assistance Network (ELAN) is a nationwide group of attorneys with experience in international trade who provide free initial consultations to small businesses on export related matters. Contact: Export Legal Assistance Network, Small Business Administration, 1667 K St., NW, Suite 1100, Washington, DC 20006; 202-778-3080; Fax: 202-778-3063; {www.fita.org/elan}.

11) **Global Learning:**

U.S. Department of Education, Business and International Education Programs. The business and international education program is designed to engage U.S. schools of business language and area programs, international study programs, public and private sector organizations, and U.S. businesses in a mutually productive relationship which will benefit the Nation's future economic interest. Approximately $3.6 million annually is available to assist U.S. institutions of higher education to promote the Nation's capacity for international understanding. Typical grantee activities include executive seminars, case studies, and export skill workshops. For more information contact: Office of Higher Education Programs, U.S. Department of Education, 600 Independence Avenue, SW, Washington, DC 20202; 202-401-9778.

12) **Export Counseling — SCORE:**

The Small Business Administration can provide export counseling to small business exporters by retired and active business executives. The Service Corps of Retired Executives (SCORE) is an overly active organization with over 12,400 volunteers and 389 SCORE chapters. Members of SCORE, with years of practical experience in international trade, assist small firms in evaluating their export potential and developing and implementing basic export marketing plans. Two of SCORE's most helpful programs are its weekly low cost workshops and its Email counseling. For more information, contact your local Small Business Administration (SBA) office listed in the government pages of your telephone book, or National SCORE Office, 401 Third St. SW, 6th Floor, Washington, DC 20024; 800-634-0245; Fax: 202-205-7636; Email: {score@sba.gov}; {www.score.org}.

13) **International Company Profiles (ICP)**

The ICP, run by the U.S. Department of Commerce, provides thorough background checks on all potential clients to reduce the risk of entering new business relationships. U.S. embassies and consulates abroad will conduct this investigation for you at a reasonable rate and return the results in approximately one month. Commercial specialists will then give a trained opinion of a possible relationship between yourself and the subject firm. All requests are held within the strictest of confidences. For more information, contact your local Export Assistance Center at {www.export.gov}.

14) **National Telecommunication and Information Administration (NTIA)**

The NTIA, through its Office of International Affairs, provides technical guidance, aids in stabilizing international telecommunications issues, deploys new technology into international markets, and works to improve global communications and expand trade opportunities for the U.S. Contact the Office of International Affairs at the NTIA: Office of International Affairs, National Telecommunications & Information Administration, Room 4701, U.S. Department of Commerce, 1401 Constitution Ave., NW, Washington, DC 20230; 202-482-1866; Fax: 202-482-1865, {www.ntia.doc.gov/oiahome/oiahome.html}.

Read All About It: Helpful Publications

The Government Printing Office (GPO) has many titles to choose from. For a listing, contact the GPO (listed below) by mail or phone and ask for the Foreign Trade and Tariff Subject Bibliography (SB-123; 021-123-00405-1).

Government Printing Office
Superintendent of Documents
Washington, DC 20402
202-512-1800
www.access.gpo.gov/su_docs

Basic Guide to Exporting:
This publication outlines the sequence of steps necessary to determine whether to, and how to, use foreign markets as a source of profits. It describes the various problems that confront smaller firms engaged in, or seeking to enter, international trade, as well as the types of assistance available. It also provides a guide to appraising the sales potential of foreign markets and to understanding the requirements of local business practices and procedures in overseas markets. The booklet is available for $13 (GPO: 003-009-00604-0) from: Superintendent of Documents, U.S. Government Printing Office, Washington, DC 20402, 202-512-1800; Fax: 202-512-2250.

Commercial News USA:
This publication describes a free export promotion service that will publicize the availability of your new product to foreign markets of more than 150 countries, and test foreign market interest in your new product. There is a small fee. Contact Commercial News USA: Associated Publications International, 317 Madison Ave., New York, NY 10017; 212-490-3999; Fax: 212-986-7864; {www.cnewsusa.com}.

Export Programs: A Business Directory of U.S. Government Resources:
This guide provides an overview of U.S. government export assistance programs and contact points for further information and expertise in utilizing these programs. Contact: Trade Information Center, U.S. Department of Commerce, Washington, DC 20230, 1-800-872-8723.

Export Trading Company (ETC) Guidebook:
This Guidebook is intended to assist those who are considering starting or expanding exporting through the various forms of an ETC. The Guidebook will also facilitate your review of the ETC Act and export trading options and serve as a planning tool for your business by showing you what it takes to export profitably and how to start doing it. Cost is $15 (GPO: 003-009-00523-0). Contact: Superintendent of Documents, Government Printing Office, Washington, DC 20402, 202-512-1800.

Foreign Labor Trends:
Published by the Department of Labor, these are a series of reports, issued annually, that describe and analyze labor trends in more than 70 countries. The reports, which are prepared by the American Embassy in each country, cover labor-management relations, trade unions, employment and unemployment, wages and working conditions, labor and government, international labor activities, and other significant developments. Contact: Office of Foreign Relations, U.S. Department of Labor, Room S 5303, 200 Constitution Ave., NW, Washington, DC 20210, 202-693-4785; Fax: 202-693-4784; {www.dol.gov/ILAB}. This publication is also available from the GPO for $1.50-$2.00.

ABC's of Exporting:
This is a special issue of Business America that takes you step by step through the exporting process. It explains the federal agencies and how they can help, as well as providing a directory of export sources. This publication is free and is available by contacting Trade Information Center, U.S. Department of Commerce, Washington, DC 20230, 1-800-872-8723.

Ag Exporter:
Monthly magazine published by the U.S. Department of Agriculture's Foreign Agricultural Service (FAS). The annual subscription cost is $27 (GPO: 701-027-00000-1). Contact: Superintendent of Documents, Government Printing Office, Washington, DC 20402; 202-512-1800.

AID Procurement Information Bulletin:
This publication advertises notices of intended procurement of AID-financed commodities. The subscription cost is free. Contact: USAID's Office of Small and Disadvantaged Business Utilization/ Minority Resource Center, U.S. Agency for International Development, Ronald Reagan Building, Washington, DC 20523-1000; 202-712-4810; Fax: 202-216-3524.

Breaking into the Trade Game: A Small Business Guide to Exporting:
The Small Business Administration has created this comprehensive guide to exporting. A must have for all exporters, new and experienced. This guide is available from the SBA website: {www.sba.gov/oit/txt/finance/pubs.html}.

U.S. Department of Commerce/ US & FCS Field Offices

Trade experts from the US & FCS are available to help you from 47 district offices and 21 branch locations throughout the U.S. The ITA trade specialists are also available at any of the 51 District Export Councils nationwide to assist U.S. firms export. For an up to date listing, go to {www.export.gov}.

Alabama
Birmingham: 950 22nd St., North, Room 707, Birmingham, AL 35203; 205-731-1331; Fax: 205-731-0076.

Alaska
Anchorage: 550 W. 7th Ave., Suite 1770, Anchorage, AK 99501; 907-271-6237; Fax: 907-271-6242.

Arizona
Phoenix: 2901 N. Central Ave., Suite 970, Phoenix, AZ 85205; 602-640-2513; Fax: 602-640-2518.
Tucson: 166 West Alameda, Tucson, AZ 85701; 520-670-5540.

Arkansas
Little Rock: 425 West Capitol Ave., TCBY Tower Building, Suite 700, Little Rock, AR 72201; 501-324-5794; Fax: 501-324-7380.

California
Bakersfield: 1706 Chester Ave., Suite 200, Bakersfield, CA 93301; 661-637-0136
Fresno: 550 E Shaw Avenue, Fresno, CA 93710; 559-227-6582
Indio: 84-245 Indio Springs Dr., Indio, CA 92203; 760-342-4455
Los Angeles: 11500 Olympic Blvd., Suite 975, Los Angeles, CA 90064; 310-235-7104; Fax: 310-235-7220.
Los Angeles: 350 So Figueroa St., Suite 509, Los Angeles, CA 90071; 213-894-4231
Monterey: 411 Pacific St., Suite 316A, Monterey, CA 93940; 831-641-9850
Newport Beach: 3300 Irvine Ave., Suite 305, Newport Beach, CA 92660; 949-660-1688; Fax: 949-660-8039.
Oakland: 530 Water St., Suite 740, Oakland, CA 94607; 510-273-7350

Ontario: 2940 Inland Empire St., Suite 121, Ontario, CA 91764; 909-466-4134
Sacramento: 917 7th Street, 2nd Floor, Sacramento, CA 95814; 916-498-5155
San Diego: 6363 Greenwich Drive, Suite 230, San Diego, CA 92123; 619-557-5395; Fax: 619-557-6176.
San Francisco: 250 Montgomery St., 14th Floor, San Francisco, CA 94104; 415-705-2300; Fax: 415-705-2297.
San Jose: 152 N Third Street, Suite 550, San Jose, CA 95113; 408-271-7300
San Rafael: 4040 Civic Center Dr., Suite 200, San Rafael, CA 94903; 415-492-4546
Ventura: 5700 Ralston St., 310, Ventura, CA 93003; 805-676-1573

Colorado
Denver: 1625 Broadway, Suite 680, Denver, CO 80202; 303-844-6001; Fax: 303-844-5651.

Connecticut
Middletown: 213 Court St., Suite 903, Middletown, CT 06457; 860-638-6950; Fax: 860-638-6970.

District of Columbia
14th and Constitution Ave., NW, Washington, DC 20230; 202-482-3917.

Delaware
Served by Philadelphia, PA, District Office.

Florida
Miami: 777 North West 72nd Ave., Box 3L2, Miami, Fl 33126; 305-526-7425.
Clearwater: 1130 Cleveland St., Clearwater, FL 33755; 727-893-3738; Fax: 727-449-2889
Ft. Lauderdale: 200 E. Las Olas Blvd., Suite 1600, Ft. Lauderdale, FL 33301; 954-356-6640.

Tallahassee: 325 John Knox Rd., #201, Tallahassee, Fl 32303; 850-942-9635.

Orlando: 20 E. Robinson St., Suite 1270, Orlando, FL 32801; 407-648-6235; Fax: 407-648-6756.

Georgia

Atlanta: 285 Peachtree Center Ave., NE, Suite 900, Atlanta, GA 30303; 404-657-1900; Fax: 404-657-1900.

Savannah: 6001 Chatham Center Dr., Suite 100, Savannah, GA 31405; 912-652-4204; Fax: 912-652-4241.

Hawaii

Honolulu: 1001 Bishop St., Suite 1140, Honolulu, HI 96813; 808-522-8040; Fax: 808-522-8045.

Idaho

Boise: 700 W. State St., 2nd Floor, Boise, ID 83720; 208-334-3857; Fax: 208-334-2787.

Illinois

Chicago: 55 W. Monroe, Room 2440, Chicago, IL 60603; 312-353-4798; Fax: 312-353-8120.

Highland Park: 508 Central Ave., Suite 206, Highland Park, IL 60035; 847-681-8010.

Peoria: 922 N. Glenwood Ave., Jobst Hall, Room 141, Peoria, IL 61606; 309-671-7815.

Rockford: 515 N. Court St., P.O. Box 1747, Rockford, IL 61110-6247; 815-987-8123; Fax: 815-987-8122.

Indiana

Indianapolis: 11405 N. Pennsylvania St., Penwood One, Suite 106, Carmel, IN 46032; 317-582-2300; Fax: 317-582-2301.

Iowa

Des Moines: 700 Locust St., Suite 100, Des Moines, IA 50309; 515-288-8614; Fax: 515-288-1437.

Kansas

Wichita: 209 E. William, Suite 300, Wichita, KS 67214; 316-263-4067.

Kentucky

Lexington: 140 E. Main St., Lexington, KY 40507; 859-225-7001.

Louisville: 601 W. Broadway, Room 634B, Louisville, KY 40202; 502-582-5066; Fax: 502-582-6573.

Somerset: 2292 S. Highway 27, Suite 240, Somerset, KY 42501; 606-677-6160.

Louisiana

New Orleans: 365 Canal St., New Orleans, LA 70130; 504-589-6546; Fax: 504-589-2337.

Shreveport: One University Place, Shreveport, LA 71115; 318-676-3064.

Maine

Portland: Maine International Trade Center, 511 Congress St., Portland, ME 04101; 207-541-7300; Fax: 207-541-7400.

Maryland

Baltimore: 401 E. Pratt St., Suite 2432, Baltimore, MD 21202; 410-962-4539; Fax: 410-962-4529.

Massachusetts

Boston: 164 Northern Ave., Suite 307, Boston, MA 02210; 617-424-5990; Fax: 617-424-5992.

Michigan

Detroit: 211 W. Fort St., Suite 2220, Detroit, MI 48226; 313-226-3650; Fax: 313-226-3657.

Grand Rapids: 301 W. Fulton St., Suite 718-S, Grand Rapids, MI 49504; 616-458-3564; Fax: 616-458-3872.

Pontiac: 250 Elizabeth Lake Road, #1300, Pontiac, MI 48341; 248-975-9600.

Minnesota

Minneapolis: 45 South 7th St., Suite 2240, Minneapolis, MN 55402; 612-348-1638; Fax: 612-348-1650.

Mississippi

Jackson: 175 East Capitol St., Suite 255, Jackson, MS 39201; 601-965-4130.

Missouri

St. Louis: 8182 Maryland Ave., Suite 303, St. Louis, MO 63105; 314-425-3302; Fax: 314-425-3381.

Kansas City: 2345 Grand St., Suite 650, Kansas City, MO 64108; 816-410-9201; Fax: 816-410-9208.

Montana

Missoula: P.O. Box 7487, Missoula, MT 59807; 406-542-6656.

Nebraska

Omaha: 11135 O St., Omaha, NE 68137; 402-597-0193.

Nevada

Las Vegas: 400 Las Vegas Blvd., Las Vegas, NV 89101; 702-229-1157.

Reno: 1755 E. Plumb Lane, #152, Reno, NV 89502; 775-784-5203; Fax: 775-784-5343.

New Hampshire

Portsmouth: 17 New Hampshire Ave., Portsmouth, NH 03801; 603-334-6074; Fax: 603-334-6110.

New Jersey

Lawrenceville: 3131 Princeton Pike, Bldg. 4, Suite 105, Lawrenceville, NJ 08648; 609-989-2100.

Newark: 744 Broad St., Suite 1505, Newark, NJ 07102; 973-645-4682.

New Mexico

Santa Fe: New Mexico Department of Economic Development, P.O. Box 20003, Santa Fe, NM 87504; 505-827-0350; Fax: 505-827-0263.

New York

Buffalo: 111 W. Huron St., Room 1312, Federal Building, Buffalo, NY 14202; 716-551-4191; Fax: 716-551-5296.

Harlem: 163 W 125th Street, Suite 904, New York City, NY 10027; 212-860-6200

Long Island: 1550 Franklin Ave., Room 207, Mineola, NY 11501; 516-739-1765

New York: 20 Exchange Place, 40th Floor, New York, NY 10005; 212-809-2642

Rochester, 400 Andrews Street, Suite 710, Rochester, NY 14604; 716-263-6480

White Plains: 707 Westchester Ave., Suite 209, White Plains, NY 10601; 914-682-6712

North Carolina

Charlotte: 521 E. Morehead Street, Suite 435, Charlotte, NC 28202; 704-333-4886.

Greensboro: 342 North Elm St., 2nd Floor, Greensboro, NC 27401; 336-333-5345; Fax: 336-333-5158.

Raleigh: 5 West Hargett Street, Suite 600, Raleigh, NC 27601; 919-715-7373.

Ohio

Akron: One Cascade Plaza, 17th Floor, Akron, OH 44308; 330-237-1264.

Cincinnati: 36 E. 7th St., Suite 2650, Cincinnati, OH 45202; 513-684-2944; Fax: 513-684-3227.

Cleveland: 600 Superior Ave., East., Suite 700, Cleveland, OH 44115; 216-522-4750; Fax: 216-522-2235.

Columbus: 280 North High Street, Suite 1400, Columbus, OH 43215; 614-365-9510

Toldeo: 300 Madison Ave., #270, Toldeo, OH 43604; 419-241-0683.

Oklahoma

Oklahoma City: 301 Northwest 63rd St., Suite 330, Oklahoma City, OK 73116; 405-608-5302; Fax: 405-608-4211.

Tulsa: 700 N Greenwood Ave., Suite 1400, Tulsa, OK 74106; 918-581-7650; Fax: 918-594-8413.

Oregon

Eugene: 1401 Williamette St., Eugene, OR 97401; 717-221-4510.

Portland: Suite 242, One World Trade Center, 121 SW Salmon St., Portland, OR 97204; 503-326-3001; Fax: 503-326-6351.

Pennsylvania

Harrisburg: 228 Walnut St., #850, P.O. Box 11698, Harrisburg, PA 17108; 717-221-4510.

Pittsburgh: 1000 Liberty Ave., Room 2002, Pittsburgh, PA 15222; 412-395-5050; Fax: 412-395-4875.

Philadelphia: The Curtis Center, Suite 580 West, Independence Sq. West, Philadelphia, PA 19106; 215-597-6101; Fax: 215-597-6123.

Puerto Rico

San Juan: 525 FD Roosevelt Ave., Suite 505, San Juan, PR 00918; 787-766-5555; Fax: 787-766-5692.

Rhode Island

Providence: One West Exchange St., Providence, RI 02903; 401-528-5104; Fax: 401-528-5067.

South Carolina

Columbia: 1201 Main Street, Suite 1720, Columbia, SC 29201, 803-765-5345; Fax. 803-253-3614.

Charleston: 5300 International Blvd., #201C, Charleston, SC 29418; 843-760-3794.

Greenville: 555 N. Pleasantburg Dr., Bldg. 1, Suite 109, Greenville, SC 29607; 864-271-1976.

South Dakota

Siouxland: Augustana College, 2001 S. Summit Ave., Room 122, Sioux Falls, SD 57197; 605-330-4264; Fax: 605-330-4266.

Tennessee

Nashville: 211 Commerce Street, 3rd Floor, Suite 100, Nashville, TN 37201; 615-259-6060.

Memphis: 650 E. Parkway S, Suite 348, Memphis, TN 38104; 901-323-1543; Fax: 901-320-9128.

Knoxville: 601 W. Summit Hill, Suite 300, Knoxville, TN 37902; 865-545-4637; Fax: 865-545-4435.

Texas

Arlington: 2000 East Lamar Blvd., Suite 450, Arlington, TX 76006; 817-277-1313.

Austin: 1700 Congress, Austin, TX 78701; 512-916-5939; Fax: 512-916-5940.

Ft. Worth: 711 Houston Street, Fort Worth, TX 76102; 817-212-2673.

Houston: 500 Dallas, Suite 1100, Houston, TX 77002; 713-718-3063; Fax: 713-718-3060.

San Antonio: 203 South Street, Suite 360, San Antonio, TX 78205; 210-228-9878.

Utah

Salt Lake City: Suite 221, 324 S. State St., Salt Lake City, UT 84111; 801-524-5116; Fax: 801-524-5886.

Vermont

Montpelier: National Life Bldg., 6th Floor, Drawer 20, Montpelier, VT 05620; 802-828-4508; Fax: 802-828-3258.

Virginia

Arlington: 1401 Wilson Blvd., Suite 1225, Arlington, VA 22209; 703-524-2885.

Richmond: 400 N. Eighth St., Suite 540, Richmond, VA 23240; 804-771-2246; Fax: 804-771-2390.

Washington

Everett: 2731 Wetmore Ave., Everett WA 98201; 425-388-3052.

Seattle: 2601 4th Ave., Suite 320, Seattle, WA 98121; 206-553-5615; Fax: 206-553-7253.

Spokane: 801 W. Riverside Ave., Suite 400, Spokane, WA 899201; 509-353-2625.

Tacoma: 950 Pacific Ave., Suite 410, Tacoma, WA 98402; 253-593-6736.

West Virginia

Charleston: 405 Capitol St., Suite 807, Charleston, WV 25300, 304-347-5123; Fax: 304-347-5408.

Wheeling: 316 Washington Ave., Wheeling, WV 26003; 304-243-5493.

Wisconsin

Milwaukee: 517 E. Wisconsin Ave., Room 596, Milwaukee,

WI 53202, 414-297-3473; Fax: 414-297-3470.

Wyoming

Served by Denver, Colorado, District Office.

State Government Assistance to Exporters

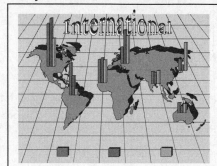

Last year state governments spent approximately $40,000,000 to help companies in their state sell goods and services overseas. This figure increased almost 50% over the previous two years. During the same period of time, federal monies devoted to maximizing companies' export capabilities remained virtually constant. This is another indicator of how the states are fertile sources of information and expertise for large and small businesses.

The underlying mission of these offices is to create jobs within their state. Usually their approach is to help companies develop overseas marketing strategies or to offer incentives to foreign companies to invest in their state. The major state trade development programs and services are outlined below.

1) **Marketing Research and Company Intelligence:**

All of the states can provide some degree of overseas marketing information. The level of detail will depend upon the resources of the state. Thirty-five states (except for California, Hawaii, Idaho, Kansas, Maryland, Minnesota, Nebraska, Nevada, New Jersey, New York, South Dakota, Texas, Washington, West Virginia, and Wyoming) say they will do customized market studies for companies. Such studies are free or available for a small fee. For example, the Commonwealth of Virginia will do an in-depth market study for a company and charge $1,000. They estimate similar surveys done by the private sector cost up to $20,000. Virginia relies on MBA students and professors within the state university system who get credit for working on such projects.

Even if a state does not perform customized studies, the trade office within a Department of Economic Development will prove to be an ideal starting place for marketing information. Some states, which do not undertake comprehensive studies for prospective exporters, will do a limited amount of research for free. These offices can also point to outside sources as well as the notable resources at the federal level that may be able to assist. And those states with offices overseas also can contact these foreign posts to identify sources in other countries. Moreover, many of the offices have people who travel abroad frequently for companies and also work with other exporters. Such bureaucrats can be invaluable for identifying the exact source for obtaining particular market or company intelligence.

2) **Company and Industry Directories:**

Many states publish directories, which are helpful to both exporters and researchers. Some states publish export/import directories which show which companies in the state are exporters and what they sell as well as which are importers and what they buy. Because many of the trade offices are also interested in foreign investment within their state, many publish directories or other reference sources disclosing which companies in their state are foreign owned, and by whom. Other state publications may include export service directories which list organizations providing services to exporters such as banks, freight forwarders, translators, and world trade organizations. Some also publish agribusiness exporter directories, which identify agricultural-related companies involved in exporting.

3) **Free Newsletters:**

All but four states (i.e., Florida, Kentucky, Ohio, and North Carolina) generate international newsletters or publish a special section within a general newsletter on items of interest to those selling overseas. These newsletters are normally free and cover topics like new trade leads, new rules and regulations for exports, and details about upcoming overseas trade shows. Such newsletters can also be a source for mailing lists for those whose clients include exporters. We haven't specifically investigated the availability of such lists, but remember that all states have a law comparable to the federal Freedom of Information Act, which allows public access to government data.

4) **Overseas Contacts:**

Finding a foreign buyer or an agent/distributor for a company is one of the primary functions of these state offices. How they do this varies from state to state. Many sponsor trade fairs and seminars overseas to attract potential buyers to products produced in their state. The more aggressive trade promotion offices may organize trade missions and escort a number of companies overseas and personally help them look for buyers or agents. Many will distribute a company's sales brochures and other literature to potential buyers around the world through their overseas offices. Some states work with the federal government and explore general trade leads and then try to match buyers with sellers. Others will cultivate potential clients in a given country and contact each directly.

5) **Export Marketing Seminars:**

Many of the states conduct free or modestly priced seminars to introduce companies to selling overseas. Some of the courses are held in conjunction with the regional International Trade Administration office of the U.S. Commerce Department. The course may be general in nature, for example, *The Basics of Exporting*, or focused on specific topics such as *International Market Research Techniques*, *Letters of Credit*, *Export Financing*, or *How to do Business with Israel*.

6) **State Grants and Loans for Exporters:**

Many states offer financial assistance for those wishing to export. Some states even provide grants (money you do not have to pay back) to those firms which cannot afford to participate in a trade mission or trade fair. This means that they provide money to those companies that are just trying to develop a customer base overseas. More typically the state will help with the financing of a sale through state-sponsored loans and loan guarantees, or assistance in identifying and applying for federal or commercial export financing.

7) **Trade Leads Databases:**

Because these offices provide mostly services, there are not many opportunities for them to develop databases. However, their trade leads program is one area where a number of offices have computerized their information. These databases consist of the names and addresses along with some background information on those overseas companies that are actively searching or might be interested in doing business with companies within the state. The number of leads in such a system could range from several hundred to five or ten thousand. None of these states seem to have made such information available on machine readable formats to those outside the office. But, in light of state Freedom of Information statutes, it may be worth making a formal inquiry if you have an interest. The states that have computerized their trade leads include: Alabama, Arkansas, Arizona, California, Colorado, Connecticut, Delaware, Florida, Georgia, Hawaii, Illinois, Indiana, Iowa, Maine, Michigan, Maryland, Minnesota, Mississippi, Missouri, Nebraska, New Jersey, New York, North Carolina, North Dakota, Ohio, Oklahoma, Oregon, New Hampshire, Pennsylvania, Puerto Rico, Rhode Island, South Dakota, Tennessee, Texas, Utah, Virginia, Washington, West Virginia, and Wisconsin.

State International Trade Offices

The foreign cities in parentheses after the telephone numbers are those locations where the state maintains a trade office.

Alabama
International Development and Trade Division, Alabama Development Office, 401 Adams Ave., Montgomery, AL 36130, 334-242-0400, 800-248-0033; Fax: 334-353-1330; Email: {idinfo@ado.state.al.us}; {www.ado.state.al.us/trade.htm}. (Stuttgart, **Germany**; Tokyo, **Japan**).

Alaska
Office of International Trade, Department of Commerce and Economic Development, 550 W. 7th Ave., Suite 1770, Anchorage, AK 99501, 907-269-8110; Fax: 907-269-8125; {www.dced.state.ak.us/trade}. (Tokyo, **Japan**; Seoul, **Korea**; Taipei, **Taiwan**; Sakhalinsk, **Russia**).

Arizona
International Trade and Investment Division, Department of Commerce, 3800 N. Central, Suite 1500, Phoenix, AZ 85012, 602-280-1300; Fax: 602-280-1305; {www.commerce.state.az.us/itrade/itrade}. (Hermosillo, **Mexico**; Mexico City, **Mexico**; Tokyo, **Japan**; Taipei, **Taiwan**; London, **UK**; Munich, **Germany**).

Arkansas
International Marketing, Arkansas Industrial Commission, One State Capitol Mall, Little Rock, AR 72201, 501-682-1121; Fax: 501-682-7394; {www.1800arkansas.com}. (Brussels, **Belgium**; Tokyo, **Japan**; Mexico City, **Mexico**; Kuala Lumpur, **Malaysia**).

California
California State World Trade Commission, 1102 Q Street, Suite 6000, Sacramento, CA 95814, 916-324-5511; Fax: 916-324-5791; {http://commerce.ca.gov/state/ttca/ttca_navigation.jsp?path=International+Business} (Tokyo, **Japan**; London, **UK**; Hong Kong; Frankfurt, **Germany**; Mexico City, **Mexico**; Taipei, **Taiwan**; Jerusalem, **Israel**; Seoul, **Korea**; Johannesburg, **South Africa**).

Export Development Office, One World Trade Center, Suite 990, Long Beach, CA 90831, 213-977-7396; Email: {expdev@commerce.ca.gov}, {commerce.ca.gov/international}.

Colorado
International Trade Office, Department of Commerce and Development, 1625 Broadway, Suite 1710, Denver, CO 80202, 303-892-3850; Fax: 303-892-3848; Email: {ito@governor.state.co.us}; {www.state.co.us/oed/ito}. (Tokyo, **Japan**; London, **UK**; Guadalajara, **Mexico**).

Connecticut
International Division, Department of Economic and Community Development, 505 Hudson St., Hartford, CT 06106, 860-270-8000; {www.ct.gov/ecd}. (Tokyo, **Japan**; Taipei, **Taiwan**; Hong Kong; Mexico City, **Mexico**).

Delaware
Delaware Development Office, International Trade Section, 820 French St., Carvel State Building, 3rd Floor, Wilmington, DE 19801, 302-577-8464; Fax: 302-577-8499; {www.state.de.us/dedo/new_web_site/frame_international_trade.html}.

District of Columbia
D.C. Office of International Business, 717 14th St. NW, Suite 1100, Box 4, Washington, DC 20005, 202-727-1576; Fax: 202-727-1588.

Florida
Office of International Affairs, Florida Department of State, The Capitol, Tallahassee, FL 32399-0250; 850-414-1727; Fax: 850-414-1734; Email: {intrel@mail.dos.state.fl.us}; {oir.dos.state. fl.us}. (Toronto, **Canada**; Taipei, **Taiwan**; Seoul, **Korea**; Frankfurt, **Germany**; Tokyo, **Japan**; London, **UK**; Sao Paulo, **Brazil**; Mexico City, **Mexico**).

Georgia
International Trade Division, Suite 1100, 285 Peachtree Center Ave., Atlanta, GA 30303, 404-657-1900; Fax: 404-657-1970; {www.georgia. org}. (Brussels, **Belgium**; Tokyo, **Japan**; Toronto, **Canada**; Seoul, **Korea**; Mexico City, **Mexico**; **Malaysia**; Sao Paulo, **Brazil**; Shang Hai, **China**; Jerusalem, **Israel**; Johannesburg, **South Africa**; Taipei, **Taiwan**).

Hawaii
Business Development and Marketing Division, Department of Business and Economic Development, P.O. Box 2359, Honolulu, HI 96804, 808-586-2404; Fax: 808-587-2427; {www.hawaii.gov/dbedt/trade/greg.html}. (Tokyo, **Japan**; Taipei, **Taiwan**).

Idaho
Division of International Business, Department of Commerce, 700 W. State St., 2nd Floor, Boise, ID 83720, 208-334-2470; Fax: 208-334-2631; {www.idoc.state.id.us/ information/exportinfo/index2.htm}. (Guadalajara, **Mexico**; Taipei, **Taiwan**; Tokyo, **Japan**; Seoul, **Korea**).

Illinois
International Business Division, Illinois Department of Commerce and Community Affairs, 100 W. Randolph St., Suite 3-400, Chicago, IL 60601, 312-814-2828; Fax: 312-814-6581; {www.illinoisbiz.biz/bus/ito/index.html}. (Brussels, **Belgium**; Causeway Bay, **Hong Kong**; Tokyo, **Japan**; Warsaw, **Poland**; Mexico City, **Mexico**; Budapest, **Hungary**).

Illinois Export Council and Illinois Export Development Authority, 321 N. Clark St., Suite 550, Chicago, IL 60610; (Export Council) 773-725-1106; (Development Authority) 312-814-6872.

Indiana
International Marketing, Department of Commerce, One North Capitol, Suite 700, Indianapolis, IN 46204, 317-232-8800; Fax 317-232-4146; {www.state.in.us/doc/business/IntTrade.html}. (Tokyo, **Japan**; Mexico City, **Mexico**; Toronto, **Canada**; Taipei, **Taiwan**; Beijing, **China**; Seoul, **Korea**; Amsterdam, **Netherlands**).

Iowa
Department of International Trade, Iowa Department of Economic Development, 200 East Grand Ave., Des Moines, IA 50309, 515-242-4743; Fax: 515-242-4918; Email: {international@ided.state.ia.us}; {www.state.ia.us/government/ided/intl}. (Frankfurt, **Germany**; Tokyo, **Japan**).

Kansas
Kansas Department of Commerce, 1000 SW Harrison St., Suite 100, Topeka, KS 66603, 785-296-4027; Fax: 785-296-5263; {http://kdoch.state.ks.us/busdev/trade_info.asp}. (Tokyo, **Japan**; Brussels, **Belgium**; Sydney, **Australia**; **UK**).

Kentucky
International Trade, Cabinet for Economic Development, 2300 Capitol Plaza Tower, 500 Mero St., Frankfort, KY 40601, 502-564-7140; Fax 502-564-7697; {www.edc.state.ky.us/kyedc/inttrade.asp}. (Tokyo, **Japan**; Brussels, **Belgium**).

Louisiana
Office of International Marketing, P.O. Box 94185, Baton Rouge, LA 70804-9185, 225-342-4319; Fax: 225-342-5389; {www.lded.state.la.us}. (Mexico City, **Mexico**; Taipei, **Taiwan**; **Netherlands**; Frankfurt, **Germany**).

Maine
International Trade Center, 511 Congress St., Portland, ME 04101, 207-541-7400, Fax: 207-541-7420, {www.mitc.com}.

Maryland
U.S. Export Assistance Center, World Trade Center, 401 East Pratt St., 7th Floor, Suite 2432, Baltimore, MD 21202, 410-962-4539; Fax: 410-962-4582. (Brussels, **Belgium**; Yokohama, **Japan**; **Hong Kong**)

Massachusetts
The Massachusetts Export Center, State Transportation Building, 10 Park Place, Suite 3720, Boston, MA 02116; {www.state.ma.us/export}. (Berlin, **Germany**; Jerusalem, **Israel**; Mexico City, **Mexico**; London, **UK**; Guangzhou, **PRC**; Rio de Janeiro, **Brazil**; **Singapore**).

Massachusetts Trade Office State Transportation Building, 10 Park Plaza, Suite 3720, Boston, MA 02116, 617-973-8650; Fax: 617-227-3488; Email: {moiti@state.ma.us}; {www.magnet.state.ma.us/moiti/}.

Michigan
International Trade Division, International Trade Authority, Michigan Department of Commerce, P.O. Box 30105, Lansing, MI 48909, 517-241-2178; {www.michigan.gov/mda}. (Toronto, **Canada**; **Hong Kong**; Brussels, **Belgium**; Tokyo, **Japan**; Mexico City, **Mexico**; Harvae, **Zimbabwe**).

Minnesota
Minnesota Trade Office, 1000 Minnesota World Trade Center, 30 E. 7th St., St. Paul, 55101, 800-657-3858, 651-297-4222; Fax: 651-296-3555; Email: mto@state.mn.us}; {www.dted.state.mn.us}. (Oslo, **Norway**; Stockholm, **Sweden**; London, **UK**; Paris, **France**; Frankfurt, **Germany**; **Hong Kong**; Osaka, **Japan**; Budapest, **Hungary**; Tokyo, **Japan**; Taipei, **Taiwan; Brussels, Belgium**).

Mississippi
Department of Economic and Community Development, P.O. Box 849, Jackson, MI 39205, 601-359-6672; Fax: 601-359-3605; {www.decd.state.ms.us/doing_busn/intl/intl_overview.htm (Seoul, **Korea**; Frankfurt, **Germany**; Taipei, **Taiwan**).

Missouri
International Trade, Department of Economic Development, 301 W. High St., Room 720C, P.O. Box 118, Jefferson City, MO 65102, 573-751-4855, Fax: 573-526-1567; Email: {missouri@mail.state.mo.us}, {www.ecodev.state.mo.us/business/internationalmarketing/}. (Tokyo, **Japan**; Dusseldorf, **Germany**; Seoul, **Korea**; Taipei, **Taiwan**; Guadalajara, **Mexico**; London, **UK**).

Montana
International Trade Office, Montana Department of Commerce, 301 S. Park Ave., Helena, MT 59601; 406-841-2752; {www.state.mt.us}, {www.commerce.state.mt.us/BRD/BRD_TradeIR.html}. (Taipei, **Taiwan**; Kumamoto, **Japan**).

Nebraska
Department of Economic Development, 301 Centennial Mall South, P.O. Box 94666, Lincoln, NE 68509, 402-471-3441; Fax: 402-471-3778; {http://international.neded.org}.

Nevada
Commission of Economic Development, 108 E. Proctor St., Capital Complex, Carson, NV 89701, 775-687-4325; Fax: 775-687-4450; {www.expand2nevada.com}.

New Hampshire
International Trade Resource Center, Department of Resources and Economic Development, 17 New Hampshire Ave., Portsmouth, NH 03801, 603-334-6074; Fax: 603-334-6110; {www.globalnh.org}.

New Jersey
Division of International Trade, Department of Commerce and Economic Development, 20 West State St., 12th Floor, P.O. Box 820, Trenton, NJ 08625, 609-777-0885; {www.state.nj.us/commerce/internat_intro.html }. (Tokyo, **Japan**; London, **UK**; Mexico City, **Mexico**).

New Mexico
Trade Division, Economic Development, 1100 St. Francis Dr., Joseph Montoya Building, Santa Fe, NM 87501, 505-827-0307; Fax: 505-827-0263; {www.edd.state.nm.us/TRADE}. (Mexico City, **Mexico**).

New York
Council for International Trade, Technology, Education and Communication, Inc. (CITEC), Peyton Hall, Main Street, Box 8561, Clarkson University, Potsdam, NY 13699; 315-268-3778; Fax: 315-268-4432; {www.citec.org} (Tokyo, **Japan**; London, **UK**; Milan, **Italy**; Toronto and Montreal, **Canada**; **Hong Kong**; Frankfurt, **Germany**).

North Carolina
International Division, Dept. of Commerce, 4320 Mail Service Center, 301 N. Wilmington St., Raleigh, NC 27699, 919-733-7193; Fax: 919-733-0110; {www.exportnc.com}. (Dusseldorf, **Germany**; **Hong Kong**; Tokyo, **Japan**; London, **UK**; Dubai, **United Arab Emirates**; Toronto, **Canada**).

North Dakota
International Trade Specialist, Department of Economic Development and Finance, 400 East Broadway, Suite 50, Bismarck, ND 58502, 701-328-5300; Fax: 701-328-5320; {www.growingnd.com/}.

Ohio
International Trade Division, Department of Development, 77 S. High St., P.O. Box 1001, Columbus, OH 43216, 614-466-5017; 614-463-1540; Email: {itd@odod.ohio.gov}, {www.odod.state.oh.us/itd}. (Brussels, **Belgium**; Tokyo, **Japan**; **Hong Kong**, Toronto, **Canada**; Mexico City, **Mexico**; **Israel**).

Oklahoma
International Trade Division, Oklahoma Department of Commerce, 700 N. Greenwood Ave., Suite 1400, Tulsa, OK 74106, 405-594-8116, Fax: 405-594-8413; {www.odoc.state.ok.us/HOMEPAGE/internat.nsf}. (Seoul, **Korea**; Mexico City, **Mexico**; **Singapore**; Antwerp, **Belgium**; Ho Chi Mnh City, **Vietnam**; Beijing, **China**; Taipei, **Taiwan**).

Oregon
International Trade Division, Oregon Economic Development Department, One World Trade Center, Suite 205, 121 Salmon St., Portland, OR 97204, 503-229-6051; Fax: 503-222-5050; {www.econ.state.or.us oregontrade/index.htm}. (Tokyo, **Japan**; Seoul, **Korea**; Taipei, **Taiwan**).

Pennsylvania
Department of Commerce, Office of International Trade, 464 Forum Building, Harrisburg, PA 17120, 717-787-7190, 888-PA-EXPORT, Fax: 717-234-4560; {www.inventpa.com}. (Frankfurt, **Germany**; Tokyo, **Japan**; Brussels, **Belgium**; Toronto, **Canada**).

Puerto Rico
Pridco, #355 FD Roosevelt Ave., Suite 404, Hato Rey, PR 00918; 787-758-4747; Fax: 787-764-1415 {www.pridco.com}.

Rhode Island
International Trade Office, Department of Economic Development, 7 Jackson Walkway, Providence, RI 02903, 401-277-2601; Fax: 401-277-2102; {www.sec.state.ri.us/bus/REIX.htm}. (Mexico City, **Mexico**).

South Carolina
International Business Development, South Carolina State Department of Commerce, P.O. Box 927, Columbia, SC 29202, 803-737-0400; Fax: 803-737-0818; {www.callsouthcarolina.com/}. (Tokyo, **Japan**; Frankfort, **Germany**; Seoul **Korea**; London, **UK**).

South Dakota
South Dakota International Business Institute, 1200 S. Jay St., Aberdeen, SD 57401, 605-626-3149, Fax: 605-626-3004; {www.sd-exports.org}.

Tennessee
Tennessee Export Office, Department of Economic and Community Development, 312 8th Avenue North, Nashville, TN 37243, 615-741-1888; {www.state.tn.us/ecd/idg.htm}.

Texas
Office of International Marketing, Texas Department of Commerce, 1700 N. Congress Ave., P.O. Box 12728, Austin, TX 78711, 512-936-0100, Fax: 512-936-0445; {www.tded.state.tx.us/trade}. (Mexico City, **Mexico**; Frankfurt, **Germany**; Tokyo, **Japan**; Taipei, **Taiwan**; Brussels, **Belgium**; Seoul, **Korea**).

Utah
International Business Development Office, 324 S. State St., Suite 500, Salt Lake City, UT 84111, 801-538-8737, Fax: 801-538-8889; {http://international.utah.gov}. (Tokyo, **Japan**).

Vermont

Vermont World Trade Office, 60 Main St., Suite 102, Burlington, VT 05401, 802-865-0493, 800-305-8321, Fax: 802-860-0091; {www.vermontworldtrade.org}.

Virginia

Virginia Economic Development Partnership, P.O. Box 798, 901 E. Byrd St., Richmond, VA 23218, 804-371-0198, Fax: 804-371-8860, Email: {exportva@vedp.state.va.us}, {www.exportvirginia.org}. (Tokyo, **Japan**; Frankfurt, **Germany**; **Hong Kong**; Mexico City, **Mexico**)

Washington

Domestic and International Trade Division, Department of Trade and Economic Development, 2001 Sixth Ave, 26th Floor, Seattle, WA 98121, 206-956-3131; Fax: 206-956-3151; {www.trade.wa.gov}. (Tokyo, **Japan**; **Canada**; Shanghai, **China**; Paris, **France**; Primorski Krai, **Russian Federation**; Taipei, **Taiwan**).

West Virginia

West Virginia Department of Development, Capitol Complex Bldg. 6, Room 517, 1900 Kanawha Blvd., Charleston, WV 25305, 304-558-2234; Fax: 304-558-1957, {www.wvdo.org/international/index.html}. (Tokyo, **Japan**; Nagaya, **Japan**; Munchen, **Germany**; Taipei, **Taiwan**).

Wisconsin

Bureau of International Business Development, Department of Development, P.O. Box 7970, 201 W. Washington Ave., Madison, WI 53707, 608-266-1018; Fax: 608-266-5551; {www.commerce.state.IE/IE-org.html}. (Frankfurt, **Germany**; **Hong Kong**; Mexico City, **Mexico**; Toronto, **Canada**; Tokyo, **Japan**; Seoul, **Korea**; **South Korea**).

Wyoming

International Trade Office, Wyoming Business Council, 214 West 15th Street, Cheyenne, WY 82002, 307-777-2800; Fax: 307-777-2838.

Overseas Travel: Business or Pleasure

The following sources and services will be helpful to anyone who is on business or vacation in any foreign country:

1) **Travel Overseas on Government Expense:**
The Office of Citizen Exchanges will pay experts, who can contribute to foreign societies' understanding of the United States, to travel abroad and participate in seminars, colloquia, or symposia. Subjects relevant to the program include economics, international political relations, U.S. social and political processes, arts and humanities, and science and technology. To see if you qualify contact: Office of Citizen Exchanges (ECA/PE/C), Bureau of Educational and Cultural Affairs, U.S. Department of State, SA-44, 301 Fourth St., SW, Washington, DC 20547; 202-619-5348; {http://exchanges.state.gov}.

2) **Citizens Arrested Overseas:**
The Arrest Unit at the State Department monitors arrests and trials to see that American citizens are not abused; acts as a liaison with family and friends in the United States; sends money or messages with written consent of arrestee; offers lists of lawyers; will forward money from the United States to detainee; tries to assure that your rights under local laws are observed. The Emergency Medical and Dietary Assistance Program includes such services as providing vitamin supplements when necessary; granting emergency transfer for emergency medical care; and short-term feeding of two or three meals a day when arrestee is detained without funds to buy his or her own meals. Contact: Arrests Unit, Citizens Emergency Center, Overseas Citizens Service, Bureau of Consular Affairs, U.S. Department of State, 2201 C St. NW, Room 4817, Washington, DC 20520, 202-647-5225; Fax: 202-647-5226; {travel.state.gov/ arrest.html}.

3) **Citizens Emergency Center:**
Emergency telephone assistance is available to United States citizens abroad under the following circumstances:

Arrests: 202-647-5225; (see details above)

Deaths: 202-647-5225; {travel.state.gov/deathrep.html}; notification of interested parties in the United States of the death abroad of American citizens; assistance in the arrangements for disposition of remains.

Financial Assistance: 202-647-5225; {travel.state.gov/money.html}; repatriation of destitute nationals, coordination of medical evacuation of non-official nationals from abroad; transmission of private funds in emergencies to destitute United States nationals abroad when commercial banking facilities are unavailable (all costs must be reimbursed).

Welfare and Whereabouts: 202-647-5225; {travel.state.gov/wwflyer.html}; search for nonofficial United States nationals who have not been heard from for an undue length of time and/or about whom there is special concern; transmission of emergency messages to United States nationals abroad. The Welfare and Whereabouts website lists all of the questions that will need to be answered upon calling the service. For other help contact: Overseas Citizen Services, Bureau of Consular Affairs, U.S. Department of State, 2201 C St. NW, Washington, DC 20520, 202-647-5225.

4) **Country Information Studies:**
For someone who wants more than what the typical travel books tell about a specific country, this series of books deals with more in-depth knowledge of the country being visited. Each book describes the origins and traditions of the people and their social and national attitudes, as well as the economics, military, political and social systems. For a more complete listing of this series and price information, contact Superintendent of Documents, Government Printing Office, Washington, DC 20402, 202-512-1800.

5) **Foreign Country Background Notes:**
Background Notes on the Countries of the World is a series of short, factual pamphlets with information on the country's land, people, history, government, political conditions, economy, foreign relations, and U.S. foreign policy. Each pamphlet also includes a factual profile, brief travel notes, a country map, and a reading list. *Background Notes* is also available online at {www.state.gov/}. Contact: Public Affairs Bureau, U.S. Department of State, Room 4827A, 2201 C St. NW, Washington, DC 20520, 202-647-2518 for a free copy of *Background Notes* for the countries you plan to visit. This material is also available from Superintendent of Documents, U.S. Government Printing Office, Washington, DC 20402, 202-512-1800. Single copies cost from $1.25 to $2.50. Order online at {bookstore.gpo.gov}.

6) **Foreign Language Materials:**
The Defense Language Institute Foreign Language Center (DLIFC) has an academic library with holdings of over 100, 000 books and periodicals in 50 different foreign languages. These materials are available through the national interlibrary loan program, which can be arranged through your local librarian. Contact: {http://dli-www.army.mil}.

7) **Foreign Language Training:**
The Foreign Service Institute is an in-house educational institution for foreign service officers, members of their families and employees of other government agencies. It provides special training in 50 foreign languages. Its instructional materials, including books and tapes, are designed to teach modern foreign languages. Instruction books must be purchased from Superintendent of Documents, U.S. Government Printing Office, Washington, DC 20402, 202-512-1800; {www.gpo.gov}. Tapes must be purchased from the National Audiovisual Center, National Archive, NTIS, Springfield, VA 22161, 1-800-788-6282 or 703-487-8400; {www.ntis.gov/nac}.

8) **Free Booklets for Travelers:**
The following booklets and guides are available free of charge:

Travel Information: Your Trip Abroad:
Contains basic information such as how to apply for a passport, customs tips, lodging information, and how American consular officers can help you in an emergency. Contact: Publications Distribution, Bureau of Public Affairs, U.S. Department of State, 2201 C St. NW, Room 5815A, Washington, DC 20520, 202-647-9859.

Customs Information:
Provides information about custom regulations both when returning to the U.S. as well as what to expect when traveling to different parts of the world. Contact: Customs Office, P.O. Box 7118, Washington, DC 20044; {www.customs.ustreas.gov}.

Visa Requirements of Foreign Governments:
Lists entry requirements of U.S. citizens traveling as tourists, and where and how to apply for visas and tourist cards. For Americans attempting to gain visas in other countries, Consular Affairs maintains a listing of the requirements for acquiring a visa in each country and which countries are not currently not accepting visas. Contact online at {travel.state.gov/ foreignentryreqs.html}. Contact: Passport Services, Bureau of Consular Affairs, U.S. Department of State, 1425 K St. NW, Room G-62, Washington, DC 20524, 202-647-0518; Email: {usvisa@state.gov}; {travel.state.gov/visa_services.html}

9) **Passport Information:**

U.S. citizens and nationals can apply for passports at all passport agencies as well as those post offices and federal and state courts authorized to accept passport applications. Due to the cost of maintaining passport services, the National Passport Information Center created a fee-financed call center with two options. 900-225-5674 charges 35 cents per minute for all calls. 888-362-8668 charges a flat rate of $4.95 per call. To avoid these charges, the NPIC has created a detailed website containing passport applications, statistics, information on how to add pages, replace a lost or stolen passport, renew an old passport, and get a listing of fees for services as well as all post offices handling passport affairs. {http://travel.state.gov/ passport_services.html}.

10) **Travel Warnings:**

Before traveling, it is always a good idea to be aware of any travel warnings for your destination. All travel warnings, general warnings, and public announcements are listed by country and are available on the Bureau of Consular Affairs website at {travel.state.gov/ travel_warnings.html}. These warnings may also be heard by telephone at any time by dialing 202-647-5225.

Index

A

Agency for International Development, 882
   procurement, 779, 781
AgExport Action Kit, 887
Agricultural products
   export incentives, 273
   loan guarantees, 273
Agriculture
   conservation programs, 248, 274, 275
   disaster assistance, 250
   facilities construction, 248
   management assistance, 273
   Native American lands, 259
   plant and animal diseases, 257
Agriculture, U.S. Department of
   procurement, 760, 780
   SBIR grants, 877
AIDS
   prevention programs, 257
Air Force Department
   procurement, 779
Airports
   grants, 253
   military, 274
Alabama
   arts grants, 794
   business assistance, 20
   business financing, 285
   business incubators, 478
   certified community development financial
     institutions, 336
   city business programs, 286
   client assistance program, 705
   corporation division, 824
   county business programs, 285
   exports, 21
   federal procurement assistance, 768
   Foundation Center collections, 830
   international trade office, 898
   inventor's resources, 862
   loan programs, 365
   microloan programs, 434
   minority business council, 682
   Minority Business Opportunity Committees, 688
   nonprofit registration, 811
   rural development, 20, 21
   SBA lenders, 501
   Small Business Administration, 22
   Small Business Development Centers, 188
   state procurement office, 782
   tax incentives, 625
   technical assistance, 389
   technology assistance, 21
   venture capital clubs, 571
   venture capital, 577, 595
   vet centers, 723
   veterans assistance, 716

   vocational rehabilitation, 695
   women and minorities, 21, 731
   women's business centers, 672
   women's business ownership representative, 668
Alaska
   arts grants, 794
   business assistance, 22
   business financing, 22, 23, 287
   certified community development financial
     institutions, 336
   certified development corporations, 456
   city business programs, 288
   client assistance program, 705
   corporation division, 824
   county business programs, 287
   energy financing, 24
   federal procurement assistance, 768
   Foundation Center collections, 831
   international trade office, 898
   inventor's resources, 862
   JOLI self-employment programs, 677
   loan programs, 365
   microloan programs, 434, 451
   Minority Business Development Centers, 686
   nonprofit registration, 812
   rural development, 22, 24
   SBA lenders, 502
   Small Business Administration, 22
   Small Business Development Centers, 189
   state conservation, 24
   state procurement office, 782
   tax incentives, 23, 625, 626
   technical assistance, 389
   vet centers, 723
   veterans assistance, 716
   vocational rehabilitation, 695
   women and minorities, 731
   women's business centers, 672
   women's business ownership representatives, 668
American Samoa
   client assistance program, 705
   vocational rehabilitation, 695
Apples
   loans, 248
Architect grants, 793
Arizona
   arts grants, 795
   business assistance, 25
   business financing, 25, 288
   business incubators, 478
   certified community development financial
     institutions, 336
   certified development corporations, 455
   city business programs, 289
   client assistance program, 705
   corporation division, 824
   county business programs, 288
   federal procurement assistance, 768

D

M

rural development, 125, 126, 127, 129, 130
SBA lenders, 547
Small Business Administration, 127
Small Business Development Centers, 219
state procurement office, 784
tax incentives, 125, 650
technical assistance, 416
technology assistance, 125
transportation assistance, 126
venture capital, 127, 589, 605
vet centers, 727
veterans assistance, 720
vocational rehabilitation, 700
women and minorities, 741
women's business centers, 674
women's business ownership representatives, 670
North Dakota
agricultural assistance, 130
arts grants, 801
business assistance, 127, 128
business financing, 128, 129, 320
business incubators, 491
Business Information Centers, 239
certified community development financial
institutions, 352
certified development corporations, 468
city business programs, 320
client assistance program, 707
Community Development Block Grants, 130
corporation division, 828
county business programs, 321
exports, 128, 129
federal procurement assistance, 774
Foundation Center collections, 835
international trade office, 900
inventor's resources, 871
JOLI self-employment programs, 678
microloan programs, 444
Native American Business Development
Centers, 688
nonprofit registration, 819
rural development, 128
SBA lenders, 548
Small Business Administration, 130
Small Business Development Centers, 220
state procurement office, 784
tax incentives, 130, 651
technical assistance, 417
technology assistance, 128, 129
Tribal Business Information Centers, 241
venture capital, 590
vet centers, 727
veterans assistance, 720
vocational rehabilitation, 701
women and minorities, 741
women's business centers, 674
women's business ownership representatives, 670
Northern Marianas Islands
client assistance program, 707
Nuclear Regulatory Commission
procurement, 781

O

Office of Citizen Exchanges, 901
Office of Federal Procurement Policy
procurement, 781
Office of Personnel Management
procurement, 765, 781
Offices of Small and Disadvantaged Business
Utilization, 779
Ohio
arts grants, 801
business assistance, 130, 133
business financing, 131, 132, 133, 321
business incubators, 492
certified community development financial
institutions, 352
certified development corporations, 468
city business programs, 321
client assistance program, 707
corporation division, 828
county business programs, 321
environmental assistance, 133
exports, 132, 133
federal procurement assistance, 774
Foundation Center collections, 835
international trade office, 900
inventor's resources, 871
JOLI self-employment programs, 678
loan programs, 379
microloan programs, 444
minority business council, 683
Minority Business Development Centers, 687
nonprofit registration, 819
rural development, 132, 133
SBA lenders, 548
services for women entrepreneurs, 665
Small Business Administration, 134
Small Business Development Centers, 220
state procurement office, 784
tax incentives, 652
technical assistance, 418
technology assistance, 131
venture capital clubs, 572
venture capital, 590, 606
vet centers, 728
veterans assistance, 720
vocational rehabilitation, 701
women and minorities, 132, 742
women's business centers, 675
women's business ownership representatives, 670
Oklahoma
arts grants, 801
business assistance, 134, 136
business financing, 136, 137, 322
business incubators, 492
Business Information Centers, 239
certified community development financial
institutions, 353
certified development companies, 469
city business programs, 322
client assistance program, 707
corporation division, 828

P

T

W